Customized version of

Ninth Edition

BIOLOGY

BIOL 1105/1106
Virginia Polytechnic Institute and State University

Kenneth A. Mason
University of Iowa

Jonathan B. Losos
Harvard University

Susan Singer
Carleton College

Based on the work of
Peter H. Raven
Director, Missouri Botanical Gardens;
Englemann Professor of Botany
Washington University

George B. Johnson
Professor Emeritus of Biology
Washington University

McGraw Hill Learning Solutions

Boston   Burr Ridge, IL   Dubuque, IA   New York   San Francisco   St. Louis
Bangkok   Bogotá   Caracas   Lisbon   London   Madrid
Mexico City   Milan   New Delhi   Seoul   Singapore   Sydney   Taipei   Toronto

The McGraw·Hill Companies

Customized Version of
Biology, Ninth Edition
BIOL 1105/1106
Virginia Polytechnic Institute and State University

This book is a McGraw-Hill Learning Solutions textbook and contains select material from *Biology*, Ninth Edition by Jonathan B. Losos, Kenneth A. Mason, Susan R. Singer, Peter H. Raven and George B. Johnson. Copyright © 2011, 2008 by The McGraw-Hill Companies, Inc. Reprinted with permission of the publisher. Many custom published texts are modified versions or adaptations of our best-selling textbooks. Some adaptations are printed in black and white to keep prices at a minimum, while others are in color.

7 8 9 0 QDB QDB 13 12 11

ISBN-13: 978-0-07-745163-9
ISBN-10: 0-07-745163-5

Learning Solutions Representative: James Doepke
Production Editor: Jessica Portz
Printer/Binder: Quad/Graphics, Dubuque

Brief Contents

Preface   v

Guided Tour   x

Contents   xxi

Part **I** *The Molecular Basis of Life*   *1*

1   The Science of Biology   1
2   The Nature of Molecules and the Properties of Water   17
3   The Chemical Building Blocks of Life   33

Part **II** *The Biology of the Cell*   *59*

4   Cell Structure   59
5   Membranes   88
6   Energy and Metabolism   107
7   How Cells Harvest Energy   122
8   Photosynthesis   147
9   Cell Communication   168
10   How Cells Divide   186

Part **III** *Genetic and Molecular Biology*   *207*

11   Sexual Reproduction and Meiosis   207
12   Patterns of Inheritance   221
13   Chromosomes, Mapping, and the Meiosis–Inheritance Connection   239
14   DNA: The Genetic Material   256
15   Genes and How They Work   278
16   Control of Gene Expression   304
17   Biotechnology   327
18   Genomics   352
19   Cellular Mechanisms & Development   372

Part **VI** *Plant Form and Function*   *729*

36   Plant Form   729
37   Vegetative Plant Development   753

38   Transport in Plants   769
39   Plant Nutrition and Soils   786
40   Plant Defense Responses   802
41   Sensory Systems in Plants   814
42   Plant Reproduction   839

Part **VII** *Animal Form and Function*   *863*

43   The Animal Body and Principles of Regulation   863
44   The Nervous System   887
45   Sensory Systems   915
46   The Endocrine System   937
47   The Musculoskeletal System   961
48   The Digestive System   981
49   The Respiratory System   1001
50   The Circulatory System   1018
51   Osmotic Regulation and the Urinary System   1038
52   The Immune System   1055
53   The Reproductive System   1084
54   Animal Development   1105

Part **VIII** *Ecology and Behavior*   *1132*

55   Behavioral Biology   1132
56   Ecology of Individuals and Populations   1162
57   Community Ecology   1185
58   Dynamics of Ecosystems   1207
59   The Biosphere   1230

Appendix A   A-1

Glossary   G-1

Credits   C-1

Index   I-1

Test =
8, 7, 14, 10

About the Authors

Pictured left to right: Susan Rundell Singer, Jonathan Losos, Kenneth Mason

Kenneth Mason is a lecturer at the University of Iowa where he teaches introductory biology. He was formerly at Purdue University where for 6 years he was responsible for the largest introductory biology course on campus and collaborated with chemistry and physics faculty on an innovative new course supported by the National Science Foundation that combined biology, chemistry, and physics. Prior to Purdue, he was on the faculty at the University of Kansas for 11 years, where he did research on the genetics of pigmentation in amphibians, publishing both original work and reviews on the topic. While there he taught a variety of courses, was involved in curricular issues, and wrote the lab manual for an upper division genetics laboratory course. His latest move to the University of Iowa was precipitated by his wife's being named president of the University of Iowa.

Jonathan Losos is the Monique and Philip Lehner Professor for the Study of Latin America in the Department of Organismic and Evolutionary Biology and curator of herpetology at the Museum of Comparative Zoology at Harvard University. Losos's research has focused on studying patterns of adaptive radiation and evolutionary diversification in lizards. The recipient of several awards, including the prestigious Theodosius Dobzhanksy and David Starr Jordan Prizes, and the Edward Osborne-Wilson Naturalist Award. Losos has published more than 100 scientific articles.

Susan Rundell Singer is the Laurence McKinley Gould Professor of the Natural Sciences in the department of biology at Carleton College in Northfield, Minnesota, where she has taught introductory biology, plant biology, genetics, plant development, and developmental genetics for 23 years. Her research interests focus on the development and evolution of flowering plants. Singer has authored numerous scientific publications on plant development, contributed chapters to developmental biology texts, and is actively involved with the education efforts of several professional societies. She received the American Society of Plant Biology's Excellence in Teaching Award, serves on the National Academies Board on Science Education, and chaired the National Research Council study committee that produced *America's Lab Report*.

Committed To Excellence

This edition continues the evolution of the new Raven & Johnson's *Biology*. The author team is committed to continually improving the text, keeping the student and learning foremost. We have an improved design and updated pedagogical features to complement the new art program and completely revised content of the transformative eighth edition of *Biology*. This latest edition of the text maintains the clear, accessible, and engaging writing style of past editions while maintaining the clear emphasis on evolution and scientific inquiry that made this a leading textbook for students majoring in biology. This emphasis on the organizing power of evolution is combined with a modern integration of the importance of cellular and molecular biology and genomics to offer our readers a text that is student-friendly while containing current content discussed from the most modern perspective.

We are committed to producing the best possible text for both student and faculty. Lead author, Kenneth Mason (University of Iowa) has taught majors biology at three different major public universities for more than 15 years. Jonathan Losos (Harvard University) is at the cutting edge of evolutionary biology research and has taught evolutionary biology to both biology majors and nonmajors students. Susan Rundell Singer (Carleton College) has been deeply involved in science education policy issues on a national level.

The extensive nature of the revision for the eighth edition allowed the incorporation of the most current possible content throughout. This has been continued in the ninth edition. Here we provide a more consistent approach to concepts so that the reader is not buried in detail in one chapter and left wondering how something works in another. In all chapters, we provide a modern perspective emphasizing the structure and function of macromolecules and the evolutionary process that has led to this structure and function.

This modern approach is illustrated with two examples. First, genomics are not given one chapter and otherwise ignored. Instead, results from the analysis of genomes are presented in context across the text. It is important that these results are provided in the context of our traditional approaches and not just lumped into a single chapter. We do not ignore the unique features of this approach and therefore provide two chapters devoted to genomics and to genome evolution.

A second example is expanded coverage of noncoding RNA. It is hard to believe how rapidly miRNA have moved from a mere curiosity to a major topic in gene expression. We have included both new text and graphics on this important topic. The results from complete genome sequencing have highlighted this important category of RNA that was largely ignored in past texts.

The revised physiology unit has been further updated to strengthen the evolutionary basis for understanding this section. The single chapter on circulation and respiration has been broken into two to provide a more reasonable amount of material for the student in each chapter. The coverage of temperature regulation has also been moved to the introductory chapter 43: The Animal Body and Principles of Regulation to provide a concrete example of regulation. All of this should enhance readability for the student as well as integrate this material even closer with the rest of the text.

The entire approach throughout the text is to emphasize important biological concepts. This conceptual approach is supported by an evolutionary perspective and an emphasis on scientific inquiry. Rather than present only dry facts, our conceptual view combines an emphasis on scientific inquiry.

Our Consistent Themes

It is important to have consistent themes that organize and unify a text. A number of themes are used throughout the book to unify the broad-ranging material that makes up modern biology. This begins with the primary goal of this textbook to provide a comprehensive understanding of evolutionary theory and the scientific basis for this view. We use an experimental framework combining both historical and contemporary research examples to help students appreciate the progressive and integrated nature of science.

Biology Is Based on an Understanding of Evolution

When Peter Raven and George Johnson began work on *Biology* in 1982 they set out to write a text that presented biology the way they taught in their classrooms—as the product of evolution. We bear in mind always that all biology "only makes sense in the light of evolution;" so this text is enhanced by a consistent evolutionary theme that is woven throughout the text, and we have enhanced this theme in the ninth edition.

The enhanced evolutionary thread can be found in obvious examples such as the two chapters on molecular evolution, but can also be seen throughout the text. As each section considers the current state of knowledge, the "what" of biological phenomenon, they also consider how each system may have arisen by evolution, the "where it came from" of biological phenomenon.

We added an explicit phylogenetic perspective to the understanding of animal form and function. This is most obvious in the numerous figures containing phylogenies in the form and function chapters. The diversity material is supported by the most up-to-date approach to phylogenies of both animals and plants. Together these current approaches add even more evolutionary support to a text that set the standard for the integration of evolution in biology.

Our approach allows evolution to be dealt with in the context in which it is relevant. The material throughout this book is considered not only in terms of present structure and function, but how that structure and function may have arisen via evolution by natural selection.

Biology Uses the Methods of Scientific Inquiry

Another unifying theme within the text is that knowledge arises from experimental work that moves us progressively forward. The use of historical and experimental approaches throughout allow the student not only to see where the field is now, but more importantly, how we arrived here. The incredible expansion of knowledge in biology has created challenges for authors in deciding what content to keep, and to what level an introductory text should strive. We have tried to keep as much historical context as possible and to provide this within an experimental framework consistently throughout the text.

We use a variety of approaches to expose the student to scientific inquiry. We use our new Scientific Thinking figures to walk through an experiment and its implications. These figures always use material that is relevant to the story being told. Data are also provided throughout the text, and other figures illustrate how we arrived at our current view of the topics that make up the different sections. Students are provided with Inquiry Questions to stimulate thinking about the material throughout the book. The questions often involve data that are presented in figures, but are not limited to this approach, also leading the student to question the material in the text as well.

Biology Is an Integrative Science

The explosion of molecular information has reverberated throughout all areas of biological study. Scientists are increasingly able to describe complicated processes in terms of the interaction of specific molecules, and this knowledge of life at the molecular level has illuminated relationships that were previously unknown. Using this cutting-edge information, we more strongly connect the different areas of biology in this edition.

One example of this integration concerns the structure and function of biological molecules—an emphasis of modern biology. This edition brings that focus to the entire book, using this as a theme to weave together the different aspects of content material with a modern perspective. Given the enormous amount of information that has accumulated in recent years, this emphasis on structure and function provides a necessary thread integrating these new perspectives into the fabric of the traditional biology text.

Although all current biology texts have added a genomics chapter, our text was one of the first to do so. This chapter has been updated, and we have added a chapter on the evolution of genomes. More importantly, the results from the analysis of genomes and the proteomes they encode have been added throughout the book wherever this information is relevant. This allows a more modern perspective throughout the book rather than limiting it to a few chapters. Examples, for instance, can be found in the diversity chapters, where classification of some organisms were updated based on new findings revealed by molecular techniques.

This systems approach to biology also shows up at the level of chapter organization. We introduce genomes in the genetics section in the context of learning about DNA and genomics. We then come back to this topic with an entire chapter at the end of the evolution unit where we look at the evolution of genomes, followed by a chapter on the evolution of development, which leads into our unit on the diversity of organisms.

Similarly, we introduce the topic of development with a chapter in the genetics section, return to it in the evolution unit, and dedicate chapters to it in both the plant and animal units. This layering of concepts is important because we believe that students best understand evolution, development, physiology, and ecology when they can reflect on the connections between the microscopic and macroscopic levels of organization.

We're excited about how we moved the previous high-quality textbook forward in a significant way for a new generation of students. All of us have extensive experience teaching undergraduate biology, and we've used this knowledge as a guide in producing a text that is up to date, beautifully illustrated, and pedagogically sound for the student. We've also worked to provide clear explicit learning objectives, and more closely integrate the text with its media support materials to provide instructors with an excellent complement to their teaching.

Ken Mason, Jonathan Losos, Susan Rundell Singer

This chapter covers one of the fastest-progressing fields in biology. It must cover fundamental topics as well as a wide variety of real and potential applications of the technology. The chapter does all of this well. There is good continuity from one section to the next, which I find important to make the text "readable."

Michael Lentz
University of North Florida

Cutting Edge Science
Changes to the Ninth Edition

Part I: The Molecular Basis of Life

The material in this section does not change much with time. However, we have updated it to make it more friendly to the student. The student is introduced to the pedagogical features that characterize the book here: learning objectives with various levels of cognitive difficulty, scientific thinking figures, and an integrated approach to guide the student through complex material.

In chapter 1, the idea of emergent properties has been clarified and material added to emphasize the nonequilibrium nature of biology. This will help introduce students to the fundamental nature of biological systems and prepare them for the rest of the book.

Part II: Biology of the Cell

The overall organization of this section was retained, but material on cell junctions and cell-to-cell interactions was moved from chapter 9 to chapter 4, where it forms a natural conclusion to cell structure. Within chapter 4 microsome/peroxisome biogenesis was clarified to complete the picture of cell structure. The nature of trans fats is clarified, a subject students are likely to have been exposed to but not understand. A brief discussion of the distribution of lipids in different membranes was also added.

Chapter 7—The organization of chapter 7 was improved for greater clarity. ATP structure and function is introduced earlier, and the opening summary section covering all of respiration was removed. This allows the information to unfold in a way that is easier to digest. A new analogy was added for the mechanism of ATP synthase to make this difficult enzyme more approachable.

Chapter 8—The section on bacterial photosynthesis was completely rewritten for clarity and accuracy. In addition to the emphasis we always had on the experimental history of photosynthesis, the scientific thinking figures for chapters 7 and 8 are complementary and cross referenced to reinforce how we accumulate evidence for complex phenomenon such as chemiosmosis.

Chapter 9—The removal of the cell junction material keeps the focus of chapter 9 on signaling through receptors, making this difficult topic more accessible. The distribution of G protein-coupled receptor genes in humans and mouse was updated.

Chapter 10—The discussion of bacterial cell division was updated again to reflect the enormous change in our view of this field. The organization of the chapter was tightened, by combining mitosis and cytokinesis as M phase. Not only is this a consensus view in the field, it simplifies the overall organization for greater clarity.

Part III: Genetic and Molecular Biology

The overall organization of this section remains the same. The splitting of transmission genetics into two chapters allows students to first be introduced to general principles, then tie these back to the behavior of chromosomes and the more complex topics related to genetic mapping.

Content changes in the molecular genetics portion of this section are intended to do two things: (1) update material that is the most rapidly changing in the entire book, and (2) introduce the idea that RNA plays a much greater role now than appreciated in the past. The view of RNA has undergone a revolution that is underappreciated in introductory textbooks. This has led to a complete updating of the section in chapter 16 on small RNAs complete with new graphics to go with the greatly expanded and reorganized text. This new section should both introduce students to exciting new material and organize it so as to make it coherent with the rest of the chapter. The new material is put into historical context and updated to distinguish between siRNA and miRNA, and the mechanisms of RNA silencing. Material on the classical bacterial operons trp and lac was also refined for greater clarity.

Chapter 11—The information on meiotic cohesins and protection of cohesins during meiosis I was clarified and updated. This is critical for students to understand how meiosis actually works as opposed to memorizing a series of events.

Chapter 12—The second example of epistasis, which did not have graphical support in the eighth edition, was removed. This allows the remaining example to be explored in greater detail. The organization of the explication of Mendel's principles was tightened to improve clarity.

Chapter 14—Material on the eukaryotic replisome was updated and the graphics for this refined from the last edition. Archaeal replication proteins are also introduced to give the student a more complete view of replication.

Chapter 15—Has been tightened considerably. The example of sickle cell anemia was moved from chapter 13 to 15, where it fits more naturally in a discussion of how mutations affect gene function.

Chapter 17—Our goal is to help students apply what they've learned about molecular biology to answering important biological questions. This chapter has been revised to balance newer technologies with approaches that continue to be used in both the research and education communities. RNAi applications to diseases like macular degeneration and next-generation sequencing technology are introduced by building on what the student already knows about DNA replication, transcription, and PCR.

Chapter 18—Our book is unique in having two chapters on genomes. The first extends the molecular unit to the scale of whole genomes, and chapter 24 focuses on comparative genomics after students have learned about evolution. This organization is core to our full integration of evolution throughout the book. Chapter 18 has been revised to demonstrate the broad relevance of genomics, from understanding the evolution of speech to identifying the source of the 2001 anthrax attacks.

Chapter 19—The material on stem cells was completely rewritten and updated. The content was reorganized to put it into an even more solid historical context using the idea of nuclear reprogramming, and how this led to both the cloning of mammals and embryonic stem cells. New information on induced pluripotent stem cells is included to keep this as current as possible. This topic is one that is of general interest and is another subject about which students have significant misinformation. We strove to provide clear, well-organized information.

Part IV: Evolution

The evolution chapters were updated with new examples. A strong emphasis on the role of experimental approaches to studying evolutionary phenomena has been maintained and enhanced.

Chapter 20—The various processes that can lead to evolutionary change within populations are discussed in detail. Notably, these processes are not considered in isolation, but explored through how they interact.

Chapter 21—This chapter presents a state-of-the-art discussion of the power of natural selection to produce evolutionary change and the ever-increasing documentation in the fossil record of evolutionary transitions through time. It also discusses a variety of phenomena that only make sense if evolution has occurred and concludes with a critique of arguments posed against the existence of evolution.

Chapter 22—The process of speciation and evolutionary diversification is considered in this chapter. It includes current disagreements on how species are identified and how speciation operates.

Chapter 23—An up-to-date discussion of not only how phylogenies are inferred, but their broad and central role in comparative biology is the focus of chapter 23.

Chapter 24—This chapter has been revised to incorporate the rapidly growing number of fully sequenced genomes in a conceptual manner. We included the paradigm-changing findings that noncoding DNA plays a critical role in regulating DNA expression. This chapter and chapter 25 illustrate how we integrate both evolution and molecular biology throughout our text.

Chapter 25—With updated examples we explore the changing perspectives on the evolution of development. Specifically, the field is shifting away from the simplified view that changes in regulatory regions of genes are responsible for the evolution of form.

Part V: Diversity of Life on Earth

In revising the diversity chapters (protist, plants, and fungi) our emphasis was on integrating an evolutionary theme. The fungi chapter was restructured to reflect the current phylogenies while keeping species that are familiar to instructors at the fore. While competitors have two plant diversity chapters, we have one. We integrated the diversity of flowers and pollination strategies, as well as fruit diversity into the plant unit to enable students to fully appreciate morphological diversity because they have already learned about plant structure and development.

Chapter 26—This chapter has been updated so instructors have the option of using it as a stand-alone diversity chapter if their syllabus is too crowded to include the extensive coverage of diversity in the unit. Endosymbiosis has been consolidated in this chapter (moving some of the content from chapter 4).

Chapter 27—Material on archaeal viruses was added to incorporate this area of active research that is often ignored. The approach to HIV drug treatments was completely redone with revised strategies and updated graphics. The discussions of prions and viroids were also revised.

Chapter 28—All health statistics in chapter 28 were updated, including information on TB, HIV and STDs. A discussion on archaeal photosynthesis was added to the section on microbial metabolism.

Chapter 30—Findings of several plant genome projects informed the revision of the plant chapter. The remarkable desiccation tolerance of moss is emphasized in a Scientific Thinking figure exploring the genes involved in desiccation tolerance. New findings on correlations between the rate of pollen tube growth and the origins of the angiosperms have also been integrated into the chapter.

Chapter 31—Since the previous edition, much has been learned about the evolution of fungi, fundamentally changing relationships among groups. We revised the fungal phylogenies in this chapter to conform with the current understanding of fungal evolution, while contextualizing the older taxonomic groupings that may be more familiar to some readers.

Chapters 32–34—These chapters have been completely overhauled to emphasize the latest understanding, synthesizing molecular and morphological information, on the phylogeny of animals. We refocused these chapters to emphasize the differences in major morphological, behavioral, and ecological features that differentiate the major animal groups, placing a strong emphasis on understanding the organism in the context of its environment. Chapter 32 is an overview, which could be used as a standalone chapter, setting the stage for Chapters 33 on non-coelomate animals and Chapter 34 on coelomates.

Chapter 35—This chapter on vertebrates was revised to incorporate current ideas on vertebrate phylogeny and to emphasize the phylogenetic approach to understanding evolutionary diversification.

Part VI: Plant Form and Function

As with the animal unit we incorporated an evolutionary theme. In the Scientific Thinking figures, as well as the text, we challenge the students to combine morphological, developmental, and molecular approaches to asking questions about plants. The goal is to help students integrate their conceptual understanding over multiple levels of organization. In addition, most of the questions at the end of the chapter are new.

Chapter 36 — The section on leaf development has been updated to include a molecular analysis of the role of a key gene, *UNIFOLIATA*, in compound leaf development.

Chapter 39 — Throughout the unit we included relevant examples to illustrate core concepts in plant biology. Here we added information about the effect of pH on germination and included a Scientific Thinking figure to more fully engage the student in considering pH effects in an agricultural context. The discussion of elevated CO_2 levels and increased temperatures on plant growth was updated. The very complex interactions affecting carbon and nitrogen content in plants is addressed at the level of plant and cell physiology. In addition, they are discussed at the ecosystem level later in the text in a more coherent presentation of the effects of climate change.

Chapter 41 — The section of phytochrome was reorganized and updated. The emphasis is on guiding the student away from the historic examples of morphological responses to different day lengths to a clear, coherent understanding of how red and far red light affect the conformation of phytochrome and the signaling pathway it affects.

Part VII: Animal Form and Function

Several organizational changes were made to this section to enhance overall coherence. The entire section was reinterpreted with the intent of better integrating evolution into all topics. The material on temperature regulation was moved from chapter 50 (8E) to the introductory chapter 43. This both provides an illustrative example to the introduction to homeostasis and removes a formerly artificial combination of temperature control and osmotic control. Respiration and circulation were made into separate chapters (49 and 50), allowing for greater clarity and removing an overly long chapter that was a barrier to understanding.

Chapter 44 — The material on synaptic plasticity was rewritten with new graphics added. And in chapter 46 the addition of learning objectives and our integrated pedagogical tools make a complex topic more approachable. A new Scientific Thinking figure was added as well.

Chapter 51 — The osmotic regulation material in this chapter is more coherent as a separate section without the temperature regulation material.

Chapter 52 — This chapter was reorganized and restructured to emphasize the existence of innate versus adaptive immunity. This replaces the old paradigm of nonspecific versus specific immunity. This reorganization and new material also emphasize the evolutionary basis of innate immunity, which exists in invertebrates and vertebrates.

Chapter 54 — The material on organizer function was updated. The Scientific Thinking figure uses molecular approaches introduced in part III and a figure that was already in the chapter. This figure is much more pedagogically useful in this repurposing than as a static figure and illustrates the use of these figures.

Part VIII: Ecology and Behavior

The ecology chapters have been revised with a particular focus on providing up-to-date information on current environmental issues, both in terms of the problems that exist and the potential action that can be taken to ameliorate them.

Chapter 55 — Completely revised with a strong emphasis on neuroethological approaches to understanding behavioral patterns, this chapter emphasizes modern molecular approaches to the study of behavior.

Chapter 56 — Considers the ecology of individuals and populations and includes up-to-date discussion of human population growth.

Chapter 57 — The ecology of communities is discussed in the context of the various ecological processes that mediate interactions between co-occurring species. With updated examples, chapter 57 illustrates how different processes can interact, as well as emphasizing the experimental approach to the study of ecology.

Chapter 58 — This chapter focuses on the dynamics of ecosystems. It has been updated to emphasize current understanding of the how ecosystems function.

Chapter 59 — The chapter has been extensively updated to provide the latest information on factors affecting the environment and human health with a clear focus on the biosphere and current environmental threats.

Chapter 60 — And finally, chapter 60 considers conservation biology, emphasizing the causes of species endangerment and what can be done. Data and examples provide the latest information and thinking on conservation issues.

Understand Biology With the Help of . . .

Integrated Learning Outcomes

Each section begins with specific Learning Outcomes that represent each major concept. At the end of each section, Learning Outcomes Reviews serve as a check to help students confirm their understanding of the concepts in that section. Questions at the end of the Learning Outcomes Review ask students to think critically about what they have read.

> Any opportunity to identify "learning outcomes" is a welcome addition; we are forced more and more to identify these in learning assessments. I would use these as a guide for students to understand the minimum material they are expected to learn from each section.
>
> *Michael Lentz*
> *University of North Florida*

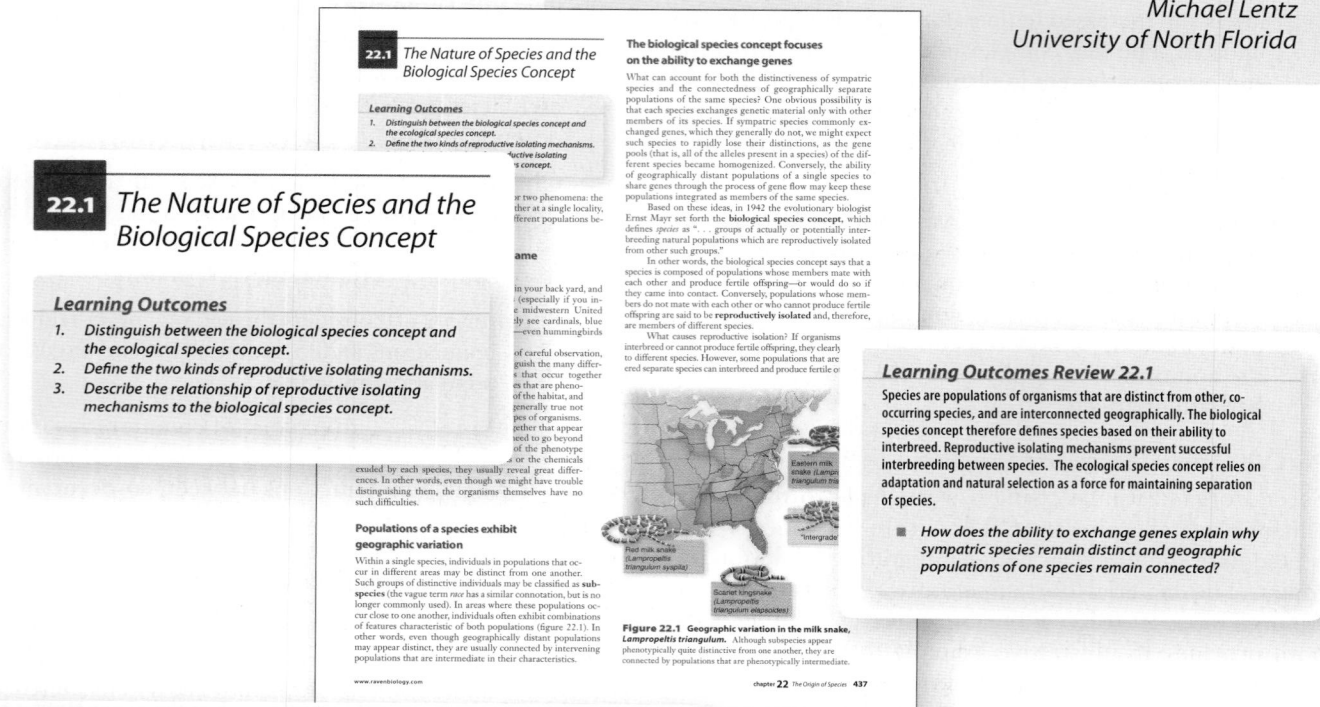

22.1 The Nature of Species and the Biological Species Concept

Learning Outcomes

1. Distinguish between the biological species concept and the ecological species concept.
2. Define the two kinds of reproductive isolating mechanisms.
3. Describe the relationship of reproductive isolating mechanisms to the biological species concept.

The biological species concept focuses on the ability to exchange genes

What can account for both the distinctiveness of sympatric species and the connectedness of geographically separate populations of the same species? One obvious possibility is that each species exchanges genetic material only with other members of its species. If sympatric species commonly exchanged genes, which they generally do not, we might expect such species to rapidly lose their distinctions, as the gene pools (that is, all of the alleles present in a species) of the different species became homogenized. Conversely, the ability of geographically distant populations of a single species to share genes through the process of gene flow may keep these populations integrated as members of the same species.

Based on these ideas, in 1942 the evolutionary biologist Ernst Mayr set forth the **biological species concept,** which defines *species* as ". . . groups of actually or potentially interbreeding natural populations which are reproductively isolated from other such groups."

In other words, the biological species concept says that a species is composed of populations whose members mate with each other and produce fertile offspring—or would do so if they came into contact. Conversely, populations whose members do not mate with each other or who cannot produce fertile offspring are said to be **reproductively isolated** and, therefore, are members of different species.

What causes reproductive isolation? If organisms interbreed or cannot produce fertile offspring, they clearly belong to different species. However, some populations that are considered separate species can interbreed and produce fertile offspring.

Learning Outcomes Review 22.1

Species are populations of organisms that are distinct from other, co-occurring species, and are interconnected geographically. The biological species concept therefore defines species based on their ability to interbreed. Reproductive isolating mechanisms prevent successful interbreeding between species. The ecological species concept relies on adaptation and natural selection as a force for maintaining separation of species.

■ *How does the ability to exchange genes explain why sympatric species remain distinct and geographic populations of one species remain connected?*

Figure 22.1 Geographic variation in the milk snake, *Lampropeltis triangulum.* Although subspecies appear phenotypically quite distinctive from one another, they are connected by populations that are phenotypically intermediate.

chapter **22** *The Origin of Species* **437**

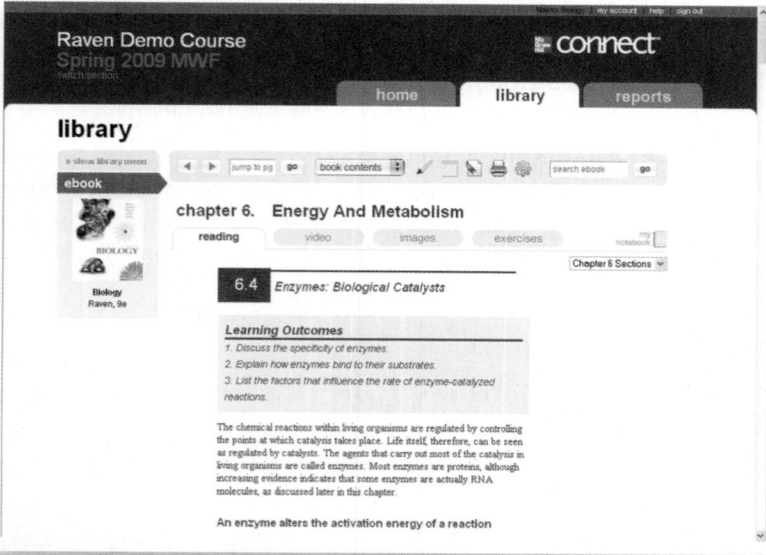

In Print and Online

The online eBook in Connect Plus™ provides students with clear understanding of concepts through a media-rich experience. Embedded animations bring key concepts to life. Also, the ebook provides an interactive experience with the Learning Outcome Review questions.

Companion Website

Students can enhance their understanding of the concepts with the rich study materials available to at www.ravenbiology.com. This open access website provides self-study options with chapter pretest quizzes to assess current understanding, animations that highlight topics students typically struggle with and textbook images that can be used for notetaking and study.

A Consistent and Instructional Visual Program

The author team collaborated with a team of medical and scientific illustrations to create the unsurpassed visual program. Focusing on consistency, accuracy, and instructional value, they created an art program that is intimately connected with the text narrative. The resulting realistic, 3-D illustrations will stimulate student interest and help instructors teach difficult concepts.

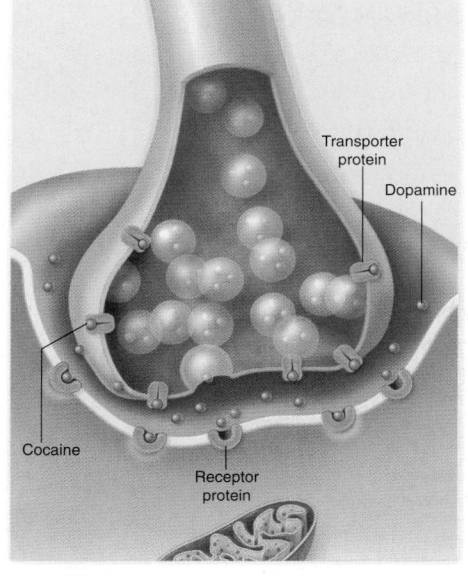

Figure 44.18 **How cocaine alters events at the synapse.**
When cocaine binds to the dopamine transporters, it prevents reuptake of dopamine so the neurotransmitter survives longer in the synapse and continues to stimulate the postsynaptic cell. Cocaine thus acts to intensify pleasurable sensations.

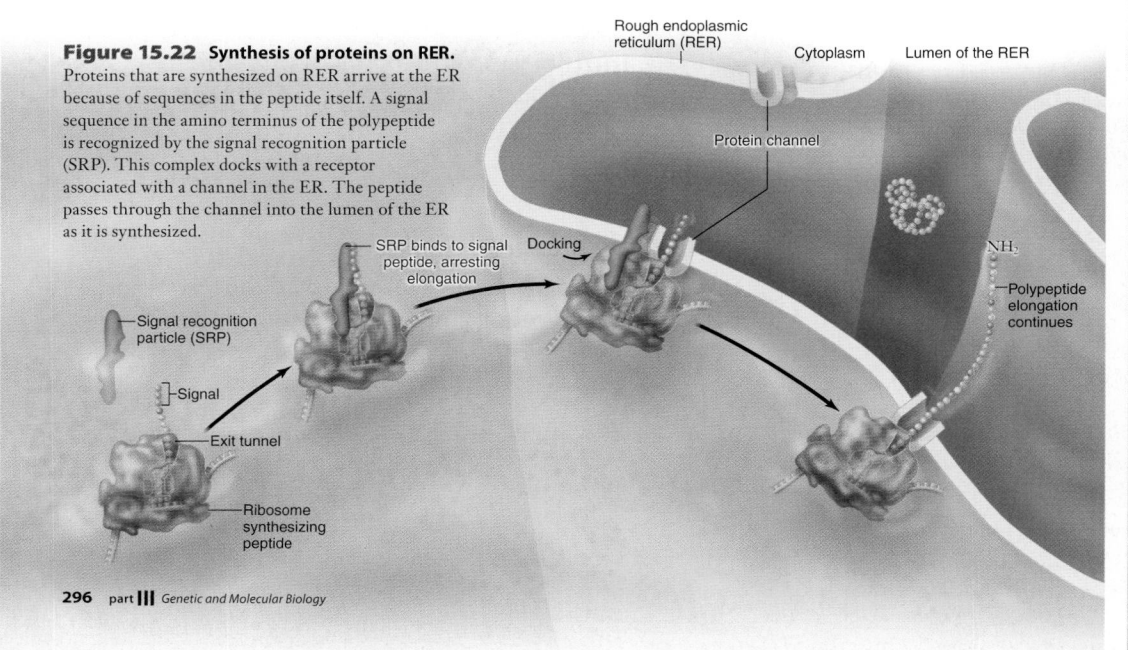

Figure 15.22 **Synthesis of proteins on RER.**
Proteins that are synthesized on RER arrive at the ER because of sequences in the peptide itself. A signal sequence in the amino terminus of the polypeptide is recognized by the signal recognition particle (SRP). This complex docks with a receptor associated with a channel in the ER. The peptide passes through the channel into the lumen of the ER as it is synthesized.

The art is quite good! The colors are well saturated and the figures are clear and often compelling, particularly in showing the molecular complexity of these molecules and cells.

Susan J Stamler
College of DuPage

Apply Your Knowledge With…

NEW Scientific Thinking Art

Key illustrations in every chapter highlight how the frontiers of knowledge are pushed forward by a combination of hypothesis and experiment. These figures begin with a hypothesis, then show how it makes explicit predictions, tests these by experiment and finally demonstrates what conclusions can be drawn, and where this leads. These provide a consistent framework to guide the student in the logic of scientific inquiry. Each illustration concludes with open-ended questions to promote scientific inquiry.

> Knowing how scientists solve problems, and then using this knowledge to solve a problem (as an example) drives home the concept of induction and deduction — I applaud this highly!
>
> *Marc LaBella*
> *Ocean County College*

SCIENTIFIC THINKING

Hypothesis: *The plasma membrane is fluid, not rigid.*
Prediction: *If the membrane is fluid, membrane proteins may diffuse laterally.*
Test: *Fuse mouse and human cells, then observe the distribution of membrane proteins over time by labeling specific mouse and human proteins.*

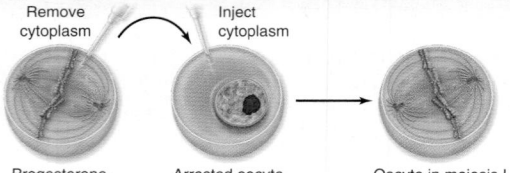

Result: *Over time, hybrid cells show increasingly intermixed proteins.*
Conclusion: *At least some membrane proteins can diffuse laterally in the membrane.*
Further Experiments: *Can you think of any other explanation for these observations? What if newly synthesized proteins were inserted into the membrane during the experiment? How could you use this basic experimental design to rule out this or other possible explanations?*

Figure 5.4   Test of membrane fluidity.

SCIENTIFIC THINKING

Hypothesis: *There are positive regulators of cell division.*
Prediction: *Frog oocytes are arrested in G_2 of meiosis I. They can be induced to mature (undergo meiosis) by progesterone treatment. If maturing oocytes contain a positive regulator of cell division, injection of cytoplasm should induce an immature oocyte to undergo meiosis.*
Test: *Oocytes are induced with progesterone, then cytoplasm from these maturing cells is injected into immature oocytes.*

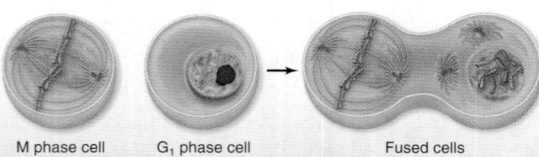

Result: *Injected oocytes progress G_2 from into meiosis I.*
Conclusion: *The progesterone treatment causes production of a positive regulator of maturation: Maturation Promoting Factor (MPF).*
Prediction: *If mitosis is driven by positive regulators, then cytoplasm from a mitotic cell should cause a G_1 cell to enter mitosis.*
Test: *M phase cells are fused with G_1 phase cells, then the nucleus from the G_1 phase cell is monitored microscopically.*

M phase cell   G₁ phase cell   Fused cells

Conclusion: *Cytoplasm from M phase cells contains a positive regulator that causes a cell to enter mitosis.*
Further Experiments: *How can both of these experiments be rationalized? What would be the next step in characterizing these factors?*

Figure 10.16 Discovery of positive regulator of cell division.

Inquiry question

? Based only on amino acid sequence, how would you recognize an integral membrane protein?

Inquiry Questions

Questions that challenge students to think about and engage in what they are reading at a more sophisticated level.

Synthesize and Tie It All Together With . . .

End-of-Chapter Conceptual Assessment Questions

Thought-provoking questions at the end of each chapter tie the concepts together by asking the student to go beyond the basics to achieve a higher level of cognitive thinking.

> I think that the end-of-chapter summary and review questions are thorough and written well. I very much like the way that they are categorized into understanding, application, and synthesizing. I use these types of questions on my exams. So I think that these end-of-chapter questions can be used as homework or in class work to help prepare students for exams.
>
> *Dr. Sharon K. Bullock*
> *UNC Charlotte*

Review Questions

UNDERSTAND

1. What property distinguished Mendel's investigation from previous studies?
   a. Mendel used true-breeding pea plants.
   b. Mendel quantified his results.
   c. Mendel examined many different traits.
   d. Mendel examined the segregation of traits.

2. The F_1 generation of the monohybrid cross purple (PP) × white (pp) flower pea plants should
   a. all have white flowers.
   b. all have a light purple or blended appearance.
   c. all have purple flowers.
   d. have (¾) purple flowers, and ¼ white flowers.

3. The F_1 plants from the previous question are allowed to self-fertilize. The phenotypic ratio for the F_2 should be
   a. all purple.   c. 3 purple:1 white.
   b. 1 purple:1 white.   d. 3 white:1 purple.

4. Which of the following is *not* a part of Mendel's five-element model?
   a. Traits have alternative forms (what we now call alleles).
   b. Parents transmit discrete traits to their offspring.
   c. If an allele is present it will be expressed.
   d. Traits do not blend.

5. An organism's _____ is/are determined by its _____.
   a. genotype; phenotype   c. alleles; phenotype
   b. phenotype; genotype   d. genes; alleles

6. Phenotypes like height in humans, which show a continuous distribution, are usually the result of
   a. an alteration of dominance for multiple alleles of a single gene.
   b. the presence of multiple alleles for a single gene.
   c. the action of one gene on multiple phenotypes.
   d. the action of multiple genes on a single phenotype.

APPLY

1. A dihybrid cross between a plant with long smooth leaves and a plant with short hairy leaves produces a long smooth F_1. If this F_1 is allowed to self-cross to produce an F_2, what would you predict for the ratio of F_2 phenotypes?
   a. 9 long smooth:3 long hairy:3 short hairy:1 short smooth
   b. 9 long smooth:3 long hairy:3 short smooth:1 short hairy
   c. 9 short hairy:3 long hairy:3 short smooth:1 long smooth
   d. 1 long smooth:1 long hairy:1 short smooth:1 short hairy

2. Consider a long smooth F_2 plant from the previous question. This plant's genotype
   a. must be homozygous for both long alleles and hairy alleles.
   b. must be heterozygous at both the leaf length gene, and the leaf hair gene.
   c. can only be inferred by another cross.
   d. cannot be determined by any means.

3. What is the probability of obtaining an individual with the genotype bb from a cross between two individuals with the genotype Bb?
   a. ½   c. ⅛
   b. ¼   d. 0

4. What is the probability of obtaining an individual with the genotype CC from a cross between two individuals with the genotypes CC and Cc?
   a. ½   c. ⅛
   b. ¼   d. ¹⁄₁₆

5. You discover a new variety of plant with color varieties of purple and white. When you intercross these, the F_1 is a lighter purple. You consider that this may be an example of blending and self-cross the F_1. If Mendel is correct, what would you predict for the F_2?
   a. 1 purple:2 white:1 light purple
   b. 1 white:2 purple:1 light purple
   c. 1 purple:2 light purple:1 white
   d. 1 light purple:2 purple:1 white

6. Mendel's model assumes that each trait is determined by a single factor with alternate forms. We now know that this is too simplistic and that
   a. a single gene may affect more than one trait.
   b. a single trait may be affected by more than one gene.
   c. a single gene always affects only one trait, but traits may be affected by more than one gene.
   d. a single gene can affect more than one trait, and traits may be affected by more than one gene.

SYNTHESIZE

1. Create a Punnett square for the following crosses and use this to predict phenotypic ratio for dominant and recessive traits. Dominant alleles are indicated by uppercase letters and recessive are indicated by lowercase letters. For parts b and c, predict ratios using probability and the product rule.
   a. A monohybrid cross between individuals with the genotype Aa and Aa
   b. A dihybrid cross between two individuals with the genotype $AaBb$
   c. A dihybrid cross between individuals with the genotype $AaBb$ and $aabb$

2. Explain how the events of meiosis can explain both segregation and independent assortment.

3. In mice, there is a yellow strain that when crossed yields 2 yellow:1 black. How could you explain this observation? How could you test this with crosses?

4. In mammals, a variety of genes affect coat color. One of these is a gene with mutant alleles that results in the complete loss of pigment, or albinism. Another controls the type of dark pigment with alleles that lead to black or brown colors. The albinistic trait is recessive, and black is dominant to brown. Two black mice are crossed and yield 9 black:4 albino:3 brown. How would you explain these results?

ONLINE RESOURCE

www.ravenbiology.com

Understand, Apply, and Synthesize—enhance your study with animations that bring concepts to life and practice tests to assess your understanding. Your instructor may also recommend the interactive eBook, individualized learning tools, and more.

238 part **III** *Genetic and Molecular Biology*

Integrated Study Quizzes

Study quizzes have been integrated into the Connect Plus ebook for students to assess their understanding of the information presented in each section. End of chapter questions are linked to the answer section of the text to provide for easy study. The notebook feature allows students to collect and manage notes and highlights from the ebook to create a custom study guide.

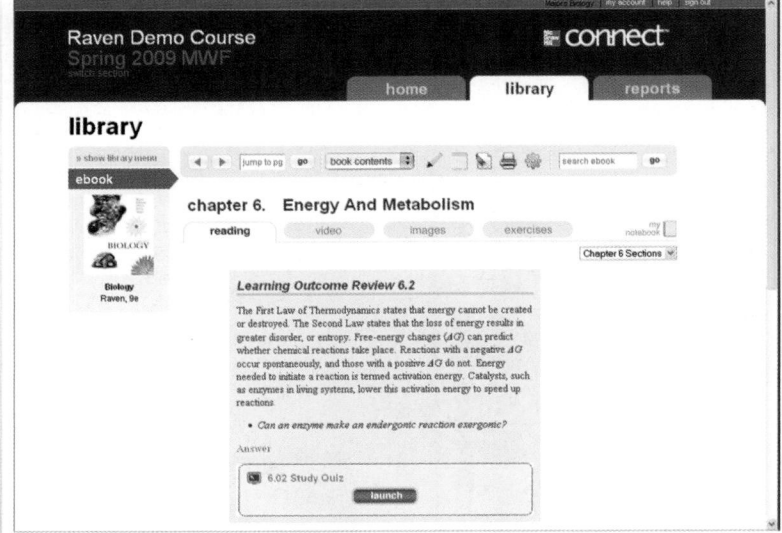

Committed to Biology Educators

McGraw-Hill Connect Biology

Connect Biology™ is a web-based assignment and assessment platform that gives students the means to better connect with their coursework, with their instructors, and with the important concepts that they will need to know for success now and in the future.

With Connect Biology you can deliver assignments, quizzes, and tests online. A robust set of questions and activities are presented and tied to the textbook's learning objectives. As an instructor, you can edit existing questions and author entirely new problems. Track individual student performance—by question, assignment, or in relation to the class overall—with detailed grade reports. Integrate grade reports easily with Learning Management Systems (LMS) such as WebCT and Blackboard. And much more.

ConnectPlus™ Biology provides students with all the advantages of Connect™ Biology, plus 24/7 access to an eBook. This media-rich version of the book includes animations, videos, and inline assessments placed appropriately throughout the chapter. Connect Plus Biology allows students to practice important skills at their own pace and on their own schedule. By purchasing eBooks from McGraw-Hill students can save as much as 50% on selected titles delivered on the most advanced eBook platforms available. Contact your McGraw-Hill sales representative to discuss eBook packaging options.

Powerful Presentation Tools

Everything you need for outstanding presentation in one place!

- **FlexArt Image PowerPoints**—including every piece of art that has been sized and cropped specifically for superior presentations as well as labels that you can edit, flexible art that can be picked up and moved, tables, and photographs

- **Animation PowerPoints**—Numerous full-color animations illustrating important processes. Harness the visual impact of concepts in motion by importing these slides into classroom presentations or online course materials

- **Lecture PowerPoints**—with fully embedded animations

- **Labeled and unlabeled JPEG images**—Full-color digital files of all illustrations, which can be readily incorporated into presentations, exams, or custom-made classroom materials

Presentation Center

In addition to the images from your book, this **online digital library** contains photos, artwork, animations, and other media from an array of McGraw-Hill textbooks that can be used to create customized lectures, visually enhance tests and quizzes, and make compelling course websites or attractive printed support materials.

Quality Test Bank

All questions have been written to fully align with the Learning Outcomes and content of the text. Provided within a computerized test bank powered by McGraw-Hill's flexible electronic testing program **EZ Test Online**, instructors can create paper and online tests or quizzes in this easy to use program! A new tagging scheme allows you to sort questions by difficulty level, topic, and section. Imagine being able to create and access your test or quiz anywhere, at any time, without installing the testing software. Now, with EZ Test Online, instructors can select questions from multiple McGraw-Hill test banks or author their own, and then either print the test for paper distribution or give it online.

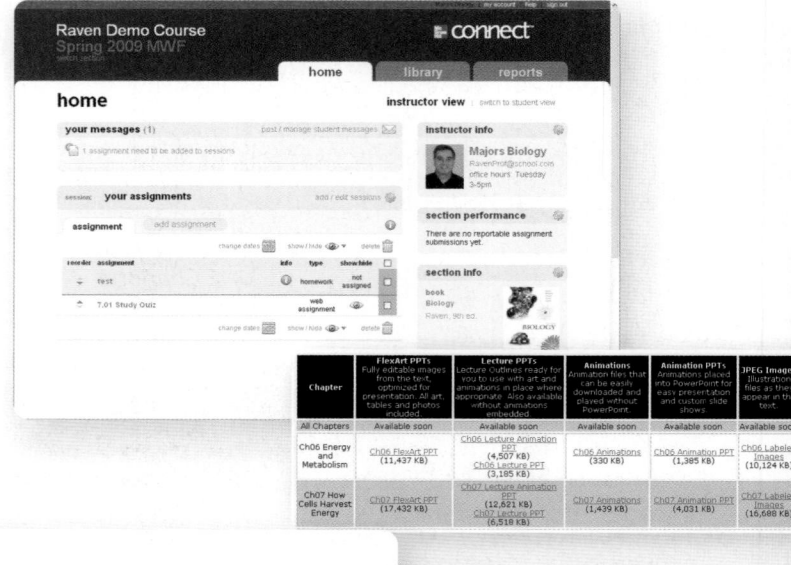

Active Learning Exercises

Supporting biology faculty in their efforts to make introductory courses more active and student-centered is critical to improving undergraduate biological education. Active learning can broadly be described as strategies and techniques in which students are engaged in their own learning, and is typically characterized by the utilization of higher order critical thinking skills. The use of these techniques is critical to biological education because of their powerful impact on students' learning and development of scientific professional skills.

Active leaning strategies are highly valued and have been shown to:

- Help make content relevant
- Be particularly adept at addressing common misconceptions
- Help students to think about their own learning (metacognition)
- Promote meaningful learning of content by emphasizing application
- Foster student interest in science

Guided Activities have been provided for instructors to use in their course for both in-class and out-of-class activities. The Guided Activities make it easy for you to incorporate active learning into your course and are flexible to fit your specific needs.

Flexible Delivery Options

Raven et al Biology is available in many formats in addition to the traditional textbook so that instructors and students have more choices when deciding which format best suits their needs.

 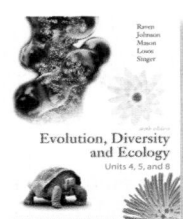 

- **Foundations of Life — Chemistry, Cells and Genetics**
  ISBN: 0-07-739750-9
  Units 1, 2 and 3

- **Evolution, Diversity and Ecology**
  ISBN: 0-07-739717-7
  Units 4, 5 and 8

- **Plants and Animals**
  ISBN: 0-07-739751-7
  Units 6 and 7

Also available, customized versions for all of your course needs. You're in charge of your course, so why not be in control of the content of your textbook? At McGraw-Hill Custom Publishing, we can help you create the ideal text — the one you've always imagined— quickly and easily. With more than 20 years of experience in custom publishing, we're experts. But at McGraw-Hill we're also innovators, leading the way with new methods and means of creating simplified value-added custom textbooks.

The options are never-ending when you work with McGraw-Hill. You already know what will work best for you and your students. And here, you can choose it.

Laboratory Manuals

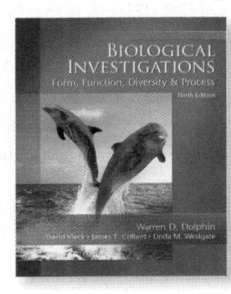

Biology Laboratory Manual, Ninth Edition
Vodopich and Moore
ISBN: 0-07-338306-6

This laboratory manual is designed for an introductory course for biology majors with a broad survey of basic laboratory techniques. The experiments and procedures are simple, safe, easy to perform, and especially appropriate for large classes. Few experiments require a second class meeting to complete the procedure. Each exercise includes many photographs, traditional topics, and experiments that help students learn about life. Procedures within each exercise are numerous and discrete so that an exercise can be tailored to the needs of the students, the style of the instructor, and the facilities available.

Biological Investigations Lab Manual, Ninth Edition
Dolphin
ISBN: 0-07-338305-8

This independent lab manual can be used for a one- or two-semester majors' level general biology lab and can be used with any majors' level general biology textbook. The labs are investigative and ask students to use more critical thinking and hands-on learning. The author emphasizes investigative, quantitative, and comparative approaches to studying the life sciences.

Focus on Evolution

Understanding Evolution, Seventh Edition
Rosenbaum and Volpe
ISBN: 0-07-338323-6

As an introduction to the principles of evolution, this paperback text is ideally suited as a main text for general evolution or as a supplement for general biology, genetics, zoology, botany, anthropology, or any life science course that utilizes evolution as the underlying theme of all life.

Committed to Quality

360° Development Process

McGraw-Hill's 360° Development Process is an ongoing, never-ending, education-oriented approach to building accurate and innovative print and digital products. It is dedicated to continual large-scale and incremental improvement, driven by multiple user feedback loops and checkpoints. This is initiated during the early planning stages of our new products, intensifies during the development and production stages, then begins again after publication in anticipation of the next edition.

This process is designed to provide a broad, comprehensive spectrum of feedback for refinement and innovation of our learning tools, for both student and instructor. The 360° Development Process includes market research, content reviews, course- and product-specific symposia, accuracy checks, and art reviews. We appreciate the expertise of the many individuals involved in this process.

Contributing Authors

Active Learning Exercises

Frank Bailey, Middle Tennessee State University

Steve Howard, Middle Tennessee State University

Michael Rutledge, Middle Tennessee State University

Chapter Contributors

Daphne Fautin, University of Kansas

Shelley Jansky, University of Wisconsin, Madison

Stephanie Pandolfi, Wayne State University

James Traniello, Boston University

Instructor's Manual

Mark Hens, University of North Carolina, Charlotte

Integrated eBook Study Guide

David Bos, Purdue University

Koy Miskin, Purdue University

Kathleen Broomall, Miami University, Oxford

Test Bank

Brian Bagatto, University of Akron

Tom Sasek, University of Louisiana at Monroe

Stephanie Pandolfi, Wayne State University

Connect Content Contributors

Susan Hengeveld, Indiana University

Salvatore Tavormina, Austin Community College

Scott Cooper, University of Wisconsin, LaCrosse

Brian Shmaefsky, Lone Star College

Phil Gibson, Oklahoma University

Morris Maduro, University of California, Riverside

Matt Neatrour, Northern Kentucky University

Leslie Jones, Valdosta State

Lynn Preston, Tarrant County College

Website

Tom Pitzer, Florida International University

Marceau Ratard, Delgado Community College

Amanda Rosenzweig, Delgado Community College

Instructor Media

Mark Browning, Purdue University

Brenda Leady, University of Toledo

Digital Board of Advisors

We are indebted to the valuable advice and direction of an outstanding group of advisors, led by Melissa Michael, University of Illinois at Urbana-Champaign. Other board members include:

Randy Phillis, University of Massachusetts

John Merrill, Michigan State

Russell Borski, North Carolina State

Deb Pires, University of California, Los Angeles

Bill Wischusen, Louisiana State University

David Scicchitano, New York City University

Michael Rutledge, Middle Tennessee State

Lynn Preston, Tarrant County College

Karen Gerhart, University of California, Davis

Jean Heitz, University of Wisconsin, Madison

Mark Lyford, University of Wyoming

General Biology Symposia

Every year McGraw-Hill conducts several General Biology Symposia, which are attended by instructors from across the country. These events are an opportunity for editors from McGraw-Hill to gather information about the needs and challenges of instructors teaching the major's biology course. It also offers a forum for the attendees to exchange ideas and experiences with colleagues they might not have otherwise met. The feedback we have received has been invaluable and has contributed to the development of Biology and its supplements. A special thank you to recent attendees:

Sylvester Allred   *Northern Arizona University*

Michael Bell   *Richland College*

Arlene Billock   *University of Louisiana Lafayette*

Stephane Boissinot   *Queens College, the City University of New York*

David Bos   *Purdue University*

Scott Bowling   *Auburn University*

Jacqueline Bowman   *Arkansas Technical University*

Arthur Buikema   *Virginia Polytechnic Institute*

Anne Bullerjahn   *Owens Community College*

Helaine Burstein   *Ohio University*

Raymond Burton   *Germanna Community College*

Peter Busher   *Boston University*

Richard Cardullo   *University of California—Riverside*

Jennifer Ciaccio   *Dixie State College*

Anne Barrett Clark   *Binghamton University*

Allison Cleveland   *University of South Florida, Tampa*

Jennifer Coleman *University of Massachusetts, Amherst*
Sehoya Cotner *University of Minnesota*
Mitch Cruzan *Portland State University*
Laura DiCaprio *Ohio University*
Kathyrn Dickson *California State College, Fullerton*
Cathy Donald-Whitney *Collin County Community College*
Stanley Faeth *Arizona State University*
Donald French *Oklahoma State University*
Douglas Gaffin *University of Oklahoma*
Karen Gerhart *University of California, Davis*
Cynthia Giffen *University of Wisconsin—Madison*
William Glider *University of Nebraska, Lincoln*
Christopher Gregg *Louisiana State University*
Stan Guffey *The University of Tennessee*
Bernard Hauser *University of Florida, Gainesville*
Jean Heitz *Unversity of Wisconsin—Madison*
Mark Hens *University of North Carolina, Greensboro*
Albert Herrera *University of Southern California*

Ralph James Hickey *Miami University of Ohio, Oxford*
Brad Hyman *University of California—Riverside*
Kyoungtae Kim *Missouri State University*
Sherry Krayesky *University of Louisiana, Lafayette*
Jerry Kudenov *University of Alaska Anchorage*
Josephine Kurdziel *University of Michigan*
Ellen Lamb *University of North Carolina—Greensboro*
Brenda Leady *University of Toledo*
Graeme Lindbeck *Valencia Community College*
Susan Meiers *Western Illinois University*
Michael Meighan *University of California, Berkeley*
John Mersfelder *Sinclair Community College*
Melissa Michael *University of Illinois at Urbana-Champaign*
Leonore Neary *Joliet Junior College*
Shawn Nordell *Saint Louis University*
John Osterman *University of Nebraska—Lincoln*
Stephanie Pandolfi *Wayne State University*
C.O. Patterson *Texas A&M University*

Nancy Pencoe *State University of West Georgia*
Roger Persell *Hunter College*
Marius Pfeiffer *Tarrant County College NE*
Steve Phelps *University of Florida*
Debra Pires *University of California, Los Angeles*
Eileen Preston *Tarrant County College NW*
Rajinder Ranu *Colorado State University*
Marceau Ratard *Delgado Community College City Park*
Melanie Rathburn *Boston University*
Robin Richardson *Winona State University*
Amanda Rosenzweig *Delgado Community College—City Park*
Laurie Russell *Saint Louis University*
Connie Russell *Angelo State University*
David Scicchitano *New York University*
Timothy Shannon *Francis Marion University*
Brian Shmaefsky *Lone Star College—Kingwood*
Richard Showman *University of South Carolina*
Robert Simons *University of California, Los Angeles*

Steve Skarda *Linn Benton Community College*
Steven D. Skopik *University of Delaware*
Phillip Sokolove *University of Maryland*
Brad Swanson *Central Michigan University*
David Thompson *Northern Kentucky University*
Maureen Tubbola *St. Cloud State University*
Ashok Upadhyaya *University of South Florida, Tampa*
Anthony Uzwiak *Rutgers University*
Rani Vajravelu *University of Central Florida*
Gary Walker *Appalachian State University*
Pat Walsh *University of Delaware*
Elizabeth Weiss-Kuziel *University of Texas at Austin*
Holly Williams *Seminole Community College*
David Williams *Valencia Community College, East Campus*
Michael Windelspecht *Appalachian State University*
Mary Wisgirda *San Jacinto College, South Campus*
Jay Zimmerman *St. John's University*

9th Edition Reviewers

Tamarah Adair *Baylor University*
Gladys Alexandre-Jouline *University of Tennessee at Knoxville*
Gregory Andraso *Gannon University*
Jorge E. Arriagada *St. Cloud State University*
David Asch *Youngstown State University*
Jeffrey G. Baguley *University of Nevada—Reno*
Suman Batish *Temple University*
Donald Baud *University of Memphis*
Peter Berget *Carnegie Mellon University*
Randall Bernot *Ball State University*
Deborah Bielser *University of Illinois—Champaign*
Wendy Binder *Loyola Marymount University*
Todd A. Blackledge *University of Akron*
Andrew R. Blaustein *Oregon State University*
Dennis Bogyo *Valdosta State University*
David Bos *Purdue University*
Robert Boyd *Auburn University*
Graciela Brelles-Marino *California State Polytechnic University—Pomona*
Joanna Brooke *DePaul University*
Roxanne Brown *Blinn College*
Mark Browning *Purdue University*
Cedric O. Buckley *Jackson State University*
Arthur L. Buikema, Jr. *Virginia Tech*
Sharon Bullock *UNC—Charlotte*
Lisa Burgess *Broward College*
Scott Carlson *Luther College*
John L. Carr *University of Louisiana—Monroe*
Laura Carruth *Georgia State University*
Dale Cassamatta *University of North Florida*
Peter Chabora *Queens College—CUNY*

Tien-Hsien Chang *Ohio State University*
Genevieve Chung *Broward College*
Cynthia Church *Metropolitan State College of Denver*
William Cohen *University of Kentucky*
James Collins *Kilgore College*
Joanne Conover *University of Connecticut*
Iris Cook *Westchester Community College*
Erica Corbett *Southeastern Oklahoma State University*
Robert Corin *College of Staten Island—CUNY*
William G. R. Crampton *University of Central Florida*
Scott Crousillac *Louisiana State University—Baton Rouge*
Karen A. Curto *University of Pittsburgh*
Denise Deal *Nassau Community College*
Philias Denette *Delgado Community College*
Mary Dettman *Seminole Community College—Oviedo*
Ann Marie DiLorenzo *Montclair State University*
Ernest DuBrul *University of Toledo*
Richard Duhrkopf *Baylor University*
Susan Dunford *University of Cincinnati*
Andrew R. Dyer *University of South Carolina—Aiken*
Carmen Eilertson *Georgia State University*
Richard P. Elinson *Duquesne University*
William L. Ellis *Pasco-Hernando Community College*
Seema Endley *Blinn College*
Gary Ervin *Mississippi State University*
Karl Fath *Queens College—CUNY*

Zen Faulkes *The University of Texas—Pan American*
Myriam Feldman *Lake Washington Technical College*
Melissa Fierke *State University of New York*
Gary L. Firestone *University of California—Berkeley*
Jason Flores *UNC—Charlotte*
Markus Friedrich *Wayne State University*
Deborah Garrity *Colorado State University*
Christopher Gee *University of North Carolina-Charlotte*
John R. Geiser *Western Michigan University*
J.P. Gibson *University of Oklahoma*
Matthew Gilg *University of North Florida*
Teresa Golden *Southeastern Oklahoma State University*
Venkat Gopalan *Ohio State University*
Michael Groesbeck *Brigham Young University*
Theresa Grove *Valdosta State University*
David Hanson *University of New Mexico*
Paul Hapeman *University of Florida*
Nargess Hassanzadeh-Kiabi *California State University—Los Angeles*
Stephen K. Herbert *University of Wyoming*
Hon Ho *State University of New York at New Paltz*
Barbara Hunnicutt *Seminole Community College*
Steve Huskey *Western Kentucky University*

Cynthia Jacobs *Arkansas Tech University*
Jason B. Jennings *Southwest Tennessee Community College*
Frank J. Jochem *Florida International University—Miami*
Norman Johnson *University of Massachusetts*
Gregory A. Jones *Santa Fe Community College*
Jerry Kaster *University of Wisconsin—Milwaukee*
Mary Jane Keith *Wichita State University*
Mary Kelley *Wayne State University*
Scott Kight *Montclair State University*
Wendy Kimber *Stevenson University*
Jeff Klahn *University of Iowa*
David S. Koetje *Calvin College*
Olga Kopp *Utah Valley University*
John C. Krenetsky *Metropolitan State College of Denver*
Patrick J. Krug *California State University—LA*
Robert Kurt *Lafayette College*
Marc J. LaBella *Ocean County College*
Ellen S. Lamb *University of North Carolina—Greensboro*
David Lampe *Duquesne University*
Grace Lasker *Lake Washington Technical College*
Kari Lavalli *Boston University*
Shannon Erickson Lee *California Sate University- Northridge*
Zhiming Liu *Eastern New Mexico University*
J. Mitchell Lockhart *Valdosta State University*
David Logan *Clark Atlanta University*

Thomas A. Lonergan   *University of New Orleans*
Andreas Madlung   *University of Puget Sound*
Lynn Mahaffy   *University of Delaware*
Jennifer Marcinkiewicz   *Kent State University*
Henri Maurice   *University of Southern Indiana*
Deanna McCullough   *University of Houston—Downtown*
Dean McCurdy   *Albion College*
Richard Merritt   *Houston Community College—Northwest*
Stephanie Miller   *Jefferson State Community College*
Thomas Miller   *University of California, Riverside*
Hector C. Miranda, Jr.   *Texas Southern University*
Jasleen Mishra   *Houston Community College*
Randy Mogg   *Columbus State Community College*
Daniel Moon   *University of North Florida*
Janice Moore   *Colorado State University*
Richard C. Moore   *Miami University*
Juan Morata   *Miami Dade College—Wolfson*
Ellyn R. Mulcahy   *Johnson County Community College*
Kimberlyn Nelson   *Pennsylvania State University*
Howard Neufeld   *Appalachian State University*
Jacalyn Newman   *University of Pittsburgh*
Margaret N. Nsofor   *Southern Illinois University—Carbondale*
Judith D. Ochrietor   *University of North Florida*
Robert O'Donnell   *SUNY—Geneseo*
Olumide Ogunmosin   *Texas Southern University*

Nathan O. Okia   *Auburn University—Montgomery*
Stephanie Pandolfi   *Michigan State University*
Peter Pappas   *County College of Morris*
J. Payne   *Bergen Community College*
Andrew Pease   *Stevenson University*
Craig Peebles   *University of Pittsburgh*
David G. Pennock   *Miami University*
Beverly Perry   *Houston Community College*
John S. Peters   *College of Charleston, SC*
Stephanie Toering Peters   *Wartburg College*
Teresa Petrino-Lin   *Barry University*
Susan Phillips   *Brevard Community College—Palm Bay*
Paul Pillitteri   *Southern Utah University*
Thomas Pitzer   *Florida International University—Miami*
Uwe Pott   *University of Wisconsin—Green Bay*
Nimala Prabhu   *Edison State College*
Lynn Preston   *Tarrant County College—NW*
Kelli Prior   *Finger Lakes Community College*
Penny L. Ragland   *Auburn Montgomery*
Marceau Ratard   *Delgado Community College*
Michael Reagan   *College of St. Benedict/ St. John's University*
Nancy A. Rice   *Western Kentucky University*
Linda Richardson   *Blinn College*
Amanda Rosenzweig   *Delgado Community College*
Cliff Ross   *University of North Florida*
John Roufaiel   *SUNY—Rockland Community College*
Kenneth Roux   *Florida State University*
Ann E. Rushing   *Baylor University*

Sangha Saha   *Harold Washington College*
Eric Saliim   *North Carolina Central University*
Thomas Sasek   *University of Louisiana—Monroe*
Leena Sawant   *Houston Community College*
Emily Schmitt   *Nova Southeastern University*
Mark Schneegurt   *Wichita State University*
Brenda Schoffstall   *Barry University*
Scott Schuette   *Southern Illinois University*
Pramila Sen   *Houston Community College*
Bin Shuai   *Wichita State University*
Susan Skambis   *Valencia Community College*
Michael Smith   *Western Kentucky University*
Ramona Smith   *Brevard Community College*
Nancy G. Solomon   *Miami University*
Sally K. Sommers Smith   *Boston University*
Melissa Spitler   *California State University—Northridge*
Ashley Spring   *Brevard Community College*
Moira Van Staaden   *Bowling Green State University*
Bruce Stallsmith   *University of Alabama—Huntsville*
Susan Stamler   *College of DuPage*
Nancy Staub   *Gonzaga University*
Stanley Stevens   *University of Memphis*
Ivan Still   *Arkansas Tech University*
Gregory W. Stunz   *Texas A&M University—Corpus Christi*
Ken D. Sumida   *Chapman University*
Rema Suniga   *Ohio Northern University*

Bradley Swanson   *Central Michigan University*
David Tam   *University of North Texas*
Franklyn Tan Te   *Miami Dade College—Wolfson*
William Terzaghi   *Wilkes University*
Melvin Thomson   *University of Wisconsin—Parkside*
Martin Tracey   *Florida International University*
James Traniello   *Boston University*
Bibit Halliday Traut   *City College of San Francisco*
Alexa Tullis   *University of Puget Sound*
Catherine Ueckert   *Northern Arizona University*
Mark VanCura   *Cape Fear CC/University of NC Pembroke*
Charles J. Venglarik   *Jefferson State Community College*
Diane Wagner   *University of Alaska—Fairbanks*
Maureen Walter   *Florida International University*
Wei Wan   *Texas A&M University*
James T. Warren, Jr.   *Penn State Erie*
Delon Washo-Krupps   *Arizona State University*
Frederick Wasserman   *Boston University*
Raymond R. White   *City College of San Francisco*
Stephen W. White   *Ozarks Technical Community College*
Kimberlyn Williams   *California State University-San Bernardino*
Martha Comstock Williams   *Southern Polytechnic State University*
David E. Wolfe   *American River College*
Amber Wyman   *Finger Lakes Community College*
Robert D. Young, Jr.   *Blinn College*

Previous Edition Reviewers and Contributors

Art Review Panel

David K. Asch   *Youngstown State University*
Karl J. Aufderheide   *Texas A&M University*
Brian Bagatto   *University of Akron*
Andrew R. Blaustein   *Oregon State University*
Nancy Maroushek Boury   *Iowa State University*
Mark Browning   *Purdue University*
Jeff Carmichael   *University of North Dakota*
Wes Colgan III   *Pikes Peak Community College*
Karen A. Curto   *University of Pittsburgh*
Donald Deters   *Bowling Green State University*
Ernest F. DuBrul   *University of Toledo*
Ralph P. Eckerlin   *Northern Virginia Community College*
Julia Emerson   *Amherst College*
Frederick B. Essig   *University of South Florida*
Sharon Eversman   *Montana State University, Bozeman*
Barbara A. Frase   *Bradley University*
T. H. Frazzetta   *University of Illinois, Urbana—Champaign*
Douglas Gaffin   *University of Oklahoma*
John R. Geiser   *Western Michigan University*

Gonzalo Giribet   *Harvard University*
John Graham   *Bowling Green State University*
Susan E. Hengeveld   *Indiana University*
Richard Hill   *Michigan State University*
David Julian   *University of Florida*
Pamela J. Lanford   *University of Maryland, College Park*
James B. Ludden   *College of DuPage*
Duncan S. MacKenzie   *Texas A&M University*
Patricia Mire   *University of Louisiana, Lafayette*
Janice Moore   *Colorado State University*
Jacalyn S. Newman   *University of Pittsburgh*
Robert Newman   *University of North Dakota*
Nicole S. Obert   *University of Illinois, Urbana-Champaign*
David G. Oppenheimer   *University of Florida*
Ellen Ott-Reeves   *Blinn College, Bryan*
Laurel Bridges Roberts   *University of Pittsburgh*
Deemah N. Schirf   *The University of Texas, San Antonio*
Mark A. Sheridan   *North Dakota State University*
Richard Showman   *University of South Carolina*

Phillip Snider Jr.   *Gadsden State Community College*
Nancy G. Solomon   *Miami University*
David Tam   *University of North Texas*
Marty Tracey   *Florida International University*
Michael J. Wade   *Indiana University*
Jyoti R. Wagle   *Houston Community College System, Central*
Andy Wang   *The University of Iowa*
Cindy Martinez Wedig   *University of Texas, Pan American*
Elizabeth A. Weiss   *University of Texas, Austin*
C. B. Wolfe   *The University of North Carolina, Charlotte*

End-of-Chapter Pedagogy and Inquiry Contributors

Arthur Buikema   *Virginia Polytechnic Institute*
Merri Lynn Casem   *California State University-Fullerton*
Mark Lyford   *University of Wyoming*
Peter Niewiarowski   *University of Akron*
Thomas Pitzer   *Florida International University*
Laurel Roberts   *University of Pittsburgh*
Michael Windelspecht   *Appalachian State University*

Reviewers and Accuracy Checkers

Barbara J. Abraham   *Hampton University*
Richard Adler   *University of Michigan, Dearborn*
Sylvester Allred   *Northern Arizona University*
Steven M. Aquilani   *Delaware County Community College*
Jonathan W. Armbruster   *Auburn University*
Gregory A. Armstrong   *The Ohio State University*
Jorge E. Arriagada   *St. Cloud State University*
David K. Asch   *Youngstown State University*
Brian Bagatto   *University of Akron*
Garen Baghdasarian   *Santa Monica College*
Anita Davelos Baines   *The University of Texas, Pan American*
Ronald A. Balsamo Jr.   *Villanova University*
Michael Bartlett   *Portland State University*
Vernon W. Bauer   *Francis Marion University*
James E. Baxter   *Ohlone College*
George W. Benz   *Middle Tennessee State University*

Gerald K. Bergtrom   *University of Wisconsin, Milwaukee*

Arlene G. Billock   *University of Louisiana, Lafayette*

Catherine S. Black   *Idaho State University*

Michael W. Black   *California Polytechnic State University*

Robert O. Blanchard   *University of New Hampshire*

Andrew R. Blaustein   *Oregon State University*

Mary A. Bober   *Santa Monica College*

Nancy Maroushek Boury   *Iowa State University*

M. Deane Bowers   *University of Colorado*

Scott A. Bowling   *Auburn University*

Benita A. Brink   *Adams State College*

Anne Bullerjahn   *Owens Community College*

Ray D. Burkett   *Southwest Tennessee Community College*

Helaine Burstein   *Ohio University*

Scott Burt   *Truman State University*

Carol T. Burton   *Bellevue Community College*

Jennifer Carr Burtwistle   *Northeast Community College*

Jorge Busciglio   *University of California, Irvine*

Pat Calie   *Eastern Kentucky University*

Christy A. Carello   *The Metropolitan State College of Denver*

Michael Carey   *University of Scranton*

Jeff Carmichael   *University of North Dakota*

Michael J. Carlisle   *Trinity Valley Community College*

John H. Caruso   *University of New Orleans*

Thomas T. Chen   *University of Connecticut*

Cynthia Church   *The Metropolitan State College of Denver*

Linda T. Collins   *University of Tennessee, Chattanooga*

Scott T. Cooper   *University of Wisconsin, La Crosse*

Joe R. Cowles   *Virginia Tech*

Nigel M. Crawford   *University of California, San Diego*

James Crowder   *Brookdale Community College*

Karen A. Curto   *University of Pittsburgh*

Bela Dadhich   *Delaware County Community College*

Lydia B. Daniels   *University of Pittsburgh*

Terry Davin   *Penn Valley Community College*

Joseph S. Davis   *University of Florida*

Neta Dean   *Stony Brook University*

Kevin W. Dees   *Wharton County Junior College*

D. Michael Denbow   *Virginia Tech*

Donald Deters   *Bowling Green State University*

Hudson DeYoe   *University of Texas, Pan American*

Randy DiDomenico   *University of Colorado*

Nd Dikeocha   *College of the Mainland*

Robert S. Dill   *Bergen Community College*

Diane M. Dixon   *Southeastern Oklahoma State University*

Kevin Dixon   *University of Illinois*

John S. Doctor   *Duquesne University*

Ernest F. DuBrul   *University of Toledo*

Charles Duggins Jr.   *University of South Carolina*

Richard P. Elinson   *Duquesne University*

Johnny El-Rady   *University of South Florida*

Frederick B. Essig   *University of South Florida*

David H. Evans   *University of Florida*

Guy E. Farish   *Adams State College*

Daphne G. Fautin   *University of Kansas*

Bruce E. Felgenhauer   *University of Louisiana, Lafayette*

Carolyn J. Ferguson   *Kansas State University*

Teresa G. Fischer   *Indian River Community College*

Irwin Forseth   *University of Maryland*

Gail Fraizer   *Kent State University*

Barbara A. Frase   *Bradley University*

Sylvia Fromherz   *University of Northern Colorado*

Phillip E. Funk   *DePaul University*

Caitlin R. Gabor   *Texas State University, San Marcos*

Purti P. Gadkari   *Wharton County Junior College*

John R. Geiser   *Western Michigan University*

Frank S. Gilliam   *Marshall University*

Miriam S. Golbert   *College of the Canyons*

Scott A. Gordon   *University of Southern Indiana*

John S. Graham   *Bowling Green State University*

David A. Gray   *California State University, Northridge*

William F. Hanna   *Massasoit Community College*

Kyle E. Harms   *Louisiana State University*

Kerry D. Heafner   *University of Louisiana, Monroe*

Susan E. Hengeveld   *Indiana University*

Charles Henry   *University of Connecticut, Storrs*

Peter Heywood   *Brown University*

Juliana G. Hinton   *McNeese State University*

Margaret L. Horton   *University of North Carolina, Greensboro*

James Horwitz   *Palm Beach Community College*

Laura A. Houston   *Montgomery College*

Feng Sheng Hu   *University of Illinois*

Allen N. Hunt   *Elizabethtown Community and Technical College*

David C. Jarrell   *University of Mary Washington*

Jennifer L. Jeffery   *Wharton County Junior College*

William Jeffery   *University of Maryland, College Park*

Lee Johnson   *The Ohio State University*

Craig T. Jordan   *The University of Texas, San Antonio*

Ronald L. Jones   *Eastern Kentucky University*

Robyn Jordan   *University of Louisiana, Monroe*

Walter S. Judd   *University of Florida*

David Julian   *University of Florida*

Daniel Kainer   *Montgomery College*

Ronald C. Kaltreider   *York College of Pennsylvania*

Thomas C. Kane   *University of Cincinnati*

Donald A. Kangas   *Truman State University*

William J. Katembe   *Delta State University*

Steven J. Kaye   *Red Rocks Community College*

Stephen R. Kelso   *University of Illinois, Chicago*

Nancy S. Kirkpatrick   *Lake Superior State University*

John Z. Kiss   *Miami University*

John C. Krenetsky   *The Metropolitan State College of Denver*

Karin E. Krieger   *University of Wisconsin, Green Bay*

David T. Kurjiaka   *University of Arizona*

Arlene T. Larson   *University of Colorado, Denver*

Peter Lavrentyev   *University of Akron*

Laura G. Leff   *Kent State University*

Michael R. Lentz   *University of North Florida*

Harvey Liftin   *Broward Community College*

Yue J. Lin   *St. John's University*

Amy Litt   *New York Botanical Garden*

Christopher R. Little   *The University of Texas, Pan American*

James Long   *Boise State University*

James O. Luken   *Coastal Carolina University*

Dennis J. Lye   *Northern Kentucky University*

P. T. Magee   *University of Minnesota, Minneapolis*

Richard Malkin   *University of California, Berkeley*

Mark D. Mamrack   *Wright State University*

Kathleen A. Marrs   *Indiana University Purdue University, Indianapolis*

Diane L. Marshall   *University of New Mexico*

Paul B. Martin   *St. Philip's College*

Peter J. Martinat   *Xavier University, Los Angeles*

Joel Maruniak   *University of Missouri*

Patricia Matthews   *Grand Valley State University*

Robin G. Maxwell   *The University of North Carolina, Greensboro*

Brenda S. McAdory   *Tennessee State University*

Nael A. McCarty   *Georgia Institute of Technology*

Brock R. McMillan   *Minnesota State University, Mankato*

Kay McMurry   *The University of Texas, Austin*

Elizabeth McPartlan   *De Anza College*

Brad Mehrtens   *University of Illinois, Urbana—Champaign*

Michael Meighan   *University of California, Berkeley*

Douglas Meikle   *Miami University*

Allen F. Mensinger   *University of Minnesota, Duluth*

Wayne B. Merkley   *Drake University*

Catherine E. Merovich   *West Virginia University*

Frank J. Messina   *Utah State University*

Brian T. Miller   *Middle Tennessee State University*

Sarah L. Milton   *Florida Atlantic University*

Subhash Minocha   *University of New Hampshire*

Hector C. Miranda Jr.   *Texas Southern University*

Patricia Mire   *University of Louisiana, Lafayette*

Robert W. Morris   *Widener University*

Satyanarayana Swamy Mruthinti   *State University of West Georgia*

Richard L. Myers   *Southwest Missouri State University*

Monica Marquez Nelson   *Joliet Junior College*

Jacalyn S. Newman   *University of Pittsburgh*

Harry Nickla   *Creighton University*

Richard A. Niesenbaum   *Muhlenberg College*

Kris M. Norenberg   *Xavier University, Louisiana*

Deborah A. O'Dell   *University of Mary Washington*

Sharman D. O'Neill   *University of California, Davis*

Cynthia P. Paul   *University of Michigan, Dearborn*

John S. Peters   *College of Charleston*

Jay Phelan   *University of California, Los Angeles*

Gregory W. Phillips   *Blinn College*

Thomas R. Pitzer   *Florida International University*

Gregory J. Podgorski   *Utah State University*

Alan Prather   *Michigan State University*

Mitch Price   *The Pennsylvania State University*

Carl Quertermus   *State University of West Georgia*

Shana Rapoport   *California State University, Northridge*

Kim Raun   *Wharton County Junior College*

Robert S. Rawding   *Gannon University*

Jill D. Reid   *Virginia Commonwealth University*

Linda R. Richardson   *Blinn College*

Robin K. Richardson   *Winona State University*

Carolyn Roberson   *Roane State Community College*

Kenneth R. Robinson   *Purdue University*

Kenneth H. Roux   *Florida State University*

Charles L. Rutherford   *Virginia Tech University*

Margaret Saha   *College of William and Mary*

Thomas Sasek   *University of Louisiana, Monroe*

Bruce M. Saul   *Augusta State University*

Deemah N. Schirf   *The University of Texas, San Antonio*

Christopher J. Schneider   *Boston University*

Timothy E. Shannon   *Francis Marion University*

Rebecca Sheller   *Southwestern University*

Mark A. Sheridan   *North Dakota State University*

Richard Showman   *University of South Carolina*

Michéle Shuster   *New Mexico State University*

William Simcik   *Tomball College, a North Harris Community College*

Rebecca B. Simmons   *University of North Dakota*

Phillip Snider Jr.   *Gadsden State Community College*

Thomas E. Snowden   *Florida Memorial College*

Dianne Snyder   *Augusta State University*

Farah Sogo   *Orange Coast College*

Nancy G. Solomon   *Miami University*

Kathryn H. Sorensen   *American River College*

Kevin N. Sorensen   *Snow College*

Bruce Stallsmith   *University of Alabama, Huntsville*
Patricia Steinke   *San Jacinto College*
Jacqueline J. Stevens   *Jackson State University*
John W. Stiller   *East Carolina University*
Antony Stretton   *University of Wisconsin, Madison*
Brett W. Strong   *Palm Beach Community College*
Gregory W. Stunz   *Texas A&M University, Corpus Christi*
Cynthia A. Surmacz   *Bloomsburg University*
Yves S. H. Tan   *Cabrillo College*
Sharon Thoma   *University of Wisconsin, Madison*
Anne M. S. Tokazewski   *Burlington County College*
Marty Tracey   *Florida International University*

Terry M. Trier   *Grand Valley State University*
Marsha R. Turell   *Houston Community College*
Linda Tyson   *Santa Fe Community College*
Rani Vajravelu   *University of Central Florida*
Jim Van Brunt   *Rogue Community College*
Judith B. Varelas   *University of Northern Colorado*
Neal J. Voelz   *St. Cloud State University*
Janice Voltzow   *University of Scranton*
Jyoti R. Wagle   *Houston Community College System, Central*
Charles Walcott   *Cornell University*
Randall Walikonis   *University of Connecticut*
Eileen Walsh   *Westchester Community College*

Steven A. Wasserman   *University of California, San Diego*
R. Douglas Watson   *University of Alabama, Birmingham*
Cindy Martinez Wedig   *University of Texas, Pan American*
Richard Weinstein   *Southern New Hampshire University*
Elizabeth A. Weiss   *University of Texas, Austin*
William R. Wellnitz   *Augusta State University*
Jonathan F. Wendel   *Iowa State University*
Sue Simon Westendorf   *Ohio University*
Vernon Lee Wiersema   *Houston Community College, Southwest*
Judy Williams   *Southeastern Oklahoma State University*
Lawrence R. Williams   *University of Houston*

Robert Winning   *Eastern Michigan University*
C. B. Wolfe   *The University of North Carolina, Charlotte*
Clarence C. Wolfe   *Northern Virginia Community College*
Eric Vivien Wong   *University of Louisville*
Gene K. Wong   *Quinnipiac University*
Denise Woodward   *The Pennsylvania State University*
Richard P. Wunderlin   *University of South Florida*
Douglas A. Wymer   *The University of West Alabama*
Lan Xu   *South Dakota State University*
H. Randall Yoder   *Lamar University*
Kathryn G. Zeiler   *Red Rocks Community College*
Scott D. Zimmerman   *Missouri State University*
Henry G. Zot   *University of West Georgia*

International Reviewers

Mari L. Acevedo   *University of Puerto Rico, Arecibo*
Heather Addy   *University of Calgary*
Heather E. Allison   *University of Liverpool*
David Backhouse   *University of New England*
Andrew Bendall   *University of Guelph*
Tony Bradshaw   *Oxford Brookes University*
D. Bruce Campbell   *Okanagan College*
Clara E. Carrasco   *University of Puerto Rico, Ponce*
Ian Cock   *Griffith University*
Margaret Cooley   *University of New South Wales*
R. S. Currah   *University of Alberta*

Logan Donaldson   *York University*
Theo Elzenga   *University of Groningen*
Neil Haave   *University of Alberta, Augustana*
Louise M. Hafner   *QUT*
Clare Hasenkampf   *University of Toronto, Scarborough*
Annika F. M. Haywood   *Memorial University of Newfoundland*
Rong-Nan Huang   *National Central University*
William Huddleston   *University of Calgary*
Wendy J. Keenleyside   *University of Guelph*
Chris Kennedy   *Simon Fraser University*

Alex Law   *Nanyang Technical University, Singapore*
Richard C. Leegood   *University of Sheffield*
R. W. Longair   *University of Calgary*
Thomas H. MacRae   *Dalhousie University*
Rolf W. Matthewes   *Simon Fraser University*
R. Ian Menz   *Flinders University*
Todd C. Nickle   *Mount Royal College*
Kirsten Poling   *University of Windsor*
Jim Provan   *Queen's University Belfast*
Roberto Quinlan   *York University*
Elsa I. Colón Reyes   *University of Puerto Rico, Aguadilla Campus*
Richard Roy   *McGill University*

Liliane Schoofs   *Katholicke Universiteit Leuren*
Joan Sharp   *Simon Fraser University*
Julie Smit   *University of Windsor*
Nguan Soon Tan   *Nanyang Technological University*
Fleur Tiver   *University of South Australia*
Llinil Torres-Ojeda   *University of Puerto Rico, Aguadilla Campus*
Han A. B. Wösten   *University of Utrecht*
H. H. Yeoh   *National University of Singapore*
Dr. Khaled Abou-Aisha   *German University in Cairo*

A Note From the Authors

A revision of this scope relies on the talents and efforts of many people working behind the scenes and we have benefited greatly from their assistance.

Jody Larson, our developmental copyeditor, labored many hours and provided countless suggestions for improving the organization and clarity of the text. She has made a tremendous contribution to the quality of the final product.

We were fortunate to again work with Electronic Publishing Services to update the art program and improve the layout of the pages. Our close collaboration resulted in a text that is pedagogically effective as well as more beautiful than any other biology text on the market.

We have the continued support of our McGraw-Hill team. Developmental editors Rose Koos and Lisa Bruflodt kept the authors on track during the development process. Sheila Frank, project manager, and David Hash, designer, ensured our text was on time and elegantly designed. Patrick Reidy, marketing manager and many more people behind the scenes have all contributed to the success or our text.

Throughout this edition we have had the support of spouses and children, who have seen less of us than they might have liked because of the pressures of getting this revision completed. They have adapted to the many hours this book draws us away from them, and, even more than us, looked forward to its completion.

As with every edition, acknowledgments would not be complete without thanking the generations of students who have used the many editions of this text. They have taught us as least as much as we have taught them, and their questions and suggestions continue to improve the text and supplementary materials.

Finally, we need to thank our reviewers and contributors. Instructors from across the country are continually invited to share their knowledge and experience with us through reviews and focus groups. The feedback we received shaped this edition, resulting in new chapters, reorganization of the table of contents, and expanded coverage in key areas. Several faculty members were asked to provide preliminary drafts of chapters to ensure that the content was as up to date and accurate as possible, and still others were asked to provide chapter outlines and assessment questions. All of these people took time out of their already busy lives to help us build a better edition of Biology for the next generation of introductory biology students, and they have our heartfelt thanks.

Contents

Part I — The Molecular Basis of Life

1 The Science of Biology 1
1.1 The Science of Life 1
1.2 The Nature of Science 4
1.3 An Example of Scientific Inquiry: Darwin and Evolution 8
1.4 Unifying Themes in Biology 12

2 The Nature of Molecules and the Properties of Water 17
2.1 The Nature of Atoms 18
2.2 Elements Found in Living Systems 22
2.3 The Nature of Chemical Bonds 23
2.4 Water: A Vital Compound 25
2.5 Properties of Water 28
2.6 Acids and Bases 29

3 The Chemical Building Blocks of Life 33
3.1 Carbon: The Framework of Biological Molecules 34
3.2 Carbohydrates: Energy Storage and Structural Molecules 38
3.3 Nucleic Acids: Information Molecules 41
3.4 Proteins: Molecules with Diverse Structures and Functions 44
3.5 Lipids: Hydrophobic Molecules 53

Part II — Biology of the Cell

4 Cell Structure 59
4.1 Cell Theory 59
4.2 Prokaryotic Cells 63
4.3 Eukaryotic Cells 65
4.4 The Endomembrane System 69
4.5 Mitochondria and Chloroplasts: Cellular Generators 73
4.6 The Cytoskeleton 75
4.7 Extracellular Structures and Cell Movement 79
4.8 Cell-to-Cell Interactions 82

5 Membranes 88
5.1 The Structure of Membranes 88
5.2 Phospholipids: The Membrane's Foundation 92
5.3 Proteins: Multifunctional Components 93
5.4 Passive Transport Across Membranes 96
5.5 Active Transport Across Membranes 99
5.6 Bulk Transport by Endocytosis and Exocytosis 102

6 Energy and Metabolism 107
6.1 The Flow of Energy in Living Systems 108
6.2 The Laws of Thermodynamics and Free Energy 109
6.3 ATP: The Energy Currency of Cells 112
6.4 Enzymes: Biological Catalysts 113
6.5 Metabolism: The Chemical Description of Cell Function 117

7 How Cells Harvest Energy 122
7.1 Overview of Respiration 123
7.2 Glycolysis: Splitting Glucose 127
7.3 The Oxidation of Pyruvate to Produce Acetyl-CoA 130
7.4 The Krebs Cycle 131
7.5 The Electron Transport Chain and Chemiosmosis 134
7.6 Energy Yield of Aerobic Respiration 137
7.7 Regulation of Aerobic Respiration 138
7.8 Oxidation Without O_2 139
7.9 Catabolism of Proteins and Fats 140
7.10 Evolution of Metabolism 142

8 Photosynthesis 147
8.1 Overview of Photosynthesis 147
8.2 The Discovery of Photosynthetic Processes 149
8.3 Pigments 151
8.4 Photosystem Organization 154
8.5 The Light-Dependent Reactions 156
8.6 Carbon Fixation: The Calvin Cycle 160
8.7 Photorespiration 163

9 Cell Communication 168
9.1 Overview of Cell Communication 168
9.2 Receptor Types 171
9.3 Intracellular Receptors 173
9.4 Signal Transduction Through Receptor Kinases 174
9.5 Signal Transduction Through G Protein-Coupled Receptors 179

10 How Cells Divide 186

10.1 Bacterial Cell Division 187
10.2 Eukaryotic Chromosomes 189
10.3 Overview of the Eukaryotic Cell Cycle 192
10.4 Interphase: Preparation for Mitosis 193
10.5 M Phase: Chromosome Segregation and the Division of Cytoplasmic Contents 194
10.6 Control of the Cell Cycle 198

Part III Genetic and Molecular Biology

11 Sexual Reproduction and Meiosis 207

11.1 Sexual Reproduction Requires Meiosis 207
11.2 Features of Meiosis 209
11.3 The Process of Meiosis 210
11.4 Summing Up: Meiosis Versus Mitosis 215

12 Patterns of Inheritance 221

12.1 The Mystery of Heredity 221
12.2 Monohybrid Crosses: The Principle of Segregation 224
12.3 Dihybrid Crosses: The Principle of Independent Assortment 228
12.4 Probability: Predicting the Results of Crosses 230
12.5 The Testcross: Revealing Unknown Genotypes 231
12.6 Extensions to Mendel 232

13 Chromosomes, Mapping, and the Meiosis–Inheritance Connection 239

13.1 Sex Linkage and the Chromosomal Theory of Inheritance 240
13.2 Sex Chromosomes and Sex Determination 241
13.3 Exceptions to the Chromosomal Theory of Inheritance 244
13.4 Genetic Mapping 244
13.5 Selected Human Genetic Disorders 249

14 DNA: The Genetic Material 256

14.1 The Nature of the Genetic Material 256
14.2 DNA Structure 259
14.3 Basic Characteristics of DNA Replication 263
14.4 Prokaryotic Replication 266
14.5 Eukaryotic Replication 271
14.6 DNA Repair 273

15 Genes and How They Work 278

15.1 The Nature of Genes 278
15.2 The Genetic Code 282
15.3 Prokaryotic Transcription 284
15.4 Eukaryotic Transcription 287
15.5 Eukaryotic pre-mRNA Splicing 289
15.6 The Structure of tRNA and Ribosomes 291
15.7 The Process of Translation 293
15.8 Summarizing Gene Expression 297
15.9 Mutation: Altered Genes 299

16 Control of Gene Expression 304

16.1 Control of Gene Expression 304
16.2 Regulatory Proteins 305
16.3 Prokaryotic Regulation 308
16.4 Eukaryotic Regulation 312
16.5 Eukaryotic Chromatin Structure 316
16.6 Eukaryotic Posttranscriptional Regulation 317
16.7 Protein Degradation 322

17 Biotechnology 327

17.1 DNA Manipulation 327
17.2 Molecular Cloning 330
17.3 DNA Analysis 335
17.4 Genetic Engineering 341
17.5 Medical Applications 343
17.6 Agricultural Applications 346

18 Genomics 352

18.1 Mapping Genomes 352
18.2 Whole-Genome Sequencing 356
18.3 Characterizing Genomes 358
18.4 Genomics and Proteomics 362
18.5 Applications of Genomics 367

19 Cellular Mechanisms of Development 372

19.1 The Process of Development 372
19.2 Cell Division 373
19.3 Cell Differentiation 375
19.4 Nuclear Reprogramming 380
19.5 Pattern Formation 383
19.6 Morphogenesis 390

Part VI Plant Form and Function

36 Plant Form 729

36.1 Organization of the Plant Body: An Overview 730
36.2 Plant Tissues 733
36.3 Roots: Anchoring and Absorption Structures 739
36.4 Stems: Support for Above-Ground Organs 743
36.5 Leaves: Photosynthetic Organs 747

37 Vegetative Plant Development 753

37.1 Embryo Development 754
37.2 Seeds 760
37.3 Fruits 761
37.4 Germination 764

38 Transport in Plants 769

38.1 Transport Mechanisms 770
38.2 Water and Mineral Absorption 773
38.3 Xylem Transport 776
38.4 The Rate of Transpiration 778
38.5 Water-Stress Responses 780
38.6 Phloem Transport 781

39 Plant Nutrition and Soils 786

39.1 Soils: The Substrates on Which Plants Depend 787
39.2 Plant Nutrients 790
39.3 Special Nutritional Strategies 792
39.4 Carbon–Nitrogen Balance and Global Change 795
39.5 Phytoremediation 797

40 Plant Defense Responses 802

40.1 Physical Defenses 802
40.2 Chemical Defenses 805
40.3 Animals that Protect Plants 809
40.4 Systemic Responses to Invaders 810

41 Sensory Systems in Plants 814

41.1 Responses to Light 815
41.2 Responses to Gravity 819
41.3 Responses to Mechanical Stimuli 821
41.4 Responses to Water and Temperature 823
41.5 Hormones and Sensory Systems 825

42 Plant Reproduction 839

42.1 Reproductive Development 840
42.2 Flower Production 842
42.3 Structure and Evolution of Flowers 848
42.4 Pollination and Fertilization 851
42.5 Asexual Reproduction 857
42.6 Plant Life Spans 859

Part VII Animal Form and Function

43 The Animal Body and Principles of Regulation 863

43.1 Organization of the Vertebrate Body 864
43.2 Epithelial Tissue 865
43.3 Connective Tissue 868
43.4 Muscle Tissue 870
43.5 Nerve Tissue 872
43.6 Overview of Vertebrate Organ Systems 872
43.7 Homeostasis 876
43.8 Regulating Body Temperature 878

44 The Nervous System 887

44.1 Nervous System Organization 888
44.2 The Mechanism of Nerve Impulse Transmission 890
44.3 Synapses: Where Neurons Communicate with Other Cells 896
44.4 The Central Nervous System: Brain and Spinal Cord 901
44.5 The Peripheral Nervous System: Sensory and Motor Neurons 909

45 Sensory Systems 915

45.1 Overview of Sensory Receptors 916
45.2 Mechanoreceptors: Touch and Pressure 917
45.3 Hearing, Vibration, and Detection of Body Position 920
45.4 Chemoreceptors: Taste, Smell, and pH 925
45.5 Vision 928
45.6 The Diversity of Sensory Experiences 933

46 The Endocrine System 937

46.1 Regulation of Body Processes by Chemical Messengers 938
46.2 Actions of Lipophilic Versus Hydrophilic Hormones 943
46.3 The Pituitary and Hypothalamus: The Body's Control Centers 946
46.4 The Major Peripheral Endocrine Glands 951
46.5 Other Hormones and Their Effects 955

47 The Musculoskeletal System 961

47.1 Types of Skeletal Systems 962
47.2 A Closer Look at Bone 963
47.3 Joints and Skeletal Movement 967
47.4 Muscle Contraction 969
47.5 Modes of Animal Locomotion 975

48 The Digestive System 981

48.1 Types of Digestive Systems 982
48.2 The Mouth and Teeth: Food Capture and Bulk Processing 984
48.3 The Esophagus and the Stomach: The Early Stages of Digestion 985
48.4 The Intestines: Breakdown, Absorption, and Elimination 987
48.5 Variations in Vertebrate Digestive Systems 990
48.6 Neural and Hormonal Regulation of the Digestive Tract 993
48.7 Accessory Organ Function 994
48.8 Food Energy, Energy Expenditure, and Essential Nutrients 995

49 The Respiratory System 1001
49.1 Gas Exchange Across Respiratory Surfaces 1002
49.2 Gills, Cutaneous Respiration, and Tracheal Systems 1004
49.3 Lungs 1006
49.4 Structures and Mechanisms of Ventilation in Mammals 1009
49.5 Transport of Gases in Body Fluids 1012

50 The Circulatory System 1018
50.1 The Components of Blood 1018
50.2 Invertebrate Circulatory Systems 1022
50.3 Vertebrate Circulatory Systems 1023
50.4 The Four-Chambered Heart and the Blood Vessels 1026
50.5 Characteristics of Blood Vessels 1030
50.6 Regulation of Blood Flow and Blood Pressure 1034

51 Osmotic Regulation and the Urinary System 1038
51.1 Osmolarity and Osmotic Balance 1038
51.2 Osmoregulatory Organs 1040
51.3 Evolution of the Vertebrate Kidney 1042
51.4 Nitrogenous Wastes: Ammonia, Urea, and Uric Acid 1044
51.5 The Mammalian Kidney 1045
51.6 Hormonal Control of Osmoregulatory Functions 1050

52 The Immune System 1055
52.1 Innate Immunity 1055
52.2 Adaptive Immunity 1061
52.3 Cell-Mediated Immunity 1066
52.4 Humoral Immunity and Antibody Production 1068
52.5 Autoimmunity and Hypersensitivity 1075
52.6 Antibodies in Medical Treatment and Diagnosis 1077
52.7 Pathogens That Evade the Immune System 1079

53 The Reproductive System 1084
53.1 Animal Reproductive Strategies 1084
53.2 Vertebrate Fertilization and Development 1087
53.3 Structure and Function of the Human Male Reproductive System 1091
53.4 Structure and Function of the Human Female Reproductive System 1094
53.5 Contraception and Infertility Treatments 1098

54 Animal Development 1105
54.1 Fertilization 1106
54.2 Cleavage and the Blastula Stage 1110
54.3 Gastrulation 1112
54.4 Organogenesis 1116
54.5 Vertebrate Axis Formation 1122
54.6 Human Development 1125

Part VIII Ecology and Behavior

55 Behavioral Biology 1132
55.1 The Natural History of Behavior 1133
55.2 Nerve Cells, Neurotransmitters, Hormones, and Behavior 1134
55.3 Behavioral Genetics 1135
55.4 Learning 1137
55.5 The Development of Behavior 1139
55.6 Animal Cognition 1141
55.7 Orientation and Migratory Behavior 1142
55.8 Animal Communication 1144
55.9 Behavioral Ecology 1147
55.10 Reproductive Strategies and Sexual Selection 1150
55.11 Altruism 1154
55.12 The Evolution of Group Living and Animal Societies 1157

56 Ecology of Individuals and Populations 1162
56.1 The Environmental Challenges 1162
56.2 Populations: Groups of a Single Species in One Place 1165
56.3 Population Demography and Dynamics 1168
56.4 Life History and the Cost of Reproduction 1171
56.5 Environmental Limits to Population Growth 1173
56.6 Factors That Regulate Populations 1175
56.7 Human Population Growth 1178

57 Community Ecology 1185
57.1 Biological Communities: Species Living Together 1186
57.2 The Ecological Niche Concept 1188
57.3 Predator–Prey Relationships 1192
57.4 The Many Types of Species Interactions 1196
57.5 Ecological Succession, Disturbance, and Species Richness 1202

58 Dynamics of Ecosystems 1207
58.1 Biogeochemical Cycles 1208
58.2 The Flow of Energy in Ecosystems 1214
58.3 Trophic-Level Interactions 1219
58.4 Biodiversity and Ecosystem Stability 1223
58.5 Island Biogeography 1226

59 The Biosphere 1230
59.1 Ecosystem Effects of Sun, Wind, and Water 1230
59.2 Earth's Biomes 1235
59.3 Freshwater Habitats 1238
59.4 Marine Habitats 1241
59.5 Human Impacts on the Biosphere: Pollution and Resource Depletion 1245
59.6 Human Impacts on the Biosphere: Climate Change 1250

Appendix A A-1 **Glossary** G-1 **Credits** C-1 **Index** I-1

Chapter

1

The Science of Biology

Chapter Outline

1.1 The Science of Life

1.2 The Nature of Science

1.3 An Example of Scientific Inquiry:
Darwin and Evolution

1.4 Unifying Themes in Biology

Introduction

You are about to embark on a journey—a journey of discovery about the nature of life. Nearly 180 years ago, a young English naturalist named Charles Darwin set sail on a similar journey on board H.M.S. Beagle; a replica of this ship is pictured here. What Darwin learned on his five-year voyage led directly to his development of the theory of evolution by natural selection, a theory that has become the core of the science of biology. Darwin's voyage seems a fitting place to begin our exploration of biology—the scientific study of living organisms and how they have evolved. Before we begin, however, let's take a moment to think about what biology is and why it's important.

1.1 The Science of Life

Learning Outcomes

1. *Explain the importance of biology as a science.*
2. *Describe the characteristics of living systems.*
3. *Recognize the hierarchical organization of living systems.*

This is the most exciting time to be studying biology in the history of the field. The amount of data available about the natural world has exploded in the last 25 years, and we are now in a position to ask and answer questions that previously were only dreamed of.

We have determined the entire sequence of the human genome and are in the process of sequencing the genomes of other species at an ever-increasing pace. We are closing in on a description of the molecular workings of the cell in unprecedented detail, and we are in the process of finally unveiling the mystery of how a single cell can give rise to the complex organization seen in multicellular organisms. With robotics, advanced imaging, and analytical techniques, we have tools available that were formerly the stuff of science fiction.

In this text, we attempt to draw a contemporary picture of the science of biology, as well as provide some history and experimental perspective on this exciting time in the discipline. In this introductory chapter, we examine the nature of biology and the foundations of science in general to put into context the information presented in the rest of the text.

Biology unifies much of natural science

The study of biology is a point of convergence for the information and tools from all of the natural sciences. Biological systems are the most complex chemical systems on Earth, and their many functions are both determined and constrained by the principles of chemistry and physics. Put another way, no new laws of nature can be gleaned from the study of biology—but that study does illuminate and illustrate the workings of those natural laws.

The intricate chemical workings of cells are based on everything we have learned from the study of chemistry. And every level of biological organization is governed by the nature of energy transactions learned from the study of thermodynamics. Biological systems do not represent any new forms of matter, and yet they are the most complex organization of matter known. The complexity of living systems is made possible by a constant source of energy—the Sun. The conversion of this energy source into organic molecules by photosynthesis is one of the most beautiful and complex reactions known in chemistry and physics.

The way we do science is changing to grapple with increasingly difficult modern problems. Science is becoming more interdisciplinary, combining the expertise from a variety of exciting new fields such as nanotechnology. Biology is at the heart of this multidisciplinary approach because biological problems often require many different approaches to arrive at solutions.

Life defies simple definition

In its broadest sense, biology is the study of living things—*the science of life*. Living things come in an astounding variety of shapes and forms, and biologists study life in many different ways. They live with gorillas, collect fossils, and listen to whales. They read the messages encoded in the long molecules of heredity and count how many times a hummingbird's wings beat each second.

What makes something "alive"? Anyone could deduce that a galloping horse is alive and a car is not, but why? We cannot say, "If it moves, it's alive," because a car can move, and gelatin can wiggle in a bowl. They certainly are not alive. Although we cannot define life with a single simple sentence, we can come up with a series of seven characteristics shared by living systems:

- **Cellular organization.** All organisms consist of one or more cells. Often too tiny to see, cells carry out the basic activities of living. Each cell is bounded by a membrane that separates it from its surroundings.
- **Ordered complexity.** All living things are both complex and highly ordered. Your body is composed of many different kinds of cells, each containing many complex

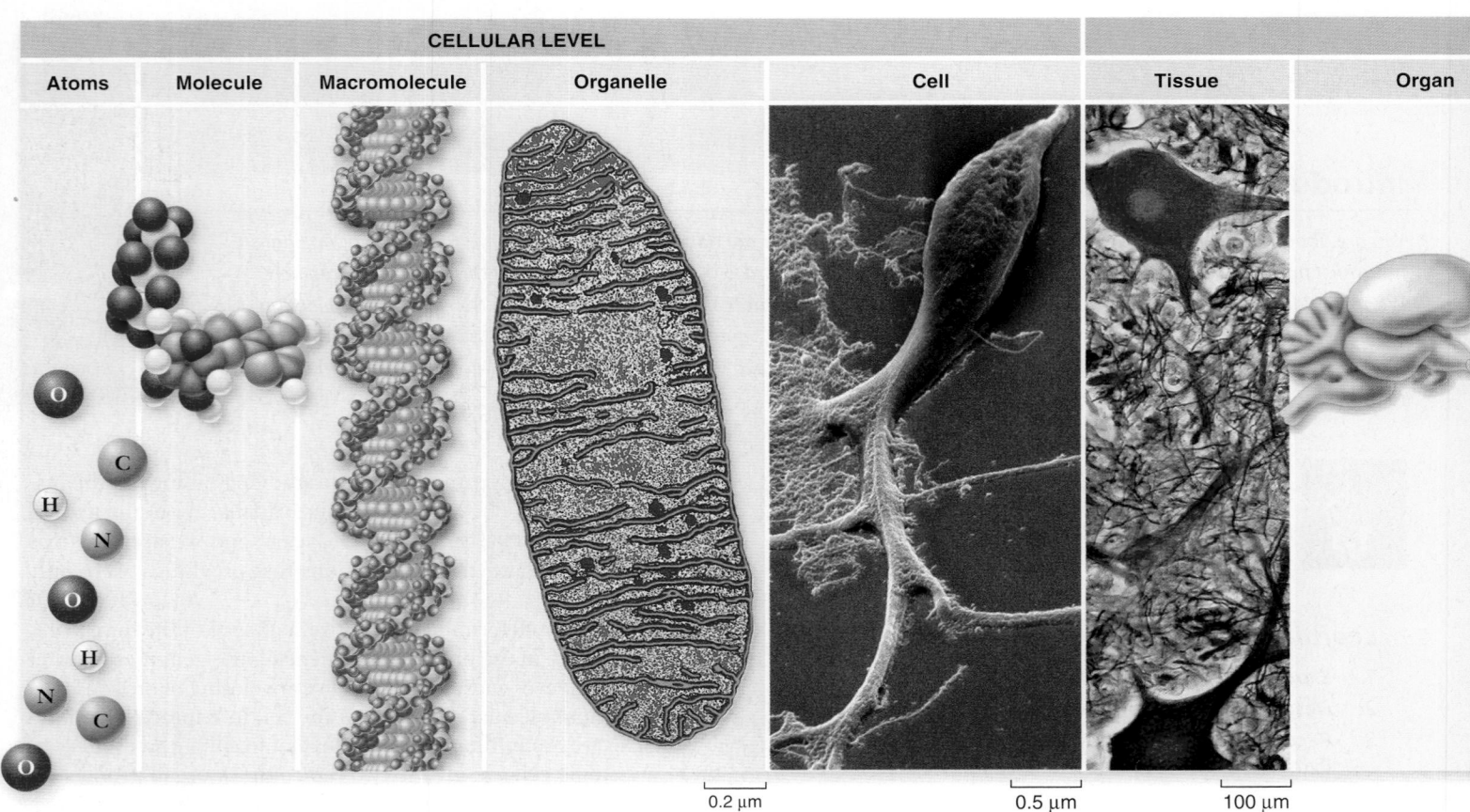

CELLULAR LEVEL

| Atoms | Molecule | Macromolecule | Organelle | Cell | Tissue | Organ |

0.2 μm   0.5 μm   100 μm

molecular structures. Many nonliving things may also be complex, but they do not exhibit this degree of ordered complexity.

- **Sensitivity.** All organisms respond to stimuli. Plants grow toward a source of light, and the pupils of your eyes dilate when you walk into a dark room.
- **Growth, development, and reproduction.** All organisms are capable of growing and reproducing, and they all possess hereditary molecules that are passed to their offspring, ensuring that the offspring are of the same species.
- **Energy utilization.** All organisms take in energy and use it to perform many kinds of work. Every muscle in your body is powered with energy you obtain from the food you eat.
- **Homeostasis.** All organisms maintain relatively constant internal conditions that are different from their environment, a process called **homeostasis.**
- **Evolutionary adaptation.** All organisms interact with other organisms and the nonliving environment in ways that influence their survival, and as a consequence, organisms evolve adaptations to their environments.

Living systems show hierarchical organization

The organization of the biological world is hierarchical—that is, each level builds on the level below it.

1. **The Cellular Level.** At the cellular level (figure 1.1), **atoms,** the fundamental elements of matter, are joined together into clusters called **molecules.** Complex biological molecules are assembled into tiny structures called **organelles** within membrane-bounded units we call **cells.** The cell is the basic unit of life. Many independent organisms are composed only of single cells. Bacteria are single cells, for example. All animals and plants, as well as most fungi and algae, are multicellular—composed of more than one cell.

2. **The Organismal Level.** Cells in complex multicellular organisms exhibit three levels of organization. The most basic level is that of **tissues,** which are groups of similar cells that act as a functional unit. Tissues, in turn, are grouped into **organs**—body structures composed of several different tissues that act as a structural and functional unit. Your brain is an organ composed of nerve cells and a variety of associated tissues that form protective coverings and contribute blood. At the third level of organization, organs are grouped into **organ systems.** The nervous system, for example, consists of sensory organs, the brain and spinal cord, and neurons that convey signals.

Figure 1.1 Hierarchical organization of living systems. Life is highly organized from the simplest atoms to complex multicellular organisms. Along this hierarchy of structure, atoms form molecules that are used to form organelles, which in turn form the functional subsystems within cells. Cells are organized into tissues, and then into organs and organ systems such as the nervous system pictured. This organization extends beyond individual organisms to populations, communities, ecosystems, and finally the entire biosphere.

ORGANISMAL LEVEL		POPULATIONAL LEVEL				
Organ system	Organism	Population	Species	Community	Ecosystem	Biosphere

3. **The Populational Level.** Individual organisms can be categorized into several hierarchical levels within the living world. The most basic of these is the **population**—a group of organisms of the same species living in the same place. All populations of a particular kind of organism together form a **species,** its members similar in appearance and able to interbreed. At a higher level of biological organization, a **biological community** consists of all the populations of different species living together in one place.

4. **Ecosystem Level.** At the highest tier of biological organization, a biological community and the physical habitat within which it lives together constitute an ecological system, or **ecosystem.** For example, the soil, water, and atmosphere of a mountain ecosystem interact with the biological community of a mountain meadow in many important ways.

5. **The Biosphere.** The entire planet can be thought of as an ecosystem that we call the biosphere.

As you move up this hierarchy, novel properties emerge. These **emergent properties** result from the way in which components interact, and they often cannot be deduced just from looking at the parts themselves. Examining individual cells, for example, gives little hint about the whole animal. You, and all humans, have the same array of cell types as a giraffe. It is because the living world exhibits many emergent properties that it is difficult to define "life."

The previous descriptions of the common features and organization of living systems begins to get at the nature of what it is to be alive. The rest of this book illustrates and expands on these basic ideas to try to provide a more complete account of living systems.

Learning Outcomes Review 1.1

Biology is a unifying science that brings together other natural sciences, such as chemistry and physics, to study living systems. Life does not have a simple definition, but living systems share a number of properties that together describe life. Living systems can also be organized hierarchically, from the cellular level to the entire biosphere, with emerging properties that may exceed the sum of the parts.

■ *Can you study biology without studying other sciences?*

1.2 The Nature of Science

Learning Outcomes

1. *Describe the types of reasoning used by biologists.*
2. *Demonstrate how to formulate a hypothesis.*

Much like life itself, the nature of science defies simple description. For many years scientists have written about the "scien-

tific method" as though there is a single way of doing science. This oversimplification has contributed to confusion on the part of nonscientists about the nature of science.

At its core, science is concerned with developing an increasingly accurate understanding of the world around us using observation and reasoning. To begin with, we assume that natural forces acting now have always acted, that the fundamental nature of the universe has not changed since its inception, and that it is not changing now. A number of complementary approaches allow understanding of natural phenomena—there is no one "right way."

Scientists also attempt to be as objective as possible in the interpretation of the data and observations they have collected. Because scientists themselves are human, this is not completely possible, but because science is a collective endeavor subject to scrutiny, it is self-correcting. One person's results are verified by others, and if the results cannot be repeated, they are rejected.

Much of science is descriptive

The classic vision of the scientific method is that observations lead to hypotheses that in turn make experimentally testable predictions. In this way, we dispassionately evaluate new ideas to arrive at an increasingly accurate view of nature. We discuss this way of doing science later in this chapter, but it is important to understand that much of science is purely descriptive: In order to understand anything, the first step is to describe it completely. Much of biology is concerned with arriving at an increasingly accurate description of nature.

The study of biodiversity is an example of descriptive science that has implications for other aspects of biology in addition to societal implications. Efforts are currently underway to classify all life on Earth. This ambitious project is purely descriptive, but it will lead to a much greater understanding of biodiversity as well as the effect our species has on biodiversity.

One of the most important accomplishments of molecular biology at the dawn of the 21st century was the completion of the sequence of the human genome. Many new hypotheses about human biology will be generated by this knowledge, and many experiments will be needed to test these hypotheses, but the determination of the sequence itself was descriptive science.

Science uses both deductive and inductive reasoning

The study of logic recognizes two opposite ways of arriving at logical conclusions: deductive and inductive reasoning. Science makes use of both of these methods, although induction is the primary way of reasoning in hypothesis-driven science.

Deductive reasoning

Deductive reasoning applies general principles to predict specific results. More than 2200 years ago, the Greek scientist Eratosthenes used Euclidean geometry and deductive reasoning to accurately estimate the circumference of the Earth (figure 1.2). Deductive reasoning is the reasoning of mathematics and

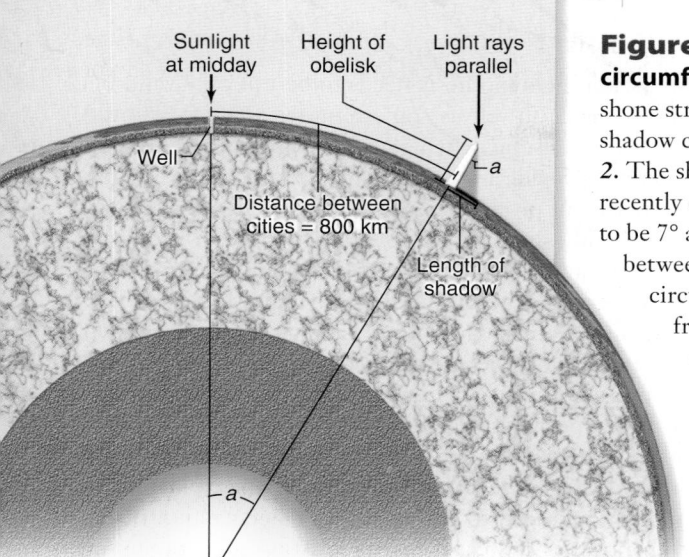

Figure 1.2 Deductive reasoning: how Eratosthenes estimated the circumference of the earth using deductive reasoning. *1.* On a day when sunlight shone straight down a deep well at Syene in Egypt, Eratosthenes measured the length of the shadow cast by a tall obelisk in the city of Alexandria, about 800 kilometers (km) away. *2.* The shadow's length and the obelisk's height formed two sides of a triangle. Using the recently developed principles of Euclidean geometry, Eratosthenes calculated the angle, *a*, to be 7° and 12′, exactly ⅟₅₀ of a circle (360°). *3.* If angle *a* is ⅟₅₀ of a circle, then the distance between the obelisk (in Alexandria) and the well (in Syene) must be equal to ⅟₅₀ the circumference of the Earth. *4.* Eratosthenes had heard that it was a 50-day camel trip from Alexandria to Syene. Assuming that a camel travels about 18.5 km per day, he estimated the distance between obelisk and well as 925 km (using different units of measure, of course). *5.* Eratosthenes thus deduced the circumference of the Earth to be 50 × 925 = 46,250 km. Modern measurements put the distance from the well to the obelisk at just over 800 km. Employing a distance of 800 km, Eratosthenes's value would have been 50 × 800 = 40,000 km. The actual circumference is 40,075 km.

philosophy, and it is used to test the validity of general ideas in all branches of knowledge. For example, if all mammals by definition have hair, and you find an animal that does not have hair, then you may conclude that this animal is not a mammal. A biologist uses deductive reasoning to infer the species of a specimen from its characteristics.

Inductive reasoning

In **inductive reasoning,** the logic flows in the opposite direction, from the specific to the general. Inductive reasoning uses specific observations to construct general scientific principles. For example, if poodles have hair, and terriers have hair, and every dog that you observe has hair, then you may conclude that all dogs have hair. Inductive reasoning leads to generalizations that can then be tested. Inductive reasoning first became important to science in the 1600s in Europe, when Francis Bacon, Isaac Newton, and others began to use the results of particular experiments to infer general principles about how the world operates.

An example from modern biology is the role of homeobox genes in development. Studies in the fruit fly, *Drosophila melanogaster,* identified genes that could cause dramatic changes in developmental fate, such as a leg appearing in the place of an antenna. When the genes themselves were isolated and their DNA sequence determined, it was found that similar genes were found in many animals, including humans. This led to the general idea that the homeobox genes act as switches to control developmental fate.

Hypothesis-driven science makes and tests predictions

Scientists establish which general principles are true from among the many that might be true through the process of systematically testing alternative proposals. If these proposals prove inconsistent with experimental observations, they are rejected as untrue. Figure 1.3 illustrates the process.

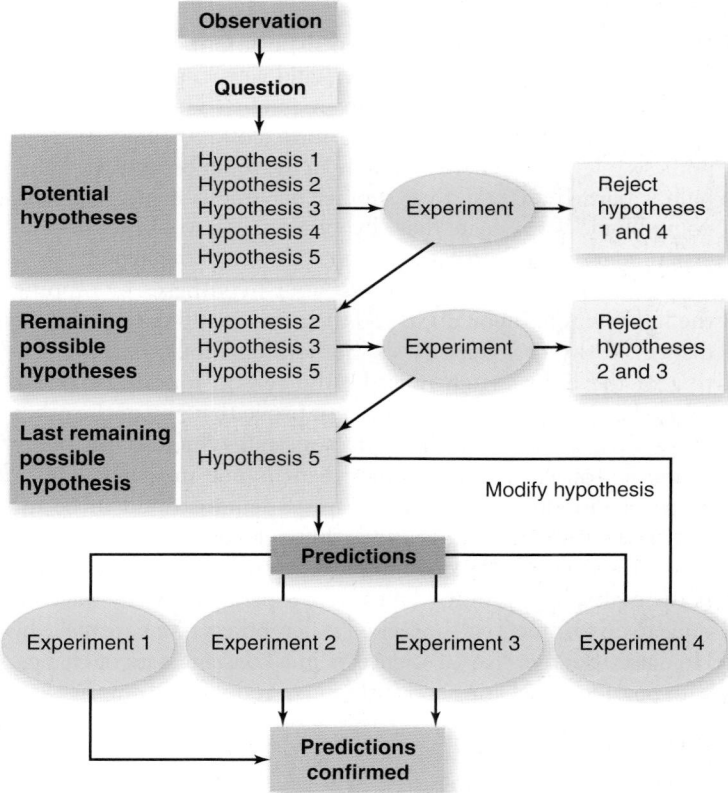

Figure 1.3 How science is done. This diagram illustrates how scientific investigations proceed. First, scientists make observations that raise a particular question. They develop a number of potential explanations (hypotheses) to answer the question. Next, they carry out experiments in an attempt to eliminate one or more of these hypotheses. Then, predictions are made based on the remaining hypotheses, and further experiments are carried out to test these predictions. The process can also be iterative. As experimental results are performed, the information can be used to modify the original hypothesis to fit each new observation.

After making careful observations, scientists construct a **hypothesis,** which is a suggested explanation that accounts for those observations. A hypothesis is a proposition that might be true. Those hypotheses that have not yet been disproved are retained. They are useful because they fit the known facts, but they are always subject to future rejection if, in the light of new information, they are found to be incorrect.

This process can also be *iterative*, that is, a hypothesis can be changed and refined with new data. For instance, geneticists George Beadle and Edward Tatum studied the nature of genetic information to arrive at their "one-gene/one-enzyme" hypothesis (see chapter 15). This hypothesis states that a gene represents the genetic information necessary to make a single enzyme. As investigators learned more about the molecular nature of genetic information, the hypothesis was refined to "one-gene/one-polypeptide" because enzymes can be made up of more than one polypeptide. With still more information about the nature of genetic information, other investigators found that a single gene can specify more than one polypeptide, and the hypothesis was refined again.

Testing hypotheses

We call the test of a hypothesis an **experiment.** Suppose that a room appears dark to you. To understand why it appears dark, you propose several hypotheses. The first might be, "There is no light in the room because the light switch is turned off." An alternative hypothesis might be, "There is no light in the room because the lightbulb is burned out." And yet another hypothesis might be, "I am going blind." To evaluate these hypotheses, you would conduct an experiment designed to eliminate one or more of the hypotheses.

For example, you might test your hypotheses by flipping the light switch. If you do so and the room is still dark, you have disproved the first hypothesis: Something other than the setting of the light switch must be the reason for the darkness. Note that a test such as this does not prove that any of the other hypotheses are true; it merely demonstrates that the one being tested is not. A successful experiment is one in which one or more of the alternative hypotheses is demonstrated to be inconsistent with the results and is thus rejected.

As you proceed through this text, you will encounter many hypotheses that have withstood the test of experiment. Many will continue to do so; others will be revised as new observations are made by biologists. Biology, like all science, is in a constant state of change, with new ideas appearing and replacing or refining old ones.

Establishing controls

Often scientists are interested in learning about processes that are influenced by many factors, or **variables.** To evaluate alternative hypotheses about one variable, all other variables must be kept constant. This is done by carrying out two experiments in parallel: a test experiment and a control experiment. In the **test experiment,** one variable is altered in a known way to test a particular hypothesis. In the **control experiment,** that variable is left unaltered. In all other respects the two experiments are identical, so any difference in the outcomes of the two experiments must result from the influence of the variable that was changed.

Much of the challenge of experimental science lies in designing control experiments that isolate a particular variable from other factors that might influence a process.

Using predictions

A successful scientific hypothesis needs to be not only valid but also useful—it needs to tell us something we want to know. A hypothesis is most useful when it makes predictions because those predictions provide a way to test the validity of the hypothesis. If an experiment produces results inconsistent with the predictions, the hypothesis must be rejected or modified. In contrast, if the predictions are supported by experimental testing, the hypothesis is supported. The more experimentally supported predictions a hypothesis makes, the more valid the hypothesis is.

As an example, in the early history of microbiology it was known that nutrient broth left sitting exposed to air becomes contaminated. Two hypotheses were proposed to explain this observation: spontaneous generation and the germ hypothesis. Spontaneous generation held that there was an inherent property in organic molecules that could lead to the spontaneous generation of life. The germ hypothesis proposed that preexisting microorganisms that were present in the air could contaminate the nutrient broth.

These competing hypotheses were tested by a number of experiments that involved filtering air and boiling the broth to kill any contaminating germs. The definitive experiment was performed by Louis Pasteur, who constructed flasks with curved necks that could be exposed to air, but that would trap any contaminating germs. When such flasks were boiled to sterilize them, they remained sterile, but if the curved neck was broken off, they became contaminated (figure 1.4).

SCIENTIFIC THINKING

Question: *What is the source of contamination that occurs in a flask of nutrient broth left exposed to the air?*

Germ Hypothesis: *Preexisting microorganisms present in the air contaminate nutrient broth.*

Prediction: *Sterilized broth will remain sterile if microorganisms are prevented from entering flask.*

Spontaneous Generation Hypothesis: *Living organisms will spontaneously generate from nonliving organic molecules in broth.*

Prediction: *Organisms will spontaneously generate from organic molecules in broth after sterilization.*

Test: *Use swan-necked flasks to prevent entry of microorganisms. To ensure that broth can still support life, break swan-neck after sterilization.*

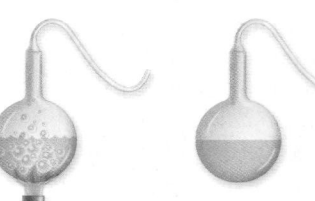

Broken neck of flask

Flask is sterilized by boiling the broth.

Unbroken flask remains sterile.

Broken flask becomes contaminated after exposure to germ-laden air.

Result: *No growth occurs in sterile swan-necked flasks. When the neck is broken off, and the broth is exposed to air, growth occurs.*

Conclusion: *Growth in broth is of preexisting microorganisms.*

Figure 1.4 Experiment to test spontaneous generation versus germ hypothesis.

This result was predicted by the germ hypothesis—that when the sterile flask is exposed to air, airborne germs are deposited in the broth and grow. The spontaneous generation hypothesis predicted no difference in results with exposure to air. This experiment disproved the hypothesis of spontaneous generation and supported the hypothesis of airborne germs under the conditions tested.

Reductionism breaks larger systems into their component parts

Scientists often use the philosophical approach of **reductionism** to understand a complex system by reducing it to its working parts. Reductionism has been the general approach of biochemistry, which has been enormously successful at unraveling the complexity of cellular metabolism by concentrating on individual pathways and specific enzymes. By analyzing all of the pathways and their components, scientists now have an overall picture of the metabolism of cells.

Reductionism has limits when applied to living systems, however—one of which is that enzymes do not always behave exactly the same in isolation as they do in their normal cellular context. A larger problem is that the complex interworking of many interconnected functions leads to emergent properties that cannot be predicted based on the workings of the parts. For example, an examination of all of the proteins and RNAs in a ribosome in isolation would not lead to predictions about the nature of protein synthesis. On a higher level, understanding the physiology of a single Canada goose, would not lead to predictions about flocking behavior. Biologists are just beginning to come to grips with this problem and to think about ways of dealing with the whole as well as the workings of the parts. The emerging field of systems biology focuses on this different approach.

Biologists construct models to explain living systems

Biologists construct models in many different ways for a variety of uses. Geneticists construct models of interacting networks of proteins that control gene expression, often even drawing cartoon figures to represent that which we cannot see. Population biologists build models of how evolutionary change occurs. Cell biologists build models of signal transduction pathways and the events leading from an external signal to internal events. Structural biologists build actual models of the structure of proteins and macromolecular complexes in cells.

Models provide a way to organize how we think about a problem. Models can also get us closer to the larger picture and away from the extreme reductionist approach. The working parts are provided by the reductionist analysis, but the model shows how they fit together. Often these models suggest other experiments that can be performed to refine or test the model.

As researchers gain more knowledge about the actual flow of molecules in living systems, more sophisticated kinetic models can be used to apply information about isolated enzymes to their cellular context. In systems biology, this modeling is being applied on a large scale to regulatory networks during development, and even to modeling an entire bacterial cell.

The nature of scientific theories

Scientists use the word **theory** in two main ways. The first meaning of *theory* is a proposed explanation for some natural phenomenon, often based on some general principle. Thus, we speak of the principle first proposed by Newton as the "theory of gravity." Such theories often bring together concepts that were previously thought to be unrelated.

The second meaning of *theory* is the body of interconnected concepts, supported by scientific reasoning and experimental evidence, that explains the facts in some area of study. Such a theory provides an indispensable framework for organizing a body of knowledge. For example, quantum theory in physics brings together a set of ideas about the nature of the universe, explains experimental facts, and serves as a guide to further questions and experiments.

To a scientist, theories are the solid ground of science, expressing ideas of which we are most certain. In contrast, to the general public, the word *theory* usually implies the opposite—a *lack* of knowledge, or a guess. Not surprisingly, this difference often results in confusion. In this text, *theory* will always be used in its scientific sense, in reference to an accepted general principle or body of knowledge.

Some critics outside of science attempt to discredit evolution by saying it is "just a theory." The hypothesis that evolution has occurred, however, is an accepted scientific fact—it is supported by overwhelming evidence. Modern evolutionary theory is a complex body of ideas, the importance of which spreads far beyond explaining evolution. Its ramifications permeate all areas of biology, and it provides the conceptual framework that unifies biology as a science. Again, the key is how well a hypothesis fits the observations. Evolutionary theory fits the observations very well.

Research can be basic or applied

In the past it was fashionable to speak of the "scientific method" as consisting of an orderly sequence of logical, either–or steps. Each step would reject one of two mutually incompatible alternatives, as though trial-and-error testing would inevitably lead a researcher through the maze of uncertainty to the ultimate scientific answer. If this were the case, a computer would make a good scientist. But science is not done this way.

As the British philosopher Karl Popper has pointed out, successful scientists without exception design their experiments with a pretty fair idea of how the results are going to come out. They have what Popper calls an "imaginative preconception" of what the truth might be. Because insight and imagination play such a large role in scientific progress, some scientists are better at science than others—just as Bruce Springsteen stands out among songwriters or Claude Monet stands out among Impressionist painters.

Some scientists perform *basic research*, which is intended to extend the boundaries of what we know. These individuals typically work at universities, and their research is usually supported by grants from various agencies and foundations.

The information generated by basic research contributes to the growing body of scientific knowledge, and it provides the scientific foundation utilized by *applied research*. Scientists who conduct applied research are often employed in some kind of industry. Their work may involve the manufacture of food additives, the creation of new drugs, or the testing of environmental quality.

Research results are written up and submitted for publication in scientific journals, where the experiments and conclusions are reviewed by other scientists. This process of careful evaluation, called *peer review*, lies at the heart of modern science. It helps to ensure that faulty research or false claims are not given the authority of scientific fact. It also provides other scientists with a starting point for testing the reproducibility of experimental results. Results that cannot be reproduced are not taken seriously for long.

Learning Outcomes Review 1.2

Much of science is descriptive, amassing observations to gain an accurate view. Both deductive reasoning and inductive reasoning are used in science. Scientific hypotheses are suggested explanations for observed phenomena. When a hypothesis has been extensively tested and no contradictory information has been found, it becomes an accepted theory. Theories are coherent explanations of observed data, but they may be modified by new information.

■ *How does a scientific theory differ from a hypothesis?*

1.3 An Example of Scientific Inquiry: Darwin and Evolution

Learning Outcomes

1. *Describe Darwin's theory of evolution by natural selection.*
2. *List evidence that supports the theory of evolution.*

Darwin's theory of evolution explains and describes how organisms on Earth have changed over time and acquired a diversity of new forms. This famous theory provides a good example of how a scientist develops a hypothesis and how a scientific theory grows and wins acceptance.

Charles Robert Darwin (1809–1882; figure 1.5) was an English naturalist who, after 30 years of study and observation, wrote one of the most famous and influential books of all time. This book, *On the Origin of Species by Means of Natural Selection*, created a sensation when it was published, and the ideas Darwin expressed in it have played a central role in the development of human thought ever since.

The idea of evolution existed prior to Darwin

In Darwin's time, most people believed that the different kinds of organisms and their individual structures resulted from di-

Figure 1.5 Charles Darwin. This newly rediscovered photograph taken in 1881, the year before Darwin died, appears to be the last ever taken of the great biologist.

rect actions of a Creator (many people still believe this). Species were thought to have been specially created and to be unchangeable over the course of time.

In contrast to these ideas, a number of earlier naturalists and philosophers had presented the view that living things must have changed during the history of life on Earth. That is, **evolution** has occurred, and living things are now different from how they began. Darwin's contribution was a concept he called *natural selection*, which he proposed as a coherent, logical explanation for this process, and he brought his ideas to wide public attention.

Darwin observed differences in related organisms

The story of Darwin and his theory begins in 1831, when he was 22 years old. He was part of a five-year navigational mapping expedition around the coasts of South America (figure 1.6), aboard H.M.S. *Beagle*. During this long voyage, Darwin had the chance to study a wide variety of plants and animals on continents and islands and in distant seas. Darwin observed a number of phenomena that were of central importance to his reaching his ultimate conclusion.

Repeatedly, Darwin saw that the characteristics of similar species varied somewhat from place to place. These geographical patterns suggested to him that lineages change gradually as species migrate from one area to another. On the Galápagos Islands, 960 km (600 miles) off the coast of Ecuador, Darwin encountered a variety of different finches on the various islands. The 14 species, although related, differed slightly in appearance, particularly in their beaks (figure 1.7).

Darwin thought it was reasonable to assume that all these birds had descended from a common ancestor arriving from the South American mainland several million years ago. Eating different foods on different islands, the finches' beaks had changed during their descent—"descent with modification," or evolution. (These finches are discussed in more detail in chapters 21 and 22.)

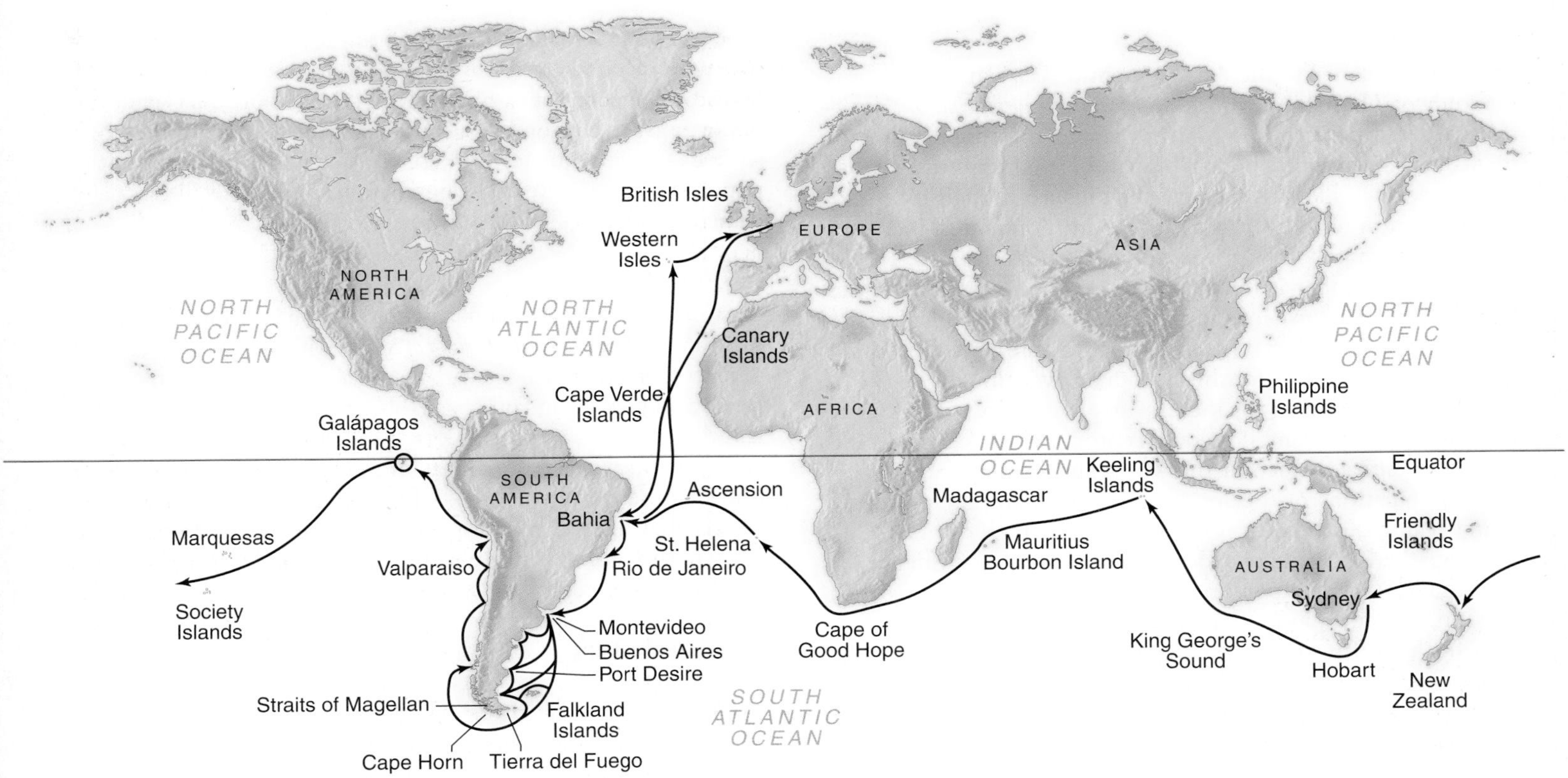

Figure 1.6 The five-year voyage of H.M.S. *Beagle*. Most of the time was spent exploring the coasts and coastal islands of South America, such as the Galápagos Islands. Darwin's studies of the animals of the Galápagos Islands played a key role in his eventual development of the concept of evolution by means of natural selection.

In a more general sense, Darwin was struck by the fact that the plants and animals on these relatively young volcanic islands resembled those on the nearby coast of South America. If each one of these plants and animals had been created independently and simply placed on the Galápagos Islands, why didn't they resemble the plants and animals of islands with similar climates—such as those off the coast of Africa, for example? Why did they resemble those of the adjacent South American coast instead?

Darwin proposed natural selection as a mechanism for evolution

It is one thing to observe the results of evolution, but quite another to understand how it happens. Darwin's great achievement lies in his ability to move beyond all the individual observations to formulate the hypothesis that evolution occurs because of natural selection.

Figure 1.7 Three Galápagos finches and what they eat. On the Galápagos Islands, Darwin observed 14 different species of finches differing mainly in their beaks and feeding habits. These three finches eat very different food items, and Darwin surmised that the different shapes of their bills represented evolutionary adaptations that improved their ability to eat the foods available in their specific habitats.

Darwin and Malthus

Of key importance to the development of Darwin's insight was his study of Thomas Malthus's *An Essay on the Principle of Population* (1798). In this book, Malthus stated that populations of plants and animals (including human beings) tend to increase geometrically, while humans are able to increase their food supply only arithmetically. Put another way, population increases by a multiplying factor—for example, in the series 2, 6, 18, 54, the starting number is multiplied by 3. Food supply increases by an additive factor—for example, the series 2, 4, 6, 8 adds 2 to each starting number. Figure 1.8 shows the difference that these two types of relationships produce over time.

Because populations increase geometrically, virtually any kind of animal or plant, if it could reproduce unchecked, would cover the entire surface of the world surprisingly quickly. Instead, populations of species remain fairly constant year after year, because death limits population numbers.

Sparked by Malthus's ideas, Darwin saw that although every organism has the potential to produce more offspring than can survive, only a limited number actually do survive and produce further offspring. Combining this observation with what he had seen on the voyage of the *Beagle*, as well as with his own experiences in breeding domestic animals, Darwin made an important association: Individuals possessing physical, behavioral, or other attributes that give them an advantage in their environment are more likely to survive and reproduce than those with less advantageous traits. By surviving, these individuals gain the opportunity to pass on their favorable characteristics to their offspring. As the frequency of these characteristics increases in the population, the nature of the population as a whole will gradually change. Darwin called this process *selection*.

Natural selection

Darwin was thoroughly familiar with variation in domesticated animals, and he began *On the Origin of Species* with a detailed discussion of pigeon breeding. He knew that animal breeders selected certain varieties of pigeons and other animals, such as dogs, to produce certain characteristics, a process Darwin called **artificial selection**.

Artificial selection often produces a great variation in traits. Domestic pigeon breeds, for example, show much greater variety than all of the wild species found throughout the world. Darwin thought that this type of change could occur in nature, too. Surely if pigeon breeders could foster variation by artificial selection, nature could do the same—a process Darwin called **natural selection.**

Darwin drafts his argument

Darwin drafted the overall argument for evolution by natural selection in a preliminary manuscript in 1842. After showing the manuscript to a few of his closest scientific friends, however, Darwin put it in a drawer, and for 16 years turned to other research. No one knows for sure why Darwin did not publish his initial manuscript—it is very thorough and outlines his ideas in detail.

The stimulus that finally brought Darwin's hypothesis into print was an essay he received in 1858. A young English naturalist named Alfred Russel Wallace (1823–1913) sent the essay to Darwin from Indonesia; it concisely set forth the hypothesis of evolution by means of natural selection, a hypothesis Wallace had developed independently of Darwin. After receiving Wallace's essay, friends of Darwin arranged for a joint presentation of their ideas at a seminar in London. Darwin then completed his own book, expanding the 1842 manuscript he had written so long ago, and submitted it for publication.

The predictions of natural selection have been tested

More than 120 years have elapsed since Darwin's death in 1882. During this period, the evidence supporting his theory has grown progressively stronger. We briefly explore some of this evidence here; in chapter 22, we will return to the theory of evolution by natural selection and examine the evidence in more detail.

The fossil record

Darwin predicted that the fossil record would yield intermediate links between the great groups of organisms—for example, between fishes and the amphibians thought to have arisen from them, and between reptiles and birds. Furthermore, natural selection predicts the relative positions in time of such transitional forms. We now know the fossil record to a degree that was unthinkable in the 19th century, and although truly "intermediate"

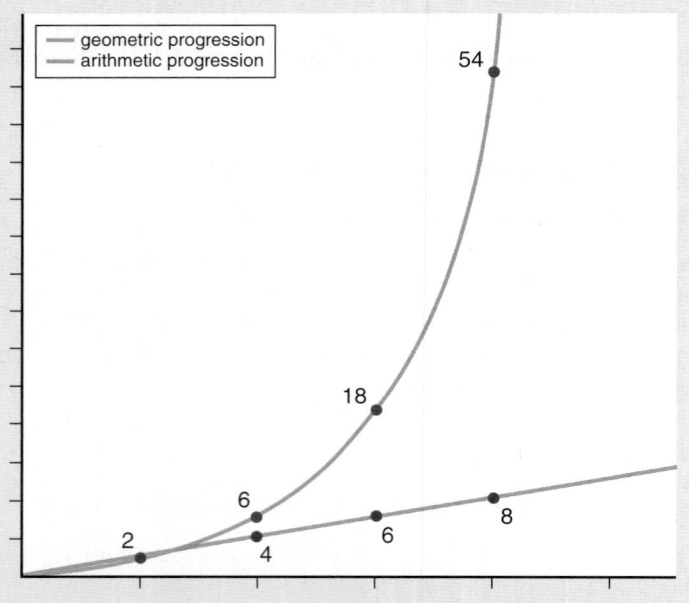

Figure 1.8 Geometric and arithmetic progressions. A geometric progression increases by a constant factor (for example, the curve shown increases ×3 for each step), whereas an arithmetic progression increases by a constant difference (for example, the line shown increases +2 for each step). Malthus contended that the human growth curve was geometric, but the human food production curve was only arithmetic.

Inquiry question

? **What is the effect of reducing the constant factor by which the geometric progression increases? Might this effect be achieved with humans? How?**

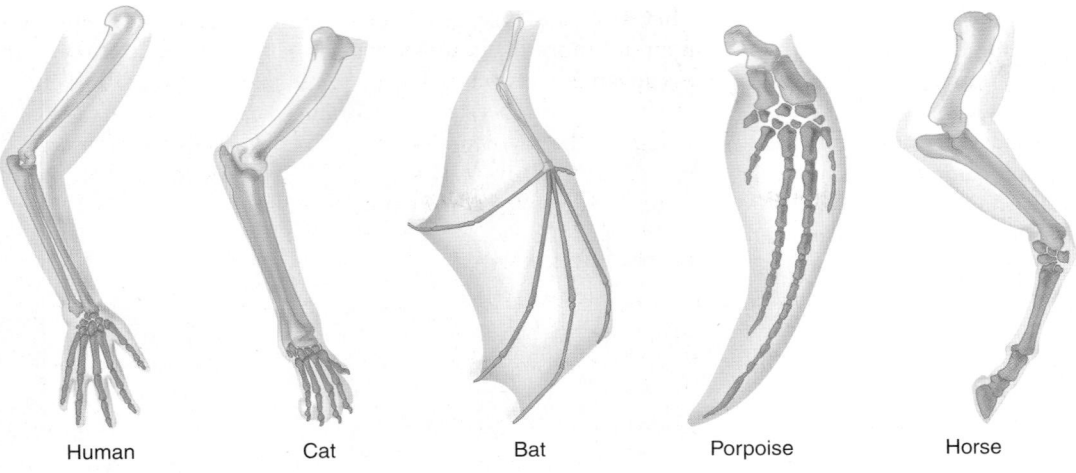

Figure 1.9 Homology among vertebrate limbs.
The forelimbs of these five vertebrates show the ways in which the relative proportions of the forelimb bones have changed in relation to the particular way of life of each organism.

Human   Cat   Bat   Porpoise   Horse

organisms are hard to determine, paleontologists have found what appear to be transitional forms and found them at the predicted positions in time.

Recent discoveries of microscopic fossils have extended the known history of life on Earth back to about 3.5 billion years ago (BYA). The discovery of other fossils has supported Darwin's predictions and has shed light on how organisms have, over this enormous time span, evolved from the simple to the complex. For vertebrate animals especially, the fossil record is rich and exhibits a graded series of changes in form, with the evolutionary sequence visible for all to see.

The age of the Earth

Darwin's theory predicted the Earth must be very old, but some physicists argued that the Earth was only a few thousand years old. This bothered Darwin, because the evolution of all living things from some single original ancestor would have required a great deal more time. Using evidence obtained by studying the rates of radioactive decay, we now know that the physicists of Darwin's time were very wrong: The Earth was formed about 4.5 BYA.

The mechanism of heredity

Darwin received some of his sharpest criticism in the area of heredity. At that time, no one had any concept of genes or how heredity works, so it was not possible for Darwin to explain completely how evolution occurs.

Even though Gregor Mendel was performing his experiments with pea plants in Brünn, Austria (now Brno, the Czech Republic), during roughly the same period, genetics was established as a science only at the start of the 20th century. When scientists began to understand the laws of inheritance (discussed in chapters 12 and 13), this problem with Darwin's theory vanished.

Comparative anatomy

Comparative studies of animals have provided strong evidence for Darwin's theory. In many different types of vertebrates, for example, the same bones are present, indicating their evolutionary past. Thus, the forelimbs shown in figure 1.9 are all constructed from the same basic array of bones, modified for different purposes.

These bones are said to be **homologous** in the different vertebrates; that is, they have the same evolutionary origin, but they now differ in structure and function. They are contrasted with **analogous** structures, such as the wings of birds and butterflies, which have similar function but different evolutionary origins.

Molecular evidence

Evolutionary patterns are also revealed at the molecular level. By comparing the genomes (that is, the sequences of all the genes) of different groups of animals or plants, we can more precisely specify the degree of relationship among the groups. A series of evolutionary changes over time should involve a continual accumulation of genetic changes in the DNA.

This difference can be seen clearly in the protein hemoglobin (figure 1.10). Rhesus monkeys, which like humans

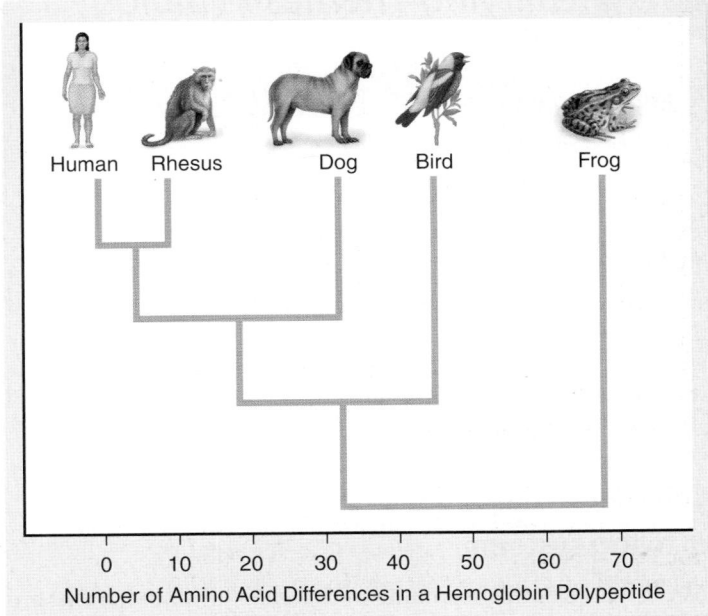

Human   Rhesus   Dog   Bird   Frog

Number of Amino Acid Differences in a Hemoglobin Polypeptide

0   10   20   30   40   50   60   70

Figure 1.10 Molecules reflect evolutionary patterns.
Vertebrates that are more distantly related to humans have a greater number of amino acid differences in the hemoglobin polypeptide.

Inquiry question

? Where do you imagine a snake might fall on the graph? Why?

chapter **1** *The Science of Biology* **11**

are primates, have fewer differences from humans in the 146-amino-acid hemoglobin β-chain than do more distantly related mammals, such as dogs. Nonmammalian vertebrates, such as birds and frogs, differ even more.

The sequences of some genes, such as the ones specifying the hemoglobin proteins, have been determined in many organisms, and the entire time course of their evolution can be laid out with confidence by tracing the origins of particular nucleotide changes in the gene sequence. The pattern of descent obtained is called a **phylogenetic tree.** It represents the evolutionary history of the gene, its "family tree." Molecular phylogenetic trees agree well with those derived from the fossil record, which is strong direct evidence of evolution. The pattern of accumulating DNA changes represents, in a real sense, the footprints of evolutionary history.

Learning Outcomes Review 1.3

Darwin observed differences in related organisms and proposed the hypothesis of evolution by natural selection to explain these differences. The predictions generated by natural selection have been tested and continue to be tested by analysis of the fossil record, genetics, comparative anatomy, and even the DNA of living organisms.

- ■ *Does Darwin's theory of evolution by natural selection explain the origin of life?*

1.4 Unifying Themes in Biology

Learning Outcomes

1. *Describe the unifying themes in biology.*
2. *Contrast living and nonliving systems.*

The study of biology encompasses a large number of different subdisciplines, ranging from biochemistry to ecology. In all of these, however, unifying themes can be identified. Among these are cell theory, the molecular basis of inheritance, the relationship between structure and function, evolution, and the emergence of novel properties.

Cell theory describes the organization of living systems

As was stated at the beginning of this chapter, all organisms are composed of cells, life's basic units (figure 1.11). Cells were discovered by Robert Hooke in England in 1665, using one of the first microscopes, one that magnified 30 times. Not long after that, the Dutch scientist Anton van Leeuwenhoek used microscopes capable of magnifying 300 times and discovered an amazing world of single-celled life in a drop of pond water. In 1839, the German biologists Matthias Schleiden and Theodor Schwann, summarizing a large number of observations by themselves and others, concluded that all living organ-

a.   60 μm

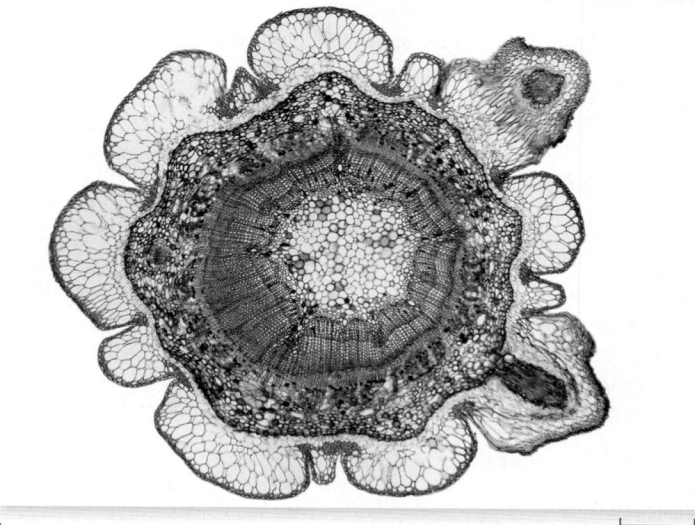

b.   568 μm

Figure 1.11 Cellular basis of life. All organisms are composed of cells. Some organisms, including the protists, shown in part *(a)* are single-celled. Others, such as the plant shown in cross section in part *(b)* consist of many cells.

isms consist of cells. Their conclusion has come to be known as the **cell theory.** Later, biologists added the idea that all cells come from preexisting cells. The cell theory, one of the basic ideas in biology, is the foundation for understanding the reproduction and growth of all organisms.

The molecular basis of inheritance explains the continuity of life

Even the simplest cell is incredibly complex—more intricate than any computer. The information that specifies what a cell is like—its detailed plan—is encoded in **deoxyribonucleic acid (DNA),** a long, cablelike molecule. Each DNA molecule is formed from two long chains of building blocks, called nucleotides, wound around each other (see chapter 14). Four different nucleotides are found in DNA, and the sequence in which they occur encodes the cell's information. Specific sequences of several hundred to many thousand nucleotides make up a **gene,** a discrete unit of information.

The continuity of life from one generation to the next—heredity—depends on the faithful copying of a cell's DNA into daughter cells. The entire set of DNA instructions that specifies a cell is called its *genome.* The sequence of the human genome, 3 billion nucleotides long, was decoded in rough draft form in 2001, a triumph of scientific investigation.

The relationship between structure and function underlies living systems

One of the unifying themes of molecular biology is the relationship between structure and function. Function in molecules, and larger macromolecular complexes, is dependent on their structure.

Although this observation may seem trivial, it has far-reaching implications. We study the structure of molecules and macromolecular complexes to learn about their function. When we know the function of a particular structure, we can infer the function of similar structures found in different contexts, such as in different organisms.

Biologists study both aspects, looking for the relationships between structure and function. On the one hand, this allows similar structures to be used to infer possible similar functions. On the other hand, this knowledge also gives clues as to what kinds of structures may be involved in a process if we know about the functionality.

For example, suppose that we know the structure of a human cell's surface receptor for insulin, the hormone that controls uptake of glucose. We then find a similar molecule in the membrane of a cell from a different species—perhaps even a very different organism, such as a worm. We might conclude that this membrane molecule acts as a receptor for an insulin-like molecule produced by the worm. In this way, we might be able to discern the evolutionary relationship between glucose uptake in worms and in humans.

The diversity of life arises by evolutionary change

The unity of life that we see in certain key characteristics shared by many related life-forms contrasts with the incredible diversity of living things in the varied environments of Earth. The underlying unity of biochemistry and genetics argues that all life has evolved from the same origin event. The diversity of life arises by evolutionary change leading to the present biodiversity we see.

Biologists divide life's great diversity into three great groups, called domains: Bacteria, Archaea, and Eukarya (figure 1.12). The domains Bacteria and Archaea are composed of single-celled organisms (*prokaryotes*) with little internal structure, and the domain Eukarya is made up of organisms (*eukaryotes*) composed of a complex, organized cell or multiple complex cells.

Within Eukarya are four main groups called kingdoms (figure 1.12). Kingdom Protista consists of all the unicellular eukaryotes except yeasts (which are fungi), as well as the multicellular algae. Because of the great diversity among the protists, many biologists feel kingdom Protista should be split into several kingdoms.

Kingdom Plantae consists of organisms that have cell walls of cellulose and obtain energy by photosynthesis. Organisms in the kingdom Fungi have cell walls of chitin and obtain energy by secreting digestive enzymes and then absorbing the products they release from the external environment. Kingdom Animalia contains organisms that lack cell walls and obtain energy by first ingesting other organisms and then digesting them internally.

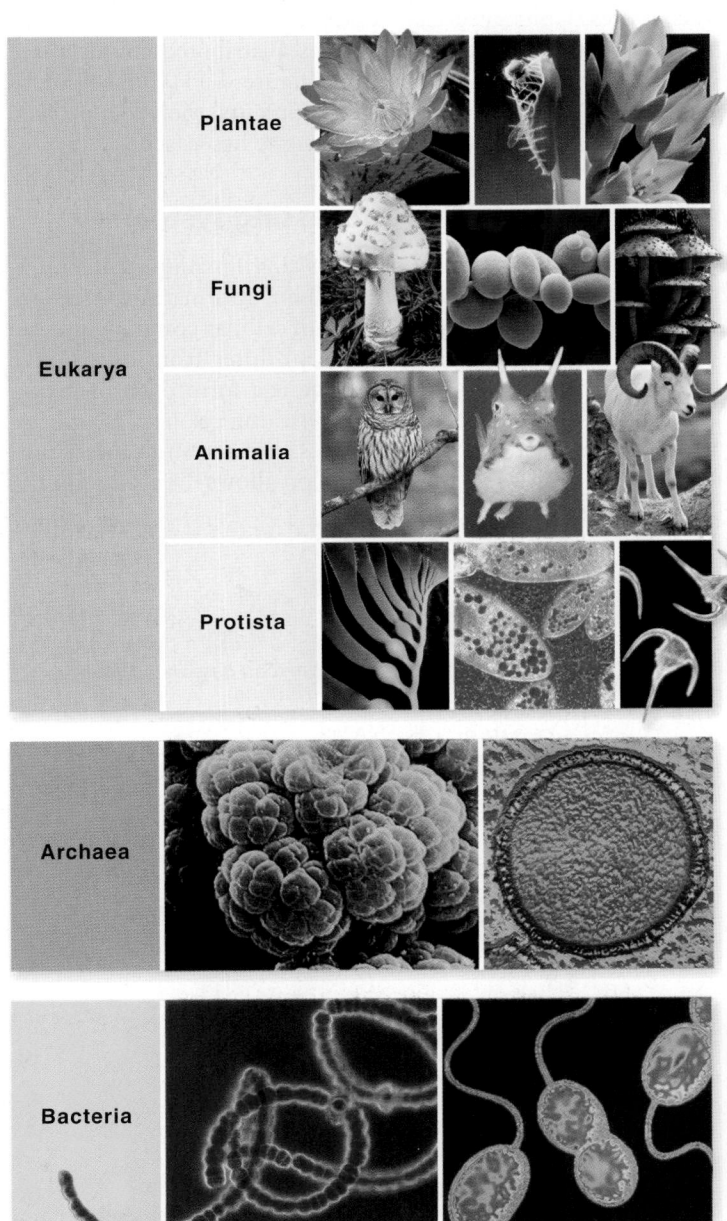

Figure 1.12 The diversity of life. Biologists categorize all living things into three overarching groups called domains: Bacteria, Archaea, and Eukarya. Domain Eukarya is composed of four kingdoms: Plantae, Fungi, Animalia, and Protista.

Evolutionary conservation explains the unity of living systems

Biologists agree that all organisms alive today have descended from some simple cellular creature that arose about 3.5 BYA. Some of the characteristics of that earliest organism have been preserved. The storage of hereditary information in DNA, for example, is common to all living things.

The retention of these conserved characteristics in a long line of descent usually reflects that they have a fundamental role in the biology of the organism—one not easily changed once adopted. A good example is provided by the homeodomain proteins, which play critical roles in early development in eukaryotes. Conserved characteristics can be seen in approximately 1850 homeodomain proteins, distributed among three different kingdoms of organisms (figure 1.13). The homeodomain proteins are powerful developmental tools that evolved early, and for which no better alternative has arisen.

Cells are information-processing systems

One way to think about cells is as highly complex nanomachines that process information. The information stored in DNA is used to direct the synthesis of cellular components, and the particular set of components can differ from cell to cell. The way that proteins fold in space is a form of information that is three-dimensional, and interesting properties emerge from the interaction of these shapes in macromolecular complexes. The control of gene expression allows differentiation of

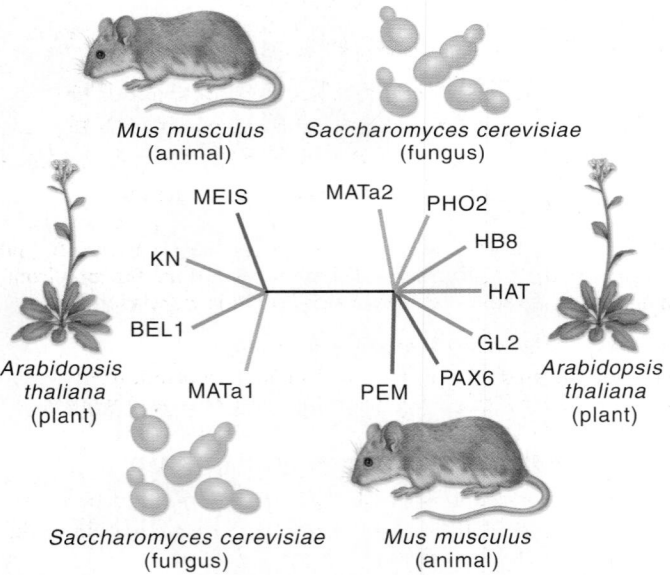

Figure 1.13 Tree of homeodomain proteins.
Homeodomain proteins are found in fungi *(brown)*, plants *(green)*, and animals *(blue)*. Based on their sequence similarities, these 11 different homeodomain proteins (uppercase letters at the ends of branches) fall into two groups, with representatives from each kingdom in each group. That means, for example, the mouse homeodomain protein PAX6 is more closely related to fungal and flowering plant proteins, such as PHO2 and GL2, than it is to the mouse protein MEIS.

cell types in time and space, leading to changes over developmental time into different tissue types—even though all cells in an organism carry the same genetic information.

Cells also process information that they receive about the environment. Cells sense their environment through proteins in their membranes, and this information is transmitted across the membrane to elaborate signal-transduction chemical pathways that can change the functioning of a cell.

This ability of cells to sense and respond to their environment is critical to the function of tissues and organs in multicellular organisms. A multicellular organism can regulate its internal environment, maintaining constant temperature, pH, and concentrations of vital ions. This homeostasis is possible because of elaborate signaling networks that coordinate the activities of different cells in different tissues.

Living systems exist in a nonequilibrium state

A key feature of living systems is that they are open systems that function far from thermodynamic equilibrium. This has a number of implications for their behavior. A constant supply of energy is necessary to maintain a stable nonequilibrium state. Consider the state of the nucleic acids, and proteins in all of your cells: at equilibrium they are not polymers, they would all be hydrolyzed to monomer nucleotides and amino acids. Second, nonequilibrium systems exhibit self-organizing properties not seen in equilibrium systems.

These self-organizing properties of living systems show up at different levels of the hierarchical organization. At the cellular level, macromolecular complexes such as the spindle necessary for chromosome separatation can self-organize. At the population level, a flock of birds, a school of fish, or the bacteria in a biofilm are all also self-organizing. This kind of interacting behavior of individual units leads to emergent properties that are not predictable from the nature of the units themselves.

Emergent properties are properties of collections of molecules, cells, individuals, that are distinct from the categorical properties that can be described by such statistics as mean and standard deviation. The mathematics necessary to describe these kind of interacting systems is nonlinear dynamics. The emerging field of systems biology is beginning to model biological systems in this way. The kinds of feedback and feedforward loops that exist between molecules in cells, or neurons in a nervous system, lead to emergent behaviors like human consciousness.

Learning Outcomes Review 1.4

Biology is a broad and complex field, but we can identify unifying themes in this complexity. Cells are the basic unit of life, and they are information-processing machines. The structures of molecules, macromolecular complexes, cells, and even higher levels of organization are related to their functions. The diversity of life can be classified and organized based on similar features; biologists identify three large domains that encompass six kingdoms. Living organisms are able to use energy to construct complex molecules from simple ones, and are thus not in a state of thermodynamic equilibrium.

■ *How do viruses fit into our definitions of living systems?*

Chapter Review

1.1 The Science of Life

Biology unifies much of the natural sciences.

The study of biological systems is interdisciplinary because solutions require many different approaches to solve a problem.

Life defies simple definition.

Although life is difficult to define, living systems have seven characteristics in common. They are composed of one or more cells; are complex and highly ordered; can respond to stimuli; can grow, reproduce, and transmit genetic information to their offspring; need energy to accomplish work; can maintain relatively constant internal conditions (homeostasis); and are capable of evolutionary adaptation to the environment.

Living systems show hierarchical organization.

The hierarchical organization of living systems progresses from atoms to the biosphere. At each higher level, emergent properties arise that are greater than the sum of the parts.

1.2 The Nature of Science

At its core, science is concerned with understanding the nature of the world by using observation and reasoning.

Much of science is descriptive.

Science is concerned with developing an increasingly accurate description of nature through observation and experimentation.

Science uses both deductive and inductive reasoning.

Deductive reasoning applies general principles to predict specific results. Inductive reasoning uses specific observations to construct general scientific principles.

Hypothesis-driven science makes and tests predictions.

A hypothesis is constructed based on observations, and it must generate experimentally testable predictions. Experiments involve a test in which a variable is manipulated, and a control in which the variable is not manipulated. Hypotheses are rejected if their predictions cannot be verified by observation or experiment.

Reductionism breaks larger systems into their component parts.

Reductionism attempts to understand a complex system by breaking it down into its component parts. It is limited because parts may act differently when isolated from the larger system.

Biologists construct models to explain living systems.

A model provides a way of organizing our thinking about a problem; models may also suggest experimental approaches.

The nature of scientific theories.

Scientists use the word *theory* in two main ways: as a proposed explanation for some natural phenomenon and as a body of concepts that explains facts in an area of study.

Research can be basic or applied.

Basic research extends the boundaries of what we know; applied research seeks to use scientific findings in practical areas such as agriculture, medicine, and industry.

1.3 An Example of Scientific Inquiry

Darwin's theory of evolution shows how a scientist develops a hypothesis and sets forth evidence, as well as how a scientific theory grows and gains acceptance.

The idea of evolution existed prior to Darwin.

A number of naturalists and philosophers had suggested living things had changed during Earth's history. Darwin's contribution was the concept of natural selection.

Darwin observed differences in related organisms.

During the voyage of the H.M.S. *Beagle*, Darwin had an opportunity to observe worldwide patterns of diversity.

Darwin proposed natural selection as a mechanism for evolution.

Darwin noted that species produce many offspring, but only a limited number survive and reproduce. He observed that the traits of offspring can be changed by artificial selection. Darwin proposed that individuals possessing traits that increase survival and reproductive success become more numerous in populations over time. This is the essence of descent with modification (natural selection). Alfred Russel Wallace independently came to the same conclusions from his own studies.

The predictions of natural selection have been tested.

Natural selection has been tested using data from many fields. Among these are the fossil record; the age of the Earth, determined by rates of radioactive decay to be 4.5 billion years; genetic experiments such as those of Gregor Mendel, showing that traits can be inherited as discrete units; comparative anatomy and the study of homologous structures; and molecular data that provides evidence for changes in DNA and proteins over time.

Taken together, these findings strongly support evolution by natural selection. No data to conclusively disprove evolution has been found.

1.4 Unifying Themes in Biology

Cell theory describes the organization of living systems.

The cell is the basic unit of life and is the foundation for understanding growth and reproduction in all organisms.

The molecular basis of inheritance explains the continuity of life.

Hereditary information, encoded in genes found in the DNA molecule, is passed on from one generation to the next.

The relationship between structure and function underlies living systems.

The function of macromolecules and their complexes is dictated by and dependent on their structure. Similarity of structure and function from one life form to another may indicate an evolutionary relationship.

The diversity of life arises by evolutionary change.

Living organisms appear to have had a common origin from which a diversity of life arose by evolutionary change. They can be grouped into three domains comprising six kingdoms based on their differences.

Evolutionary conservation explains the unity of living systems.

The underlying similarities in biochemistry and genetics support the contention that all life evolved from a single source.

Cells are information-processing systems.

Cells can sense and respond to environmental changes through proteins located on their cell membranes. Differential expression of stored genetic information is the basis for different cell types.

Living systems exist in a nonequilibrium state.

Organisms are open systems that need a constant supply of energy to maintain their stable nonequilibrium state. Living things are able to self-organize, creating levels of complexity that may exhibit emergent properties.

UNDERSTAND

1. Which of the following is NOT a property of life?

   a. Energy utilization   c. Order
   b. Movement   d. Homeostasis

2. The process of inductive reasoning involves

   a. the use of general principles to predict a specific result.
   b. the generation of specific predictions based on a belief system.
   c. the use of specific observations to develop general principles.
   d. the use of general principles to support a hypothesis.

3. A hypothesis in biology is best described as

   a. a possible explanation of an observation.
   b. an observation that supports a theory.
   c. a general principle that explains some aspect of life.
   d. an unchanging statement that correctly predicts some aspect of life.

4. A scientific theory is

   a. a guess about how things work in the world.
   b. a statement of how the world works that is supported by experimental data.
   c. a belief held by many scientists.
   d. both a and c.

5. The cell theory states that

   a. cells are small.
   b. cells are highly organized.
   c. there is only one basic type of cell.
   d. all living things are made up of cells.

6. The molecule DNA is important to biological systems because

   a. it can be replicated.
   b. it encodes the information for making a new individual.
   c. it forms a complex, double-helical structure.
   d. nucleotides form genes.

7. The organization of living systems is

   a. linear with cells at one end and the biosphere at the other.
   b. circular with cells in the center.
   c. hierarchical with cells at the base, and the biosphere at the top.
   d. chaotic and beyond description.

8. The idea of evolution

   a. was original to Darwin.
   b. was original to Wallace.
   c. predated Darwin and Wallace.
   d. both a and b.

APPLY

1. What is the significance of Pasteur's experiment to test the germ hypothesis?

   a. It proved that heat can sterilize a broth.
   b. It demonstrated that cells can arise spontaneously.
   c. It demonstrated that some cells are germs.
   d. It demonstrated that cells can only arise from other cells.

2. Which of the following is NOT an example of reductionism?

   a. Analysis of an isolated enzyme's function in an experimental assay
   b. Investigation of the effect of a hormone on cell growth in a Petri dish
   c. Observation of the change in gene expression in response to specific stimulus
   d. An evaluation of the overall behavior of a cell

3. How is the process of natural selection different from that of artificial selection?

   a. Natural selection produces more variation.
   b. Natural selection makes an individual better adapted.
   c. Artificial selection is a result of human intervention.
   d. Artificial selection results in better adaptations.

4. How does the fossil record help support the theory of evolution by natural selection?

   a. It demonstrates that simple organisms predate more complex organisms.
   b. It provides evidence of change in the form of organisms over time.
   c. It shows that diversity existed millions of years ago.
   d. Both a and b.

5. The theory of evolution by natural selection is a good example of how science proceeds because

   a. it rationalizes a large body of observations.
   b. it makes predictions that have been tested by a variety of approaches.
   c. it represents Darwin's belief of how life has changed over time.
   d. both a and b.

6. In which domain of life would you find only single-celled organisms?

   a. Eukarya   c. Archaea
   b. Bacteria   d. Both b and c

7. Evolutionary conservation occurs when a characteristic is

   a. important to the life of the organism.
   b. not influenced by evolution.
   c. reduced to its least complex form.
   d. found in more primitive organisms.

SYNTHESIZE

1. Exobiology is the study of life on other planets. In recent years, scientists have sent various spacecraft out into the galaxy in search for extraterrestrial life. Assuming that all life shares common properties, what should exobiologists be looking for as they explore other worlds?

2. The classic experiment by Pasteur (see figure 1.4) tested the hypothesis that cells arise from other cells. In this experiment cell growth was measured following sterilization of broth in a swan-neck flask or in a flask with a broken neck.

   a. Which variables were kept the same in these two experiments?
   b. How does the shape of the flask affect the experiment?
   c. Predict the outcome of each experiment based on the two hypotheses.
   d. Some bacteria (germs) are capable of producing heat-resistant spores that protect the cell and allow it to continue to grow after the environment cools. How would the outcome of this experiment have been affected if spore-forming bacteria were present in the broth?

Chapter **2**

The Nature of Molecules and the Properties of Water

Chapter Outline

2.1 The Nature of Atoms

2.2 Elements Found in Living Systems

2.3 The Nature of Chemical Bonds

2.4 Water: A Vital Compound

2.5 Properties of Water

2.6 Acids and Bases

Introduction

About 12.5 billion years ago, an enormous explosion probably signalled the beginning of the universe. This explosion started a process of star building and planetary formation that eventually led to the formation of Earth, about 4.5 billion years ago (BYA). Around 3.5 BYA, life began on Earth and started to diversify. To understand the nature of life on Earth, we first need to understand the nature of the matter that forms the building blocks of all life.

The earliest speculations about the world around us included this most basic question, "What is it made of?" The ancient Greeks recognized that larger things may be built of smaller parts. This concept was formed into a solid experimental scientific idea in the early 20th century, when physicists began trying to break atoms apart. From those humble beginnings to the huge particle accelerators used by the modern physicists of today, the picture of the atomic world emerges as fundamentally different from the tangible, macroscopic world around us.

To understand how living systems are assembled, we must first understand a little about atomic structure, about how atoms can be linked together by chemical bonds to make molecules, and about the ways in which these small molecules are joined together to make larger molecules, until finally we arrive at the structures of cells and then of organisms. Our study of life on Earth therefore begins with physics and chemistry. For many of you, this chapter will be a review of material encountered in other courses.

The Nature of Atoms

Learning Outcomes

1. *Define element, atomic number, atomic mass, and isotope.*
2. *Describe atomic structure, the relationships of subatomic particles, and how these relationships determine chemical properties.*
3. *Explain the discrete energy levels in which electrons orbit the nucleus of an atom.*

Any substance in the universe that has mass and occupies space is defined as *matter*. All matter is composed of extremely small particles called **atoms.** Because of their size, atoms are difficult to study. Not until early in the 20th century did scientists carry out the first experiments revealing the physical nature of atoms (figure 2.1).

Atomic structure includes a central nucleus and orbiting electrons

Objects as small as atoms can be "seen" only indirectly, by using complex technology such as tunneling microscopy (figure 2.2). We now know a great deal about the complexities of atomic structure, but the simple view put forth in 1913 by the Danish physicist Niels Bohr provides a good starting point for understanding atomic theory. Bohr proposed that every atom possesses an orbiting cloud of tiny subatomic particles called *electrons* whizzing around a core, like the planets of a miniature solar system. At the center of each atom is a small, very dense nucleus formed of two other kinds of subatomic particles: *protons* and *neutrons* (figure 2.3).

Atomic number and the elements

Within the nucleus, the cluster of protons and neutrons is held together by a force that works only over short, subatomic distances. Each proton carries a positive (+) charge, and each neutron has no charge. Each electron carries a negative (−) charge. Typically, an atom has one electron for each proton and is, thus, electrically neutral. Different atoms are defined by the number of protons, a quantity called the *atomic number*. The chemical behavior of an atom is due to the number and configuration of electrons, as we will see later in this chapter. Atoms with the same atomic number (that is, the same number of protons) have the same chemical properties and are said to belong to the same element. Formally speaking, an *element* is any substance that cannot be broken down to any other substance by ordinary chemical means.

Atomic mass

The terms *mass* and *weight* are often used interchangeably, but they have slightly different meanings. *Mass* refers to the amount of a substance, but *weight* refers to the force gravity exerts on a substance. An object has the same mass whether it is on the Earth or the Moon, but its weight will be greater on the Earth because the Earth's gravitational force is greater than the Moon's. The *atomic mass* of an atom is equal to the sum of the masses of

SCIENTIFIC THINKING

Hypothesis: *Atoms are composed of diffuse positive charge with embedded negative charge (electrons).*

Prediction: *If alpha particles (α), which are helium nuclei, are shot at a thin foil of gold, the α-particles will not be deflected much by the diffuse positive charge or by the light electrons.*

Test: *α-Particles are shot at a thin sheet of gold foil surrounded by a detector screen, which shows flashes of light when hit by the particles.*

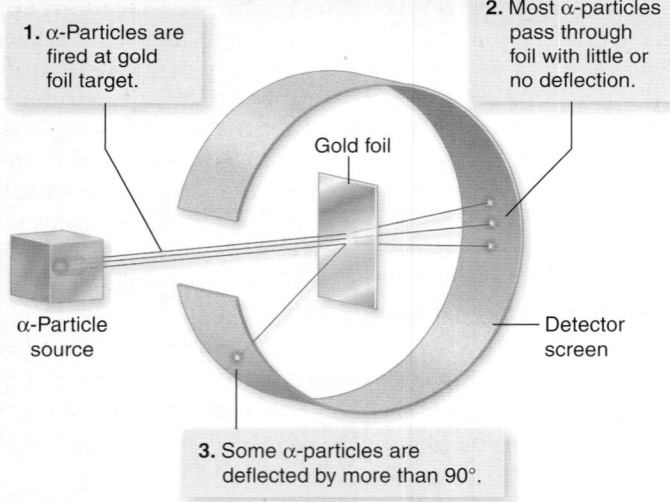

1. α-Particles are fired at gold foil target.

2. Most α-particles pass through foil with little or no deflection.

Gold foil

α-Particle source

Detector screen

3. Some α-particles are deflected by more than 90°.

Result: *Most particles are not deflected at all, but a small percentage of particles are deflected at angles of 90° or more.*

Conclusion: *The hypothesis is not supported. The large deflections observed led to a view of the atom as composed of a very small central region containing positive charge (the nucleus) surrounded by electrons.*

Further Experiments: *How does the Bohr atom with its quantized energy for electrons extend this model?*

Figure 2.1 Rutherford scattering experiment. Large-angle scattering of α particles led Rutherford to propose the existence of the nucleus.

Figure 2.2 Scanning tunneling microscope image. The scanning tunneling microscope is a nonoptical way of imaging that allows atoms to be visualized. This image shows a lattice of oxygen atoms (dark blue) on a rhodium crystal (light blue).

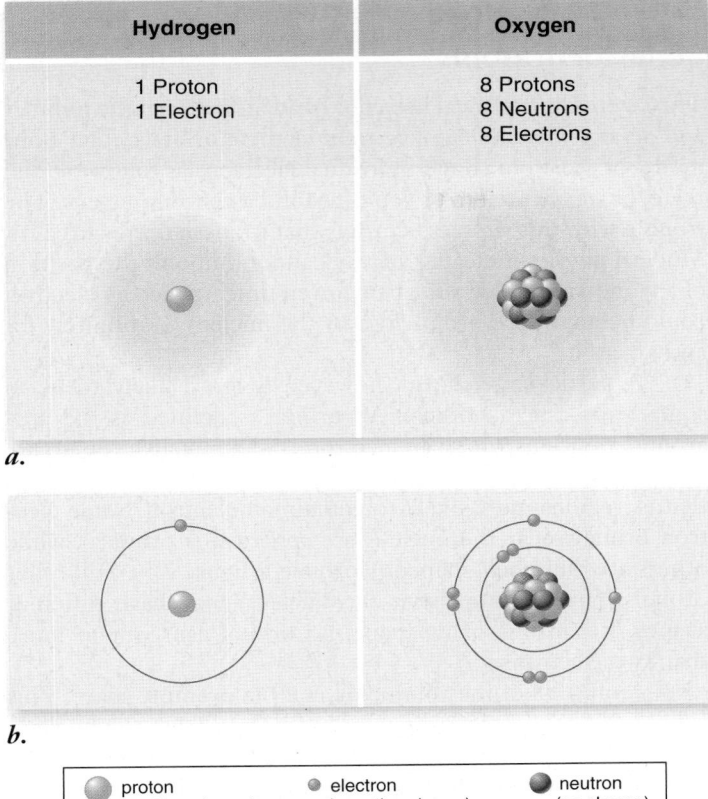

Hydrogen	Oxygen
1 Proton 1 Electron	8 Protons 8 Neutrons 8 Electrons

a.

b.

proton (positive charge)	electron (negative charge)	neutron (no charge)

Figure 2.3 Basic structure of atoms. All atoms have a nucleus consisting of protons and neutrons, except hydrogen, the smallest atom, which usually has only one proton and no neutrons in its nucleus. Oxygen typically has eight protons and eight neutrons in its nucleus. In the simple "Bohr model" of atoms pictured here, electrons spin around the nucleus at a relatively far distance. *a.* Atoms are depicted as a nucleus with a cloud of electrons (not shown to scale). *b.* The electrons are shown in discrete energy levels. These are described in greater detail in the text.

its protons and neutrons. Atoms that occur naturally on Earth contain from 1 to 92 protons and up to 146 neutrons.

The mass of atoms and subatomic particles is measured in units called *daltons*. To give you an idea of just how small these units are, note that it takes 602 million million billion (6.02 × 10^{23}) daltons to make 1 gram (g). A proton weighs approximately 1 dalton (actually 1.007 daltons), as does a neutron (1.009 dal-

tons). In contrast, electrons weigh only 1/1840 of a dalton, so they contribute almost nothing to the overall mass of an atom.

Electrons

The positive charges in the nucleus of an atom are neutralized, or counterbalanced, by negatively charged electrons, which are located in regions called **orbitals** that lie at varying distances around the nucleus. Atoms with the same number of protons and electrons are electrically neutral; that is, they have no net charge, and are therefore called *neutral atoms*.

Electrons are maintained in their orbitals by their attraction to the positively charged nucleus. Sometimes other forces overcome this attraction, and an atom loses one or more electrons. In other cases, atoms gain additional electrons. Atoms in which the number of electrons does not equal the number of protons are known as *ions*, and they are charged particles. An atom having more protons than electrons has a net positive charge and is called a **cation**. For example, an atom of sodium (Na) that has lost one electron becomes a sodium ion (Na^+), with a charge of +1. An atom having fewer protons than electrons carries a net negative charge and is called an **anion**. A chlorine atom (Cl) that has gained one electron becomes a chloride ion (Cl^-), with a charge of –1.

Isotopes

Although all atoms of an element have the same number of protons, they may not all have the same number of neutrons. Atoms of a single element that possess different numbers of neutrons are called **isotopes** of that element.

Most elements in nature exist as mixtures of different isotopes. Carbon (C), for example, has three isotopes, all containing six protons (figure 2.4). Over 99% of the carbon found in nature exists as an isotope that also contains six neutrons. Because the total mass of this isotope is 12 daltons (6 from protons plus 6 from neutrons), it is referred to as carbon-12 and is symbolized ^{12}C. Most of the rest of the naturally occurring carbon is carbon-13, an isotope with seven neutrons. The rarest carbon isotope is carbon-14, with eight neutrons. Unlike the other two isotopes, carbon-14 is unstable: This means that its nucleus tends to break up into elements with lower atomic numbers. This nuclear breakup, which emits a significant amount of energy, is called *radioactive decay*, and isotopes that decay in this fashion are **radioactive isotopes**.

Some radioactive isotopes are more unstable than others, and therefore they decay more readily. For any given isotope, however, the rate of decay is constant. The decay time is usually expressed as the *half-life*, the time it takes for one-half of the

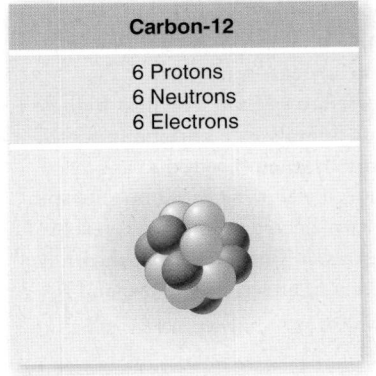

Carbon-12
6 Protons 6 Neutrons 6 Electrons

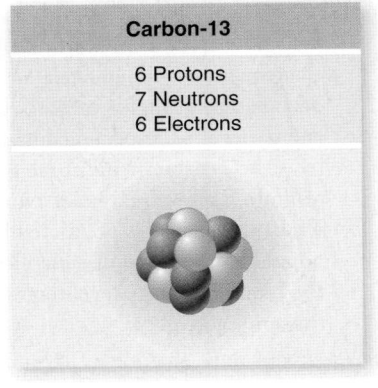

Carbon-13
6 Protons 7 Neutrons 6 Electrons

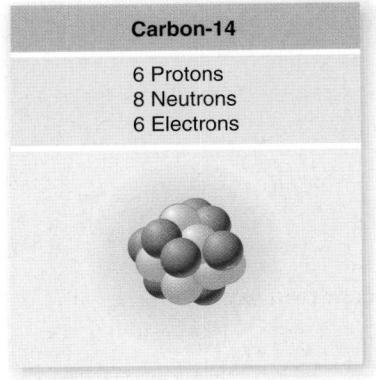

Carbon-14
6 Protons 8 Neutrons 6 Electrons

Figure 2.4 The three most abundant isotopes of carbon. Isotopes of a particular element have different numbers of neutrons.

atoms in a sample to decay. Carbon-14, for example, often used in the carbon dating of fossils and other materials, has a half-life of 5730 years. A sample of carbon containing 1 g of carbon-14 today would contain 0.5 g of carbon-14 after 5730 years, 0.25 g 11,460 years from now, 0.125 g 17,190 years from now, and so on. By determining the ratios of the different isotopes of carbon and other elements in biological samples and in rocks, scientists are able to accurately determine when these materials formed.

Radioactivity has many useful applications in modern biology. Radioactive isotopes are one way to label, or "tag," a specific molecule and then follow its progress, either in a chemical reaction or in living cells and tissue. The downside, however, is that the energetic subatomic particles emitted by radioactive substances have the potential to severely damage living cells, producing genetic mutations and, at high doses, cell death. Consequently, exposure to radiation is carefully controlled and regulated. Scientists who work with radioactivity follow strict handling protocols and wear radiation-sensitive badges to monitor their exposure over time to help ensure a safe level of exposure.

Electrons determine the chemical behavior of atoms

The key to the chemical behavior of an atom lies in the number and arrangement of its electrons in their orbitals. The Bohr model of the atom shows individual electrons as following discrete, or distinct, circular orbits around a central nucleus. The trouble with this simple picture is that it doesn't reflect reality. Modern physics indicates that we cannot pinpoint the position of any individual electron at any given time. In fact, an electron could be anywhere, from close to the nucleus to infinitely far away from it.

A particular electron, however, is more likely to be in some areas than in others. An orbital is defined as the area around a nucleus where an electron is most likely to be found. These orbitals represent probability distributions for electrons, that is, regions more likely to contain an electron. Some electron orbitals near the nucleus are spherical (s orbitals), while others are dumbbell-shaped (p orbitals) (figure 2.5). Still other orbitals, farther away from the nucleus, may have different shapes. Regardless of its shape, no orbital can contain more than two electrons.

Almost all of the volume of an atom is empty space. This is because the electrons are usually far away from the nucleus, relative to its size. If the nucleus of an atom were the size of a golf ball, the orbit of the nearest electron would be a mile away. Consequently, the nuclei of two atoms never come close enough in nature to interact with each other. It is for this reason that an atom's electrons, not its protons or neutrons, determine its chemical behavior, and it also explains why the isotopes of an element, all of which have the same arrangement of electrons, behave the same way chemically.

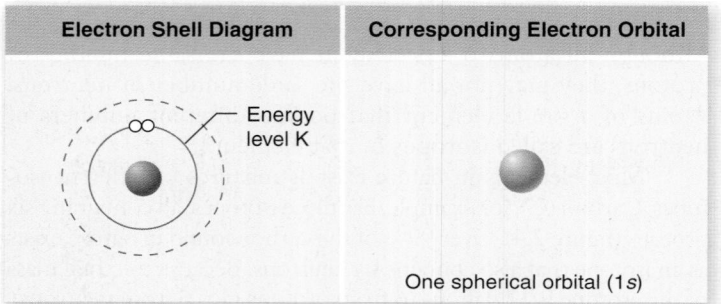

a.

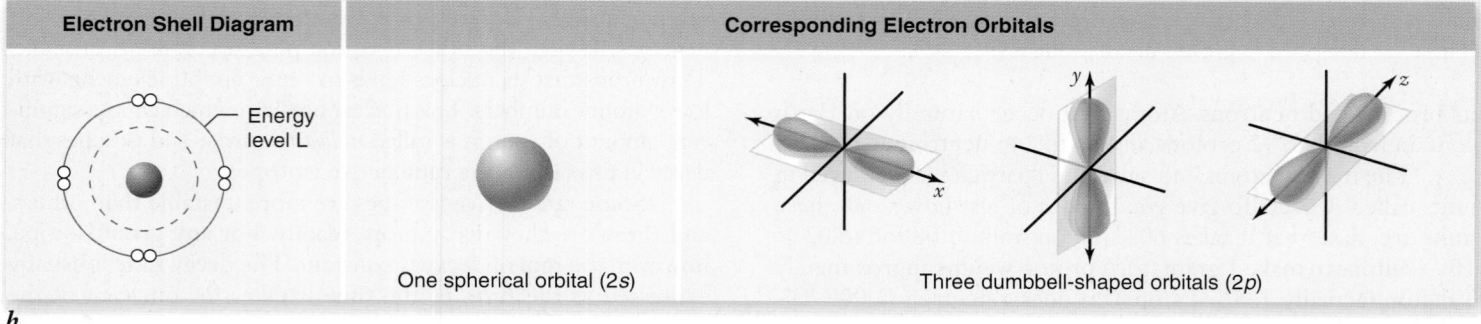

b.

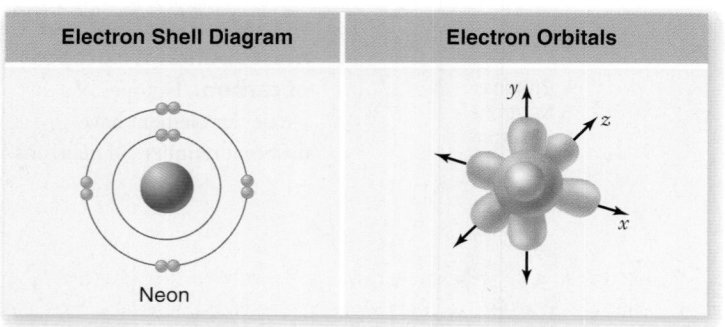

c.

Figure 2.5 Electron orbitals. *a.* The lowest energy level, or electron shell—the one nearest the nucleus—is level K. It is occupied by a single *s* orbital, referred to as 1*s*. *b.* The next highest energy level, L, is occupied by four orbitals: one *s* orbital (referred to as the 2*s* orbital) and three *p* orbitals (each referred to as a 2*p* orbital). Each orbital holds two paired electrons with opposite spin. Thus, the K level is populated by two electrons, and the L level is populated by a total of eight electrons. *c.* The neon atom shown has the L and K energy levels completely filled with electrons and is thus unreactive.

Atoms contain discrete energy levels

Because electrons are attracted to the positively charged nucleus, it takes work to keep them in their orbitals, just as it takes work to hold a grapefruit in your hand against the pull of gravity. The formal definition of energy is the ability to do work.

The grapefruit held above the ground is said to possess *potential energy* because of its position. If you release it, the grapefruit falls, and its potential energy is reduced. On the other hand, if you carried the grapefruit to the top of a building, you would increase its potential energy. Electrons also have a potential energy that is related to their position. To oppose the attraction of the nucleus and move the electron to a more distant orbital requires an input of energy, which results in an electron with greater potential energy. The chlorophyll that makes plants green captures energy from light during photosynthesis in this way. As you'll see in chapter 8—light energy excites electrons in the chlorophyll molecule. Moving an electron closer to the nucleus has the opposite effect: Energy is released, usually as radiant energy (heat or light), and the electron ends up with less potential energy (figure 2.6).

One of the initially surprising aspects of atomic structure is that electrons within the atom have discrete **energy levels.** These discrete levels correspond to quanta (sing., quantum), which means specific amount of energy. To use the grapefruit analogy again, it is as though a grapefruit could only be raised to particular floors of a building. Every atom exhibits a ladder of potential energy values, a discrete set of orbitals at particular energetic "distances" from the nucleus.

Because the amount of energy an electron possesses is related to its distance from the nucleus, electrons that are the same distance from the nucleus have the same energy, even if they occupy different orbitals. Such electrons are said to occupy the same energy level. The energy levels are denoted with letters K, L, M, and so on (see figure 2.6). Be careful not to confuse energy levels, which are drawn as rings to indicate an electron's *energy*, with orbitals, which have a variety of three-dimensional shapes and indicate an electron's most likely *location*. Electron orbitals are arranged so that as they are filled, this fills each energy level in successive order. This filling of orbitals and energy levels is what is responsible for the chemical reactivity of elements.

During some chemical reactions, electrons are transferred from one atom to another. In such reactions, the loss of an electron is called **oxidation,** and the gain of an electron is called *reduction.*

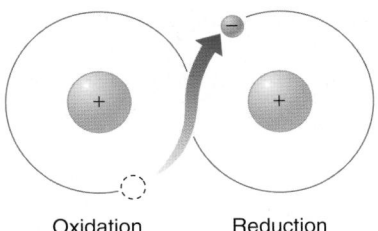

Oxidation   Reduction

Notice that when an electron is transferred in this way, it keeps its energy of position. In organisms, chemical energy is stored in high-energy electrons that are transferred from one atom to another in reactions involving oxidation and reduction (described in chapter 7). When the processes of oxidation and reduction are coupled, which often happens, one atom or molecule is oxidized while another is reduced in the same reaction. We call these combinations *redox reactions.*

Learning Outcomes Review 2.1

An atom consists of a nucleus of protons and neutrons surrounded by a cloud of electrons. For each atom, the number of protons is the atomic number; atoms with the same atomic number constitute an element. Atoms of a single element that have different numbers of neutrons are called isotopes. Electrons, which determine the chemical behavior of an element, are located about a nucleus in orbitals representing discrete energy levels. No orbital can contain more than two electrons, but many orbitals may have the same energy level, and thus contain electrons with the same energy.

■ *If the number of protons exceeds the number of neutrons, is the charge on the atom positive or negative?*

■ *If the number of protons exceeds electrons?*

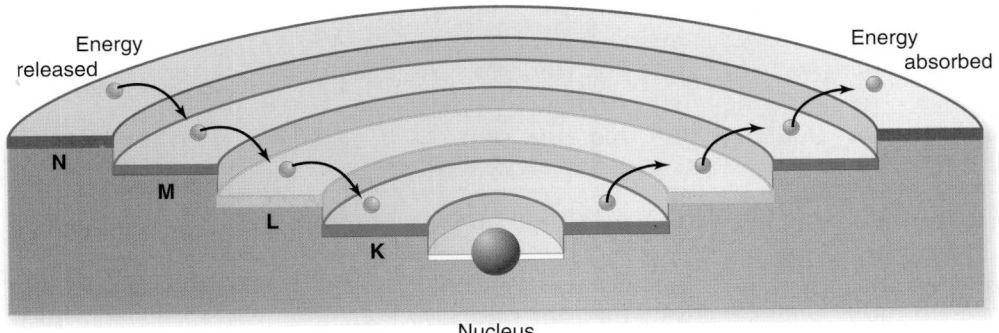

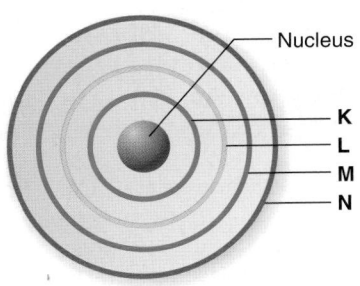

Figure 2.6 Atomic energy levels. Electrons have energy of position. When an atom absorbs energy, an electron moves to a higher energy level, farther from the nucleus. When an electron falls to lower energy levels, closer to the nucleus, energy is released. The first two energy levels are the same as shown in the previous figure.

Elements Found in Living Systems

Ninety elements occur naturally, each with a different number of protons and a different arrangement of electrons. When the 19th-century Russian chemist Dmitri Mendeleev arranged the known elements in a table according to their atomic number, he discovered one of the great generalizations of science: The elements exhibit a pattern of chemical properties that repeats itself in groups of eight. This periodically repeating pattern lent the table its name: the periodic table of elements (figure 2.7).

The periodic table displays elements according to atomic number and properties

The eight-element periodicity that Mendeleev found is based on the interactions of the electrons in the outermost energy level of the different elements. These electrons are called **valence electrons,** and their interactions are the basis for the elements' differing chemical properties. For most of the atoms important to life, the outermost energy level can contain no more than eight electrons; the chemical behavior of an element reflects how many of the eight positions are filled. Elements possessing all eight electrons in their outer energy level (two for helium) are *inert*, or nonreactive. These elements, which include helium (He), neon (Ne), argon (Ar), and so on, are termed the *noble gases*. In sharp contrast, elements with seven electrons (one fewer than the maximum number of eight) in their outer energy level, such as fluorine (F), chlorine (Cl), and bromine (Br), are highly reactive. They tend to gain the extra electron needed to fill the energy level. Elements with only one electron in their outer energy level, such as lithium (Li), sodium (Na), and potassium (K), are also very reactive. They tend to lose the single electron in their outer level.

Mendeleev's periodic table leads to a useful generalization, the **octet rule,** or *rule of eight* (Latin *octo*, "eight"): Atoms tend to establish completely full outer energy levels. For the main group elements of the periodic table, the rule of eight is accomplished by one filled *s* orbital and three filled *p* orbitals (figure 2.8). The exception to this is He, in the first row, which needs only two electrons to fill the 1*s* orbital. Most chemical behavior of biological interest can be predicted quite accurately from this simple rule, combined with the tendency of atoms to balance positive and negative charges. For instance, you read earlier that sodium ion (Na^+) has lost an electron, and chloride ion (Cl^-) has gained an electron. In the following section, we describe how these ions react to form table salt.

Of the 90 naturally occurring elements on Earth, only 12 (C, H, O, N, P, S, Na, K, Ca, Mg, Fe, Cl) are found in living systems in more than trace amounts (0.01% or higher). These elements all have atomic numbers less than 21, and thus, have low atomic masses. Of these 12, the first 4 elements (carbon, hydrogen, oxygen, and nitrogen) constitute 96.3% of the weight of your body. The majority of molecules that make up your body are compounds of carbon, which we call *organic* compounds.

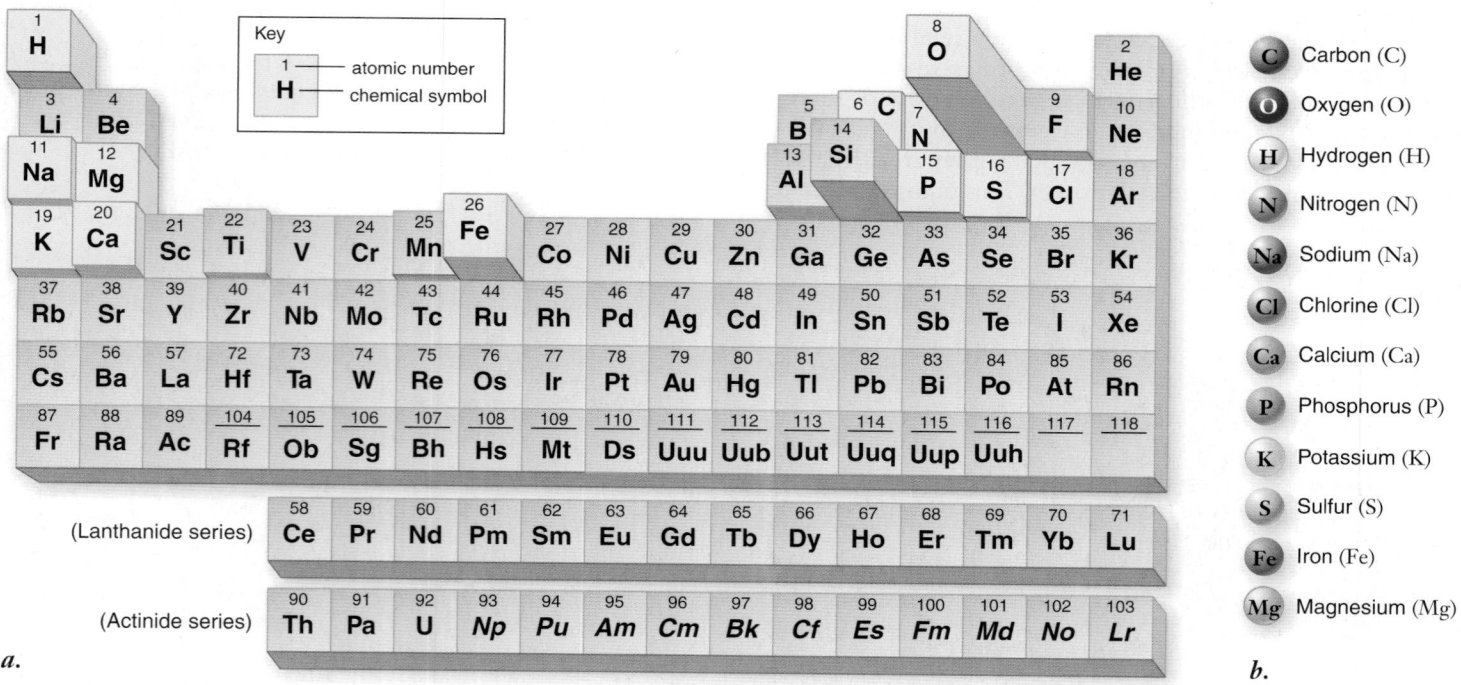

Figure 2.7 Periodic table of the elements. *a.* In this representation, the frequency of elements that occur in the Earth's crust is indicated by the height of the block. Elements shaded in green are found in living systems in more than trace amounts. *b.* Common elements found in living systems are shown in colors that will be used throughout the text.

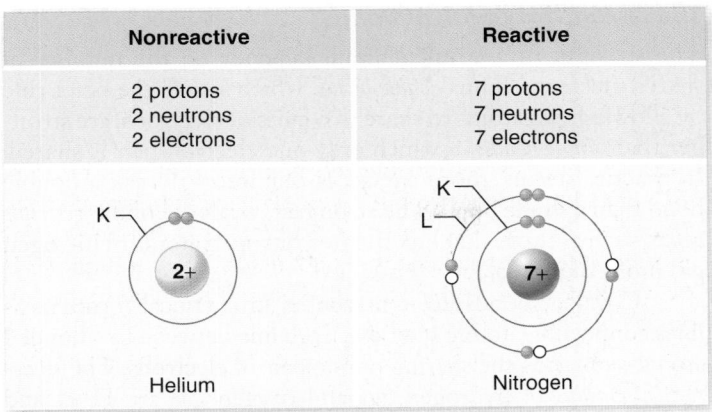

Nonreactive	Reactive
2 protons 2 neutrons 2 electrons	7 protons 7 neutrons 7 electrons
Helium	Nitrogen

Figure 2.8 Electron energy levels for helium and nitrogen. Green balls represent electrons, blue ball represents the nucleus with number of protons indicated by number of (+) charges. Note that the helium atom has a filled K shell and is thus unreactive, whereas the nitrogen atom has five electrons in the L shell, three of which are unpaired, making it reactive.

These organic compounds contain primarily these four elements (CHON), explaining their prevalence in living systems. Some trace elements, such as zinc (Zn) and iodine (I), play crucial roles in living processes even though they are present in tiny amounts. Iodine deficiency, for example, can lead to enlargement of the thyroid gland, causing a bulge at the neck called a goiter.

Learning Outcomes Review 2.2

The periodic table shows the elements in terms of atomic number and repeating chemical properties. Only 12 elements are found in significant amounts in living organisms: C, H, O, N, P, S, Na, K, Ca, Mg, Fe, and Cl.

■ *Why are the noble gases more stable than other elements in the periodic table?*

2.3 The Nature of Chemical Bonds

Learning Outcomes

1. *Relate position in the periodic table to the formation of ions.*
2. *Explain how complex molecules can be built from many atoms by covalent bonds.*
3. *Contrast polar and nonpolar covalent bonds.*

A group of atoms held together by energy in a stable association is called a *molecule*. When a molecule contains atoms of more than one element, it is called a *compound*. The atoms in a molecule are joined by *chemical bonds*; these bonds can result when atoms with opposite charges attract each other (ionic bonds), when two atoms share one or more pairs of electrons

TABLE 2.1	Bonds and Interactions	
Name	**Basis of Interaction**	**Strength**
Covalent bond	Sharing of electron pairs	Strong
Ionic bond	Attraction of opposite charges	↑
Hydrogen bond	Sharing of H atom	
Hydrophobic interaction	Forcing of hydrophobic portions of molecules together in presence of polar substances	↓
van der Waals attraction	Weak attractions between atoms due to oppositely polarized electron clouds	Weak

(covalent bonds), or when atoms interact in other ways (table 2.1). We will start by examining *ionic bonds*, which form when atoms with opposite electrical charges (ions) attract.

Ionic bonds form crystals

Common table salt, the molecule sodium chloride (NaCl), is a lattice of ions in which the atoms are held together by ionic bonds (figure 2.9). Sodium has 11 electrons: 2 in the inner

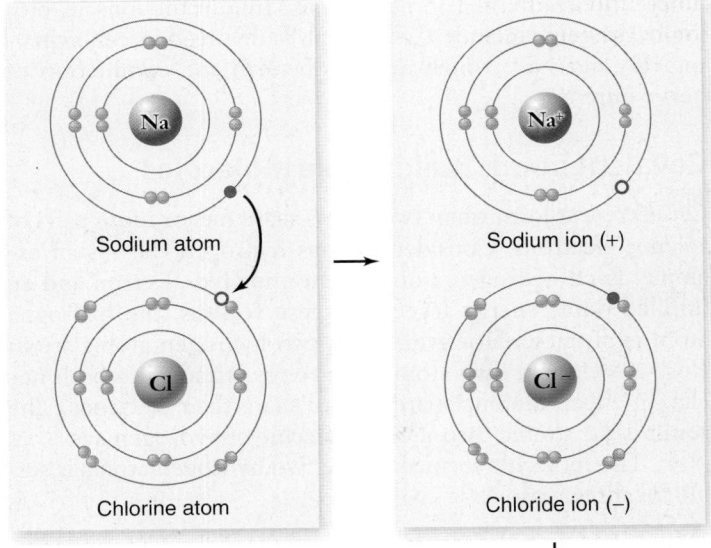

a.

Figure 2.9 The formation of ionic bonds by sodium chloride.
a. When a sodium atom donates an electron to a chlorine atom, the sodium atom becomes a positively charged sodium ion, and the chlorine atom becomes a negatively charged chloride ion. *b.* The electrostatic attraction of oppositely charged ions leads to the formation of a lattice of Na^+ and Cl^-.

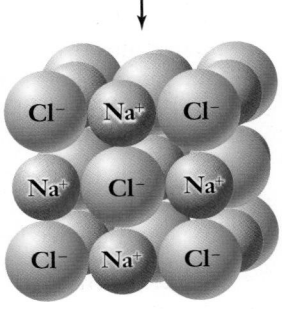

b. NaCl crystal

energy level (K), 8 in the next level (L), and 1 in the outer (valence) level (M). The single, unpaired valence electron has a strong tendency to join with another unpaired electron in another atom. A stable configuration can be achieved if the valence electron is lost to another atom that also has an unpaired electron. The loss of this electron results in the formation of a positively charged sodium ion, Na^+.

The chlorine atom has 17 electrons: 2 in the K level, 8 in the L level, and 7 in the M level. As you can see in the figure, one of the orbitals in the outer energy level has an unpaired electron (red circle). The addition of another electron fills that level and causes a negatively charged chloride ion, Cl^-, to form.

When placed together, metallic sodium and gaseous chlorine react swiftly and explosively, as the sodium atoms donate electrons to chlorine to form Na^+ and Cl^- ions. Because opposite charges attract, the Na^+ and Cl^- remain associated in an *ionic compound*, NaCl, which is electrically neutral. The electrical attractive force holding NaCl together, however, is not directed specifically between individual Na^+ and Cl^- ions, and no individual sodium chloride molecules form. Instead, the force exists between any one ion and *all* neighboring ions of the opposite charge. The ions aggregate in a crystal matrix with a precise geometry. Such aggregations are what we know as salt crystals. If a salt such as NaCl is placed in water, the electrical attraction of the water molecules, for reasons we will point out later in this chapter, disrupts the forces holding the ions in their crystal matrix, causing the salt to dissolve into a roughly equal mixture of free Na^+ and Cl^- ions.

Because living systems always include water, ions are more important than ionic crystals. Important ions in biological systems include Ca^{2+}, which is involved in cell signaling, K^+ and Na^+, which are involved in the conduction of nerve impulses.

Covalent bonds build stable molecules

Covalent bonds form when two atoms share one or more pairs of valence electrons. Consider gaseous hydrogen (H_2) as an example. Each hydrogen atom has an unpaired electron and an unfilled outer energy level; for these reasons, the hydrogen atom is unstable. However, when two hydrogen atoms are in close association, each atom's electron is attracted to both nuclei. In effect, the nuclei are able to share their electrons. The result is a diatomic (two-atom) molecule of hydrogen gas.

The molecule formed by the two hydrogen atoms is stable for three reasons:

1. **It has no net charge.** The diatomic molecule formed as a result of this sharing of electrons is not charged because it still contains two protons and two electrons.
2. **The octet rule is satisfied.** Each of the two hydrogen atoms can be considered to have two orbiting electrons in its outer energy level. This state satisfies the octet rule, because each shared electron orbits both nuclei and is included in the outer energy level of both atoms.
3. **It has no unpaired electrons.** The bond between the two atoms also pairs the two free electrons.

Unlike ionic bonds, covalent bonds are formed between two individual atoms, giving rise to true, discrete molecules.

The strength of covalent bonds

The strength of a covalent bond depends on the number of shared electrons. Thus *double bonds*, which satisfy the octet rule by allowing two atoms to share two pairs of electrons, are stronger than *single bonds*, in which only one electron pair is shared. In practical terms, more energy is required to break a double bond than a single bond. The strongest covalent bonds are *triple bonds*, such as those that link the two nitrogen atoms of nitrogen gas molecules (N_2).

Covalent bonds are represented in chemical formulas as lines connecting atomic symbols. Each line between two bonded atoms represents the sharing of one pair of electrons. The *structural formulas* of hydrogen gas and oxygen gas are H—H and O=O, respectively, and their *molecular formulas* are H_2 and O_2. The structural formula for N_2 is N≡N.

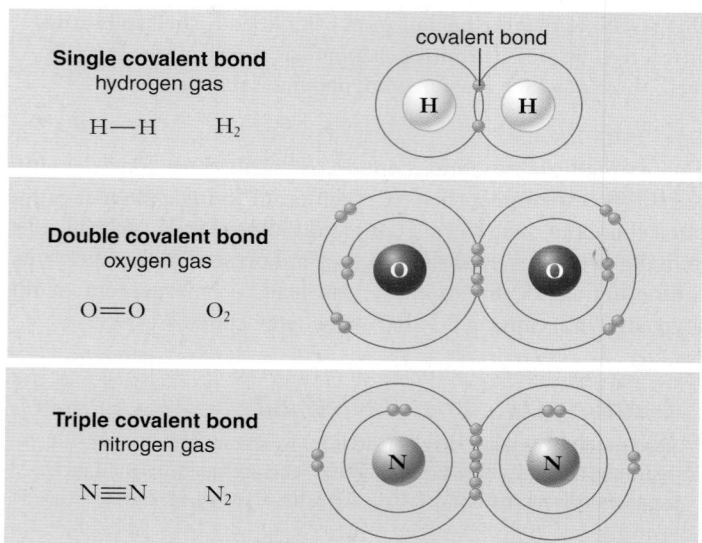

Molecules with several covalent bonds

A vast number of biological compounds are composed of more than two atoms. An atom that requires two, three, or four additional electrons to fill its outer energy level completely may acquire them by sharing its electrons with two or more other atoms.

For example, the carbon atom (C) contains six electrons, four of which are in its outer energy level and are unpaired. To satisfy the octet rule, a carbon atom must form four covalent bonds. Because four covalent bonds may form in many ways, carbon atoms are found in many different kinds of molecules. CO_2 (carbon dioxide), CH_4 (methane), and C_2H_5OH (ethanol) are just a few examples.

Polar and nonpolar covalent bonds

Atoms differ in their affinity for electrons, a property called **electronegativity.** In general, electronegativity increases left to right across a row of the periodic table and decreases down the column. Thus the elements in the upper-right corner have the highest electronegativity.

For bonds between identical atoms, for example, between two hydrogen or two oxygen atoms, the affinity for electrons is obviously the same, and the electrons are equally shared. Such bonds are termed **nonpolar.** The resulting compounds (H_2 or O_2) are also referred to as nonpolar.

For atoms that differ greatly in electronegativity, electrons are not shared equally. The shared electrons are more likely to be closer to the atom with greater electronegativity, and less likely to be near the atom of lower electronegativity. In this case, although the molecule is still electrically neutral (same number of protons as electrons), the distribution of charge is not uniform. This unequal distribution results in regions of partial negative charge near the more electronegative atom, and regions of partial positive charge near the less electronegative atom. Such bonds are termed **polar covalent bonds,** and the molecules polar molecules. When drawing polar molecules, these partial charges are usually symbolized by the lowercase Greek letter delta (δ). The partial charge seen in a polar covalent bond is relatively small—far less than the unit charge of an ion. For biological molecules, we can predict polarity of bonds by knowing the relative electronegativity of a small number of important atoms (table 2.2). Notice that although C and H differ slightly in electronegativity, this small difference is negligible, and C–H bonds are considered nonpolar.

Because of its importance in the chemistry of water, we will explore the nature of polar and nonpolar molecules in the following section on water. Water (H_2O) is a polar molecule with electrons more concentrated around the oxygen atom.

Chemical reactions alter bonds

The formation and breaking of chemical bonds, which is the essence of chemistry, is termed a *chemical reaction.* All chemical reactions involve the shifting of atoms from one molecule or ionic compound to another, without any change in the number or identity of the atoms. For convenience, we refer to the original molecules before the reaction starts as *reactants,* and the molecules resulting from the chemical reaction as *products.* For example:

$$6H_2O + 6CO_2 \longrightarrow C_6H_{12}O_6 + 6O_2$$
$$\underset{reactants}{\quad} \longrightarrow \underset{products}{\quad}$$

You may recognize this reaction as a simplified form of the photosynthesis reaction, in which water and carbon dioxide are combined to produce glucose and oxygen. Most animal life ultimately depends on this reaction, which takes place in plants. (Photosynthetic reactions will be discussed in detail in chapter 8.)

TABLE 2.2	Relative Electronegativities of Some Important Atoms
Atom	**Electronegativity**
O	3.5
N	3.0
C	2.5
H	2.1

The extent to which chemical reactions occur is influenced by three important factors:

1. **Temperature.** Heating the reactants increases the rate of a reaction because the reactants collide with one another more often. (Care must be taken that the temperature is not so high that it destroys the molecules.)
2. **Concentration of reactants and products.** Reactions proceed more quickly when more reactants are available, allowing more frequent collisions. An accumulation of products typically slows the reaction and, in reversible reactions, may speed the reaction in the reverse direction.
3. **Catalysts.** A catalyst is a substance that increases the rate of a reaction. It doesn't alter the reaction's equilibrium between reactants and products, but it does shorten the time needed to reach equilibrium, often dramatically. In living systems, proteins called enzymes catalyze almost every chemical reaction.

Many reactions in nature are reversible. This means that the products may themselves be reactants, allowing the reaction to proceed in reverse. We can write the preceding reaction in the reverse order:

$$C_6H_{12}O_6 + 6O_2 \longrightarrow 6H_2O + 6CO_2$$
$$\underset{reactants}{\quad} \longrightarrow \underset{products}{\quad}$$

This reaction is a simplified version of the oxidation of glucose by cellular respiration, in which glucose is broken down into water and carbon dioxide in the presence of oxygen. Virtually all organisms carry out forms of glucose oxidation; details are covered later, in chapter 7.

Learning Outcomes Review 2.3

An ionic bond is an attraction between ions of opposite charge in an ionic compound. A covalent bond is formed when two atoms share one or more pairs of electrons. Complex biological compounds are formed in large part by atoms that can form one or more covalent bonds: C, H, O, and N. A polar covalent bond is formed by unequal sharing of electrons. Nonpolar bonds exhibit equal sharing of electrons.

■ *How is a polar covalent bond different from an ionic bond?*

2.4 Water: A Vital Compound

Learning Outcomes

1. *Relate how the structure of water leads to hydrogen bonds.*
2. *Describe water's cohesive and adhesive properties.*

Of all the common molecules, only water exists as a liquid at the relatively low temperatures that prevail on the Earth's surface. Three-fourths of the Earth is covered by liquid water

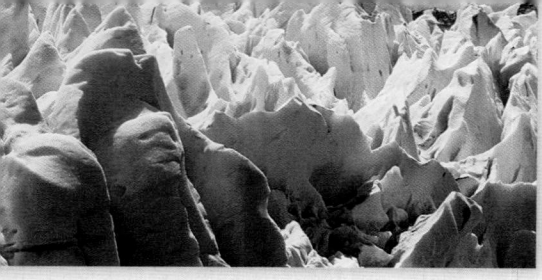
a. Solid

b. Liquid

c. Gas

Figure 2.10 Water takes many forms. *a.* When water cools below 0°C, it forms beautiful crystals, familiar to us as snow and ice. *b.* Ice turns to liquid when the temperature is above 0°C. *c.* Liquid water becomes steam when the temperature rises above 100°C, as seen in this hot spring at Yellowstone National Park.

(figure 2.10). When life was beginning, water provided a medium in which other molecules could move around and interact, without being held in place by strong covalent or ionic bonds. Life evolved in water for 2 billion years before spreading to land. And even today, life is inextricably tied to water. About two-thirds of any organism's body is composed of water, and all organisms require a water-rich environment, either inside or outside it, for growth and reproduction. It is no accident that tropical rain forests are bursting with life, while dry deserts appear almost lifeless except when water becomes temporarily plentiful, such as after a rainstorm.

Water's structure facilitates hydrogen bonding

Water has a simple molecular structure, consisting of an oxygen atom bound to two hydrogen atoms by two single covalent bonds (figure 2.11). The resulting molecule is stable: It satisfies the octet rule, has no unpaired electrons, and carries no net electrical charge.

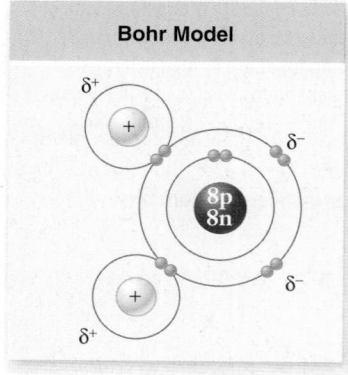
a.

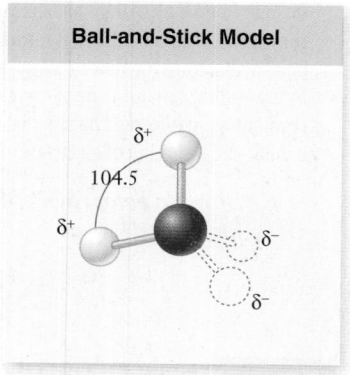
c.

Figure 2.11 Water has a simple molecular structure.
a. Each water molecule is composed of one oxygen atom and two hydrogen atoms. The oxygen atom shares one electron with each hydrogen atom.
b. The greater electronegativity of the oxygen atom makes the water molecule polar: Water carries two partial negative charges (δ^-) near the oxygen atom and two partial positive charges (δ^+), one on each hydrogen atom. *c.* Space-filling model shows what the molecule would look like if it were visible.

The single most outstanding chemical property of water is its ability to form weak chemical associations, called **hydrogen bonds.** These bonds form between the partially negative O atoms and the partially positive H atoms of two water molecules. Although these bonds have only 5–10% of the strength of covalent bonds, they are important to DNA and protein structure, and thus responsible for much of the chemical organization of living systems.

The electronegativity of O is much greater than that of H (see table 2.2), and so the bonds between these atoms are highly polar. *The polarity of water underlies water's chemistry and the chemistry of life.*

If we consider the shape of a water molecule, we see that its two covalent bonds have a partial charge at each end: δ^- at the oxygen end and δ^+ at the hydrogen end. The most stable arrangement of these charges is a *tetrahedron (a pyramid with a triangle as its base)*, in which the two negative and two positive charges are approximately equidistant from one another. The oxygen atom lies at the center of the tetrahedron, the hydrogen atoms occupy two of the apexes (corners), and the partial negative charges occupy the other two apexes (figure 2.11*b*). The bond angle between the two covalent oxygen–hydrogen bonds is 104.5°. This value is slightly less than the bond angle of a regular tetrahedron, which would be 109.5°. In water, the partial negative charges occupy more space than the partial positive regions, so the oxygen–hydrogen bond angle is slightly compressed.

Water molecules are cohesive

The polarity of water allows water molecules to be attracted to one another: that is, water is *cohesive.* The oxygen end of each water molecule, which is δ^-, is attracted to the hydrogen end, which is δ^+, of other molecules. The attraction produces hydrogen bonds among water molecules (figure 2.12). Each hydrogen bond is individually very weak and transient, lasting on average only a hundred-billionth (10^{-11}) of a second. The cumulative effects of large numbers of these bonds, however, can be enormous. Water forms an abundance of hydrogen bonds, which are responsible for many of its important physical properties (table 2.3).

Water's cohesion is responsible for its being a liquid, not a gas, at moderate temperatures. The cohesion of liquid water is also responsible for its **surface tension.** Small insects can walk on water (figure 2.13) because at the air–water interface, all the surface water molecules are hydrogen-bonded to molecules below them.

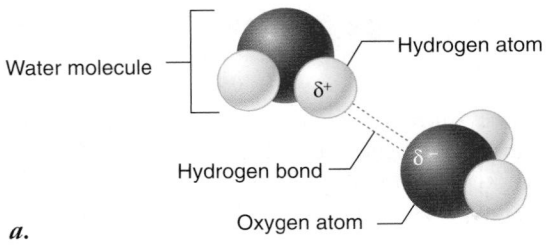

Water molecule

Hydrogen atom

δ+

Hydrogen bond

δ−

Oxygen atom

a.

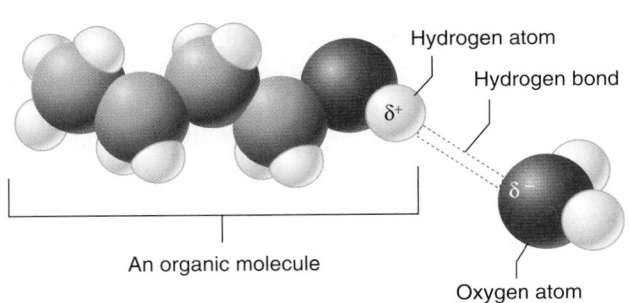

Hydrogen atom

Hydrogen bond

δ+

An organic molecule

δ−

Oxygen atom

b.

Figure 2.12 Structure of a hydrogen bond. *a.* Hydrogen bond between two water molecules. *b.* Hydrogen bond between an organic molecule (*n*-butanol) and water. H in *n*-butanol forms a hydrogen bond with oxygen in water. This kind of hydrogen bond is possible any time H is bound to a more electronegative atom (see table 2.2).

Water molecules are adhesive

The polarity of water causes it to be attracted to other polar molecules as well. This attraction for other polar substances is called *adhesion.* Water adheres to any substance with which it can form hydrogen bonds. This property explains why substances containing polar molecules get "wet" when they are immersed in water, but those that are composed of nonpolar molecules (such as oils) do not.

The attraction of water to substances that have electrical charges on their surface is responsible for capillary action. If a glass tube with a narrow diameter is lowered into a beaker of water, the water will rise in the tube above the level of the water in the beaker,

Figure 2.13 Cohesion. Some insects, such as this water strider, literally walk on water. Because the surface tension of the water is greater than the force of one foot, the strider glides atop the surface of the water rather than sinking. The high surface tension of water is due to hydrogen bonding between water molecules.

because the adhesion of water to the glass surface, drawing it upward, is stronger than the force of gravity, pulling it downward. The narrower the tube, the greater the electrostatic forces between the water and the glass, and the higher the water rises (figure 2.14).

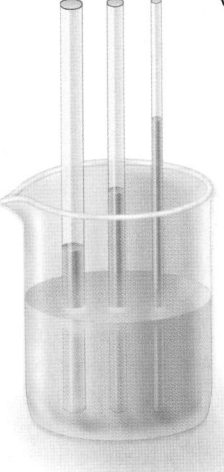

Figure 2.14 Adhesion. Capillary action causes the water within a narrow tube to rise above the surrounding water level; the adhesion of the water to the glass surface, which draws water upward, is stronger than the force of gravity, which tends to pull it down. The narrower the tube, the greater the surface area available for adhesion for a given volume of water, and the higher the water rises in the tube.

TABLE 2.3	The Properties of Water	
Property	**Explanation**	**Example of Benefit to Life**
Cohesion	Hydrogen bonds hold water molecules together.	Leaves pull water upward from the roots; seeds swell and germinate.
High specific heat	Hydrogen bonds absorb heat when they break and release heat when they form, minimizing temperature changes.	Water stabilizes the temperature of organisms and the environment.
High heat of vaporization	Many hydrogen bonds must be broken for water to evaporate.	Evaporation of water cools body surfaces.
Lower density of ice	Water molecules in an ice crystal are spaced relatively far apart because of hydrogen bonding.	Because ice is less dense than water, lakes do not freeze solid, allowing fish and other life in lakes to survive the winter.
Solubility	Polar water molecules are attracted to ions and polar compounds, making these compounds soluble.	Many kinds of molecules can move freely in cells, permitting a diverse array of chemical reactions.

2.5 Properties of Water

Water moderates temperature through two properties: its high specific heat and its high heat of vaporization. Water also has the unusual property of being less dense in its solid form, ice, than as a liquid. Water acts as a solvent for polar molecules and exerts an organizing effect on nonpolar molecules. All these properties result from its polar nature.

Water's high specific heat helps maintain temperature

The temperature of any substance is a measure of how rapidly its individual molecules are moving. In the case of water, a large input of thermal energy is required to break the many hydrogen bonds that keep individual water molecules from moving about. Therefore, water is said to have a high **specific heat,** which is defined as the amount of heat 1 g of a substance must absorb or lose to change its temperature by 1 degree Celsius (°C). Specific heat measures the extent to which a substance resists changing its temperature when it absorbs or loses heat. Because polar substances tend to form hydrogen bonds, the more polar it is, the higher is its specific heat. The specific heat of water (1 calorie/g/°C) is twice that of most carbon compounds and nine times that of iron. Only ammonia, which is more polar than water and forms very strong hydrogen bonds, has a higher specific heat than water (1.23 cal/g/°C). Still, only 20% of the hydrogen bonds are broken as water heats from 0° to 100°C.

Because of its high specific heat, water heats up more slowly than almost any other compound and holds its temperature longer. Because organisms have a high water content, water's high specific heat allows them to maintain a relatively constant internal temperature. The heat generated by the chemical reactions inside cells would destroy the cells if not for the absorption of this heat by the water within them.

Water's high heat of vaporization facilitates cooling

The **heat of vaporization** is defined as the amount of energy required to change 1 g of a substance from a liquid to a gas. A considerable amount of heat energy (586 cal) is required to accomplish this change in water. As water changes from a liquid to a gas it requires energy (in the form of heat) to break its many hydrogen bonds. The evaporation of water from a surface cools that surface. Many organisms dispose of excess body heat by evaporative cooling, for example, through sweating in humans and many other vertebrates.

Solid water is less dense than liquid water

At low temperatures, water molecules are locked into a crystal-like lattice of hydrogen bonds, forming solid ice (see figure 2.10*a*). Interestingly, ice is less dense than liquid water because the hydrogen bonds in ice space the water molecules relatively far apart. This unusual feature enables icebergs to float. If water did not have this property, nearly all bodies of water would be ice, with only the shallow surface melting every year. The buoyancy of ice is important ecologically because it means bodies of water freeze from the top down and not the bottom up. Because ice floats on the surface of lakes in the winter and the water beneath the ice remains liquid, fish and other animals keep from freezing.

The solvent properties of water help move ions and polar molecules

Water molecules gather closely around any substance that bears an electrical charge, whether that substance carries a full charge (ion) or a charge separation (polar molecule). For example, sucrose (table sugar) is composed of molecules that contain polar hydroxyl (OH) groups. A sugar crystal dissolves rapidly in water because water molecules can form hydrogen bonds with individual hydroxyl groups of the sucrose molecules. Therefore, sucrose is said to be *soluble* in water. Water is termed the *solvent*, and sugar is called the *solute*. Every time a sucrose molecule dissociates, or breaks away, from a solid sugar crystal, water molecules surround it in a cloud, forming a *hydration shell* that prevents it from associating with other sucrose molecules. Hydration shells also form around ions such as Na^+ and Cl^- (figure 2.15).

Water organizes nonpolar molecules

Water molecules always tend to form the maximum possible number of hydrogen bonds. When nonpolar molecules such as oils, which do not form hydrogen bonds, are placed in water, the water molecules act to exclude them. The nonpolar molecules aggregate, or clump together, thus minimizing their disruption of the hydrogen bonding of water. In effect, they shrink from contact with water, and for this reason they are referred to as **hydrophobic** (Greek *hydros*, "water," and *phobos*, "fearing"). In contrast, polar molecules, which readily form hydrogen bonds with water, are said to be **hydrophilic** ("water-loving").

The tendency of nonpolar molecules to aggregate in water is known as **hydrophobic exclusion.** By forcing the hydrophobic portions of molecules together, water causes these molecules to

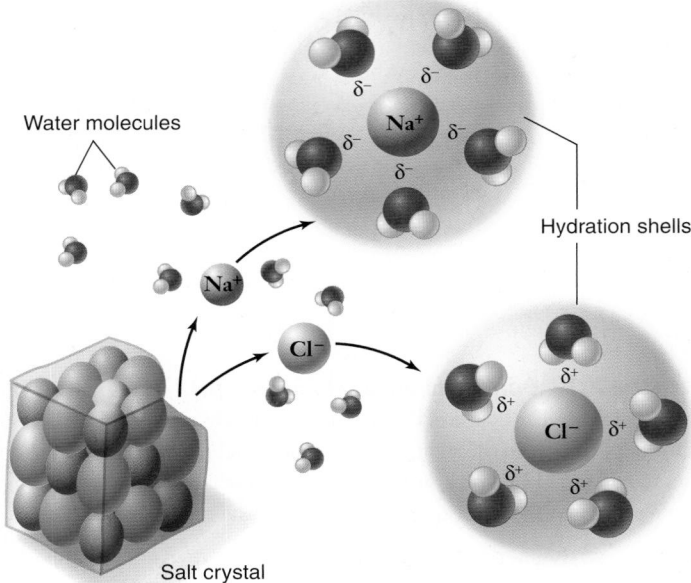

Figure 2.15 Why salt dissolves in water. When a crystal of table salt dissolves in water, individual Na^+ and Cl^- ions break away from the salt lattice and become surrounded by water molecules. Water molecules orient around Na^+ so that their partial negative poles face toward the positive Na^+; water molecules surrounding Cl^- orient in the opposite way, with their partial positive poles facing the negative Cl^-. Surrounded by hydration shells, Na^+ and Cl^- never reenter the salt lattice.

assume particular shapes. This property can also affect the structure of proteins, DNA, and biological membranes. In fact, the interaction of nonpolar molecules and water is critical to living systems.

Water can form ions

The covalent bonds of a water molecule sometimes break spontaneously. In pure water at 25°C, only 1 out of every 550 million water molecules undergoes this process. When it happens, a proton (hydrogen atom nucleus) dissociates from the molecule. Because the dissociated proton lacks the negatively charged electron it was sharing, its positive charge is no longer counterbalanced, and it becomes a hydrogen ion, H^+. The rest of the dissociated water molecule, which has retained the shared electron from the covalent bond, is negatively charged and forms a hydroxide ion, OH^-. This process of spontaneous ion formation is called *ionization:*

$$H_2O \longrightarrow OH^- + H^+$$
water   *hydroxide ion*   *hydrogen ion (proton)*

At 25°C, 1 liter (L) of water contains one ten-millionth (or 10^{-7}) mole of H^+ ions. A **mole** (mol) is defined as the weight of a substance in grams that corresponds to the atomic masses of all of the atoms in a molecule of that substance. In the case of H^+, the atomic mass is 1, and a mole of H^+ ions would weigh 1 g. One mole of any substance always contains 6.02×10^{23} molecules of the substance. Therefore, the **molar concentration** of hydrogen ions in pure water, represented as $[H^+]$, is 10^{-7} mol/L. (In reality, the H^+ usually associates with another water molecule to form a hydronium ion, H_3O^+.)

2.6 Acids and Bases

The concentration of hydrogen ions, and concurrently of hydroxide ions, in a solution is described by the terms *acidity* and *basicity*, respectively. Pure water, having an $[H^+]$ of 10^{-7} mol/L, is considered to be neutral, that is, neither acidic nor basic. Recall that for every H^+ ion formed when water dissociates, an OH^- ion is also formed, meaning that the dissociation of water produces H^+ and OH^- in equal amounts.

The pH scale measures hydrogen ion concentration

The *pH scale* (figure 2.16) is a more convenient way to express the hydrogen ion concentration of a solution. This scale defines *pH*, which stands for "partial hydrogen," as the negative logarithm of the hydrogen ion concentration in the solution:

$$pH = -\log [H^+]$$

Because the logarithm of the hydrogen ion concentration is simply the exponent of the molar concentration of H^+, the pH equals the exponent times –1. For water, therefore, an $[H^+]$ of 10^{-7} mol/L corresponds to a pH value of 7. This is the neutral point—a balance between H^+ and OH^-—on the pH scale. This balance occurs because the dissociation of water produces equal amounts of H^+ and OH^-.

Note that, because the pH scale is *logarithmic*, a difference of 1 on the scale represents a 10-fold change in $[H^+]$. A solution with a pH of 4 therefore has 10 times the $[H^+]$ of a solution with a pH of 5 and 100 times the $[H^+]$ of a solution with a pH of 6.

Acids

Any substance that dissociates in water to increase the $[H^+]$ (and lower the pH) is called an **acid.** The stronger an acid is, the more hydrogen ions it produces and the lower its pH. For example, hydrochloric acid (HCl), which is abundant in your stomach, ionizes completely in water. A dilution of 10^{-1} mol/L of HCl dissociates to form 10^{-1} mol/L of H^+, giving the solution

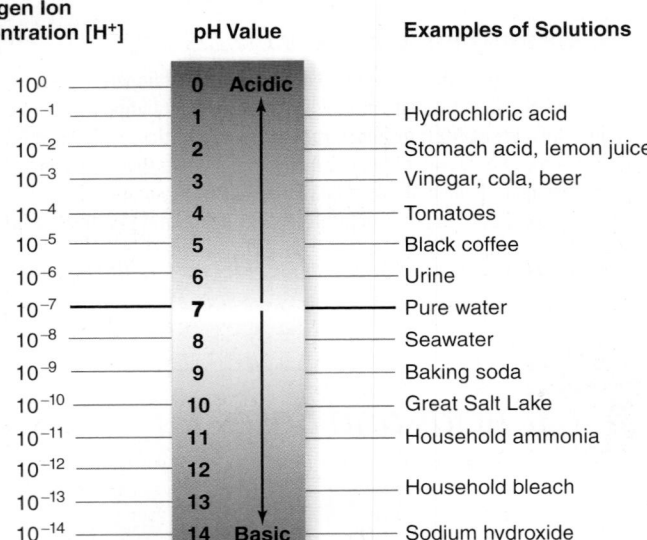

Hydrogen Ion Concentration [H⁺]	pH Value	Examples of Solutions

Figure 2.16 The pH scale. The pH value of a solution indicates its concentration of hydrogen ions. Solutions with a pH less than 7 are acidic, whereas those with a pH greater than 7 are basic. The scale is logarithmic, which means that a pH change of 1 represents a 10-fold change in the concentration of hydrogen ions. Thus, lemon juice is 100 times more acidic than tomato juice, and seawater is 10 times more basic than pure water, which has a pH of 7.

a pH of 1. The pH of champagne, which bubbles because of the carbonic acid dissolved in it, is about 2.

Bases

A substance that combines with H⁺ when dissolved in water, and thus lowers the [H⁺], is called a **base.** Therefore, basic (or alkaline) solutions have pH values above 7. Very strong bases, such as sodium hydroxide (NaOH), have pH values of 12 or more. Many common cleaning substances, such as ammonia and bleach, accomplish their action because of their high pH.

Buffers help stabilize pH

The pH inside almost all living cells, and in the fluid surrounding cells in multicellular organisms, is fairly close to neutral, 7. Most of the enzymes in living systems are extremely sensitive to pH. Often even a small change in pH will alter their shape, thereby disrupting their activities. For this reason, it is important that a cell maintain a constant pH level.

But the chemical reactions of life constantly produce acids and bases within cells. Furthermore, many animals eat substances that are acidic or basic. Cola drinks, for example, are moderately strong (although dilute) acidic solutions. Despite such variations in the concentrations of H⁺ and OH⁻, the pH of an organism is kept at a relatively constant level by buffers (figure 2.17).

A **buffer** is a substance that resists changes in pH. Buffers act by releasing hydrogen ions when a base is added and absorbing hydrogen ions when acid is added, with the overall effect of keeping [H⁺] relatively constant.

Within organisms, most buffers consist of pairs of substances, one an acid and the other a base. The key buffer in human blood is an acid–base pair consisting of carbonic acid

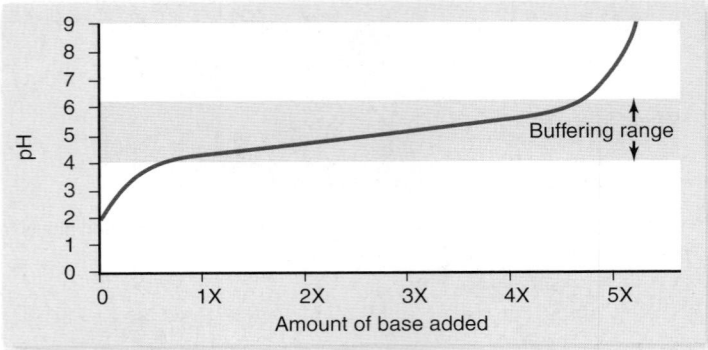

Figure 2.17 Buffers minimize changes in pH. Adding a base to a solution neutralizes some of the acid present, and so raises the pH. Thus, as the curve moves to the right, reflecting more and more base, it also rises to higher pH values. A buffer makes the curve rise or fall very slowly over a portion of the pH scale, called the "buffering range" of that buffer.

Inquiry question

? For this buffer, adding base raises pH more rapidly below pH 4 than above it. What might account for this behavior?

(acid) and bicarbonate (base). These two substances interact in a pair of reversible reactions. First, carbon dioxide (CO_2) and H_2O join to form carbonic acid (H_2CO_3), which in a second reaction dissociates to yield bicarbonate ion (HCO_3^-) and H⁺.

If some acid or other substance adds H⁺ to the blood, the HCO_3^- acts as a base and removes the excess H⁺ by forming H_2CO_3. Similarly, if a basic substance removes H⁺ from the blood, H_2CO_3 dissociates, releasing more H⁺ into the blood. The forward and reverse reactions that interconvert H_2CO_3 and HCO_3^- thus stabilize the blood's pH.

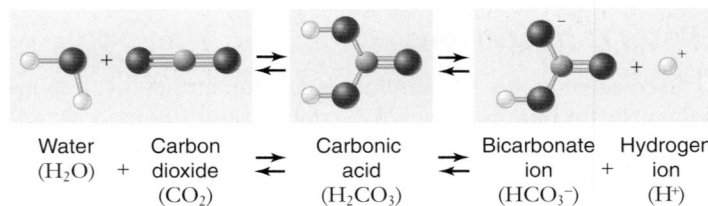

| Water (H_2O) | + | Carbon dioxide (CO_2) | | Carbonic acid (H_2CO_3) | | Bicarbonate ion (HCO_3^-) | + | Hydrogen ion (H⁺) |

The reaction of carbon dioxide and water to form carbonic acid is a crucial one because it permits carbon, essential to life, to enter water from the air. The Earth's oceans are rich in carbon because of the reaction of carbon dioxide with water.

In a condition called blood acidosis, human blood, which normally has a pH of about 7.4, drops to a pH of about 7.1. This condition is fatal if not treated immediately. The reverse condition, blood alkalosis, involves an increase in blood pH of a similar magnitude and is just as serious.

Learning Outcomes Review 2.6

Acid solutions have a high [H⁺] , and basic solutions have a low [H⁺] (and therefore a high [OH⁻]). The pH of a solution is the negative logarithm of its [H⁺]. Low pH values indicate acids, and high pH values indicate bases. Even small changes in pH can be harmful to life. Buffer systems in organisms help to maintain pH within a narrow range.

■ *A change of 2 pH units indicates what change in [H⁺]?*

2.1 The Nature of Atoms

All matter is composed of atoms (see figure 2.3).

Atomic structure includes a central nucleus and orbiting electrons.

Electrically neutral atoms have the same number of protons as electrons. Atoms that gain or lose electrons are called ions.

Each element is defined by its atomic number, the number of protons in the nucleus. Atomic mass is the sum of the mass of protons and neutrons in an atom. Isotopes are forms of a single element with different numbers of neutrons, and thus different atomic mass. Radioactive isotopes are unstable.

Electrons determine the chemical behavior of atoms.

The potential energy of electrons increases as distance from the nucleus increases. Electron orbitals are probability distributions. S-orbitals are spherical; other orbitals have different shapes, such as the dumbbell-shaped p-orbitals.

Atoms contain discrete energy levels.

Energy levels correspond to quanta (sing. quantum) of energy, a "ladder" of energy levels that an electron may have.

The loss of electrons from an atom is called oxidation. The gain of electrons is called reduction. Electrons can be transferred from one atom to another in coupled redox reactions.

2.2 Elements Found in Living Systems

The periodic table displays elements according to atomic number and properties.

Atoms tend to establish completely full outer energy levels (the octet rule). Elements with filled outermost orbitals are inert.

Ninety elements occur naturally in the Earth's crust. Twelve of these elements are found in living organisms in greater than trace amounts: C, H, O, N, P, S, Na, K, Ca, Mg, Fe, and Cl.

Compounds of carbon are called organic compounds. The majority of molecules in living systems are composed of C bound to H, O, and N.

2.3 The Nature of Chemical Bonds

Molecules contain two or more atoms joined by chemical bonds. Compounds contain two or more different elements.

Ionic bonds form crystals.

Ions with opposite electrical charges form ionic bonds, such as NaCl (see figure 2.9b).

Covalent bonds build stable molecules.

A molecule formed by a covalent bond is stable because it has no net charge, the octet rule is satisfied, and it has no unpaired electrons. Covalent bonds may be single, double, or triple, depending on the number of pairs of electrons shared. Nonpolar covalent bonds involve equal sharing of electrons between atoms. Polar covalent bonds involve unequal sharing of electrons.

Chemical reactions alter bonds.

Temperature, reactant concentration, and the presence of catalysts affect reaction rates. Most biological reactions are reversible, such as the conversion of carbon dioxide and water into carbohydrates.

2.4 Water: A Vital Compound

Water's structure facilitates hydrogen bonding.

Hydrogen bonds are weak interactions between a partially positive H in one molecule and a partially negative O in another molecule (see figure 2.11).

Water molecules are cohesive.

Cohesion is the tendency of water molecules to adhere to one another due to hydrogen bonding. The cohesion of water is responsible for its surface tension.

Water molecules are adhesive.

Adhesion occurs when water molecules adhere to other polar molecules. Capillary action results from water's adhesion to the sides of narrow tubes, combined with its cohesion.

2.5 Properties of Water

Water's high specific heat helps maintain temperature.

The specific heat of water is high because it takes a considerable amount of energy to disrupt hydrogen bonds.

Water's high heat of vaporization facilitates cooling.

Breaking hydrogen bonds to turn liquid water into vapor takes a lot of energy. Many organisms lose excess heat through evaporative cooling, such as sweating.

Solid water is less dense than liquid water.

Hydrogen bonds are spaced farther apart in the solid phase of water than in the liquid phase. As a result, ice floats.

The solvent properties of water help move ions and polar molecules.

Water's polarity makes it a good solvent for polar substances and ions. Polar molecules or portions of molecules are attracted to water (hydrophilic). Molecules that are nonpolar are repelled by water (hydrophobic). Water makes nonpolar molecules clump together.

Water organizes nonpolar molecules.

Nonpolar molecules will aggregate to avoid water. This maximizes the hydrogen bonds that water can make. This hydrophobic exclusion can affect the structure of DNA, proteins and biological membranes.

Water can form ions.

Water dissociates into H^+ and OH^-. The concentration of H^+, shown as $[H^+]$, in pure water is 10^{-7} mol/L.

2.6 Acids and Bases (see figure 2.16)

The pH scale measures hydrogen ion concentration.

pH is defined as the negative logarithm of $[H^+]$. Pure water has a pH of 7. A difference of 1 pH unit means a 10-fold change in $[H^+]$.

Acids have a greater $[H^+]$ and therefore a lower pH; bases have a lower $[H^+]$ and therefore a higher pH.

Buffers help stabilize pH.

Carbon dioxide and water react reversibly to form carbonic acid. A buffer resists changes in pH by absorbing or releasing H^+. The key buffer in the human blood is the carbonic acid/bicarbonate pair.

UNDERSTAND

1. The property that distinguishes an atom of one element (carbon, for example) from an atom of another element (oxygen, for example) is
   a. the number of electrons.
   b. the number of protons.
   c. the number of neutrons.
   d. the combined number of protons and neutrons.

2. If an atom has one valence electron, that is, a single electron in its outer energy level, it will most likely form
   a. one polar, covalent bond.
   b. two nonpolar, covalent bonds.
   c. two covalent bonds.
   d. an ionic bond.

3. An atom with a net positive charge must have more
   a. protons than neutrons.
   b. protons than electrons.
   c. electrons than neutrons.
   d. electrons than protons.

4. The isotopes carbon-12 and carbon-14 differ in
   a. the number of neutrons.
   b. the number of protons.
   c. the number of electrons.
   d. both b and c.

5. Which of the following is NOT a property of the elements most commonly found in living organisms?
   a. The elements have a low atomic mass.
   b. The elements have an atomic number less than 21.
   c. The elements possess eight electrons in their outer energy level.
   d. The elements are lacking one or more electrons from their outer energy level.

6. Ionic bonds arise from
   a. shared valence electrons.
   b. attractions between valence electrons.
   c. charge attractions between valence electrons.
   d. attractions between ions of opposite charge.

7. A substance with a high concentration of hydrogen ions
   a. is called a base.   c. has a high pH.
   b. is called an acid.   d. both b and c.

APPLY

1. Using the periodic table on page 22, which of the following atoms would you predict could form a positively charged ion (cation)?
   a. Fluorine (F)   c. Potassium (K)
   b. Neon (Ne)   d. Sulfur (S)

2. Refer to the element pictured. How many covalent bonds could this atom form?
   a. Two
   b. Three
   c. Four
   d. None

3. A molecule with polar covalent bonds would
   a. be soluble in water.
   b. not be soluble in water.
   c. contain atoms with very similar electronegativity.
   d. contain atoms that have gained or lost electrons.

4. Hydrogen bonds are formed
   a. between any molecules that contain hydrogen.
   b. only between water molecules.
   c. when hydrogen is part of a polar bond.
   d. when two atoms of hydrogen share an electron.

5. Which of the following properties of water is NOT a consequence of its ability to form hydrogen bonds?
   a. Cohesiveness
   b. High specific heat
   c. Ability to function as a solvent
   d. Neutral pH

6. The decay of radioactive isotopes involves changes to the nucleus of atoms. Explain how this differs from the changes in atoms that occur during chemical reactions.

SYNTHESIZE

1. Elements that form ions are important for a range of biological processes. You have learned something about the cations sodium (Na^+), calcium (Ca^{2+}) and potassium (K^+) in this chapter. Use your knowledge of the definition of a cation to identify other examples from the periodic table.

2. A popular theme in science fiction literature has been the idea of silicon-based life-forms in contrast to our carbon-based life. Evaluate the possibility of silicon-based life based on the chemical structure and potential for chemical bonding of a silicon atom.

3. Recent efforts by NASA to search for signs of life on Mars have focused on the search for evidence of liquid water rather than looking directly for biological organisms (living or fossilized). Use your knowledge of the influence of water on life on Earth to construct an argument justifying this approach.

ONLINE RESOURCE

www.ravenbiology.com

Understand, Apply, and Synthesize—enhance your study with animations that bring concepts to life and practice tests to assess your understanding. Your instructor may also recommend the interactive eBook, individualized learning tools, and more.

Chapter 3

The Chemical Building Blocks of Life

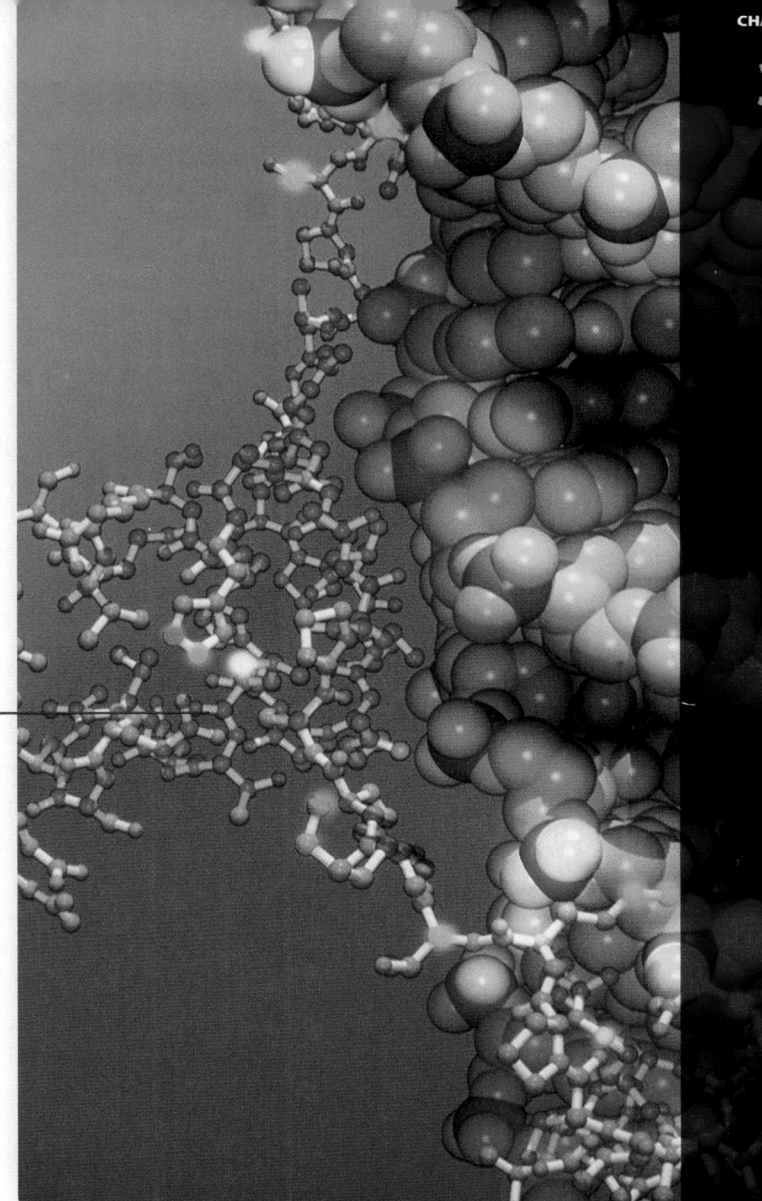

Chapter Outline

3.1   Carbon: The Framework of Biological Molecules

3.2   Carbohydrates: Energy Storage and Structural Molecules

3.3   Nucleic Acids: Information Molecules

3.4   Proteins: Molecules with Diverse Structures and Functions

3.5   Lipids: Hydrophobic Molecules

Introduction

A cup of water contains more molecules than there are stars in the sky. But many molecules are much larger than water molecules. Many thousands of distinct biological molecules are long chains made of thousands or even billions of atoms. These enormous assemblages, which are almost always synthesized by living things, are macromolecules. *As you may know, biological macromolecules can be divided into four categories:* carbohydrates, nucleic acids, proteins, *and* lipids, *and they are the basic chemical building blocks from which all organisms are composed.*

We take the existence of these classes of macromolecules for granted now, but as late as the 19th century many theories of "vital forces" were associated with living systems. One such theory held that cells contained a substance, protoplasm, that was responsible for the chemical reactions in living systems. Any disruption of cells was thought to disturb the protoplasm. Such a view makes studying the chemical reactions of cells in the lab (in vitro) impossible. The demonstration of fermentation in a cell-free system marked the beginning of modern biochemistry (figure 3.1). This approach involves studying biological molecules outside of cells to infer their role inside cells. Because these biological macromolecules all involve carbon-containing compounds, we begin with a brief summary of carbon and its chemistry.

Hypothesis: *Chemical reactions, such as the fermentation reaction in yeast, are controlled by enzymes and do not require living cells.*

Prediction: *If yeast cells are broken open, these enzymes should function outside of the cell.*

Test: *Yeast is mixed with quartz sand and diatomaceous earth and then ground in a mortar and pestle. The resulting paste is wrapped in canvas and subjected to 400–500 atm pressure in a press. Fermentable and nonfermentable substrates are added to the resulting fluid, with fermentation being measured by the production of CO_2.*

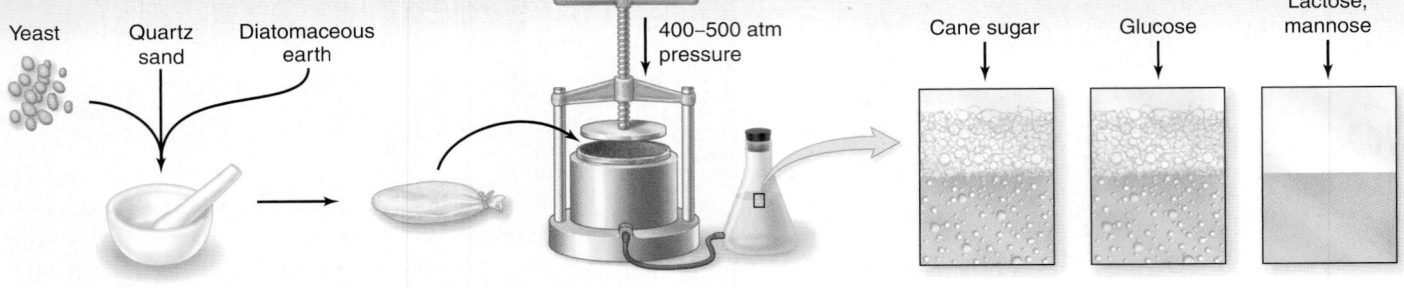

Grind in mortar/pestle.   Wrap in canvas and apply pressure in a press.

Result: *When a fermentable substrate (cane sugar, glucose) is used, CO_2 is produced, when a nonfermentable substrate (lactose, mannose) is used, no CO_2 is produced. In addition, visual inspection of the fluid shows no visible yeast cells.*

Conclusion: *The hypothesis is supported. The fermentation reaction can occur in the absence of live yeast.*

Historical Significance: *Although this is not precisely the intent of the original experiment, it represents the first use of a cell-free system. Such systems allow for the study of biochemical reactions in vitro and the purification of proteins involved. We now know that the "fermentation reaction" is actually a complex series of reactions. Would such a series of reactions be your first choice for this kind of demonstration?*

Figure 3.1 The demonstration of cell-free fermentation. Eduard Buchner's (1860–1917) demonstration of fermentation by fluid produced from yeast, but not containing any live cells both argued against the protoplasm theory and provided a method for future biochemists to examine the chemistry of life outside of cells.

3.1 Carbon: The Framework of Biological Molecules

Learning Outcomes

1. *Describe the relationship between functional groups and macromolecules.*
2. *Recognize the different kinds of isomers.*
3. *List the different kinds of biological macromolecules.*

In chapter 2, we reviewed the basics of chemistry. Biological systems obey all the laws of chemistry. Thus, chemistry forms the basis of living systems.

The framework of biological molecules consists predominantly of carbon atoms bonded to other carbon atoms or to atoms of oxygen, nitrogen, sulfur, phosphorus, or hydrogen. Because carbon atoms can form up to four covalent bonds, molecules containing carbon can form straight chains, branches, or even rings, balls, tubes, and coils.

Molecules consisting only of carbon and hydrogen are called *hydrocarbons*. Because carbon–hydrogen covalent bonds store considerable energy, hydrocarbons make good fuels. Gasoline, for example, is rich in hydrocarbons, and propane gas, an-

other hydrocarbon, consists of a chain of three carbon atoms, with eight hydrogen atoms bound to it. The chemical formula for propane is C_3H_8. Its structural formula is

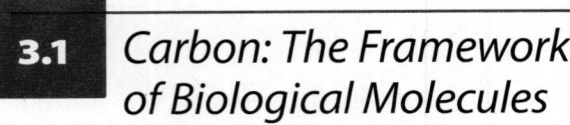

Propane structural formula

Theoretically speaking, the length of a chain of carbon atoms is unlimited. As described in the rest of this chapter, the four main types of biological molecules often consist of huge chains of carbon-containing compounds.

Functional groups account for differences in molecular properties

Carbon and hydrogen atoms both have very similar electronegativities. Electrons in C—C and C—H bonds are therefore evenly distributed, with no significant differences in charge over the molecular surface. For this reason, hydrocarbons are nonpolar. Most biological molecules produced by cells, however, also contain other atoms. Because these other atoms frequently have different electronegativities, molecules containing them exhibit regions of partial positive or negative charge. They are polar. These molecules can be thought of as a C—H core to which specific molecular groups, called **functional groups,** are attached. One such common functional group is —OH, called a *hydroxyl group.*

Functional groups have definite chemical properties that they retain no matter where they occur. Both the hydroxyl and carbonyl (C=O) groups, for example, are polar because of the electronegativity of the oxygen atoms (see chapter 2). Other common functional groups are the acidic carboxyl (COOH), phosphate (PO_4), and the basic amino (NH_2) group. Many of these functional groups can also participate in hydrogen bonding. Hydrogen bond donors and acceptors can be predicted based on their electronegativities shown in table 2.2. Figure 3.2 illustrates these biologically important functional groups and lists the macromolecules in which they are found.

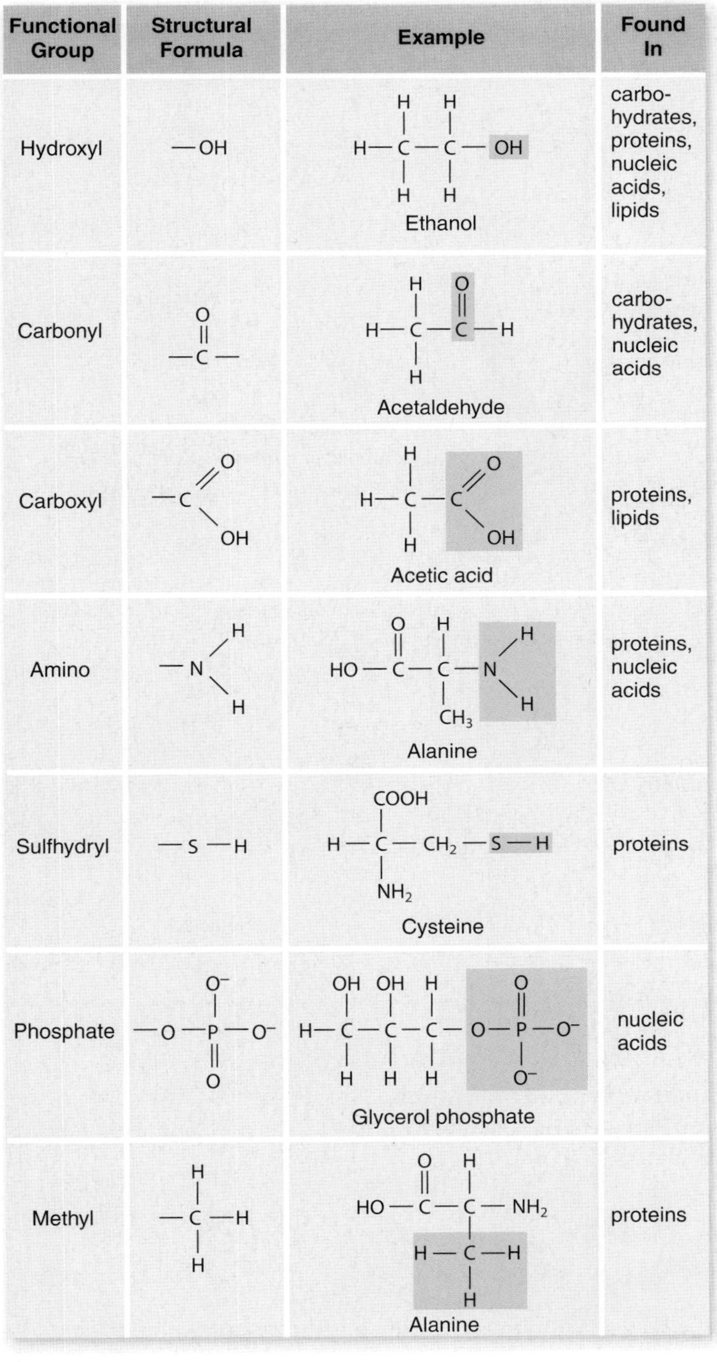

Isomers have the same molecular formulas but different structures

Organic molecules having the same molecular or empirical formula can exist in different forms called **isomers.** If there are differences in the actual structure of their carbon skeleton, we call them *structural isomers.* Later you will see that glucose and fructose are structural isomers of $C_6H_{12}O_6$. Another form of isomers, called *stereoisomers,* have the same carbon skeleton but differ in how the groups attached to this skeleton are arranged in space.

Enzymes in biological systems usually recognize only a single, specific stereoisomer. A subcategory of stereoisomers, called *enantiomers,* are actually mirror images of each other. A molecule that has mirror-image versions is called a *chiral* molecule. When carbon is bound to four different molecules, this inherent asymmetry exists (figure 3.3).

Chiral compounds are characterized by their effect on polarized light. Polarized light has a single plane, and chiral molecules rotate this plane either to the right (Latin, *dextro*) or left (Latin, *levo*). We therefore call the two chiral forms *D* for *dextrorotatory* and *L* for *levorotatory.* Living systems tend to produce only a single enantiomer of the two possible forms; for example, in most organisms we find primarily D-sugars and L-amino acids.

Functional Group	Structural Formula	Example	Found In
Hydroxyl	—OH	Ethanol	carbo-hydrates, proteins, nucleic acids, lipids
Carbonyl	$\overset{O}{\underset{\|}{-C-}}$	Acetaldehyde	carbo-hydrates, nucleic acids
Carboxyl	$-C\overset{O}{\underset{OH}{}}$	Acetic acid	proteins, lipids
Amino	$-N\overset{H}{\underset{H}{}}$	Alanine	proteins, nucleic acids
Sulfhydryl	—S—H	Cysteine	proteins
Phosphate	$-O-\overset{O^-}{\underset{O}{P}}-O-$	Glycerol phosphate	nucleic acids
Methyl	$-\overset{H}{\underset{H}{C}}-H$	Alanine	proteins

Figure 3.2 The primary functional chemical groups. These groups tend to act as units during chemical reactions and give specific chemical properties to the molecules that possess them. Amino groups, for example, make a molecule more basic, and carboxyl groups make a molecule more acidic. These functional groups are also not limited to the examples in the "Found In" column but are widely distributed in biological molecules.

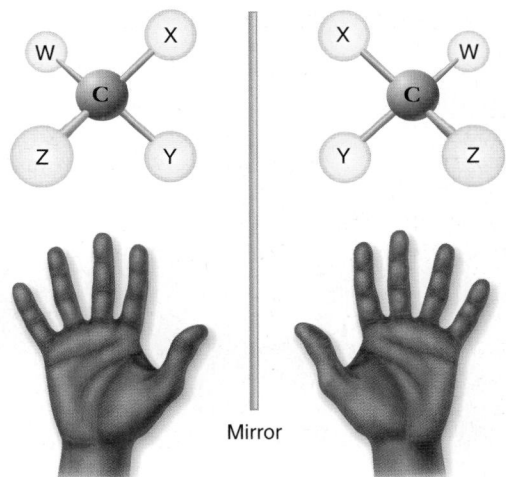

Figure 3.3 Chiral molecules. When carbon is bound to four different groups, the resulting molecule is said to be chiral (from Greek *cheir,* meaning "hand."). A chiral molecule will have stereoisomers that are mirror images. The two molecules shown have the same four groups but cannot be superimposed, much like your two hands cannot be superimposed but must be flipped to match. These types of stereoisomers are called *enantiomers.*

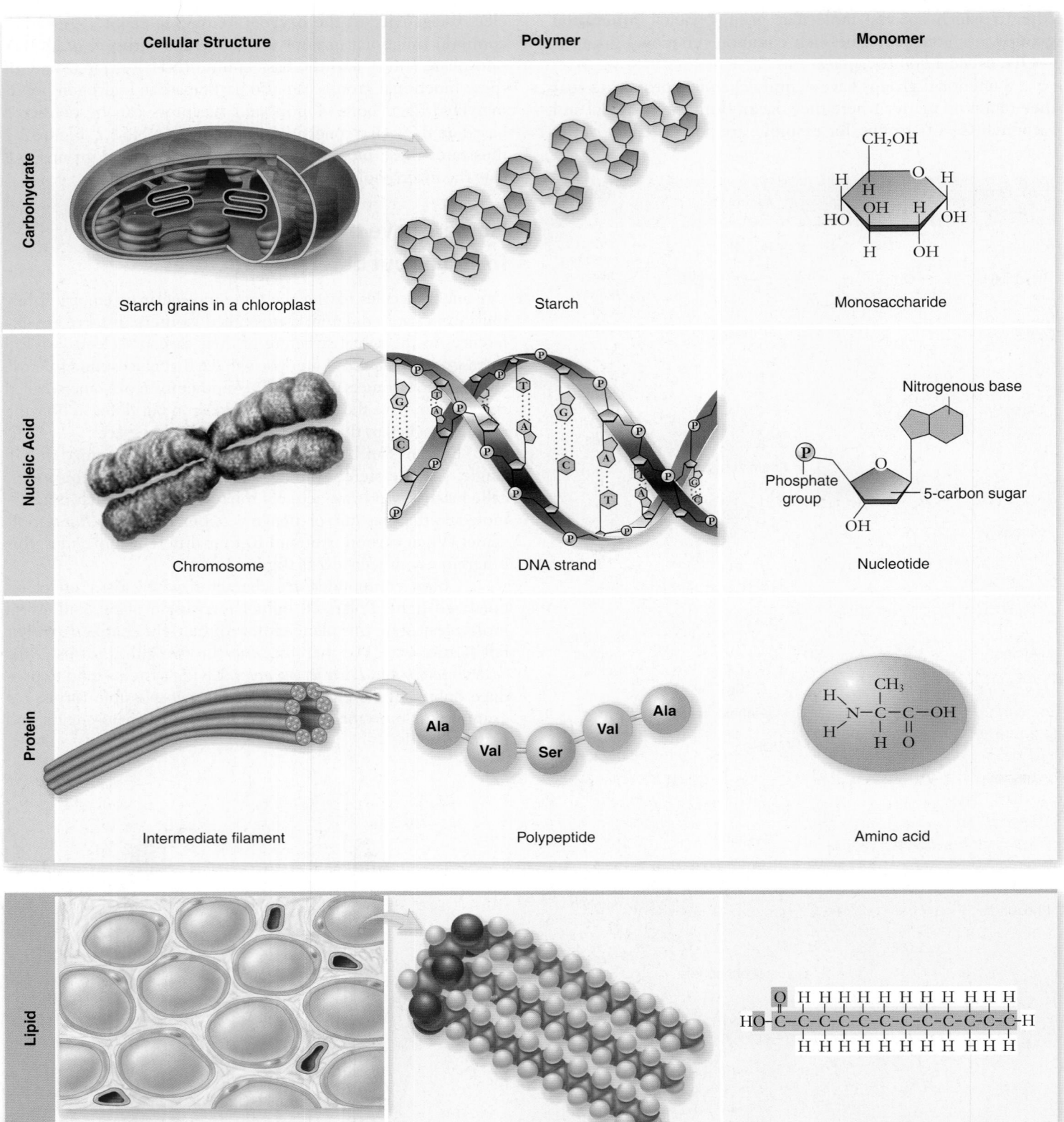

Cellular Structure	Polymer	Monomer

Carbohydrate

Starch grains in a chloroplast — Starch — Monosaccharide

Nucleic Acid

Chromosome — DNA strand — Nucleotide

Nitrogenous base

Phosphate group — 5-carbon sugar

Protein

Intermediate filament — Polypeptide — Amino acid

Lipid

Adipose cell with fat droplets — Triglyceride — Fatty acid

Figure 3.4 Polymer macromolecules. The four major biological macromolecules are shown. Carbohydrates, nucleic acids, and proteins all form polymers and are shown with the monomers used to make them. Lipids do not fit this simple monomer–polymer relationship, however, because they are constructed from glycerol and fatty acids. All four types of macromolecules are also shown in their cellular context.

TABLE 3.1	Macromolecules		
Macromolecule	**Subunit**	**Function**	**Example**
C A R B O H Y D R A T E S			
Starch, glycogen	Glucose	Energy storage	Potatoes
Cellulose	Glucose	Structural support in plant cell walls	Paper; strings of celery
Chitin	Modified glucose	Structural support	Crab shells
N U C L E I C A C I D S			
DNA	Nucleotides	Encodes genes	Chromosomes
RNA	Nucleotides	Needed for gene expression	Messenger RNA
P R O T E I N S			
Functional	Amino acids	Catalysis; transport	Hemoglobin
Structural	Amino acids	Support	Hair; silk
L I P I D S			
Fats	Glycerol and three fatty acids	Energy storage	Butter; corn oil; soap
Phospholipids	Glycerol, two fatty acids, phosphate, and polar R groups	Cell membranes	Phosphatidylcholine
Prostaglandins	Five-carbon rings with two nonpolar tails	Chemical messengers	Prostaglandin E (PGE)
Steroids	Four fused carbon rings	Membranes; hormones	Cholesterol; estrogen
Terpenes	Long carbon chains	Pigments; structural support	Carotene; rubber

Biological macromolecules include carbohydrates, nucleic acids, proteins, and lipids

Remember that biological macromolecules are traditionally grouped into carbohydrates, nucleic acids, proteins, and lipids (table 3.1). In many cases, these macromolecules are polymers. A **polymer** is a long molecule built by linking together a large number of small, similar chemical subunits called **monomers.** They are like railroad cars coupled to form a train. The nature of a polymer is determined by the monomers used to build the polymer. Here are some examples. Complex carbohydrates such as starch are polymers composed of simple ring-shaped sugars. Nucleic acids (DNA and RNA) are polymers of nucleotides (figure 3.4). Proteins are polymers of amino acids, and lipids are polymers of fatty acids (see figure 3.4). These long chains are built via chemical reactions termed *dehydration reactions* and are broken down by *hydrolysis reactions.*

The dehydration reaction

Despite the differences between monomers of these major polymers, the basic chemistry of their synthesis is similar: To form a covalent bond between two monomers, an —OH group is removed from one monomer, and a hydrogen atom (H) is removed from the other (figure 3.5a). For example, this simple chemistry is the same for linking amino acids together to make a protein or assembling glucose units together to make starch. This reaction is also used to link fatty acids to glycerol in lipids. This chemical reaction is called condensation, or a **dehydration reaction,** because the removal of —OH and —H is the same as the removal of a molecule of water (H_2O). For every subunit added to a macromolecule, one water molecule is removed. These and other biochemical reactions require that the reacting substances are held close together and that the correct chemical bonds are stressed and broken. This process of positioning and stressing, termed *catalysis*, is carried out within cells by enzymes.

The hydrolysis reaction

Cells disassemble macromolecules into their constituent subunits through reactions that are the reverse of dehydration—a molecule of water is added instead of removed (figure 3.5b). In this process, called **hydrolysis,** a hydrogen atom is attached to one subunit and a hydroxyl group to the other, breaking a specific covalent bond in the macromolecule.

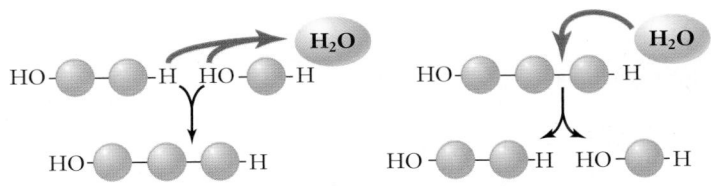

a. Dehydration reaction   *b.* Hydrolysis reaction

Figure 3.5 Making and breaking macromolecules.
a. Biological macromolecules are polymers formed by linking monomers together through dehydration reactions. This process releases a water molecule for every bond formed. *b.* Breaking the bond between subunits involves hydrolysis, which reverses the loss of a water molecule by dehydration.

3.2 Carbohydrates: Energy Storage and Structural Molecules

Learning Outcomes

1. *Describe the structure of a sugar.*
2. *Name the different forms of carbohydrate molecules.*
3. *Relate the structure of polysaccharides to their functions*

Monosaccharides are simple sugars

Carbohydrates are a loosely defined group of molecules that all contain carbon, hydrogen, and oxygen in the molar ratio 1:2:1. Their empirical formula (which lists the number of atoms in the molecule with subscripts) is $(CH_2O)_n$, where n is the number of carbon atoms. Because they contain many carbon–hydrogen (C—H) bonds, which release energy when oxidation occurs, carbohydrates are well suited for energy storage. Sugars are among the most important energy-storage molecules, and they exist in several different forms.

The simplest of the carbohydrates are the **monosaccharides** (Greek *mono*, "single," and Latin *saccharum*, "sugar"). Simple sugars contain as few as three carbon atoms, but those that play the central role in energy storage have six (figure 3.6). The empirical formula of six-carbon sugars is:

$$C_6H_{12}O_6 \qquad or \qquad (CH_2O)_6$$

Six-carbon sugars can exist in a straight-chain form, but dissolved in water (an aqueous environment) they almost always form rings.

The most important of the six-carbon monosaccharides for energy storage is glucose, which you first encountered in the examples of chemical reactions in chapter 2. Glucose has seven energy-storing C—H bonds (figure 3.7). Depending on the orientation of the carbonyl group (C=O) when the ring is closed, glucose can exist in two different forms: alpha (α) or beta (β).

Sugar isomers have structural differences

Glucose is not the only sugar with the formula $C_6H_{12}O_6$. Both structural isomers and stereoisomers of this simple six-carbon skeleton exist in nature. Fructose is a structural isomer that differs in the position of the carbonyl carbon (C==O); galactose is a stereoisomer that differs in the position of —OH and —H groups relative to the ring (figure 3.8). These differences often account for substantial functional differences between the isomers. Your taste buds can discern them: Fructose tastes much sweeter than glucose, despite the fact that both sugars have identical chemical composition. Enzymes that act on different sugars can distinguish both the structural and stereoisomers of this basic six-carbon skeleton. The different stereoisomers of glucose are also important in the polymers that can be made using glucose as a monomer, as you will see later in this chapter.

Disaccharides serve as transport molecules in plants and provide nutrition in animals

Most organisms transport sugars within their bodies. In humans, the glucose that circulates in the blood does so as a simple monosaccharide. In plants and many other organisms, however, glucose is converted into a transport form before it is moved from place to place within the organism. In such a form, it is less readily metabolized during transport.

Transport forms of sugars are commonly made by linking two monosaccharides together to form a **disaccharide** (Greek *di*, "two"). Disaccharides serve as effective reservoirs of glucose because the enzymes that normally use glucose in the organism cannot break the bond linking the two monosaccharide subunits. Enzymes that can do so are typically present only in the tissue that uses glucose.

3-carbon Sugar	5-carbon Sugars		6-carbon Sugars		

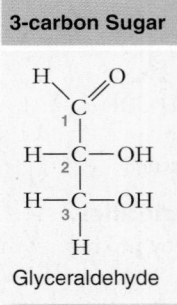

Glyceraldehyde

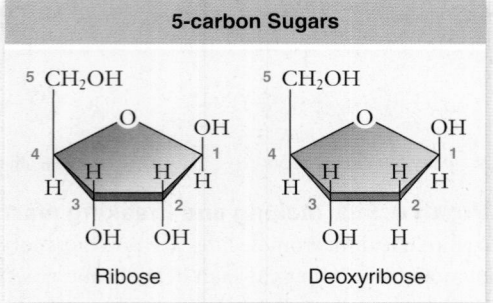

Ribose   Deoxyribose

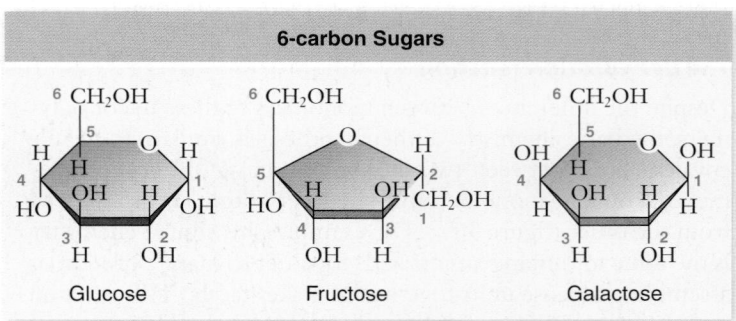

Glucose   Fructose   Galactose

Figure 3.6 Monosaccharides. Monosaccharides, or simple sugars, can contain as few as three carbon atoms and are often used as building blocks to form larger molecules. The five-carbon sugars ribose and deoxyribose are components of nucleic acids (see figure 3.15). The carbons are conventionally numbered from the more oxidized end.

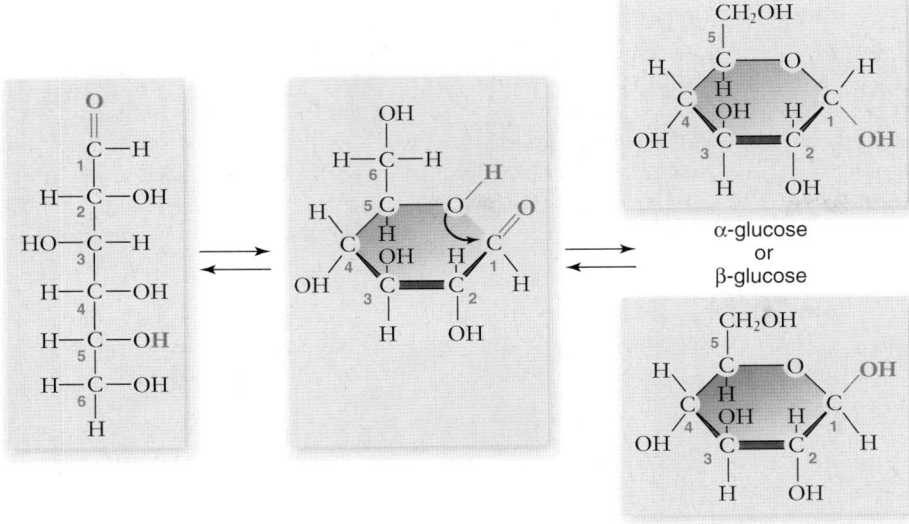

Figure 3.7 Structure of the glucose molecule. Glucose is a linear, six-carbon molecule that forms a six-membered ring in solution. Ring closure occurs such that two forms can result: α-glucose and β-glucose. These structures differ only in the position of the —OH bound to carbon 1. The structure of the ring can be represented in many ways; shown here are the most common, with the carbons conventionally numbered (in *blue*) so that the forms can be compared easily. The heavy lines in the ring structures represent portions of the molecule that are projecting out of the page toward you.

Transport forms differ depending on which monosaccharides are linked to form the disaccharide. Glucose forms transport disaccharides with itself and with many other monosaccharides, including fructose and galactose. When glucose forms a disaccharide with the structural isomer fructose, the resulting disaccharide is *sucrose*, or table sugar (figure 3.9*a*). Sucrose is the form most plants use to transport glucose and is the sugar that most humans and other animals eat. Sugarcane and sugar beets are rich in sucrose.

When glucose is linked to the stereoisomer galactose, the resulting disaccharide is *lactose*, or milk sugar. Many mammals supply energy to their young in the form of lactose. Adults often have greatly reduced levels of lactase, the enzyme required to cleave lactose into its two monosaccharide components, and thus they cannot metabolize lactose efficiently. This can result in lactose intolerance in humans. Most of the energy that is channeled into lactose production is therefore reserved for offspring. For this reason, lactose as an energy source is primarily for offspring in mammals.

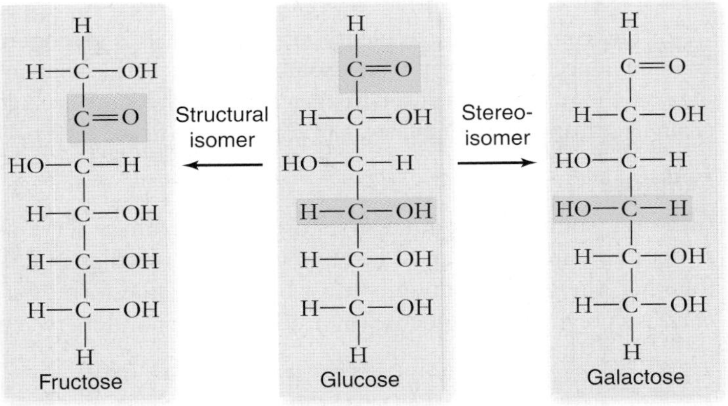

Polysaccharides provide energy storage and structural components

Polysaccharides are longer polymers made up of monosaccharides that have been joined through dehydration reactions. **Starch,** a storage polysaccharide, consists entirely of α-glucose molecules linked in long chains. **Cellulose,** a structural polysaccharide, also consists of glucose molecules linked in chains, but these molecules are β-glucose. Because starch is built from α-glucose we call the linkages α linkages; cellulose has β linkages.

Starches and Glycogen

Organisms store the metabolic energy contained in monosaccharides by converting them into disaccharides, such as *maltose* (figure 3.9*b*). These are then linked together into the insoluble polysaccharides called *starches*. These polysaccharides differ mainly in how the polymers branch.

The starch with the simplest structure is *amylose*. It is composed of many hundreds of α-glucose molecules linked together in long, unbranched chains. Each linkage occurs between the carbon 1

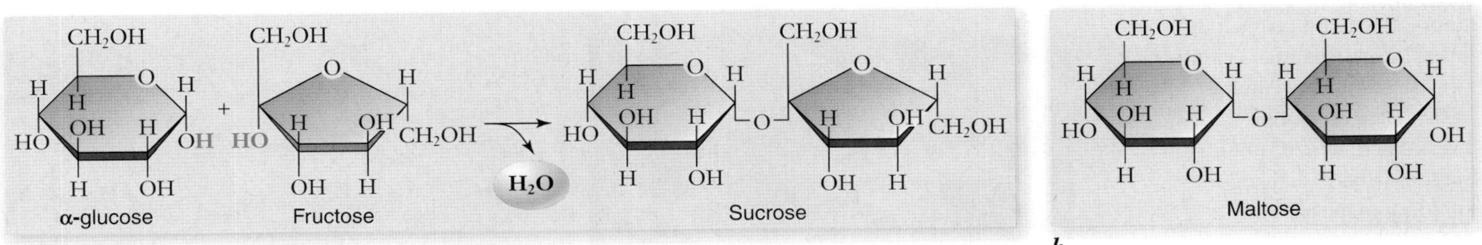

Figure 3.8 Isomers and stereoisomers. Glucose, fructose, and galactose are isomers with the empirical formula $C_6H_{12}O_6$. A structural isomer of glucose, such as fructose, has identical chemical groups bonded to different carbon atoms. Notice that this results in a five-membered ring in solution (see figure 3.6). A stereoisomer of glucose, such as galactose, has identical chemical groups bonded to the same carbon atoms but in different orientations (the —OH at carbon 4).

Figure 3.9 How disaccharides form. Some disaccharides are used to transport glucose from one part of an organism's body to another; one example is sucrose (*a*), which is found in sugarcane. Other disaccharides, such as maltose (*b*), are used in grain for storage.

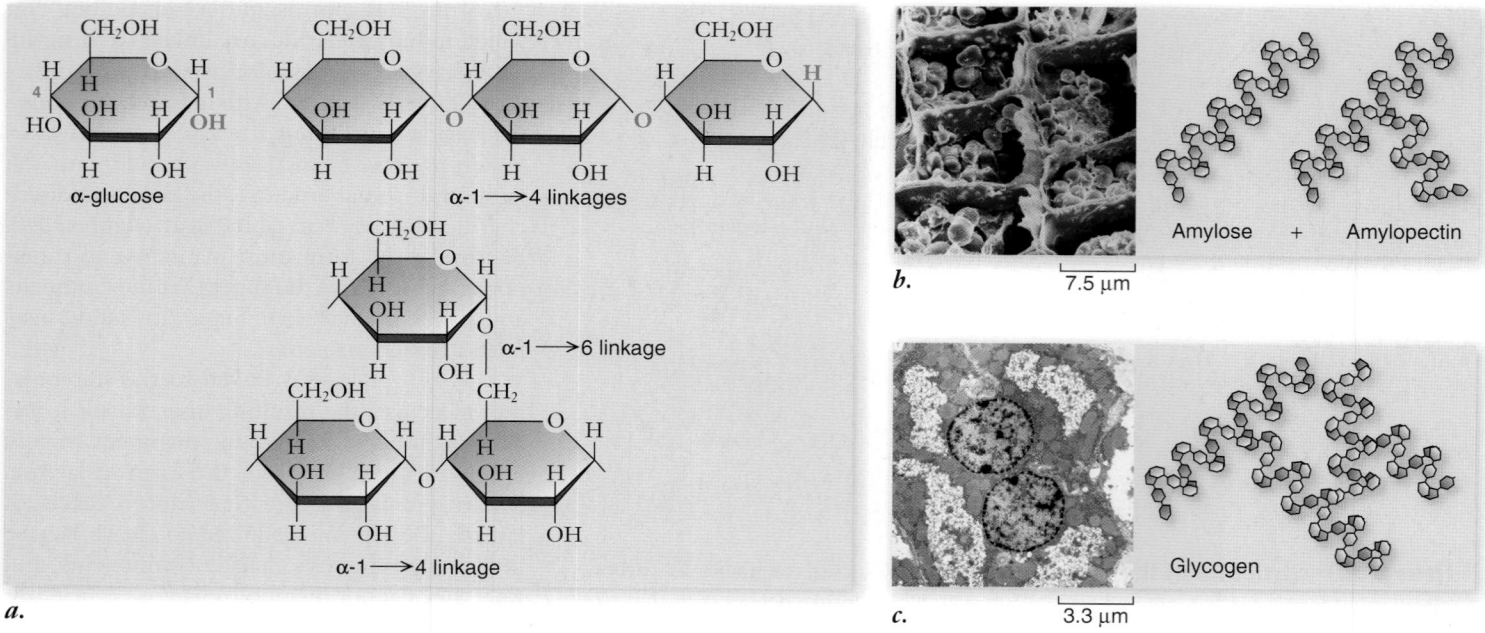

Figure 3.10 Polymers of glucose: Starch and glycogen. *a.* Starch chains consist of polymers of α-glucose subunits joined by α-(1→4) glycosidic linkages. These chains can be branched by forming similar α-(1→6) glycosidic bonds. These storage polymers then differ primarily in their degree of branching. *b.* Starch is found in plants and is composed of amylose and amylopectin, which are unbranched and branched, respectively. The branched form is insoluble and forms starch granules in plant cells. *c.* Glycogen is found in animal cells and is highly branched and also insoluble, forming glycogen granules.

(C-1) of one glucose molecule and the C-4 of another, making them α-(1→4) linkages (figure 3.10*a*). The long chains of amylose tend to coil up in water, a property that renders amylose insoluble. Potato starch is about 20% amylose (figure 3.10*b*).

Most plant starch, including the remaining 80% of potato starch, is a somewhat more complicated variant of amylose called *amylopectin*. Pectins are branched polysaccharides with the branches occurring due to bonds between the C-1 of one molecule and the C-6 of another [α-(1→6) linkages]. These short amylose branches consist of 20 to 30 glucose subunits (figure 3.10*b*).

The comparable molecule to starch in animals is **glycogen.** Like amylopectin, glycogen is an insoluble polysaccharide containing branched amylose chains. Glycogen has a much longer average chain length and more branches than plant starch (figure 3.10*c*).

Cellulose

Although some chains of sugars store energy, others serve as structural material for cells. For two glucose molecules to link together, the glucose subunits must be of the same form. *Cellulose* is a polymer of β-glucose (figure 3.11). The bonds between

Figure 3.11 Polymers of glucose: Cellulose. Starch chains consist of α-glucose subunits, and cellulose chains consist of β-glucose subunits. *a.* Thus the bonds between adjacent glucose molecules in cellulose are β-(1→4) glycosidic linkages. *b.* Cellulose is unbranched and forms long fibers. Cellulose fibers can be very strong and are quite resistant to metabolic breakdown, which is one reason wood is such a good building material.

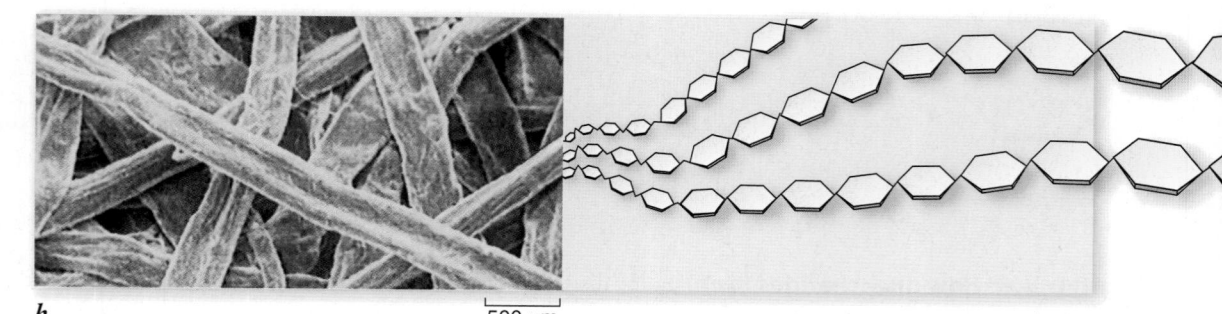

adjacent glucose molecules still exist between the C-1 of the first glucose and the C-4 of the next glucose, but these are β-(1⟶4) linkages.

The properties of a chain of glucose molecules consisting of all β-glucose are very different from those of starch. These long, unbranched β-linked chains make tough fibers. Cellulose is the chief component of plant cell walls (see figure 3.11b). It is chemically similar to amylose, with one important difference: The starch-hydrolyzing enzymes that occur in most organisms cannot break the bond between two β-glucose units because they only recognize α linkages.

Because cellulose cannot be broken down readily by most creatures, it works well as a biological structural material. But some animals, such as cows, are able to break down cellulose by means of symbiotic bacteria and protists in their digestive tracts. These organisms provide the necessary enzymes for cleaving the β-(1⟶4) linkages, thus enabling access to a rich source of energy.

Chitin

Chitin, the structural material found in arthropods and many fungi, is a polymer of *N*-acetylglucosamine, a substituted version of glucose. When cross-linked by proteins, it forms a tough, resistant surface material that serves as the hard exoskeleton of insects and crustaceans (figure 3.12; see chapter 34). Few organisms are able to digest chitin, but most possess a chitinase enzyme, probably to protect against fungi.

Learning Outcomes Review 3.2

Monosaccharides have three to six or more carbon atoms typically arranged in a ring form. Disaccharides consist of two linked monosaccharides; polysaccharides are long chains of monosaccharides. Structural differences between sugar isomers can lead to functional differences. Starches are branched polymers of α-glucose used for energy storage. Cellulose in plants consists of unbranched chains of β-glucose that are not easily digested.

■ *How do the structures of starch, glycogen, and cellulose affect their function?*

Figure 3.12 Chitin. Chitin is the principal structural element in the external skeletons of many invertebrates, such as this lobster.

Nucleic Acids: Information Molecules

Learning Outcomes

1. **Describe the structure of nucleotides.**
2. **Compare and contrast the structures of DNA and RNA.**
3. **Explain the functions of DNA and RNA.**
4. **Recognize other nucleotides involved in energy metabolism.**

The biochemical activity of a cell depends on production of a large number of proteins, each with a specific sequence. The information necessary to produce the correct proteins is passed through generations of organisms, even though the protein molecules themselves are not.

Nucleic acids carry information inside cells, just as disks contain the information in a computer or road maps display information needed by travelers. Two main varieties of nucleic acids are **deoxyribonucleic acid (DNA;** figure 3.13) and **ribonucleic acid (RNA).**

DNA encodes the genetic information used to assemble proteins (as discussed in detail in chapter 15) similar to the way the letters on this page encode information. Unique among macromolecules, nucleic acids are able to serve as templates to produce precise copies of themselves. This characteristic allows genetic information to be preserved during cell division and

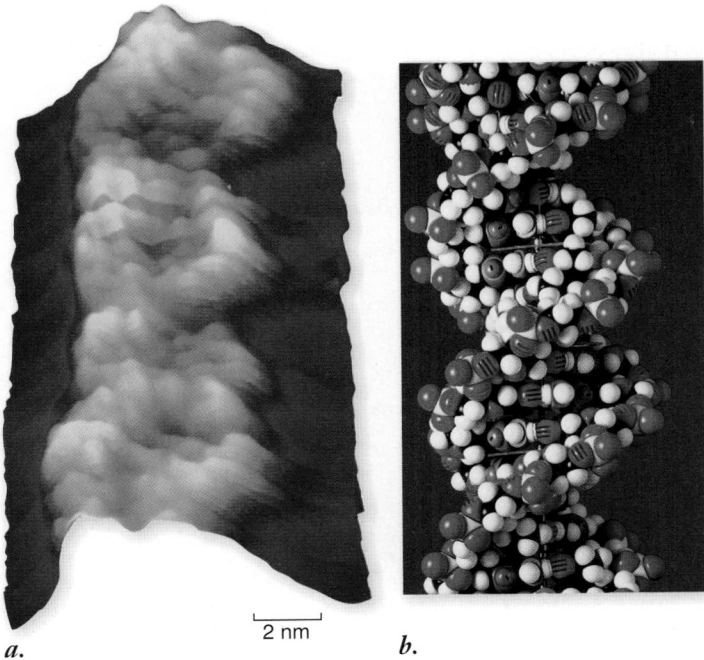

2 nm

a.   *b.*

Figure 3.13 Images of DNA. *a.* A scanning-tunneling micrograph of DNA (false color; 2,000,000×) showing approximately three turns of the DNA double helix. *b.* A space-filling model for comparison to the image of actual DNA in (*a*).

during the reproduction of organisms. DNA, found primarily in the nuclear region of cells, contains the genetic information necessary to build specific organisms.

Cells use a type of RNA called messenger RNA (mRNA) to direct the synthesis of proteins. mRNA consists of transcribed single-stranded copies of portions of the DNA. These transcripts serve as blueprints specifying the amino acid sequences of proteins. This process will be described in detail in chapter 15.

Nucleic acids are nucleotide polymers

Nucleic acids are long polymers of repeating subunits called **nucleotides.** Each nucleotide consists of three components: a pentose, or five-carbon sugar (ribose in RNA and deoxyribose in DNA); a phosphate (—PO₄) group; and an organic nitrogenous (nitrogen-containing) base (figure 3.14). When a nucleic acid polymer forms, the phosphate group of one nucleotide binds to the hydroxyl group from the pentose sugar of another, releasing water and forming a *phosphodiester bond* by a dehydration reaction. A **nucleic acid,** then, is simply a chain of five-carbon sugars linked together by phosphodiester bonds with a nitrogenous base protruding from each sugar (see figure 3.15a). These chains of nucleotides, *polynucleotides*, have different ends: a phosphate on one end and an —OH from a sugar on the other end. We conventionally refer to these ends as 5′ ("five-prime," —PO₄) and 3′ ("three-prime," —OH) taken from the carbon numbering of the sugar (figure 3.15a).

Two types of nitrogenous bases occur in nucleotides (3.15b). The first type, *purines*, are large, double-ring molecules found in both DNA and RNA; the two types of purines are adenine (A) and guanine (G). The second type, *pyrimidines*, are smaller, single-ring molecules; they include cytosine (C, in both

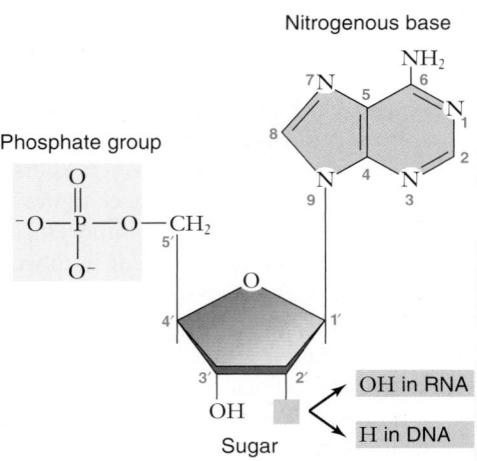

Figure 3.14 Structure of a nucleotide. The nucleotide subunits of DNA and RNA are made up of three elements: a five-carbon sugar (ribose or deoxyribose), an organic nitrogenous base (adenine is shown here), and a phosphate group. Notice that all the numbers on the sugar are given as "primes" (1′, 2′, etc.) to distinguish them from the numbering on the rings of the bases.

DNA and RNA), thymine (T, in DNA only), and uracil (U, in RNA only).

DNA carries the genetic code

Organisms use sequences of nucleotides in DNA to encode the information specifying the amino acid sequences of their proteins. This method of encoding information is very similar to the way in which sequences of letters encode information in a sentence.

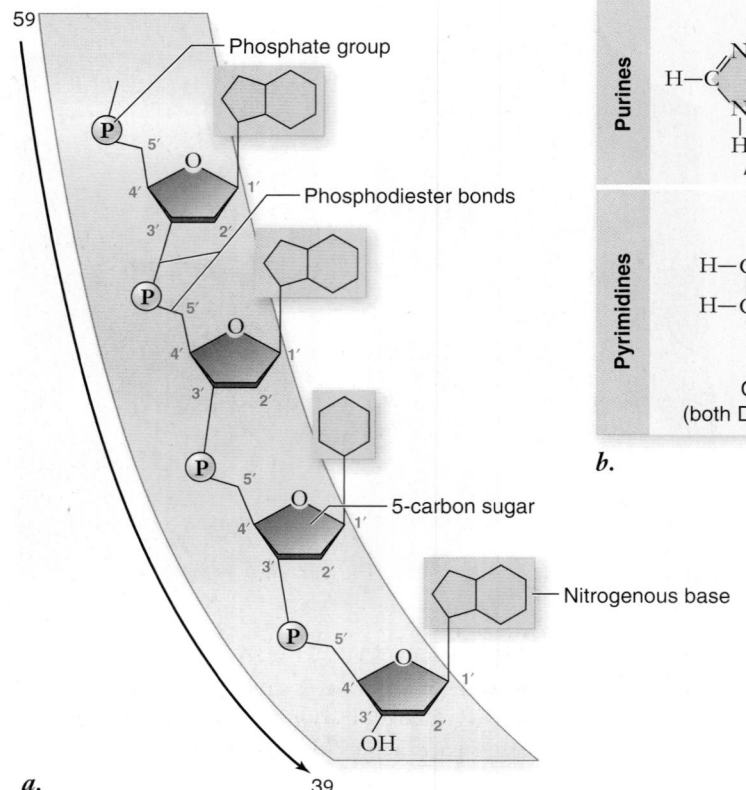

b.

Figure 3.15 The structure of a nucleic acid and the organic nitrogenous bases. *a.* In a nucleic acid, nucleotides are linked to one another via phosphodiester bonds formed between the phosphate of one nucleotide and the sugar of the next nucleotide. We call this the sugar-phosphate backbone, and the organic bases protrude from this chain. The backbone also has different ends: a 5′ phosphate end and a 3′ hydroxyl end (the numbers come from the numbers in the sugars). *b.* The organic nitrogenous bases can be either purines or pyrimidines. The base thymine is found in DNA. The base uracil is found in RNA.

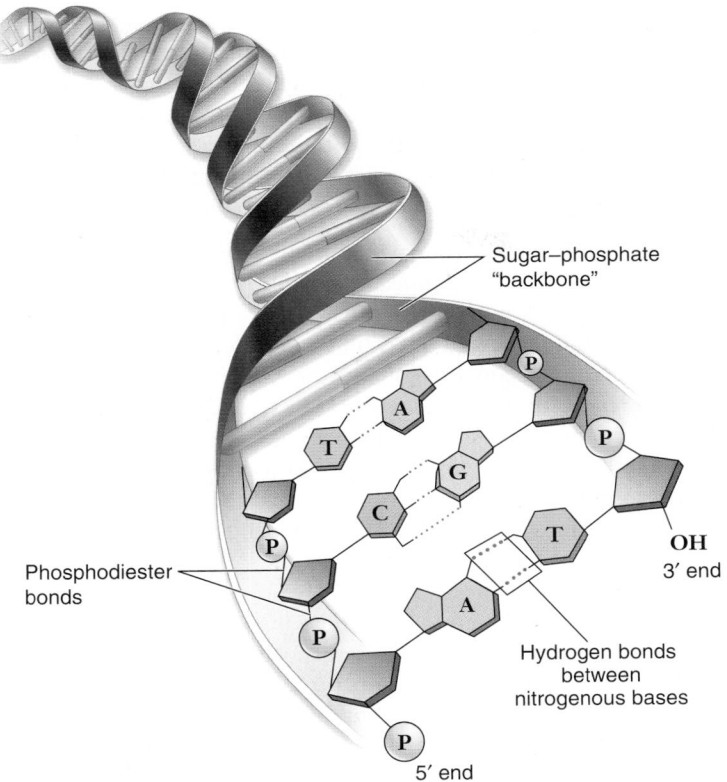

Figure 3.16 The structure of DNA. DNA consists of two polynucleotide chains running in opposite directions wrapped about a single helical axis. Hydrogen bond formation (dashed lines) between the nitrogenous bases, called base-pairing, causes the two chains of DNA to bind to each other and form a double helix.

A sentence written in English consists of a combination of the 26 different letters of the alphabet in a certain order; the code of a DNA molecule consists of different combinations of the four types of nucleotides in specific sequences, such as CGCTTACG. The information encoded in DNA is used in the everyday functioning of the organism and is passed on to the organism's descendants.

DNA molecules in organisms exist not as single chains folded into complex shapes, like proteins, but rather as two chains wrapped about each other in a long linear molecule in eukaryotes, and a circular molecule in most prokaryotes. The two strands of a DNA polymer wind around each other like the outside and inside rails of a spiral staircase. Such a spiral shape is called a helix, and a helix composed of two chains is called a **double helix.** Each step of DNA's helical staircase is composed of a base-pair. The pair consists of a base in one chain attracted by hydrogen bonds to a base opposite it on the other chain (figure 3.16).

The base-pairing rules are rigid: Adenine can pair only with thymine (in DNA) or with uracil (in RNA), and cytosine can pair only with guanine. The bases that participate in base-pairing are said to be **complementary** to each other. Additional details of the structure of DNA and how it interacts with RNA in the production of proteins are presented in chapters 14 and 15.

RNA is a transcript of a DNA strand

RNA is similar to DNA, but with two major chemical differences. First, RNA molecules contain ribose sugars, in which the C-2 is bonded to a hydroxyl group. (In DNA, this hydroxyl group is replaced by a hydrogen atom.) Second, RNA molecules use uracil in place of thymine. Uracil has the same structure as thymine, except that one of its carbons lacks a methyl ($—CH_3$) group.

Transcribing the DNA message into a chemically different molecule such as RNA allows the cell to distinguish between the original information-storage molecule and the transcript. DNA molecules are always double-stranded (except for a few single-stranded DNA viruses), whereas the RNA molecules transcribed from DNA are typically single-stranded (figure 3.17). These differences allow DNA to store hereditary information and RNA to use this information to specify the sequence of amino acids in proteins.

Other nucleotides are vital components of energy reactions

In addition to serving as subunits of DNA and RNA, nucleotide bases play other critical roles in the life of a cell. For example, adenine is a key component of the molecule **adenosine**

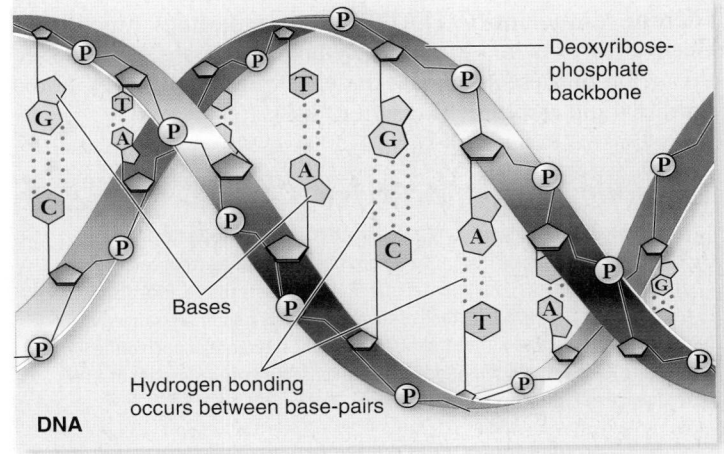

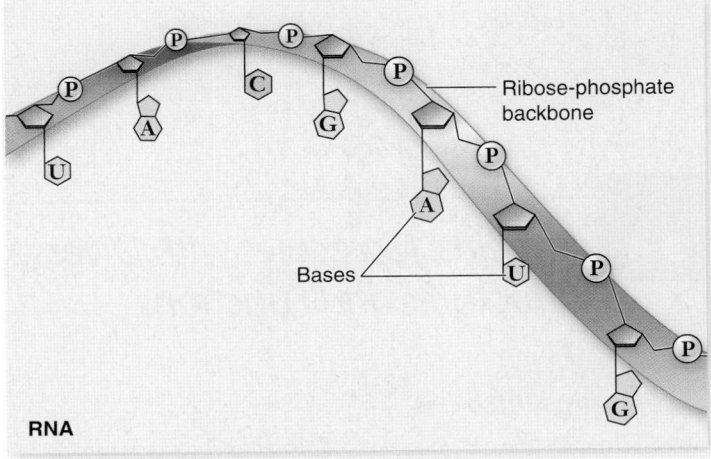

Figure 3.17 DNA versus RNA. DNA forms a double helix, uses deoxyribose as the sugar in its sugar–phosphate backbone, and uses thymine among its nitrogenous bases. RNA is usually single-stranded, uses ribose as the sugar in its sugar–phosphate backbone, and uses uracil in place of thymine.

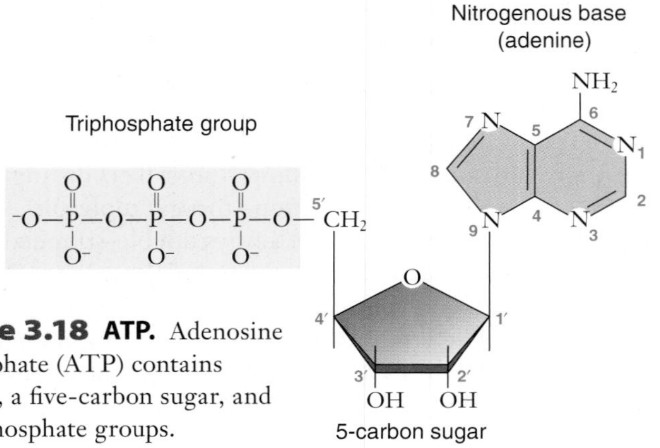

Triphosphate group

Nitrogenous base (adenine)

Figure 3.18 ATP. Adenosine triphosphate (ATP) contains adenine, a five-carbon sugar, and three phosphate groups.

5-carbon sugar

triphosphate (**ATP;** figure 3.18)—the energy currency of the cell. Cells use ATP as energy in a variety of transactions, the way we use money in society. ATP is used to drive energetically unfavorable chemical reactions, to power transport across membranes, and to power the movement of cells.

Two other important nucleotide-containing molecules are **nicotinamide adenine dinucleotide (NAD⁺)** and **flavin adenine dinucleotide (FAD).** These molecules function as electron carriers in a variety of cellular processes. You will see the action of these molecules in detail when we discuss photosynthesis and respiration (chapters 7–8).

Learning Outcomes Review 3.3

A nucleic acid is a polymer composed of alternating phosphate and five-carbon sugar groups with a nitrogenous base protruding from each sugar. In DNA, this sugar is deoxyribose. In RNA, the sugar is ribose. RNA also contains the base uracil instead of thymine. DNA is a double-stranded helix that stores hereditary information as a specific sequence of nucleotide bases. RNA is a single-stranded molecule consisting of a transcript of a DNA sequence that directs protein synthesis.

■ *If an RNA molecule is copied from a DNA strand, what is the relationship between the sequence of bases in RNA and each DNA strand?*

3.4 Proteins: Molecules with Diverse Structures and Functions

Learning Outcomes

1. Describe the possible levels of protein structure.
2. Explain how motifs and domains contribute to protein structure.
3. Understand the relationship between amino acid sequence and their three-dimensional structure.

Proteins are the most diverse group of biological macromolecules, both chemically and functionally. Because proteins have so many different functions in cells we could not begin to list them all. We can, however, group these functions into the following seven categories. This list is a summary only, however; details are covered in later chapters.

1. **Enzyme catalysis.** Enzymes are biological catalysts that facilitate specific chemical reactions. Because of this property, the appearance of enzymes was one of the most important events in the evolution of life. Enzymes are three-dimensional globular proteins that fit snugly around the molecules they act on. This fit facilitates chemical reactions by stressing particular chemical bonds.
2. **Defense.** Other globular proteins use their shapes to "recognize" foreign microbes and cancer cells. These cell-surface receptors form the core of the body's endocrine and immune systems.
3. **Transport.** A variety of globular proteins transport small molecules and ions. The transport protein hemoglobin, for example, transports oxygen in the blood. Membrane transport proteins help move ions and molecules across the membrane.
4. **Support.** Protein fibers play structural roles. These fibers include keratin in hair, fibrin in blood clots, and collagen. The last one, collagen, forms the matrix of skin, ligaments, tendons, and bones and is the most abundant protein in a vertebrate body.
5. **Motion.** Muscles contract through the sliding motion of two kinds of protein filaments: actin and myosin. Contractile proteins also play key roles in the cell's cytoskeleton and in moving materials within cells.
6. **Regulation.** Small proteins called hormones serve as intercellular messengers in animals. Proteins also play many regulatory roles within the cell—turning on and shutting off genes during development, for example. In addition, proteins receive information, acting as cell-surface receptors.
7. **Storage.** Calcium and iron are stored in the body by binding as ions to storage proteins.

Table 3.2 summarizes these functions and includes examples of the proteins that carry them out in the human body.

Proteins are polymers of amino acids

Proteins are linear polymers made with 20 different amino acids. **Amino acids,** as their name suggests, contain an amino group ($—NH_2$) and an acidic carboxyl group ($—COOH$). The specific order of amino acids determines the protein's structure and function. Many scientists believe amino acids were among the first molecules formed on the early Earth. It seems highly likely that the oceans that existed early in the history of the Earth contained a wide variety of amino acids.

Amino acid structure

The generalized structure of an amino acid is shown here as amino and carboxyl groups bonded to a central carbon atom, with an additional hydrogen and a functional side group

TABLE 3.2	The Many Functions of Protein		
Function	**Class of Protein**	**Examples**	**Examples of Use**
Enzyme catalysis	Enzymes	Glycosidases	Cleave polysaccharides
		Proteases	Break down proteins
		Polymerases	Synthesize nucleic acids
		Kinases	Phosphorylate sugars and proteins
Defense	Immunoglobulins	Antibodies	Mark foreign proteins for elimination
	Toxins	Snake venom	Blocks nerve function
	Cell-surface antigens	MHC* proteins	"Self" recognition
Transport	Circulating transporters	Hemoglobin	Carries O_2 and CO_2 in blood
		Myoglobin	Carries O_2 and CO_2 in muscle
		Cytochromes	Electron transport
	Membrane transporters	Sodium–potassium pump	Excitable membranes
		Proton pump	Chemiosmosis
		Glucose transporter	Transports glucose into cells
Support	Fibers	Collagen	Forms cartilage
		Keratin	Forms hair, nails
		Fibrin	Forms blood clots
Motion	Muscle	Actin	Contraction of muscle fibers
		Myosin	Contraction of muscle fibers
Regulation	Osmotic proteins	Serum albumin	Maintains osmotic concentration of blood
	Gene regulators	*lac* Repressor	Regulates transcription
	Hormones	Insulin	Controls blood glucose levels
		Vasopressin	Increases water retention by kidneys
		Oxytocin	Regulates uterine contractions and milk production
Storage	Ion-binding	Ferritin	Stores iron, especially in spleen
		Casein	Stores ions in milk
		Calmodulin	Binds calcium ions

*MHC, major histocompatibility complex.

indicated by R. These components completely fill the bonds of the central carbon:

$$H_2N-\overset{\overset{\displaystyle R}{|}}{\underset{\underset{\displaystyle H}{|}}{C}}-COOH$$

The unique character of each amino acid is determined by the nature of the R group. Notice that unless the R group is an H atom, as in glycine, amino acids are chiral and can exist as two enantiomeric forms: D or L. In living systems, only the L-amino acids are found in proteins, and D-amino acids are rare.

The R group also determines the chemistry of amino acids. Serine, in which the R group is —CH₂OH, is a polar molecule. Alanine, which has —CH₃ as its R group, is nonpolar.

The 20 common amino acids are grouped into five chemical classes, based on their R group:

1. Nonpolar amino acids, such as leucine, often have R groups that contain —CH₂ or —CH₃.
2. Polar uncharged amino acids, such as threonine, have R groups that contain oxygen (or —OH).
3. Charged amino acids, such as glutamic acid, have R groups that contain acids or bases that can ionize.
4. Aromatic amino acids, such as phenylalanine, have R groups that contain an organic (carbon) ring with alternating single and double bonds. These are also nonpolar.
5. Amino acids that have special functions have unique properties. Some examples are methionine, which is often the first amino acid in a chain of amino acids; proline, which causes kinks in chains; and cysteine, which links chains together.

chapter **3** *The Chemical Building Blocks of Life* **45**

Each amino acid affects the shape of a protein differently, depending on the chemical nature of its side group. For example, portions of a protein chain with numerous nonpolar amino acids tend to fold into the interior of the protein by hydrophobic exclusion.

Peptide bonds

In addition to its R group, each amino acid, when ionized, has a positive amino (NH_3^+) group at one end and a negative carboxyl (COO^-) group at the other. The amino and carboxyl groups on a pair of amino acids can undergo a dehydration reaction to form a covalent bond. The covalent bond that links two amino acids is called a **peptide bond** (figure 3.19). The two amino acids linked by such a bond are not free to rotate around the N—C linkage because the peptide bond has a partial double-bond character. This is different from the N—C and C—C bonds to the central carbon of the amino acid. This lack of rotation about the peptide bond is one factor that determines the structural character of the coils and other regular shapes formed by chains of amino acids.

A protein is composed of one or more long unbranched chains. Each chain is called a **polypeptide** and is composed of amino acids linked by peptide bonds. The terms *protein* and *polypeptide* tend to be used loosely and may be confusing. For proteins that include only a single polypeptide chain, the two terms are synonymous.

The pioneering work of Frederick Sanger in the early 1950s provided the evidence that each kind of protein has a specific amino acid sequence. Using chemical methods to remove successive amino acids and then identify them, Sanger succeeded in determining the amino acid sequence of insulin. In so doing he demonstrated clearly that this protein had a defined sequence, which was the same for all insulin molecules in

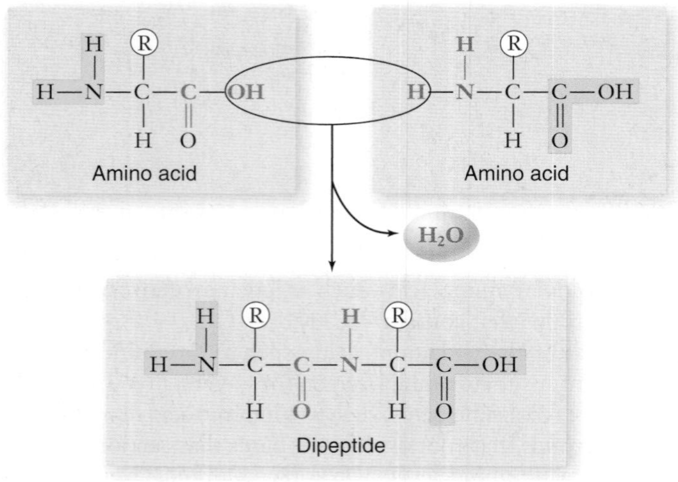

Figure 3.19 The peptide bond. A peptide bond forms when the amino end of one amino acid joins to the carboxyl end of another. Reacting amino and carboxyl groups are shown in red and nonreacting groups are highlighted in green. Notice that the resulting dipeptide still has an amino end and a carboxyl end. Because of the partial double-bond nature of peptide bonds, the resulting peptide chain cannot rotate freely around these bonds.

the solution. Although many different amino acids occur in nature, only 20 commonly occur in proteins. Figure 3.20 illustrates these 20 amino acids and their side groups.

Proteins have levels of structure

The shape of a protein determines its function. One way to study the shape of something as small as a protein is to look at it with very short wavelength energy—in other words, with X-rays. X-rays can be passed through a crystal of protein to produce a diffraction pattern. This pattern can then be analyzed by a painstaking procedure that allows the investigator to build up a three-dimensional picture of the position of each atom. The first protein to be analyzed in this way was myoglobin, and the related protein hemoglobin was analyzed soon thereafter.

As more and more proteins were studied, a general principle became evident: In every protein studied, essentially all the internal amino acids are nonpolar ones—amino acids such as leucine, valine, and phenylalanine. Water's tendency to hydrophobically exclude nonpolar molecules literally shoves the nonpolar portions of the amino acid chain into the protein's interior (figure 3.21). This tendency forces the nonpolar amino acids into close contact with one another, leaving little empty space inside. Polar and charged amino acids are restricted to the surface of the protein, except for the few that play key functional roles.

The structure of proteins is usually discussed in terms of a hierarchy of four levels: *primary, secondary, tertiary,* and *quaternary* (figure 3.22). We will examine this view and then integrate it with a more modern approach arising from our increasing knowledge of protein structure.

Primary structure: amino acid sequence

The **primary structure** of a protein is its amino acid sequence. Because the R groups that distinguish the amino acids play no role in the peptide backbone of proteins, a protein can consist of any sequence of amino acids. Thus, because any of 20 different amino acids might appear at any position, a protein containing 100 amino acids could form any of 20^{100} different amino acid sequences (that's the same as 10^{130}, or 1 followed by 130 zeros—more than the number of atoms known in the universe). This important property of proteins permits great diversity.

Consider the protein hemoglobin, the protein your blood uses to transport oxygen. Hemoglobin is composed of two α-globin peptide chains and two β-globin peptide chains. The α-globin chains differ from the β-globin ones in the sequence of amino acids. Furthermore, any alteration in the normal sequence of either of the types of globin proteins, even by a single amino acid, can have drastic effects on how the protein functions.

Secondary structure: Hydrogen bonding patterns

The amino acid side groups are not the only portions of proteins that form hydrogen bonds. The peptide groups of the main chain can also do so. These hydrogen bonds can be with water or with other peptide groups. If the peptide groups formed too many hydrogen bonds with water, the proteins would tend to behave like a random coil and wouldn't produce

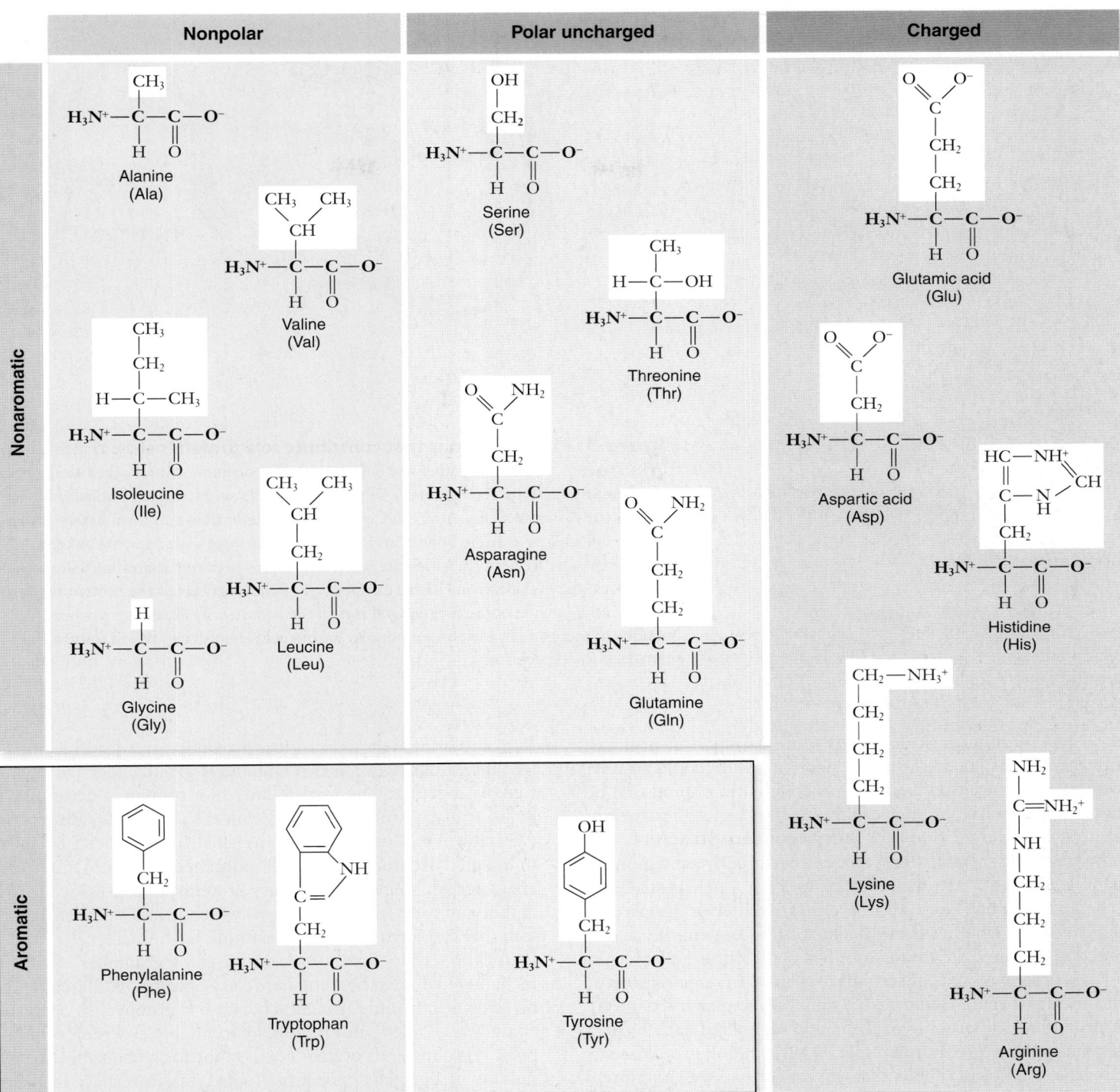

Figure 3.20 The 20 common amino acids. Each amino acid has the same chemical backbone, but differs in the side, or R, group. Seven of the amino acids are nonpolar because they have —CH₂ or —CH₃ in their R groups. Two of the seven contain ring structures with alternating double and single bonds, which classifies them also as aromatic. Another five are polar because they have oxygen or a hydroxyl group in their R groups. Five others are capable of ionizing to a charged form. The remaining three special-function amino acids have chemical properties that allow them to help form links between protein chains or kinks in proteins.

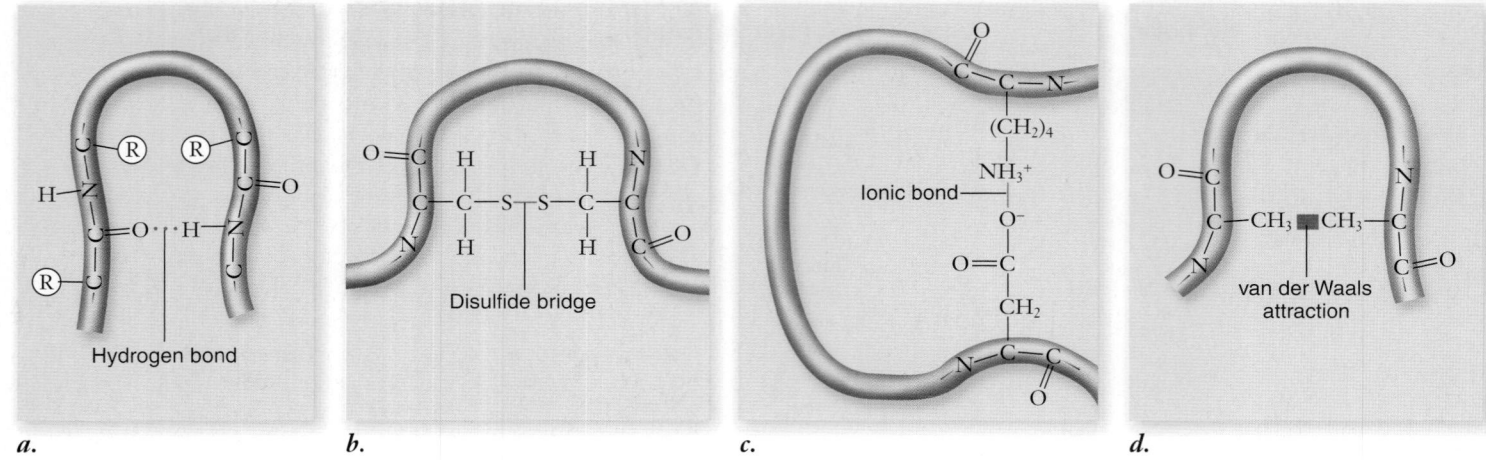

a. b. c. d.

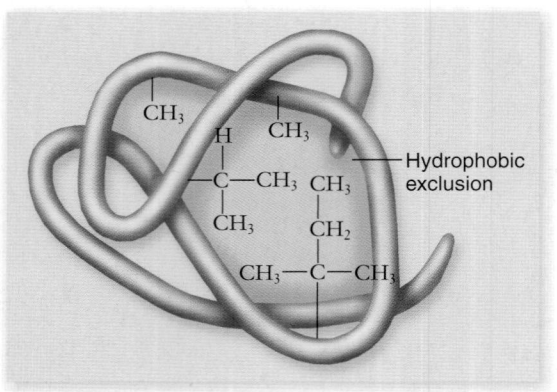

e.

Figure 3.21 **Interactions that contribute to a protein's shape.** Aside from the bonds that link together the amino acids in a protein, several other weaker forces and interactions determine how a protein will fold. *a.* Hydrogen bonds can form between the different amino acids. *b.* Covalent disulfide bridges can form between two cysteine side chains. *c.* Ionic bonds can form between groups with opposite charge. *d.* van der Waals attractions, which are weak attractions between atoms due to oppositely polarized electron clouds, can occur. *e.* Polar portions of the protein tend to gather on the outside of the protein and interact with water, whereas the hydrophobic portions of the protein, including nonpolar amino acid chains, are shoved toward the interior of the protein.

the kinds of globular structures that are common in proteins. Linus Pauling suggested that the peptide groups could interact with one another if the peptide was coiled into a spiral that he called the **α helix.** We now call this sort of regular interaction of groups in the peptide backbone **secondary structure.** Another form of secondary structure can occur between regions of peptide aligned next to each other to form a planar structure called a **β sheet.** These can be either parallel or antiparallel depending on whether the adjacent sections of peptide are oriented in the same direction, or opposite direction.

These two kinds of secondary structure create regions of the protein that are cylindrical (α helices) and planar (β sheets). A protein's final structure can include regions of each type of secondary structure. For example, DNA-binding proteins usually have regions of α helix that can lay across DNA and interact directly with the bases of DNA. Porin proteins that form holes in membranes are composed of β sheets arranged to form a pore in the membrane. Finally in hemoglobin, the α- and β-globin peptide chains that make up the final molecule each have characteristic regions of secondary structure.

Tertiary structure: Folds and links

The final folded shape of a globular protein is called its **tertiary structure.** This tertiary structure contains regions that have secondary structure and determines how these are further arranged in space to produce the overall structure. A protein is initially driven into its tertiary structure by hydrophobic exclusion from water. Ionic bonds between oppositely charged

R groups bring regions into close proximity, and disulfide bonds (covalent links between two cysteine R groups) lock particular regions together. The final folding of a protein is determined by its primary structure—the chemical nature of its side groups (see figure 3.21 and 3.22). Many small proteins can be fully unfolded ("denatured") and will spontaneously refold into their characteristic shape. Other larger proteins tend to associate together and form insoluble clumps when denatured, such as the film that can form when you heat milk for hot chocolate.

The tertiary structure is stabilized by a number of forces including hydrogen bonding between R groups of different amino acids, electrostatic attraction between R groups with opposite charge (also called salt bridges), hydrophobic exclusion of nonpolar R groups, and covalent bonds in the form of disulfides. The stability of a protein, once it has folded into its tertiary shape, is strongly influenced by how well its interior fits together. When two nonpolar chains in the interior are very close together, they experience a form of molecular attraction called van der Waals forces. Individually quite weak, these forces can add up to a strong attraction when many of them come into play, like the combined strength of hundreds of hooks and loops on a strip of Velcro. These forces are effective only over short distances, however. No "holes" or cavities exist in the interior of proteins. The variety of different nonpolar amino acids, with a different-sized R group with its own distinctive shape, allows nonpolar chains to fit very precisely within the protein interior.

It is therefore not surprising that changing a single amino acid can drastically alter the structure, and thus the function of a

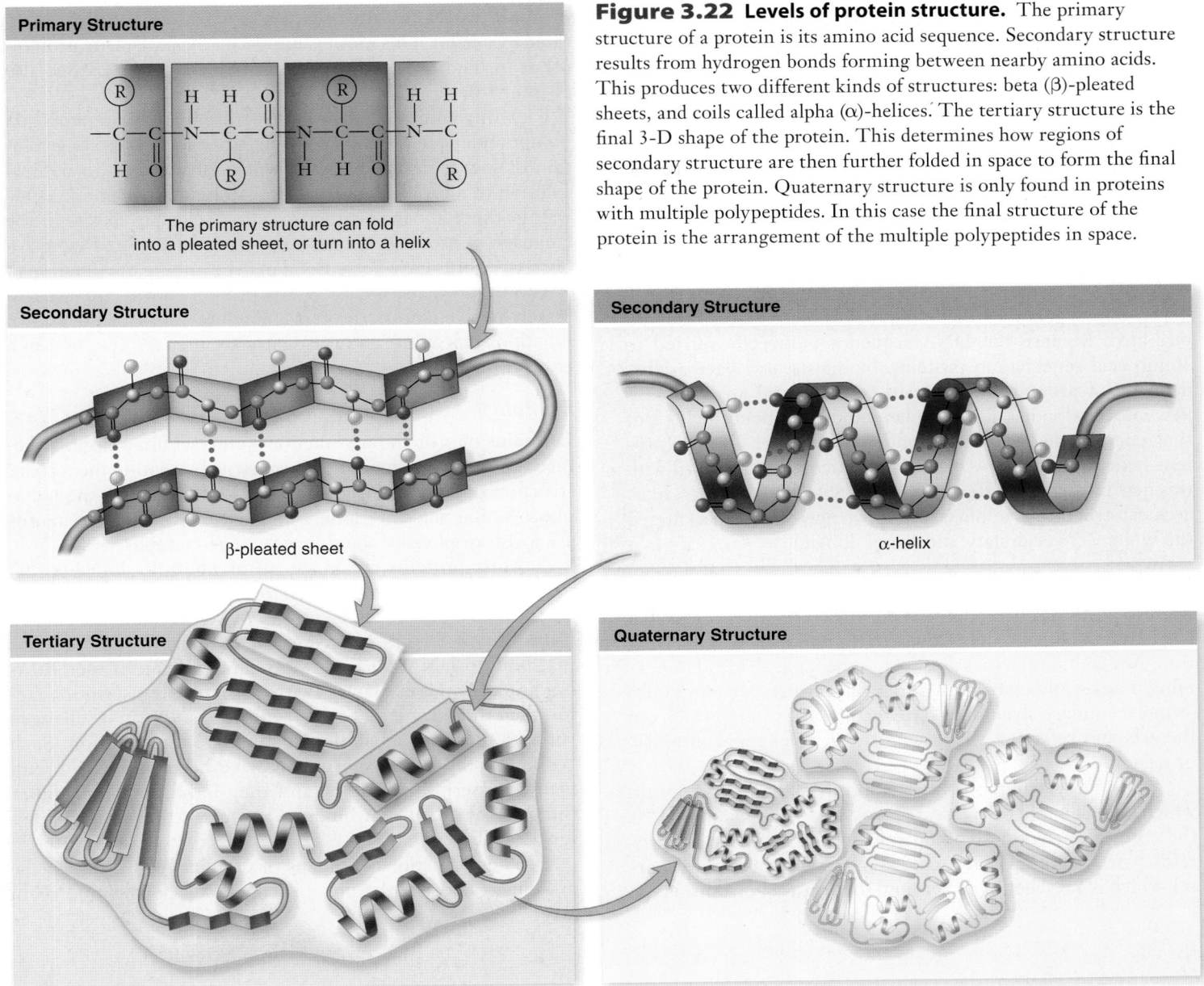

Primary Structure

The primary structure can fold into a pleated sheet, or turn into a helix

Secondary Structure

β-pleated sheet

Secondary Structure

α-helix

Tertiary Structure

Quaternary Structure

Figure 3.22 Levels of protein structure. The primary structure of a protein is its amino acid sequence. Secondary structure results from hydrogen bonds forming between nearby amino acids. This produces two different kinds of structures: beta (β)-pleated sheets, and coils called alpha (α)-helices. The tertiary structure is the final 3-D shape of the protein. This determines how regions of secondary structure are then further folded in space to form the final shape of the protein. Quaternary structure is only found in proteins with multiple polypeptides. In this case the final structure of the protein is the arrangement of the multiple polypeptides in space.

protein. The sickle cell version of hemoglobin (HbS), for example, is a change of a single glutamic acid for a valine in the β-globin chain. This change substitutes a charged amino acid for a nonpolar one on the surface of the protein, leading the protein to become sticky and form clumps. Another variant of hemoglobin called HbE, actually the most common in human populations, causes a change from glutamic acid to lysine at a different site in the β-globin chain. In this case the structural change is not as dramatic, but it still impairs function, resulting in blood disorders called anemia and thalassemia. More than 700 structural variants of hemoglobin are known, with up to 7% of the world's population being carriers of forms that are medically important.

Quaternary structure: Subunit arrangements

When two or more polypeptide chains associate to form a functional protein, the individual chains are referred to as subunits of the protein. The arrangement of these subunits is termed its **quaternary structure**. In proteins composed of subunits, the interfaces where the subunits touch one another are often nonpolar, and they play a key role in transmitting information between the subunits about individual subunit activities.

Remember that the protein hemoglobin is composed of two α-chain subunits and two β-chain subunits. Each α- and β-globin chain has a primary structure consisting of a specific sequence of amino acids. This then assumes a characteristic secondary structure consisting of α helices and β sheets that are then arranged into a specific tertiary structure for each α- and β-globin subunit. Lastly, these subunits are then arranged into their final quaternary structure. This is the final structure of the protein. For proteins that consist of only a single peptide chain, the enzyme lysozyme for example, the tertiary structure is the final structure of the protein.

Motifs and domains are additional structural characteristics

To directly determine the sequence of amino acids in a protein is a laborious task. Although the process has been automated, it remains slow and difficult.

The ability to sequence DNA changed this situation rather suddenly. Sequencing DNA was a much simpler process, and even before it was automated, the number of known sequences rose quickly. With the advent of automation, the known sequences increased even more dramatically. Today the entire sequence of hundreds of bacterial genomes and more than a dozen animal genomes, including that of humans, has been determined. Because the DNA sequence is directly related to amino acid sequence in proteins, biologists now have a large database of protein sequences to compare and analyze. This new information has also stimulated thought about the logic of the genetic code and whether underlying patterns exist in protein structure. Our view of protein structure has evolved with this new information. Researchers still view the four-part hierarchical structure as important, but two new terms have entered the biologist's vocabulary: motif and domain.

Motifs

As biologists discovered the 3-D structure of proteins (an even more laborious task than determining the sequence), they noticed similarities between otherwise dissimilar proteins. These similar structures are called **motifs,** or sometimes "supersecondary structure." The term *motif* is borrowed from the arts and refers to a recurring thematic element in music or design.

One very common protein motif is the β-α-β motif, which creates a fold or crease; the so-called "Rossmann fold" at the core of nucleotide-binding sites in a wide variety of proteins. A second motif that occurs in many proteins is the β barrel, which is a β sheet folded around to form a tube. A third type of motif, the helix-turn-helix, consists of two α helices separated by a bend. This motif is important because many proteins use it to bind to the DNA double helix (figure 3.23; see also chapter 16).

Motifs indicate a logic to structure that investigators still do not understand. Do they simply represent a reuse by evolution of something that already works, or are they an optimal solution to a problem, such as how to bind a nucleotide? One way to think about it is that if amino acids are letters in the language of proteins, then motifs represent repeated words or phrases. Motifs have been useful in determining the function of unknown proteins. Databases of protein motifs are used to search new unknown proteins. Finding motifs with known functions may allow an investigator to infer the function of a new protein.

Domains

Domains of proteins are functional units within a larger structure. They can be thought of as substructure within the tertiary structure of a protein (see figure 3.23). To continue the metaphor: Amino acids are letters in the protein language, motifs are words or phrases, and domains are paragraphs.

Most proteins are made up of multiple domains that perform different parts of the protein's function. In many cases, these domains can be physically separated. For example, transcription factors (discussed in chapter 16) are proteins that bind to DNA and initiate its transcription. If the DNA-binding region is exchanged with a different transcription factor, then the specificity of the factor for DNA can be changed without changing its ability to stimulate transcription. Such "domain-swapping" experiments have been performed with many transcription factors, and they indicate, among other things, that the DNA-binding and activation domains are functionally separate.

These functional domains of proteins may also help the protein to fold into its proper shape. As a polypeptide chain

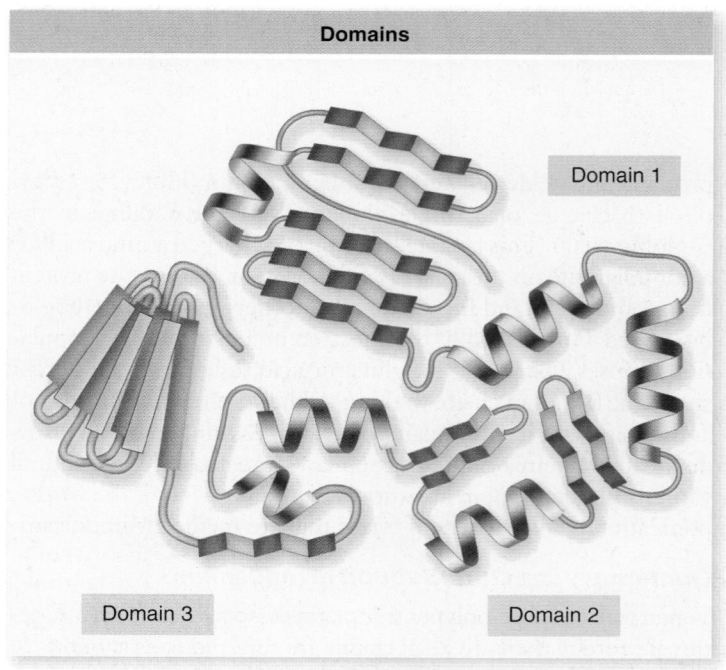

Figure 3.23 Motifs and domains. The elements of secondary structure can combine, fold, or crease to form motifs. These motifs are found in different proteins and can be used to predict function. Proteins also are made of larger domains, which are functionally distinct parts of a protein. The arrangement of these domains in space is the tertiary structure of a protein.

folds, the domains take their proper shape, each more or less independently of the others. This action can be demonstrated experimentally by artificially producing the fragment of a polypeptide that forms the domain in the intact protein, and showing that the fragment folds to form the same structure as it exhibits in the intact protein. A single polypeptide chain connects the domains of a protein, like a rope tied into several adjacent knots.

Domains can also correspond to the structure of the genes that encode them. Later, in chapter 15, you will see that genes in eukaryotes are often in pieces within the genome, and these pieces, called *exons*, sometimes encode the functional domains of a protein. This finding led to the idea of evolution acting by shuffling protein-encoding domains.

The process of folding relies on chaperone proteins

Until recently, scientific investigators thought that newly made proteins fold spontaneously, randomly trying out different configurations as hydrophobic interactions with water shoved nonpolar amino acids into the protein's interior until the final structure was arrived at. We now know this view is too simple. Protein chains can fold in so many different ways that trial and error would simply take too long. In addition, as the open chain folds its way toward its final form, nonpolar "sticky" interior portions are exposed during intermediate stages. If these intermediate forms are placed in a test tube in an environment identical to that inside a cell, they stick to other, unwanted protein partners, forming a gluey mess.

How do cells avoid having their proteins clump into a mass? A vital clue came in studies of unusual mutations that prevent viruses from replicating in bacterial cells. It turns out that the virus proteins produced inside the cells could not fold properly. Further study revealed that normal cells contain **chaperone proteins,** which help other proteins to fold correctly.

Molecular biologists have now identified many proteins that act as molecular chaperones. This class of proteins has multiple subclasses, and representatives have been found in essentially every organism that has been examined. Furthermore, these proteins seem to be essential for viability as well, illustrating their fundamental importance. Many are heat shock proteins, produced in greatly increased amounts when cells are exposed to elevated temperature. High temperatures cause proteins to unfold, and heat shock chaperone proteins help the cell's proteins to refold properly.

One class of these proteins, called chaperonins, has been extensively studied. In the bacterium *Escherichia coli* (*E. coli*), one example is the essential protein GroE chaperonin. In mutants in which the GroE chaperonin is inactivated, fully 30% of the bacterial proteins fail to fold properly. Chaperonins associate to form a large macromolecular complex that resembles a cylindrical container. Proteins can move into the container, and the container itself can change its shape considerably (figure 3.24). Experiments have shown that an improperly folded protein can enter the chaperonin and be refolded. Although we don't know exactly how this happens, it seems to involve changes in the hydrophobicity of the interior of the chamber.

The flexibility of the structure of chaperonins is amazing. We tend to think of proteins as being fixed structures, but this is clearly not the case for chaperonins and this flexibility is necessary for their function. It also illustrates that even domains that may be very widely separated in a very large protein are still functionally connected. The folding process within a chaperonin harnesses the hydrolysis of ATP to power these changes in structure necessary for function. This entire process can occur in a cyclic manner until the appropriate structure is achieved. Cells use these chaperonins both to accomplish the original folding of some proteins and to restore the structure of incorrectly folded ones.

Some diseases may result from improper folding

Chaperone protein deficiencies may be implicated in certain diseases in which key proteins are improperly folded. Cystic fibrosis

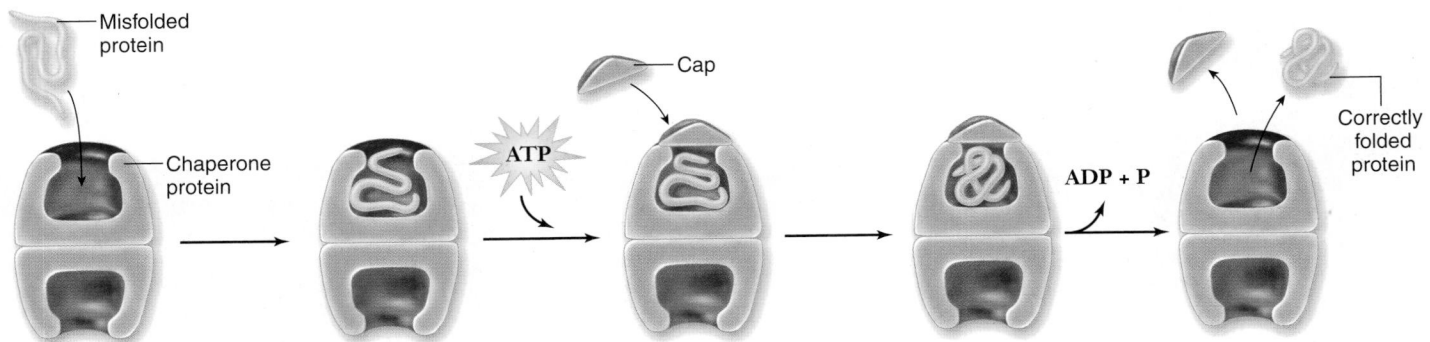

Chance for protein to refold

Figure 3.24 How one type of chaperone protein works. This barrel-shaped chaperonin is from the GroE family of chaperone proteins. It is composed of two identical rings each with seven identical subunits, each of which has three distinct domains. An incorrectly folded protein enters one chamber of the barrel, and a cap seals the chamber. Energy from the hydrolysis of ATP fuels structural alterations to the chamber, changing it from hydrophobic to hydrophilic. This change allows the protein to refold. After a short time, the protein is ejected, either folded or unfolded, and the cycle can repeat itself.

is a hereditary disorder in which a mutation disables a vital protein that moves ions across cell membranes. As a result, people with cystic fibrosis have thicker than normal mucus. This results in breathing problems, lung disease, and digestive difficulties, among other things. One interesting feature of the molecular analysis of this disease has been the number of different mutations found in human populations. One diverse class of mutations all result in problems with protein folding. The number of different mutations that can result in improperly folded proteins may be related to the fact that the native protein often fails to fold properly.

Denaturation inactivates proteins

If a protein's environment is altered, the protein may change its shape or even unfold completely. This process is called **denaturation** (figure 3.25). Proteins can be denatured when the pH, temperature, or ionic concentration of the surrounding solution changes.

Denatured proteins are usually biologically inactive. This action is particularly significant in the case of enzymes. Because practically every chemical reaction in a living organism is catalyzed by a specific enzyme, it is vital that a cell's enzymes work properly.

The traditional methods of food preservation, salt curing and pickling, involve denaturation of proteins. Prior to the general availability of refrigerators and freezers, the only practical

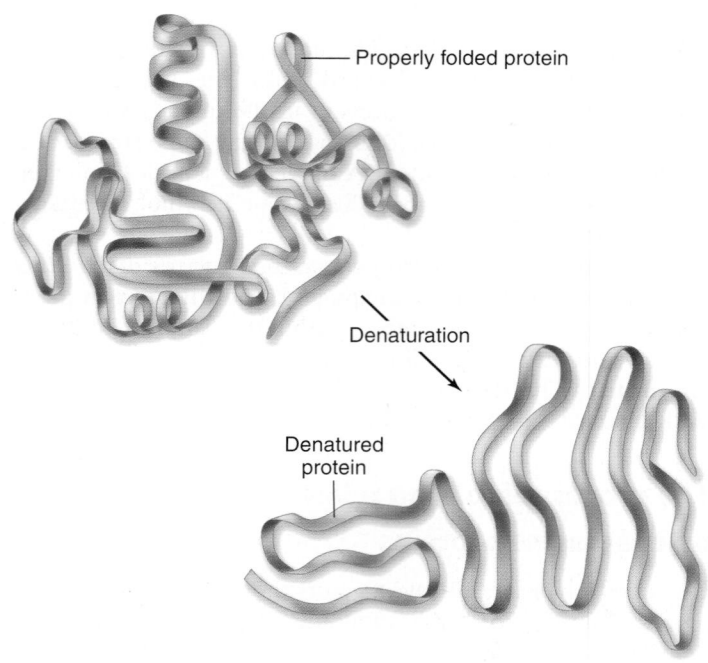

Figure 3.25 Protein denaturation. Changes in a protein's environment, such as variations in temperature or pH, can cause a protein to unfold and lose its shape in a process called denaturation. In this denatured state, proteins are biologically inactive.

SCIENTIFIC THINKING

Hypothesis: *The 3-D structure of a protein is the thermodynamically stable structure. It depends only on the primary structure of the protein and the solution conditions.*

Prediction: *If a protein is denatured and allowed to renature under native conditions, it will refold into the native structure.*

Test: *Ribonuclease is treated with a reducing agent to break disulfide bonds and is then treated with urea to completely unfold the protein. The disulfide bonds are reformed under nondenaturing conditions to see if the protein refolds properly.*

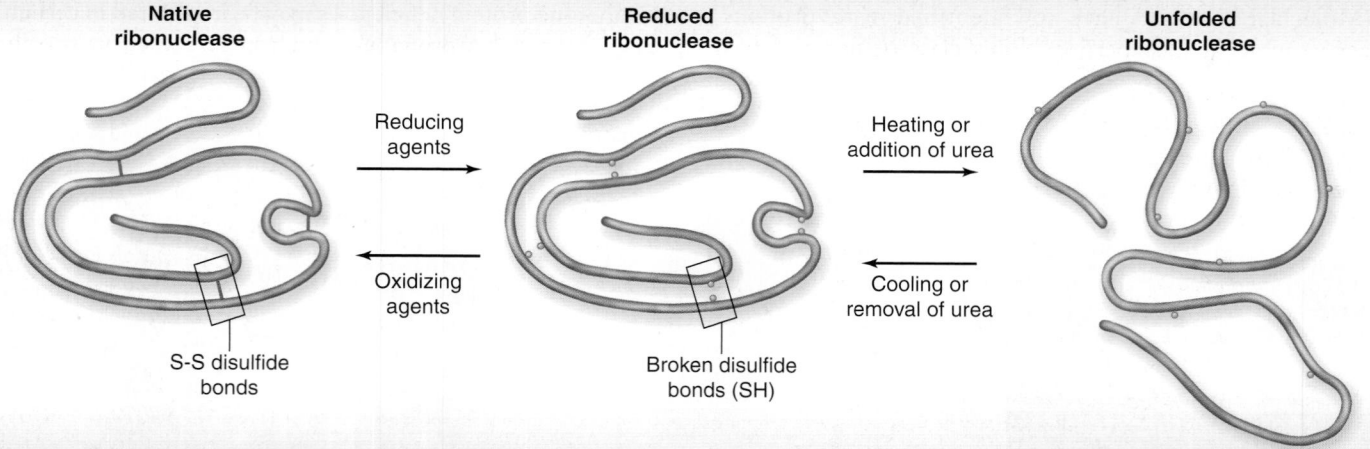

Result: *Denatured Ribonuclease refolds properly under nondenaturing conditions.*

Conclusion: *The hypothesis is supported. The information in the primary structure (amino acid sequence) is sufficient for refolding to occur. This implies that protein folding results in the thermodynamically stable structure.*

Further Experiments: *If the disulfide bonds were allowed to reform under denaturing conditions, would we get the same result? How can we rule out that the protein had not been completely denatured and therefore retained some structure?*

Figure 3.26 Primary structure determines tertiary structure.

way to keep microorganisms from growing in food was to keep the food in a solution containing a high concentration of salt or vinegar, which denatured the enzymes of most microorganisms and prevented them from growing on the food.

Most enzymes function within a very narrow range of environmental conditions. Blood-borne enzymes that course through a human body at a pH of about 7.4 would rapidly become denatured in the highly acidic environment of the stomach. Conversely, the protein-degrading enzymes that function at a pH of 2 or less in the stomach would be denatured in the relatively basic pH of the blood. Similarly, organisms that live near oceanic hydrothermal vents have enzymes that work well at these extremes of temperature (over 100°C). They cannot survive in cooler waters, because their enzymes do not function properly at lower temperatures. Any given organism usually has a tolerance range of pH, temperature, and salt concentration. Within that range, its enzymes maintain the proper shape to carry out their biological functions.

When a protein's normal environment is reestablished after denaturation, a small protein may spontaneously refold into its natural shape, driven by the interactions between its nonpolar amino acids and water (figure 3.26). This process is termed *renaturation*, and it was first established for the enzyme ribonuclease (RNase). The renaturation of RNase led to the doctrine that primary structure determines tertiary structure. Larger proteins can rarely refold spontaneously, however, because of the complex nature of their final shape, so this simple idea needs to be qualified.

The fact that some proteins can spontaneously renature implies that tertiary structure is strongly influenced by primary structure. In an extreme example, the *E. coli* ribosome can be taken apart and put back together experimentally. Although this process requires temperature and ion concentration shifts, it indicates an amazing degree of self-assembly. That complex structures can arise by self-assembly is a key idea in the study of modern biology.

It is important to distinguish denaturation from **dissociation.** For proteins with quaternary structure, the subunits may be dissociated without losing their individual tertiary structure. For example, the four subunits of hemoglobin may dissociate into four individual molecules (two α-globins and two β-globins) without denaturation of the folded globin proteins. They readily reassume their four-subunit quaternary structure.

Learning Outcomes

1. *Understand the structure of triglycerides.*
2. *Explain how fats function as energy-storage molecules.*
3. *Apply knowledge of the structure of phospholipids to the formation of membranes.*

Lipids are a somewhat loosely defined group of molecules with one main chemical characteristic: They are insoluble in water. Storage fats such as animal fat are one kind of lipid. Oils such as those from olives, corn, and coconut are also lipids, as are waxes such as beeswax and earwax. Even some vitamins are lipids!

Lipids have a very high proportion of nonpolar carbon–hydrogen (C—H) bonds, and so long-chain lipids cannot fold up like a protein to confine their nonpolar portions away from the surrounding aqueous environment. Instead, when they are placed in water, many lipid molecules spontaneously cluster together and expose what polar (hydrophilic) groups they have to the surrounding water, while confining the nonpolar (hydrophobic) parts of the molecules together within the cluster. You may have noticed this effect when you add oil to a pan containing water, and the oil beads up into cohesive drops on the water's surface. This spontaneous assembly of lipids is of paramount importance to cells, as it underlies the structure of cellular membranes.

Fats consist of complex polymers of fatty acids attached to glycerol

Many lipids are built from a simple skeleton made up of two main kinds of molecules: fatty acids and glycerol. Fatty acids are long-chain hydrocarbons with a carboxylic acid (COOH) at one end. Glycerol is a three-carbon polyalcohol (three —OH groups). Many lipid molecules consist of a glycerol molecule with three fatty acids attached, one to each carbon of the glycerol backbone. Because it contains three fatty acids, a fat molecule is commonly called a **triglyceride** (the more accurate chemical name is *triacylglycerol*). This basic structure is depicted in figure 3.27. The three fatty acids of a triglyceride need not be identical, and often they are very different from one another. The hydrocarbon chains of fatty acids vary in length. The most common are even-numbered chains of 14 to 20 carbons. The many C—H bonds of fats serve as a form of long-term energy storage.

If all of the internal carbon atoms in the fatty acid chains are bonded to at least two hydrogen atoms, the fatty acid is said to be **saturated,** which refers to its having all the hydrogen atoms possible (see figure 3.27). A fatty acid that has double bonds between one or more pairs of successive carbon atoms is said to be **unsaturated.** Fatty acids with one double bond are called monounsaturated, and those with more than one double bond are termed **polyunsaturated.** Most naturally occurring unsaturated fatty acids have double bonds with a cis configuration where the carbon chain is on the same side before and after the double bond (double bonds in fatty acids in 3.27*b* are all cis).

Structural Formula	Structural Formula
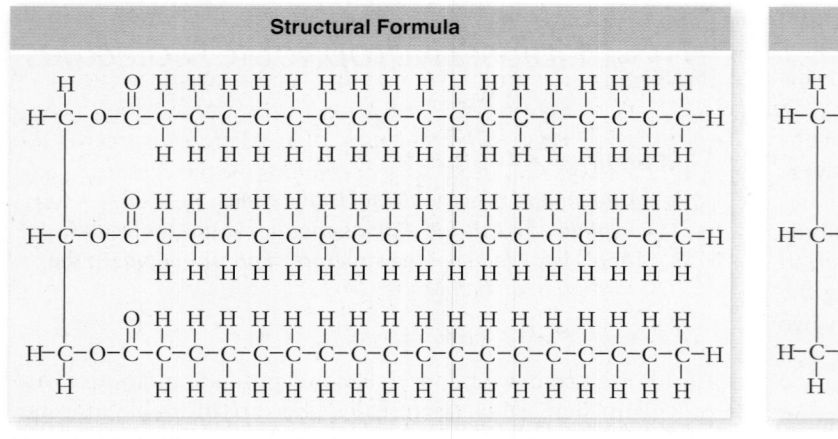	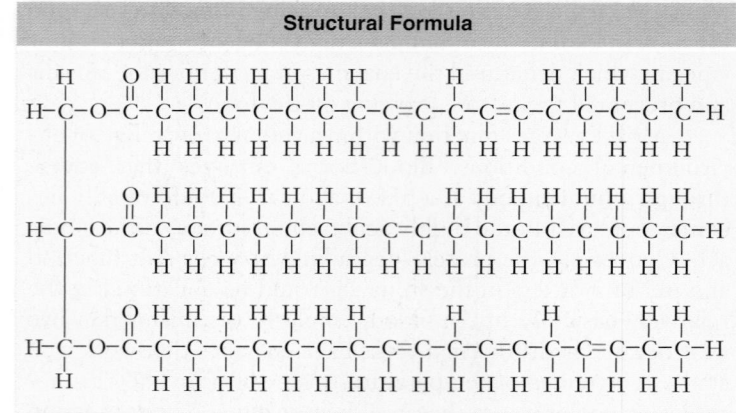

Space-Filling Model	Space-Filling Model
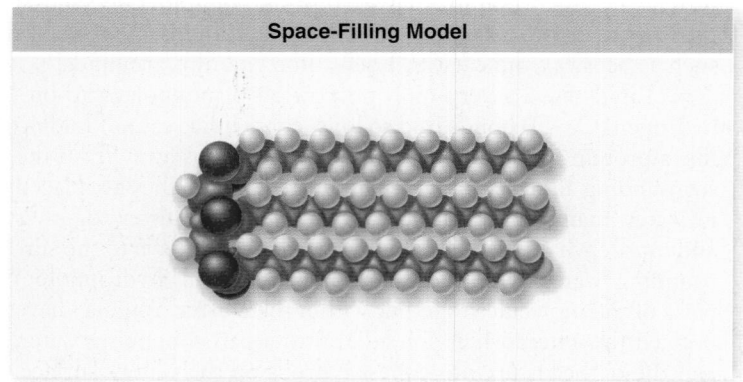	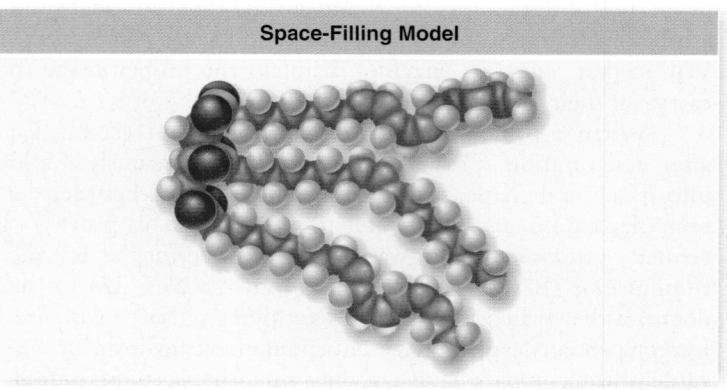

a.   *b.*

Figure 3.27 Saturated and unsaturated fats. *a.* A saturated fat is composed of triglycerides that contain three saturated fatty acids (the kind that have no double bonds). A saturated fat therefore has the maximum number of hydrogen atoms bonded to its carbon chain. Most animal fats are saturated. *b.* Unsaturated fat is composed of triglycerides that contain three unsaturated fatty acids (the kind that have one or more double bonds). These have fewer than the maximum number of hydrogen atoms bonded to the carbon chain. This example includes both a monounsaturated and two polyunsaturated fatty acids. Plant fats are typically unsaturated. The many kinks of the double bonds prevent the triglyceride from closely aligning, which makes them liquid oils at room temperature.

When fats are partially hydrogenated industrially, this can produce double bonds with a trans configuration where the carbon chain is on opposite sides before and after the double bond. These are the so called trans fats. These have been linked to elevated levels of low-density lipoprotein (LDL) "bad cholesterol" and lowered levels of high-density lipoprotein (HDL) "good cholesterol." This condition is thought to be associated with an increased risk for coronary heart disease.

Having double bonds changes the behavior of the molecule because free rotation cannot occur about a C=C double bond as it can with a C—C single bond. This characteristic mainly affects melting point: that is, whether the fatty acid is a solid fat or a liquid oil at room temperature. Fats containing polyunsaturated fatty acids have low melting points because their fatty acid chains bend at the double bonds, preventing the fat molecules from aligning closely with one another. Most saturated fats, such as animal fat or those in butter, are solid at room temperature.

Placed in water, triglycerides spontaneously associate together, forming fat globules that can be very large relative to the size of the individual molecules. Because fats are insoluble in water, they can be deposited at specific locations within an organism, such as in vesicles of adipose tissue.

Organisms contain many other kinds of lipids besides fats (figure 3.28). *Terpenes* are long-chain lipids that are components of many biologically important pigments, such as chlorophyll and the visual pigment retinal. Rubber is also a terpene. *Steroids*, another class of lipid, are composed of four carbon rings. Most animal cell membranes contain the steroid cholesterol. Other steroids, such as testosterone and estrogen, function as hormones in multicellular animals. *Prostaglandins* are a group of about 20 lipids that are modified fatty acids, with two nonpolar "tails" attached to a five-carbon ring. Prostaglandins act as local chemical messengers in many vertebrate tissues. Later chapters explore the effects of some of these complex fatty acids.

Fats are excellent energy-storage molecules

Most fats contain over 40 carbon atoms. The ratio of energy-storing C—H bonds in fats is more than twice that of carbohydrates (see section 3.2), making fats much more efficient molecules for storing chemical energy. On average, fats yield about 9 kilocalories (kcal) of chemical energy per gram, as compared with about 4 kcal/g for carbohydrates.

Most fats produced by animals are saturated (except some fish oils), whereas most plant fats are unsaturated (see

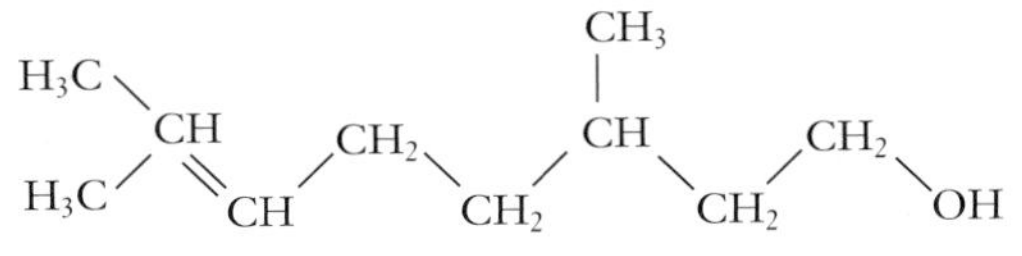

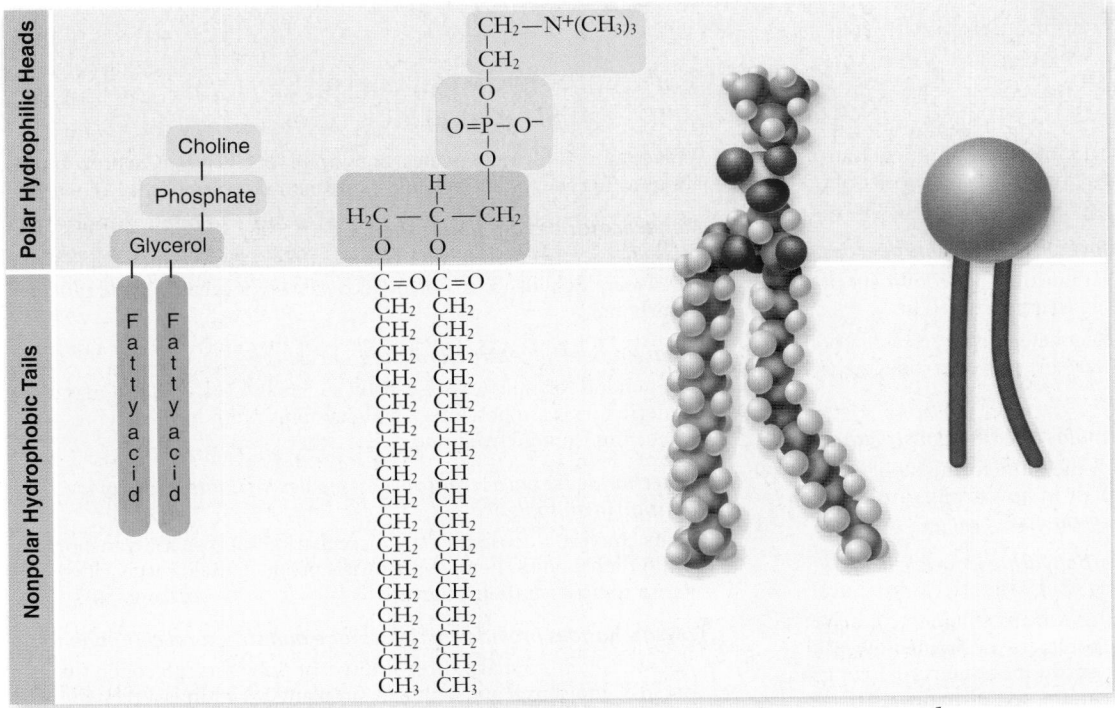

a. Terpene (citronellol)

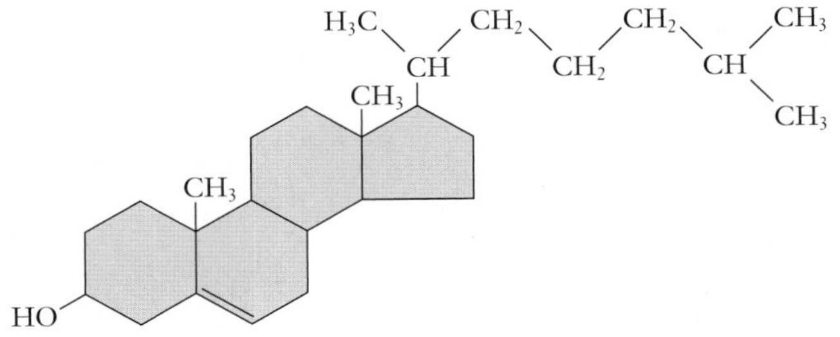

b. Steroid (cholesterol)

Figure 3.28 Other kinds of lipids. *a.* Terpenes are found in biological pigments, such as chlorophyll and retinal, and *(b)* steroids play important roles in membranes and as the basis for a class of hormones involved in chemical signaling.

figure 3.27). The exceptions are the tropical plant oils (palm oil and coconut oil), which are saturated even though they are liquid at room temperature. An oil may be converted into a solid fat by chemically adding hydrogen. Most peanut butter is usually artificially hydrogenated to make the peanut fats solidify, preventing them from separating out as oils while the jar sits on the store shelf. However, artificially hydrogenating unsaturated fats produces the *trans*-fatty acids described above.

When an organism consumes excess carbohydrate, it is converted into starch, glycogen, or fats reserved for future use. The reason that many humans in developed countries gain weight as they grow older is that the amount of energy they need decreases with age, but their intake of food does not. Thus, an increasing proportion of the carbohydrates they ingest is converted into fat.

A diet heavy in fats is one of several factors thought to contribute to heart disease, particularly atherosclerosis. In atherosclerosis, sometimes referred to as "hardening of the arteries," fatty substances called plaque adhere to the lining of blood vessels, blocking the flow of blood. Fragments of a plaque can break off from a deposit and clog arteries to the brain, causing a stroke.

Phospholipids form membranes

Complex lipid molecules called **phospholipids** are among the most important molecules of the cell because they form the core of all biological membranes. An individual phospholipid can be thought of as a substituted triglyceride, that is, a triglyceride with a phosphate replacing one of the fatty acids. The basic structure of a phospholipid includes three kinds of subunits:

1. *Glycerol*, a three-carbon alcohol, in which each carbon bears a hydroxyl group. Glycerol forms the backbone of the phospholipid molecule.
2. *Fatty acids*, long chains of —CH_2 groups (hydrocarbon chains) ending in a carboxyl (—COOH) group. Two fatty acids are attached to the glycerol backbone in a phospholipid molecule.
3. *A phosphate group* (—PO_4^{2-}) attached to one end of the glycerol. The charged phosphate group usually has a charged organic molecule linked to it, such as choline, ethanolamine, or the amino acid serine.

The phospholipid molecule can be thought of as having a polar "head" at one end (the phosphate group) and two long, very nonpolar "tails" at the other (figure 3.29). This structure is essential for how these molecules function, although it first

Figure 3.29 Phospholipids.
The phospholipid phosphatidylcholine is shown as *(a)* a schematic, *(b)* a formula, *(c)* a space-filling model, and *(d)* an icon used in depictions of biological membranes.

chapter **3** *The Chemical Building Blocks of Life* **55**

appears paradoxical. Why would a molecule need to be soluble in water, but also not soluble in water? The formation of a membrane shows the unique properties of such a structure.

In water, the nonpolar tails of nearby lipid molecules aggregate away from the water, forming spherical *micelles*, with the tails facing inward (figure 3.30*a*). This is actually how detergent molecules work to make grease soluble in water. The grease is soluble within the nonpolar interior of the micelle and the polar surface of the micelle is soluble in water. With phospholipids, a more complex structure forms in which two layers of molecules line up, with the hydrophobic tails of each layer pointing toward one another, or inward, leaving the hydrophilic heads oriented outward, forming a bilayer (figure 3.30*b*). Lipid bilayers are the basic framework of biological membranes, discussed in detail in chapter 5.

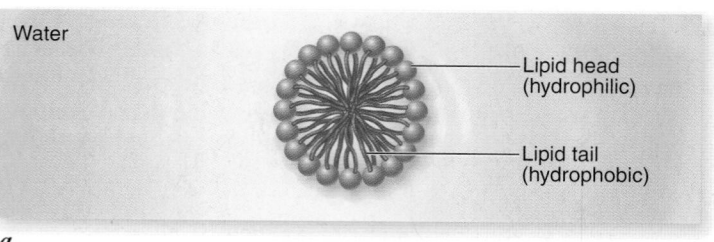
a.

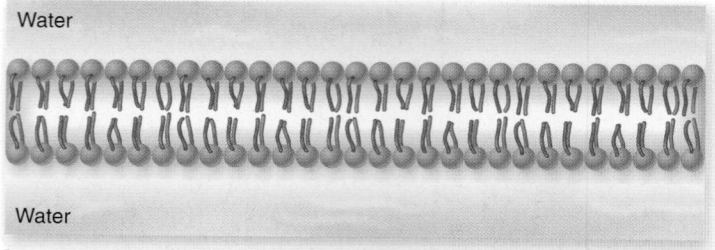
b.

Figure 3.30 Lipids spontaneously form micelles or lipid bilayers in water. In an aqueous environment, lipid molecules orient so that their polar (hydrophilic) heads are in the polar medium, water, and their nonpolar (hydrophobic) tails are held away from the water. *a.* Droplets called micelles can form, or *(b)* phospholipid molecules can arrange themselves into two layers; in both structures, the hydrophilic heads extend outward and the hydrophobic tails inward. This second example is called a phospholipid bilayer.

Learning Outcomes Review 3.5

Triglycerides are made of fatty acids linked to glycerol. Fats can contain twice as many C—H bonds as carbohydrates and thus they store energy efficiently. Because the C—H bonds in lipids are nonpolar, they are not water-soluble and aggregate together in water. Phospholipids replace one fatty acid with a hydrophilic phosphate group. This allows them to spontaneously form bilayers, which are the basis of biological membranes.

■ *Why do phospholipids form membranes while triglycerides form insoluble droplets?*

Chapter Review

3.1 Carbon: The Framework of Biological Molecules

Carbon, the backbone of all biological molecules, can form four covalent bonds and make long chains. Hydrocarbons consist of carbon and hydrogen, and their bonds store considerable energy.

Functional groups account for differences in molecular properties.

Functional groups are small molecular entities that confer specific chemical characteristics when attached to a hydrocarbon.

Carbon and hydrogen have similar electronegativity so C—H bonds are not polar. Oxygen and nitrogen have greater electronegativity, leading to polar bonds.

Isomers have the same molecular formulas but different structures.

Structural isomers are molecules with the same formula but different structures; stereoisomers differ in how groups are attached. Enantiomers are mirror-image stereoisomers.

Biological macromolecules include carbohydrates, nucleic acids, proteins, and lipids.

Most important biological macromolecules are polymers—long chains of monomer units. Biological polymers are formed by elimination of water (H and OH) from two monomers (dehydration reaction). They are broken down by adding water (hydrolysis).

3.2 Carbohydrates: Energy Storage and Structural Molecules

The empirical formula of a carbohydrate is $(CH_2O)_n$. Carbohydrates are used for energy storage and as structural molecules.

Monosaccharides are simple sugars.

Simple sugars contain three to six or more carbon atoms. Examples are glyceraldehyde (3 carbons), deoxyribose (5 carbons), and glucose (6 carbons).

Sugar isomers have structural differences.

The general formula for six-carbon sugars is $C_6H_{12}O_6$, and many isomeric forms are possible. Living systems often have enzymes for converting isomers from one to the other.

Disaccharides serve as transport molecules in plants and provide nutrition in animals.

Plants convert glucose into the disaccharide sucrose for transport within their bodies. Female mammals produce the disaccharide lactose to nourish their young.

Polysaccharides provide energy storage and structural components.

Glucose is used to make three important polymers: glycogen (in animals), and starch and cellulose (in plants). Chitin is a related structural material found in arthropods and many fungi.

3.3 Nucleic Acids: Information Molecules

Deoxyribonucleic acid (DNA) and ribonucleic acid (RNA) are polymers composed of nucleotide monomers. Cells use nucleic acids for information storage and transfer.

Nucleic acids are nucleotide polymers.

Nucleic acids contain four different nucleotide bases. In DNA these are adenine, guanine, cytosine, and thymine. In RNA, thymine is replaced by uracil.

DNA carries the genetic code.

DNA exists as a double helix held together by specific base pairs: adenine with thymine and guanine with cytosine. The nucleic acid sequence constitutes the genetic code.

RNA is a transcript of a DNA strand.

RNA is made by copying DNA. This transcript is then used as a template to make proteins.

Other nucleotides are vital components of energy reactions.

Adenosine triphosphate (ATP) provides energy in cells; NAD^+ and FAD transport electrons in cellular processes.

3.4 Proteins: Molecules with Diverse Structures and Functions

Most enzymes are proteins. Proteins also provide defense, transport, motion, and regulation, among many other roles.

Proteins are polymers of amino acids.

Amino acids are joined by peptide bonds to make polypeptides. The 20 common amino acids are characterized by R groups that determine their properties.

Proteins have levels of structure.

Protein structure is defined by the following hierarchy: primary (amino acid sequence), secondary (hydrogen bonding patterns), tertiary (three-dimensional folding), and quaternary (associations between two or more polypeptides).

Motifs and domains are additional structural characteristics.

Motifs are similar structural elements found in dissimilar proteins. They can create folds, creases, or barrel shapes. Domains are functional subunits or sites within a tertiary structure.

The process of folding relies on chaperone proteins.

Chaperone proteins assist in the folding of proteins. Heat shock proteins are an example of chaperone proteins.

Some diseases may result from improper folding.

Some forms of cystic fibrosis and Alzheimer disease are associated with misfolded proteins.

Denaturation inactivates proteins.

Denaturation refers to an unfolding of tertiary structure, which usually destroys function. Some denatured proteins may recover function when conditions are returned to normal. This implies that primary structure strongly influences tertiary structure.

Disassociation refers to separation of quaternary subunits with no changes to their tertiary structure.

3.5 Lipids: Hydrophobic Molecules

Lipids are insoluble in water because they have a high proportion of nonpolar C—H bonds.

Fats consist of complex polymers of fatty acids attached to glycerol.

Many lipids exist as triglycerides, three fatty acids connected to a glycerol molecule. Saturated fatty acids contain the maximum number of hydrogen atoms. Unsaturated fatty acids contain one or more double bonds between carbon atoms.

Fats are excellent energy-storage molecules.

The energy stored in the C—H bonds of fats is more than twice that of carbohydrates: 9 kcal/g compared with 4 kcal/g. For this reason, excess carbohydrate is converted to fat for storage.

Phospholipids form membranes

Phospholipids contain two fatty acids and one phosphate attached to glycerol. In phospholipid-bilayer membranes, the phosphate heads are hydrophilic and cluster on the two faces of the membrane, and the hydrophobic tails are in the center.

Review Questions

UNDERSTAND

1. How is a polymer formed from multiple monomers?
   a. From the growth of the chain of carbon atoms
   b. By the removal of an —OH group and a hydrogen atom
   c. By the addition of an —OH group and a hydrogen atom
   d. Through hydrogen bonding

2. Why are carbohydrates important molecules for energy storage?
   a. The C—H bonds found in carbohydrates store energy.
   b. The double bonds between carbon and oxygen are very strong.
   c. The electronegativity of the oxygen atoms means that a carbohydrate is made up of many polar bonds.
   d. They can form ring structures in the aqueous environment of a cell.

3. Plant cells store energy in the form of _____, and animal cells store energy in the form of _____.
   a. fructose; glucose
   b. disaccharides; monosaccharides
   c. cellulose; chitin
   d. starch; glycogen

4. Which carbohydrate would you find as part of a molecule of RNA?
   a. Galactose
   b. Deoxyribose
   c. Ribose
   d. Glucose

5. A molecule of DNA or RNA is a polymer of
   a. monosaccharides.
   b. nucleotides.
   c. amino acids.
   d. fatty acids.

6. What makes cellulose different from starch?

    a. Starch is produced by plant cells, and cellulose is produced by animal cells.

    b. Cellulose forms long filaments, and starch is highly branched.

    c. Starch is insoluble, and cellulose is soluble.

    d. All of the above.

7. What monomers make up a protein?

    a. Monosaccharides   c. Amino acids

    b. Nucleotides   d. Fatty acids

8. A triglyceride is a form of _____ composed of _____.

    a. lipid; fatty acids and glucose

    b. lipid; fatty acids and glycerol

    c. carbohydrate; fatty acids

    d. lipid; cholesterol

APPLY

1. Amino acids are linked together to form a protein by

    a. phosphodiester bonds.

    b. β-(1⟶4) linkages.

    c. peptide bonds.

    d. hydrogen bonds.

2. Which of the following is NOT a difference between DNA and RNA?

    a. Deoxyribose sugar versus ribose sugar

    b. Thymine versus uracil

    c. Double-stranded versus single-stranded

    d. Phosphodiester versus hydrogen bonds

3. Which part of an amino acid has the greatest influence on the overall structure of a protein?

    a. The (—NH$_2$) amino group

    b. The R group

    c. The (—COOH) carboxyl group

    d. Both a and c

4. A mutation that alters a single amino acid within a protein can alter

    a. the primary level of protein structure.

    b. the secondary level of protein structure.

    c. the tertiary level of protein structure.

    d. all of the above.

5. Two different proteins have the same domain in their structure. From this we can infer that they have

    a. the same primary structure.

    b. similar function.

    c. very different functions.

    d. the same primary structure but different function.

6. What chemical property of lipids accounts for their insolubility in water?

    a. The COOH group of fatty acids

    b. The large number of nonpolar C—H bonds

    c. The branching of saturated fatty acids

    d. The C═C bonds found in unsaturated fatty acids

7. The spontaneous formation of a lipid bilayer in an aqueous environment occurs because

    a. the polar head groups of the phospholipids can interact with water.

    b. the long fatty acid tails of the phospholipids can interact with water.

    c. the fatty acid tails of the phospholipids are hydrophobic.

    d. both a and c.

SYNTHESIZE

1. How do the four biological macromolecules differ from one another? How does the structure of each relate to its function?

2. Hydrogen bonds and hydrophobic interactions each play an important role in stabilizing and organizing biological macromolecules. Consider the four macromolecules discussed in this chapter. Describe how these affect the form and function of each type of macromolecule. Would a disruption in the hydrogen bonds affect form and function? Hydrophobic interactions?

3. Plants make both starch and cellulose. Would you predict that the enzymes involved in starch synthesis could also be used by the plant for cellulose synthesis? Construct an argument to explain this based on the structure and function of the enzymes and the polymers synthesized.

ONLINE RESOURCE

www.ravenbiology.com

Understand, Apply, and Synthesize—enhance your study with animations that bring concepts to life and practice tests to assess your understanding. Your instructor may also recommend the interactive eBook, individualized learning tools, and more.

Chapter 4

Cell Structure

Chapter Outline

4.1 Cell Theory

4.2 Prokaryotic Cells

4.3 Eukaryotic Cells

4.4 The Endomembrane System

4.5 Mitochondria and Chloroplasts: Cellular Generators

4.6 The Cytoskeleton

4.7 Extracellular Structures and Cell Movement

4.8 Cell-to-Cell Interactions

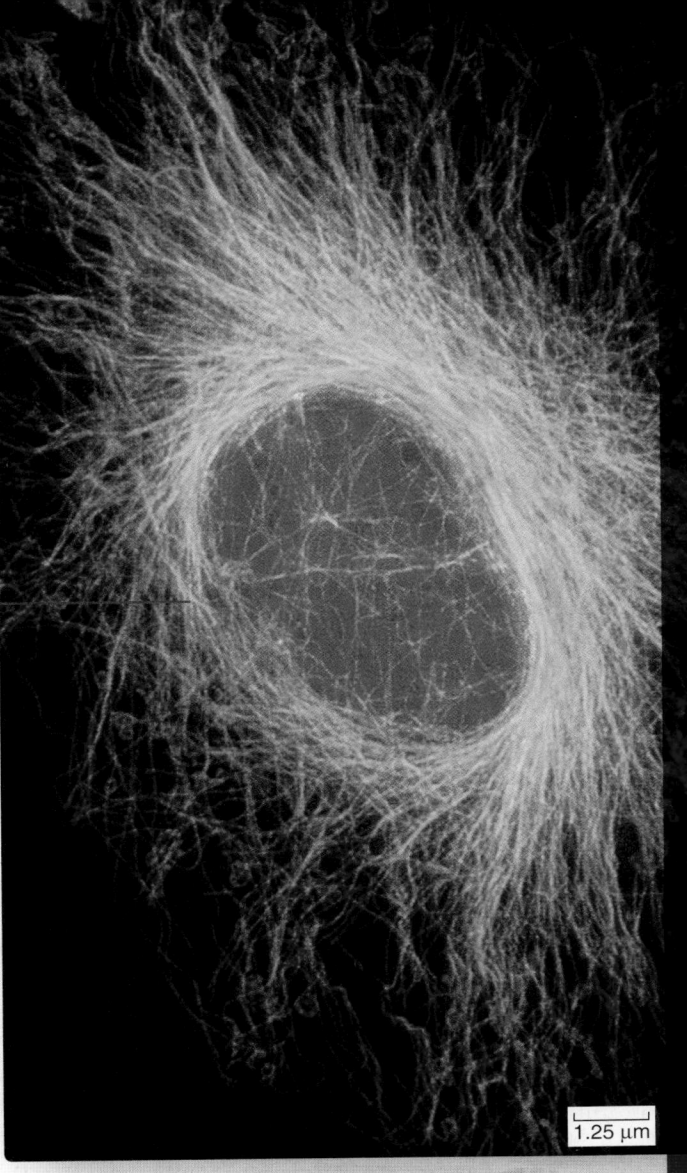

1.25 μm

Part II Biology of the Cell

Introduction

All organisms are composed of cells. The gossamer wing of a butterfly is a thin sheet of cells and so is the glistening outer layer of your eyes. The hamburger or tomato you eat is composed of cells, and its contents soon become part of your cells. Some organisms consist of a single cell too small to see with the unaided eye. Others, such as humans, are composed of many specialized cells, such as the fibroblast cell shown in the striking fluorescence micrograph on this page. Cells are so much a part of life that we cannot imagine an organism that is not cellular in nature. In this chapter, we take a close look at the internal structure of cells. In chapters 4 to 10, we will focus on cells in action—how they communicate with their environment, grow, and reproduce.

4.1 Cell Theory

Learning Outcomes

1. *Explain the cell theory.*
2. *Describe the factors that limit cell size.*
3. *Categorize structural and functional similarities in cells.*

Cells are characteristically microscopic in size. Although there are exceptions, a typical eukaryotic cell is 10 to 100 micrometers (μm) (10 to 100 millionths of a meter) in diameter, while most prokaryotic cells are only 1 to 10 μm in diameter.

Because cells are so small, they were not discovered until the invention of the microscope in the 17th century. Robert Hooke was the first to observe cells in 1665, naming the shapes he saw in cork *cellulae* (Latin, "small rooms"). This is known to us as *cells*. Another early microscopist, Anton van Leeuwenhoek first observed living cells, which he termed "animalcules," or little animals. After these early efforts, a century and a half passed before biologists fully recognized the importance of cells. In 1838, botanist Matthias Schleiden stated that all plants "are aggregates of fully individualized, independent, separate beings, namely the cells themselves." In 1839, Theodor Schwann reported that all animal tissues also consist of individual cells. Thus, the cell theory was born.

Cell theory is the unifying foundation of cell biology

The cell theory was proposed to explain the observation that all organisms are composed of cells. It sounds simple, but it is a far-reaching statement about the organization of life.

In its modern form, the *cell theory* includes the following three principles:

1. All organisms are composed of one or more cells, and the life processes of metabolism and heredity occur within these cells.
2. Cells are the smallest living things, the basic units of organization of all organisms.
3. Cells arise only by division of a previously existing cell.

Although life likely evolved spontaneously in the environment of early Earth, biologists have concluded that no additional cells are originating spontaneously at present. Rather, life on Earth represents a continuous line of descent from those early cells.

Cell size is limited

Most cells are relatively small for reasons related to the diffusion of substances into and out of cells. The rate of diffusion is affected by a number of variables, including (1) surface area available for diffusion, (2) temperature, (3) concentration gradient of diffusing substance, and (4) the distance over which diffusion must occur. As the size of a cell increases, the length of time for diffusion from the outside membrane to the interior of the cell increases as well. Larger cells need to synthesize more macromolecules, have correspondingly higher energy requirements, and produce a greater quantity of waste. Molecules used for energy and biosynthesis must be transported through the membrane. Any metabolic waste produced must be removed, also passing through the membrane. The rate at which this transport occurs depends on both the distance to the membrane and the area of membrane available. For this reason, an organism made up of many relatively small cells has an advantage over one composed of fewer, larger cells.

The advantage of small cell size is readily apparent in terms of the **surface area-to-volume ratio.** As a cell's size increases, its volume increases much more rapidly than its surface area. For a spherical cell, the surface area is proportional to the square of the radius, whereas the volume is proportional to the cube of the radius. Thus, if the radii of two cells differ by a factor of 10, the larger cell will have 10^2, or 100 times, the surface area, but 10^3, or 1000 times, the volume of the smaller cell (figure 4.1).

The cell surface provides the only opportunity for interaction with the environment, because all substances enter and exit a cell via this surface. The membrane surrounding the cell

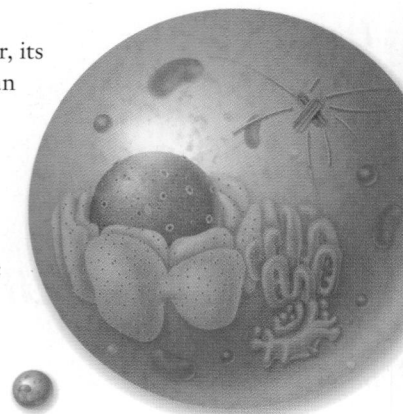

Figure 4.1 Surface area-to-volume ratio. As a cell gets larger, its volume increases at a faster rate than its surface area. If the cell radius increases by 10 times, the surface area increases by 100 times, but the volume increases by 1000 times. A cell's surface area must be large enough to meet the metabolic needs of its volume.

Cell radius (*r*)	1 unit	10 unit
Surface area ($4\pi r^2$)	12.57 unit^2	1257 unit^2
Volume ($\frac{4}{3}\pi r^3$)	4.189 unit^3	4189 unit^3
Surface Area / Volume	3	0.3

plays a key role in controlling cell function. Because small cells have more surface area per unit of volume than large ones, control over cell contents is more effective when cells are relatively small.

Although most cells are small, some quite large cells do exist. These cells have apparently overcome the surface area-to-volume problem by one or more adaptive mechanisms. For example, some cells, such as skeletal muscle cells, have more than one nucleus, allowing genetic information to be spread around a large cell. Some other large cells, such as neurons, are long and skinny, so that any given point within the cell is close to the plasma membrane. This permits diffusion between the inside and outside of the cell to still be rapid.

Microscopes allow visualization of cells and components

Other than egg cells, not many cells are visible to the naked eye (figure 4.2). Most are less than 50 μm in diameter, far smaller than the period at the end of this sentence. So, to visualize cells we need the aid of technology. The development of microscopes and their refinement over the centuries has allowed us to continually explore cells in greater detail.

The resolution problem

How do we study cells if they are too small to see? The key is to understand why we can't see them. The reason we can't see such small objects is the limited resolution of the human eye. *Resolution* is the minimum distance two points can be apart and still be distinguished as two separate points. When two objects are closer together than about 100 μm, the light reflected from each strikes the same photoreceptor cell at the rear of the eye. Only when the objects are farther than 100 μm apart can the light from each strike different cells, allowing your eye to resolve them as two distinct objects rather than one.

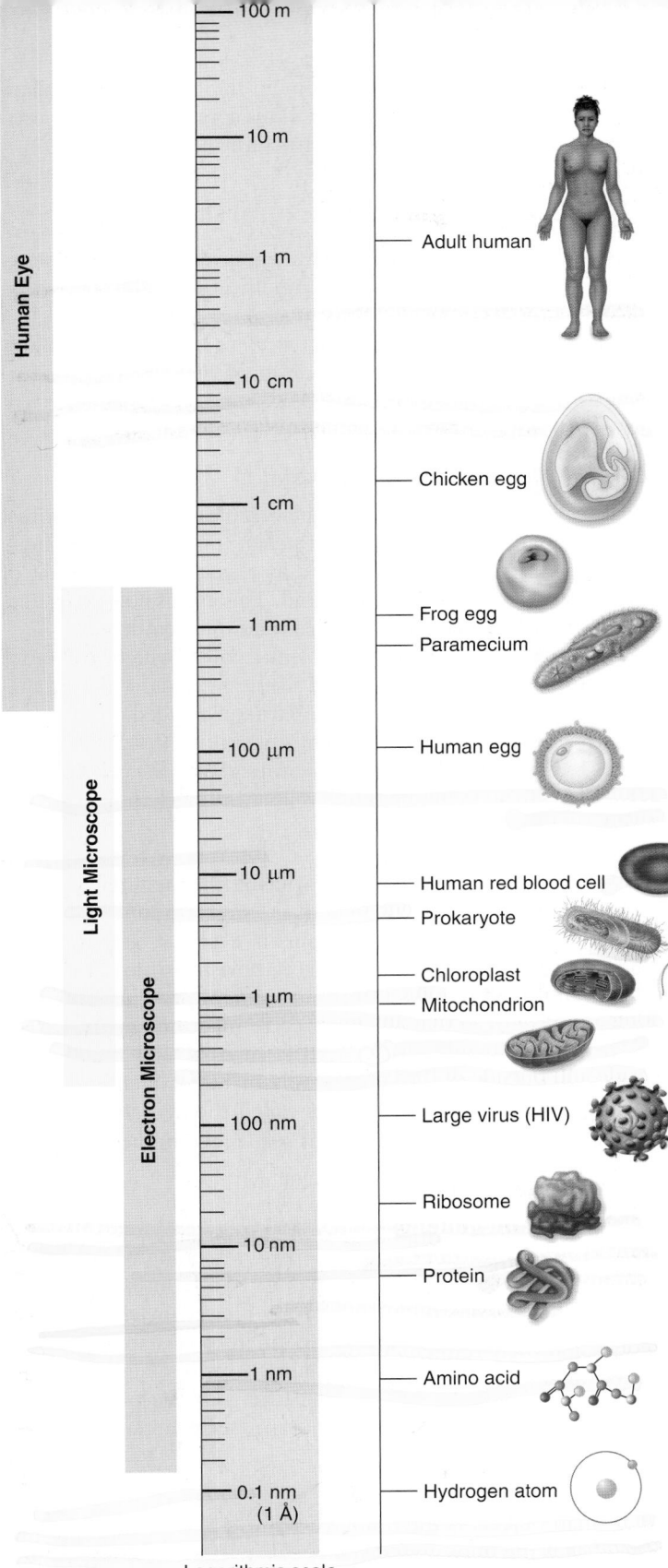

100 m

10 m

1 m — Adult human

10 cm

1 cm — Chicken egg

— Frog egg
1 mm — Paramecium

100 μm — Human egg

10 μm — Human red blood cell
— Prokaryote

1 μm — Chloroplast
— Mitochondrion

100 nm — Large virus (HIV)

— Ribosome
10 nm

— Protein

1 nm — Amino acid

0.1 nm — Hydrogen atom
(1 Å)

Logarithmic scale

Human Eye

Light Microscope

Electron Microscope

Figure 4.2 The size of cells and their contents. Except for vertebrate eggs, which can typically be seen with the unaided eye, most cells are microscopic in size. Prokaryotic cells are generally 1 to 10 μm across.

$1 \text{ m} = 10^2 \text{ cm} = 10^3 \text{ mm} = 10^6 \text{ μm} = 10^9 \text{ nm}$

Types of microscopes

One way to overcome the limitations of our eyes is to increase magnification so that small objects appear larger. The first microscopists used glass lenses to magnify small cells and cause them to appear larger than the 100-μm limit imposed by the human eye. The glass lens increases focusing power. Because the glass lens makes the object appear closer, the image on the back of the eye is bigger than it would be without the lens.

Modern *light microscopes*, which operate with visible light, use two magnifying lenses (and a variety of correcting lenses) to achieve very high magnification and clarity (table 4.1). The first lens focuses the image of the object on the second lens, which magnifies it again and focuses it on the back of the eye. Microscopes that magnify in stages using several lenses are called *compound microscopes.* They can resolve structures that are separated by at least 200 nanometers (nm).

Light microscopes, even compound ones, are not powerful enough to resolve many of the structures within cells. For example, a cell membrane is only 5 nm thick. Why not just add another magnifying stage to the microscope to increase its resolving power? This doesn't work because when two objects are closer than a few hundred nanometers, the light beams reflecting from the two images start to overlap each other. The only way two light beams can get closer together and still be resolved is if their wavelengths are shorter. One way to avoid overlap is by using a beam of electrons rather than a beam of light. Electrons have a much shorter wavelength, and an *electron microscope*, employing electron beams, has 1000 times the resolving power of a light microscope. *Transmission electron microscopes,* so called because the electrons used to visualize the specimens are transmitted through the material, are capable of resolving objects only 0.2 nm apart—which is only twice the diameter of a hydrogen atom!

A second kind of electron microscope, the *scanning electron microscope,* beams electrons onto the surface of the specimen. The electrons reflected back from the surface, together with other electrons that the specimen itself emits as a result of the bombardment, are amplified and transmitted to a screen, where the image can be viewed and photographed. Scanning electron microscopy yields striking three-dimensional images. This technique has improved our understanding of many biological and physical phenomena (see table 4.1).

Using stains to view cell structure

Although resolution remains a physical limit, we can improve the images we see by altering the sample. Certain chemical stains increase the contrast between different cellular components. Structures within the cell absorb or exclude the stain differentially, producing contrast that aids resolution.

Stains that bind to specific types of molecules have made these techniques even more powerful. This method uses antibodies that bind, for example, to a particular protein. This process, called *immunohistochemistry,* uses antibodies generated in animals such as rabbits or mice. When these animals are injected with specific proteins, they produce antibodies that bind to the injected protein. The antibodies are then purified and chemically bonded to enzymes, to stains, or to fluorescent molecules. When cells are incubated in a solution containing the antibodies, the antibodies

TABLE 4.1	Microscopes

LIGHT MICROSCOPES

Bright-field microscope:
Light is transmitted through a specimen, giving little contrast. Staining specimens improves contrast but requires that cells be fixed (not alive), which can distort or alter components.

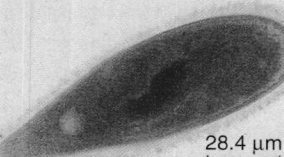
28.4 μm

Dark-field microscope:
Light is directed at an angle toward the specimen. A condenser lens transmits only light reflected off the specimen. The field is dark, and the specimen is light against this dark background.

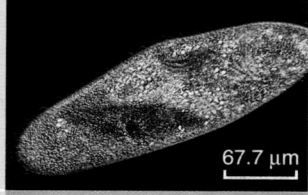
67.7 μm

Phase-contrast microscope:
Components of the microscope bring light waves out of phase, which produces differences in contrast and brightness when the light waves recombine.

32.8 μm

Differential-interference–contrast microscope:
Polarized light is split into two beams that have slightly different paths through the sample. Combining these two beams produces greater contrast, especially at the edges of structures.

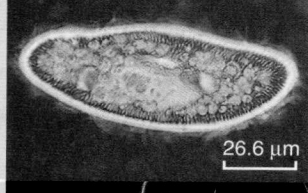
26.6 μm

Fluorescence microscope:
Fluorescent stains absorb light at one wavelength, then emit it at another. Filters transmit only the emitted light.

10.2 μm

Confocal microscope:
Light from a laser is focused to a point and scanned across the fluorescently stained specimen in two directions. This produces clear images of one plane of the specimen. Other planes of the specimen are excluded to prevent the blurring of the image. Multiple planes can be used to reconstruct a 3-D image.

25.0 μm

ELECTRON MICROSCOPES

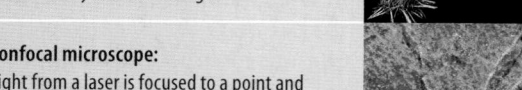

Transmission electron microscope:
A beam of electrons is passed through the specimen. Electrons that pass through are used to expose film. Areas of the specimen that scatter electrons appear dark. False coloring enhances the image.

2.56 μm

Scanning electron microscope:
An electron beam is scanned across the surface of the specimen, and electrons are knocked off the surface. Thus, the topography of the specimen determines the contrast and the content of the image. False coloring enhances the image.

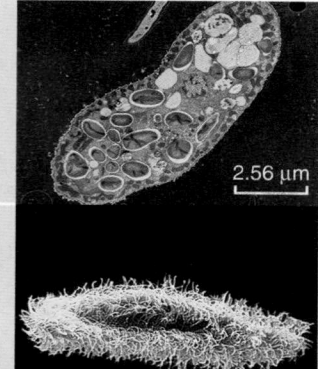
6.76 μm

bind to cellular structures that contain the target molecule and can be seen with light microscopy. This approach has been used extensively in the analysis of cell structure and function.

All cells exhibit basic structural similarities

The general plan of cellular organization varies between different organisms, but despite these modifications, all cells resemble one another in certain fundamental ways. Before we begin a detailed examination of cell structure, let's first summarize four major features all cells have in common: (1) a nucleoid or nucleus where genetic material is located, (2) cytoplasm, (3) *ribosomes* to synthesize proteins, and (4) a plasma membrane.

Centrally located genetic material

Every cell contains DNA, the hereditary molecule. In **prokaryotes,** the simplest organisms, most of the genetic material lies in a single circular molecule of DNA. It typically resides near the center of the cell in an area called the **nucleoid.** This area is not segregated, however, from the rest of the cell's interior by membranes.

By contrast, the DNA of eukaryotes, which are more complex organisms, is contained in the nucleus, which is surrounded by a double-membrane structure called the nuclear envelope. In both types of organisms, the DNA contains the genes that code for the proteins synthesized by the cell. (Details of nucleus structure are described later in the chapter.)

The cytoplasm

A semifluid matrix called the **cytoplasm** fills the interior of the cell. The cytoplasm contains all of the sugars, amino acids, and proteins the cell uses to carry out its everyday activities. Although it is an aqueous medium, cytoplasm is more like jello than water due to the high concentration of proteins and other macromolecules. We call any discrete macromolecular structure in the cytoplasm specialized for a particular function an **organelle.** The part of the cytoplasm that contains organic molecules and ions in solution is called the **cytosol** to distinguish it from the larger organelles suspended in this fluid.

The plasma membrane

The **plasma membrane** encloses a cell and separates its contents from its surroundings. The plasma membrane is a phospholipid bilayer about 5 to 10 nm (5 to 10 billionths of a meter) thick, with proteins embedded in it. Viewed in cross section with the electron microscope, such membranes appear as two dark lines separated by a lighter area. This distinctive appearance arises from the tail-to-tail packing of the phospholipid molecules that make up the membrane (see chapter 5).

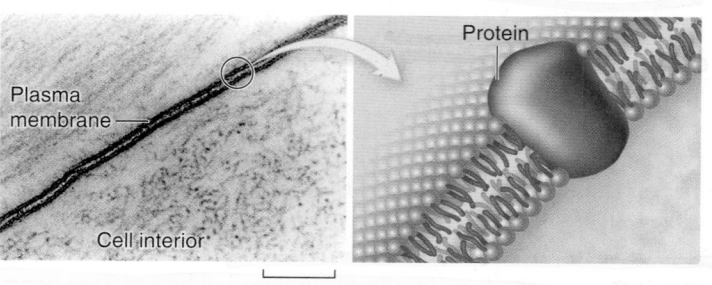
Plasma membrane
Cell interior
Protein
0.054 μm

The proteins of the plasma membrane are generally responsible for a cell's ability to interact with the environment. *Transport proteins* help molecules and ions move across the plasma membrane, either from the environment to the interior of the cell or vice versa. *Receptor proteins* induce changes within the cell when they come in contact with specific molecules in the environment, such as hormones, or with molecules on the surface of neighboring cells. These molecules can function as *markers* that identify the cell as a particular type. This interaction between cell surface molecules is especially important in multicellular organisms, whose cells must be able to recognize one another as they form tissues.

We'll examine the structure and function of cell membranes more thoroughly in chapter 5.

Learning Outcomes Review 4.1

All organisms are single cells or aggregates of cells, and all cells arise from preexisting cells. Cell size is limited primarily by the efficiency of diffusion across the plasma membrane. As a cell becomes larger, its volume increases more quickly than its surface area. Past a certain point, diffusion cannot support the cell's needs. All cells are bounded by a plasma membrane and filled with cytoplasm. The genetic material is found in the central portion of the cell; and in eukaryotic cells, it is contained in a membrane-bounded nucleus.

■ ***Would finding life on Mars change our view of cell theory?***

4.2 Prokaryotic Cells

Learning Outcomes

1. ***Describe the organization of prokaryotic cells.***
2. ***Distinguish between bacterial and archaeal cell types.***

When cells were visualized with microscopes, two basic cellular architectures were recognized: eukaryotic and prokaryotic. These terms refer to the presence or absence, respectively, of a membrane-bounded nucleus that contains genetic material. We have already mentioned that in addition to lacking a nucleus, prokaryotic cells do not have an internal membrane system or numerous membrane-bounded organelles.

Prokaryote cells have relatively simple organization

Prokaryotes are the simplest organisms. Prokaryotic cells are small. They consist of cytoplasm surrounded by a plasma mem-

brane and are encased within a rigid **cell wall.** They have no distinct interior compartments (figure 4.3). A prokaryotic cell is like a one-room cabin in which eating, sleeping, and watching TV all occur.

Prokaryotes are very important in the ecology of living organisms. Some harvest light by photosynthesis, others break down dead organisms and recycle their components. Still others cause disease or have uses in many important industrial processes. There are two main domains of prokaryotes: archaea and bacteria. Chapter 28 covers prokaryotic diversity in more detail.

Although prokaryotic cells do contain organelles like **ribosomes,** which carry out protein synthesis, most lack the membrane-bounded organelles characteristic of eukaryotic cells. It was long thought that prokaryotes also lack the elaborate cytoskeleton found in eukaryotes, but we have now found they have molecules related to both actin and tubulin, which form two of the cytoskeletal elements described later in the chapter. The actin-like proteins form supporting fibrils near the surface of the cell, but the cytoplasm of a prokaryotic cell does not appear to have an extensive internal support structure. Consequently, the strength of the cell comes primarily from its rigid cell wall (see figure 4.3).

The plasma membrane of a prokaryotic cell carries out some of the functions organelles perform in eukaryotic cells. For example, some photosynthetic bacteria, such as the

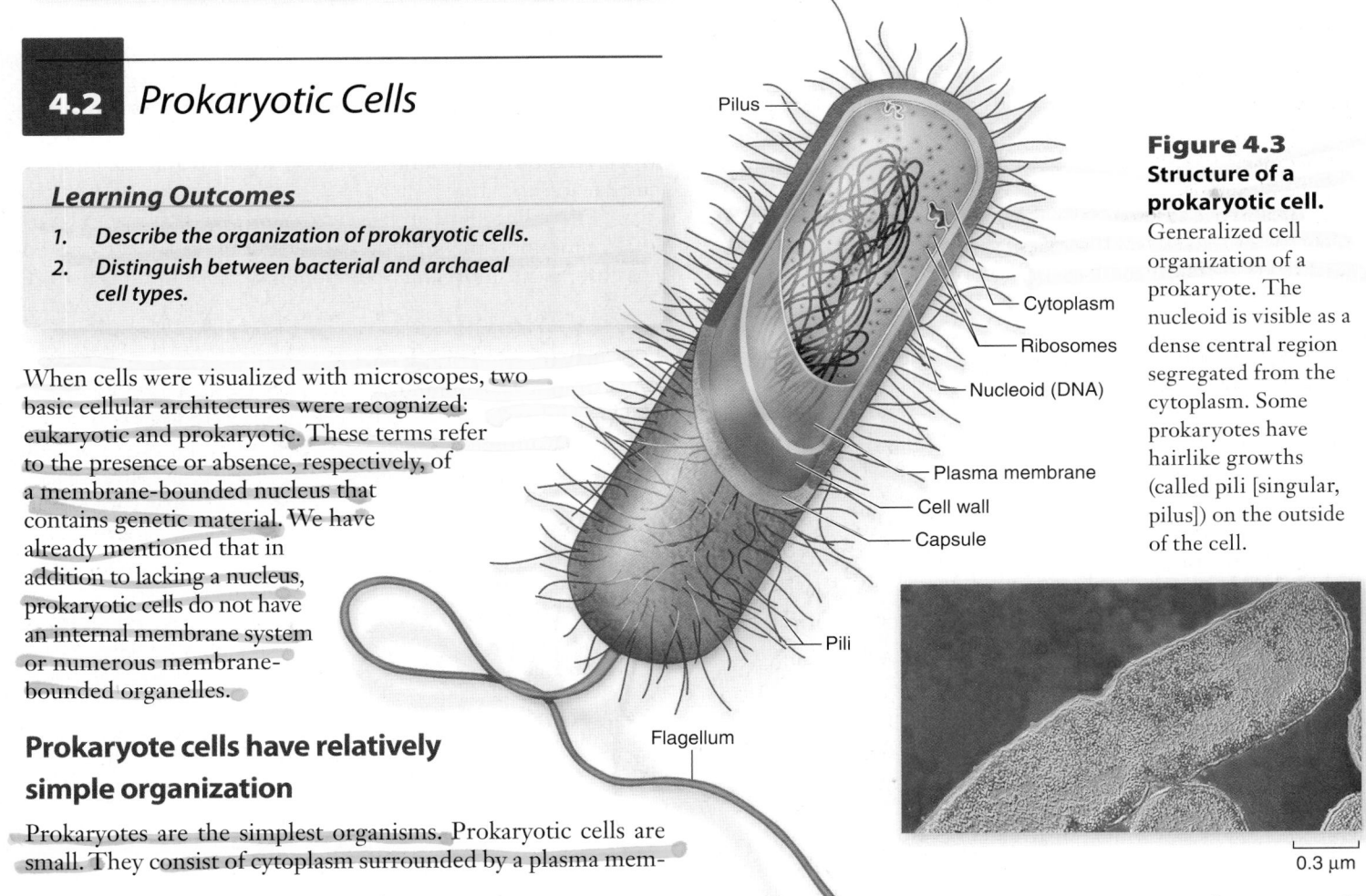

Figure 4.3
Structure of a prokaryotic cell. Generalized cell organization of a prokaryote. The nucleoid is visible as a dense central region segregated from the cytoplasm. Some prokaryotes have hairlike growths (called pili [singular, pilus]) on the outside of the cell.

Pilus
Cytoplasm
Ribosomes
Nucleoid (DNA)
Plasma membrane
Cell wall
Capsule
Pili
Flagellum

0.3 μm

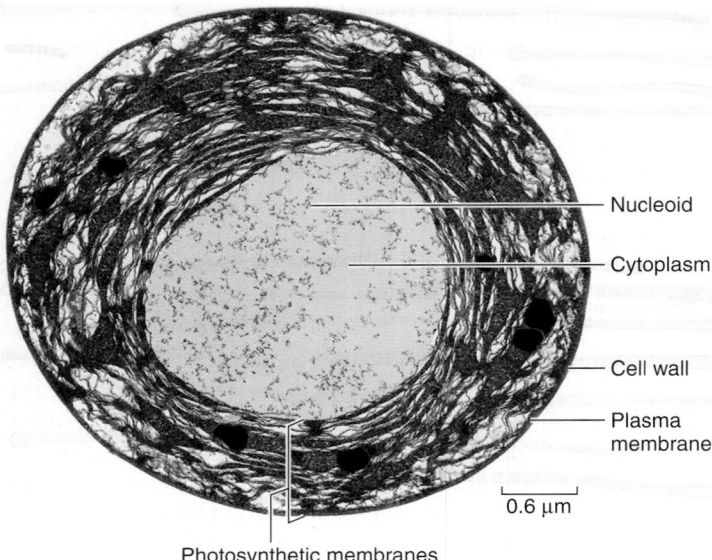

Figure 4.4 Electron micrograph of a photosynthetic bacterial cell. Extensive folded photosynthetic membranes are shown in green in this false color electron micrograph of a *Prochloron* cell.

Inquiry question

? What modifications would you include if you wanted to make a cell as large as possible?

cyanobacterium *Prochloron* (figure 4.4), have an extensively folded plasma membrane, with the folds extending into the cell's interior. These membrane folds contain the bacterial pigments connected with photosynthesis. In eukaryotic plant cells, photosynthetic pigments are found in the inner membrane of the chloroplast.

Because a prokaryotic cell contains no membrane-bounded organelles, the DNA, enzymes, and other cytoplasmic constituents have access to all parts of the cell. Reactions are not compartmen-

talized as they are in eukaryotic cells, and the whole prokaryote operates as a single unit.

Bacterial cell walls consist of peptidoglycan

Most bacterial cells are encased by a strong cell wall. This cell wall is composed of *peptidoglycan*, which consists of a carbohydrate matrix (polymers of sugars) that is cross-linked by short polypeptide units. Details about the structure of this cell wall are discussed in chapter 28. Cell walls protect the cell, maintain its shape, and prevent excessive uptake or loss of water. The exception is the class Mollicutes, which includes the common genus *Mycoplasma*, which lack a cell wall. Plants, fungi, and most protists also have cell walls but with a chemical structure different from peptidoglycan.

The susceptibility of bacteria to antibiotics often depends on the structure of their cell walls. The drugs penicillin and vancomycin, for example, interfere with the ability of bacteria to cross-link the peptides in their peptidoglycan cell wall. Like removing all the nails from a wooden house, this destroys the integrity of the structural matrix, which can no longer prevent water from rushing in and swelling the cell to bursting.

Some bacteria also secrete a jelly-like protective capsule of polysaccharide around the cell. Many disease-causing bacteria have such a capsule, which enables them to adhere to teeth, skin, food—or to practically any surface that will support their growth.

Archaea lack peptidoglycan

We are still learning about the physiology and structure of archaea. Many of these organisms are difficult to culture in the laboratory, and so this group has not yet been studied in detail. More is known about their genetic makeup than about any other feature.

The cell walls of archaea are composed of various chemical compounds, including polysaccharides and proteins, and possibly even inorganic components. A common feature

Figure 4.5 Some prokaryotes move by rotating their flagella.
a. The photograph shows *Vibrio cholerae*, the microbe that causes the serious disease cholera. *b.* The bacterial flagellum is a complex structure. The motor proteins, powered by a proton gradient, are anchored in the plasma membrane. Two rings are found in the cell wall. The motor proteins cause the entire structure to rotate. *c.* As the flagellum rotates it creates a spiral wave down the structure. This powers the cell forward.

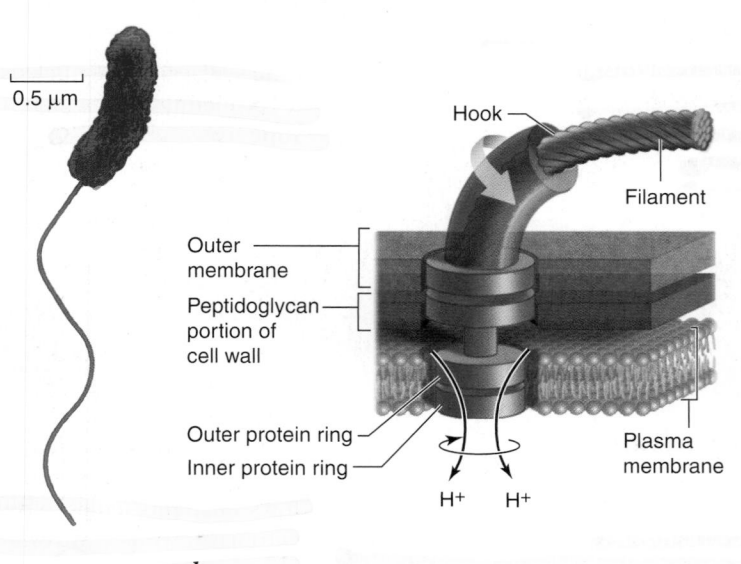
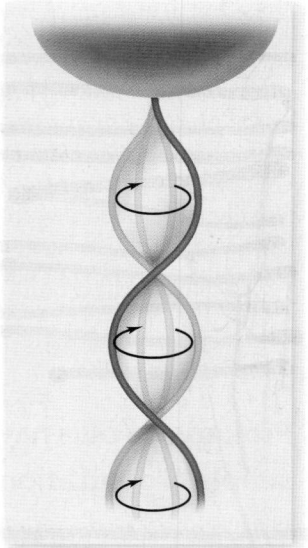

a.　　*b.*　　*c.*

distinguishing archaea from bacteria is the nature of their membrane lipids. The chemical structure of archaeal lipids is distinctly different from that of lipids in bacteria and can include saturated hydrocarbons that are covalently attached to glycerol at both ends, such that their membrane is a monolayer. These features seem to confer greater thermal stability to archaeal membranes, although the tradeoff seems to be an inability to alter the degree of saturation of the hydrocarbons—meaning that archaea with this characteristic cannot adapt to changing environmental temperatures.

The cellular machinery that replicates DNA and synthesized proteins in archaea is more closely related to eukaryotic systems than to bacterial systems. Even though they share a similar overall cellular architecture with prokaryotes, archaea appear to be more closely related on a molecular basis to eukaryotes.

Some prokaryotes move by means of rotating flagella

Flagella (singular, *flagellum*) are long, threadlike structures protruding from the surface of a cell that are used in locomotion. Prokaryotic flagella are protein fibers that extend out from the cell. There may be one or more per cell, or none, depending on the species. Bacteria can swim at speeds of up to 70 cell lengths per second by rotating their flagella like screws (figure 4.5). The rotary motor uses the energy stored in a gradient that transfers protons across the plasma membrane to power the movement of the flagellum. Interestingly, the same principle, in which a proton gradient powers the rotation of a molecule, is used in eukaryotic mitochondria and chloroplasts by an enzyme that synthesizes ATP (see chapters 7 and 8).

Learning Outcomes Review 4.2

Prokaryotes are small cells that lack complex interior organization. The two domains of prokaryotes are archaea and bacteria. The cell wall of bacteria is composed of peptidoglycan, which is not found in archaea. Archaea have cell walls made from a variety of polysaccharides and peptides, as well as membranes containing unusual lipids. Some bacteria move using a rotating flagellum.

■ *What features do bacteria and archaea share?*

4.3 Eukaryotic Cells

Learning Outcomes

1. *Compare the organization of eukaryotic and prokaryotic cells.*
2. *Discuss the role of the nucleus in eukaryotic cells.*
3. *Describe the role of ribosomes in protein synthesis.*

Eukaryotic cells (figures 4.6 and 4.7) are far more complex than prokaryotic cells. The hallmark of the eukaryotic cell is compartmentalization. This is achieved through a combination of an extensive **endomembrane system** that weaves through the cell interior and by numerous *organelles*. These organelles include membrane-bounded structures that form compartments within which multiple biochemical processes can proceed simultaneously and independently.

Plant cells often have a large, membrane-bounded sac called a **central vacuole**, which stores proteins, pigments, and waste materials. Both plant and animal cells contain **vesicles**—smaller sacs that store and transport a variety of materials. Inside the nucleus, the DNA is wound tightly around proteins and packaged into compact units called **chromosomes.**

All eukaryotic cells are supported by an internal protein scaffold, the **cytoskeleton.** Although the cells of animals and some protists lack cell walls, the cells of fungi, plants, and many protists have strong cell walls composed of cellulose or chitin fibers embedded in a matrix of other polysaccharides and proteins. Through the rest of this chapter, we will examine the internal components of eukaryotic cells in more detail.

The nucleus acts as the information center

The largest and most easily seen organelle within a eukaryotic cell is the **nucleus** (Latin, "kernel" or "nut"), first described by the botanist Robert Brown in 1831. Nuclei are roughly spherical in shape, and in animal cells, they are typically located in the central region of the cell (figure 4.8*a*). In some cells, a network of fine cytoplasmic filaments seems to cradle the nucleus in this position.

The nucleus is the repository of the genetic information that enables the synthesis of nearly all proteins of a living eukaryotic cell. Most eukaryotic cells possess a single nucleus, although the cells of fungi and some other groups may have several to many nuclei. Mammalian erythrocytes (red blood cells) lose their nuclei when they mature. Many nuclei exhibit a dark-staining zone called the **nucleolus,** which is a region where intensive synthesis of ribosomal RNA is taking place.

The nuclear envelope

The surface of the nucleus is bounded by *two* phospholipid bilayer membranes, which together make up the **nuclear envelope** (see figure 4.8). The outer membrane of the nuclear envelope is continuous with the cytoplasm's interior membrane system, called the *endoplasmic reticulum* (described later).

Scattered over the surface of the nuclear envelope are what appear as shallow depressions in the electron micrograph but are in fact structures called **nuclear pores** (see figure 4.8*b*, *c*). These pores form 50 to 80 nm apart at locations where the two membrane layers of the nuclear envelope pinch together. They have a complex structure with a cytoplasmic face, a nuclear face, and a central ring embedded in the membrane. The proteins that make up this nuclear pore complex are arranged in a circle with a large central hole. The complex allows small molecules to diffuse freely between nucleoplasm and cytoplasm while controlling the passage of proteins and RNA–protein complexes. Passage is restricted primarily to two kinds

Figure 4.6 Structure of an animal cell. In this generalized diagram of an animal cell, the plasma membrane encases the cell, which contains the cytoskeleton and various cell organelles and interior structures suspended in a semifluid matrix called the cytoplasm. Some kinds of animal cells possess finger-like projections called microvilli. Other types of eukaryotic cells—for example, many protist cells—may possess flagella, which aid in movement, or cilia, which can have many different functions.

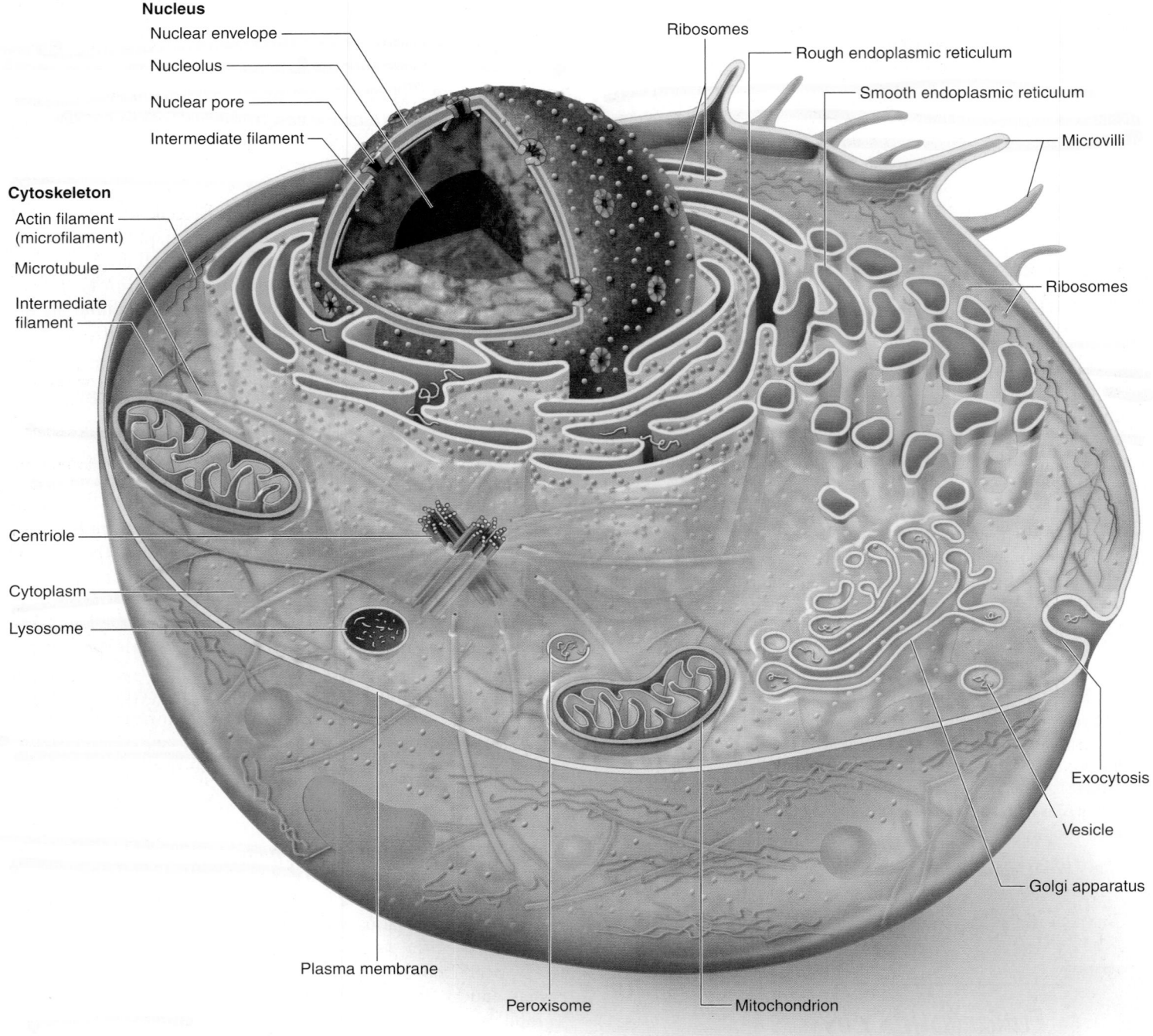

Nucleus
Nuclear envelope
Nucleolus
Nuclear pore
Intermediate filament

Cytoskeleton
Actin filament (microfilament)
Microtubule
Intermediate filament

Centriole

Cytoplasm

Lysosome

Plasma membrane

Peroxisome

Mitochondrion

Ribosomes

Rough endoplasmic reticulum

Smooth endoplasmic reticulum

Microvilli

Ribosomes

Exocytosis

Vesicle

Golgi apparatus

Figure 4.7 Structure of a plant cell. Most mature plant cells contain a large central vacuole, which occupies a major portion of the internal volume of the cell, and organelles called chloroplasts, within which photosynthesis takes place. The cells of plants, fungi, and some protists have cell walls, although the composition of the walls varies among the groups. Plant cells have cytoplasmic connections to one another through openings in the cell wall called plasmodesmata. Flagella occur in sperm of a few plant species, but are otherwise absent from plant and fungal cells. Centrioles are also usually absent.

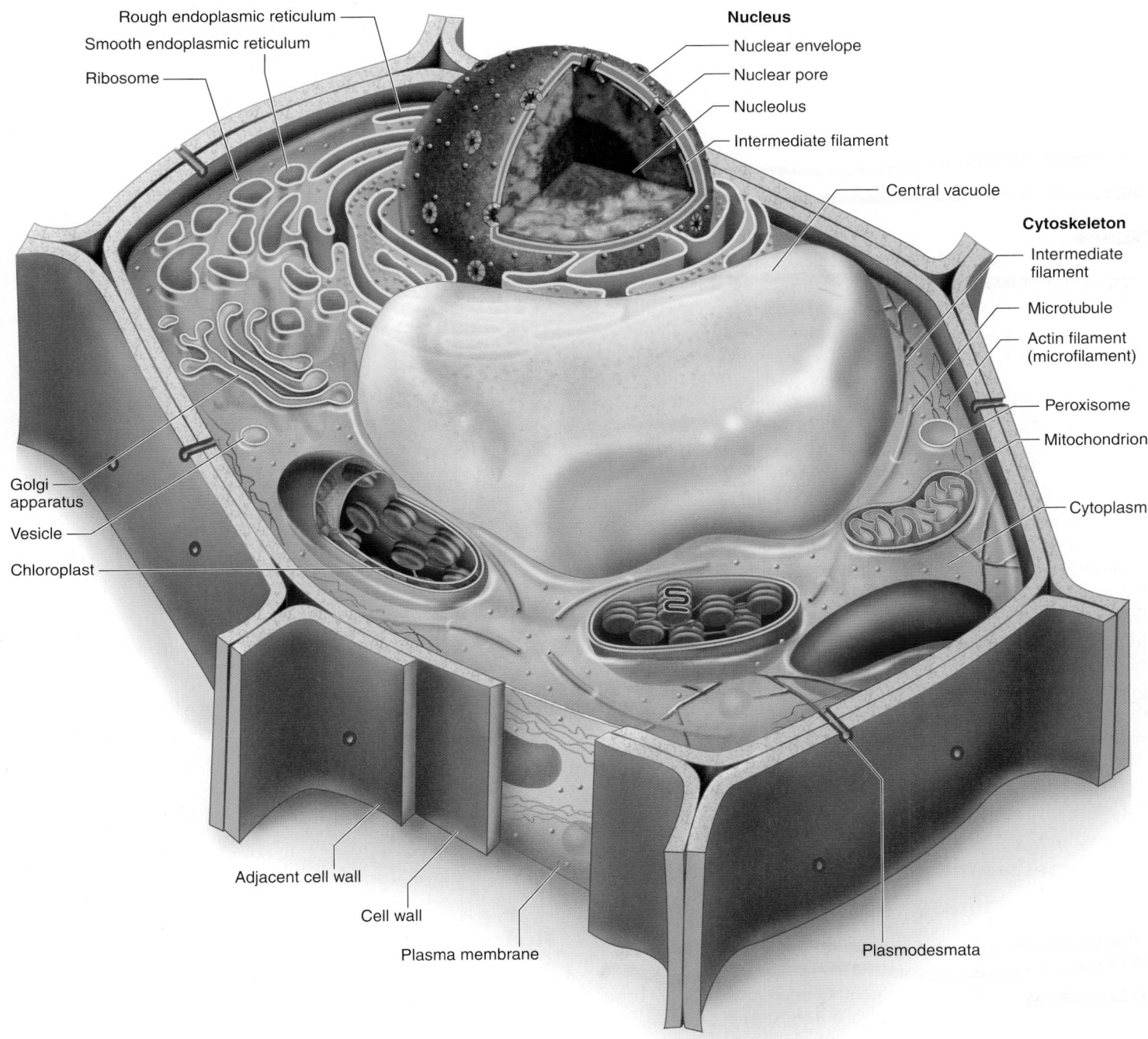

Rough endoplasmic reticulum

Smooth endoplasmic reticulum

Ribosome

Nucleus
Nuclear envelope
Nuclear pore
Nucleolus
Intermediate filament

Central vacuole

Cytoskeleton
Intermediate filament
Microtubule
Actin filament (microfilament)
Peroxisome
Mitochondrion
Cytoplasm

Golgi apparatus
Vesicle
Chloroplast

Adjacent cell wall
Cell wall
Plasma membrane
Plasmodesmata

of molecules: (1) proteins moving into the nucleus to be incorporated into nuclear structures or to catalyze nuclear activities and (2) RNA and RNA–protein complexes formed in the nucleus and exported to the cytoplasm.

The inner surface of the nuclear envelope is covered with a network of fibers that make up the nuclear lamina (see figure 4.8d). This is composed of intermediate filament fibers called *nuclear lamins*. This structure gives the nucleus its shape and is also involved in the deconstruction and reconstruction of the nuclear envelope that accompanies cell division.

Chromatin: DNA packaging

In both prokaryotes and eukaryotes, DNA contains the hereditary information specifying cell structure and function. In most prokaryotes, the DNA is organized into a single circular chromosome. In eukaryotes, the DNA is divided into multiple linear chromosomes. The DNA in these chromosomes is organized with proteins into a complex structure called **chromatin.**

Chromatin is usually in a more extended form that allows regulatory proteins to attach to specific nucleotide sequences along the DNA and regulate gene expression. Without this access, DNA could not direct the day-to-day activities of the cell. When cells divide, the chromatin must be further compacted into a more highly condensed form.

The nucleolus: Ribosomal subunit manufacturing

Before cells can synthesize proteins in large quantity, they must first construct a large number of ribosomes to carry out this synthesis. Hundreds of copies of the genes encoding the ribosomal RNAs are clustered together on the chromosome, facilitating ribsosome construction. By transcribing RNA molecules from this cluster, the cell rapidly generates large numbers of the molecules needed to produce ribosomes.

The clusters of ribosomal RNA genes, the RNAs they produce, and the ribosomal proteins all come together within the nucleus during ribosome production. These ribosomal assembly areas are easily visible within the nucleus as one or more dark-staining regions called nucleoli (singular, nucleolus). Nucleoli can be seen under the light microscope even when the chromosomes are uncoiled.

Ribosomes are the cell's protein synthesis machinery

Although the DNA in a cell's nucleus encodes the amino acid sequence of each protein in the cell, the proteins are not assembled there. A simple experiment demonstrates this: If a brief pulse of radioactive amino acid is administered to a cell, the radioactivity shows up associated with newly made protein in the cytoplasm, not in the nucleus. When investigators first carried out these experiments, they found that protein synthesis is associated with large RNA–protein complexes (called ribosomes) outside the nucleus.

Ribosomes are among the most complex molecular assemblies found in cells. Each ribosome is composed of two

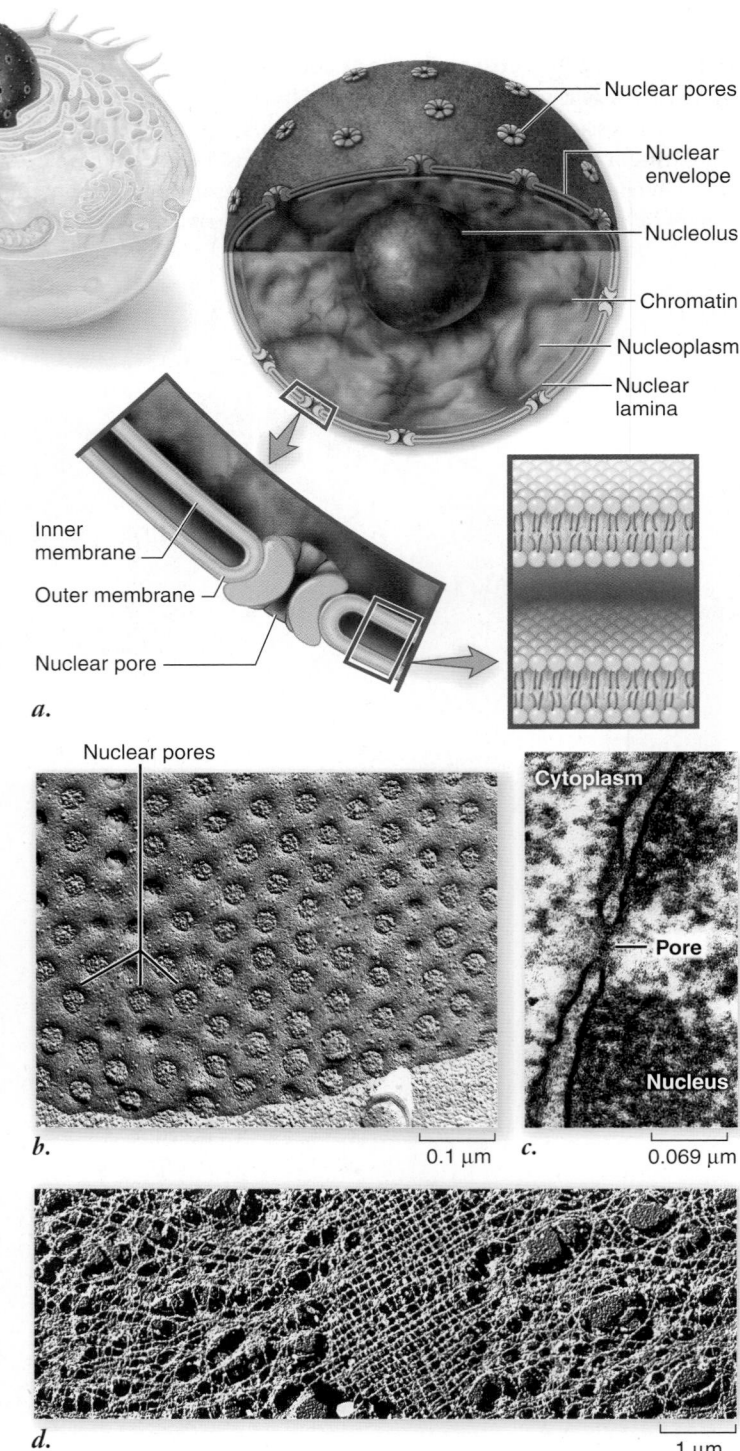

Figure 4.8 The nucleus. *a.* The nucleus is composed of a double membrane called the nuclear envelope, enclosing a fluid-filled interior containing chromatin. The individual nuclear pores extend through the two membrane layers of the envelope. *b.* A freeze-fracture electron micrograph (see figure 5.3) of a cell nucleus, showing many nuclear pores. *c.* A transmission electron micrograph of the nuclear membrane showing a single nuclear pore. The dark material within the pore is protein, which acts to control access through the pore. *d.* The nuclear lamina is visible as a dense network of fibers made of intermediate filaments. The nucleus has been colored purple in the micrographs.

(b): © Dr. Richard Kessel & Dr. Gene Shih/Visuals Unlimited

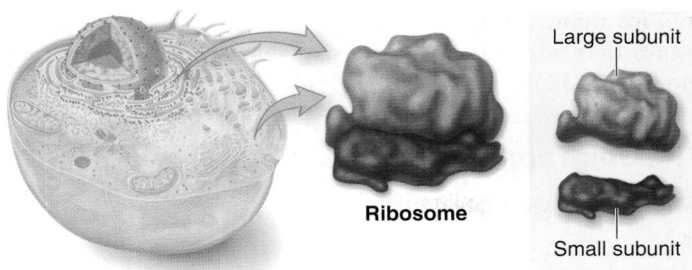

Figure 4.9 A ribosome. Ribosomes consist of a large and a small subunit composed of rRNA and protein. The individual subunits are synthesized in the nucleolus and then move through the nuclear pores to the cytoplasm, where they assemble to translate mRNA. Ribosomes serve as sites of protein synthesis.

subunits (figure 4.9), and each subunit is composed of a combination of RNA, called **ribosomal RNA (rRNA),** and proteins. The subunits join to form a functional ribosome only when they are actively synthesizing proteins. This complicated process requires the two other main forms of RNA: **messenger RNA (mRNA),** which carries coding information from DNA, and **transfer RNA (tRNA),** which carries amino acids. Ribosomes use the information in mRNA to direct the synthesis of a protein. This process will be described in more detail in chapter 15.

Ribosomes are found either free in the cytoplasm or associated with internal membranes, as described in the following section. Free ribosomes synthesize proteins that are found in the cytoplasm, nuclear proteins, mitochondrial proteins, and proteins found in other organelles not derived from the endomembrane system. Membrane-associated ribosomes synthesize membrane proteins, proteins found in the endomembrane system, and proteins destined for export from the cell.

Ribosomes can be thought of as "universal organelles" because they are found in all cell types from all three domains of life. As we build a picture of the minimal essential functions for cellular life, ribosomes will be on the short list. Life is protein-based, and ribosomes are the factories that make proteins.

Learning Outcomes Review 4.3

In contrast to prokaryotic cells, eukaryotic cells exhibit compartmentalization. Eukaryotic cells contain an endomembrane system and organelles that carry out specialized functions. The nucleus, composed of a double membrane connected to the endomembrane system, contains the cell's genetic information. Material moves between the nucleus and cytoplasm through nuclear pores. Ribosomes translate mRNA, which is transcribed from DNA in the nucleus, into polypeptides that make up proteins. Ribosomes are a universal organelle found in all known cells.

- ■ *Would you expect cells in different organs in complex animals to have the same structure?*

The Endomembrane System

The interior of a eukaryotic cell is packed with membranes so thin that they are invisible under the low resolving power of light microscopes. This endomembrane system fills the cell, dividing it into compartments, channeling the passage of molecules through the interior of the cell, and providing surfaces for the synthesis of lipids and some proteins. The presence of these membranes in eukaryotic cells marks one of the fundamental distinctions between eukaryotes and prokaryotes.

The largest of the internal membranes is called the **endoplasmic reticulum (ER).** *Endoplasmic* means "within the cytoplasm," and *reticulum* is Latin for "a little net." Like the plasma membrane, the ER is composed of a phospholipid bilayer embedded with proteins. It weaves in sheets through the interior of the cell, creating a series of channels between its folds (figure 4.10). Of the many compartments in eukaryotic cells, the two largest are the inner region of the ER, called the **cisternal space** or **lumen,** and the region exterior to it, the cytosol, which is the fluid component of the cytoplasm containing dissolved organic molecules such as proteins and ions.

The rough ER is a site of protein synthesis

The **rough ER (RER)** gets its name from its surface appearance, which is pebbly due to the presence of ribosomes. The RER is not easily visible with a light microscope, but it can be seen using the electron microscope. It appears to be composed of flattened sacs, the surfaces of which are bumpy with ribosomes (see figure 4.10).

The proteins synthesized on the surface of the RER are destined to be exported from the cell, sent to lysosomes or vacuoles (described in a later section), or embedded in the plasma membrane. These proteins enter the cisternal space as a first step in the pathway that will sort proteins to their eventual destinations. This pathway also involves vesicles and the Golgi apparatus, described later. The sequence of the protein being synthesized determines whether the ribosome will become associated with the ER or remain a cytoplasmic ribosome.

In the ER, newly synthesized proteins can be modified by the addition of short-chain carbohydrates to form **glycoproteins.** Those proteins destined for secretion are separated from other products and later packaged into vesicles. The ER also manufactures membranes by producing membrane proteins and phospholipid molecules. The membrane

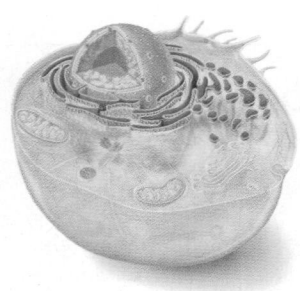

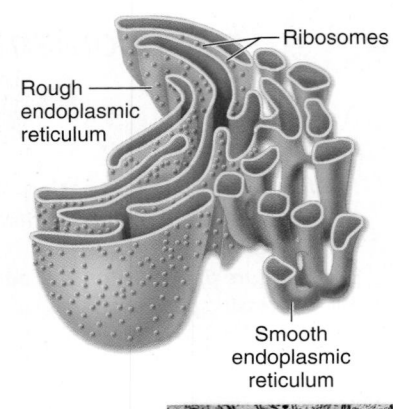

Ribosomes

Rough endoplasmic reticulum

Smooth endoplasmic reticulum

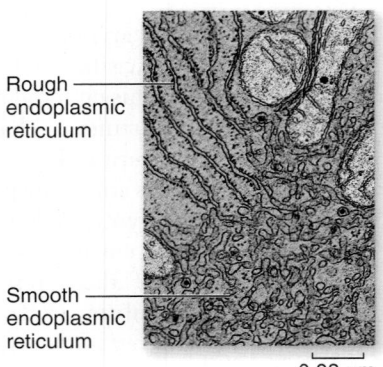

Rough endoplasmic reticulum

Smooth endoplasmic reticulum

0.08 μm

Figure 4.10 The endoplasmic reticulum. Rough ER (RER), blue in the drawing, is composed more of flattened sacs and forms a compartment throughout the cytoplasm. Ribosomes associated with the cytoplasmic face of the RER extrude newly made proteins into the interior, or lumen. The smooth ER (SER), green in the drawing, is a more tubelike structure connected to the RER. The micrograph has been colored to match the drawing.

proteins are inserted into the ER's own membrane, which can then expand and pinch off in the form of vesicles to be transferred to other locations.

The smooth ER has multiple roles

Regions of the ER with relatively few bound ribosomes are referred to as **smooth ER (SER).** The SER appears more like a network of tubules than the flattened sacs of the RER. The membranes of the SER contain many embedded enzymes. Enzymes anchored within the ER, for example, catalyze the synthesis of a variety of carbohydrates and lipids. Steroid hormones are synthesized in the SER as well. The majority of membrane lipids are assembled in the SER and then sent to whatever parts of the cell need membrane components.

The SER is used to store Ca^{2+} in cells. This keeps the cytoplasmic level low, allowing Ca^{2+} to be used as a signaling molecule. In muscle cells, for example, Ca^{2+} is used to trigger muscle contraction. In other cells, Ca^{2+} release from SER stores is involved in diverse signaling pathways.

The ratio of SER to RER depends on a cell's function. In multicellular animals such as ourselves, great variation exists in this ratio. Cells that carry out extensive lipid synthesis, such as those in the testes, intestine, and brain, have abundant SER. Cells that synthesize proteins that are secreted, such as antibodies, have much more extensive RER.

Another role of the SER is the modification of foreign substances to make them less toxic. In the liver, the enzymes of the SER carry out this detoxification. This action can include neutralizing substances that we have taken for a therapeutic reason, such as penicillin. Thus, relatively high doses are prescribed for some drugs to offset our body's efforts to

remove them. Liver cells have extensive SER as well as enzymes that can process a variety of substances by chemically modifying them.

The Golgi apparatus sorts and packages proteins

Flattened stacks of membranes, often interconnected with one another, form a complex called the **Golgi body.** These structures are named for Camillo Golgi, the 19th-century physician who first identified them. The number of stacked membranes within the Golgi body ranges from 1 or a few in protists, to 20 or more in animal cells and to several hundred in plant cells. They are especially abundant in glandular cells, which manufacture and secrete substances. The Golgi body is often referred to as the **Golgi apparatus** (figure 4.11).

The Golgi apparatus functions in the collection, packaging, and distribution of molecules synthesized at one location and used at another within the cell or even outside of it. A Golgi body has a front and a back, with distinctly different membrane compositions at these opposite ends. The front, or receiving end, is called the *cis* face and is usually located near ER. Materials move to the *cis* face in transport vesicles that bud off the ER. These vesicles fuse with the *cis* face, emptying their contents into the interior, or lumen, of the Golgi apparatus. The ER-synthesized molecules then pass through the channels of the Golgi apparatus until they reach the back, or discharging end,

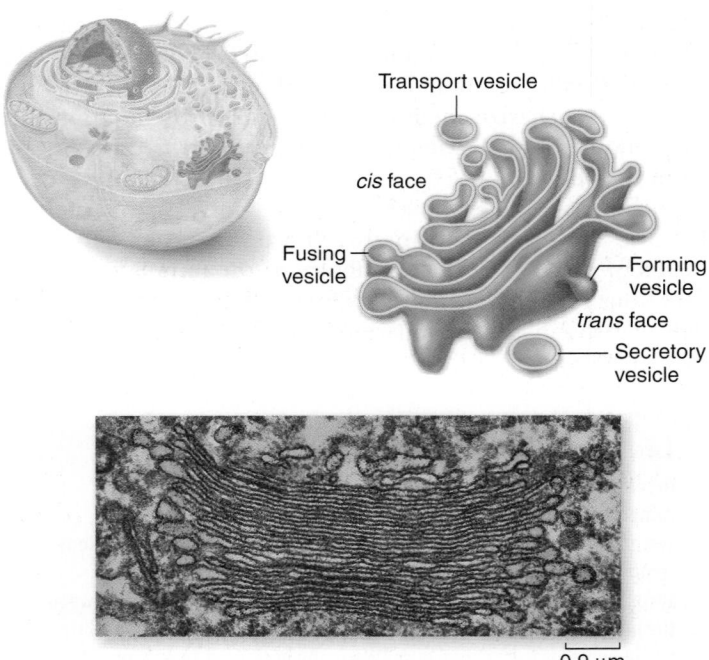

Transport vesicle

cis face

Fusing vesicle

Forming vesicle

trans face

Secretory vesicle

0.9 μm

Figure 4.11 The Golgi apparatus. The Golgi apparatus is a smooth, concave, membranous structure. It receives material for processing in transport vesicles on the *cis* face and sends the material packaged in transport or secretory vesicles off the *trans* face. The substance in a vesicle could be for export out of the cell or for distribution to another region within the same cell.

called the *trans* face, where they are discharged in secretory vesicles (figure 4.12).

Proteins and lipids manufactured on the rough and smooth ER membranes are transported into the Golgi apparatus and modified as they pass through it. The most common alteration is the addition or modification of short sugar chains, forming glycoproteins and glycolipids. In many instances, enzymes in the Golgi apparatus modify existing glycoproteins and glycolipids made in the ER by cleaving a sugar from a chain or by modifying one or more of the sugars.

The newly formed or altered glycoproteins and glycolipids collect at the ends of the Golgi bodies in flattened, stacked membrane folds called **cisternae** (Latin, "collecting vessels"). Periodically, the membranes of the cisternae push together, pinching off small, membrane-bounded secretory vesicles containing the glycoprotein and glycolipid molecules. These vesicles then diffuse to other locations in the cell, distributing the newly synthesized molecules to their appropriate destinations.

Another function of the Golgi apparatus is the synthesis of cell wall components. Noncellulose polysaccharides that form part of the cell wall of plants are synthesized in the Golgi apparatus and sent to the plasma membrane where they can be added to the cellulose that is assembled on the exterior of the cell. Other polysaccharides secreted by plants are also synthesized in the Golgi apparatus.

Lysosomes contain digestive enzymes

Membrane-bounded digestive vesicles, called **lysosomes,** are also components of the endomembrane system. They arise from the Golgi apparatus. They contain high levels of degrading enzymes, which catalyze the rapid breakdown of proteins, nucleic acids, lipids, and carbohydrates. Throughout the lives of eukaryotic cells, lysosomal enzymes break down old organelles and recycle their component molecules. This makes room for newly formed organelles. For example, mitochondria are replaced in some tissues every 10 days.

The digestive enzymes in the lysosome are optimally active at acid pH. Lysosomes are activated by fusing with a food vesicle produced by *phagocytosis* (a specific type of endocytosis; see chapter 5) or by fusing with an old or worn-out organelle. The fusion event activates proton pumps in the lysosomal membrane, resulting in a lower internal pH. As the interior pH falls, the arsenal of digestive enzymes contained in the lysosome is activated. This leads to the degradation of macromolecules in the food vesicle or the destruction of the old organelle.

A number of human genetic disorders, collectively called lysosomal storage disorders, affect lysosomes. For example, the genetic abnormality called Tay–Sachs disease is caused by the loss of function of a single lysosomal enzyme. This enzyme is necessary to break down a membrane glycolipid found in nerve cells. Accumulation of glycolipid in lysosomes affects nerve cell function, leading to a variety of clinical symptoms such as seizures and muscle rigidity.

In addition to breaking down organelles and other structures within cells, lysosomes eliminate other cells that

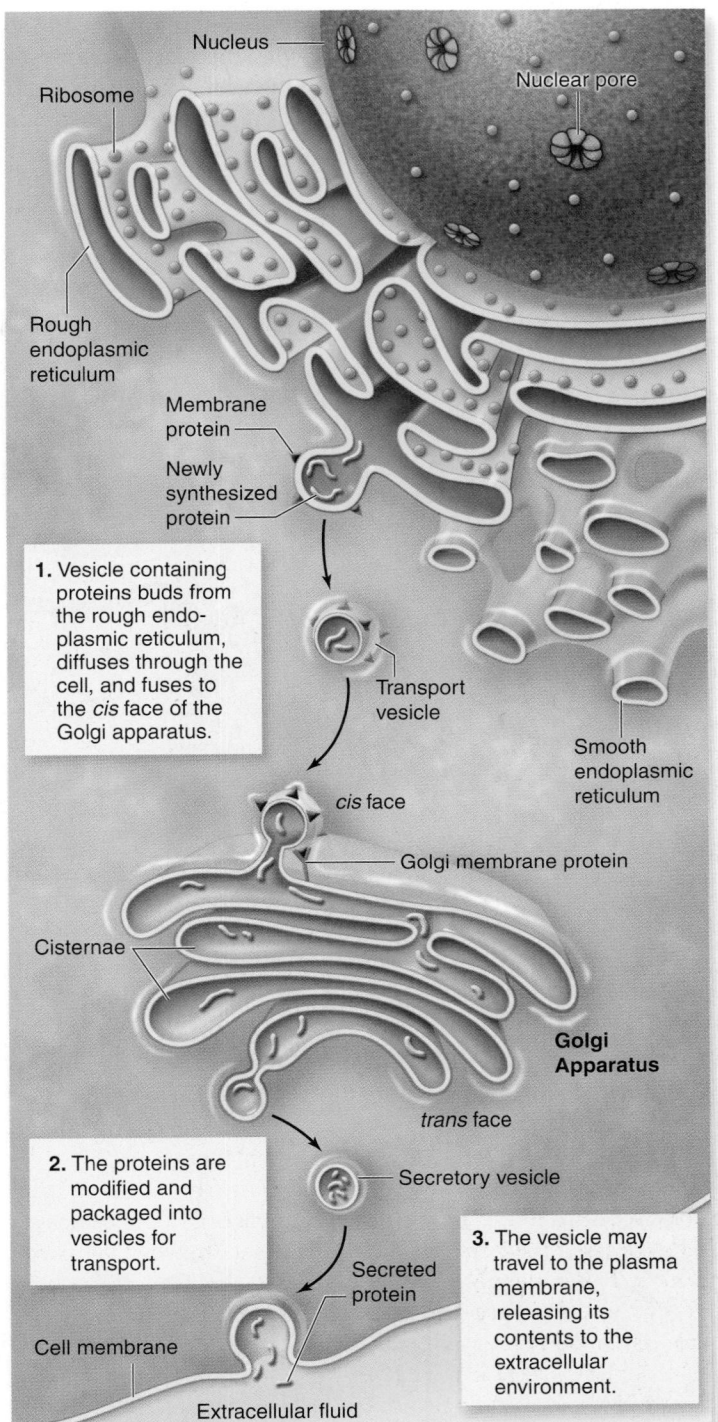

Figure 4.12 Protein transport through the endomembrane system. Proteins synthesized by ribosomes on the RER are translocated into the internal compartment of the ER. These proteins may be used at a distant location within the cell or secreted from the cell. They are transported within vesicles that bud off the rough ER. These transport vesicles travel to the *cis* face of the Golgi apparatus. There they can be modified and packaged into vesicles that bud off the *trans* face of the Golgi apparatus. Vesicles leaving the *trans* face transport proteins to other locations in the cell, or fuse with the plasma membrane, releasing their contents to the extracellular environment.

the cell has engulfed by phagocytosis. When a white blood cell, for example, phagocytizes a passing pathogen, lysosomes fuse with the resulting "food vesicle," releasing their enzymes into the vesicle and degrading the material within (figure 4.13).

Microbodies are a diverse category of organelles

Eukaryotic cells contain a variety of enzyme-bearing, membrane-enclosed vesicles called **microbodies.** These are found in the cells of plants, animals, fungi, and protists. The distribution of enzymes into microbodies is one of the principal ways eukaryotic cells organize their metabolism.

Peroxisomes: Peroxide utilization

An important type of microbody is the **peroxisome** (figure 4.14), which contains enzymes involved in the oxidation of fatty acids. If these oxidative enzymes were not isolated within microbodies, they would tend to short-circuit the metabolism of the cytoplasm, which often involves adding hydrogen atoms to oxygen. Because many peroxisomal proteins are synthesized by cytoplasmic ribosomes, the organelles themselves were long thought to form by the addition of lipids and proteins, leading to growth. As they grow larger, they divide to produce new peroxisomes. Although division of peroxisomes still appears to occur, it is now clear that peroxisomes can form from the fusion of ER-derived vesicles. These vesicles then import peroxisomal proteins to form a mature peroxisome. Genetic screens have isolated some 32 genes that encode proteins involved in biogenesis and maintenance of peroxisomes. The human genetic diseases called peroxisome biogenesis disorders (PBDs) appear to be caused by mutations in some of these genes.

Peroxisomes get their name from the hydrogen peroxide produced as a by-product of the activities of oxidative enzymes. Hydrogen peroxide is dangerous to cells because of its violent

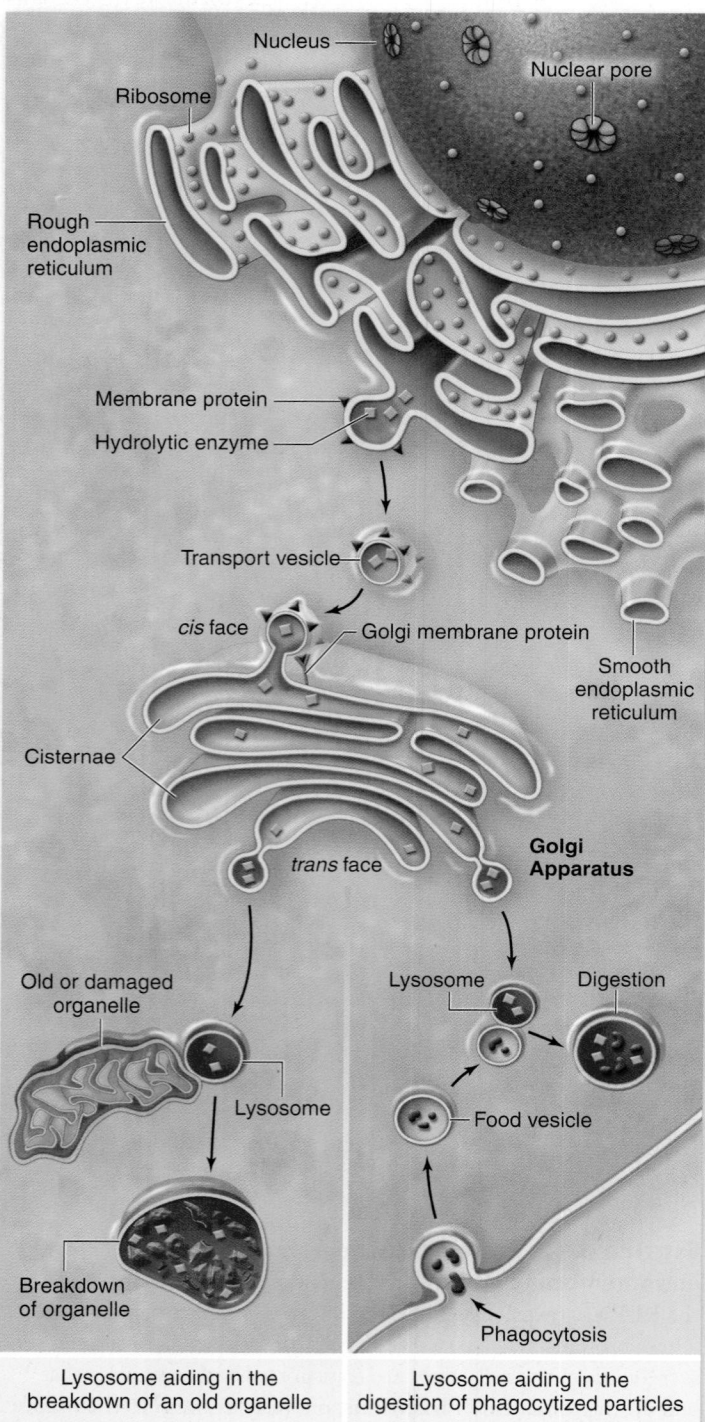

Figure 4.13 Lysosomes. Lysosomes are formed from vesicles budding off the Golgi. They contain hydrolytic enzymes that digest particles or cells taken into the cell by phagocytosis, and break down old organelles.

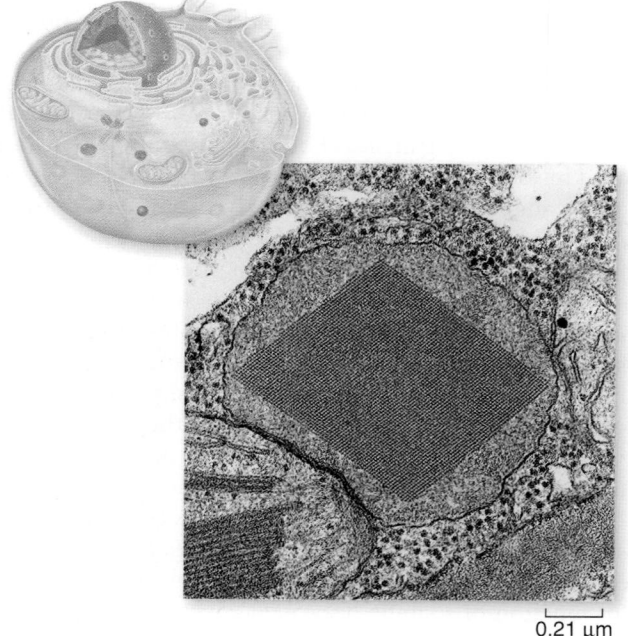

0.21 μm

Figure 4.14 A peroxisome. Peroxisomes are spherical organelles that may contain a large crystal structure composed of protein. Peroxisomes contain digestive and detoxifying enzymes that produce hydrogen peroxide as a by-product. A peroxisome has been colored green in the electron micrograph.

chemical reactivity. However, peroxisomes also contain the enzyme catalase, which breaks down hydrogen peroxide into its harmless constituents—water and oxygen.

Plants use vacuoles for storage and water balance

Plant cells have specialized membrane-bounded structures called **vacuoles.** The most conspicuous example is the large central vacuole seen in most plant cells (figure 4.15). In fact, *vacuole* actually means blank space, referring to its appearance in the light microscope. The membrane surrounding this vacuole is called the **tonoplast** because it contains channels for water that are used to help the cell maintain its tonicity, or osmotic balance (see osmosis in chapter 5).

For many years biologists assumed that only one type of vacuole existed and that it served multiple functions. The functions assigned to this vacuole included water balance and storage of both useful molecules (such as sugars, ions and pigments) and waste products. The vacuole was also thought to store enzymes involved in the breakdown of macromolecules and those used in detoxifying foreign substances. Old textbooks of plant physiology referred to vacuoles as the attic of the cell for the variety of substances thought to be stored there.

Studies of tonoplast transporters and the isolation of vacuoles from a variety of cell types have led to a more complex view of vacuoles. These studies have made it clear that different vacuolar types can be found in different cells. These vacuoles are specialized, depending on the function of the cell.

The central vacuole is clearly important for a number of roles in all plant cells. The central vacuole and the water channels of the tonoplast maintain the tonicity of the cell, allowing the cell to expand and contract depending on conditions. The central vacuole is also involved in cell growth by occupying most of the volume of the cell. Plant cells grow by expanding the vacuole, rather than by increasing cytoplasmic volume.

Vacuoles with a variety of functions are also found in some types of fungi and protists. One form is the contractile vacuole, found in some protists, which can pump water and is used to maintain water balance in the cell. Other vacuoles are used for storage or to segregate toxic materials from the rest of the cytoplasm. The number and kind of vacuoles found in a cell depends on the needs of the particular cell type.

Learning Outcomes Review 4.4

The endoplasmic reticulum (ER) is an extensive system of folded membranes that spatially organize the cell's biosynthetic activities. Smooth ER (SER) is the site of lipid and membrane synthesis and is used to store Ca^{2+}. Rough ER (RER) is covered with ribosomes and is a site of protein synthesis. Proteins from the RER are transported by vesicles to the Golgi apparatus where they are modified, packaged, and distributed to their final location. Lysosomes are vesicles that contain digestive enzymes used to degrade materials such as invaders or worn-out components. Peroxisomes carry out oxidative metabolism that generates peroxides. Vacuoles are membrane-bounded structures that have roles ranging from storage to cell growth in plants. They are also found in some fungi and protists.

■ *How do ribosomes on the RER differ from cytoplasmic ribosomes?*

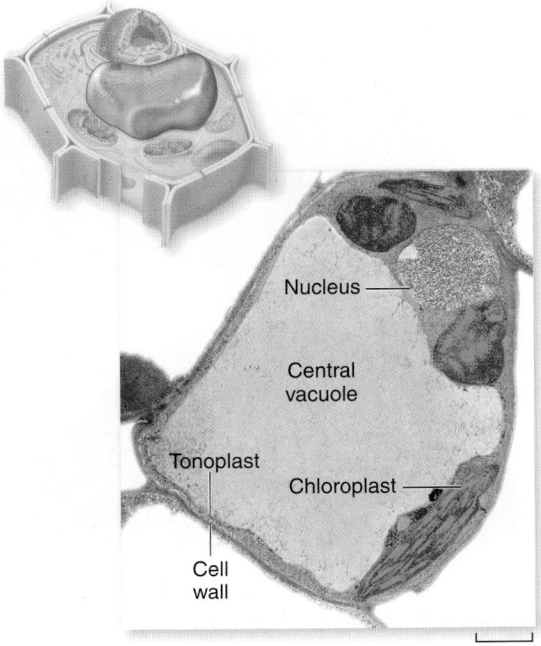

Figure 4.15 The central vacuole. A plant's central vacuole stores dissolved substances and can expand in size to increase the tonicity of a plant cell. Micrograph shown with false color.

Nucleus

Central vacuole

Tonoplast

Chloroplast

Cell wall

0.9 μm

4.5 Mitochondria and Chloroplasts: Cellular Generators

Learning Outcomes

1. Describe the structure of mitochondria and chloroplasts.
2. Compare the function of mitochondria and chloroplasts.
3. Explain the probable origin of mitochondria and chloroplasts.

Mitochondria and chloroplasts share structural and functional similarities. Structurally, they are both surrounded by a double membrane, and both contain their own DNA and protein synthesis machinery. Functionally, they are both involved in energy metabolism, as we will explore in detail in later chapters on energy metabolism and photosynthesis.

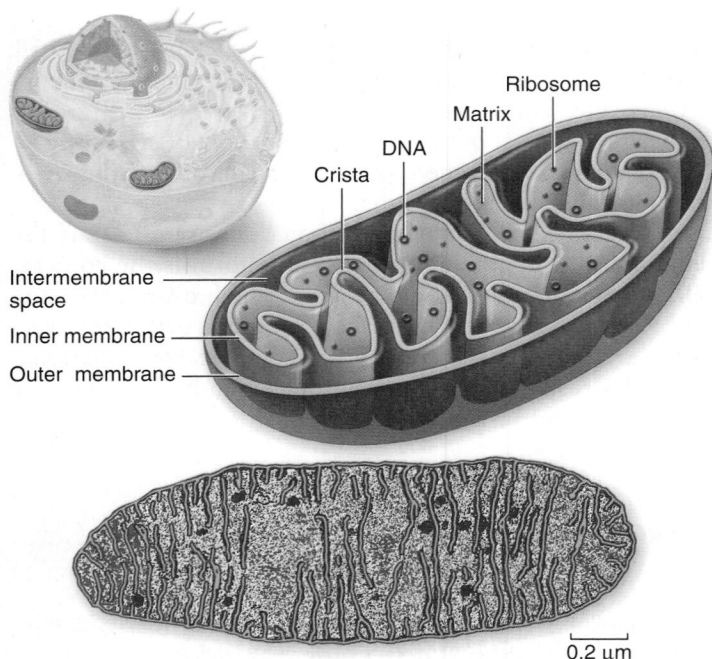

Figure 4.16 Mitochondria. The inner membrane of a mitochondrion is shaped into folds called cristae that greatly increase the surface area for oxidative metabolism. A mitochondrion in cross section and cut lengthwise is shown colored red in the micrograph.

Mitochondria metabolize sugar to generate ATP

Mitochondria (singular, *mitochondrion*) are typically tubular or sausage-shaped organelles about the size of bacteria that are found in all types of eukaryotic cells (figure 4.16). Mitochondria are bounded by two membranes: a smooth outer membrane, and an inner folded membrane with numerous contiguous layers called **cristae** (singular, *crista*).

The cristae partition the mitochondrion into two compartments: a **matrix,** lying inside the inner membrane; and an outer compartment, or **intermembrane space,** lying between the two mitochondrial membranes. On the surface of the inner membrane, and also embedded within it, are proteins that carry out oxidative metabolism, the oxygen-requiring process by which energy in macromolecules is used to produce ATP (chapter 7).

Mitochondria have their own DNA; this DNA contains several genes that produce proteins essential to the mitochondrion's role in oxidative metabolism. Thus, the mitochondrion, in many respects, acts as a cell within a cell, containing its own genetic information specifying proteins for its unique functions. The mitochondria are not fully autonomous, however, because most of the genes that encode the enzymes used in oxidative metabolism are located in the cell nucleus.

A eukaryotic cell does not produce brand-new mitochondria each time the cell divides. Instead, the mitochondria themselves divide in two, doubling in number, and these are partitioned between the new cells. Most of the components required for mitochondrial division are encoded by genes in the nucleus and are translated into proteins by cytoplasmic ribosomes. Mitochondrial replication is, therefore, impossible without nuclear participation, and mitochondria thus cannot be grown in a cell-free culture.

Chloroplasts use light to generate ATP and sugars

Plant cells and cells of other eukaryotic organisms that carry out photosynthesis typically contain from one to several hundred **chloroplasts.** Chloroplasts bestow an obvious advantage on the organisms that possess them: They can manufacture their own food. Chloroplasts contain the photosynthetic pigment chlorophyll that gives most plants their green color.

The chloroplast, like the mitochondrion, is surrounded by two membranes (figure 4.17). However, chloroplasts are larger and more complex than mitochondria. In addition to the outer and inner membranes, which lie in close association with each other, chloroplasts have closed compartments of stacked membranes called **grana** (singular, *granum*), which lie inside the inner membrane.

A chloroplast may contain a hundred or more grana, and each granum may contain from a few to several dozen disk-shaped structures called **thylakoids.** On the surface of the thylakoids are the light-capturing photosynthetic pigments, to be discussed in depth in chapter 8. Surrounding the thylakoid is a fluid matrix called the *stroma*. The enzymes used to synthesize glucose during photosynthesis are found in the stroma.

Like mitochondria, chloroplasts contain DNA, but many of the genes that specify chloroplast components are also located in the nucleus. Some of the elements used in photosynthesis, including the specific protein components necessary to accomplish the reaction, are synthesized entirely within the chloroplast.

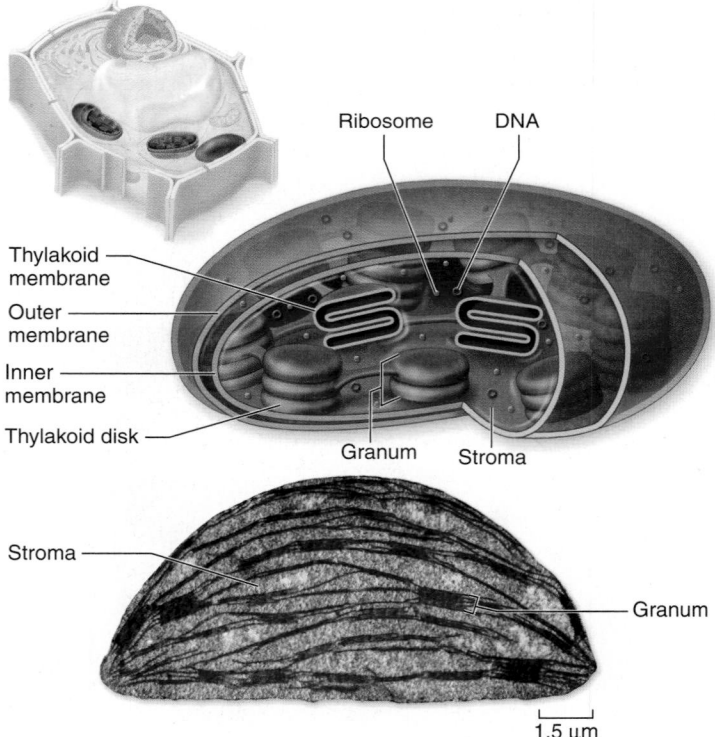

Figure 4.17 Chloroplast structure. The inner membrane of a chloroplast surrounds a membrane system of stacks of closed chlorophyll-containing vesicles called thylakoids, within which photosynthesis occurs. Thylakoids are typically stacked one on top of the other in columns called grana. The chloroplast has been colored green in the micrograph.

Other DNA-containing organelles in plants, called *leuco-plasts*, lack pigment and a complex internal structure. In root cells and some other plant cells, leucoplasts may serve as starch storage sites. A leucoplast that stores starch (amylose) is sometimes termed an **amyloplast.** These organelles—chloroplasts, leucoplasts, and amyloplasts—are collectively called **plastids.** All plastids are produced by the division of existing plastids.

Mitochondria and chloroplasts arose by endosymbiosis

Symbiosis is a close relationship between organisms of different species that live together. As noted in chapter 29, the theory of **endosymbiosis** proposes that some of today's eukaryotic organelles evolved by a symbiosis arising between two cells that were each free-living. One cell, a prokaryote, was engulfed by and became part of another cell, which was the precursor of modern eukaryotes (figure 4.18).

According to the endosymbiont theory, the engulfed prokaryotes provided their hosts with certain advantages associated with their special metabolic abilities. Two key eukaryotic organelles are believed to be the descendants of these endosymbiotic prokaryotes: mitochondria, which are thought to have originated as bacteria capable of carrying out oxidative metabolism, and chloroplasts, which apparently arose from photosynthetic bacteria. This is discussed in detail in chapter 29.

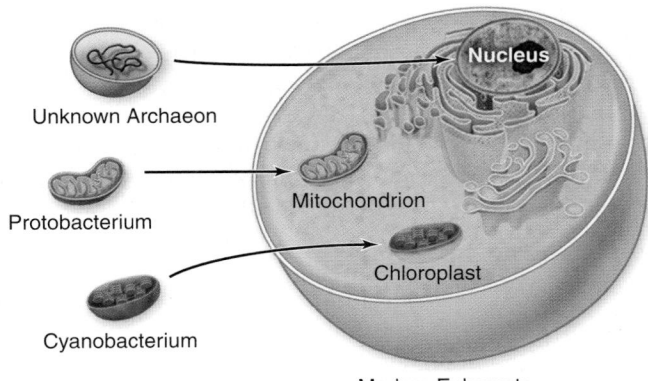

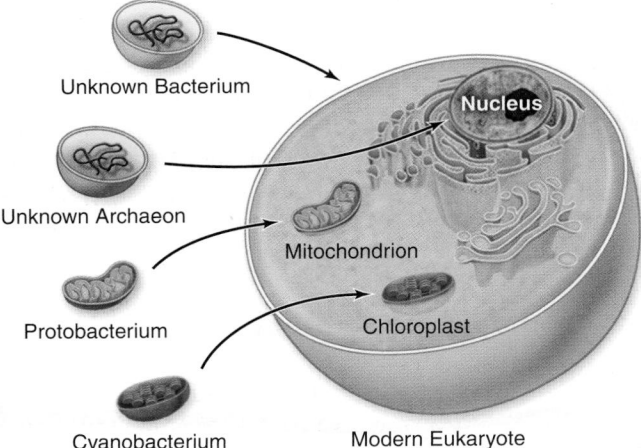

Figure 4.18 Possible origins of eukaryotic cells. Both mitochondria and chloroplasts are thought to have arisen by endosymbiosis where a free-living cell is taken up but not digested. The nature of the engulfing cell is unknown. Two possibilities are The engulfing cell *(top)* is an archaeon that gave rise to the nuclear genome and cytoplasmic contents. The engulfing cell *(bottom)* consists of a nucleus derived from an archaeon in a bacterial cell. This could arise by a fusion event or by engulfment of the archaeon by the bacterium.

The cytoplasm of all eukaryotic cells is crisscrossed by a network of protein fibers that supports the shape of the cell and anchors organelles to fixed locations. This network, called the cytoskeleton, is a dynamic system, constantly assembling and disassembling. Individual fibers consist of polymers of identical protein subunits that attract one another and spontaneously assemble into long chains. Fibers disassemble in the same way, as one subunit after another breaks away from one end of the chain.

Three types of fibers compose the cytoskeleton

Eukaryotic cells may contain the following three types of cytoskeletal fibers, each formed from a different kind of subunit: (1) actin filaments, sometimes called microfilaments, (2) microtubules, and (3) intermediate filaments.

Actin filaments (microfilaments)

Actin filaments are long fibers about 7 nm in diameter. Each filament is composed of two protein chains loosely twined together like two strands of pearls (figure 4.19). Each "pearl," or subunit, on the chain is the globular protein **actin.** Actin filaments exhibit polarity, that is, they have plus (+) and minus (–) ends. These designate the direction of growth of the filaments.

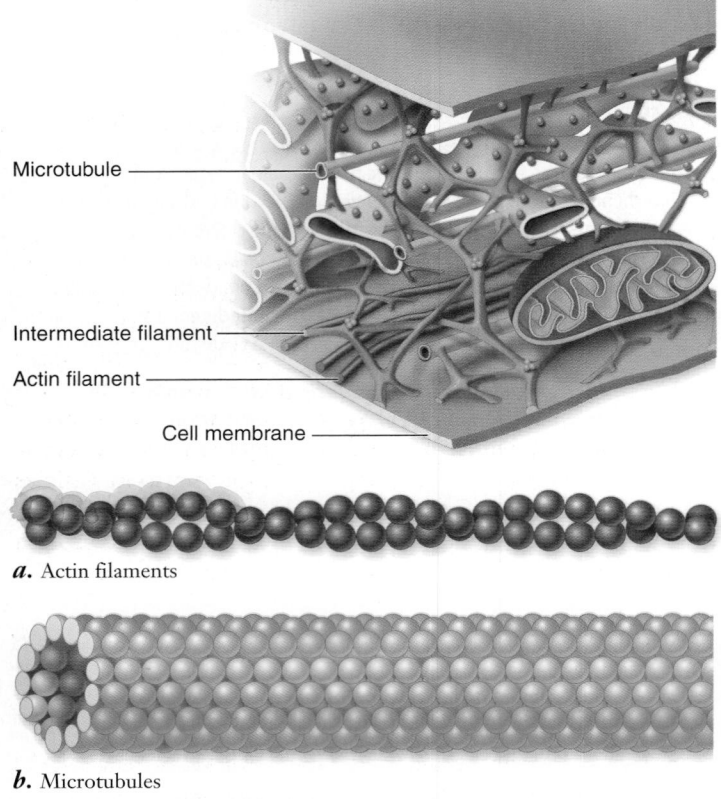

Microtubule

Intermediate filament

Actin filament

Cell membrane

a. Actin filaments

b. Microtubules

c. Intermediate filament

Figure 4.19 Molecules that make up the cytoskeleton.
a. Actin filaments: Actin filaments, also called *microfilaments,* are made of two strands of the globular protein actin twisted together. They are often found in bundles or in a branching network. Actin filaments in many cells are concentrated below the plasma membrane in bundles known as stress fibers, which may have a contractile function. *b. Microtubules:* Microtubules are composed of α- and β-tubulin protein subunits arranged side by side to form a tube. Microtubules are comparatively stiff cytoskeletal elements and have many functions in the cell including intracellular transport and the separation of chromosomes during mitosis. *c. Intermediate filaments:* Intermediate filaments are composed of overlapping staggered tetramers of protein. These tetramers are then bundled into cables. This molecular arrangement allows for a ropelike structure that imparts tremendous mechanical strength to the cell.

Actin molecules spontaneously form these filaments, even in a test tube.

Cells regulate the rate of actin polymerization through other proteins that act as switches, turning on polymerization when appropriate. Actin filaments are responsible for cellular movements such as contraction, crawling, "pinching" during division, and formation of cellular extensions.

Microtubule

Microtubules, the largest of the cytoskeletal elements, are hollow tubes about 25 nm in diameter, each composed of a ring of 13 protein protofilaments (see figure 4.19). Globular proteins consisting of dimers of α- and β-*tubulin* subunits polymerize to form the 13 protofilaments. The protofilaments are arrayed side by side around a central core, giving the microtubule its characteristic tube shape.

In many cells, microtubules form from nucleation centers near the center of the cell and radiate toward the periphery. They are in a constant state of flux, continually polymerizing and depolymerizing. The average half-life of a microtubule ranges from as long as 10 minutes in a nondividing animal cell to as short as 20 seconds in a dividing animal cell. The ends of the microtubule are designated as plus (+) (away from the nucleation center) or minus (–) (toward the nucleation center).

Along with facilitating cellular movement, microtubules organize the cytoplasm and are responsible for moving materials within the cell itself, as described shortly.

Intermediate filaments

The most durable element of the cytoskeleton in animal cells is a system of tough, fibrous protein molecules twined together in an overlapping arrangement (see figure 4.19). These *intermediate filaments* are characteristically 8 to 10 nm in diameter—between the size of actin filaments and microtubules. Once formed, intermediate filaments are stable and usually do not break down.

Intermediate filaments constitute a mixed group of cytoskeletal fibers. The most common type, composed of protein subunits called *vimentin,* provides structural stability for many kinds of cells. *Keratin,* another class of intermediate filament, is found in epithelial cells (cells that line organs and body cavities) and associated structures such as hair and fingernails. The intermediate filaments of nerve cells are called *neurofilaments.*

Centrosomes are microtubule-organizing centers

Centrioles are barrel-shaped organelles found in the cells of animals and most protists. They occur in pairs, usually located at right angles to each other near the nuclear membranes (figure 4.20). The region surrounding the pair in almost all animal cells is referred to as a *centrosome.* Surrounding the centrioles in the centrosome is the **pericentriolar material,** which contains ring-shaped structures composed of tubulin. The pericentriolar material can nucleate the assembly of microtubules in animal cells. Structures with this function are called *microtubule-organizing centers.* The centrosome is also responsible for the reorganization of microtubules that occurs during

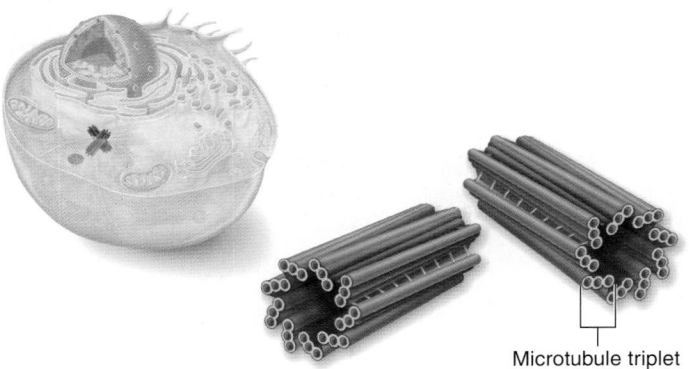

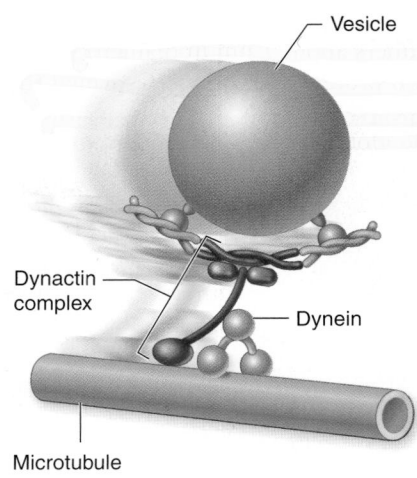

Figure 4.21 Molecular motors. Vesicles can be transported along microtubules using motor proteins that use ATP to generate force. The vesicles are attached to motor proteins by connector molecules, such as the dynactin complex shown here. The motor protein dynein moves the connected vesicle along microtubules.

Figure 4.20 Centrioles. Each centriole is composed of nine triplets of microtubules. Centrioles are usually not found in plant cells. In animal cells they help to organize microtubules.

cell division. The centrosomes of plants and fungi lack centrioles, but still contain microtubule-organizing centers. You will learn more about the actions of the centrosomes when we describe the process of cell division in chapter 10.

The cytoskeleton helps move materials within cells

Actin filaments and microtubules often orchestrate their activities to affect cellular processes. For example, during cell reproduction (see chapter 10), newly replicated chromosomes move to opposite sides of a dividing cell because they are attached to shortening microtubules. Then, in animal cells, a belt of actin pinches the cell in two by contracting like a purse string.

Muscle cells also use actin filaments, which slide along filaments of the motor protein myosin when a muscle contracts. The fluttering of an eyelash, the flight of an eagle, and the awkward crawling of a baby all depend on these cytoskeletal movements within muscle cells.

Not only is the cytoskeleton responsible for the cell's shape and movement, but it also provides a scaffold that holds certain enzymes and other macromolecules in defined areas of the cytoplasm. For example, many of the enzymes involved in cell metabolism bind to actin filaments, as do ribosomes. By moving and anchoring particular enzymes near one another, the cytoskeleton, like the endoplasmic reticulum, helps organize the cell's activities.

Molecular motors

All eukaryotic cells must move materials from one place to another in the cytoplasm. One way cells do this is by using the channels of the endoplasmic reticulum as an intracellular highway. Material can also be moved using vesicles loaded with cargo that can move along the cytoskeleton like a railroad track. For example, in a nerve cell with an axon that may extend far from the cell body, vesicles can be moved along tracks of microtubules from the cell body to the end of the axon.

Four components are required to move material along microtubules: (1) a vesicle or organelle that is to be transported, (2) a motor protein that provides the energy-driven motion, (3) a connector molecule that connects the vesicle to the motor molecule, and (4) microtubules on which the vesicle will ride like a train on a rail (figure 4.21).

The direction a vesicle is moved depends on the type of motor protein involved and the fact that microtubules are organized with their plus ends toward the periphery of the cell. In one case, a protein called kinectin binds vesicles to the motor protein *kinesin*. Kinesin uses ATP to power its movement toward the cell periphery, dragging the vesicle with it as it travels along the microtubule toward the plus end (figure 4.22). As nature's tiniest motors, these proteins pull the transport vesicles along the microtubular tracks. Another set of vesicle proteins, called the dynactin complex, binds vesicles to the motor protein *dynein* (see figure 4.22), which directs movement in the opposite

---

SCIENTIFIC THINKING

Hypothesis: *Kinesin molecules can act as molecular motors and move along microtubules using energy from ATP.*

Test: *A microscope slide is covered with purified kinesin. Purified microtubules are added in a buffer containing ATP. The microtubules are monitored under a microscope using a video recorder to capture any movement.*

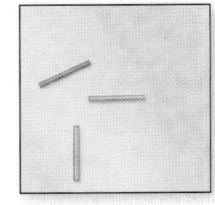 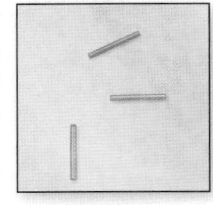 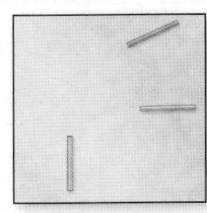

Frame 1   Frame 2   Frame 3

Result: *Over time, the movement of individual microtubules can be observed in the microscope. This is shown schematically in the figure by the movement of specific microtubules shown in color.*

Conclusion: *Kinesin acts as a molecular motor moving along (in this case actually moving) microtubules.*

Further Experiments: *Are there any further controls that are not shown in this experiment? What additional conclusions could be drawn by varying the amount of kinesin sticking to the slide?*

Figure 4.22 Demonstration of kinesin as molecular motor. Microtubules can be observed moving over a slide coated with kinesin.

TABLE 4.2   Eukaryotic Cell Structures and their Functions

Structure		Description	Function
Plasma membrane		Phospholipid bilayer with embedded proteins	Regulates what passes into and out of cell; cell-to-cell recognition; connection and adhesion; cell communication
Nucleus		Structure (usually spherical) that contains chromosomes and is surrounded by double membrane	Instructions for protein synthesis and cell reproduction; contains genetic information
Chromosomes		Long threads of DNA that form a complex with protein	Contain hereditary information used to direct synthesis of proteins
Nucleolus		Site of genes for rRNA synthesis	Synthesis of rRNA and ribosome assembly
Ribosomes		Small, complex assemblies of protein and RNA, often bound to ER	Sites of protein synthesis
Endoplasmic reticulum (ER)		Network of internal membranes	Intracellular compartment forms transport vesicles; participates in lipid synthesis and synthesis of membrane or secreted proteins
Golgi apparatus		Stacks of flattened vesicles	Packages proteins for export from cell; forms secretory vesicles
Lysosomes		Vesicles derived from Golgi apparatus that contain hydrolytic digestive enzymes	Digest worn-out organelles and cell debris; digest material taken up by endocytosis
Microbodies		Vesicles that are formed from incorporation of lipids and proteins and that contain oxidative and other enzymes	Isolate particular chemical activities from rest of cell
Mitochondria		Bacteria-like elements with double membrane	"Power plants" of the cell; sites of oxidative metabolism
Chloroplasts		Bacteria-like elements with double membrane surrounding a third, thylakoid membrane containing chlorophyll, a photosynthetic pigment	Sites of photosynthesis
Cytoskeleton		Network of protein filaments	Structural support; cell movement; movement of vesicles within cells
Flagella (cilia)		Cellular extensions with 9 + 2 arrangement of pairs of microtubles	Motility or moving fluids over surfaces
Cell wall		Outer layer of cellulose or chitin; or absent	Protection; support

direction along microtubules toward the minus end, inward toward the cell's center. (Dynein is also involved in the movement of eukaryotic flagella, as discussed later.) The destination of a particular transport vesicle and its content is thus determined by the nature of the linking protein embedded within the vesicle's membrane.

The major eukaryotic cell structures and their respective functions are summarized in table 4.2.

Learning Outcomes Review 4.6

The three principal fibers of the cytoskeleton are actin filaments (microfilaments), microtubules, and intermediate filaments. These fibers interact to modulate cell shape and permit cell movement. They also act to move materials within the cytoplasm. Material is also moved in large cells using vesicles and molecular motors. The motor proteins move vesicles along tracks of microtubules.

■ *What advantage does the cytoskeleton give to large eukaryotic cells?*

4.7 Extracellular Structures and Cell Movement

Learning Outcomes

1. *Describe how cells move.*
2. *Identify the different cytoskeletal elements involved in cell movement.*
3. *Classify the elements of extracellular matrix in animal cells.*

Essentially all cell motion is tied to the movement of actin filaments, microtubules, or both. Intermediate filaments act as intracellular tendons, preventing excessive stretching of cells. Actin filaments play a major role in determining the shape of cells. Because actin filaments can form and dissolve so readily, they enable some cells to change shape quickly.

Some cells crawl

The arrangement of actin filaments within the cell cytoplasm allows cells to crawl, literally! Crawling is a significant cellular phenomenon, essential to such diverse processes as inflammation, clotting, wound healing, and the spread of cancer. White blood cells in particular exhibit this ability. Produced in the bone marrow, these cells are released into the circulatory system and then eventually crawl out of venules and into the tissues to destroy potential pathogens.

At the leading edge of a crawling cell, actin filaments rapidly polymerize, and their extension forces the edge of the cell forward. This extended region is stabilized when microtubules polymerize into the newly formed region. Overall forward movement of the cell is then achieved through the action of the protein **myosin,** which is best known for its role in muscle contraction. Myosin motors along the actin filaments contract, pulling the contents of the cell toward the newly extended front edge.

Cells crawl when these steps occur continuously, with a leading edge extending and stabilizing, and then motors contracting to pull the remaining cell contents along. Receptors on the cell surface can detect molecules outside the cell and stimulate extension in specific directions, allowing cells to move toward particular targets.

Flagella and cilia aid movement

Earlier in this chapter, we described the structure of prokaryotic flagella. Eukaryotic cells have a completely different kind of flagellum, consisting of a circle of nine microtubule pairs surrounding two central microtubules. This arrangement is referred to as the *9 + 2 structure* (figure 4.23).

As pairs of microtubules move past each other using arms composed of the motor protein dynein, the eukaryotic flagellum *undulates*, rather than rotates. When examined carefully, each flagellum proves to be an outward projection of the cell's interior, containing cytoplasm and enclosed by the plasma membrane. The microtubules of the flagellum are derived from a **basal body,** situated just below the point where the flagellum protrudes from the surface of the cell.

The flagellum's complex microtubular apparatus evolved early in the history of eukaryotes. Today the cells of many

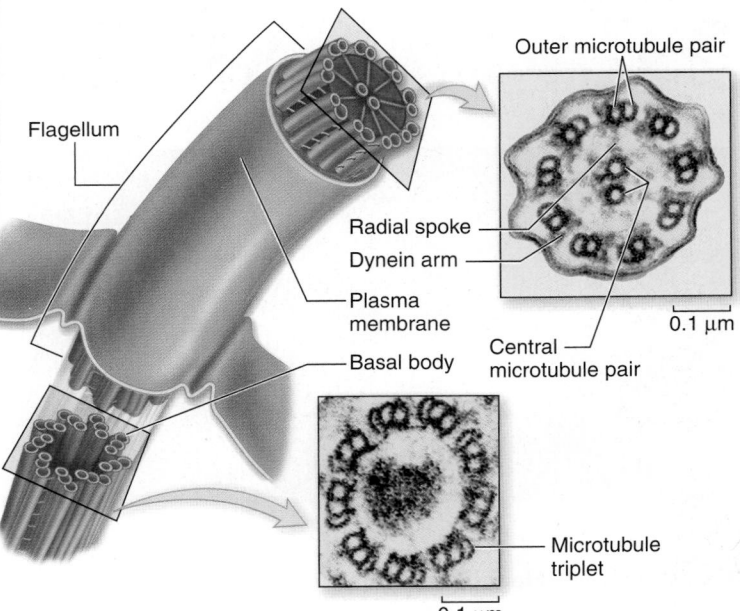

Figure 4.23 Flagella and cilia. A eukaryotic flagellum originates directly from a basal body. The flagellum has two microtubules in its core connected by radial spokes to an outer ring of nine paired microtubules with dynein arms (9 + 2 structure). The basal body consists of nine microtubule triplets connected by short protein segments. The structure of cilia is similar to that of flagella, but cilia are usually shorter.

multicellular and some unicellular eukaryotes no longer possess flagella and are nonmotile. Other structures, called **cilia** (singular, *cilium*), with an organization similar to the 9 + 2 arrangement of microtubules can still be found within them. Cilia are short cellular projections that are often organized in rows. They are more numerous than flagella on the cell surface, but have the same internal structure.

In many multicellular organisms, cilia carry out tasks far removed from their original function of propelling cells through water. In several kinds of vertebrate tissues, for example, the beating of rows of cilia move water over the tissue surface. The sensory cells of the vertebrate ear also contain conventional cilia surrounded by actin-based stereocilia; sound waves bend these structures and provide the initial sensory input for hearing. Thus, the 9 + 2 structure of flagella and cilia appears to be a fundamental component of eukaryotic cells (figure 4.24).

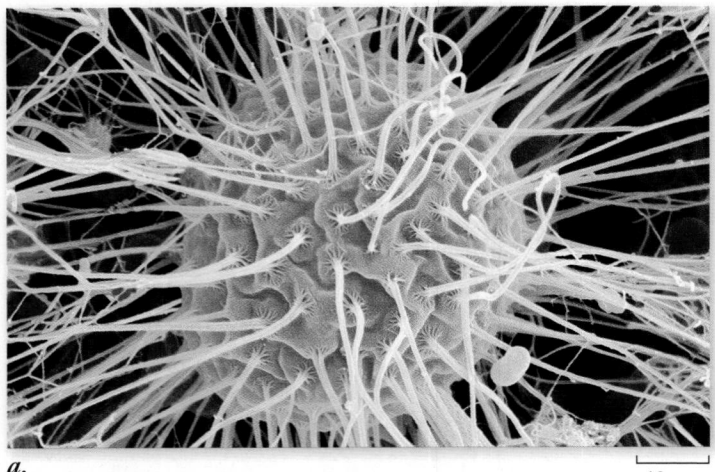

a.   40 μm

b.   66.6 μm

Figure 4.24 Flagella and cilia. *a.* A green alga with numerous flagella that allow it to move through the water. *b.* Paramecia are covered with many cilia, which beat in unison to move the cell. The cilia can also be used to move fluid into the paramecium's mouth to ingest material.

Inquiry question

? The passageways of the human trachea (the path of airflow into and out of the lungs) are known to be lined with ciliated cells. What function could these cilia perform?

Plant cell walls provide protection and support

The cells of plants, fungi, and many types of protists have cell walls, which protect and support the cells. The cell walls of these eukaryotes are chemically and structurally different from prokaryotic cell walls. In plants and protists, the cell walls are composed of fibers of the polysaccharide cellulose, whereas in fungi, the cell walls are composed of chitin.

In plants, **primary walls** are laid down when the cell is still growing. Between the walls of adjacent cells a sticky substance, called the **middle lamella,** glues the cells together (figure 4.25). Some plant cells produce strong **secondary walls,** which are deposited inside the primary walls of fully expanded cells.

Animal cells secrete an extracellular matrix

Animal cells lack the cell walls that encase plants, fungi, and most protists. Instead, animal cells secrete an elaborate mixture of glycoproteins into the space around them, forming

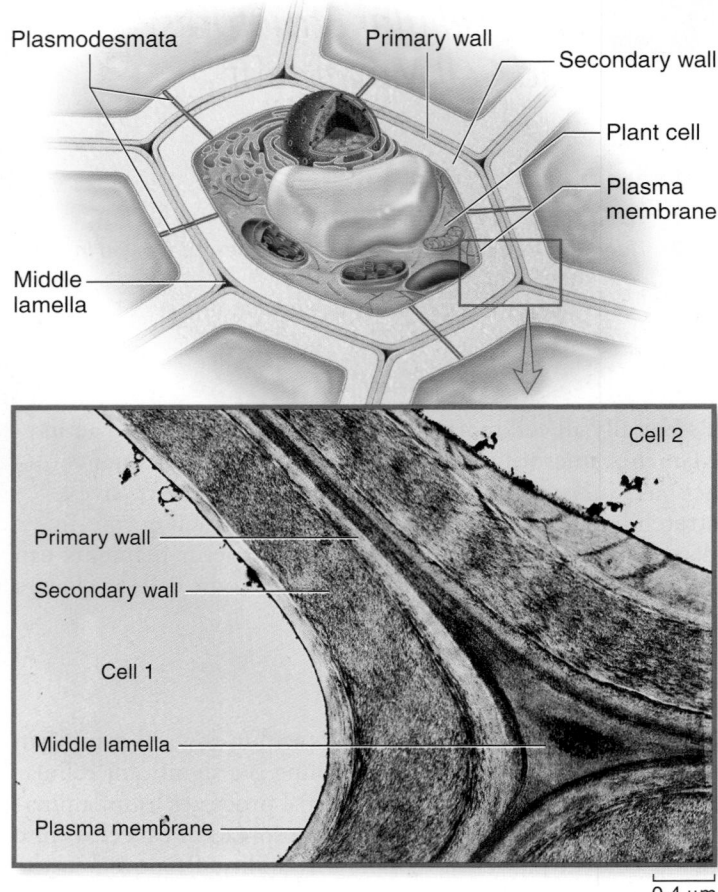

Figure 4.25 Cell walls in plants. Plant cell walls are thick, strong, and rigid. Primary cell walls are laid down when the cell is young. Thicker secondary cell walls may be added later when the cell is fully grown.

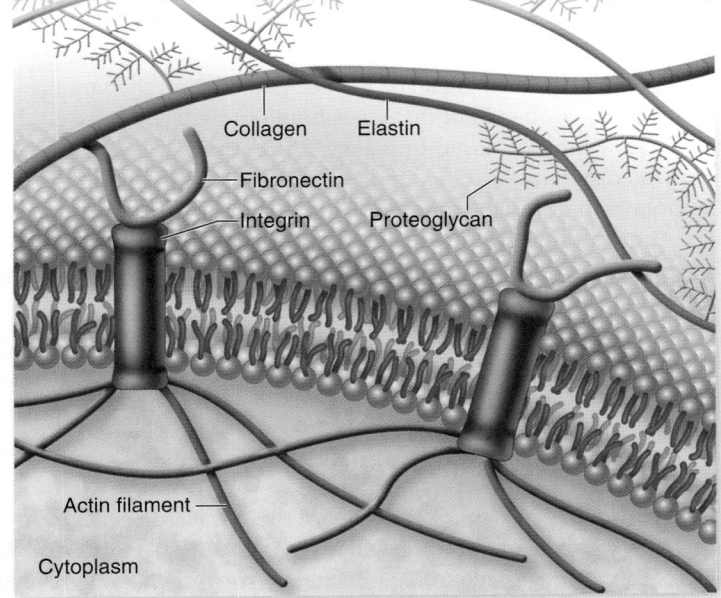

Collagen   Elastin

Fibronectin

Integrin   Proteoglycan

Actin filament

Cytoplasm

Figure 4.26 The extracellular matrix. Animal cells are surrounded by an extracellular matrix composed of various glycoproteins that give the cells support, strength, and resilience.

the *extracellular matrix (ECM)* (figure 4.26). The fibrous protein collagen, the same protein found in cartilage, tendons, and ligaments may be abundant in the ECM. Strong fibers of collagen and another fibrous protein, elastin, are embedded within a complex web of other glycoproteins, called proteoglycans, that form a protective layer over the cell surface.

The ECM of some cells is attached to the plasma membrane by a third kind of glycoprotein, *fibronectin*. Fibronectin molecules bind not only to ECM glycoproteins but also to proteins called **integrins**. Integrins are an integral part of the plasma membrane, extending into the cytoplasm, where they are attached to the microfilaments and intermediate filaments of the cytoskeleton. Linking ECM and cytoskeleton, integrins allow the ECM to influence cell behavior in important ways. They can alter gene expression and cell migration patterns by a combination of mechanical and chemical signaling pathways. In this way, the ECM can help coordinate the behavior of all the cells in a particular tissue.

Table 4.3 compares and reviews the features of three types of cells.

EUKARYOTES

TABLE 4.3	A Comparison of Prokaryotic, Animal, and Plant Cells		
	Prokaryote	**Animal**	**Plant**
EXTERIOR STRUCTURES			
Cell wall	Present (protein-polysaccharide)	Absent	Present (cellulose)
Cell membrane	Present	Present	Present
Flagella/cilia	Flagella may be present	May be present (9 + 2 structure)	Absent except in sperm of a few species (9 + 2 structure)
INTERIOR STRUCTURES			
Endoplasmic reticulum	Absent	Usually present	Usually present
Ribosomes	Present	Present	Present
Microtubules	Absent	Present	Present
Centrioles	Absent	Present	Absent
Golgi apparatus	Absent	Present	Present
Nucleus	Absent	Present	Present
Mitochondria	Absent	Present	Present
Chloroplasts	Absent	Absent	Present
Chromosomes	Single; circle of DNA	Multiple; DNA–protein complex	Multiple; DNA–protein complex
Lysosomes	Absent	Usually present	Present
Vacuoles	Absent	Absent or small	Usually a large single vacuole

4.8 Cell-to-Cell Interactions

Learning Outcomes

1. **Differentiate between types of cell junctions.**
2. **Describe the roles of surface proteins.**

In multicellular organisms, not only must cells be able to communicate with one another, they must also be organized in specific ways. With the exception of a few primitive types of organisms, the hallmark of multicellular life is the organization of highly specialized groups of cells into *tissues*, such as blood and muscle. Remarkably, each cell within a tissue performs the functions of that tissue and no other, even though all cells of the body are derived from a single fertilized cell and contain the same genetic information—all of the genes found in the genome.

This kind of tissue organization requires that cells have both identity and specific kinds of cell-to-cell connections. As an organism develops, the cells acquire their identities by carefully controlling the *expression* of those genes, turning on the specific set of genes that encode the functions of each cell type. How do cells sense where they are? How do they "know" which type of tissue they belong to? Table 4.4 provides a summary of the kinds of connections seen between cells that are explored in the following sections.

Surface proteins give cells identity

One key set of genes functions to mark the surfaces of cells, identifying them as being of a particular type. When cells make contact, they "read" each other's cell surface markers and react accordingly. Cells that are part of the same tissue type recognize each other, and they frequently respond by forming connections between their surfaces to better coordinate their functions.

Glycolipids

Most tissue-specific cell surface markers are glycolipids, that is, lipids with carbohydrate heads. The glycolipids on the surface of red blood cells are also responsible for the A, B, and O blood types.

MHC proteins

One example of the function of cell surface markers is the recognition of "self" and "nonself" cells by the immune system. This function is vital for multicellular organisms, which need to defend themselves against invading or malignant cells. The immune system of vertebrates uses a particular set of markers to distinguish self from nonself cells, encoded by genes of the

TABLE 4.4	Cell-to-Cell Connections and Cell Identity		
Type of Connection	**Structure**	**Function**	**Example**
Surface markers	Variable, integral proteins or glycolipids in plasma membrane	Identify the cell	MHC complexes, blood groups, antibodies
Tight junctions	Tightly bound, leakproof, fibrous protein seal that surrounds cell	Organizing junction; holds cells together such that materials pass *through* but not *between* the cells	Junctions between epithelial cells in the gut
Anchoring junction (Desmosome)	Intermediate filaments of cytoskeleton linked to adjoining cells through cadherins	Anchoring junction; binds cells together	Epithelium
Anchoring junction (Adherens junction)	Transmembrane fibrous proteins	Anchoring junction; connects extracellular matrix to cytoskeleton	Tissues with high mechanical stress, such as the skin
Communicating junction (Gap junction)	Six transmembrane connexon proteins creating a pore that connects cells	Communicating junction; allows passage of small molecules from cell to cell in a tissue	Excitable tissue such as heart muscle
Communicating junction (Plasmodesmata)	Cytoplasmic connections between gaps in adjoining plant cell walls	Communicating junction between plant cells	Plant tissues

major histocompatibility complex (MHC). Cell recognition in the immune system is covered in chapter 52.

Cell connections mediate cell-to-cell adhesion

Most cells in a multicellular organism are in physical contact with other cells at all times, usually as members of organized tissues such as those in a leaf or those in your lungs, heart, or gut. These cells and the mass of other cells clustered around them form long-lasting or permanent connections with one another called *cell junctions.*

The nature of the physical connections between the cells of a tissue in large measure determines what the tissue is like. Indeed, a tissue's proper functioning often depends critically on how the individual cells are arranged within it. Just as a house cannot maintain its structure without nails and cement, so a tissue cannot maintain its characteristic architecture without the appropriate cell junctions.

Cell junctions are divided into three categories, based on their functions: tight, anchoring, and communicating junctions (figure 4.27).

Tight junctions

Tight junctions connect the plasma membranes of adjacent cells in a sheet. This sheet of cells acts as a wall within the organ, keeping molecules on one side or the other (figure 4.27a).

Creating sheets of cells. The cells that line an animal's digestive tract are organized in a sheet only one cell thick. One surface of the sheet faces the inside of the tract, and the other

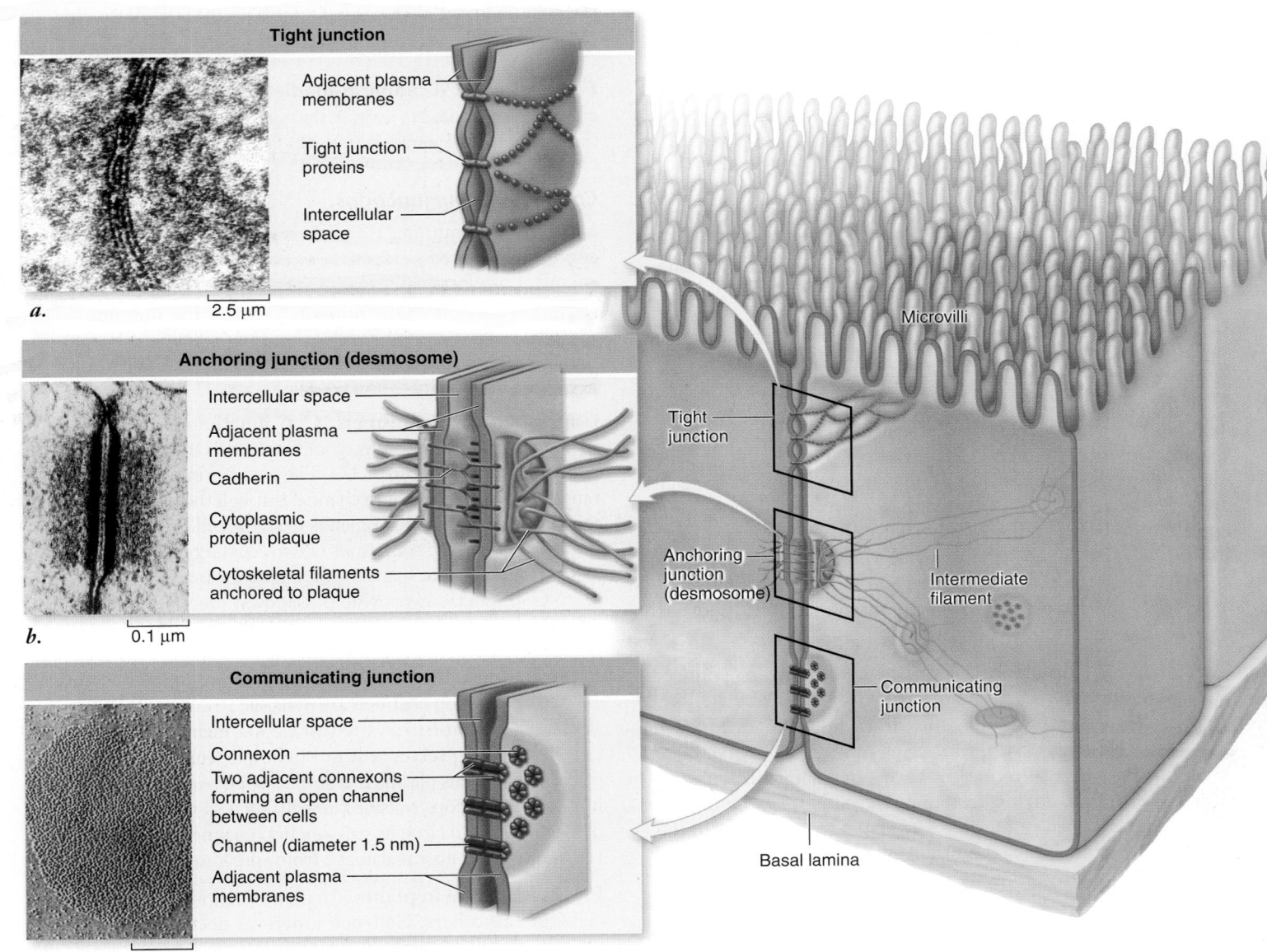

Figure 4.27 An overview of cell junction types. Here, the diagram of gut epithelial cells on the right illustrates the comparative structures and locations of common cell junctions. The detailed models on the left show the structures of the three major types of cell junctions: *(a)* tight junction; *(b)* anchoring junction, the example shown is a desmosome; *(c)* communicating junction, the example shown is a gap junction.

faces the extracellular space, where blood vessels are located. Tight junctions encircle each cell in the sheet, like a belt cinched around a person's waist. The junctions between neighboring cells are so securely attached that there is no space between them for leakage. Hence, nutrients absorbed from the food in the digestive tract must pass directly through the cells in the sheet to enter the bloodstream because they cannot pass through spaces between cells.

Partitioning the sheet. The tight junctions between the cells lining the digestive tract also partition the plasma membranes of these cells into separate compartments. Transport proteins in the membrane facing the inside of the tract carry nutrients from that side to the cytoplasm of the cells. Other proteins, located in the membrane on the opposite side of the cells, transport those nutrients from the cytoplasm to the extracellular fluid, where they can enter the bloodstream.

For the sheet to absorb nutrients properly, these proteins must remain in the correct locations within the fluid membrane. Tight junctions effectively segregate the proteins on opposite sides of the sheet, preventing them from drifting within the membrane from one side of the sheet to the other. When tight junctions are experimentally disrupted, just this sort of migration occurs.

Anchoring junctions

Anchoring junctions mechanically attach the cytoskeleton of a cell to the cytoskeletons of other cells or to the extracellular matrix. These junctions are most common in tissues subject to mechanical stress, such as muscle and skin epithelium.

Cadherin and intermediate filaments. *Desmosomes* connect the cytoskeletons of adjacent cells (figure 4.27b), and *hemidesmosomes* anchor epithelial cells to a basement membrane. Proteins called **cadherins,** most of which are single-pass transmembrane glycoproteins, create the critical link. Proteins link the short cytoplasmic end of a cadherin to the intermediate filaments in the cytoskeleton. The other end of the cadherin molecule projects outward from the plasma membrane, joining directly with a cadherin protruding from an adjacent cell similar to a firm handshake, binding the cells together. Connections between proteins tethered to the intermediate filaments are much more secure than connections between free-floating membrane proteins.

Cadherin and actin filaments. Cadherins can also connect the actin frameworks of cells in cadherin-mediated junctions (figure 4.28). When they do, they form less stable links between cells than when they connect intermediate filaments. Many kinds of actin-linking cadherins occur in different tissues. For example, during vertebrate development, the migration of neurons in the embryo is associated with changes in the type of cadherin expressed on their plasma membranes.

Integrin-mediated links. Anchoring junctions called **adherens junctions** connect the actin filaments of one cell with those of neighboring cells or with the extracellular matrix. The linking proteins in these junctions are members of a large superfamily of cell-surface receptors called integrins that bind to a protein component of the extracellular matrix. At least 20 different integrins exist each with a differently shaped binding domain.

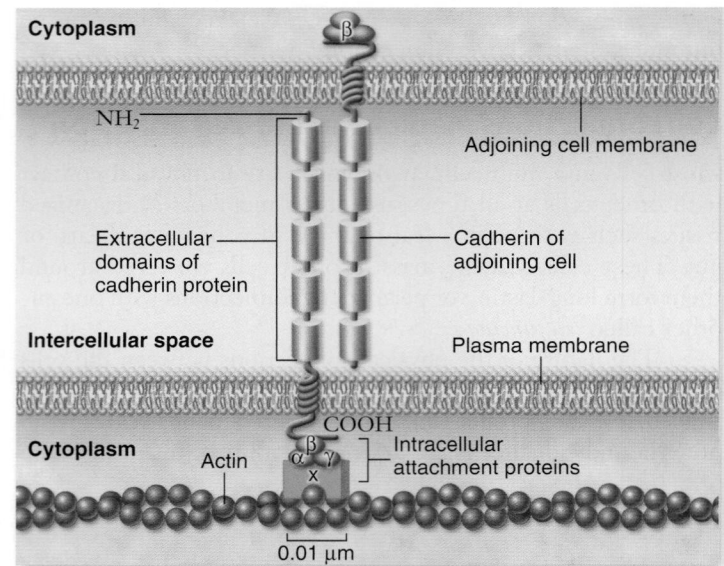

Figure 4.28 A cadherin-mediated junction. The cadherin molecule is anchored to actin in the cytoskeleton and passes through the membrane to interact with the cadherin of an adjoining cell.

Communicating junctions

Many cells communicate with adjacent cells through direct connections called *communicating junctions*. In these junctions, a chemical or electrical signal passes directly from one cell to an adjacent one. Communicating junctions permit small molecules or ions to pass from one cell to the other. In animals, these direct communication channels between cells are called *gap junctions*, and in plants, *plasmodesmata*.

Gap junctions in animals. Gap junctions are composed of structures called connexons, complexes of six identical transmembrane proteins (see figure 4.27c). The proteins in a connexon are arranged in a circle to create a channel through the plasma membrane that protrudes several nanometers from the cell surface. A gap junction forms when the connexons of two cells align perfectly, creating an open channel that spans the plasma membranes of both cells.

Gap junctions provide passageways large enough to permit small substances, such as simple sugars and amino acids, to pass from one cell to the next. Yet the passages are small enough to prevent the passage of larger molecules, such as proteins.

Gap junction channels are dynamic structures that can open or close in response to a variety of factors, including Ca^{2+} and H^+ ions. This gating serves at least one important function. When a cell is damaged, its plasma membrane often becomes leaky. Ions in high concentrations outside the cell, such as Ca^{2+}, flow into the damaged cell and close its gap junction channels. This isolates the cell and so prevents the damage from spreading to other cells.

Plasmodesmata in plants. In plants, cell walls separate every cell from all others. Cell–cell junctions occur only at holes or gaps in the walls, where the plasma membranes of adjacent cells can come into contact with one another. Cytoplasmic connections that form across the touching plasma membranes are called **plasmodesmata** (singular, *plasmodesma*) (figure 4.29). The majority of living cells within a higher plant are connected to their neighbors by these junctions.

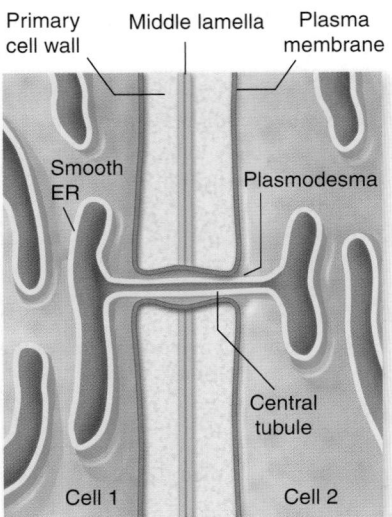

Primary cell wall   Middle lamella   Plasma membrane

Smooth ER

Plasmodesma

Central tubule

Cell 1   Cell 2

Figure 4.29 Plasmodesmata. Plant cells can communicate through specialized openings in their cell walls, called plasmodesmata, where the cytoplasm of adjoining cells are connected.

Plasmodesmata function much like gap junctions in animal cells, although their structure is more complex. Unlike gap junctions, plasmodesmata are lined with plasma membrane and contain a central tubule that connects the endoplasmic reticulum of the two cells.

Chapter Review

4.1 Cell Theory

Cell theory is the unifying foundation of cell biology.
All organisms are composed of one or more cells. Cells arise only by division of preexisting cells.

Cell size is limited.
Cell size is constrained by the diffusion distance. As cell size increases, diffusion becomes inefficient.

Microscopes allow visualization of cells and components.
Magnification gives better resolution than is possible with the naked eye. Staining with chemicals enhances contrast of structures.

All cells exhibit basic structural similarities.
All cells have centrally located DNA, a semifluid cytoplasm, and an enclosing plasma membrane.

4.2 Prokaryotic Cells (see figure 4.3)

Prokaryotic cells have relatively simple organization.
Prokaryotic cells contain DNA and ribosomes, but they lack a nucleus, an internal membrane system, and membrane-bounded organelles. A rigid cell wall surrounds the plasma membrane.

Bacterial cell walls consist of peptidoglycan.
Peptidoglycan is composed of carbohydrate cross-linked with short peptides.

Archaea lack peptidoglycan.
Archaeal cell walls do not contain peptidoglycan, and they have unique plasma membranes.

Some prokaryotes move by means of rotating flagella.
Prokaryotic flagella rotate because of proton transfer across the plasma membrane.

4.3 Eukaryotic Cells (see figures 4.6 and 4.7)
Eukaryotic cells have a membrane-bounded nucleus, an endomembrane system, and many different organelles.

The nucleus acts as the information center.
The nucleus is surrounded by an envelope of two phospholipid bilayers; the outer layer is contiguous with the ER. Pores allow exchange of small molecules. The nucleolus is a region of the nucleoplasm where rRNA is transcribed and ribosomes are assembled.

In most prokaryotes, DNA is organized into a single circular chromosome. In eukaryotes, numerous chromosomes are present.

Ribosomes are the cell's protein synthesis machinery.
Ribosomes translate mRNA to produce polypeptides. They are found in all cell types.

4.4 The Endomembrane System
The endoplasmic reticulum (ER) creates channels and passages within the cytoplasm (see figure 4.10).

The rough ER is a site of protein synthesis.
The rough ER (RER), studded with ribosomes, synthesizes and modifies proteins and manufactures membranes.

The smooth ER has multiple roles.
The smooth endoplasmic reticulum (SER) lacks ribosomes; it is involved in carbohydrate and lipid synthesis and detoxification.

The Golgi apparatus sorts and packages proteins.

The Golgi apparatus receives vesicles from the ER, modifies and packages macromolecules, and transports them (see figure 4.11).

Lysosomes contain digestive enzymes.

Lysosomes break down macromolecules and recycle the components of old organelles (see figure 4.13).

Microbodies are a diverse category of organelles.

Plants use vacuoles for storage and water balance.

4.5 Mitochondria and Chloroplasts: Cellular Generators

Mitochondria and chloroplasts have a double-membrane structure, contain their own DNA, and can divide independently.

Mitochondria metabolize sugar to generate ATP.

The inner membrane of mitochondria is extensively folded into layers called cristae. Proteins on the surface and in the inner membrane carry out metabolism to produce ATP (see figure 4.16).

Chloroplasts use light to generate ATP and sugars.

Chloroplasts capture light energy via thylakoid membranes arranged in stacks called grana, and use it to synthesize glucose (see figure 4.17).

Mitochondria and chloroplasts arose by endosymbiosis.

The endosymbiont theory proposes that mitochondria and chloroplasts were once prokaryotes engulfed by another cell.

4.6 The Cytoskeleton

The cytoskeleton consists of crisscrossed protein fibers that support the shape of the cell and anchor organelles (see figure 4.19).

Three types of fibers compose the cytoskeleton.

Actin filaments, or microfilaments, are long, thin polymers involved in cellular movement. Microtubules are hollow structures that move materials within a cell. Intermediate filaments serve a wide variety of functions.

Centrosomes are microtubule-organizing centers.

Centrosomes help assemble the nuclear division apparatus of animal cells (see figure 4.20).

The cytoskeleton helps move materials within cells.

Molecular motors move vesicles along microtubules, like a train on a railroad track. Kinesin and dynein are two motor proteins.

4.7 Extracellular Structures and Cell Movement

Some cells crawl.

Cell crawling occurs as actin polymerization forces the cell membrane forward, while myosin pulls the cell body forward.

Flagella and cilia aid movement.

Eukaryotic flagella have a 9 + 2 structure and arise from a basal body. Cilia are shorter and more numerous than flagella.

Plant cell walls provide protection and support.

Plants have cell walls composed of cellulose fibers. The middle lamella, between cell walls, holds adjacent cells together.

Animal cells secrete an extracellular matrix.

Glycoproteins are the main component of the extracellular matrix (ECM) of animal cells.

4.8 Cell-to-Cell Interactions (see figure 4.27)

Surface proteins give cells identity.

Glycolipids and MHC proteins on cell surfaces help distinguish self from nonself.

Cell connections mediate cell-to-cell adhesion.

Cell junctions include tight junctions, anchoring junctions, and communicating junctions. In animals, gap junctions allow the passage of small molecules between cells. In plants, plasmodesmata penetrate the cell wall and connect cells.

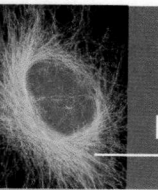

Review Questions

UNDERSTAND

1. Which of the following statements is NOT part of the cell theory?
   a. All organisms are composed of one or more cells.
   b. Cells come from other cells by division.
   c. Cells are the smallest living things.
   d. Eukaryotic cells have evolved from prokaryotic cells.

2. All cells have all of the following except
   a. plasma membrane.   c. cytoplasm.
   b. genetic material.   d. cell wall.

3. Eukaryotic cells are more complex than prokaryotic cells. Which of the following are found only in a eukaryotic cell?
   a. Cell wall
   b. Plasma membrane
   c. Endoplasmic reticulum
   d. Ribosomes

4. Which of the following are differences between bacteria and archaea?
   a. The molecular architecture of their cell walls
   b. The type of ribosomes found in each
   c. Archaea have an internal membrane system that bacteria lack.
   d. Both a and b

5. The cytoskeleton includes
   a. microtubules made of actin filaments.
   b. microfilaments made of tubulin.
   c. intermediate filaments made of twisted fibers of vimentin and keratin.
   d. smooth endoplasmic reticulum.

6. The smooth endoplasmic reticulum is
   a. involved in protein synthesis.
   b. a site of protein glycosylation.
   c. used to store a variety of ions.
   d. the site of lipid and membrane synthesis.

7. Plasmodesmata in plants and gap junctions in animals are functionally similar in that
   a. each is used to anchor layers of cells.
   b. they form channels between cells that allow diffusion of small molecules.
   c. they form tight junctions between cells.
   d. they are anchored to the extracellular matrix.

APPLY

1. The most important factor that limits the size of a cell is the
   a. quantity of proteins and organelles a cell can make.
   b. rate of diffusion of small molecules.
   c. surface area-to-volume ratio of the cell.
   d. amount of DNA in the cell.

2. All eukaryotic cells possess each of the following except
   a. mitochondria.   c. cytoskeleton.
   b. cell wall.   d. nucleus.

3. Which of these organelles is NOT associated with the production or sorting of proteins in a cell?
   a. Ribosomes
   b. Smooth endoplasmic reticulum (SER)
   c. Rough endoplasmic reticulum (RER)
   d. Golgi apparatus

4. Different motor proteins like kinesin and myosin are similar in that they can
   a. interact with microtubules.
   b. use energy from ATP to produce movement.
   c. interact with actin.
   d. do both a and b.

5. The protein sorting pathway involves the following organelles/compartments in order:
   a. SER, RER, transport vesicle, Golgi.
   b. RER, lysosome, Golgi.
   c. RER, transport vesicle, Golgi, final destination.
   d. Golgi, transport vesicle, RER, final destination.

6. Chloroplasts and mitochondria have many common features because both
   a. are present in plant cells.
   b. arose by endosymbiosis.
   c. function to oxidize glucose.
   d. function to produce glucose.

7. Eukaryotic cells are composed of three types of cytoskeletal filaments. How are these three filaments similar?
   a. They contribute to the shape of the cell.
   b. They are all made of the same type of protein.
   c. They are all the same size and shape.
   d. They are all equally dynamic and flexible.

SYNTHESIZE

1. The smooth endoplasmic reticulum is the site of synthesis of the phospholipids that make up all the membranes of a cell—especially the plasma membrane. Use the diagram of an animal cell (see figure 4.6) to trace a pathway that would carry a phospholipid molecule from the SER to the plasma membrane. What endomembrane compartments would the phospholipids travel through? How can a phospholipid molecule move between membrane compartments?

2. Use the information provided in table 4.3 to develop a set of predictions about the properties of mitochondria and chloroplasts if these organelles were once free-living prokaryotic cells. How do your predictions match with the evidence for endosymbiosis?

3. In evolutionary theory, homologous traits are those with a similar structure and function derived from a common ancestor. Analogous traits represent adaptations to a similar environment, but from distantly related organisms. Consider the structure and function of the flagella found on eukaryotic and prokaryotic cells. Are the flagella an example of a homologous or analogous trait? Defend your answer.

4. The protist, *Giardia intestinalis*, is the organism associated with water-borne diarrheal diseases. *Giardia* is an unusual eukaryote because it seems to lack mitochondria. Provide two possible evolutionary scenarios for this in the context of the endosymbiotic theory.

ONLINE RESOURCE

www.ravenbiology.com

Understand, Apply, and Synthesize—enhance your study with animations that bring concepts to life and practice tests to assess your understanding. Your instructor may also recommend the interactive eBook, individualized learning tools, and more.

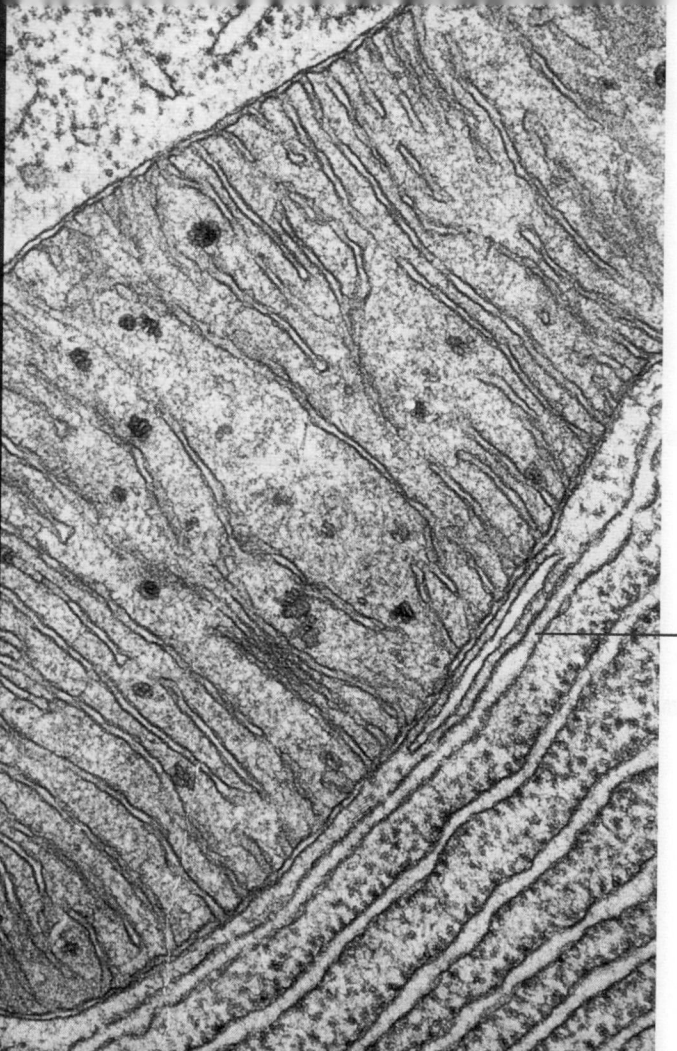

0.16 µm

Chapter 5

Membranes

Chapter Outline

5.1 The Structure of Membranes

5.2 Phospholipids: The Membrane's Foundation

5.3 Proteins: Multifunctional Components

5.4 Passive Transport Across Membranes

5.5 Active Transport Across Membranes

5.6 Bulk Transport by Endocytosis and Exocytosis

Introduction

A cell's interactions with the environment are critical, a give-and-take that never ceases. Without it, life could not exist. Living cells are encased within a lipid membrane through which few water-soluble substances can pass. The membrane also contains protein passageways that permit specific substances to move into and out of the cell and allow the cell to exchange information with its environment. Eukaryotic cells also contain internal membranes like those of the mitochondrion and endoplasmic reticulum pictured here. We call the delicate skin of lipids with embedded protein molecules that encase the cell a plasma membrane. *This chapter examines the structure and function of this remarkable membrane.*

5.1 The Structure of Membranes

Learning Outcomes

1. Describe the components of biological membranes.
2. Explain the fluid mosaic model of membrane structure.

The membranes that encase all living cells are two phospholipid sheets that are only 5–10 nanometers thick; more than 10,000 of these sheets piled on one another would just equal the thickness of this sheet of paper. Biologists established the components of membranes—not only lipids, but also proteins and other molecules—through biochemical assays, but the organization of the membrane components remained elusive.

We begin by considering the theories that have been advanced about membrane structure. We then look at the individual components of membranes more closely.

The fluid mosaic model shows proteins embedded in a fluid lipid bilayer

The lipid layer that forms the foundation of a cell's membranes is a bilayer formed of **phospholipids** (figure 5.1). For many years, biologists thought that the protein components of the cell membrane covered the inner and outer surfaces of the phospholipid bilayer like a coat of paint. An early model portrayed the membrane as a sandwich; a phospholipid bilayer between two layers of globular protein.

In 1972, S. Jonathan Singer and Garth J. Nicolson revised the model in a simple but profound way: They proposed that the globular proteins are *inserted* into the lipid bilayer, with their nonpolar segments in contact with the nonpolar interior of the bilayer and their polar portions protruding out from the membrane surface. In this model, called the *fluid mosaic model*, a mosaic of proteins floats in or on the fluid lipid bilayer like boats on a pond (figure 5.2).

We now recognize two categories of membrane proteins based on their association with the membrane. *Integral membrane proteins* are embedded in the membrane, and *peripheral proteins* are associated with the surface of the membrane.

Cellular membranes consist of four component groups

A eukaryotic cell contains many membranes. Although they are not all identical, they share the same fundamental architecture. Cell membranes are assembled from four components (table 5.1):

1. **Phospholipid bilayer.** Every cell membrane is composed of phospholipids in a bilayer. The other components of the membrane are embedded within the bilayer, which provides a flexible matrix and, at the same time, imposes a barrier to permeability. Animal cell membranes also contain cholesterol, a steroid with a polar hydroxyl group (—OH). Plant cells have a much lower cholesterol content.

2. **Transmembrane proteins.** A major component of every membrane is a collection of proteins that float in the lipid bilayer. These proteins have a variety of functions, including transport and communication across the membrane. Many integral membrane proteins are not fixed in position. They can move about, just as the phospholipid molecules do. Some membranes are

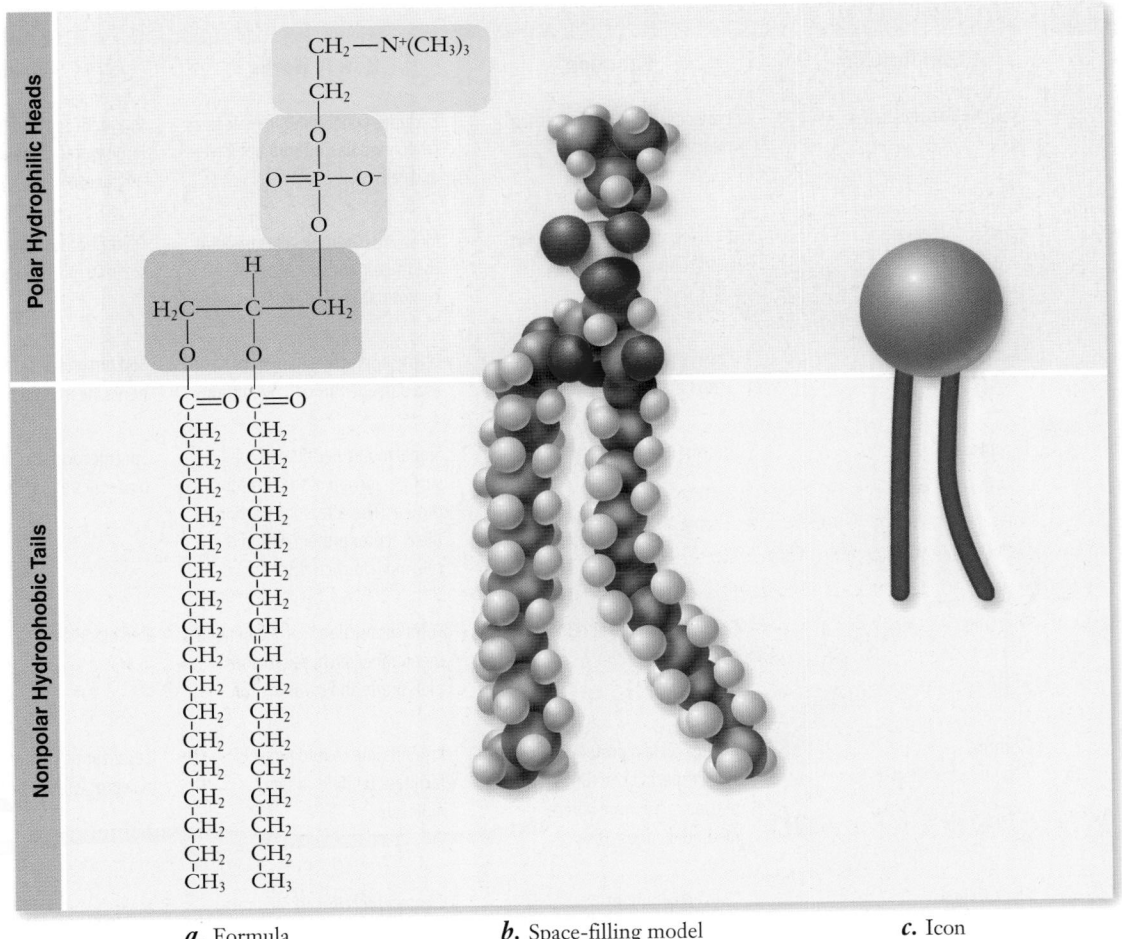

a. Formula   *b.* Space-filling model   *c.* Icon

Figure 5.1 Different views of phospholipid structure. Phospholipids are composed of glycerol (*pink*) linked to two fatty acids and a phosphate group. The phosphate group (*yellow*) can have additional molecules attached, such as the positively charged choline (*green*) shown. Phosphatidylcholine is a common component of membranes, it is shown in (*a*) with its chemical formula, (*b*) as a space-filling model, and (*c*) as the icon that is used in most of the figures in this chapter.

Figure 5.2 The fluid mosaic model of cell membranes.

Integral proteins protrude through the plasma membrane, with nonpolar regions that tether them to the membrane's hydrophobic interior. Carbohydrate chains are often bound to the extracellular portion of these proteins, forming glycoproteins. Peripheral membrane proteins are associated with the surface of the membrane. Membrane phospholipids can be modified by the addition of carbohydrates to form glycolipids. Inside the cell, actin filaments and intermediate filaments interact with membrane proteins. Outside the cell, many animal cells have an elaborate extracellular matrix composed primarily of glycoproteins.

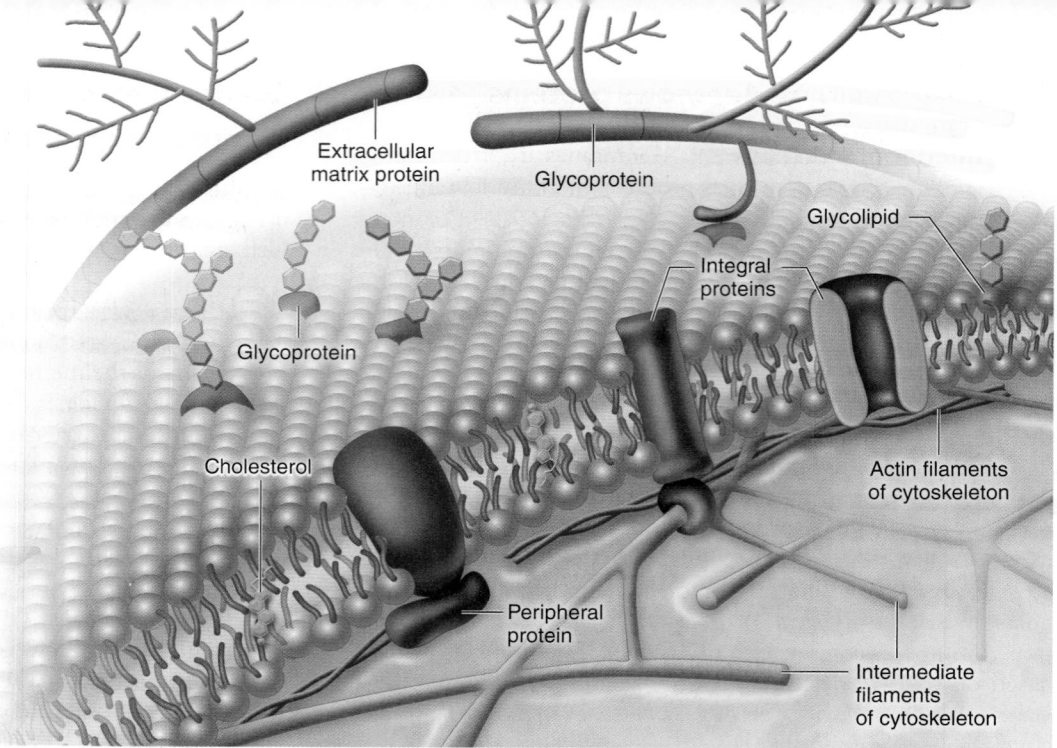

TABLE 5.1	Components of the Cell Membrane			
Component	**Composition**	**Function**	**How It Works**	**Example**
Phospholipid bilayer	Phospholipid molecules	Provides permeability barrier, matrix for proteins	Excludes water-soluble molecules from nonpolar interior of bilayer and cell	Bilayer of cell is impermeable to large water-soluble molecules, such as glucose
Transmembrane proteins	Carriers	Actively or passively transport molecules across membrane	Move specific molecules through the membrane in a series of conformational changes	Glycophorin carrier for sugar transport; sodium–potassium pump
	Channels	Passively transport molecules across membrane	Create a selective tunnel that acts as a passage through membrane	Sodium and potassium channels in nerve, heart, and muscle cells
	Receptors	Transmit information into cell	Signal molecules bind to cell-surface portion of the receptor protein. This alters the portion of the receptor protein within the cell, inducing activity	Specific receptors bind peptide hormones and neurotransmitters
Interior protein network	Spectrins	Determine shape of cell	Form supporting scaffold beneath membrane, anchored to both membrane and cytoskeleton	Red blood cell
	Clathrins	Anchor certain proteins to specific sites, especially on the exterior plasma membrane in receptor-mediated endocytosis	Proteins line coated pits and facilitate binding to specific molecules	Localization of low-density lipoprotein receptor within coated pits
Cell-surface markers	Glycoproteins	"Self" recognition	Create a protein/carbohydrate chain shape characteristic of individual	Major histocompatibility complex protein recognized by immune system
	Glycolipid	Tissue recognition	Create a lipid/carbohydrate chain shape characteristic of tissue	A, B, O blood group markers

crowded with proteins, but in others, the proteins are more sparsely distributed.

3. **Interior protein network.** Membranes are structurally supported by intracellular proteins that reinforce the membrane's shape. For example, a red blood cell has a characteristic biconcave shape because a scaffold made of a protein called spectrin links proteins in the plasma membrane with actin filaments in the cell's cytoskeleton.

   Membranes use networks of other proteins to control the lateral movements of some key membrane proteins, anchoring them to specific sites.

4. **Cell-surface markers.** As you learned in the preceding chapter, membrane sections assemble in the endoplasmic reticulum, transfer to the Golgi apparatus, and then are transported to the plasma membrane. The ER adds chains of sugar molecules to membrane proteins and lipids, converting them into **glycoproteins** and **glycolipids.** Different cell types exhibit different varieties of these glycoproteins and glycolipids on their surfaces, which act as cell identity markers.

Originally, it was believed that because of its fluidity, the plasma membrane was uniform, with lipids and proteins free to diffuse rapidly in the plane of the membrane. However, in the last decade evidence has accumulated suggesting the plasma membrane is not homogeneous and contains microdomains with distinct lipid and protein composition. One type of microdomain, the *lipid raft*, is heavily enriched with cholesterol, which fills space between the phospholipids, packing them more tightly together than the surrounding membrane.

Although the distribution of membrane lipids is symmetrical in the ER where they are synthesized, this distribution is asymmetrical in the plasma membrane, Golgi apparatus, and endosomes. This is accomplished by enzymes that transport lipids across the bilayer from one face to the other.

Electron microscopy has provided structural evidence

Electron microscopy allows biologists to examine the delicate, filmy structure of a cell membrane. We discussed two types of electron microscopes in chapter 4: the transmission electron microscope (TEM) and the scanning electron microscope (SEM). Both provide illuminating views of membrane structure.

When examining cell membranes with electron microscopy, specimens must be prepared for viewing. In one method of preparing a specimen, the tissue of choice is embedded in a hard epoxy matrix. The epoxy block is then cut with a microtome, a machine with a very sharp blade that makes incredibly thin, transparent "epoxy shavings" less than 1 μm thick that peel away from the block of tissue.

These shavings are placed on a grid, and a beam of electrons is directed through the grid with the TEM. At the high magnification an electron microscope provides, resolution is good enough to reveal the double layers of a membrane. False color can be added to the micrograph to enhance detail.

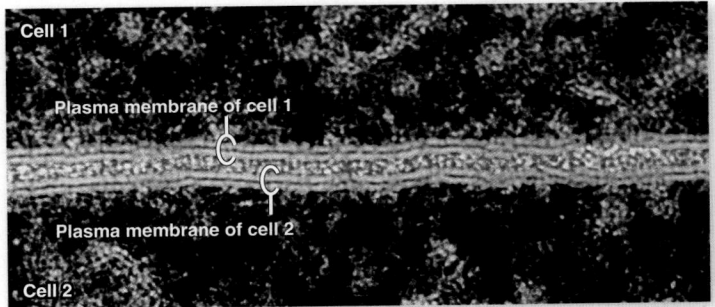

Cell 1
Plasma membrane of cell 1
Plasma membrane of cell 2
Cell 2

0.038 μm

Freeze-fracturing a specimen is another way to visualize the inside of the membrane (figure 5.3). The tissue is embedded

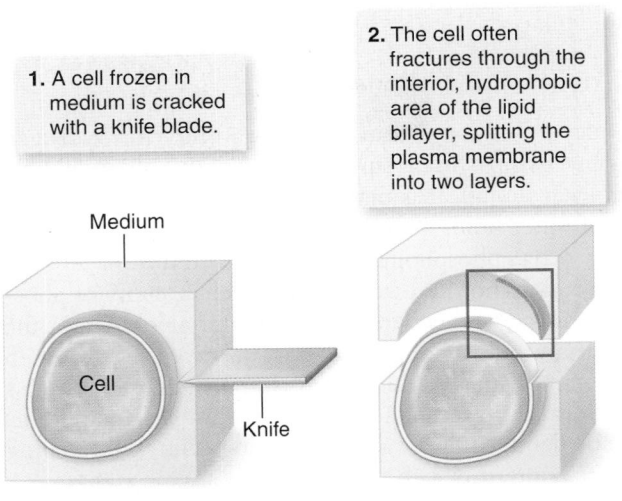

1. A cell frozen in medium is cracked with a knife blade.

2. The cell often fractures through the interior, hydrophobic area of the lipid bilayer, splitting the plasma membrane into two layers.

Medium

Cell

Knife

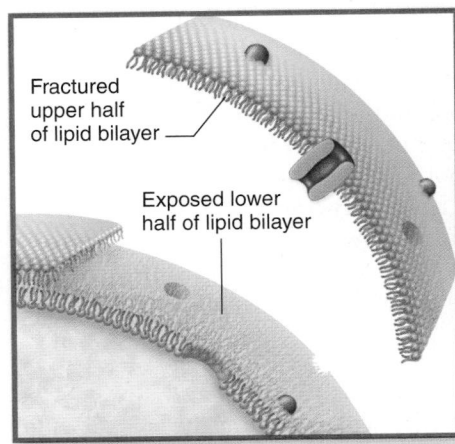

3. The plasma membrane separates such that proteins and other embedded membrane structures remain within one or the other layers of the membrane.

Fractured upper half of lipid bilayer

Exposed lower half of lipid bilayer

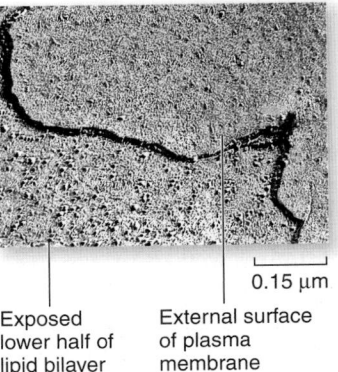

4. The exposed membrane is coated with platinum, which forms a replica of the membrane. The underlying membrane is dissolved away, and the replica is then viewed with electron microscopy.

0.15 μm

Exposed lower half of lipid bilayer

External surface of plasma membrane

Figure 5.3 Viewing a plasma membrane with freeze-fracture microscopy.

in a medium and quick frozen with liquid nitrogen. The frozen tissue is then "tapped" with a knife, causing a crack between the phospholipid layers of membranes. Proteins, carbohydrates, pits, pores, channels, or any other structure affiliated with the membrane will pull apart (whole, usually) and stick with one or the other side of the split membrane.

Next, a very thin coating of platinum is evaporated onto the fractured surface, forming a replica or "cast" of the surface. After the topography of the membrane has been preserved in the cast, the actual tissue is dissolved away, and the cast is examined with electron microscopy, creating a textured and three-dimensional view of the membrane.

Learning Outcomes Review 5.1

Cellular membranes contain four components: (1) a phospholipid bilayer, (2) transmembrane proteins, (3) an internal protein network providing structural support, and (4) cell-surface markers composed of glycoproteins and glycolipids. The fluid mosaic model of membrane structure includes both the fluid nature of the membrane and the mosaic composition of proteins floating in the phospholipid bilayer. Transmission electron microscopy (TEM) and scanning electron microscopy (SEM) have provided evidence supporting the fluid mosaic model.

■ *If the plasma membrane were just a phospholipid bilayer, how would this affect its function?*

5.2 Phospholipids: The Membrane's Foundation

Learning Outcomes

1. **List the different components of phospholipids.**
2. **Explain how membranes form spontaneously.**
3. **Describe the factors involved in membrane fluidity.**

Like the fat molecules (triglycerides) described in chapter 3, a phospholipid has a backbone derived from the three-carbon polyalcohol *glycerol*. Attached to this backbone are one to three fatty acids, long chains of carbon atoms ending in a carboxyl (—COOH) group. A triglyceride molecule has three such chains, one attached to each carbon in the backbone. Because these chains are nonpolar, they do not form hydrogen bonds with water, and triglycerides are not water-soluble.

A phospholipid, by contrast, has only two fatty acid chains attached to its backbone. The third carbon of the glycerol carries a phosphate group, thus the name *phospho*lipid. An additional polar organic molecule is often added to the phosphate group as well.

From this simple molecular framework, a large variety of lipids can be constructed by varying the polar organic group attached to the phosphate and the fatty acid chains attached to the glycerol. Mammalian membranes, for example, contain hundreds of chemically distinct species of lipids.

Phospholipids spontaneously form bilayers

The phosphate groups are charged, and other molecules attached to them are polar or charged. This creates a huge change in the molecule's physical properties compared with a triglyceride. The strongly polar phosphate end is hydrophilic, or "water-loving," while the fatty acid end is strongly nonpolar and hydrophobic, or "water-fearing." The two nonpolar fatty acids extend in one direction, roughly parallel to each other, and the polar phosphate group points in the other direction. To represent this structure, phospholipids are often diagrammed as a polar head with two dangling nonpolar tails, as in figure 5.1c.

What happens when a collection of phospholipid molecules is placed in water? The polar water molecules repel the long, nonpolar tails of the phospholipids while seeking partners for hydrogen bonding. Because of the polar nature of the water molecules, the nonpolar tails of the phospholipids end up packed closely together, sequestered as far as possible from water. Every phospholipid molecule is oriented with its polar head toward water and its nonpolar tails away. When *two* layers form with the tails facing each other, no tails ever come in contact with water. The resulting structure is the phospholipid bilayer. Phospholipid bilayers form spontaneously, driven by the tendency of water molecules to form the maximum number of hydrogen bonds.

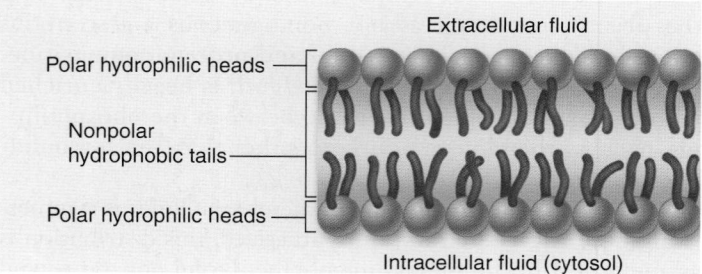

The nonpolar interior of a lipid bilayer impedes the passage of any water-soluble substances through the bilayer, just as a layer of oil impedes the passage of a drop of water. This barrier to water-soluble substances is the key biological property of the lipid bilayer.

The phospholipid bilayer is fluid

A lipid bilayer is stable because water's affinity for hydrogen bonding never stops. Just as surface tension holds a soap bubble together, even though it is made of a liquid, so the hydrogen bonding of water holds a membrane together. Although water continually drives phospholipid molecules into the bilayer configuration, it does not have any effect on the mobility of phospholipids relative to their lipid and nonlipid neighbors in the bilayer. Because phospholipids interact relatively weakly with one another, individual phospholipids and unanchored proteins are comparatively free to move about within the membrane. This can be demonstrated vividly by fusing cells and watching their proteins intermix with time (figure 5.4).

Membrane fluidity can change

The degree of membrane fluidity changes with the composition of the membrane itself. Much like triglycerides can be solid or liquid at room temperature, depending on their fatty acid

Hypothesis: *The plasma membrane is fluid, not rigid.*

Prediction: *If the membrane is fluid, membrane proteins may diffuse laterally.*

Test: *Fuse mouse and human cells, then observe the distribution of membrane proteins over time by labeling specific mouse and human proteins.*

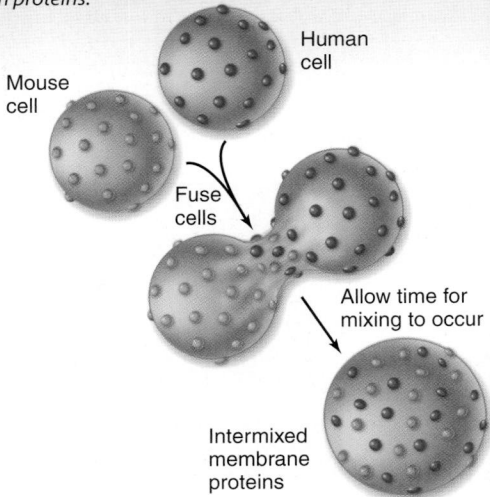

Mouse cell

Human cell

Fuse cells

Allow time for mixing to occur

Intermixed membrane proteins

Result: *Over time, hybrid cells show increasingly intermixed proteins.*

Conclusion: *At least some membrane proteins can diffuse laterally in the membrane.*

Further Experiments: *Can you think of any other explanation for these observations? What if newly synthesized proteins were inserted into the membrane during the experiment? How could you use this basic experimental design to rule out this or other possible explanations?*

Figure 5.4 **Test of membrane fluidity.**

composition, membrane fluidity can be altered by changing the membrane's fatty acid composition.

Saturated fats tend to make the membrane less fluid because they pack together well. Unsaturated fats make the membrane more fluid—the "kinks" introduced by the double bonds keep them from packing tightly. You saw this effect on fats and oils earlier in chapter 3. Most membranes also contain sterols such as cholesterol, which can either increase or decrease membrane fluidity, depending on the temperature.

Changes in the environment can have drastic effects on the membranes of single-celled organisms such as bacteria. Increasing temperature makes a membrane more fluid, and decreasing temperature makes it less fluid. Bacteria have evolved mechanisms to maintain a constant membrane fluidity despite fluctuating temperatures. Some bacteria contain enzymes called *fatty acid desaturases* that can introduce double bonds into fatty acids in membranes. Genetic studies, involving either the inactivation of these enzymes or the introduction of them into cells that normally lack them, indicate that the action of these enzymes confers cold tolerance. At colder temperatures, the double bonds introduced by fatty acid desaturase make the membrane more fluid, counteracting the environmental effect of reduced temperature.

Learning Outcomes Review 5.2

Biological membranes consist of a phospholipid bilayer. Each phospholipid has a hydrophilic (phosphate) head and a hydrophobic (lipid) tail. In water, phospholipid molecules spontaneously form a bilayer, with phosphate groups facing out toward the water and lipid tails facing in, where they are sequestered from water. Membrane fluidity varies with composition and conditions: unsaturated fats disturb packing of the lipid tails and make the membrane more fluid, as do higher temperatures.

■ *Would a phospholipid bilayer form in a nonpolar solvent?*

5.3 *Proteins: Multifunctional Components*

Learning Outcomes

1. *List the functions of membrane proteins.*
2. *Explain how proteins can associate with the membrane.*
3. *Identify a transmembrane domain.*

Cell membranes contain a complex assembly of proteins enmeshed in the fluid soup of phospholipid molecules. This very flexible organization permits a broad range of interactions with the environment, some directly involving membrane proteins.

Proteins and protein complexes perform key functions

Although cells interact with their environment through their plasma membranes in many ways, we will focus on six key classes of membrane protein in this chapter and in chapter 9 (figure 5.5).

1. **Transporters.** Membranes are very selective, allowing only certain solutes to enter or leave the cell, either through channels or carriers composed of proteins.
2. **Enzymes.** Cells carry out many chemical reactions on the interior surface of the plasma membrane, using enzymes attached to the membrane.
3. **Cell-surface receptors.** Membranes are exquisitely sensitive to chemical messages, which are detected by receptor proteins on their surfaces.
4. **Cell-surface identity markers.** Membranes carry cell-surface markers that identify them to other cells. Most cell types carry their own ID tags, specific combinations of cell-surface proteins and protein complexes such as glycoproteins that are characteristic of that cell type.
5. **Cell-to-cell adhesion proteins.** Cells use specific proteins to glue themselves to one another. Some act by forming temporary interactions, and others form a more permanent bond. (See chapter 9.)
6. **Attachments to the cytoskeleton.** Surface proteins that interact with other cells are often anchored to the cytoskeleton by linking proteins.

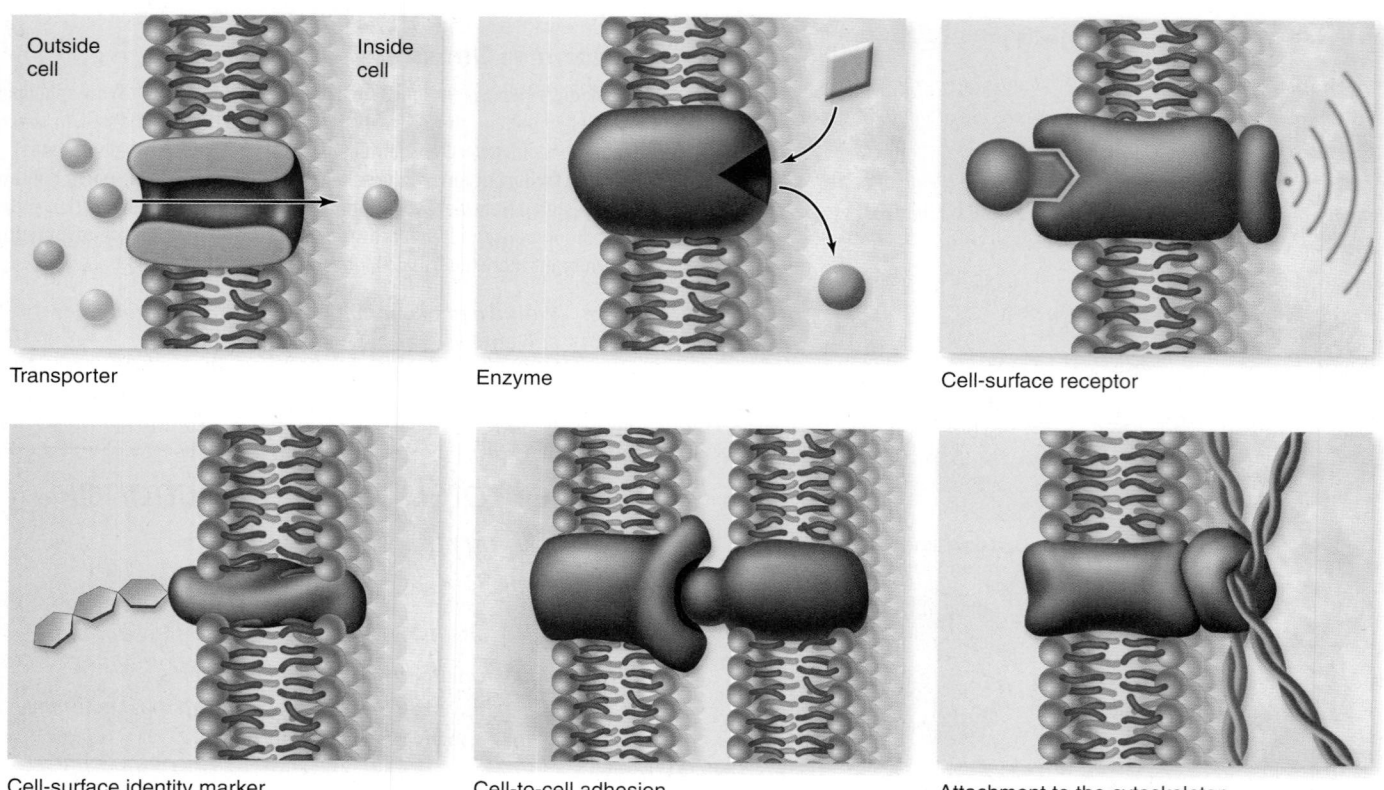

Outside cell · Inside cell

Transporter

Enzyme

Cell-surface receptor

Cell-surface identity marker

Cell-to-cell adhesion

Attachment to the cytoskeleton

Figure 5.5 Functions of plasma membrane proteins. Membrane proteins act as transporters, enzymes, cell-surface receptors, and cell-surface identity markers, as well as aiding in cell-to-cell adhesion and securing the cytoskeleton.

Inquiry question

? According to the fluid mosaic model, membranes are held together by hydrophobic interactions. Considering the forces that some cells may experience, why do membranes not break apart every time an animal moves?

Structural features of membrane proteins relate to function

As we've just detailed, membrane proteins can serve a variety of functions. These diverse functions arise from the diverse structures of these proteins, yet they also have common structural features related to their role as membrane proteins.

The anchoring of proteins in the bilayer

Some membrane proteins are attached to the surface of the membrane by special molecules that associate strongly with phospholipids. Like a ship tied to a floating dock, these anchored proteins are free to move about on the surface of the membrane tethered to a phospholipid. The anchoring molecules are modified lipids that have (1) nonpolar regions that insert into the internal portion of the lipid bilayer and (2) chemical bonding domains that link directly to proteins.

Protein anchored to phospholipid

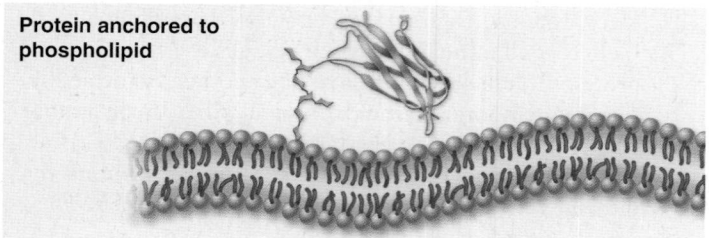

In contrast, other proteins actually span the lipid bilayer (transmembrane proteins). The part of the protein that extends through the lipid bilayer and that is in contact with the nonpolar interior are α-helices or β-pleated sheets (see chapter 3) that consist of nonpolar amino acids. Because water avoids nonpolar amino acids, these portions of the protein are held within the interior of the lipid bilayer. The polar ends protrude from both sides of the membrane. Any movement of the protein out of the membrane, in either direction, brings the nonpolar regions of the protein into contact with water, which "shoves" the protein back into the interior. These forces prevent the transmembrane proteins from simply popping out of the membrane and floating away.

Transmembrane domains

Cell membranes contain a variety of different transmembrane proteins, which differ in the way they traverse the lipid bilayer. The primary difference lies in the number of times that the protein crosses the membrane. Each membrane-spanning region is called a **transmembrane domain.** These domains are composed of hydrophobic amino acids usually arranged into α helices (figure 5.6).

Proteins need only a single transmembrane domain to be anchored in the membrane, but they often have more than one such domain. An example of a protein with a single transmembrane domain is the linking protein that attaches the spectrin network of the cytoskeleton to the interior of the plasma membrane.

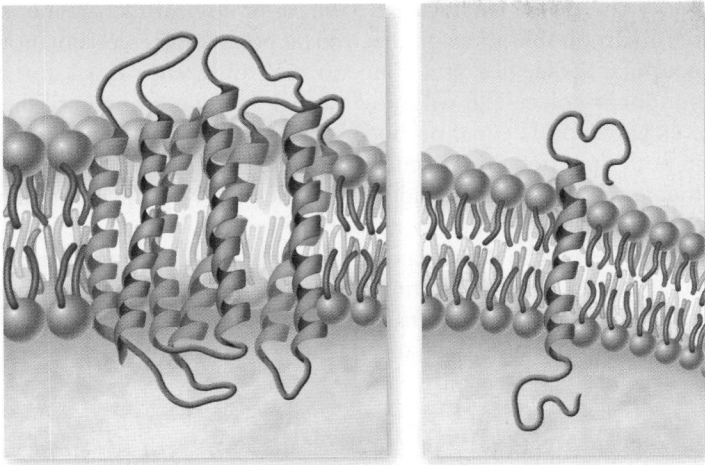

a.   *b.*

Figure 5.6 Transmembrane domains. Integral membrane proteins have at least one hydrophobic transmembrane domain (shown in blue) to anchor them in the membrane. *a.* Receptor protein with seven transmembrane domains. *b.* Protein with single transmembrane domain.

Biologists classify some types of receptors based on the number of transmembrane domains they have, such as G protein–coupled receptors with seven membrane-spanning domains (chapter 9). These receptors respond to external molecules, such as epinephrine, and initiate a cascade of events inside the cell.

Another example is bacteriorhodopsin, one of the key transmembrane proteins that carries out photosynthesis in halophilic (salt-loving) archaea. It contains seven nonpolar helical segments that traverse the membrane, forming a structure within the membrane through which protons pass during the light-driven pumping of protons (figure 5.7).

Pores

Some transmembrane proteins have extensive nonpolar regions with secondary configurations of β-pleated sheets instead of α helices (chapter 3). The β sheets form a characteristic motif, folding back and forth in a cylinder so the sheets arrange themselves like a pipe through the membrane. This forms a polar environment in the interior of the β sheets spanning the membrane. This so-called *β barrel*, open on both ends, is a common feature of the porin class of proteins that are found within the outer membrane of some bacteria. The openings allow molecules to pass through the membrane (figure 5.8).

Learning Outcomes Review 5.3

Proteins in the membrane confer the main differences between membranes of different cells. Their functions include transport, enzymatic action, reception of extracellular signals, cell-to-cell interactions, and cell identity markers. Peripheral proteins can be anchored in the membrane by modified lipids. Integral membrane proteins span the membrane and have one or more hydrophobic regions, called transmembrane domains, that anchor them.

■ *Why are transmembrane domains hydrophobic?*

Inquiry question

? Based only on amino acid sequence, how would you recognize an integral membrane protein?

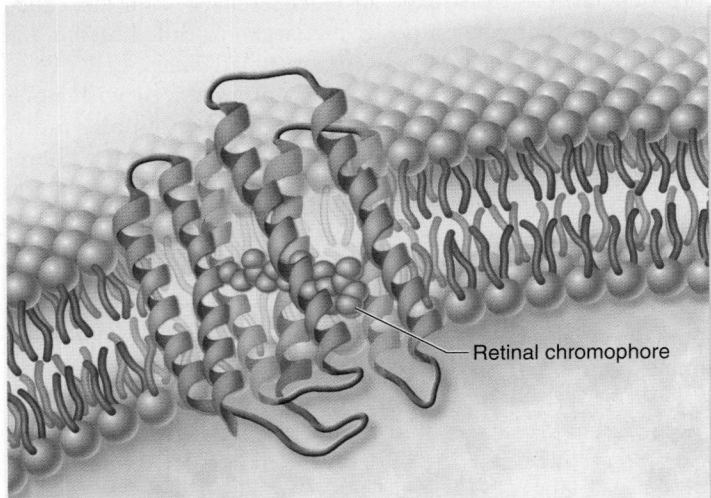

Figure 5.7 Bacteriorhodopsin. This transmembrane protein mediates photosynthesis in the archaean *Halobacterium salinarium*. The protein traverses the membrane seven times with hydrophobic helical strands that are within the hydrophobic center of the lipid bilayer. The helical regions form a structure across the bilayer through which protons are pumped by the retinal chromophore *(green)* using energy from light.

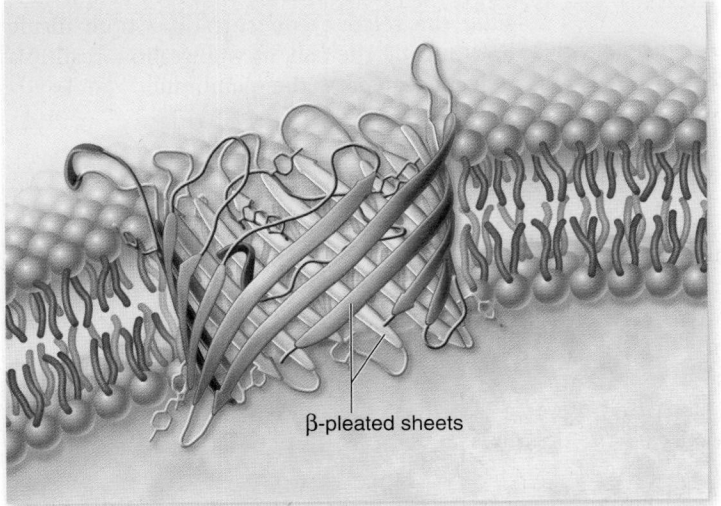

Figure 5.8 A pore protein. The bacterial transmembrane protein porin creates large open tunnels called pores in the outer membrane of a bacterium. Sixteen strands of β-pleated sheets run antiparallel to one another, creating a so-called β barrel in the bacterial outer cell membrane. The tunnel allows water and other materials to pass through the membrane.

Passive Transport Across Membranes

Learning Outcomes

1. *Compare simple diffusion and facilitated diffusion.*
2. *Differentiate between channel proteins and carrier proteins.*
3. *Explain the movement of water by osmosis.*

Many substances can move in and out of the cell without the cell's having to expend energy. This type of movement is termed **passive transport.** Some ions and molecules can pass through the membrane fairly easily and do so because of a *concentration gradient*—a difference between the concentration on the inside of the membrane and that on the outside. Some substances also move in response to a gradient, but do so through specific channels formed by proteins in the membrane.

Transport can occur by simple diffusion

Molecules and ions dissolved in water are in constant random motion. This random motion causes a net movement of these substances from regions of high concentration to regions of lower concentration, a process called **diffusion** (figure 5.9).

Net movement driven by diffusion will continue until the concentration is the same in all regions. Consider what happens when you add a drop of colored ink to a bowl of water. Over time the ink becomes dispersed throughout the solution. This is due to diffusion of the ink molecules. In the context of cells, we are usually concerned with differences in concentration of molecules across the plasma membrane. We need to consider the relative concentrations both inside and outside the cell, as well as how readily a molecule can cross the membrane.

Figure 5.9 Diffusion. If a drop of colored ink is dropped into a beaker of water (*a*) its molecules dissolve (*b*) and diffuse (*c*). Eventually, diffusion results in an even distribution of ink molecules throughout the water (*d*).

The major barrier to crossing a biological membrane is the hydrophobic interior that repels polar molecules but not nonpolar molecules. If a concentration difference exists for a nonpolar molecule, it will move across the membrane until the concentration is equal on both sides. At this point, movement in both directions still occurs, but there is no net change in either direction. This includes molecules like O_2 and nonpolar organic molecules such as steroid hormones.

The plasma membrane has limited permeability to small polar molecules and very limited permeability to larger polar molecules and ions. The movement of water, one of the most important polar molecules, is discussed in its own section later on.

Proteins allow membrane diffusion to be selective

Many important molecules required by cells cannot easily cross the plasma membrane. These molecules can still enter the cell by diffusion through specific channel proteins or carrier proteins embedded in the plasma membrane, provided there is a higher concentration of the molecule outside the cell than inside. We call this process of diffusion mediated by a membrane protein **facilitated diffusion. Channel proteins** have a hydrophilic interior that provides an aqueous channel through which polar molecules can pass when the channel is open. **Carrier proteins,** in contrast to channels, bind specifically to the molecule they assist, much like an enzyme binds to its substrate. These channels and carriers are usually selective for one type of molecule, and thus the cell membrane is said to be **selectively permeable.**

Facilitated diffusion of ions through channels

You saw in chapter 2 that atoms with an unequal number of protons and electrons have an electric charge and are called ions. Those that carry a positive charge are called *cations* and those that carry a negative charge are called *anions.*

Because of their charge, ions interact well with polar molecules such as water, but are repelled by nonpolar molecules such as the interior of the plasma membrane. Therefore, ions cannot move between the cytoplasm of a cell and the extracellular fluid without the assistance of membrane transport proteins.

Ion channels possess a hydrated interior that spans the membrane. Ions can diffuse through the channel in either direction, depending on their relative concentration across the membrane (figure 5.10). Some channel proteins can be opened or closed in response to a stimulus. These channels are called *gated channels,* and depending on the nature of the channel, the stimulus can be either chemical or electrical.

Three conditions determine the direction of net movement of the ions: (1) their relative concentrations on either side of the membrane, (2) the voltage difference across the membrane and for the gated channels, and

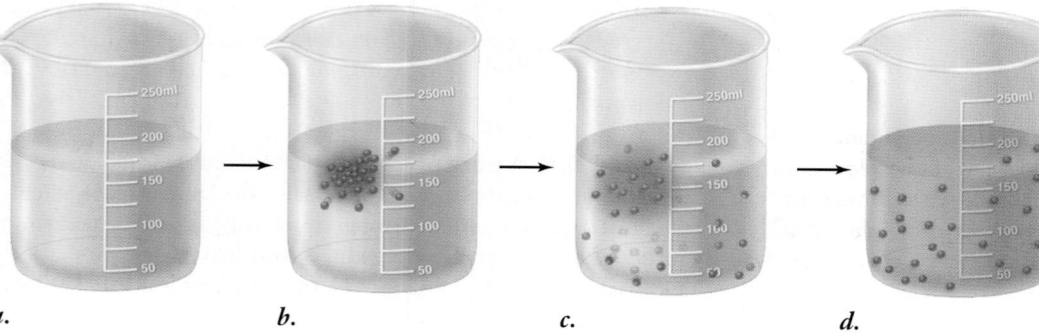

a.   *b.*   *c.*   *d.*

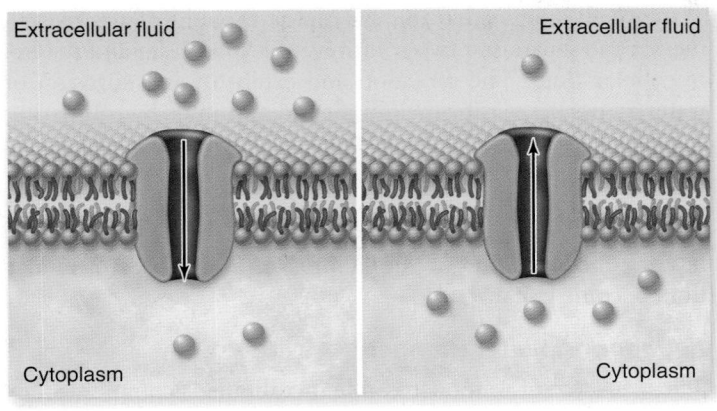

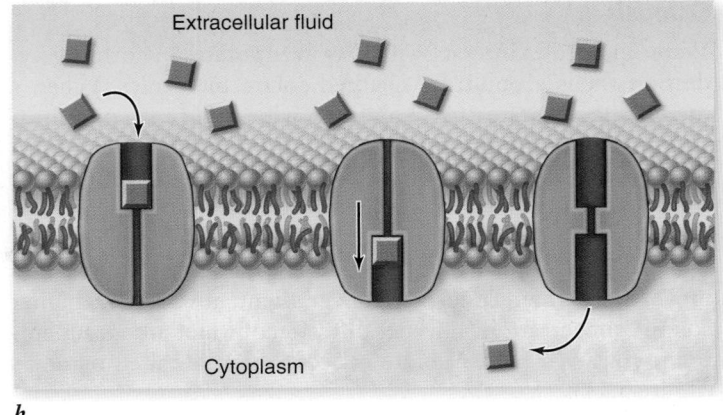

a.   *b.*

Figure 5.10 Facilitated diffusion. Diffusion can be facilitated by membrane proteins. *a.* The movement of ions through a channel is shown. On the left the concentration is higher outside the cell, so the ions move into the cell. On the right the situation is reversed. In both cases, transport continues until the concentration is equal on both sides of the membrane. At this point, ions continue to cross the membrane in both directions, but there is no net movement in either direction. *b.* Carrier proteins bind specifically to the molecules they transport. In this case, the concentration is higher outside the cell, so molecules bind to the carrier on the outside. The carrier's shape changes, allowing the molecule to cross the membrane. This is reversible, so net movement continues until the concentration is equal on both sides of the membrane.

(3) the state of the gate (open or closed). A voltage difference is an electrical potential difference across the membrane called a *membrane potential.* Changes in membrane potential form the basis for transmission of signals in the nervous system and some other tissues. (We discuss this topic in detail in chapter 45.) Each type of channel is specific for a particular ion, such as calcium (Ca^{2+}), sodium (Na^+), potassium (K^+), or chloride (Cl^-), or in some cases, for more than one cation or anion. Ion channels play an essential role in signaling by the nervous system.

Facilitated diffusion by carrier proteins

Carrier proteins can help transport both ions and other solutes, such as some sugars and amino acids, across the membrane. Transport through a carrier is still a form of diffusion and therefore requires a concentration difference across the membrane.

Carriers must bind to the molecule they transport, so the relationship between concentration and rate of transport differs from that due to simple diffusion. As concentration increases, transport by simple diffusion shows a linear increase in rate of transport. But when a carrier protein is involved, a concentration increase means that more of the carriers are bound to the transported molecule. At high enough concentrations all carriers will be occupied, and the rate of transport will be constant. This means that the carrier exhibits *saturation.*

This situation is somewhat like that of a stadium (the cell) where a crowd must pass through turnstiles to enter. If there are unoccupied turnstiles, you can go right through, but when all are occupied, you must wait. When ticket holders are passing through the gates at maximum speed, the rate at which they enter cannot increase, no matter how many are waiting outside.

Facilitated diffusion in red blood cells

Several examples of facilitated diffusion can be found in the plasma membrane of vertebrate red blood cells (RBCs). One RBC carrier protein, for example, transports a different molecule in each direction: chloride ion (Cl^-) in one direction and bicarbonate ion (HCO_3^-) in the opposite direction. As you will learn in chapter 51, this carrier is important in the uptake and release of carbon dioxide.

The glucose transporter is a second vital facilitated diffusion carrier in RBCs. Red blood cells keep their internal concentration of glucose low through a chemical trick: They immediately add a phosphate group to any entering glucose molecule, converting it to a highly charged glucose phosphate that can no longer bind to the glucose transporter, and therefore cannot pass back across the membrane. This maintains a steep concentration gradient for unphosphorylated glucose, favoring its entry into the cell.

The glucose transporter that assists the entry of glucose into the cell does not appear to form a channel in the membrane. Instead, this transmembrane protein appears to bind to a glucose molecule and then to flip its shape, dragging the glucose through the bilayer and releasing it on the inside of the plasma membrane. After it releases the glucose, the transporter reverts to its original shape and is then available to bind the next glucose molecule that comes along outside the cell.

Osmosis is the movement of water across membranes

The cytoplasm of a cell contains ions and molecules, such as sugars and amino acids, dissolved in water. The mixture of these substances and water is called an *aqueous solution.* Water is termed the **solvent,** and the substances dissolved in the water are **solutes.** Both water and solutes tend to diffuse from regions of high concentration to ones of low concentration; that is, they diffuse down their concentration gradients.

When two regions are separated by a membrane, what happens depends on whether the solutes can pass freely through that membrane. Most solutes, including ions and sugars, are not lipid-soluble and, therefore, are unable to cross the lipid bilayer. The concentration gradient of these solutes can lead to the movement of water.

Osmosis

Water molecules interact with dissolved solutes by forming hydration shells around the charged solute molecules. When a membrane separates two solutions with different concentrations of solutes, the concentrations of *free* water molecules on the two sides of the membrane also differ. The side with higher solute concentration has tied up more water molecules in hydration shells and thus has fewer free water molecules.

As a consequence of this difference, free water molecules move down their concentration gradient, toward the higher solute concentration. This net diffusion of water across a membrane toward a higher solute concentration is called **osmosis** (figure 5.11).

The concentration of *all* solutes in a solution determines the **osmotic concentration** of the solution. If two solutions have unequal osmotic concentrations, the solution with the higher concentration is **hypertonic** (Greek *hyper*; "more than"), and the solution with the lower concentration is **hypotonic** (Greek *hypo*, "less than"). When two solutions have the same osmotic concentration, the solutions are **isotonic** (Greek *iso*, "equal"). The terms *hyperosmotic*, *hypoosmotic*, and *isosmotic* are also used to describe these conditions.

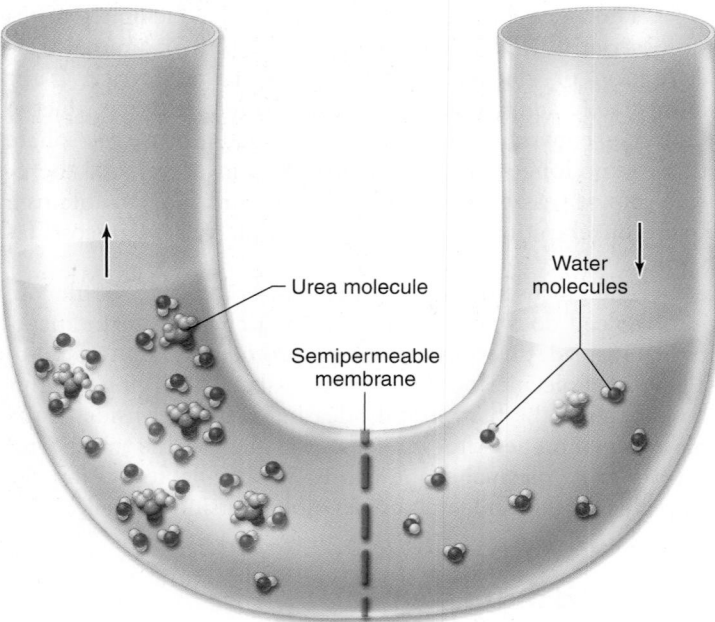

Urea molecule

Water molecules

Semipermeable membrane

Figure 5.11 Osmosis. Concentration differences in charged or polar molecules that cannot cross a semipermeable membrane result in movement of water, which can cross the membrane. Water molecules form hydrogen bonds with charged or polar molecules creating a hydration shell around them in solution. A higher concentration of polar molecules (urea) shown on the left side of the membrane leads to water molecules gathering around each urea molecule. These water molecules are no longer free to diffuse across the membrane. The polar solute has reduced the concentration of free water molecules, creating a gradient. This causes a net movement of water by diffusion from right to left in the U-tube, raising the level on the left and lowering the level on the right.

A cell in any environment can be thought of as a plasma membrane separating two solutions: the cytoplasm and the extracellular fluid. The direction and extent of any diffusion of water across the plasma membrane is determined by comparing the osmotic strength of these solutions. Put another way, water diffuses out of a cell in a hypertonic solution (that is, the cytoplasm of the cell is hypotonic, compared with the extracellular fluid). This loss of water causes the cell to shrink until the osmotic concentrations of the cytoplasm and the extracellular fluid become equal.

Aquaporins: Water channels

The transport of water across the membrane is complex. Studies on artificial membranes show that water, despite its polarity, can cross the membrane, but this flow is limited. Water flow in living cells is facilitated by **aquaporins,** which are specialized channels for water.

A simple experiment demonstrates this. If an amphibian egg is placed in hypotonic spring water (the solute concentration in the cell is higher than that of the surrounding water), it does not swell. If aquaporin mRNA is then injected into the egg, the channel proteins are expressed and appear in the egg's plasma membrane. Water can now diffuse into the egg, causing it to swell.

More than 11 different kinds of aquaporins have been found in mammals. These fall into two general classes: those that are specific for only water, and those that allow other small hydrophilic molecules, such as glycerol or urea, to cross the membrane as well. This latter class explains how some membranes allow the easy passage of small hydrophilic substances.

The human genetic disease, hereditary (nephrogenic) diabetes insipidus (NDI), has been shown to be caused by a nonfunctional aquaporin protein. This disease causes the excretion of large volumes of dilute urine, illustrating the importance of aquaporins to our physiology.

Osmotic pressure

What happens to a cell in a hypotonic solution? (That is, the cell's cytoplasm is hypertonic relative to the extracellular fluid.) In this situation, water diffuses into the cell from the extracellular fluid, causing the cell to swell. The pressure of the cytoplasm pushing out against the cell membrane, or hydrostatic pressure, increases. The amount of water that enters the cell depends on the difference in solute concentration between the cell and the extracellular fluid. This is measured as **osmotic pressure,** defined as the force needed to stop osmotic flow.

If the membrane is strong enough, the cell reaches an equilibrium, at which the osmotic pressure, which tends to drive water into the cell, is exactly counterbalanced by the hydrostatic pressure, which tends to drive water back out of the cell. However, a plasma membrane by itself cannot withstand large internal pressures, and an isolated cell under such conditions would burst like an overinflated balloon (figure 5.12).

Accordingly, it is important for animal cells, which only have plasma membranes, to maintain osmotic balance. In contrast, the cells of prokaryotes, fungi, plants, and many protists are surrounded by strong cell walls, which can withstand high internal pressures without bursting.

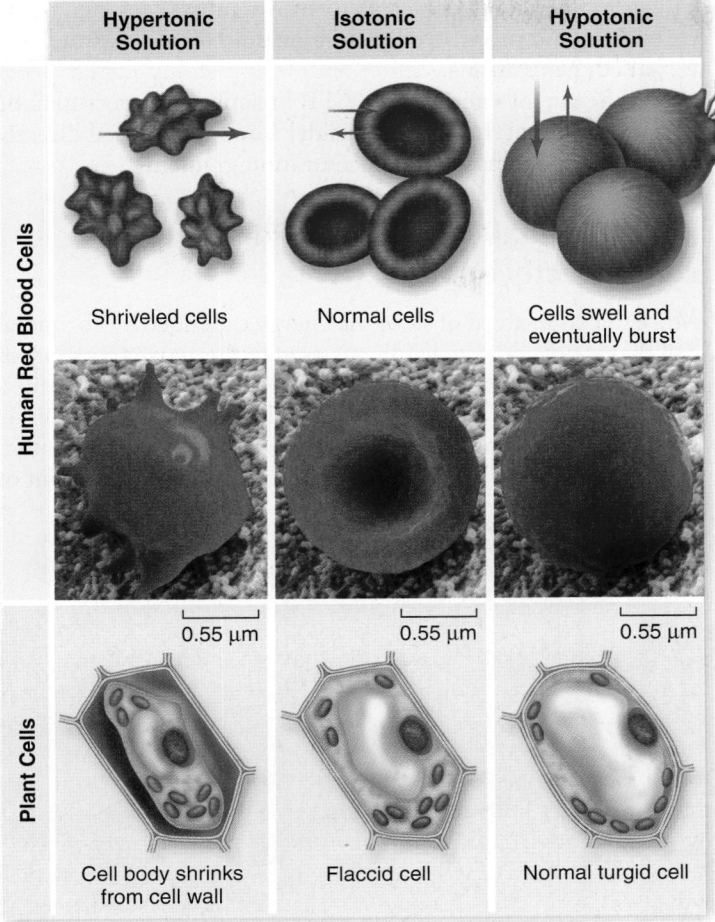

| Hypertonic Solution | Isotonic Solution | Hypotonic Solution |

Human Red Blood Cells

Shriveled cells | Normal cells | Cells swell and eventually burst

0.55 μm | 0.55 μm | 0.55 μm

Plant Cells

Cell body shrinks from cell wall | Flaccid cell | Normal turgid cell

Figure 5.12 How solutes create osmotic pressure. In a hypertonic solution, water moves out of the cell, causing the cell to shrivel. In an isotonic solution, water diffuses into and out of the cell at the same rate, with no change in cell size. In a hypotonic solution, water moves into the cell. Direction and amount of water movement is shown with blue arrows *(top)*. As water enters the cell from a hypotonic solution, pressure is applied to the plasma membrane until the cell ruptures. Water enters the cell due to osmotic pressure from the higher solute concentration in the cell. Osmotic pressure is measured as the force needed to stop osmosis. The strong cell wall of plant cells can withstand the hydrostatic pressure to keep the cell from rupturing. This is not the case with animal cells.

Maintaining osmotic balance

Organisms have developed many strategies for solving the dilemma posed by being hypertonic to their environment and therefore having a steady influx of water by osmosis.

Extrusion. Some single-celled eukaryotes, such as the protist *Paramecium,* use organelles called contractile vacuoles to remove water. Each vacuole collects water from various parts of the cytoplasm and transports it to the central part of the vacuole, near the cell surface. The vacuole possesses a small pore that opens to the outside of the cell. By contracting rhythmically, the vacuole pumps out (extrudes) through this pore the water that is continuously drawn into the cell by osmotic forces.

Isosmotic Regulation. Some organisms that live in the ocean adjust their internal concentration of solutes to match that of the surrounding seawater. Because they are isosmotic with respect to their environment, no net flow of water occurs into or out of these cells.

Many terrestrial animals solve the problem in a similar way, by circulating a fluid through their bodies that bathes cells in an isotonic solution. The blood in your body, for example, contains a high concentration of the protein albumin, which elevates the solute concentration of the blood to match that of your cells' cytoplasm.

Turgor. Most plant cells are hypertonic to their immediate environment, containing a high concentration of solutes in their central vacuoles. The resulting internal hydrostatic pressure, known as **turgor pressure,** presses the plasma membrane firmly against the interior of the cell wall, making the cell rigid. Most green plants depend on turgor pressure to maintain their shape, and thus they wilt when they lack sufficient water.

Learning Outcomes Review 5.4

Passive transport involves diffusion, which requires a concentration gradient. Hydrophobic molecules can diffuse directly through the membrane (simple diffusion). Polar molecules and ions can also diffuse through the membrane, but only with the aid of a channel or carrier protein (facilitated diffusion). Channel proteins assist by forming a hydrophilic passageway through the membrane, whereas carrier proteins bind to the molecule they assist. Water passes through the membrane and through aquaporins in response to solute concentration differences inside and outside the cell. This process is called osmosis.

■ *If you require intravenous (IV) medication in the hospital, what should the concentration of solutes in the IV solution be relative to your blood cells?*

5.5 Active Transport Across Membranes

Learning Outcomes

1. **Differentiate between active transport and diffusion.**
2. **Describe the function of the Na⁺/K⁺ pump.**
3. **Explain the energetics of coupled transport.**

Diffusion, facilitated diffusion, and osmosis are passive transport processes that move materials down their concentration gradients, but cells can also actively move substances across a cell membrane *up* their concentration gradients. This process requires the expenditure of energy, typically from ATP, and is therefore called **active transport.**

Active transport uses energy to move materials against a concentration gradient

Like facilitated diffusion, active transport involves highly selective protein carriers within the membrane that bind to the transported substance, which could be an ion or a simple molecule, such as a sugar, an amino acid, or a nucleotide. These carrier proteins are called **uniporters** if they transport a single type of molecule and symporters or antiporters if they transport two different molecules together. **Symporters** transport two molecules in the same direction, and **antiporters** transport two molecules in opposite directions. These terms can also be used to describe facilitated diffusion carriers.

Active transport is one of the most important functions of any cell. It enables a cell to take up additional molecules of a substance that is already present in its cytoplasm in concentrations higher than in the extracellular fluid. Active transport also enables a cell to move substances out of its cytoplasm and into the extracellular fluid, despite higher external concentrations.

The use of energy from ATP in active transport may be direct or indirect. Let's first consider how ATP is used directly to move ions against their concentration gradients.

The sodium–potassium pump runs directly on ATP

More than one-third of all of the energy expended by an animal cell that is not actively dividing is used in the active transport of sodium (Na^+) and potassium (K^+) ions. Most animal cells have a low internal concentration of Na^+, relative to their surroundings, and a high internal concentration of K^+. They maintain these concentration differences by actively pumping Na^+ out of the cell and K^+ in.

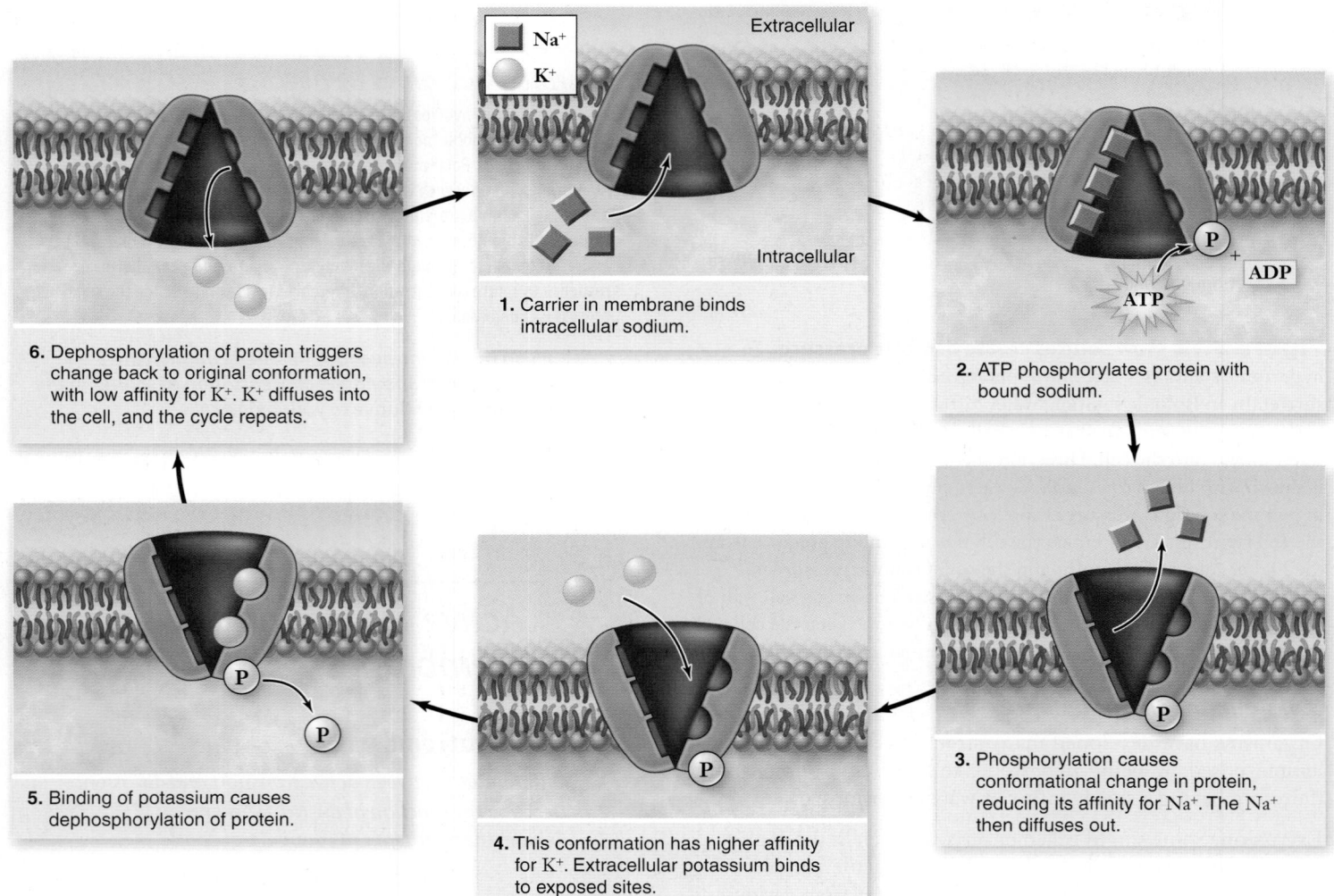

Na⁺
K⁺

Extracellular

Intracellular

1. Carrier in membrane binds intracellular sodium.

2. ATP phosphorylates protein with bound sodium.

P + ADP
ATP

3. Phosphorylation causes conformational change in protein, reducing its affinity for Na^+. The Na^+ then diffuses out.

4. This conformation has higher affinity for K^+. Extracellular potassium binds to exposed sites.

5. Binding of potassium causes dephosphorylation of protein.

6. Dephosphorylation of protein triggers change back to original conformation, with low affinity for K^+. K^+ diffuses into the cell, and the cycle repeats.

Figure 5.13 The sodium–potassium pump. The protein carrier known as the sodium–potassium pump transports sodium (Na^+) and potassium (K^+) across the plasma membrane. For every three Na^+ transported out of the cell, two K^+ are transported into it. The sodium–potassium pump is fueled by ATP hydrolysis. The affinity of the pump for Na^+ and K^+ is changed by adding or removing phosphate (P), which changes the conformation of the protein.

The remarkable protein that transports these two ions across the cell membrane is known as the **sodium–potassium pump** (figure 5.13). This carrier protein uses the energy stored in ATP to move these two ions. In this case, the energy is used to change the conformation of the carrier protein, which changes its affinity for either Na^+ ions or K^+ ions. This is an excellent illustration of how subtle changes in the structure of a protein affect its function.

The important characteristic of the sodium–potassium pump is that it is an active transport mechanism, transporting Na^+ and K^+ from areas of low concentration to areas of high concentration. This transport is the opposite of passive transport by diffusion; it is achieved only by the constant expenditure of metabolic energy. The sodium–potassium pump works through the following series of conformational changes in the transmembrane protein (summarized in figure 5.13):

Step 1. Three Na^+ bind to the cytoplasmic side of the protein, causing the protein to change its conformation.

Step 2. In its new conformation, the protein binds a molecule of ATP and cleaves it into adenosine diphosphate (ADP) and phosphate (P_i). ADP is released, but the phosphate group is covalently linked to the protein. The protein is now phosphorylated.

Step 3. The phosphorylation of the protein induces a second conformational change in the protein. This change translocates the three Na^+ across the membrane, so they now face the exterior. In this new conformation, the protein has a low affinity for Na^+, and the three bound Na^+ break away from the protein and diffuse into the extracellular fluid.

Step 4. The new conformation has a high affinity for K^+, two of which bind to the extracellular side of the protein as soon as it is free of the Na^+.

Step 5. The binding of the K^+ causes another conformational change in the protein, this time resulting in the hydrolysis of the bound phosphate group.

Step 6. Freed of the phosphate group, the protein reverts to its original shape, exposing the two K^+ to the cytoplasm. This conformation has a low affinity for K^+, so the two bound K^+ dissociate from the protein and diffuse into the interior of the cell. The original conformation has a high affinity for Na^+. When these ions bind, they initiate another cycle.

In every cycle, three Na^+ leave the cell and two K^+ enter. The changes in protein conformation that occur during the cycle are rapid, enabling each carrier to transport as many as 300 Na^+ per second. The sodium–potassium pump appears to exist in all animal cells, although cells vary widely in the number of pump proteins they contain.

Coupled transport uses ATP indirectly

Some molecules are moved against their concentration gradient by using the energy stored in a gradient of a different molecule. In this process, called *coupled transport*, the energy released

as one molecule moves down its concentration gradient is captured and used to move a different molecule against its gradient. As you just saw, the energy stored in ATP molecules can be used to create a gradient of Na^+ and K^+ across the membrane. These gradients can then be used to power the transport of other molecules across the membrane.

As one example, let's consider the active transport of glucose across the membrane in animal cells. Glucose is such an important molecule that there are a variety of transporters for it, one of which was discussed earlier under passive transport. In a multicellular organism, intestinal epithelial cells can have a higher concentration of glucose inside the cell than outside, so these cells need to be able to transport glucose against its concentration gradient. This requires energy and a different transporter than the one involved in facilitated diffusion of glucose.

The active glucose transporter uses the Na^+ gradient produced by the sodium–potassium pump as a source of energy to power the movement of glucose into the cell. In this system, both glucose and Na^+ bind to the transport protein, which allows Na^+ to pass into the cell down its concentration gradient, capturing the energy and using it to move glucose into the cell. In this kind of cotransport, both molecules are moving in the same direction across the membrane; therefore the transporter is a symporter (figure 5.14).

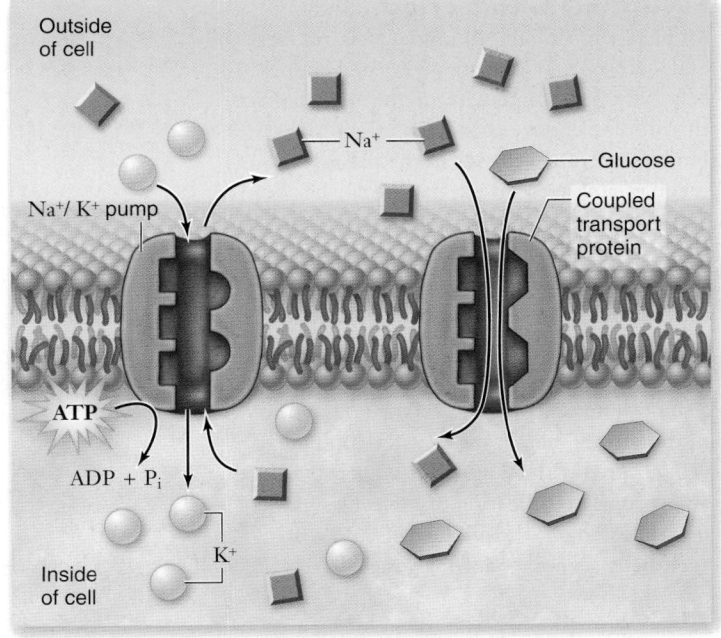

Figure 5.14 Coupled transport. A membrane protein transports Na^+ into the cell, down its concentration gradient, at the same time it transports a glucose molecule into the cell. The gradient driving the Na^+ entry allows sugar molecules to be transported against their concentration gradient. The Na^+ gradient is maintained by the Na^+/K^+ pump. ADP = adenosine diphosphate; ATP = adenosine triphosphate; P_i = inorganic phosphate

In a related process, called *countertransport*, the inward movement of Na$^+$ is coupled with the outward movement of another substance, such as Ca^{2+} or H$^+$. As in cotransport, both Na$^+$ and the other substance bind to the same transport protein, which in this case is an antiporter, as the substances bind on opposite sides of the membrane and are moved in opposite directions. In countertransport, the cell uses the energy released as Na$^+$ moves down its concentration gradient into the cell to eject a substance against its concentration gradient. In both cotransport and countertransport, the potential energy in the concentration gradient of one molecule is used to transport another molecule against its concentration gradient. They differ only in the direction that the second molecule moves relative to the first.

Learning Outcomes Review 5.5

Active transport requires both a carrier protein and energy, usually in the form of ATP, to move molecules against a concentration gradient. The sodium–potassium pump uses ATP to moved Na$^+$ in one direction and K$^+$ in the other to create and maintain concentration differences of these ions. In coupled transport, a favorable concentration gradient of one molecule is used to move a different molecule against its gradient, such as in the transport of glucose by Na$^+$.

■ **Can active transport involve a channel protein. Why or why not?**

Learning Outcomes

1. **Distinguish between endocytosis and exocytosis.**
2. **Explain how endocytosis can be specific.**

The lipid nature of cell plasma membranes raises a second problem. The substances cells require for growth are mostly large, polar molecules that cannot cross the hydrophobic barrier a lipid bilayer creates. How do these substances get into cells? Two processes are involved in this **bulk transport:** *endocytosis* and *exocytosis*.

Bulk material enters the cell in vesicles

In **endocytosis,** the plasma membrane envelops food particles and fluids. Cells use three major types of endocytosis: phagocytosis, pinocytosis, and receptor-mediated endocytosis (figure 5.15). Like active transport, these processes also require energy expenditure.

Figure 5.15 Endocytosis. Both *(a)* phagocytosis and *(b)* pinocytosis are forms of endocytosis. *c.* In receptor-mediated endocytosis, cells have pits coated with the protein clathrin that initiate endocytosis when target molecules bind to receptor proteins in the plasma membrane. Photo inserts (false color has been added to enhance distinction of structures): *(a)* A TEM of phagocytosis of a bacterium, *Rickettsia tsutsugamushi,* by a mouse peritoneal mesothelial cell. The bacterium enters the host cell by phagocytosis and replicates in the cytoplasm. *(b)* A TEM of pinocytosis in a smooth muscle cell. *(c)* A coated pit appears in the plasma membrane of a developing egg cell, covered with a layer of proteins. When an appropriate collection of molecules gathers in the coated pit, the pit deepens and will eventually seal off to form a vesicle.

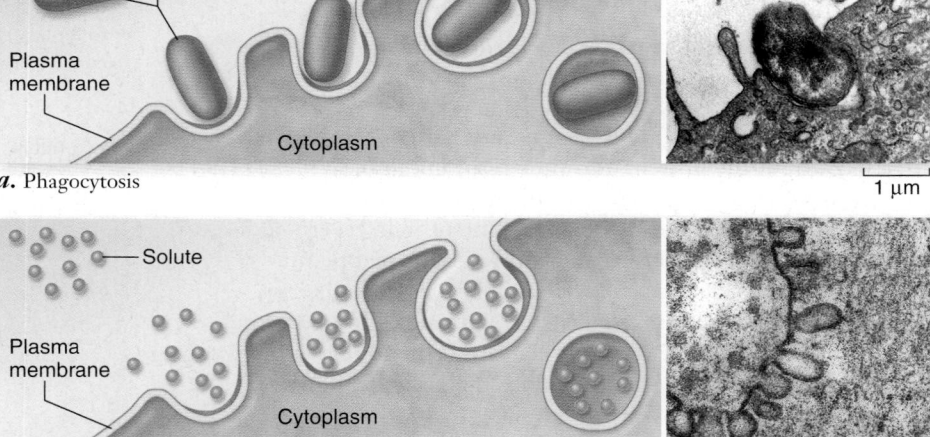

a. Phagocytosis   1 µm

b. Pinocytosis   0.1 µm

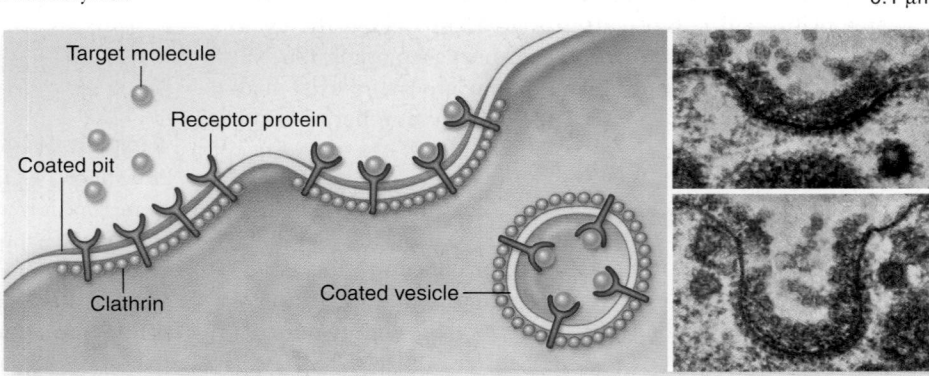
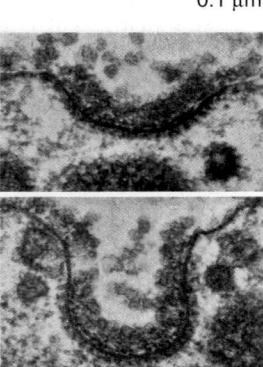

c. Receptor-mediated endocytosis   0.093 µm

Phagocytosis and pinocytosis

If the material the cell takes in is particulate (made up of discrete particles), such as an organism or some other fragment of organic matter (figure 5.15*a*), the process is called **phagocytosis** (Greek *phagein*, "to eat," + *cytos*, "cell"). If the material the cell takes in is liquid (figure 5.15*b*), the process is called **pinocytosis** (Greek *pinein*, "to drink"). Pinocytosis is common among animal cells. Mammalian egg cells, for example, "nurse" from surrounding cells; the nearby cells secrete nutrients that the maturing egg cell takes up by pinocytosis.

Virtually all eukaryotic cells constantly carry out these kinds of endocytotic processes, trapping particles and extracellular fluid in vesicles and ingesting them. Endocytosis rates vary from one cell type to another. They can be surprisingly high; some types of white blood cells ingest up to 25% of their cell volume each hour.

Receptor-mediated endocytosis

Molecules are often transported into eukaryotic cells through **receptor-mediated endocytosis.** These molecules first bind to specific receptors in the plasma membrane—they have a conformation that fits snugly into the receptor. Different cell types contain a characteristic battery of receptor types, each for a different kind of molecule in their membranes.

The portion of the receptor molecule that lies inside the membrane is trapped in an indented pit coated on the cytoplasmic side with the protein *clathrin*. Each pit acts like a molecular mousetrap, closing over to form an internal vesicle when the right molecule enters the pit (figure 5.15*c*). The trigger that releases the trap is the binding of the properly fitted target molecule to the embedded receptor. When binding occurs, the cell reacts by initiating endocytosis; the process is highly specific and very fast. The vesicle is now inside the cell carrying its cargo.

One type of molecule that is taken up by receptor-mediated endocytosis is low-density lipoprotein (LDL). LDL molecules bring cholesterol into the cell where it can be in-corporated into membranes. Cholesterol plays a key role in determining the stiffness of the body's membranes. In the human genetic disease familial hypercholesterolemia, the LDL receptors lack tails, so they are never fastened in the clathrin-coated pits and as a result, do not trigger vesicle formation. The cholesterol stays in the bloodstream of affected individuals, accumulating as plaques inside arteries and leading to heart attacks.

It is important to understand that endocytosis in itself does not bring substances directly into the cytoplasm of a cell. The material taken in is still separated from the cytoplasm by the membrane of the vesicle.

Material can leave the cell by exocytosis

The reverse of endocytosis is **exocytosis**, the discharge of material from vesicles at the cell surface (figure 5.16). In plant cells, exocytosis is an important means of exporting the materials needed to construct the cell wall through the plasma membrane. Among protists, contractile vacuole discharge is considered a form of exocytosis. In animal cells, exocytosis provides a mechanism for secreting many hormones, neurotransmitters, digestive enzymes, and other substances.

The mechanisms for transport across cell membranes are summarized in table 5.2.

Learning Outcomes Review 5.6

Large molecules and other bulky materials can enter a cell by endocytosis and leave the cell by exocytosis. These processes require energy. Endocytosis may be mediated by specific receptor proteins in the membrane that trigger the formation of vesicles.

■ *What feature unites transport by receptor-mediated endocytosis, transport by a carrier, and catalysis by an enzyme?*

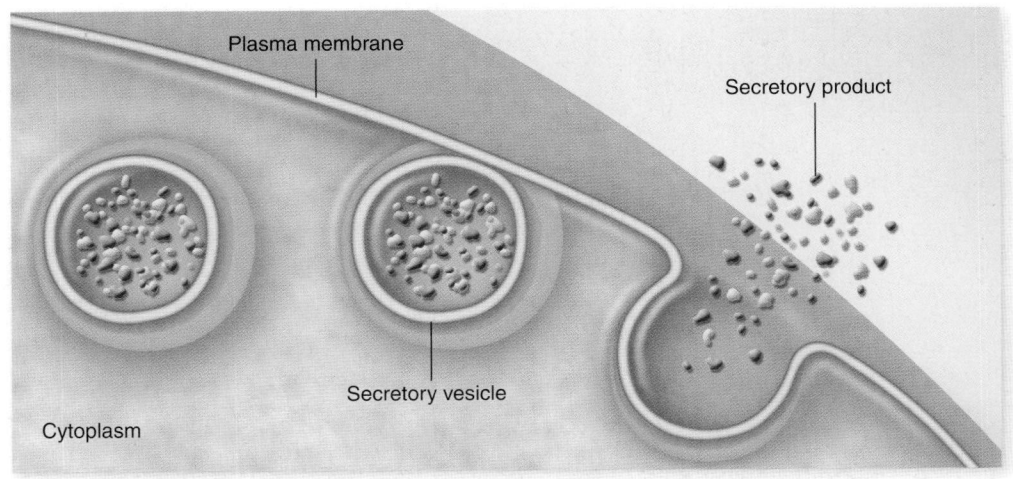

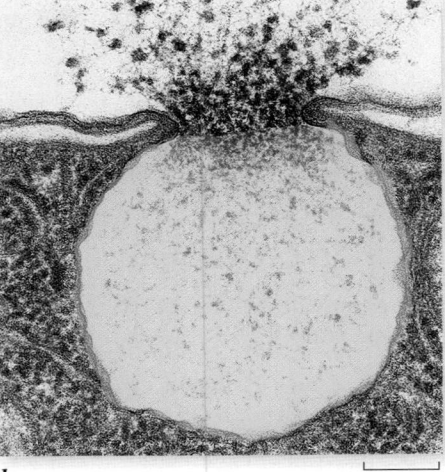

0.069 μm

a.

b.

Figure 5.16 Exocytosis. *a.* Proteins and other molecules are secreted from cells in small packets called vesicles, whose membranes fuse with the plasma membrane, releasing their contents outside the cell. *b.* A false-colored transmission electron micrograph showing exocytosis.

TABLE 5.2

Mechanisms for Transport Across Cell Membranes

Process		How It Works	Example
PASSIVE PROCESSES			
Diffusion			
Direct		Random molecular motion produces net migration of nonpolar molecules toward region of lower concentration	Movement of oxygen into cells
Facilitated Diffusion			
Protein channel		Polar molecules or ions move through a protein channel; net movement is toward region of lower concentration	Movement of ions in or out of cell
Protein carrier		Molecule binds to carrier protein in membrane and is transported across; net movement is toward region of lower concentration	Movement of glucose into cells
Osmosis			
Aquaporins		Diffusion of water across the membrane via osmosis; requires osmotic gradient	Movement of water into cells placed in a hypotonic solution
ACTIVE PROCESSES			
Active Transport			
Protein carrier			
Na^+/K^+ pump		Carrier uses energy to move a substance across a membrane against its concentration gradient	Na^+ and K^+ against their concentration gradients
Coupled transport		Molecules are transported across a membrane against their concentration gradients by the cotransport of sodium ions or protons down their concentration gradients	Coupled uptake of glucose into cells against its concentration gradient using a Na^+ gradient
Endocytosis			
Membrane vesicle			
Phagocytosis		Particle is engulfed by membrane, which folds around it and forms a vesicle	Ingestion of bacteria by white blood cells
Pinocytosis		Fluid droplets are engulfed by membrane, which forms vesicles around them	"Nursing" of human egg cells
Receptor-mediated endocytosis		Endocytosis triggered by a specific receptor, forming clathrin-coated vesicles	Cholesterol uptake
Exocytosis			
Membrane vesicle		Vesicles fuse with plasma membrane and eject contents	Secretion of mucus; release of neurotransmitters

5.1 The Structure of Membranes

The fluid mosaic model shows proteins embedded in a fluid lipid bilayer.

Membranes are sheets of phospholipid bilayers with associated proteins (figure 5.2). Hydrophobic regions of a membrane are oriented inward and hydrophilic regions oriented outward. In the fluid mosaic model, proteins float on or in the lipid bilayer.

Cellular membranes consist of four component groups.

In eukaryotic cells, membranes have four components: a phosopholipid bilayer, transmembrane proteins (integral membrane proteins), an interior protein network, and cell-surface markers. The interior protein network is composed of cytoskeletal filaments and peripheral membrane proteins, which are associated with the membrane but are not an integral part. Membranes contain glycoproteins and glycolipids on the surface that act as cell identity markers.

Electron microscopy has provided structural evidence.

Transmission electron microscopy (TEM) and scanning electron microscopy (SEM) have confirmed the structure predicted by the fluid mosaic model.

5.2 Phospholipids: The Membrane's Foundation

Phospholipids are composed of two fatty acids and a phosphate group linked to a three-carbon glycerol molecule.

Phospholipids spontaneously form bilayers.

The phosphate group of a phospholipid is polar and hydrophilic; the fatty acids are nonpolar and hydrophobic, and they orient away from the polar head of the phospholipids. The nonpolar interior of the lipid bilayer impedes the passage of water and water-soluble substances.

The phospholipid bilayer is fluid.

Hydrogen bonding of water keeps the membrane in its bilayer configuration; however, phospholipids and unanchored proteins in the membrane are loosely associated and can diffuse laterally.

Membrane fluidity can change.

Membrane fluidity depends on the fatty acid composition of the membrane. Unsaturated fats tend to make the membrane more fluid because of the "kinks" of double bonds in the fatty acid tails. Temperature also affects fluidity. Some bacteria have enzymes that alter the fatty acids of the membrane to compensate for temperature changes.

5.3 Proteins: Multifunctional Components

Proteins and protein complexes perform key functions.

Transporters are integral membrane proteins that carry specific substances through the membrane. Enzymes often occur on the interior surface of the membrane. Cell-surface receptors respond to external chemical messages and change conditions inside the cell; cell identity markers on the surface allow recognition of the body's cells as "self." Cell-to-cell adhesion proteins glue cells together; surface proteins that interact with other cells anchor to the cytoskeleton.

Structural features of membrane proteins relate to function.

Surface proteins are attached to the surface by nonpolar regions that associate with polar regions of phospholipids. Transmembrane proteins may cross the bilayer a number of times, and each membrane-spanning region is called a transmembrane domain. Such a domain is composed of hydrophobic amino acids usually arranged in α-helices. In certain proteins, β-pleated sheets in the nonpolar region form a pipelike passageway having a polar environment. An example is the porin class of proteins.

5.4 Passive Transport Across Membranes

Transport can occur by simple diffusion.

Simple diffusion is the passive movement of a substance along a chemical or electrical gradient. Biological membranes pose a barrier to hydrophilic polar molecules, while they allow hydrophobic substances to diffuse freely.

Proteins allow membrane diffusion to be selective.

Ions and large hydrophilic molecules cannot cross the phospholipid bilayer. Diffusion can still occur with the help of proteins, thus we call this facilitated diffusion. These proteins can be either channels, or carriers. Channels allow the diffusion of ions based on concentration and charge across the membrane. They are specific for different ions, but form an aqueous pore in the membrane. Carrier proteins bind to the molecules they transport, much like an enzyme. The rate of transport by a carrier is limited by the number of carriers in the membrane.

Osmosis is the movement of water across membranes.

The direction of movement due to osmosis depends on the solute concentration on either side of the membrane (figure 5.12). Solutions can be isotonic, hypotonic, or hypertonic. Cells in an isotonic solution are in osmotic balance; cells in a hypotonic solution will gain water; and cells in a hypertonic solution will lose water. Aquaporins are water channels that facilitate the diffusion of water.

5.5 Active Transport Across Membranes

Active transport uses energy to move materials against a concentration gradient.

Active transport uses specialized protein carriers that couple a source of energy to transport. They are classified based on the number of molecules and direction of transport. Uniporters transport a specific molecule in one direction; symporters transport two molecules in the same direction; and antiporters transport two molecules in opposite directions.

The sodium–potassium pump runs directly on ATP.

The sodium–potassium pump moves Na^+ out of the cell and K^+ into the cell against their concentration gradients using ATP. In every cycle of the pump, three Na^+ leave the cell and two K^+ enter it. This pump appears to be almost universal in animal cells.

Coupled transport uses ATP indirectly.

Coupled transport occurs when the energy released by a diffusing molecule is used to transport a different molecule against its concentration gradient in the same direction. Countertransport is similar to coupled transport, but the two molecules move in opposite directions.

5.6 Bulk Transport by Endocytosis and Exocytosis

Bulk transport moves large quantities of substances that cannot pass through the cell membrane.

Bulk material enters the cell in vesicles.

In endocytosis, the cell membrane surrounds material and pinches off to form a vesicle. In receptor-mediated endocytosis, specific molecules bind to receptors on the cell membrane.

Material can leave the cell by exocytosis.

In exocytosis, material in a vesicle is discharged when the vesicle fuses with the membrane.

UNDERSTAND

1. The fluid mosaic model of the membrane describes the membrane as
   a. containing a significant quantity of water in the interior.
   b. composed of fluid phospholipids on the outside and protein on the inside.
   c. composed of protein on the outside and fluid phospholipids on the inside.
   d. made of proteins and lipids that can freely move.

2. What chemical property characterizes the interior of the phospholipid bilayer?
   a. It is hydrophobic.
   b. It is hydrophilic.
   c. It is polar.
   d. It is saturated.

3. The transmembrane domain of an integral membrane protein
   a. is composed of hydrophobic amino acids.
   b. often forms an α-helical structure.
   c. can cross the membrane multiple times.
   d. is all of the above.

4. The specific function of a membrane within a cell is determined by the
   a. degree of saturation of the fatty acids within the phospholipid bilayer.
   b. location of the membrane within the cell.
   c. presence of lipid rafts and cholesterol.
   d. type and number of membrane proteins.

5. The movement of water across a membrane is dependent on
   a. the solvent concentration.
   b. the solute concentration.
   c. the presence of carrier proteins.
   d. membrane potential.

6. If a cell is in an isotonic environment, then
   a. the cell will gain water and burst.
   b. no water will move across the membrane.
   c. the cell will lose water and shrink.
   d. osmosis still occurs, but there is no net gain or loss of cell volume.

7. Which of the following is NOT a mechanism for bringing material into a cell?
   a. Exocytosis
   b. Endocytosis
   c. Pinocytosis
   d. Phagocytosis

APPLY

1. A bacterial cell that can alter the composition of saturated and unsaturated fatty acids in its membrane lipids is adapted to a cold environment. If this cell is shifted to a warmer environment, it will react by
   a. increasing the amount of cholesterol in its membrane.
   b. altering the amount of protein present in the membrane.
   c. increasing the degree of saturated fatty acids in its membrane.
   d. increasing the percentage of unsaturated fatty acids in its membrane.

2. What variable(s) influence(s) whether a nonpolar molecule can move across a membrane by passive diffusion?
   a. The structure of the phospholipids bilayer
   b. The difference in concentration of the molecule across the membrane

c. The presence of transport proteins in the membrane
d. All of the above

3. Which of the following does NOT contribute to the selective permeability of a biological membrane?
   a. Specificity of the carrier proteins in the membrane
   b. Selectivity of channel proteins in the membrane
   c. Hydrophobic barrier of the phospholipid bilayer
   d. Hydrogen bond formation between water and phosphate groups

4. How are *active* transport and *coupled* transport related?
   a. They both use ATP to move molecules.
   b. Active transport establishes a concentration gradient, but coupled transport doesn't.
   c. Coupled transport uses the concentration gradient established by active transport.
   d. Active transport moves one molecule, but coupled transport moves two.

5. A cell can use the process of facilitated diffusion to
   a. concentrate a molecule such as glucose inside a cell.
   b. remove all of a toxic molecule from a cell.
   c. move ions or large polar molecules across the membrane regardless of concentration.
   d. move ions or large polar molecules from a region of high concentration to a region of low concentration.

SYNTHESIZE

1. Figure 5.4 describes a classic experiment demonstrating the ability of proteins to move within the plane of the cell's plasma membrane. The following table outlines three different experiments using the fusion of labeled mouse and human cells.

Experiment	Conditions	Temperature (°C)	Result
1	Fuse human and mouse cells	37	Intermixed membrane proteins
2	Fuse human and mouse cells in presence of ATP inhibitors	37	Intermixed membrane proteins
3	Fuse human and mouse cells	4	No intermixing of membrane proteins

What conclusions can you reach about the movement of these proteins?

2. Each compartment of the endomembrane system of a cell is connected to the plasma membrane. Create a simple diagram of a cell including the RER, Golgi apparatus, vesicle, and the plasma membrane. Starting with the RER, use two different colors to represent the inner and outer halves of the bilayer for each of these membranes. What do you observe?

3. The distribution of lipids in the ER membrane is symmetric, that is, it is the same in both leaflets of the membrane. The Golgi apparatus and plasma membrane do not have symmetric distribution of membrane lipids. What kinds of processes could achieve this outcome?

ONLINE RESOURCE

www.ravenbiology.com

Mc Graw Hill **connect**™
|BIOLOGY

Understand, Apply, and Synthesize—enhance your study with animations that bring concepts to life and practice tests to assess your understanding. Your instructor may also recommend the interactive eBook, individualized learning tools, and more.

Chapter 6

Energy and Metabolism

Chapter Outline

6.1 The Flow of Energy in Living Systems

6.2 The Laws of Thermodynamics and Free Energy

6.3 ATP: The Energy Currency of Cells

6.4 Enzymes: Biological Catalysts

6.5 Metabolism: The Chemical Description of Cell Function

Introduction

Life can be viewed as a constant flow of energy, channeled by organisms to do the work of living. Each of the significant properties by which we define life—order, growth, reproduction, responsiveness, and internal regulation—requires a constant supply of energy. Both the lion and the giraffe need to eat to provide energy for a wide variety of cellular functions. Deprived of a source of energy, life stops. Therefore, a comprehensive study of life would be impossible without discussing bioenergetics, *the analysis of how energy powers the activities of living systems. In this chapter, we focus on energy—what it is and how it changes during chemical reactions.*

The Flow of Energy in Living Systems

Thermodynamics is the branch of chemistry concerned with energy changes. Cells are governed by the laws of physics and chemistry, so we must understand these laws in order to understand how cells function.

Energy can take many forms

Energy is defined as the capacity to do work. We think of energy as existing in two states: kinetic energy and potential energy (figure 6.1). **Kinetic energy** is the energy of motion. Moving objects perform work by causing other matter to move. **Potential energy** is stored energy. Objects that are not actively moving but have the capacity to do so possess potential energy. A boulder perched on a hilltop has gravitational potential energy. As it begins to roll downhill, some of its potential energy is converted into kinetic energy. Much of the work that living organisms carry out involves transforming potential energy into kinetic energy.

Energy can take many forms: mechanical energy, heat, sound, electric current, light, or radioactivity. Because it can exist in so many forms, energy can be measured in many ways. Heat is the most convenient way of measuring energy because all other forms of energy can be converted into heat. In fact, the term *thermodynamics* means "heat changes."

The unit of heat most commonly employed in biology is the kilocalorie (kcal). One kilocalorie is equal to 1000 calories (cal). One calorie is the heat required to raise the temperature of one gram of water one degree Celsius (°C). (You are probably more used to seeing the term *Calorie* with a capital C. This is used on food labels and is actually the same as kilocalorie.) Another energy unit, often used in physics, is the *joule*; one joule equals 0.239 cal.

The sun provides energy for living systems

Energy flows into the biological world from the Sun. It is estimated that the Sun provides the Earth with more than 13×10^{23} calories per year, or 40 million billion calories per second! Plants, algae, and certain kinds of bacteria capture a fraction of this energy through photosynthesis.

In photosynthesis, energy absorbed from sunlight is used to combine small molecules (water and carbon dioxide) into more complex ones (sugars). This process converts carbon from an inorganic to an organic form. In the process, energy from the Sun is stored as potential energy in the covalent bonds between atoms in the sugar molecules.

Breaking the bonds between atoms requires energy. In fact, the strength of a covalent bond is measured by the amount of energy required to break it. For example, it takes 98.8 kcal to break one mole (6.023×10^{23}) of the carbon–hydrogen (C—H) bonds found in organic molecules. Fat molecules have many C—H bonds, and breaking those bonds provides lots of energy.

a. Potential energy

b. Kinetic energy

Figure 6.1 Potential and kinetic energy. *a.* Objects that have the capacity to move but are not moving have potential energy. The energy required for the girl to climb to the top of the slide is stored as potential energy. *b.* Objects that are in motion have kinetic energy. The stored potential energy is released as kinetic energy as the girl slides down.

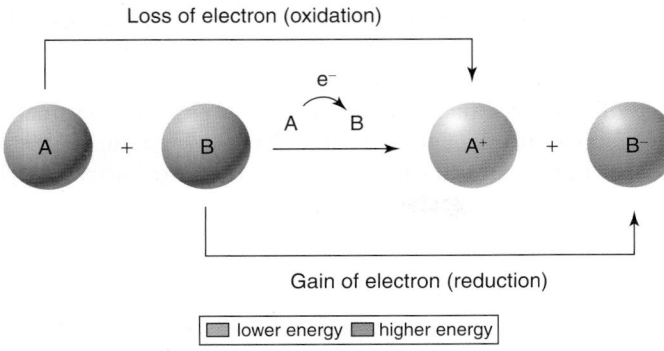

Loss of electron (oxidation)

e⁻

A + B → A⁺ + B⁻

Gain of electron (reduction)

☐ lower energy ☐ higher energy

Figure 6.2 Redox reactions. Oxidation is the loss of an electron; reduction is the gain of an electron. In this example, the charges of molecules A and B appear as superscripts in each molecule. Molecule A loses energy as it loses an electron, and molecule B gains that energy as it gains an electron.

This is one reason animals store fat. The oxidation of one mole of a 16-carbon fatty acid that is completely saturated with hydrogens yields 2340 kcal.

Oxidation–reduction reactions transfer electrons while bonds are made or broken

During a chemical reaction, the energy stored in chemical bonds may be used to make new bonds. In some of these reactions, electrons actually pass from one atom or molecule to another. An atom or molecule that loses an electron is said to be oxidized, and the process by which this occurs is called **oxidation.** The name comes from the fact that oxygen is the most common electron acceptor in biological systems. Conversely, an atom or molecule that gains an electron is said to be reduced, and the process is called *reduction*. The reduced form of a molecule has a higher level of energy than the oxidized form (figure 6.2).

Oxidation and reduction always take place together, because every electron that is lost by one atom through oxidation is gained by another atom through reduction. Therefore, chemical reactions of this sort are called **oxidation–reduction,** or **redox,** *reactions*. Oxidation–reduction reactions play a key role in the flow of energy through biological systems.

In the next two chapters, you will learn the details of how organisms derive energy from the oxidation of organic compounds via respiration, as well as from the energy in sunlight via photosynthesis.

Learning Outcomes Review 6.1

Energy is defined as the capacity to do work. The two forms of energy are kinetic energy, or energy of motion, and potential energy, or stored energy. The ultimate source of energy for living systems is the Sun. Organisms derive their energy from oxidation–reduction reactions. In oxidation, a molecule loses an electron; in reduction, a molecule gains an electron.

■ *What energy source might ecosystems at the bottom of the ocean use?*

6.2 The Laws of Thermodynamics and Free Energy

Learning Outcomes

1. **Explain the laws of thermodynamics.**
2. **Recognize how free energy can be used to predict the outcome of chemical reactions.**
3. **Contrast the course of a reaction with and without an enzyme catalyst.**

All activities of living organisms—growing, running, thinking, singing, reading these words—involve changes in energy. A set of two universal laws we call the laws of thermodynamics govern all energy changes in the universe, from nuclear reactions to a bird flying through the air.

The First Law states that energy cannot be created or destroyed

The **First Law of Thermodynamics** concerns the amount of energy in the universe. Energy cannot be created or destroyed; it can only change from one form to another (from potential to kinetic, for example). The total amount of energy in the universe remains constant.

The lion eating a giraffe at the beginning of this chapter is acquiring energy. Rather than creating new energy or capturing the energy in sunlight, the lion is merely transferring some of the potential energy stored in the giraffe's tissues to its own body, just as the giraffe obtained the potential energy stored in the plants it ate while it was alive.

Within any living organism, chemical potential energy stored in some molecules can be shifted to other molecules and stored in different chemical bonds. It can also be converted into other forms, such as kinetic energy, light, or electricity. During each conversion, some of the energy dissipates into the environment as **heat,** which is a measure of the random motion of molecules (and therefore a measure of one form of kinetic energy). Energy continuously flows through the biological world in one direction, with new energy from the Sun constantly entering the system to replace the energy dissipated as heat.

Heat can be harnessed to do work only when there is a heat gradient—that is, a temperature difference between two areas. Cells are too small to maintain significant internal temperature differences, so heat energy is incapable of doing the work of cells. Instead, cells must rely on chemical reactions for energy.

Although the total amount of energy in the universe remains constant, the energy available to do work decreases as more of it is progressively lost as heat.

The Second Law states that some energy is lost as disorder increases

The **Second Law of Thermodynamics** concerns the transformation of potential energy into heat, or random molecular motion. It states that the disorder in the universe, more formally called **entropy,** is continuously increasing. Put simply, disorder is more likely than order. For example, it is much more likely that a column of bricks will tumble over than that a pile of bricks will arrange themselves spontaneously to form a column.

In general, energy transformations proceed spontaneously to convert matter from a more ordered, less stable form to a less ordered, but more stable form. For this reason, the second law is sometimes called "time's arrow." Looking at the photographs in figure 6.3, you could put the pictures into correct sequence using the information that time had elapsed with only natural processes occurring. Although it might be great if our rooms would straighten themselves up, we know from experience how much work it takes to do so.

The Second Law of Thermodynamics can also be stated simply as "entropy increases." When the universe formed, it held all the potential energy it will ever have. It has become progressively more disordered ever since, with every energy exchange increasing the amount of entropy.

Chemical reactions can be predicted based on changes in free energy

It takes energy to break the chemical bonds that hold the atoms in a molecule together. Heat energy, because it increases atomic motion, makes it easier for the atoms to pull apart. Both chemical bonding and heat have a significant influence on a molecule. Chemical bonding reduces disorder; heat increases it. The net effect, the amount of energy actually available to break and subsequently form other chemical bonds, is called the *free energy* of that molecule. In a more general sense, **free energy** is defined as the energy available to do work in any system.

For a molecule within a cell, where pressure and volume usually do not change, the free energy is denoted by the symbol G (for "Gibbs free energy"). G is equal to the energy contained in a molecule's chemical bonds (called **enthalpy** and designated H) together with the energy term (TS) related to the degree of disorder in the system, where S is the symbol for *entropy* and T is the absolute temperature expressed in the Kelvin scale ($K = °C + 273$):

$$G = H - TS$$

Chemical reactions break some bonds in the reactants and form new ones in the products. Consequently, reactions can produce changes in free energy. When a chemical reaction occurs under conditions of constant temperature, pressure, and volume—as do most biological reactions—the change symbolized by the Greek capital letter delta, Δ, in free energy (ΔG) is simply:

$$\Delta G = \Delta H - T\Delta S$$

We can use the change in free energy, or ΔG, to predict whether a chemical reaction is spontaneous or not. For some reactions, the ΔG is positive, which means that the products of the reaction contain *more* free energy than the reactants; the bond energy *(H)* is higher, or the disorder *(S)* in the system is lower. Such reactions do not proceed spontaneously because they require an input of energy. Any reaction that requires an input of energy is said to be **endergonic** ("inward energy").

For other reactions, the ΔG is negative. In this case, the products of the reaction contain less free energy than the reactants; either the bond energy is lower, or the disorder is higher, or both. Such reactions tend to proceed spontaneously. These reactions release the excess free energy as heat and are thus said to be **exergonic** ("outward energy"). Any chemical reaction tends to proceed spontaneously if the difference in disorder *(TΔS)* is *greater* than the difference in bond energies between reactants and products *(ΔH)*.

Note that *spontaneous* does not mean the same thing as *instantaneous.* A spontaneous reaction may proceed very slowly. Figure 6.4 sums up endergonic and exergonic reactions.

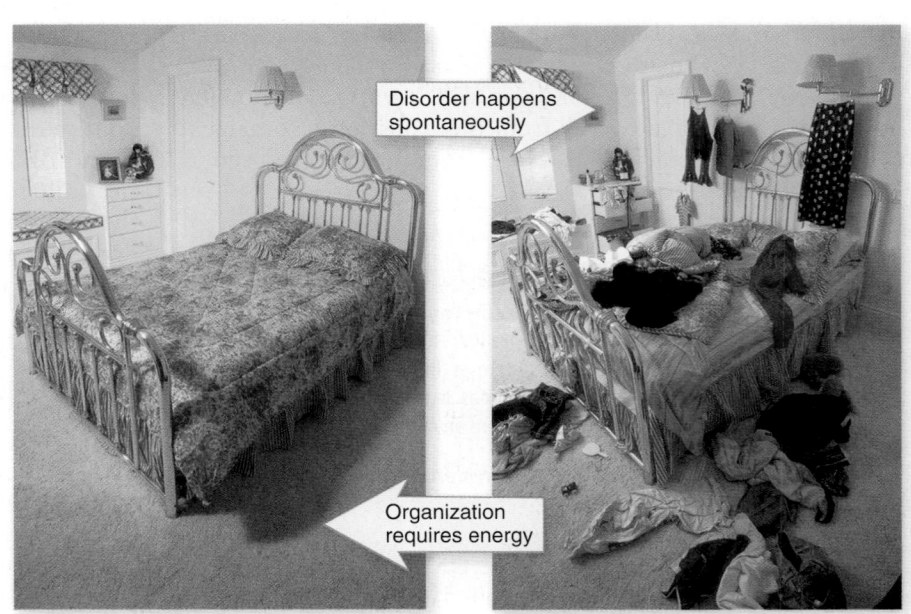

Figure 6.3 Entropy in action. As time elapses, the room shown at right becomes more disorganized. Entropy has increased in this room. It takes energy to restore it to the ordered state shown at left.

Disorder happens spontaneously

Organization requires energy

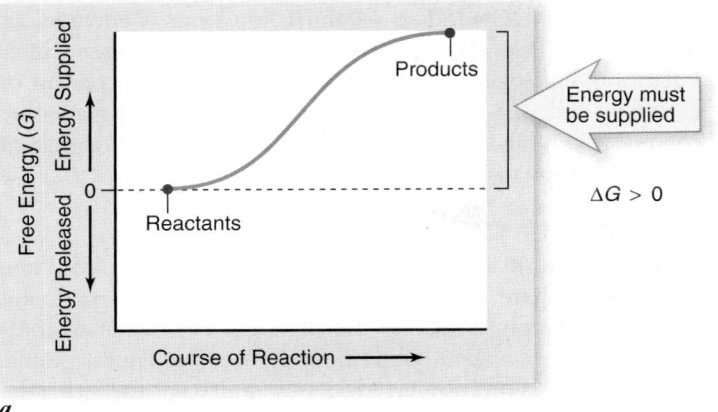

a.

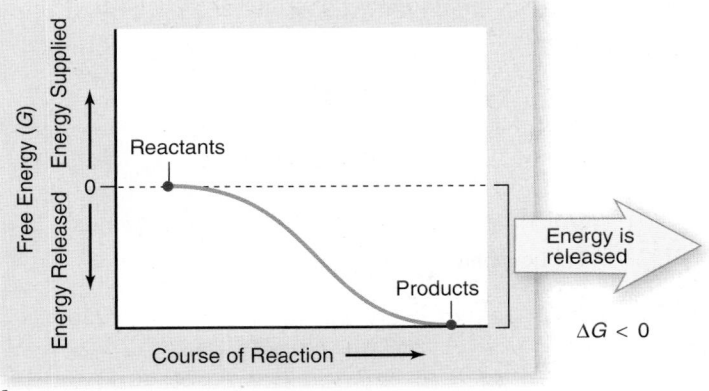

b.

Figure 6.4 Energy in chemical reactions. *a.* In an endergonic reaction, the products of the reaction contain more energy than the reactants, and the extra energy must be supplied for the reaction to proceed. *b.* In an exergonic reaction, the products contain less energy than the reactants, and the excess energy is released.

Because chemical reactions are reversible, a reaction that is exergonic in the forward direction will be endergonic in the reverse direction. For each reaction, an equilibrium exists at some point between the relative amounts of reactants and products. This equilibrium has a numeric value and is called the *equilibrium constant*. This characteristic of reactions provides us with another way to think about free energy changes: an exergonic reaction has an equilibrium favoring the products, and an endergonic reaction has an equilibrium favoring the reactants.

Spontaneous chemical reactions require activation energy

If all chemical reactions that release free energy tend to occur spontaneously, why haven't all such reactions already occurred? Consider the gasoline tank of your car: The oxidation of the hydrocarbons in gasoline is an exergonic reaction, but your gas tank does not spontaneously explode. One reason is that most reactions require an input of energy to get started. In the case of your car, this input consists of the electrical sparks in the engine's cylinders, producing a controlled explosion.

Activation energy

Before new chemical bonds can form, even bonds that contain less energy, existing bonds must first be broken, and that requires energy input. The extra energy needed to destabilize existing chemical bonds and initiate a chemical reaction is called **activation energy** (figure 6.5).

The rate of an exergonic reaction depends on the activation energy required for the reaction to begin. Reactions with larger activation energies tend to proceed more slowly because fewer molecules succeed in getting over the initial energy hurdle. The rate of reactions can be increased in two ways: (1) by increasing the energy of reacting molecules or (2) by lowering activation energy. Chemists often drive important industrial reactions by increasing the energy of the reacting molecules, which is frequently accomplished simply by heating up the reactants. The other strategy is to use a catalyst to lower the activation energy.

How catalysts work

Activation energies are not constant. Stressing particular chemical bonds can make them easier to break. The process of influencing chemical bonds in a way that lowers the activation energy needed to initiate a reaction is called **catalysis,** and substances that accomplish this are known as *catalysts* (see figure 6.5).

Catalysts cannot violate the basic laws of thermodynamics; they cannot, for example, make an endergonic reaction proceed spontaneously. By reducing the activation energy, a catalyst accelerates both the forward and the reverse reactions by exactly the same amount. Therefore, a catalyst does not alter the proportion of reactant that is ultimately converted into product.

To understand this, imagine a bowling ball resting in a shallow depression on the side of a hill. Only a narrow rim of dirt below the ball prevents it from rolling down the hill. Now imagine digging away that rim of dirt. If you remove enough dirt from below the ball, it will start to roll down the hill—but

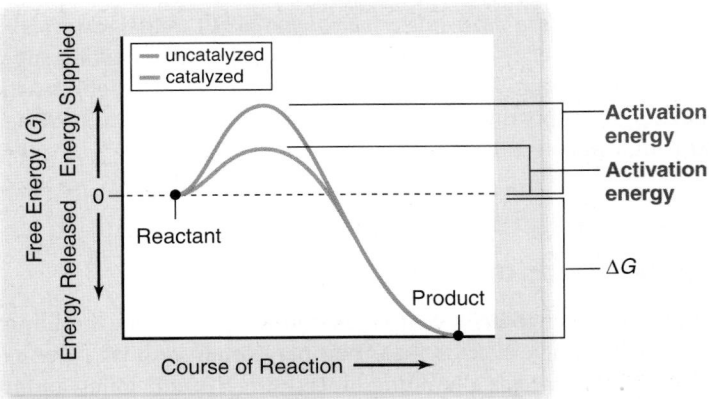

Figure 6.5 Activation energy and catalysis. Exergonic reactions do not necessarily proceed rapidly because activation energy must be supplied to destabilize existing chemical bonds. Catalysts accelerate particular reactions by lowering the amount of activation energy required to initiate the reaction. Catalysts do not alter the free-energy change produced by the reaction.

removing dirt from below the ball will *never* cause the ball to roll up the hill. Removing the lip of dirt simply allows the ball to move freely; gravity determines the direction it then travels.

Similarly, the direction in which a chemical reaction proceeds is determined solely by the difference in free energy between reactants and products. Like digging away the soil below the bowling ball on the hill, catalysts reduce the energy barrier that is preventing the reaction from proceeding. Only exergonic reactions can proceed spontaneously, and catalysts cannot change that. What catalysts *can* do is make a reaction proceed much faster. In living systems, enzymes act as catalysts.

Learning Outcomes Review 6.2

The First Law of Thermodynamics states that energy cannot be created or destroyed. The Second Law states that the loss of energy results in greater disorder, or entropy. Free-energy changes (ΔG) can predict whether chemical reactions take place. Reactions with a negative ΔG occur spontaneously, and those with a positive ΔG do not. Energy needed to initiate a reaction is termed activation energy. Catalysts, such as enzymes in living systems, lower this activation energy to speed up reactions.

■ **Can an enzyme make an endergonic reaction exergonic?**

6.3 ATP: The Energy Currency of Cells

Learning Outcomes

1. **Describe the role of ATP in short-term energy storage.**
2. **Explain what "high-energy" bonds are in ATP.**

The chief "currency" all cells use for their energy transactions is the nucleotide *adenosine triphosphate (ATP)*. ATP powers almost every energy-requiring process in cells, from making sugars, to supplying activation energy for chemical reactions, to actively transporting substances across membranes, to moving through the environment and growing.

Cells store and release energy in the bonds of ATP

You saw in chapter 3 that nucleotides serve as the building blocks for nucleic acids, but they play other cellular roles as well. ATP is used as a building block for RNA molecules, and it also has a critical function as a portable source of energy on demand for endergonic cellular processes.

The structure of ATP

Like all nucleotides, ATP is composed of three smaller components (figure 6.6). The first component is a five-carbon sugar, ribose, which serves as the framework to which the other two

subunits are attached. The second component is adenine, an organic molecule composed of two carbon–nitrogen rings. Each of the nitrogen atoms in the ring has an unshared pair of electrons and weakly attracts hydrogen ions, making adenine chemically a weak base. The third component of ATP is a chain of three phosphates.

How ATP stores energy

The key to how ATP stores energy lies in its triphosphate group. Phosphate groups are highly negatively charged, and thus they strongly repel one another. This electrostatic repulsion makes the covalent bonds joining the phosphates unstable. The molecule is often referred to as a "coiled spring," with the phosphates straining away from one another.

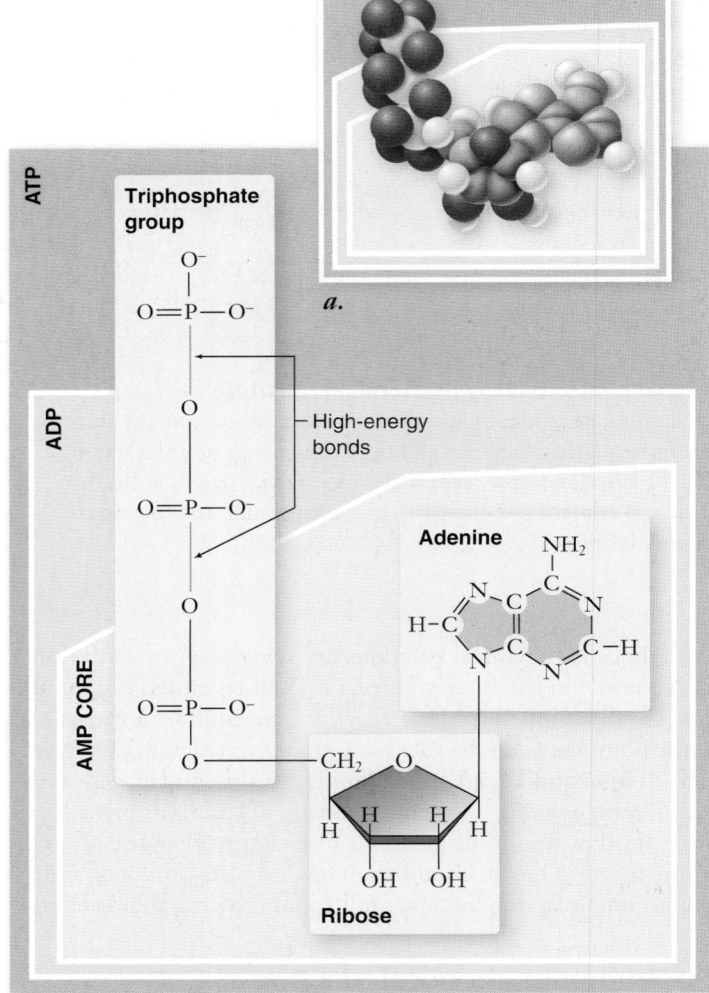

Figure 6.6 The ATP molecule. The model (*a*) and the structural diagram (*b*) both show that ATP has a core of AMP. Addition of one phosphate to AMP yields ADP, and addition of a second phosphate yields ATP. These two terminal phosphates are attached by high-energy bonds so that removing either by hydrolysis is an exergonic reaction that releases energy. ADP, adenosine diphosphate; AMP, adenosine monophosphate; ATP, adenosine triphosphate.

The unstable bonds holding the phosphates together in the ATP molecule have a low activation energy and are easily broken by hydrolysis. When they break, they can transfer a considerable amount of energy. In other words, the hydrolysis of ATP has a negative ΔG, and the energy it releases can be used to perform work.

In most reactions involving ATP, only the outermost high-energy phosphate bond is hydrolyzed, cleaving off the phosphate group on the end. When this happens, ATP becomes *adenosine diphosphate (ADP)* plus an **inorganic phosphate (P_i),** and energy equal to 7.3 kcal/mol is released under standard conditions. The liberated phosphate group usually attaches temporarily to some intermediate molecule. When that molecule is dephosphorylated, the phosphate group is released as P_i.

Both of the two terminal phosphates can be hydrolyzed to release energy, leaving *adenosine monophosphate (AMP)*, but the third phosphate is not attached by a high-energy bond. With only one phosphate group, AMP has no other phosphates to provide the electrostatic repulsion that makes the bonds holding the two terminal phosphate groups high-energy bonds.

ATP hydrolysis drives endergonic reactions

Cells use ATP to drive endergonic reactions. These reactions do not proceed spontaneously because their products possess more free energy than their reactants. However, if the cleavage of ATP's terminal high-energy bond releases more energy than the other reaction consumes, the two reactions can be coupled so that the energy released by the hydrolysis of ATP can be used to supply the endergonic reaction with the energy it needs. Coupled together, these reactions result in a net release of energy (–ΔG) and are therefore exergonic and proceed spontaneously. Because almost all the endergonic reactions in cells require less energy than is released by the cleavage of ATP, ATP can provide most of the energy a cell needs.

Inquiry question

When ATP hydrolysis is coupled with an endergonic reaction and supplies more than enough energy, is the overall process endergonic or exergonic? Would the ΔG for the overall process be negative or positive?

ATP cycles continuously

The same feature that makes ATP an effective energy donor—the instability of its phosphate bonds—prevents it from being a good long-term energy-storage molecule. Fats and carbohydrates serve that function better.

The use of ATP can be thought of as a cycle: Cells use exergonic reactions to provide the energy needed to synthesize ATP from ADP + P_i; they then use the hydrolysis of ATP to provide energy to drive the endergonic reactions they need (figure 6.7).

Most cells do not maintain large stockpiles of ATP. Instead, they typically have only a few seconds' supply of ATP at any given time, and they continually produce more from ADP and P_i. It is estimated that even a sedentary individual turns over an amount of ATP in one day roughly equal to his body weight. This statistic makes clear the importance of ATP synthesis. In the next two chapters we will explore in detail the cellular mechanisms for synthesizing ATP.

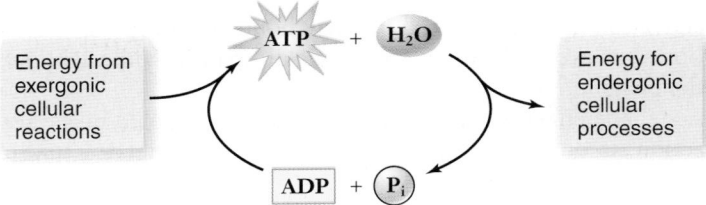

Figure 6.7 The ATP cycle. ATP is synthesized and hydrolyzed in a cyclic fashion. The synthesis of ATP from ADP + P_i is endergonic and is powered by exergonic cellular reactions. The hydrolysis of ATP to ADP + P_i is exergonic, and the energy released is used to power endergonic cellular functions such as muscle contraction. ADP, adenosine diphosphate; ATP, adenosine triphosphate; P_i, inorganic phosphate.

Learning Outcomes Review 6.3

ATP is a nucleotide with three phosphate groups. Endergonic cellular processes can be driven by coupling to the exergonic hydrolysis of the two terminal phosphates. The bonds holding the terminal phosphate groups together are easily broken, releasing energy like a coiled spring. The cell is constantly building ATP using exergonic reactions and breaking it down to drive endergonic reactions.

■ *If the molecular weight of ATP is 507.18 g/mol, and the ΔG for hydrolysis is –7.3 kcal/mol how much energy is released over the course of the day by a 100-kg man?*

6.4 Enzymes: Biological Catalysts

Learning Outcomes

1. Discuss the specificity of enzymes.
2. Explain how enzymes bind to their substrates.
3. List the factors that influence the rate of enzyme-catalyzed reactions.

The chemical reactions within living organisms are regulated by controlling the points at which catalysis takes place. Life itself, therefore, can be seen as regulated by catalysts. The agents that carry out most of the catalysis in living organisms are called enzymes. Most enzymes are proteins, although increasing evidence indicates that some enzymes are actually RNA molecules, as discussed later in this chapter.

An enzyme alters the activation energy of a reaction

The unique three-dimensional shape of an enzyme enables it to stabilize a temporary association between **substrates**—the molecules that will undergo the reaction. By bringing two substrates together in the correct orientation or by stressing particular chemical bonds of a substrate, an enzyme lowers the activation energy required for new bonds to form. The reaction thus proceeds much more quickly than it would without the enzyme.

The enzyme itself is not changed or consumed in the reaction, so only a small amount of an enzyme is needed, and it can be used over and over.

As an example of how an enzyme works, let's consider the reaction of carbon dioxide and water to form carbonic acid. This important enzyme-catalyzed reaction occurs in vertebrate red blood cells:

$$CO_2 + H_2O \rightleftharpoons H_2CO_3$$

carbon   water   carbonic
dioxide   acid

This reaction may proceed in either direction, but because it has a large activation energy, the reaction is very slow in the absence of an enzyme: Perhaps 200 molecules of carbonic acid form in an hour in a cell in the absence of any enzyme. Reactions that proceed this slowly are of little use to a cell. Vertebrate red blood cells overcome this problem by employing an enzyme within their cytoplasm called *carbonic anhydrase* (enzyme names usually end in "–ase"). Under the same conditions, but in the presence of carbonic anhydrase, an estimated 600,000 molecules of carbonic acid form every *second!* Thus, the enzyme increases the reaction rate by more than one million times.

Thousands of different kinds of enzymes are known, each catalyzing one or a few specific chemical reactions. By facilitating particular chemical reactions, the enzymes in a cell determine the course of metabolism—the collection of all chemical reactions—in that cell.

Different types of cells contain different sets of enzymes, and this difference contributes to structural and functional variations among cell types. For example, the chemical reactions taking place within a red blood cell differ from those that occur within a nerve cell, in part because different cell types contain different arrays of enzymes.

Active sites of enzymes conform to fit the shape of substrates

Most enzymes are globular proteins with one or more pockets or clefts, called **active sites,** on their surface (figure 6.8). Substrates bind to the enzyme at these active sites, forming an **enzyme–substrate complex** (figure 6.10). For catalysis to occur within the complex, a substrate molecule must fit precisely into an active site. When that happens, amino acid side groups of the enzyme end up very close to certain bonds of the substrate. These side groups interact chemically with the substrate, usually stressing or distorting a particular bond and consequently lowering the activation energy needed to break the bond. After the bonds of the substrates are broken, or new bonds are formed, the substrates have been converted to products. These products then dissociate from the enzyme, leaving the enzyme ready to bind its next substrate and begin the cycle again.

Proteins are not rigid. The binding of a substrate induces the enzyme to adjust its shape slightly, leading to a better *induced fit* between enzyme and substrate (see figure 6.9).

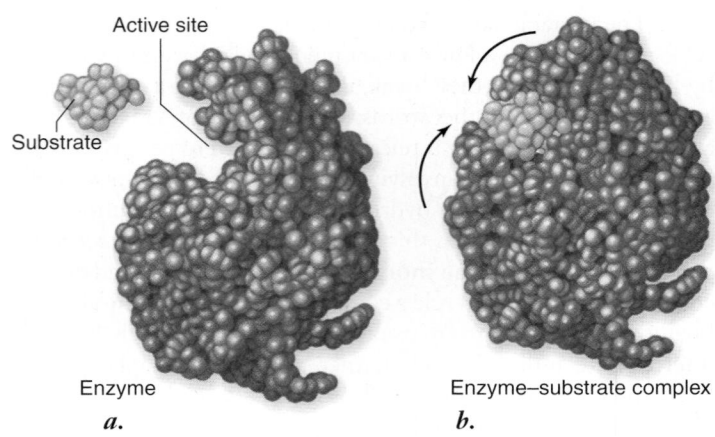

Active site

Substrate

Enzyme
a.

Enzyme–substrate complex
b.

Figure 6.8 Enzyme binding its substrate. *a.* The active site of the enzyme lysozyme fits the shape of its substrate, a peptidoglycan that makes up bacterial cell walls. *b.* When the substrate, indicated in yellow, slides into the groove of the active site, the protein is induced to alter its shape slightly and bind the substrate more tightly. This alteration of the shape of the enzyme to better fit the substrate is called induced fit.

This interaction may also facilitate the binding of other substrates; in such cases, one substrate "activates" the enzyme to receive other substrates.

Enzymes occur in many forms

Although many enzymes are suspended in the cytoplasm of cells, not attached to any structure, other enzymes function as

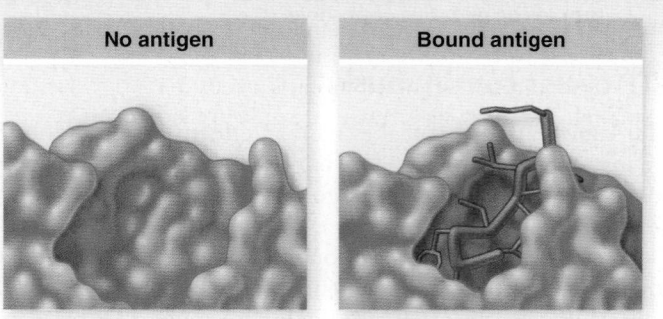

SCIENTIFIC THINKING

Hypothesis: *Protein structure is flexible not rigid.*

Prediction: *Antibody–antigen binding can involve a change in protein structure.*

Test: *Determine crystal structure of a fragment of a specific antibody with no antigen bound, and with antigen bound for comparison.*

No antigen   Bound antigen

Result: *After binding, the antibody folds around the antigen forming a pocket.*

Conclusion: *In this case, binding involves an induced-fit kind of change in conformation.*

Further Experiments: *Why is this experiment easier to do with an antibody than with an enzyme? Can this experiment be done with an enzyme?*

Figure 6.9 Induced-fit binding of antibody to antigen.

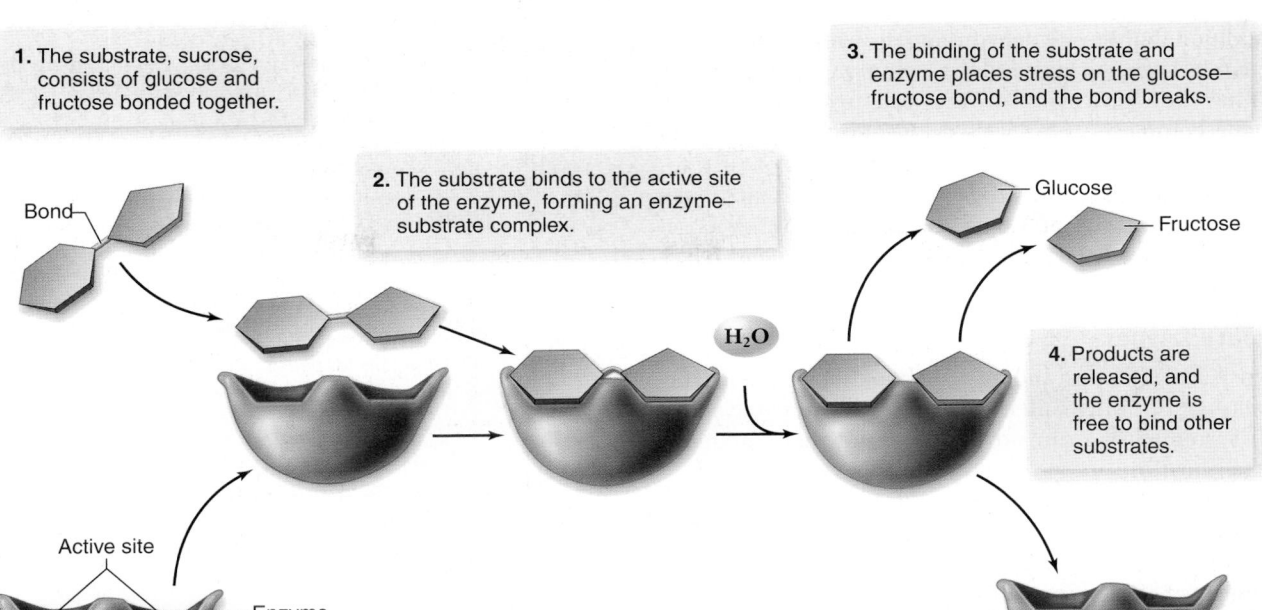

1. The substrate, sucrose, consists of glucose and fructose bonded together.

2. The substrate binds to the active site of the enzyme, forming an enzyme–substrate complex.

3. The binding of the substrate and enzyme places stress on the glucose–fructose bond, and the bond breaks.

4. Products are released, and the enzyme is free to bind other substrates.

Bond

Glucose

Fructose

H_2O

Active site

Enzyme sucrase

Figure 6.10 The catalytic cycle of an enzyme. Enzymes increase the speed at which chemical reactions occur, but they are not altered permanently themselves as they do so. In the reaction illustrated here, the enzyme sucrase is splitting the sugar sucrose into two simpler sugars: glucose and fructose.

integral parts of cell membranes and organelles. Enzymes may also form associations called *multienzyme complexes* to carry out reaction sequences. And, as mentioned earlier, evidence exists that some enzymes may consist of RNA rather than being only protein.

Multienzyme complexes

Often several enzymes catalyzing different steps of a sequence of reactions are associated with one another in noncovalently bonded assemblies called **multienzyme complexes.** The bacterial pyruvate dehydrogenase multienzyme complex, shown in figure 6.11, contains enzymes that carry out three sequential reactions in oxidative metabolism. Each complex has multiple copies of each of the three enzymes—60 protein subunits in all. The many subunits work together to form a molecular machine that performs multiple functions.

Multienzyme complexes offer the following significant advantages in catalytic efficiency:

1. The rate of any enzyme reaction is limited by how often the enzyme collides with its substrate. If a series of sequential reactions occurs within a multienzyme complex, the product of one reaction can be delivered to the next enzyme without releasing it to diffuse away.

2. Because the reacting substrate doesn't leave the complex while it goes through the series of reactions, unwanted side reactions are prevented.

3. All of the reactions that take place within the multienzyme complex can be controlled as a unit.

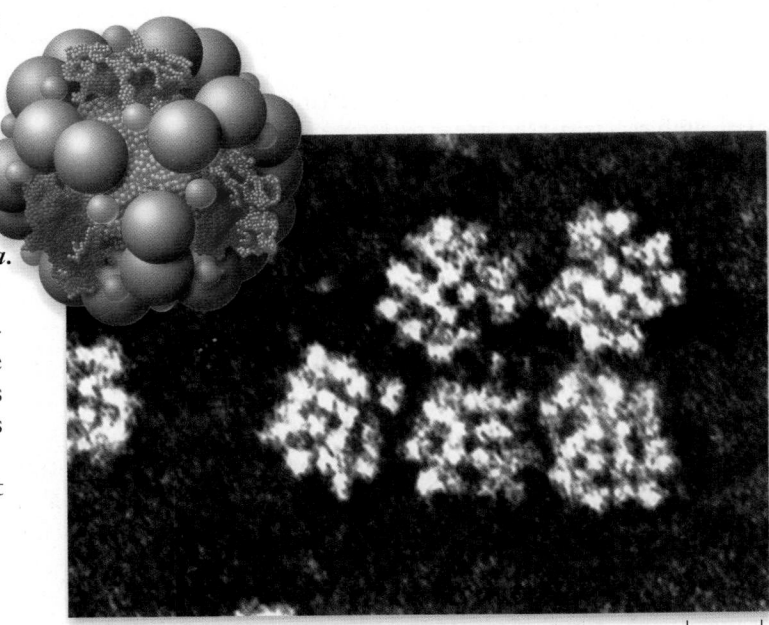

a.

b.

0.050 μm

Figure 6.11 A complex enzyme: pyruvate dehydrogenase. Pyruvate dehydrogenase, which catalyzes the oxidation of pyruvate, is one of the most complex enzymes known. *a.* A model of the enzyme showing the arrangement of the 60 protein subunits. *b.* Many of the protein subunits are clearly visible in the electron micrograph.

In addition to pyruvate dehydrogenase, which controls entry to the Krebs cycle during aerobic respiration (see chapter 7), several other key processes in the cell are catalyzed by multienzyme complexes. One well-studied system is the fatty acid synthetase complex that catalyzes the synthesis of fatty acids from two-carbon precursors. Seven different enzymes make up this multienzyme complex, and the intermediate reaction products remain associated with the complex for the entire series of reactions.

Nonprotein enzymes

Until a few years ago, most biology textbooks contained statements such as "Proteins called enzymes are the catalysts of biological systems." We can no longer make that statement without qualification.

Thomas J. Cech and colleagues at the University of Colorado reported in 1981 that certain reactions involving RNA molecules appear to be catalyzed in cells by RNA itself, rather than by enzymes. This initial observation has been corroborated by additional examples of RNA catalysis. Like enzymes, these RNA catalysts, which are loosely called "ribozymes," greatly accelerate the rate of particular biochemical reactions and show extraordinary substrate specificity.

Research has revealed at least two sorts of ribozymes. Some ribozymes have folded structures and catalyze reactions on themselves, a process called *intra*molecular catalysis. Other ribozymes act on other molecules without being changed themselves, a process called *inter*molecular catalysis.

The most striking example of the role of RNA as enzyme is emerging from recent work on the structure and function of the ribosome. For many years it was thought that RNA was a structural framework for this vital organelle, but it is now clear that ribosomal RNA plays a key role in ribosome function. The ribosome itself is a ribozyme.

The ability of RNA, an informational molecule, to act as a catalyst has stirred great excitement because it seems to answer the question—Which came first, the protein or the nucleic acid? It now seems at least possible that RNA evolved first and may have catalyzed the formation of the first proteins.

Environmental and other factors affect enzyme function

The rate of an enzyme-catalyzed reaction is affected by the concentrations of both the substrate and the enzyme that works on it. In addition, any chemical or physical factor that alters the enzyme's three-dimensional shape—such as temperature, pH, and the binding of regulatory molecules—can affect the enzyme's ability to catalyze the reaction.

Temperature

Increasing the temperature of an uncatalyzed reaction increases its rate because the additional heat increases random molecular movement. This motion can add stress to molecular bonds and affect the activation energy of a reaction.

The rate of an enzyme-catalyzed reaction also increases with temperature, but only up to a point called the *optimum*

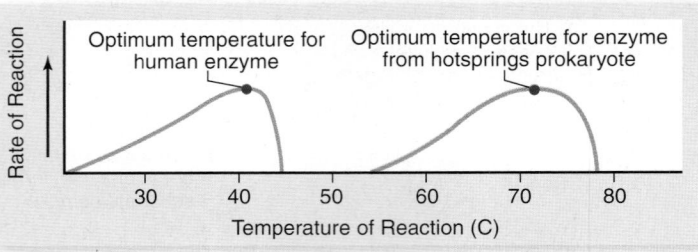

a.

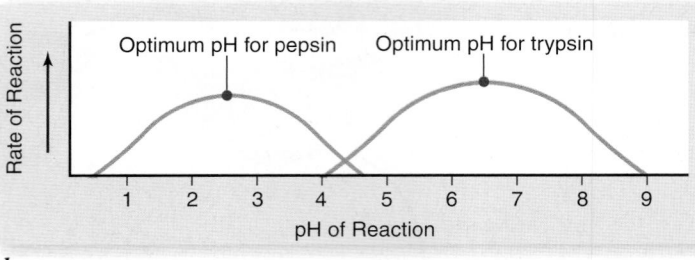

b.

Figure 6.12 Enzyme sensitivity to the environment. The activity of an enzyme is influenced by both (*a*) temperature and (*b*) pH. Most human enzymes, such as the protein-degrading enzyme trypsin, work best at temperatures of about 40°C and within a pH range of 6 to 8. The hot springs prokaryote tolerates a higher environmental temperature and a correspondingly higher temperature optimum for enzymes. Pepsin works in the acidic environment of the stomach and has a lower optimum pH.

temperature (figure 6.12*a*). Below this temperature, the hydrogen bonds and hydrophobic interactions that determine the enzyme's shape are not flexible enough to permit the induced fit that is optimum for catalysis. Above the optimum temperature, these forces are too weak to maintain the enzyme's shape against the increased random movement of the atoms in the enzyme. At higher temperatures, the enzyme denatures, as described in chapter 3.

Most human enzymes have an optimum temperature between 35°C and 40°C—a range that includes normal body temperature. Prokaryotes that live in hot springs have more stable enzymes (that is, enzymes held together more strongly), so the optimum temperature for those enzymes can be 70°C or higher. In each case the optimal temperature for the enzyme corresponds to the "normal" temperature usually encountered in the body or the environment, depending on the type of organism.

pH

Ionic interactions between oppositely charged amino acid residues, such as glutamic acid (−) and lysine (+), also hold enzymes together. These interactions are sensitive to the hydrogen ion concentration of the fluid in which the enzyme is dissolved, because changing that concentration shifts the balance between positively and negatively charged amino acid residues. For this reason, most enzymes have an *optimum pH* that usually ranges from pH 6 to 8.

Enzymes able to function in very acidic environments are proteins that maintain their three-dimensional shape even in the presence of high hydrogen ion concentrations. The enzyme pepsin, for example, digests proteins in the stomach at pH 2, a very acidic level (figure 6.12b).

Inhibitors and activators

Enzyme activity is also sensitive to the presence of specific substances that can bind to the enzyme and cause changes in its shape. Through these substances, a cell is able to regulate which of its enzymes are active and which are inactive at a particular time. This ability allows the cell to increase its efficiency and to control changes in its characteristics during development. A substance that binds to an enzyme and *decreases* its activity is called an **inhibitor.** Very often, the end product of a biochemical pathway acts as an inhibitor of an early reaction in the pathway, a process called *feedback inhibition* (discussed later in this chapter).

Enzyme inhibition occurs in two ways: **Competitive inhibitors** compete with the substrate for the same active site, occupying the active site and thus preventing substrates from binding; **noncompetitive inhibitors** bind to the enzyme in a location other than the active site, changing the shape of the enzyme and making it unable to bind to the substrate (figure 6.13).

Many enzymes can exist in either an active or inactive conformation; such enzymes are called *allosteric enzymes.* Most noncompetitive inhibitors bind to a specific portion of the enzyme called an **allosteric site.** These sites serve as chemical on/off switches; the binding of a substance to the site can switch the enzyme between its active and inactive configurations. A substance that binds to an allosteric site and reduces enzyme activity is called an **allosteric inhibitor** (figure 6.13b).

This kind of control is also used to activate enzymes. An **allosteric activator** binds to allosteric sites to keep an enzyme in its active configuration, thereby *increasing* enzyme activity.

Enzyme cofactors

Enzyme function is often assisted by additional chemical components known as **cofactors.** These can be metal ions that are often found in the active site participating directly in catalysis. For example, the metallic ion zinc is used by some enzymes, such as protein-digesting carboxypeptidase, to draw electrons away from their position in covalent bonds, making the bonds less stable and easier to break. Other metallic elements, such as molybdenum and manganese, are also used as cofactors. Like zinc, these substances are required in the diet in small amounts.

When the cofactor is a nonprotein organic molecule, it is called a **coenzyme.** Many of the small organic molecules essential in our diets that we call vitamins function as coenzymes. For example the B vitamins B_6 and B_{12}, both function as coenzymes for a number of different enzymes. Modified nucleotides are also used as coenzymes.

In numerous oxidation–reduction reactions that are catalyzed by enzymes, the electrons pass in pairs from the active site of the enzyme to a coenzyme that serves as the electron acceptor. The coenzyme then transfers the electrons to a different enzyme, which releases them (and the energy they bear) to the substrates in another reaction. Often, the electrons combine with protons (H^+) to form hydrogen atoms. In this way, coenzymes shuttle energy in the form of hydrogen atoms from one enzyme to another in a cell. The role of coenzymes and the specifics of their action will be explored in detail in the following two chapters.

Learning Outcomes Review 6.4

Enzymes are biological catalysts that accelerate chemical reactions inside the cell. Enzymes bind to their substrates based on molecular shape, which allows them to be highly specific. Enzyme activity is affected by conditions such as temperature and pH and the presence of inhibitors or activators. Some enzymes also require an inorganic cofactor or an organic coenzyme.

■ *Why do proteins and RNA function as enzymes but DNA does not?*

6.5 Metabolism: The Chemical Description of Cell Function

Learning Outcomes

1. *Explain the kinds of reactions that make up metabolism.*
2. *Discuss what is meant by a metabolic pathway.*
3. *Recognize that metabolism is a product of evolution.*

Living chemistry, the total of all chemical reactions carried out by an organism, is called **metabolism.** Those chemical reactions that expend energy to build up molecules are called *anabolic* reactions, or **anabolism.** Reactions that harvest energy by breaking down molecules are called *catabolic* reactions, or **catabolism.** This section presents a general overview of metabolic processes that will be described in much greater detail in later chapters.

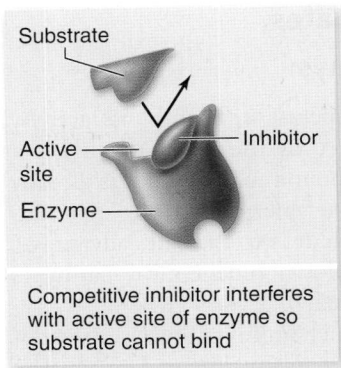

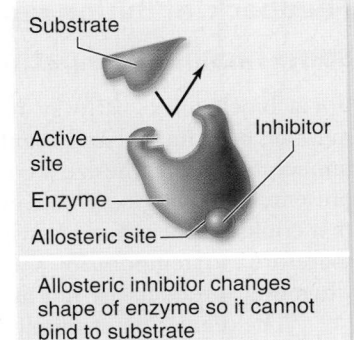

Competitive inhibitor interferes with active site of enzyme so substrate cannot bind

Allosteric inhibitor changes shape of enzyme so it cannot bind to substrate

a. Competitive inhibition   *b.* Noncompetitive inhibition

Figure 6.13 How enzymes can be inhibited. *a.* In competitive inhibition, the inhibitor has a shape similar to the substrate and competes for the active site of the enzyme. *b.* In noncompetitive inhibition, the inhibitor binds to the enzyme at the allosteric site, a place away from the active site, effecting a conformational change in the enzyme, making it unable to bind to its substrate.

Biochemical pathways organize chemical reactions in cells

Organisms contain thousands of different kinds of enzymes that catalyze a bewildering variety of reactions. Many of these reactions in a cell occur in sequences called **biochemical pathways.** In such pathways, the product of one reaction becomes the substrate for the next (figure 6.14). Biochemical pathways are the organizational units of metabolism—the elements an organism controls to achieve coherent metabolic activity.

Many sequential enzyme steps in biochemical pathways take place in specific compartments of the cell; for example, the steps of the Krebs cycle (see chapter 7) occur in the matrix inside mitochondria in eukaryotes. By determining where many of the enzymes that catalyze these steps are located, we can "map out" a model of metabolic processes in the cell.

Biochemical pathways may have evolved in stepwise fashion

In the earliest cells, the first biochemical processes probably involved energy-rich molecules scavenged from the environment. Most of the molecules necessary for these processes are thought to have existed independently in the "organic soup" of the early oceans.

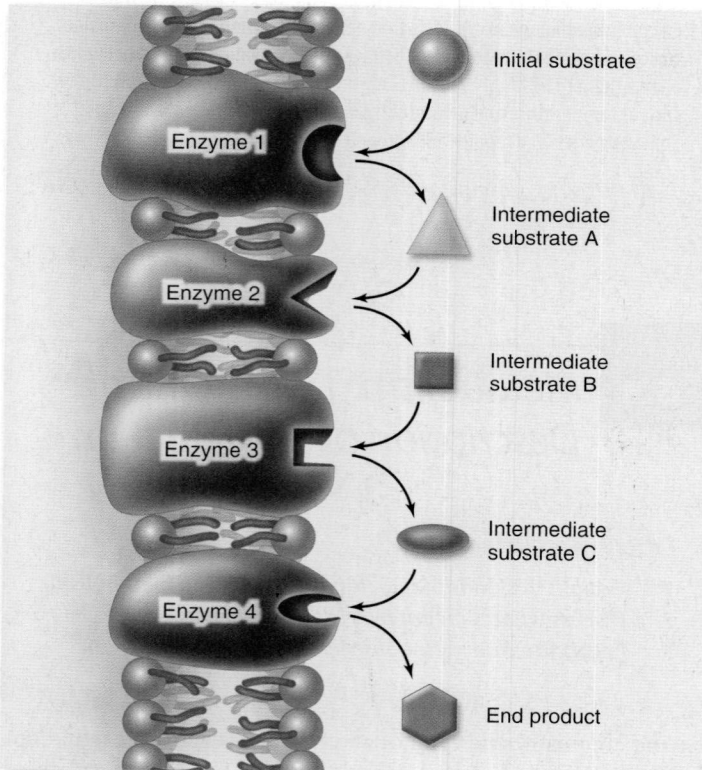

Figure 6.14 A biochemical pathway. The original substrate is acted on by enzyme 1, changing the substrate to a new intermediate, substrate A, recognized as a substrate by enzyme 2. Each enzyme in the pathway acts on the product of the previous stage. These enzymes may be either soluble or arranged in a membrane as shown.

The first catalyzed reactions were probably simple, one-step reactions that brought these molecules together in various combinations. Eventually, the energy-rich molecules became depleted in the external environment, and only organisms that had evolved some means of making those molecules from other substances could survive. Thus, a hypothetical reaction,

$$\begin{array}{c} F \\ + \longrightarrow H \\ G \end{array}$$

where two energy-rich molecules (F and G) react to produce compound H and release energy, became more complex when the supply of F in the environment ran out.

A new reaction was added in which the depleted molecule, F, is made from another molecule, E, which was also present in the environment:

$$\begin{array}{c} E \longrightarrow F \\ + \longrightarrow H \\ G \end{array}$$

When the supply of E was in turn exhausted, organisms that were able to make E from some other available precursor, D, survived. When D was depleted, those organisms in turn were replaced by ones able to synthesize D from another molecule, C:

$$\begin{array}{c} C \longrightarrow D \longrightarrow E \longrightarrow F \\ + \longrightarrow H \\ G \end{array}$$

This hypothetical biochemical pathway would have evolved slowly through time, with the final reactions in the pathway evolving first and earlier reactions evolving later.

Looking at the pathway now, we would say that the "advanced" organism, starting with compound C, is able to synthesize H by means of a series of steps. This is how the biochemical pathways within organisms are thought to have evolved—not all at once, but one step at a time, backwards.

Feedback inhibition regulates some biochemical pathways

For a biochemical pathway to operate efficiently, its activity must be coordinated and regulated by the cell. Not only is it unnecessary to synthesize a compound when plenty is already present, but doing so would waste energy and raw materials that could be put to use elsewhere. It is to the cell's advantage, therefore, to temporarily shut down biochemical pathways when their products are not needed.

The regulation of simple biochemical pathways often depends on an elegant feedback mechanism: The end-product of the pathway binds to an allosteric site on the enzyme that catalyzes the first reaction in the pathway. This mode of regulation is called **feedback inhibition** (figure 6.15).

In the hypothetical pathway we just described, the enzyme catalyzing the reaction C $\longrightarrow$ D would possess an allosteric site for H, the end-product of the pathway. As the pathway churned out its product and the amount of H in the cell increased, it would become more likely that an H molecule would encounter

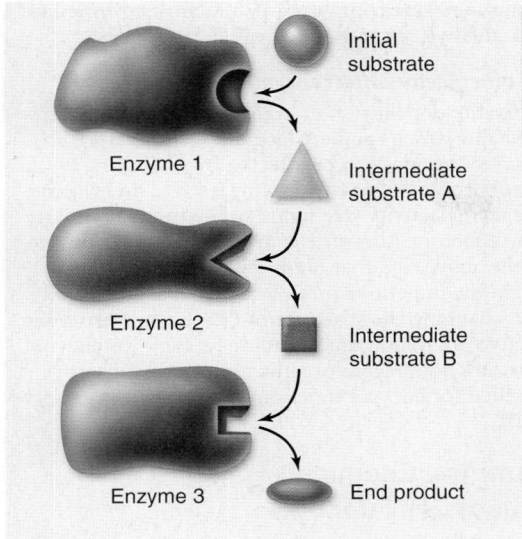

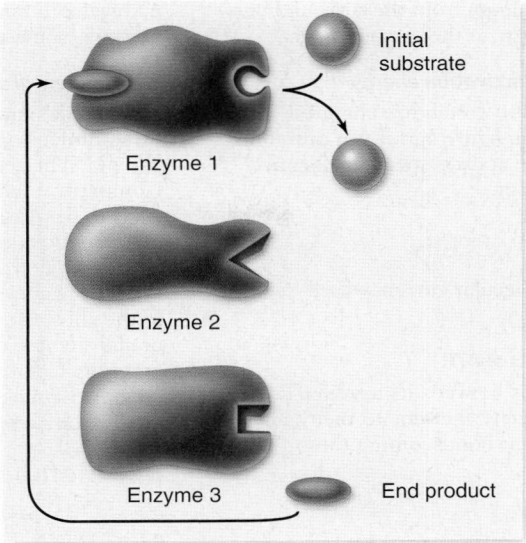

a.   b.

Figure 6.15 Feedback inhibition. *a.* A biochemical pathway with no feedback inhibition. *b.* A biochemical pathway in which the final end-product becomes the allosteric inhibitor for the first enzyme in the pathway. In other words, the formation of the pathway's final end-product stops the pathway. The pathway could be the synthesis of an amino acid, a nucleotide, or another important cellular molecule.

the allosteric site on the C $\longrightarrow$ D enzyme. Binding to the allosteric site would essentially shut down the reaction C $\longrightarrow$ D and in turn effectively shut down the whole pathway.

In this chapter we have reviewed the basics of energy and its transformations as carried out in living systems. Chemical bonds are the primary location of energy storage and release, and cells have developed elegant methods of making and breaking chemical bonds to create the molecules they need. Enzymes facilitate these reactions by serving as catalysts. In the following chapters you will learn the details of the mechanisms by which organisms harvest, store, and utilize energy.

Learning Outcomes Review 6.5

Metabolism is the sum of all chemical reactions in a cell. Anabolic reactions use energy to build up molecules. Catabolic reactions release energy by breaking down molecules. In a metabolic pathway, the end-product of one reaction is the substrate for the next reaction. Evolution may have favored organisms that could use precursor molecules to synthesize a nutrient. Over time, more reactions would be linked together as novel enzymes arose by mutation.

■ *Is a catabolic pathway likely to be subject to feedback inhibition?*

Chapter Review

6.1 The Flow of Energy in Living Systems

Thermodynamics is the study of energy changes.

Energy can take many forms.

Energy is the capacity to do work. Potential energy is stored energy, and kinetic energy is the energy of motion. Energy can take many forms: mechanical, heat, sound, electric current, light, or radioactive radiation. Energy is measured in units of heat known as kilocalories.

The Sun provides energy for living systems.

Photosynthesis stores light energy from the Sun as potential energy in the covalent bonds of sugar molecules. Breaking these bonds in living cells releases energy for use in other reactions.

Oxidation–reduction reactions transfer electrons while bonds are made or broken.

Oxidation is a reaction involving the loss of electrons. Reduction is the gain of electrons (see figure 6.2). These two reactions take place together and are therefore termed redox reactions.

6.2 The Laws of Thermodynamics and Free Energy

The First Law states that energy cannot be created or destroyed.

Virtually all activities of living organisms require energy. Energy changes form as it moves through organisms and their biochemical systems, but it is not created or destroyed.

The Second Law states that some energy is lost as disorder increases.

The disorder, or entropy, of the universe is continuously increasing. In an open system like the Earth, which is receiving energy from the Sun, this may not be the case. To increase order however, energy must be expended. In energy conversions, some energy is always lost as heat.

Chemical reactions can be predicted based on changes in free energy.

Free energy (G) is the energy available to do work in any system. Changes in free energy (ΔG) predict the direction of reactions. Reactions with a negative ΔG are spontaneous (exergonic) reactions, and reactions with a positive ΔG are not spontaneous (endergonic).

Endergonic chemical reactions absorb energy from the surroundings, whereas exergonic reactions release energy to the surroundings.

Spontaneous chemical reactions require activation energy.

Activation energy is the energy required to destabilize chemical bonds and initiate chemical reactions (see figure 6.5). Even exergonic reactions require this activation energy. Catalysts speed up chemical reactions by lowering the activation energy.

6.3 ATP: The Energy Currency of Cells

Adenosine triphosphate (ATP) is the molecular currency used for cellular energy transactions.

Cells store and release energy in the bonds of ATP.

The energy of ATP is stored in the bonds between its terminal phosphate groups. These groups repel each other due to their negative charge and therefore the covalent bonds joining these phosphates are unstable.

ATP hydrolysis drives endergonic reactions.

Enzymes hydrolyze the terminal phosphate group of ATP to release energy for reactions. If ATP hydrolysis is coupled to an endergonic reaction with a positive ΔG with magnitude less than that for ATP hydrolysis, the two reactions together will be exergonic.

ATP cycles continuously.

ATP hydrolysis releases energy to drive endergonic reactions, and it is synthesized with energy from exergonic reactions (see figure 6.7).

6.4 Enzymes: Biological Catalysts

An enzyme alters the activation energy of a reaction.

Enzymes lower the activation energy needed to initiate a chemical reaction.

Active sites of enzymes conform to fit the shape of substrates.

Substrates bind to the active site of an enzyme. Enzymes adjust their shape to the substrate so there is a better fit (see figure 6.8).

Enzymes occur in many forms.

Enzymes can be free in the cytosol or exist as components bound to membranes and organelles. Enzymes involved in a biochemical pathway can form multienzyme complexes. While most enzymes are proteins, some are actually RNA molecules, called ribozymes.

Environmental and other factors affect enzyme function.

An enzyme's functionality depends on its ability to maintain its three-dimensional shape, which can be affected by temperature and pH. The activity of enzymes can be affected by inhibitors. Competitive inhibitors compete for the enzyme's active site, which leads to decreased enzyme activity (see figure 6.13). Enzyme activity can be controlled by effectors. Allosteric enzymes have a second site, located away from the active site, that binds effectors to activate or inhibit the enzyme. Noncompetitive inhibitors and activators bind to the allosteric site, changing the structure of the enzyme to inhibit or activate it. Cofactors are nonorganic metals necessary for enzyme function. Coenzymes are nonprotein organic molecules, such as certain vitamins, needed for enzyme function. Often coenzymes serve as electron acceptors.

6.5 Metabolism: The Chemical Description of Cell Function

Metabolism is the sum of all biochemical reactions in a cell. Anabolic reactions require energy to build up molecules, and catabolic reactions break down molecules and release energy.

Biochemical pathways organize chemical reactions in cells.

Chemical reactions in biochemical pathways use the product of one reaction as the substrate for the next.

Biochemical pathways may have evolved in stepwise fashion.

In the primordial "soup" of the early oceans, many reactions were probably single-step reactions combining two molecules. As one of the substrate molecules was depleted, organisms having an enzyme that could synthesize the substrate would have a selective advantage. In this manner, biochemical pathways are thought to have evolved "backward" with new reactions producing limiting substrates for existing reactions.

Feedback inhibition regulates some biochemical pathways.

Biosynthetic pathways are often regulated by the end product of the pathway. Feedback inhibition occurs when the end-product of a reaction combines with an enzyme's allosteric site to shut down the enzyme's activity (see figure 6.15).

Review Questions

UNDERSTAND

1. A covalent bond between two atoms represents what kind of energy?
   a. Kinetic energy
   b. Potential energy
   c. Mechanical energy
   d. Solar energy

2. During a redox reaction the molecule that gains an electron has been
   a. reduced and now has a higher energy level.
   b. oxidized and now has a lower energy level.
   c. reduced and now has a lower energy level.
   d. oxidized and now has a higher energy level.

3. An endergonic reaction has the following properties
   a. $+\Delta G$ and the reaction is spontaneous.
   b. $+\Delta G$ and the reaction is not spontaneous.
   c. $-\Delta G$ and the reaction is spontaneous.
   d. $-\Delta G$ and the reaction is not spontaneous.

4. A spontaneous reaction is one in which
   a. the reactants have a higher free energy than the products.
   b. the products have a higher free energy than the reactants.
   c. an input of energy is required.
   d. entropy is decreased.

5. What is *activation energy*?
   a. The thermal energy associated with random movements of molecules
   b. The energy released through breaking chemical bonds
   c. The difference in free energy between reactants and products
   d. The energy required to initiate a chemical reaction

6. Which of the following is NOT a property of a catalyst?
   a. A catalyst reduces the activation energy of a reaction.
   b. A catalyst lowers the free energy of the reactants.
   c. A catalyst does not change as a result of the reaction.
   d. A catalyst works in both the forward and reverse directions of a reaction.

7. Where is the energy stored in a molecule of ATP?
   a. Within the bonds between nitrogen and carbon
   b. In the carbon-to-carbon bonds found in the ribose
   c. In the phosphorus-to-oxygen double bond
   d. In the bonds connecting the two terminal phosphate groups

APPLY

1. Cells use ATP to drive endergonic reactions because
   a. ATP is the universal catalyst.
   b. energy released by ATP hydrolysis makes ΔG for coupled reactions more negative.
   c. energy released by ATP hydrolysis makes ΔG for coupled reactions more positive.
   d. the conversion of ATP to ADP is also endergonic.

2. Which of the following statements is NOT true about enzymes?
   a. Enzymes use the three-dimensional shape of their active site to bind reactants.
   b. Enzymes lower the activation energy for a reaction.
   c. Enzymes make ΔG for a reaction more negative.
   d. Enzymes can catalyze the forward and reverse directions of a reaction.

3. What is the function of the *active site* of an enzyme?
   a. Bind the substrate, forming an enzyme–substrate complex
   b. Side groups within the active site interact with the substrate
   c. Bind to regulatory molecules, thereby altering the enzymes conformation
   d. Both a and b

4. The discovery of ribozymes meant that
   a. only proteins have catalytic function.
   b. only nucleic acids have catalytic function.
   c. RNAs can act as enzymes.
   d. RNA has the same function as protein.

5. Enzymes have similar responses to both changes in temperature and pH. The effect of both is on the
   a. rate of movement of the substrate molecules.
   b. strength of the chemical bonds within the substrate.
   c. three-dimensional shape of the enzyme.
   d. rate of movement of the enzyme.

6. In feedback inhibition, the
   a. first enzyme in a pathway is inhibited by its own product.
   b. last enzyme in a pathway is inhibited by its own product.
   c. first enzyme in a pathway is inhibited by the end-product of the pathway.
   d. last enzyme in a pathway is inhibited by the end-product of the pathway.

SYNTHESIZE

1. Examine the graph showing the rate of reaction versus temperature for an enzyme–catalyzed reaction in a human.
   a. Describe what is happening to the enzyme at around 40°C.
   b. Explain why the line touches the *x*-axis at approximately 20°C and 45°C.
   c. Average body temperature for humans is 37°C. Suggest a reason why the temperature optimum of this enzyme is greater than 37°C.

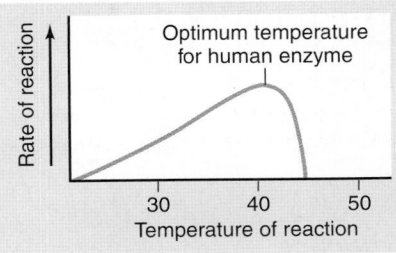

2. Phosphofructokinase functions to add a phosphate group to a molecule of fructose-6-phosphate. This enzyme functions early in glycolysis, an energy-yielding biochemical pathway discussed in chapter 7. The enzyme has an active site that binds fructose and ATP. An allosteric inhibitory site also binds ATP when cellular levels of ATP are very high.
   a. Predict the rate of the reaction if the levels of cellular ATP are low.
   b. Predict the rate of the reaction if levels of cellular ATP are very high.
   c. Describe what is happening to the enzyme when levels of ATP are very high.

ONLINE RESOURCE

www.ravenbiology.com

Understand, Apply, and Synthesize—enhance your study with animations that bring concepts to life and practice tests to assess your understanding. Your instructor may also recommend the interactive eBook, individualized learning tools, and more.

How Cells Harvest Energy

Chapter Outline

7.1 Overview of Respiration

7.2 Glycolysis: Splitting Glucose

7.3 The Oxidation of Pyruvate to Produce Acetyl-CoA

7.4 The Krebs Cycle

7.5 The Electron Transport Chain and Chemiosmosis

7.6 Energy Yield of Aerobic Respiration

7.7 Regulation of Aerobic Respiration

7.8 Oxidation Without O_2

7.9 Catabolism of Proteins and Fats

7.10 Evolution of Metabolism

Introduction

Life is driven by energy. All the activities organisms carry out—the swimming of bacteria, the purring of a cat, your thinking about these words—use energy. In this chapter, we discuss the processes all cells use to derive chemical energy from organic molecules and to convert that energy to ATP. Then, in chapter 8, we will examine photosynthesis, which uses light energy to make chemical energy. We consider the conversion of chemical energy to ATP first because all organisms, both the plant, a photosynthesizer, and the caterpillar feeding on the plant, pictured in the photo are capable of harvesting energy from chemical bonds. Energy harvest via respiration is a universal process.

- Foods contains carbs, proteins, fats
- Carbs + fats = C-H and C-O bonds

- Extracting energy from complex organic mixtures:
1. Digestion → large molecules to small
2. other enzymes break down C-H, C-O bonds and harvest their energy.

Learning Outcomes

1. Characterize oxidation–dehydrogenation reactions in biological systems.
2. Understand the role of electron carriers in energy metabolism.
3. Describe the role of ATP in biological systems.

Plants, algae, and some bacteria harvest the energy of sunlight through photosynthesis, converting radiant energy into chemical energy. These organisms, along with a few others that use chemical energy in a similar way, are called **autotrophs** ("self-feeders"). All other organisms live on the organic compounds autotrophs produce, using them as food, and are called **heterotrophs** ("fed by others"). At least 95% of the kinds of organisms on Earth—all animals and fungi, and most protists and prokaryotes—are heterotrophs. Autotrophs also extract energy from organic compounds—they just have the additional capacity to use the energy from sunlight to synthesize these compounds. The process by which energy is harvested is **cellular respiration**—the oxidation of organic compounds to extract energy from chemical bonds.

Autotrophs = photosynthesis
95%
Heterotrophs - eat what autotrophs make

Cells oxidize organic compounds to drive metabolism

Most foods contain a variety of carbohydrates, proteins, and fats, all rich in energy-laden chemical bonds. Carbohydrates and fats, as you recall from chapter 3, possess many carbon–hydrogen (C—H) bonds, as well as carbon–oxygen (C—O) bonds.

The job of extracting energy from the complex organic mixture in most foods is tackled in stages. First, enzymes break down the large molecules into smaller ones, a process called

Respiration - when energy is harvested by autotrophs

digestion (see chapter 48). Then, other enzymes dismantle these fragments a bit at a time, harvesting energy from C—H and other chemical bonds at each stage.

The reactions that break down these molecules share a common feature: They are oxidations. Energy metabolism is therefore concerned with redox reactions, and to understand the process we must follow the fate of the electrons lost from the food molecules.

These reactions are not the simple transfer of electrons, however; they are also **dehydrogenations**. That is, the electrons lost are accompanied by protons, so that what is really lost is a hydrogen atom, not just an electron.

Cellular respiration is the complete oxidation of glucose

In chapter 6, you learned that an atom that loses electrons is said to be *oxidized*, and an atom accepting electrons is said to be *reduced*. Oxidation reactions are often coupled with reduction reactions in living systems, and these paired reactions are called *redox reactions*. Cells utilize enzyme-facilitated redox reactions to take energy from food sources and convert it to ATP.

Redox reactions

Oxidation–reduction reactions play a key role in the flow of energy through biological systems because the electrons that pass from one atom to another carry energy with them. The amount of energy an electron possesses depends on its orbital position, or energy level, around the atom's nucleus. When this electron departs from one atom and moves to another in a redox reaction, the electron's energy is transferred with it.

Figure 7.1 shows how an enzyme catalyzes a redox reaction involving an energy-rich substrate molecule, with the help of a cofactor, **nicotinamide adenosine dinucleotide (NAD⁺)**. In this reaction, NAD⁺ accepts a pair of electrons from the substrate, along with a proton, to form **NADH** (this process is described in more detail shortly). The oxidized product is now released from the enzyme's active site, as is NADH.

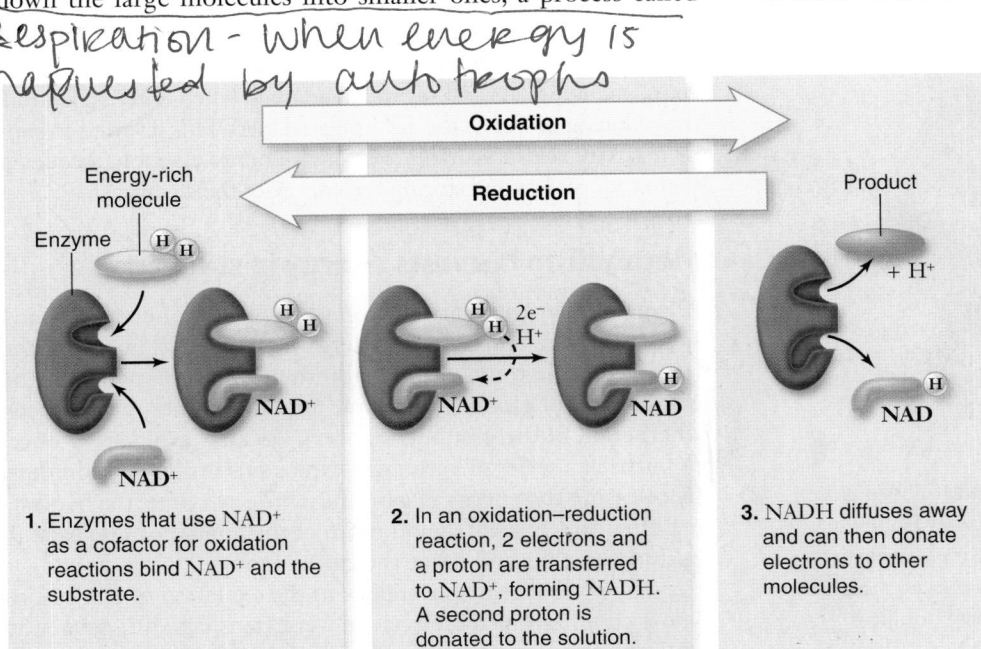

1. Enzymes that use NAD⁺ as a cofactor for oxidation reactions bind NAD⁺ and the substrate.
2. In an oxidation–reduction reaction, 2 electrons and a proton are transferred to NAD⁺, forming NADH. A second proton is donated to the solution.
3. NADH diffuses away and can then donate electrons to other molecules.

Figure 7.1 Oxidation–reduction reactions often employ cofactors. Cells use a chemical cofactor called nicotinamide adenosine dinucleotide (NAD⁺) to carry out many oxidation–reduction reactions. Two electrons and a proton are transferred to NAD⁺ with another proton donated to the solution. Molecules that gain electrons are said to be reduced, and ones that lose energetic electrons are said to be oxidized. NAD⁺ oxidizes energy-rich molecules by acquiring their electrons (in the figure, this proceeds 1 ⟶ 2 ⟶ 3) and then reduces other molecules by giving the electrons to them (in the figure, this proceeds 3 ⟶ 2 ⟶ 1). NADH is the reduced form of NAD⁺.

In the overall process of cellular energy harvest dozens of redox reactions take place, and a number of molecules, including NAD^+, act as electron acceptors. During each transfer of electrons energy is released. This energy may be captured and used to make ATP or to form other chemical bonds; the rest is lost as heat.

At the end of this process, high-energy electrons from the initial chemical bonds have lost much of their energy, and these depleted electrons are transferred to a final electron acceptor (figure 7.2). When this acceptor is oxygen, the process is called **aerobic respiration.** When the final electron acceptor is an inorganic molecule other than oxygen, the process is called **anaerobic respiration,** and when it is an organic molecule, the process is called **fermentation.**

"Burning" carbohydrates

Chemically, there is little difference between the catabolism of carbohydrates in a cell and the burning of wood in a fireplace. In both instances, the reactants are carbohydrates and oxygen, and the products are carbon dioxide, water, and energy:

$$\underset{\text{glucose}}{C_6H_{12}O_6} + \underset{\text{oxygen}}{6\,O_2} \longrightarrow \underset{\substack{\text{carbon}\\\text{dioxide}}}{6\,CO_2} + \underset{\text{water}}{6\,H_2O} + \text{energy (heat and ATP)}$$

The change in free energy in this reaction is −686 kcal/mol (or −2870 kJ/mol) under standard conditions (that is, at room temperature, 1 atm pressure, and so forth). In the conditions that exist inside a cell, the energy released can be as high as −720 kcal/mol (−3012 kJ/mol) of glucose. This means that under actual cellular conditions, more energy is released than under standard conditions.

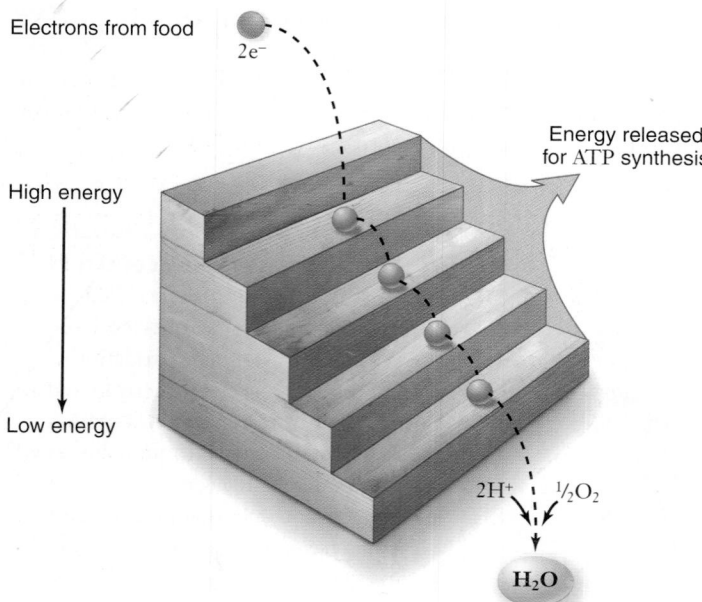

Figure 7.2 How electron transport works. This diagram shows how ATP is generated when electrons transfer from one energy level to another. Rather than releasing a single explosive burst of energy, electrons "fall" to lower and lower energy levels in steps, releasing stored energy with each fall as they tumble to the lowest (most electronegative) electron acceptor, O_2.

The same amount of energy is released whether glucose is catabolized or burned, but when it is burned, most of the energy is released as heat. Cells harvest useful energy from the catabolism of glucose by using a portion of the energy to drive the production of ATP.

Electron carriers play a critical role in energy metabolism

During respiration, glucose is oxidized to CO_2. If the electrons were given directly to O_2, the reaction would be combustion, and cells would burst into flames. Instead, as you have just seen, the cell transfers the electrons to intermediate electron carriers, then eventually to O_2.

Many forms of electron carriers are used in this process: (1) soluble carriers that move electrons from one molecule to another, (2) membrane-bound carriers that form a redox chain, and (3) carriers that move within the membrane. The common feature of all of these carriers is that they can be reversibly oxidized and reduced. Some of these carriers, such as the iron-containing cytochromes, can carry just electrons, and some carry both electrons and protons.

NAD^+ is one of the most important electron (and proton) carriers. As shown on the left in figure 7.3, the NAD^+ molecule is composed of two nucleotides bound together. The two nucleotides that make up NAD^+, nicotinamide monophosphate (NMP) and adenosine monophosphate (AMP), are joined head-to-head by their phosphate groups. The two nucleotides serve different functions in the NAD^+ molecule: AMP acts as the core, providing a shape recognized by many enzymes; NMP is the active part of the molecule, because it is readily reduced, that is, it easily accepts electrons.

When NAD^+ acquires two electrons and a proton from the active site of an enzyme, it is reduced to NADH, shown on the right in figure 7.3. The NADH molecule now carries the two energetic electrons and can supply them to other molecules and reduce them.

This ability to supply high-energy electrons is critical to both energy metabolism and to the biosynthesis of many organic molecules, including fats and sugars. In animals, when ATP is plentiful, the reducing power of the accumulated NADH is diverted to supplying fatty acid precursors with high-energy electrons, reducing them to form fats and storing the energy of the electrons.

Metabolism harvests energy in stages

It is generally true that the larger the release of energy in any single step, the more of that energy is released as heat, and the less is available to be channeled into more useful paths. In the combustion of gasoline, the same amount of energy is released whether all of the gasoline in a car's gas tank explodes at once, or burns in a series of very small explosions inside the cylinders. By releasing the energy in gasoline a little at a time, the harvesting efficiency is greater, and more of the energy can be used to push the pistons and move the car.

The same principle applies to the oxidation of glucose inside a cell. If all of the electrons were transferred to oxygen in one explosive step, releasing all of the free energy at once, the cell

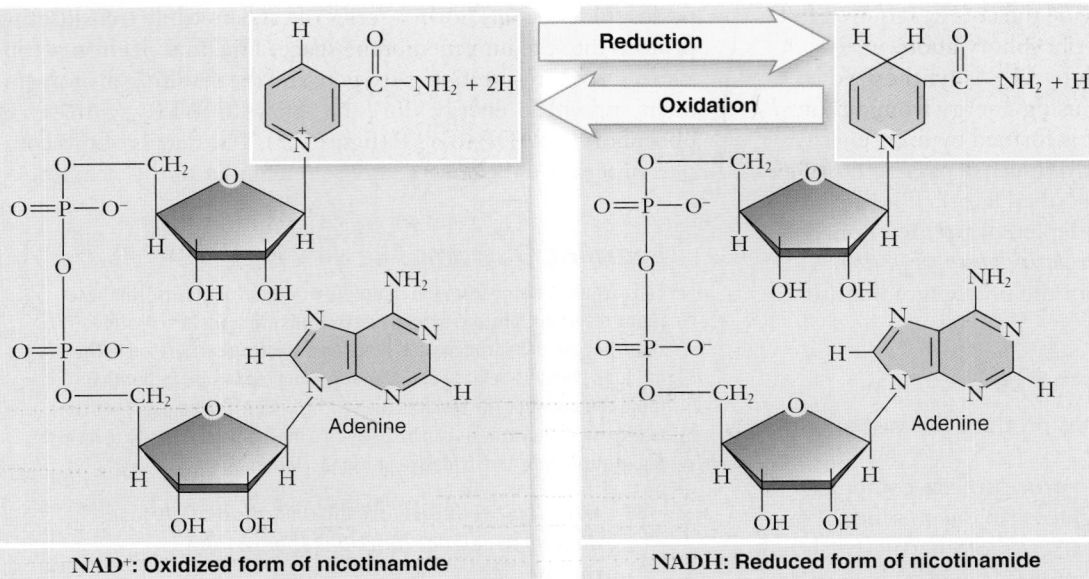

Figure 7.3 **NAD⁺ and**
Figure 7.3 NAD⁺ and
NADH. This dinucleotide
serves as an "electron
shuttle" during cellular
respiration. NAD⁺ accepts a
pair of electrons and a proton
from catabolized
macromolecules and is
reduced to NADH.

NAD⁺: Oxidized form of nicotinamide   NADH: Reduced form of nicotinamide

would recover very little of that energy in a useful form. Instead, cells burn their fuel much as a car does, a little at a time.

The electrons in the C—H bonds of glucose are stripped off in stages in the series of enzyme-catalyzed reactions collectively referred to as glycolysis and the Krebs cycle. The electrons are removed by transferring them to NAD⁺, as described earlier, or to other electron carriers.

The energy released by all of these oxidation reactions is also not all released at once (see figure 7.2). The electrons are passed to another set of electron carriers called the **electron transport chain,** which is located in the mitochondrial inner membrane. Movement of electrons through this chain produces potential energy in the form of an electrochemical gradient. We examine this process in more detail later in this chapter.

ATP plays a central role in metabolism

The previous chapter introduced ATP as the energy currency of the cell. Cells use ATP to power most of those activities that require work—one of the most obvious of which is movement. Tiny fibers within muscle cells pull against one another when muscles contract. Mitochondria can move a meter or more along the narrow nerve cells that extend from your spine to your feet. Chromosomes are pulled apart by microtubules during cell division. All of these movements require the expenditure of energy by ATP hydrolysis. Cells also use ATP to drive endergonic reactions that would otherwise not occur spontaneously (see chapter 6).

How does ATP drive an endergonic reaction? The enzyme that catalyzes a particular reaction has two binding sites on its surface: one for the reactant and another for ATP. The ATP site splits the ATP molecule, liberating over 7 kcal ($\Delta G = -7.3$ kcal/mol) of chemical energy. This energy pushes the reactant at the second site "uphill," reaching the activation energy and driving the endergonic reaction. Thus endergonic reactions coupled to ATP hydrolysis become favorable.

The many steps of cellular respiration have as their ultimate goal the production of ATP. ATP synthesis is itself an endergonic reaction, which requires cells to perform exergonic reactions to drive this synthesis.

Cells make ATP by two fundamentally different mechanisms

The synthesis of ATP can be accomplished by two distinct mechanisms: one that involves chemical coupling with an intermediate bound to phosphate, and another that relies on an electrochemical gradient of protons for the potential energy to phosphorylate ADP.

1. In *substrate-level phosphorylation*, ATP is formed by transferring a phosphate group directly to ADP from a phosphate-bearing intermediate, or substrate (figure 7.4). During **glycolysis,** the initial breakdown of glucose (discussed later), the chemical bonds of glucose are shifted

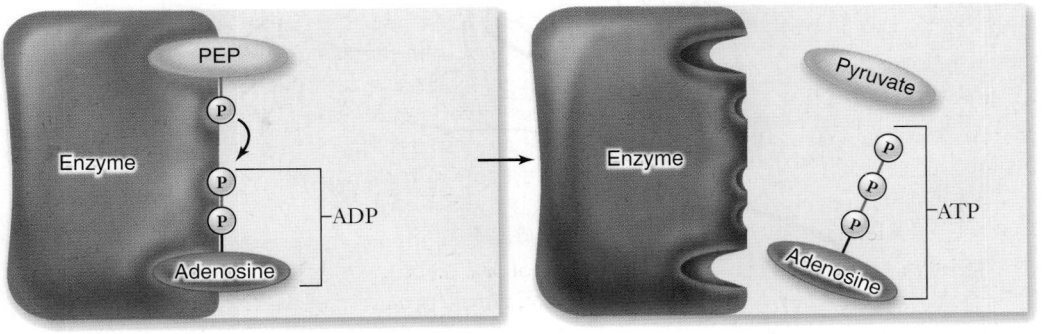

Figure 7.4 Substrate-level phosphorylation. Some molecules, such as phosphoenolpyruvate (PEP), possess a high-energy phosphate (P) bond similar to the bonds in ATP. When PEP's phosphate group is transferred enzymatically to ADP, the energy in the bond is conserved, and ATP is created.

around in reactions that provide the energy required to form ATP by substrate-level phosphorylation.

2. In **oxidative phosphorylation,** ATP is synthesized by the enzyme **ATP synthase,** using energy from a proton (H^+) gradient. This gradient is formed by high-energy electrons from the oxidation of glucose passing down an electron transport chain (described later). These electrons, with their energy depleted, are then donated to oxygen, hence the term *oxidative phosphorylation*. ATP synthase uses the energy from the proton gradient to catalyze the reaction:

$$ADP + P_i \longrightarrow ATP$$

Eukaryotes and aerobic prokaryotes produce the vast majority of their ATP this way.

In most organisms, these two processes are combined. To harvest energy to make ATP from glucose in the presence of oxygen, the cell carries out a complex series of enzyme-catalyzed reactions that remove energetic electrons via oxidation reactions. These electrons are then used in an electron transport chain that passes the electrons down a series of carriers while translocating protons into the intermembrane space. The final electron acceptor in aerobic respiration is oxygen, and the resulting proton gradient provides energy for the enzyme ATP synthase to phosphorylate ADP to ATP (figure 7.5). The details of this complex process will be covered in the remainder of this chapter.

Learning Outcomes Review 7.1

Cells acquire energy from the complete oxidation of glucose. In these redox reactions, protons as well as electrons are transferred, and thus they are dehydrogenation reactions. Electron carriers aid in the gradual, stepwise release of the energy from oxidation, rather than rapid combustion. The result is the synthesis of ATP, a portable source of energy. ATP synthesis can occur by two mechanisms: substrate level phosphorylation and oxidative phosphorylation.

■ **Why don't cells just link the oxidation of glucose directly to cellular functions that require the energy?**

Figure 7.5 An overview of aerobic respiration.

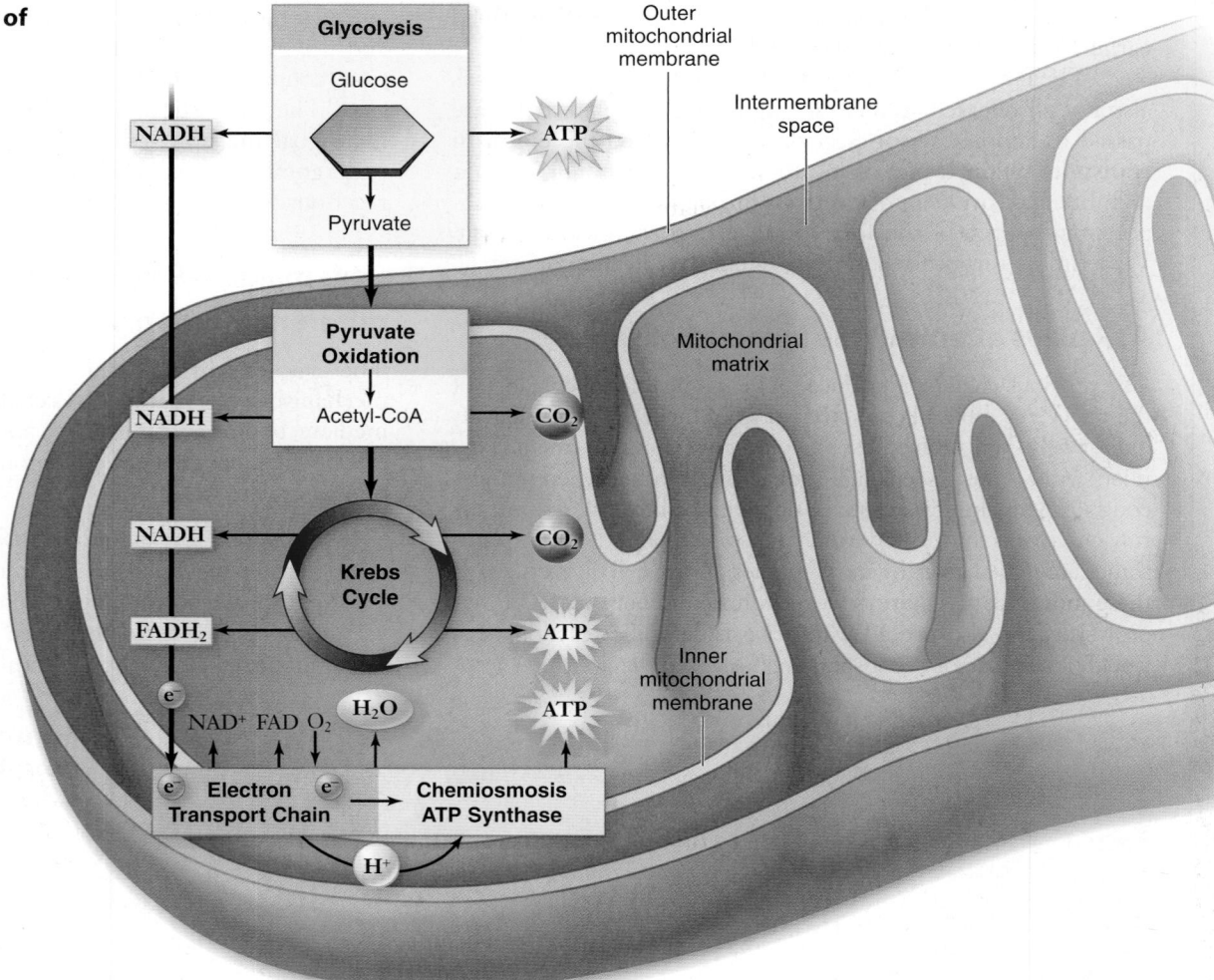

Glycolysis: Splitting Glucose

Learning Outcomes

1. **Describe the process of glycolysis.**
2. **Calculate the energy yield from glycolysis.**
3. **Distinguish between aerobic respiration and fermentation.**

Glucose molecules can be dismantled in many ways, but primitive organisms evolved a glucose-catabolizing process that releases enough free energy to drive the synthesis of ATP in enzyme-coupled reactions. Glycolysis occurs in the cytoplasm and converts glucose into two 3-carbon molecules of pyruvate (figure 7.6). For each molecule of glucose that passes through this transformation, the cell nets two ATP molecules.

Priming changes glucose into an easily cleaved form

The first half of glycolysis consists of five sequential reactions that convert one molecule of glucose into two molecules of the 3-carbon compound *glyceraldehyde 3-phosphate (G3P)*. These reactions require the expenditure of ATP, so they are an endergonic process.

Step A: Glucose priming Three reactions "prime" glucose by changing it into a compound that can be cleaved readily into two 3-carbon phosphorylated molecules. Two of these reactions transfer a phosphate from ATP, so this step requires the cell to use two ATP molecules.

Step B: Cleavage and rearrangement In the first of the remaining pair of reactions, the 6-carbon product of step A is split into two 3-carbon molecules. One is G3P, and the other is then converted to G3P by the second reaction (figure 7.7).

ATP is synthesized by substrate-level phosphorylation

In the second half of glycolysis, five more reactions convert G3P into pyruvate in an energy-yielding process that generates ATP.

Step C: Oxidation Two electrons (and one proton) are transferred from G3P to NAD^+, forming NADH. A molecule of P_i is also added to G3P to produce 1,3-bisphosphoglycerate (BPG). The phosphate incorporated will later be transferred to ADP by substrate-level phosphorylation to allow a net yield of ATP.

Step D: ATP generation Four reactions convert BPG into pyruvate. This process generates two ATP molecules per G3P (see figures 7.4 and 7.7) produced in Step B.

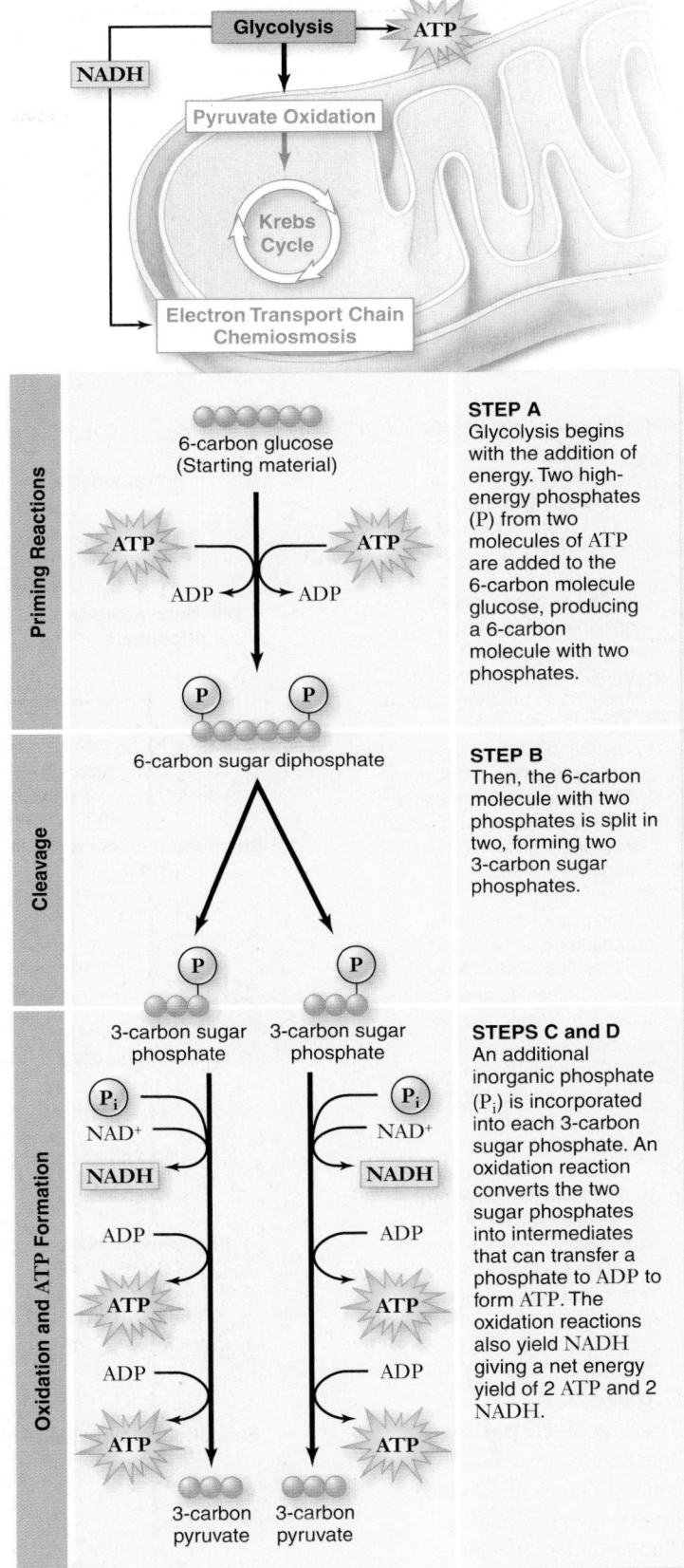

STEP A
Glycolysis begins with the addition of energy. Two high-energy phosphates (P) from two molecules of ATP are added to the 6-carbon molecule glucose, producing a 6-carbon molecule with two phosphates.

STEP B
Then, the 6-carbon molecule with two phosphates is split in two, forming two 3-carbon sugar phosphates.

STEPS C and D
An additional inorganic phosphate (P_i) is incorporated into each 3-carbon sugar phosphate. An oxidation reaction converts the two sugar phosphates into intermediates that can transfer a phosphate to ADP to form ATP. The oxidation reactions also yield NADH giving a net energy yield of 2 ATP and 2 NADH.

Figure 7.6 How glycolysis works.

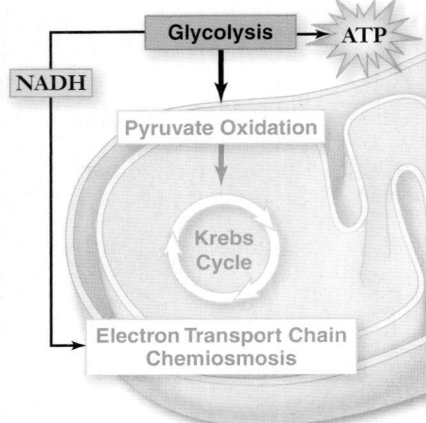

Glycolysis → ATP

NADH

Pyruvate Oxidation

Krebs Cycle

Electron Transport Chain Chemiosmosis

1. Phosphorylation of glucose by ATP.

2–3. Rearrangement, followed by a second ATP phosphorylation.

4–5. The 6-carbon molecule is split into two 3-carbon molecules—one G3P, another that is converted into G3P in another reaction.

6. Oxidation followed by phosphorylation produces two NADH molecules and two molecules of BPG, each with one high-energy phosphate bond.

7. Removal of high-energy phosphate by two ADP molecules produces two ATP molecules and leaves two 3PG molecules.

8–9. Removal of water yields two PEP molecules, each with a high-energy phosphate bond.

10. Removal of high-energy phosphate by two ADP molecules produces two ATP molecules and two pyruvate molecules.

Figure 7.7
The glycolytic pathway.
The first five reactions convert a molecule of glucose into two molecules of G3P. The second five reactions convert G3P into pyruvate.

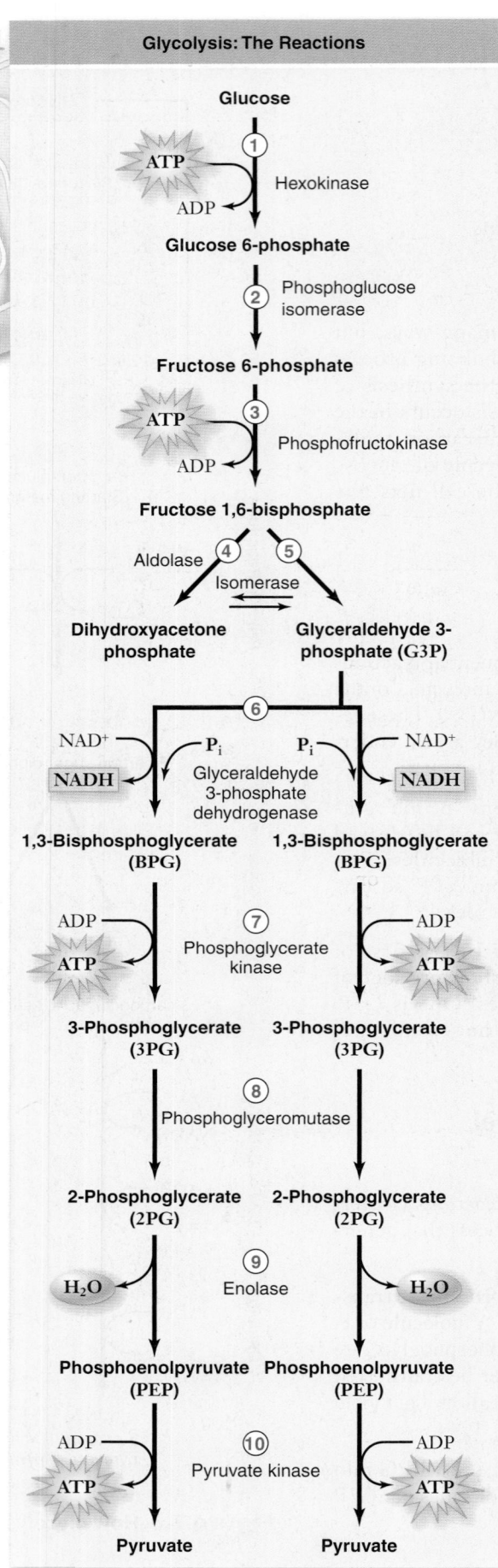

Glycolysis: The Reactions

Glucose

① Hexokinase

ATP → ADP

Glucose 6-phosphate

② Phosphoglucose isomerase

Fructose 6-phosphate

③ Phosphofructokinase

ATP → ADP

Fructose 1,6-bisphosphate

Aldolase ④ ⑤ Isomerase

Dihydroxyacetone phosphate

Glyceraldehyde 3-phosphate (G3P)

⑥ Glyceraldehyde 3-phosphate dehydrogenase

NAD^+ + P_i → **NADH**

P_i + NAD^+ → **NADH**

1,3-Bisphosphoglycerate (BPG)

1,3-Bisphosphoglycerate (BPG)

⑦ Phosphoglycerate kinase

ADP → ATP

ADP → ATP

3-Phosphoglycerate (3PG)

3-Phosphoglycerate (3PG)

⑧ Phosphoglyceromutase

2-Phosphoglycerate (2PG)

2-Phosphoglycerate (2PG)

⑨ Enolase

H_2O

H_2O

Phosphoenolpyruvate (PEP)

Phosphoenolpyruvate (PEP)

⑩ Pyruvate kinase

ADP → ATP

ADP → ATP

Pyruvate

Pyruvate

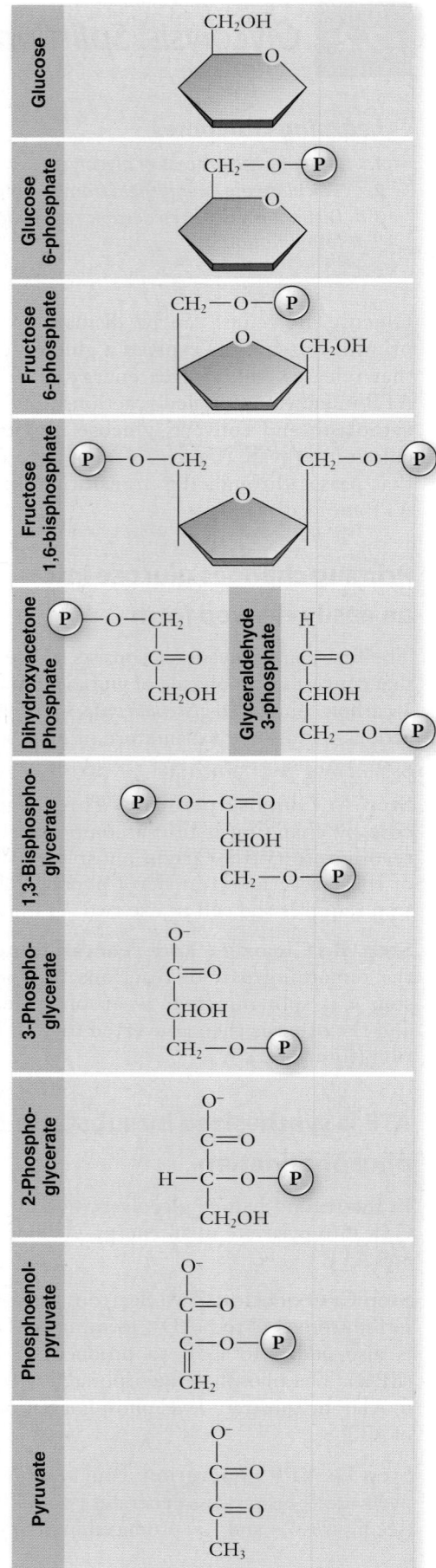

Glucose

Glucose 6-phosphate

Fructose 6-phosphate

Fructose 1,6-bisphosphate

Dihydroxyacetone Phosphate

Glyceraldehyde 3-phosphate

1,3-Bisphospho-glycerate

3-Phospho-glycerate

2-Phospho-glycerate

Phosphoenol-pyruvate

Pyruvate

Because each glucose molecule is split into two G3P molecules, the overall reaction sequence has a net yield of two molecules of ATP, as well as two molecules of NADH and two of pyruvate:

4 ATP (2 ATP for each of the 2 G3P molecules in step D)
− 2 ATP (used in the two reactions in step A)
_____
2 ATP (net yield for entire process)

The hydrolysis of one molecule of ATP yields a ΔG of −7.3 kcal/mol under standard conditions. Thus cells harvest a maximum of 14.6 kcal of energy per mole of glucose from glycolysis.

A brief history of glycolysis

Although far from ideal in terms of the amount of energy it releases, glycolysis does generate ATP. For more than a billion years during the anaerobic first stages of life on Earth, glycolysis was the primary way heterotrophic organisms generated ATP from organic molecules.

Like many biochemical pathways, glycolysis is believed to have evolved backward, with the last steps in the process being the most ancient. Thus, the second half of glycolysis, the ATP-yielding breakdown of G3P, may have been the original process. The synthesis of G3P from glucose would have appeared later, perhaps when alternative sources of G3P were depleted.

Why does glycolysis take place in modern organisms, since its energy yield in the absence of oxygen is comparatively little? The answer is that evolution is an incremental process: Change occurs by improving on past successes. In catabolic metabolism, glycolysis satisfied the one essential evolutionary criterion—it was an improvement. Cells that could not carry out glycolysis were at a competitive disadvantage, and only cells capable of glycolysis survived. Later improvements in catabolic metabolism built on this success. Metabolism evolved as one layer of reactions added to another. Nearly every present-day organism carries out glycolysis, as a metabolic memory of its evolutionary past.

The last section of this chapter discusses the evolution of metabolism in more detail.

NADH must be recycled to continue respiration

Inspect for a moment the net reaction of the glycolytic sequence:

$$\text{glucose} + 2\ \text{ADP} + 2\ P_i + 2\ \text{NAD}^+ \longrightarrow 2\ \text{pyruvate} + 2\ \text{ATP} + 2\ \text{NADH} + 2\ H^+ + 2\ H_2O$$

You can see that three changes occur in glycolysis: (1) Glucose is converted into two molecules of pyruvate; (2) two molecules of ADP are converted into ATP via substrate-level phosphorylation; and (3) two molecules of NAD$^+$ are reduced to NADH. This leaves the cell with two problems: extracting the energy that remains in the two pyruvate molecules, and regenerating NAD$^+$ to be able to continue glycolysis.

Recycling NADH

As long as food molecules that can be converted into glucose are available, a cell can continually churn out ATP to drive its activities. In doing so, however, it accumulates NADH and depletes the pool of NAD$^+$ molecules. A cell does not contain a large amount of NAD$^+$, and for glycolysis to continue, NADH must be recycled into NAD$^+$. Some molecule other than NAD$^+$ must ultimately accept the electrons taken from G3P and be reduced. Two processes can carry out this key task (figure 7.8):

1. **Aerobic respiration.** Oxygen is an excellent electron acceptor. Through a series of electron transfers, electrons taken from G3P can be donated to oxygen, forming water. This process occurs in the mitochondria of eukaryotic cells in the presence of oxygen. Because air is rich in oxygen, this process is also referred to as *aerobic metabolism*. A significant amount of ATP is also produced.
2. **Fermentation.** When oxygen is unavailable, an organic molecule, such as acetaldehyde in wine fermentation, can accept electrons instead. This reaction plays an important role in the metabolism of most organisms, even those capable of aerobic respiration.

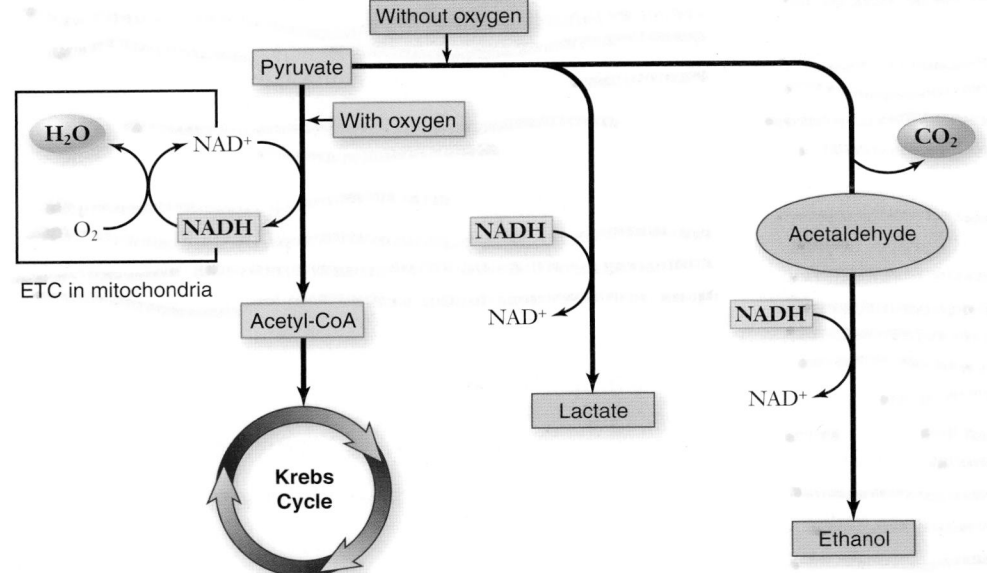

Figure 7.8 The fate of pyruvate and NADH produced by glycolysis. In the presence of oxygen, NADH is oxidized by the electron transport chain (ETC) in mitochondria using oxygen as the final electron acceptor. This regenerates NAD$^+$, allowing glycolysis to continue. The pyruvate produced by glycolysis is oxidized to acetyl-CoA, which enters the Krebs cycle. In the absence of oxygen, pyruvate is instead reduced, oxidizing NADH and regenerating NAD$^+$ thus allowing glycolysis to continue. Direct reduction of pyruvate, as in muscle cells, produces lactate. In yeast, carbon dioxide is first removed from pyruvate, producing acetaldehyde, which is then reduced to ethanol.

The fate of pyruvate

The fate of the pyruvate that is produced by glycolysis depends on which of these two processes takes place. The aerobic respiration path starts with the oxidation of pyruvate to produce acetyl coenzyme A (acetyl-CoA), which is then further oxidized in a series of reactions called the Krebs cycle. The fermentation path, by contrast, uses the reduction of all or part of pyruvate to oxidize NADH back to NAD$^+$. We examine aerobic respiration next; fermentation is described in detail in a later section.

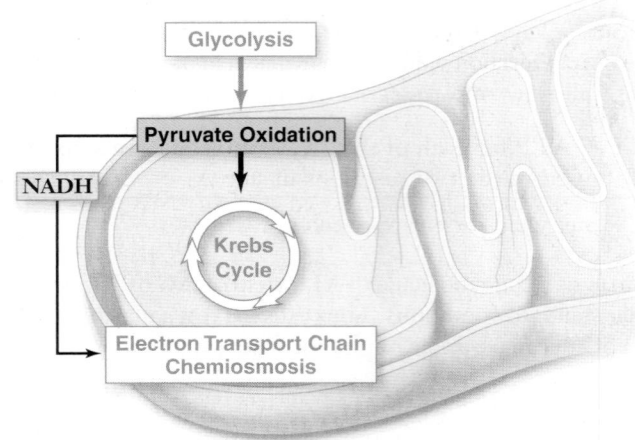

Learning Outcomes Review 7.2

Glycolysis splits the 6-carbon molecule glucose into two 3-carbon molecules of pyruvate. This process uses two ATP molecules in "priming" reactions and eventually produces four molecules of ATP per glucose for a net yield of two ATP. The oxidation reactions of glycolysis require NAD$^+$ and produce NADH. When oxygen is abundant, NAD$^+$ is regenerated in the electron transport chain using O$_2$ as an acceptor. When oxygen is absent, NAD$^+$ is regenerated in a fermentation reaction using an organic molecule as an electron receptor.

■ *Does glycolysis taking place in the cytoplasm argue for or against the endosymbiotic origin of mitochondria?*

7.3 The Oxidation of Pyruvate to Produce Acetyl-CoA

Learning Outcome

1. *Explain how the oxidation of pyruvate joins glycolysis with the Krebs cycle.*

In the presence of oxygen, the oxidation of glucose that begins in glycolysis continues where glycolysis leaves off—with pyruvate. In eukaryotic organisms, the extraction of additional energy from pyruvate takes place exclusively inside mitochondria. In prokaryotes similar reactions take place in the cytoplasm and at the plasma membrane.

The cell harvests pyruvate's considerable energy in two steps. First, pyruvate is oxidized to produce a two-carbon compound and CO$_2$, with the electrons transferred to NAD$^+$ to produce NADH. Next, the two-carbon compound is oxidized to CO$_2$ by the reactions of the Krebs cycle.

Pyruvate is oxidized in a "decarboxylation" reaction that cleaves off one of pyruvate's three carbons. This carbon departs as CO$_2$ (figure 7.9). The remaining 2-carbon compound, called an acetyl group, is then attached to coenzyme A; this entire molecule is called *acetyl-CoA*. A pair of electrons and one associated proton is transferred to the electron carrier NAD$^+$, reducing it to NADH, with a second proton donated to the solution.

The reaction involves three intermediate stages, and it is catalyzed within mitochondria by a *multienzyme complex*. As chapter 6 noted, a multienzyme complex organizes a series of enzymatic steps so that the chemical intermediates do not diffuse away or undergo other reactions. Within the complex, component polypeptides pass

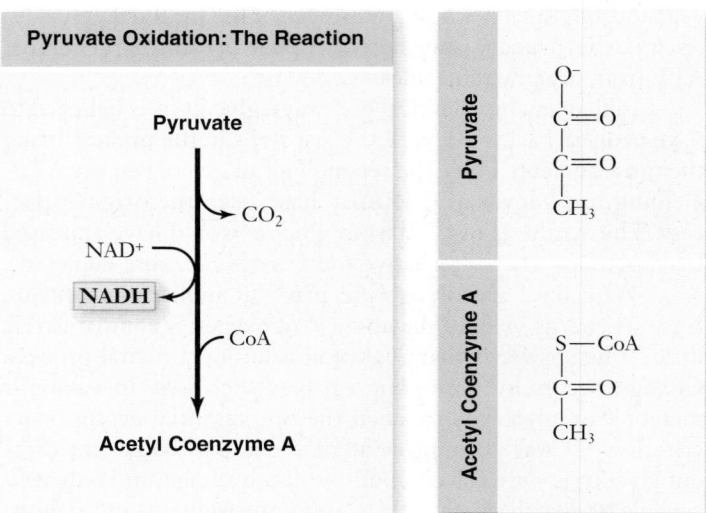

Figure 7.9 The oxidation of pyruvate. This complex reaction uses NAD$^+$ to accept electrons, reducing it to NADH. The product, acetyl coenzyme A (acetyl-CoA), feeds the acetyl unit into the Krebs cycle, and the CoA is recycled for another oxidation of pyruvate. NADH provides energetic electrons for the electron transport chain.

the substrates from one enzyme to the next without releasing them. *Pyruvate dehydrogenase*, the complex of enzymes that removes CO$_2$ from pyruvate, is one of the largest enzymes known; it contains 60 subunits! The reaction can be summarized as:

$$\text{pyruvate} + NAD^+ + CoA \longrightarrow \text{acetyl-CoA} + NADH + CO_2 + H^+$$

The molecule of NADH produced is used later to produce ATP. The acetyl group is fed into the Krebs cycle, with the CoA being recycled for another oxidation of pyruvate. The Krebs cycle then completes the oxidation of the original carbons from glucose.

Learning Outcome Review 7.3

Pyruvate is oxidized in the mitochondria to produce acetyl-CoA and CO$_2$. Acetyl-CoA is the molecule that links glycolysis and the reactions of the Krebs cycle.

■ *What are the advantages and disadvantages of a multienzyme complex?*

7.4 *The Krebs Cycle*

Learning Outcomes
1. **Describe the three segments and nine reactions of the Krebs cycle.**
2. **Explain the fate of the electrons produced by the Krebs cycle.**

In this third stage, the acetyl group from pyruvate is oxidized in a series of nine reactions called the *Krebs cycle*. These reactions occur in the matrix of mitochondria.

In this cycle, the 2-carbon acetyl group of acetyl-CoA combines with a 4-carbon molecule called oxaloacetate. The resulting 6-carbon molecule, citrate, then goes through a several-step sequence of electron-yielding oxidation reactions, during which two CO_2 molecules split off, restoring oxaloacetate. The regenerated oxaloacetate is used to bind to another acetyl group for the next round of the cycle.

In each turn of the cycle, a new acetyl group is added and two carbons are lost as two CO_2 molecules, and more electrons are transferred to electron carriers. These electrons are then used by the electron transport chain to drive *proton pumps* that generate ATP.

The Krebs cycle has three segments:

An overview

The nine reactions of the Krebs cycle can be grouped into three overall segments. These are described in the following sections and summarized in figure 7.10.

Segment A: Acetyl-CoA plus oxaloacetate This reaction produces the 6-carbon citrate molecule.

Segment B: Citrate rearrangement and decarboxylation Five more steps, which have been simplified in figure 7.10, reduce citrate to a 5-carbon intermediate and then to 4-carbon succinate. During these reactions, two NADH and one ATP are produced.

Segment C: Regeneration of oxaloacetate Succinate undergoes three additional reactions, also simplified in the figure, to become oxaloacetate. During these reactions, one NADH is produced; in addition, a molecule of flavin adenine dinucleotide (FAD), another cofactor, becomes reduced to $FADH_2$.

The specifics of each reaction are described next.

Figure 7.10 How the Krebs cycle works.

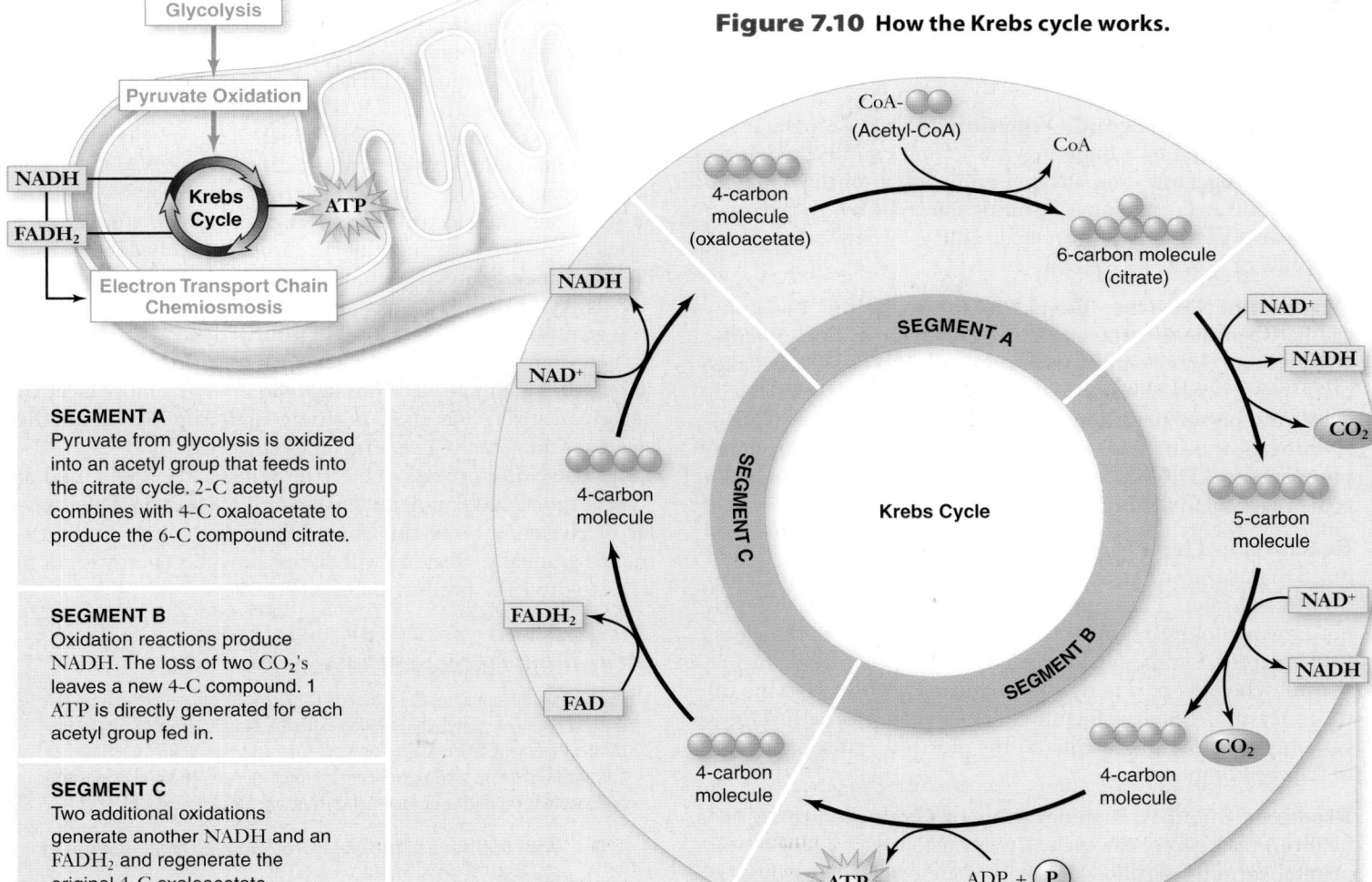

SEGMENT A
Pyruvate from glycolysis is oxidized into an acetyl group that feeds into the citrate cycle. 2-C acetyl group combines with 4-C oxaloacetate to produce the 6-C compound citrate.

SEGMENT B
Oxidation reactions produce NADH. The loss of two CO_2's leaves a new 4-C compound. 1 ATP is directly generated for each acetyl group fed in.

SEGMENT C
Two additional oxidations generate another NADH and an $FADH_2$ and regenerate the original 4-C oxaloacetate.

The Krebs cycle extracts electrons and synthesizes one ATP

Figure 7.11 summarizes the sequence of the Krebs cycle reactions. A 2-carbon group from acetyl-CoA enters the cycle at the beginning, and two CO_2 molecules, one ATP, and four pairs of electrons are produced.

Reaction 1: Condensation Citrate is formed from acetyl-CoA and oxaloacetate. This condensation reaction is irreversible, committing the 2-carbon acetyl group to the Krebs cycle. The reaction is inhibited when the cell's ATP concentration is high and stimulated when it is low. The result is that when the cell possesses ample amounts of ATP, the Krebs cycle shuts down, and acetyl-CoA is channeled into fat synthesis.

Reactions 2 and 3: Isomerization Before the oxidation reactions can begin, the hydroxyl (—OH) group of citrate must be repositioned. This rearrangement is done in two steps: First, a water molecule is removed from one carbon; then water is added to a different carbon. As a result, an —H group and an —OH group change positions. The product is an isomer of citrate called *isocitrate*. This rearrangement facilitates the subsequent reactions.

Reaction 4: The First Oxidation In the first energy-yielding step of the cycle, isocitrate undergoes an oxidative decarboxylation reaction. First, isocitrate is oxidized, yielding a pair of electrons that reduce a molecule of NAD^+ to NADH. Then the oxidized intermediate is decarboxylated; the central carboxyl group splits off to form CO_2, yielding a 5-carbon molecule called α-*ketoglutarate*.

Reaction 5: The Second Oxidation Next, α-ketoglutarate is decarboxylated by a multienzyme complex similar to pyruvate dehydrogenase. The succinyl group left after the removal of CO_2 joins to coenzyme A, forming *succinyl-CoA*. In the process, two electrons are extracted, and they reduce another molecule of NAD^+ to NADH.

Reaction 6: Substrate-Level Phosphorylation The linkage between the 4-carbon succinyl group and CoA is a high-energy bond. In a coupled reaction similar to those that take place in glycolysis, this bond is cleaved, and the energy released drives the phosphorylation of guanosine diphosphate (GDP), forming guanosine triphosphate (GTP). GTP can transfer a phosphate to ADP converting it into ATP. The 4-carbon molecule that remains is called *succinate*.

Reaction 7: The Third Oxidation Next, succinate is oxidized to *fumarate* by an enzyme located in the inner mitochondrial membrane. The free-energy change in this reaction is not large enough to reduce NAD^+. Instead, FAD is the electron acceptor. Unlike NAD^+, FAD is not free to diffuse within the mitochondrion; it is tightly associated with its enzyme in the inner mitochondrial membrane. Its reduced form, $FADH_2$, can only contribute electrons to the electron transport chain in the membrane.

Reactions 8 and 9: Regeneration of Oxaloacetate In the final two reactions of the cycle, a water molecule is added to fumarate, forming *malate*. Malate is then oxidized, yielding a 4-carbon molecule of *oxaloacetate* and two electrons that reduce a molecule of NAD^+ to NADH. Oxaloacetate, the molecule that began the cycle, is now free to combine with another 2-carbon acetyl group from acetyl-CoA and begin the cycle again.

Glucose becomes CO_2 and potential energy

In the process of aerobic respiration, glucose is entirely consumed. The 6-carbon glucose molecule is cleaved into a pair of 3-carbon pyruvate molecules during glycolysis. One of the carbons of each pyruvate is then lost as CO_2 in the conversion of pyruvate to acetyl-CoA. The two other carbons from acetyl-CoA are lost as CO_2 during the oxidations of the Krebs cycle.

All that is left to mark the passing of a glucose molecule into six CO_2 molecules is its energy, some of which is preserved in four ATP molecules and in the reduced state of 12 electron carriers. Ten of these carriers are NADH molecules; the other two are $FADH_2$.

Following the electrons in the reactions reveals the direction of transfer

As you examine the changes in electrical charge in the reactions that oxidize glucose, a good strategy for keeping the transfers clear is always to *follow the electrons*. For example, in glycolysis, an enzyme extracts two hydrogens—that is, two electrons and two protons—from glucose and transfers both electrons and one of the protons to NAD^+. The other proton is released as a hydrogen ion, H^+, into the surrounding solution. This transfer converts NAD^+ into NADH; that is, two negative electrons ($2e^-$) and one positive proton (H^+) are added to one positively charged NAD^+ to form NADH, which is electrically neutral.

As mentioned earlier, energy captured by NADH is not harvested all at once. The two electrons carried by NADH are passed along the electron transport chain, which consists of a series of electron carriers, mostly proteins, embedded within the inner membranes of mitochondria.

NADH delivers electrons to the beginning of the electron transport chain, and oxygen captures them at the end. The oxygen then joins with hydrogen ions to form water. At each step in the chain, the electrons move to a slightly more electronegative carrier, and their positions shift slightly. Thus, the electrons move *down* an energy gradient.

The entire process of electron transfer releases a total of 53 kcal/mol (222 kJ/mol) under standard conditions. The transfer of electrons along this chain allows the energy to be extracted gradually. Next, we will discuss how this energy is put to work to drive the production of ATP.

Learning Outcomes Review 7.4

The Krebs cycle completes the oxidation of glucose begun with glycolysis. In the first segment, acetyl-CoA is added to oxaloacetate to produce citrate. In the next segment, five reactions produce succinate, two NADH from NAD^+, and one ATP. Finally, succinate undergoes three more reactions to regenerate oxaloacetate, producing one more NADH and one $FADH_2$ from FAD.

■ *What happens to the electrons removed from glucose at this point?*

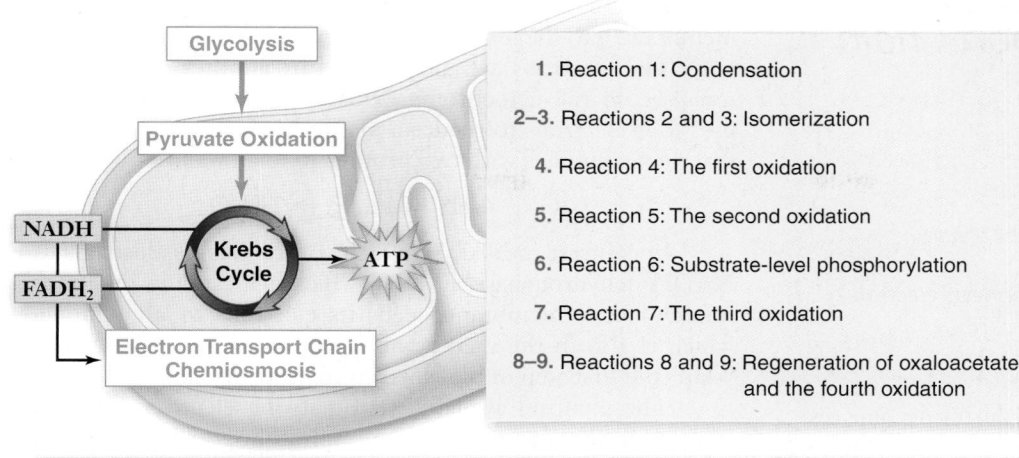

Figure 7.11 The Krebs cycle. This series of reactions takes place within the matrix of the mitochondrion. For the complete breakdown of a molecule of glucose, the two molecules of acetyl-CoA produced by glycolysis and pyruvate oxidation each have to make a trip around the Krebs cycle. Follow the different carbons through the cycle, and notice the changes that occur in the carbon skeletons of the molecules and where oxidation reactions take place as they proceed through the cycle.

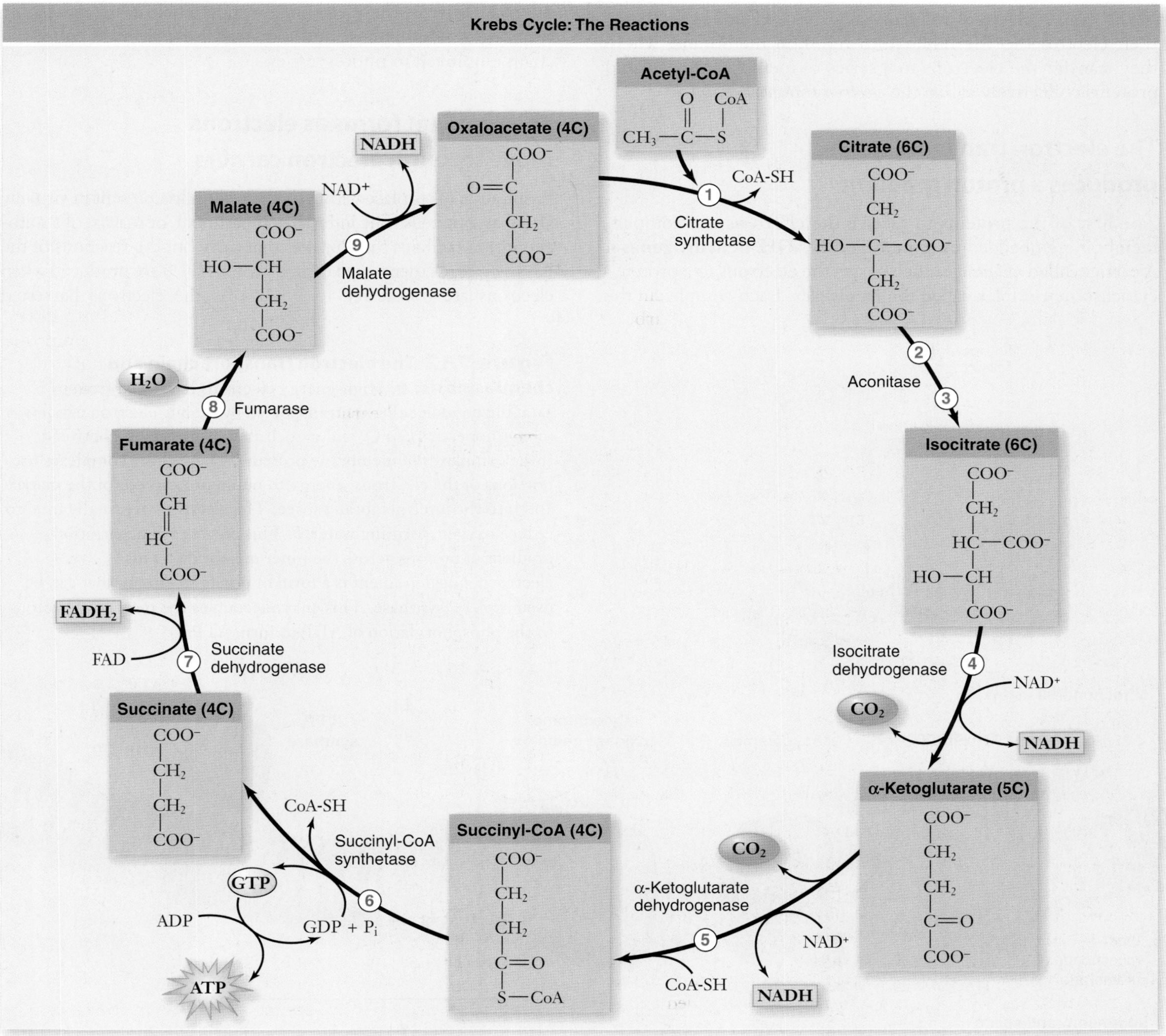

1. Reaction 1: Condensation

2–3. Reactions 2 and 3: Isomerization

4. Reaction 4: The first oxidation

5. Reaction 5: The second oxidation

6. Reaction 6: Substrate-level phosphorylation

7. Reaction 7: The third oxidation

8–9. Reactions 8 and 9: Regeneration of oxaloacetate and the fourth oxidation

Krebs Cycle: The Reactions

Acetyl-CoA

$$CH_3-\overset{\overset{\displaystyle O}{\|}}{C}-\overset{\displaystyle CoA}{S}$$

Oxaloacetate (4C)

COO^-
$O=C$
CH_2
COO^-

Citrate (6C)

COO^-
CH_2
$HO-C-COO^-$
CH_2
COO^-

Malate (4C)

COO^-
$HO-CH$
CH_2
COO^-

NADH   NAD⁺

① Citrate synthetase   CoA-SH

⑨ Malate dehydrogenase

② Aconitase ③

Isocitrate (6C)

COO^-
CH_2
$HC-COO^-$
$HO-CH$
COO^-

H_2O ⑧ Fumarase

Fumarate (4C)

COO^-
CH
$\|$
HC
COO^-

Isocitrate dehydrogenase ④   NAD⁺

CO_2 NADH

FADH₂   FAD   ⑦ Succinate dehydrogenase

Succinate (4C)

COO^-
CH_2
CH_2
COO^-

CoA-SH

Succinyl-CoA synthetase

Succinyl-CoA (4C)

COO^-
CH_2
CH_2
$C=O$
$S-CoA$

α-Ketoglutarate (5C)

COO^-
CH_2
CH_2
$C=O$
COO^-

GTP   ⑥   GDP + P_i

ADP

ATP

CO_2 α-Ketoglutarate dehydrogenase   ⑤   NAD⁺

CoA-SH   **NADH**

chapter **7** *How Cells Harvest Energy*

The Electron Transport Chain and Chemiosmosis

The NADH and FADH$_2$ molecules formed during aerobic respiration each contain a pair of electrons that were gained when NAD$^+$ and FAD were reduced. The NADH molecules carry their electrons to the inner mitochondrial membrane, where they transfer the electrons to a series of membrane-associated proteins collectively called the *electron transport chain.*

The electron transport chain produces a proton gradient

The first of the proteins to receive the electrons is a complex, membrane-embedded enzyme called **NADH dehydrogenase.** A carrier called *ubiquinone* then passes the electrons to a protein–cytochrome complex called the *bc$_1$ complex.* Each complex in the

chain operates as a proton pump, driving a proton out across the membrane into the intermembrane space (figure 7.12*a*).

The electrons are then carried by another carrier, *cytochrome c,* to the cytochrome oxidase complex. This complex uses four electrons to reduce a molecule of oxygen. Each oxygen then combines with two protons to form water:

$$O_2 + 4\,H^+ + 4\,e^- \longrightarrow 2\,H_2O$$

In contrast to NADH, which contributes its electrons to NADH dehydrogenase, FADH$_2$, which is located in the inner mitochondrial membrane, feeds its electrons to ubiquinone, which is also in the membrane. Electrons from FADH$_2$ thus "skip" the first step in the electron transport chain.

The plentiful availability of a strong electron acceptor, oxygen, is what makes oxidative respiration possible. As you'll see in chapter 8, the electron transport chain used in aerobic respiration is similar to, and may well have evolved from, the chain employed in photosynthesis.

The gradient forms as electrons move through electron carriers

Respiration takes place within the mitochondria present in virtually all eukaryotic cells. The internal compartment, or matrix, of a mitochondrion contains the enzymes that carry out the reactions of the Krebs cycle. As mentioned earlier, protons (H$^+$) are produced when electrons are transferred to NAD$^+$. As the electrons harvested

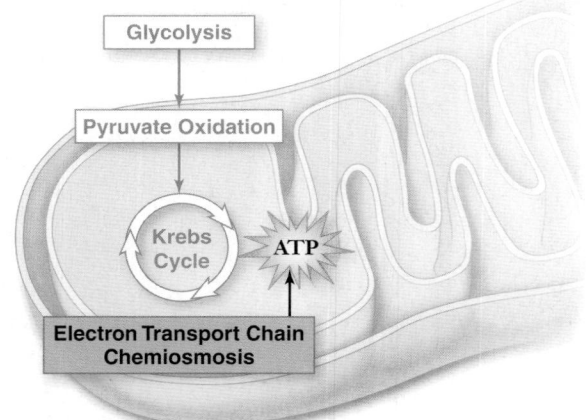

Figure 7.12 The electron transport chain and chemiosmosis. *a.* High-energy electrons harvested from catabolized molecules are transported by mobile electron carriers (ubiquinone, marked Q, and cytochrome c, marked C) between three complexes of membrane proteins. These three complexes use portions of the electrons' energy to pump protons out of the matrix and into the intermembrane space. The electrons are finally used to reduce oxygen, forming water. *b.* This creates a concentration gradient of protons across the inner membrane. This electrochemical gradient is a form of potential energy that can be used by ATP synthase. This enzyme couples the reentry of protons to the phosphorylation of ADP to form ATP.

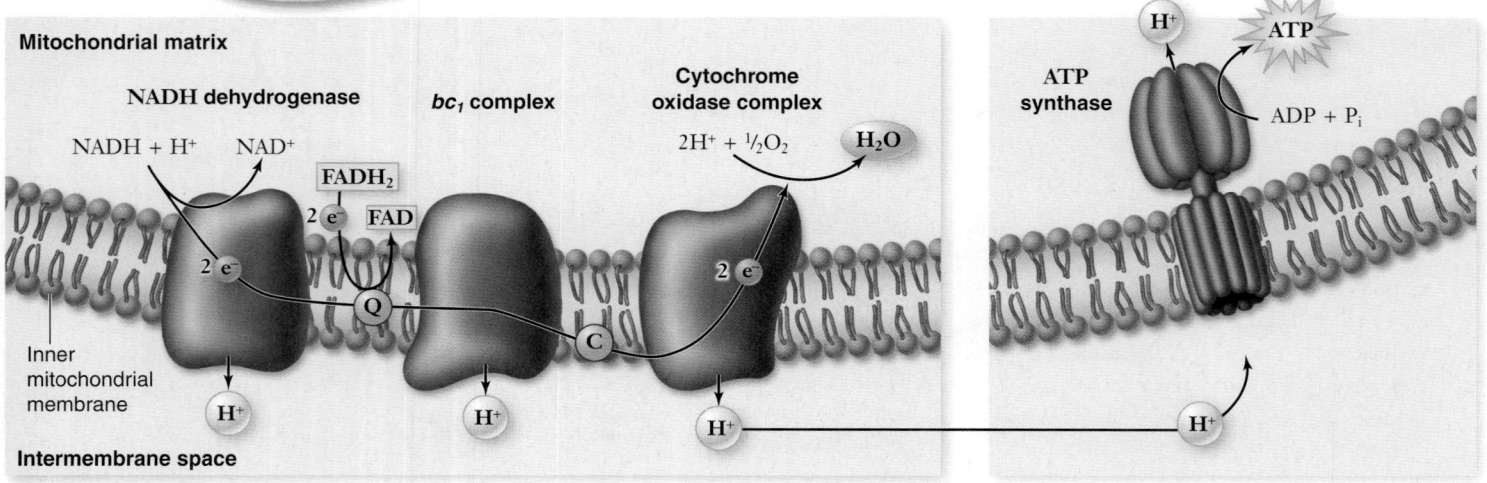

a. The electron transport chain

b. Chemiosmosis

by oxidative respiration are passed along the electron transport chain, the energy they release transports protons out of the matrix and into the outer compartment called the intermembrane space.

Three transmembrane complexes of the electron transport chain in the inner mitochondrial membrane actually accomplish the proton transport (see figure 7.12a). The flow of highly energetic electrons induces a change in the shape of pump proteins, which causes them to transport protons across the membrane. The electrons contributed by NADH activate all three of these proton pumps, whereas those contributed by $FADH_2$ activate only two because of where they enter the chain. In this way a proton gradient is formed between the intermembrane space and the matrix.

Chemiosmosis utilizes the electrochemical gradient to produce ATP

Because the mitochondrial matrix is negative compared with the intermembrane space, positively charged protons are at- tracted to the matrix. The higher outer concentration of protons also tends to drive protons back in by diffusion, but because membranes are relatively impermeable to ions, this process occurs only very slowly. Most of the protons that re- enter the matrix instead pass through ATP synthase, an enzyme that uses the energy of the gradient to catalyze the synthesis of ATP from ADP and P_i. Because the chemical formation of ATP is driven by a diffusion force similar to osmosis, this process is referred to as *chemiosmosis* (figure 7.12b). The newly formed ATP is transported by facilitated diffusion to the many places in the cell where enzymes require energy to drive endergonic reactions. This chemiosmotic mechanism for the coupling of electron transport and ATP synthesis was controversial when it was proposed. Over the years, experimental evidence accumulated to support this hypothesis (figure 7.13).

The energy released by the reactions of cellular respiration ultimately drives the proton pumps that produce the

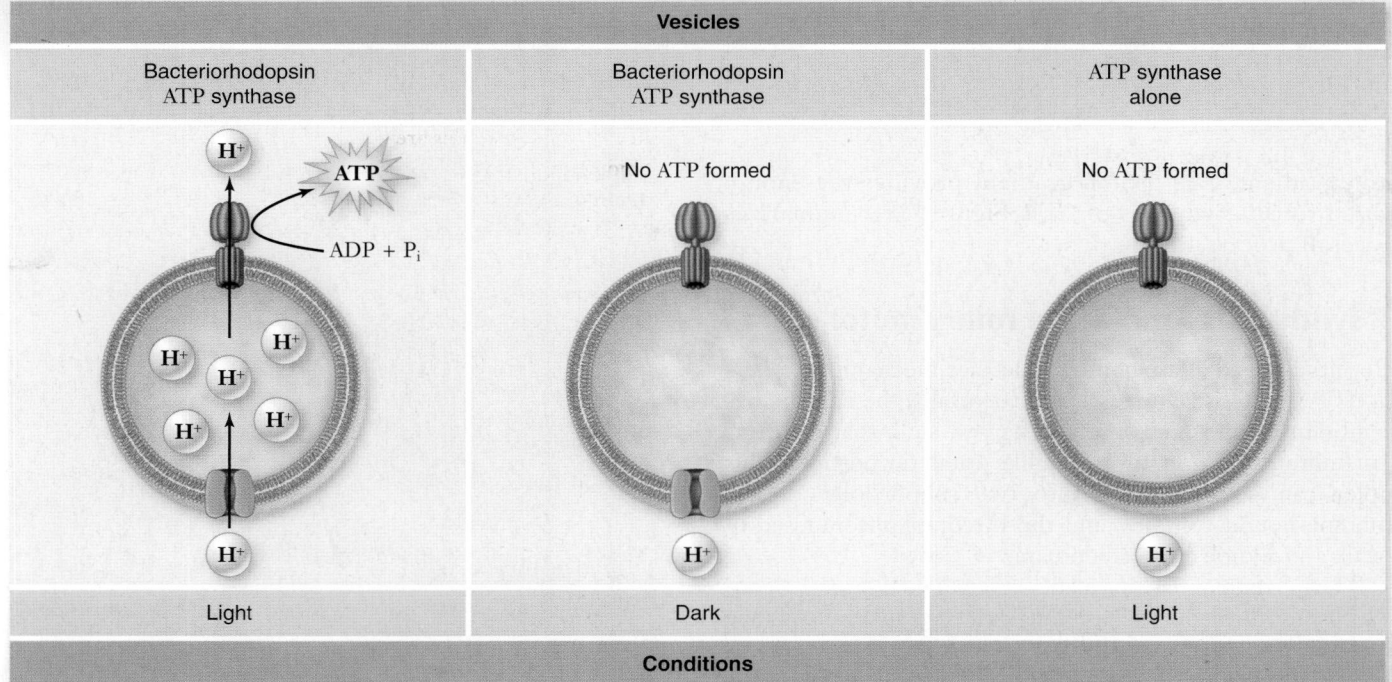

SCIENTIFIC THINKING

Hypothesis: ATP synthase enzyme uses a proton gradient to provide energy for phosphorylation reaction.

Prediction: The source of the proton gradient should not matter. A proton gradient formed by the light-driven pump bacteriorhodopsin should power phosphorylation in the light but not in the dark.

Test: Artificial vesicles are made with bacteriorhodopsin and ATP synthase, and ATP synthase alone. These are illuminated with light and assessed for ATP production.

Result: The vesicle with both bacteriorhodopsin and ATP synthase can form ATP in the light but not in the dark. The vesicle with ATP synthase alone cannot form ATP in the light.

Conclusion: ATP synthase is able to utilize a proton gradient for energy to form ATP.

Further Experiments: What other controls would be appropriate for this type of experiment? Why is this experiment a better test of the chemiosmotic hypothesis than the acid bath experiment in Jangendorf/chapter 8 (see figure 8.16)?

Figure 7.13 Evidence for the chemiosmotic synthesis of ATP by ATP synthase.

Figure 7.14 Aerobic respiration in the mitochondria. The entire process of aerobic respiration is shown in cellular context. Glycolysis occurs in the cytoplasm with the pyruvate and NADH produced entering the mitochondria. Here, pyruvate is oxidized and fed into the Krebs cycle to complete the oxidation process. All the energetic electrons harvested by oxidations in the overall process are transferred by NADH and FADH$_2$ to the electron transport chain. The electron transport chain uses the energy released during electron transport to pump protons across the inner membrane. This creates an electrochemical gradient that contains potential energy. The enzyme ATP synthase uses this gradient to phosphorylate ADP to form ATP.

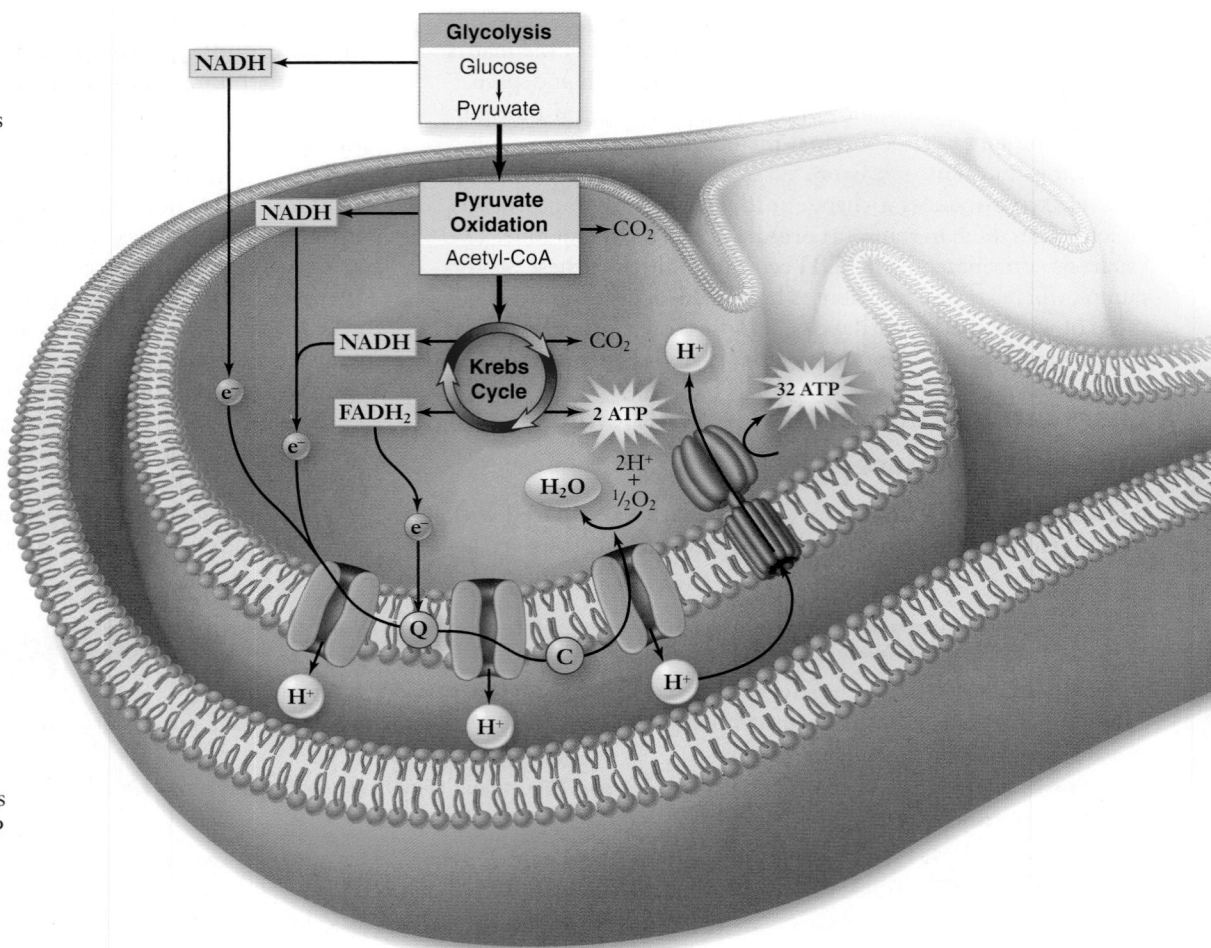

proton gradient. The proton gradient provides the energy required for the synthesis of ATP. Figure 7.14 summarizes the overall process.

ATP synthase is a molecular rotary motor

ATP synthase uses a fascinating molecular mechanism to perform ATP synthesis (figure 7.15). Structurally, the enzyme has a membrane-bound portion and a narrow stalk that connects the membrane portion to a knoblike catalytic portion. This complex can be dissociated into two subportions: the F$_0$ membrane-bound complex, and the F$_1$ complex composed of the stalk and a knob, or head domain.

The F$_1$ complex has enzymatic activity. The F$_0$ complex contains a channel through which protons move across the membrane down their concentration gradient. As they do so, their movement causes part of the F$_0$ complex and the stalk to rotate relative to the knob. The mechanical energy of this rotation is used to change the conformation of the catalytic domain in the F$_1$ complex.

Thus, the synthesis of ATP is achieved by a tiny rotary motor, the rotation of which is driven directly by a gradient of protons. The flow of protons is like that of water in a hydroelectric power plant. Like the flow of water driven by gravity causes a turbine to rotate and generate electrical current, the proton gradient produces the energy that drives the rotation of the ATP synthase generator.

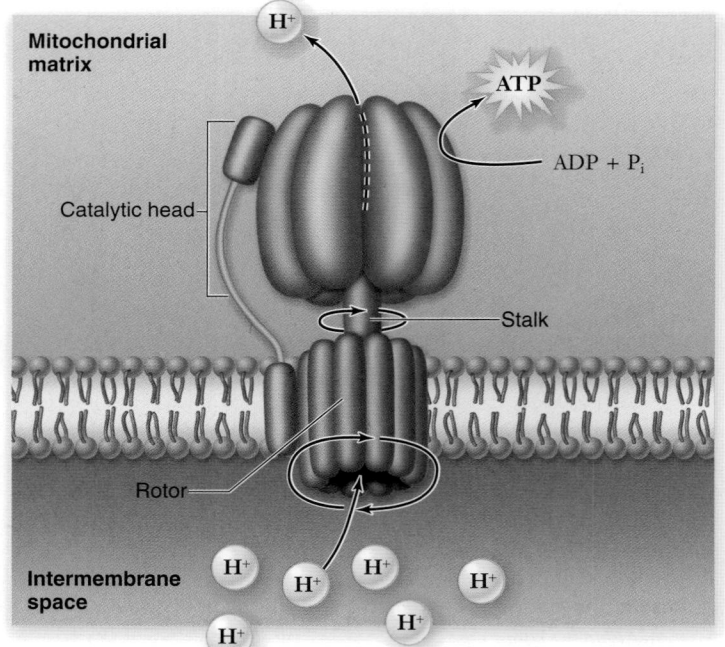

Figure 7.15 The ATP rotary engine. Protons move across the membrane down their concentration gradient. The energy released causes the rotor and stalk structures to rotate. This mechanical energy alters the conformation of the ATP synthase enzyme to catalyze the formation of ATP.

7.6 Energy Yield of Aerobic Respiration

How much metabolic energy in the form of ATP does a cell gain from aerobic breakdown of glucose? Knowing the steps involved in the process, we can calculate the theoretical yield of ATP and compare it with the actual yield.

The theoretical yield for eukaryotes is 36 molecules of ATP per glucose molecule

The chemiosmotic model suggests that one ATP molecule is generated for each proton pump activated by the electron transport chain. Because the electrons from NADH activate three pumps and those from FADH$_2$ activate two, we would expect each molecule of NADH and FADH$_2$ to generate three and two ATP molecules, respectively.

In doing this accounting, remember that everything downstream of glycolysis must be multiplied by 2 because two pyruvates are produced per molecule of glucose. A total of 10 NADH molecules is generated by respiration: 2 from glycolysis, 2 from the oxidation of pyruvate (1×2), and another 6 from the Krebs cycle (3×2). Also, two FADH$_2$ are produced (1×2). Finally, two ATP are generated directly by glycolysis and another two ATP from the Krebs cycle (1×2). This gives a total of $10 \times 3 = 30$ ATP from NADH, plus $2 \times 2 = 4$ ATP from FADH$_2$, plus 4 ATP, for a total of 38 ATP (figure 7.16).

This number is accurate for bacteria, but it does not hold for eukaryotes because the NADH produced in the cytoplasm by glycolysis needs to be transported into the mitochondria by active transport, which costs one ATP per NADH transported. This reduces the predicted yield for eukaryotes to 36 ATP.

The actual yield for eukaryotes is 30 molecules of ATP per glucose molecule

The amount of ATP actually produced in a eukaryotic cell during aerobic respiration is somewhat lower than 36, for two reasons. First, the inner mitochondrial membrane is somewhat "leaky" to protons, allowing some of them to reenter the matrix without passing through ATP synthase. Second, mitochondria often use the proton gradient generated by chemiosmosis for purposes other than ATP synthesis (such as transporting pyruvate into the matrix).

Consequently, the actual measured values of ATP generated by NADH and FADH$_2$ are closer to 2.5 for each NADH, and 1.5 for each FADH$_2$. With these corrections, the overall harvest of ATP from a molecule of glucose in a eukaryotic cell is calculated as: 4 ATP from substrate-level

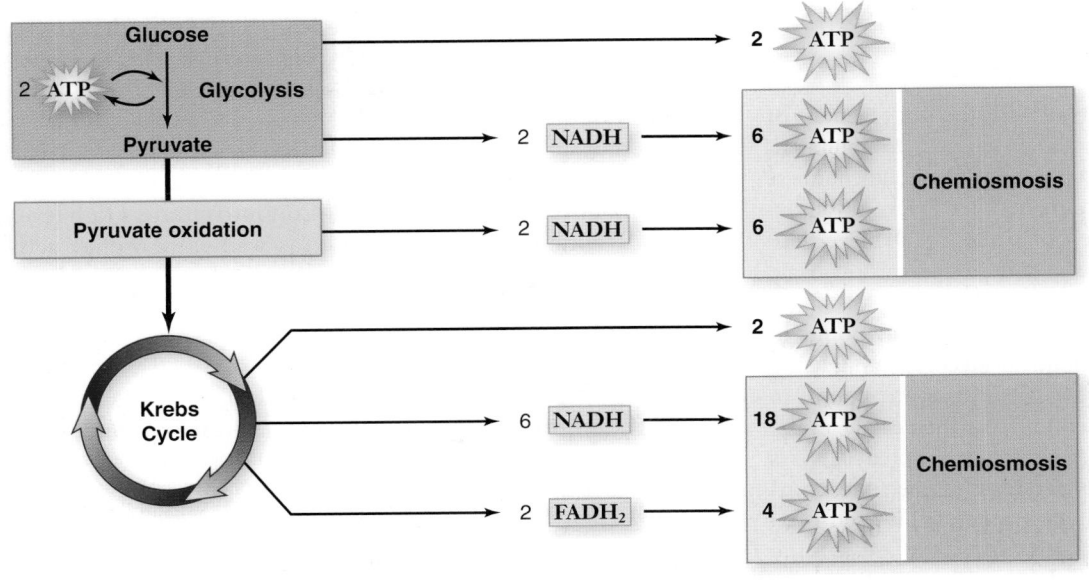

Figure 7.16 Theoretical ATP yield. The theoretical yield of ATP harvested from glucose by aerobic respiration totals 38 molecules. In eukaryotes this is reduced to 36 because it takes 1 ATP to transport each molecule of NADH that is generated by glycolysis in the cytoplasm into the mitochondria.

Total net ATP yield = **38**
(36 in eukaryotes)

phosphorylation + 25 ATP from NADH (2.5×10) + 3 ATP from $FADH_2$ (1.5×2) − 2 ATP for transport of glycolytic NADH = 30 molecules of ATP.

We mentioned earlier that the catabolism of glucose by aerobic respiration, in contrast to that by glycolysis alone, has a large energy yield. Aerobic respiration in a eukaryotic cell harvests about (7.3×30)/686 = 32% of the energy available in glucose. (By comparison, a typical car converts only about 25% of the energy in gasoline into useful energy.)

The higher yield of aerobic respiration was one of the key factors that fostered the evolution of heterotrophs. As this mechanism for producing ATP evolved, nonphotosynthetic organisms could more successfully base their metabolism on the exclusive use of molecules derived from other organisms. As long as some organisms captured energy by photosynthesis, others could exist solely by feeding on them.

Learning Outcome Review 7.6

Passage of electrons down the electron transport chain produces roughly three ATP per NADH (two ATP per $FADH_2$). This process plus the ATP generated by substrate-level phosphorylation could yield a maximum of 38 ATP for the complete oxidation of glucose. But NADH generated in the cytoplasm yields only two ATP/NADH because transporting the NADH into the mitochondria uses ATP. Therefore the theoretical total is 36 ATP per glucose in eukaryotes.

■ *Why is the expected yield not necessarily the same as the actual yield in a cell?*

7.7 Regulation of Aerobic Respiration

Learning Outcome

1. *Understand the control points for cellular respiration.*

When cells possess plentiful amounts of ATP, the key reactions of glycolysis, the Krebs cycle, and fatty acid breakdown are inhibited, slowing ATP production. The regulation of these biochemical pathways by the level of ATP is an example of feedback inhibition. Conversely, when ATP levels in the cell are low, ADP levels are high, and ADP activates enzymes in the pathways of carbohydrate catabolism to stimulate the production of more ATP.

Control of glucose catabolism occurs at two key points in the catabolic pathway, namely at a point in glycolysis and at the beginning of the Krebs cycle (figure 7.17). The control point in glycolysis is the enzyme phosphofructokinase, which catalyzes the conversion of fructose phosphate to fructose bisphosphate. This is the first reaction of glycolysis that is not readily reversible, committing the substrate to the glycolytic sequence. ATP itself is an allosteric inhibitor (see chapter 6) of phosphofructokinase, as is the Krebs cycle intermediate citrate. High levels of both ATP and citrate inhibit phosphofructokinase. Thus, under conditions when

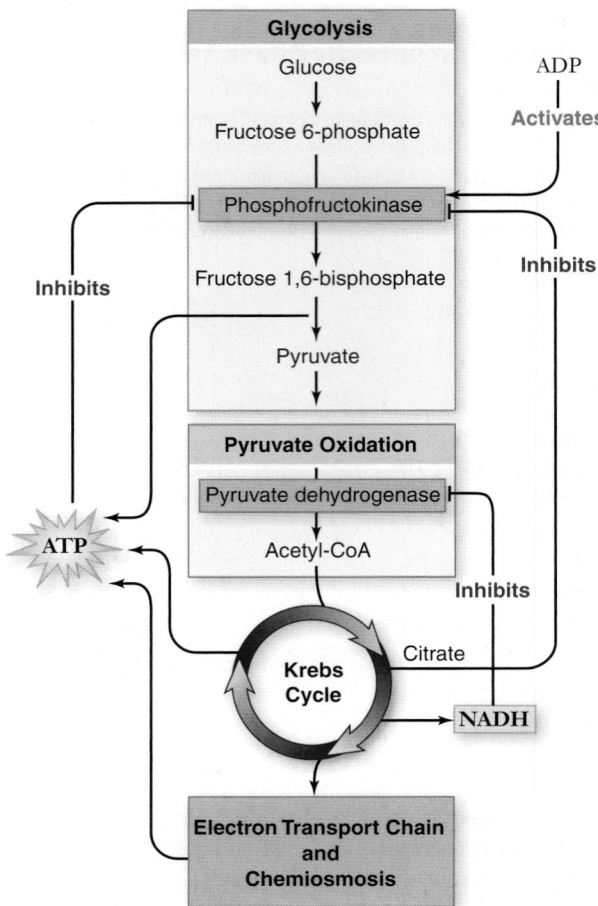

Figure 7.17 Control of glucose catabolism. The relative levels of ADP and ATP and key intermediates NADH and citrate control the catabolic pathway at two key points: the committing reactions of glycolysis and the Krebs cycle.

ATP is in excess, or when the Krebs cycle is producing citrate faster than it is being consumed, glycolysis is slowed.

The main control point in the oxidation of pyruvate occurs at the committing step in the Krebs cycle with the enzyme pyruvate dehydrogenase, which converts pyruvate to acetyl-CoA. This enzyme is inhibited by high levels of NADH, a key product of the Krebs cycle.

Another control point in the Krebs cycle is the enzyme citrate synthetase, which catalyzes the first reaction, the conversion of oxaloacetate and acetyl-CoA into citrate. High levels of ATP inhibit citrate synthetase (as well as phosphofructokinase, pyruvate dehydrogenase, and two other Krebs cycle enzymes), slowing down the entire catabolic pathway.

Learning Outcome Review 7.7

Respiration is controlled by levels of ATP in the cell and levels of key intermediates in the process. The control point for glycolysis is the enzyme phosphofructokinase, which is inhibited by ATP or citrate (or both). The main control point in oxidation of pyruvate is the enzyme pyruvate dehydrogenase, inhibited by NADH.

■ *How does feedback inhibition ensure economic production of ATP?*

7.8 Oxidation Without O₂

Learning Outcomes

1. *Compare anaerobic and aerobic respiration.*
2. *Distinguish the role of fermentation in anaerobic metabolism.*

In the presence of oxygen, cells can use oxygen to produce a large amount of ATP. But even when no oxygen is present to accept electrons, some organisms can still respire *anaerobically*, using inorganic molecules as final electron acceptors for an electron transport chain.

For example, many prokaryotes use sulfur, nitrate, carbon dioxide, or even inorganic metals as the final electron acceptor in place of oxygen (figure 7.18). The free energy released by using these other molecules as final electron acceptors is not as great as that using oxygen because they have a lower affinity for electrons. The amount of ATP produced is less, but the process is still respiration and not fermentation.

Methanogens use carbon dioxide

Among the heterotrophs that practice anaerobic respiration are Archaea such as thermophiles and methanogens. Methanogens use carbon dioxide (CO_2) as the electron acceptor, reducing CO_2 to CH_4 (methane). The hydrogens are de-

rived from organic molecules produced by other organisms. Methanogens are found in diverse environments, including soil and the digestive systems of ruminants like cows.

Sulfur bacteria use sulfate

Evidence of a second anaerobic respiratory process among primitive bacteria is seen in a group of rocks about 2.7 BYA, known as the Woman River iron formation. Organic material in these rocks is enriched for the light isotope of sulfur, ^{32}S, relative to the heavier isotope, ^{34}S. No known geochemical process produces such enrichment, but biological sulfur reduction does, in a process still carried out today by certain prokaryotes.

In this sulfate respiration, the prokaryotes derive energy from the reduction of inorganic sulfates (SO_4) to hydrogen sulfide (H_2S). The hydrogen atoms are obtained from organic molecules other organisms produce. These prokaryotes thus are similar to methanogens, but they use SO_4 as the oxidizing (that is, electron-accepting) agent in place of CO_2.

The early sulfate reducers set the stage for the evolution of photosynthesis, creating an environment rich in H_2S. As discussed in chapter 8, the first form of photosynthesis obtained hydrogens from H_2S using the energy of sunlight.

Fermentation uses organic compounds as electron acceptors

In the absence of oxygen, cells that cannot utilize an alternative electron acceptor for respiration must rely exclusively on

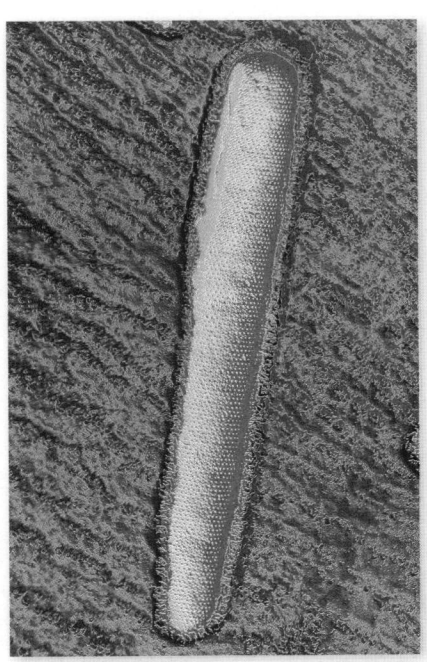

a.

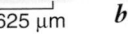

0.625 µm

b.

Figure 7.18 Sulfur-respiring prokaryote. *a.* The micrograph shows the archaeal species *Thermoproteus tenax*. This organism can use elemental sulfur as a final electron acceptor for anaerobic respiration. *b.* *Thermoproteus* is often found in sulfur-containing hot springs such as the Norris Geyser Basin in Yellowstone National Park shown here.

glycolysis to produce ATP. Under these conditions, the electrons generated by glycolysis are donated to organic molecules in a process called *fermentation*. This process recycles NAD^+, the electron acceptor that allows glycolysis to proceed.

Bacteria carry out more than a dozen kinds of fermentation reactions, often using pyruvate or a derivative of pyruvate to accept the electrons from NADH. Organic molecules other than pyruvate and its derivatives can be used as well; the important point is that the process regenerates NAD^+:

$$\text{organic molecule} + \text{NADH} \longrightarrow \text{reduced organic molecule} + NAD^+$$

Often the reduced organic compound is an organic acid—such as acetic acid, butyric acid, propionic acid, or lactic acid—or an alcohol.

Ethanol fermentation

Eukaryotic cells are capable of only a few types of fermentation. In one type, which occurs in yeast, the molecule that accepts electrons from NADH is derived from pyruvate, the end-product of glycolysis.

Yeast enzymes remove a terminal CO_2 group from pyruvate through decarboxylation, producing a 2-carbon molecule called acetaldehyde. The CO_2 released causes bread made with yeast to rise. The acetaldehyde accepts a pair of electrons from NADH, producing NAD^+ and ethanol (ethyl alcohol) (figure 7.19).

This particular type of fermentation is of great interest to humans, because it is the source of the ethanol in wine and beer. Ethanol is a by-product of fermentation that is actually toxic to yeast; as it approaches a concentration of about 12%, it begins to kill the yeast. That explains why naturally fermented wine contains only about 12% ethanol.

Lactic acid fermentation

Most animal cells regenerate NAD^+ without decarboxylation. Muscle cells, for example, use the enzyme lactate dehydrogenase to transfer electrons from NADH back to the pyruvate that is produced by glycolysis. This reaction converts pyruvate into lactic acid and regenerates NAD^+ from NADH (see figure 7.19). It therefore closes the metabolic circle, allowing glycolysis to continue as long as glucose is available.

Circulating blood removes excess lactate, the ionized form of lactic acid, from muscles, but when removal cannot keep pace with production, the accumulating lactic acid interferes with muscle function and contributes to muscle fatigue.

Learning Outcomes Review 7.8

Nitrate, sulfur, and CO_2 are all used as terminal electron acceptors in anaerobic respiration of different organisms. Organic molecules can also accept electrons in fermentation reactions that regenerate NAD^+. Fermentation reactions produce a variety of compounds, including ethanol in yeast and lactic acid in humans.

■ **In what kinds of ecosystems would you expect to find anaerobic respiration?**

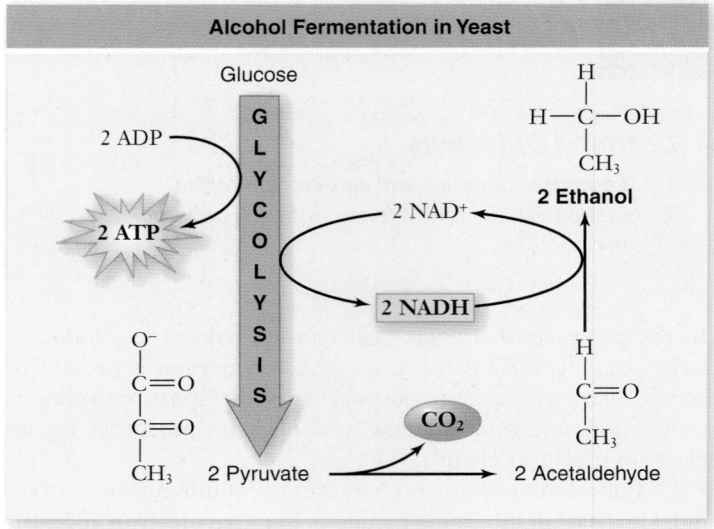

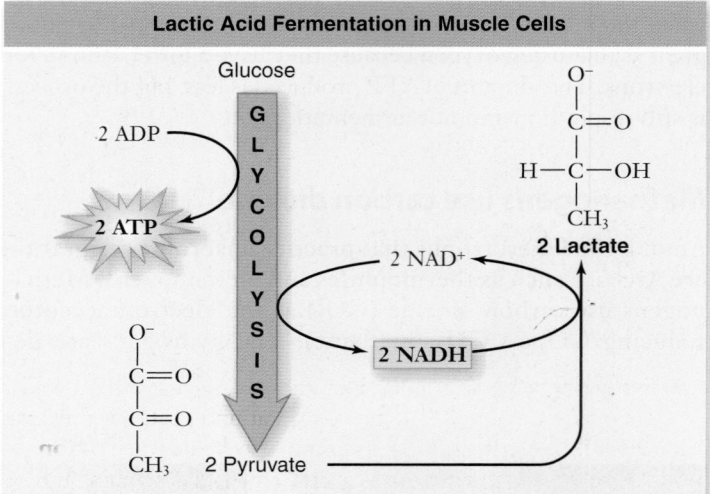

Figure 7.19 Fermentation. Yeasts carry out the conversion of pyruvate to ethanol. Muscle cells convert pyruvate into lactate, which is less toxic than ethanol. In each case, the reduction of a metabolite of glucose has oxidized NADH back to NAD^+ to allow glycolysis to continue under anaerobic conditions.

7.9 Catabolism of Proteins and Fats

Learning Outcomes

1. *Identify the points at which proteins and fats enter energy metabolism.*
2. *Describe the linkages between catabolic and anabolic pathways.*

Thus far we have focused on the aerobic respiration of glucose, which organisms obtain from the digestion of carbohydrates or from photosynthesis. Organic molecules other than glucose,

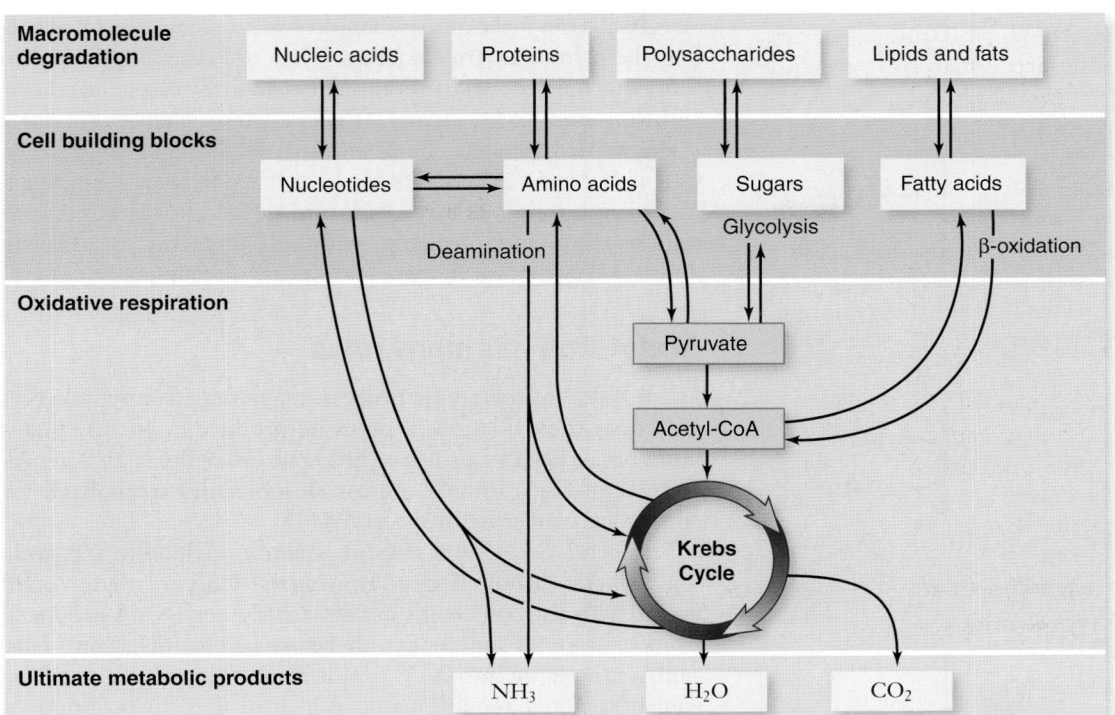

Figure 7.20 How cells extract chemical energy. All eukaryotes and many prokaryotes extract energy from organic molecules by oxidizing them. The first stage of this process, breaking down macromolecules into their constituent parts, yields little energy. The second stage, oxidative or aerobic respiration, extracts energy, primarily in the form of high-energy electrons, and produces water and carbon dioxide. Key intermediates in these energy pathways are also used for biosynthetic pathways, shown by reverse arrows.

particularly proteins and fats, are also important sources of energy (figure 7.20).

Catabolism of proteins removes amino groups

Proteins are first broken down into their individual amino acids. The nitrogen-containing side group (the amino group) is then removed from each amino acid in a process called **deamination**. A series of reactions converts the carbon chain that remains into a molecule that enters glycolysis or the Krebs cycle. For example, alanine is converted into pyruvate, glutamate into α-ketoglutarate (figure 7.21), and aspartate into oxaloacetate. The reactions of glycolysis and the Krebs cycle then extract the high-energy electrons from these molecules and put them to work making ATP.

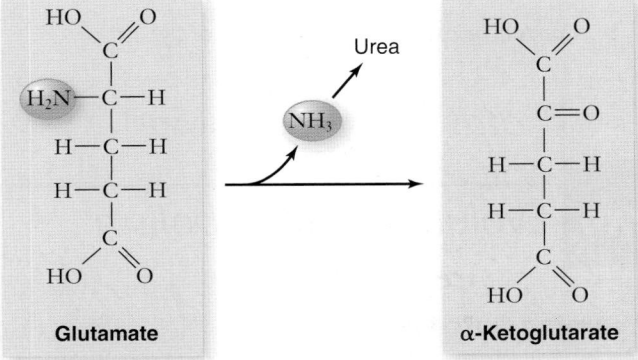

Figure 7.21 Deamination. After proteins are broken down into their amino acid constituents, the amino groups are removed from the amino acids to form molecules that participate in glycolysis and the Krebs cycle. For example, the amino acid glutamate becomes α-ketoglutarate, a Krebs cycle intermediate, when it loses its amino group.

Catabolism of fatty acids produces acetyl groups

Fats are broken down into fatty acids plus glycerol. Long-chain fatty acids typically have an even number of carbons, and the many C—H bonds provide a rich harvest of energy. Fatty acids are oxidized in the matrix of the mitochondrion. Enzymes remove the 2-carbon acetyl groups from the end of each fatty acid until the entire fatty acid is converted into acetyl groups (figure 7.22). Each acetyl group is combined with coenzyme A to form acetyl-CoA. This process is known as **β oxidation.** This process is oxygen-dependent, which explains why aerobic exercise burns fat, but anaerobic exercise does not.

How much ATP does the catabolism of fatty acids produce? Let's compare a hypothetical 6-carbon fatty acid with the 6-carbon glucose molecule, which we've said yields about 30 molecules of ATP in a eukaryotic cell. Two rounds of β oxidation would convert the fatty acid into three molecules of acetyl-CoA. Each round requires one molecule of ATP to prime the process, but it also produces one molecule of NADH and one of $FADH_2$. These molecules together yield four molecules of ATP (assuming 2.5 ATPs per NADH, and 1.5 ATPs per $FADH_2$).

The oxidation of each acetyl-CoA in the Krebs cycle ultimately produces an additional 10 molecules of ATP. Overall, then, the ATP yield of a 6-carbon fatty acid is approximately: 8 (from two rounds of β oxidation) − 2 (for priming those two rounds) + 30 (from oxidizing the three acetyl-CoAs) = 36 molecules of ATP. Therefore, the respiration of a 6-carbon fatty acid yields 20% more ATP than the respiration of glucose.

Moreover, a fatty acid of that size would weigh less than two thirds as much as glucose, so a gram of fatty acid contains more than twice as many kilocalories as a gram of glucose. You can see from this fact why fat is a storage molecule for excess

Figure 7.22

β oxidation. Through a series of reactions known as β oxidation, the last two carbons in a fatty acid combine with coenzyme A to form acetyl-CoA, which enters the Krebs cycle. The fatty acid, now two carbons shorter, enters the pathway again and keeps reentering until all its carbons have been used to form acetyl-CoA molecules. Each round of β oxidation uses one molecule of ATP and generates one molecule each of FADH$_2$ and NADH.

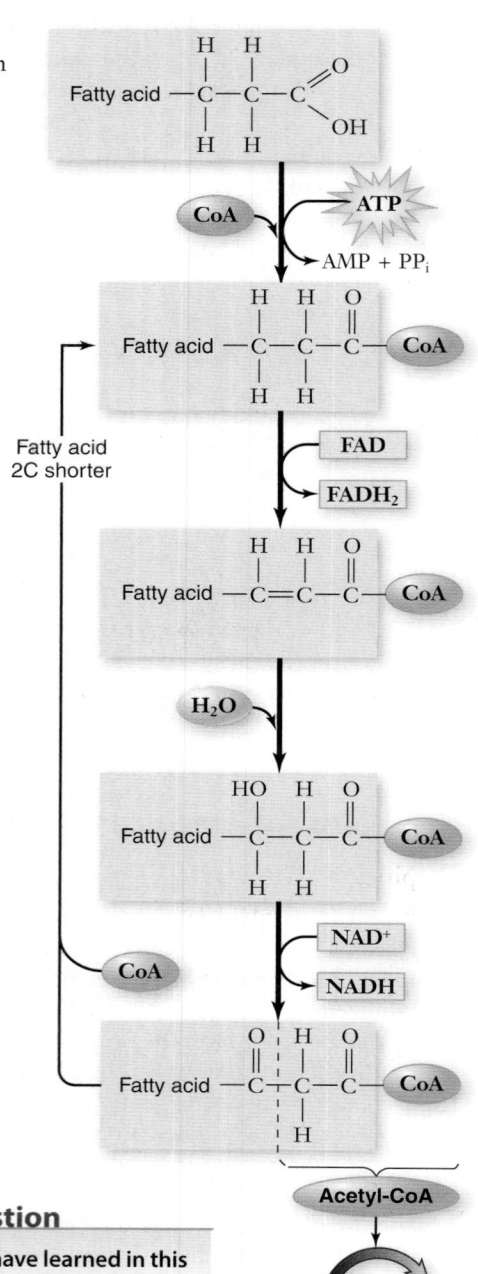

Inquiry question

? Given what you have learned in this chapter, how many ATP would be produced by the oxidation of a fatty acid that has 16 carbons?

Cells can make glucose, amino acids, and fats, as well as getting them from external sources. They use reactions similar to those that break down these substances. In many cases, the reverse pathways even share enzymes if the free-energy changes are small. For example, gluconeogenesis, the process of making new glucose, uses all but three enzymes of the glycolytic pathway. Thus, much of glycolysis runs forward or backward, depending on the concentrations of the intermediates—with only three key steps having different enzymes for forward and reverse directions.

Acetyl-CoA has many roles

Many different metabolic processes generate acetyl-CoA. Not only does the oxidation of pyruvate produce it, but the metabolic breakdown of proteins, fats, and other lipids also generates acetyl-CoA. Indeed, almost all molecules catabolized for energy are converted into acetyl-CoA.

Acetyl-CoA has a role in anabolic metabolism as well. Units of two carbons derived from acetyl-CoA are used to build up the hydrocarbon chains in fatty acids. Acetyl-CoA produced from a variety of sources can therefore be channeled into fatty acid synthesis or into ATP production, depending on the organism's energy requirements. Which of these two options is taken depends on the level of ATP in the cell.

When ATP levels are high, the oxidative pathway is inhibited, and acetyl-CoA is channeled into fatty acid synthesis. This explains why many animals (humans included) develop fat reserves when they consume more food than their activities require. Alternatively, when ATP levels are low, the oxidative pathway is stimulated, and acetyl-CoA flows into energy-producing oxidative metabolism.

Learning Outcomes Review 7.9

Proteins can be broken into their constituent amino acids, which are then deaminated and can enter metabolism at glycolysis or different steps of the Krebs cycle. Fats can be broken into units of acetyl-CoA by β oxidation and then fed into the Krebs cycle. Many metabolic processes can be used reversibly, to either build up (anabolism) or break down (catabolism) the major biological macromolecules. Key intermediates, such as pyruvate and acetyl-CoA, connect these processes.

■ **Can fats be oxidized in the absence of O$_2$?**

energy in many types of animals. If excess energy were stored instead as carbohydrate, as it is in plants, animal bodies would have to be much bulkier.

A small number of key intermediates connect metabolic pathways

Oxidation pathways of food molecules are interrelated in that a small number of key intermediates, such as pyruvate and acetyl-CoA, link the breakdown from different starting points. These key intermediates allow the interconversion of different types of molecules, such as sugars and amino acids (see figure 7.20).

7.10 Evolution of Metabolism

Learning Outcome

1. Describe one possible hypothesis for the evolution of metabolism.

We talk about cellular respiration as a continuous series of stages, but it is important to note that these stages evolved over time, and metabolism has changed a great deal in that time.

Both anabolic processes and catabolic processes evolved in concert with each other. We do not know the details of this biochemical evolution, or the order of appearance of these processes. Therefore the following timeline is based on the available geochemical evidence and represents a hypothesis rather than a strict timeline.

The earliest life forms degraded carbon-based molecules present in the environment

The most primitive forms of life are thought to have obtained chemical energy by degrading, or breaking down, organic molecules that were abiotically produced, that is, carbon-containing molecules formed by inorganic processes on the early Earth.

The first major event in the evolution of metabolism was the origin of the ability to harness chemical bond energy. At an early stage, organisms began to store this energy in the bonds of ATP.

The evolution of glycolysis also occurred early

The second major event in the evolution of metabolism was glycolysis, the initial breakdown of glucose. As proteins evolved diverse catalytic functions, it became possible to capture a larger fraction of the chemical bond energy in organic molecules by breaking chemical bonds in a series of steps.

Glycolysis undoubtedly evolved early in the history of life on Earth, because this biochemical pathway has been retained by all living organisms. It is a chemical process that does not appear to have changed for more than 2 billion years.

Anoxygenic photosynthesis allowed the capture of light energy

The third major event in the evolution of metabolism was anoxygenic photosynthesis. Early in the history of life, a different way of generating ATP evolved in some organisms. Instead of obtaining energy for ATP synthesis by reshuffling chemical bonds, as in glycolysis, these organisms developed the ability to use light to pump protons out of their cells and to use the resulting proton gradient to power the production of ATP through chemiosmosis.

Photosynthesis evolved in the absence of oxygen and works well without it. Dissolved H_2S, present in the oceans of the early Earth beneath an atmosphere free of oxygen gas, served as a ready source of hydrogen atoms for building organic molecules. Free sulfur was produced as a by-product of this reaction.

Oxygen-forming photosynthesis used a different source of hydrogen

The substitution of H_2O for H_2S in photosynthesis was the fourth major event in the history of metabolism. Oxygen-forming photosynthesis employs H_2O rather than H_2S as a source of hydrogen atoms and their associated electrons. Because it garners its electrons from reduced oxygen rather than from reduced sulfur, it generates oxygen gas rather than free sulfur.

More than 2 BYA, small cells capable of carrying out this oxygen-forming photosynthesis, such as cyanobacteria, became the dominant forms of life on Earth. Oxygen gas began to accumulate in the atmosphere. This was the beginning of a great transition that changed conditions on Earth permanently. Our atmosphere is now 20.9% oxygen, every molecule of which is derived from an oxygen-forming photosynthetic reaction.

Nitrogen fixation provided new organic nitrogen

Nitrogen is available from dead organic matter, and from chemical reactions that generated the original organic molecules. For life to expand, a new source of nitrogen was needed. Nitrogen fixation was the fifth major step in the evolution of metabolism. Proteins and nucleic acids cannot be synthesized from the products of photosynthesis because both of these biologically critical molecules contain nitrogen. Obtaining nitrogen atoms from N_2 gas, a process called *nitrogen fixation*, requires breaking an $N \equiv N$ triple bond.

This important reaction evolved in the hydrogen-rich atmosphere of the early Earth, where no oxygen was present. Oxygen acts as a poison to nitrogen fixation, which today occurs only in oxygen-free environments or in oxygen-free compartments within certain prokaryotes.

Aerobic respiration utilized oxygen

Respiration is the sixth and final event in the history of metabolism. Aerobic respiration employs the same kind of proton pumps as photosynthesis and is thought to have evolved as a modification of the basic photosynthetic machinery.

Biologists think that the ability to carry out photosynthesis without H_2S first evolved among purple nonsulfur bacteria, which obtain their hydrogens from organic compounds instead. It was perhaps inevitable that among the descendants of these respiring photosynthetic bacteria, some would eventually do without photosynthesis entirely, subsisting only on the energy and electrons derived from the breakdown of organic molecules. The mitochondria within all eukaryotic cells are thought to be descendants of these bacteria.

The complex process of aerobic metabolism developed over geological time, as natural selection favored organisms with more efficient methods of obtaining energy from organic molecules. The process of photosynthesis, as you have seen in this concluding section, has also developed over time, and the rise of photosynthesis changed life on Earth forever. The next chapter explores photosynthesis in detail.

Learning Outcome Review 7.10

Major milestones in the evolution of metabolism include the evolution of pathways to extract energy from organic compounds, the pathways of photosynthesis, and those of nitrogen fixation. Photosynthesis began as an anoxygenic process that later evolved to produce free oxygen, thus allowing the evolution of aerobic metabolism.

■ *What evidence can you cite for this hypothesis of the evolution of metabolism?*

7.1 Overview of Respiration

Cells oxidize organic compounds to drive metabolism.

Cellular respiration is the complete oxidation of glucose.

Aerobic respiration uses oxygen as the final electron acceptor for redox reactions. Anaerobic respiration utilizes inorganic molecules as acceptors, and fermentation uses organic molecules.

Electron carriers play a critical role in energy metabolism.

Electron carriers can be reversibly oxidized and reduced. For example, NAD^+ is reduced to NADH by acquiring two electrons; NADH supplies these electrons to other molecules to reduce them.

Metabolism harvests energy in stages.

Mitochondria of eukaryotic cells move electrons in steps via the electron transport chain to capture energy efficiently.

ATP plays a central role in metabolism.

The ultimate goal of cellular respiration is synthesis of ATP, which is used to power most of the cell's activities.

Cells make ATP by two fundamentally different mechanisms.

Substrate-level phosphorylation transfers a phosphate directly to ADP (see figure 7.4). Oxidative phosphorylation generates ATP via the enzyme ATP synthase, powered by a proton gradient.

7.2 Glycolysis: Splitting Glucose (see figure 7.6)

Glycolysis converts glucose into two 3-carbon molecules of pyruvate. Each molecule of glucose yields two net ATP molecules.

Priming changes glucose into an easily cleaved form.

Priming reactions add two phosphates to glucose; this is cleaved into two 3-carbon molecules of glyceraldehyde 3-phosphate (G3P).

ATP is synthesized by substrate-level phosphorylation.

Oxidation of G3P transfers electrons to NAD^+, yielding NADH. After four more reactions, the final product is two molecules of pyruvate. Glycolysis produces 2 net ATP, 2 NADH, and 2 pyruvate.

NADH must be recycled into NAD^+ to continue respiration.

In the presence of oxygen, NADH passes electrons to the electron transport chain. In the absence of oxygen, NADH passes the electrons to an organic molecule such as acetaldehyde (fermentation).

7.3 The Oxidation of Pyruvate to Produce Acetyl-CoA

Pyruvate is oxidized to yield 1 CO_2, 1 NADH, and 1 acetyl-CoA. Acetyl-CoA enters the Krebs cycle as 2-carbon acetyl units.

7.4 The Krebs Cycle

The Krebs cycle extracts electrons and synthesizes one ATP.

The first reaction is an irreversible condensation that produces citrate; it is inhibited when ATP is plentiful. The second and third reactions rearrange citrate to isocitrate. The fourth and fifth reactions are oxidations; in each reaction, one NAD^+ is reduced to NADH. The sixth reaction is a substrate-level phosphorylation producing GTP, and from that ATP. The seventh reaction is another oxidation that reduces FAD to $FADH_2$. Reactions eight and nine regenerate oxaloacetate, including one final oxidation that reduces NAD^+ to NADH.

Glucose becomes CO_2 and potential energy.

As a glucose molecule is broken down to CO_2, some of its energy is preserved in 4 ATPs, 10 NADH, and 2 $FADH_2$.

Following the electrons in the reactions reveals the direction of transfer.

7.5 The Electron Transport Chain and Chemiosmosis (see figure 7.12)

The electron transport chain produces a proton gradient.

In the inner mitochondrial membrane, NADH is oxidized to NAD^+ by NADH dehydrogenase. Electrons move through ubiquinone and the bc_1 complex to cytochrome oxidase, where they join with H^+ and O_2 to form H_2O. This results in three protons being pumped into the intermembrane space. For $FADH_2$, electrons are passed directly to ubiquinone. Thus only two protons are pumped into the intermembrane space.

The gradient forms as electrons move through electron carriers

Chemiosmosis utilizes the electrochemical gradient to produce ATP

ATP synthase is a molecular rotary motor.

Protons diffuse back into the mitochondrial matrix via the ATP synthase channel. The enzyme uses this energy to synthesize ATP (see figure 7.15).

7.6 Energy Yield of Aerobic Respiration

The theoretical yield for eukaryotes is 36 molecules of ATP per glucose molecule.

The actual yield for eukaryotes is 30 molecules of ATP per glucose molecule (see figure 7.16).

7.7 Regulation of Aerobic Respiration

Glucose catabolism is controlled by the concentration of ATP molecules and intermediates in the Krebs cycle (see figure 7.17).

7.8 Oxidation Without O_2 (see figure 7.8)

In the absence of oxygen other final electron acceptors can be used for respiration.

Methanogens use carbon dioxide.

Sulfur bacteria use sulfate.

Fermentation uses organic compounds as electron acceptors.

Fermentation is the regeneration of NAD^+ by oxidation of NADH and reduction of an organic molecule. In yeast, pyruvate is decarboxylated, then reduced to ethanol. In animals, pyruvate is reduced directly to lactate.

7.9 Catabolism of Proteins and Fats

Catabolism of proteins removes amino groups (see figure 7.20).

Catabolism of fatty acids produces acetyl groups.

Fatty acids are converted to acetyl groups by successive rounds of β-oxidation (see figure 7.22). These acetyl groups feed into the Krebs cycle to be oxidized and generate NADH for electron transport.

A small number of key intermediates connect metabolic pathways.

Acetyl-CoA has many roles.
With high ATP, acetyl-CoA is converted into fatty acids.

7.10 Evolution of Metabolism

Major milestones are recognized in the evolution of metabolism; the order of events is hypothetical.

The earliest life forms degraded carbon-based molecules present in the environment.

The evolution of glycolysis also occurred early.

Anoxygenic photosynthesis allowed the capture of light energy.

Oxygen-forming photosynthesis used a different source of hydrogen.

Nitrogen fixation provided new organic nitrogen.

Aerobic respiration utilized oxygen.

Review Questions

UNDERSTAND

1. An *autotroph* is an organism that
   a. extracts energy from organic sources.
   b. converts energy from sunlight into chemical energy.
   c. relies on the energy produced by other organisms as an energy source.
   d. does both a and b.

2. Which of the following processes is (are) required for the complete oxidation of glucose?
   a. The Krebs cycle
   b. Glycolysis
   c. Pyruvate oxidation
   d. All of the above

3. Which of the following is NOT a product of glycolysis?
   a. ATP   c. CO_2
   b. Pyruvate   d. NADH

4. Glycolysis produces ATP by
   a. phosphorylating organic molecules in the priming reactions.
   b. the production of glyceraldehyde 3-phosphate.
   c. substrate-level phosphorylation.
   d. the reduction of NAD^+ to NADH.

5. What is the role of NAD^+ in the process of cellular respiration?
   a. It functions as an electron carrier.
   b. It functions as an enzyme.
   c. It is the final electron acceptor for anaerobic respiration.
   d. It is a nucleotide source for the synthesis of ATP.

6. The reactions of the Krebs cycle occur in the
   a. inner membrane of the mitochondria.
   b. intermembrane space of the mitochondria.
   c. the cytoplasm.
   d. matrix of the mitochondria.

7. The electrons carried by NADH and $FADH_2$ can be
   a. pumped into the intermembrane space.
   b. transferred to the ATP synthase.
   c. moved between proteins in the inner membrane of the mitochondrion.
   d. transported into the matrix of the mitochondrion.

APPLY

1. Which of the following is NOT a true statement regarding cellular respiration?
   a. Enzymes catalyze reactions that transfer electrons.
   b. Electrons have a higher potential energy at the end of the process.
   c. Carbon dioxide gas is a by-product.
   d. The process involves multiple redox reactions.

2. The direct source of energy for the ATP produced by ATP synthase comes from
   a. the electron transport chain.
   b. the proton gradient.
   c. substrate-level phosphorylation.
   d. the oxidation reactions occurring during respiration.

3. Can cellular respiration occur in the absence of O_2?
   a. No, O_2 is necessary as the final electron acceptor.
   b. No, anaerobic organisms only need glycolysis and fermentation.
   c. Yes, because oxygen can be generated by splitting H_2O.
   d. Yes, but it requires an alternative to O_2 as a final electron acceptor.

4. Why is fermentation an important metabolic function in cells?
   a. It generates glucose for the cell in the absence of O_2.
   b. It oxidizes NADH to NAD^+.
   c. It oxidizes pyruvate.
   d. It produces ATP.

5. Which of the following statements is NOT true about the oxidation of pyruvate?
   a. Pyruvate oxidation occurs in the cytoplasm.
   b. Pyruvate oxidation only occurs if oxygen is present.
   c. Pyruvate is converted into acetyl-CoA.
   d. Pyruvate oxidation results in the production of NADH.

6. A chemical agent that makes holes in the inner membrane of the mitochondria would
   a. stop the movement of electrons down the electron transport chain.
   b. stop ATP synthesis.
   c. stop the Krebs cycle.
   d. all of the above.

7. Yeast cells that have mutations in genes that encode enzymes in glycolysis can still grow on glycerol. They are able to utilize glycerol because it
   a. enters glycolysis after the step affected by the mutation.
   b. can feed into the Krebs cycle and generate ATP via electron transport and chemiosmosis.
   c. can be utilized by fermentation.
   d. can donate electrons directly to the electron transport chain.

SYNTHESIZE

1. Use the following table to outline the relationship between the molecules and the metabolic reactions.

Molecules	Glycolysis	Cellular Respiration
Glucose		
Pyruvate		
Oxygen		
ATP		
CO_2		

2. Human babies and hibernating or cold-adapted animals are able to maintain body temperature (a process called *thermogenesis*) due to the presence of brown fat. Brown fat is characterized by a high concentration of mitochondria. These brown fat mitochondria have a special protein located within their inner membranes. *Thermogenin* is a protein that functions as a passive proton transporter. Propose a likely explanation for the role of brown fat in thermogenesis based on your knowledge of metabolism, transport, and the structure and function of mitochondria.

3. Recent data indicate a link between colder temperatures and weight loss. If adults retain brown fat, how could this be explained?

ONLINE RESOURCE

www.ravenbiology.com

Understand, Apply, and Synthesize—enhance your study with animations that bring concepts to life and practice tests to assess your understanding. Your instructor may also recommend the interactive eBook, individualized learning tools, and more.

Chapter 8

Photosynthesis

Chapter Outline

8.1   Overview of Photosynthesis

8.2   The Discovery of Photosynthetic Processes

8.3   Pigments

8.4   Photosystem Organization

8.5   The Light-Dependent Reactions

8.6   Carbon Fixation: The Calvin Cycle

8.7   Photorespiration

Introduction

The rich diversity of life that covers our Earth would be impossible without photosynthesis. Almost every oxygen atom in the air we breathe was once part of a water molecule, liberated by photosynthesis. All the energy released by the burning of coal, firewood, gasoline, and natural gas, and by our bodies' burning of all the food we eat—directly or indirectly—has been captured from sunlight by photosynthesis. It is vitally important, then, that we understand photosynthesis. Research may enable us to improve crop yields and land use, important goals in an increasingly crowded world. In chapter 7, we described how cells extract chemical energy from food molecules and use that energy to power their activities. In this chapter, we examine photosynthesis, the process by which organisms such as the aptly named sunflowers in the picture capture energy from sunlight and use it to build food molecules that are rich in chemical energy.

8.1 Overview of Photosynthesis

Learning Outcomes

1. **Explain the reaction for photosynthesis.**
2. **Describe the structure of the chloroplast.**

Life is powered by sunshine. The energy used by most living cells comes ultimately from the Sun and is captured by plants, algae, and bacteria through the process of photosynthesis.

The diversity of life is only possible because our planet is awash in energy streaming Earthward from the Sun. Each day, the radiant energy that reaches Earth equals the power from about 1 million Hiroshima-sized atomic bombs. Photosynthesis captures about 1% of this huge supply of energy (an amount equal to 10,000 Hiroshima bombs) and uses it to provide the energy that drives all life.

Photosynthesis combines CO_2 and H_2O, producing glucose and O_2

Photosynthesis occurs in a wide variety of organisms, and it comes in different forms. These include a form of photosynthesis that does not produce oxygen (anoxygenic) and a form that does (oxygenic). Anoxygenic photosynthesis is found in four different bacterial groups: purple bacteria, green sulfur bacteria, green nonsulfur bacteria, and heliobacteria. Oxygenic photosynthesis is found in cyanobacteria, seven groups of algae, and essentially all land plants. These two types of photosynthesis share similarities in the types of pigments they use to trap light energy, but they differ in the arrangement and action of these pigments.

In the case of plants, photosynthesis takes place primarily in the leaves. Figure 8.1 illustrates the levels of organization in a plant leaf. As you learned in chapter 4, the cells of plant leaves contain organelles called chloroplasts, which carry out the photosynthetic process. No other structure in a plant cell is able to carry out photosynthesis (figure 8.2). Photosynthesis takes place in three stages:

1. capturing energy from sunlight;
2. using the energy to make ATP and to reduce the compound NADP$^+$, an electron carrier, to NADPH; and
3. using the ATP and NADPH to power the synthesis of organic molecules from CO_2 in the air.

The first two stages require light and are commonly called the **light-dependent reactions.**

The third stage, the formation of organic molecules from CO_2, is called **carbon fixation.** This process takes place via a cyclic series of reactions. As long as ATP and NADPH are available, the carbon fixation reactions can occur either in the presence or in the absence of light, and so these reactions are also called the **light-independent reactions.**

The following simple equation summarizes the overall process of photosynthesis:

$$6\ CO_2 + 12\ H_2O + \text{light} \longrightarrow C_6H_{12}O_6 + 6\ H_2O + 6\ O_2$$

carbon dioxide   *water*   *glucose*   *water*   *oxygen*

You may notice that this equation is the reverse of the reaction for respiration. In respiration, glucose is oxidized to CO_2 using O_2 as an electron acceptor. In photosynthesis, CO_2 is reduced to glucose using electrons gained from the oxidation of water. The oxidation of H_2O and the reduction of CO_2 requires energy that is provided by light. Although this statement is an oversimplification, it provides a useful "global perspective."

In plants, photosynthesis takes place in chloroplasts

In the preceding chapter, you saw that a mitochondrion's complex structure of internal and external membranes contribute to its function. The same is true for the structure of the chloroplast.

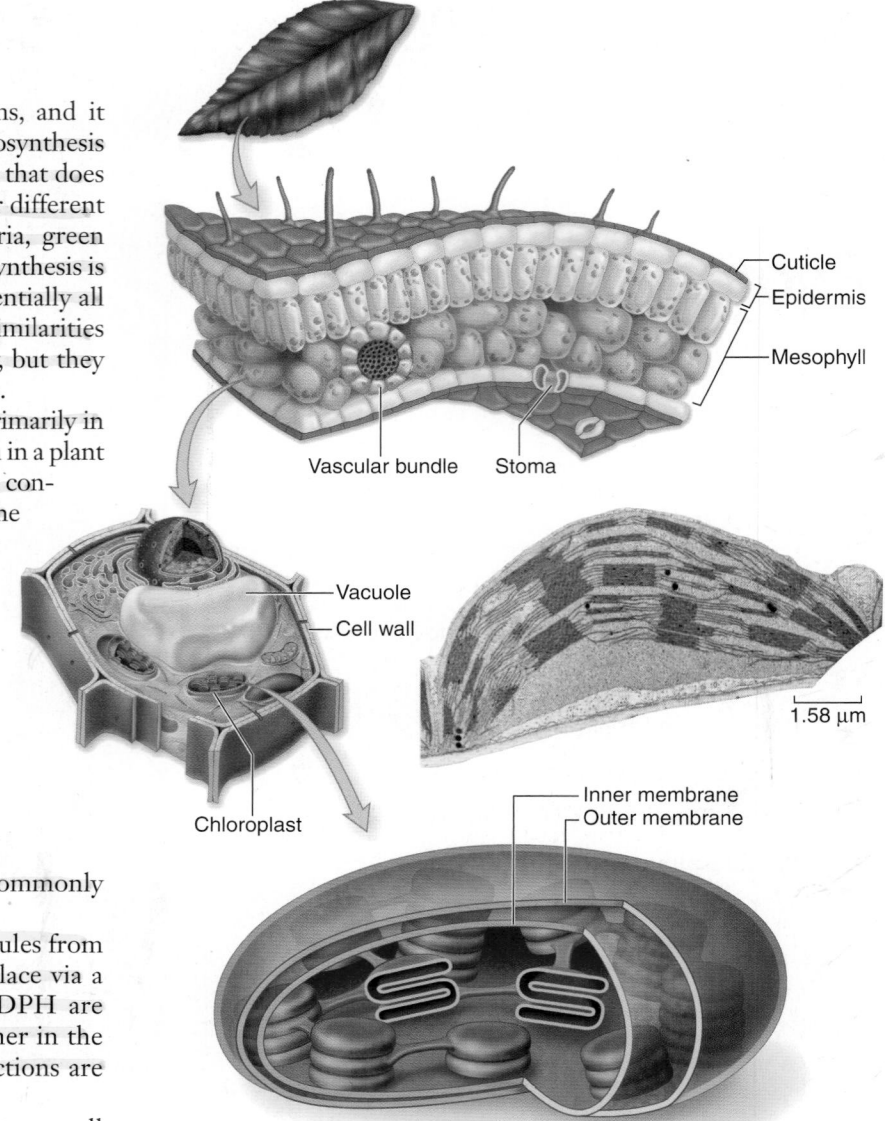

Figure 8.1 Journey into a leaf. A plant leaf possesses a thick layer of cells (the mesophyll) rich in chloroplasts. The inner membrane of the chloroplast is organized into flattened structures called thylakoid disks, which are stacked into columns called grana. The rest of the interior is filled with a semifluid substance called stroma.

The internal membrane of chloroplasts, called the *thylakoid membrane*, is a continuous phospholipid bilayer organized into flattened sacs that are found stacked on one another in columns called *grana* (singular, *granum*). The thylakoid membrane contains **chlorophyll** and other photosynthetic pigments for capturing light energy along with the machinery to make ATP. Connections between grana are termed *stroma lamella*.

Surrounding the thylakoid membrane system is a semiliquid substance called **stroma.** The stroma houses the enzymes needed to assemble organic molecules from CO_2 using energy from ATP coupled with reduction via NADPH. In the thylakoid membrane, photosynthetic pigments are clustered together to form **photosystems,** which show distinct organization within the thylakoid.

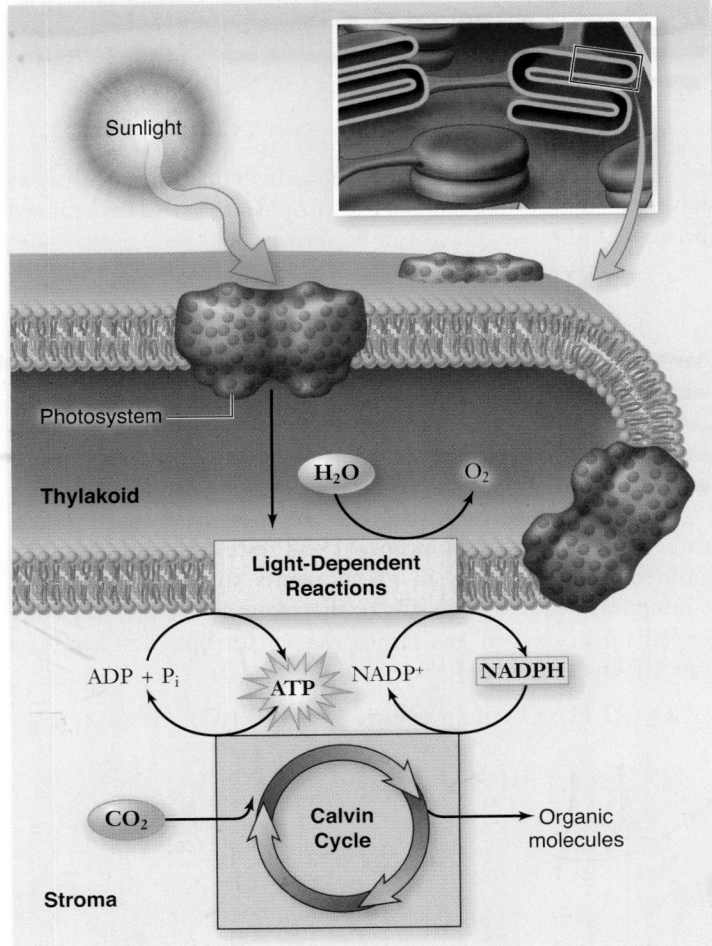

Figure 8.2 Overview of photosynthesis. In the light-dependent reactions, photosystems in the thylakoid absorb photons of light and use this energy to generate ATP and NADPH. Electrons lost from the photosystems are replaced by the oxidation of water, producing O_2 as a by-product. The ATP and NADPH produced by the light reactions is used during carbon fixation via the Calvin cycle in the stroma.

Each pigment molecule within the photosystem is capable of capturing photons, which are packets of energy. When light of a proper wavelength strikes a pigment molecule in the photosystem, the resulting excitation passes from one pigment molecule to another.

The excited electron is not transferred physically—rather, its *energy* passes from one molecule to another. The passage is similar to the transfer of kinetic energy along a row of upright dominoes. If you push the first one over, it falls against the next, and that one against the next, and so on, until all of the dominoes have fallen down.

Eventually, the energy arrives at a key chlorophyll molecule in contact with a membrane-bound protein that can accept an electron. The energy is transferred as an excited electron to that protein, which passes it on to a series of other membrane proteins that put the energy to work making ATP and NADPH.

These compounds are then used to build organic molecules. The photosystem thus acts as a large antenna, gathering the light energy harvested by many individual pigment molecules.

Learning Outcomes Review 8.1

Photosynthesis consists of light-dependent reactions that require sunlight, and others that convert CO_2 into organic molecules. The overall reaction is essentially the reverse of respiration and produces O_2 as a by-product. The chloroplast's inner membrane, the thylakoid, is the site in which photosynthetic pigments are clustered, allowing passage of energy from one molecule to the next. The thylakoid membrane is organized into flattened sacs stacked in columns called grana.

■ *How is the structure of the chloroplast similar to the mitochondria?*

8.2 The Discovery of Photosynthetic Processes

Learning Outcomes

1. Describe experiments that support our understanding of photosynthesis.
2. Explain the difference between the light-dependent and light-independent reactions.

The story of how we learned about photosynthesis begins over 300 years ago, and it continues to this day. It starts with curiosity about how plants manage to grow, often increasing their organic mass considerably.

Plants do not increase mass from soil and water alone

From the time of the Greeks, plants were thought to obtain their food from the soil, literally sucking it up with their roots. A Belgian doctor, Jan Baptista van Helmont (1580–1644) thought of a simple way to test this idea.

He planted a small willow tree in a pot of soil, after first weighing the tree and the soil. The tree grew in the pot for several years, during which time van Helmont added only water. At the end of five years, the tree was much larger, its weight having increased by 74.4 kg. However, the soil in the pot weighed only 57 g less than it had five years earlier. With this experiment, van Helmont demonstrated that the substance of the plant was not produced only from the soil. He incorrectly concluded, however, that the water he had been adding mainly accounted for the plant's increased biomass.

A hundred years passed before the story became clearer. The key clue was provided by the English scientist Joseph Priestly (1733–1804). On the 17th of August, 1771, Priestly put a living sprig of mint into air in which a wax candle had burnt out. On the 27th of the same month, Priestly found that another candle could be burned in this same air. Somehow, the vegetation seemed to have restored the air. Priestly found that while a mouse could not breathe candle-exhausted air, air "restored" by vegetation was not "at all inconvenient to a mouse." The key clue was that *living vegetation adds something to the air.*

How does vegetation "restore" air? Twenty-five years later, the Dutch physician Jan Ingenhousz (1730–1799) solved the puzzle. He demonstrated that air was restored only in the presence of sunlight and only by a plant's green leaves, not by its roots. He proposed that the green parts of the plant carry out a process that uses sunlight to split carbon dioxide into carbon and oxygen. He suggested that the oxygen was released as O_2 gas into the air, while the carbon atom combined with water to form carbohydrates. Other research refined his conclusions, and by the end of the nineteenth century, the overall reaction for photosynthesis could be written as:

$$CO_2 + H_2O + \text{light energy} \longrightarrow (CH_2O) + O_2$$

It turns out, however, that there's more to it than that. When researchers began to examine the process in more detail in the twentieth century, the role of light proved to be unexpectedly complex.

Photosynthesis includes both light-dependent and light-independent reactions

At the beginning of the twentieth century, the English plant physiologist F. F. Blackman (1866–1947) came to the startling conclusion that photosynthesis is in fact a multistage process, only one portion of which uses light directly.

Blackman measured the effects of different light intensities, CO_2 concentrations, and temperatures on photosynthesis. As long as light intensity was relatively low, he found photosynthesis could be accelerated by increasing the amount of light, but not by increasing the temperature or CO_2 concentration (figure 8.3). At high light intensities, however, an increase in temperature or CO_2 concentration greatly accelerated photosynthesis.

Blackman concluded that photosynthesis consists of an initial set of what he called "light" reactions, that are largely independent of temperature but depend on light, and a second set of "dark" reactions (more properly called light-independent reactions), that seemed to be independent of light but limited by CO_2.

Do not be confused by Blackman's labels—the so-called "dark" reactions occur in the light (in fact, they require the products of the light-dependent reactions); his use of the word *dark* simply indicates that light is not *directly* involved in those reactions.

Blackman found that increased temperature increased the rate of the light-independent reactions, but only up to about 35°C. Higher temperatures caused the rate to fall off rapidly. Because many plant enzymes begin to be denatured at 35°C, Blackman concluded that enzymes must carry out the light-independent reactions.

O_2 comes from water, not from CO_2

In the 1930s, C. B. van Niel (1897–1985) working at the Hopkins Marine Station at Stanford, discovered that purple sulfur bacteria do not release oxygen during photosynthesis; instead, they convert hydrogen sulfide (H_2S) into globules of pure elemental sulfur that accumulate inside them. The process van Niel observed was:

$$CO_2 + 2\ H_2S + \text{light energy} \longrightarrow (CH_2O) + H_2O + 2\ S$$

The striking parallel between this equation and Ingenhousz's equation led van Niel to propose that the generalized process of photosynthesis can be shown as:

$$CO_2 + 2\ H_2A + \text{light energy} \longrightarrow (CH_2O) + H_2O + 2\ A$$

In this equation, the substance H_2A serves as an electron donor. In photosynthesis performed by green plants, H_2A is water, whereas in purple sulfur bacteria, H_2A is hydrogen sulfide. The product, A, comes from the splitting of H_2A. Therefore, the O_2 produced during green plant photosynthesis results from splitting water, not carbon dioxide.

When isotopes came into common use in the early 1950s, van Niel's revolutionary proposal was tested. Investigators examined photosynthesis in green plants supplied with water containing heavy oxygen (^{18}O); they found that the ^{18}O label ended up in oxygen gas rather than in carbohydrate, just as van Niel had predicted:

$$CO_2 + 2\ H_2{}^{18}O + \text{light energy} \longrightarrow (CH_2O) + H_2O + {}^{18}O_2$$

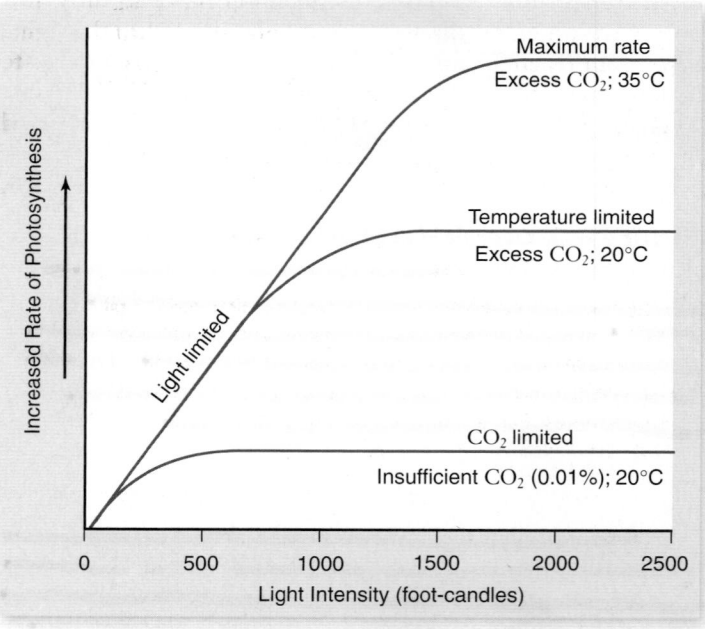

Figure 8.3 Discovery of the light-independent reactions. Blackman measured photosynthesis rates under differing light intensities, CO_2 concentrations, and temperatures. As this graph shows, light is the limiting factor at low light intensities, but temperature and CO_2 concentration are the limiting factors at higher light intensities. This implies the existence of reactions using CO_2 that involve enzymes.

Inquiry question

? Blackman found that increasing light intensity above 2000 foot-candles did not lead to any further increase in the rate of photosynthesis. Can you suggest a hypothesis that would explain this?

In algae and green plants, the carbohydrate typically produced by photosynthesis is glucose. The complete balanced equation for photosynthesis in these organisms thus becomes:

$$6\,CO_2 + 12\,H_2O + \text{light energy} \longrightarrow C_6H_{12}O_6 + 6\,H_2O + 6\,O_2$$

ATP and NADPH from light-dependent reactions reduce CO₂ to make sugars

In his pioneering work on the light-dependent reactions, van Niel proposed that the H^+ ions and electrons generated by the splitting of water were used to convert CO_2 into organic matter in a process he called *carbon fixation.* In the 1950s, Robin Hill (1899–1991) demonstrated that van Niel was right, light energy could be harvested and used in a reduction reaction. Chloroplasts isolated from leaf cells were able to reduce a dye and release oxygen in response to light. Later experiments showed that the electrons released from water were transferred to $NADP^+$ and that illuminated chloroplasts deprived of CO_2 accumulate ATP. If CO_2 is introduced, neither ATP nor NADPH accumulate, and the CO_2 is assimilated into organic molecules.

These experiments are important for three reasons: First, they firmly demonstrate that photosynthesis in plants occurs within chloroplasts. Second, they show that the light-dependent reactions use light energy to reduce $NADP^+$ and to manufacture ATP. Third, they confirm that the ATP and NADPH from this early stage of photosynthesis are then used in the subsequent reactions to reduce carbon dioxide, forming simple sugars.

Learning Outcomes Review 8.2

Early experiments indicated that plants "restore" air to usable form, that is, produce oxygen—but only in the presence of sunlight. Further experiments showed that there are both light-dependent and independent reactions. The light-dependent reactions produce O_2 from H_2O, and generate ATP and NADPH. The light-independent reactions synthesize organic compounds through carbon fixation.

■ *Where does the carbon in your body come from?*

Learning Outcomes

1. **Explain how pigments are important to photosynthesis.**
2. **Relate the absorption spectrum of a pigment to its color.**

For plants to make use of the energy of sunlight, some biochemical structure must be present in chloroplasts and the thylakoids that can absorb this energy. Molecules that absorb light energy in the visible range are termed **pigments.** We are most familiar with them as dyes that impart a certain color to clothing or other materials. The color that we see is the color that is not absorbed—that is, it is reflected. To understand how plants use pigments to capture light energy, we must first review current knowledge about the nature of light.

Light is a form of energy

The wave nature of light produces an electromagnetic spectrum that differentiates light based on its wavelength (figure 8.4). We are most familiar with the visible range of this spectrum because we can actually see it, but visible light is only a small part of the entire spectrum. Visible light can be divided into its separate colors by the use of a prism, which separates light based on wavelength.

A particle of light, termed a **photon,** acts like a discrete bundle of energy. We use the wave concept of light to understand different colors of light and the particle nature of light to understand the energy transfers that occur during photosynthesis. Thus, we will refer both to wavelengths of light and to photons of light throughout the chapter.

The energy in photons

The energy content of a photon is inversely proportional to the wavelength of the light: Short-wavelength light contains photons of higher energy than long-wavelength light (see figure 8.4). X-rays, which contain a great deal of energy, have very short wavelengths—much shorter than those of visible light.

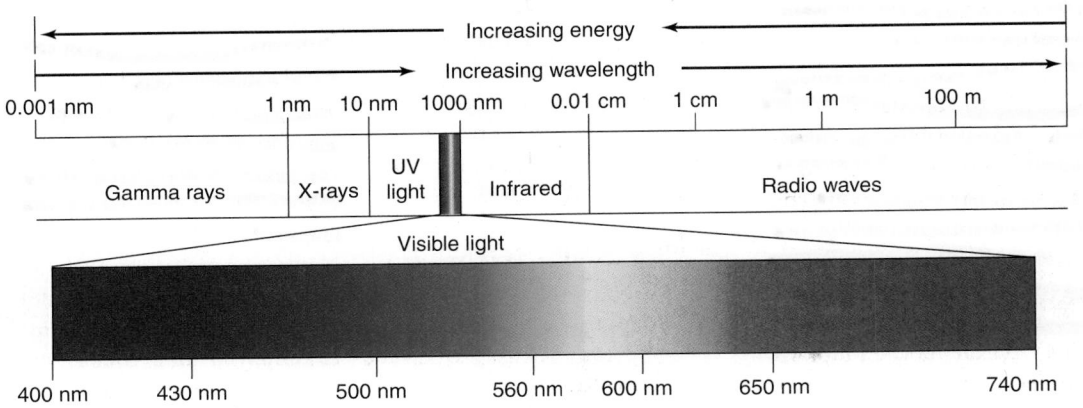

Figure 8.4 The electromagnetic spectrum. Light is a form of electromagnetic energy conveniently thought of as a wave. The shorter the wavelength of light, the greater its energy. Visible light represents only a small part of the electromagnetic spectrum between 400 and 740 nm.

A beam of light is able to remove electrons from certain molecules, creating an electrical current. This phenomenon is called the **photoelectric effect,** and it occurs when photons transfer energy to electrons. The strength of the photoelectric effect depends on the wavelength of light; that is, short wavelengths are much more effective than long ones in producing the photoelectric effect because they have more energy.

In photosynthesis, chloroplasts are acting as photoelectric devices: They absorb sunlight and transfer the excited electrons to a carrier. As we unravel the details of this process, it will become clear how this process traps energy and uses it to synthesize organic compounds.

Each pigment has a characteristic absorption spectrum

When a photon strikes a molecule with the amount of energy needed to excite an electron, then the molecule will absorb the photon raising the electron to a higher energy level. Whether the photon's energy is absorbed depends on how much energy it carries (defined by its wavelength), and also on the chemical nature of the molecule it hits.

As described in chapter 2, electrons occupy discrete energy levels in their orbits around atomic nuclei. To boost an electron into a different energy level requires just the right amount of energy, just as reaching the next rung on a ladder requires you to raise your foot just the right distance. A specific atom, therefore, can absorb only certain photons of light—namely, those that correspond to the atom's available energy levels. As a result, each molecule has a characteristic **absorption spectrum,** the range and efficiency of photons it is capable of absorbing.

As mentioned earlier, pigments are good absorbers of light in the visible range. Organisms have evolved a variety of different pigments, but only two general types are used in green plant photosynthesis: chlorophylls and carotenoids. In some organisms, other molecules also absorb light energy.

Chlorophyll absorption spectra

Chlorophylls absorb photons within narrow energy ranges. Two kinds of chlorophyll in plants, chlorophyll *a* and chlorophyll *b*, preferentially absorb violet-blue and red light (figure 8.5). Neither of these pigments absorbs photons with wavelengths between about 500 and 600 nm; light of these wavelengths is reflected. When these reflected photons are subsequently absorbed by the retinal pigment in our eyes, we perceive them as green.

Chlorophyll *a* is the main photosynthetic pigment in plants and cyanobacteria and the only pigment that can act directly to convert light energy to chemical energy. **Chlorophyll *b*,** acting as an **accessory pigment,** or secondary light-absorbing pigment, complements and adds to the light absorption of chlorophyll *a*.

Chlorophyll *b* has an absorption spectrum shifted toward the green wavelengths. Therefore, chlorophyll *b* can absorb photons that chlorophyll *a* cannot, greatly increasing the proportion of the photons in sunlight that plants can harvest. In addition, a variety of different accessory pigments are found in plants, bacteria, and algae.

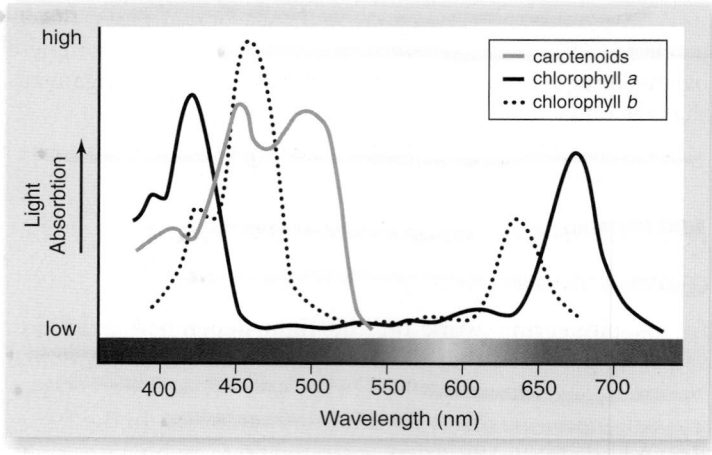

Figure 8.5 **Absorption spectra for chlorophyll and carotenoids.** The peaks represent wavelengths of light of sunlight absorbed by the two common forms of photosynthetic pigment, chlorophylls *a* and *b*, and the carotenoids. Chlorophylls absorb predominantly violet-blue and red light in two narrow bands of the spectrum and reflect green light in the middle of the spectrum. Carotenoids absorb mostly blue and green light and reflect orange and yellow light.

Structure of chlorophylls

Chlorophylls absorb photons by means of an excitation process analogous to the photoelectric effect. These pigments contain a complex ring structure, called a *porphyrin ring*, with alternating single and double bonds. At the center of the ring is a magnesium atom (figure 8.6).

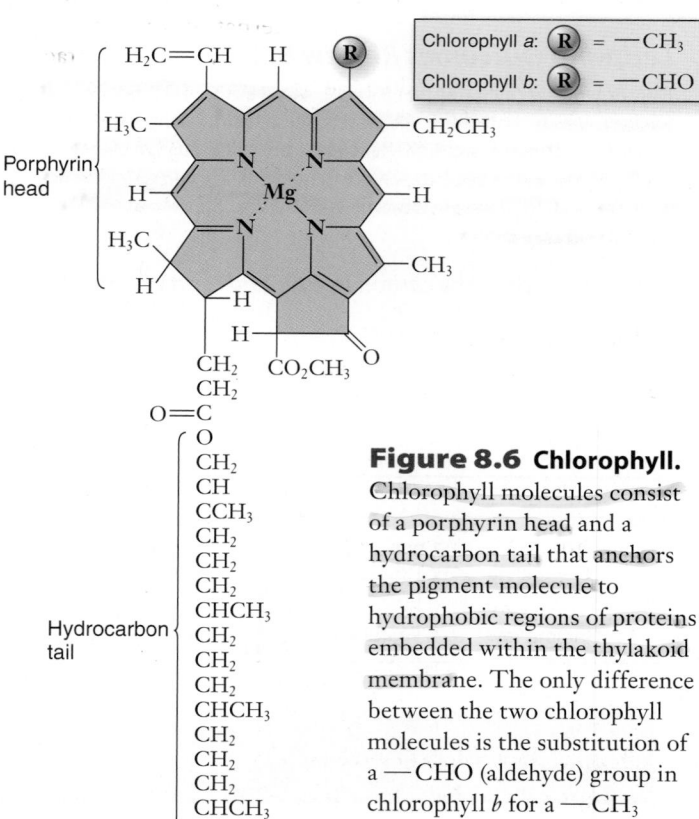

Figure 8.6 **Chlorophyll.** Chlorophyll molecules consist of a porphyrin head and a hydrocarbon tail that anchors the pigment molecule to hydrophobic regions of proteins embedded within the thylakoid membrane. The only difference between the two chlorophyll molecules is the substitution of a —CHO (aldehyde) group in chlorophyll *b* for a —CH₃ (methyl) group in chlorophyll *a*.

Hypothesis: *All wavelengths of light are equally effective in promoting photosynthesis.*

Prediction: *Illuminating plant cells with light broken into different wavelengths by a prism will produce the same amount of O_2 for all wavelengths.*

Test: *A filament of algae immobilized on a slide is illuminated by light that has passed through a prism. Motile bacteria that require O_2 for growth are added to the slide.*

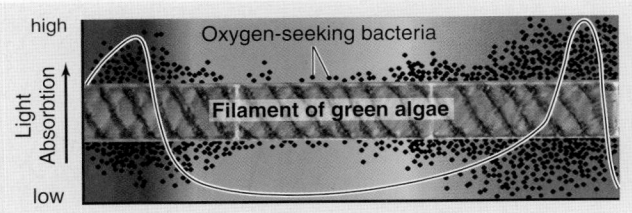

Result: *The bacteria move to regions of high O_2, or regions of most active photosynthesis. This is in the purple/blue and red regions of the spectrum.*

Conclusion: *All wavelengths are not equally effective at promoting photosynthesis. The most effective constitute the action spectrum for photosynthesis.*

Further Experiments: *How does the action spectrum relate to the various absorption spectra in figure 8.5?*

Figure 8.7 Determination of an action spectrum for photosynthesis.

Photons excite electrons in the porphyrin ring, which are then channeled away through the alternating carbon single- and double-bond system. Different small side groups attached to the outside of the ring alter the absorption properties of the molecule in the different kinds of chlorophyll (see figure 8.6). The precise absorption spectrum is also influenced by the local microenvironment created by the association of chlorophyll with different proteins.

The **action spectrum** of photosynthesis—that is, the relative effectiveness of different wavelengths of light in promoting photosynthesis—corresponds to the absorption spectrum for chlorophylls. This is demonstrated in the experiment in figure 8.7. All plants, algae, and cyanobacteria use chlorophyll *a* as their primary pigments.

It is reasonable to ask why these photosynthetic organisms do not use a pigment like retinal (the pigment in our eyes), which has a broad absorption spectrum that covers the range of 500 to 600 nm. The most likely hypothesis involves *photoefficiency.* Although retinal absorbs a broad range of wavelengths, it does so with relatively low efficiency. Chlorophyll, in contrast, absorbs in only two narrow bands, but does so with high efficiency. Therefore, plants and most other photosynthetic organisms achieve far higher overall energy capture rates with chlorophyll than with other pigments.

Carotenoids and other accessory pigments

Carotenoids consist of carbon rings linked to chains with alternating single and double bonds. They can absorb photons with a wide range of energies, although they are not always highly efficient in transferring this energy. Carotenoids assist in photosynthesis by capturing energy from light composed of wavelengths that are not efficiently absorbed by chlorophylls (figure 8.5; see also figure 8.8).

Carotenoids also perform a valuable role in scavenging free radicals. The oxidation–reduction reactions that occur in the chloroplast can generate destructive free radicals. Carotenoids can act as general-purpose antioxidants to lessen damage. Thus carotenoids have a protective role in addition to their role as light-absorbing molecules. This protective role is not surprising, because unlike the chlorophylls, carotenoids are found in many different kinds of organisms, including members of all three domains of life.

A typical carotenoid is β-carotene, which contains two carbon rings connected by a chain of 18 carbon atoms with alternating single and double bonds. Splitting a molecule of β-carotene into equal halves produces two molecules of vitamin A. Oxidation of vitamin A produces retinal, the

Oak leaf in summer

Oak leaf in autumn

Figure 8.8 Fall colors are produced by carotenoids and other accessory pigments. During the spring and summer, chlorophyll in leaves masks the presence of carotenoids and other accessory pigments. When cool fall temperatures cause leaves to cease manufacturing chlorophyll, the chlorophyll is no longer present to reflect green light, and the leaves reflect the orange and yellow light that carotenoids and other pigments do not absorb.

pigment used in vertebrate vision. This connection explains why eating carrots, which are rich in β-carotene, may enhance vision.

Phycobiloproteins are accessory pigments found in cyanobacteria and some algae. These pigments are composed of proteins attached to a tetrapyrrole group. These pyrrole rings contain a system of alternating double bonds similar to those found in other pigments and molecules that transfer electrons. Phycobiloproteins can be organized into complexes called phycobilisomes to form another light-harvesting complex that can absorb green light, which is typically reflected by chlorophyll. These complexes are probably ecologically important to cyanobacteria, helping them to exist in low-light situations in oceans. In this habitat, green light remains because red and blue light has been absorbed by green algae closer to the surface.

Learning Outcomes Review 8.3

A pigment is a molecule that can absorb light energy; its absorption spectrum shows the wavelengths at which it absorbs energy most efficiently. A pigment's color results from the wavelengths it does not absorb, which we then see. The main photosynthetic pigment is chlorophyll, which exists in several forms with slightly different absorption spectra. Many photosynthetic organisms have accessory pigments with absorption spectra different from chlorophyll; these increase light capture.

■ *What is the difference between an action spectrum and an absorption spectrum?*

8.4 *Photosystem Organization*

Learning Outcomes

1. *Describe the nature of photosystems.*
2. *Understand what happens in the reaction center.*

One way to study the role that pigments play in photosynthesis is to measure the correlation between the output of photosynthesis and the intensity of illumination—that is, how much photosynthesis is produced by how much light. Experiments on plants show that the output of photosynthesis increases linearly at low light intensities, but finally becomes saturated (no further increase) at high-intensity light. Saturation occurs because all of the light-absorbing capacity of the plant is in use.

Production of one O_2 molecule requires many chlorophyll molecules

Given the saturation observed with increasing light intensity, the next question is how many chlorophyll molecules have actually absorbed a photon. The question can be phrased this way: "Does saturation occur when all chlorophyll molecules have absorbed photons?" Finding an answer required being able to measure both photosynthetic output (on the basis of O_2 production) and the number of chlorophyll molecules present.

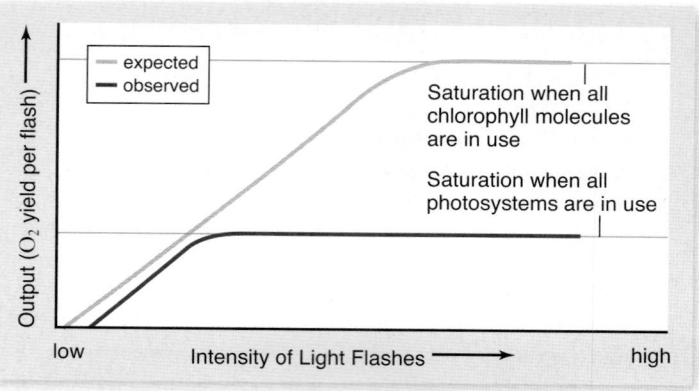

Figure 8.9 Saturation of photosynthesis. When photosynthetic saturation is achieved, further increases in intensity cause no increase in output. This saturation occurs far below the level expected for the number of individual chlorophyll molecules present. This led to the idea of organized photosystems, each containing many chlorophyll molecules. These photosystems saturate at a lower O_2 yield than that expected for the number of individual chlorophyll molecules.

Inquiry question

 Under what experimental conditions would you expect the saturation levels for a given number of chlorophyll molecules to be higher?

Using the unicellular algae *Chlorella*, investigators could obtain these values. Illuminating a *Chlorella* culture with pulses of light with increasing intensity should increase the yield of O_2 per pulse until the system becomes saturated. Then O_2 production can be compared with the number of chlorophyll molecules present in the culture.

The observed level of O_2 per chlorophyll molecule at saturation, however, turned out to be only one molecule of O_2 per 2500 chlorophyll molecules (figure 8.9). This result was very different from what was expected, and it led to the idea that light is absorbed not by independent pigment molecules, but rather by clusters of chlorophyll and accessory pigment molecules (photosystems). Light is absorbed by any one of hundreds of pigment molecules in a photosystem, and each pigment molecule transfers its excitation energy to a single molecule with a lower energy level than the others.

A generalized photosystem contains an antenna complex and a reaction center

In chloroplasts and all but one class of photosynthetic prokaryotes, light is captured by photosystems. Each photosystem is a network of chlorophyll *a* molecules, accessory pigments, and associated proteins held within a protein matrix on the surface of the photosynthetic membrane. Like a magnifying glass focusing light on a precise point, a photosystem channels the excitation energy gathered by any one of its pigment molecules to a specific molecule, the reaction center chlorophyll. This molecule then passes the energy out of the photosystem as excited electrons that are put to work driving the synthesis of ATP and organic molecules.

A photosystem thus consists of two closely linked components: (1) an *antenna complex* of hundreds of pigment molecules that gather photons and feed the captured light energy to the reaction center; and (2) a *reaction center* consisting of one or more chlorophyll *a* molecules in a matrix of protein, that passes excited electrons out of the photosystem.

The antenna complex

The **antenna complex** is also called a light-harvesting complex, which accurately describes its role. This light-harvesting complex captures photons from sunlight (figure 8.10) and channels them to the reaction center chlorophylls.

In chloroplasts, light-harvesting complexes consist of a web of chlorophyll molecules linked together and held tightly in the thylakoid membrane by a matrix of proteins. Varying amounts of carotenoid accessory pigments may also be present. The protein matrix holds individual pigment molecules in orientations that are optimal for energy transfer.

The excitation energy resulting from the absorption of a photon passes from one pigment molecule to an adjacent molecule on its way to the reaction center. After the transfer, the excited electron in each molecule returns to the low-energy level it had before the photon was absorbed. Consequently, it is energy, not the excited electrons themselves, that passes from one pigment molecule to the next. The antenna complex funnels the energy from many electrons to the reaction center.

The reaction center

The **reaction center** is a transmembrane protein–pigment complex. The reaction center of purple photosynthetic bacteria is simpler than the one in chloroplasts but better understood. A pair of bacteriochlorophyll *a* molecules acts as a trap for photon energy, passing an excited electron to an acceptor precisely positioned as its neighbor. Note that here in the reaction center, the excited electron itself is transferred, and not just the energy, as was the case in the pigment–pigment transfers of the antenna complex. This difference allows the energy

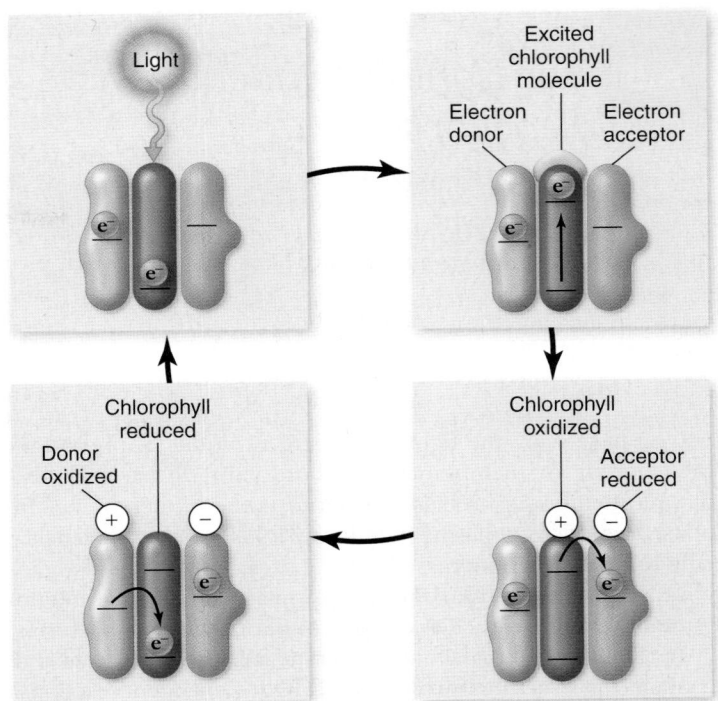

Figure 8.11 Converting light to chemical energy. When a chlorophyll in the reaction center absorbs a photon of light, an electron is excited to a higher energy level. This light-energized electron can be transferred to the primary electron acceptor, reducing it. The oxidized chlorophyll then fills its electron "hole" by oxidizing a donor molecule. The source of this donor varies with the photosystem as discussed in the text.

absorbed from photons to move away from the chlorophylls, and it is the key conversion of light into chemical energy.

Figure 8.11 shows the transfer of excited electrons from the reaction center to the primary electron acceptor. By energizing an electron of the reaction center chlorophyll, light creates a strong electron donor where none existed before. The chlorophyll transfers the energized electron to the primary acceptor (a molecule of quinone), reducing the quinone and converting it to a strong electron donor. A nearby weak electron donor then passes a low-energy electron to the chlorophyll, restoring it to its original condition. The quinone transfers its electrons to another acceptor, and the process is repeated.

In plant chloroplasts, water serves as this weak electron donor. When water is oxidized in this way, oxygen is released along with two protons (H^+).

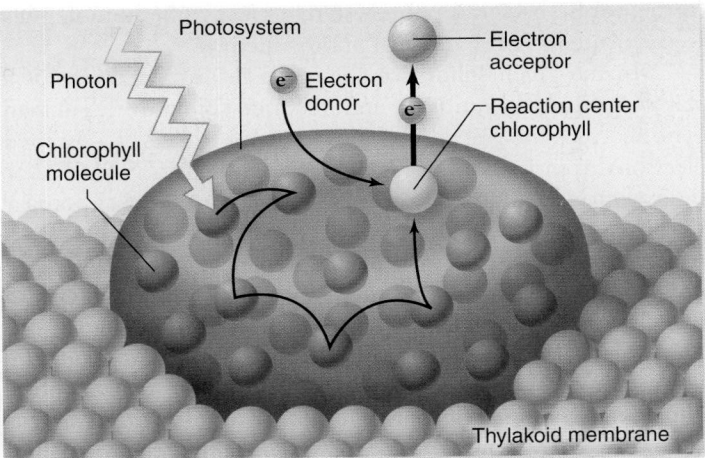

Figure 8.10 How the antenna complex works. When light of the proper wavelength strikes any pigment molecule within a photosystem, the light is absorbed by that pigment molecule. The excitation energy is then transferred from one molecule to another within the cluster of pigment molecules until it encounters the reaction center chlorophyll *a*. When excitation energy reaches the reaction center chlorophyll, electron transfer is initiated.

Learning Outcomes Review 8.4

Chlorophylls and accessory pigments are organized into photosystems found in the thylakoid membrane. The photosystem can be subdivided into an antenna complex, which is involved in light harvesting, and a reaction center, where the photochemical reactions occur. In the reaction center, an excited electron is passed to an acceptor; this transfers energy away from the chlorophylls and is key to the conversion of light into chemical energy.

■ *Why were photosystems an unexpected finding?*

8.5 The Light-Dependent Reactions

Learning Outcomes

1. Compare the function of the two photosystems in green plants.
2. Explain how the light reactions generate ATP and NADPH.

As you have seen, the light-dependent reactions of photosynthesis occur in membranes. In photosynthetic bacteria, the plasma membrane itself is the photosynthetic membrane. In many bacteria, the plasma membrane folds in on itself repeatedly to produce an increased surface area. In plants and algae, photosynthesis is carried out by chloroplasts, which are thought to be the evolutionary descendants of photosynthetic bacteria.

The internal thylakoid membrane is highly organized and contains the structures involved in the light-dependent reactions. For this reason, the reactions are also referred to as the thylakoid reactions. The thylakoid reactions take place in four stages:

1. **Primary photoevent.** A photon of light is captured by a pigment. This primary photoevent excites an electron within the pigment.
2. **Charge separation.** This excitation energy is transferred to the reaction center, which transfers an energetic electron to an acceptor molecule, initiating electron transport.
3. **Electron transport.** The excited electrons are shuttled along a series of electron carrier molecules embedded within the photosynthetic membrane. Several of them react by transporting protons across the membrane, generating a proton gradient. Eventually the electrons are used to reduce a final acceptor, NADPH.
4. **Chemiosmosis.** The protons that accumulate on one side of the membrane now flow back across the membrane through ATP synthase where chemiosmotic synthesis of ATP takes place, just as it does in aerobic respiration (see chapter 7).

These four processes make up the two stages of the light-dependent reactions mentioned at the beginning of this chapter. Steps 1 through 3 represent the stage of capturing energy from light; step 4 is the stage of producing ATP (and, as you'll see, NADPH). In the rest of this section we discuss the evolution of photosystems and the details of photosystem function in the light-dependent reactions.

Some bacteria use a single photosystem

Photosynthetic pigment arrays are thought to have evolved more than 2 BYA in bacteria similar to the purple and green bacteria alive today. In these bacteria, a single photosystem is used that generates ATP via electron transport. This process then returns the electrons to the reaction center. For this reason, it is called

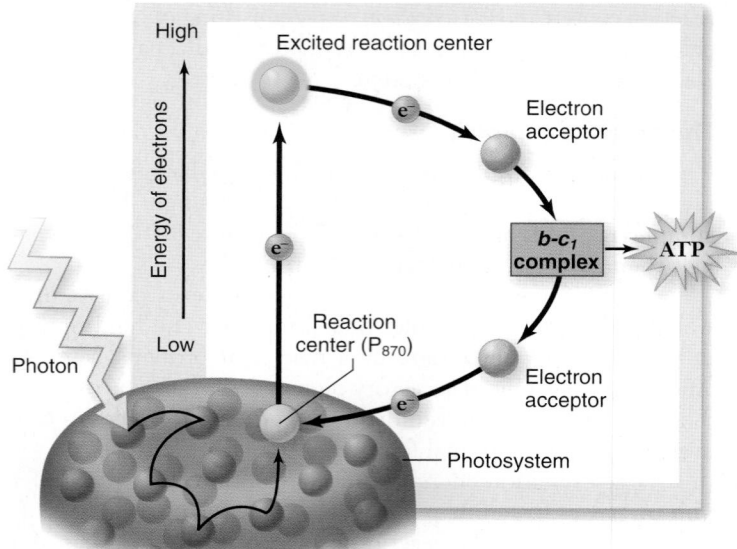

Figure 8.12 The path of an electron in purple nonsulfur bacteria. When a light-energized electron is ejected from the photosystem reaction center (P_{870}) it returns to the photosystem via a cyclic path that produces ATP but not NADPH.

cyclic photophosphorylation. These systems do not evolve oxygen and are thus referred to as anoxygenic photosynthesis.

In the purple nonsulfur bacteria, peak absorption occurs at a wavelength of 870 nm (near infrared, not visible to the human eye), and thus the reaction center pigment is called P_{870}. Absorption of a photon by chlorophyll P_{870} does not raise an electron to a high enough level to be passed to NADP, thus they must generate reducing power in a different way.

When the P_{870} reaction center absorbs a photon, the excited electron is passed to an electron transport chain that passes the electrons back to the reaction center, generating a proton gradient for ATP synthesis (figure 8.12). The proteins in the purple bacterial photosystem appear to be homologous to the proteins in the modern photosystem II.

In the green sulfur bacteria, peak absorption occurs at a wavelength of 840 nm (near infrared, not visible to the human eye), and thus the reaction center pigment is called P_{840}. Excited electrons from this photosystem can be passed to NADPH, or returned to the chlorophyll by an electron transport chain similar to the purple bacteria. To replace electrons passed to NADPH, hydrogen sulfide is used as an electron donor. The proteins in the green sulfur bacterial photosystem appear to be homologous to the proteins in the modern photosystem I.

Neither of these systems generate sufficient oxidizing power to oxidize H_2O. They are thus anoxygenic and take place under anaerobic conditions. The linked photosystems of cyanobacteria and plant chloroplasts generate the oxidizing power necessary to oxidize H_2O, allowing it to serve as a source of both electrons and protons.

Chloroplasts have two connected photosystems

In contrast to the sulfur bacteria, plants have two linked photosystems. This overcomes the limitations of cyclic photophosphorylation by providing an alternative source of electrons from the oxidation of water. The oxidation of water also generates O_2, thus oxygenic photosynthesis. The noncyclic transfer of electrons also produces NADPH, which can be used in the biosynthesis of carbohydrates.

One photosystem, called **photosystem I,** has an absorption peak of 700 nm, so its reaction center pigment is called P_{700}. This photosystem functions in a way analogous to the photosystem found in the sulfur bacteria discussed earlier. The other photosystem, called **photosystem II,** has an absorption peak of 680 nm, so its reaction center pigment is called P_{680}. This photosystem can generate an oxidation potential high enough to oxidize water. Working together, the two photosystems carry out a noncyclic transfer of electrons that is used to generate both ATP and NADPH.

The photosystems were named I and II in the order of their discovery, and not in the order in which they operate in the light-dependent reactions. In plants and algae, the two photosystems are specialized for different roles in the overall process of oxygenic photosynthesis. Photosystem I transfers electrons ultimately to $NADP^+$, producing NADPH. The electrons lost from photosystem I are replaced by electrons from photosystem II. Photosystem II with its high oxidation potential can oxidize water to replace the electrons transferred to photosystem I. Thus there is an overall flow of electrons from water to NADPH.

These two photosystems are connected by a complex of electron carriers called the **cytochrome/b_6-f complex** (explained shortly). This complex can use the energy from the passage of electrons to move protons across the thylakoid membrane to generate the proton gradient used by an ATP synthase enzyme.

The two photosystems work together in noncyclic photophosphorylation

Evidence for the action of two photosystems came from experiments that measured the rate of photosynthesis using two light beams of different wavelengths: one red and the other far-red. Using both beams produced a rate greater than the sum of the rates using individual beams of these wavelengths (figure 8.13). This surprising result, called the *enhancement effect,* can be explained by a mechanism involving two photosystems acting in series (that is, one after the other), one photosystem absorbs preferentially in the red, the other in the far-red.

Plants use photosystems II and I in series, first one and then the other, to produce both ATP and NADPH. This two-stage process is called **noncyclic photophosphorylation** because the path of the electrons is not a circle—the electrons ejected from the photosystems do not return to them, but rather end up in NADPH. The photosystems are replenished with electrons obtained by splitting water.

The scheme shown in figure 8.14, called a *Z diagram,* illustrates the two electron-energizing steps, one catalyzed by each photosystem. The horizontal axis shows the progress of the light reactions and the relative positions of the complexes, and the vertical axis shows relative energy levels of electrons. The electrons originate from water, which holds onto its electrons very tightly (redox potential = +820 mV), and end up in NADPH, which holds its electrons much more loosely (redox potential = −320 mV).

Photosystem II acts first. High-energy electrons generated by photosystem II are used to synthesize ATP and are then

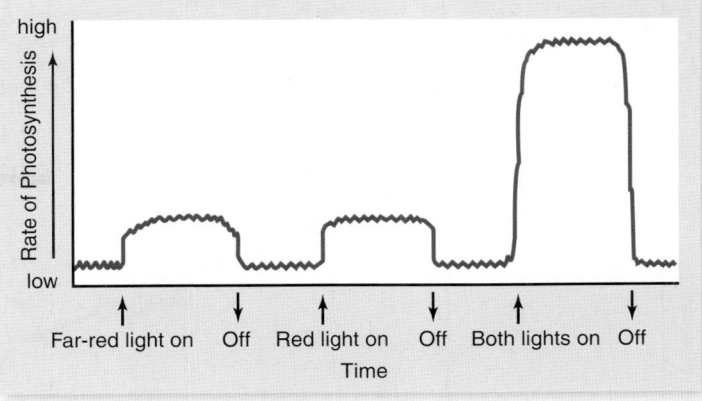

Figure 8.13 The enhancement effect. The rate of photosynthesis when red and far-red light are provided together is greater than the sum of the rates when each wavelength is provided individually. This result baffled researchers in the 1950s. Today, it provides key evidence that photosynthesis is carried out by two photochemical systems that act in series. One absorbs maximally in the far red, the other in the red portion of the spectrum.

? Inquiry question

What would you conclude if "both lights on" did not change the relative rate of photosynthesis?

passed to photosystem I to drive the production of NADPH. For every pair of electrons obtained from a molecule of water, one molecule of NADPH and slightly more than one molecule of ATP are produced.

Photosystem II

The reaction center of photosystem II closely resembles the reaction center of purple bacteria. It consists of a core of 10 transmembrane protein subunits with electron transfer components and two P_{680} chlorophyll molecules arranged around this core. The light-harvesting antenna complex consists of molecules of chlorophyll *a* and accessory pigments bound to several protein chains. The reaction center of photosystem II differs from the reaction center of the purple bacteria in that it also contains four manganese atoms. These manganese atoms are essential for the oxidation of water.

Although the chemical details of the oxidation of water are not entirely clear, the outline is emerging. Four manganese atoms are bound in a cluster to reaction center proteins. Two water molecules are also bound to this cluster of manganese atoms. When the reaction center of photosystem II absorbs a photon, an electron in a P_{680} chlorophyll molecule is excited, which transfers this electron to an acceptor. The oxidized P_{680} then removes an electron from a manganese atom. The oxidized manganese atoms, with the aid of reaction center proteins, remove electrons from oxygen atoms in the two water molecules. This process requires the reaction center to absorb four photons to complete the oxidation of two water molecules, producing one O_2 in the process.

The role of the b_6-f complex

The primary electron acceptor for the light-energized electrons leaving photosystem II is a quinone molecule. The reduced

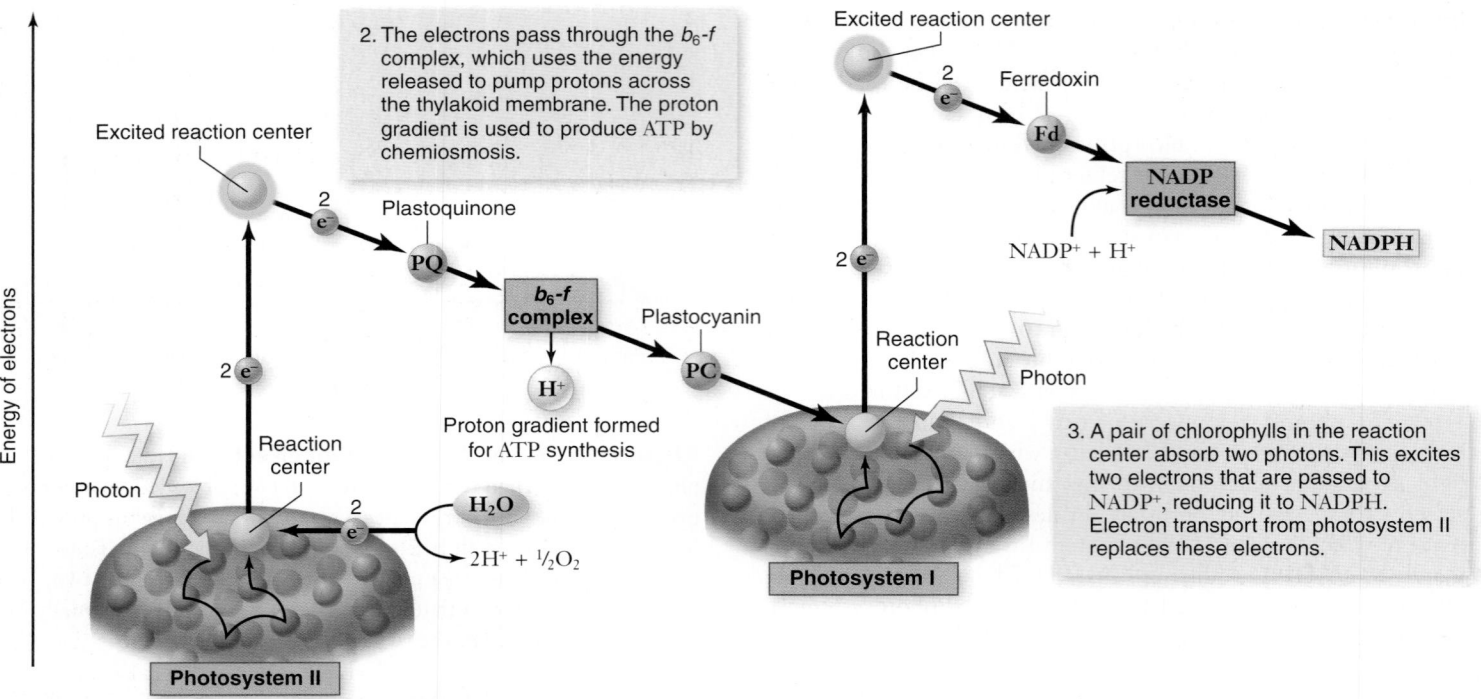

2. The electrons pass through the b_6-f complex, which uses the energy released to pump protons across the thylakoid membrane. The proton gradient is used to produce ATP by chemiosmosis.

3. A pair of chlorophylls in the reaction center absorb two photons. This excites two electrons that are passed to $NADP^+$, reducing it to NADPH. Electron transport from photosystem II replaces these electrons.

1. A pair of chlorophylls in the reaction center absorb two photons of light. This excites two electrons that are transferred to plastoquinone (PQ). Loss of electrons from the reaction center produces an oxidation potential capable of oxidizing water.

Figure 8.14 Z diagram of photosystems I and II. Two photosystems work sequentially and have different roles. Photosystem II passes energetic electrons to photosystem I via an electron transport chain. The electrons lost are replaced by oxidizing water. Photosystem I uses energetic electrons to reduce $NADP^+$ to NADPH.

quinone that results from accepting a pair of electrons (*plastoquinone*) is a strong electron donor; it passes the excited electron pair to a proton pump called the **b_6-f complex** embedded within the thylakoid membrane (figure 8.15). This complex closely resembles the bc_1 complex in the respiratory electron transport chain of mitochondria, discussed in chapter 7.

Arrival of the energetic electron pair causes the b_6-f complex to pump a proton into the thylakoid space. A small, copper-containing protein called *plastocyanin* then carries the electron pair to photosystem I.

Photosystem I

The reaction center of photosystem I consists of a core transmembrane complex consisting of 12 to 14 protein subunits with two bound P_{700} chlorophyll molecules. Energy is fed to it by an antenna complex consisting of chlorophyll *a* and accessory pigment molecules.

Photosystem I accepts an electron from plastocyanin into the "hole" created by the exit of a light-energized electron. The absorption of a photon by photosystem I boosts the electron leaving the reaction center to a very high energy level. The electrons are passed to an iron–sulfur protein called *ferredoxin*. Unlike photosystem II and the bacterial photosystem, the plant photosystem I does not rely on quinones as electron acceptors.

Making NADPH

Photosystem I passes electrons to ferredoxin on the stromal side of the membrane (outside the thylakoid). The reduced ferredoxin carries an electron with very high potential. Two of them, from

two molecules of reduced ferredoxin, are then donated to a molecule of $NADP^+$ to form NADPH. The reaction is catalyzed by the membrane-bound enzyme *NADP reductase*.

Because the reaction occurs on the stromal side of the membrane and involves the uptake of a proton in forming NADPH, it contributes further to the proton gradient established during photosynthetic electron transport. The function of the two photosystems is summarized in figure 8.15.

ATP is generated by chemiosmosis

Protons are pumped from the stroma into the thylakoid compartment by the b_6-f complex. The splitting of water also produces added protons that contribute to the gradient. The thylakoid membrane is impermeable to protons, so this creates an electrochemical gradient that can be used to synthesize ATP.

ATP synthase

The chloroplast has ATP synthase enzymes in the thylakoid membrane that form a channel, allowing protons to cross back out into the stroma. These channels protrude like knobs on the external surface of the thylakoid membrane. As protons pass out of the thylakoid through the ATP synthase channel, ADP is phosphorylated to ATP and released into the stroma (see figure 8.15). The stroma contains the enzymes that catalyze the reactions of carbon fixation—the Calvin cycle reactions.

This mechanism is the same as that seen in the mitochondrial ATP synthase, and, in fact, the two enzymes are evolutionarily related. This similarity in generating a proton gradient by

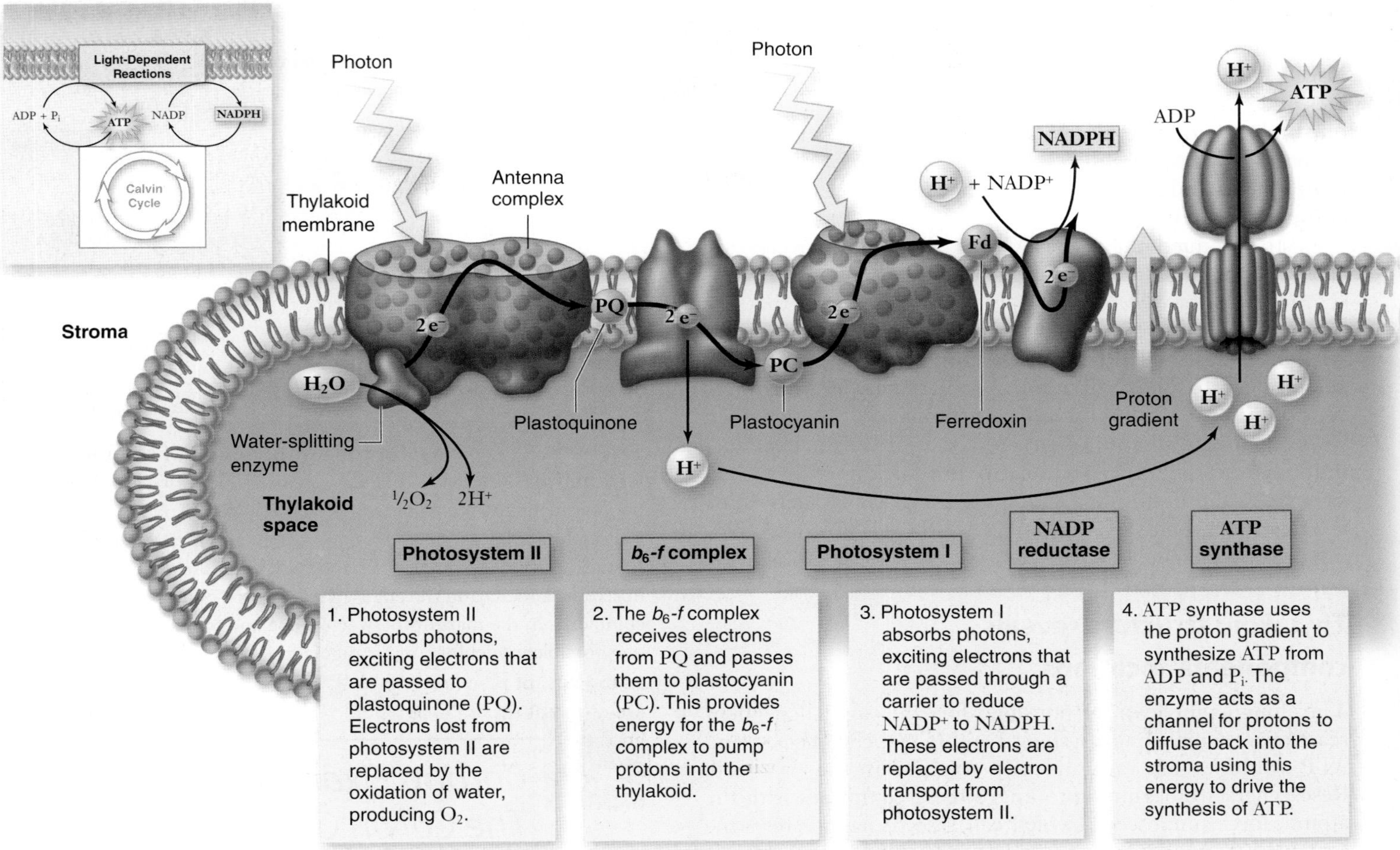
Light-Dependent Reactions
ADP + P_i
ATP
NADP
NADPH
Calvin Cycle
Photon
Photon
Thylakoid membrane
Antenna complex
Stroma
H_2O
2e⁻
PQ
2 e⁻
PC
2e⁻
Fd
2 e⁻
H^+ + $NADP^+$
NADPH
ADP
H^+
ATP
Water-splitting enzyme
Plastoquinone
Plastocyanin
Ferredoxin
Proton gradient
H^+
H^+
H^+
H^+
Thylakoid space
½O_2 2H^+
Photosystem II
b_6-f complex
Photosystem I
NADP reductase
ATP synthase
1. Photosystem II absorbs photons, exciting electrons that are passed to plastoquinone (PQ). Electrons lost from photosystem II are replaced by the oxidation of water, producing O_2.
2. The b_6-f complex receives electrons from PQ and passes them to plastocyanin (PC). This provides energy for the b_6-f complex to pump protons into the thylakoid.
3. Photosystem I absorbs photons, exciting electrons that are passed through a carrier to reduce $NADP^+$ to NADPH. These electrons are replaced by electron transport from photosystem II.
4. ATP synthase uses the proton gradient to synthesize ATP from ADP and P_i. The enzyme acts as a channel for protons to diffuse back into the stroma using this energy to drive the synthesis of ATP.

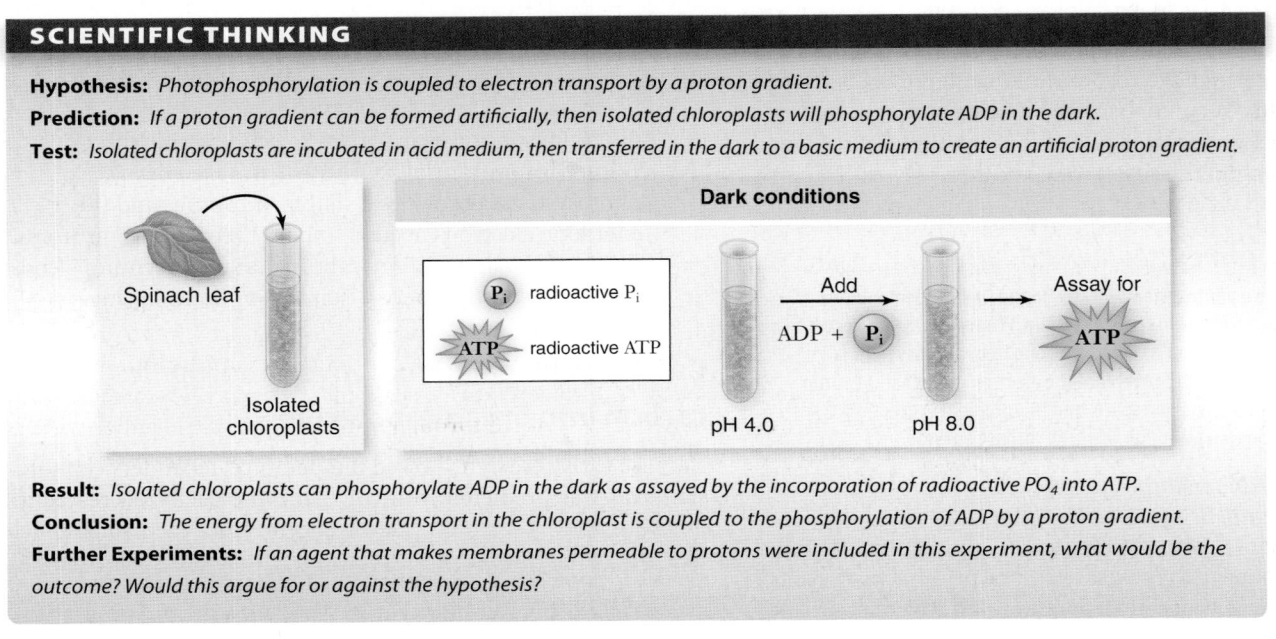

Figure 8.15 The photosynthetic electron transport system and ATP synthase. The two photosystems are arranged in the thylakoid membrane joined by an electron transport system that includes the b_6-f complex. These function together to create a proton gradient that is used by ATP synthase to synthesize ATP.

electron transport and ATP by chemiosmosis illustrates the similarities in structure and function in mitochondria and chloroplasts. Evidence for this chemiosmotic mechanism for photophosphorylation was actually discovered earlier (figure 8.16) and formed the background for experiments using the mitochondrial ATP synthase.

SCIENTIFIC THINKING

Hypothesis: *Photophosphorylation is coupled to electron transport by a proton gradient.*

Prediction: *If a proton gradient can be formed artificially, then isolated chloroplasts will phosphorylate ADP in the dark.*

Test: *Isolated chloroplasts are incubated in acid medium, then transferred in the dark to a basic medium to create an artificial proton gradient.*

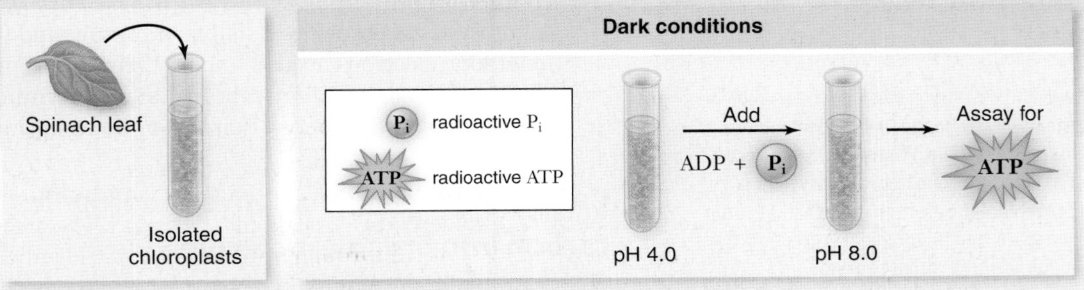
Spinach leaf
Isolated chloroplasts
Dark conditions
P_i radioactive P_i
ATP radioactive ATP
pH 4.0
Add
ADP + P_i
pH 8.0
Assay for
ATP

Result: *Isolated chloroplasts can phosphorylate ADP in the dark as assayed by the incorporation of radioactive PO_4 into ATP.*

Conclusion: *The energy from electron transport in the chloroplast is coupled to the phosphorylation of ADP by a proton gradient.*

Further Experiments: *If an agent that makes membranes permeable to protons were included in this experiment, what would be the outcome? Would this argue for or against the hypothesis?*

Figure 8.16 The Jagendorf acid bath experiment.

The production of additional ATP

The passage of an electron pair from water to NADPH in noncyclic photophosphorylation generates one molecule of NADPH and slightly more than one molecule of ATP. But as you will learn later in this chapter, building organic molecules takes more energy than that—it takes 1.5 ATP molecules per NADPH molecule to fix carbon.

To produce the extra ATP, many plant species are capable of short-circuiting photosystem I, switching photosynthesis into a *cyclic photophosphorylation* mode, so that the light-excited electron leaving photosystem I is used to make ATP instead of NADPH. The energetic electrons are simply passed back to the b_6-f complex, rather than passing on to NADP+. The b_6-f complex pumps protons into the thylakoid space, adding to the proton gradient that drives the chemiosmotic synthesis of ATP. The relative proportions of cyclic and noncyclic photophosphorylation in these plants determine the relative amounts of ATP and NADPH available for building organic molecules.

Thylakoid structure reveals components' locations

The four complexes responsible for the light-dependent reactions—namely photosystems I and II, cytochrome b_6-f, and ATP synthase—are not randomly arranged in the thylakoid. Researchers are beginning to image these complexes with the atomic force microscope, which can resolve nanometer scale structures, and a picture is emerging in which photosystem II is found primarily in the grana, whereas photosystem I and ATP synthase are found primarily in the stroma lamella. Photosystem I and ATP synthase may also be found in the edges of the grana that are not stacked. The cytochrome b_6-f complex is found in the borders between grana and stroma lamella. One possible model for the arrangement of the complexes is shown in figure 8.17.

The thylakoid itself is no longer thought of only as stacked disks. Some models of the thylakoid, based on electron microscopy and other imaging, depict the grana as folds of the interconnecting stroma lamella. This kind of arrangement is more similar to the folds seen in bacterial photosynthesis, and it would therefore allow for more flexibility in how the various complexes are arranged relative to one another.

Learning Outcomes Review 8.5

The chloroplast has two photosystems located in the thylakoid membrane that are connected by an electron transport chain. Photosystem I passes an electron to NADPH. This electron is replaced by one from photosystem II. Photosystem II can oxidize water to replace the electron it has lost. A proton gradient is built up in the thylakoid space, and this gradient is used to generate ATP as protons pass through the ATP synthase enzyme.

■ *If the thylakoid membrane were leaky to protons, would ATP still be produced? Would NADPH?*

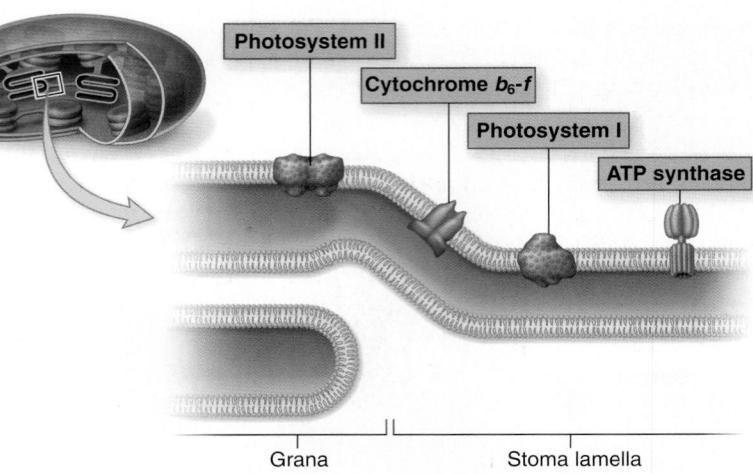

Figure 8.17 Model for the arrangement of complexes within the thylakoid. The arrangement of the two kinds of photosystems and the other complexes involved in photosynthesis is not random. Photosystem II is concentrated within grana, especially in stacked areas. Photosystem I and ATP synthase are concentrated in stroma lamella and the edges of grana. The cytochrome b_6-f complex is in the margins between grana and stroma lamella. This is one possible model for this arrangement.

8.6 Carbon Fixation: The Calvin Cycle

Learning Outcomes

1. Describe carbon fixation.
2. Explain how the Calvin cycle produces glucose.

Carbohydrates contain many C—H bonds and are highly reduced compared with CO_2. To build carbohydrates, cells use energy and a source of electrons produced by the light-dependent reactions of the thylakoids:

1. **Energy.** ATP (provided by cyclic and noncyclic photophosphorylation) drives the endergonic reactions.
2. **Reduction potential.** NADPH (provided by photosystem I) provides a source of protons and the energetic electrons needed to bind them to carbon atoms. Much of the light energy captured in photosynthesis ends up invested in the energy-rich C—H bonds of sugars.

Calvin cycle reactions convert inorganic carbon into organic molecules

Because early research showed temperature dependence, photosynthesis was predicted to involve enzyme-catalyzed reactions. These reactions form a cycle of enzyme-catalyzed steps much like the Krebs cycle of respiration. Unlike the Krebs cycle, however, carbon fixation is geared toward producing new compounds, so the nature of the cycles is quite different.

The cycle of reactions that allow carbon fixation is called the **Calvin cycle,** after its discoverer, Melvin Calvin (1911–1997). Because the first intermediate of the cycle, phosphoglycerate, contains three carbon atoms, this process is also called **C₃ photosynthesis.**

The key step in this process—the event that makes the reduction of CO_2 possible—is the attachment of CO_2 to a highly specialized organic molecule. Photosynthetic cells produce this molecule by reassembling the bonds of two intermediates in glycolysis—fructose 6-phosphate and glyceraldehyde 3-phosphate (G3P)—to form the energy-rich 5-carbon sugar **ribulose 1,5-bisphosphate (RuBP).**

CO_2 reacts with RuBP to form a transient 6-carbon intermediate that immediately splits into two molecules of the three-carbon *3-phosphoglycerate (PGA).* This overall reaction is called the *carbon fixation reaction* because inorganic carbon (CO_2) has been incorporated into an organic form: the acid PGA. The enzyme that carries out this reaction, **ribulose bisphosphate carboxylase/oxygenase** (usually abbreviated **rubisco**) is a large, 16-subunit enzyme found in the chloroplast stroma.

Carbon is transferred through cycle intermediates, eventually producing glucose

We will consider how the Calvin cycle can produce one molecule of glucose, although this glucose is not produced directly by the cycle (figure 8.18). In a series of reactions, six molecules of CO_2 are bound to six RuBP by rubisco to produce 12 molecules of

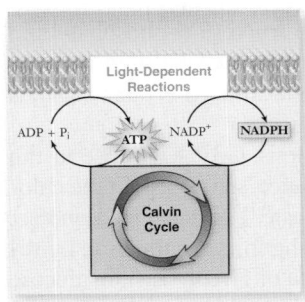

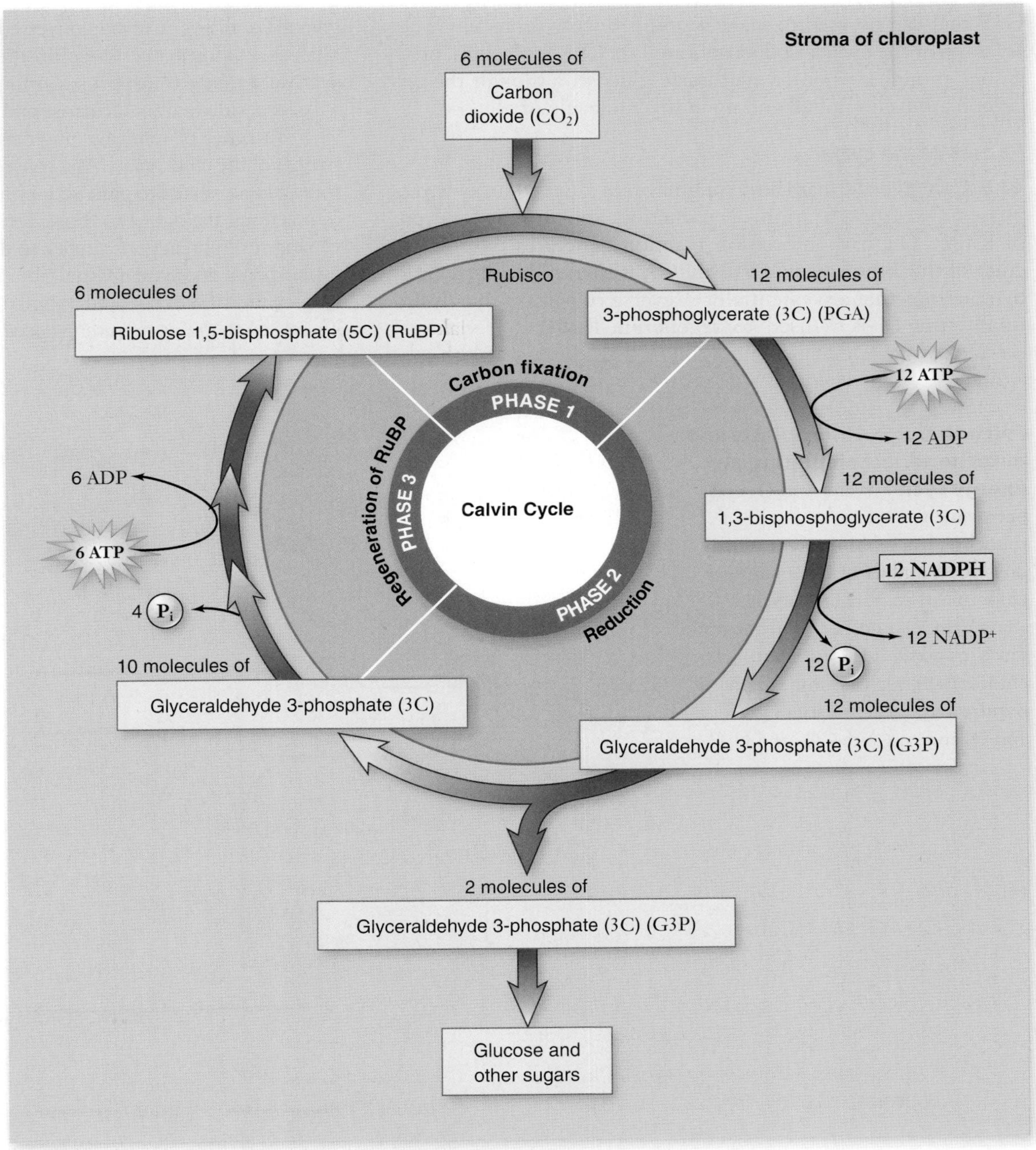

Figure 8.18 The Calvin cycle. The Calvin cycle accomplishes carbon fixation: converting inorganic carbon in the form of CO_2 into organic carbon in the form of carbohydrates. The cycle can be broken down into three phases: (1) carbon fixation, (2) reduction, and (3) regeneration of RuBP. For every six CO_2 molecules fixed by the cycle, a molecule of glucose can be synthesized from the products of the reduction reactions, G3P. The cycle uses the ATP and NADPH produced by the light reactions.

Stroma of chloroplast

6 molecules of
Carbon dioxide (CO_2)

Rubisco

6 molecules of
Ribulose 1,5-bisphosphate (5C) (RuBP)

12 molecules of
3-phosphoglycerate (3C) (PGA)

Carbon fixation
PHASE 1

12 ATP
12 ADP

Regeneration of RuBP
PHASE 3

6 ADP

6 ATP

Calvin Cycle

12 molecules of
1,3-bisphosphoglycerate (3C)

12 NADPH
12 NADP⁺

4 P_i

PHASE 2
Reduction

12 P_i

10 molecules of
Glyceraldehyde 3-phosphate (3C)

12 molecules of
Glyceraldehyde 3-phosphate (3C) (G3P)

2 molecules of
Glyceraldehyde 3-phosphate (3C) (G3P)

Glucose and other sugars

Light-Dependent Reactions

ADP + P$_i$ ATP   NADP⁺   NADPH

Calvin Cycle

PGA (containing 12 × 3 = 36 carbon atoms in all, 6 from CO_2 and 30 from RuBP). The 36 carbon atoms then undergo a cycle of reactions that regenerates the six molecules of RuBP used in the initial step (containing 6 × 5 = 30 carbon atoms). This leaves two molecules of *glyceraldehyde 3-phosphate (G3P)* (each with three carbon atoms) as the net gain. (You may recall G3P as also being the product of the first half of glycolysis, described in chapter 7.) These two molecules of G3P can then be used to make one molecule of glucose.

The net equation of the Calvin cycle is:

$$6\ CO_2 + 18\ ATP + 12\ NADPH + water \longrightarrow$$
$$2\ glyceraldehyde\ 3\text{-}phosphate + 16\ P_i + 18\ ADP + 12\ NADP^+$$

With six full turns of the cycle, six molecules of carbon dioxide enter, two molecules of G3P are produced, and six molecules of RuBP are regenerated. Thus six turns of the cycle produce two G3P that can be used to make a single glucose molecule. The six turns of the cycle also incorporated six CO_2 molecules, providing enough carbon to synthesize glucose, although the six carbon atoms do not all end up in this molecule of glucose.

Phases of the cycle

The Calvin cycle can be thought of as divided into three phases: (1) carbon fixation, (2) reduction, and (3) regeneration of RuBP. The carbon fixation reaction generates two molecules of the 3-carbon acid PGA; PGA is then reduced to G3P by reactions that are essentially a reverse of part of glycolysis; finally, the PGA is used to regenerate RuBP. Three turns

around the cycle incorporate enough carbon to produce a new molecule of G3P, and six turns incorporate enough carbon to synthesize one glucose molecule.

We now know that light is required *indirectly* for different segments of the CO_2 reduction reactions. Five of the Calvin cycle enzymes—including rubisco—are light-activated; that is, they become functional or operate more efficiently in the presence of light. Light also promotes transport of required 3-carbon intermediates across chloroplast membranes. And finally, light promotes the influx of Mg^{2+} into the chloroplast stroma, which further activates the enzyme rubisco.

Output of the Calvin cycle

Glyceraldehyde 3-phosphate is a 3-carbon sugar, a key intermediate in glycolysis. Much of it is transported out of the chloroplast to the cytoplasm of the cell, where the reversal of several reactions in glycolysis allows it to be converted to fructose 6-phosphate and glucose 1-phosphate. These products can then be used to form sucrose, a major transport sugar in plants. (Sucrose, table sugar, is a disaccharide made of fructose and glucose.)

In times of intensive photosynthesis, G3P levels rise in the stroma of the chloroplast. As a consequence, some G3P in the chloroplast is converted to glucose 1-phosphate. This takes place in a set of reactions analogous to those occurring in the cytoplasm, by reversing several reactions similar to those of glycolysis. The glucose 1-phosphate is then combined into an insoluble polymer, forming long chains of starch stored as bulky starch grains in the cytoplasm. These starch grains represent stored glucose for later use.

Figure 8.19 Chloroplasts and mitochondria: completing an energy cycle. Water and O_2 cycle between chloroplasts and mitochondria within a plant cell, as do glucose and CO_2. Cells with chloroplasts require an outside source of CO_2 and H_2O and generate glucose and O_2. Cells without chloroplasts, such as animal cells, require an outside source of glucose and O_2 and generate CO_2 and H_2O.

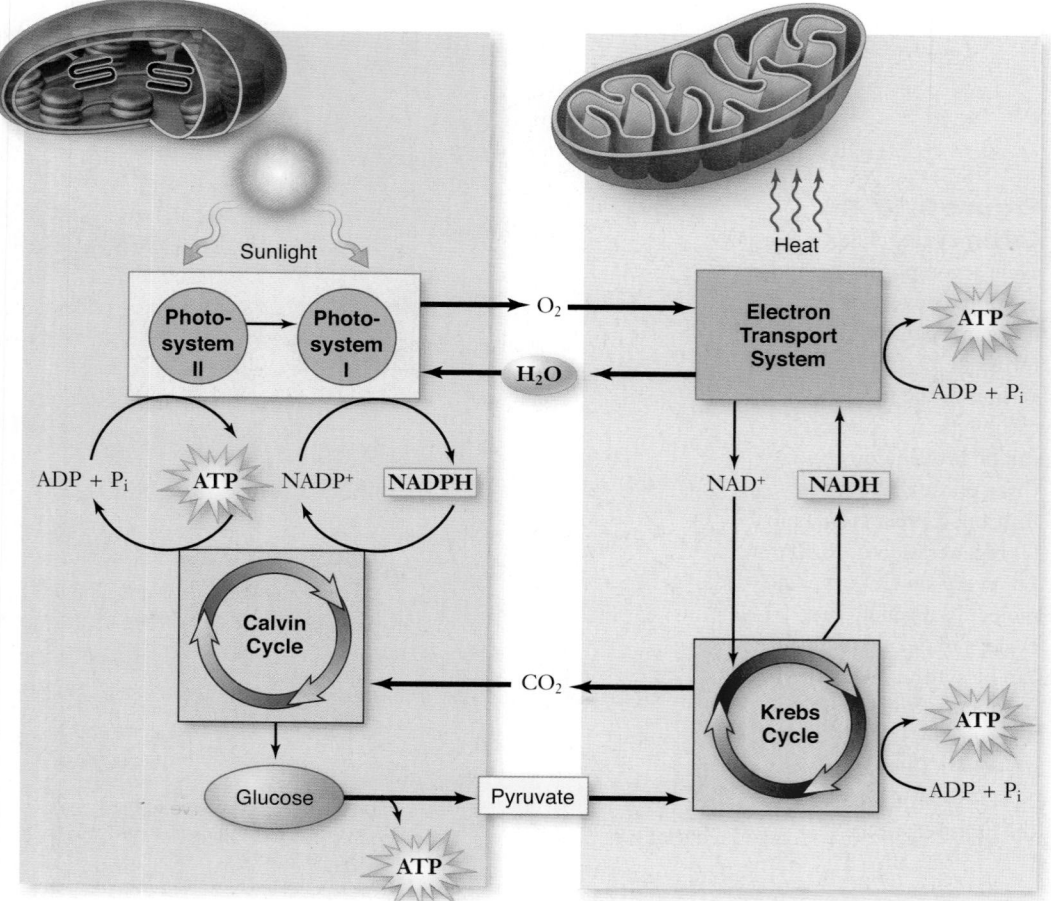

The energy cycle

The energy-capturing metabolisms of the chloroplasts studied in this chapter and the mitochondria studied in chapter 7 are intimately related (figure 8.19). Photosynthesis uses the products of respiration as starting substrates, and respiration uses the products of photosynthesis as starting substrates. The production of glucose from G3P even uses part of the ancient glycolytic pathway, run in reverse. Also, the principal proteins involved in electron transport and ATP production in plants are evolutionarily related to those in mitochondria.

Photosynthesis is but one aspect of plant biology, although it is an important one. In chapters 36 through 42, we examine plants in more detail. We have discussed photosynthesis as a part of cell biology because photosynthesis arose long before plants did, and because most organisms depend directly or indirectly on photosynthesis for the energy that powers their lives.

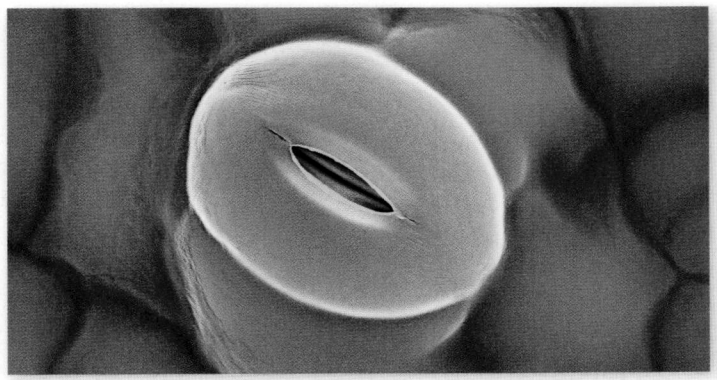

Figure 8.20 Stoma. A closed stoma in the leaf of a tobacco plant. Each stoma is formed from two guard cells whose shape changes with turgor pressure to open and close. Under dry conditions plants close their stomata to conserve water.

Learning Outcomes Review 8.6

Carbon fixation takes place in the stroma of the chloroplast, where inorganic CO_2 is incorporated into an organic molecule. The key intermediate is the 5-carbon sugar RuBP that combines with CO_2 in a reaction catalyzed by the enzyme rubisco. The cycle can be broken down into three stages: carbon fixation, reduction, and regeneration of RuBP. ATP and NADPH from the light reactions provide energy and electrons for the reduction reactions, which produce G3P. Glucose is synthesized when two molecules of G3P are combined.

- **How does the Calvin cycle compare with glycolysis?**

8.7 Photorespiration

Learning Outcomes

1. **Explain the action of rubisco in oxidizing RuBP.**
2. **Compare the function of carbon fixation in the C_3, C_4, and CAM pathways.**

Evolution does not necessarily result in optimum solutions. Rather, it favors workable solutions that can be derived from features that already exist. Photosynthesis is no exception. Rubisco, the enzyme that catalyzes the key carbon-fixing reaction of photosynthesis, provides a decidedly suboptimal solution. This enzyme has a second enzymatic activity that interferes with carbon fixation, namely that of *oxidizing* RuBP. In this process, called **photorespiration**, O_2 is incorporated into RuBP, which undergoes additional reactions that actually release CO_2. Hence, photorespiration releases CO_2, essentially undoing carbon fixation.

Photorespiration reduces the yield of photosynthesis

The carboxylation and oxidation of RuBP are catalyzed at the same active site on rubisco, and CO_2 and O_2 compete with each other at this site. Under normal conditions at 25°C, the rate of the carboxylation reaction is four times that of the oxidation reaction, meaning that 20% of photosynthetically fixed carbon is lost to photorespiration.

This loss rises substantially as temperature increases, because under hot, arid conditions, specialized openings in the leaf called *stomata* (singular, *stoma*) (figure 8.20) close to conserve water. This closing also cuts off the supply of CO_2 entering the leaf and does not allow O_2 to exit (figure 8.21). As a result, the low-CO_2 and high-O_2 conditions within the leaf favor photorespiration.

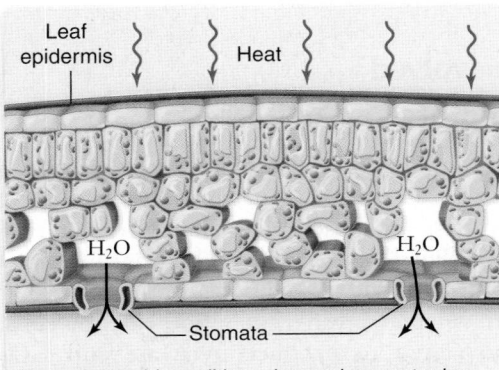

Under hot, arid conditions, leaves lose water by evaporation through openings in the leaves called stomata.

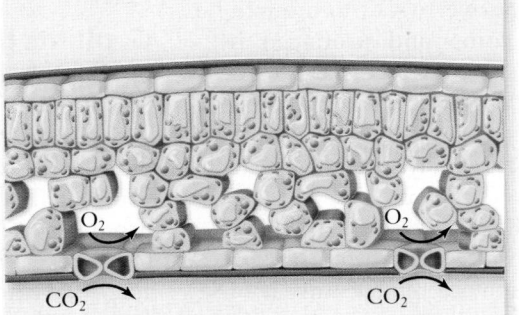

The stomata close to conserve water but as a result, O_2 builds up inside the leaves, and CO_2 cannot enter the leaves.

Figure 8.21 Conditions favoring photorespiration. In hot, arid environments, stomata close to conserve water, which also prevents CO_2 from entering and O_2 from exiting the leaf. The high-O_2/low-CO_2 conditions favor photorespiration.

**Figure 8.22
Comparison of C₃ and C₄ pathways of carbon fixation.** *a.* The C₃ pathway uses the Calvin cycle to fix carbon. All reactions occur in mesophyll cells using CO₂ that diffuses in through stomata. *b.* The C₄ pathway incorporates CO₂ into a 4-carbon molecule of malate in mesophyll cells. This is transported to the bundle sheath cells where it is converted back into CO₂ and pyruvate, creating a high level of CO₂. This allows efficient carbon fixation by the Calvin cycle.

a. C₃ pathway

b. C₄ pathway

Plants that fix carbon using only C₃ photosynthesis (the Calvin cycle) are called **C₃ plants** (figure 8.22*a*). Other plants add CO₂ to phosphoenolpyruvate (PEP) to form a 4-carbon molecule. This reaction is catalyzed by the enzyme PEP *carboxylase.* This enzyme has two advantages over rubisco: it has a much greater affinity for CO₂ than rubisco, and it does not have oxidase activity.

The 4-carbon compound produced by PEP carboxylase undergoes further modification, only to be eventually decarboxylated. The CO₂ released by this decarboxylation is then used by rubisco in the Calvin cycle. This allows CO₂ to be pumped directly to the site of rubisco, which increases the local concentration of CO₂ relative to O₂, minimizing photorespiration. The 4-carbon compound produced by PEP carboxylase allows CO₂ to be stored in an organic form, to then be released in a different cell, or at a different time to keep the level of CO₂ high relative to O₂.

The reduction in the yield of carbohydrate as a result of photorespiration is not trivial. C₃ plants lose between 25% and 50% of their photosynthetically fixed carbon in this way. The rate depends largely on temperature. In tropical climates, especially those in which the temperature is often above 28°C, the problem is severe, and it has a major effect on tropical agriculture.

The two main groups of plants that initially capture CO₂ using PEP carboxylase differ in how they maintain high levels of CO₂ relative to O₂. In **C₄ plants** (figure 8.22*b*), the capture of CO₂ occurs in one cell and the decarboxylation occurs in an adjacent cell. This represents a spatial solution to the problem of photorespiration. The second group, **CAM plants,** perform both reactions in the same cell, but capture CO₂ using PEP carboxylase at night, then decarboxylate during the day. CAM stands for **crassulacean acid metabolism,** after the plant family Crassulaceae (the stonecrops, or hens-and-chicks), in which it was first discovered. This mechanism represents a temporal solution to the photorespiration problem.

C₄ plants have evolved to minimize photorespiration

The C₄ plants include corn, sugarcane, sorghum, and a number of other grasses. These plants initially fix carbon using PEP carboxylase in mesophyll cells. This reaction produces the organic acid oxaloacetate, which is converted to malate and transported to bundle-sheath cells that surround the leaf veins. Within the bundle-sheath cells, malate is decarboxylated to produce pyruvate and CO₂ (figure 8.23). Because the bundle-sheath cells are impermeable to CO₂, the local level of CO₂ is high and carbon fixation by rubisco and the Calvin cycle is efficient. The

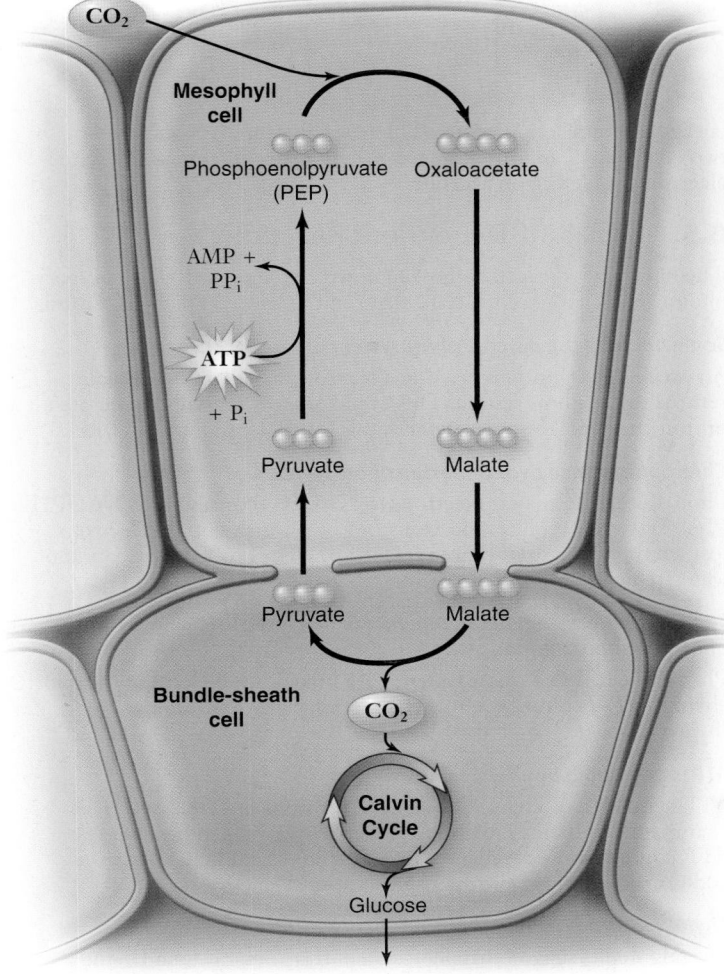

Figure 8.23 Carbon fixation in C₄ plants. This process is called the C₄ pathway because the first molecule formed, oxaloacetate, contains four carbons. The oxaloacetate is converted to malate, which moves into bundle-sheath cells where it is decarboxylated back to CO_2 and pyruvate. This produces a high level of CO_2 in the bundle-sheath cells that can be fixed by the usual C₃ Calvin cycle with little photorespiration. The pyruvate diffuses back into the mesophyll cells, where it is converted back to PEP to be used in another C₄ fixation reaction.

pyruvate produced by decarboxylation is transported back to the mesophyll cells, where it is converted back to PEP, thereby completing the cycle.

The C₄ pathway, although it overcomes the problems of photorespiration, does have a cost. The conversion of pyruvate back to PEP requires breaking two high-energy bonds in ATP. Thus each CO_2 transported into the bundle-sheath cells cost the equivalent of two ATP. To produce a single glucose, this requires 12 additional ATP compared with the Calvin cycle alone. Despite this additional cost, C₄ photosynthesis is advantageous in hot dry climates where photorespiration would remove more than half of the carbon fixed by the usual C₃ pathway alone.

Figure 8.24 Carbon fixation in CAM plants. CAM plants also use both C₄ and C₃ pathways to fix carbon and minimize photorespiration. In CAM plants, the two pathways occur in the same cell but are separated in time: The C₄ pathway is utilized to fix carbon at night, then CO_2 is released from these accumulated stores during the day to drive the C₃ pathway. This achieves the same effect of minimizing photorespiration while also minimizing loss of water by opening stomata at night when temperatures are lower.

The Crassulacean acid pathway splits photosynthesis into night and day

A second strategy to decrease photorespiration in hot regions has been adopted by the CAM plants. These include many succulent (water-storing) plants, such as cacti, pineapples, and some members of about two dozen other plant groups.

In these plants, the stomata open during the night and close during the day (figure 8.24). This pattern of stomatal opening and closing is the reverse of that in most plants. CAM plants initially fix CO_2 using PEP carboxylase to produce oxaloacetate. The oxaloacetate is often converted into other organic acids, depending on the particular CAM plant. These organic compounds accumulate during the night and are stored in the vacuole. Then during the day, when the stomata are closed, the organic acids are decarboxylated to yield high levels of CO_2. These high levels of CO_2 drive the Calvin cycle and minimize photorespiration.

Like C₄ plants, CAM plants use both C₃ and C₄ pathways. They differ in that they use both of these pathways in the same cell: the C₄ pathway at night and the C₃ pathway during the day. In C₄ plants the two pathways occur in different cells.

Learning Outcomes Review 8.7

Rubisco can also oxidize RuBP under conditions of high O_2 and low CO_2. In plants that use only C₃ metabolism (Calvin cycle), up to 20% of fixed carbon is lost to this photorespiration. Plants adapted to hot, dry environments are capable of storing CO_2 as a 4-carbon molecule and avoiding some of this loss; they are called C₄ plants. In CAM plants, CO_2 is fixed at night into a C₄ organic compound; in the daytime, this compound is used as a source of CO_2 C₃ metabolism when stomata are closed to prevent water loss.

■ *How do C₄ plants and CAM plants differ?*

8.1 Overview of Photosynthesis

Photosynthesis is the conversion of light energy into chemical energy (see figure 8.2).

Photosynthesis combines CO_2 and H_2O, producing glucose and O_2.
Photosynthesis has three stages: absorbing light energy, using this energy to synthesize ATP and NADPH, and using the ATP and NADPH to convert CO_2 to organic molecules. The first two stages consist of light-dependent reactions, and the third stage of light-independent reactions.

In plants, photosynthesis takes place in chloroplasts.
Chloroplasts contain internal thylakoid membranes and a fluid matrix called stroma. The photosystems involved in energy capture are found in the thylakoid membranes, and enzymes for assembling organic molecules are in the stroma.

8.2 The Discovery of Photosynthetic Processes

Plants do not increase mass from soil and water alone.
Early investigations revealed that plants produce O_2 from carbon dioxide and water in the presence of light.

Photosynthesis includes both light-dependent and light-independent reactions.
The light-dependent reactions require light; the light-independent reactions occur in both daylight and darkness. The rate of photosynthesis depends on the amount of light, the CO_2 concentration, and temperature.

O_2 comes from water, not from CO_2.
The use of isotopes revealed the individual origins and fates of different molecules in photosynthetic reactions.

ATP and NADPH from light-dependent reactions reduce CO_2 to make sugars.
Carbon fixation requires ATP and NADPH, which are products of the light-dependent reactions. As long as these are available, CO_2 is reduced by enzymes in the stroma to form simple sugars.

8.3 Pigments

Light is a form of energy.
Light exists both as a wave and as a particle (photon). Light can remove electrons from some metals by the photoelectric effect, and in photosynthesis, chloroplasts act as photoelectric devices.

Each pigment has a characteristic absorption spectrum.
Chlorophyll *a* is the only pigment that can convert light energy into chemical energy. Chlorophyll *b* is an accessory pigment that increases the harvest of photons for photosynthesis.
Carotenoids and other accessory pigments further increase a plant's ability to harvest photons.

8.4 Photosystem Organization (see figure 8.10)

Production of one O_2 molecule requires many chlorophyll molecules.
Measurement of O_2 output led to the idea of photosystems—clusters of pigment molecules that channel energy to a reaction center.

A generalized photosystem contains an antenna complex and a reaction center.
A photosystem is a network of chlorophyll *a*, accessory pigments, and proteins embedded in the thylakoid membrane. Pigment molecules of the antenna complex harvest photons and feed light energy to the reaction center. The reaction center is composed of two chlorophyll *a* molecules in a protein matrix that pass an excited electron to an electron acceptor.

8.5 The Light-Dependent Reactions

The light reactions can be broken down into four processes: primary photoevent, charge separation, electron transport, and chemiosmosis.

Some bacteria use a single photosystem (figure 8.12).
An excited electron moves along a transport chain and eventually returns to the photosystem. This cyclic process is used to generate a proton gradient. In some bacteria, this can also produce NADPH.

Chloroplasts have two connected photosystems.
Photosystem I transfers electrons to $NADP^+$, reducing it to NADPH. Photosystem II replaces electrons lost by photosystem I. Electrons lost from photosystem II are replaced by electrons from oxidation of water, which also produces O_2.

The two photosystems work together in noncyclic photophosphorylation.
Photosystem II and photosystem I are linked by an electron transport chain; the b_6-f complex in this chain pumps protons into the thylakoid space.

ATP is generated by chemiosmosis.
ATP synthase is a channel enzyme; as protons flow through the channel down their gradient, ADP is phosphorylated producing ATP, similar to the mechanism in mitochondria. Plants can make additional ATP by cyclic photophosphorylation.

Thylakoid structure reveals components' locations.
Imaging studies suggest that photosystem II is primarily found in the grana, while photosystem I and ATP synthase are found in the stroma lamella.

8.6 Carbon Fixation: The Calvin Cycle (see figure 8.18)

Calvin cycle reactions convert inorganic carbon into organic molecules.
The Calvin cycle, also known as C_3 photosynthesis, uses CO_2, ATP, and NADPH to build simple sugars.

Carbon is transferred through cycle intermediates, eventually producing glucose.
The Calvin cycle occurs in three stages: carbon fixation via the enzyme rubisco's action on RuBP and CO_2; reduction of the resulting 3-carbon PGA to G3P, generating ATP and NADPH; and regeneration of RuBP. Six turns of the cycle fix enough carbon to produce two excess G3Ps used to make one molecule of glucose.

8.7 Photorespiration

Photorespiration reduces the yield of photosynthesis.
Rubisco can catalyze the oxidation of RuBP, reversing carbon fixation. Dry, hot conditions tend to increase this reaction.

C_4 plants have evolved to minimize photorespiration.
C_4 plants fix carbon by adding CO_2 to a 3-carbon molecule, forming oxaloacetate. Carbon is fixed in one cell by the C_4 pathway, then CO_2 is released in another cell for the Calvin cycle (see figure 8.23).

The Crassulacean acid pathway splits photosynthesis into night and day.
CAM plants use the C_4 pathway during the day when stomata are closed, and the Calvin cycle at night in the same cell.

UNDERSTAND

1. The *light-dependent* reactions of photosynthesis are responsible for the production of
   a. glucose.
   b. CO_2.
   c. ATP and NADPH.
   d. H_2O.

2. Which region of a chloroplast is associated with the capture of light energy?
   a. Thylakoid membrane
   b. Outer membrane
   c. Stroma
   d. Both a and c

3. The colors of light that are most effective for photosynthesis are
   a. red, blue, and violet.
   b. green, yellow, and orange.
   c. infrared and ultraviolet.
   d. All colors of light are equally effective.

4. During noncyclic photosynthesis, photosystem I functions to _____, and photosystem II functions to _____.
   a. synthesize ATP; produce O_2
   b. reduce $NADP^+$; oxidize H_2O
   c. reduce CO_2; oxidize NADPH
   d. restore an electron to its reaction center; gain an electron from water

5. How is a reaction center pigment in a photosystem different from a pigment in the antenna complex?
   a. The reaction center pigment is a chlorophyll molecule.
   b. The antenna complex pigment can only reflect light.
   c. The reaction center pigment loses an electron when it absorbs light energy.
   d. The antenna complex pigments are not attached to proteins.

6. The ATP and NADPH from the light reactions are used
   a. in glycolysis in roots.
   b. directly in most biochemical reactions in the cell.
   c. during the reactions of the Calvin cycle to produce glucose.
   d. to synthesize chlorophyll.

7. The carbon fixation reaction converts
   a. inorganic carbon into an organic acid.
   b. CO_2 into glucose.
   c. inactive rubisco into active rubisco.
   d. an organic acid into CO_2.

8. C_4 plants initially fix carbon by
   a. the same pathway as C_3 plants, but they modify this product.
   b. incorporating CO_2 into oxaloacetate, which is converted to malate.
   c. incorporating CO_2 into citrate via the Krebs cycle.
   d. incorporating CO_2 into glucose via reverse glycolysis.

APPLY

1. The overall flow of electrons in the light reactions is from
   a. antenna pigments to the reaction center.
   b. H_2O to CO_2.
   c. photosystem I to photosystem II.
   d. H_2O to NADPH.

2. Where in a chloroplast would you find the highest concentration of protons?
   a. In the stroma
   b. In the lumen of the thylakoid
   c. In the intermembrane space
   d. In the antenna complex

3. How does the reaction center of photosystem I regain an electron during noncyclic photosynthesis?
   a. The electron is recycled directly back to the reaction center pigment.
   b. The electron is donated from H_2O.
   c. The electron is donated from photosystem II.
   d. The electron is donated from NADPH.

4. If the Calvin cycle runs through six turns
   a. all of the fixed carbon will end up in the same glucose molecule.
   b. 12 carbons will be fixed by the process.
   c. enough carbon will be fixed to make one glucose, but they will not all be in the same molecule.
   d. one glucose will be converted into six CO_2.

5. Which of the following are similarities between the structure and function of mitochondria and chloroplasts?
   a. They both create internal proton gradients by electron transport.
   b. They both generate CO_2 by oxidation reactions.
   c. They both have an outer membrane and an inner membrane system.
   d. Both a and c are correct.

6. Carbon fixation by the C_4 pathway produces
   a. the same product as is produced by the Calvin cycle.
   b. an organic acid, but a 4-carbon one not a 3-carbon.
   c. a 3-carbon organic acid that is converted to the 4-carbon malate.
   d. RuBP.

7. If the thylakoid membrane became leaky to ions, what would you predict to be the result on the light reactions?
   a. It would stop ATP production.
   b. It would stop NADPH production.
   c. It would stop the oxidation of H_2O.
   d. All of the above are correct.

8. The overall process of photosynthesis
   a. results in the reduction of CO_2 and the oxidation of H_2O.
   b. results in the reduction of H_2O and the oxidation of CO_2.
   c. consumes O_2 and produces CO_2.
   d. produces O_2 from CO_2.

SYNTHESIZE

1. Compare and contrast the fixation of carbon in C_3, C_4, and CAM plants.

2. Diagram the relationship between the reactants and products of photosynthesis and respiration.

3. Do plant cells need mitochondria? Explain your answer.

ONLINE RESOURCE

www.ravenbiology.com

Understand, Apply, and Synthesize—enhance your study with animations that bring concepts to life and practice tests to assess your understanding. Your instructor may also recommend the interactive eBook, individualized learning tools, and more.

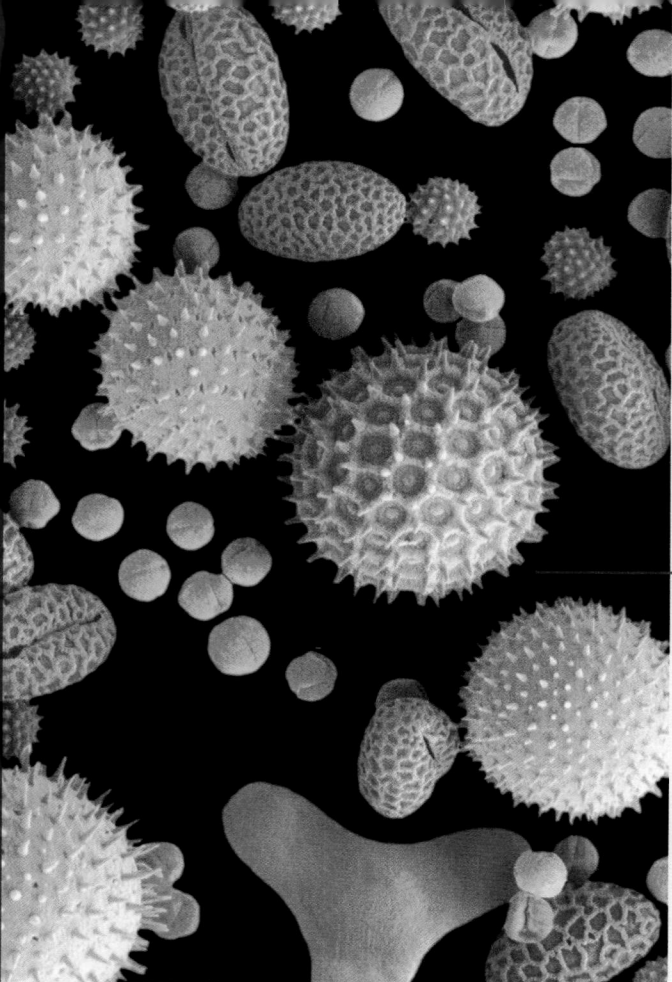

Chapter 9

Cell Communication

Chapter Outline

9.1 Overview of Cell Communication

9.2 Receptor Types

9.3 Intracellular Receptors

9.4 Signal Transduction Through Receptor Kinases

9.5 Signal Transduction Through G Protein-Coupled Receptors

Introduction

Springtime is a time of rebirth and renewal. Trees that have appeared dead produce new leaves and buds, and flowers sprout from the ground. For sufferers of seasonal allergy, this is not quite such a pleasant time. The pollen in the micrograph and other allergens produced stimulate the immune system to produce the molecule histamine and other molecules that form cellular signals. These signals cause inflammation, mucus secretion, vasodilation, and other responses that together cause the runny nose, itching watery eyes, and other symptoms that make up the allergic reaction. We treat allergy symptoms by using drugs called antihistamines that interfere with this cellular signaling. The popular drug loratadine (better known as Claritin), for example, acts by blocking the receptor for histamine, thus preventing its action.

We will begin this chapter with a general overview of signaling, and the kinds of receptors cells use to respond to signals. Then we will look in more detail at how these different types of receptors can elicit a response from cells, and finally, how cells make connections with one another.

9.1 Overview of Cell Communication

Learning Outcomes

1. *Explain the different ways that cells communicate.*
2. *Describe how cells use signal transduction pathways.*

Communication between cells is common in nature. Cell signaling occurs in all multicellular organisms, providing an indispensable mechanism for cells to influence one another. Effective signaling requires a signaling molecule, called a **ligand,** and a molecule to which the signal binds, called a **receptor protein.** The interaction of these two components initiates the process of *signal transduction*, which converts the information in the signal into a cellular response (figure 9.1).

The cells of multicellular organisms use a variety of molecules as signals, including but not limited to, peptides, large

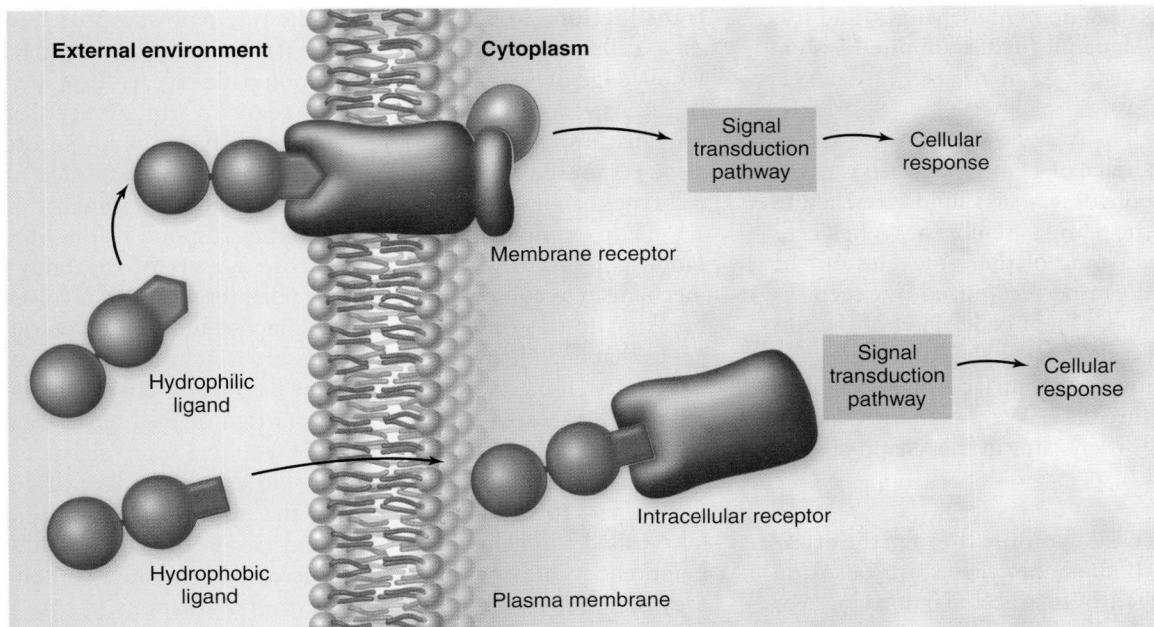

Labels in figure: External environment; Cytoplasm; Signal transduction pathway; Cellular response; Membrane receptor; Hydrophilic ligand; Signal transduction pathway; Cellular response; Intracellular receptor; Hydrophobic ligand; Plasma membrane

proteins, individual amino acids, nucleotides, and steroids and other lipids. Even dissolved gases such as NO (nitric oxide) are used as signals.

Any cell of a multicellular organism is exposed to a constant stream of signals. At any time, hundreds of different chemical signals may be present in the environment surrounding the cell. Each cell responds only to certain signals, however, and ignores the rest, like a person following the conversation of one or two individuals in a noisy, crowded room.

How does a cell "choose" which signals to respond to? The number and kind of receptor molecules determine this. When a ligand approaches a receptor protein that has a complementary shape, the two can bind, forming a complex. This binding induces a change in the receptor protein's shape, ultimately producing a response in the cell via a signal transduction pathway. In this way, a given cell responds to the signaling molecules that fit the particular set of receptor proteins it possesses and ignores those for which it lacks receptors.

Signaling is defined by the distance from source to receptor

Cells can communicate through any of four basic mechanisms, depending primarily on the distance between the signaling and responding cells (figure 9.2). These mechanisms are (1) direct contact, (2) paracrine signaling, (3) endocrine signaling, and (4) synaptic signaling.

In addition to using these four basic mechanisms, some cells actually send signals to themselves, secreting signals that bind to specific receptors on their own plasma membranes. This process, called *autocrine signaling*, is thought to play an

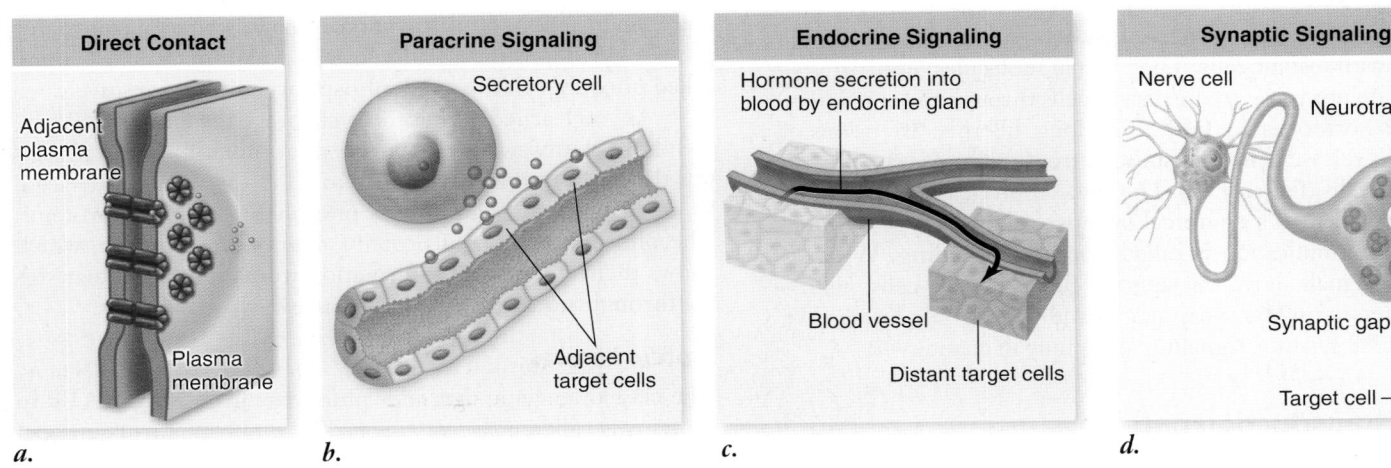

Figure 9.2 Four kinds of cell signaling. Cells communicate in several ways. *a.* Two cells in direct contact with each other may send signals across gap junctions. *b.* In paracrine signaling, secretions from one cell have an effect only on cells in the immediate area. *c.* In endocrine signaling, hormones are released into the organism's circulatory system, which carries them to the target cells. *d.* Chemical synapse signaling involves transmission of signal molecules, called neurotransmitters, from a neuron over a small synaptic gap to the target cell.

important role in reinforcing developmental changes, and it is an important component of signaling in the immune system (chapter 52).

Direct contact

As you saw in chapter 5, the surface of a eukaryotic cell is richly populated with proteins, carbohydrates, and lipids attached to and extending outward from the plasma membrane. When cells are very close to one another, some of the molecules on the plasma membrane of one cell can be recognized by receptors on the plasma membrane of an adjacent cell. Many of the important interactions between cells in early development occur by means of direct contact between cell surfaces. Cells also signal through gap junctions (figure 9.2*a*). We'll examine contact-dependent interactions more closely later in this chapter.

Paracrine signaling

Signal molecules released by cells can diffuse through the extracellular fluid to other cells. If those molecules are taken up by neighboring cells, destroyed by extracellular enzymes, or quickly removed from the extracellular fluid in some other way, their influence is restricted to cells in the immediate vicinity of the releasing cell. Signals with such short-lived, local effects are called **paracrine** signals (figure 9.2*b*).

Like direct contact, paracrine signaling plays an important role in early development, coordinating the activities of clusters of neighboring cells. The immune response in vertebrates also involves paracrine signaling between immune cells (chapter 52).

Endocrine signaling

A released signal molecule that remains in the extracellular fluid may enter the organism's circulatory system and travel widely throughout the body. These longer-lived signal molecules, which may affect cells very distant from the releasing cell, are called **hormones,** and this type of intercellular communication is known as **endocrine signaling** (figure 9.2*c*). Chapter 46 discusses endocrine signaling in detail. Both animals and plants use this signaling mechanism extensively.

Synaptic signaling

In animals, the cells of the nervous system provide rapid communication with distant cells. Their signal molecules, **neurotransmitters,** do not travel to the distant cells through the circulatory system as hormones do. Rather, the long, fiberlike extensions of nerve cells release neurotransmitters from their tips very close to the target cells (figure 9.2*d*). The association of a neuron and its target cell is called a **chemical synapse,** and this type of intercellular communication is called **synaptic signaling.** Whereas paracrine signals move through the fluid between cells, neurotransmitters cross the synaptic gap and persist only briefly. We will examine synaptic signaling more fully in chapter 44.

Signal transduction pathways lead to cellular responses

The types of signaling outlined earlier are descriptive and say nothing about how cells respond to signals. The events that occur within the cell on receipt of a signal are called **signal transduction.** These events form discrete pathways that lead to a cellular response to the signal received by receptors. Knowledge of these signal transduction pathways has exploded in recent years and indicates a high degree of complexity that explains how in some cases different cell types can have the same response to different signals, and in other cases different cell types can have a different response to the same signal.

For example, a variety of cell types respond to the hormone glucagon by mobilizing glucose as part of the body's mechanism to control blood glucose (chapter 46). This involves breaking down stored glycogen into glucose and turning on the genes that encode the enzymes necessary to synthesize glucose. In contrast, the hormone epinephrine has diverse effects on different cell types. We have all been startled or frightened by a sudden event. Your heart beats faster, you feel more alert, and you can even feel the hairs on your skin stand up. All of this is due in part to your body releasing the hormone epinephrine (also called adrenaline) into the bloodstream. This leads to the heightened state of alertness and increased heart rate and energy that prepare us to respond to extreme situations.

These differing effects of epinephrine depend on the different cell types with receptors for this hormone. In the liver, cells are stimulated to mobilize glucose while in the heart muscle cells contract more forcefully to increase blood flow. In addition, blood vessels respond by expanding in some areas and contracting in others to redirect blood flow to the liver, heart, and skeletal muscles. These different reactions depend on the fact that each cell type has a receptor for epinephrine, but different sets of proteins that respond to this signal.

Phosphorylation is key in control of protein function

The function of a signal transduction pathway is to change the behavior or nature of a cell. This action may require changing the composition of proteins that make up a cell or altering the activity of cellular proteins. Many proteins are inactive or nonfunctional as they are initially synthesized and require modification after synthesis for activation. In other cases, a protein may require modification for deactivation. A major source of control for protein function is the addition or removal of phosphate groups, called **phosphorylation** or **dephosphorylation,** respectively.

As you learned in preceding chapters, the end result of the metabolic pathways of cellular respiration and photosynthesis was the phosphorylation of ADP to ATP. The ATP synthesized by these processes can donate phosphate groups to proteins. The phosphorylation of proteins alters their function, which allows them to transmit information from an extracellular signal through a signal transduction pathway.

Protein kinases

The class of enzyme that adds phosphate groups from ATP to proteins is called a *protein kinase.* These phosphate groups can be added to the three amino acids that have an OH as part of their R group, namely serine, threonine, and tyrosine. We categorize protein kinases based on which of these three substrates they alter (figure 9.3). Most cytoplasmic protein kinases fall into the serine/threonine kinase class.

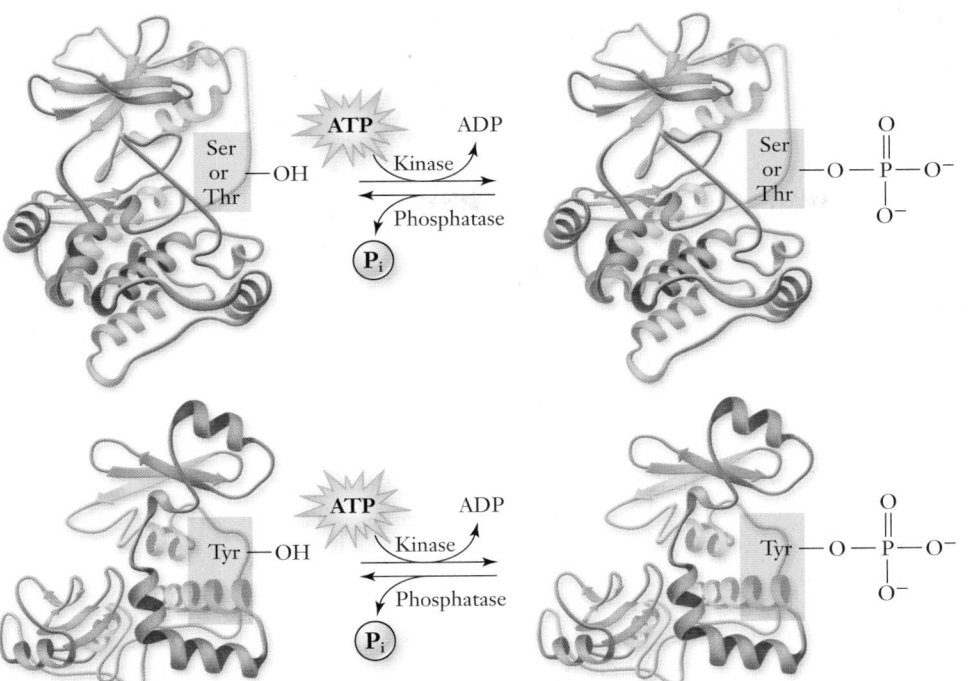

Figure 9.3 **Phosphorylation of proteins.** Many proteins are controlled by their phosphorylation state: that is, they are activated by phosphorylation and deactivated by dephosphorylation or the reverse. The enzymes that add phosphate groups are called kinases. These form two classes depending on the amino acid the phosphate is added to, either serine/threonine kinases or tyrosine kinases. The action of kinases is reversed by protein phosphatase enzymes.

Phosphatases

Part of the reason for the versatility of phosphorylation as a form of protein modification is that it is reversible. Another class of enzymes called **phosphatases** removes phosphate groups, reversing the action of kinases (see figure 9.3). Thus, a protein activated by a kinase can be deactivated by a phosphatase, or the reverse.

Learning Outcomes Review 9.1

Cell communication involves chemical signals, or ligands, that bind to cellular receptors. Binding of ligand to receptor initiates signal transduction pathways that lead to a cellular response. Different cells may have the same response to one signal and the same signal can also elicit different responses in different cells. The phosphorylation–dephosphorylation of proteins is a common mechanism of controlling protein function found in signaling pathways.

■ *How are receptor ligand interactions similar to enzyme substrate interactions?*

9.2 Receptor Types

Learning Outcome

1. **Contrast the different types of receptors.**

The first step in understanding cell signaling is to consider the receptors themselves. Cells must have a specific receptor to be able to respond to a particular signaling molecule. The interaction of a receptor and its ligand is an example of molecular recognition, a process in which one molecule fits specifically based on its complementary shape with another molecule. This interaction causes subtle changes in the structure of the receptor, thereby activating it. This is the beginning of any signal transduction pathway.

Receptors are defined by location

The nature of these receptor molecules depends on their location and on the kind of ligands they bind. Intracellular receptors bind hydro-phobic ligands, which can easily cross the membrane, inside the cell. In contrast, cell surface or membrane receptors bind hydrophilic ligands, which cannot easily cross the membrane, outside the cell (figure 9.1). Membrane receptors consist of transmembrane proteins that are in contact with both the cytoplasm and the extracellular environment. Table 9.1 summarizes the types of receptors and communication mechanisms discussed in this chapter.

Membrane receptors include three subclasses

When a receptor is a transmembrane protein, the ligand binds to the receptor outside of the cell and never actually crosses the plasma membrane. In this case, the receptor itself, and not the signaling molecule is responsible for information crossing the membrane. Membrane receptors can be categorized based on their structure and function.

Channel-linked receptors

Chemically gated ion channels are receptor proteins that allow the passage of ions (figure 9.4a). The receptor proteins that bind many neurotransmitters have the same basic structure. Each is a membrane protein with multiple transmembrane domains, meaning that the chain of amino acids threads back and forth across the plasma membrane several times. In the center of the protein is a pore that connects the extracellular fluid with the cytoplasm. The pore is big enough for ions to pass through, so the protein functions as an **ion channel.**

TABLE 9.1	Receptors Involved in Cell Signaling		
Receptor Type	**Structure**	**Function**	**Example**
Intracellular Receptors	No extracellular signal-binding site	Receives signals from lipid-soluble or noncharged, nonpolar small molecules	Receptors for NO, steroid hormone, vitamin D, and thyroid hormone
Cell Surface Receptors			
Chemically gated ion channels	Multipass transmembrane protein forming a central pore	Molecular "gates" triggered chemically to open or close	Neurons
Enzymatic receptors	Single-pass transmembrane protein	Binds signal extracellularly; catalyzes response intracellularly	Phosphorylation of protein kinases
G protein-coupled receptors	Seven-pass transmembrane protein with cytoplasmic binding site for G protein	Binding of signal to receptor causes GTP to bind a G protein; G protein, with attached GTP, detaches to deliver the signal inside the cell	Peptide hormones, rod cells in the eyes

The channel is said to be chemically gated because it opens only when a chemical (the neurotransmitter) binds to it. The type of ion that flows across the membrane when a chemically gated ion channel opens depends on the shape and charge structure of the channel. Sodium, potassium, calcium, and chloride ions all have specific ion channels.

The acetylcholine receptor found in muscle cell membranes functions as an Na^+ channel. When the receptor binds to its ligand, the neurotransmitter acetylcholine, the channel opens allowing Na^+ to flow into the muscle cell. This is a critical step linking the signal from a motor neuron to muscle cell contraction (chapter 44).

Enzymatic receptors

Many cell surface receptors either act as enzymes or are directly linked to enzymes (figure 9.4b). When a signal molecule binds to the receptor, it activates the enzyme. In almost all

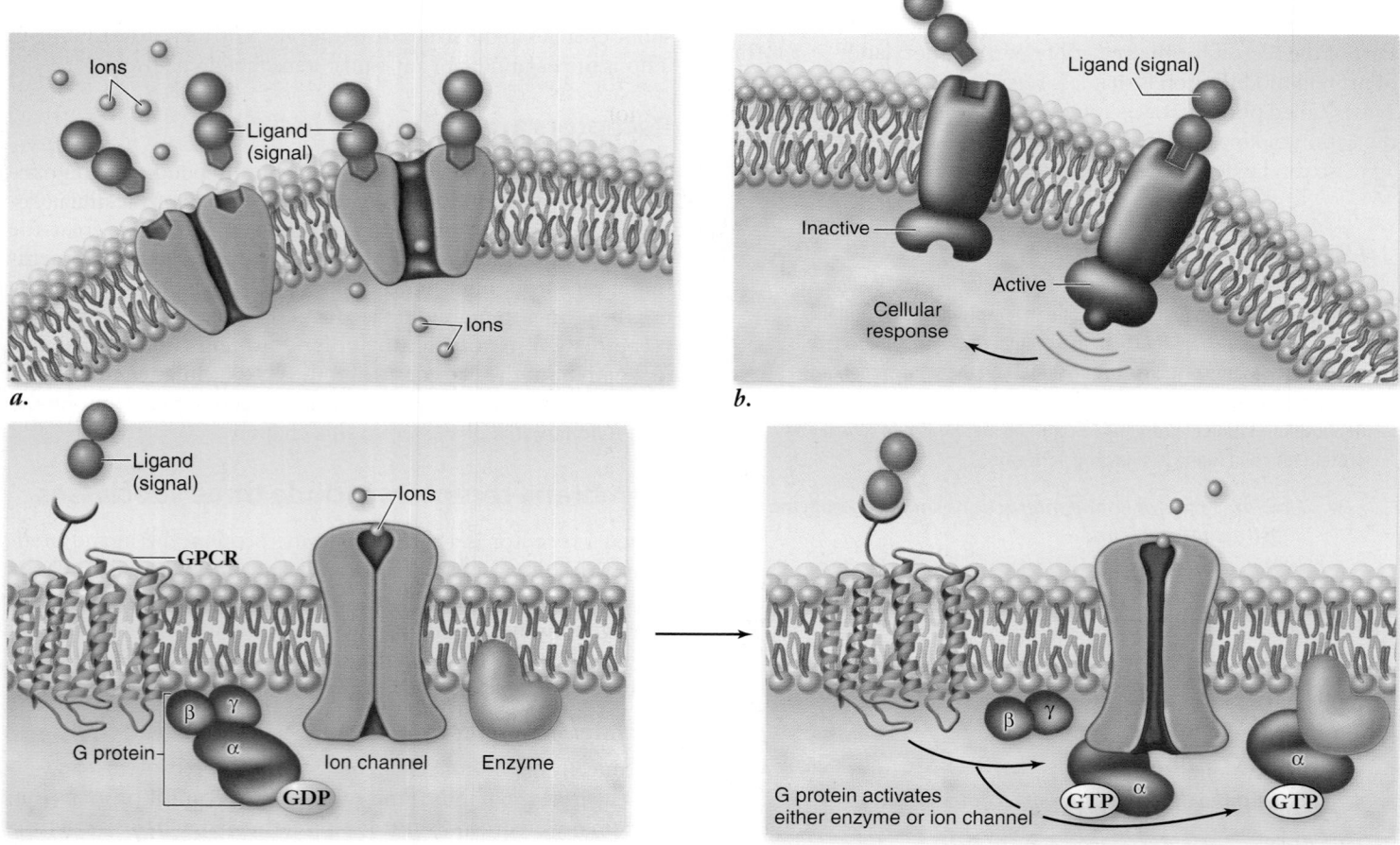

Figure 9.4 Cell surface receptors. *a.* Chemically gated ion channels form a pore in the plasma membrane that can be opened or closed by chemical signals. They are usually selective, allowing the passage of only one type of ion. *b.* Enzymatic receptors bind to ligands on the extracellular surface. A catalytic region on their cytoplasmic portion transmits the signal across the membrane by acting as an enzyme in the cytoplasm. *c.* G protein-coupled receptors (GPCR) bind to ligands outside the cell and to G proteins inside the cell. The G protein then activates an enzyme or ion channel, transmitting signals from the cell's surface to its interior.

cases, these enzymes are **protein kinases,** enzymes that add phosphate groups to proteins. We discuss these receptors in detail in a later section of this chapter.

G Protein-coupled receptors

A third class of cell surface receptors acts indirectly on enzymes or ion channels in the plasma membrane with the aid of an assisting protein, called a **G protein.** The G protein, which is so named because it binds the nucleotide *guanosine triphosphate* (GTP), can be thought of as being inserted between the receptors and the enzyme (effector). That is, the ligand binds to the receptor, activating it, which activates the G protein, which in turn activates the effector protein (figure 9.4c). These receptors are also discussed in detail later on.

Membrane receptors can generate second messengers

Some enzymatic receptors and most G protein-coupled receptors utilize other substances to relay the message within the cytoplasm. These other substances, small molecules or ions called **second messengers,** alter the behavior of cellular proteins by binding to them and changing their shape. (The original signal molecule is considered the "first messenger.") Two common second messengers are **cyclic adenosine monophosphate (cyclic-AMP,** or **cAMP)** and calcium ions. The role of these second messengers will be explored in more detail in a later section.

Learning Outcome Review 9.2

Receptors may be internal (intracellular receptors) or external (membrane receptors). Membrane receptors include channel-linked receptors, enzymatic receptors, and G protein-coupled receptors. Signal transduction through membrane receptors often involves the production of a second signaling molecule, or second messenger, inside the cell.

■ *Would a hydrophobic molecule be expected to have an internal or membrane receptor?*

Learning Outcomes
1. *Identify the chemical nature of ligands for intracellular receptors.*
2. *Describe the action of intracellular receptors.*

Many cell signals are lipid-soluble or very small molecules that can readily pass through the plasma membrane of the target cell and into the cell, where they interact with an *intracellular receptor.* Some of these ligands bind to protein receptors located in the cytoplasm, others pass across the nuclear membrane as well and bind to receptors within the nucleus.

Steroid hormone receptors affect gene expression

Of all of the receptor types discussed in this chapter, the action of the steroid hormone receptors is the simplest and most direct.

Steroid hormones form a large class of compounds, including cortisol, estrogen, progesterone, and testosterone, that share a common nonpolar structure. Estrogen, progesterone, and testosterone are involved in sexual development and behavior (chapter 53). Other steroid hormones, such as cortisol, also have varied effects depending on the target tissue, ranging from the mobilization of glucose to the inhibition of white blood cells to control inflammation. Their anti-inflammatory action is the basis of their use in medicine.

The nonpolar structure allows these hormones to cross the membrane and bind to intracellular receptors. The location of steroid hormone receptors prior to hormone binding is cytoplasmic, but their primary site of action is in the nucleus. Binding of the hormone to the receptor causes the complex to shift from the cytoplasm to the nucleus (figure 9.5). As the

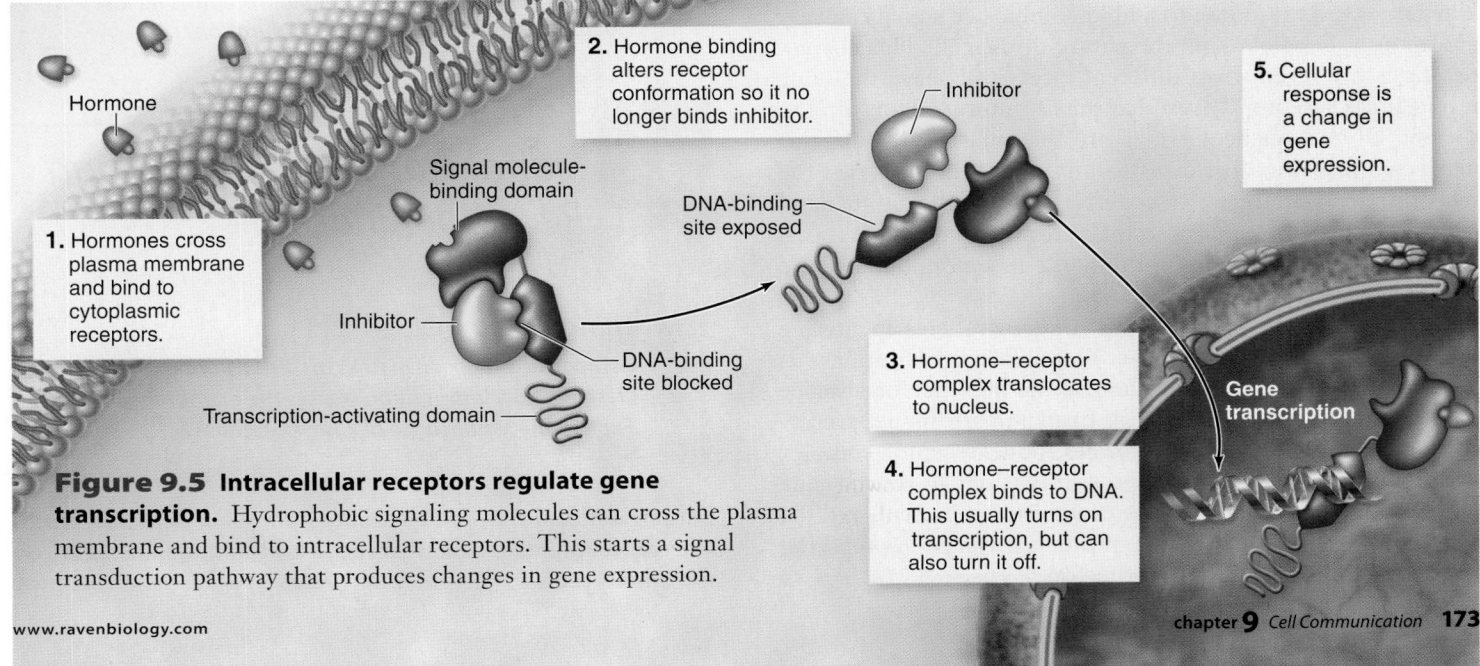

Figure 9.5 Intracellular receptors regulate gene transcription. Hydrophobic signaling molecules can cross the plasma membrane and bind to intracellular receptors. This starts a signal transduction pathway that produces changes in gene expression.

ligand–receptor complex makes it all the way to the nucleus of the cell, these receptors are often called **nuclear receptors.**

Steroid receptor action

The primary function of steroid hormone receptors, as well as receptors for a number of other small, lipid-soluble signal molecules such as vitamin D and thyroid hormone, is to act as regulators of gene expression (see chapter 16).

All of these receptors have similar structures; the genes that code for them appear to be the evolutionary descendants of a single ancestral gene. Because of their structural similarities, they are all part of the *nuclear receptor superfamily.*

Each of these receptors has three functional domains—

1. a hormone-binding domain,
2. a DNA-binding domain, and
3. a domain that can interact with coactivators to affect the level of gene transcription.

In its inactive state, the receptor typically cannot bind to DNA because an inhibitor protein occupies the DNA-binding site. When the signal molecule binds to the hormone-binding site, the conformation of the receptor changes, releasing the inhibitor and exposing the DNA-binding site, allowing the receptor to attach to specific nucleotide sequences on the DNA (see figure 9.5). This binding activates (or, in a few instances, suppresses) particular genes, usually located adjacent to the hormone-binding sequences. In the case of cortisol, which is a glucocorticoid hormone that can increase levels of glucose in cells, a number of different genes involved in the synthesis of glucose have binding sites for the hormone receptor complex.

The lipid-soluble ligands that intracellular receptors recognize tend to persist in the blood far longer than water-soluble signals. Most water-soluble hormones break down within minutes, and neurotransmitters break down within seconds or even milliseconds. In contrast, a steroid hormone such as cortisol or estrogen persists for hours.

Specificity and the role of coactivators

The target cell's response to a lipid-soluble cell signal can vary enormously, depending on the nature of the cell. This characteristic is true even when different target cells have the same intracellular receptor. Given that the receptor proteins bind to specific DNA sequences, which are the same in all cells, this may seem puzzling. It is explained in part by the fact that the receptors act in concert with **coactivators,** and the number and nature of these molecules can differ from cell to cell. Thus, a cell's response depends on not only the receptors but also the coactivators present.

The hormone estrogen has different effects in uterine tissue than in mammary tissue. This differential response is mediated by coactivators and not by the presence or absence of a receptor in the two tissues. In mammary tissue, a critical coactivator is lacking and the hormone–receptor complex instead interacts with another protein that acts to reduce gene expression. In uterine tissue, the coactivator is present, and the expression of genes that encode proteins involved in preparing the uterus for pregnancy are turned on.

Other intracellular receptors act as enzymes

A very interesting example of a receptor acting as an enzyme is found in the receptor for nitric oxide (NO). This small gas molecule diffuses readily out of the cells where it is produced and passes directly into neighboring cells, where it binds to the enzyme guanylyl cyclase. Binding of NO activates this enzyme, enabling it to catalyze the synthesis of *cyclic guanosine monophosphate (cGMP)*, an intracellular messenger molecule that produces cell-specific responses such as the relaxation of smooth muscle cells.

When the brain sends a nerve signal to relax the smooth muscle cells lining the walls of vertebrate blood vessels, acetylcholine released by the nerve cell binds to receptors on epithelial cells. This causes an increase in intracellular Ca^{2+} in the epithelial cell that stimulates nitric oxide synthase to produce NO. The NO diffuses into the smooth muscle, where it increases the level of cGMP, leading to relaxation. This relaxation allows the vessel to expand and thereby increases blood flow. This explains the use of nitroglycerin to treat the pain of angina caused by constricted blood vessels to the heart. The nitroglycerin is converted by cells to NO, which then acts to relax the blood vessels.

The drug sildenafil (better known as Viagra) also functions via this signal transduction pathway by binding to and inhibiting the enzyme cGMP phosphodiesterase, which breaks down cGMP. This keeps levels of cGMP high, thereby stimulating production of NO. The reason for Viagra's selective effect is that it binds to a form of cGMP phosphodiesterase found in cells in the penis. This allows relaxation of smooth muscle in erectile tissue, thereby increasing blood flow.

Learning Outcomes Review 9.3

Hydrophobic signaling molecules can cross the membrane and bind to intracellular receptors. The steroid hormone receptors act by directly influencing gene expression. On binding hormone, the hormone–receptor moves into the nucleus to turn on (or sometimes turn off) gene expression. This also requires another protein called a coactivator that functions with the hormone–receptor. Thus, the cell's response to a hormone depends on the presence of a receptor and coactivators as well.

- *Would these types of intracellular receptors be fast acting, or have effects of longer duration?*

9.4 *Signal Transduction Through Receptor Kinases*

Learning Outcomes

1. *Compare the function of RTKs to steroid hormone receptors.*
2. *Describe how information crosses the membrane in RTKs.*
3. *Explain the significance of kinase cascades.*

Earlier you read that protein kinases phosphorylate proteins to alter protein function and that the most common kinases act on the amino acids serine, threonine, and tyrosine. The **receptor** tyrosine kinases (RTK) influence the cell cycle, cell migration, cell metabolism, and cell proliferation—virtually all aspects of the cell are affected by signaling through these receptors. Alterations to the function of these receptors and their signaling pathways can lead to cancers in humans and other animals.

Some of the earliest examples of cancer-causing genes, or oncogenes, involve RTK function (discussed in chapter 10). The cancer-causing simian sarcoma virus carries a gene for platelet-derived growth factor. When the virus infects a cell, the cell overproduces and secretes platelet-derived growth factor, causing overgrowth of the surrounding cells. Another virus, avian erythroblastosis virus, carries an altered form of the epidermal growth factor receptor that lacks most of its extracellular domain. When this virus infects a cell the altered receptors produced are stuck in the "on" state. The continuous signaling from this receptor leads to cells that have lost the normal controls over growth.

Receptor tyrosine kinases recognize hydrophilic ligands and form a large class of membrane receptors in animal cells. Plants possess receptors with a similar overall structure and function, but they are serine–threonine kinases. These plant receptors have been named **plant receptor kinases.**

Because these receptors are performing similar functions in plant and animal cells but differ in their substrates, the duplication and divergence of each kind of receptor kinase probably occurred after the plant–animal divergence. The proliferation of these types of signaling molecules is thought to be coincident with the independent evolution of multicellularity in each group.

In this section, we will concentrate on the RTK family of receptors that has been extensively studied in a variety of animal cells.

RTKs are activated by autophosphorylation

Receptor tyrosine kinases have a relatively simple structure consisting of a single transmembrane domain that anchors them in the membrane, an extracellular ligand-binding domain, and an intracellular kinase domain. This kinase domain contains the catalytic site of the receptor, which acts as a protein kinase that adds phosphate groups to tyrosines. On ligand binding to a specific receptor, two of these receptor–ligand complexes associate together (often referred to as dimerization) and phosphorylate each other, a process called *autophosphorylation* (figure 9.6).

The autophosphorylation event transmits across the membrane the signal that began with the binding of the ligand to the receptor. The next step, propagation of the signal in the

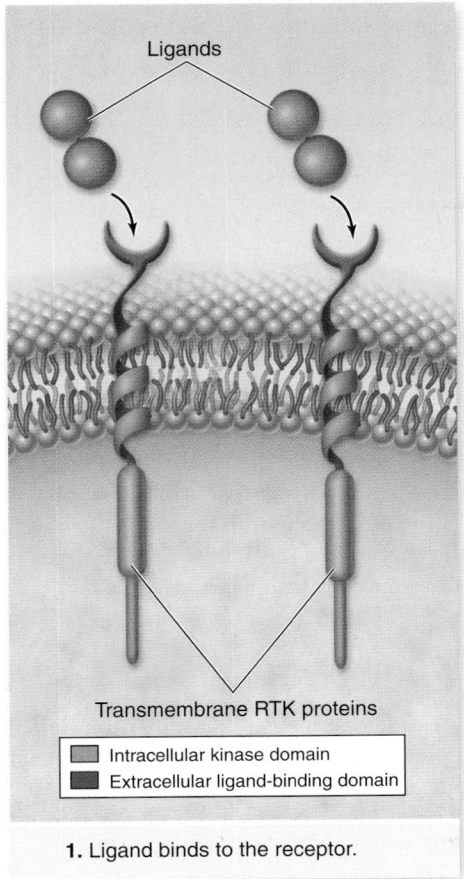

1. Ligand binds to the receptor.

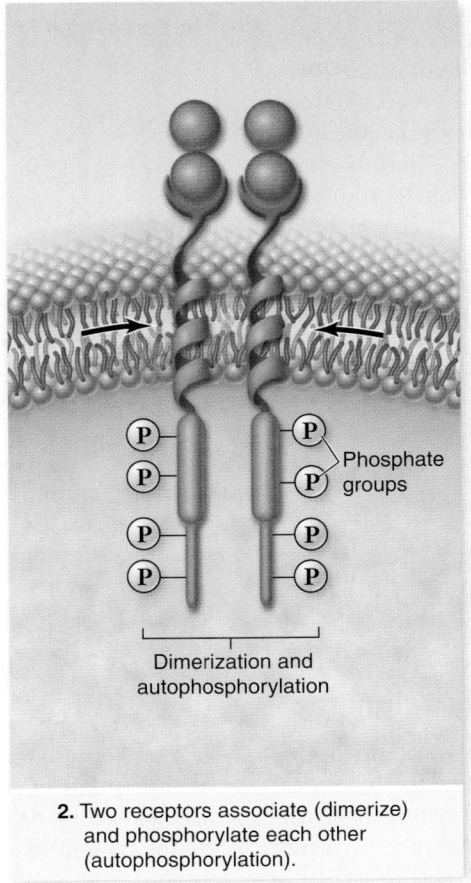

2. Two receptors associate (dimerize) and phosphorylate each other (autophosphorylation).

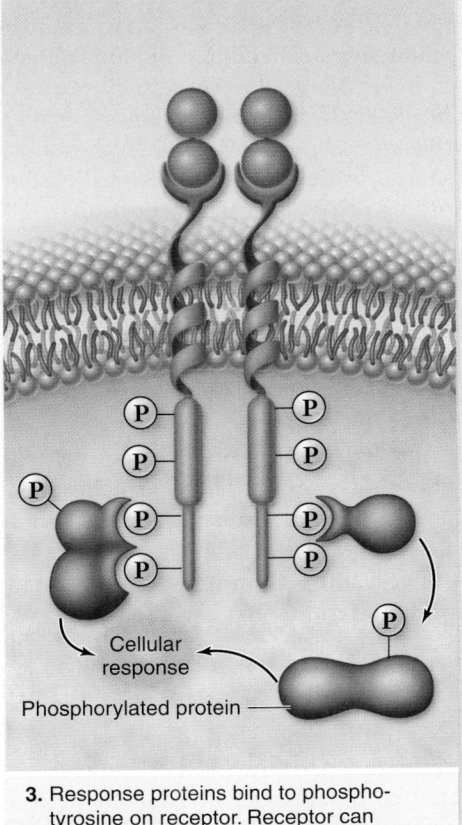

3. Response proteins bind to phosphotyrosine on receptor. Receptor can phosphorylate other response proteins.

Figure 9.6 Activation of a receptor tyrosine kinase (RTK). These membrane receptors bind hormones or growth factors that are hydrophilic and cannot cross the membrane. The receptor is a transmembrane protein with an extracellular ligand binding domain and an intracellular kinase domain. Signal transduction pathways begin with response proteins binding to phosphotyrosine on receptor, and by receptor phosphorylation of response proteins.

chapter **9** *Cell Communication*

cytoplasm, can take a variety of different forms. These forms include activation of the tyrosine kinase domain to phosphorylate other intracellular targets or interaction of other proteins with the phosphorylated receptor.

The cellular response after activation depends on the possible response proteins in the cell. Two different cells can have the same receptor yet a different response, depending on what response proteins are present in the cytoplasm. For example fibroblast growth factor stimulates cell division in fibroblasts but stimulates nerve cells to differentiate rather than to divide.

Phosphotyrosine domains mediate protein–protein interactions

One way that the signal from the receptor can be propagated in the cytoplasm is via proteins that bind specifically to phosphorylated tyrosines in the receptor. When the receptor is activated, regions of the protein outside of the catalytic site are phosphorylated. This creates "docking" sites for proteins that bind specifically to phosphotyrosine. The proteins that bind to these phosphorylated tyrosines can initiate intracellular events to convert the signal from the ligand into a response (see figure 9.6).

The insulin receptor

The use of docking proteins is illustrated by the insulin receptor. The hormone insulin is part of the body's control system to maintain a constant level of blood glucose. The role of insulin is to lower blood glucose, acting by binding to an RTK. Another protein called the *insulin response protein* binds to the phosphorylated receptor and is itself phosphorylated. The insulin response protein passes the signal on by binding to additional proteins that lead to the activation of the enzyme glycogen synthase, which converts glucose to glycogen (figure 9.7), thereby lowering blood glucose. Other proteins activated by the insulin receptor act to inhibit the synthesis of enzymes involved in making glucose, and to increase the number of glucose transporter proteins in the plasma membrane.

Adapter proteins

Another class of proteins, **adapter proteins,** can also bind to phosphotyrosines. These proteins themselves do not participate in signal transduction but act as a link between the receptor and proteins that initiate downstream signaling events. For example, the Ras protein discussed later, is activated by adapter proteins binding to a receptor.

Protein kinase cascades can amplify a signal

One important class of cytoplasmic kinases are **mitogen-activated protein (MAP) kinases.** A *mitogen* is a chemical that stimulates cell division by activating the normal pathways that control division. The MAP kinases are activated by a signaling module called a *phosphorylation cascade* or a **kinase cascade.** This module is a series of protein kinases that phosphorylate each other in succession. The final step in the cascade is the activation by phosphorylation of MAP kinase itself (figure 9.8).

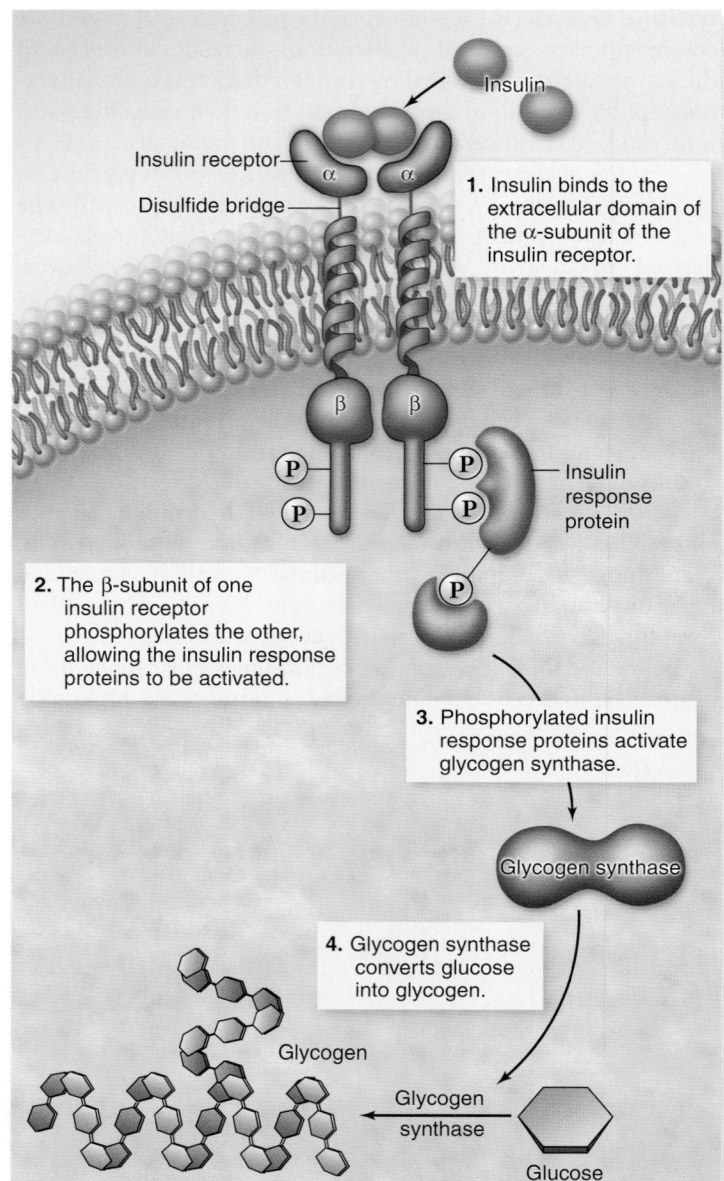

Figure 9.7 The insulin receptor. The insulin receptor is a receptor tyrosine kinase that initiates a variety of cellular responses related to glucose metabolism. One signal transduction pathway that this receptor mediates leads to the activation of the enzyme glycogen synthase. This enzyme converts glucose to glycogen.

One function of a kinase cascade is to amplify the original signal. Because each step in the cascade is an enzyme, it can act on a number of substrate molecules. With each enzyme in the cascade acting on many substrates this produces a large amount of the final product (see figure 9.8). This allows a small number of initial signaling molecules to produce a large response.

The cellular response to this cascade in any particular cell depends on the targets of the MAP kinase, but usually involves phosphorylating transcription factors that then activate gene expression (chapter 16). An example of this kind of signaling

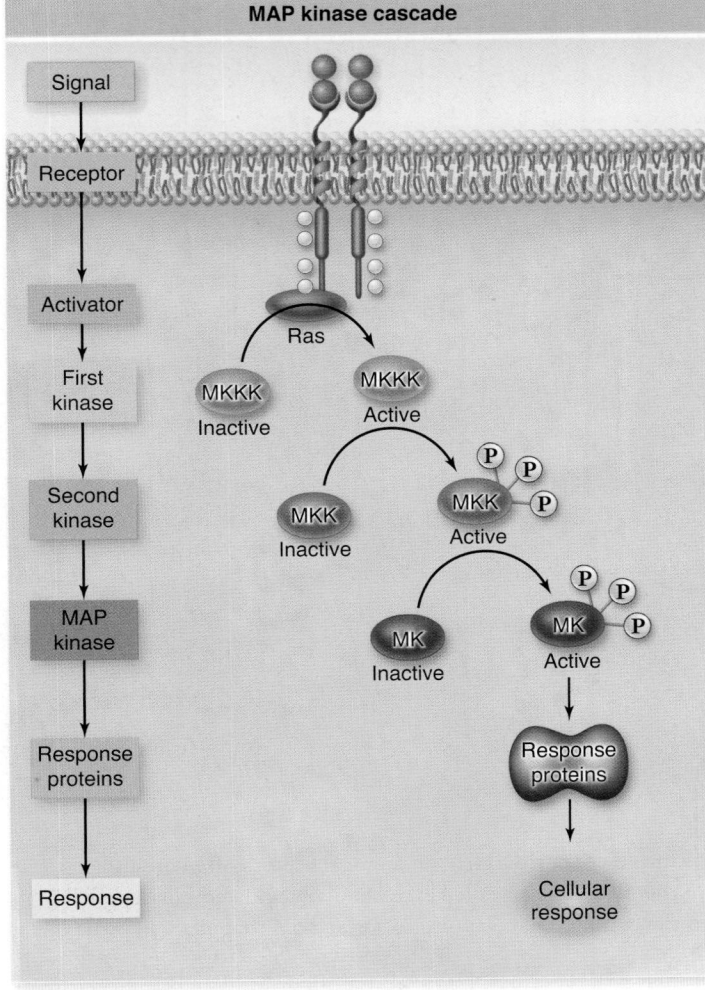

MAP kinase cascade

Signal

Receptor

Activator

First kinase

Second kinase

MAP kinase

Response proteins

Response

Ras

MKKK Inactive — MKKK Active

MKK Inactive — MKK Active

MK Inactive — MK Active

Response proteins

Cellular response

a.

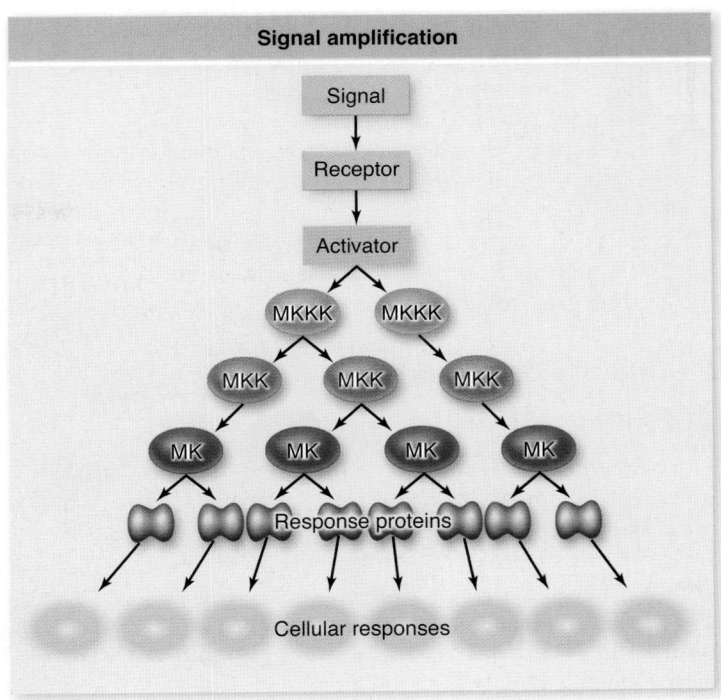

Signal amplification

Signal

Receptor

Activator

MKKK MKKK

MKK MKK MKK

MK MK MK MK

Response proteins

Cellular responses

b.

Figure 9.8 MAP kinase cascade leads to signal amplification. *a.* Phosphorylation cascade is shown as a flowchart on the left. The corresponding cellular events are shown on the right, beginning with the receptor in the plasma membrane. Each kinase is named starting with the last, the MAP kinase (MK), which is phosphorylated by a MAP kinase kinase (MKK), which is in turn phosphorylated by a MAP kinase kinase kinase (MKKK). The cascade is linked to the receptor protein by an activator protein. *b.* At each step the enzymatic action of the kinase on multiple substrates leads to amplification of the signal.

through growth factor receptors is provided in chapter 10 and illustrates how signal transduction initiated by a growth factor can control the process of cell division through a kinase cascade.

Scaffold proteins organize kinase cascades

The proteins in a kinase cascade need to act sequentially to be effective. One way the efficiency of this process can be increased is to organize them in the cytoplasm. Proteins called *scaffold proteins* are thought to organize the components of a kinase cascade into a single protein complex, the ultimate in a signaling module. The scaffold protein binds to each individual kinase such that they are spatially organized for optimal function (figure 9.9).

The advantages of this kind of organization are many. A physically arranged sequence is clearly more efficient than one that depends on diffusion to produce the appropriate order of events. This organization also allows the segregation of signaling modules in different cytoplasmic locations.

The disadvantage of this kind of organization is that it reduces the amplification effect of the kinase cascade. Enzymes held in one place are not free to find new substrate molecules, but must rely on substrates being nearby.

The best studied example of a scaffold protein comes from mating behavior in budding yeast. Yeast cells respond to mating pheromones with changes in cell morphology and gene expression, mediated by a protein kinase cascade. A protein called Ste5 was originally identified as a protein required for mating behavior, but no enzymatic activity could be detected for this protein. It has now been shown that this protein interacts with all of the members of the kinase cascade and acts as a scaffold protein that organizes the cascade and insulates it from other signaling pathways.

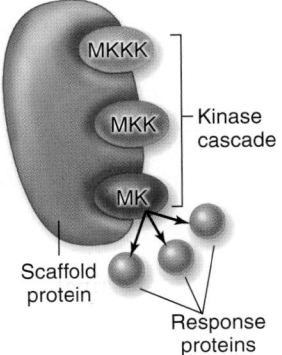

MKKK

MKK

MK

Kinase cascade

Scaffold protein

Response proteins

Figure 9.9 Kinase cascade can be organized by scaffold proteins. The scaffold protein binds to each kinase in the cascade, organizing them so each substrate is next to its enzyme. This organization also sequesters the kinases from other signaling pathways in the cytoplasm.

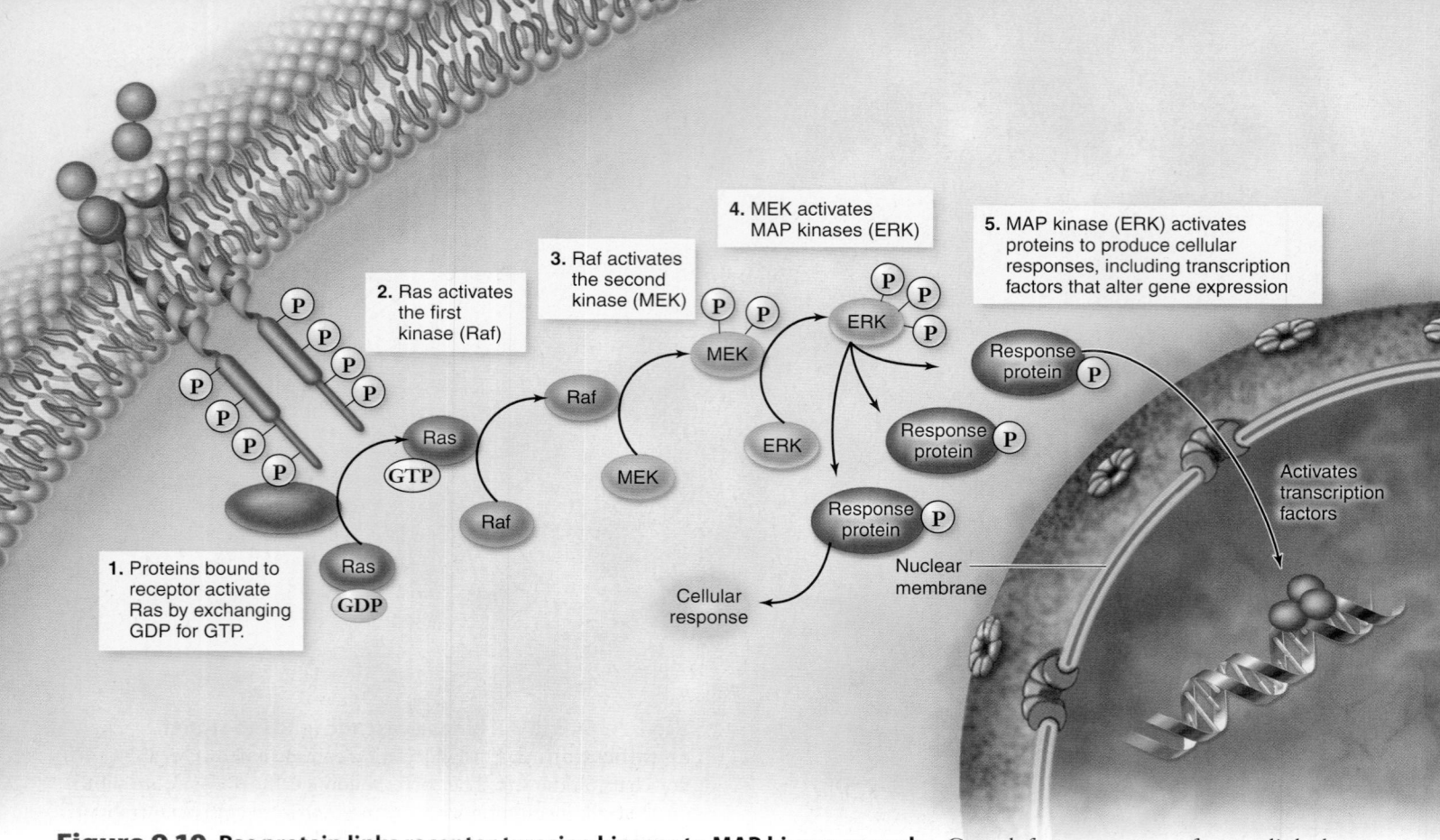

Figure 9.10 Ras protein links receptor tyrosine kinases to MAP kinase cascade. Growth factor receptors often are linked to a MAP kinase cascade by the Ras protein. The figure shows the activation of the MAP kinase called extracellular regulated kinase (ERK). Activated ERK phosphorylates a number of response proteins that can act in the cytoplasm and transcription factors that move into the nucleus to turn on the genes needed for cell cycle progression.

Labels in figure:

1. Proteins bound to receptor activate Ras by exchanging GDP for GTP.

2. Ras activates the first kinase (Raf)

3. Raf activates the second kinase (MEK)

4. MEK activates MAP kinases (ERK)

5. MAP kinase (ERK) activates proteins to produce cellular responses, including transcription factors that alter gene expression

Activates transcription factors

Nuclear membrane

Cellular response

Response protein

Ras proteins link receptors with kinase cascades

The link between the RTK and the MAP kinase cascade is a small GTP-binding protein (G protein) called **Ras.** The Ras protein is mutated in many human tumors, indicative of its central role in linking growth factor receptors to their cellular response.

The Ras protein is active when bound to GTP and inactive when bound to GDP. When an RTK, such as a growth factor receptor, is activated, it binds to adapter proteins that then act on Ras to stimulate the exchange of GDP for GTP, activating Ras. The Ras protein then activates the first kinase in the MAP kinase cascade (figure 9.10).

One key to signaling through this pathway is that Ras can regulate itself. The Ras protein has intrinsic GTPase activity, hydrolyzing GTP to GDP and P_i, leaving the GDP bound to Ras, which is now inactivated. The action of the RTK turns on Ras, which can be thought of as a switch that can turn itself off. This is one reason that stimulation of cell division by growth factors is short-lived.

RTKs are inactivated by internalization

It is important to cells that signaling pathways are only activated transiently. Continued activation could render the cell unable to respond to other signals or to respond inappropriately to a signal that is no longer relevant. Consequently, inactivation is as important for the control of signaling as activation. Receptor tyrosine kinases can be inactivated by two basic mechanisms—dephosphorylation and internalization. Internalization is by endocytosis, in which the receptor is taken up into the cytoplasm in a vesicle where it can be degraded or recycled.

The enzymes in the kinase cascade are all controlled by dephosphorylation by phosphatase enzymes. This leads to termination of the response at both the level of the receptor and the response proteins.

Learning Outcomes Review 9.4

Receptor tyrosine kinases (RTK) are membrane receptors that can phosphorylate tyrosine. When activated, they autophosphorylate, creating binding domains for other proteins. These proteins transmit the signal inside the cell. One form of signaling pathway involves the MAP kinase cascade, a series of kinases that each activate the next in the series. This ends with a MAP kinase that activates transcription factors to alter gene expression.

■ *Ras protein is mutated in many human cancers. What are possible reasons for this?*

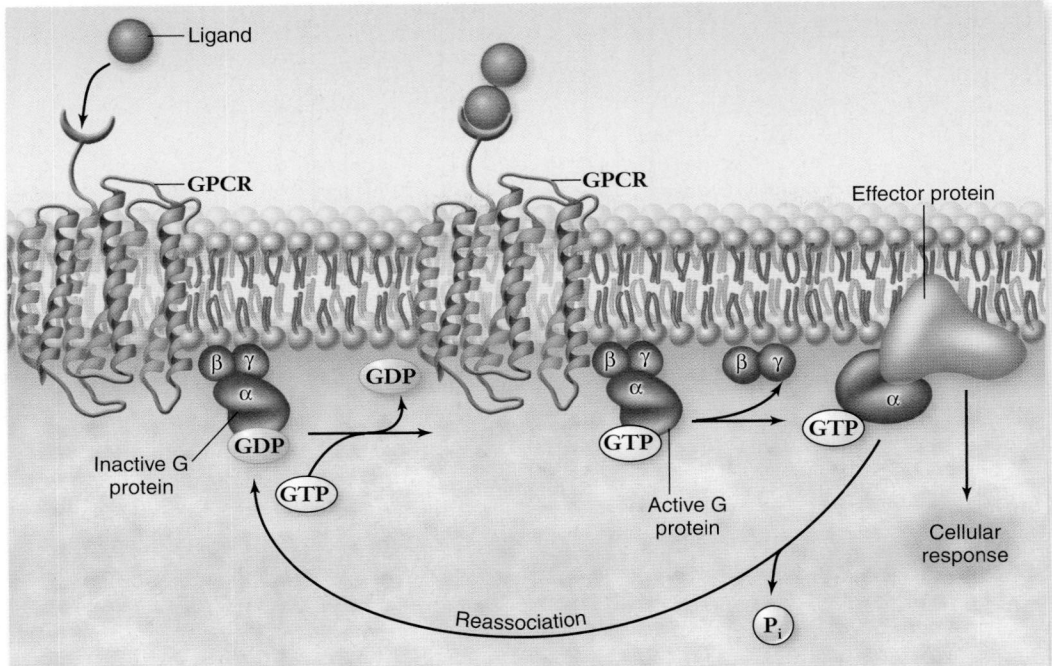

Figure 9.11 The action of G protein-coupled receptors. G protein-coupled receptors act through a heterotrimeric G protein that links the receptor to an effector protein. When ligand binds to the receptor, it activates an associated G protein, exchanging GDP for GTP. The active G protein complex dissociates into G_α and $G_{\beta\gamma}$. The G_α subunit (bound to GTP) is shown activating an effector protein. The effector protein may act directly on cellular proteins or produce a second messenger to cause a cellular response. G_α can hydrolyze GTP inactivating the system, then reassociate with $G_{\beta\gamma}$.

9.5 Signal Transduction Through G Protein-Coupled Receptors

Learning Outcomes

1. **Contrast signaling through GPCRs and RTKs.**
2. **Relate the function of second messengers to signal transduction pathways.**

The single largest category of receptor type in animal cells is **G protein-coupled receptors (GPCRs),** so named because the receptors act by coupling with a G protein. G proteins are proteins that bind guanosine nucleotides, such as Ras discussed previously.

The latest count of genes encoding GPCRs in the human genome is 799 with about half of these encoding odorant receptors involved in the sense of taste and smell. In the mouse, over 1000 different odorant receptors are involved in the sense of smell. The family of GPCRs has been subdivided into 5 groups: Rhodopsin, Secretin, Adhesion, Glutamate, and Frizzled/Taste 2 based on structure and function. The names refer to the first discovered member of each group; for example, Rhodopsin is the GPCR involved in light sensing in mammals. In this section, we will concentrate on the basic mechanism of activation and some of the possible signal transduction pathways.

G proteins link receptors with effector proteins

The function of the G protein in signaling by GPCRs is to provide a link between a receptor that receives signals and effector proteins that produce cellular responses. The G protein functions as a switch that is turned on by the receptor. In its "on" state, the G protein activates effector proteins to cause a cellular response.

All G proteins are active when bound to GTP and inactive when bound to GDP. The main difference between the G proteins in GPCRs and the Ras protein described earlier is that these G proteins are composed of three subunits, called α, β, and γ. As a result, they are often called *heterotrimeric G proteins*. When a ligand binds to a GPCR and activates its associated G protein, the G protein exchanges GDP for GTP and dissociates into two parts consisting of the G_α subunit bound to GTP, and the G_β and G_γ subunits together ($G_{\beta\gamma}$). The signal can then be propagated by either the G_α or the $G_{\beta\gamma}$ components, thereby acting to turn on effector proteins. The hydrolysis of bound GTP to GDP by G_α causes reassociation of the heterotrimer and restores the "off" state of the system (figure 9.11).

The effector proteins are usually enzymes. An effector protein might be a protein kinase that phosphorylates proteins to directly propagate the signal, or it may produce a second messenger to initiate a signal transduction pathway.

Effector proteins produce multiple second messengers

Often, the effector proteins activated by G proteins produce a second messenger. Two of the most common effectors are *adenylyl cyclase* and *phospholipase C*, which produce cAMP and IP_3 plus DAG, respectively.

Cyclic-AMP

All animal cells studied thus far use cAMP as a second messenger (chapter 46). When a signaling molecule binds to a GPCR that uses the enzyme **adenylyl cyclase** as an effector, a large amount of

ATP

$$\text{ATP} \xrightarrow{\text{Adenylyl cyclase}} \text{cAMP} + \text{PP}_i$$

cAMP + PP$_i$

cAMP

PP$_i$

a.

Figure 9.12 Production of second messengers. Second messengers are signaling molecules produced within the cell. *a.* The nucleotide ATP is converted by the enzyme adenylyl cyclase into cyclic AMP, or cAMP, and pyrophosphate (PP$_i$). *b.* The inositol phospholipid PIP$_2$ is composed of two lipids and a phosphate attached to glycerol. The phosphate is also attached to the sugar inositol. This molecule can be cleaved by the enzyme phospholipase C to produce two different second messengers: DAG, made up of the glycerol with the two lipids, and IP$_3$, inositol triphosphate.

Extracellular space

Plasma membrane

Cytoplasm

DAG

Cleaved by phospholipase C

Phospholipase C

IP$_3$

PIP$_2$

DAG + IP$_3$

b.

cAMP is produced within the cell (figure 9.12*a*). The cAMP then binds to and activates the enzyme protein kinase A (PKA), which adds phosphates to specific proteins in the cell (figure 9.13).

The effect of this phosphorylation on cell function depends on the identity of the cell and the proteins that are phosphorylated. In muscle cells, for example, PKA activates an enzyme necessary to break down glycogen and inhibits another enzyme necessary to synthesize glycogen. This leads to an increase in glucose available to the muscle. By contrast, in the kidney the action of PKA leads to the production of water channels that can increase the permeability of tubule cells to water.

Disruption of cAMP signaling can have a variety of effects. The symptoms of the disease cholera are due to altered cAMP levels in cells in the gut. The bacterium *Vibrio cholerae* produces a toxin that binds to a GPCR in the epithelium of the gut, causing it to be locked into an "on" state. This causes a large increase in intracellular cAMP that, in these cells, causes Cl⁻ ions to be transported out of the cell. Water follows the Cl⁻, leading to diarrhea and dehydration characteristic of the disease.

The molecule cAMP is also an extracellular signal. In the slime mold *Dictyostelium discoideum*, secreted cAMP acts as a signal for aggregation under conditions of starvation.

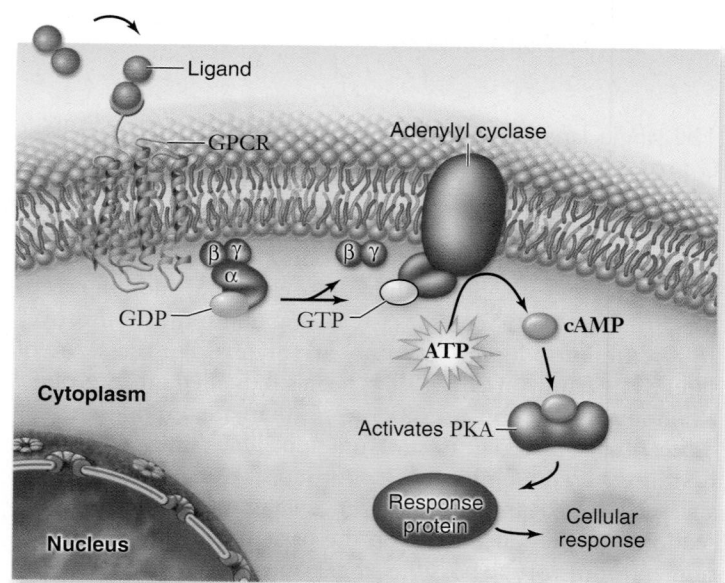

Figure 9.13 cAMP signaling pathway. Extracellular signal binds to a GPCR, activating a G protein. The G protein then activates the effector protein adenylyl cyclase, which catalyzes the conversion of ATP to cAMP. The cAMP then activates protein kinase A (PKA), which phosphorylates target proteins to cause a cellular response.

Question: *What is the receptor for cAMP?*

Hypothesis: *A previously identified G protein-coupled receptor is the cAMP receptor.*

Prediction: *If the function of the cAMP receptor is removed, then cells will not respond to starvation by aggregating.*

Test: *Use G protein-coupled receptor gene to direct synthesis of antisense RNA complementary to the normal mRNA. This will eliminate gene expression by the cellular copy of the G protein-coupled receptor.*

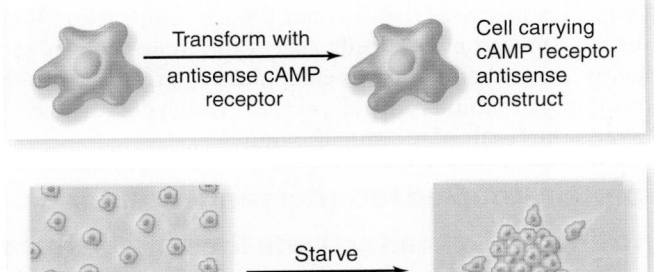

Transform with antisense cAMP receptor → Cell carrying cAMP receptor antisense construct

Wild-type → Starve → Aggregated cells

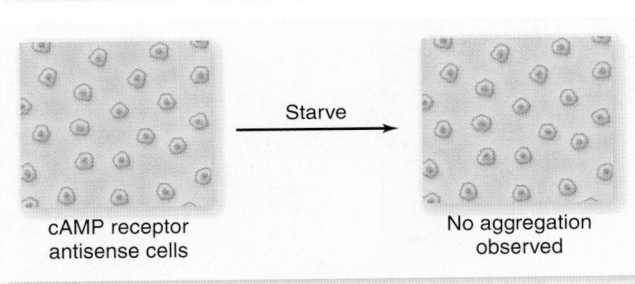

cAMP receptor antisense cells → Starve → No aggregation observed

Result: *Cells transformed with the antisense construct do not aggregate normally.*

Conclusion: *Previously identified G protein-coupled receptor is the cAMP receptor, which controls the aggregation response.*

Further Experiments: *How can this kind of experiment be used to unravel other aspects of this signaling system?*

Figure 9.14 **The receptor for cAMP in *D. discoideum* is a GPCR.**

Experiments have shown that the receptor for this signal is also a GPCR (figure 9.14).

Inositol phosphates

A common second messenger is produced from the molecules called inositol phospholipids. These are inserted into the plasma membrane by their lipid ends and have the *inositol phosphate* portion protruding into the cytoplasm. The most common inositol phospholipid is phosphatidylinositol-4,5-bisphosphate (PIP_2). This molecule is a substrate of the effector protein phospholipase C, which cleaves PIP_2 to yield **diacylglycerol (DAG)** and **inositol-1,4,5-trisphosphate (IP_3)** (see figure 9.12*b*).

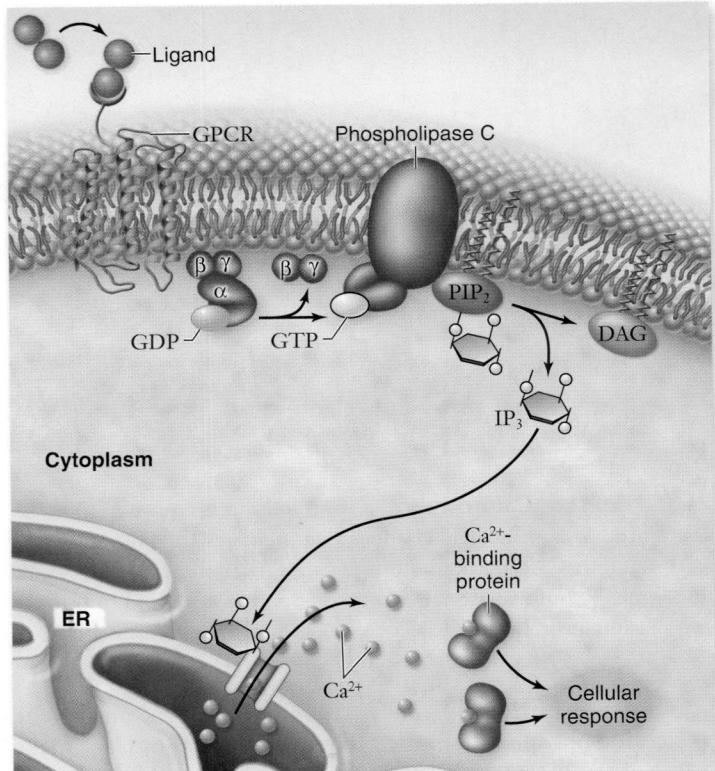

Figure 9.15 **Inositol phospholipid and Ca^{2+} signaling.** Extracellular signal binds to a GPCR activating a G protein. The G protein activates the effector protein phospholipase C, which converts PIP_2 to DAG and IP_3. IP_3 is then bound to a channel-linked receptor on the endoplasmic reticular (ER) membrane, causing the ER to release stored Ca^{2+} into the cytoplasm. The Ca^{2+} then binds to Ca^{2+}-binding proteins such as calmodulin and PKC to cause a cellular response.

Both of these compounds then act as second messengers with a variety of cellular effects. DAG, like cAMP, can activate a protein kinase, in this case protein kinase C (PKC).

Calcium

Calcium ions (Ca^{2+}) serve widely as second messengers. Ca^{2+} levels inside the cytoplasm are normally very low (less than 10^{-7} M), whereas outside the cell and in the endoplasmic reticulum, Ca^{2+} levels are quite high (about 10^{-3} M). The endoplasmic reticulum has receptor proteins that act as ion channels to release Ca^{2+}. One of the most common of these receptors can bind the second messenger IP_3 to release Ca^{2+}, linking signaling through inositol phosphates with signaling by Ca^{2+} (figure 9.15).

The result of the outflow of Ca^{2+} from the endoplasmic reticulum depends on the cell type. For example, in skeletal muscle cells Ca^{2+} stimulates muscle contraction but in endocrine cells it stimulates the secretion of hormones.

Ca^{2+} initiates some cellular responses by binding to *calmodulin*, a 148-amino-acid cytoplasmic protein that contains four binding sites for Ca^{2+} (figure 9.16). When four Ca^{2+} ions are bound to calmodulin, the calmodulin/Ca^{2+} complex is able to bind to other proteins to activate them. These proteins include

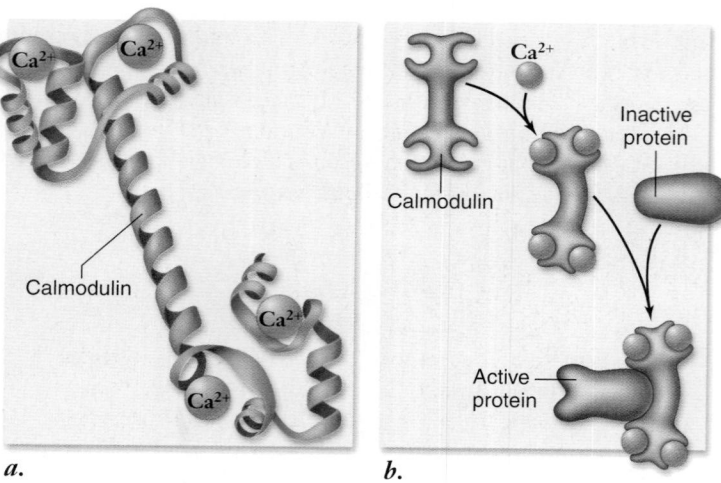

Figure 9.16 Calmodulin. *a.* Calmodulin is a protein containing 148 amino acid residues that mediates Ca²⁺ function. *b.* When four Ca²⁺ are bound to the calmodulin molecule, it undergoes a conformational change that allows it to bind to other cytoplasmic proteins and effect cellular responses.

protein kinases, ion channels, receptor proteins, and cyclic nucleotide phosphodiesterases. These many uses of Ca²⁺ make it one of the most versatile second messengers in cells.

Different receptors can produce the same second messengers

As mentioned previously, the two hormones glucagon and epinephrine can both stimulate liver cells to mobilize glucose. The reason that these different signals have the same effect is that they both act by the same signal transduction pathway to stimulate the breakdown and inhibit the synthesis of glycogen.

The binding of either hormone to its receptor activates a G protein that simulates adenylyl cyclase. The production of cAMP leads to the activation of PKA, which in turn activates another protein kinase called phosphorylase kinase. Activated phosphorylase kinase then activates glycogen phosphorylase, which cleaves off units of glucose-6-phosphate from the glycogen polymer (figure 9.17). The action of multiple kinases again leads to amplification such that a few signaling molecules result in a large number of glucose molecules being released.

At the same time, PKA also phosphorylates the enzyme glycogen synthase, but in this case it inhibits the enzyme, thus preventing the synthesis of glycogen. In addition, PKA phosphorylates other proteins that activate the expression of genes encoding the enzymes needed to synthesize glucose. This convergence of signal transduction pathways from different receptors leads to the same result—glucose is mobilized.

Receptor subtypes can lead to different effects in different cells

We also saw earlier how a single signaling molecule, epinephrine, can have different effects in different cells. One way this happens is through the existence of multiple forms of the same receptor. The receptor for epinephrine actually has nine different subtypes, or isoforms. These are encoded by different genes and are actually different receptor molecules. The sequences of these proteins are very similar, especially in the ligand-binding domain, which allows them to bind epinephrine. They differ mainly in their cytoplasmic domains, which interact with G proteins. This leads to different isoforms activating different G proteins, thereby leading to different signal transduction pathways.

Thus, in the heart, muscle cells have one isoform of the receptor that, when bound to epinephrine, activates a G protein that activates adenylyl cyclase, leading to increased cAMP. This increases the rate and force of contraction. In the intestine, smooth muscle cells have a different isoform of the receptor that, when bound to epinephrine, activates a different G protein that inhibits adenylyl cyclase, which decreases cAMP. This has the result of relaxing the muscle.

G protein-coupled receptors and receptor tyrosine kinases can activate the same pathways

Different receptor types can affect the same signaling module. For example, RTKs were shown to activate the MAP kinase cascade,

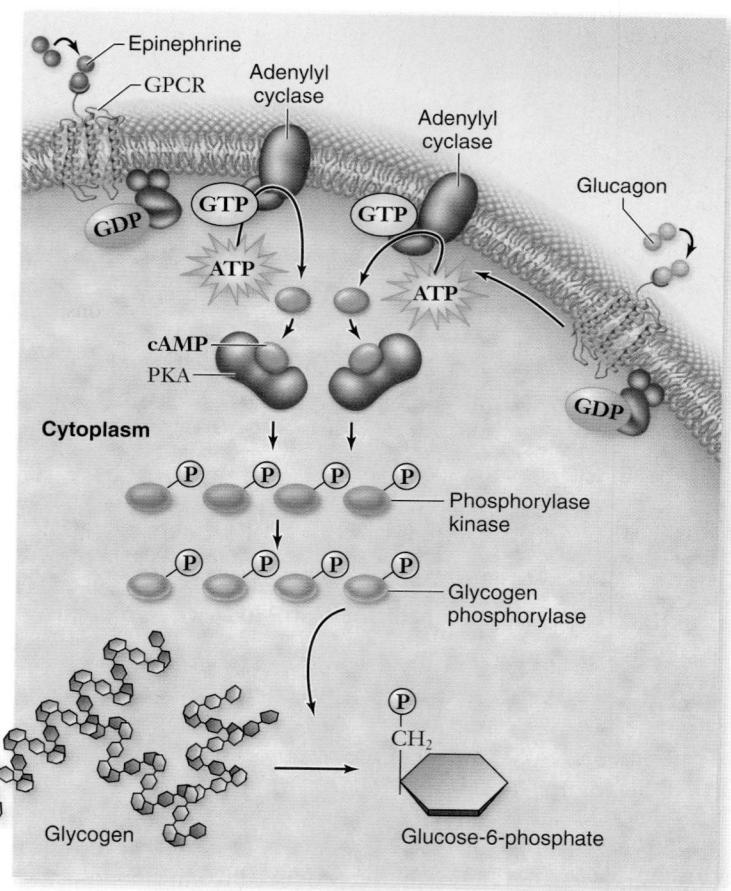

Figure 9.17 Different receptors can activate the same signaling pathway. The hormones glucagon and epinephrine both act through GPCRs. Each of these receptors acts via a G protein that activates adenylyl cyclase, producing cAMP. The activation of PKA begins a kinase cascade that leads to the breakdown of glycogen.

but GPCRs can also activate this same cascade. Similarly, the activation of phospholipase C was mentioned previously in the context of GPCR signaling, but it can also be activated by RTKs.

This cross-reactivity may appear to introduce complications into cell function, but in fact it provides the cell with an incredible amount of flexibility. Cells have a large, but limited number of intracellular signaling modules, which can be turned on and off by different kinds of membrane receptors. This leads to signaling networks that interconnect possible cellular effectors with multiple incoming signals.

The Internet represents an example of a network in which many different kinds of computers are connected globally. This network can be broken down into subnetworks that are connected to the overall network. Because of the nature of the connections, when you send an e-mail message across the Internet, it can reach its destination through many different pathways. Likewise, the cell has interconnected networks of signaling pathways in which many different signals, receptors, and response proteins are interconnected. Specific pathways like the MAP kinase cascade, or signaling through second messengers like cAMP and Ca^{2+}, represent subnetworks within the global signaling network. A specific signal can activate different pathways in different cells, or different signals can activate the same pathway. We do not yet understand the cell at this level, but the field of systems biology is moving toward such global understanding of cell function.

Learning Outcomes Review 9.5

Signaling through GPCRs uses a three-part system—a receptor, a G protein, and an effector protein. G proteins are active when bound to GTP and inactive when bound to GDP. A ligand binding to the receptor activates the G protein, which then activates the effector protein. Effector proteins include adenylyl cyclase, which produces the second messenger cAMP. Another effector protein, phospholipase C, cleaves the inositol phosphates and results in the release of Ca^{2+} from the ER.

■ **There are far more GPCRs than any other receptor type. What is a possible explanation for this?**

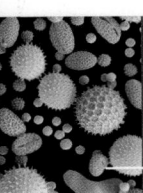

Chapter Review

9.1 Overview of Cell Communication (figure 9.1)

Cell communication requires signal molecules, called ligands, binding to specific receptor proteins producing a cellular response.

Signaling is defined by the distance from source to receptor (figure 9.2).

Direct contact—molecules on the plasma membrane of one cell contact the receptor molecules on an adjacent cell.

Paracrine signaling—short-lived signal molecules are released into the extracellular fluid and influence neighboring cells.

Endocrine signaling—long-lived hormones enter the circulatory system and are carried to target cells some distance away.

Synaptic signaling—short-lived neurotransmitters are released by neurons into the gap, called a synapse, between nerves and target cells.

Signal transduction pathways lead to cellular responses.

Intracellular events initiated by a signaling event are called signal transduction.

Phosphorylation is key in control of protein function.

Proteins can be controlled by phosphate added by kinase and removed by phosphatase enzymes.

9.2 Receptor Types (figure 9.4)

Receptors are defined by location.

Receptors are broadly defined as intracellular or cell-surface receptors (membrane receptors).

Membrane receptors are transmembrane proteins that transfer information across the membrane, but not the signal molecule.

Membrane receptors include three subclasses.

Channel-linked receptors are chemically gated ion channels that allow specific ions to pass through a central pore.

Enzymatic receptors are enzymes activated by binding a ligand; these enzymes are usually protein kinases.

G protein-coupled receptors interact with G proteins that control the function of effector proteins: enzymes or ion channels.

Membrane receptors can generate second messengers.

Some enzymatic and most G protein-coupled receptors produce second messengers, to relay messages in the cytoplasm.

9.3 Intracellular Receptors (figure 9.5)

Many cell signals are lipid-soluble and readily pass through the plasma membrane and bind to receptors in the cytoplasm or nucleus.

Steroid hormone receptors affect gene expression.

Steroid hormones bind cytoplasmic receptors then are transported to the nucleus. Thus, they are called nuclear receptors. These can directly affect gene expression, usually activating transcription of the genes they control.

Nuclear receptors have three functional domains: hormone-binding, DNA-binding, and transcription-activating domains.

Ligand binding changes receptor shape, releasing an inhibitor occupying the DNA-binding site.

A cell's response to a lipid-soluble signal depends on the hormone–receptor complex and the other protein coactivators present.

Other intracellular receptors act as enzymes.

9.4 Signal Transduction Through Receptor Kinases

Receptor kinases in plants and animals recognize hydrophilic ligands and influence the cell cycle, cell migration, cell metabolism, and cell proliferation.

Because they are involved in growth control, alterations of receptor kinases and their signaling pathways can lead to cancer.

RTKs are activated by autophosphorylation.

The activated receptor can also phosphorylate other intracellular proteins.

Phosphotyrosine domains mediate protein–protein interactions.

Adapter proteins can bind to phosphotryrosine and act as links between the receptors and downstream signaling events.

Protein kinase cascades can amplify a signal.

Scaffold proteins organize kinase cascades.

Scaffold proteins and protein kinases form a single complex where the enzymes act sequentially and are optimally functional.

Internalized receptors are degraded or recycled.

Ras proteins link receptors with kinase cascades.

RTKs are inactivated by internalization.

9.5 Signal Transduction Through G Protein-Coupled Receptors (figure 9.11)

G protein-coupled receptors function through activation of G proteins.

G proteins link receptors with effector proteins.

G proteins are active bound to GTP and inactive bound to GDP. Receptors promote exchange of GDP for GTP.

The activated G protein dissociates into two parts, G_α and $G_{\beta\gamma}$, each of which can act on effector proteins.

G_α also hydrolyzes GTP to GDP to inactivate the G protein.

Effector proteins produce multiple second messengers.

Two common effector proteins are adenylyl cyclase and phospholipase C, which produce second messengers known as cAMP, and DAG and IP_3, respectively.

Ca^{2+} is also a second messenger. Ca^{2+} release is triggered by IP_3 binding to channel-linked receptors in the ER.

Ca^{2+} can bind to a cytoplasmic protein calmodulin, which in turn activates other proteins, producing a variety of responses.

Different receptors can produce the same second messengers.

Different GPCR receptors can converge to activate the same effector enzyme and thus produce the same second messenger.

Receptor subtypes can lead to different effects in different cells.

Epinephrine causes increased contraction in heart muscle but relaxation in smooth muscle.

G protein-coupled receptors and receptor tyrosine kinases can activate the same pathways.

Both RTKs and GPCRs can activate MAP kinase cascades.

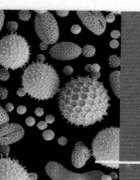

Review Questions

UNDERSTAND

1. Paracrine signaling is characterized by ligands that are
   a. produced by the cell itself.
   b. secreted by neighboring cells.
   c. present on the plasma membrane of neighboring cells.
   d. secreted by distant cells.

2. Signal transduction pathways
   a. are necessary for signals to cross the membrane.
   b. include the intracellular events stimulated by an extracellular signal.
   c. include the extracellular events stimulated by an intracellular signal.
   d. are only found in cases where the signal can cross the membrane.

3. The function of a _____ is to add phosphates to proteins, whereas a _____ functions to remove the phosphates.
   a. tyrosine; serine
   b. protein phosphatase; protein dephosphatase
   c. protein kinase; protein phosphatase
   d. receptor; ligand

4. Which of the following receptor types is not a membrane receptor?
   a. Channel-linked receptor
   b. Enzymatic receptor
   c. G protein-coupled receptor
   d. Steroid hormone receptors

5. How does the function of an intracellular receptor differ from that of a membrane receptor?
   a. The intracellular receptor binds a ligand.
   b. The intracellular receptor binds DNA.
   c. The intracellular receptor activates a kinase.
   d. The intracellular receptor functions as a second messenger.

6. Signaling through receptor tyrosine kinases often
   a. leads to the production of the second messenger cAMP.
   b. leads to the production of the second messenger IP_3.
   c. stimulates gene expression directly.
   d. leads to the activation of a cascade of kinase enzymes.

7. What is the function of Ras during tyrosine kinase cell signaling?

   a. It activates the opening of channel-linked receptors.
   b. It is an enzyme that synthesizes second messengers.
   c. It links the receptor protein to the MAP kinase pathway.
   d. It phosphorylates other enzymes as part of a pathway.

8. Which of the following best describes the immediate effect of ligand binding to a G protein-coupled receptor?

   a. The G protein trimer releases a GDP and binds a GTP.
   b. The G protein trimer dissociates from the receptor.
   c. The G protein trimer interacts with an effector protein.
   d. The α subunit of the G protein becomes phosphorylated.

APPLY

1. The action of steroid hormone receptors

   a. stimulates a cascade of phosphorylation reactions.
   b. leads to a direct affect on gene expression.
   c. stimulates a second messenger that activates. gene expression.
   d. activates a G protein that stimulates gene expression.

2. The ion Ca^{++} can act as a second messenger because it is

   a. produced by the enzyme calcium synthase.
   b. normally at a high level in the cytoplasm.
   c. normally at a low level in the cytoplasm.
   d. stored in the cytoplasm.

3. The response to signaling through G protein-coupled receptors can vary in different cells because

   a. all receptors act through the same G protein.
   b. different isoforms of a receptor bind the same ligand but activate different effectors.
   c. the amount of receptor in the membrane differs in different cell types.
   d. different receptors can activate the same effector.

4. Signaling through G proteins is self-limiting because G proteins

   a. are degraded, shutting the pathway off.
   b. only bind to GDP and not GTP.
   c. are internalized, shutting the pathway off.
   d. hydrolyze GTP to GDP inactivating themselves.

5. The same signal can have different effects in different cells because there

   a. are different receptor subtypes that initiate different signal transduction pathways.
   b. may be different coactivators in different cells.

   c. may be different target proteins in different cells' signal transduction pathways.
   d. all of the above.

6. The receptors for steroid hormones and peptide hormones are fundamentally different because

   a. of the great difference in size of the molecule.
   b. peptides are one of the four major polymers and steroids are simple ringed structures.
   c. peptides are hydrophilic and steroids are hydrophobic.
   d. peptides are hydrophobic and steroids are hydrophilic.

SYNTHESIZE

1. Describe the common features found in all examples of cellular signaling discussed in this chapter. Provide examples to illustrate your answer.

2. The sheet of cells that form the gut epithelium folds into peaks called villi and valleys called crypts. The cells within the crypt region secrete a protein, Netrin-1, that becomes concentrated within the crypts. Netrin-1 is the ligand for a receptor protein that is found on the surface of all gut epithelial cells. Netrin-1 binding triggers a signal pathway that promotes cell growth. Gut epithelial cells undergo apoptosis (cell death) in the absence of Netrin-1 ligand binding.

   a. How would you characterize the type of signaling (autocrine, paracrine, endocrine) found in this system?
   b. Predict where the greatest amount of cell growth and cell death would occur in the epithelium.
   c. The loss of the Netrin-1 receptor is associated with some types of colon cancer. Suggest an explanation for the link between this signaling pathway and tumor formation.

ONLINE RESOURCE

www.ravenbiology.com

Understand, Apply, and Synthesize—enhance your study with animations that bring concepts to life and practice tests to assess your understanding. Your instructor may also recommend the interactive eBook, individualized learning tools, and more.

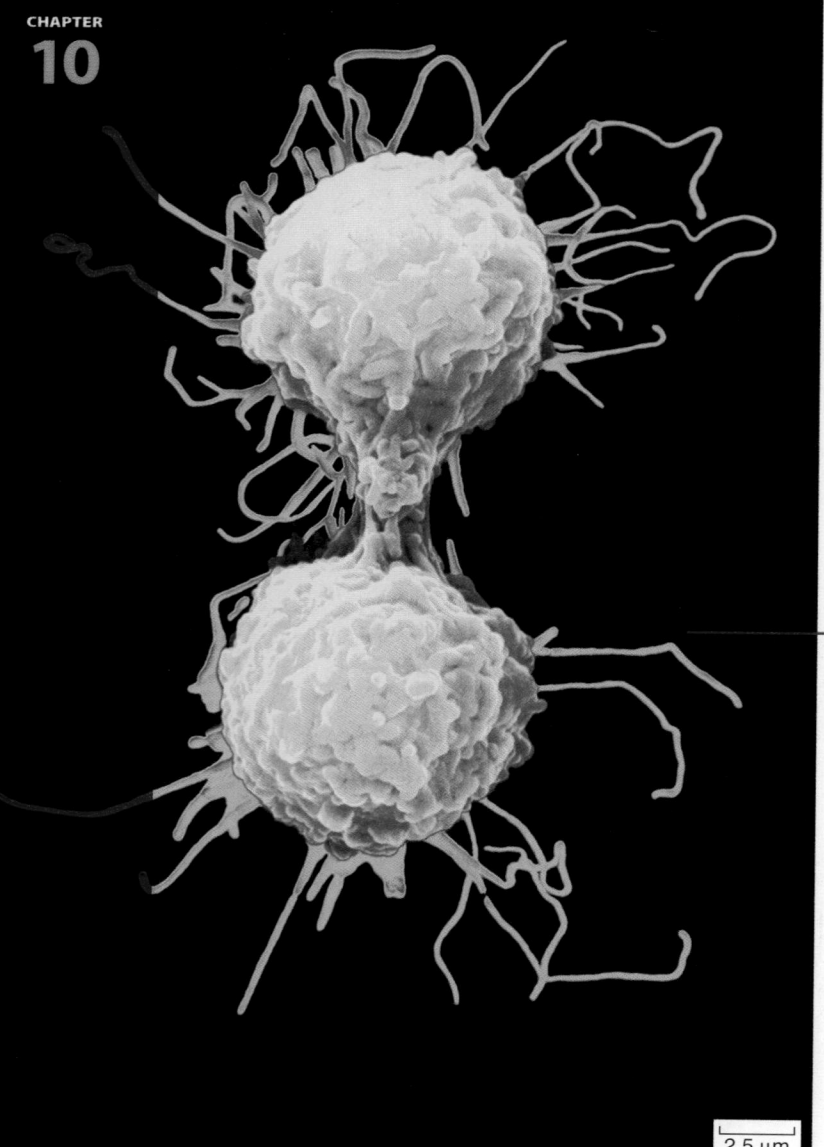

2.5 µm

Chapter **10**

How Cells Divide

Chapter Outline

10.1 Bacterial Cell Division

10.2 Eukaryotic Chromosomes

10.3 Overview of the Eukaryotic Cell Cycle

10.4 Interphase: Preparation for Mitosis

10.5 M Phase: Chromosome Segregation and the Division of Cytoplasmic Contents

10.6 Control of the Cell Cycle

Introduction

All species of organisms—bacteria, alligators, the weeds in a lawn—grow and reproduce. From the smallest creature to the largest, all species produce offspring like themselves and pass on the hereditary information that makes them what they are. In this chapter, we examine how cells, like the white blood cell shown in the figure, divide and reproduce. Cell division is necessary for the growth of organisms, for wound healing, and to replace cells that are lost regularly, such as those in your skin and in the lining of your gut. The mechanism of cell reproduction and its biological consequences have changed significantly during the evolution of life on Earth. The process is complex in eukaryotes, involving both the replication of chromosomes and their separation into daughter cells. Much of what we are learning about the causes of cancer relates to how cells control this process, and in particular their tendency to divide, a mechanism that in broad outline remains the same in all eukaryotes.

10.1 Bacterial Cell Division

Learning Outcome

1. **Describe the process of binary fission.**

Bacteria divide as a way of reproducing themselves. Although bacteria exchange DNA, they do not have a sexual cycle like eukaryotes. Thus all growth in a bacterial population is due to division to produce new cells. The reproduction of bacteria is clonal—that is, each cell produced by cell division is an identical copy of the original cell.

Binary fission is a simple form of cell division

Cell division in both bacterial and eukaryotic cells produces two new cells with the same genetic information as the original. Despite the differences in these cell types, the essentials of the process are the same: duplication and segregation of genetic information into daughter cells, and division of cellular contents. We begin by looking at the simpler process, **binary fission**, which occurs in bacteria.

Most bacteria have a genome made up of a single, circular DNA molecule. In spite of its apparent simplicity, the DNA molecule of the bacterium *Escherichia coli* is actually on the order of 500 times longer than the cell itself! Thus, this "simple" structure is actually packaged very tightly to fit into the cell. Although not found in a nucleus, the DNA is located in a region called the *nucleoid* that is distinct from the cytoplasm around it.

The compaction and organization of the nucleoid involves a class of proteins called structural maintenance of chromosome, or SMC, proteins. These are ancient proteins that have evolved to perform a number of roles related to DNA compression and cohesion. In eukaryotes the cohesin and condensin proteins discussed later in the chapter are SMC proteins.

During binary fission, the chromosome is replicated, and the two products are partitioned to each end of the cell prior to the actual division of the cell. One key feature of bacterial cell division is that replication and partitioning of the chromosome occur as a concerted process. In contrast, DNA replication in eukaryotic cells occurs early in division, and chromosome separation occurs much later.

Proteins control chromosome separation and septum formation

Binary fission begins with the replication of the bacterial DNA at a specific site—the origin of replication (see chapter 14)—and proceeds both directions around the circular DNA to a specific site of termination (figure 10.1). The cell grows by elongation, and division occurs roughly at midcell. For many years, it was thought that newly replicated *E. coli* DNA molecules were passively segregated by attachment to and growth of the membrane as the cell elongated. Experiments that follow the movement of the origin of replication show that it is at

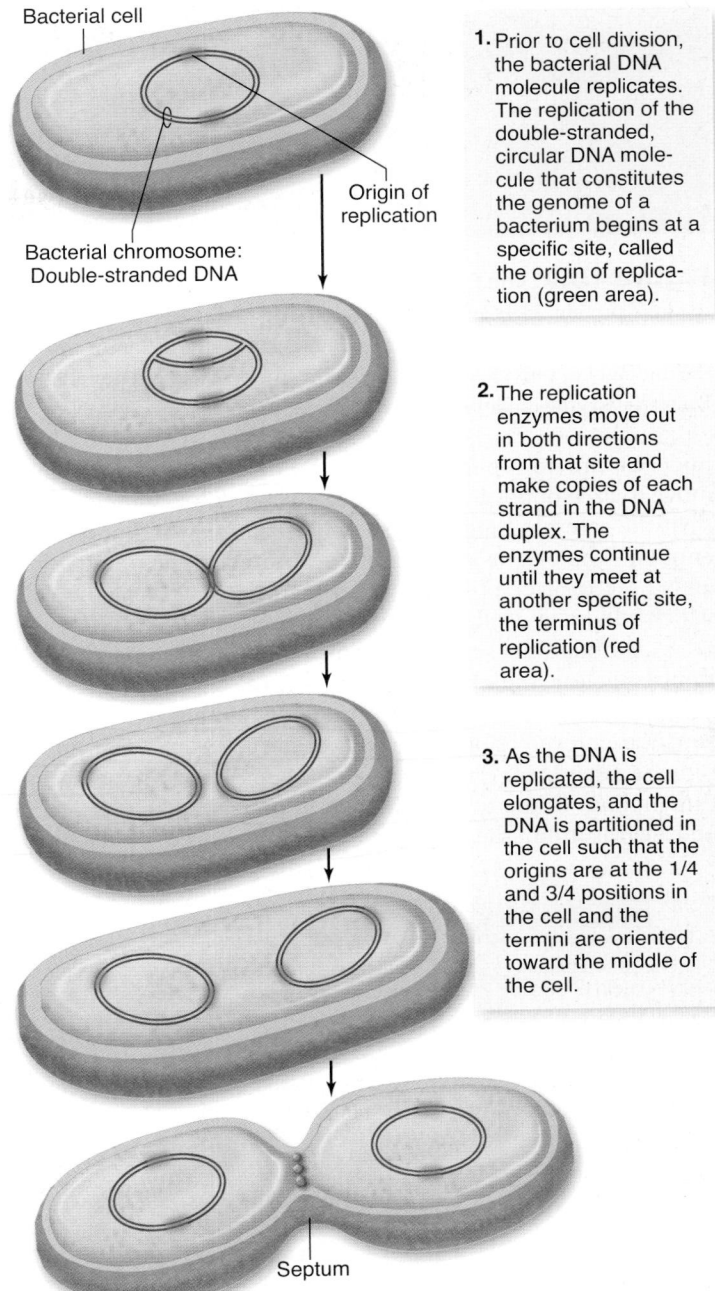

1. Prior to cell division, the bacterial DNA molecule replicates. The replication of the double-stranded, circular DNA molecule that constitutes the genome of a bacterium begins at a specific site, called the origin of replication (green area).

2. The replication enzymes move out in both directions from that site and make copies of each strand in the DNA duplex. The enzymes continue until they meet at another specific site, the terminus of replication (red area).

3. As the DNA is replicated, the cell elongates, and the DNA is partitioned in the cell such that the origins are at the 1/4 and 3/4 positions in the cell and the termini are oriented toward the middle of the cell.

4. Septation then begins, in which new membrane and cell wall material begin to grow and form a septum at approximately the midpoint of the cell. A protein molecule called FtsZ (orange dots) facilitates this process.

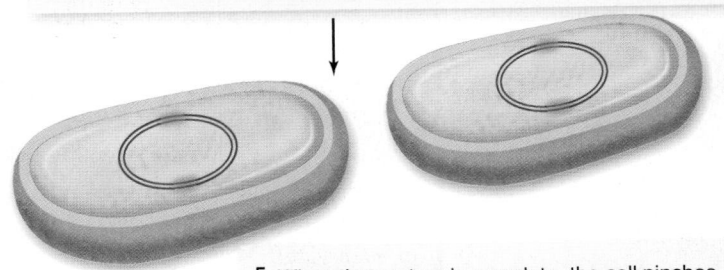

5. When the septum is complete, the cell pinches in two, and two daughter cells are formed, each containing a bacterial DNA molecule.

Figure 10.1 Binary fission.

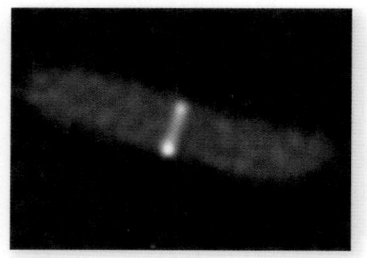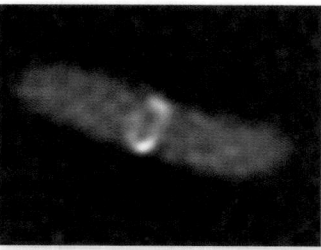

Figure 10.2 The FtsZ protein. In these dividing *E. coli* bacteria, the FtsZ protein is labeled with fluorescent dye to show its location during binary fission. The protein assembles into a ring at approximately the midpoint of the cell, where it facilitates septation and cell division. Bacteria carrying mutations in the *FtsZ* gene are unable to divide.

midcell prior to replication, then the newly replicated origins move toward opposite ends of the cell. This movement is faster than the rate of elongation, showing that growth alone is not enough. The origins appear to be captured at the one quarter and three quarter positions relative to the length of the cell, which will be midcell of the two daughter cells.

Although the actual mechanism of chromosome segregation is unclear, the order of events is not. During replication, first the origin, then the rest of the newly replicated chromosomes are moved to opposite ends of the cell as two new nucleoids are assembled. The final event of replication is decatenation (untangling) of the final replication products. After replication and segregation, the midcell region is cleared of daughter nucleoids, and division occurs. The force behind chromosome segregation has been attributed to DNA replication itself, transcription, and the polymerization of actin-like molecules. At this point, no single model appears to explain the process, and it may involve more than one.

The cell's other components are partitioned by the growth of new membrane and production of the **septum** (see figure 10.1). This process, termed **septation,** usually occurs at the midpoint of the cell. It begins with the formation of a ring composed of many copies of the protein FtsZ (figure 10.2). Next, accumulation of a number of other proteins occurs, including ones embedded in the membrane. This structure contracts inward radially until the cell pinches off into two new cells. The midcell location of the FtsZ ring is caused by an oscillation between the two poles of an inhibitor of FtsZ formation.

The FtsZ protein is found in most prokaryotes, including archaea. It can form filaments and rings, and recent three-dimensional crystals show a high degree of similarity to eukaryotic tubulin. However, its role in bacterial division is quite different from the role of tubulin in mitosis in eukaryotes.

The evolution of eukaryotic cells included much more complex genomes composed of multiple linear chromosomes housed in a membrane-bounded nucleus. These complex genomes may be possible due to the evolution of mechanisms that delay chromosome separation after replication. Although it is unclear how this ability to keep chromosomes together evolved, it does seem more closely related to binary fission than we once thought (figure 10.3).

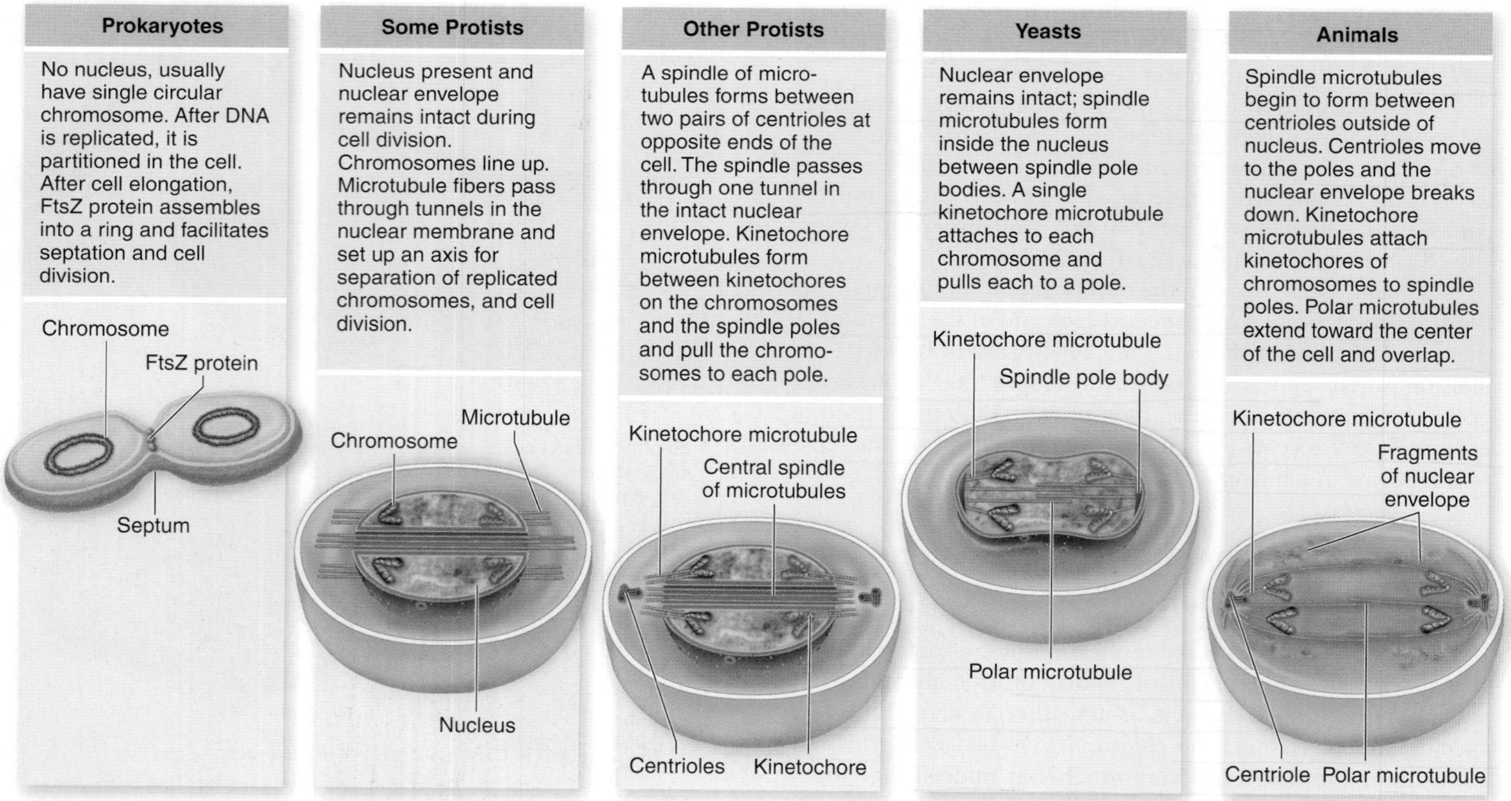

Prokaryotes	Some Protists	Other Protists	Yeasts	Animals
No nucleus, usually have single circular chromosome. After DNA is replicated, it is partitioned in the cell. After cell elongation, FtsZ protein assembles into a ring and facilitates septation and cell division.	Nucleus present and nuclear envelope remains intact during cell division. Chromosomes line up. Microtubule fibers pass through tunnels in the nuclear membrane and set up an axis for separation of replicated chromosomes, and cell division.	A spindle of microtubules forms between two pairs of centrioles at opposite ends of the cell. The spindle passes through one tunnel in the intact nuclear envelope. Kinetochore microtubules form between kinetochores on the chromosomes and the spindle poles and pull the chromosomes to each pole.	Nuclear envelope remains intact; spindle microtubules form inside the nucleus between spindle pole bodies. A single kinetochore microtubule attaches to each chromosome and pulls each to a pole.	Spindle microtubules begin to form between centrioles outside of nucleus. Centrioles move to the poles and the nuclear envelope breaks down. Kinetochore microtubules attach kinetochores of chromosomes to spindle poles. Polar microtubules extend toward the center of the cell and overlap.

Figure 10.3 A comparison of protein assemblies during cell division among different organisms. The prokaryotic protein FtsZ has a structure that is similar to that of the eukaryotic protein tubulin. Tubulin is the protein component of microtubules, which are fibers used to separate chromosomes in eukaryotic cell division.

10.2 Eukaryotic Chromosomes

no relationship b/w # of ↑ and complexity

Learning Outcomes

1. Describe the structure of eukaryotic chromosomes.
2. Distinguish between homologues and sister chromatids.

all identical except for 1 pair; sexual pair.

TABLE 10.1	Chromosome Number in Selected Eukaryotes
Group	**Total Number of Chromosomes**
F U N G I	
Neurospora (haploid)	7
Saccharomyces (a yeast)	16
I N S E C T S	
Mosquito	6
Drosophila	8
Honeybee	diploid females 32, haploid males 16
Silkworm	56
P L A N T S	
Haplopappus gracilis	2
Garden pea	14
Corn	20
Bread wheat	42
Sugarcane	80
Horsetail	216
Adder's tongue fern	1262
V E R T E B R A T E S	
Opossum	22
Frog	26
Mouse	40
Human	46
Chimpanzee	48
Horse	64
Chicken	78
Dog	78

Chromosomes were first observed by the German embryologist Walther Flemming (1843–1905) in 1879, while he was examining the rapidly dividing cells of salamander larvae. When Flemming looked at the cells through what would now be a rather primitive light microscope, he saw minute threads within their nuclei that appeared to be dividing lengthwise. Flemming called their division **mitosis**, based on the Greek word *mitos*, meaning "thread."

Chromosome number varies among species

Since their initial discovery, chromosomes have been found in the cells of all eukaryotes examined. Their number may vary enormously from one species to another. A few kinds of organisms have only a single pair of chromosomes, whereas some ferns have more than 500 pairs (table 10.1). Most eukaryotes have between 10 and 50 chromosomes in their body cells.

Human cells each have 46 chromosomes, consisting of 23 nearly identical pairs (figure 10.4). Each of these 46 chromosomes contains hundreds or thousands of genes that play important roles in determining how a person's body develops and functions. Human embryos missing even one chromosome, a condition called *monosomy*, do not survive in most cases. Having an extra copy of any one chromosome, a condition called *trisomy*, is usually fatal except where the smallest chromosomes are involved. (You'll learn more about human chromosome abnormalities in chapter 13.)

Eukaryotic chromosomes exhibit complex structure

Researchers have learned a great deal about chromosome structure and composition in the more than 125 years since their

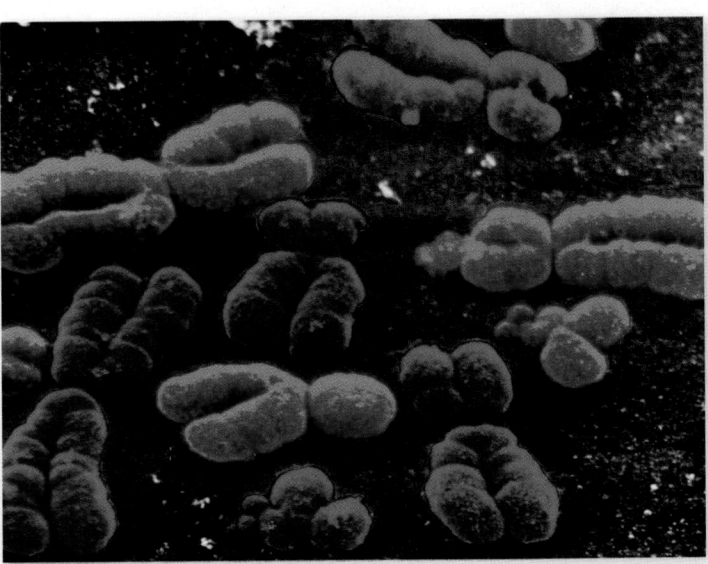

10.5 μm

Figure 10.4 Human chromosomes. This scanning electron micrograph shows human chromosomes as they appear immediately before nuclear division. Each DNA molecule has already replicated, forming identical copies held together at a visible constriction called the centromere. False color has been added to the chromosomes.

discovery. But despite intense research, the exact structure of eukaryotic chromosomes during the cell cycle remains unclear. The structures described in this chapter represent the currently accepted model.

Composition of chromatin

Chromosomes are composed of *chromatin*, a complex of DNA and protein; most chromosomes are about 40% DNA and 60% protein. A significant amount of RNA is also associated with chromosomes because chromosomes are the sites of RNA synthesis.

The DNA of a single chromosome is one very long, double-stranded fiber that extends unbroken through the chromosome's entire length. A typical human chromosome contains about 140 million (1.4×10^8) nucleotides in its DNA. If we think of each nucleotide as a "word," then the amount of information an average chromosome contains would fill about 280 printed books of 1000 pages each, with 500 "words" per page.

If we could lay out the strand of DNA from a single chromosome in a straight line, it would be about 5 cm (2 in.) long. Fitting such a strand into a cell nucleus is like cramming a string the length of a football field into a baseball—and that's only 1 of 46 chromosomes! In the cell, however, the DNA is coiled, allowing it to fit into a much smaller space than would otherwise be possible.

The organization of chromatin in the nondividing nucleus is not well understood, but geneticists have recognized for years that some domains of chromatin, called **heterochromatin,** are not expressed, and other domains of chromatin, called **euchromatin,** are expressed. This genetically measurable state is also related to the physical state of chromatin, although researchers are just beginning to see the details.

Chromosome structure

If we gently disrupt a eukaryotic nucleus and examine the DNA with an electron microscope, we find that it resembles a string of beads (figure 10.5). Every 200 nucleotides (nt), the DNA duplex (double strand) is coiled around a core of eight **histone proteins.** Unlike most proteins, which have an overall negative charge, histones are positively charged because of an abundance of the basic amino acids arginine and lysine. Thus, they are strongly attracted to the negatively charged phosphate groups of the DNA, and the histone cores act as "magnetic forms" that promote and guide the coiling of the DNA. The complex of DNA and histone proteins is termed a **nucleosome.**

Further coiling occurs when the string of nucleosomes is wrapped into higher order coils called *solenoids.* The precise path of this higher order folding of chromatin is still a subject of some debate, but it leads to a fiber with a diameter of 30 nm and thus is often called the 30-nm fiber. This 30-nm fiber is the usual state of interphase (nondividing) chromatin.

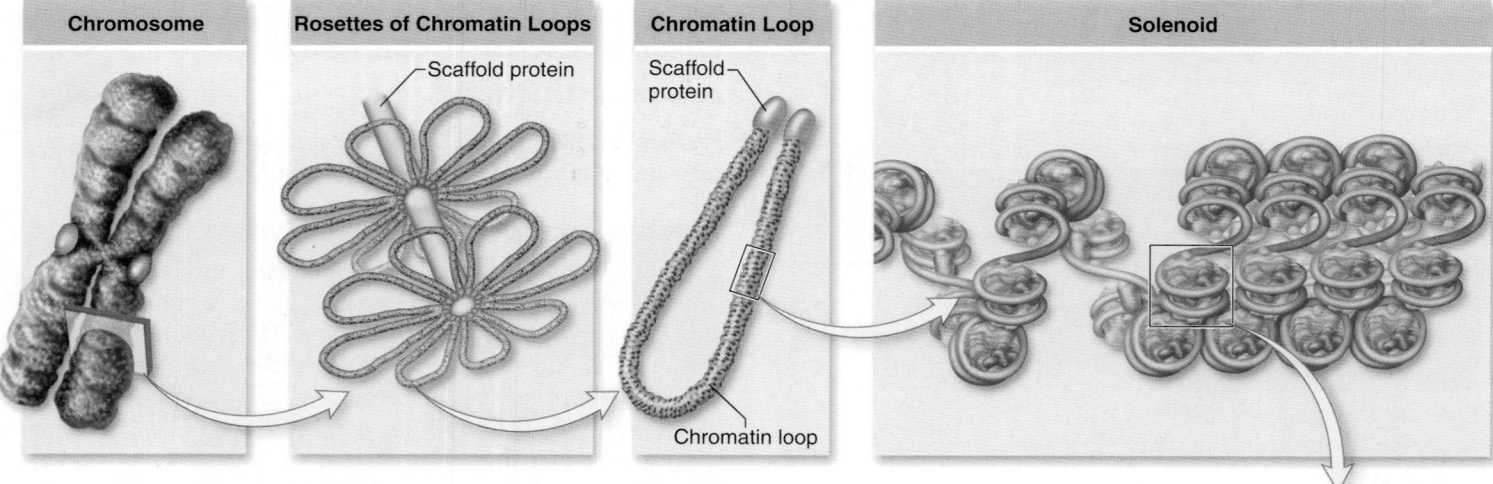

| Chromosome | Rosettes of Chromatin Loops | Chromatin Loop | Solenoid |

Scaffold protein

Scaffold protein

Chromatin loop

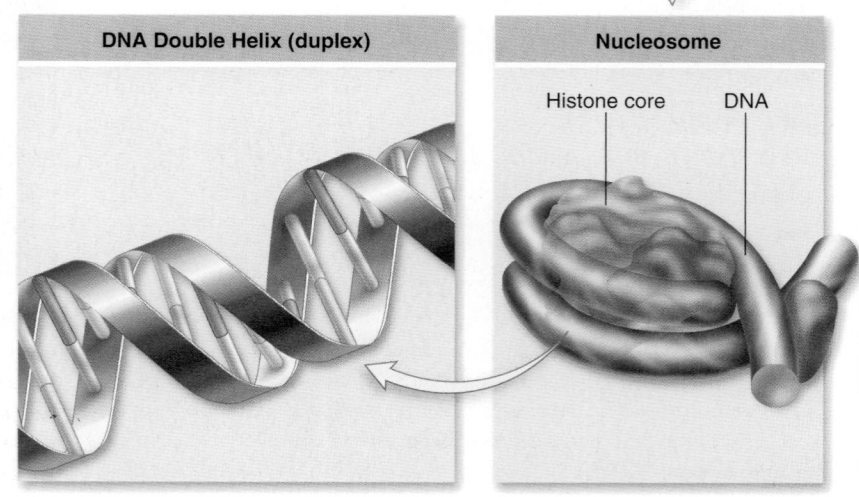

DNA Double Helix (duplex)

Nucleosome

Histone core   DNA

Figure 10.5 Levels of eukaryotic chromosomal organization. Each chromosome consists of a long double-stranded DNA molecule. These strands require further packaging to fit into the cell nucleus. The DNA duplex is tightly bound to and wound around proteins called histones. The DNA-wrapped histones are called nucleosomes. The nucleosomes are further coiled into a solenoid. This solenoid is then organized into looped domains. The final organization of the chromosome is unknown, but it appears to involve further radial looping into rosettes around a preexisting scaffolding of protein. The arrangement illustrated here is one of many possibilities.

During mitosis the chromatin in the solenoid is arranged around a scaffold of protein assembled at this time to achieve maximum compaction of the chromosomes. This process prepares the chromosomes for the events of mitosis described later. The exact nature of this compaction is unknown, but one long-standing model involves radial looping of the solenoid about the protein scaffold, aided by a complex of proteins called **condensin.**

Chromosome karyotypes

Chromosomes vary in size, staining properties, the location of the centromere (a constriction found on all chromosomes, described shortly), the relative length of the two arms on either side of the centromere, and the positions of constricted regions along the arms. The particular array of chromosomes an individual organism possesses is called its **karyotype.** The karyotype in figure 10.6 shows the set of chromosomes from a normal human cell.

When defining the number of different chromosomes in a species, geneticists count the **haploid (*n*)** number of chromosomes. This refers to one complete set of chromosomes necessary to define an organism. For humans and many other species, the total number of chromosomes in a cell is called the **diploid (*2n*)** number, which is twice the haploid number. For humans, the haploid number is 23 and the diploid number is 46. Diploid

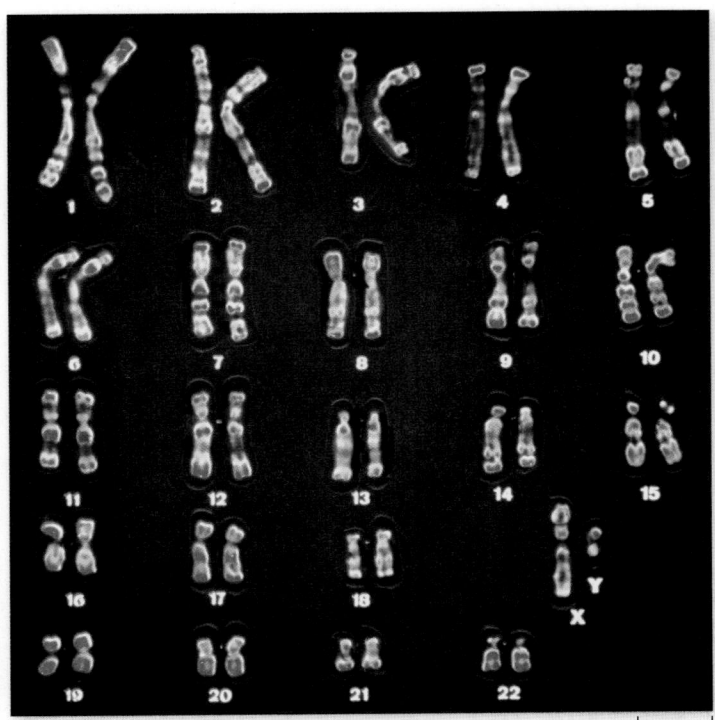

Figure 10.6 A human karyotype. The individual chromosomes that make up the 23 pairs differ widely in size and in centromere position. In this preparation of a male karyotype, the chromosomes have been specifically stained to indicate differences in their composition and to distinguish them clearly from one another. Notice that members of a chromosome pair are very similar but not identical.

9.2 μm

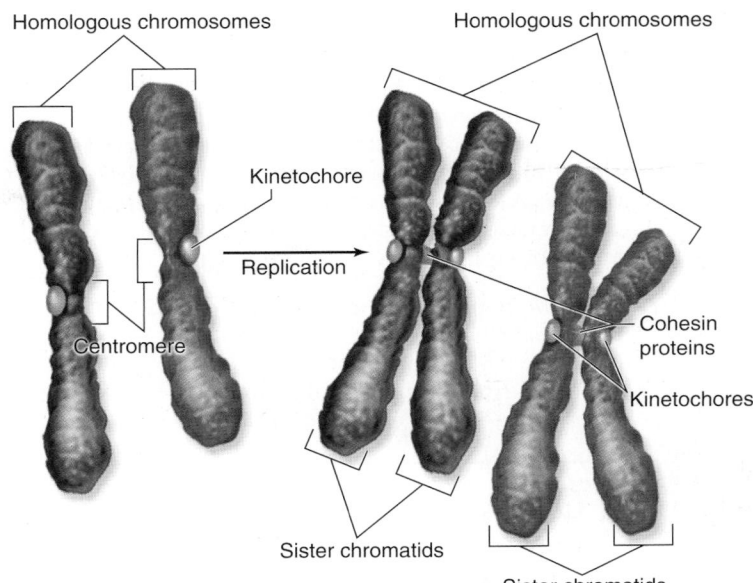

Figure 10.7 The difference between homologous chromosomes and sister chromatids. Homologous chromosomes are the maternal and paternal copies of the same chromosome—say, chromosome number 16. Sister chromatids are the two replicas of a single chromosome held together at their centromeres by cohesin proteins after DNA replication. The kinetochore (described later in the chapter) is composed of proteins found at the centromere that attach to microtubules during mitosis.

chromosomes reflect the equal genetic contribution that each parent makes to offspring. We refer to the maternal and paternal chromosomes as being **homologous,** and each one of the pair is termed a **homologue.**

Chromosome replication

Chromosomes as seen in a karyotype are only present for a brief period during cell division. Prior to replicating, each chromosome is composed of a single DNA molecule that is arranged into the 30-nm fiber described earlier. After replication, each chromosome is composed of two identical DNA molecules held together by a complex of proteins called **cohesins.** As the chromosomes become more condensed and arranged about the protein scaffold, they become visible as two strands that are held together. At this point, we still call this one chromosome, but it is composed of two sister **chromatids** (figure 10.7).

The fact that the products of replication are held together is critical to the division process. One problem that a cell must solve is how to ensure that each new cell receives a complete set of chromosomes. If we were designing a system, we might use some kind of label to identify each chromosome, much like most of us use when we duplicate files on a computer. The cell has no mechanism to label chromosomes; instead, it keeps the products of replication together until the moment of chromosome segregation, ensuring that one copy of each chromosome goes to each daughter cell. This separation of sister chromatids is the key event in the mitotic process described in detail shortly.

10.3 Overview of the Eukaryotic Cell Cycle

Learning Outcome

1. **Describe the eukaryotic cell cycle.**

Compared with prokaryotes, the increased size and more complex organization of eukaryotic genomes required radical changes in the partitioning of replicated genomes into daughter cells. The **cell cycle** requires the duplication of the genome, its accurate segregation, and the division of cellular contents.

The cell cycle is divided into five phases

The cell cycle is divided into phases based on the key events of genome duplication and segregation. The cell cycle is usually diagrammed using the metaphor of a clock face (figure 10.8).

- **G_1 (gap phase 1)** is the primary growth phase of the cell. The term *gap phase* refers to its filling the gap between cytokinesis and DNA synthesis. For most cells, this is the longest phase.
- **S (synthesis)** is the phase in which the cell synthesizes a replica of the genome.
- **G_2 (gap phase 2)** is the second growth phase, and preparation for separation of the newly replicated genome. This phase fills the gap between DNA synthesis and the beginning of mitosis. During this phase, mitochondria and other organelles replicate, and microtubules begin to assemble at a spindle.

  G_1, S, and G_2 together constitute **interphase,** the portion of the cell cycle between cell divisions.
- **Mitosis** is the phase of the cell cycle in which the spindle apparatus assembles, binds to the chromosomes, and moves the sister chromatids apart. Mitosis is the essential step in the separation of the two daughter genomes. It is traditionally subdivided into five stages: prophase, prometaphase, metaphase, anaphase, and telophase.
- **Cytokinesis** is the phase of the cell cycle when the cytoplasm divides, creating two daughter cells. In animal

cells, the microtubule spindle helps position a contracting ring of actin that constricts like a drawstring to pinch the cell in two. In cells with a cell wall, such as plant cells, a plate forms between the dividing cells.

Mitosis and cytokinesis together are usually referred to collectively as M phase, to distinguish the dividing phase from interphase.

The duration of the cell cycle varies depending on cell type

The time it takes to complete a cell cycle varies greatly. Cells in animal embryos can complete their cell cycle in under 20 min; the shortest known animal nuclear division cycles occur in fruit fly embryos (8 min). These cells simply divide their nuclei as quickly as they can replicate their DNA, without cell growth. Half of their cycle is taken up by S, half by M, and essentially none by G_1 or G_2.

Because mature cells require time to grow, most of their cycles are much longer than those of embryonic tissue. Typically, a dividing mammalian cell completes its cell cycle in about 24 hr, but some cells, such as certain cells in the human liver, have cell cycles lasting more than a year. During the cycle, growth occurs throughout the G_1 and G_2 phases, as well as during the S phase. The M phase takes only about an hour, a small fraction of the entire cycle.

Most of the variation in the length of the cell cycle between organisms or cell types occurs in the G_1 phase. Cells often pause in G_1 before DNA replication and enter a resting state called the **G_0 phase;** cells may remain in this phase for

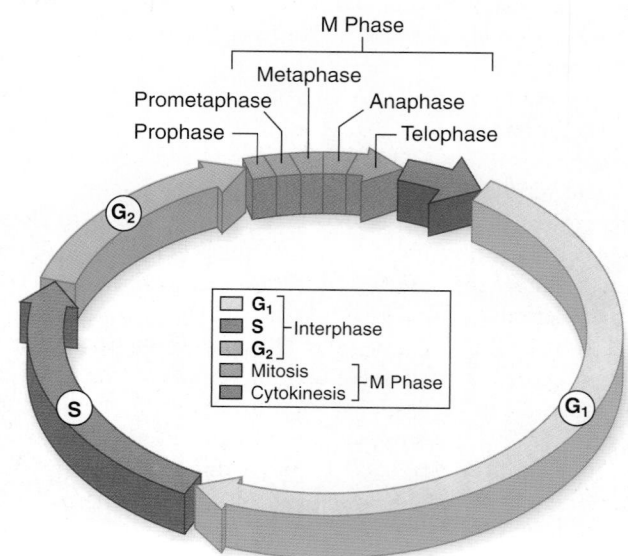

Figure 10.8 The cell cycle. The cell cycle is depicted as a circle. The first gap phase, G_1, involves growth and preparation for DNA synthesis. During S phase, a copy of the genome is synthesized. The second gap phase, G_2, prepares the cell for mitosis. During mitosis, replicated chromosomes are partitioned. Cytokinesis divides the cell into two cells with identical genomes.

days to years before resuming cell division. At any given time, most of the cells in an animal's body are in G_0 phase. Some, such as muscle and nerve cells, remain there permanently; others, such as liver cells, can resume G_1 phase in response to factors released during injury.

Learning Outcome Review 10.3

Cell division in eukaryotes is a complex process that involves five phases: a first gap phase (G_1); a DNA synthesis phase (S); a second gap phase (G_2); mitosis (M), during which chromatids are separated; and cytokinesis in which a cell becomes two separate cells.

■ **When during the cycle is a cell irreversibly committed to dividing?**

10.4 Interphase: Preparation for Mitosis

Learning Outcomes

1. **Describe the events that take place during interphase.**
2. **Explain the structure of the centromere after S phase.**

The events that occur during interphase—the G_1, S, and G_2 phases—are very important for the successful completion of mitosis. During G_1, cells undergo the major portion of their growth. During the S phase, each chromosome replicates to produce two sister chromatids, which remain attached to each other at the centromere. In the G_2 phase, the chromosomes coil even more tightly.

The **centromere** is a point of constriction on the chromosome containing certain repeated DNA sequences that bind specific proteins. These proteins make up a disklike structure called the **kinetochore.** This disk functions as an attachment site for microtubules necessary to separate the chromosomes during cell division (figure 10.9). As seen in figure 10.6, each chromosome's centromere is located at a characteristic site along the length of the chromosome.

After the S phase, the sister chromatids appear to share a common centromere, but at the molecular level the DNA of the centromere has actually already replicated, so there are two complete DNA molecules. Functionally, however, the two chromatids have a single centromere due to their being attached by cohesin proteins at the centromere site (figure 10.10). In metazoan animals, most of the cohesins that hold sister chromatids together after replication appear to be replaced by condensin during the process of chromosome compaction. This leaves the chromosomes still attached tightly at the centromere, but loosely attached elsewhere.

The cell grows throughout interphase. The G_1 and G_2 segments of interphase are periods of active growth, during which proteins are synthesized and cell organelles are pro-

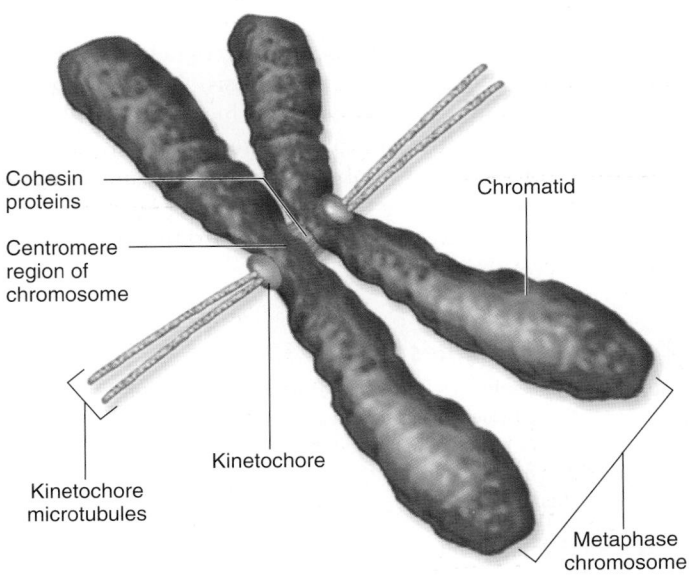

Figure 10.9 Kinetochores. Separation of sister chromatids during mitosis depends on microtubules attaching to proteins found in the kinetochore. These kinetochore proteins are assembled on the centromere of chromosomes. The centromeres of the two sister chromatids are held together by cohesin proteins.

duced. The cell's DNA replicates only during the S phase of the cell cycle.

After the chromosomes have replicated in S phase, they remain fully extended and uncoiled, although cohesin proteins are associated with them at this stage. In G_2 phase, they begin

2.0 μm

Figure 10.10 Proteins found at the centromere. In this image DNA, a cohesin protein and a kinetochore protein have all been labeled with a different colored fluorescent dye. Cohesin (*red*), which holds centromeres together, lies between the sister chromatids (*blue*). Each sister chromatid has its own separate kinetochore (*green*).

the process of condensation, coiling ever more tightly. Special *motor proteins* are involved in the rapid final condensation of the chromosomes that occurs early in mitosis. Also during G_2 phase, the cells begin to assemble the machinery they will later use to move the chromosomes to opposite poles of the cell. In animal cells, a pair of microtubule-organizing centers called *centrioles* replicate, producing one for each pole. All eukaryotic cells undertake an extensive synthesis of **tubulin,** the protein that forms microtubules.

Learning Outcomes Review 10.4

Interphase includes the G_1, S, and G_2 phases of the cell cycle. During interphase, the cell grows; replicates chromosomes, organelles, and centrioles; and synthesizes components needed for mitosis, including tubulin. Cohesin proteins hold chromatids together at the centromere of each chromosome.

■ *How would a mutation that deleted cohesin proteins affect cell division?*

10.5 M Phase: Chromosome Segregation and the Division of Cytoplasmic Contents

Learning Outcomes

1. **Describe the phases of mitosis.**
2. **Understand the importance of chromatid cohesion.**
3. **Compare cytokinesis in plants and animals.**

The process of mitosis is one of the most dramatic and beautiful biological processes that can be readily observed. In our attempts to understand this process, we have divided it into discrete phases but it should always be remembered that this is a dynamic, continuous process, not a set of discrete steps. This process is shown both schematically and in micrographs in figure 10.11.

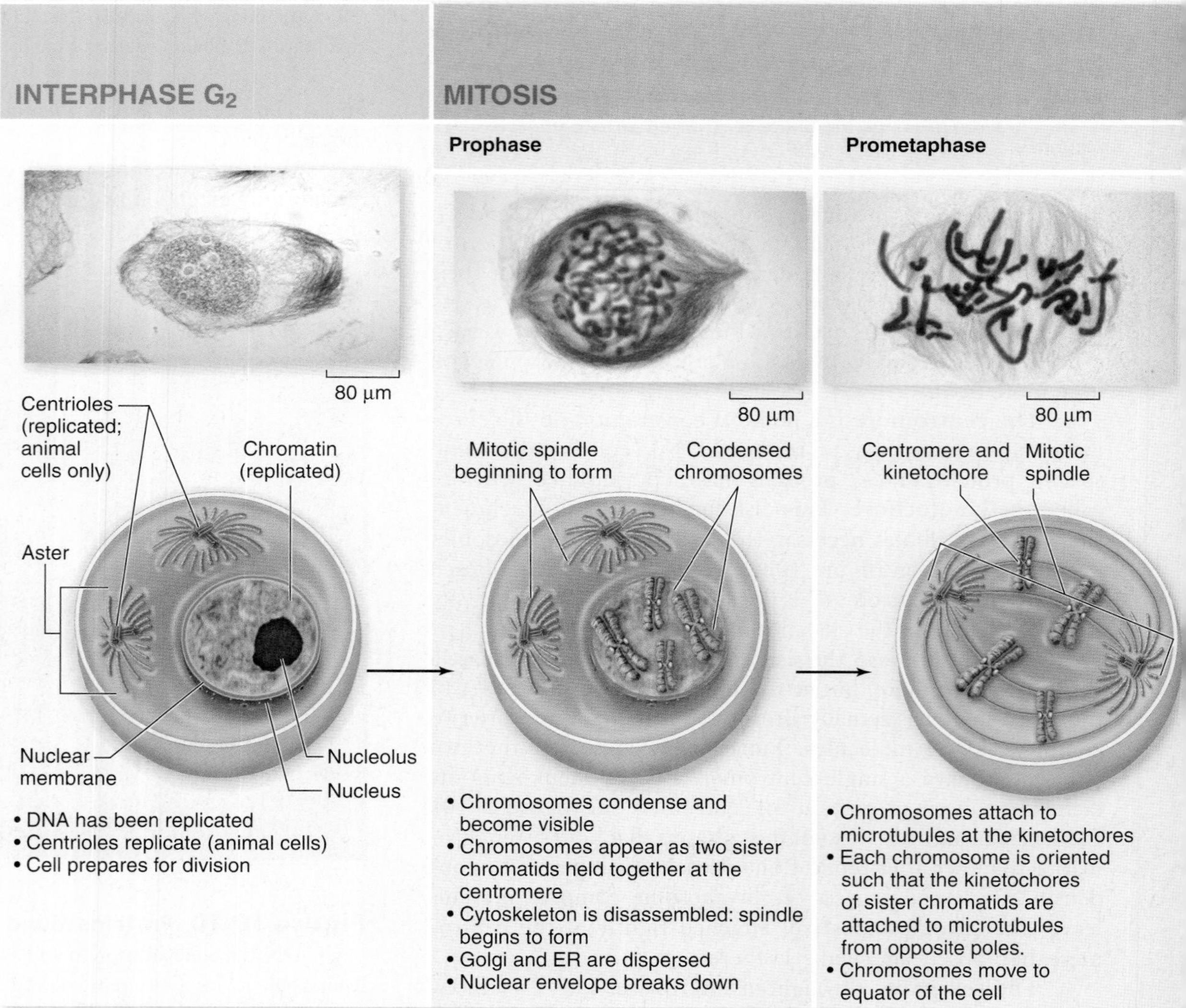

Figure 10.11 Mitosis and cytokinesis.
Mitosis is conventionally divided into five stages—prophase, prometaphase, metaphase, anaphase, and telophase—which together act to separate duplicated chromosomes. This is followed by cytokinesis, which divides the cell into two separate cells. Photos depict mitosis and cytokinesis in a plant, the African blood lily (*Haemanthus katharinae*), with chromosomes stained blue and microtubules stained red. Drawings depict mitosis and cytokinesis in animal cells.

INTERPHASE G_2

80 μm

Centrioles (replicated; animal cells only)

Chromatin (replicated)

Aster

Nuclear membrane

Nucleolus

Nucleus

- DNA has been replicated
- Centrioles replicate (animal cells)
- Cell prepares for division

MITOSIS

Prophase

80 μm

Mitotic spindle beginning to form

Condensed chromosomes

- Chromosomes condense and become visible
- Chromosomes appear as two sister chromatids held together at the centromere
- Cytoskeleton is disassembled: spindle begins to form
- Golgi and ER are dispersed
- Nuclear envelope breaks down

Prometaphase

80 μm

Centromere and kinetochore

Mitotic spindle

- Chromosomes attach to microtubules at the kinetochores
- Each chromosome is oriented such that the kinetochores of sister chromatids are attached to microtubules from opposite poles.
- Chromosomes move to equator of the cell

During prophase, the mitotic apparatus forms

When the chromosome condensation initiated in G_2 phase reaches the point at which individual condensed chromosomes first become visible with the light microscope, the first stage of mitosis, **prophase,** has begun. The condensation process continues throughout prophase; consequently, chromosomes that start prophase as minute threads appear quite bulky before its conclusion. Ribosomal RNA synthesis ceases when the portion of the chromosome bearing the rRNA genes is condensed.

The spindle and centrioles

The assembly of the **spindle** apparatus that will later separate the sister chromatids occurs during prophase. The normal microtubule structure in the cell disassembled in the G_2 phase is replaced by the spindle. In animal cells, the two centriole pairs formed during G_2 phase begin to move apart early in prophase, forming between them an axis of microtubules referred to as spindle fibers. By the time the centrioles reach the opposite poles of the cell, they have established a bridge of microtubules, called the spindle apparatus, between them. In plant cells, a similar bridge of microtubular fibers forms between opposite poles of the cell, although centrioles are absent in plant cells.

In animal cell mitosis, the centrioles extend a radial array of microtubules toward the nearby plasma membrane when they reach the poles of the cell. This arrangement of microtubules is called an **aster.** Although the aster's function is not fully understood, it probably braces the centrioles against the membrane and stiffens the point of microtubular attachment during the retraction of the spindle. Plant cells, which have rigid cell walls, do not form asters.

Breakdown of the nuclear envelope

During the formation of the spindle apparatus, the nuclear envelope breaks down, and the endoplasmic reticulum reabsorbs its components. At this point, the microtubular spindle fibers extend completely across the cell, from one pole to the other. Their orientation determines the plane in which the cell will subsequently divide, through the center of the cell at right angles to the spindle apparatus.

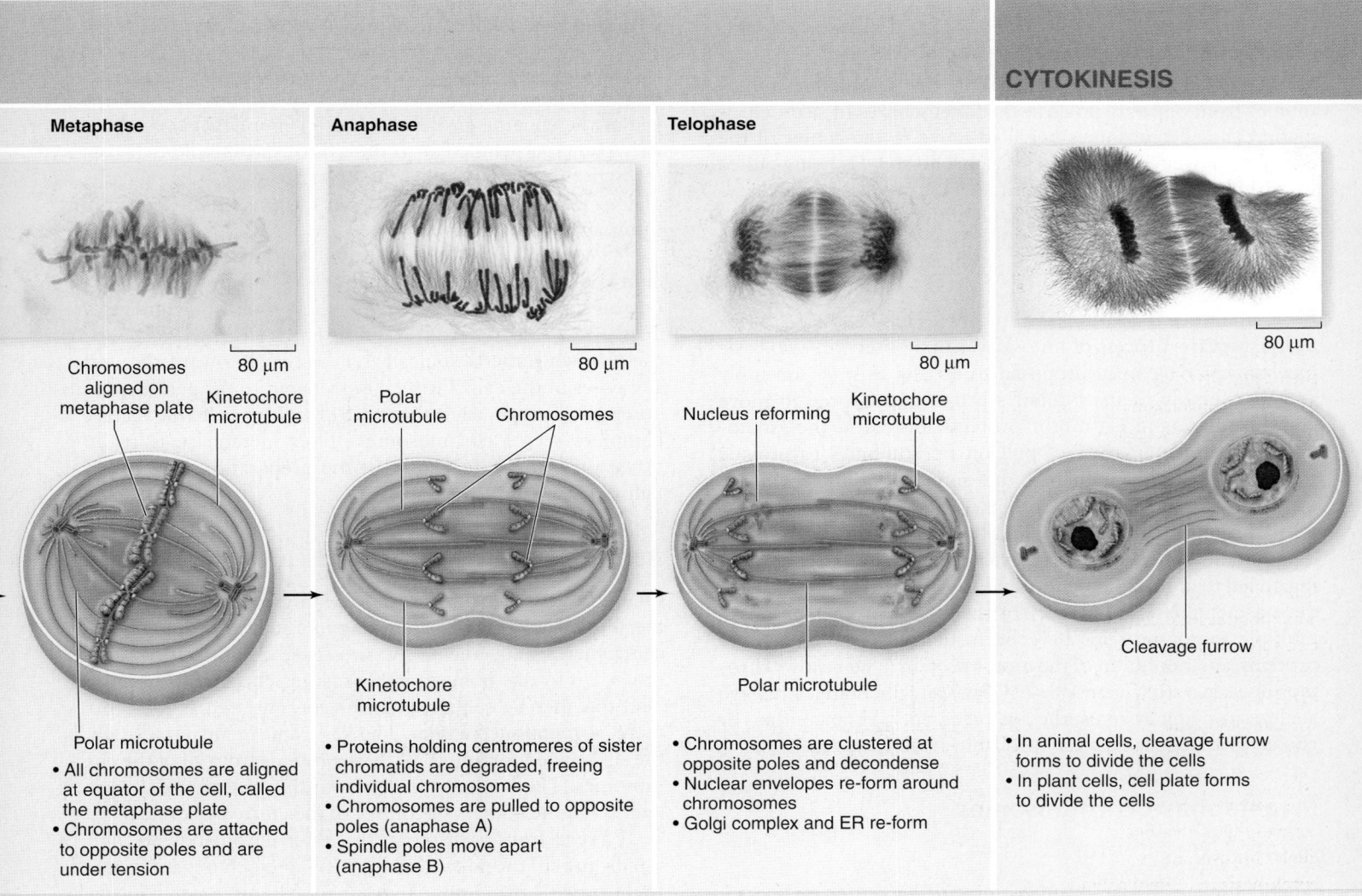

CYTOKINESIS

Metaphase

80 μm

Chromosomes aligned on metaphase plate

Kinetochore microtubule

Polar microtubule

- All chromosomes are aligned at equator of the cell, called the metaphase plate
- Chromosomes are attached to opposite poles and are under tension

Anaphase

80 μm

Polar microtubule

Chromosomes

Kinetochore microtubule

- Proteins holding centromeres of sister chromatids are degraded, freeing individual chromosomes
- Chromosomes are pulled to opposite poles (anaphase A)
- Spindle poles move apart (anaphase B)

Telophase

80 μm

Nucleus reforming

Kinetochore microtubule

Polar microtubule

- Chromosomes are clustered at opposite poles and decondense
- Nuclear envelopes re-form around chromosomes
- Golgi complex and ER re-form

80 μm

Cleavage furrow

- In animal cells, cleavage furrow forms to divide the cells
- In plant cells, cell plate forms to divide the cells

During prometaphase, chromosomes attach to the spindle

The transition from prophase to **prometaphase** occurs following the disassembly of the nuclear envelope. During prometaphase the condensed chromosomes become attached to the spindle by their kinetochores. Each chromosome possesses two kinetochores, one attached to the centromere region of each sister chromatid (see figure 10.9).

Microtubule attachment

As prometaphase continues, a second group of microtubules grow from the poles of the cell toward the centromeres. These microtubules are captured by the kinetochores on each pair of sister chromatids. This results in the kinetochores of each sister chromatid being connected to opposite poles of the spindle.

This bipolar attachment is critical to the process of mitosis; any mistakes in microtubule positioning can be disastrous. For example, the attachment of the kinetochores of both sister chromatids to the same pole leads to a failure of sister chromatid separation, and they will be pulled to the same pole ending up in the same daughter cell, with the other daughter cell missing that chromosome.

Movement of chromosomes to the cell center

With each chromosome attached to the spindle by microtubules from opposite poles to the kinetochores of sister chromatids, the chromosomes begin to move to the center of the cell. This movement is jerky, as if a chromosome is being pulled toward both poles at the same time. This process is called *congression*, and it eventually leads to all of the chromosomes being arranged at the equator of the cell with the sister chromatids of each chromosome oriented to opposite poles by their kinetochore microtubules.

The force that moves chromosomes has been of great interest since the process of mitosis was first observed. Two basic mechanisms have been proposed to explain this: (1) assembly and disassembly of microtubules provides the force to move chromosomes, and (2) motor proteins located at the kinetochore and poles of the cell pull on microtubules to provide force. Data have been obtained that support both mechanisms.

In support of the microtubule-shortening proposal, isolated chromosomes can be pulled by microtubule disassembly. The spindle is a very dynamic structure, with microtubules being added to at the kinetochore and shortened at the poles, even during metaphase. In support of the motor protein proposal, multiple motor proteins have been identified as kinetochore proteins, and inhibition of the motor protein dynein slows chromosome separation at anaphase. Like many phenomena that we analyze in living systems, the answer is not a simple either–or choice; both mechanisms are probably at work.

In metaphase, chromosomes align at the equator

The alignment of the chromosomes in the center of the cell signals the third stage of mitosis, **metaphase.** When viewed with a light microscope, the chromosomes appear to array

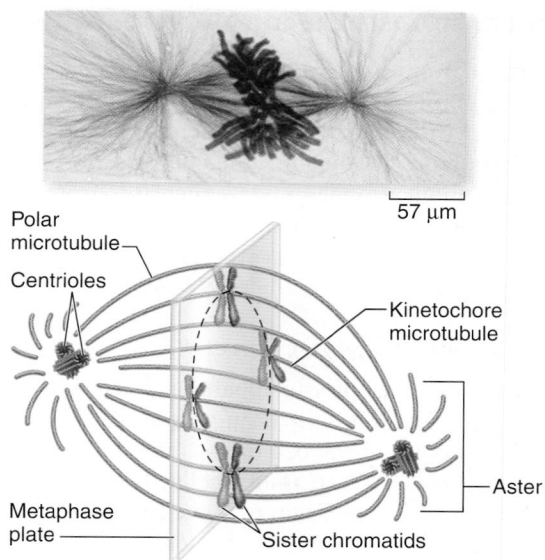

Figure 10.12 Metaphase. In metaphase, the chromosomes are arrayed at the midpoint of the cell. The imaginary plane through the equator of the cell is called the metaphase plate. As the spindle itself is a three dimensional structure, the chromosomes are arrayed in a rough circle on the metaphase plate.

themselves in a circle along the inner circumference of the cell, just as the equator girdles the Earth (figure 10.12). An imaginary plane perpendicular to the axis of the spindle that passes through this circle is called the *metaphase plate*. The metaphase plate is not an actual structure, but rather an indication of the future axis of cell division.

Positioned by the microtubules attached to the kinetochores of their centromeres, all of the chromosomes line up on the metaphase plate. At this point their centromeres are neatly arrayed in a circle, equidistant from the two poles of the cell, with microtubules extending back toward the opposite poles of the cell. The cell is prepared to properly separate sister chromatids, such that each daughter cell will receive a complete set of chromosomes. Thus metaphase is really a transitional phase in which all the preparations are checked before the action continues.

At anaphase, the chromatids separate

Of all the stages of mitosis, shown in figure 10.11, **anaphase** is the shortest and the most amazing to watch. It begins when the centromeres split, freeing the two sister chromatids from each other. Up to this point in mitosis, sister chromatids have been held together by cohesin proteins concentrated at the centromere, as mentioned earlier. The key event in anaphase, then, is the simultaneous removal of these proteins from all of the chromosomes. The control and details of this process are discussed later on in the context of control of the entire cell cycle.

Freed from each other, the sister chromatids are pulled rapidly toward the poles to which their kinetochores are attached. In the process, two forms of movement take place simultaneously, each driven by microtubules. These movements are often called anaphase A and anaphase B to distinguish them.

First, during anaphase A, the *kinetochores are pulled toward the poles* as the microtubules that connect them to the poles shorten. This shortening process is not a contraction; the microtubules do not get any thicker. Instead, tubulin subunits are removed from the kinetochore ends of the microtubules. As more subunits are removed, the chromatid-bearing microtubules are progressively disassembled, and the chromatids are pulled ever closer to the poles of the cell.

Second, during anaphase B, the *poles move apart* as microtubular spindle fibers physically anchored to opposite poles slide past each other, away from the center of the cell (figure 10.13). Because another group of microtubules attach the chromosomes to the poles, the chromosomes move apart, too. If a flexible membrane surrounds the cell, it becomes visibly elongated.

When the sister chromatids separate in anaphase, the accurate partitioning of the replicated genome—the essential element of mitosis—is complete.

During telophase, the nucleus re-forms

In **telophase,** the spindle apparatus disassembles as the microtubules are broken down into tubulin monomers that can be used to construct the cytoskeletons of the daughter cells. A nuclear envelope forms around each set of sister chromatids, which can now be called chromosomes because they are no longer attached at the centromere. The chromosomes soon begin to uncoil into the more extended form that permits gene expression. One of the early group of genes expressed after mitosis is complete are the rRNA genes, resulting in the reappearance of the nucleolus.

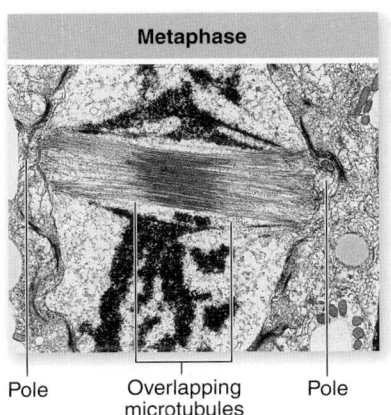

Metaphase

Pole | Overlapping microtubules | Pole

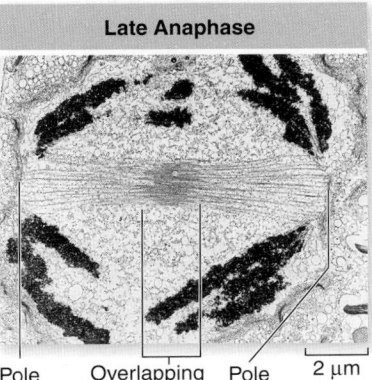

Late Anaphase

Pole | Overlapping microtubules | Pole | 2 µm

Figure 10.13 Microtubules slide past each other as the chromosomes separate. In these electron micrographs of dividing diatoms, the overlap of the microtubules lessens markedly during spindle elongation as the cell passes from metaphase to anaphase. During anaphase B the poles move farther apart as the chromosomes move toward the poles.

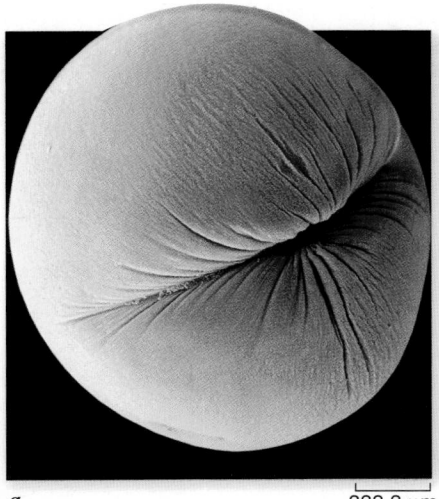
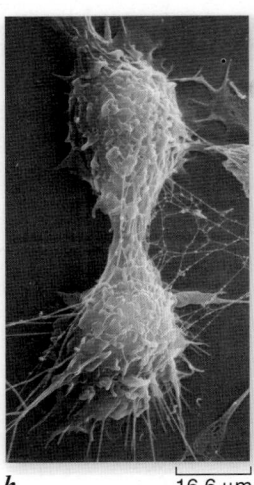

a. 333.3 µm   *b.* 16.6 µm

Figure 10.14 Cytokinesis in animal cells. *a.* A cleavage furrow forms around a dividing frog egg. *b.* The completion of cytokinesis in an animal cell. The two daughter cells are still joined by a thin band of cytoplasm occupied largely by microtubules.

Telophase can be viewed as a reversal of the process of prophase, bringing the cell back to the state of interphase. Mitosis is complete at the end of telophase. The eukaryotic cell has partitioned its replicated genome into two new nuclei positioned at opposite ends of the cell. Other cytoplasmic organelles, including mitochondria and chloroplasts (if present), were reassorted to areas that will separate and become the daughter cells.

Cell division is still not complete at the end of mitosis, however, because the division of the cell body proper has not yet begun. The phase of the cell cycle when the cell actually divides is called **cytokinesis.** It generally involves the cleavage of the cell into roughly equal halves.

In animal cells, a belt of actin pinches off the daughter cells

In animal cells and the cells of all other eukaryotes that lack cell walls, cytokinesis is achieved by means of a constricting belt of actin filaments. As these filaments slide past one another, the diameter of the belt decreases, pinching the cell and creating a **cleavage furrow** around the cell's circumference (figure 10.14*a*).

As constriction proceeds, the furrow deepens until it eventually slices all the way into the center of the cell. At this point, the cell is divided in two (figure 10.14*b*).

In plant cells, a cell plate divides the daughter cells

Plant cell walls are far too rigid to be squeezed in two by actin filaments. Instead, these cells assemble membrane components in their interior, at right angles to the spindle apparatus. This expanding membrane partition, called a **cell plate,** continues to grow outward until it reaches the interior surface of the plasma membrane and fuses with it, effectively dividing the cell in two

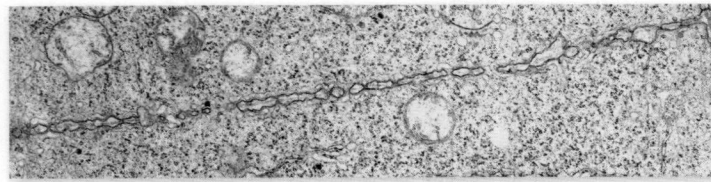

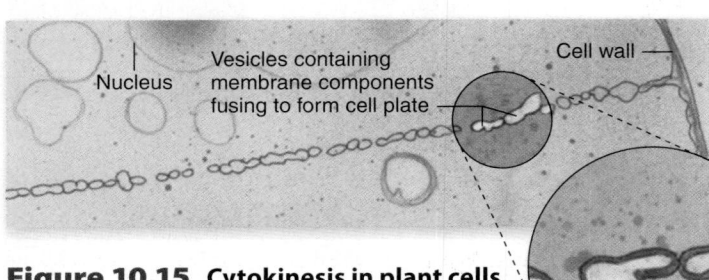

Figure 10.15 Cytokinesis in plant cells. In this photomicrograph and companion drawing, a cell plate is forming between daughter nuclei. The cell plate forms from the fusion of Golgi-derived vesicles. Once the plate is complete, there will be two cells.

(figure 10.15). Cellulose is then laid down on the new membranes, creating two new cell walls. The space between the daughter cells becomes impregnated with pectins and is called a *middle lamella*.

In fungi and some protists, daughter nuclei are separated during cytokinesis

In most fungi and some groups of protists, the nuclear membrane does not dissolve, and as a result, all the events of mitosis occur entirely *within* the nucleus. Only after mitosis is complete in these organisms does the nucleus divide into two daughter nuclei; then, during cytokinesis, one nucleus goes to each daughter cell. This separate nuclear division phase of the cell cycle does not occur in plants, animals, or most protists.

After cytokinesis in any eukaryotic cell, the two daughter cells contain all the components of a complete cell. Whereas mitosis ensures that both daughter cells contain a full complement of chromosomes, no similar mechanism ensures that organelles such as mitochondria and chloroplasts are distributed equally between the daughter cells. But as long as at least one of each organelle is present in each cell, the organelles can replicate to reach the number appropriate for that cell.

Learning Outcomes Review 10.5

Mitosis is divided into phases: prophase, prometaphase, metaphase, anaphase, and telophase. The early phases involve restructuring the cell to create the microtubule spindle that pulls chromosomes to the equator of the cell in metaphase. Chromatids for each chromosome remain attached at the centromere by cohesin proteins. Chromatids are then pulled to opposite poles during anaphase when cohesin proteins are destroyed. The nucleus is re-formed in telophase, and cytokinesis then divides the cell cytoplasm and organelles. In animal cells, actin pinches the cell in two; in plant cells, a cell plate forms in the middle of the dividing cell.

- **What would happen to a chromosome that loses cohesin protein between sister chromatids before metaphase?**

10.6 *Control of the Cell Cycle*

Learning Outcomes

1. **Distinguish the role of checkpoints in the control of the cell cycle.**
2. **Understand the role of the anaphase-promoting complex/cyclosome in mitosis.**
3. **Describe cancer in terms of cell cycle control.**

Our knowledge of how the cell cycle is controlled, although still incomplete, has grown enormously in the past 30 years. Our current view integrates two basic concepts. First, the cell cycle has two irreversible points: the replication of genetic material and the separation of the sister chromatids. Second, the cell cycle can be put on hold at specific points called *checkpoints*. At any of these checkpoints, the process is checked for accuracy and can be halted if there are errors. This leads to extremely high fidelity overall for the entire process. The checkpoint organization also allows the cell cycle to respond to both the internal state of the cell, including nutritional state and integrity of genetic material, and to signals from the environment, which are integrated at major checkpoints.

Research uncovered cell cycle control factors

The history of investigation into control of the cell cycle is instructive in two ways. First, it allows us to place modern observations into context; second, we can see how biologists using very different approaches often end up at the same place. The following brief history introduces three observations and then shows how they can be integrated into a single mechanism.

Discovery of MPF

Research on the activation of frog oocytes led to the discovery of a substance that was first called *maturation-promoting factor (MPF)*. Frog oocytes, which go on to become egg cells, become arrested near the end of their development at the G_2 stage before meiosis I, which is the division leading to the production of gametes (chapter 11). They remain in this arrested state and await hormonal signaling to complete this division process.

Cytoplasm taken from a variety of actively dividing cells could prematurely induce cell division when injected into oocytes (figure 10.16). These experiments indicated the presence of a positive regulator of cell cycle progression in the cytoplasm of dividing cells: MPF. These experiments also fit well with cell fusion experiments done with mitotic and interphase cells that also indicated a cytoplasmic positive regulator that could induce mitosis (figure 10.16).

Further studies highlighted two key aspects of MPF. First, MPF activity varied during the cell cycle: low in early G_2, rising throughout this phase, and then peaking in mitosis (figure 10.17). Second, the enzymatic activity of MPF involved

Hypothesis: *There are positive regulators of cell division.*

Prediction: *Frog oocytes are arrested in G$_2$ of meiosis I. They can be induced to mature (undergo meiosis) by progesterone treatment. If maturing oocytes contain a positive regulator of cell division, injection of cytoplasm should induce an immature oocyte to undergo meiosis.*

Test: *Oocytes are induced with progesterone, then cytoplasm from these maturing cells is injected into immature oocytes.*

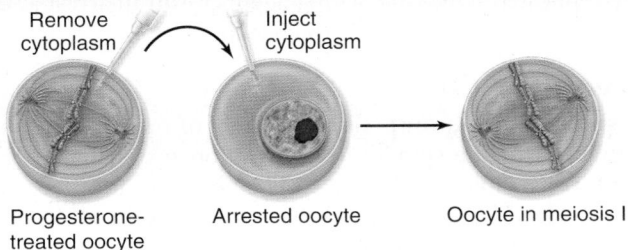

Result: *Injected oocytes progress from G$_2$ into meiosis I.*

Conclusion: *The progesterone treatment causes production of a positive regulator of maturation: Maturation Promoting Factor (MPF).*

Prediction: *If mitosis is driven by positive regulators, then cytoplasm from a mitotic cell should cause a G$_1$ cell to enter mitosis.*

Test: *M phase cells are fused with G$_1$ phase cells, then the nucleus from the G$_1$ phase cell is monitored microscopically.*

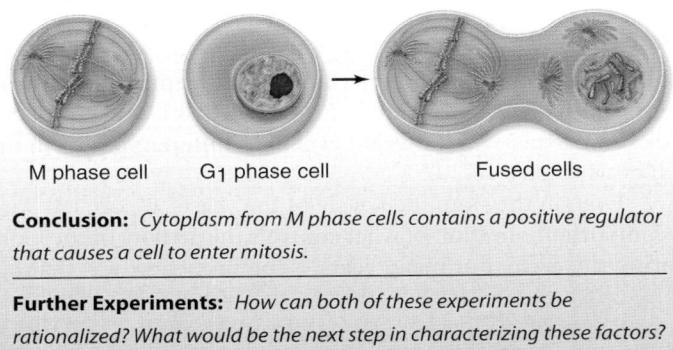

Conclusion: *Cytoplasm from M phase cells contains a positive regulator that causes a cell to enter mitosis.*

Further Experiments: *How can both of these experiments be rationalized? What would be the next step in characterizing these factors?*

Figure 10.16 Discovery of positive regulator of cell division.

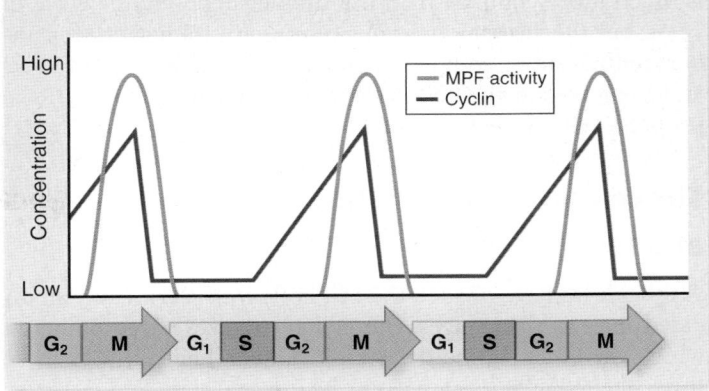

Figure 10.17 Correlation of MPF activity, amount of cyclin protein, and stages of the cell cycle. Cyclin concentration and MPF activity are shown plotted vs. stage of the cell cycle. MPF activity changes in a repeating pattern through the cell cycle. This also correlates with the level of mitotic cyclin in the cell, which shows a similar pattern. The reason for this correlation is that cyclin is actually one component of MPF, the other being a cyclin-dependent kinase (Cdk). Together these act as a positive regulator of cell division.

Despite much effort, no identified enzymatic activity was associated with these proteins. Their hallmark was the timing of their production and not any intrinsic activity.

Genetic analysis of the cell cycle

Geneticists using two different yeasts, budding yeast and fission yeast, as model systems set out to determine the genes necessary for control of the cell cycle. By isolating mutants that were halted during division, they identified genes that were necessary for cell cycle progression. These studies indicated that in yeast, there were two critical control points: the commitment to DNA synthesis, called START, as it meant committing to divide, and the commitment to mitosis. One particular gene, named *cdc2*, from fission yeast, was shown to be critical for passing both of these boundaries.

MPF is cyclin plus cdc2

All of these findings came together in an elegant fashion with the following observations. First, the protein encoded by the *cdc2* gene was shown to be a protein kinase. Second, the purification and identification of MPF showed that it was composed of both a cyclin component and a kinase component. Last, the kinase itself was the cdc2 protein!

The cdc2 protein was the first identified **cyclin-dependent kinase (Cdk),** that is, a protein kinase enzyme that is only active when complexed with cyclin. This finding led to the renaming of MPF as *mitosis*-promoting factor, as its role was clearly more general than simply promoting the maturation of frog oocytes.

These Cdk enzymes are the key positive drivers of the cell division cycle. They are often called the engine that drives cell division. The control of the cell cycle in higher eukaryotes

the phosphorylation of proteins. This second point is not surprising given the importance of phosphorylation as a reversible switch on the activity of proteins (see chapter 9). The first observation indicated that MPF itself was not always active, but rather was being regulated with the cell cycle, and the second showed the possible enzymatic activity of MPF.

Discovery of cyclins

Other researchers examined proteins produced during the early divisions in sea urchin embryos. They identified proteins that were produced in synchrony with the cell cycle, and named them **cyclins** (see figure 10.17). These observations were extended in another marine invertebrate, the surf clam. Two forms of cyclin were found that cycled at slightly different times, reaching peaks at the G$_1$/S and G$_2$/M boundaries.

is much more complex than the simple single-engine cycle of yeast, but the yeast model remains a useful framework for understanding more complex regulation. The discovery of Cdks and their role in the cell cycle is an excellent example of the progressive nature of science.

The cell cycle can be halted at three checkpoints

Although we have divided the cell cycle into phases and subdivided mitosis into stages, the cell recognizes three points at which the cycle can be delayed or halted. The cell uses these three checkpoints to both assess its internal state and integrate external signals (figure 10.18): G_1/S, G_2/M, and late metaphase (the spindle checkpoint). Passage through these checkpoints is controlled by the Cdk enzymes described earlier and also in the following section.

G_1/S checkpoint

The **G_1/S checkpoint** is the primary point at which the cell "decides" whether or not to divide. This checkpoint is therefore the primary point at which external signals can influence events of the cycle. It is the phase during which growth factors (discussed later on) affect the cycle and also the phase that links cell division to cell growth and nutrition.

In yeast systems, where the majority of the genetic analysis of the cell cycle has been performed, this checkpoint is called START. In animals, it is called the restriction point (R point). In all systems, once a cell has made this irreversible commitment to replicate its genome, it has committed to divide. Damage to DNA can halt the cycle at this point, as can starvation conditions or lack of growth factors.

G_2/M checkpoint

The **G_2/M checkpoint** has received a large amount of attention because of its complexity and its importance as the stimulus for the events of mitosis. Historically, Cdks active at this checkpoint were first identified as MPFs, a term that has now evolved into **M phase-promoting factor (MPF).**

Passage through this checkpoint represents the commitment to mitosis. This checkpoint assesses the success of DNA replication and can stall the cycle if DNA has not been accurately replicated. DNA-damaging agents result in arrest at this checkpoint as well as at the G_1/S checkpoint.

Spindle checkpoint

The **spindle checkpoint** ensures that all of the chromosomes are attached to the spindle in preparation for anaphase. The second irreversible step in the cycle is the separation of chromosomes during anaphase, and therefore it is critical that they are properly arrayed at the metaphase plate.

Cyclin-dependent kinases drive the cell cycle

The primary molecular mechanism of cell cycle control is phosphorylation, which you may recall is the addition of a phosphate group to the amino acids serine, threonine, and tyrosine in proteins (chapter 9). The enzymes that accomplish this phosphorylation are the Cdks (figure 10.19).

The action of Cdks

The first important cell cycle kinase was identified in fission yeast and named Cdc2 (now also called Cdk1). In yeast, this Cdk can partner with different cyclins at different points in the cell cycle (figure 10.20).

Even in the simplified cycle of the yeasts, we are left with the important question of what controls the activity of the Cdks during the cycle. For many years, a common view was that cyclins drove the cell cycle—that is, the periodic synthesis and destruction of cyclins acted as a clock. More recently, it has become clear that the Cdc2 kinase is also itself controlled by

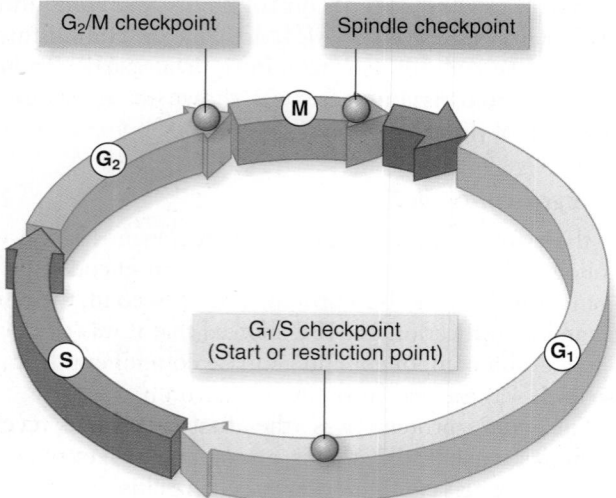

Figure 10.18 Control of the cell cycle. Cells use a centralized control system to check whether proper conditions have been achieved before passing three key checkpoints in the cell cycle.

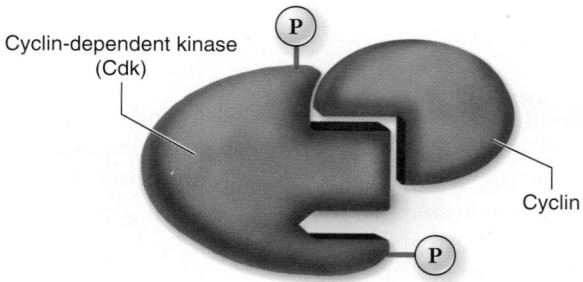

Figure 10.19 Cdk enzyme forms a complex with cyclin. Cdk is a protein kinase that activates numerous cell proteins by phosphorylating them. Cyclin is a regulatory protein required to activate Cdk. This complex is also called mitosis-promoting factor (MPF). The activity of Cdk is also controlled by the pattern of phosphorylation: phosphorylation at one site (represented by the red site) inactivates the Cdk, and phosphorylation at another site (represented by the green site) activates the Cdk.

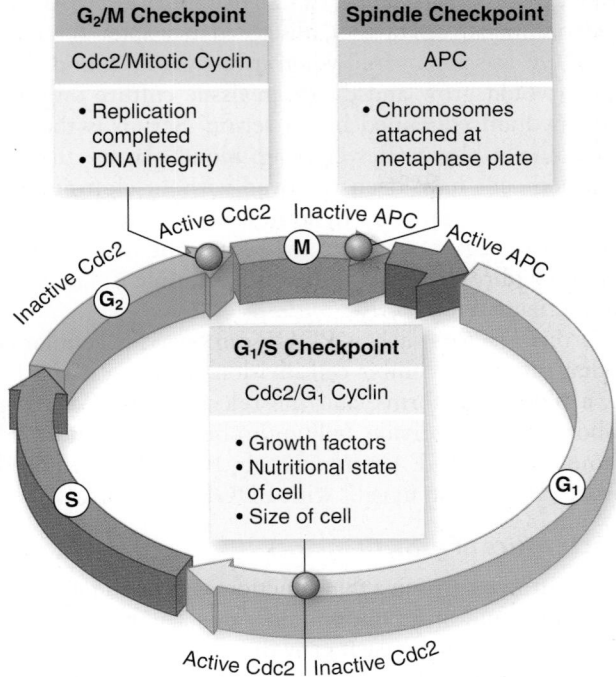

G₂/M Checkpoint

Cdc2/Mitotic Cyclin

- Replication completed
- DNA integrity

Spindle Checkpoint

APC

- Chromosomes attached at metaphase plate

Inactive Cdc2

Active Cdc2   Inactive APC   Active APC

Inactive Cdc2

G₂

M

G₁/S Checkpoint

Cdc2/G₁ Cyclin

- Growth factors
- Nutritional state of cell
- Size of cell

S

G₁

Active Cdc2 | Inactive Cdc2

Figure 10.20 Checkpoints of the yeast cell cycle. The simplest cell cycle that has been studied in detail is the fission yeast. This is controlled by three main checkpoints and a single Cdk enzyme, called Cdc2. The Cdc2 enzyme partners with different cyclins to control the G₁/S and G₂/M checkpoints. The spindle checkpoint is controlled by the anaphase-promoting complex (APC).

phosphorylation: Phosphorylation at one site activates Cdc2, and phosphorylation at another site inactivates it (see figure 10.19). Full activation of the Cdc2 kinase requires complexing with a cyclin and the appropriate pattern of phosphorylation.

As the G₁/S checkpoint is approached, the triggering signal in yeast appears to be the accumulation of G₁ cyclins. These form a complex with Cdc2 to create the active G₁/S Cdk, which phosphorylates a number of targets that bring about the increased enzyme activity for DNA replication.

The action of MPF

MPF and its role at the G₂/M checkpoint has been extensively analyzed in a number of different experimental systems. The control of MPF is sensitive to agents that disrupt or delay replication and to agents that damage DNA. It was once thought that MPF was controlled solely by the level of the M phase-specific cyclins, but it has now become clear that this is not the case.

Although M phase cyclin is necessary for MPF function, activity is controlled by inhibitory phosphorylation of the kinase component, Cdc2. The critical signal in this process is the removal of the inhibitory phosphates by a protein, phosphatase. This action forms a molecular switch based on positive feedback because the active MPF further activates its own activating phosphatase.

The checkpoint assesses the balance of the kinase that adds inhibitory phosphates with the phosphatase that removes them. Damage to DNA acts through a complex pathway that includes damage sensing and a response to tip the balance toward the inhibitory phosphorylation of MPF. Later on, we describe how some cancers overcome this inhibition.

The anaphase-promoting complex

The molecular details of the sensing system at the spindle checkpoint are not clear. The presence of all chromosomes at the metaphase plate and the tension on the microtubules between opposite poles are both important. The signal is transmitted through the **anaphase-promoting complex,** also called the *cyclosome (APC/C).*

The function of the APC/C is to trigger anaphase itself. As described earlier, the sister chromatids at metaphase are still held together by the protein complex cohesin. The APC does not act directly on cohesin, but rather acts by marking a protein called *securin* for destruction. The securin protein acts as an inhibitor of another protease called *separase* that appears to be specific for the cohesin complex. Once inhibition is lifted, separase destroys cohesin.

This process has been analyzed in detail in budding yeast, where it has been shown that the separase enzyme specifically degrades a component of cohesin called Scc1. This leads to the release of the sister chromatids and results in their sudden movement toward opposite poles during anaphase.

In vertebrates, most cohesin is removed from the sister chromatids during chromosome condensation, possibly with cohesin being replaced by condensin. At metaphase, the majority of the cohesin that remains on vertebrate chromatids is concentrated at the centromere (figure 10.10). The destruction of this cohesin explains the anaphase movement of chromosomes and the apparent "division" of the centromeres.

The APC/C has a number of roles in mitosis: it activates the protease that removes the cohesins holding sister chromatids together, and it is necessary for the destruction of mitotic cyclins to drive the cell out of mitosis. The APC/C complex marks proteins for destruction by the proteosome, the organelle responsible for the controlled degradation of proteins (chapter 16). The signal to degrade a protein is the addition of a molecule called *ubiquitin,* and the APC/C acts as a ubiquitin ligase. As we learn more about the APC/C and its functions, it is clear that the control of its activity is a key regulator of the cell cycle.

In multicellular eukaryotes, many Cdks and external signals act on the cell cycle

The major difference between more complex animals and single-celled eukaryotes such as fungi and protists is twofold: First, multiple Cdks control the cycle as opposed to the single Cdk in yeasts; and second, animal cells respond to a greater variety of external signals than do yeasts, which primarily respond to signals necessary for mating.

In higher eukaryotes there are more Cdk enzymes and more cyclins that can partner with these multiple Cdks, but their basic role is the same as in the yeast cycle. A more complex cell cycle is shown in figure 10.21. These more complex controls allow the integration of more input into control of the cycle. With the evolution of more complex forms of organization (tissues, organs, and organ systems), more complex forms of cell cycle control evolved as well.

A multicellular body's organization cannot be maintained without severely limiting cell proliferation—so that only certain cells divide, and only at appropriate times. The way cells inhibit individual growth of other cells is apparent in mammalian cells growing in tissue culture: A single layer of cells expands over a culture plate until the growing border of cells comes into contact with neighboring cells, and then the cells stop dividing. If a sector of cells is cleared away, neighboring cells rapidly refill that sector and then stop dividing again on cell contact.

How are cells able to sense the density of the cell culture around them? When cells come in contact with one another, receptor proteins in the plasma membrane activate a signal transduction pathway that acts to inhibit Cdk action. This prevents entry into the cell cycle.

Growth factors and the cell cycle

Growth factors act by triggering intracellular signaling systems. Fibroblasts, for example, possess numerous receptors on their plasma membranes for one of the first growth factors to be identified, **platelet-derived growth factor (PDGF).** The PDGF recep-

tor is a receptor tyrosine kinase (RTK) that initiates a MAP kinase cascade to stimulate cell division (discussed in chapter 9).

PDGF was discovered when investigators found that fibroblasts would grow and divide in tissue culture only if the growth medium contained blood serum. Serum is the liquid that remains in blood after clotting; blood plasma, the liquid from which cells have been removed without clotting, would not work. The researchers hypothesized that platelets in the blood clots were releasing into the serum one or more factors required for fibroblast growth. Eventually, they isolated such a factor and named it PDGF.

Growth factors such as PDGF can override cellular controls that otherwise inhibit cell division. When a tissue is injured, a blood clot forms, and the release of PDGF triggers neighboring cells to divide, helping to heal the wound. Only a tiny amount of PDGF (approximately 10^{-10} M) is required to stimulate cell division in cells with PDGF receptors.

Characteristics of growth factors

Over 50 different proteins that function as growth factors have been isolated, and more undoubtedly exist. A specific cell surface receptor recognizes each growth factor, its binding site fitting that growth factor precisely. These growth factor receptors often initiate MAP kinase cascades in which the final kinase enters the nucleus and activates transcription factors by phosphorylation. These transcription factors stimulate the production of G_1 cyclins and the proteins that are necessary for cell cycle progression (figure 10.22).

The cellular selectivity of a particular growth factor depends on which target cells bear its unique receptor. Some growth factors, such as PDGF and epidermal growth factor (EGF), affect a broad range of cell types, but others affect only specific types. For example, nerve growth factor (NGF) promotes the growth of certain classes of neurons, and erythropoietin triggers cell division in red blood cell precursors. Most animal cells need a combination of several different growth factors to overcome the various controls that inhibit cell division.

The G_0 phase

If cells are deprived of appropriate growth factors, they stop at the G_1 checkpoint of the cell cycle. With their growth and division arrested, they remain in this dormant G_0 phase.

The ability to enter G_0 accounts for the incredible diversity seen in the length of the cell cycle in different tissues. Epithelial cells lining the human gut divide more than twice a day, constantly renewing this lining. By contrast, liver cells divide only once every year or two, spending most of their time in the G_0 phase. Mature neurons and muscle cells usually never leave G_0.

Cancer is a failure of cell cycle control

The unrestrained, uncontrolled growth of cells in humans leads to the disease called **cancer.** Cancer is essentially a disease of cell division—a failure of cell division control.

The p53 gene

Recent work has identified one of the culprits in cancer. Officially dubbed *p53,* this gene plays a key role in the G_1 checkpoint of cell division.

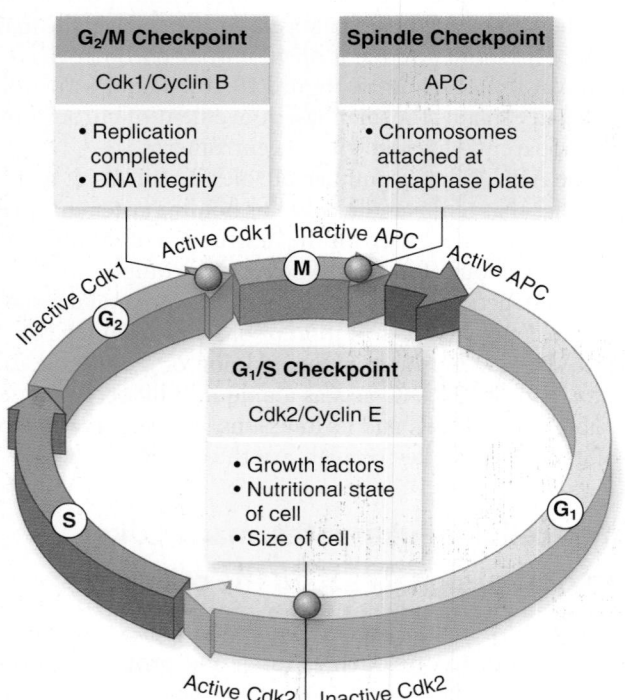

Figure 10.21 Checkpoints of the mammalian cell cycle. The more complex mammalian cell cycle is shown. This cycle is still controlled through three main checkpoints. These integrate internal and external signals to control progress through the cycle. These inputs control the state of two different Cdk–cyclin complexes and the anaphase-promoting complex (APC).

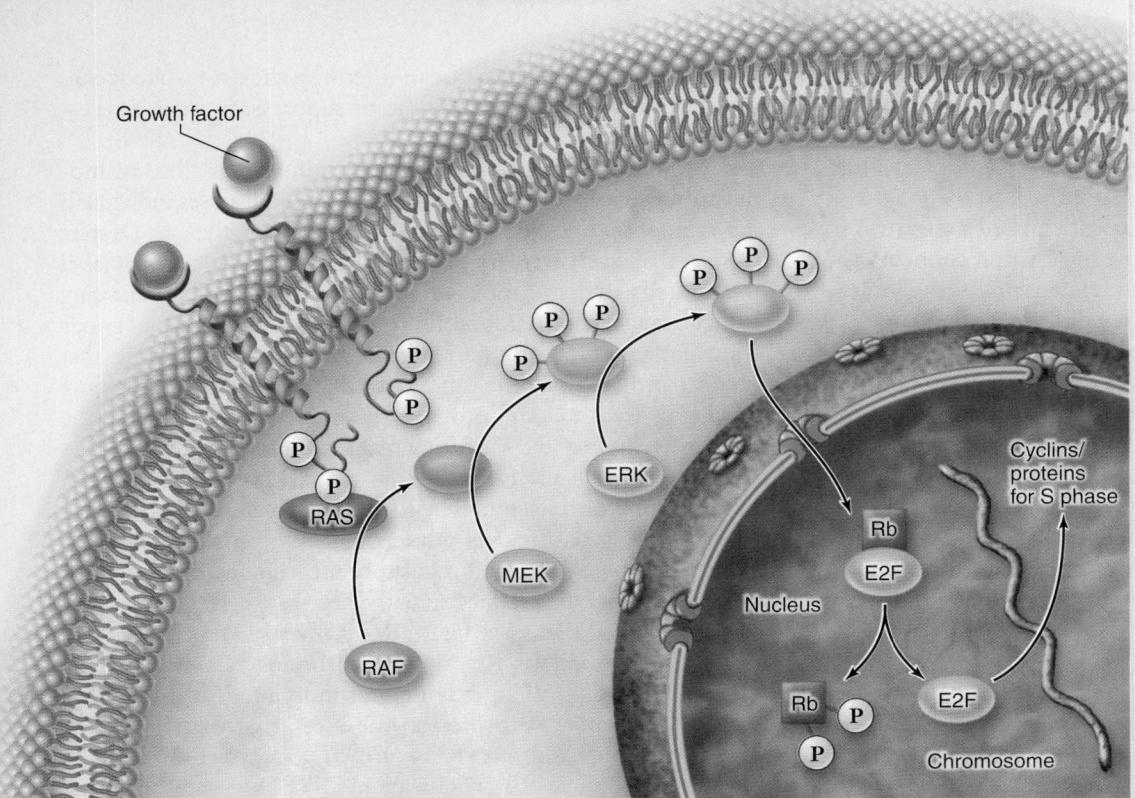

Figure 10.22 **The cell proliferation-signaling pathway.** Binding of a growth factor sets in motion a MAP kinase intracellular signaling pathway (described in chapter 9), which activates nuclear regulatory proteins that trigger cell division. In this example, when the nuclear retinoblastoma protein (Rb) is phosphorylated, another nuclear protein (the transcription factor E2F) is released and is then able to stimulate the production of cyclin and other proteins necessary for S phase.

The gene's product, the p53 protein, monitors the integrity of DNA, checking that it is undamaged. If the p53 protein detects damaged DNA, it halts cell division and stimulates the activity of special enzymes to repair the damage. Once the DNA has been repaired, p53 allows cell division to continue. In cases where the DNA damage is irreparable, p53 then directs the cell to kill itself.

By halting division in damaged cells, the *p53* gene prevents the development of many mutated cells, and it is therefore considered a **tumor-suppressor gene** although its activities are not limited to cancer prevention. Scientists have found that *p53* is entirely absent or damaged beyond use in the majority of cancerous cells they have examined. It is precisely because *p53* is nonfunctional that cancer cells are able to repeatedly undergo cell division without being halted at the G_1 checkpoint (figure 10.23).

Proto-oncogenes

The disease we call cancer is actually many different diseases, depending on the tissue affected. The common theme in all cases is the loss of control over the cell cycle. Research has identified numerous so-called **oncogenes**, genes that can, when introduced into a cell, cause it to become a cancer cell. This identification then led to the discovery of **proto-oncogenes**, which are normal cellular genes that become oncogenes when mutated.

The action of proto-oncogenes is often related to signalling by growth factors, and their mutation can lead to loss of growth control in multiple ways. Some proto-oncogenes encode receptors for growth factors, and others encode proteins involved in signal transduction that act after growth factor receptors. If a receptor for a growth factor becomes mutated such that it is permanently "on," the cell is no longer dependent on the presence of the growth factor for cell division. This is analogous

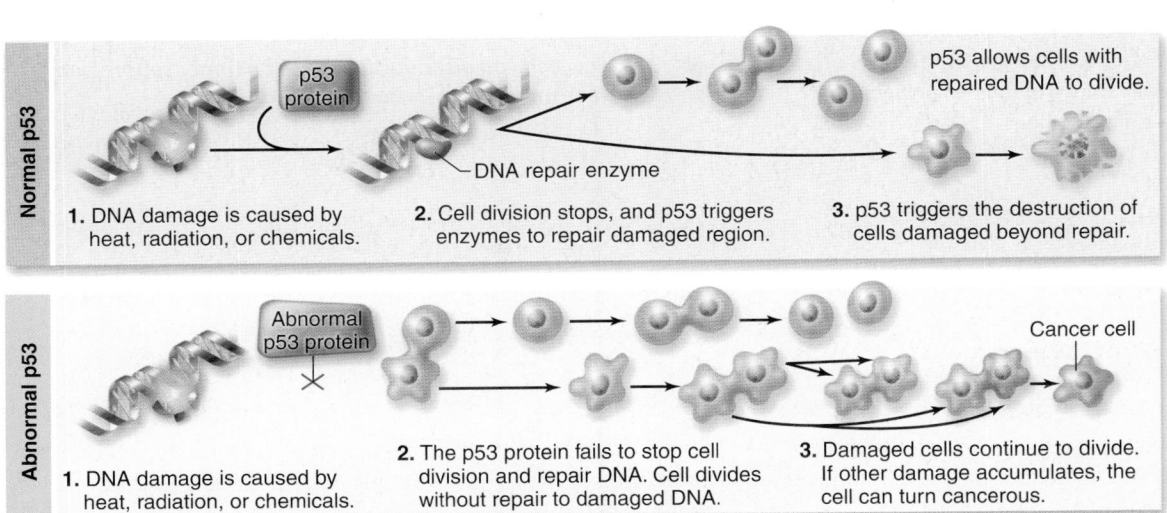

Figure 10.23 Cell division, cancer, and p53 protein. Normal p53 protein monitors DNA, destroying cells that have irreparable damage to their DNA. Abnormal p53 protein fails to stop cell division and repair DNA. As damaged cells proliferate, cancer develops.

to a light switch that is stuck on: The light will always be on. PDGF and EGF receptors both fall into the category of proto-oncogenes. Only one copy of a proto-oncogene needs to undergo this mutation for uncontrolled division to take place; thus, this change acts like a dominant mutation.

The number of proto-oncogenes identified has grown to more than 50 over the years. This line of research connects our understanding of cancer with our understanding of the molecular mechanisms governing cell cycle control.

Tumor-suppressor genes

After the discovery of proto-oncogenes, a second category of genes related to cancer was identified: the tumor-suppressor genes. We mentioned earlier that the *p53* gene acts as a tumor-suppressor gene, and a number of other such genes exist.

Both copies of a tumor-suppressor gene must lose function for the cancerous phenotype to develop, in contrast to the muta-

tions in proto-oncogenes. Put another way, the proto-oncogenes act in a dominant fashion, and tumor suppressors act in a recessive fashion.

The first tumor-suppressor identified was the **retinoblastoma susceptibility gene (Rb),** which predisposes individuals for a rare form of cancer that affects the retina of the eye. Despite the fact that a cell heterozygous for a mutant *Rb* allele is normal, it is inherited as a dominant in families. The reason is that inheriting a single mutant copy of *Rb* means the individual has only one "good" copy left, and during the hundreds of thousands of divisions that occur to produce the retina, any error that damages the remaining good copy leads to a cancerous cell. A single cancerous cell in the retina then leads to the formation of a retinoblastoma tumor.

The role of the Rb protein in the cell cycle is to integrate signals from growth factors. The Rb protein is called a "pocket protein" because it has binding pockets for other proteins. Its role is therefore to bind important regulatory proteins and prevent them from stimulating the production of the necessary cell cycle proteins, such as cyclins or Cdks (see figure 10.21) discussed previously.

The binding of Rb to other proteins is controlled by phosphorylation: When it is dephosphorylated, it can bind a variety of regulatory proteins, but loses this capacity when phosphorylated. The action of growth factors results in the phosphorylation of Rb protein by a Cdk. This then brings us full circle, because the phosphorylation of Rb releases previously bound regulatory proteins, resulting in the production of S phase cyclins that are necessary for the cell to pass the G_1/S boundary and begin chromosome replication.

Figure 10.24 summarizes the types of genes that can cause cancer when mutated.

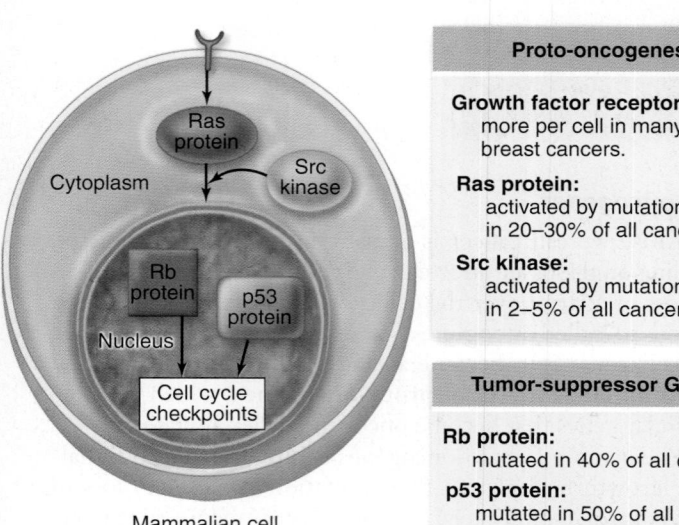

Proto-oncogenes

Growth factor receptor:
more per cell in many breast cancers.

Ras protein:
activated by mutations in 20–30% of all cancers.

Src kinase:
activated by mutations in 2–5% of all cancers.

Tumor-suppressor Genes

Rb protein:
mutated in 40% of all cancers.

p53 protein:
mutated in 50% of all cancers.

Mammalian cell

Figure 10.24 Key proteins associated with human cancers. Mutations in genes encoding key components of the cell division-signaling pathway are responsible for many cancers. Among them are proto-oncogenes encoding growth factor receptors, protein relay switches such as Ras protein, and kinase enzymes such as Src, which act after Ras and growth factor receptors. Mutations that disrupt tumor-suppressor proteins, such as Rb and p53, also foster cancer development.

Learning Outcomes Review 10.6

Cyclin proteins are produced in synchrony with the cell cycle. These proteins complex with cyclin-dependent kinases to drive the cell cyle. Three checkpoints exist in the cell cycle: the G_1/S checkpoint, the G_2/M checkpoint, and the spindle checkpoint. The cell cycle can be halted at these checkpoints if the process is not accurate. The anaphase-promoting complex/cyclosome (APC/C) triggers anaphase by lifting inhibition on a protease that removes cohesin holding chromatids together. The loss of cell cycle control leads to cancer, which can occur by a combination of two basic mechanisms: proto-oncogenes that gain function to become oncogenes, and tumor-suppressor genes that lose function and allow cell proliferation.

■ *How can you distinguish between a tumor suppressor gene and a proto-oncogene?*

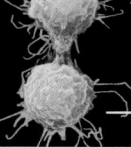

10.1 Bacterial Cell Division

Binary fission is a simple form of cell division.

Prokaryotic cell division is clonal, resulting in two identical cells. Bacterial DNA replication and partitioning of the chromosome are concerted processes.

Proteins control chromosome separation and septum formation.

DNA replication begins at a specific point, the origin, and proceeds bidirectionally to a specific termination site. Newly replicated chromosomes are segregated to opposite poles at the same time as they are replicated. New cells are separated by septation, which involves insertion of new cell membrane and other cellular materials at the midpoint of the cell. A ring of FtsZ and proteins embedded in the cell membrane expands radially inward, pinching the cell into two new cells.

10.2 Eukaryotic Chromosomes

Chromosome number varies among species.

The gain or loss of chromosomes is usually lethal.

Eukaryotic chromosomes exhibit complex structure.

Chromosomes are composed of chromatin, a complex of DNA, and protein. Heterochromatin is not expressed and euchromatin is expressed. The DNA of a single chromosome is a very long, double-stranded fiber. The DNA is wrapped around a core of eight histones to form a nucleosome, which can be further coiled into a 30-nm fiber in interphase cells. During mitosis, chromosomes are further condensed by arranging coiled 30-nm fibers radially around a protein scaffold.

Newly replicated chromosomes remain attached at a constricted area called a centromere, consisting of repeated DNA sequences. After replication, a chromosome consists of two sister chromatids held together at the centromere by a complex of proteins called cohesins (figure 10.7).

10.3 Overview of the Eukaryotic Cell Cycle (figure 10.8)

The cell cycle is divided into five phases.

The phases of the cell cycle are gap 1 (G_1), synthesis (S), gap 2 (G_2), mitosis, and cytokinesis (C). G_1, S, and G_2 are collectively called interphase, and mitosis and cytokinesis together are called M phase.

The duration of the cell cycle varies depending on cell type.

The length of a cell cycle varies with age, cell type, and species. Cells can exit G_1 and enter a nondividing phase called G_0; the G_0 phase can be temporary or permanent.

10.4 Interphase: Preparation for Mitosis

G_1, S, and G_2, are the three subphases of interphase. G_1 is the primary growth phase; during S phase, DNA synthesis occurs. G_2 phase occurs after S phase and before mitosis.

The centromere binds proteins assembled into a disklike structure called a kinetochore where microtubules attach during mitosis. The centromeric DNA is replicated, but the two DNA strands are held together by cohesin proteins.

10.5 M Phase: Chromosome Segregation and the Division of Cytoplasmic Contents (figure 10.11)

During prophase, the mitotic apparatus forms.

In prophase, chromosomes condense, the spindle is formed, and the nuclear envelope disintegrates. In animals cells, centriole pairs separate and migrate to opposite ends of the cell, establishing the axis of nuclear division.

During prometaphase, chromosomes attach to the spindle.

In metaphase, chromosomes align at the equator.

Chromatids of each chromosome are connected to opposite poles by kinetochore microtubules. They are held at the equator of the cell by the tension of being pulled toward opposite poles.

At anaphase, the chromatids separate.

At this point, cohesin proteins holding sister chromatids together at the centromeres are destroyed, and the chromatids are pulled to opposite poles. This movement is called anaphase A, and the movement of poles farther apart is called anaphase B.

During telophase, the nucleus re-forms.

Telophase reverses the events of prophase and prepares the cell for cytokinesis.

In animals cells, a belt of actin pinches off the daughter cells.

A contractile ring of actin under the membrane contracts during cytokinesis.

In plant cells, a cell plate divides the daughter cells.

Fusion of vesicles produces a new membrane in the middle of the cell to produce the cell plate.

In fungi and some protists, daughter nuclei are separated during cytokinesis.

10.6 Control of the Cell Cycle (figure 10.18)

Research uncovered cell cycle control factors.

Experiments showed that there are positive regulators of mitosis, and that there are proteins produced in synchrony with the cell cycle (cyclins). The positive regulators are cyclin-dependent kinases (Cdks). Cdks are complexes of a kinase and a regulatory molecule called cyclin. They phosphorylate proteins to drive the cell cycle.

The cell cycle can be halted at three checkpoints.

Checkpoints are points at which the cell can assess the accuracy of the process and stop if needed. The G_1/S checkpoint is a commitment to divide; the G_2/M checkpoint ensures DNA integrity; and the spindle checkpoint ensures that all chromosomes are attached to spindle fibers, with bipolar orientation.

Cyclin-dependent kinases drive the cell cycle.

The cycle progresses by the action of Cdks. Yeast have only one CDK enzyme; vertebrates have more than four enzymes. During the G_1 phase, G_1 cyclin combines with Cdc2 kinase to form the Cdk that triggers entry into S phase.

The anaphase-promoting complex/cyclosome (APC/C) activates a protease that removes cohesins holding the centromeres of sister chromatids together; the result is to trigger anaphase, separating the chromatids and drawing them to opposite poles. The APC/C also triggers destruction of mitotic cyclins to exit mitosis.

In multicellular eukaryotes, many Cdks and external signals act on the cell cycle.

Growth factors, like platelet-derived growth factor (PDGF), stimulate cell division. This acts through a MAP kinase cascade that results in the production of cyclins and activation of Cdks to stimulate cell division in fibroblasts after tissue injury.

Cancer is a failure of cell cycle control.

Mutations in proto-oncogenes have dominant, gain-of-function effects leading to cancer. Mutations in tumor-suppressor genes are recessive; loss of function of both copies leads to cancer.

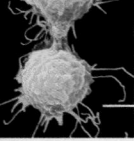

UNDERSTAND

1. Binary fission in prokaryotes does not require the
   a. replication of DNA.
   b. elongation of the cell.
   c. separation of daughter cells by septum formation.
   d. assembly of the nuclear envelope.

2. Chromatin is composed of
   a. RNA and protein.   c. sister chromatids.
   b. DNA and protein.   d. chromosomes.

3. What is a nucleosome?
   a. A region in the cell's nucleus that contains euchromatin
   b. A region of DNA wound around histone proteins
   c. A region of a chromosome made up of multiple loops of chromatin
   d. A 30-nm fiber found in chromatin

4. What is the role of cohesin proteins in cell division?
   a. They organize the DNA of the chromosomes into highly condensed structures.
   b. They hold the DNA of the sister chromatids together.
   c. They help the cell divide into two daughter cells.
   d. They connect microtubules and chromosomes.

5. The kinetochore is a structure that functions to
   a. connect the centromere to microtubules.
   b. connect centrioles to microtubules.
   c. aid in chromosome condensation.
   d. aid in chromosomes cohesion.

6. Separation of the sister chromatids occurs during
   a. prophase.   c. anaphase.
   b. prometaphase.   d. telophase.

7. Why is cytokinesis an important part of cell division?
   a. It is responsible for the proper separation of genetic information.
   b. It is responsible for the proper separation of the cytoplasmic contents.
   c. It triggers the movement of a cell through the cell cycle.
   d. It allows cells to halt at checkpoints.

APPLY

1. What steps in the cell cycle represent irreversible commitments?
   a. The S/G_2 checkpoint   c. Anaphase
   b. The G_1/S checkpoint   d. Both b and c

2. Cyclin-dependent kinases (Cdks) are regulated by
   a. the periodic destruction of cyclins.
   b. bipolar attachment of chromosomes to the spindle.
   c. DNA synthesis.
   d. both a and b.

3. The bacterial SMC proteins, eukaryotic cohesin proteins, and condensin proteins share a similar structure. Functionally they all
   a. interact with microtubules.
   b. can act as kinase enzymes.
   c. interact with DNA to compact or hold strands together.
   d. connect chromosomes to cytoskeletal elements.

4. Genetically, proto-oncogenes act in a dominant fashion. This is because
   a. there is only one copy of each proto-oncogene in the genome.
   b. they act in a gain-of-function fashion to turn on the cell cycle.
   c. they act in a loss-of-function fashion to turn off the cell cycle.
   d. they require that both genomic copies are altered to affect function.

5. The metaphase to anaphase transition involves
   a. new force being generated to pull the chromatids apart.
   b. an increase in force on sister chromatids to pull them apart.
   c. completing DNA replication of centromeres allowing chromosomes to be pulled apart.
   d. loss of cohesion between sister chromatids.

6. The main difference between bacterial cell division and eukaryotic cell division is that
   a. since bacteria only have one chromosome, they can count the number of copies in the cell.
   b. eukaryotes mark their chromosomes to identify them and bacteria do not.
   c. bacterial DNA replication and chromosome segregation are concerted processes but in eukaryotes they are separated in time.
   d. none of the above

7. In animal cells, cytokinesis is accomplished by a contractile ring containing actin. The related process in bacteria is
   a. chromosome segregation, which also appears to use an actin-like protein.
   b. septation via a ring of FtsZ protein, which is an actin-like protein.
   c. cytokinesis, which requires formation of a cell plate via vesicular fusion.
   d. septation via a ring of FtsZ protein, which is a tubulin-like protein.

SYNTHESIZE

1. Regulation of the cell cycle is very complex and involves multiple proteins. In yeast, a complex of cdc2 and a mitotic cyclin is responsible for moving the cell past the G_2/M checkpoint. The activity of the cyclin-dependent kinase cdc2 is inhibited when it is phosphorylated by the kinase, Wee-1. What would you predict would be the phenotype of a Wee-1 mutant yeast? What other genes could be altered in a Wee-1 deficient mutant strain that would make the cells act normally?

2. Review your knowledge of signaling pathways (chapter 9). Create an outline illustrating how a growth factor (ligand) can lead to the production of a cyclin protein that would trigger S phase.

3. Compare and contrast how mutations in cellular proto-oncogenes and in tumor suppressor genes can lead to cancer cells.

ONLINE RESOURCE

www.ravenbiology.com

Understand, Apply, and Synthesize—enhance your study with animations that bring concepts to life and practice tests to assess your understanding. Your instructor may also recommend the interactive eBook, individualized learning tools, and more.

Chapter

11

Sexual Reproduction and Meiosis

Chapter Outline

11.1   Sexual Reproduction Requires Meiosis

11.2   Features of Meiosis

11.3   The Process of Meiosis

11.4   Summing Up: Meiosis Versus Mitosis

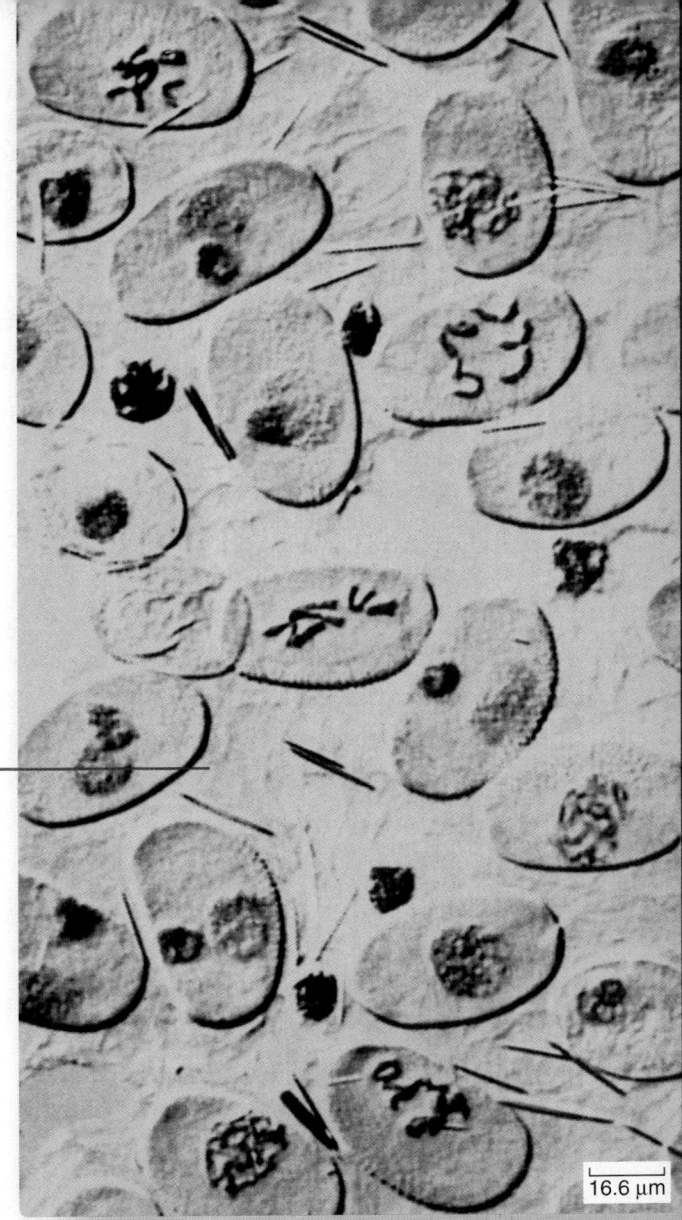

16.6 μm

Part ▮▮▮ Genetic and Molecular Biology

Introduction

Most animals and plants reproduce sexually. Gametes of opposite sex unite to form a cell that, dividing repeatedly by mitosis, eventually gives rise to an adult body with some 100 trillion cells. The gametes that form the initial cell are the products of a special form of cell division called meiosis, *visible in the photo above, and the subject of this chapter. Meiosis is far more intricate than mitosis, and the details behind it are not as well understood. The basic process, however, is clear. Also clear are the profound consequences of sexual reproduction: It plays a key role in generating the tremendous genetic diversity that is the raw material of evolution.*

11.1 Sexual Reproduction Requires Meiosis

Learning Outcomes

1.   *Understand the function of meiosis in sexual reproduction.*
2.   *Distinguish between germ-line and somatic cells.*

The essence of sexual reproduction is the genetic contribution of two cells. This mode of reproduction imposes difficulties for sexually reproducing organisms that biologists recognized early on. We are only recently making progress on the underlying mechanism for the elaborate behavior of chromosomes during meiosis. To begin, we briefly consider the history of meiosis and its relationship to sexual reproduction.

Meiosis reduces the number of chromosomes

Only a few years after Walther Flemming's discovery of chromosomes in 1879, Belgian cytologist Edouard van Beneden was surprised to find different numbers of chromosomes in different types of cells in the roundworm *Ascaris*. Specifically, he observed that the **gametes** (eggs and sperm) each contained two chromosomes, but all of the nonreproductive cells, or **somatic cells,** of embryos and mature individuals each contained four.

From his observations, van Beneden proposed in 1883 that an egg and a sperm, each containing half the complement of chromosomes found in other cells, fuse to produce a single cell called a **zygote.** The zygote, like all of the cells ultimately derived from it, contains two copies of each chromosome. The fusion of gametes to form a new cell is called **fertilization,** or **syngamy.**

It was clear even to early investigators that gamete formation must involve some mechanism that reduces the number of chromosomes to half the number found in other cells. If it did not, the chromosome number would double with each fertilization, and after only a few generations, the number of chromosomes in each cell would become impossibly large. For example, in just 10 generations, the 46 chromosomes present in human cells would increase to over 47,000 (46×2^{10}).

The number of chromosomes does not explode in this way because of a special reduction division, **meiosis.** Meiosis occurs during gamete formation, producing cells with half the normal number of chromosomes. The subsequent fusion of two of these cells ensures a consistent chromosome number from one generation to the next.

Sexual life cycles have both haploid and diploid stages

Meiosis and fertilization together constitute a cycle of reproduction. Two sets of chromosomes are present in the somatic cells of adult individuals, making them *diploid* cells, but only one set is present in the gametes, which are thus *haploid*. Reproduction that involves this alternation of meiosis and fertilization is called **sexual reproduction.** Its outstanding characteristic is that offspring inherit chromosomes from *two* parents (figure 11.1). You, for example, inherited 23 chromosomes from your mother (maternal homologue), and 23 from your father (paternal homologue).

The life cycles of all sexually reproducing organisms follow a pattern of alternation between diploid and haploid chromosome numbers, but there is some variation in the life cycles. Many types of algae, for example, spend the majority of their life cycle in a haploid state. The zygote undergoing meiosis produces haploid cells that then undergo mitosis. Some plants and some algae alternate between a multicellular haploid phase and a multicellular diploid phase (specific examples can be found in chapters 30 and 31). In most animals, the diploid state dominates; the zygote first undergoes mitosis to produce diploid cells. Then later in the life cycle, some of these diploid cells undergo meiosis to produce haploid gametes (figure 11.2).

Germ-line cells are set aside early in animal development

In animals, the single diploid zygote undergoes mitosis to give rise to all of the cells in the adult body. The cells that will eventually undergo meiosis to produce gametes are set aside from somatic cells early in the course of development. These cells are referred to as **germ-line cells.**

Both the somatic cells and the gamete-producing germ-line cells are diploid, but whereas somatic cells undergo mitosis to form genetically identical, diploid daughter cells, gamete-producing germ-line cells undergo meiosis to produce haploid gametes (see figure 11.2).

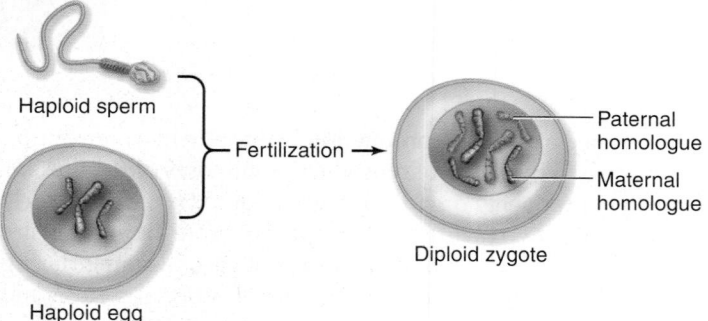

Figure 11.1 Diploid cells carry chromosomes from two parents. A diploid cell contains two versions of each chromosome, a maternal homologue contributed by the haploid egg of the mother, and a paternal homologue contributed by the haploid sperm of the father.

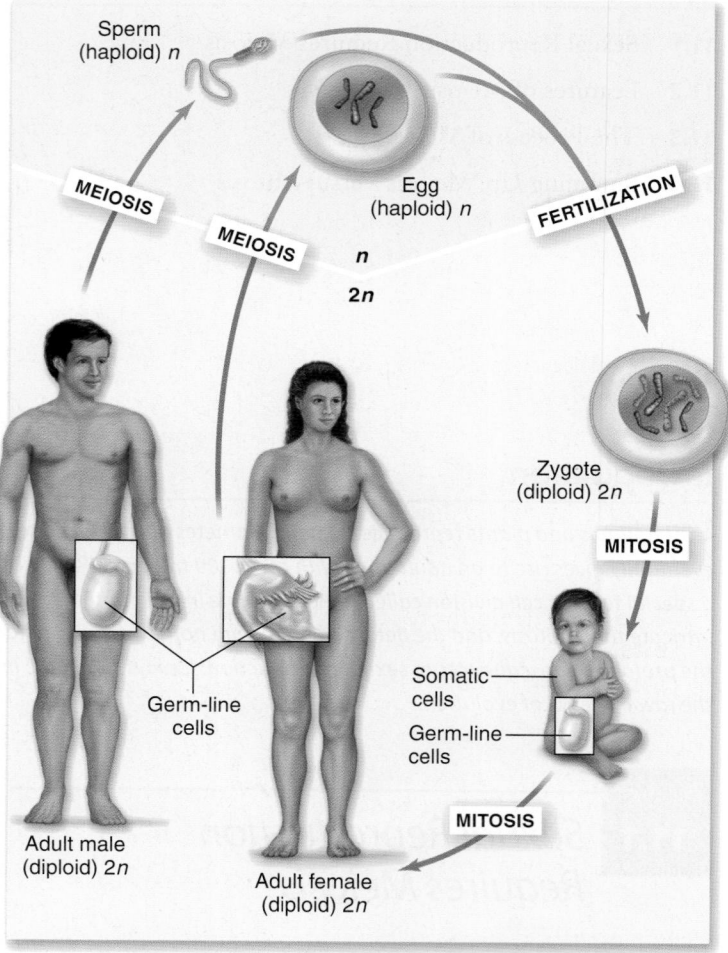

Figure 11.2 The sexual life cycle in animals. In animals, the zygote undergoes mitotic divisions and gives rise to all the cells of the adult body. Germ-line cells are set aside early in development and undergo meiosis to form the haploid gametes (eggs or sperm). The rest of the body cells are called somatic cells.

11.2 Features of Meiosis

Learning Outcomes

1. Describe how homologous chromosomes pair during meiosis.
2. Explain why meiosis I is called the reductive division.

The mechanism of meiotic cell division varies in important details in different organisms. These variations are particularly evident in the chromosomal separation mechanisms:

Those found in protists and fungi are very different from those in plants and animals, which we describe here.

Meiosis in a diploid organism consists of two rounds of division, called **meiosis I** and **meiosis II**, with each round containing prophase, metaphase, anaphase, and telophase stages. Before describing the details of this process, we first examine the features of meiosis that distinguish it from mitosis.

Homologous chromosomes pair during meiosis

During early prophase I of meiosis, homologous chromosomes find each other and become closely associated, a process called pairing, or **synapsis** (figure 11.3*a*). Despite a long history of investigation, molecular details remain unclear. Biologists have used electron microscopy, data from genetic crosses, and biochemical analysis to shed light on synapsis. Thus far the results of their investigations have not been integrated into a complete picture.

The synaptonemal complex

It is clear that homologous chromosomes find their proper partners and become intimately associated during prophase I. This process includes the formation in many species of an elaborate structure called the **synaptonemal complex,** consisting of the homologues paired closely along a lattice of proteins between them (figure 11.3*b*). The components of the synaptonemal complex include a meiosis-specific form of cohesin, a type of protein that joins sister chromatids during mitosis (described in chapter 10). This form of cohesin helps to join homologues as well as sister chromatids. The result is that all four chromatids of the two homologues are closely associated during this phase of meiosis. This structure is also sometimes called a *tetrad* or *bivalent.*

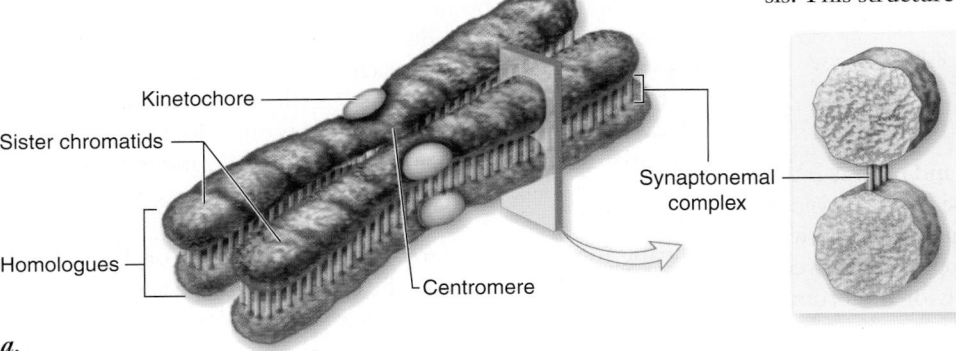
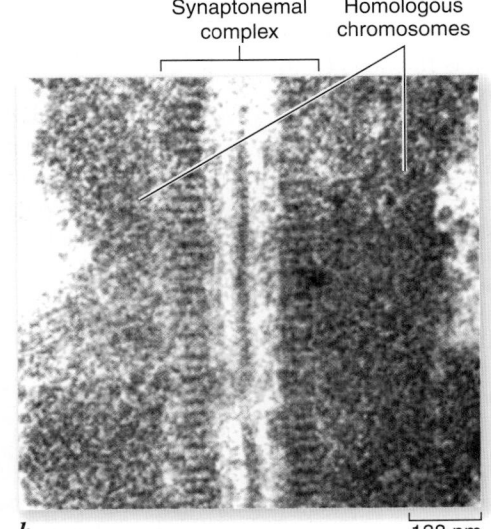
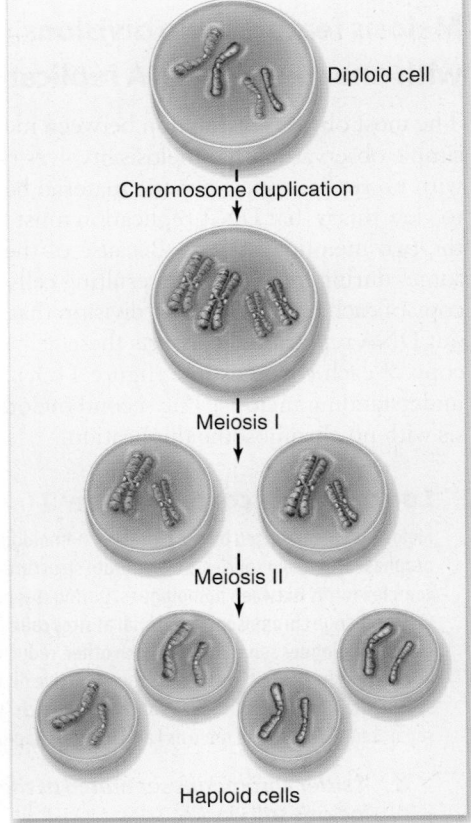

Figure 11.3 Unique features of meiosis. *a.* Homologous chromosomes pair during prophase I of meiosis. This process, called synapsis, produces homologues connected by a structure called the synaptonemal complex. The paired homologues can physically exchange parts, a process called crossing over. *b.* The synaptonemal complex of the ascomycete *Neotiella rutilans*, a cup fungus. *c.* This pairing allows the homologous pairs, and not sister chromatids, to separate as a unit during meiosis I. Because chromosomes are not duplicated again before meiosis II, disjunction of sister chromatids yields the final haploid products.

The exchange of genetic material between homologues

While homologues are paired during prophase I, another process unique to meiosis occurs: genetic **recombination**, or **crossing over**. This process literally allows the homologues to exchange chromosomal material. The cytological observation of this phenomenon is called crossing over, and its detection genetically is called recombination—because alleles of genes that were formerly on separate homologues can now be found on the same homologue. (Genetic recombination is covered in detail in chapter 13.)

The sites of crossing over are called **chiasmata** (singular, *chiasma*), and these sites of contact are maintained until anaphase I. The physical connection of homologues due to crossing over and the continued connection of the sister chromatids lock homologues together.

Homologue association and separation

The association between the homologues persists throughout meiosis I and dictates the behavior of the chromosomes. During metaphase I, the paired homologues move to the metaphase plate and become oriented with homologues of each pair attached to opposite poles of the spindle. By contrast, in mitosis homologues behave independently of one another.

Then, during anaphase I, homologues are pulled to opposite poles for each pair of chromosomes. This again is in contrast to mitosis, in which sister chromatids, not homologues, are pulled to opposite poles.

You can now see why the first division is termed the "reduction division"—it results in daughter cells that contain one homologue from each chromosome pair. The second meiotic division does not further reduce the number of chromosomes; it will merely separate the sister chromatids for each homologue.

Meiosis features two divisions with one round of DNA replication

The most obvious distinction between meiosis and mitosis is the simple observation that meiosis involves two successive divisions with no replication of genetic material between them. One way to view this is that DNA replication must be suppressed between the two meiotic divisions. Because of the behavior of chromosomes during meiosis I, the resulting cells contain one replicated copy of each chromosome. A division that acts like mitosis, without DNA replication, converts these cells into ones with a single copy of each chromosome (figure 11.3c). This is the last key to understanding meiosis: The second meiotic division is like mitosis with no chromosome duplication.

Learning Outcomes Review 11.2

Meiosis is characterized by the pairing of homologous chromosomes during prophase I. In many species, an elaborate structure called the synaptonemal complex forms between homologues. During this pairing, homologues may exchange chromosomal material at sites called chiasmata. In meiosis I, the homologues separate from each other, reducing the chromosome number to the haploid state (thus the reductive division). It is followed by a second division without replication, during which sister chromatids become separated. The result of meiosis I and II is four haploid cells.

■ *If sister chromatids separated at the first division, would meiosis still work?*

Learning Outcomes

1. **Describe the behavior of chromosomes through both meiotic divisions.**
2. **Explain the importance of monopolar attachment of homologous pairs at metaphase I.**
3. **Differentiate between the events of anaphase I and anaphase II of meiosis.**

To understand meiosis, it is necessary to carefully follow the behavior of chromosomes during each division. The events of meiosis depend on homologues exchanging chromosomal material by crossing over. This allows sister chromatid cohesion around the sites of exchange to hold homologues together. The loss of sister chromatid cohesion is then different on the chromosome arms and at the centromeres: it is lost at anaphase I on the chromosome arms but is retained at the centromeres until anaphase II.

Prophase I sets the stage for the reductive division

Meiotic cells have an interphase period that is similar to mitosis with G_1, S, and G_2 phases. After interphase, germ-line cells enter meiosis I. In prophase I, the DNA coils tighter, and individual chromosomes first become visible under the light microscope as a matrix of fine threads. Because the DNA has already replicated before the onset of meiosis, each of these threads actually consists of two sister chromatids joined at their centromeres. In prophase I, homologous chromosomes become closely associated in synapsis, exchange segments by crossing over, and then separate.

Synapsis

During interphase in germ-line cells, the ends of the chromatids seem to be attached to the nuclear envelope at specific sites. The sites the homologues attach to are adjacent, so that during prophase I the members of each homologous pair of chromosomes are brought close together. Homologous pairs then align side by side, apparently guided by heterochromatin sequences, in the process of synapsis.

This association joins homologues along their entire length. The sister chromatids of each homologue are also joined by the cohesin complex in a process called *sister chromatid cohesion* (similar to what happens during mitosis). This brings all four chromatids for each set of paired homologues into close association.

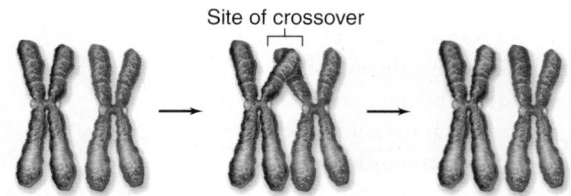

Figure 11.4 The results of crossing over. During crossing over, homologous chromosomes may exchange segments.

Meiosis I		Mitosis	

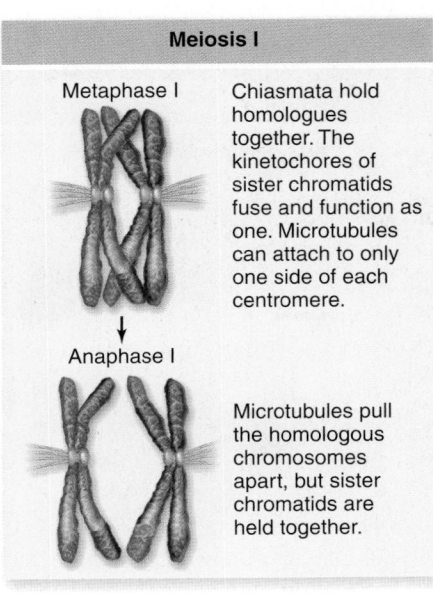

Meiosis I

Metaphase I

Chiasmata hold homologues together. The kinetochores of sister chromatids fuse and function as one. Microtubules can attach to only one side of each centromere.

Anaphase I

Microtubules pull the homologous chromosomes apart, but sister chromatids are held together.

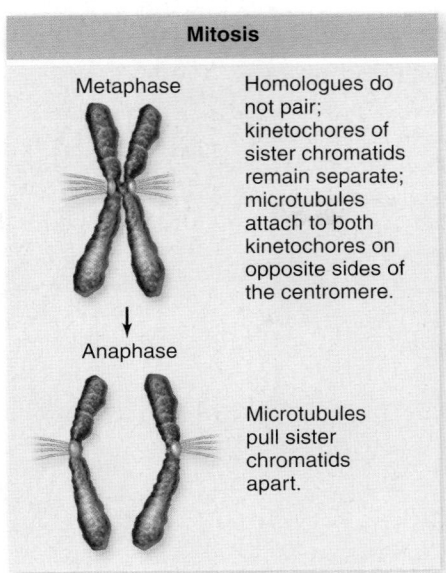

Mitosis

Metaphase

Homologues do not pair; kinetochores of sister chromatids remain separate; microtubules attach to both kinetochores on opposite sides of the centromere.

Anaphase

Microtubules pull sister chromatids apart.

Figure 11.5 Alignment of chromosomes differs between meiosis I and mitosis. In metaphase I of meiosis I, the chiasmata and connections between sister chromatids hold homologous chromosomes together; paired kinetochores for sister chromatids of each homologue become attached to microtubules from one pole. By the end of meiosis I, connections between sister chromatid arms are broken as microtubules shorten, pulling the homologous chromosomes apart. The sister chromatids remain joined by their centromeres. In mitosis, microtubules from opposite poles attach to the kinetochore of each sister centromere; when the connections between sister centromeres are broken microtubules shorten, pulling the sister chromatids to opposite poles.

Crossing over

Along with the synaptonemal complex that forms during prophase I (see figure 11.3), another kind of structure appears that correlates in timing with the recombination process. These are called *recombination nodules*, and they are thought to contain the enzymatic machinery necessary to break and rejoin chromatids of homologous chromosomes.

Crossing over involves a complex series of events in which DNA segments are exchanged between nonsister chromatids (figure 11.4). Crossing over between sister chromatids is suppressed during meiosis. Reciprocal crossovers between nonsister chromatids are controlled such that each chromosome arm usually has one or a few crossovers per meiosis, no matter what the size of the chromosome. Human chromosomes typically have two or three.

When crossing over is complete, the synaptonemal complex breaks down, and the homologous chromosomes become less tightly associated but remain attached by chiasmata. At this point, there are four chromatids for each type of chromosome (two homologous chromosomes, each of which consists of two sister chromatids).

The four chromatids do not separate completely because they are held together in two ways: (1) The two sister chromatids of each homologue, recently created by DNA replication, are held together by their common centromeres; and (2) the paired homologues are held together at the points where crossing over occurred by sister chromatid cohesion around the site of exchange. These points are the chiasmata that can be observed microscopically. Like small rings moving down two strands of rope, the chiasmata move to the end of the chromosome arm before metaphase I.

While the elaborate behavior of chromosome pairing is taking place, other events must occur during prophase I. The nuclear envelope must be dispersed, along with the interphase structure of microtubules. The microtubules are formed into a spindle, just as in mitosis.

During metaphase I, paired homologues align

By metaphase I, the second stage of meiosis I, the chiasmata have moved down the paired chromosomes to the ends. At this point, they are called *terminal chiasmata*. Terminal chiasmata

hold the homologous chromosomes together in metaphase I so that homologues can be aligned at the equator of the cell.

The capture of microtubules by kinetochores occurs such that the kinetochores of sister chromatids act as a single unit. This results in microtubules from opposite poles becoming attached to the kinetochores of *homologues*, and not to those of sister chromatids (figure 11.5).

The ability of sister centromeres to behave as a unit during meiosis I is not understood. It has been suggested, based on electron microscope data, that the centromere–kinetochore complex of sister chromatids is compacted during meiosis I, allowing them to function as a single unit.

The monopolar attachment of centromeres of sister chromatids would be disastrous in mitosis, but it is critical to meiosis I. It produces tension on the homologues, which are joined by chiasmata and sister chromatid cohesion, pulling paired homologues to the equator of the cell. In this way, each joined pair of homologues lines up on the metaphase plate (see figure 11.5).

The orientation of each pair on the spindle axis is random; either the maternal or the paternal homologue may be oriented toward a given pole (figure 11.6; see also figure 11.7).

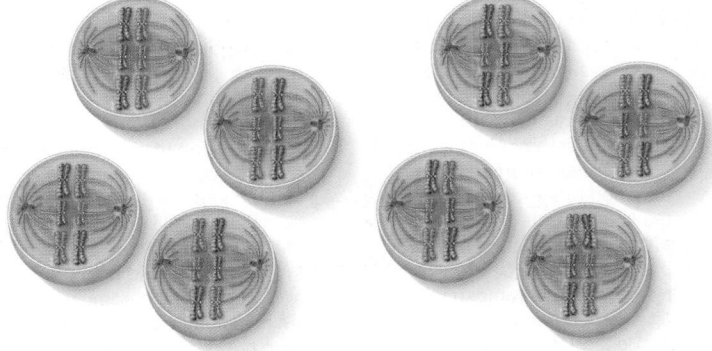

Figure 11.6 Random orientation of chromosomes on the metaphase plate. The number of possible chromosome orientations equals 2 raised to the power of the number of chromosome pairs. In this hypothetical cell with three chromosome pairs, eight (2^3) possible orientations exist. Each orientation produces gametes with different combinations of parental chromosomes.

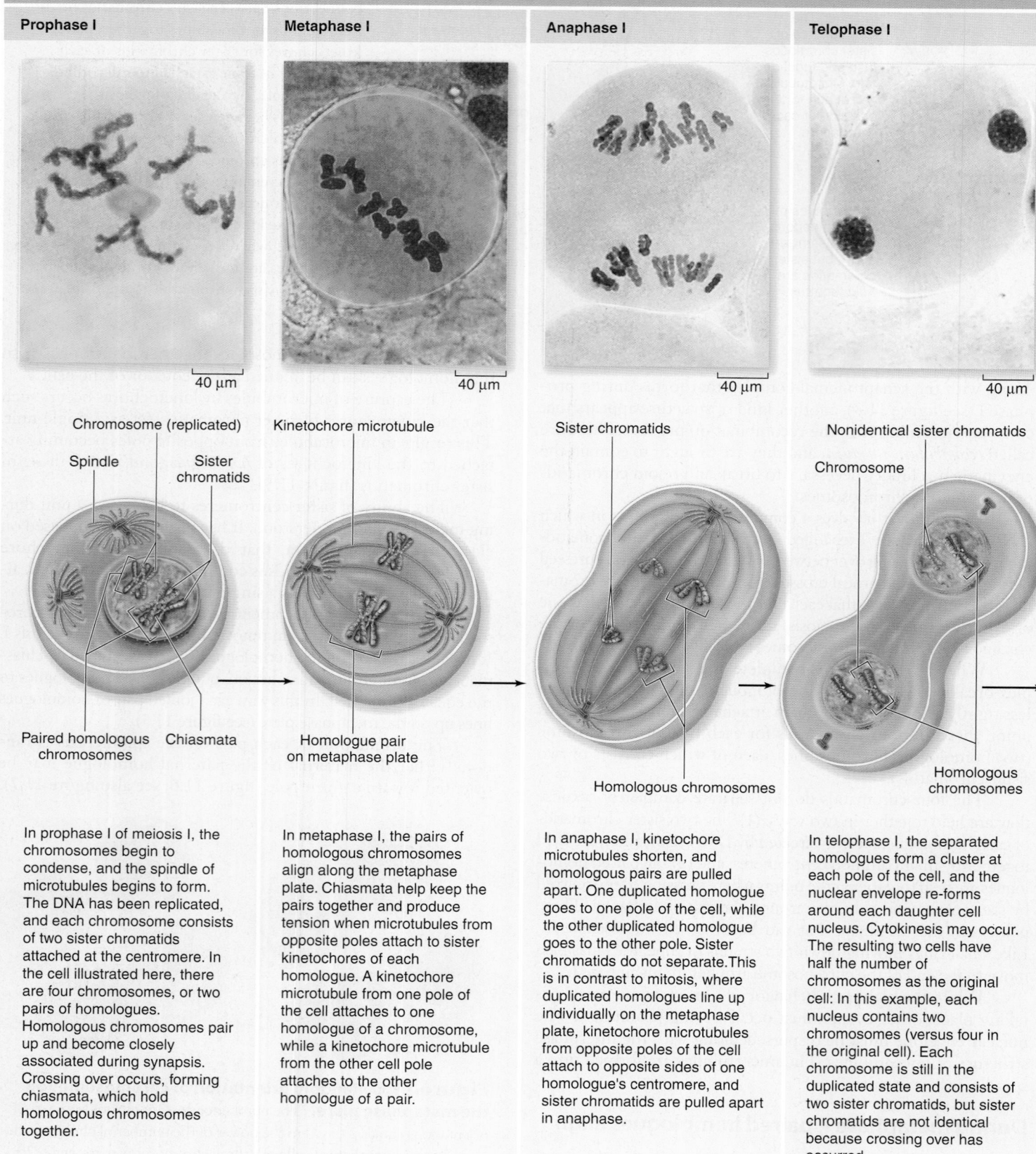

Prophase I

Chromosome (replicated)

Spindle | Sister chromatids

Paired homologous chromosomes | Chiasmata

In prophase I of meiosis I, the chromosomes begin to condense, and the spindle of microtubules begins to form. The DNA has been replicated, and each chromosome consists of two sister chromatids attached at the centromere. In the cell illustrated here, there are four chromosomes, or two pairs of homologues. Homologous chromosomes pair up and become closely associated during synapsis. Crossing over occurs, forming chiasmata, which hold homologous chromosomes together.

Metaphase I

Kinetochore microtubule

Homologue pair on metaphase plate

In metaphase I, the pairs of homologous chromosomes align along the metaphase plate. Chiasmata help keep the pairs together and produce tension when microtubules from opposite poles attach to sister kinetochores of each homologue. A kinetochore microtubule from one pole of the cell attaches to one homologue of a chromosome, while a kinetochore microtubule from the other cell pole attaches to the other homologue of a pair.

Anaphase I

Sister chromatids

Homologous chromosomes

In anaphase I, kinetochore microtubules shorten, and homologous pairs are pulled apart. One duplicated homologue goes to one pole of the cell, while the other duplicated homologue goes to the other pole. Sister chromatids do not separate. This is in contrast to mitosis, where duplicated homologues line up individually on the metaphase plate, kinetochore microtubules from opposite poles of the cell attach to opposite sides of one homologue's centromere, and sister chromatids are pulled apart in anaphase.

Telophase I

Nonidentical sister chromatids

Chromosome

Homologous chromosomes

In telophase I, the separated homologues form a cluster at each pole of the cell, and the nuclear envelope re-forms around each daughter cell nucleus. Cytokinesis may occur. The resulting two cells have half the number of chromosomes as the original cell: In this example, each nucleus contains two chromosomes (versus four in the original cell). Each chromosome is still in the duplicated state and consists of two sister chromatids, but sister chromatids are not identical because crossing over has occurred.

Figure 11.7 **The stages of meiosis.** Meiosis in plant cells (photos) and animal cells (drawings) is shown.

MEIOSIS II

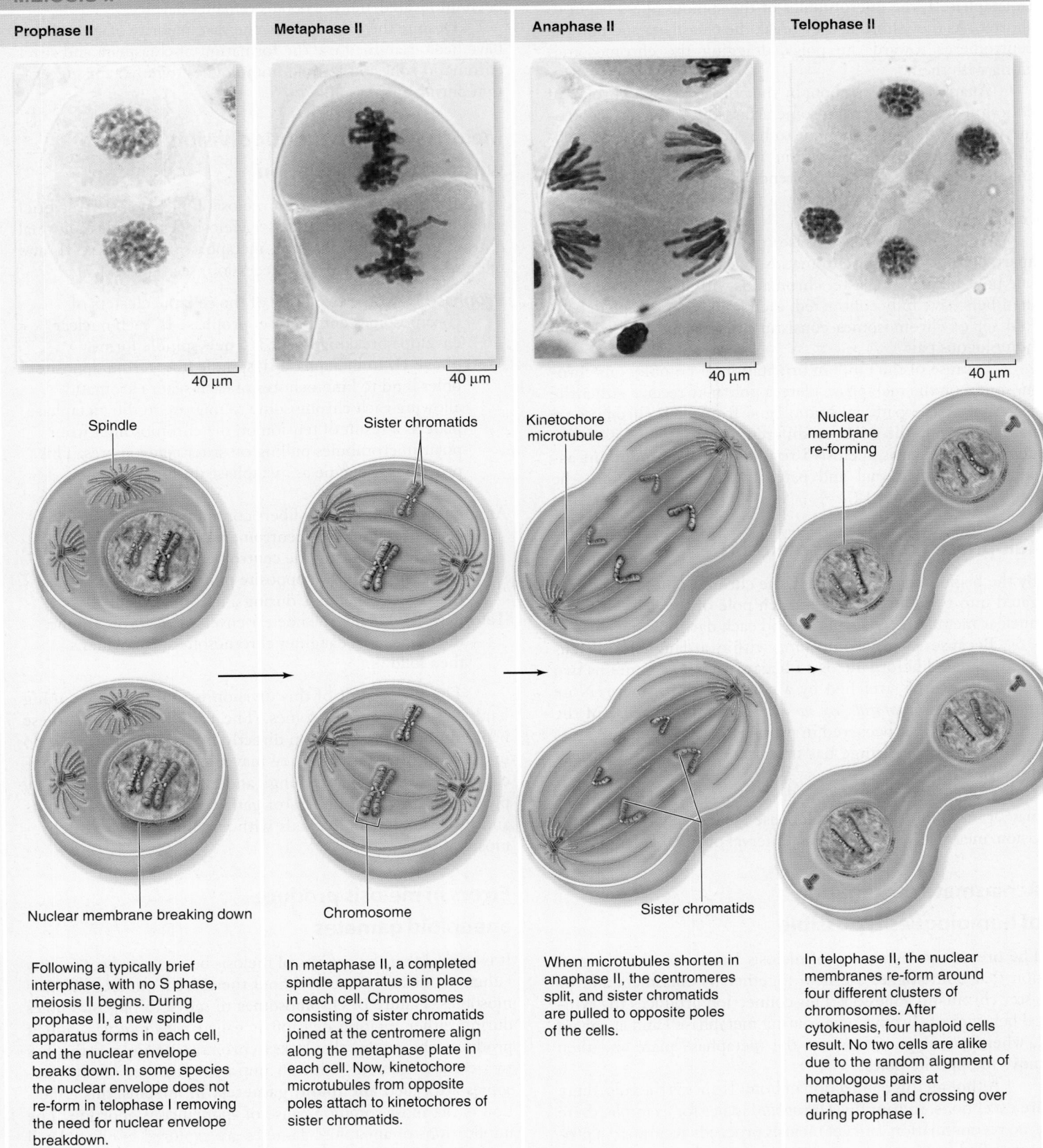

| Prophase II | Metaphase II | Anaphase II | Telophase II |

40 µm   40 µm   40 µm   40 µm

Spindle

Sister chromatids

Kinetochore microtubule

Nuclear membrane re-forming

Nuclear membrane breaking down

Chromosome

Sister chromatids

Following a typically brief interphase, with no S phase, meiosis II begins. During prophase II, a new spindle apparatus forms in each cell, and the nuclear envelope breaks down. In some species the nuclear envelope does not re-form in telophase I removing the need for nuclear envelope breakdown.

In metaphase II, a completed spindle apparatus is in place in each cell. Chromosomes consisting of sister chromatids joined at the centromere align along the metaphase plate in each cell. Now, kinetochore microtubules from opposite poles attach to kinetochores of sister chromatids.

When microtubules shorten in anaphase II, the centromeres split, and sister chromatids are pulled to opposite poles of the cells.

In telophase II, the nuclear membranes re-form around four different clusters of chromosomes. After cytokinesis, four haploid cells result. No two cells are alike due to the random alignment of homologous pairs at metaphase I and crossing over during prophase I.

chapter **11** *Sexual Reproduction and Meiosis*

Anaphase I results from the differential loss of sister chromatid cohesion along the arms

In anaphase I, the microtubules of the spindle fibers begin to shorten. As they shorten, they break the chiasmata and pull the centromeres toward the poles, dragging the chromosomes along with them.

Anaphase I comes about by the release of sister chromatid cohesion along the chromosome arms, but not at the centromeres. This release is thought to be the result of the destruction of meiosis-specific cohesin in a process analogous to anaphase in mitosis. The difference is that the destruction is inhibited at the centromeres by a mechanism that is only recently becoming clear.

As a result of this release, the homologues are pulled apart, but not the sister chromatids. Each homologue moves to one pole, taking both sister chromatids with it. When the spindle fibers have fully contracted, each pole has a complete haploid set of chromosomes consisting of one member of each homologous pair.

Because of the random orientation of homologous chromosomes on the metaphase plate, a pole may receive either the maternal or the paternal homologue from each chromosome pair. As a result, the genes on different chromosomes assort independently; that is, meiosis I results in the **independent assortment** of maternal and paternal chromosomes into the gametes (see chapter 12).

Telophase I completes meiosis I

By the beginning of telophase I, the chromosomes have segregated into two clusters, one at each pole of the cell. Now the nuclear membrane re-forms around each daughter nucleus.

Because each chromosome within a daughter nucleus had replicated before meiosis I began, each now contains two sister chromatids attached by a common centromere. Note that *the sister chromatids are no longer identical* because of the crossing over that occurred in prophase I (see figure 11.7); as you will see, this change has important implications for genetic variability.

Cytokinesis, the division of the cytoplasm and its contents, may or may not occur after telophase I. The second meiotic division, meiosis II, occurs after an interval of variable length.

Achiasmate segregation of homologues is possible

The preceding description of meiosis I relies on the observation that homologues are held together by chiasmata and by sister chromatid cohesion. This connection produces the critical behavior of chromosomes during metaphase I and anaphase I, when homologues move to the metaphase plate and then move to opposite poles.

Although this connection of homologues is the rule, there are exceptions. In fruit fly (*Drosophila*) males for example, there is no recombination, and yet meiosis proceeds accurately, a process called **achiasmate segregation** ("without chiasmata").

This seems to involve an alternative mechanism for joining homologues and then allowing their segregation during anaphase I. Telomeres and other heterochromatic sequences have been implicated, but the details remain unclear.

Despite these exceptions, the vast majority of species that have been examined use the formation of chiasmata and sister chromatid cohesion to hold homologues together for segregation during anaphase I.

Meiosis II is like a mitotic division without DNA replication

Typically, interphase between meiosis I and meiosis II is brief and does not include an S phase: Meiosis II resembles a normal mitotic division. Prophase II, metaphase II, anaphase II, and telophase II follow in quick succession (see figure 11.7).

Prophase II. At the two poles of the cell, the clusters of chromosomes enter a brief prophase II, each nuclear envelope breaking down as a new spindle forms.

Metaphase II. In metaphase II, spindle fibers from opposite poles bind to kinetochores of each sister chromatid, allowing each chromosome to migrate to the metaphase plate as a result of tension on the chromosomes from polar microtubules pulling on sister centromeres. This process is the same as metaphase during a mitotic division.

Anaphase II. The spindle fibers contract, and the cohesin complex joining the centromeres of sister chromatids is destroyed, splitting the centromeres and pulling the sister chromatids to opposite poles. This process is also the same as anaphase during a mitotic division.

Telophase II. Finally, the nuclear envelope re-forms around the four sets of daughter chromosomes. Cytokinesis then follows.

The final result of this division is four cells containing haploid sets of chromosomes. The cells that contain these haploid nuclei may develop directly into gametes, as they do in animals. Alternatively, they may themselves divide mitotically, as they do in plants, fungi, and many protists, eventually producing greater numbers of gametes or, as in some plants and insects, adult individuals with varying numbers of chromosome sets.

Errors in meiosis produce aneuploid gametes

It is critical that the process of meiosis be accurate because any failure produces gametes without the correct number of chromosomes. Failure of chromosomes to move to opposite poles during either meiotic division is called *nondisjunction*, and it produces one gamete that lacks a chromosome and one that has two copies. Gametes with an improper number of chromosomes are called **aneuploid gametes.** In humans, this condition is the most common cause of spontaneous abortion. The implications of aneuploid gametes are explored in more detail in chapter 13.

11.4 Summing Up: Meiosis Versus Mitosis

The key to meiosis is understanding the differences between meiosis and mitosis. The basic machinery in both processes is the same, but the behavior of chromosomes is distinctly different during the first meiotic division (figure 11.8).

Meiosis is characterized by four distinct features:

1. Homologous pairing and crossing over joins maternal and paternal homologues during meiosis I.
2. Sister chromatids remain connected at the centromere and segregate together during anaphase I.
3. Kinetochores of sister chromatids are attached to the same pole in meiosis I and to opposite poles in mitosis.
4. DNA replication is suppressed between the two meiotic divisions.

Although the underlying molecular mechanisms are unclear, we will consider what we know of each of these features in the following sections.

Homologous pairing is specific to meiosis

The pairing of homologues during prophase I of meiosis is the first deviation from mitosis and sets the stage for all of the subsequent differences (see figure 11.8). How homologues find each other and become aligned is one of the great mysteries of meiosis. Some cytological evidence implicates telomeres and other specific sites as being necessary for pairing, but this finding does little to clarify the essential process.

Some light has been shed on the mechanisms with the discovery of meiosis-specific cohesin proteins. In yeast, the protein Rec8 replaces the mitotic Scc1 protein as part of the cohesin complex. You saw in chapter 10 that Scc1 is destroyed during anaphase of mitosis to allow sister chromatids to be pulled to opposite poles. The replacement of this critical cohesin component with a meiosis-specific version seems to be a common feature in systems analyzed to date.

Synaptonemal complex proteins have been identified in diverse species, but these proteins show little sequence conservation. This is despite the similarity of structures observed cytologically. The transverse elements, while showing no sequence conservation, do share the feature of coiled-coil domains that promote protein–protein interactions.

The molecular details of the recombination process that produces crossing over are complex, but many of the proteins involved have been identified. The process is initiated with the introduction of a double-strand break in one homologue. This explains the similarity in the machinery necessary for meiotic recombination and the machinery involved in the repair of double-strand breaks in DNA. Recombination probably first evolved as a repair mechanism and was later co-opted for use in disjoining chromosomes. The importance of recombination for proper disjunction is clear from the observation in many organisms that loss of function for recombination proteins also results in higher levels of nondisjunction.

Sister chromatid cohesion is maintained through meiosis I but released in meiosis II

Meiosis I is characterized by the segregation of homologues, not sister chromatids, during anaphase. For this separation to occur, the centromeres of sister chromatids must move to the same pole, or cosegregate, during anaphase I. This means that meiosis-specific cohesin proteins must first be removed from the chromosome arms, then later from sister centromeres.

Homologues are joined by chiasmata, and sister chromatid cohesion around the site of exchange then holds homologues together. The destruction of Rec8 protein on the chromosome arms appears to be what allows homologues to be pulled apart at anaphase I.

This leaves the key distinction between meiosis and mitosis being the maintenance of sister chromatid cohesion at the centromere during all of meiosis I, but the loss of cohesion from the chromosome arms during anaphase I (see figure 11.8). Recently, some light was shed on this problem with the identification of conserved proteins, called Shugoshin (a Japanese term meaning "guardian spirit") required for cohesin protection from separase-mediated cleavage during meiosis I (figure 11.9). Mice have two Shugoshins: Sgo-1 and Sgo-2. Depletion of Sgo-2 results in early sister chromatid separation. This leaves the problem of why Sgo-2 acts only at anaphase I and not anaphase II. It has been suggested that the tension produced by anaphase II causes Sgo-2 to migrate from the centromere to the kinetochore.

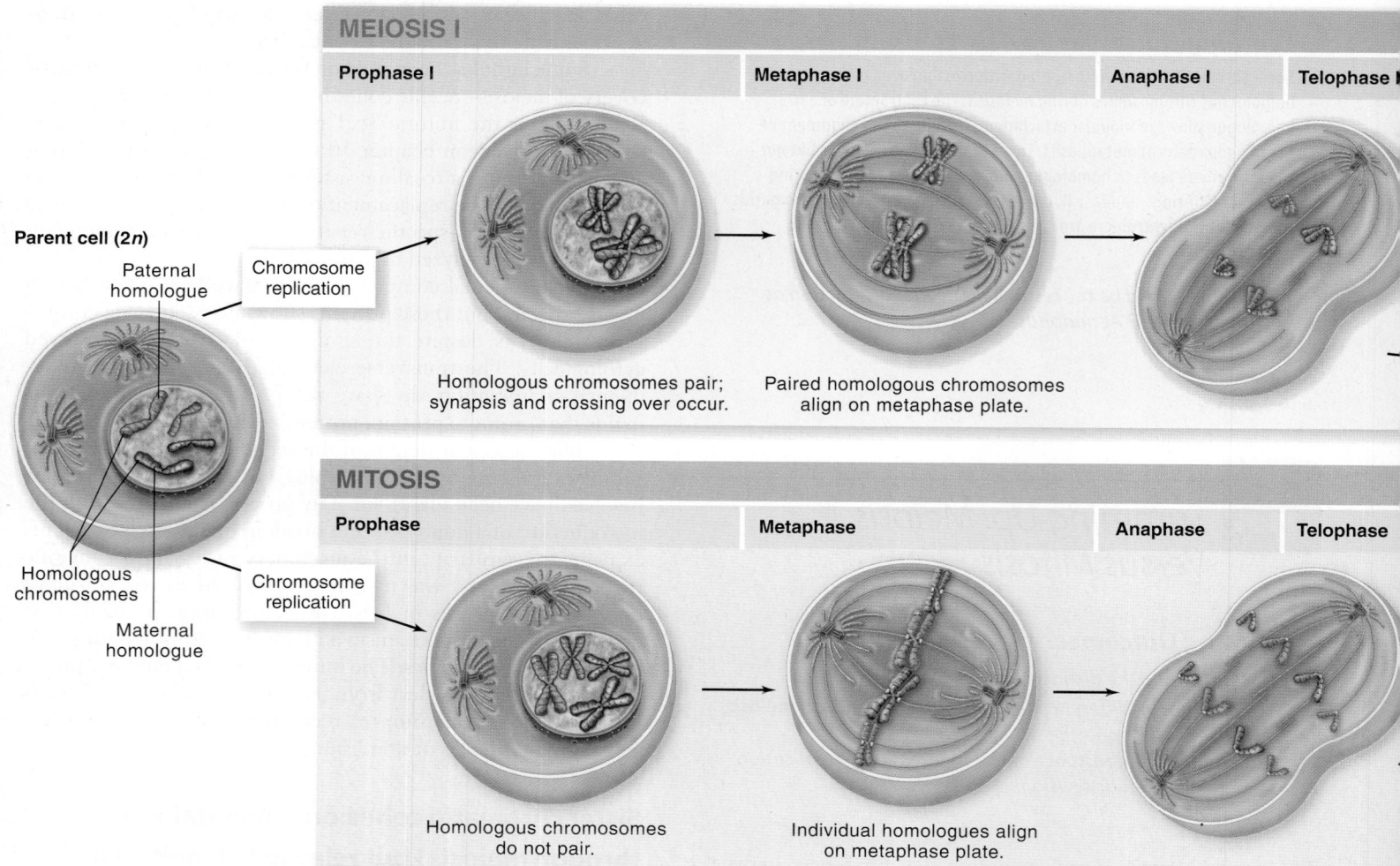

MEIOSIS I

Prophase I	Metaphase I	Anaphase I	Telophase

Homologous chromosomes pair; synapsis and crossing over occur.

Paired homologous chromosomes align on metaphase plate.

Parent cell (2*n*)

Paternal homologue

Chromosome replication

Homologous chromosomes

Maternal homologue

MITOSIS

Prophase	Metaphase	Anaphase	Telophase

Chromosome replication

Homologous chromosomes do not pair.

Individual homologues align on metaphase plate.

Sister kinetochores are attached to the same pole during meiosis I

The cosegregation of sister centromeres requires that the kinetochores of sister chromatids are attached to the same pole during meiosis I. This attachment is in contrast to both mitosis (see figure 11.8) and meiosis II, in which sister kinetochores must become attached to opposite poles.

The underlying basis of this monopolar attachment of sister kinetochores is unclear, but it seems to be based on structural differences between centromere–kinetochore complexes in meiosis I and in mitosis. Mitotic kinetochores visualized with the electron microscope appear to be recessed, making bipolar attachment more likely. Meiosis I kinetochores protrude more, making monopolar attachment easier.

It is clear that both the maintenance of sister chromatid cohesion at the centromere and monopolar attachment are required for the segregation of homologues that distinguishes meiosis I from mitosis.

Replication is suppressed between meiotic divisions

After a mitotic division, a new round of DNA replication must occur before the next division. For meiosis to succeed in halving the number of chromosomes, this replication must be suppressed between the two divisions. The detailed mechanism of suppression of replication between meiotic division is unknown. One clue is the observation that the level of one of the cyclins, cyclin B, is reduced between meiotic divisions, but is not lost completely, as it is between mitotic divisions.

During mitosis, the destruction of mitotic cyclin is necessary for a cell to enter another division cycle. The result of this maintenance of cyclin B between meiotic divisions in germ-line cells is the failure to form initiation complexes necessary for DNA replication to proceed. This failure to form initiation complexes appears to be critical to suppressing DNA replication.

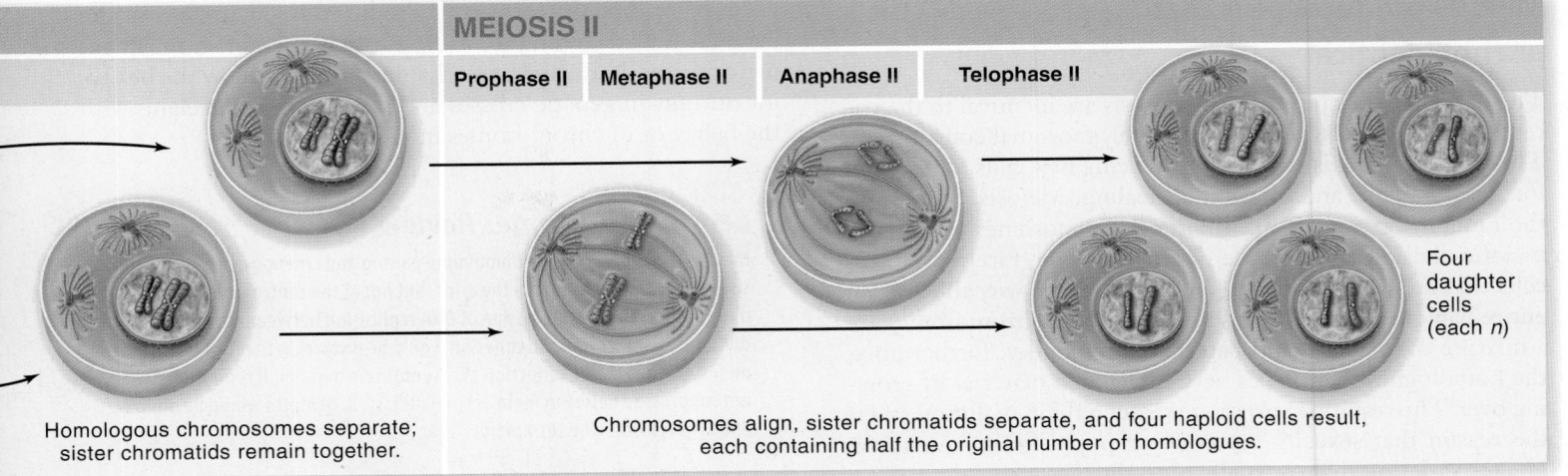

MEIOSIS II

| Prophase II | Metaphase II | Anaphase II | Telophase II |

Four daughter cells (each *n*)

Homologous chromosomes separate; sister chromatids remain together.

Chromosomes align, sister chromatids separate, and four haploid cells result, each containing half the original number of homologues.

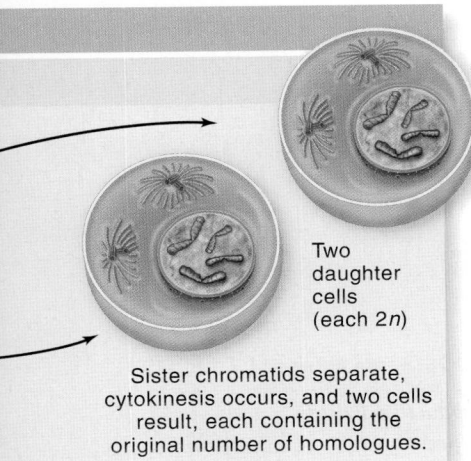

Two daughter cells (each 2*n*)

Sister chromatids separate, cytokinesis occurs, and two cells result, each containing the original number of homologues.

Figure 11.8 A comparison of meiosis and mitosis. Meiosis involves two nuclear divisions with no DNA replication between them. It thus produces four daughter cells, each with half the original number of chromosomes. Crossing over occurs in prophase I of meiosis. Mitosis involves a single nuclear division after DNA replication. It thus produces two daughter cells, each containing the original number of chromosomes.

Inquiry question

? If the chromosomes of a mitotic cell behaved the same as chromosomes in meiosis I, would the resulting cells have the proper chromosomal constitution?

SCIENTIFIC THINKING

Question: *Why are cohesin proteins at the centromeres of sister chromatids not destroyed at anaphase I of meiosis?*

Hypothesis: *Meiosis-specific cohesin component Rec8 is protected by another protein at centromeres.*

Prediction: *If Rec8 and the centromere protecting protein are both expressed in mitotic cells, chromosome separation will be prevented. This is lethal to a dividing cell.*

Test: *Fission yeast strain is designed to produce Rec8 instead of normal mitotic cohesin. These cells are transformed with a cDNA library that expresses all cellular proteins. Transformed cells are duplicated onto media containing dye for dead cells (allows expression of Rec8 and cDNA), and media that will result in loss of plasmid cDNA (expresses only Rec8). Cells containing cDNA for protecting protein will be dead in presence of Rec8.*

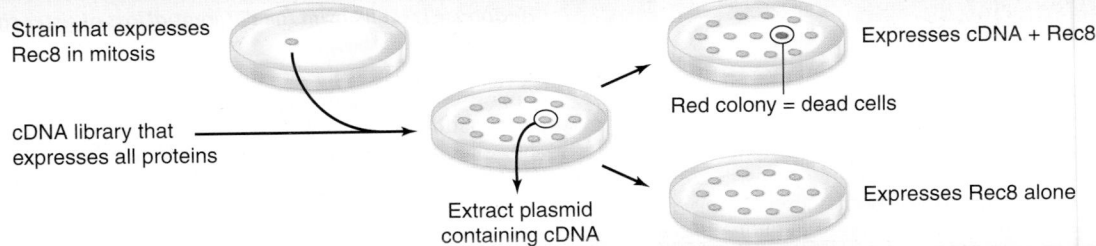

Strain that expresses Rec8 in mitosis

cDNA library that expresses all proteins

Extract plasmid containing cDNA

Expresses cDNA + Rec8

Red colony = dead cells

Expresses Rec8 alone

Result: *Transformed cells that die on the plates where Rec8 is coexpressed with cDNA identify the protecting protein. When the cDNA is extracted and analyzed, the encoded protein localizes to the centromeres of meiotic cells.*

Conclusion: *This screen identifies a protein with Rec8 protecting activity.*

Further Experiments: *If the gene encoding the protecting protein is deleted from cells, what would be the expected phenotype? In mitotic cells? In meiotic cells?*

Figure 11.9 Identification of meiosis-specific cohesin protector.

Meiosis produces cells that are not identical

The daughter cells produced by mitosis are identical to the parental cell, at least in terms of their chromosomal constitution. This exact copying is critical to producing new cells for growth, for development, and for wound healing. Meiosis, because of the random orientation of different chromosomes at the first meiotic division and because of crossing over, rarely produces cells that are identical. The gametes from meiosis all carry an entire haploid set of chromosomes, but these chromosomes are a mixture of maternal and paternal homologues; furthermore, the homologues themselves have exchanged material by crossing over. The resulting variation is essential for evolution and is the reason that sexually reproducing populations have much greater variation than asexually reproducing ones.

Meiosis is not only critical for the process of sexual reproduction, but is also the foundation for understanding the basis of heredity. The different cells produced by meiosis form the basis for understanding the behavior of observable traits in genetic crosses. In the next two chapters we will follow the behavior of traits in genetic crosses and see how this correlates with the behavior of chromosomes in meiosis.

Learning Outcomes Review 11.4

Meiosis is characterized by homologue pairing and crossing over; by loss of sister chromatid cohesion in the arms, but not at the centromere at the first division; and by the suppression of DNA replication between the two meiotic divisions. Sister chromatid cohesion would be disastrous in mitosis, but in meiosis I it allows the reduction of chromosome number. If replication were not suppressed between meiosis I and meiosis II, gametes would be diploid, and zygotes would be tetraploid.

■ **What features of meiosis lead to genetic variation in the products?**

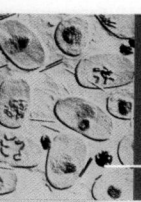

Chapter Review

11.1 Sexual Reproduction Requires Meiosis (figure 11.2)

Meiosis reduces the number of chromosomes.

Eggs and sperm are haploid (1n) cells, which contain one set of all chromosomes, and products of meiotic division.

Sexual life cycles have both haploid and diploid stages.

During fertilization, or syngamy, the fusion of two haploid gametes results in a diploid (2n) zygote, which contains two sets of chromosomes. Meiosis and fertilization constitute a reproductive cycle in sexual organisms as they alternate between diploid and haploid chromosome numbers. Somatic cells divide by mitosis and form the body of an organism.

Germ-line cells are set aside early in animal development.

Cells that eventually will form haploid gametes by meiosis are called germ-line cells. These are set aside early in development in animals.

11.2 Features of Meiosis

Homologous chromosomes pair during meiosis.

The pairing of homologous chromosomes, called synapsis, occurs during early prophase I. Paired homologues are often joined by the synaptonemal complex (see figure 11.3). During synapsis, crossing over occurs between homologous chromosomes, exchanging chromosomal material (see figure 11.4). Because the homologues are paired, they move as a unit to the metaphase plate during metaphase I. During anaphase I, homologues of each pair are pulled to opposite poles, producing two cells that each have one complete set of chromosomes.

Meiosis features two divisions with one round of DNA replication.

Meiosis II is like mitosis but without replication of DNA. Sister chromatids are pulled to opposite poles to yield four haploid cells.

11.3 The Process of Meiosis (see figures 11.7 and 11.8)

Prophase I sets the stage for the reductive division.

Meiotic cells have an interphase period similar to mitosis with G_1, S, and G_2 phases. This is followed by prophase I in which homologous chromosomes align along their entire length. The sister chromatids are held together by cohesin proteins. Homologues exchange chromosomal material by crossing over, which assists in holding the homologues together during meiosis I. The nuclear envelope disperses and the spindle apparatus forms.

During metaphase I, paired homologues align.

Spindle fibers attach to the kinetochores of the homologues; the kinetochores of sister chromatids behave as a single unit. Homologues of each pair become attached by kinetochore microtubules to opposite poles, and homologous pairs move to the metaphase plate as a unit. The orientation of each homologous pair on the equator is random; either the maternal or paternal homologue may be oriented toward a given pole.

Anaphase I results from the differential loss of sister chromatid cohesion along the arms.

During anaphase I the homologues of each pair are pulled to opposite poles as kinetochore microtubules shorten. Loss of sister chromatid cohesion on the arms but not at the centromeres allows homologues to separate, but sister chromatids to stay together. This is due to the loss of cohesin proteins on the arms but not at the centromere. At the end of anaphase I each pole has a complete set of haploid chromosomes, consisting of one member of each homologous pair. Because of the random orientation of homologous pairs at metaphase I, meiosis I results in the independent assortment of maternal and paternal chromosomes in gametes.

Telophase I completes meiosis I.

During telophase I the nuclear envelope re-forms around each daughter nucleus. This phase does not occur in all species. Cytokinesis may or may not occur after telophase I.

Achiasmate segregation of homologues is possible.

Although homologues are usually held together by chiasmata, some systems are able to segregate chromosomes without this.

Meiosis II is like a mitotic division without DNA replication.

A brief interphase with no DNA replication occurs after meiosis I. During meiosis II, cohesin proteins at the centromeres that hold sister chromatids together are destroyed, allowing each to migrate to opposite poles of the cell. The result of meiosis I and II is four cells, each containing haploid sets of chromosomes that are not identical. Once completed, the haploid cells may produce gametes or divide mitotically to produce even more gametes or haploid adults.

Errors in meiosis produce aneuploid gametes.

Errors occur during meiosis because of nondisjunction, the failure of chromosomes to move to opposite poles. It may result in aneuploid gametes: one gamete with no chromosome, and another gamete with two copies of a chromosome.

11.4 Summing Up: Meiosis Versus Mitosis

Four distinct features of meiosis I are not found in mitosis: Maternal and paternal homologues pair, and exchange genetic information by crossing over; the kinetochores of sister chromatids function as a unit during meiosis I, allowing sister chromatids to cosegregate during anaphase I; kinetochores of sister chromatids are connected to a single pole in meiosis I and to opposite poles in mitosis; and DNA replication is suppressed between meiosis I and meiosis II.

Homologous pairing is specific to meiosis.

How homologues find each other during meiosis is not known. The proteins of the synaptonemal complex do not seem to be conserved in different species, but there are meiosis-specific cohesin proteins. These are involved in the differential destruction of cohesins on the arms versus the centromere during meiosis I. The recombination process that occurs between paired homologues is better known. This process uses proteins involved in DNA repair and starts with a double-stranded break in DNA.

Sister chromatid cohesion is maintained through meiosis I but released in meiosis II.

Shugoshin protein protects centromeric cohesin in anaphase I, so that sister chromatids remain connected. Cohesins on the arms are not protected and are thus degraded during anaphase I, allowing homologues to move to opposite poles.

Sister kinetochores are attached to the same pole during meiosis I.

Kinetochores of sister chromatids must be attached to the same spindle fibers (monopolar attachment) to segregate together.

Replication is suppressed between meiotic divisions.

Suppression of replication may be related to the maintenance of some cyclin proteins that are degraded at the end of mitosis.

Meiosis produces cells that are not identical.

Because of the independent assortment of homologues and the process of crossing over, gametes show great variation.

Review Questions

UNDERSTAND

1. In comparing somatic cells and gametes, somatic cells are
   a. diploid with half the number of chromosomes.
   b. haploid with half the number of chromosomes.
   c. diploid with twice the number of chromosomes.
   d. haploid with twice the number of chromosomes.

2. What are *homologous* chromosomes?
   a. The two halves of a replicated chromosome
   b. Two identical chromosomes from one parent
   c. Two genetically identical chromosomes, one from each parent
   d. Two genetically similar chromosomes, one from each parent

3. Chiasmata form
   a. between homologous chromosomes.
   b. sister chromatids.
   c. between replicated copies of the same chromosomes.
   d. sex chromosomes but not autosomes.

4. Crossing over involves each of the following with the exception of
   a. the transfer of DNA between two nonsister chromatids.
   b. the transfer of DNA between two sister chromatids.
   c. the formation of a synaptonemal complex.
   d. the alignment of homologous chromosomes.

5. During anaphase I
   a. sister chromatids separate and move to the poles.
   b. homologous chromosomes move to opposite poles.
   c. homologous chromosomes align at the middle of the cell.
   d. all the chromosomes align independently at the middle of the cell.

6. At metaphase I the kinetochores of sister chromatids are
   a. attached to microtubules from the same pole.
   b. attached to microtubules from opposite poles.
   c. held together with cohesin proteins.
   d. not attached to any microtubules.

7. What occurs during anaphase of meiosis II?
   a. The homologous chromosomes align.
   b. Sister chromatids are pulled to opposite poles.
   c. Homologous chromosomes are pulled to opposite poles.
   d. The haploid chromosomes line up.

APPLY

1. Which of the following does *not* contribute to genetic diversity?
   a. Independent assortment
   b. Recombination
   c. Metaphase of meiosis II
   d. Metaphase of meiosis I

2. How does DNA replication differ between mitosis and meiosis?

   a. DNA replication takes less time in meiosis because the cells are haploid.

   b. During meiosis, there is only one round of replication for two divisions.

   c. During mitosis, there is only one round of replication every other division.

   d. DNA replication is exactly the same in mitosis and meiosis.

3. Which of the following is *not* a distinct feature of meiosis?

   a. Pairing and exchange of genetic material between homologous chromosomes

   b. Attachment of sister kinetochores to spindle microtubules

   c. Movement of sister chromatids to the same pole

   d. Suppression of DNA replication

4. Which phase of meiosis I is most similar to the comparable phase in mitosis?

   a. Prophase I   c. Anaphase I

   b. Metaphase I   d. Telophase I

5. Structurally, meiotic cohesins have different components than mitotic cohesins. This leads to the following functional difference:

   a. During metaphase I, the sister kinetochores become attached to the same pole.

   b. Centromeres remain attached during anaphase I of meiosis.

   c. Centromeres remain attached through both divisions.

   d. Centromeric cohesins are destroyed at anaphase I, and cohesins along the arms are destroyed at anaphase II.

6. Mutations that affect DNA repair often also affect the accuracy of meiosis. This is because

   a. the proteins involved in the repair of double-strand breaks are also involved in crossing over.

   b. the proteins involved in DNA repair are also involved in sister chromatid cohesion.

   c. DNA repair only occurs on condensed chromosomes such as those found in meiosis.

   d. cohesin proteins are also necessary for DNA repair.

SYNTHESIZE

1. Diagram the process of meiosis for an imaginary cell with six chromosomes in a diploid cell.

   a. How many homologous pairs are present in this cell? Create a drawing that distinguishes between homologous pairs.

   b. Label each homologue to indicate whether it is maternal (M) or paternal (P).

   c. Draw a new cell showing how these chromosomes would arrange themselves during metaphase of meiosis I. Do all the maternal homologues have to line up on the same side of the cell?

   d. How would this picture differ if you were diagramming anaphase of meiosis II?

2. Mules are the offspring of the mating of a horse and a donkey. Mules are unable to reproduce. A horse has a total of 64 chromosomes, whereas donkeys have 62 chromosomes. Use your knowledge of meiosis to predict the diploid chromosome number of a mule. Propose a possible explanation for the inability of mules to reproduce.

3. Compare the processes of *independent assortment* and *crossing over*. Which process has the greatest influence on genetic diversity?

4. Aneuploid gametes are cells that contain the wrong number of chromosomes. Aneuploidy occurs as a result of *nondisjunction*, or lack of separation of the chromosomes during either phase of meiosis.

   a. At what point in meiotic cell division would nondisjunction occur?

   b. Imagine a cell had a diploid chromosome number of four. Create a diagram to illustrate the effects of nondisjunction of one pair of homologous chromosomes in meiosis I versus meiosis II.

ONLINE RESOURCE

www.ravenbiology.com

Understand, Apply, and Synthesize—enhance your study with animations that bring concepts to life and practice tests to assess your understanding. Your instructor may also recommend the interactive eBook, individualized learning tools, and more.

Chapter

12

Patterns of Inheritance

Chapter Outline

12.1 The Mystery of Heredity

12.2 Monohybrid Crosses: The Principle of Segregation

12.3 Dihybrid Crosses: The Principle of Independent Assortment

12.4 Probability: Predicting the Results of Crosses

12.5 The Testcross: Revealing Unknown Genotypes

12.6 Extensions to Mendel

Introduction

Every living creature is a product of the long evolutionary history of life on Earth. All organisms share this history, but as far as we know, only humans wonder about the processes that led to their origin and investigate the possibilities. We are far from understanding everything about our origins, but we have learned a great deal. Like a partially completed jigsaw puzzle, the boundaries of this elaborate question have fallen into place, and much of the internal structure is becoming apparent. In this chapter, we discuss one piece of the puzzle—the enigma of heredity. Why do individuals, like the children in this picture, differ so much in appearance despite the fact that we are all members of the same species? And, why do members of a single family tend to resemble one another more than they resemble members of other families?

12.1 The Mystery of Heredity

Learning Outcomes

1. *Describe explanations for inheritance prior to Mendel.*
2. *Explain the advantages of Mendel's experimental system.*

As far back as written records go, patterns of resemblance among the members of particular families have been noted and commented on (figure 12.1), but there was no coherent model to explain these patterns. Before the 20th century, two concepts provided the basis for most thinking about heredity. The first was that heredity occurs within species. The second was that traits are transmitted directly from parents to offspring. Taken together, these ideas led to a view of inheritance as resulting from a blending of traits within fixed, unchanging species.

Figure 12.1 Heredity and family resemblance. Family resemblances are often strong—a visual manifestation of the mechanism of heredity.

Inheritance itself was viewed as traits being borne through fluid, usually identified as blood, that led to their blending in offspring. This older idea persists today in the use of the term "bloodlines" when referring to the breeding of domestic animals such as horses.

Taken together, however, these two classical assumptions led to a paradox. If no variation enters a species from outside, and if the variation within each species blends in every generation, then all members of a species should soon have the same appearance. It is clear that this does not happen—individuals within most species differ from one another, and they differ in characteristics that are transmitted from generation to generation.

Early plant biologists produced hybrids and saw puzzling results

The first investigator to achieve and document successful experimental **hybridizations** was Josef Kölreuter, who in 1760 cross-fertilized (or crossed, for short) different strains of tobacco and obtained fertile offspring. The hybrids differed in appearance from both parent strains. When individuals within the hybrid generation were crossed, their offspring were highly variable. Some of these offspring resembled plants of the hybrid generation (their parents), but a few resembled the original strains (their grandparents). The variation observed in second-generation offspring contradicts the theory of direct transmission. This can be seen as the beginning of modern genetics.

Over the next hundred years, other investigators elaborated on Kölreuter's work. T. A. Knight, an English landholder, in 1823 crossed two varieties of the garden pea, *Pisum sativum* (figure 12.2). One of these varieties had green seeds, and the other had yellow seeds. Both varieties were **true-breeding,** meaning that the offspring produced from self-fertilization remained uniform from one generation to the next. All of the progeny (offspring) of the cross between the two varieties had yellow seeds. Among the offspring of these hybrids, however, some plants produced yellow seeds and others, less common, produced green seeds.

Other investigators made observations similar to Knight's, namely that alternative forms of observed traits were being distributed among the offspring. A modern geneticist would say the alternative forms of each trait were **segregating** among the progeny of a mating, meaning that some offspring exhibited one form of a trait (yellow seeds), and other offspring from the same mating exhibited a different form (green seeds). This segregation of alternative forms of a trait provided the clue that led Gregor Mendel to his understanding of the nature of heredity.

Within these deceptively simple results were the makings of a scientific revolution. Nevertheless, another century passed before the process of segregation was fully appreciated.

Mendel used mathematics to analyze his crosses

Born in 1822 to peasant parents, Gregor Mendel (figure 12.3) was educated in a monastery and went on to study science and mathematics at the University of Vienna, where he failed his examinations for a teaching certificate. He returned to the monastery and spent the rest of his life there, eventually becoming abbot. In the garden of the monastery, Mendel initiated his own series of experiments on plant hybridization. The results of these experiments would ultimately change our views of heredity irrevocably.

Practical considerations for use of the garden pea

For his experiments, Mendel chose the garden pea, the same plant Knight and others had studied. The choice was a good one for several reasons. First, many earlier investigators had produced hybrid peas by crossing different varieties, so Mendel knew that he could expect to observe segregation of traits among the offspring.

Figure 12.2 The garden pea, *Pisum sativum.* Easy to cultivate and able to produce many distinctive varieties, the garden pea was a popular experimental subject in investigations of heredity as long as a century before Gregor Mendel's experiments.

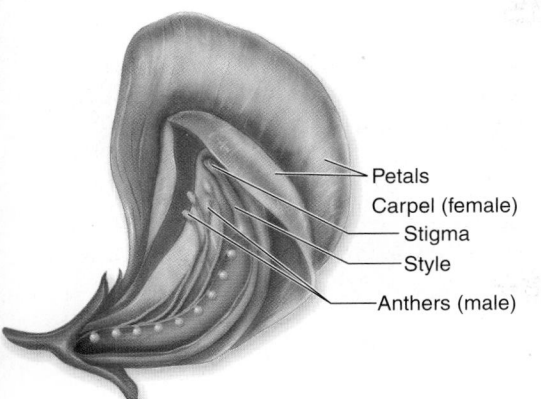
Petals
Carpel (female)
Stigma
Style
Anthers (male)

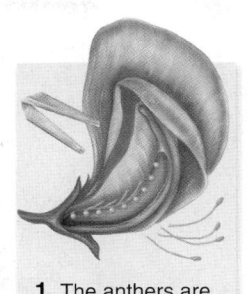
1. The anthers are cut away on the purple flower.

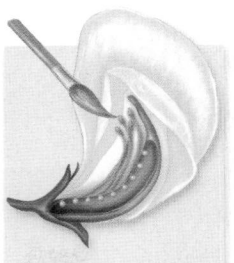
2. Pollen is obtained from the white flower.

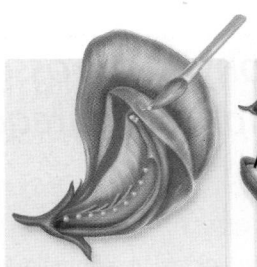
3. Pollen is transferred to the purple flower.

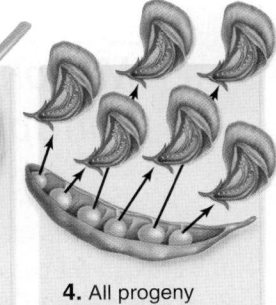
4. All progeny result in purple flowers.

Figure 12.3 How Mendel conducted his experiments. In a pea plant flower, petals enclose both the male anther (containing pollen grains, which give rise to haploid sperm) and the female carpel (containing ovules, which give rise to haploid eggs). This ensures self-fertilization will take place unless the flower is disturbed. Mendel collected pollen from the anthers of a white flower, then placed that pollen onto the stigma of a purple flower with anthers removed. This cross fertilization yields all hybrid seeds that give rise to purple flowers. Using pollen from a white flower to fertilize a purple flower gives the same result.

Inquiry question

 What confounding problems could have been seen if Mendel had chosen another plant with exposed male and female structures?

Second, a large number of pure varieties of peas were available. Mendel initially examined 34 varieties. Then, for further study, he selected lines that differed with respect to seven easily distinguishable traits, such as round versus wrinkled seeds and yellow versus green seeds, the latter a trait that Knight had studied.

Third, pea plants are small and easy to grow, and they have a relatively short generation time. A researcher can therefore conduct experiments involving numerous plants, grow several generations in a single year, and obtain results relatively quickly.

A fourth advantage of studying peas is that both the male and female sexual organs are enclosed within each pea flower (see figure 12.3), and gametes produced by the male and female parts of the same flower can fuse to form viable offspring, a process termed **self-fertilization.** This self-fertilization takes place automatically within an individual flower if it is not disturbed. It is also possible to prevent self-fertilization by removing a flower's male parts before fertilization occurs, then introduce pollen from a different strain, thus performing *cross-pollination* that results in *cross-fertilization* (see figure 12.3).

Mendel's experimental design

Mendel was careful to focus on only a few specific differences between the plants he was using and to ignore the countless other differences he must have seen. He also had the insight to realize that the differences he selected must be comparable. For example, he recognized that trying to study the inheritance of round seeds versus tall height would be useless.

Mendel usually conducted his experiments in three stages:

1. Mendel allowed plants of a given variety to self-cross for multiple generations to assure himself that the traits he was studying were indeed true-breeding, that is, transmitted unchanged from generation to generation.

2. Mendel then performed crosses between true-breeding varieties exhibiting alternative forms of traits. He also performed **reciprocal crosses:** using pollen from a white-flowered plant to fertilize a purple-flowered plant, then using pollen from a purple-flowered plant to fertilize a white-flowered plant.

3. Finally, Mendel permitted the hybrid offspring produced by these crosses to self-fertilize for several generations, allowing him to observe the inheritance of alternative forms of a trait. Most important, he counted the numbers of offspring exhibiting each trait in each succeeding generation.

This quantification of results is what distinguished Mendel's research from that of earlier investigators, who only noted differences in a qualitative way. Mendel's mathematical analysis of experimental results led to the inheritance model that we still use today.

Learning Outcomes Review 12.1

Prior to Mendel, concepts of inheritance did not form a consistent model. The dominant view was of blending inheritance, in which traits of parents were carried by fluid and "blended" in offspring. Plant hybridizers before Mendel, however, had already cast doubt on this model by observing characteristics in hybrids that seemed to change in second-generation offspring. Mendel's experiments with plants involved quantifying types of offspring and mathematically analyzing his observations.

■ *Which was more important to Mendel's success: his approach, or his choice of experimental material?*

Monohybrid Crosses: The Principle of Segregation

Learning Outcomes

1. Evaluate the outcome of a monohybrid cross.
2. Explain Mendel's principle of segregation.
3. Compare the segregation of alleles with the behavior of homologues in meiosis.

A *monohybrid cross* is a cross that follows only two variations on a single trait, such as white- and purple-colored flowers. This deceptively simple kind of cross can lead to important conclusions about the nature of inheritance.

The seven characteristics, or characters, Mendel studied in his experiments possessed two variants that differed from one another in ways that were easy to recognize and score (figure 12.4). We examine in detail Mendel's crosses with flower color. His experiments with other characters were similar, and they produced similar results.

The F_1 generation exhibits only one of two traits, without blending

When Mendel crossed white-flowered and purple-flowered plants, the hybrid offspring he obtained did not have flowers of intermediate color, as the hypothesis of blending inheritance would predict. Instead, in every case the flower color of the offspring resembled that of one of their parents. These offspring are customarily referred to as the **first filial generation,** or **F_1.** In a cross of white-flowered and purple-flowered plants, the F_1 offspring all had purple flowers, as other scientists had reported before Mendel.

Mendel referred to the form of each trait expressed in the F_1 plants as **dominant,** and to the alternative form that was not expressed in the F_1 plants as **recessive.** For each of the seven pairs of contrasting traits that Mendel examined, one of the pair proved to be dominant and the other recessive.

The F_2 generation exhibits both traits in a 3:1 ratio

After allowing individual F_1 plants to mature and self-fertilize, Mendel collected and planted the seeds from each plant to see what the offspring in the **second filial generation,** or **F_2,** would look like. He found that although most F_2 plants had purple flowers, some exhibited white flowers, the recessive trait. Although hidden in the F_1 generation, the recessive trait had reappeared among some F_2 individuals.

Believing the proportions of the F_2 types would provide some clue about the mechanism of heredity, Mendel counted the numbers of each type among the F_2 progeny. In the cross between the purple-flowered F_1 plants, he obtained a total of 929 F_2 individuals. Of these, 705 (75.9%) had purple flowers, and 224 (24.1%) had white flowers (see figure 12.4).

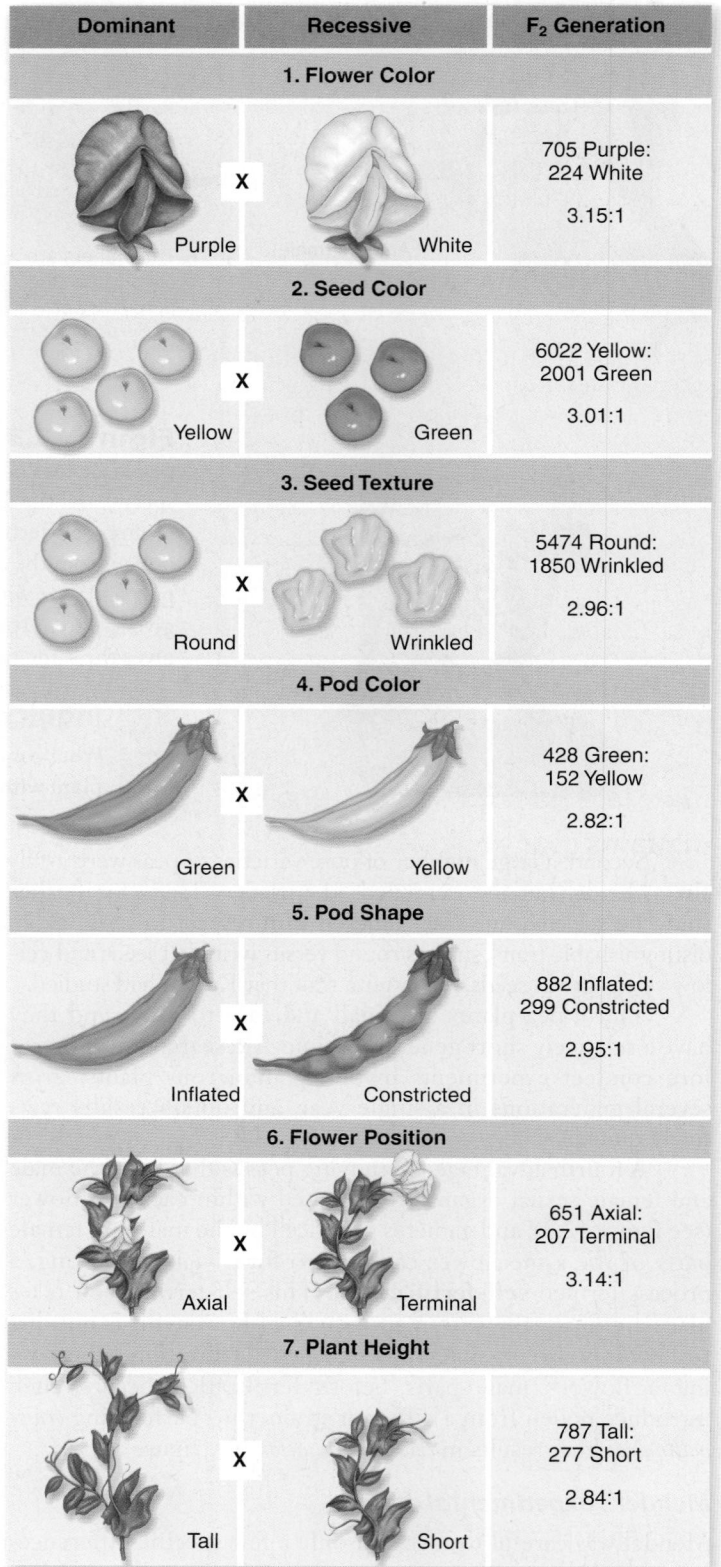

Dominant	Recessive	F_2 Generation
1. Flower Color		
Purple	White	705 Purple: 224 White 3.15:1
2. Seed Color		
Yellow	Green	6022 Yellow: 2001 Green 3.01:1
3. Seed Texture		
Round	Wrinkled	5474 Round: 1850 Wrinkled 2.96:1
4. Pod Color		
Green	Yellow	428 Green: 152 Yellow 2.82:1
5. Pod Shape		
Inflated	Constricted	882 Inflated: 299 Constricted 2.95:1
6. Flower Position		
Axial	Terminal	651 Axial: 207 Terminal 3.14:1
7. Plant Height		
Tall	Short	787 Tall: 277 Short 2.84:1

Figure 12.4 Mendel's seven traits. Mendel studied how differences among varieties of peas were inherited when the varieties were crossed. Similar experiments had been done before, but Mendel was the first to quantify the results and appreciate their significance. Results are shown for seven different monohybrid crosses. The F_1 generation is not shown in the table.

Approximately ¼ of the F_2 individuals, therefore, exhibited the recessive form of the character.

Mendel obtained the same numerical result with the other six characters he examined: Of the F_2 individuals, ¾ exhibited the dominant trait, and ¼ displayed the recessive trait (see figure 12.4). In other words, the dominant-to-recessive ratio among the F_2 plants was always close to 3:1.

The 3:1 ratio is actually 1:2:1

Mendel went on to examine how the F_2 plants passed traits to subsequent generations. He found that plants exhibiting the recessive trait were always true-breeding. For example, the white-flowered F_2 individuals reliably produced white-flowered offspring when they were allowed to self-fertilize. By contrast, only ⅓ of the dominant, purple-flowered F_2 individuals (¼ of all F_2 offspring) proved true-breeding, but ⅔ were not. This last class of plants produced dominant and recessive individuals in the third filial generation (F_3) in a 3:1 ratio.

This result suggested that, for the entire sample, the 3:1 ratio that Mendel observed in the F_2 generation was really a disguised 1:2:1 ratio: ¼ true-breeding dominant individuals, ½ not-true-breeding dominant individuals, and ¼ true-breeding recessive individuals (figure 12.5).

Mendel's Principle of Segregation explains monohybrid observations

From his experiments, Mendel was able to understand four things about the nature of heredity:

- The plants he crossed did not produce progeny of intermediate appearance, as a hypothesis of blending inheritance would have predicted. Instead, different plants inherited each trait intact, as a discrete characteristic.
- For each pair of alternative forms of a trait, one alternative was not expressed in the F_1 hybrids, although it reappeared in some F_2 individuals. *The trait that "disappeared" must therefore be latent (present but not expressed) in the F_1 individuals.*
- The pairs of alternative traits examined were segregated among the progeny of a particular cross, some individuals exhibiting one trait and some the other.
- These alternative traits were expressed in the F_2 generation in the ratio of ¾ dominant to ¼ recessive. This characteristic 3:1 segregation is referred to as the **Mendelian ratio** for a monohybrid cross.

Mendel's five-element model

To explain these results, Mendel proposed a simple model that has become one of the most famous in the history of science, containing simple assumptions and making clear predictions. The model has five elements:

1. Parents do not transmit physiological traits directly to their offspring. Rather, they transmit discrete information for the traits, what Mendel called "factors." We now call these factors *genes*.

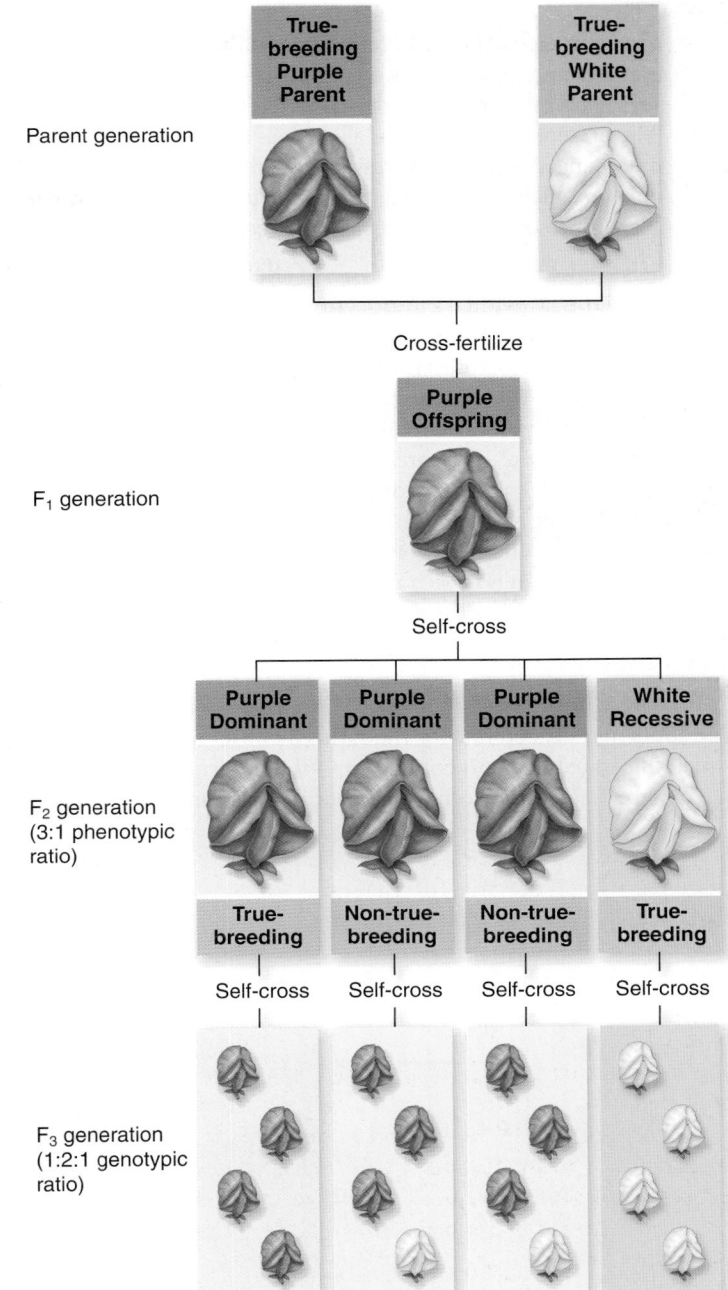

Figure 12.5 The F_2 generation is a disguised 1:2:1 ratio. By allowing the F_2 generation to self-fertilize, Mendel found from the offspring (F_3) that the ratio of F_2 plants was 1 true-breeding dominant: 2 not-true-breeding dominant: and 1 true-breeding recessive.

2. Each individual receives one copy of each gene from each parent. We now know that genes are carried on chromosomes, and each adult individual is diploid, with one set of chromosomes from each parent.
3. Not all copies of a gene are identical. The alternative forms of a gene are called **alleles.** When two haploid gametes containing the same allele fuse during fertilization, the resulting offspring is said to be **homozygous.** When the two haploid gametes contain different alleles, the resulting offspring is said to be **heterozygous.**

4. The two alleles remain discrete—they neither blend with nor alter each other. Therefore, when the individual matures and produces its own gametes, the alleles segregate randomly into these gametes.

5. The presence of a particular allele does not ensure that the trait it encodes will be expressed. In heterozygous individuals, only one allele is expressed (the dominant one), and the other allele is present but unexpressed (the recessive one).

Geneticists now refer to the total set of alleles that an individual contains as the individual's **genotype**. The physical appearance or other observable characteristics of that individual, which result from an allele's expression, is termed the individual's **phenotype**. In other words, the genotype is the blueprint, and the phenotype is the visible outcome in an individual.

This also allows us to present Mendel's ratios in more modern terms. The 3:1 ratio of dominant to recessive is the monohybrid phenotypic ratio. The 1:2:1 ratio of homozygous dominant to heterozygous to homozygous recessive is the monohybrid genotypic ratio. The genotypic ratio "collapses" into the phenotypic ratio due to the action of the dominant allele making the heterozygote appear the same as homozygous dominant.

The principle of segregation

Mendel's model accounts for the ratios he observed in a neat and satisfying way. His main conclusion—that alternative alleles for a character segregate from each other during gamete formation and remain distinct—has since been verified in many other organisms. It is commonly referred to as Mendel's first law of heredity, or the **Principle of Segregation.** It can be simply stated as: *The two alleles for a gene segregate during gamete formation and are rejoined at random, one from each parent, during fertilization.*

The physical basis for allele segregation is the behavior of chromosomes during meiosis. As you saw in chapter 11, homologues for each chromosome disjoin during anaphase I of meiosis. The second meiotic division then produces gametes that contain only one homologue for each chromosome.

It is a tribute to Mendel's intellect that his analysis arrived at the correct scheme, even though he had no knowledge of the cellular mechanisms of inheritance; neither chromosomes nor meiosis had yet been described.

The Punnett square allows symbolic analysis

To test his model, Mendel first expressed it in terms of a simple set of symbols. He then used the symbols to interpret his results.

Consider again Mendel's cross of purple-flowered with white-flowered plants. By convention, we assign the symbol *P* (uppercase) to the dominant allele, associated with the production of purple flowers, and the symbol *p* (lowercase) to the recessive allele, associated with the production of white flowers.

In this system, the genotype of an individual that is true-breeding for the recessive white-flowered trait would be designated *pp*. Similarly, the genotype of a true-breeding purple-flowered

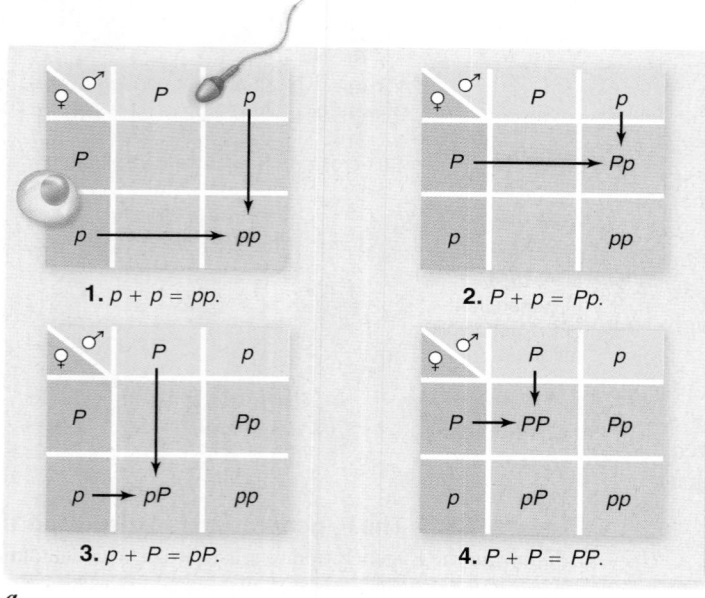

a.

Figure 12.6 Using a Punnett square to analyze Mendel's cross.

a. To make a Punnett square, place the different female gametes along the side of a square and the different male gametes along the top. Each potential zygote is represented as the intersection of a vertical line and a horizontal line. *b.* In Mendel's cross of purple by white flowers, each parent makes only one type of gamete. The F₁ are all purple, *Pp*, heterozygotes. These F₁ offspring make two types of gametes that can be combined to produce three kinds of F₂ offspring: *PP* homozygous dominant (purple); *Pp* heterozygous (also purple); and *pp* homozygous recessive (white). The phenotypic ratio is 3 purple:1 white. The genotypic ratio is 1 *PP*:2 *Pp*:1 *pp*.

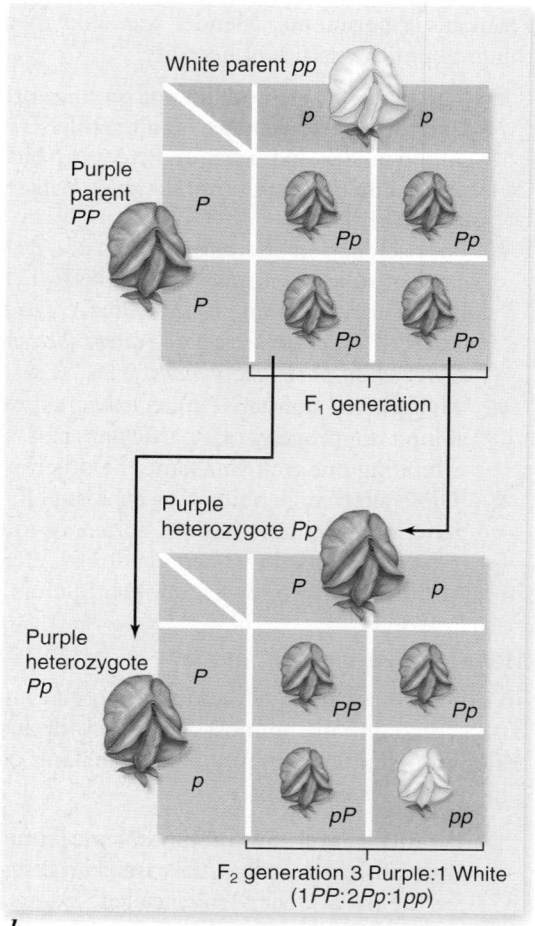

b.

TABLE 12.1 Some Dominant and Recessive Traits in Humans

Recessive Traits	Phenotypes	Dominant Traits	Phenotypes
Albinism	Lack of melanin pigmentation	Middigital hair	Presence of hair on middle segment of fingers
Alkaptonuria	Inability to metabolize homogentisic acid	Brachydactyly	Short fingers
Red-green color blindness	Inability to distinguish red or green wavelengths of light	Huntington disease	Degeneration of nervous system, starting in middle age
Cystic fibrosis	Abnormal gland secretion, leading to liver degeneration and lung failure	Phenylthiocarbamide (PTC) sensitivity	Ability to taste PTC as bitter
Duchenne muscular dystrophy	Wasting away of muscles during childhood	Camptodactyly	Inability to straighten the little finger
Hemophilia	Inability of blood to clot properly, some clots form but the process is delayed	Hypercholesterolemia (the most common human Mendelian disorder)	Elevated levels of blood cholesterol and risk of heart attack
Sickle cell anemia	Defective hemoglobin that causes red blood cells to curve and stick together	Polydactyly	Extra fingers and toes

individual would be designated *PP*. In contrast, a heterozygote would be designated *Pp* (dominant allele first). Using these conventions and denoting a cross between two strains with ×, we can symbolize Mendel's original purple × white cross as *PP* × *pp*.

Because a white-flowered parent (*pp*) can produce only *p* gametes, and a true-breeding purple-flowered parent (*PP, homozygous dominant*) can produce only *P* gametes, the union of these gametes can produce only heterozygous *Pp* offspring in the F₁ generation. Because the *P* allele is dominant, all of these F₁ individuals are expected to have purple flowers.

When F₁ individuals are allowed to self-fertilize, the *P* and *p* alleles segregate during gamete formation to produce both *P* gametes and *p* gametes. Their subsequent union at fertilization to form F₂ individuals is random.

The F₂ possibilities may be visualized in a simple diagram called a **Punnett square,** named after its originator, the English geneticist R. C. Punnett (figure 12.6*a*). Mendel's model, analyzed in terms of a Punnett square, clearly predicts that the F₂ generation should consist of ¾ purple-flowered plants and ¼ white-flowered plants, a phenotypic ratio of 3:1 (figure 12.6*b*).

Some human traits exhibit dominant/recessive inheritance

A number of human traits have been shown to display both dominant and recessive inheritance (table 12.1 provides a sample of these). Researchers cannot perform controlled crosses in humans the way Mendel did with pea plants, instead geneticists study crosses that have already been performed—in other words, family histories. The organized methodology we use is a **pedigree,** a consistent graphical representation of matings and offspring over multiple generations for a particular trait. The information in the pedigree may allow geneticists to deduce a model for the mode of inheritance of the trait. In analyzing these pedigrees, it is important to realize that disease-causing alleles are usually quite rare in the general population.

A dominant pedigree: Juvenile glaucoma

One of the most extensive pedigrees yet produced traced the inheritance of a form of blindness caused by a dominant allele. The disease allele causes a form of hereditary juvenile glaucoma. The disease causes degeneration of nerve fibers in the optic nerve, leading to blindness.

This pedigree followed inheritance over three centuries, following the origin back to a couple in a small town in northwestern France who died in 1495. A small portion of this pedigree is shown in figure 12.7. The dominant nature of the trait is obvious from the

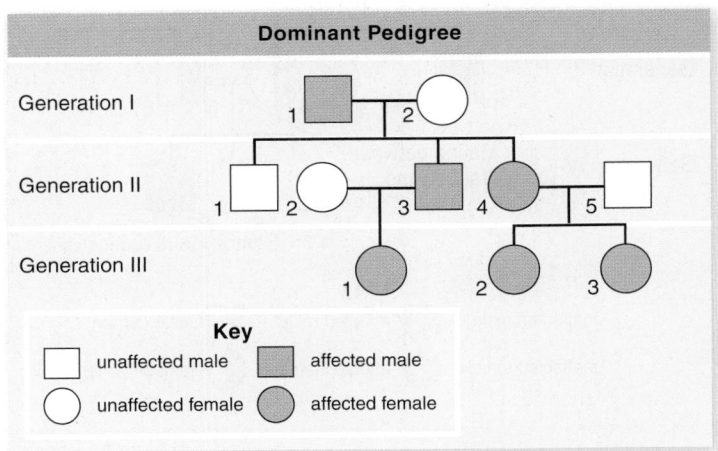

Figure 12.7 Dominant pedigree for hereditary juvenile glaucoma. Males are shown as squares and females are shown as circles. Affected individuals are shown shaded. The dominant nature of this trait can be seen in the trait appearing in every generation, a feature of dominant traits.

Inquiry question

? If one of the affected females in the third generation married an unaffected male, could she produce unaffected offspring? If so, what are the chances of having unaffected offspring?

fact that every generation shows the trait. This is extremely unlikely for a recessive trait as it would require large numbers of unrelated individuals to be carrying the disease allele.

A recessive pedigree: Albinism

An example of inheritance of a recessive human trait is albinism, a condition in which the pigment melanin is not produced. Long thought to be due to a single gene, multiple genes are now known that lead to albinism; the common feature is the loss of pigment from hair, skin, and eyes. The loss of pigment makes albinistic individuals sensitive to the sun. The tanning effect we are all familiar with from exposure to the sun is due to increased numbers of pigment-producing cells, and increased production of pigment. This is lacking in albinistic individuals due to the lack of any pigment to begin with.

The pedigree in figure 12.8 is for a form of albinism due to a nonfunctional allele of the enzyme tyrosinase, which is required for the formation of melanin pigment. The genetic characteristics of this form of albinism are: females and males are affected equally, most affected individuals have unaffected parents, a single affected parent usually does not have affected offspring, and affected offspring are more frequent when parents are related. Each of these features can be see in figure 12.8, and all of this fits a recessive mode of inheritance.

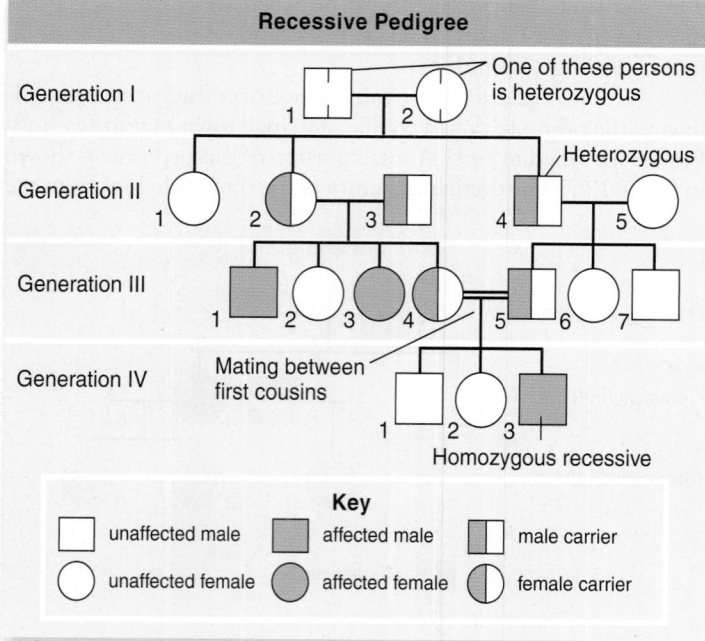

Figure 12.8 Recessive pedigree for albinism. One of the two individuals in the first generation must be heterozygous and individuals II-2 and II-4 must be heterozygous. Notice that for each affected individual, neither parent is affected, but both must be heterozygous (carriers). The double line indicates a consanguineous mating (between relatives) that, in this case, produced affected offspring.

? Inquiry question

From a genetic disease standpoint, why is it never advisable for close relatives to mate and have children?

12.3 Dihybrid Crosses: The Principle of Independent Assortment

Learning Outcomes

1. *Evaluate the outcome of a dihybrid cross.*
2. *Explain Mendel's Principle of Independent Assortment.*
3. *Understand the physical basis of independent assortment.*

The Principle of Segregation explains the behavior of alternative forms of a single trait in a monohybrid cross. The next step is to extend this to follow the behavior of two different traits in a single cross: a **dihybrid cross.**

With an understanding of the behavior of single traits, Mendel went on to ask if different traits behaved independently in hybrids. He first established a series of true-breeding lines of peas that differed in two of the seven characters he had studied. He then crossed contrasting pairs of the true-breeding lines to create heterozygotes. These heterozygotes are now doubly heterozygous, or dihybrid. Finally, he self-crossed the dihybrid F_1 plants to produce an F_2 generation, and counted all progeny types.

Traits in a dihybrid cross behave independently

Consider a cross involving different seed shape alleles (round, *R*, and wrinkled, *r*) and different seed color alleles (yellow, *Y*, and green, *y*). Crossing round yellow (*RR YY*) with wrinkled green (*rr yy*), produces heterozygous F_1 individuals having the same phenotype (namely round and yellow) and the same genotype (*Rr Yy*). Allowing these dihybrid F_1 individuals to self-fertilize produces an F_2 generation.

The F_2 generation exhibits four types of progeny in a 9:3:3:1 ratio

In analyzing these results, we first consider the number of possible phenotypes. We expect to see the two parental phenotypes: round yellow and wrinkled green. If the traits behave independently, then we can also expect one trait from each parent to produce plants with round green seeds and others with wrinkled yellow seeds.

Next consider what types of gametes the F_1 individuals can produce. Again, we expect the two types of gametes found in the parents: *RY* and *ry*. If the traits behave independently, then we can also expect the gametes *Ry* and *rY*. Using modern language, two genes each with two alleles can be combined four ways to produce these gametes: *RY, ry, Ry,* and *rY*.

A dihybrid Punnett square

We can then construct a Punnett square with these gametes to generate all possible progeny. This is a 4 × 4 square with 16 possible outcomes. Filling in the Punnett square produces all possible offspring (figure 12.9). From this we can see that there are 9 round yellow, 3 wrinkled yellow, 3 round green, and 1 wrinkled green. This predicts a phenotypic ratio of 9:3:3:1 for traits that behave independently.

Mendel's Principle of Independent Assortment explains dihybrid results

What did Mendel actually observe? From a total of 556 seeds from self-fertilized dihybrid plants, he observed the following results:

- 315 round yellow (signified *R__ Y__*, where the underscore indicates the presence of either allele),
- 108 round green (*R__ yy*),
- 101 wrinkled yellow (*rr Y__*), and
- 32 wrinkled green (*rr yy*).

These results are very close to a 9:3:3:1 ratio. (The expected 9:3:3:1 ratio from this many offspring would be 313:104:104:35.)

The alleles of two genes appeared to behave independently of each other. Mendel referred to this phenomenon as the traits assorting independently. Note that this *independent assortment* of different genes in no way alters the segregation of individual pairs of alleles for each gene. Round versus wrinkled seeds occur in a ratio of approximately 3:1 (423:133); so do yellow versus green seeds (416:140). Mendel obtained similar results for other pairs of traits.

We call this Mendel's second law of heredity, or the **Principle of Independent Assortment.** This can also be stated simply: *In a dihybrid cross, the alleles of each gene assort independently.* A more precise statement would be: *the segregation of different allele pairs is independent.* This statement more closely ties independent assortment to the behavior of chromosomes during meiosis (see chapter 11). The independent alignment of different homologous chromosome pairs during metaphase I leads to the independent segregation of the different allele pairs.

Learning Outcomes Review 12.3

Mendel's analysis of dihybrid crosses revealed that the segregation of allele pairs for different traits is independent; this finding is known as Mendel's Principle of Independent Assortment. When individuals that differ in two traits are crossed, and their progeny are intercrossed, the result is four different types that occur in a ratio of 9:3:3:1, Mendel's dihybrid ratio. This occurs because of the independent behavior of different homologous pairs of chromosomes during meiosis I.

- *Which is more important in terms of explaining Mendel's laws, meiosis I or meiosis II?*

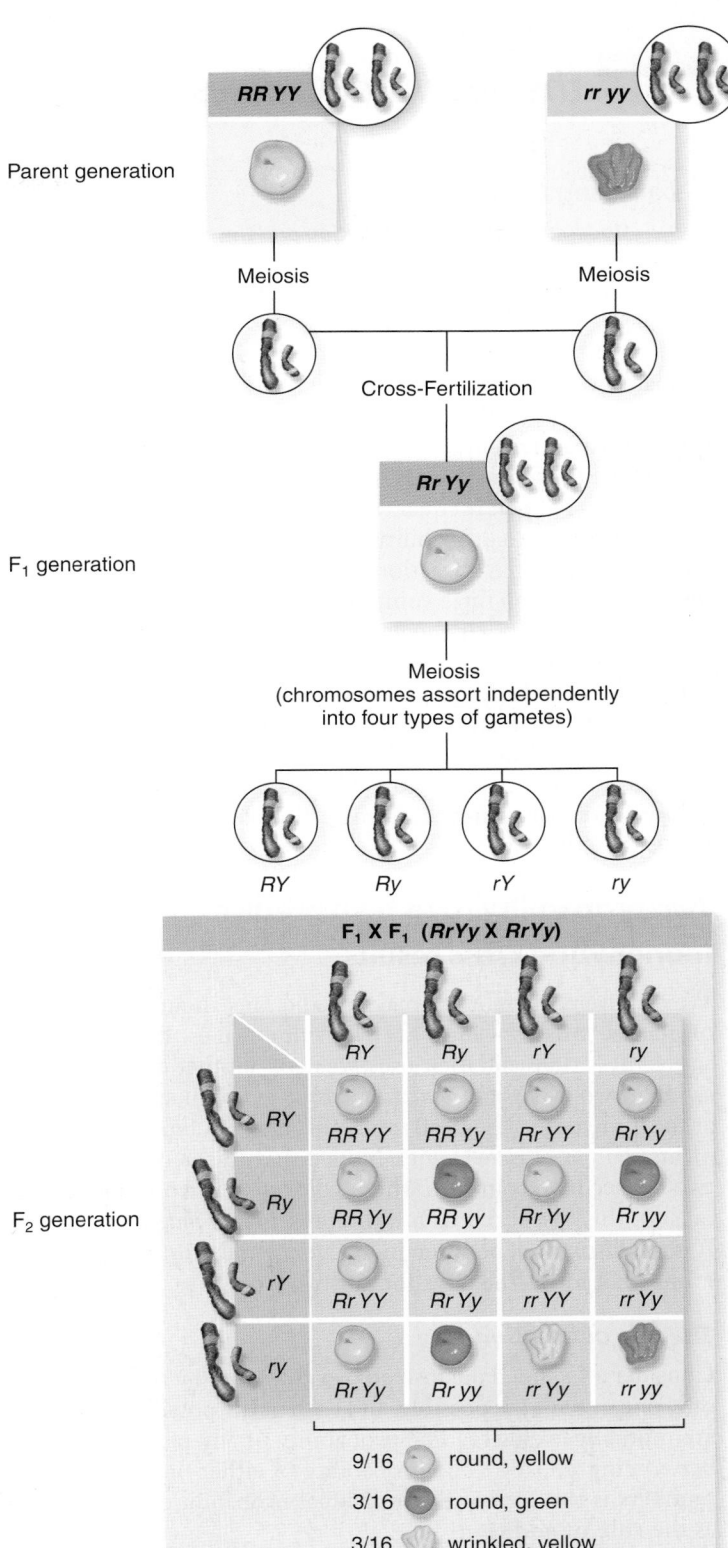

Figure 12.9 Analyzing a dihybrid cross. This Punnett square shows the results of Mendel's dihybrid cross between plants with round yellow seeds and plants with wrinkled green seeds. The ratio of the four possible combinations of phenotypes is predicted to be 9:3:3:1, the ratio that Mendel found.

Probability: Predicting the Results of Crosses

Probability allows us to predict the likelihood of the outcome of random events. Because the behavior of different chromosomes during meiosis is independent, we can use probability to predict the outcome of crosses. The probability of an event that is certain to happen is equal to 1. In contrast, an event that can never happen has a probability of 0. Therefore, probabilities for all other events have fractional values, between 0 and 1. For instance, when you flip a coin, two outcomes are possible; there is only one way to get the event "heads" so the probability of heads is one divided by two, or ½. In the case of genetics, consider a pea plant heterozygous for the flower color alleles P and p. This individual can produce two types of gametes in equal numbers, again due to the behavior of chromosomes during meiosis. There is one way to get a P gamete, so the probability of any particular gamete carrying a P allele is 1 divided by 2 or ½, just like the coin toss.

Two probability rules help predict monohybrid cross results

We can use probability to make predictions about the outcome of genetic crosses using only two simple rules. Before we describe these rules and their uses, we need another definition. We say that two events are *mutually exclusive* if both cannot happen at the same time. The heads and tails of a coin flip are examples of mutually exclusive events. Notice that this is different from two consecutive coin flips where you can get two heads or two tails. In this case, each coin flip represents an *independent event*. It is the distinction between independent and mutually exclusive events that forms the basis for our two rules.

The rule of addition

Consider a six-sided die instead of a coin: for any roll of the die, only one outcome is possible, and each of the possible outcomes are mutually exclusive. The probability of any particular number coming up is ⅙. The probability of either of two different numbers is the sum of the individual probabilities, or restated as the **rule of addition:**

For two mutually exclusive events, the probability of either event occurring is the sum of the individual probabilities.

Probability of rolling either a 2 or a 6
is = ⅙ + ⅙ = ²⁄₆ = ⅓

To apply this to our cross of heterozygous purple F_1, four mutually exclusive outcomes are possible: PP, Pp, pP, and pp. The probability of being heterozygous is the same as the probability of being either Pp or pP, or ¼ plus ¼, or ½.

Probability of F_2 heterozygote = ¼Pp + ¼pP = ½

In the previous example, of 379 total offspring, we would expect about 190 to be heterozygotes. (The actual number is 189.5.)

The rule of multiplication

The second rule, and by far the most useful for genetics, deals with the outcome of independent events. This is called the **product rule,** or **rule of multiplication,** and it states that the probability of two independent events both occurring is the *product* of their individual probabilities.

We can apply this to a monohybrid cross in which offspring are formed by gametes from each of two parents. For any particular outcome then, this is due to two independent events: the formation of two different gametes. Consider the purple F_1 parents from earlier. They are all Pp (heterozygotes), so the probability that a particular F_2 individual will be pp (homozygous recessive) is the probability of receiving a p gamete from the male (½) times the probability of receiving a p gamete from the female (½), or ¼:

Probability of pp homozygote = ½p (male parent) × ½p
(female parent) = ¼pp

This is actually the basis for the Punnett square that we used before. Each cell in the square was the product of the probabilities of the gametes that contribute to the cell. We then use the addition rule to sum the probabilities of the mutually exclusive events that make up each cell.

We can use the result of a probability calculation to predict the number of homozygous recessive offspring in a cross between heterozygotes. For example, out of 379 total offspring, we would expect about 95 to exhibit the homozygous recessive phenotype. (The actual calculated number is 94.75.)

Dihybrid cross probabilities are based on monohybrid cross probabilities

Probability analysis can be extended to the dihybrid case. For our purple F_1 by F_1 cross, there are four possible outcomes, three of which show the dominant phenotype. Thus the probability of any offspring showing the dominant phenotype is ¾, and the probability of any offspring showing the recessive phenotype is ¼. Now we can use this and the product rule to predict the outcome of a dihybrid cross. We will use our example of seed shape and color from earlier, but now examine it using probability.

If the alleles affecting seed shape and seed color segregate independently, then the probability that a particular pair of alleles for seed shape would occur together with a particular pair of alleles for seed color is the product of the individual probabilities for each pair. For example, the probability that an individual with wrinkled green seeds ($rr\,yy$) would appear in the F_2 generation would be equal to the probability of obtaining wrinkled seeds (¼) times the probability of obtaining green seeds (¼), or ¹⁄₁₆.

Probability of $rr\,yy$ = ¼ rr × ¼ yy = ¹⁄₁₆ $rr\,yy$

Because of independent assortment, we can think of the dihybrid cross of consisting of two independent monohybrid crosses; since these are independent events, the product rule applies. So, we can calculate the probabilities for each dihybrid phenotype:

Probability of round yellow ($R\_\_\ Y\_\_$) =
¾ $R\_\_$ × ¾ $Y\_\_$ = $^9/_{16}$

Probability of round green ($R\_\_\ yy$) =
¾ $R\_\_$ × ¼ yy = $^3/_{16}$

Probability of wrinkled yellow ($rr\ Y\_\_$) =
¼ rr × ¾ $Y\_\_$ = $^3/_{16}$

Probability of wrinkled green ($rr\ yy$) =
¼ rr ×¼ yy = $^1/_{16}$

The hypothesis that color and shape genes are independently sorted thus predicts that the F_2 generation will display a 9:3:3:1 phenotypic ratio. These ratios can be applied to an observed total offspring to predict the expected number in each phenotypic group. The underlying logic and the results are the same as obtained using the Punnett square.

Learning Outcomes Review 12.4

The rule of addition states that the probability of either of two events occurring is the sum of their individual probabilities. The rule of multiplication states that the probability of two independent events both occurring is the product of their individual probabilities. These rules can be applied to genetic crosses to determine the probability of particular genotypes and phenotypes. Results can then be compared against these predictions.

■ *How would you calculate the probability of all dominant phenotype F_2 progeny in a trihybrid cross?*

The Testcross: Revealing Unknown Genotypes

Learning Outcome

1. *Interpret data from test crosses to infer genotypes.*

To test his model further, Mendel devised a simple and powerful procedure called the **testcross**. In a testcross, an individual with unknown genotype is crossed with the homozygous recessive genotype—that is, the recessive parental variety. The contribution of the homozygous recessive parent can be ignored, because this parent can contribute only recessive alleles.

Consider a purple-flowered pea plant. It is impossible to tell whether such a plant is homozygous or heterozygous simply by looking at it. To learn its genotype, you can perform a testcross to a white-flowered plant. In this cross, the two possible test plant genotypes will give different results (figure 12.10):

Alternative 1: Unknown individual is homozygous dominant (PP) $PP × pp$: All offspring have purple flowers (Pp).

Alternative 2: Unknown individual is heterozygous (Pp) $Pp × pp$: ½ of offspring have white flowers (pp), and ½ have purple flowers (Pp).

Put simply, the appearance of the recessive phenotype in the offspring of a testcross indicates that the test individual's genotype is heterozygous.

For each pair of alleles Mendel investigated, he observed phenotypic F_2 ratios of 3:1 (see figure 12.4) and testcross ratios of 1:1, just as his model had predicted. Testcrosses can also be used to determine the genotype of an individual when two genes are involved. Mendel often

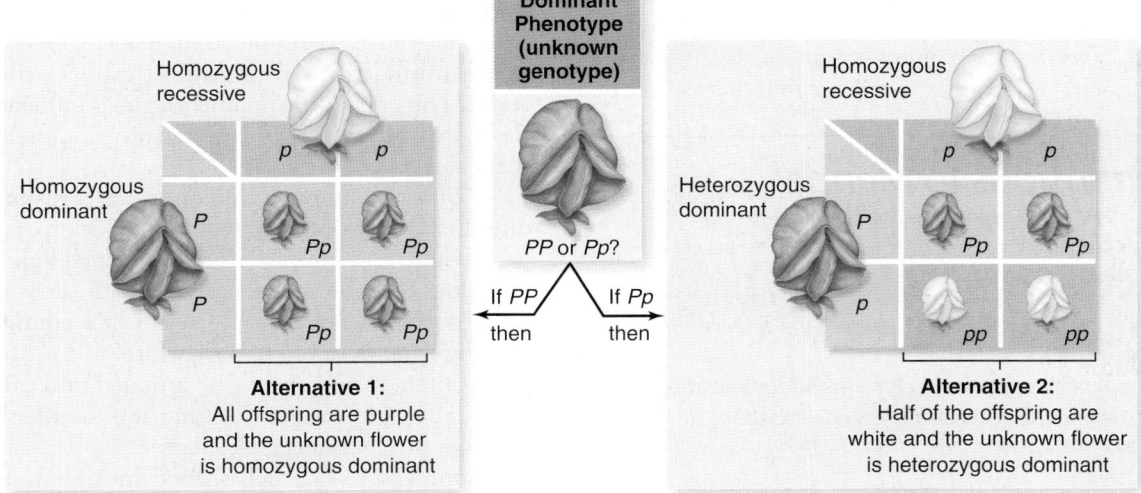

Figure 12.10 A testcross. To determine whether an individual exhibiting a dominant phenotype, such as purple flowers, is homozygous or heterozygous for the dominant allele, Mendel crossed the individual in question with a plant that he knew to be homozygous recessive—in this case, a plant with white flowers.

TABLE 12.2	Dihybrid Testcross	
Actual Genotype	**Results of Testcross**	
	Trait A	**Trait B**
AABB	Trait A breeds true	Trait B breeds true
AaBB	————	Trait B breeds true
AABb	Trait A breeds true	————
AaBb	————	————

performed testcrosses to verify the genotypes of dominant-appearing F_2 individuals.

An F_2 individual exhibiting both dominant traits ($A\_\_ B\_\_$) might have any of the following genotypes: $AABB$, $AaBB$, $AABb$, or $AaBb$. By crossing dominant-appearing F_2 individuals with homozygous recessive individuals (that is, $A\_\_ B\_\_ \times aabb$), Mendel was able to determine whether either or both of the traits bred true among the progeny, and so to determine the genotype of the F_2 parent (table 12.2).

Testcrossing is a powerful tool that simplifies genetic analysis. We will use this method of analysis in the next chapter, when we explore genetic mapping.

Learning Outcome Review 12.5

Individuals showing the dominant phenotype can be either homozygous dominant or heterozygous. Unknown genotypes can be revealed using a testcross, which is a cross to a homozygous recessive individual. Heterozygotes produce both dominant and recessive phenotypes in equal numbers as a result of the testcross.

■ *In a dihybrid testcross of a doubly heterozygous individual, what would be the expected phenotypic ratio?*

12.6 Extensions to Mendel

Learning Outcomes

1. *Describe how assumptions in Mendel's model result in oversimplification.*
2. *Discuss a genetic explanation for continuous variation.*
3. *Explain the genetic basis for observed alterations to Mendel's ratios.*

Although Mendel's results did not receive much notice during his lifetime, three different investigators independently rediscovered his pioneering paper in 1900, 16 years after his death. They came across it while searching the literature in prepara-

tion for publishing their own findings, which closely resembled those Mendel had presented more than 30 years earlier.

In the decades following the rediscovery of Mendel's ideas, many investigators set out to test them. However, scientists attempting to confirm Mendel's theory often had trouble obtaining the same simple ratios he had reported.

The reason that Mendel's simple ratios were not obtained had to do with the traits that others examined. A number of assumptions are built into Mendel's model that are oversimplifications. These assumptions include that each trait is specified by a single gene with two alternative alleles; that there are no environmental effects; and that gene products act independently. The idea of dominance also hides a wealth of biochemical complexity. In the following sections, you'll see how Mendel's simple ideas can be extended to provide a more complete view of genetics (table 12.3).

In polygenic inheritance, more than one gene can affect a single trait

Often, the relationship between genotype and phenotype is more complicated than a single allele producing a single trait. Most phenotypes also do not reflect simple two-state cases like purple or white flowers.

Consider Mendel's crosses between tall and short pea plants. In reality, the "tall" plants actually have normal height, and the "short" plants are dwarfed by an allele at a single gene. But in most species, including humans, height varies over a continuous range, rather than having discrete values. This continuous distribution of a phenotype has a simple genetic explanation: more than one gene is at work. The mode of inheritance operating in this case is often called **polygenic inheritance.**

In reality, few phenotypes result from the action of only one gene. Instead, most characters reflect multiple additive contributions to the phenotype by several genes. When multiple genes act jointly to influence a character, such as height or weight, the character often shows a range of small differences. When these genes segregate independently, a gradation in the degree of difference can be observed when a group consisting of many individuals is examined (figure 12.11). We call this gradation **continuous variation,** and we call such traits **quantitative traits.** The greater the number of genes influencing a character, the more continuous the expected distribution of the versions of that character.

This continuous variation in traits is similar to blending different colors of paint: Combining one part red with seven parts white, for example, produces a much lighter shade of pink than does combining five parts red with three parts white. Different ratios of red to white result in a continuum of shades, ranging from pure red to pure white.

Often, variations can be grouped into categories, such as different height ranges. Plotting the numbers in each height category produces a curve called a *histogram*, such as that shown in figure 12.11. The bell-shaped histogram approximates an idealized *normal distribution*, in which the central tendency is characterized by the mean, and the spread of the curve indicates the amount of variation.

Even simple-appearing traits can have this kind of polygenic basis. For example, human eye colors are often described in

TABLE 12.3	When Mendel's Laws/Results May Not Be Observed	
Genetic Occurrence	**Definition**	**Examples**
Polygenic inheritance	More than one gene can affect a single trait.	• Four genes are involved in determining eye color. • Human height
Pleiotropy	A single gene can affect more than one trait.	• A pleiotropic allele dominant for yellow fur in mice is recessive for a lethal developmental defect. • Cystic fibrosis • Sickle cell anemia
Multiple alleles for one gene	Genes may have more than two alleles.	ABO blood types in humans
Dominance is not always complete	• In incomplete dominance the heterozygote is intermediate. • In codominance no single allele is dominant, and the heterozygote shows some aspect of both homozygotes.	• Japanese four o'clocks • Human blood groups
Environmental factors	Genes may be affected by the environment.	Siamese cats
Gene interaction	Products of genes can interact to alter genetic ratios.	• The production of a purple pigment in corn • Coat color in mammals

simple terms with brown dominant to blue, but this is actually incorrect. Extensive analysis indicates that at least four genes are involved in determining eye color. This leads to more complex inheritance patterns than initially reported. For example, blue-eyed parents can have brown-eyed offspring, although it is rare.

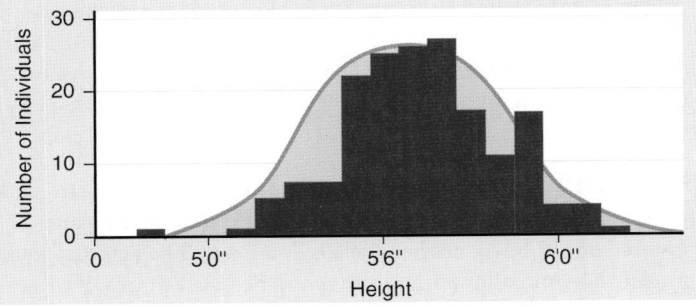

Figure 12.11 Height is a continuously varying trait. The photo and accompanying graph show variation in height among students of the 1914 class at the Connecticut Agricultural College. Because many genes contribute to height and tend to segregate independently of one another, the cumulative contribution of different combinations of alleles to height forms a *continuous* distribution of possible heights, in which the extremes are much rarer than the intermediate values. Variation can also arise due to environmental factors such as nutrition.

In pleiotropy, a single gene can affect more than one trait

Not only can more than one gene affect a single trait, but a single gene can affect more than one trait. Considering the complexity of biochemical pathways and the interdependent nature of organ systems in multicellular organisms, this should be no surprise.

An allele that has more than one effect on phenotype is said to be **pleiotropic.** The pioneering French geneticist Lucien Cuenot studied yellow fur in mice, a dominant trait, and found he was unable to obtain a pure-breeding yellow strain by crossing individual yellow mice with each other. Individuals homozygous for the yellow allele died, because the yellow allele was pleiotropic: One effect was yellow coat color, but another was a lethal developmental defect.

A pleiotropic allele may be dominant with respect to one phenotypic consequence (yellow fur) and recessive with respect to another (lethal developmental defect). Pleiotropic effects are difficult to predict, because a gene that affects one trait often performs other, unknown functions.

Pleiotropic effects are characteristic of many inherited disorders in humans, including cystic fibrosis and sickle cell anemia (discussed in chapter 13). In these disorders, multiple symptoms (phenotypes) can be traced back to a single gene defect. Cystic fibrosis patients exhibit clogged blood vessels, overly sticky mucus, salty sweat, liver and pancreas failure, and several other symptoms. It is often difficult to deduce the nature of the primary defect from the range of a gene's pleiotropic effects. As it turns out, all these symptoms of cystic fibrosis are pleiotropic effects of a single defect, a mutation in a gene that encodes a chloride ion transmembrane channel.

Genes may have more than two alleles

Mendel always looked at genes with two alternative alleles. Although any diploid individual can carry only two alleles for a gene, there may be more than two alleles in a population. The example of ABO blood types in humans, described later on, involves an allelic series with three alleles.

If you think of a gene as a sequence of nucleotides in a DNA molecule, then the number of possible alleles is huge because even a single nucleotide change could produce a new allele. In reality, the number of alleles possible for any gene is constrained, but usually more than two alleles exist for any gene in an outbreeding population. The dominance relationships of these alleles cannot be predicted, but can be determined by observing the phenotypes for the various heterozygous combinations.

Dominance is not always complete

Mendel's idea of dominant and recessive traits can seem hard to explain in terms of modern biochemistry. For example, if a recessive trait is caused by the loss of function of an enzyme encoded by the recessive allele, then why should a heterozygote, with only half the activity of this enzyme, have the same appearance as a homozygous dominant individual?

The answer is that enzymes usually act in pathways and not alone. These pathways, as you have seen in earlier chapters, can be highly complex in terms of inputs and outputs, and they can sometimes tolerate large reductions in activity of single enzymes in the pathway without reductions in the level of the end-product. When this is the case, complete dominance will be observed; however, not all genes act in this way.

Incomplete dominance

In **incomplete dominance,** the heterozygote is intermediate in appearance between the two homozygotes. For example, in a cross between red- and white-flowering Japanese four o'clocks, described in figure 12.12, all the F_1 offspring have pink flowers—indicating that neither red nor white flower color was dominant. Looking only at the F_1, we might conclude that this is a case of blending inheritance. But when two of the F_1 pink flowers are crossed, they produce red-, pink-, and white-flowered plants in a 1:2:1 ratio. In this case the phenotypic ratio is the same as the genotypic ratio because all three genotypes can be distinguished.

Codominance

Most genes in a population possess several different alleles, and often no single allele is dominant; instead, each allele has its own effect, and the heterozygote shows some aspect of the phenotype of both homozygotes. The alleles are said to be **codominant.** Codominance can be distinguished from incomplete dominance by the appearance of the heterozygote. In incomplete dominance, the heterozygote is intermediate between the two homozygotes, whereas in codominance, some aspect of both alleles is seen in the heterozygote. One of the clearest human examples is found in the human blood groups.

The different phenotypes of human blood groups are based on the response of the immune system to proteins on the surface of red blood cells. In homozygotes a single type of protein is found on the surface of cells, and in heterozygotes, two kinds of protein are found, leading to codominance.

The human ABO blood group system

The gene that determines ABO blood types encodes an enzyme that adds sugar molecules to proteins on the surface of red

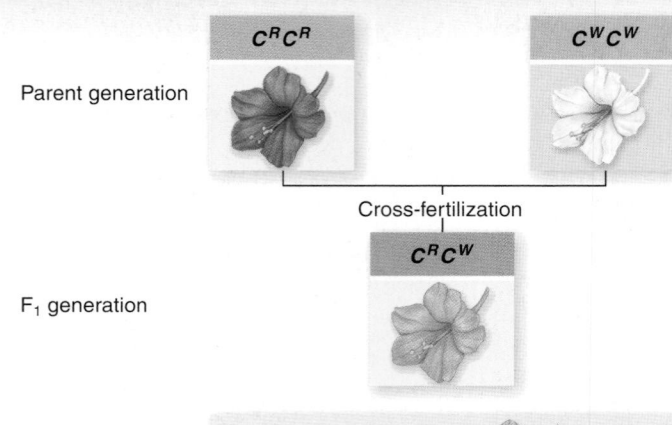
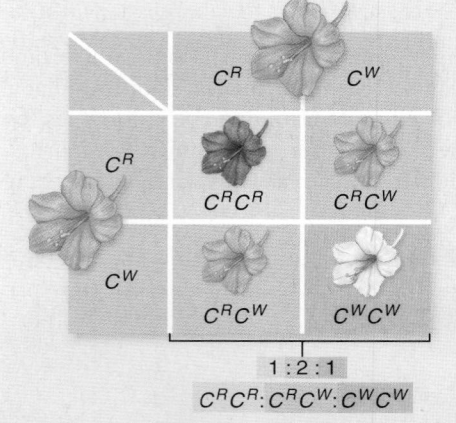
Figure 12.12 Incomplete dominance. In a cross between a red-flowered (genotype C^RC^R) Japanese four o'clock and a white-flowered one (C^WC^W), neither allele is dominant. The heterozygous progeny have pink flowers and the genotype C^RC^W. If two of these heterozygotes are crossed, the phenotypes of their progeny occur in a ratio of 1:2:1 (red:pink:white).

blood cells. These sugars act as recognition markers for the immune system (see chapter 52). The gene that encodes the enzyme, designated I, has three common alleles: I^A, whose product adds galactosamine; I^B, whose product adds galactose; and i, which codes for a protein that does not add a sugar.

The three alleles of the I gene can be combined to produce six different genotypes. An individual heterozygous for the I^A and

I^B alleles produces both forms of the enzyme and exhibits both galactose and galactosamine on red blood cells. Because both alleles are expressed simultaneously in heterozygotes, the I^A and I^B alleles are codominant. Both I^A and I^B are dominant over the i allele, because both I^A and I^B alleles lead to sugar addition, whereas the i allele does not. The different combinations of the three alleles produce four different phenotypes (figure 12.13):

1. Type A individuals add only galactosamine. They are either I^AI^A homozygotes or I^Ai heterozygotes (two genotypes).
2. Type B individuals add only galactose. They are either I^BI^B homozygotes or I^Bi heterozygotes (two genotypes).
3. Type AB individuals add both sugars and are I^AI^B heterozygotes (one genotype).
4. Type O individuals add neither sugar and are ii homozygotes (one genotype).

These four different cell-surface phenotypes are called the **ABO blood groups.**

A person's immune system can distinguish among these four phenotypes. If a type A individual receives a transfusion of type B blood, the recipient's immune system recognizes the "foreign" antigen (galactose) and attacks the donated blood cells, causing them to clump, or agglutinate. The same thing would happen if the donated blood is type AB. However, if the donated blood is type O, no immune attack occurs, because there are no galactose antigens.

In general, any individual's immune system can tolerate a transfusion of type O blood, and so type O is termed the "universal donor." Because neither galactose nor galactosamine is foreign to type AB individuals (whose red blood cells have both sugars), those individuals may receive any type of blood, and type AB is termed the "universal recipient." Nevertheless, matching blood is preferable for any transfusion.

Phenotypes may be affected by the environment

Another assumption, implicit in Mendel's work, is that the environment does not affect the relationship between genotype and phenotype. For example, the soil in the abbey yard where Mendel performed his experiments was probably not uniform, and yet its possible effect on the expression of traits was ignored. But in reality, although the expression of genotype produces phenotype, the environment can affect this relationship.

Environmental effects are not limited to the external environment. For example, the alleles of some genes encode heat-sensitive products, that are affected by differences in internal body temperature. The *ch* allele in Himalayan rabbits and Siamese cats encodes a heat-sensitive version of the enzyme tyrosinase, which as you may recall is involved in albinism (figure 12.14). The Ch version of the enzyme is inactivated at temperatures above about 33°C. At the surface of the torso and head of these animals, the temperature is above 33°C and tyrosinase is inactive, producing a whitish coat. At the extremities, such as the tips of the ears and tail, the temperature is usually below 33°C and the enzyme is active, allowing production of melanin that turns the coat in these areas a dark color.

> ### Inquiry question
> **?** Many studies of identical twins separated at birth have revealed phenotypic differences in their development (height, weight, etc.). If these are identical twins, can you propose an explanation for these differences?

In epistasis, interactions of genes alter genetic ratios

The last simplistic assumption in Mendel's model is that the products of genes do not interact. But the products of genes may not act independently of one another, and the interconnected behavior of gene products can change the ratio expected by independent assortment, even if the genes are on different chromosomes that do exhibit independent assortment.

Alleles	Blood Type	Sugars Exhibited	Donates and Receives
I^AI^A, I^Ai (I^A dominant to i)	A	Galactosamine	Receives A and O Donates to A and AB
I^BI^B, I^Bi (I^B dominant to i)	B	Galactose	Receives B and O Donates to B and AB
I^AI^B (codominant)	AB	Both galactose and galactosamine	Universal receiver Donates to AB
ii (i is recessive)	O	None	Receives O Universal donor

Figure 12.13 ABO blood groups illustrate both codominance and multiple alleles. There are three alleles of the *I* gene: I^A, I^B, and i. I^A and I^B are both dominant to i (see types A and B), but codominant to each other (see type AB). The genotypes that give rise to each blood type are shown with the associated phenotypes in terms of sugars added to surface proteins and the body's reaction after a blood transfusion.

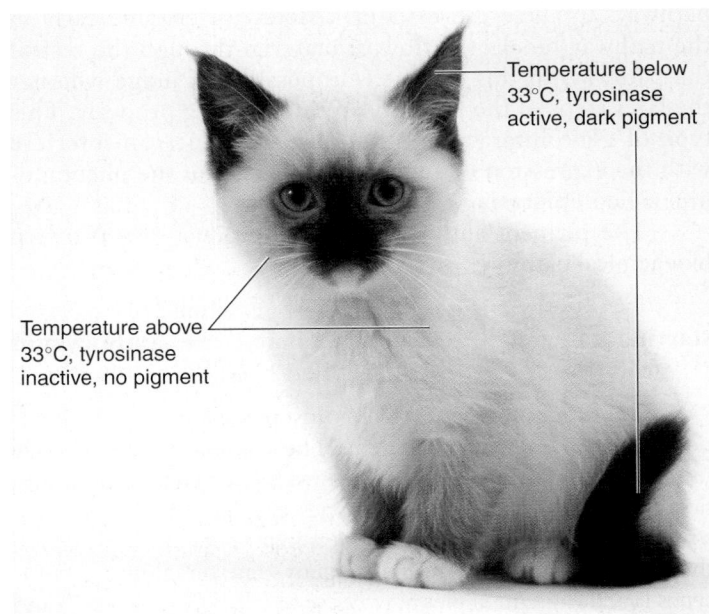

Temperature below 33°C, tyrosinase active, dark pigment

Temperature above 33°C, tyrosinase inactive, no pigment

Figure 12.14 Siamese cat. The pattern of coat color is due to an allele that encodes a temperature-sensitive form of the enzyme tyrosinase.

Given the interconnected nature of metabolism, it should not come as a surprise that many gene products are not independent. Genes that act in the same metabolic pathway, for example, should show some form of dependence at the level of function. In such cases, the ratio Mendel would predict is not readily observed, but it is still there in an altered form.

In the tests of Mendel's ideas that followed the rediscovery of his work, scientists had trouble obtaining Mendel's simple ratios, particularly with dihybrid crosses. Sometimes, it was not possible to identify successfully each of the four phenotypic classes expected, because two or more of the classes looked alike.

An example of this comes from the analysis of particular varieties of corn, *Zea mays*. Some commercial varieties exhibit a purple pigment called anthocyanin in their seed coats, whereas others do not. In 1918, geneticist R. A. Emerson crossed two true-breeding corn varieties, each lacking anthocyanin pigment. Surprisingly, all of the F_1 plants produced purple seeds.

When two of these pigment-producing F_1 plants were crossed to produce an F_2 generation, 56% were pigment producers and 44% were not. This is clearly not what Mendel's ideas would lead us to expect. Emerson correctly deduced that two genes were involved in producing pigment, and that the second cross had thus been a dihybrid cross. According to Mendel's theory, gametes in a dihybrid cross could combine in 16 equally possible ways—so the puzzle was to figure out how these 16 combinations could occur in the two phenotypic groups of progeny. Emerson multiplied the fraction that were pigment producers (0.56) by 16 to obtain 9, and multiplied the fraction that lacked pigment (0.44) by 16 to obtain 7. Emerson therefore had a *modified ratio* of 9:7 instead of the usual 9:3:3:1 ratio (figure 12.15).

This modified ratio is easily rationalized by considering the function of the products encoded by these genes. When gene products act sequentially, as in a biochemical pathway, an allele expressed as a defective enzyme early in the pathway blocks the flow of material through the rest of the pathway. In this case, it is impossible to judge whether the later steps of the pathway are functioning properly. This type of gene interaction, in which one gene can interfere with the expression of another, is the basis of the phenomenon called **epistasis.**

The pigment anthocyanin is the product of a two-step biochemical pathway:

$$\text{starting molecule} \xrightarrow{\text{enzyme 1}} \text{intermediate} \xrightarrow{\text{enzyme 2}} \text{anthocyanin}$$
(colorless)   (colorless)   (purple)

To produce pigment, a plant must possess at least one functional copy of each enzyme's gene. The dominant alleles encode functional enzymes, and the recessive alleles encode nonfunctional enzymes. Of the 16 genotypes predicted by random assortment, 9 contain at least one dominant allele of both genes; they therefore produce purple progeny. The remaining 7 genotypes lack dominant alleles at *either or both* loci (3 + 3 + 1 = 7) and so produce colorless progeny, giving the phenotypic ratio of 9:7 that Emerson observed (see figure 12.15).

You can see that although this ratio is not the expected dihybrid ratio, it is a modification of the expected ratio.

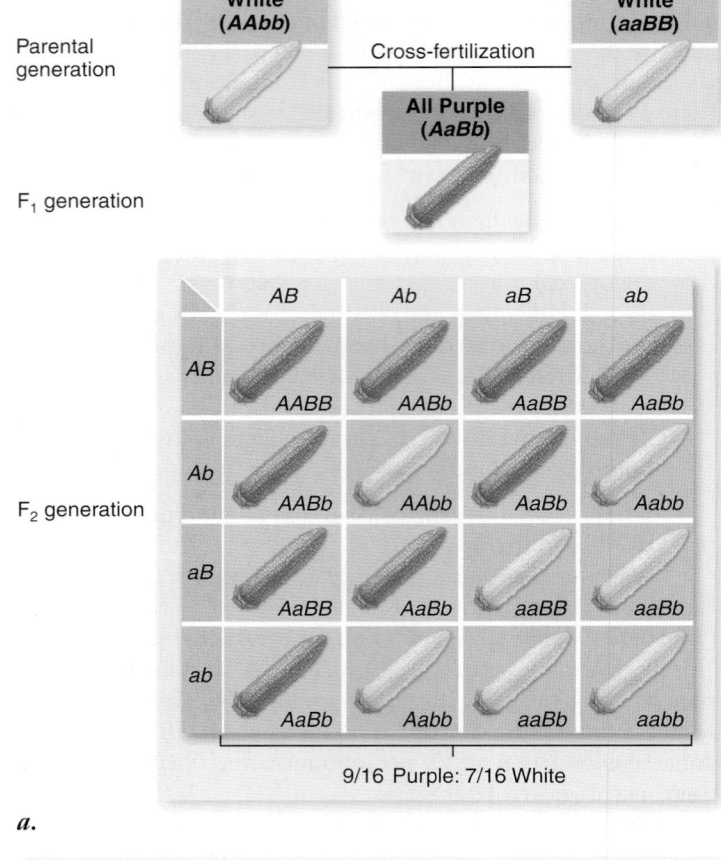

Figure 12.15 How epistasis affects grain color.
a. Crossing some white varieties of corn yields an all purple F_1. Self-crossing the F_1 yields 9 purple:7 white. This can be explained by the presence of two genes, each encoding an enzyme necessary for the production of purple pigment. Unless both enzymes are active (genotype is $A\_B\_$), no pigment is expressed. *b.* The biochemical pathway for pigment production with enzymes encoded by A and B genes.

Learning Outcomes Review 12.6

Mendel's model assumes that each trait is specified by one gene with only two alleles, no environmental effects alter a trait, and gene products act independently. All of these prove to be oversimplifications. Traits produced by the action of multiple genes (polygenic inheritance) have continuous variation. One gene can affect more than one trait (pleiotropy). Genes may have more than two alleles, and these may not show simple dominance. In incomplete dominance, the heterozygote is intermediate between the two homozygotes, and in codominance the heterozygote shows aspects of both homozygotes, both of which alter the monohybrid ratio. The action of genes is not always independent, which can result in modified dihybrid ratios.

■ *In the cross in figure 12.15, what proportion of F_2 will be white because they are homozygous recessive for one of the two genes?*

12.1 The Mystery of Heredity

Early plant biologists produced hybrids and saw puzzling results.

Plant breeders noticed that some forms of a trait can disappear in one generation only to reappear later, that is, they segregate rather than blend.

Mendel used mathematics to analyze his crosses.

Mendel's experiments involved reciprocal crosses between true-breeding pea varieties followed by one or more generations of self-fertilization. His mathematical analysis of experimental results led to the present model of inheritance.

12.2 Monohybrid Crosses: The Principle of Segregation (see figure 12.5)

The F_1 generation exhibits only one of two traits, without blending.

Mendel called the trait visible in the F_1 the dominant trait; the other he termed recessive.

The F_2 generation exhibits both traits in a 3:1 ratio.

When F_1 plants are self-fertilized, the F_2 shows a consistent ratio of 3 dominant:1 recessive. We call this 3:1 ratio the Mendelian monohybrid ratio.

The 3:1 ratio is actually 1:2:1.

Mendel then examined the F_2 and found the recessive F_2 plants always bred true, but only one out of three dominant F_2 bred true. This means the 3:1 ratio is actually 1 true-breeding dominant:2 non-true-breeding dominant:1 recessive.

Mendel's Principle of Segregation explains monohybrid observations.

Traits are determined by discrete factors we now call genes. These exist in alternative forms we call alleles. Individuals carrying two identical alleles for a gene are said to be homozygous, and individuals carrying different alleles are said to be heterozygous. The genotype is the entire set of alleles of all genes possessed by an individual. The phenotype is the individual's appearance due to these alleles.

The Principle of Segregation states that during gamete formation, the two alleles of a gene separate (segregate). Parental alleles then randomly come together to form the diploid zygote. The physical basis of segregation is the separation of homologues during anaphase of meiosis I.

The Punnett square allows symbolic analysis.

Punnett squares are formed by placing the gametes from one parent along the top of the square with the gametes from the other parent along the side. Zygotes formed from gamete combinations form the blocks of the square (see figure 12.6).

Some human traits exhibit dominant/recessive inheritance.

Certain human traits have been found to have a Mendelian basis (see table 12.1). Inheritance patterns in human families can be analyzed and inferred using a pedigree diagram of earlier generations.

12.3 Dihybrid Crosses: The Principle of Independent Assortment (see figure 12.9)

Traits in a dihybrid cross behave independently.

If parents differing in two traits are crossed, the F_1 will be all dominant. Each F_1 parent can produce four different gametes that can be combined to produce 16 possible outcomes in the F_2. This yields a phenotypic ratio of 9:3:3:1 of the four possible phenotypes.

Mendel's Principle of Independent Assortment explains dihybrid results.

The Principle of Independent Assortment states that different traits segregate independently of one another. The physical basis of independent assortment is the independent behavior of different pairs of homologous chromosomes during meiosis I.

12.4 Probability: Predicting the Results of Crosses

Two probability rules help predict monohybrid cross results.

The rule of addition states that the probability of two independent events occurring is the sum of their individual probabilities. The rule of multiplication, or product rule, states that the probability of two independent events *both* occurring is the product of their individual probabilities.

Dihybrid cross probabilities are based on monohybrid cross probabilities.

A dihybrid cross is essentially two independent monohybrid crosses. The product rule applies and can be used to predict the cross's outcome.

12.5 The Testcross: Revealing Unknown Genotypes (see figure 12.10)

In a testcross, an unknown genotype is crossed with a homozygous recessive genotype. The F_1 offspring will all be the same if the unknown genetoype is homozygous dominant. The F_1 offspring will exhibit a 1:1 dominant:recessive ratio if the unknown genotype is heterozygous.

12.6 Extensions to Mendel

In polygenic inheritance, more than one gene can affect a single trait.

Many traits, such as human height, are due to multiple additive contributions by many genes, resulting in continuous variation.

In pleiotropy, a single gene can affect more than one trait.

A pleiotropic effect occurs when an allele affects more than one trait. These effects are difficult to predict.

Genes may have more than two alleles.

There may be more than two alleles of a gene in a population. Given the possible number of DNA sequences, this is not surprising.

Dominance is not always complete.

In incomplete dominance the heterozygote exhibits an intermediate phenotype; the monohybrid genotypic and phenotypic ratios are the same (see figure 12.12). Codominant alleles each contribute to the phenotype of a heterozygote.

Phenotypes may be affected by the environment.

Genotype determines phenotype, but the environment will have an effect on this relationship. Environment means both external and internal factors. For example, in Siamese cats, a temperature-sensitive enzyme produces more pigment in the colder peripheral areas of the body.

In epistasis, interactions of genes alter genetic ratios.

Genes encoding enzymes that act in a single biochemical pathway are not independent. In corn, anthocyanin pigment production requires the action of two enzymes. Doubly heterozygous individuals for these enzymes yield a 9:7 ratio when self-crossed (see figure 12.15).

UNDERSTAND

1. What property distinguished Mendel's investigation from previous studies?

    a. Mendel used true-breeding pea plants.
    b. Mendel quantified his results.
    c. Mendel examined many different traits.
    d. Mendel examined the segregation of traits.

2. The F_1 generation of the monohybrid cross purple (PP) × white (pp) flower pea plants should

    a. all have white flowers.
    b. all have a light purple or blended appearance.
    c. all have purple flowers.
    d. have (¾) purple flowers, and ¼ white flowers.

3. The F_1 plants from the previous question are allowed to self-fertilize. The phenotypic ratio for the F_2 should be

    a. all purple.   c. 3 purple:1 white.
    b. 1 purple:1 white.   d. 3 white:1 purple.

4. Which of the following is *not* a part of Mendel's five-element model?

    a. Traits have alternative forms (what we now call alleles).
    b. Parents transmit discrete traits to their offspring.
    c. If an allele is present it will be expressed.
    d. Traits do not blend.

5. An organism's _____ is/are determined by its _____.

    a. genotype; phenotype   c. alleles; phenotype
    b. phenotype; genotype   d. genes; alleles

6. Phenotypes like height in humans, which show a continuous distribution, are usually the result of

    a. an alteration of dominance for multiple alleles of a single gene.
    b. the presence of multiple alleles for a single gene.
    c. the action of one gene on multiple phenotypes.
    d. the action of multiple genes on a single phenotype.

APPLY

1. A dihybrid cross between a plant with long smooth leaves and a plant with short hairy leaves produces a long smooth F_1. If this F_1 is allowed to self-cross to produce an F_2, what would you predict for the ratio of F_2 phenotypes?

    a. 9 long smooth:3 long hairy:3 short hairy:1 short smooth
    b. 9 long smooth:3 long hairy:3 short smooth:1 short hairy
    c. 9 short hairy:3 long hairy:3 short smooth:1 long smooth
    d. 1 long smooth:1 long hairy:1 short smooth:1 short hairy

2. Consider a long smooth F_2 plant from the previous question. This plant's genotype

    a. must be homozygous for both long alleles and hairy alleles.
    b. must be heterozygous at both the leaf length gene, and the leaf hair gene.
    c. can only be inferred by another cross.
    d. cannot be determined by any means.

3. What is the probability of obtaining an individual with the genotype bb from a cross between two individuals with the genotype Bb?

    a. ½   c. ⅛
    b. ¼   d. 0

4. What is the probability of obtaining an individual with the genotype CC from a cross between two individuals with the genotypes CC and Cc?

    a. ½   c. ⅛
    b. ¼   d. ¹⁄₁₆

5. You discover a new variety of plant with color varieties of purple and white. When you intercross these, the F_1 is a lighter purple. You consider that this may be an example of blending and self-cross the F_1. If Mendel is correct, what would you predict for the F_2?

    a. 1 purple:2 white:1 light purple
    b. 1 white:2 purple:1 light purple
    c. 1 purple:2 light purple:1 white
    d. 1 light purple:2 purple:1 white

6. Mendel's model assumes that each trait is determined by a single factor with alternate forms. We now know that this is too simplistic and that

    a. a single gene may affect more than one trait.
    b. a single trait may be affected by more than one gene.
    c. a single gene always affects only one trait, but traits may be affected by more than one gene.
    d. a single gene can affect more than one trait, and traits may be affected by more than one gene.

SYNTHESIZE

1. Create a Punnett square for the following crosses and use this to predict phenotypic ratio for dominant and recessive traits. Dominant alleles are indicated by uppercase letters and recessive are indicated by lowercase letters. For parts b and c, predict ratios using probability and the product rule.

    a. A monohybrid cross between individuals with the genotype Aa and Aa
    b. A dihybrid cross between two individuals with the genotype $AaBb$
    c. A dihybrid cross between individuals with the genotype $AaBb$ and $aabb$

2. Explain how the events of meiosis can explain both segregation and independent assortment.

3. In mice, there is a yellow strain that when crossed yields 2 yellow:1 black. How could you explain this observation? How could you test this with crosses?

4. In mammals, a variety of genes affect coat color. One of these is a gene with mutant alleles that results in the complete loss of pigment, or albinism. Another controls the type of dark pigment with alleles that lead to black or brown colors. The albinistic trait is recessive, and black is dominant to brown. Two black mice are crossed and yield 9 black:4 albino:3 brown. How would you explain these results?

ONLINE RESOURCE

www.ravenbiology.com

Understand, Apply, and Synthesize—enhance your study with animations that bring concepts to life and practice tests to assess your understanding. Your instructor may also recommend the interactive eBook, individualized learning tools, and more.

Chapter **13**

Chromosomes, Mapping, and the Meiosis–Inheritance Connection

Chapter Outline

13.1 Sex Linkage and the Chromosomal Theory of Inheritance

13.2 Sex Chromosomes and Sex Determination

13.3 Exceptions to the Chromosomal Theory of Inheritance

13.4 Genetic Mapping

13.5 Selected Human Genetic Disorders

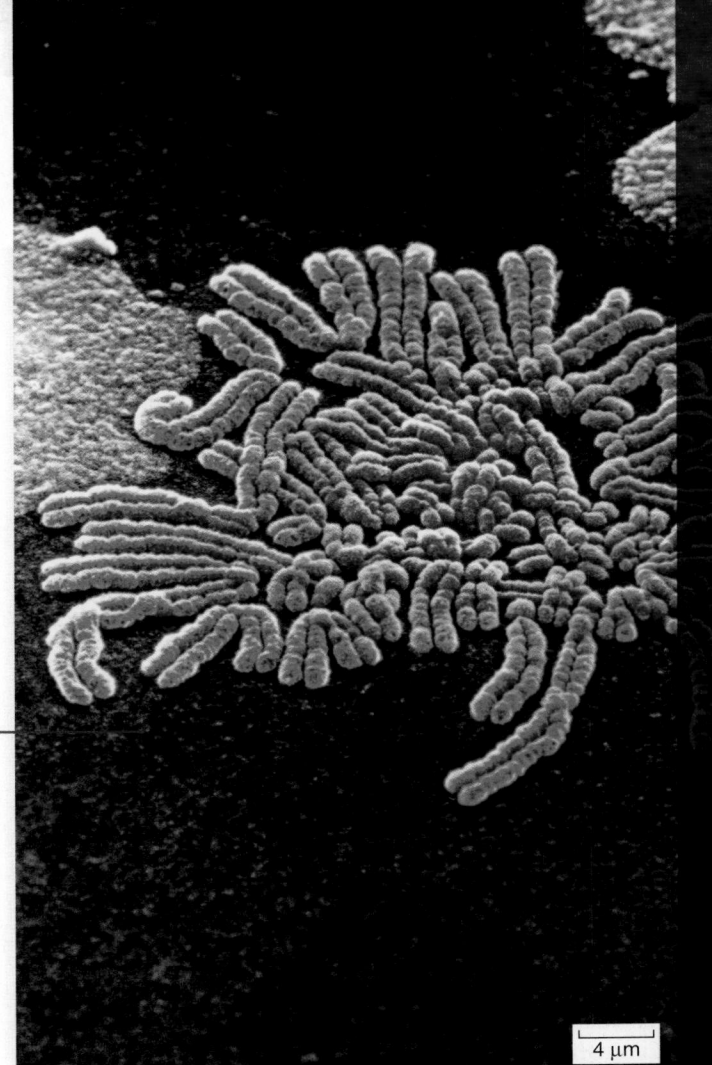

4 μm

Introduction

Mendel's experiments opened the door to understanding inheritance, but many questions remained. In the early part of the 20th century, we did not know the nature of the factors whose behavior Mendel had described. The next step, which involved many researchers in the early part of the century, was uniting information about the behavior of chromosomes, seen in the picture, and the inheritance of traits. The basis for Mendel's principles of segregation and independent assortment lie in events that occur during meiosis.

The behavior of chromosomes during meiosis not only explains Mendel's principles, but leads to new and different approaches to the study of heredity. The ability to construct genetic maps is one of the most powerful tools of classical genetic analysis. The tools of genetic mapping developed in flies and other organisms in combination with information from the Human Genome Project now allow us to determine the location of genes and isolate those that are involved in genetic diseases.

Sex Linkage and the Chromosomal Theory of Inheritance

Learning Outcomes

1. Describe sex-linked inheritance in fruit flies.
2. Explain the evidence for genes being on chromosomes.

A central role for chromosomes in heredity was first suggested in 1900 by the German geneticist Carl Correns, in one of the papers announcing the rediscovery of Mendel's work. Soon after, observations that similar chromosomes paired with one another during meiosis led directly to the **chromosomal theory of inheritance**, first formulated by the American Walter Sutton in 1902.

Morgan correlated the inheritance of a trait with sex chromosomes

In 1910, Thomas Hunt Morgan, studying the fruit fly *Drosophila melanogaster*, discovered a mutant male fly with white eyes instead of red (figure 13.1).

Morgan immediately set out to determine whether this new trait would be inherited in a Mendelian fashion. He first crossed the mutant male to a normal red-eyed female to see whether the red-eyed or white-eyed trait was dominant. All of the F₁ progeny had red eyes, so Morgan concluded that red eye color was dominant over white.

The F₁ cross

Following the experimental procedure that Mendel had established long ago, Morgan then crossed the red-eyed flies from the F₁ generation with each other. Of the 4252 F₂ progeny Morgan examined, 782 (18%) had white eyes. Although the ratio of red eyes to white eyes in the F₂ progeny was greater than 3:1, the results of the cross nevertheless provided clear evidence that eye color segregates. However, something about the outcome was strange and totally unpredicted by Mendel's theory—*all of the white-eyed F₂ flies were males!* (Figure 13.2)

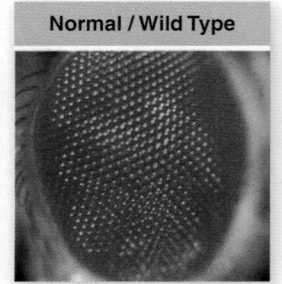
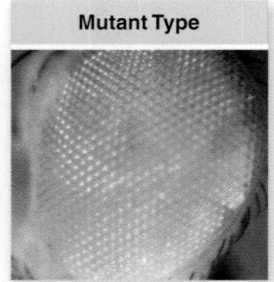

Normal / Wild Type   **Mutant Type**

Figure 13.1 Red-eyed (wild type) and white-eyed (mutant) *Drosophila*. Mutations are heritable alterations in genetic material. By studying the inheritance pattern of white and red alleles (located on the X chromosome), Morgan first demonstrated that genes are on chromosomes.

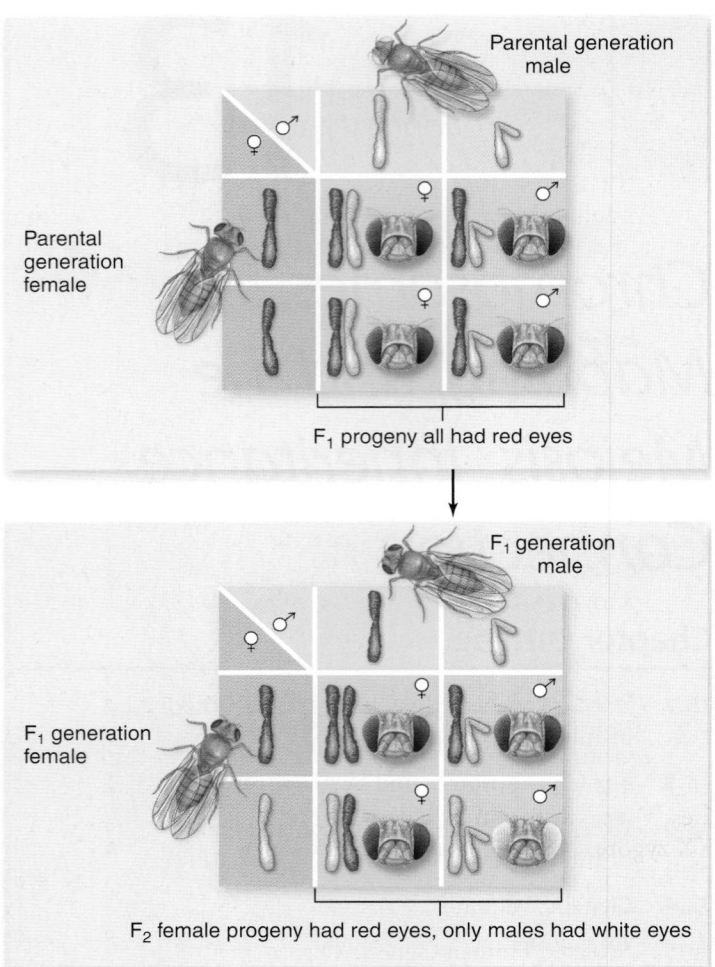

F₁ progeny all had red eyes

F₂ female progeny had red eyes, only males had white eyes

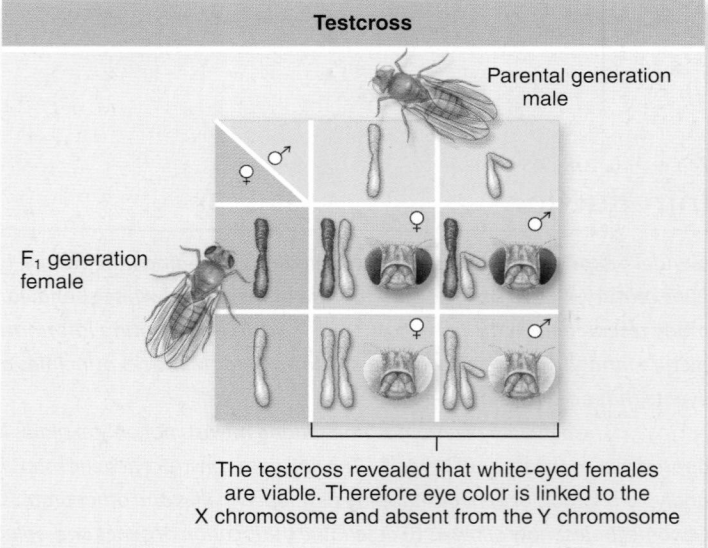

The testcross revealed that white-eyed females are viable. Therefore eye color is linked to the X chromosome and absent from the Y chromosome

Figure 13.2 The chromosomal basis of sex linkage. White-eyed male flies are crossed to red-eyed females. The F₁ flies all have red eyes, as expected for a recessive white-eye allele. In the F₂, all of the white-eyed flies are male because the Y chromosome lacks the white-eye (*white*) gene. Inheritance of the sex chromosomes correlates with eye color, showing the *white* gene is on the X chromosome.

The testcross

Morgan sought an explanation for this result. One possibility was simply that white-eyed female flies don't exist; such individuals might not be viable for some unknown reason. To test this idea, Morgan testcrossed the female F_1 progeny with the original white-eyed male. He obtained white-eyed and red-eyed flies of both sexes in a 1:1:1:1 ratio, just as Mendel's theory had predicted (figure 13.2). Therefore, white-eyed female flies are viable. Given that white-eyed females can exist, Morgan turned to the nature of the chromosomes in males and females for an explanation.

The gene for eye color lies on the X chromosome

In *Drosophila*, the sex of an individual is determined by the number of copies it has of a particular chromosome, the **X chromosome.** Observations of *Drosophila* chromosomes revealed that female flies have two X chromosomes, but male flies have only one. In males, the single X chromosome pairs in meiosis with a dissimilar partner called the **Y chromosome.** These two chromosomes are termed **sex chromosomes** because of their association with sex.

During meiosis, a female produces only X-bearing gametes, but a male produces both X-bearing and Y-bearing gametes. When fertilization involves an X sperm, the result is an XX zygote, which develops into a female; when fertilization involves a Y sperm, the result is an XY zygote, which develops into a male.

The solution to Morgan's puzzle is that the gene causing the white-eye trait in *Drosophila* resides only on the X chromosome—it is absent from the Y chromosome. (We now know that the Y chromosome in flies carries almost no functional genes.) A trait determined by a gene on the X chromosome is said to be **sex-linked,** or X-linked, because it is associated with the sex of the individual. Knowing the white-eye trait is recessive to the red-eye trait, we can now see that Morgan's result was a natural consequence of the Mendelian segregation of chromosomes (see figure 13.2).

Morgan's experiment was one of the most important in the history of genetics because it presented the first clear evidence that the genes determining Mendelian traits do indeed reside on the chromosomes, as Sutton had proposed. Mendelian traits segregate in genetic crosses because homologues separate during gamete formation.

Learning Outcomes Review 13.1

Morgan showed that the trait for white eyes in *Drosophila* segregated with the sex of offspring. X and Y chromosomes also segregate with sex, this correlates the behavior of a trait with the behavior of chromosomes. This finding supported the chromosomal theory of inheritance, which states that traits are carried on chromosomes.

■ *What are the expectations for a cross of white-eyed females to red-eyed males?*

13.2 Sex Chromosomes and Sex Determination

Learning Outcomes

1. *Describe the relationship between sex chromosomes and sex determination.*
2. *Explain dosage compensation in mammals and its genetic consequences.*

The structure and number of sex chromosomes vary in different species (table 13.1). In the fruit fly, *Drosophila*, females are XX and males XY, which is also the case for humans and other mammals. However, in birds, the male has two Z chromosomes, and the female has a Z and a W chromosome. Some insects, such as grasshoppers, have no Y chromosome—females are XX and males are characterized as XO (O indicates the absence of a chromosome).

In humans, the Y chromosome generally determines maleness

In chapter 10, you learned that humans have 46 chromosomes (23 pairs). Twenty-two of these pairs are perfectly matched in both males and females and are called **autosomes.** The remaining pair are the sex chromosomes: XX in females, and XY in males.

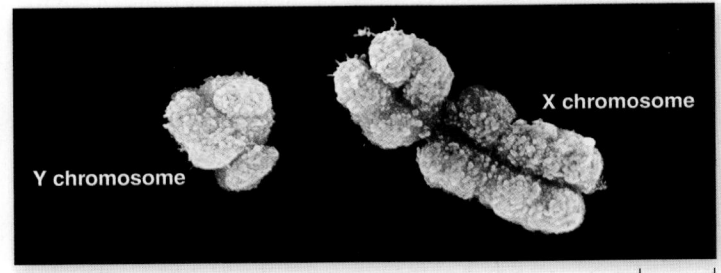

2.8 μm

TABLE 13.1	Sex Determination in Some Organisms		
		Female	**Male**
Humans, *Drosophila*		XX	XY
Birds		ZW	ZZ
Grasshoppers		XX	XO
Honeybees		Diploid	Haploid

The Y chromosome in males is highly condensed. Because few genes on the Y chromosome are expressed, recessive alleles on a male's single X chromosome have no *active* counterpart on the Y chromosome.

The "default" setting in human embryonic development is for production of a female. Some of the active genes on the Y chromosome, notably the *SRY* gene, are responsible for the masculinization of genitalia and secondary sex organs, producing features associated with "maleness" in humans. Consequently, any individual with *at least one Y chromosome* is normally a male.

The exceptions to this rule actually provide support for this mechanism of sex determination. For example, movement of part of the Y chromosome to the X chromosome can cause otherwise XX individuals to develop as male. There is also a genetic disorder that causes a failure to respond to the androgen hormones (androgen insensitivity syndrome) that causes XY individuals to develop as female. Lastly, mutations in *SRY* itself can cause XY individuals to develop as females.

This form of sex determination seen in humans is shared among mammals, but is not universal in vertebrates. Among fishes and some species of reptiles, environmental factors can cause changes in the expression of this sex-determining gene, and thus in the sex of the adult individual.

Some human genetic disorders display sex linkage

From ancient times, people have noted conditions that seem to affect males to a greater degree than females. Red-green color blindness is one well-known condition that is more common in males because the gene affected is carried on the X chromosome.

Another example is hemophilia, a disease that affects a single protein in a cascade of proteins involved in the formation of blood clots. Thus, in an untreated hemophiliac, even minor cuts will not stop bleeding. This form of hemophilia is caused by an X-linked recessive allele; women who are heterozygous for the allele are asymptomatic carriers, and men who receive an X chromosome with the recessive allele exhibit the disease.

The allele for hemophilia was introduced into a number of different European royal families by Queen Victoria of England. Because these families kept careful genealogical records, we have an extensive pedigree for this condition. In the five generations after Victoria, ten of her male descendants have had hemophilia as shown in the pedigree in figure 13.3.

The Russian house of Romanov inherited this condition through Alexandra Feodorovna, a granddaughter of Queen

Figure 13.3 **The royal hemophilia pedigree.** Queen Victoria, shown at the bottom center of the photo, was a carrier for hemophilia. Two of Victoria's four daughters, Alice and Beatrice, inherited the hemophilia allele from Victoria. Two of Alice's daughters are standing behind Victoria (wearing feathered boas): Princess Irene of Prussia *(right)* and Alexandra *(left)*, who would soon become czarina of Russia. Both Irene and Alexandra were also carriers of hemophilia. From the pedigree, it is clear that Alice introduced hemophilia into the Russian and Prussian royal houses, and Victoria's daughter Beatrice introduced it into the Spanish royal house. Victoria's son Leopold, himself a victim, also transmitted the disorder in a third line of descent. Half-shaded symbols represent carriers with one normal allele and one defective allele; fully shaded symbols represent affected individuals.

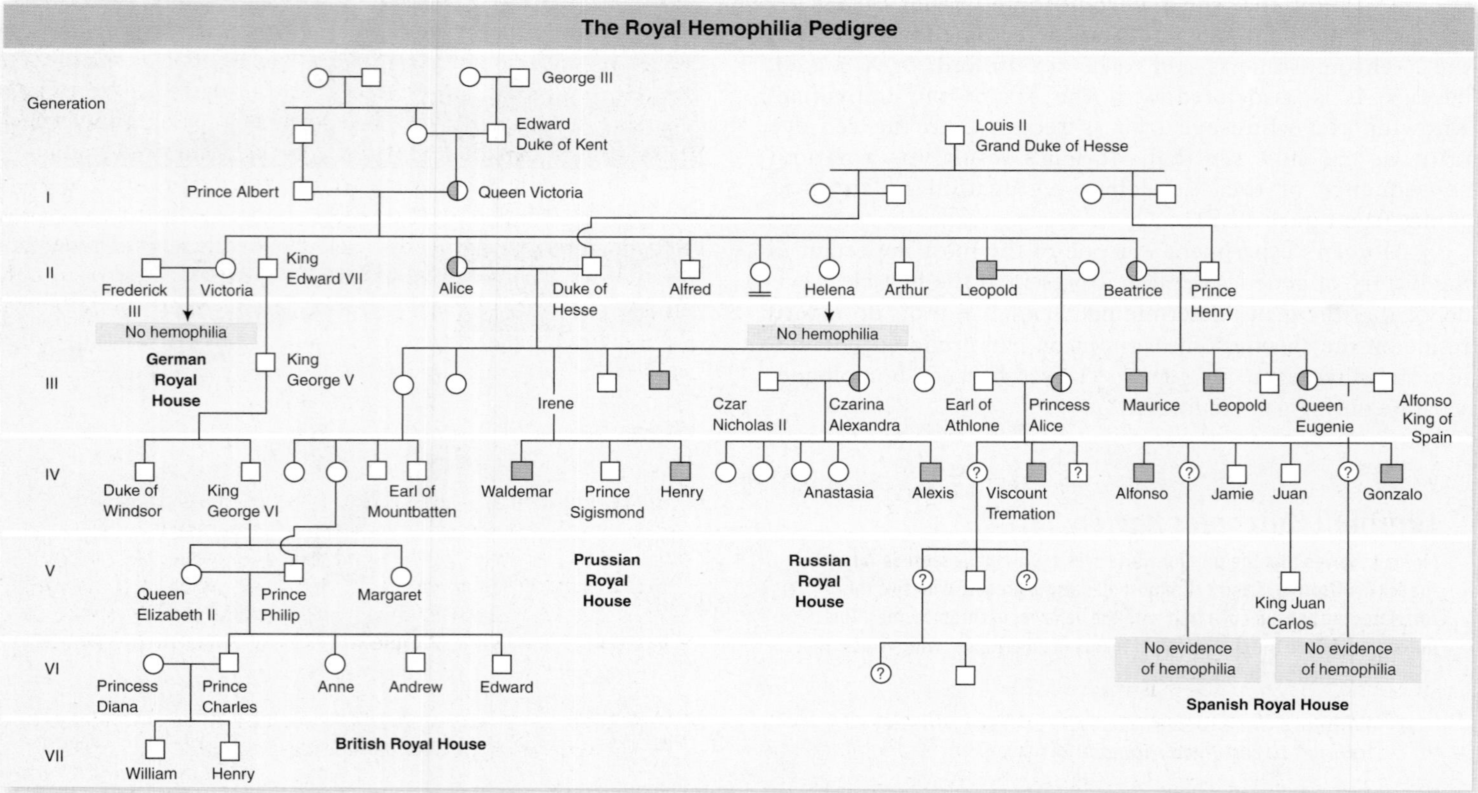

The Royal Hemophilia Pedigree

Generation

George III

Edward
Duke of Kent

Louis II
Grand Duke of Hesse

I

Prince Albert — Queen Victoria

II

Frederick III — Victoria — King Edward VII — Alice — Duke of Hesse — Alfred — Helena — Arthur — Leopold — Beatrice — Prince Henry

No hemophilia

No hemophilia

German Royal House

III

King George V — Irene — Czar Nicholas II — Czarina Alexandra — Earl of Athlone — Princess Alice — Maurice — Leopold — Queen Eugenie — Alfonso King of Spain

IV

Duke of Windsor — King George VI — Earl of Mountbatten — Waldemar — Prince Sigismond — Henry — Anastasia — Alexis — Viscount Tremation — Alfonso — Jamie — Juan — Gonzalo

Prussian Royal House

Russian Royal House

V

Queen Elizabeth II — Prince Philip — Margaret — King Juan Carlos

No evidence of hemophilia

No evidence of hemophilia

Spanish Royal House

VI

Princess Diana — Prince Charles — Anne — Andrew — Edward

VII

William — Henry

British Royal House

Victoria. She married Czar Nicholas II, and their only son, Alexis, was afflicted with the disease. The entire family was executed during the Russian revolution. (Recently, a woman who had long claimed to be Anastasia, a surviving daughter, was shown not to be a Romanov using modern genetic techniques to test her remains.)

Ironically, this condition has not affected the current British royal family, because Victoria's son Edward, who became King Edward VII, did not receive the hemophilia allele. All of the subsequent rulers of England are his descendants.

Dosage compensation prevents doubling of sex-linked gene products

Although males have only one copy of the X chromosome and females have two, female cells do not produce twice as much of the proteins encoded by genes on the X chromosome. Instead, one of the X chromosomes in females is inactivated early in embryonic development, shortly after the embryo's sex is determined. This inactivation is an example of **dosage compensation,** which ensures an equal level of expression from the sex chromosomes despite a differing number of sex chromosomes in males and females. (In *Drosophila*, by contrast, dosage compensation is achieved by increasing the level of expression on the male X chromosome.)

Which X chromosome is inactivated in females varies randomly from cell to cell. If a woman is heterozygous for a sex-linked trait, some of her cells will express one allele and some the other. The inactivated X chromosome is highly condensed, making it visible as an intensely staining **Barr body,** seen below, attached to the nuclear membrane.

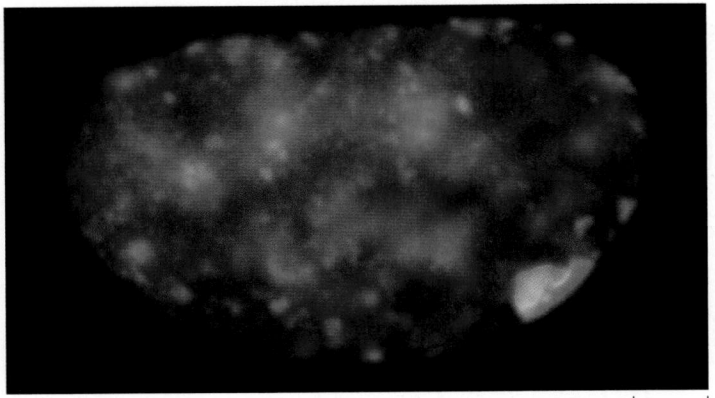

4 μm

X chromosome inactivation can lead to genetic mosaics

X chromosome inactivation to produce dosage compensation is not unique to humans but is true of all mammals. Females that are heterozygous for X chromosome alleles are **genetic mosaics:** Their individual cells may express different alleles, depending on which chromosome is inactivated.

One example is the calico cat, a female that has a patchy distribution of dark fur, orange fur, and white fur (figure 13.4). The dark fur and orange fur are due to heterozygosity for a gene on the

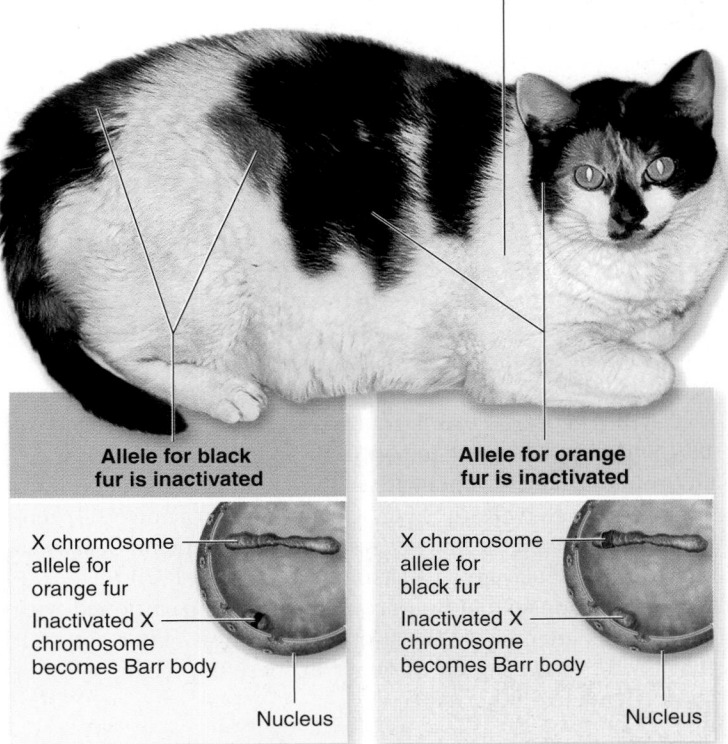

Second gene causes patchy distribution of pigment: white fur = no pigment, orange or black fur = pigment

Allele for black fur is inactivated

Allele for orange fur is inactivated

X chromosome allele for orange fur

Inactivated X chromosome becomes Barr body

Nucleus

X chromosome allele for black fur

Inactivated X chromosome becomes Barr body

Nucleus

Figure 13.4 A calico cat. The cat is heterozygous for alleles of a coat color gene that produce either black fur or orange fur. This gene is on the X chromosome, so the different-colored fur is due to inactivation of one X chromosome. The patchy distribution and white color is due to a second gene that is epistatic to the coat color gene and thus masks its effects.

X chromosome that determines pigment color. One allele results in dark fur, and another allele results in orange fur. Which of these colors is observed in any particular patch is due to inactivation of one X chromosome: If the chromosome containing the orange allele is inactivated, then the fur will be dark, and vice versa.

The patchy distribution of color, and the presence of white fur, is due to a second gene that is epistatic to the fur color gene (see chapter 12). That is, the presence of this second gene produces a patchy distribution of pigment, with some areas totally lacking pigment. In the areas that lack pigment, the effect of either fur color allele is masked. Thus, in this one animal we can see an excellent example of both epistasis and X inactivation.

Learning Outcomes Review 13.2

Sex determination begins with the presence or absence of certain chromosomes termed the sex chromosomes. Additional factors may influence sex determination in different species. In humans, males are XY, and therefore they exhibit recessive traits for alleles on the X chromosome. In mammalian females, one X chromosome in each cell becomes inactivated to balance the levels of gene expression. This random inactivation can lead to genetic mosaics.

- **Would you expect an XXX individual to be viable? If so, would that individual be male or female?**

Exceptions to the Chromosomal Theory of Inheritance

Learning Outcomes

1. Explain why the presence of DNA in organelles leads to non-Mendelian inheritance.
2. Describe the inheritance pattern of organelle DNA.

Although the chromosomal theory explains most inheritance, there are exceptions. Primarily, these are due to the presence of DNA in organelle genomes, specifically in mitochondria and chloroplasts. Non-Mendelian inheritance via organelles was studied in depth by Ruth Sager, who in the face of universal skepticism constructed the first map of chloroplast genes in *Chlamydomonas*, a unicellular green alga, in the 1960s and 1970s.

Mitochondria and chloroplasts are not partitioned with the nuclear genome by the process of meiosis. Thus any trait that is due to the action of genes in these organelles will not show Mendelian inheritance.

Mitochondrial genes are inherited from the female parent

Organelles are usually inherited from only one parent, generally the mother. When a zygote is formed, it receives an equal contribution of the nuclear genome from each parent, but it gets all of its mitochondria from the egg cell, which contains a great deal more cytoplasm (and thus organelles). As the zygote divides, these original mitochondria divide as well and are partitioned randomly.

As a result, the mitochondria in every cell of an adult organism can be traced back to the original maternal mitochondria present in the egg. This mode of uniparental (one-parent) inheritance from the mother is called **maternal inheritance.**

In humans, the disease Leber's hereditary optic neuropathy (LHON) shows maternal inheritance. The genetic basis of this disease is a mutant allele for a subunit of NADH dehydrogenase. The mutant allele reduces the efficiency of electron flow in the electron transport chain in mitochondria (see chapter 7), in turn reducing overall ATP production. Some nerve cells in the optic system are particularly sensitive to reduction in ATP production, resulting in neural degeneration.

A mother with this disease will pass it on to all of her progeny, whereas a father with the disease will not pass it on to any of his progeny. Note that this condition differs from sex-linked inheritance because males and females are equally affected.

Chloroplast genes may also be passed on uniparentally

The inheritance pattern of chloroplasts is also usually maternal, although both paternal and biparental inheritance of chloroplasts may be observed in some species. Carl Correns first hypothesized in 1909 that chloroplasts were responsible for inheritance of variegation

(mixed green and white leaves) in the plant commonly known as the four o'clock (*Mirabilis jalapa*). The offspring exhibited the phenotype of the female parent, regardless of the male's phenotype.

In Sager's work on *Chlamydomonas*, resistance to the antibiotic streptomycin was shown to be transmitted via the chloroplast DNA from only the mt^+ mating type. The mt^- mating type does not contribute chloroplast DNA to the zygote formed by fusion of mt^+ and mt^- gametes.

Learning Outcomes Review 13.3

The genomes of mitochondria and chloroplasts divide independently of the nucleus. These organelles are carried in the cytoplasm of the egg cell, so any traits determined by these genomes are maternally inherited and thus do not follow Mendelian rules. In some species, however, chloroplasts may be passed on paternally or biparentally.

- **How can you explain the lack of mt^- chloroplast DNA in Chlamydomonas zygotes from mt^- by mt^+ crosses?**

Genetic Mapping

Learning Outcomes

1. Recognize that genes on the same chromosome may not assort independently.
2. Explain how recombination frequency is related to genetic distance.
3. Review how data from testcrosses is used to construct genetic maps.

We have seen that Mendelian traits are determined by genes located on chromosomes and that the independent assortment of Mendelian traits reflects the independent assortment of chromosomes in meiosis. This is fine as far as it goes, but it is still incomplete. Of Mendel's seven traits in figure 12.4, six are on different chromosomes and two are on the same chromosome, yet all show independent assortment with one another. The two on the same chromosome should not behave the same as those that are on different chromosomes. In fact, organisms generally have many more genes that assort independently than the number of chromosomes. This means that independent assortment cannot be due only to the random alignment of chromosomes during meiosis.

Inquiry question

? Mendel did not examine plant height and pod shape in his dihybrid crosses. The genes for these traits are very close together on the same chromosome. How would this have changed Mendel's results?

The solution to this problem is found in an observation that was introduced in chapter 11: the crossing over of homologues during meiosis. In prophase I of meiosis, homologues appear to physically exchange material by crossing over (figure 13.5). In chapter 11, you saw how this was part of the mechanism that allows homologues, and not sister chromatids, to disjoin at anaphase I.

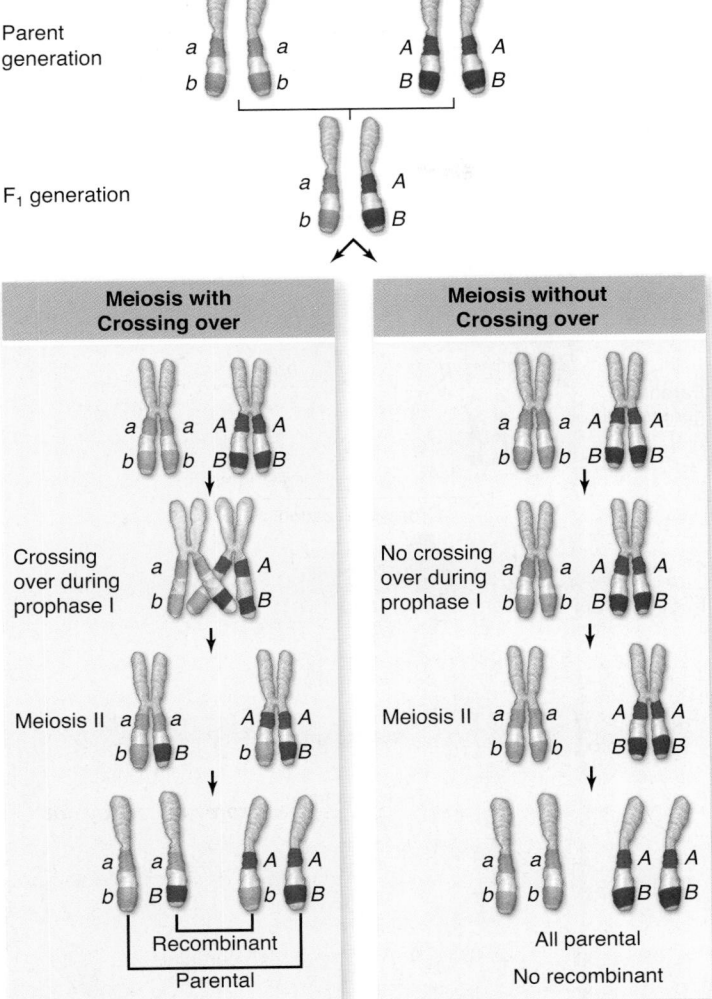

Figure 13.5 Crossing over exchanges alleles on homologues. When a crossover occurs between two loci, it leads to the production of recombinant chromosomes. If no crossover occurs, then the chromosomes will carry the parental combination of alleles.

Genetic recombination exchanges alleles on homologues

Consider a dihybrid cross performed using the Mendelian framework. Two true-breeding parents that each differ with respect to two traits are crossed, producing doubly heterozygous F_1 progeny. If the genes for the two traits are on a single chromosome, then during meiosis we would expect alleles for both loci to segregate together and produce only gametes that resemble the two parental types. But if a crossover occurs between the two loci, then each homologue would carry one allele from each parent and produce gametes that combine these parental traits (see figure 13.5). We call gametes with this new combination of alleles *recombinant* gametes as they are formed by recombining the parental alleles.

The first investigator to provide evidence for this was Morgan, who studied three genes on the X chromosome of *Drosophila*. He found an excess of parental types, which he explained as due to the genes all being on the X chromosome and therefore coinherited (inherited together). He went further,

suggesting that the recombinant genotypes were due to crossing over between homologues during meiosis.

Experiments performed independently by Barbara McClintock and Harriet Creighton in maize and by Curt Stern in *Drosophila* provided evidence for this physical exchange of genetic material. The experiment done by Creighton and McClintock is detailed in figure 13.6. In this experiment, they used a chromosome with two alterations visible under a microscope: a knob on one end of the chromosome and an extension of the other end making it longer. In addition to these visible markers, this chromosome also carried a gene that determines kernel color (colored or colorless) and a gene that determines kernel texture (waxy or starchy).

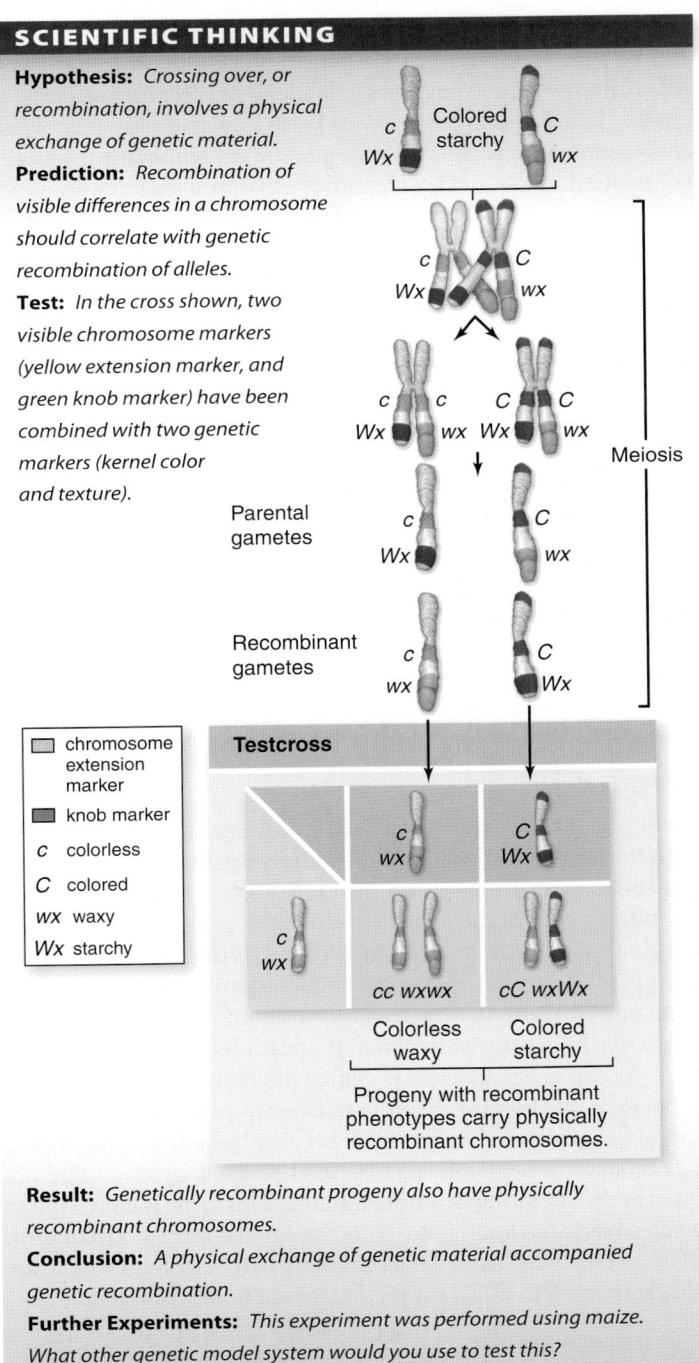

SCIENTIFIC THINKING

Hypothesis: *Crossing over, or recombination, involves a physical exchange of genetic material.*

Prediction: *Recombination of visible differences in a chromosome should correlate with genetic recombination of alleles.*

Test: *In the cross shown, two visible chromosome markers (yellow extension marker, and green knob marker) have been combined with two genetic markers (kernel color and texture).*

Result: *Genetically recombinant progeny also have physically recombinant chromosomes.*

Conclusion: *A physical exchange of genetic material accompanied genetic recombination.*

Further Experiments: *This experiment was performed using maize. What other genetic model system would you use to test this?*

Figure 13.6 The Creighton and McClintock experiment.

The long chromosome, which also had the knob, carried the dominant colored allele for kernel color (*C*) and the recessive waxy allele for kernel texture *(wx)*. Heterozygotes were constructed with this chromosome paired with a visibly normal chromosome carrying the recessive colorless allele for kernel color *(c)* and the dominant starchy allele for kernel texture *(Wx)* (see figure 13.6). These plants appeared colored and starchy because they were heterozygous for both loci, and they were also heterozygous for the two visibly distinct chromosomes.

These plants, heterozygous for both chromosomal and genetic markers, were test crossed to colorless waxy plants with normal appearing chromosomes. The progeny were analyzed for both physical recombination (using a microscope to observe chromosome appearance) and genetic recombination (by examining the phenotype of progeny). The results were striking: All of the progeny that were genetically recombinant (appear colored starchy or colorless waxy) also now had only one of the chromosomal markers. That is, genetic recombination was accompanied by physical exchange of chromosomal material.

Recombination is the basis for genetic maps

The ability to map the location of genes on chromosomes using data from genetic crosses is one of the most powerful tools of genetics. The insight that allowed this technique, like many great insights, is so simple as to seem obvious in retrospect.

Morgan had already suggested that the frequency with which a particular group of recombinant progeny appeared was a reflection of the relative location of genes on the chromosome. An undergraduate in Morgan's laboratory, Alfred Sturtevant put this observation on a quantitative basis. Sturtevant reasoned that the frequency of recombination observed in crosses could be used as a measure of genetic distance. That is, as physical distance on a chromosome increases, so does the probability of recombination (crossover) occurring between the gene loci. Using this logic, the frequency of recombinant gametes produced is a measure of their distance apart on a chromosome.

Linkage data

To be able to measure recombination frequency easily, investigators used a testcross instead of intercrossing the F₁ progeny to produce an F₂ generation. In a testcross, as described earlier, the phenotypes of the progeny reflect the gametes produced by the doubly heterozygous F₁ individual. In the case of recombination, progeny that appear parental have not undergone crossover, and progeny that appear recombinant have experienced a crossover between the two loci in question (see figure 13.5).

When genes are close together, the number of recombinant progeny is much lower than the number of parental progeny, and the genes are defined on this basis as being **linked.** The number of recombinant progeny divided by total progeny gives a value defined as the **recombination frequency.** This value is converted to a percentage, and each 1% of recombination is termed a **map unit.** This unit has been named the centimorgan (cM) for T. H. Morgan, although it is also called simply a map unit (m.u.) as well.

Constructing maps

Constructing genetic maps then becomes a simple process of performing testcrosses with doubly heterozygous individuals

and counting progeny to determine percent recombination. This is best shown with an example using a two-point cross.

Drosophila homozygous for two mutations, vestigial wings *(vg)* and black body *(b)*, are crossed to flies homozygous for the wild type, or normal alleles, of these genes *(vg⁺ b⁺)*. The doubly

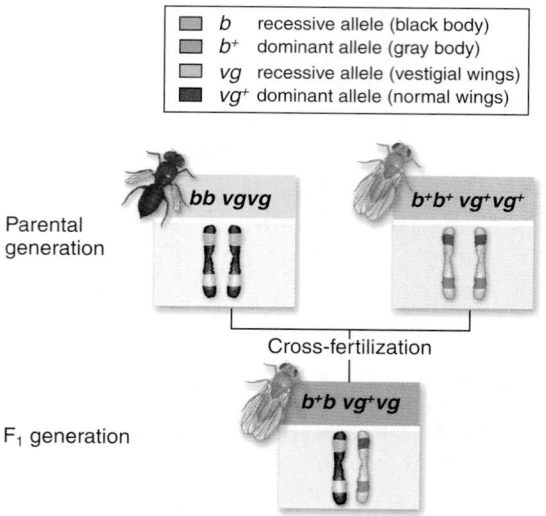

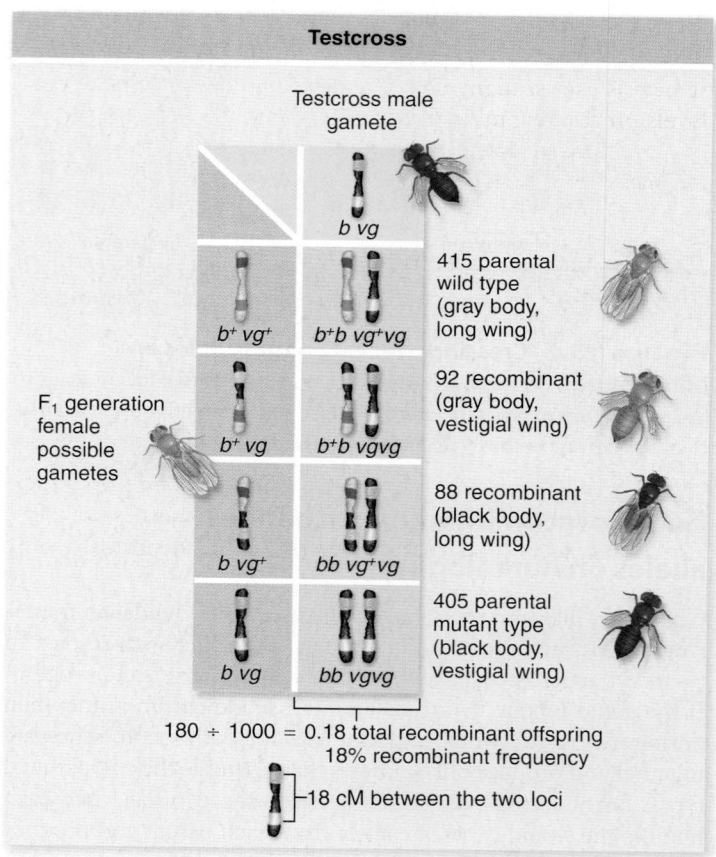

Figure 13.7 Two-point cross to map genes. Flies homozygous for long wings *(vg⁺)* and gray bodies *(b⁺)* are crossed to flies homozygous for vestigial wings *(vg)* and black bodies *(b)*. Both vestigial wing and black body are recessive to the normal (wild-type) long wing and grey body. The F₁ progeny are then testcrossed to homozygous vestigial black to produce the progeny for mapping. Data are analyzed in the text.

heterozygous F₁ progeny are then testcrossed to homozygous recessive individuals *(vg b/vg b)*, and progeny are counted (figure 13.7). The data are shown here:

vestigial wings, black body *(vg b)*	405	(parental)
long wings, gray body *(vg⁺ b⁺)*	415	(parental)
vestigial wings, gray body *(vg b⁺)*	92	(recombinant)
long wings, black body *(vg⁺ b)*	88	(recombinant)
Total Progeny	1000	

The numbers of recombinant progeny are added together, and this sum is divided by total progeny to produce the recombination frequency. The recombination frequency is 92 + 88 divided by 1000, or 0.18. Converting this number to a percentage yields 18 cM as the map distance between these two loci.

Multiple crossovers can yield independent assortment results

As the distance separating loci increases, the probability of recombination occurring between them during meiosis also increases. What happens when more than one recombination event occurs?

If homologues undergo two crossovers between loci, then the parental combination is restored. This leads to an underestimate of the true genetic distance because not all events can be noted. As a result, the relationship between true distance on a chromosome and the recombination frequency is not linear. It begins as a straight line, but the slope decreases; the curve levels off at a recombination frequency of 0.5 (figure 13.8).

At long distances, multiple events between loci become frequent. In this case, odd numbers of crossovers (1, 3, 5) produce recombinant gametes, and no crossover or even numbers of crossovers (0, 2, 4) produce parental gametes. At large enough distances, these frequencies are about equal, leading to the number of recombinant gametes being equal to the number of parental gametes, and the loci exhibit independent assortment! This is how Mendel could use two loci on the same chromosome and have them assort independently.

Inquiry question

? **What would Mendel have observed in a dihybrid cross if the two loci were 10 cM apart on the same chromosome? Is this likely to have led him to the idea of independent assortment?**

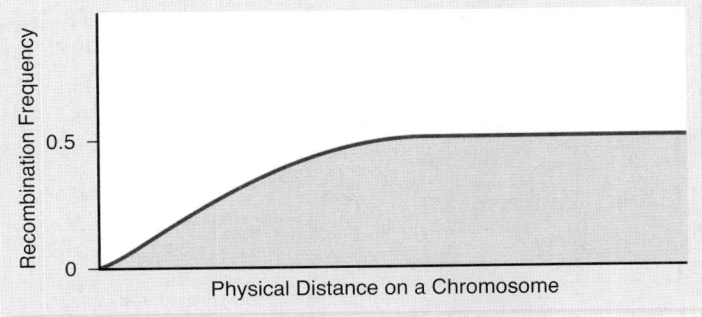

Figure 13.8 Relationship between true distance and recombination frequency. As distance on a chromosome increases, the recombinants are not all detected due to double crossovers. This leads to a curve that levels off at 0.5.

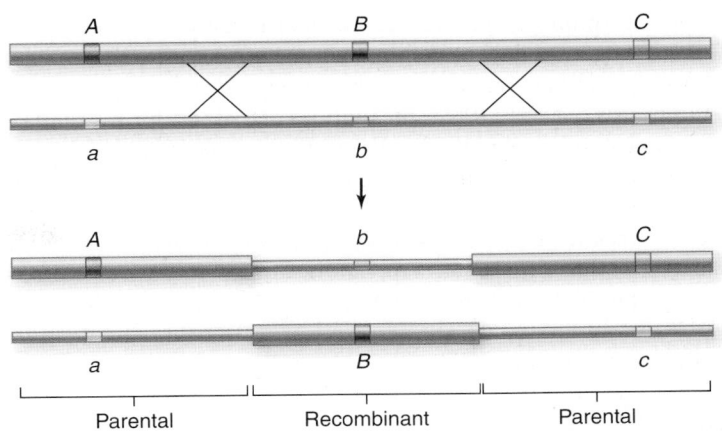

Figure 13.9 Use of a three-point cross to order genes. In a two-point cross, the outside loci appear parental for double crossovers. With the addition of a third locus, the two crossovers can still be detected because the middle locus will be recombinant. This double crossover class should be the least frequent, so whatever locus has recombinant alleles in this class must be in the middle.

Three-point crosses can be used to put genes in order

Because multiple crossovers reduce the number of observed recombinant progeny, longer map distances are not accurate. As a result, when geneticists try to construct maps from a series of two-point crosses, determining the order of genes is problematic. Using three loci instead of two, or a three-point cross, can help solve the problem.

In a three-point cross, the gene in the middle allows us to see recombination events on either side. For example, a double crossover for the two outside loci is actually a single crossover between the middle locus and each outside locus (figure 13.9).

The probability of two crossovers is equal to the product of the probability of each individual crossover, each of which is relatively low. Therefore, in any three-point cross, the class of offspring with two crossovers is the least frequent class. Analyzing these individuals to see which locus is recombinant identifies the locus that lies in the middle of the three loci in the cross (see figure 13.9).

In practice, geneticists use three-point crosses to determine the order of genes, then use data from the closest two-point crosses to determine distances. Longer distances are generated by simple addition of shorter distances. This avoids using inaccurate measures from two-point crosses between distant loci.

Genetic maps can be constructed for the human genome

Human genes can be mapped, but the data must be derived from historical pedigrees, such as those of the royal families of Europe mentioned earlier. The principle is the same—genetic distance is still proportional to recombination frequency—but the analysis requires the use of complex statistics and summing data from many families.

The difficulty of mapping in humans

Looking at nonhuman animals with extensive genetic maps, the majority of genetic markers have been found at loci where alleles cause morphological changes, such as variant eye color, body color, or wing morphology in flies. In humans, such alleles generally, but not always, correspond to what we consider disease states. As recently as the early 1980s, the number of markers for the human genome numbered in the hundreds. Because the human genome is so large, however, this low number of markers would never provide dense enough coverage to use for mapping.

Another consideration is that the disease-causing alleles are those that we wish to map, but they occur at low frequencies in the population. Any one family would be highly unlikely to carry multiple disease alleles, the segregation of which would allow for mapping.

Anonymous markers

This situation changed with the development of **anonymous markers,** genetic markers that can be detected using molecular techniques, but that do not cause a detectable phenotype. The nature of these markers has evolved with technology, leading to a standardized set of markers scattered throughout the genome. These markers, which have a relatively high density, can be detected using techniques that are easy to automate. As a result of analysis, geneticists now have several thousand markers to work with, instead of hundreds, and have produced a human genetic map that would have been unthinkable 25 years ago (figure 13.10). (In the following chapters of this unit, you'll learn about some of the molecular techniques that have been developed for use with genomes.)

Single-nucleotide polymorphisms (SNPs)

The information developed from sequencing the human genome can then be used to identify and map single bases that differ between individuals. Any differences between individuals

in populations are termed *polymorphisms;* polymorphisms affecting a single base of a gene locus are called **single-nucleotide polymorphisms (SNPs).** Over 2 million such differences have been identified and are being placed on both the genetic map and the human genome sequence. This confluence of techniques will enable the ultimate resolution of genetic analysis.

The recent progress in gene mapping applies to more than just the relatively small number of genes that show simple Mendelian inheritance. The development of a high-resolution genetic map, and the characterization of millions of SNPs, opens up the possibility of being able to characterize complex quantitative traits in humans as well.

On a more practical level, the types of molecular markers described earlier are used in forensic analysis. Although not quite as rapid as some television programs would have you believe, this does allow rapid DNA testing of crime scene samples to help eliminate or confirm crime suspects and for paternity testing.

Learning Outcomes Review 13.4

Crossing over during meiosis exchanges alleles on homologues. This recombination of alleles can be used to map the location of genes. Genes that are close together are said to be linked, and exhibit an excess of parental versus recombinant types in a testcross. The frequency of recombination in testcrosses is used as a measure of genetic distance. Loci separated by large distances have multiple crossovers between them, which can lead to independent assortment.

- ■ *If two genes assort independently, can you tell if they are on a single chromosome and far apart or on two different chromosomes?*

Figure 13.10 **The human X chromosome gene map.** Only a partial map for the human X chromosome is presented here, a more detailed map would require a much larger figure. The black bands represent staining patterns that can be seen under the microscope, and the constriction represents the centromere. Analysis of the sequence of the X chromosome indicates 1098 genes on the X chromosome. Many of these may have mutant alleles that can affect disease states. By analyzing inheritance patterns of affected and unaffected individuals, the 59 diseases shown have been traced to specific segments of the X chromosome, indicated by brackets.

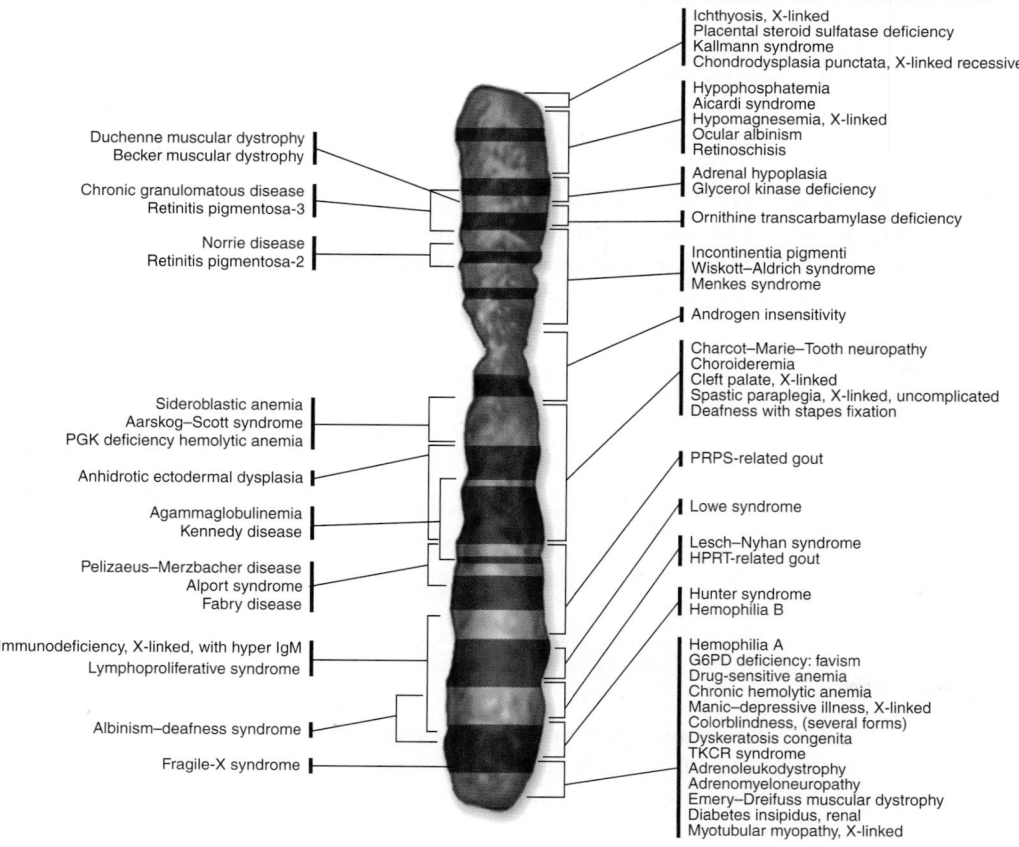

Duchenne muscular dystrophy
Becker muscular dystrophy

Chronic granulomatous disease
Retinitis pigmentosa-3

Norrie disease
Retinitis pigmentosa-2

Sideroblastic anemia
Aarskog–Scott syndrome
PGK deficiency hemolytic anemia

Anhidrotic ectodermal dysplasia

Agammaglobulinemia
Kennedy disease

Pelizaeus–Merzbacher disease
Alport syndrome
Fabry disease

Immunodeficiency, X-linked, with hyper IgM
Lymphoproliferative syndrome

Albinism–deafness syndrome

Fragile-X syndrome

Ichthyosis, X-linked
Placental steroid sulfatase deficiency
Kallmann syndrome
Chondrodysplasia punctata, X-linked recessive

Hypophosphatemia
Aicardi syndrome
Hypomagnesemia, X-linked
Ocular albinism
Retinoschisis

Adrenal hypoplasia
Glycerol kinase deficiency

Ornithine transcarbamylase deficiency

Incontinentia pigmenti
Wiskott–Aldrich syndrome
Menkes syndrome

Androgen insensitivity

Charcot–Marie–Tooth neuropathy
Choroideremia
Cleft palate, X-linked
Spastic paraplegia, X-linked, uncomplicated
Deafness with stapes fixation

PRPS-related gout

Lowe syndrome

Lesch–Nyhan syndrome
HPRT-related gout

Hunter syndrome
Hemophilia B

Hemophilia A
G6PD deficiency: favism
Drug-sensitive anemia
Chronic hemolytic anemia
Manic–depressive illness, X-linked
Colorblindness, (several forms)
Dyskeratosis congenita
TKCR syndrome
Adrenoleukodystrophy
Adrenomyeloneuropathy
Emery–Dreifuss muscular dystrophy
Diabetes insipidus, renal
Myotubular myopathy, X-linked

13.5 Selected Human Genetic Disorders

Learning Outcomes

1. Explain how mutations can cause disease.
2. Describe the consequences of nondisjunction in humans.
3. Recognize how genomic imprinting can lead to non-Mendelian inheritance.

Diseases that run in families have been known for many years. These can be nonlife-threatening like albinism, or may result in premature death like Huntington's, which were used as examples of recessive and dominant traits in humans previously. A small sample of diseases due to alterations of alleles of a single gene is provided in table 13.2. We will discuss the nature of these genetic changes later in chapter 15. In this section we discuss some of the genetic disorders that have been found in human populations.

Sickle cell anemia is due to altered hemoglobin

The first human disease shown to be the result of a mutation in a protein was sickle cell anemia. It is caused by a defect in the oxygen carrier molecule, hemoglobin, that leads to impaired oxygen delivery to tissues. The defective hemoglobin molecules stick to one another, leading to stiff, rodlike structures that alter the shape of the red blood cells that carry them. These red blood cells take on a characteristic shape that led to the name "sickle cell" (figure 13.11).

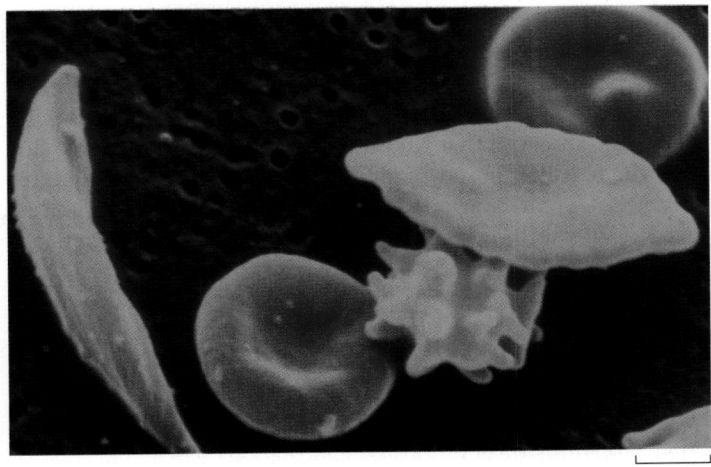

1 μm

Figure 13.11 Sickle cell anemia. In individuals homozygous for the sickle cell trait, many of the red blood cells have sickled or irregular shapes, such as the cell on the far left.

Individuals homozygous for the sickle cell allele exhibit intermittent illness and reduced life span. Individuals heterozygous for the sickle cell allele are indistinguishable from normal individuals in a normal oxygen environment, although their red cells do exhibit reduced ability to carry oxygen.

The sickle cell allele is particularly prevalent in people of African descent. In some regions of Africa, up to 45% of the population is heterozygous for the trait, and 6% are homozygous. This proportion of heterozygotes is higher than would be expected on the basis of chance alone. It turns out that heterozygosity confers a greater resistance to the blood-borne parasite

TABLE 13.2	Some Important Genetic Disorders			
Disorder	**Symptom**	**Defect**	**Dominant/Recessive**	**Frequency Among Human Births**
Cystic fibrosis	Mucus clogs lungs, liver, and pancreas	Failure of chloride ion transport mechanism	Recessive	1/2500 (Caucasians)
Sickle cell anemia	Blood circulation is poor	Abnormal hemoglobin molecules	Recessive	1/600 (African Americans)
Tay–Sachs disease	Central nervous system deteriorates in infancy	Defective enzyme (hexosaminidase A)	Recessive	1/3500 (Ashkenazi Jews)
Phenylketonuria	Brain fails to develop in infancy, treatable with dietary restriction	Defective enzyme (phenylalanine hydroxylase)	Recessive	1/12,000
Hemophilia	Blood fails to clot	Defective blood-clotting factor VIII	X-linked recessive	1/10,000 (Caucasian males)
Huntington disease	Brain tissue gradually deteriorates in middle age	Production of an inhibitor of brain cell metabolism	Dominant	1/24,000
Muscular dystrophy (Duchenne)	Muscles waste away	Degradation of myelin coating of nerves stimulating muscles	X-linked recessive	1/3700 (males)
Hypercholesterolemia	Excessive cholesterol levels in blood lead to heart disease	Abnormal form of cholesterol cell surface receptor	Dominant	1/500

that causes malaria. In regions of central Africa where malaria is endemic, the sickle cell allele also occurs at a high frequency.

The sickle cell allele is not the end of the story for the β-globin gene; a large number of other alterations of this gene have been observed that lead to anemias. In fact, for hemoglobin, which is composed of two α-globins and two β-globins, over 700 structural variants have been cataloged. It is estimated that 7% of the human population worldwide are carriers for different inherited hemoglobin disorders.

The Human Gene Mutation Database has cataloged the nature of many disease alleles, including the sickle cell allele. The majority of alleles seem to be simple changes. Almost 60% of the close to 28,000 alleles in the Human Gene Mutation Database are single-base substitutions. Another 23% are due to small insertions or deletions of less than 20 bases. The rest of the alleles are made of more complex alterations. It is clear that simple changes in genes can have profound effects.

Nondisjunction of chromosomes changes chromosome number

The failure of homologues or sister chromatids to separate properly during meiosis is called **nondisjunction.** This failure leads to the gain or loss of a chromosome, a condition called **aneuploidy.** The frequency of aneuploidy in humans is surprisingly high, being estimated to occur in 5% of conceptions.

Nondisjunction of autosomes

Humans who have lost even one copy of an autosome are called **monosomics,** and generally do not survive embryonic development. In all but a few cases, humans who have gained an extra autosome (called **trisomics**) also do not survive. Data from clinically recognized spontaneous abortions indicate levels of aneuploidy as high as 35%.

Five of the smallest human autosomes—those numbered 13, 15, 18, 21, and 22—can be present as three copies and still allow the individual to survive, at least for a time. The presence of an extra chromosome 13, 15, or 18 causes severe developmental defects, and infants with such a genetic makeup die within a few months. In contrast, individuals who have an extra copy of chromosome 21 or, more rarely, chromosome 22, usually survive to adulthood. In these people, the maturation of the skeletal system is delayed, so they generally are short and have poor muscle tone. Their mental development is also affected, and children with trisomy 21 are always mentally retarded to some degree.

The developmental defect produced by trisomy 21 (figure 13.12) was first described in 1866 by J. Langdon Down; for this reason, it is called Down syndrome. About 1 in every 750 children exhibits Down syndrome, and the frequency is comparable in all racial groups. Similar conditions also occur in chimpanzees and other related primates.

In humans, the defect occurs when a particular small portion of chromosome 21 is present in three copies instead of two. In 97% of the cases examined, all of chromosome 21 is present in three copies. In the other 3%, a small portion of chromosome 21 containing the critical segment has been added to another chromosome by a process called *translocation* (see chapter 15);

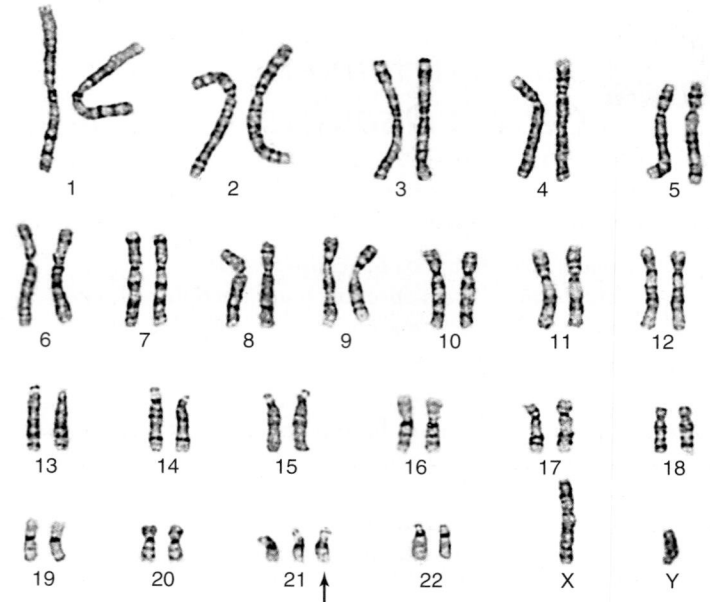

Figure 13.12 Down syndrome. As shown in this male karyotype, Down syndrome is associated with trisomy of chromosome 21 (arrow shows third copy of chromosome 21).

it exists along with the normal two copies of chromosome 21. This latter condition is known as *translocation Down syndrome.*

In mothers younger than 20 years of age, the risk of giving birth to a child with Down syndrome is about 1 in 1700; in mothers 20 to 30 years old, the risk is only about 1 in 1400. However, in mothers 30 to 35 years old, the risk rises to 1 in 750, and by age 45, the risk is as high as 1 in 16 (figure 13.13).

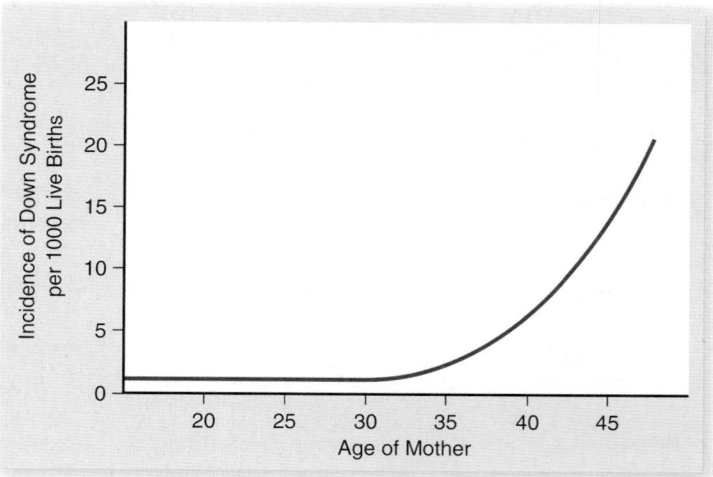

Figure 13.13 Correlation between maternal age and the incidence of Down syndrome. As women age, the chances they will bear a child with Down syndrome increase. After a woman reaches 35, the frequency of Down syndrome rises rapidly.

Inquiry question

? Over a five-year period between ages 20 and 25, the incidence of Down syndrome increases 0.1 per thousand; over a five-year period between ages 35 and 40, the incidence increases to 8.0 per thousand, 80 times as great. The period of time is the same in both instances. What has changed?

Primary nondisjunctions are far more common in women than in men because all of the eggs a woman will ever produce have developed to the point of prophase in meiosis I by the time she is born. By the time a woman has children, her eggs are as old as she is. Therefore, there is a much greater chance for cell-division problems of various kinds, including those that cause primary nondisjunction, to accumulate over time in female gametes. In contrast, men produce new sperm daily. For this reason, the age of the mother is more critical than that of the father for couples contemplating childbearing.

Nondisjunction of sex chromosomes

Individuals who gain or lose a sex chromosome do not generally experience the severe developmental abnormalities caused by similar changes in autosomes. Although such individuals have somewhat abnormal features, they often reach maturity and in some cases may be fertile.

X chromosome nondisjunction. When X chromosomes fail to separate during meiosis, some of the gametes produced possess both X chromosomes, and so are XX gametes; the other gametes have no sex chromosome and are designated "O" (figure 13.14).

If an XX gamete combines with an X gamete, the resulting XXX zygote develops into a female with one functional X chromosome and two Barr bodies. She may be taller in stature but is otherwise normal in appearance.

If an XX gamete instead combines with a Y gamete, the effects are more serious. The resulting XXY zygote develops into a male who has many female body characteristics and, in some cases but not all, diminished mental capacity. This condition, called *Klinefelter syndrome*, occurs in about 1 out of every 500 male births.

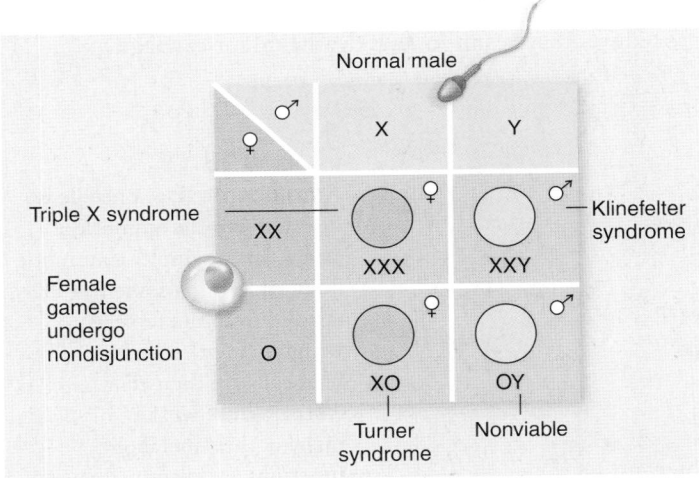

Figure 13.14 How nondisjunction can produce abnormalities in the number of sex chromosomes. When nondisjunction occurs in the production of female gametes, the gamete with two X chromosomes (XX) produces Klinefelter males (XXY) and triple-X females (XXX). The gamete with no X chromosome (O) produces Turner females (XO) and nonviable OY males lacking any X chromosome.

Inquiry question

? Can you think of two nondisjunction scenarios that would produce an XXY male?

If an O gamete fuses with a Y gamete, the resulting OY zygote is nonviable and fails to develop further; humans cannot survive when they lack the genes on the X chromosome. But if an O gamete fuses with an X gamete, the XO zygote develops into a sterile female of short stature, with a webbed neck and sex organs that never fully mature during puberty. The mental abilities of an XO individual are in the low-normal range. This condition, called *Turner syndrome*, occurs roughly once in every 5000 female births.

Y chromosome nondisjunction. The Y chromosome can also fail to separate in meiosis, leading to the formation of YY gametes. When these gametes combine with X gametes, the XYY zygotes develop into fertile males of normal appearance. The frequency of the XYY genotype (*Jacob syndrome*) is about 1 per 1000 newborn males.

Genomic imprinting depends on the parental origin of alleles

By the late 20th century, geneticists were confident that they understood the basic mechanisms governing inheritance. It came as quite a surprise when mouse geneticists found an important exception to classical Mendelian genetics that appears to be unique to mammals. In **genomic imprinting,** the phenotype caused by a specific allele is exhibited when the allele comes from one parent, but not from the other.

The basis for genomic imprinting is the expression of a gene depending on passage through maternal or paternal germ lines. Some genes are inactivated in the paternal germ line and therefore are not expressed in the zygote. Other genes are inactivated in the maternal germ line, with the same result. This condition makes the zygote effectively haploid for an imprinted gene. The expression of variant alleles of imprinted genes depends on the parent of origin. Furthermore, imprinted genes seem to be concentrated in particular regions of the genome. These regions include genes that are both maternally and paternally imprinted.

Prader–Willi and Angelman syndromes

An example of genomic imprinting in humans involves the two diseases Prader–Willi syndrome (PWS) and Angelman syndrome (AS). The effects of PWS include respiratory distress, obesity, short stature, mild mental retardation, and obsessive–compulsive behavior. The effects of AS include developmental delay, severe mental retardation, hyperactivity, aggressive behavior, and inappropriate laughter.

Genetic studies have implicated genes on chromosome 15 for both disorders, but the pattern of inheritance is complementary. The most common cause of both syndromes is a deletion of material on chromosome 15 and, in fact, the same deletion can cause either syndrome. The determining factor is the parental origin of the normal and deleted chromosomes. If the chromosome with the deletion is paternally inherited it causes PWS, if the chromosome with the deletion is maternally inherited it causes AS.

The region of chromosome 15 that is lost is subject to imprinting, with some genes being inactivated in the maternal germ line, and others in the paternal germ line. In PWS, genes are inactivated in the maternal germ line, such that deletion or other functional loss of paternally derived alleles produces the syndrome. The opposite is true for AS syndrome: Genes are inactivated in the paternal germ line, such that loss of maternally derived alleles leads to the syndrome.

Molecular basis of genomic imprinting

Although genomic imprinting is not well understood, at least one aspect seems clear: The basis for inactivating genes appears to be linked to modifications of the DNA itself. DNA can be modified by the addition of methyl groups, termed *methylation*. This modification is correlated with inactivity of genes. The proteins that are associated with chromosomes can also be modified, leading to effects on gene expression. The control of gene expression is discussed in more detail in the following chapters.

Some genetic defects can be detected early in pregnancy

Although most genetic disorders cannot yet be cured, we are learning a great deal about them, and progress toward successful therapy is being made in many cases. In the absence of a cure, however, the only recourse is to try to avoid producing children with these conditions. The process of identifying parents at risk for having children with genetic defects and of assessing the genetic state of early embryos is called **genetic counseling.**

Pedigree analysis

One way of assessing risks is through pedigree analysis, often employed as an aid in genetic counseling. By analyzing a person's pedigree, it is sometimes possible to estimate the likelihood that the person is a carrier for certain disorders. For example, if a counseling client's family history reveals that a relative has been afflicted with a recessive genetic disorder, such as cystic fibrosis, it is possible that the client is a heterozygous carrier of the recessive allele for that disorder.

When a couple is expecting a child, and pedigree analysis indicates that both of them have a significant chance of being heterozygous carriers of a deleterious recessive allele, the pregnancy is said to be high-risk. In such cases, a significant probability exists that their child will exhibit the clinical disorder.

Another class of high-risk pregnancy is that in which the mothers are older than 35. As discussed earlier, the frequency of Down syndrome increases dramatically in the pregnancies of older women (see figure 13.13).

Amniocentesis

When a pregnancy is diagnosed as high-risk, many women elect to undergo **amniocentesis,** a procedure that permits the prenatal diagnosis of many genetic disorders. In the fourth month of pregnancy, a sterile hypodermic needle is inserted into the expanded uterus of the mother, removing a small sample of the amniotic fluid that bathes the fetus (figure 13.15). Within the fluid are free-floating cells derived from the fetus; once removed, these cells can be grown in cultures in the laboratory.

During amniocentesis, the position of the needle and that of the fetus are usually observed by means of *ultrasound*. The sound waves used in ultrasound are not harmful to mother or fetus, and they permit the person withdrawing the amniotic fluid to do so without damaging the fetus. In addition, ultrasound can be used to examine the fetus for signs of major abnormalities. However, about 1 out of 200 amniocentesis procedures may result in fetal death and miscarriage.

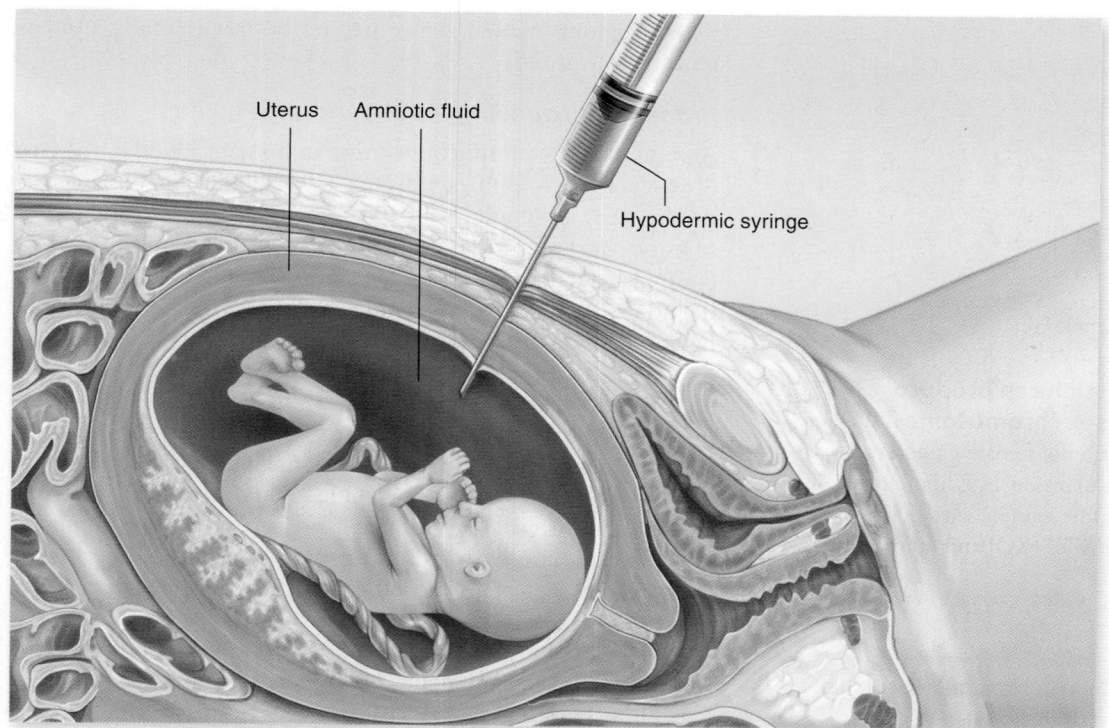

Figure 13.15
Amniocentesis. A needle is inserted into the amniotic cavity, and a sample of amniotic fluid, containing some free cells derived from the fetus, is withdrawn into a syringe. The fetal cells are then grown in culture, and their karyotype and many of their metabolic functions are examined.

Uterus   Amniotic fluid

Hypodermic syringe

Figure 13.16 Chorionic villi sampling. Cells can be taken from the chorionic villi as early as the eighth to tenth week of pregnancy. Cells are removed by suction with a tube inserted through the cervix. These cells can then be grown in culture and examined for karyotypes and tested biochemically for defects.

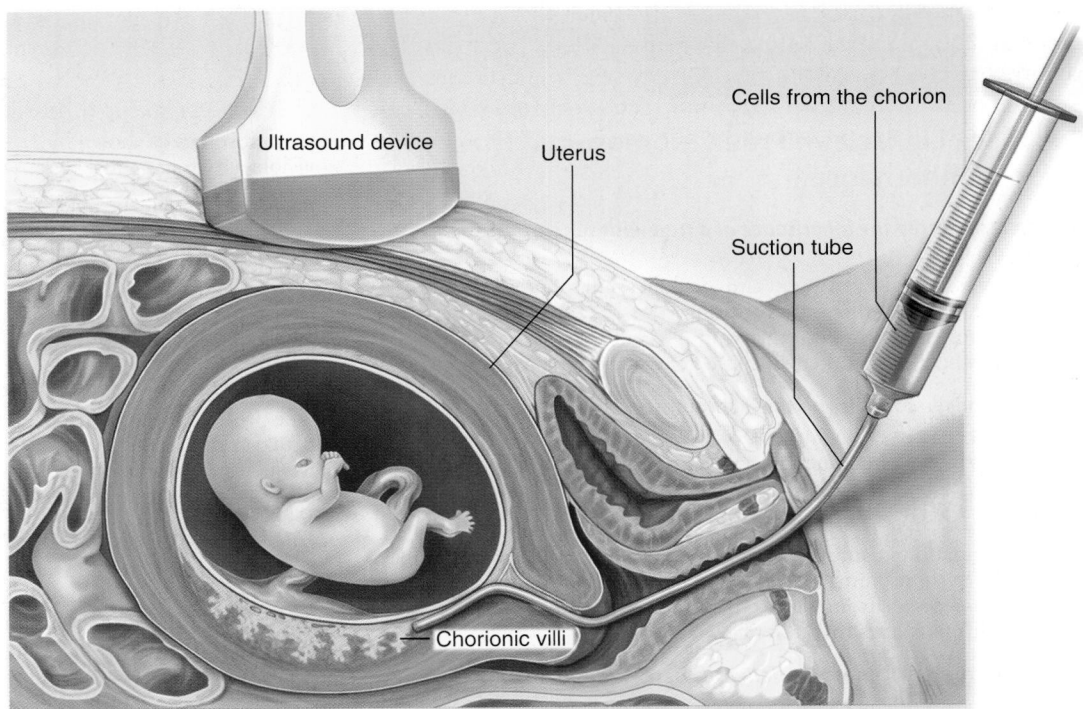

Chorionic villi sampling

In recent years, physicians have increasingly turned to a new, less invasive procedure for genetic screening called **chorionic villi sampling.** Using this method, the physician removes cells from the chorion, a membranous part of the placenta that nourishes the fetus (figure 13.16). This procedure can be used earlier in pregnancy (by the eighth week) and yields results much more rapidly than does amniocentesis. Risks from chorionic villi sampling are comparable to those for amniocentesis.

To test for certain genetic disorders, genetic counselors look for three characteristics in the cultures of cells obtained from amniocentesis or chorionic villi sampling. First, analysis of the karyotype can reveal aneuploidy (extra or missing chromosomes) and gross chromosomal alterations. Second, in many cases it is possible to test directly for the proper functioning of enzymes involved in genetic disorders. The lack of normal enzymatic activity signals the presence of the disorder. As examples, the lack of the enzyme responsible for breaking down phenylalanine indicates phenylketonuria (PKU); the absence of the enzyme responsible for the breakdown of gangliosides indicates Tay–Sachs disease; and so forth. Additionally, with information from the Human Genome Project, more disease alleles for genetic disorders are known. If there are a small number of alleles for a specific disease in the population, these can be identified as well.

With the changes in human genetics brought about by the Human Genome Project (see chapter 18), it is possible to design tests for many more diseases. Difficulties still exist in discerning the number and frequency of disease-causing alleles, but these problems are not insurmountable. At present, tests for at least 13 genes with alleles that lead to clinical syndromes are available. This number is bound to rise and to be expanded to include alleles that do not directly lead to disease states but that predispose a person for a particular disease.

Inquiry question

? Based on what you read in this chapter, what reasons could a mother have to undergo CVS, considering its small but potential risks?

Learning Outcomes Review 13.5

Mutations in DNA that result in altered proteins can cause hereditary diseases. Pedigree studies and genetic testing may clarify the risk of disease. At the chromosome level, nondisjunction during meiosis can result in gametes with too few or too many chromosomes, most of which produce inviable offspring. Imprinting refers to inactivation of alleles depending on which parent the alleles come from; offspring in whom imprinting occurs appear haploid for the affected gene even though they are diploid.

■ *During spermatogenesis, is there any difference in outcome between first and second division nondisjunction?*

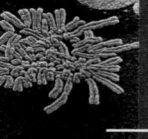

13.1 Sex Linkage and the Chromosomal Theory of Inheritance

Morgan correlated the inheritance of a trait with sex chromosomes (see figure 13.2).

Morgan crossed red-eyed and white-eyed flies and found differences in inheritance based on the sex of offspring. All white-eyed offspring were males, but testcrosses showed that white-eyed females were possible, supporting the idea that the white-eye gene was on the X chromsome.

The gene for eye color lies on the X chromosome.

The inheritance of eye color in *Drosophila* segregates with the X chromosome, a phenomenon termed sex-linked inheritance.

13.2 Sex Chromosomes and Sex Determination

Sex determination in animals is usually associated with a chromosomal difference. In some animals, females have two similar sex chromosomes and males have sex chromosomes that differ. In other species, females have sex chromosomes that differ (see table 13.1).

In humans the Y chromosome generally determines maleness.

The Y chromosome is highly condensed and does not have active counterparts to most genes on the X chromosome. The *SRY* gene on the Y chromosome is responsible for the masculinization of genitalia and secondary sex organs. An XY individual can develop into a sterile female due to mutations in the *SRY* gene or the failure of the embryo to respond to androgens.

Some human genetic disorders display sex linkage (see figure 13.3).

Human genetic disorders show sex linkage when the relevant gene is on the X chromosome; hemophilia is an example.

Dosage compensation prevents doubling of sex-linked gene products.

In fruit flies, males double the gene expression from their single X chromosome. In mammals, one of the X chromosomes in a female is randomly inactivated during development.

X-chromosome inactivation can lead to genetic mosaics.

In a mammalian female that is heterozygous for X-chromosome alleles, X inactivation produces a mosaic pattern, as shown in the coat color of calico cats (see figure 13.4).

13.3 Exceptions to the Chromosomal Theory of Inheritance

Mitochondrial genes are inherited from the female parent.

Mitochondria have their own genomes and divide independently; they are passed to offspring in the cytoplasm of the egg cell.

Chloroplast genes may also be passed on uniparentally.

Chloroplasts also reside in the cytoplasm, have their own genomes, and divide independently. They are usually inherited maternally.

13.4 Genetic Mapping

Mendel's independent assortment is too simplistic. Genes on the same chromosome may or may not segregate independently.

Genetic recombination exchanges alleles on homologues.

Homologous chromosomes may exchange alleles by crossing over (see figure 13.5). This occurs by breakage and rejoining of chromosomes as shown by crosses in which chromosomes carry both visible and genetic markers (see figure 13.6).

Recombination is the basis for genetic maps.

Genes close together on a single chromosome are said to be linked. The further apart two linked genes are, the greater the frequency of recombination. This allows genetic maps to be constructed based on recombination frequency. A map unit is expressed as the percentage of recombinant progeny.

Multiple crossovers can yield independent assortment results.

The probability of multiple crossovers increases with distance between two genes and results in an underestimate of recombination frequency. The maximum recombination frequency is 50%, the same value as for independent assortment.

Three-point crosses can be used to put genes in order (see figure 13.9).

If three genes are used instead of two, data from multiple crossovers can be used to order genes. Longer map distances fail to reflect the effect of multiple crossovers and thus underestimate true distance. By evaluating intervening genes with less separation, more accurate distances can be obtained.

Genetic maps can be constructed for the human genome.

Human genetic mapping was difficult because it required multiple disease-causing alleles segregating in a family. The process has been made easier by the use of anonymous markers, identifiable molecular markers that do not cause a phenotype. Single-nucleotide polymorphisms (SNPs) can be used to detect differences between individuals for identification.

13.5 Selected Human Genetic Disorders

Sickle cell anemia is due to altered hemoglobin.

The phenotypes in sickle cell anemia can all be traced to alterations in the structure of hemoglobin that affect the shape of red blood cells. Over 700 variants of hemoglobin structure have been characterized, some of which also cause disorders.

Nondisjunction of chromosomes changes chromosome number.

Nondisjunction is the failure of homologues or sister chromatids to separate during meiosis. The result is aneuploidy: monosomy or trisomy of a chromosome in the zygote. Most aneuploidies are lethal, but some, such as trisomy 21 in humans (Down syndrome), can result in viable offspring. X-chromosome nondisjunction occurs when X chromosomes fail to separate during meiosis. The resulting gamete carries either XX or O (zero sex chromosomes) (see figure 13.14). Y-chromosome nondisjunction results in YY gametes.

Genomic imprinting depends on the parental origin of alleles.

In genomic imprinting, the expression of a gene depends on whether it passes through the maternal or paternal germ line. Imprinted genes appear to be inactivated by methylation. Imprinting produces a haploid phenotype.

Some genetic defects can be detected early in pregnancy.

Genetic defects in humans can be determined by pedigree analysis, amniocentesis, or chorionic villi sampling.

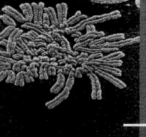

UNDERSTAND

1. Why is the white-eye phenotype always observed in males carrying the white-eye allele?
   a. Because the trait is dominant
   b. Because the trait is recessive
   c. Because the allele is located on the X chromosome and males only have one X
   d. Because the allele is located on the Y chromosome and only males have Y chromosomes

2. In an organism's genome, *autosomes* are
   a. the chromosomes that differ between the sexes.
   b. chromosomes that are involved in sex determination.
   c. only inherited from the mother (maternal inheritance).
   d. all of the chromosomes other than sex chromosomes.

3. What cellular process is responsible for genetic recombination?
   a. The independent alignment of homologous pairs during meiosis I
   b. Separation of the homologues in meiosis I
   c. Separation of the chromatids during meiosis II
   d. Crossing over between homologues

4. The map distance between two genes is determined by the
   a. recombination frequency.
   b. frequency of parental types.
   c. ratio of genes to length of a chromosome.
   d. ratio of parental to recombinant progeny.

5. How many map units separate two alleles if the recombination frequency is 0.07?
   a. 700 cM   b. 70 cM   c. 7 cM   d. 0.7 cM

6. How does maternal inheritance of mitochondrial genes differ from sex linkage?
   a. Mitochondrial genes do not contribute to the phenotype of an individual.
   b. Because mitochondria are inherited from the mother, only females are affected.
   c. Since mitochondria are inherited from the mother, females and males are equally affected.
   d. Mitochondrial genes must be dominant. Sex-linked traits are typically recessive.

7. Which of the following genotypes due to nondisjunction of sex chromosomes is lethal?
   a. XXX   b. XXY   c. OY   d. XO

APPLY

1. Dosage compensation is needed to
   a. balance expression from autosomes relative to sex chromosomes.
   b. balance expression from two autosomes in a diploid cell.
   c. balance expression of sex chromosomes in both sexes.
   d. inactivate female-specific autosomal chromosomes.

2. As real genetic distances increases, the distance calculated by recombination frequency becomes an
   a. overestimate due to multiple crossovers that cannot be scored.
   b. underestimate due to multiple crossovers that cannot be scored.
   c. underestimate due to multiple crossovers adding to recombination frequency.
   d. overestimate due to multiple crossovers adding to recombination frequency.

3. Down syndrome is the result of trisomy for chromosome 21. Why is this trisomy viable and trisomy for most other chromosomes is not?
   a. Chromosome 21 is a large chromosome and excess genetic material is less harmful.
   b. Chromosome 21 behaves differently in meiosis I than the other chromosomes.
   c. Chromosome 21 is a small chromosome with few genes so this does less to disrupt the genome.
   d. Chromosome 21 is less prone to nondisjunction than other chromosomes.

4. Genes that are on the same chromosome can show independent assortment
   a. when they are far enough apart for two crossovers to occur.
   b. when they are far enough apart that odd numbers of crossovers is about equal to even.
   c. only if recombination is low for that chromosome.
   d. only if the genes show genomic imprinting.

5. We use three-point crosses to order genes because this allows us to
   a. control for dosage compensation.
   b. control for genomic imprinting.
   c. detect multiple recombination events, and these infrequent events give us the order.
   d. detect multiple recombination events, and these frequent events give us the order.

6. During the process of spermatogenesis, a nondisjunction event that occurs during the second division would be
   a. worse than the first division because all four meiotic products would be aneuploid.
   b. better than the first division because only two of the four meiotic products would be aneuploid.
   c. the same outcome as the first division with all four products aneuploid.
   d. the same outcome as the first division as only two products would be aneuploid.

SYNTHESIZE

1. Color blindness is caused by a sex-linked, recessive gene. If a woman, whose father was color blind, marries a man with normal color vision, what percentage of their children will be color blind? What percentage of male children? Of female children?

2. Assume that the genes for seed color and seed shape are located on the same chromosome. A plant heterozygous for both genes is testcrossed wrinkled green with the following results:

green, wrinkled	645
green, round	36
yellow, wrinkled	29
yellow, round	590

   What were the genotypes of the parents, and how far apart are these genes?

3. Is it possible to have a calico cat that is male? Why or why not?

ONLINE RESOURCE

www.ravenbiology.com0

Understand, Apply, and Synthesize—enhance your study with animations that bring concepts to life and practice tests to assess your understanding. Your instructor may also recommend the interactive eBook, individualized learning tools, and more.

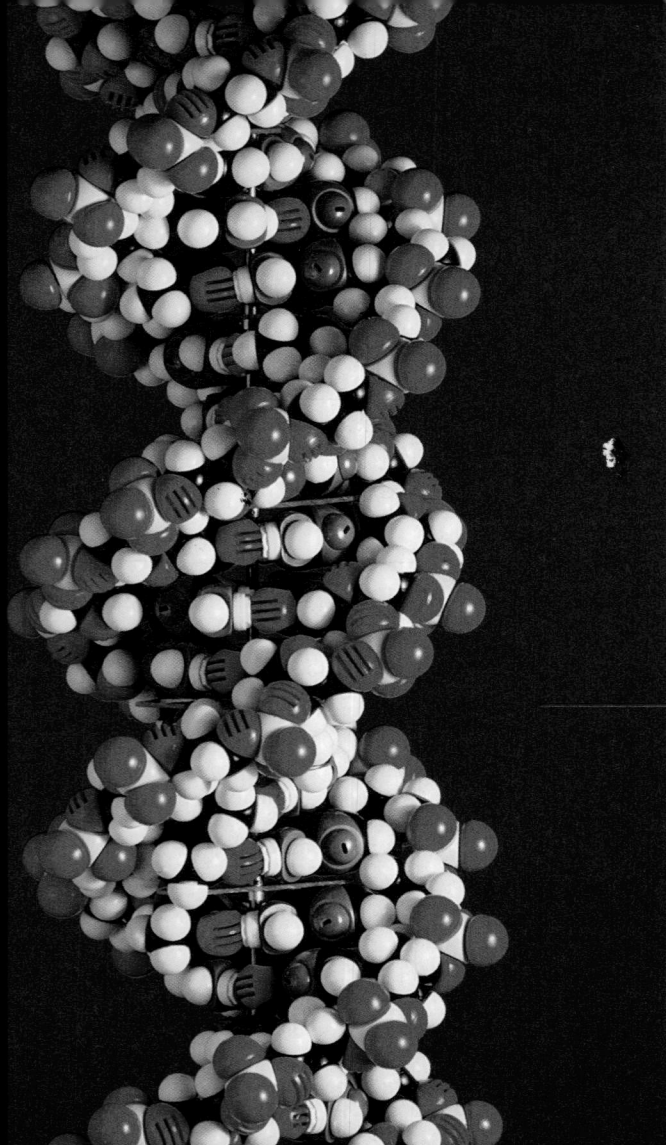

Chapter

14

DNA: The Genetic Material

Chapter Outline

14.1 The Nature of the Genetic Material

14.2 DNA Structure

14.3 Basic Characteristics of DNA Replication

14.4 Prokaryotic Replication

14.5 Eukaryotic Replication

14.6 DNA Repair

Introduction

The realization that patterns of heredity can be explained by the segregation of chromosomes in meiosis raised a question that occupied biologists for over 50 years: What is the exact nature of the connection between hereditary traits and chromosomes? This chapter describes the chain of experiments that led to our current understanding of DNA, modeled in the picture, and of the molecular mechanisms of heredity. These experiments are among the most elegant in science. And, just as in a good detective story, each discovery has led to new questions. But however erratic and lurching the course of the experimental journey may appear, our picture of heredity has become progressively clearer, the image more sharply defined.

14.1 The Nature of the Genetic Material

Learning Outcomes

1. Describe the phenomenon of transformation.
2. Evaluate the evidence for DNA as genetic material.

In the previous two chapters, you learned about the nature of inheritance and how genes, which contain the information to specify traits, are located on chromosomes. This finding led to the question of what part of the chromosome actually contains the genetic information. Specifically, biologists wondered about the chemical identity of the genetic information. They knew that chromosomes are composed primarily of both protein and DNA. Which of these organic molecules actually makes up the genes?

Starting in the late 1920s and continuing for about 30 years, a series of investigations addressed this question. DNA consists of four chemically similar nucleotides. In contrast, protein contains 20 different amino acids that are much more chemically diverse than nucleotides. These characteristics seemed initially to indicate greater informational capacity in protein than in DNA.

However, experiments began to reveal evidence in favor of DNA. We describe three of those major findings in this section.

Griffith finds that bacterial cells can be transformed

The first clue came in 1928 with the work of the British microbiologist Frederick Griffith. Griffith was trying to make a vaccine that would protect against influenza, which was thought at the time to be caused by the bacteria *Streptococcus pneumoniae*. There are two forms of this bacteria: The normal virulent form that causes pneumonia, and a mutant, nonvirulent form that does not. The normal virulent form of this bacterium is referred to as the S form because it forms smooth colonies on a culture dish. The mutant, nonvirulent form, which lacks an enzyme needed to manufacture the polysaccharide coat, is called the R form because it forms rough colonies.

Griffith performed a series of simple experiments in which mice were infected with these bacteria, then monitored for disease symptoms (figure 14.1). Mice infected with the virulent S form died from pneumonia, whereas infection with the nonvirulent R form had no effect. This result shows that the polysaccharide coat is necessary for virulence. If the virulent

S form is first heat-killed, infection does not harm the mice, showing that the coat itself is not sufficient to cause disease. Lastly, infecting mice with a mixture of heat-killed S form with live R form caused pneumonia and death in the mice. This was unexpected as neither treatment alone caused disease. Furthermore, high levels of live S form bacteria were found in the lungs of the dead mice.

Somehow, the information specifying the polysaccharide coat had passed from the dead, virulent S bacteria to the live, coatless R bacteria in the mixture, permanently altering the coatless R bacteria into the virulent S variety. Griffith called this transfer of virulence from one cell to another, **transformation.** Our modern interpretation is that genetic material was actually transferred between the cells. *dead cells → live cells*

Avery, MacLeod, and McCarty identify the transforming principle

The agent responsible for transforming *Streptococcus* went undiscovered until 1944. In a classic series of experiments, Oswald Avery and his coworkers Colin MacLeod and Maclyn McCarty identified the substance responsible for transformation in Griffith's experiment.

They first prepared the mixture of dead S *Streptococcus* and live R *Streptococcus* that Griffith had used. Then they removed as much of the protein as they could from their preparation, eventually achieving 99.98% purity. They found that despite the removal of nearly all protein, the transforming activity was not reduced.

→ protein isnt responsible

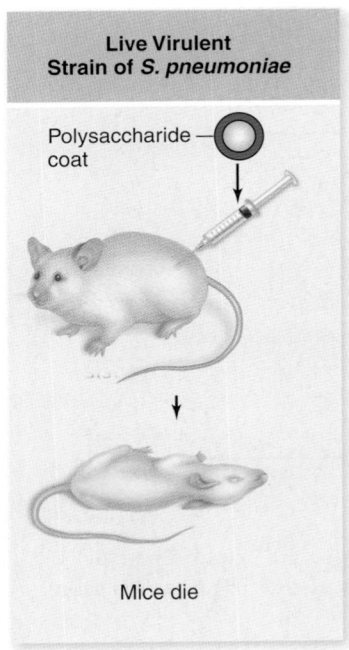
Live Virulent Strain of *S. pneumoniae*
Polysaccharide coat
Mice die
a.

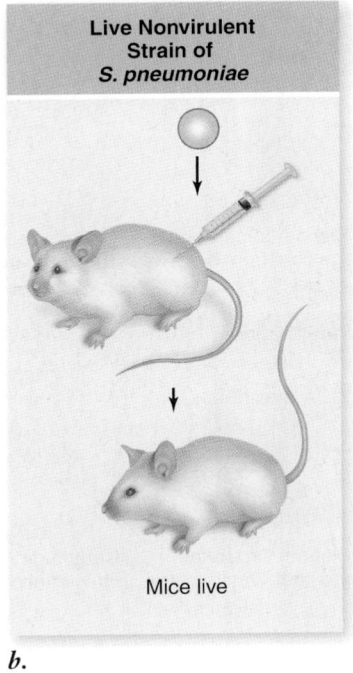
Live Nonvirulent Strain of *S. pneumoniae*
Mice live
b.

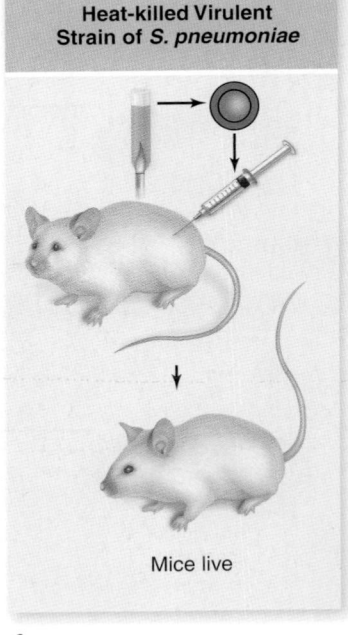
Heat-killed Virulent Strain of *S. pneumoniae*
Mice live
c.

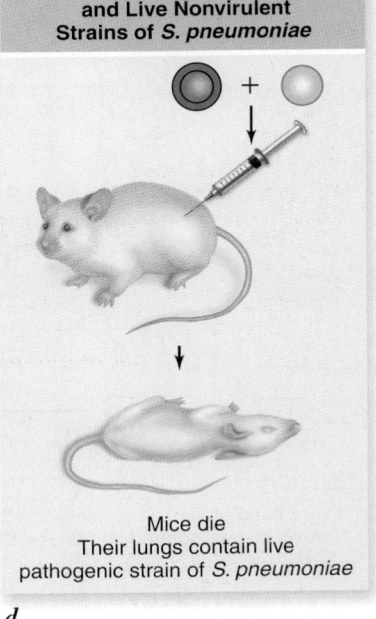
Mixture of Heat-Killed Virulent and Live Nonvirulent Strains of *S. pneumoniae*
Mice die
Their lungs contain live pathogenic strain of *S. pneumoniae*
d.

Figure 14.1 Griffith's experiment. Griffith was trying to make a vaccine against pneumonia and instead discovered transformation. *a.* Injecting live virulent bacteria into mice produces pneumonia. Injection of nonvirulent bacteria (*b*) or heat-killed virulent bacteria (*c*) had no effect. *d.* However, a mixture of heat-killed virulent and live nonvirulent bacteria produced pneumonia in the mice. This indicates the genetic information for virulence was transferred from dead, virulent cells to live, nonvirulent cells, transforming them from nonvirulent to virulent.

chapter **14** *DNA: The Genetic Material*

Moreover, the properties of this substance resembled those of DNA in several ways:

1. The elemental composition agreed closely with that of DNA.
2. When spun at high speeds in an ultracentrifuge, it migrated to the same level (density) as DNA.
3. Extracting lipids and proteins did not reduce transforming activity.
4. Protein-digesting enzymes did not affect transforming activity, nor did RNA-digesting enzymes.
5. DNA-digesting enzymes destroyed all transforming activity.

These experiments supported the identity of DNA as the substance transferred between cells by transformation and indicated that the genetic material, at least in this bacterial species, is DNA.

DNA is supported

Hershey and Chase demonstrate that phage genetic material is DNA

Avery's results were not widely accepted at first because many biologists continued to believe that proteins were the reposi-tory of hereditary information. But additional evidence sup-porting Avery's conclusion was provided in 1952 by Alfred Hershey and Martha Chase, who experimented with viruses that infect bacteria. These viruses are called **bacteriophages,** or more simply, **phages.**

Viruses, described in more detail in chapter 27, are much simpler than cells; they generally consist of genetic material (DNA or RNA) surrounded by a protein coat. The phage used in these experiments is called a *lytic* phage because infection causes the cell to burst, or lyse. When such a phage infects a bacterial cell, it first binds to the cell's outer surface and then injects its genetic information into the cell. There, the viral genetic information is expressed by the bacterial cell's machin-ery, leading to production of thousands of new viruses. The buildup of viruses eventually causes the cell to lyse, releasing progeny phage.

The phage used by Hershey and Chase contains only DNA and protein, and therefore it provides the simplest possible system to differentiate the roles of DNA and pro-tein. Hershey and Chase set out to identify the molecule that the phage injects into the bacterial cells. To do this, they needed a method to label both DNA and protein in unique ways that would allow them to be distinguished. Nucleotides

SCIENTIFIC THINKING

Hypothesis: DNA is the genetic material in bacteriophage.

Prediction: The phage life cycle requires reprogramming the cell to make phage proteins. The information for this must be introduced into the cell during infection.

Test: DNA can be specifically labeled using radioactive phosphate (^{32}P), and protein can be specifically labeled using radioactive sulfur (^{35}S). Phage are grown on either ^{35}S or ^{32}P, then used to infect cells in two experiments. The phage heads remain attached to the outside of the cell and can be removed by brief agitation in a blender. The cell suspension can be collected by centrifugation, leaving the phage heads in the supernatant.

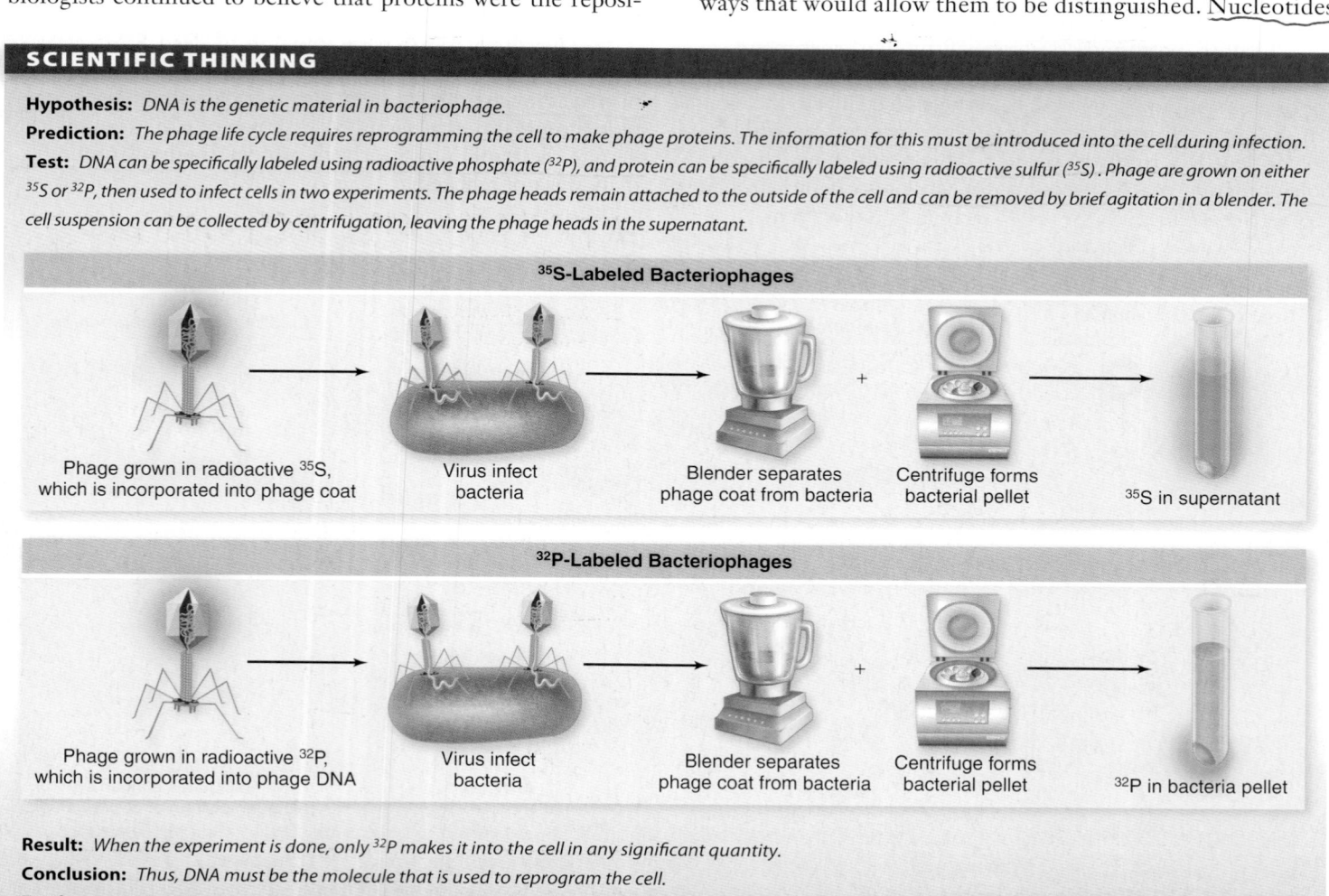

^{35}S-Labeled Bacteriophages

Phage grown in radioactive ^{35}S, which is incorporated into phage coat → Virus infect bacteria → Blender separates phage coat from bacteria + Centrifuge forms bacterial pellet → ^{35}S in supernatant

^{32}P-Labeled Bacteriophages

Phage grown in radioactive ^{32}P, which is incorporated into phage DNA → Virus infect bacteria → Blender separates phage coat from bacteria + Centrifuge forms bacterial pellet → ^{32}P in bacteria pellet

Result: When the experiment is done, only ^{32}P makes it into the cell in any significant quantity.

Conclusion: Thus, DNA must be the molecule that is used to reprogram the cell.

Further Experiments: How does this experiment complement or extend the work of Avery on the identity of the transforming principle?

Figure 14.2 Hershey–Chase experiment showed DNA is genetic material for phage.

contain phosphorus, but proteins do not, and some amino acids contain sulfur, but DNA does not. Thus, the radioactive ^{32}P isotope can be used to label DNA specifically, and the isotope ^{35}S can be used to label proteins specifically. The two isotopes are easily distinguished based on the particles they emit when they decay.

Two experiments were performed (figure 14.2). In one, viruses were grown on a medium containing ^{32}P, which was incorporated into DNA; in the other, viruses were grown on medium containing ^{35}S, which was incorporated into coat proteins. Each group of labeled viruses was then allowed to infect separate bacterial cultures.

After infection, the bacterial cell suspension was agitated in a blender to remove the infecting viral particles from the surfaces of the bacteria. This step ensured that only the part of the virus that had been injected into the bacterial cells—that is, the genetic material—would be detected.

Each bacterial suspension was then centrifuged to produce a pellet of cells for analysis. In the ^{32}P experiment, a large amount of radioactive phosphorus was found in the cell pellet, but in the ^{35}S experiment, very little radioactive sulfur was found in the pellet (see figure 14.2). Hershey and Chase deduced that DNA, and not protein, constituted the genetic information that viruses inject into bacteria. ← DNA

Learning Outcomes Review 14.1

Experiments with pneumonia-causing bacteria showed that virulence could be passed from one cell to another, a phenomenon termed transformation. When the factor responsible for transformation was purified, it was shown to be DNA. Labeling experiments with phage also indicated that the genetic material was DNA and not protein.

■ **Why was protein an attractive candidate for the genetic material?**

Learning Outcomes

1. Describe the data available to Watson and Crick.
2. Explain the details of the Watson and Crick structure.
3. Explain the importance of complementarity for DNA structure and function.

A Swiss chemist, Friedrich Miescher, discovered DNA in 1869, only four years after Mendel's work was published—although it is unlikely that Miescher knew of Mendel's experiments.

Miescher extracted a white substance from the nuclei of human cells and fish sperm. The proportion of nitrogen and phosphorus in the substance was different from that found in any other known constituent of cells, which convinced Miescher that he had discovered a new biological substance. He called this substance "nuclein" because it seemed to be specifically associated with the nucleus. Because Miescher's nuclein was slightly acidic, it came to be called *nucleic acid*.

DNA's components were known, but its three-dimensional structure was a mystery

Although the three-dimensional structure of the DNA molecule was not elucidated until Watson and Crick, it was known that it contained three main components (figure 14.3):

1. a five-carbon sugar
2. a phosphate (PO_4) group

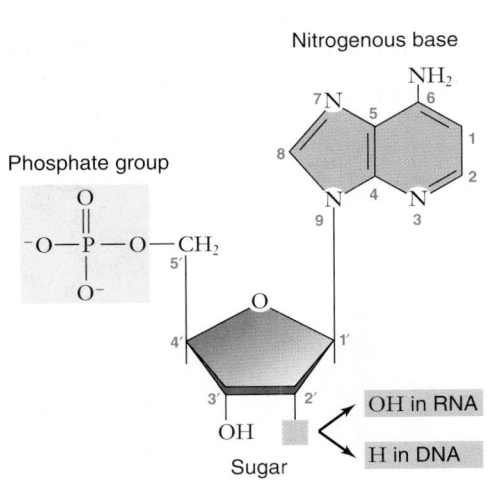

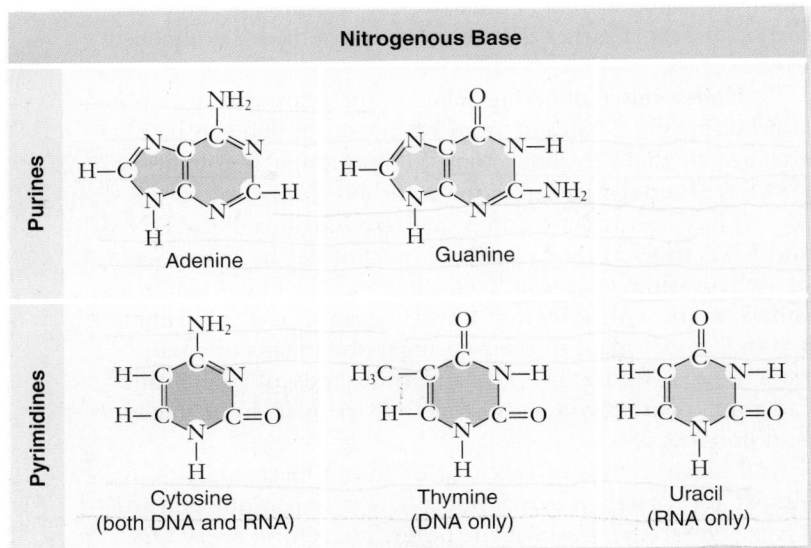

Figure 14.3 Nucleotide subunits of DNA and RNA. The nucleotide subunits of DNA and RNA are composed of three components: a five-carbon sugar (deoxyribose in DNA and ribose in RNA); a phosphate group; and a nitrogenous base (either a purine or a pyrimidine).

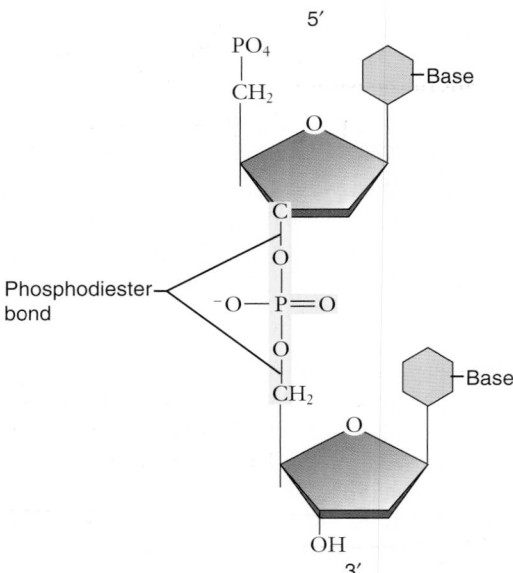

Figure 14.4   A phosphodiester bond.

3. a nitrogen-containing (nitrogenous) base. The base may be a **purine** (adenine, A, or guanine, G), a two-ringed structure; or a **pyrimidine** (thymine, T, or cytosine, C), a single-ringed structure. RNA contains the pyrimidine uracil (U) in place of thymine.

The convention in organic chemistry is to number the carbon atoms of a molecule and then to use these numbers to refer to any functional group attached to a carbon atom (see chapter 3). In the ribose sugars found in nucleic acids, four of the carbon atoms together with an oxygen atom form a five-membered ring. As illustrated in figure 14.3, the carbon atoms are numbered 1′ to 5′, proceeding clockwise from the oxygen atom; the prime symbol (′) indicates that the number refers to a carbon in a sugar rather than to the atoms in the bases attached to the sugars.

Under this numbering scheme, the phosphate group is attached to the 5′ carbon atom of the sugar, and the base is attached to the 1′ carbon atom. In addition, a free hydroxyl (—OH) group is attached to the 3′ carbon atom.

The 5′ phosphate and 3′ hydroxyl groups allow DNA and RNA to form long chains of nucleotides by the process of dehydration synthesis (see chapter 3). The linkage is called a **phosphodiester bond** because the phosphate group is now linked to the two sugars by means of a pair of ester bonds (figure 14.4). Many thousands of nucleotides can join together via these linkages to form long nucleic acid polymers.

Linear strands of DNA or RNA, no matter how long, almost always have a free 5′ phosphate group at one end and a free 3′ hydroxyl group at the other. Therefore, every DNA and RNA molecule has an intrinsic polarity, and we can refer unambiguously to each end of the molecule. By convention, the sequence of bases is usually written in the 5′-to-3′ direction.

Chargaff, Franklin, and Wilkins obtained some structural evidence

To understand the model that Watson and Crick proposed, we need to review the evidence that they had available to construct their model.

Chargaff's rules

A careful study carried out by Erwin Chargaff showed that the nucleotide composition of DNA molecules varied in complex ways, depending on the source of the DNA. This strongly suggested that DNA was not a simple repeating polymer and that it might have the information-encoding properties genetic material requires. Despite DNA's complexity, however, Chargaff observed an important underlying regularity in the ratios of the bases found in native DNA: *The amount of adenine present in DNA always equals the amount of thymine, and the amount of guanine always equals the amount of cytosine*. These findings are commonly referred to as *Chargaff's rules*:

1. The proportion of A always equals that of T, and the proportion of G always equals that of C, or: A = T, and G = C.
2. It follows that there is always an equal proportion of purines (A and G) and pyrimidines (C and T).

As mounting evidence indicated that DNA stored the hereditary information, investigators began to puzzle over how such a seemingly simple molecule could carry out such a complex coding function.

Franklin: X-ray diffraction patterns of DNA

Another line of evidence provided more direct information about the possible structure of DNA. The British chemist Rosalind Franklin (figure 14.5a) used the technique of X-ray diffraction to analyze DNA. In X-ray diffraction, a molecule is bombarded with a beam of X-rays. The rays are bent, or

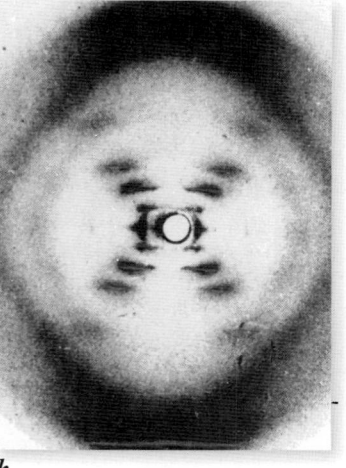

a.   *b.*

Figure 14.5 Rosalind Franklin's X-ray diffraction patterns. *a.* Rosalind Franklin. *b.* This X-ray diffraction photograph of DNA fibers, made in 1953 by Rosalind Franklin was interpreted to show the helical structure of DNA.

Figure 14.6 The DNA double helix. James Watson (*left*) and Francis Crick (*right*) deduced the structure of DNA in 1953 from Chargaff's rules, knowing the proper tautomeric forms of the bases and using Franklin's diffraction studies.

diffracted, by the molecules they encounter, and the diffraction pattern is recorded on photographic film. The patterns resemble the ripples created by tossing a rock into a smooth lake (figure 14.5*b*). When analyzed mathematically, the diffraction pattern can yield information about the three-dimensional structure of a molecule.

X-ray diffraction works best on substances that can be prepared as perfectly regular crystalline arrays. At the time Franklin conducted her analysis, it was impossible to obtain true crystals of natural DNA, so she had to use DNA in the form of fibers. Maurice Wilkins, another researcher working in the same laboratory, had been able to prepare more uniformly oriented DNA fibers than anyone else at the time. Using these fibers, Franklin succeeded in obtaining crude diffraction information on natural DNA. The diffraction patterns she obtained suggested that the DNA molecule had the shape of a helix, or corkscrew, with a consistent diameter of about 2 nm and a complete helical turn every 3.4 nm.

Tautomeric forms of bases

One piece of evidence important to Watson and Crick was the form of the bases themselves. Because of the alternating double and single bonds in the bases, they actually exist in equilibrium between two different forms when in solution. The different forms have to do with keto (C=O) versus enol (C—OH) groups and amino (—NH₂) versus imino (=NH) groups that are attached to the bases. These structural forms are called *tautomers*.

[handwritten:] C=O vs C-OH and amino vs imino

The importance of this distinction is that the two forms exhibit very different hydrogen-bonding possibilities. The predominant forms of the bases contain the keto and amino groups (see figure 14.3), but a prominent biochemistry text of the time actually contained the opposite, and incorrect, information. Legend has it that Watson learned the correct forms while having lunch with a biochemist friend.

The Watson–Crick model fits the available evidence

*[handwritten:] * pre-dominant form = keto-amino*

Learning informally of Franklin's results before they were published in 1953, James Watson and Francis Crick, two young investigators at Cambridge University, quickly worked out a likely structure for the DNA molecule (figure 14.6), which we now know was substantially correct. Watson and Crick did not perform a single experiment themselves related to DNA structure; rather, they built detailed molecular models based on the information available.

The key to the model was their understanding that each DNA molecule is actually made up of *two* chains of nucleotides that are intertwined—the double helix.

The phosphodiester backbone

The two strands of the double helix are made up of long polymers of nucleotides, and as described earlier, each strand is made up of repeating sugar and phosphate units joined by phosphodiester bonds (figure 14.7). We call this the *phosphodiester backbone* of the

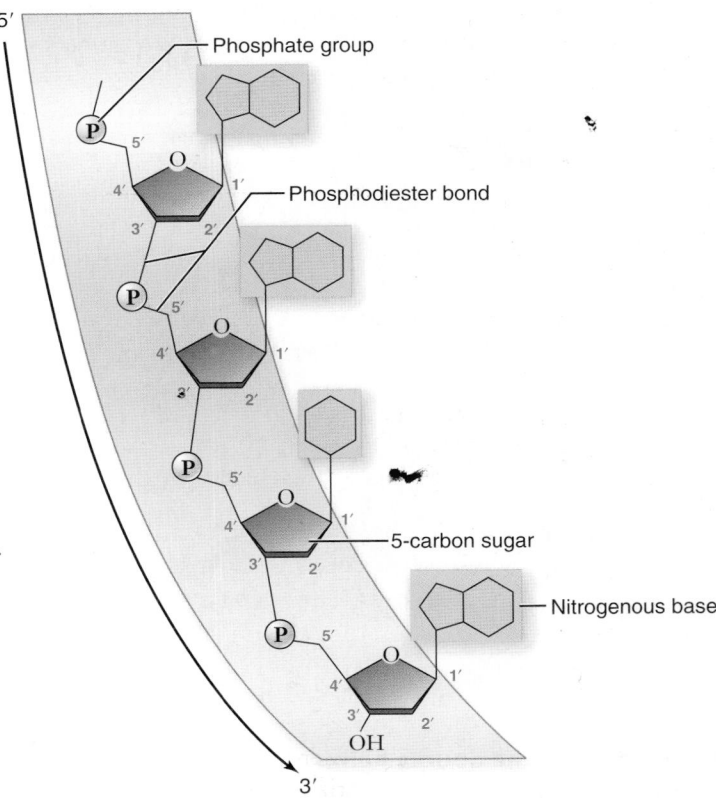

Figure 14.7 Structure of a single strand of DNA. The phosphodiester backbone is composed of alternating sugar and phosphate groups. The bases are attached to each sugar.

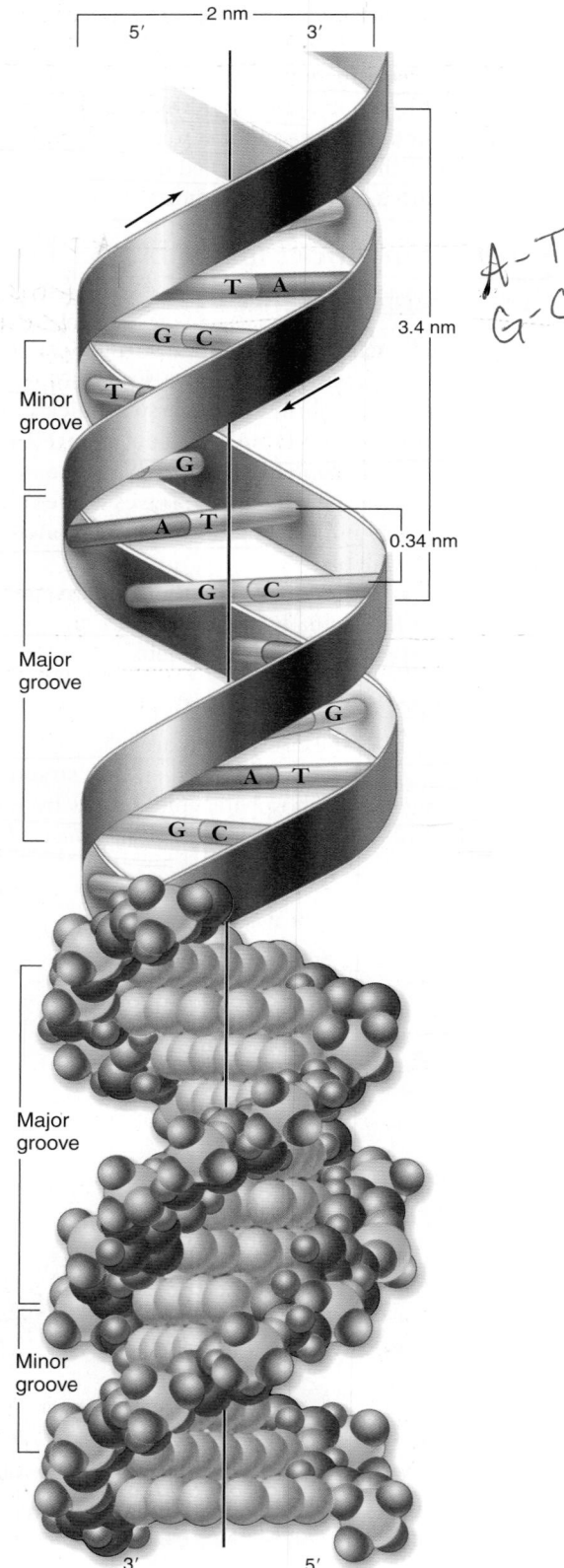

Figure 14.8 The double helix. Shown with the phosphodiester backbone as a ribbon on top and a space-filling model on the bottom. The bases protrude into the interior of the helix where they hold it together by base-pairing. The backbone forms two grooves, the larger major groove and the smaller minor groove.

molecule. The two strands of the backbone are then wrapped about a common axis forming a double helix (figure 14.8). The helix is often compared to a spiral staircase, in which the two strands of the double helix are the handrails on the staircase.

Complementarity of bases

Watson and Crick proposed that the two strands were held together by formation of hydrogen bonds between bases on opposite strands. These bonds would result in specific **base-pairs:** Adenine (A) can form two hydrogen bonds with thymine (T) to form an A–T base-pair, and guanine (G) can form three hydrogen bonds with cytosine (C) to form a G–C base-pair (figure 14.9).

Note that this configuration also pairs a two-ringed purine with a single-ringed pyrimidine in each case, so that the diameter of each base-pair is the same. This consistent diameter is indicated by the X-ray diffraction data.

We refer to this pattern of base-pairing as *complementary*, which means that although the strands are not identical, they each can be used to specify the other by base-pairing. If the sequence of one strand is ATGC, then the complementary strand sequence must be TACG. This characteristic becomes critical for DNA replication and expression, as you will see later in this chapter.

The Watson–Crick model also explained Chargaff's results: In a double helix, adenine forms two hydrogen bonds with thymine, but it will not form hydrogen bonds properly with cytosine. Similarly, guanine forms three hydrogen bonds with cytosine, but it will not form hydrogen bonds properly with thymine. Because of this base-pairing, adenine and thymine always occur in the same proportions in any DNA molecule, as do guanine and cytosine.

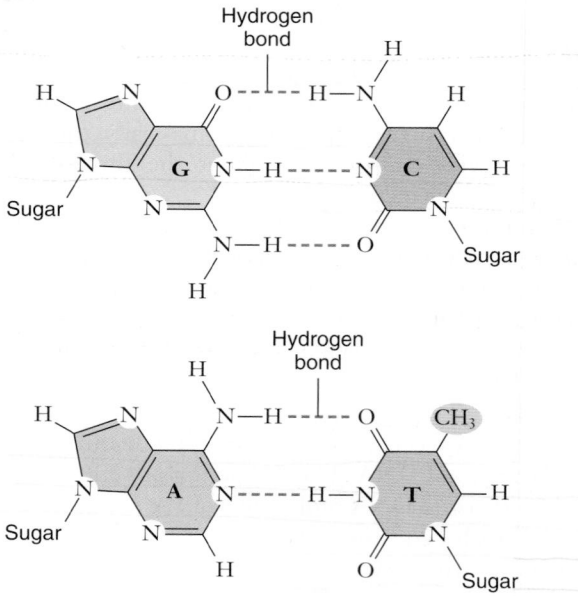

Figure 14.9 Base-pairing holds strands together. The hydrogen bonds that form between A and T and between G and C are shown with dashed lines. These produce AT and GC base-pairs that hold the two strands together. This always pairs a purine with a pyrimidine, keeping the diameter of the double helix constant.

Inquiry question

? **Does the Watson–Crick model account for all of the data discussed in the text?**

Antiparallel configuration

As stated earlier, a single phosphodiester strand has an inherent polarity, meaning that one end terminates in a 3′ OH and the other end terminates in a 5′ PO$_4$. Strands are thus referred to as having either a 5′-to-3′ or a 3′-to-5′ polarity. Two strands could be put together in two ways: with the polarity the same in each (parallel) or with the polarity opposite (antiparallel). Native double-stranded DNA always has the antiparallel configuration, with one strand running 5′ to 3′ and the other running 3′ to 5′ (see figure 14.8). In addition to its complementarity, this antiparallel nature also has important implications for DNA replication. *DNA is antiparallel*

The Watson–Crick DNA molecule

In the Watson and Crick model, each DNA molecule is composed of two complementary phosphodiester strands that each form a helix with a common axis. These strands are antiparallel, with the bases extending into the interior of the helix. The bases from opposite strands form base-pairs with each other to join the two complementary strands (see figures 14.8 and 14.9).

Although the hydrogen bonds between each individual base-pair are low-energy bonds, the sum of bonds between the many base-pairs of the polymer has enough energy that the entire molecule is stable. To return to our spiral staircase analogy—the backbone is the handrails, the base-pairs are the steps.

Although the Watson–Crick model provided a rational structural for DNA, researchers had to answer further questions about how DNA could be replicated, a crucial step in cell division, and also about how cells could repair damaged or otherwise altered DNA. We explore these questions in the rest of this chapter. (In the following chapter, we continue with the genetic code and the connection between the code and protein synthesis.)

Learning Outcomes Review 14.2

Chargaff showed that in DNA, the amount of adenine was equal to the amount of thymine, and the amount of guanosine was equal to that of cytosine. X-ray diffraction studies by Franklin and Wilkins indicated that DNA formed a helix. Watson and Crick built a model consisting of two antiparallel strands wrapped in a helix about a common axis. The two strands are held together by hydrogen bonds between the bases: adenine pairs with thymine and guanine pairs with cytosine. The two strands are thus complementary to each other.

■ *Why was information about the proper tautomeric form of the bases critical?*

14.3 Basic Characteristics of DNA Replication

Learning Outcomes

1. Explain the basic mechanism of DNA replication.
2. Describe the requirements for DNA replication.

The accurate replication of DNA prior to cell division is a basic and crucial function. Research has revealed that this complex process requires the participation of a large number of cellular proteins. Before geneticists could look for these details, however, they needed to perform some groundwork on the general mechanisms.

Meselson and Stahl demonstrate the semiconservative mechanism

The Watson–Crick model immediately suggested that the basis for copying the genetic information is complementarity. One chain of the DNA molecule may have any conceivable base sequence, but this sequence completely determines the sequence of its partner in the duplex.

In replication, the sequence of parental strands must be duplicated in daughter strands. That is, one parental helix with two strands must yield two daughter helices with four strands. The two daughter molecules are then separated during the course of cell division.

Three models of DNA replication are possible (figure 14.10):

1. In a *conservative model*, both strands of the parental duplex would remain intact (conserved), and new DNA copies would consist of all-new molecules. Both daughter strands would contain all-new molecules.

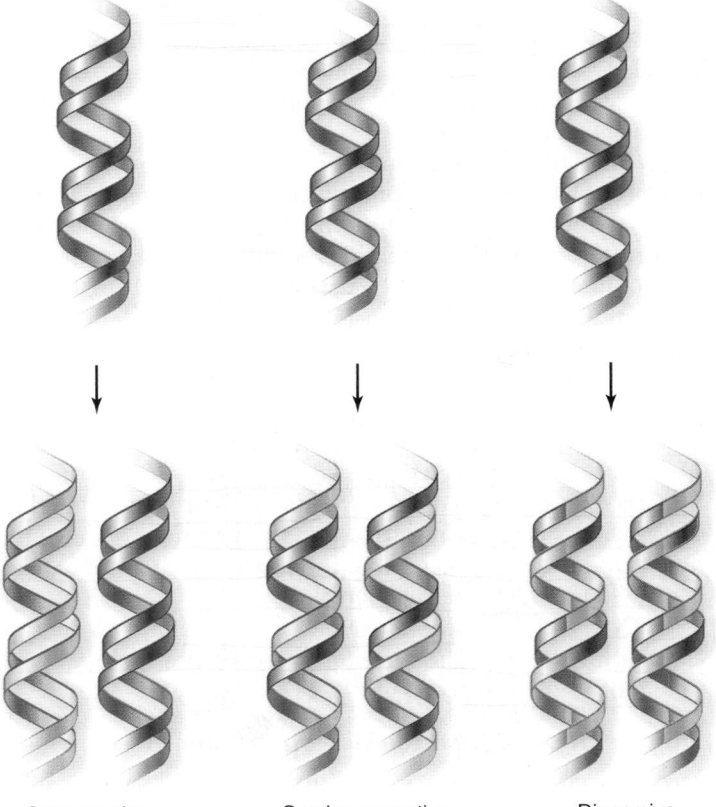

Conservative   Semiconservative   Dispersive

Figure 14.10 Three possible models for DNA replication. The conservative model produces one entirely new molecule and conserves the old. The semiconservative model produces two hybrid molecules of old and new strands. The dispersive model produces hybrid molecules with each strand a mixture of old and new.

2. In a **semiconservative model,** one strand of the parental duplex remains intact in daughter strands (semiconserved); a new complementary strand is built for each parental strand consisting of new molecules. Daughter strands would consist of one parental strand and one newly synthesized strand.

3. In a *dispersive model,* copies of DNA would consist of mixtures of parental and newly synthesized strands; that is, the new DNA would be dispersed throughout each strand of both daughter molecules after replication.

Notice that these three models suggest general mechanisms of replication, without specifying any molecular details of the process.

The Meselson–Stahl experiment

The three models for DNA replication were evaluated in 1958 by Matthew Meselson and Franklin Stahl. To distinguish between these models, they labeled DNA and then followed the labeled DNA through two rounds of replication (figure 14.11).

The label Meselson and Stahl used was a heavy isotope of nitrogen (^{15}N), not a radioactive label. Molecules containing ^{15}N have a greater density than those containing the common ^{14}N isotope. Ultracentrifugation can be used to separate molecules that have different densities.

Bacteria were grown in a medium containing ^{15}N, which became incorporated into the bases of the bacterial DNA. After several generations, the DNA of these bacteria was denser than that of bacteria grown in a medium containing the normally available ^{14}N. Meselson and Stahl then transferred the bacteria from the ^{15}N medium to ^{14}N medium and collected the DNA at various time intervals.

The DNA for each interval was dissolved in a solution containing a heavy salt, cesium chloride. This solution was spun at very high speeds in an ultracentrifuge. The enormous centrifugal forces caused cesium ions to migrate toward the bottom of the centrifuge tube, creating a gradient of cesium concentration, and thus of density. Each DNA strand floated or sank in the gradient until it reached the point at which its density exactly matched the density of the cesium at that location. Because ^{15}N strands are denser than ^{14}N strands, they migrated farther down the tube.

The DNA collected immediately after the transfer of bacteria to new ^{14}N medium was all of one density equal to that of ^{15}N DNA alone. However, after the bacteria completed a first round of DNA replication, the density of their DNA had decreased to a value intermediate between ^{14}N DNA alone and ^{15}N DNA. After the second round of replication, two density classes of DNA were observed: one intermediate and one equal to that of ^{14}N DNA (see figure 14.11).

Interpretation of the Meselson–Stahl findings

Meselson and Stahl compared their experimental data with the results that would be predicted on the basis of the three models.

1. The conservative model was not consistent with the data because after one round of replication, two densities should have been observed: DNA strands would either be all-heavy (parental) or all-light (daughter). This model is rejected.

2. The semiconservative model is consistent with all observations: After one round of replication, a single

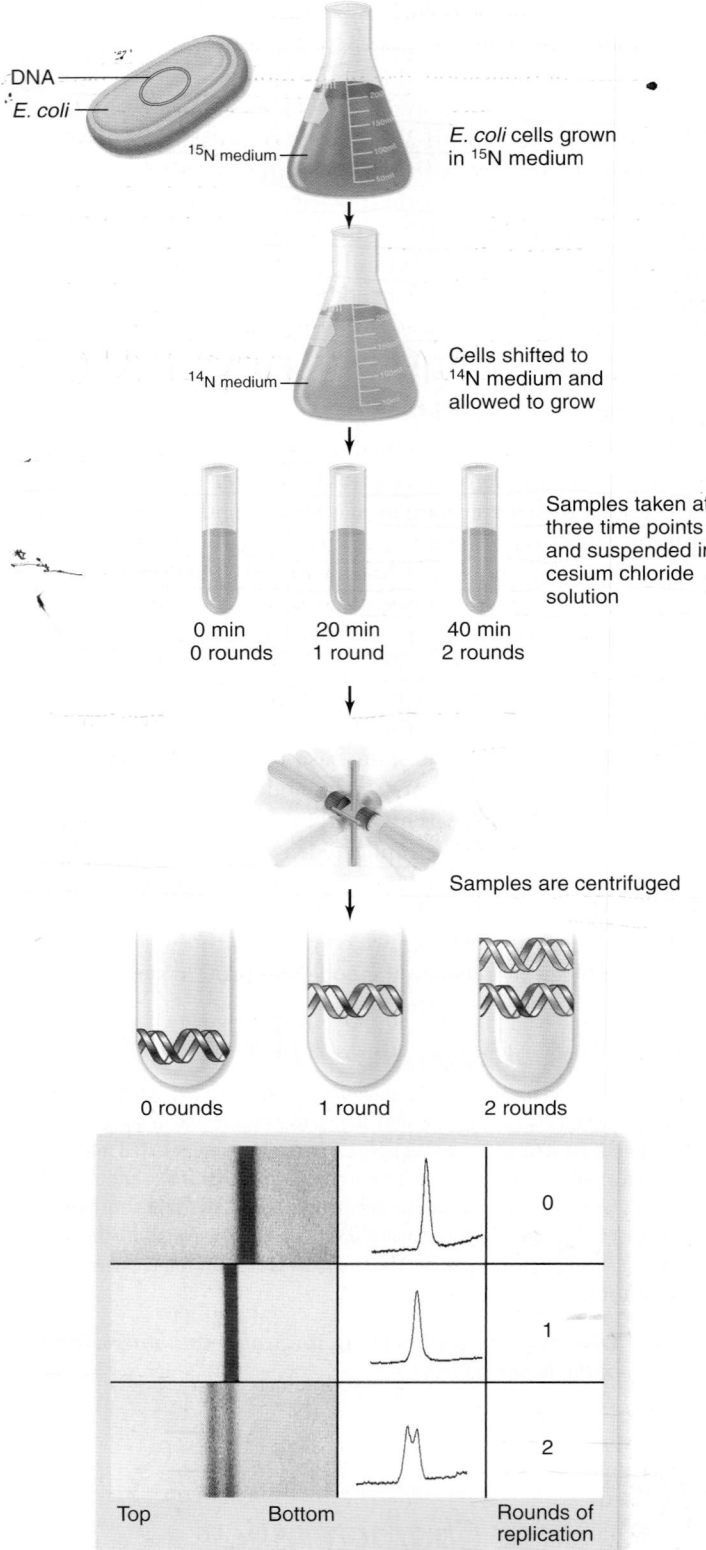

Figure 14.11 The Meselson–Stahl experiment. Bacteria grown in heavy ^{15}N medium are shifted to light ^{14}N medium and grown for two rounds of replication. Samples are taken at time points corresponding to zero, one, and two rounds of replication and centrifuged in cesium chloride to form a gradient. The actual data are shown at the bottom with the interpretation of semiconservative replication shown schematically.

density would be predicted because all DNA molecules would have a light strand and a heavy strand. After two rounds of replication, half of the molecules would have two light strands, and half would have a light strand and a heavy strand—and so two densities would be observed. Therefore, the results support the semiconservative model.

3. The dispersive model was consistent with the data from the first round of replication, because in this model, every DNA helix would consist of strands that are mixtures of ½ light (new) and ½ heavy (old) molecules. But after two rounds of replication, the dispersive model would still yield only a single density; DNA strands would be composed of ¾ light and ¼ heavy molecules. Instead, two densities were observed. Therefore, this model is also rejected.

The basic mechanism of DNA replication is semiconservative. At the simplest level, then, DNA is replicated by opening up a DNA helix and making copies of both strands to produce two daughter helices, each consisting of one old strand and one new strand.

DNA replication requires a template, nucleotides, and a polymerase enzyme

Replication requires three things: something to copy, something to do the copying, and the building blocks to make the copy. The parental DNA molecules serve as a template, enzymes perform the actions of copying the template, and the building blocks are nucleoside triphosphates.

The process of replication can be thought of as having a beginning where the process starts; a middle where the majority of building blocks are added; and an end where the process is finished. We use the terms *initiation*, *elongation*, and *termination* to describe a biochemical process. Although this may seem overly simplistic, in fact, discrete functions are usually required for initiation and termination that are not necessary for elongation.

A number of enzymes work together to accomplish the task of assembling a new strand, but the enzyme that actually matches the existing DNA bases with complementary nucleotides and then links the nucleotides together to make the new strand is **DNA polymerase** (figure 14.12). All DNA

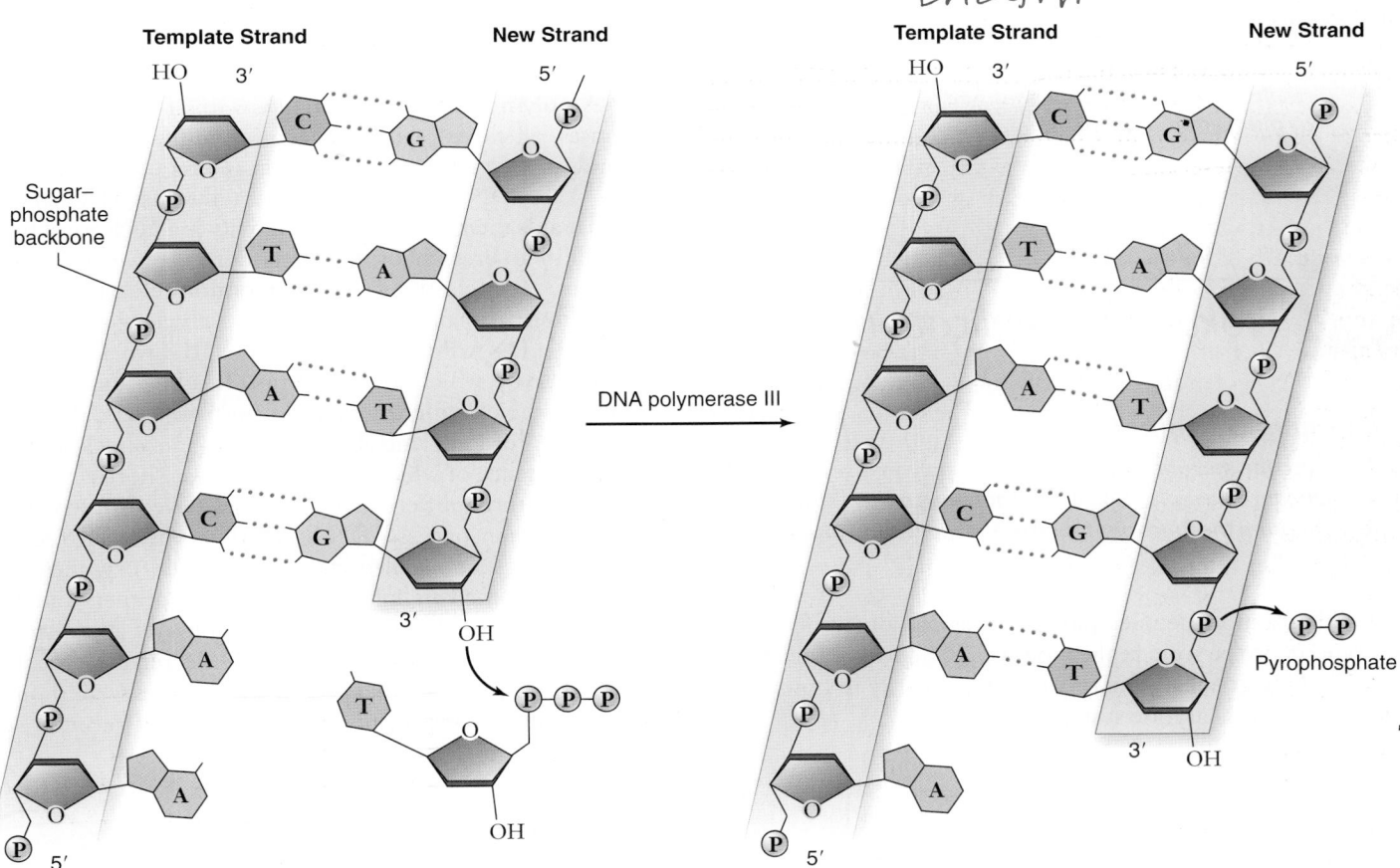

Figure 14.12 Action of DNA polymerase. DNA polymerases add nucleotides to the 3′ end of a growing chain. The nucleotide added depends on the base that is in the template strand. Each new base must be complementary to the base in the template strand. With the addition of each new nucleoside triphosphate, two of its phosphates are cleaved off as pyrophosphate.

Inquiry question

? Why do you think it is important that the sugar–phosphate backbone of DNA is held together by covalent bonds, and the cross-bridges between the two strands are held together by hydrogen bonds?

polymerases that have been examined have several common features. They all add new bases to the 3' end of existing strands. That is, they synthesize in a 5'-to-3' direction by extending a strand base-paired to the template. All DNA polymerases also require a *primer* to begin synthesis; they cannot begin without a strand of RNA or DNA base-paired to the template. RNA polymerases do not have this requirement, so they usually synthesize the primers.

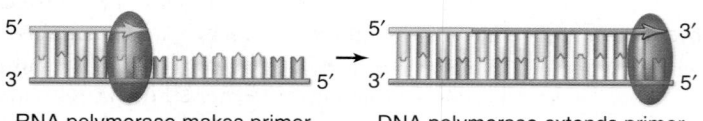

RNA polymerase makes primer → DNA polymerase extends primer

Learning Outcomes Review 14.3

Meselson and Stahl showed that the basic mechanism of replication is semiconservative: Each new DNA helix is composed of one old strand and one new strand. The process of replication requires a template to copy, nucleoside triphosphate building blocks, and the enzyme DNA polymerase. DNA polymerases synthesize DNA in a 5'-to-3' direction from a primer, usually RNA.

■ *In the Meselson–Stahl experiment, what would the results be if the DNA was denatured prior to separation by ultracentrifugation?*

14.4 Prokaryotic Replication

Learning Outcomes

1. *Describe the functions of E. coli DNA polymerases.*
2. *Explain why replication is discontinuous on one strand.*
3. *Diagram the functions found at the replication fork.*

To build up a more detailed picture of replication, we first concentrate on prokaryotic replication using *E. coli* as a model. We can then look at eukaryotic replication primarily in how it differs from the prokaryotic system.

Prokaryotic replication starts at a single origin

Replication in *E. coli* initiates at a specific site, the origin (called *oriC*), and ends at a specific site, the terminus. The sequence of *oriC* consists of repeated nucleotides that bind an initiator protein and an AT-rich sequence that can be opened easily during initiation of replication. (A–T base-pairs have only two hydrogen bonds, compared with the three hydrogen bonds in G–C base-pairs.)

After initiation, replication proceeds bidirectionally from this unique origin to the unique terminus (figure 14.13). We call the DNA controlled by an origin a **replicon**. In this case, the chromosome plus the origin forms a single replicon.

E. coli has at least three different DNA polymerases

As mentioned earlier, DNA polymerase refers to a group of enzymes responsible for the building of a new DNA strand from the template. The first DNA polymerase isolated in *E. coli* was given the name **DNA polymerase I (Pol I)**. At first, investigators assumed this polymerase was responsible for the bulk synthesis of DNA during replication. A mutant was isolated, however, that had no Pol I activity, but could still replicate its chromosome. Two additional polymerases were isolated from this strain of *E. coli* and were named **DNA polymerase II (Pol II)** and **DNA polymerase III (Pol III)**. As with all other known polymerases, all three of these enzymes synthesize polynucleotide strands only in the 5'-to-3' direction and require a primer.

Many DNA polymerases have additional enzymatic activity that aids their function. This activity is a nuclease activity, or the ability to break phosphodiester bonds between nucleotides. Nucleases are classified as either **endonucleases** (which cut DNA internally) or **exonucleases** (which chew away at an end of DNA). DNA Pol I, Pol II, and Pol III have 3'-to-5' exonuclease activity, which serves as a proofreading function because it allows the enzyme to remove a mispaired base. In addition, the DNA Pol I enzyme also has a 5'-to-3' exonuclease activity, the importance of which will become clear shortly.

The three different polymerases have different roles in the replication process. DNA Pol III is the main replication enzyme; it is responsible for the bulk of DNA synthesis. DNA Pol I acts on the lagging strand to remove primers and replace them with DNA. The Pol II enzyme does not appear to play a role in replication but is involved in DNA repair processes.

For many years, these three polymerases were thought to be the only DNA polymerases in *E. coli*, but recently several

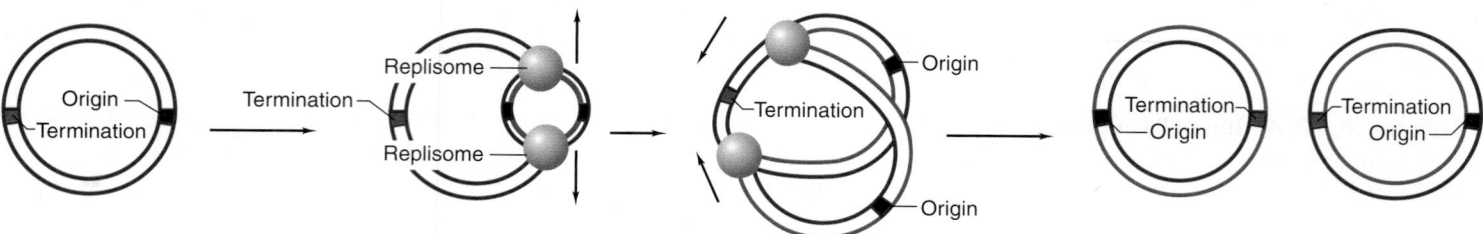

Figure 14.13 Replication is bidirectional from a unique origin. Replication initiates from a unique origin. Two separate replisomes are loaded onto the origin and initiate synthesis in the opposite directions on the chromosome. These two replisomes continue in opposite directions until they come to a unique termination site.

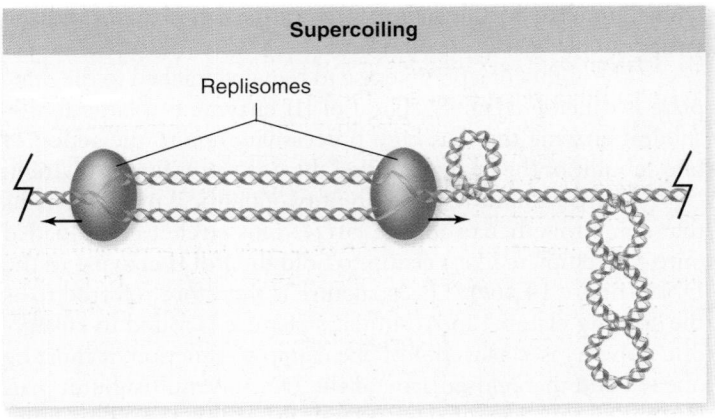

Supercoiling

Replisomes

No Supercoiling

Replisomes

DNA gyrase

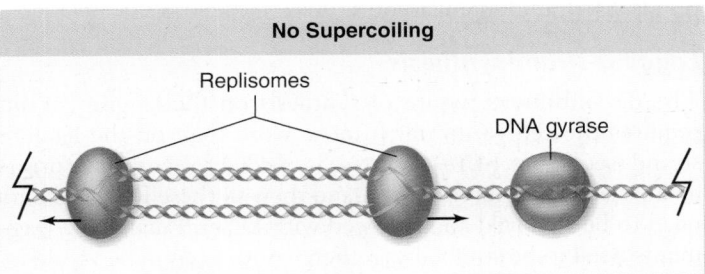

Figure 14.14 Unwinding the helix causes torsional strain. If the ends of a linear DNA molecule are constrained, as they are in the cell, unwinding the helix produces torsional strain. This can cause the double helix to further coil in space (supercoiling). The enzyme DNA gyrase can relieve supercoiling.

new ones have been identified. There are now five known polymerases, although not all are active in DNA replication.

Unwinding DNA requires energy and causes torsional strain

Although some DNA polymerases can unwind DNA as they synthesize new DNA, another class of enzymes has the single function of unwinding DNA strands to make this process more efficient. Enzymes that use energy from ATP to unwind the DNA template are called **helicases.**

The single strands of DNA produced by helicase action are unstable because the process exposes the hydrophobic bases to water. Cells solve this problem by using a protein, called single-strand-binding protein (SSB), to coat exposed single strands.

The unwinding of the two strands introduces torsional strain in the DNA molecule. Imagine two rubber bands twisted together. If you now unwind the rubber bands, what happens? The rubber bands, already twisted about each other, will further coil in space. When this happens with a DNA molecule it is called **supercoiling** (figure 14.14). The branch of mathematics that studies how forms twist and coil in space is called *topology*, and therefore we describe this coiling of the double helix as the *topological state* of DNA. This state describes how the double helix itself coils in space. You have already seen an example of this coiling with DNA wrapped about histone proteins in the nucleosomes of eukaryotic chromosomes (see chapter 10).

Enzymes that can alter the topological state of DNA are called **topoisomerases.** Topoisomerase enzymes act to relieve the torsional strain caused by unwinding and to prevent this supercoiling from happening. **DNA gyrase** is the topoisomerase involved in DNA replication (see figure 14.14).

Replication is semidiscontinuous

Earlier, DNA was described as being antiparallel—meaning that one strand runs in the 3′-to-5′ direction, and its complementary strand runs in the 5′-to-3′ direction. The antiparallel nature of DNA combined with the nature of the polymerase enzymes puts constraints on the replication process. Because polymerases can synthesize DNA in only one direction, and the two DNA strands run in opposite directions, polymerases on the two strands must be synthesizing DNA in opposite directions (figure 14.15).

The requirement of DNA polymerases for a primer means that on one strand primers need to be added as the helix

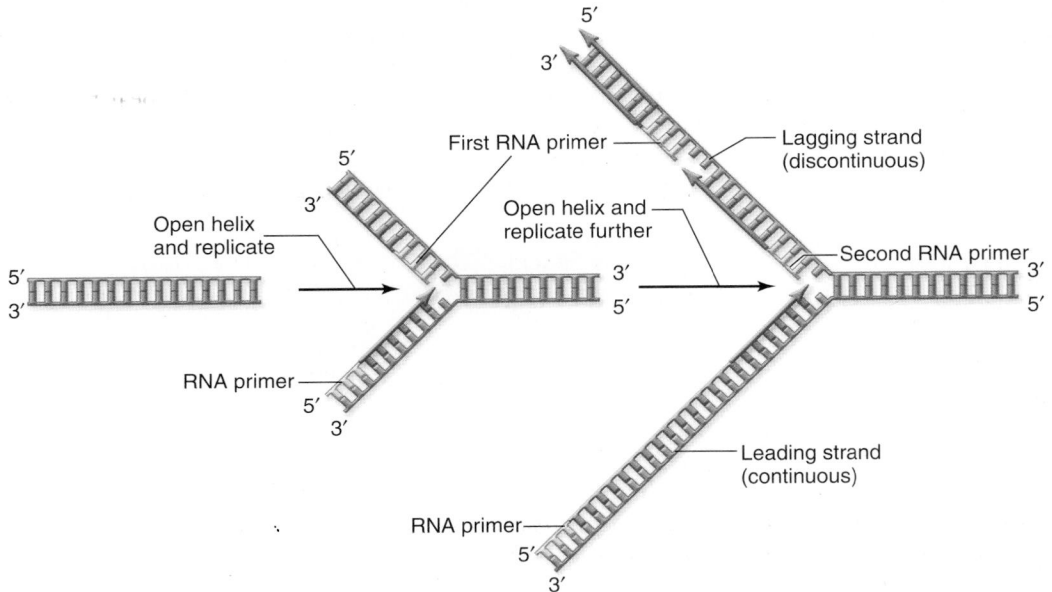

Figure 14.15 Replication is semidiscontinuous. The 5′-to-3′ synthesis of the polymerase and the antiparallel nature of DNA mean that only one strand, the leading strand, can be synthesized continuously. The other strand, the lagging strand, must be made in pieces, each with its own primer.

First RNA primer

Lagging strand (discontinuous)

Open helix and replicate

Open helix and replicate further

Second RNA primer

RNA primer

Leading strand (continuous)

RNA primer

is opened up (see figure 14.15). This means that one strand can be synthesized in a continuous fashion from an initial primer, but the other strand must be synthesized in a discontinuous fashion with multiple priming events and short sections of DNA being assembled. The strand that is continuous is called the **leading strand,** and the strand that is discontinuous is the **lagging strand.** DNA fragments synthesized on the lagging strand are named **Okazaki fragments** in honor of the man who first experimentally demonstrated discontinuous synthesis. They introduce a need for even more enzymatic activity on the lagging strand, as is described next.

Synthesis occurs at the replication fork

The partial opening of a DNA helix to form two single strands has a forked appearance, and is thus called the **replication fork.** All of the enzymatic activities that we have discussed plus a few more are found at the replication fork (table 14.1). Synthesis on the leading strand and on the lagging strand proceed in different ways, however.

Priming

The primers required by DNA polymerases during replication are synthesized by the enzyme *DNA primase.* This enzyme is an RNA polymerase that synthesizes short stretches of RNA 10–20 bp (base-pairs) long that function as primers for DNA polymerase. Later on, the RNA primer is removed and replaced with DNA.

Leading-strand synthesis

Synthesis on the leading strand is relatively simple. A single priming event is required, and then the strand can be extended indefinitely by the action of DNA Pol III. If the enzyme re-

mains attached to the template, it can synthesize around the entire circular *E. coli* chromosome.

The ability of a polymerase to remain attached to the template is called *processivity.* The Pol III enzyme is a large multisubunit enzyme that has high processivity due to the action of one subunit of the enzyme, called the β *subunit* (figure 14.16a).

The β subunit is made up of two identical protein chains that come together to form a circle. This circle can be loaded onto the template like a clamp to hold the Pol II enzyme to the DNA (figure 14.16b). This structure is therefore referred to as the "sliding clamp," and a similar structure is found in eukaryotic polymerases as well. For the clamp to function, it must be opened and then closed around the DNA. A multisubunit protein called the clamp loader accomplishes this task. This function is also found in eukaryotes.

Lagging-strand synthesis

The discontinuous nature of synthesis on the lagging strand requires the cell to do much more work than on the leading strand (see figure 14.15). Primase is needed to synthesize primers for each Okazaki fragment, and then all these RNA primers need to be removed and replaced with DNA. Finally, the fragments need to be stitched together.

DNA Pol II accomplishes the synthesis of Okazaki fragments. The removal and replacement of primer segments, however, is accomplished by DNA Pol I. Using its 5′-to-3′ exonuclease activity, it can remove primers in front and then replace them by using its usual 5′-to-3′ polymerase activity. The synthesis is primed by the previous Okazaki fragment, which is composed of DNA and has a free 3′ OH that can be extended.

TABLE 14.1	DNA Replication Enzymes of *E. coli*		
Protein	**Role**	**Size (kDa)**	**Molecules per Cell**
Helicase	Unwinds the double helix	300	20
Primase	Synthesizes RNA primers	60	50
Single-strand binding protein	Stabilizes single-stranded regions	74	300
DNA gyrase	Relieves torque	400	250
DNA polymerase III	Synthesizes DNA	≈900	20
DNA polymerase I	Erases primer and fills gaps	103	300
DNA ligase	Joins the ends of DNA segments; DNA repair	74	300

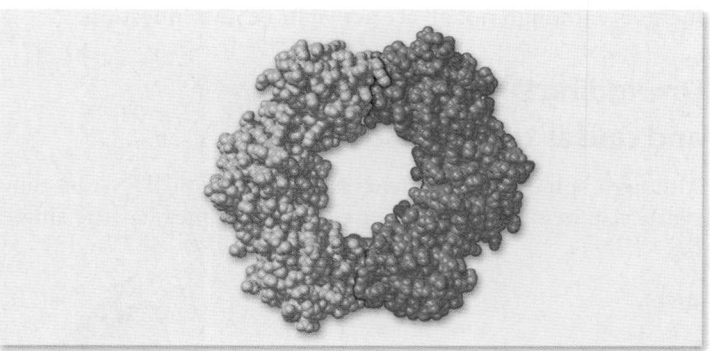

a.

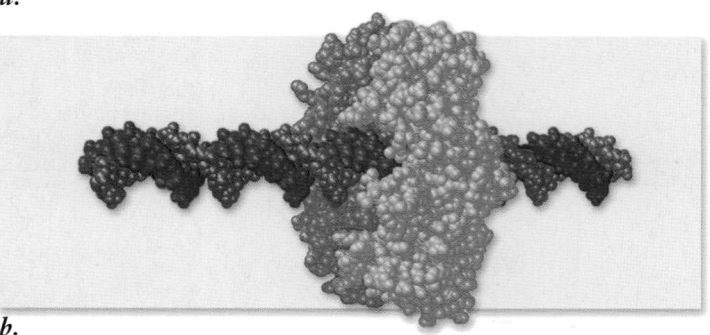

b.

Figure 14.16 The DNA polymerase sliding clamp. *a.* The β subunit forms a ring that can encircle DNA. *b.* The β subunit is shown attached to the DNA. This forms the "sliding clamp" that keeps the polymerase attached to the template.

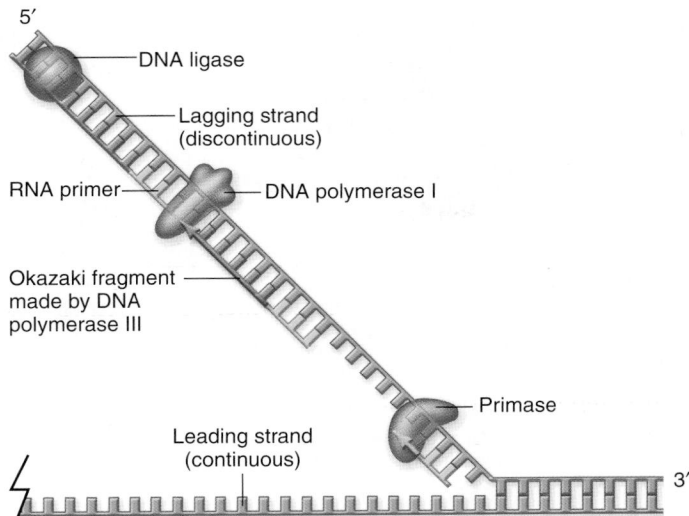

Figure 14.17 Lagging-strand synthesis. The action of primase synthesizes the primers needed by DNA polymerase III (not shown). These primers are removed by DNA polymerase I using its 5′-to-3′ exonuclease activity, then extending the previous Okazaki fragment to replace the RNA. The nick between Okazaki fragments after primer removal is sealed by DNA ligase.

This leaves only the last phosphodiester bond to be formed where synthesis by Pol I ends. This is done by **DNA ligase,** which seals this "nick," eventually joining the Okazaki fragments into complete strands. All of this activity on the lagging strand is summarized in figure 14.17.

 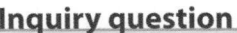

Inquiry question

? What is the role of DNA ligase? What would happen to DNA replication in a cell where this enzyme is not functional?

Termination

Termination occurs at a specific site located roughly opposite *oriC* on the circular chromosome. The last stages of replication produce two daughter molecules that are intertwined like two rings in a chain. These intertwined molecules are unlinked by the same enzyme that relieves torsional strain at the replication fork—DNA gyrase.

The replisome contains all the necessary enzymes for replication

The enzymes involved in DNA replication form a macromolecular assembly called the **replisome.** This assembly can be thought of as the "replication organelle," just as the ribosome is the organelle that synthesizes protein. The replisome has two main subcomponents: the *primosome,* and a complex of two DNA Pol III enzymes, one for each strand. The primosome is composed of primase and helicase, along with a number of accessory proteins. The need for constant priming on the lagging strand explains the need for the primosome complex as part of the replisome.

The two Pol III complexes include two synthetic core subunits, each with its own β subunit. The entire replisome complex is held together by a number of proteins that includes the clamp loader. The clamp loader is required to periodically load a β subunit on the lagging strand and to transfer the Pol III to this new β subunit (figure 14.18).

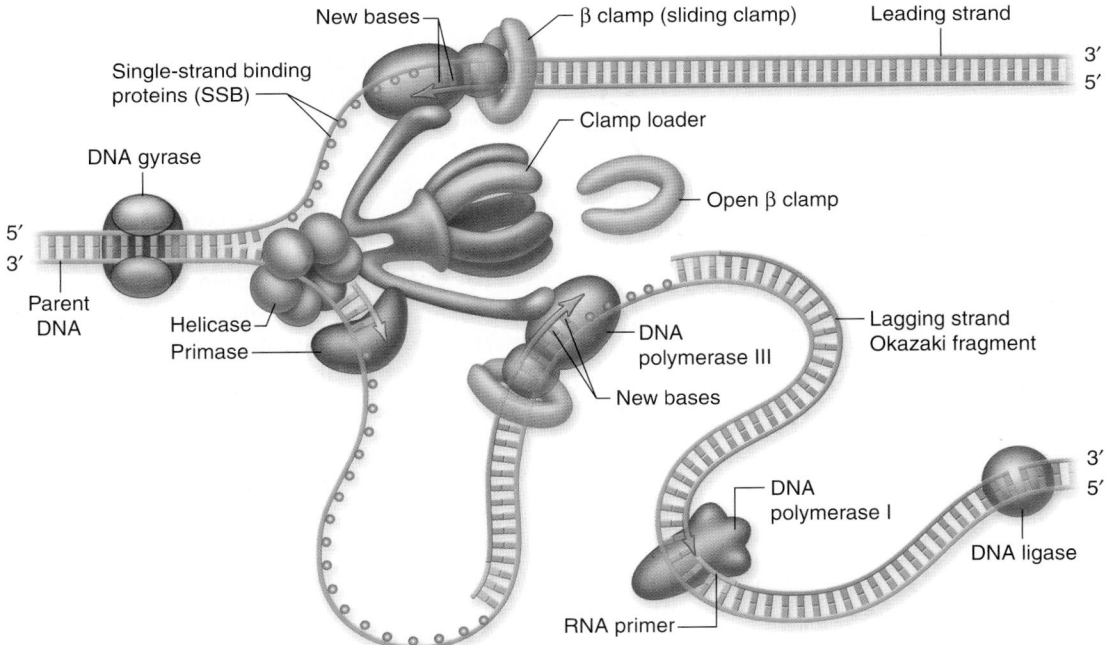

Figure 14.18 The replication fork. A model for the structure of the replication fork with two polymerase III enzymes held together by a large complex of accessory proteins. These include the "clamp loader," which loads the β subunit sliding clamp periodically on the lagging strand. The polymerase III on the lagging strand periodically releases its template and reassociates along with the β clamp. The loop in the lagging-strand template allows both polymerases to move in the same direction despite DNA being antiparallel. Primase, which makes primers for the lagging-strand fragments, and helicase are also associated with the central complex. Polymerase I removes primers and ligase joins the fragments together.

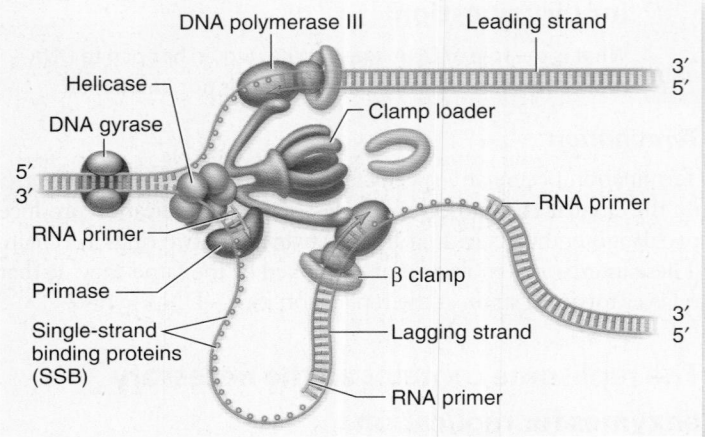

1. A DNA polymerase III enzyme is active on each strand. Primase synthesizes new primers for the lagging strand.

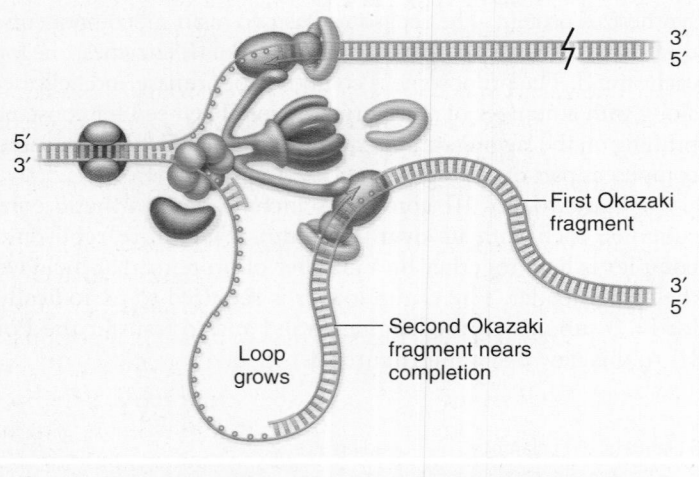

2. The "loop" in the lagging-strand template allows replication to occur 5′-to-3′ on both strands, with the complex moving to the left.

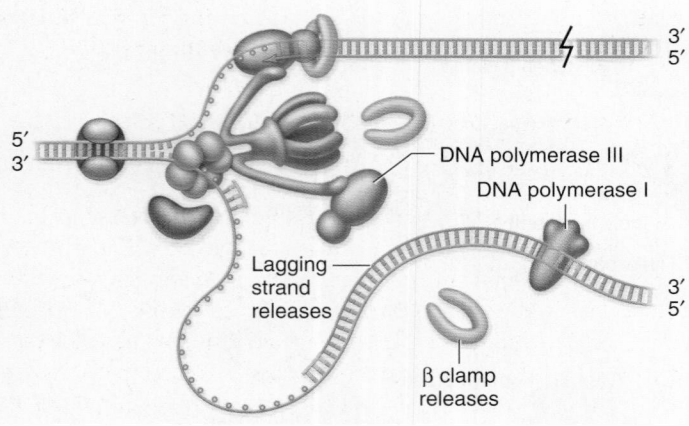

3. When the polymerase III on the lagging strand hits the previously synthesized fragment, it releases the β clamp and the template strand. DNA polymerase I attaches to remove the primer.

Figure 14.19 DNA synthesis by the replisome. The semidiscontinuous synthesis of DNA is illustrated in stages using the model from figure 14.18.

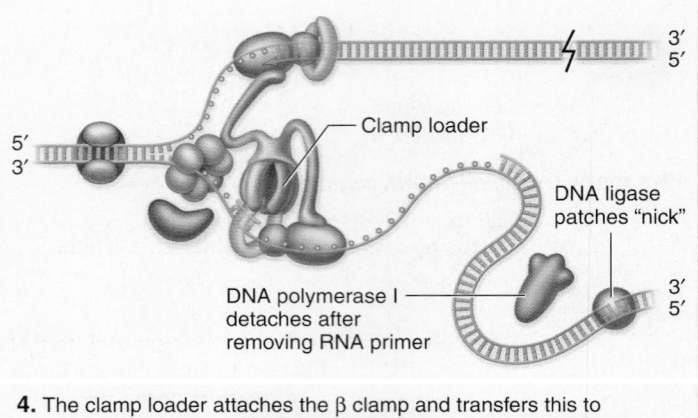

4. The clamp loader attaches the β clamp and transfers this to polymerase III, creating a new loop in the lagging-strand template. DNA ligase joins the fragments after DNA polymerase I removes the primers.

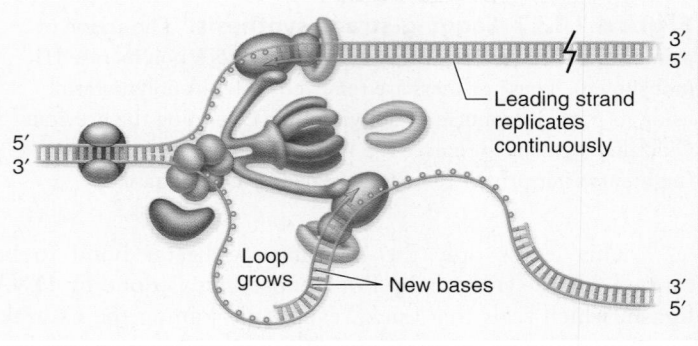

5. After the β clamp is loaded, the DNA polymerase III on the lagging strand adds bases to the next Okazaki fragment.

Even given the difficulties with lagging-strand synthesis, the two Pol III enzymes in the replisome are active on both leading and lagging strands simultaneously. How can the two strands be synthesized in the same direction when the strands are antiparallel? The model first proposed, still with us in some form, involves a loop formed in the lagging strand, so that the polymerases can move in the same direction (see figure 14.18). Current evidence also indicates that this replication complex is probably stationary, with the DNA strand moving through it like thread in a sewing machine, rather than the complex moving along the DNA strands. This stationary complex also pushes the newly synthesized DNA outward, which may aid in chromosome segregation. This process is summarized in figure 14.19.

Learning Outcomes Review 14.4

E. coli has three DNA polymerases: DNA Pol I, II, and III. Synthesis on one strand is discontinuous because DNA is antiparallel, and polymerases only synthesize in the 5′-to-3′ direction. Replication occurs at the replication fork, where the two strands are separated. Assembled here is a massive complex, the replisome, containing DNA polymerase III, primase, helicase, and other proteins. The lagging strand requires DNA polymerase I to remove the primers and replace them with DNA, and ligase to join Okazaki fragments.

■ *How are the nuclease functions of the different polymerases used during replication?*

14.5 Eukaryotic Replication

Learning Outcomes

1. *Compare eukaryotic replication with prokaryotic.*
2. *Explain the function of telomeres.*
3. *Identify the link between telomerase and cell division.*

Eukaryotic replication is complicated by two main factors: the larger amount of DNA organized into multiple chromosomes, and the linear structure of the chromosomes. This process requires new enzymatic activities only for dealing with the ends of chromosomes; otherwise the basic enzymology is the same.

Eukaryotic replication requires multiple origins

The sheer amount of DNA and how it is packaged constitute a problem for eukaryotes (figure 14.20). Eukaryotes usually have multiple chromosomes that are each larger than the *E. coli*

9.09 μm

Figure 14.20 DNA of a single human chromosome. This chromosome has been relieved of most of its packaging proteins, leaving the DNA in its native form. The residual protein scaffolding appears as the dark material in the lower part of the micrograph.

chromosome. If only a single unique origin existed for each chromosome, the length of time necessary for replication would be prohibitive. This problem is solved by the use of multiple origins of replication for each chromosome, resulting in multiple *replicons*.

The origins are not as sequence-specific as *oriC*, and their recognition seems to depend on chromatin structure as well as on sequence. The number of origins used can also be adjusted during the course of development, so that early on, when cell divisions need to be rapid, more origins are activated. Each origin must be used only once per cell cycle.

The enzymology of eukaryotic replication is more complex

The replication machinery of eukaryotes is similar to that found in bacteria, but it is larger and more complex. The initiation phase of replication requires more factors to assemble both helicase and primase complexes onto the template, then load the polymerase with its sliding clamp unit.

The eukaryotic primase is interesting in that it is a complex of both an RNA polymerase and a DNA polymerase. It first makes short RNA primers, then extends these with DNA to produce the final primer. The reason for this added complexity is unclear.

The main replication polymerase itself is also a complex of two different enzymes that work together. One is called *DNA polymerase epsilon* (pol ε) and the other *DNA polymerase delta* (pol δ). The sliding clamp subunit that allows the enzyme complex to stay attached to the template is called PCNA (for proliferating cell nuclear antigen). This unusual name reflects the fact that PCNA was first identified as an antibody-inducing protein in proliferating (dividing) cells. The PCNA sliding clamp forms a trimer, but this structure is similar to the β subunit sliding clamp. The clamp loader is also similar to the bacterial structure. Despite the additional complexity, the action of the replisome is similar to that described earlier for *E. coli*, and the replication fork has essentially the same components.

Archaeal replication proteins are similar to eukaryotic proteins

Despite their lack of a membrane-bounded nucleus, Archaeal replication proteins are more similar to eukaryotes than to bacterial. The main replication polymerase is most similar to eukaryotic pol δ, and the sliding clamp is similar to the PCNA protein. The clamp loading complex is also more similar to eukaryotic than bacterial. The most interesting conclusion from all of these data are that all three domains of life have similar functions involved in replicating chromosomes. All three domains assemble similar protein complexes with clamp loader, sliding clamp, two polymerases, helicase, and primase at the replication fork.

Linear chromosomes have specialized ends

The specialized structures found on the ends of eukaryotic chromosomes are called **telomeres.** These structures protect

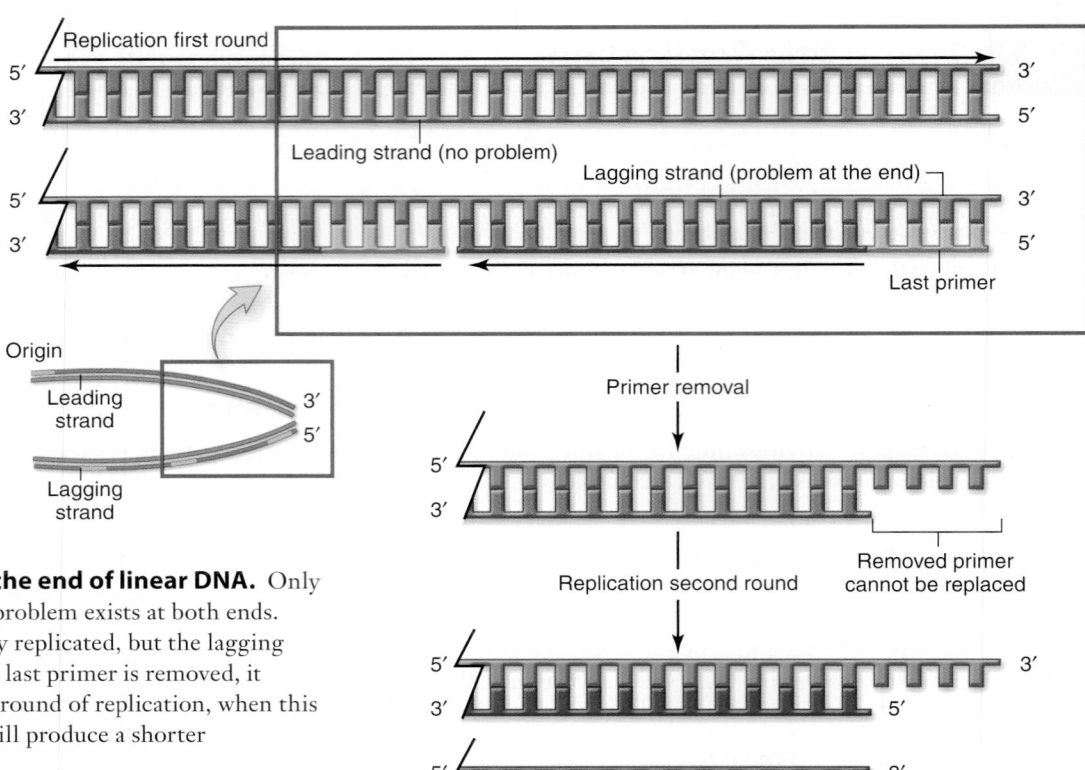

Figure 14.21 Replication of the end of linear DNA. Only one end is shown for simplicity; the problem exists at both ends. The leading strand can be completely replicated, but the lagging strand cannot be finished. When the last primer is removed, it cannot be replaced. During the next round of replication, when this shortened template is replicated, it will produce a shorter chromosome.

the ends of chromosomes from nucleases and maintain the integrity of linear chromosomes. These telomeres are composed of specific DNA sequences, but they are not made by the replication complex.

Replicating ends

The very structure of a linear chromosome causes a cell problems in replicating the ends. The directionality of polymerases, combined with their requirement for a primer, create this problem.

Consider a simple linear molecule like the one in figure 14.21. Replication of one end of each template strand is simple, namely the 5′ end of the leading-strand template. When the polymerase reaches this end, synthesizing in the 5′-to-3′ direction, it eventually runs out of template and is finished.

But on the other strand's end, the 3′ end of the lagging strand, removal of the last primer on this end leaves a gap. This gap cannot be primed, meaning that the polymerase complex cannot finish this end properly. The result would be a gradual shortening of chromosomes with each round of cell division (see figure 14.21).

The action of telomerase

When the sequence of telomeres was determined, they were found to be composed of short repeated sequences of DNA. This repeating nature is easily explained by their synthesis. They are made by an enzyme called **telomerase,** which uses an internal RNA as a template and not the DNA itself (figure 14.22).

Figure 14.22 Action of telomerase. Telomerase contains an internal RNA that the enzyme uses as a template to extend the DNA of the chromosome end. Multiple rounds of synthesis by telomerase produce repeated sequences. This single strand is completed by normal synthesis using it as a template (not shown).

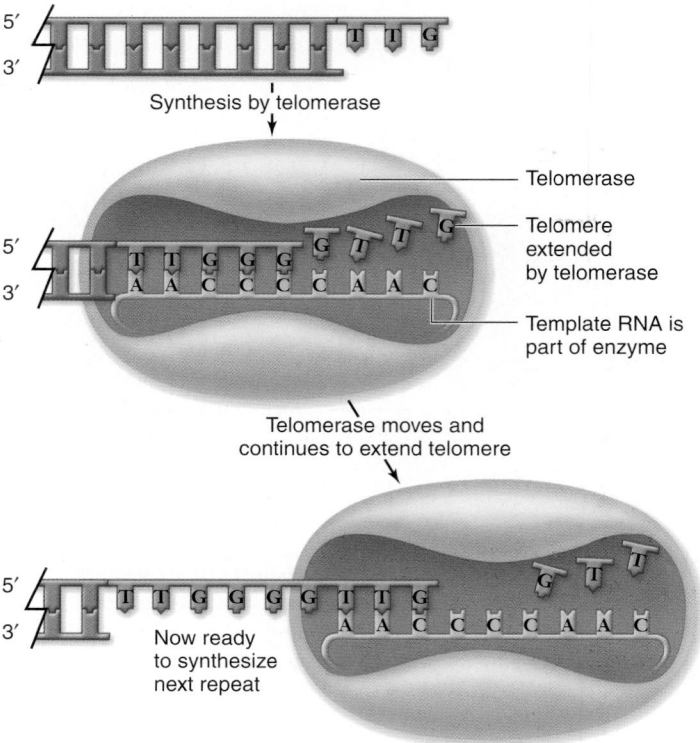

The use of the internal RNA template allows short stretches of DNA to be synthesized, composed of repeated nucleotide sequences complementary to the RNA of the enzyme. The other strand of these repeated units is synthesized by the usual action of the replication machinery copying the strand made by telomerase.

Telomerase, aging, and cancer

A gradual shortening of the ends of chromosomes occurs in the absence of telomerase activity. During embryonic and childhood development in humans, telomerase activity is high, but it is low in most somatic cells of the adult. The exceptions are cells that must divide as part of their function, such as lymphocytes. The activity of telomerase in somatic cells is kept low by preventing the expression of the gene encoding this enzyme.

Evidence for the shortening of chromosomes in the absence of telomerase was obtained by producing mice with no telomerase activity. These mice appear to be normal for up to six generations, but they show steadily decreasing telomere length that eventually leads to nonviable offspring.

This finding indicates a relationship between cell senescence (aging) and telomere length. Normal cells undergo only a specified number of divisions when grown in culture. This limit is at least partially based on telomere length.

Support for the relationship between senescence and telomere length comes from experiments in which telomerase was introduced into fibroblasts in culture. These cells have their lifespan increased relative to controls that have no added telomerase. Interestingly, these cells do not show the hallmarks of malignant cells, indicating that activation of telomerase alone does not make cells malignant.

A relationship has been found, however, between telomerase and cancer. Cancer cells do continue to divide indefinitely, and this would not be possible if their chromosomes were being continually shortened. Cancer cells generally show activation of telomerase, which allows them to maintain telomere length; but this is clearly only one aspect of conditions that allow them to escape normal growth controls.

Inquiry question

? How does the structure of eukaryotic genomes affect replication? Does this introduce problems that are not faced by prokaryotes?

Learning Outcomes Review 14.5

Eukarotic replication is complicated by a large amount of DNA organized into chromosomes, and by the linear nature of chromosomes. Eukaryotes replicate a large amount of DNA in a short time by using multiple origins of replication. Linear chromosomes end in telomeres, and the length of telomeres is correlated with the ability of cells to divide. The enzyme telomerase synthesizes the telomeres. Cancer cells show activation of telomerase, which extends the ability of the cells to divide.

■ *What might be the result of abnormal shortening of telomeres or a lack of telomerase activity?*

Learning Outcomes

1. *Explain why DNA repair is critical for cells.*
2. *Describe the different forms of DNA repair.*

As you learned earlier, many DNA polymerases have 3′-to-5′exonuclease activity that allows "proofreading" of added bases. This action increases the accuracy of replication, but errors still occur. Without error correction mechanisms, cells would accumulate errors at an unacceptable rate, leading to high levels of deleterious or lethal mutations. A balance must exist between the introduction of new variation by mutation, and the effects of deleterious mutations on the individual.

Cells are constantly exposed to DNA-damaging agents

In addition to errors in DNA replication, cells are constantly exposed to agents that can damage DNA. These agents include radiation, such as UV light and X-rays, and chemicals in the environment. Agents that damage DNA can lead to mutations, and any agent that increases the number of mutations above background levels is called a **mutagen.**

The number of potentially mutagenic agents that organisms encounter is huge. Sunlight itself includes radiation in the UV range and is thus mutagenic. Ozone normally screens out much of the harmful UV radiation in sunlight, but some remains. The relationship between sunlight and mutations is shown clearly by the increase in skin cancer in regions of the southern hemisphere that are underneath a seasonal "ozone hole."

Organisms also may encounter mutagens in their diet in the form of either contaminants in food or natural plant products that can damage DNA. When a simple test was designed to detect mutagens, screening of possible sources indicated an amazing diversity of mutagens in the environment and in natural sources. As a result, consumer products are now screened to reduce the load of mutagens we are exposed to, but we cannot escape natural sources.

DNA repair restores damaged DNA

Cells cannot escape exposure to mutagens, but systems have evolved that enable cells to repair some damage. These DNA repair systems are vital to continued existence, whether a cell is a free-living, single-celled organism or part of a complex multicellular organism.

The importance of DNA repair is indicated by the multiplicity of repair systems that have been discovered and characterized. All cells that have been examined show multiple pathways for repairing damaged DNA and for reversing errors that occur during replication. These systems are not perfect, but they do reduce the mutational load on organisms to an acceptable level. In the rest of this section, we illustrate the action of DNA repair by concentrating on two examples drawn from these multiple repair pathways.

Repair can be either specific or nonspecific

DNA repair falls into two general categories: specific and nonspecific. Specific repair systems target a single kind of lesion in DNA and repair only that damage. Nonspecific forms of repair use a single mechanism to repair multiple kinds of lesions in DNA.

Photorepair: A specific repair mechanism

Photorepair is specific for one particular form of damage caused by UV light, namely the *thymine dimer*. Thymine dimers are formed by a photochemical reaction of UV light and adjacent thymine bases in DNA. The UV radiation causes the thymines to react, covalently linking them together: a thymine dimer (figure 14.23).

Repair of these thymine dimers can be accomplished by multiple pathways, including photorepair. In photorepair, an en-

zyme called a *photolyase* absorbs light in the visible range and uses this energy to cleave the thymine dimer. This action restores the two thymines to their original state (see figure 14.23). It is interesting that sunlight in the UV range can cause this damage, and sunlight in the visible range can be used to repair the damage. Photorepair does not occur in cells deprived of visible light.

The photolyase enzyme has been found in many different species, ranging from bacteria, to single-celled eukaryotes, to humans. The ubiquitous nature of this enzyme illustrates the importance of this form of repair. For as long as cells have existed on Earth, they have been exposed to UV light and its potential to damage DNA.

Excision repair: A nonspecific repair mechanism

A common form of nonspecific repair is **excision repair.** In this pathway, a damaged region is removed, or excised, and is then replaced by DNA synthesis (figure 14.24). In *E. coli*, this action is accomplished by proteins encoded by the *uvr A, B,* and

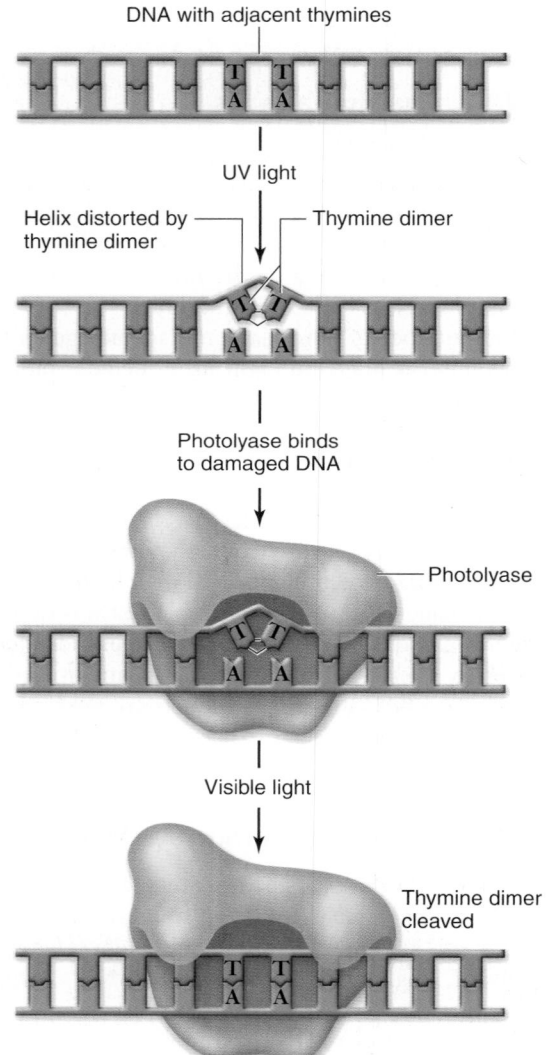

DNA with adjacent thymines

UV light

Helix distorted by thymine dimer — Thymine dimer

Photolyase binds to damaged DNA

— Photolyase

Visible light

Thymine dimer cleaved

Figure 14.23 Repair of thymine dimer by photorepair.
UV light can catalyze a photochemical reaction to form a covalent bond between two adjacent thymines, thereby creating a thymine dimer. A photolyase enzyme recognizes the damage and binds to the thymine dimer. The enzyme absorbs visible light and uses the energy to cleave the thymine dimer.

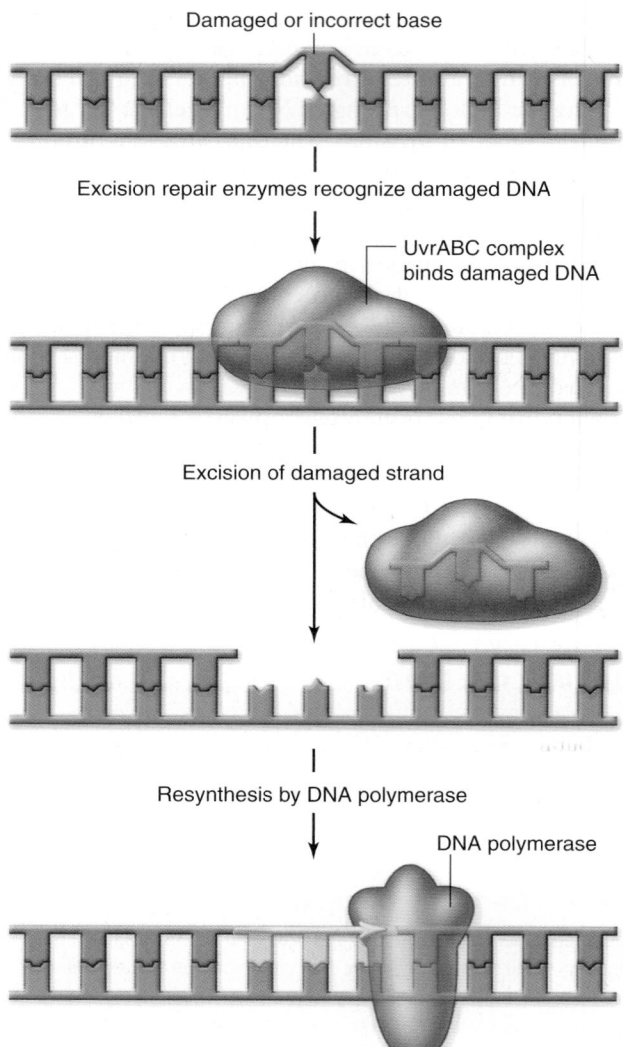

Damaged or incorrect base

Excision repair enzymes recognize damaged DNA

UvrABC complex binds damaged DNA

Excision of damaged strand

Resynthesis by DNA polymerase

DNA polymerase

Figure 14.24 Repair of damaged DNA by excision repair. Damaged DNA is recognized by the uvr complex, which binds to the damaged region and removes it. Synthesis by DNA polymerase replaces the damaged region. DNA ligase finishes the process (not shown).

C genes. Although these genes were identified based on mutations that increased sensitivity of the cell to UV light (hence the "uvr" in their names), their proteins can act on damage due to other mutagens.

Excision repair follows three steps: (1) recognition of damage, (2) removal of the damaged region, and (3) resynthesis using the information on the undamaged strand as a template (see figure 14.24). Recognition and excision are accomplished by the UvrABC complex. The UvrABC complex binds to damaged DNA and then cleaves a single strand on either side of the damage, removing it. In the synthesis stage, DNA pol I or pol II replaces the damaged DNA. This restores the original information in the damaged strand by using the information in the complementary strand.

Other repair pathways

Cells have other forms of nonspecific repair, and these fall into two categories: error-free and error-prone. It may seem strange to have an error-prone pathway, but it can be thought of as a last-ditch effort to save a cell that has been exposed to such massive damage that it has overwhelmed the error-free systems. In fact, this system in *E. coli* is part of what is called the "SOS response."

Cells can also repair damage that produces breaks in DNA. These systems use enzymes related to those that are involved in recombination during meiosis (see chapter 11). It is thought that recombination uses enzymes that originally evolved for DNA repair.

The number of different systems and the wide spectrum of damage that can be repaired illustrate the importance of maintaining the integrity of the genome. Accurate replication of the genome is useless if a cell cannot reverse errors that can occur during this process or repair damage due to environmental causes.

Inquiry question

? Cells are constantly exposed to DNA-damaging agents, ranging from UV light to by-products of oxidative metabolism. How does the cell deal with this, and what would happen if the cell had no way of dealing with this?

Learning Outcomes Review 14.6

The ability to repair DNA is critical because of replication errors and the constant presence of damaging agents that can cause mutation. Cells have multiple repair pathways; some of these systems are specific for a single type of damage, such as photorepair that reverses thymine dimers caused by UV light. Other systems are nonspecific, such as excision repair that removes and replaces damaged regions.

■ *Could a cell survive with no form of DNA repair?*

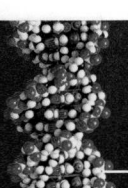

Chapter Review

14.1 The Nature of the Genetic Material

Griffith finds that bacterial cells can be transformed.
Nonvirulent *S. pneumoniae* could take up an unknown substance from a virulent strain and become virulent.

Avery, MacLeod, and McCarty identify the transforming principle.
The transforming substance could be inactivated by DNA-digesting enzymes, but not by protein-digesting enzymes.

Hershey and Chase demonstrate that phage genetic material is DNA.
Radioactive labeling showed that the infectious agent of phage is its DNA, and not its protein.

14.2 DNA Structure

DNA's components were known, but its three-dimensional structure was a mystery.
The nucleotide building blocks for DNA contain deoxyribose and the bases adenine (A), guanine (G), cytosine (C), and thymine (T). Phosphodiester bonds are formed between the 5' phosphate of one nucleotide and the 3' hydroxyl of another nucleotide (see figure 14.4).

Chargaff, Franklin, and Wilkins obtained some structural evidence.
Chargaff found equal amounts of adenine and thymine, and of cytosine and guanine, in DNA. The bases exist primarily in keto and enol forms that exhibit hydrogen bonding. X-ray diffraction studies by Franklin and Wilkins indicated that DNA had a helical structure.

The Watson-Crick model fits the available evidence (see figures 14.8 and 14.9).
DNA consists of two antiparallel polynucleotide strands wrapped about a common helical axis. These strands are held together by hydrogen bonds forming specific base pairs (A/T and G/C). The two strands are complementary; one strand can specify the other.

14.3 Basic Characteristics of DNA Replication

Meselson and Stahl demonstrate the semiconservative mechanism (see figure 14.11).
Semiconservative replication uses each strand of a DNA molecule to specify the synthesis of a new strand. Meselson and Stahl showed this by using a heavy isotope of nitrogen and separating the replication products. Replication produces two new molecules each composed of one new strand and one old strand.

DNA replication requires a template, nucleotides, and a polymerase enzyme.
All new DNA molecules are produced by DNA polymerase copying a template. All known polymerases synthesize new DNA in the 5'-to-3' direction. These enzymes also require a primer. The building blocks used in replication are deoxynucleotide triphosphates with high-energy bonds; they do not require any additional energy.

14.4 Prokaryotic Replication

Prokaryotic replication starts at a single origin.
The *E. coli* origin has AT-rich sequences that are easily opened. The chromosome and its origin form a replicon.

E. coli has at least three different DNA polymerases.
Some DNA polymerases can also degrade DNA from one end, called exonuclease activity. Pol I, II, and III all have 3′-to-5′ exonuclease activity that can remove mispaired bases. Pol I can remove bases in the 5′-to-3′ direction, important to removing RNA primers.

Unwinding DNA requires energy and causes torsional strain.
DNA helicase uses energy from ATP to unwind DNA. The torsional strain introduced is removed by the enzyme DNA gyrase.

Replication is semidiscontinuous.
Replication is discontinuous on one strand (see figure 14.15). The continuous strand is called the leading strand, and the discontinuous strand is called the lagging strand.

Synthesis occurs at the replication fork.
The partial opening of a DNA strand forms two single-stranded regions called the replication fork. At the fork, synthesis on the leading strand requires a single primer, and the polymerase stays attached to the template because of the β subunit that acts as a sliding clamp. On the lagging strand, DNA primase adds primers periodically, and DNA Pol III synthesizes the Okazaki fragments. DNA Pol I removes primer segments, and DNA ligase joins the fragments.

The replisome contains all the necessary enzymes for replication.
The replisome consists of two copies of Pol III, DNA primase, DNA helicase, and a number of accessory proteins. It moves in one direction by creating a loop in the lagging strand, allowing the antiparallel template strands to be copied in the same direction (see figures 14.18 and 14.19).

14.5 Eukaryotic Replication

Eukaryotic replication requires multiple origins.
The sheer size and organization of eukaryotic chromosomes requires multiple origins of replication to be able to replicate DNA in the time available in S phase.

The enzymology of eukaryotic replication is more complex.
The eukaryotic primase synthesizes a short stretch of RNA and then switches to making DNA. This primer is extended by the main replication polymerase, which is a complex of two enzymes. The sliding clamp subunit was originally identified as protein produced by proliferating cells and is called PCNA.

Archaeal replication proteins are similar to eukaryotic proteins.
The replication proteins of archaea, including the sliding clamp, clamp loader, and DNA polymerases, are more similar to those of eukaryotes than to prokaryotes.

Linear chromosomes have specialized ends.
The ends of linear chromosomes are called telomeres. They are made by telomerase, not by the replication complex. Telomerase contains an internal RNA that acts as a template to extend the DNA of the chromosome end. Adult cells lack telomerase activity, and telomere shortening correlates with senescence.

14.6 DNA Repair

Cells are constantly exposed to DNA-damaging agents.
Errors from replication and damage induced by agents such as UV light and chemical mutagens can lead to mutations.

DNA repair restores damaged DNA.
Without repair mechanisms, cells would accumulate mutations until inviability occurred.

Repair can be either specific or nonspecific.
The enzyme photolyase uses energy from visible light to cleave thymine dimers caused by UV light. Excision repair is nonspecific. In prokaryotes, the uvr system can remove a damaged region of DNA.

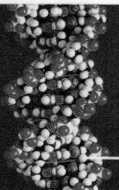

Review Questions

UNDERSTAND

1. What was the key finding from Griffith's experiments using live and heat-killed pathogenic bacteria?
   a. Bacteria with a smooth coat could kill mice.
   b. Bacteria with a rough coat are not lethal.
   c. DNA is the genetic material.
   d. Genetic material can be transferred from dead to live bacteria.

2. Which of the following is *not* a component of DNA?
   a. The pyrimidine uracil   c. The purine adenine
   b. Five-carbon sugars   d. Phosphate groups

3. Chargaff studied the composition of DNA from different sources and found that
   a. the number of phosphate groups always equals the number of five-carbon sugars.
   b. the proportions of A equal that of C and G equals T.
   c. the proportions of A equal that of T and G equals C.
   d. purines bind to pyrimidines.

4. The bonds that hold two complementary strands of DNA together are
   a. hydrogen bonds.   c. ionic bonds.
   b. peptide bonds.   d. phosphodiester bonds.

5. The basic mechanism of DNA replication is semiconservative with two new molecules,
    a. each with new strands.
    b. one with all new strands and one with all old strands.
    c. each with one new and one old strand.
    d. each with a mixture of old and new strands.

6. One common feature of all DNA polymerases is that they
    a. synthesize DNA in the 3′-to-5′ direction.
    b. synthesize DNA in the 5′-to-3′ direction.
    c. synthesize DNA in both directions by switching strands.
    d. do not require a primer.

7. Which of the following is *not* part of the Watson–Crick model of the structure of DNA?
    a. DNA is composed of two strands.
    b. The two DNA strands are oriented in parallel (5′-to-3′).
    c. Purines bind to pyrimidines.
    d. DNA forms a double helix.

APPLY

1. If one strand of a DNA is: 5′ ATCGTTAAGCGAGTCA 3′, then the complementary strand would be:
    a. 5′ TAGCAATTCGCTCAGT 3′.
    b. 5′ ACTGAGCGAATTGCTA 3′.
    c. 5′ TGACTCGCTTAACGAT 3′.
    d. 5′ ATCGTTAAGCGAGTCA 3′.

2. Hershey and Chase used radioactive phosphorus and sulfur to
    a. label DNA and protein with the same molecule.
    b. differentially label DNA and protein.
    c. identify the transforming principle.
    d. Both (b) and (c) are correct.

3. The Meselson and Stahl experiment used a density label to be able to
    a. determine the directionality of DNA replication.
    b. differentially label DNA and protein.
    c. distinguish between newly replicated and old strands.
    d. distinguish between replicated DNA and RNA primers.

4. The difference in leading- versus lagging-strand synthesis is a consequence of
    a. only the physical structure of DNA.
    b. only the activity of DNA polymerase enzymes.
    c. both the physical structure of DNA and the action of polymerase enzyme.
    d. the larger size of the lagging strand.

5. If the activity of DNA ligase was removed from replication, this would have a greater affect on
    a. synthesis on the lagging strand versus the leading strand.
    b. synthesis on the leading strand versus the lagging strand.
    c. priming of DNA synthesis versus actual DNA synthesis.
    d. photorepair of DNA versus DNA replication.

6. Successful DNA synthesis requires all of the following *except*
    a. helicase.   b. endonuclease.
    c. DNA primase.   d. DNA ligase.

7. The synthesis of telomeres
    a. uses DNA polymerase, but without the sliding clamp.
    b. uses enzymes involved in DNA repair.
    c. requires telomerase, which does not need a template.
    d. requires telomerase, which uses an internal RNA as a template.

8. Which type of enzyme is involved in excision repair?
    a. Photolyase   c. Endonuclease
    b. DNA polymerase III   d. Telomerase

SYNTHESIZE

1. The work by Griffith provided the first indication that DNA was the genetic material. Review the four experiments outlined in figure 14.1. Predict the likely outcome for the following variations on this classic research.
    a. Heat-killed pathogenic and heat-killed nonpathogenic
    b. Heat-killed pathogenic and live nonpathogenic in the presence of an enzyme that digests proteins (proteases)
    c. Heat-killed pathogenic and live nonpathogenic in the presence of an enzyme that digests DNA (endonuclease)

2. In the Meseleson–Stahl experiment, a control experiment was done to show that the hybrid bands after one round of replication were in fact two complete strands, one heavy and one light. Using the same experimental setup as detailed in the text, how can this be addressed?

3. Enzyme function is critically important for the proper replication of DNA. Predict the consequence of a loss of function for each of the following enzymes.
    a. DNA gyrase   c. DNA ligase
    b. DNA polymerase III   d. DNA polymerase I

ONLINE RESOURCE

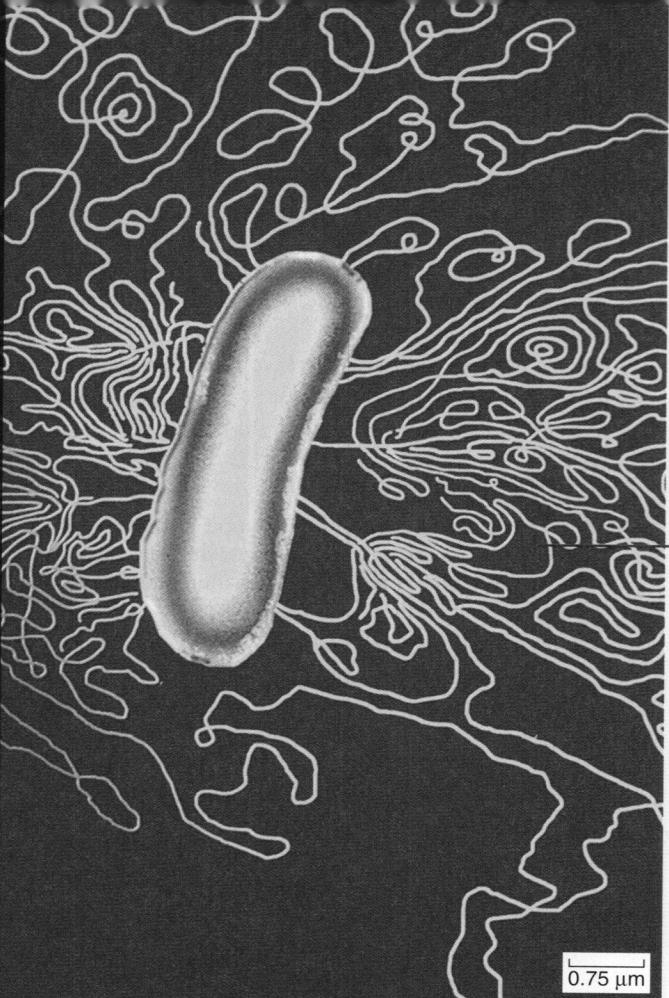

0.75 μm

Chapter 15

Genes and How They Work

Chapter Outline

15.1 The Nature of Genes

15.2 The Genetic Code

15.3 Prokaryotic Transcription

15.4 Eukaryotic Transcription

15.5 Eukaryotic pre-mRNA Splicing

15.6 The Structure of tRNA and Ribosomes

15.7 The Process of Translation

15.8 Summarizing Gene Expression

15.9 Mutation: Altered Genes

Introduction

You've seen how genes specify traits and how those traits can be followed in genetic crosses. You've also seen that the information in genes resides in the DNA molecule; the picture above shows all the DNA within the entire E. coli chromosome. Information in DNA is replicated by the cell and then partitioned equally during the process of cell division. The information in DNA is much like a blueprint for a building. The construction of the building uses the information in the blueprint, but requires building materials and carpenters and other skilled laborers using a variety of tools working together to actually construct the building. Similarly, the information in DNA requires nucleotide and amino acid building blocks, multiple forms of RNA, and many proteins acting in a coordinated fashion to make up the structure of a cell.

We now turn to the nature of the genes themselves and how cells extract the information in DNA in the process of gene expression. Gene expression can be thought of as the conversion of genotype into the phenotype.

15.1 The Nature of Genes

Learning Outcomes

1. Describe the evidence for the one-gene/one-polypeptide hypothesis.
2. Distinguish between transcription and translation.
3. List the roles played by RNA in gene expression.

We know that DNA encodes proteins, but this knowledge alone tells us little about how the information in DNA can control cellular functions. Researchers had evidence that genetic mutations affected proteins, and in particular enzymes, long before the structure and code of DNA was known. In this section we review the evidence of the link between genes and enzymes.

Garrod concluded that inherited disorders can involve specific enzymes

In 1902, the British physician Archibald Garrod noted that certain diseases among his patients seemed to be more prevalent in particular families. By examining several generations of these families, he found that some of the diseases behaved as though they were the product of simple recessive alleles. Garrod concluded that these disorders were Mendelian traits, and that they had resulted from changes in the hereditary information in an ancestor of the affected families.

Garrod investigated several of these disorders in detail. In alkaptonuria, patients produced urine that contained homogentisic acid (alkapton). This substance oxidized rapidly when exposed to air, turning the urine black. In normal individuals, homogentisic acid is broken down into simpler substances. With considerable insight, Garrod concluded that patients suffering from alkaptonuria lack the enzyme necessary to catalyze this breakdown. He speculated that many other inherited diseases might also reflect enzyme deficiencies.

Beadle and Tatum showed that genes specify enzymes

From Garrod's finding, it took but a short leap of intuition to surmise that the information encoded within the DNA of chromosomes acts to specify particular enzymes. This point was not actually established, however, until 1941, when a series of experiments by George Beadle and Edward Tatum at Stanford University provided definitive evidence. Beadle and Tatum deliberately set out to create mutations in chromosomes and verified that they behaved in a Mendelian fashion in crosses. These alterations to single genes were analyzed for their effects on the organism (figure 15.1).

Neurospora crassa, the bread mold

One of the reasons Beadle and Tatum's experiments produced clear-cut results was their choice of experimental organism, the bread mold *Neurospora crassa*. This fungus can be grown readily in the laboratory on a defined medium consisting of only a carbon source (glucose), a vitamin (biotin), and inorganic salts. This type of medium is called "minimal" because it represents the minimal requirements to support growth. Any cells that can grow on minimal medium must be able to synthesize all necessary biological molecules.

Beadle and Tatum exposed *Neurospora* spores to X-rays, expecting that the DNA in some of the spores would experience damage in regions encoding the ability to make compounds needed for normal growth (see figure 15.1). Such a mutation would cause cells to be unable to grow on minimal medium. Such mutations are called **nutritional mutations** because cells carrying them grow only if the medium is supplemented with additional nutrients.

Nutritional mutants

To identify mutations causing metabolic deficiencies, Beadle and Tatum placed subcultures of individual fungal cells grown on a rich medium onto minimal medium. Any cells that had lost the ability to make compounds necessary for growth would not grow on minimal medium. Using this approach, Beadle and Tatum succeeded in isolating and identifying many nutritional mutants.

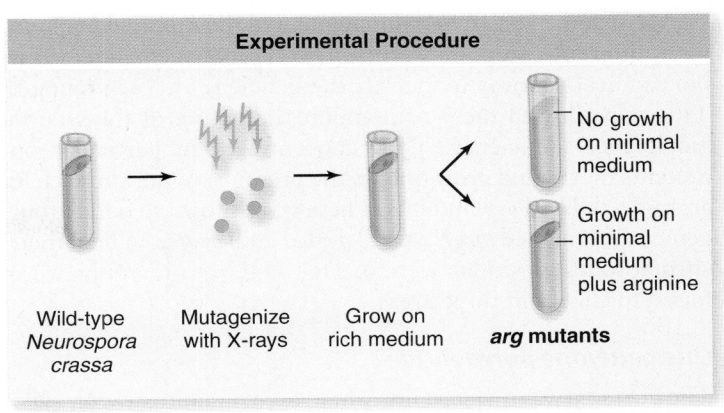

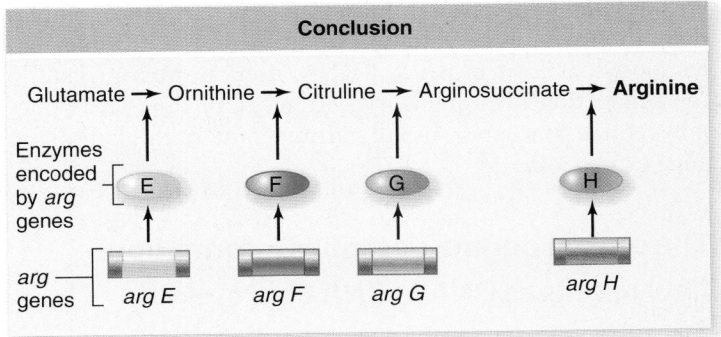

Figure 15.1 The Beadle and Tatum experiment.
Wild-type *Neurospora* were mutagenized with X-rays to produce mutants deficient in the synthesis of arginine (top panel). The specific defect in each mutant was identified by growing on medium supplemented with intermediates in the biosynthetic pathway for arginine (middle panel). A mutant will grow only on media supplemented with an intermediate produced after the defective enzyme in the pathway for each mutant. The enzymes in the pathway can then be correlated with genes on chromosomes (bottom panel).

Next, the researchers supplemented the minimal medium with different compounds known to be intermediates in this biochemical pathway to identify the deficiency in each mutant. This step allowed them to pinpoint the nature of the strain's biochemical deficiency. They concentrated in particular on mutants that would grow only in the presence of the amino acid arginine, dubbed *arg* mutants. These were shown to define four genes they named *argE, argF, argG,* and *argH*. When their chromosomal positions were located, the *arg* mutations were found to cluster in three areas.

One gene/one polypeptide

The next step was to determine where each mutation was blocked in the biochemical pathway for arginine biosynthesis. To do this, they supplemented the medium with each intermediate in the pathway to see which intermediate would support a mutant's growth. If the mutation affects an enzyme in the pathway that acts prior to the intermediate used as a supplement, then growth should be supported—but not if the mutation affects a step after the intermediate used (see figure 15.1). For each enzyme in the arginine biosynthetic pathway, Beadle and Tatum were able to isolate a mutant strain with a defective form of that enzyme. The mutation was always located at one of a few specific chromosomal sites, and each mutation had a unique location. Thus, each of the mutants they examined had a defect in a single enzyme, caused by a mutation at a single site on a chromosome.

Beadle and Tatum concluded that genes specify the structure of enzymes, and that each gene encodes the structure of one enzyme (see figure 15.1). They called this relationship the *one-gene/one-enzyme hypothesis.* Today, because many enzymes contain multiple polypeptide subunits, each encoded by a separate gene, the relationship is more commonly referred to as the **one-gene/one-polypeptide hypothesis.** This hypothesis clearly states the molecular relationship between genotype and phenotype.

As you learn more about genomes and gene expression, you'll find that this clear relationship is overly simple. As described later in this chapter, eukaryotic genes are more complex than those of prokaryotes. In addition, some enzymes are composed, at least in part, of RNA, itself an intermediate in the production of proteins. Nevertheless, this one-gene/one-polypeptide concept is a useful starting point for thinking about gene expression.

The central dogma describes information flow in cells as DNA to RNA to protein

The conversion of genotype to phenotype requires information stored in DNA to be converted to protein. The nature of information flow in cells was first described by Francis Crick as the **central dogma of molecular biology.** Information passes in one direction from the gene (DNA) to an RNA copy of the gene, and the RNA copy directs the sequential assembly of a chain of amino acids into a protein (figure 15.2). Stated briefly,

$$DNA \longrightarrow RNA \longrightarrow protein$$

The central dogma provides an intellectual framework that describes information flow in biological systems. We call the

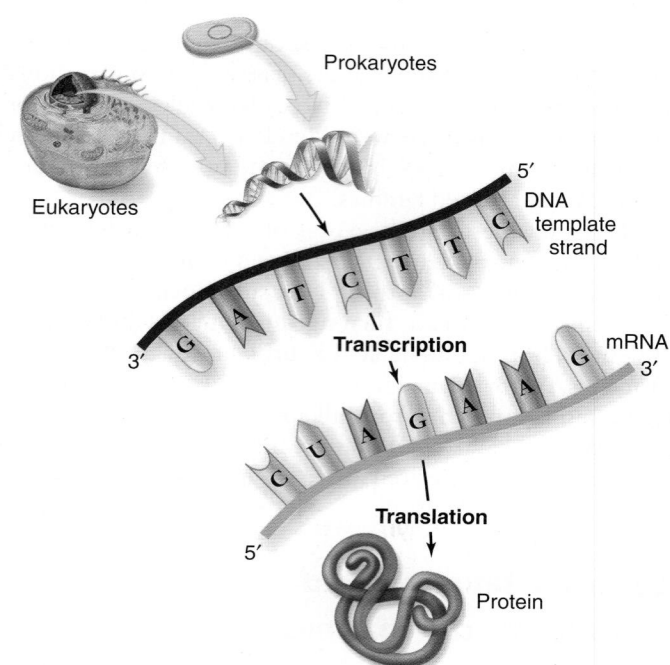

Figure 15.2 The central dogma of molecular biology. DNA is transcribed to make mRNA, which is translated to make a protein.

DNA-to-RNA step **transcription** because it produces an exact copy of the DNA, much as a legal transcription contains the exact words of a court proceeding. The RNA-to-protein step is termed **translation** because it requires translating from the nucleic acid to the protein "languages."

Since the original formulation of the central dogma, a class of viruses called **retroviruses** was discovered that can convert their RNA genome into a DNA copy, using the viral enzyme **reverse transcriptase.** This conversion violates the direction of information flow of the central dogma, and the discovery forced an updating of the possible flow of information to include this "reverse" flow from RNA to DNA.

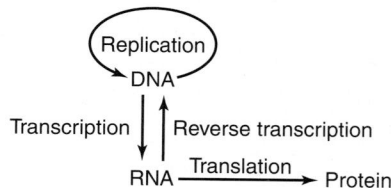

Transcription makes an RNA copy of DNA

The process of transcription produces an RNA copy of the information in DNA. That is, transcription is the DNA-directed synthesis of RNA by the enzyme RNA polymerase (figure 15.3). This process uses the principle of complementarity, described in chapter 14, to use DNA as a template to make RNA.

Because DNA is double-stranded and RNA is single-stranded, only one of the two DNA strands needs to be copied. We call the strand that is copied the **template strand.** The RNA transcript's sequence is complementary to the template strand. The strand of DNA not used as a template is called the **coding strand.** It has the same sequence as the RNA transcript,

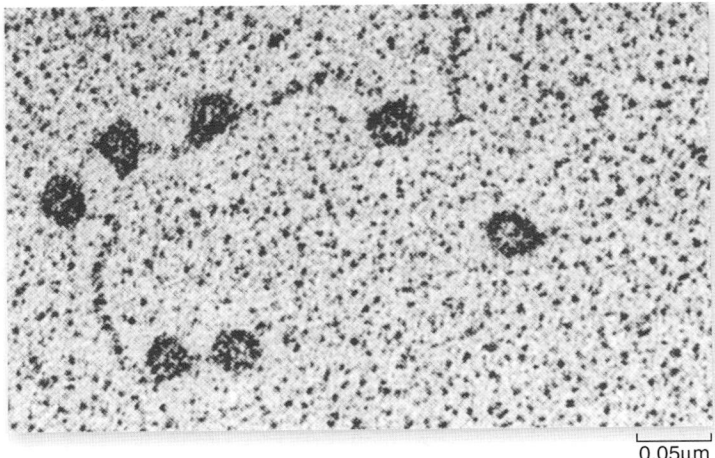

Figure 15.3 RNA polymerase. In this electron micrograph, the dark circles are RNA polymerase molecules synthesizing RNA from a DNA template.

except that U (uracil) in the RNA is T (thymine) in the DNA-coding strand. Another naming convention for the two strands of the DNA is to call the coding strand the sense strand, as it has the same "sense" as the RNA. The template strand would then be the antisense strand.

Coding (sense) 5′–TCAGCCGTCAGCT–3′ ⎤
                                                    ⎬ DNA
Template (antisense) 3′–AGTCGGCAGTCGA–5′ ⎦

                         ↓ Transcription

Coding 5′–UCAGCCGUCAGCU– 3′ mRNA

The RNA transcript used to direct the synthesis of polypeptides is termed *messenger RNA (mRNA)*. Its name reflects its use by the cell to carry the DNA message to the ribosome for processing.

> **Inquiry question**
>
> **?** It is widely accepted that RNA polymerase has no proofreading capacity. Would you expect high or low levels of error in transcription compared with DNA replication? Why do you think it is more important for DNA polymerase than for RNA polymerase to proofread?

Translation uses information in RNA to synthesize proteins

The process of translation is by necessity much more complex than transcription. In this case, RNA cannot be used as a direct template for a protein because there is no complementarity—that is, a sequence of amino acids cannot be aligned to an RNA template based on any kind of "chemical fit." Molecular geneticists suggested that some kind of adapter molecule must exist that can interact with both RNA and amino acids, and *transfer RNA (tRNA)* was found to fill this role. This need for an intermediary adds a level of complexity to the process that is not seen in either DNA replication or transcription of RNA.

Translation takes place on the ribosome, the cellular protein-synthesis machinery, and it requires the participation of multiple kinds of RNA and many proteins. Here we provide an outline of the processes; all are described in detail in the sections that follow.

RNA has multiple roles in gene expression

All RNAs are synthesized from a DNA template by transcription. Gene expression requires the participation of multiple kinds of RNA, each with different roles in the overall process. Here is a brief summary of these roles, which are described in detail later.

Messenger RNA. Even before the details of gene expression were unraveled, geneticists recognized that there must be an intermediate form of the information in DNA that can be transported out of the eukaryotic nucleus to the cytoplasm for ribosomal processing. This hypothesis was called the "messenger hypothesis," and we retain this language in the name *messenger RNA* (mRNA).

Ribosomal RNA. The class of RNA found in ribosomes is called **ribosomal RNA (rRNA).** There are multiple forms of rRNA, and rRNA is found in both ribosomal subunits. This rRNA is critical to the function of the ribosome.

Transfer RNA. The intermediary adapter molecule between mRNA and amino acids, as mentioned earlier, is **transfer RNA (tRNA).** Transfer RNA molecules have amino acids covalently attached to one end and an anticodon that can base-pair with an mRNA codon at the other. The tRNAs act to interpret information in mRNA and to help position the amino acids on the ribosome.

Small nuclear RNA. Small nuclear RNAs (snRNAs) are part of the machinery that is involved in nuclear processing of eukaryotic "pre-mRNA." We discuss this splicing reaction later in the chapter.

SRP RNA. In eukaryotes, where some proteins are synthesized by ribosomes on the rough endoplasmic reticulum (RER), this process is mediated by the **signal recognition particle,** or **SRP,** described later in the chapter. The SRP contains both RNA and proteins.

Micro-RNA. This class of RNA was discovered relatively recently. These very short RNAs, called **micro-RNAs,** or **miRNA,** have gone from unknown to a major class of regulatory molecules in a very short period of time.

> ### Learning Outcomes Review 15.1
> Garrod showed that altered enzymes can cause metabolic disorders. Beadle and Tatum demonstrated that each gene encodes a unique enzyme. Genetic information flows from DNA (genes) to protein (enzymes) using messenger RNA as an intermediate. Transcription converts information in DNA into an RNA transcript, and translation converts this information into protein. RNA comes in several varieties having different functions; these include mRNA (the transcript), tRNA (the intermediary), and rRNA (in ribosomes), as well as snRNA, SNP RNA, and micro-RNA.
>
> ■ *Why do cells need an adapter molecule like tRNA between RNA and protein?*

The Genetic Code

How does the order of nucleotides in a DNA molecule encode the information that specifies the order of amino acids in a polypeptide? The answer to this essential question came in 1961, through an experiment led by Francis Crick and Sydney Brenner. That experiment was so elegant and the result so critical to understanding the genetic code that we describe it here in detail.

The code is read in groups of three

Crick and Brenner reasoned that the genetic code most likely consisted of a series of blocks of information called **codons,** each corresponding to an amino acid in the encoded protein. They further hypothesized that the information within one codon was probably a sequence of three nucleotides. With four DNA nucleotides (G, C, T, and A), using two in each codon can produce only 4^2, or 16, different codons—not enough to code for 20 amino acids. However, three nucleotides results in 4^3, or 64, different combinations of three, more than enough.

Spaced or unspaced codons?

In theory, the sequence of codons in a gene could be punctuated with nucleotides between the codons that are not used, like the spaces that separate the words in this sentence. Alternatively, the codons could lie immediately adjacent to each other, forming a continuous sequence of nucleotides.

If the information in the genetic message is separated by spaces, then altering any single word would not affect the entire sentence. In contrast, if all of the words are run together but read in groups of three, then any alteration that is not in groups of three would alter the entire sentence. These two ways of using information in DNA imply different methods of translating the information into protein.

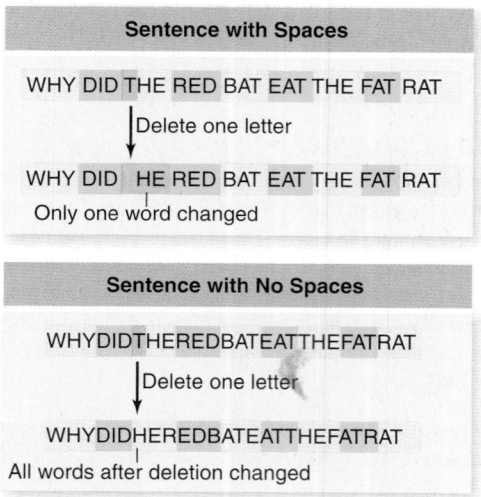

Determining that codons are unspaced

To choose between these alternative mechanisms, Crick and his colleagues used a chemical to create mutations that caused single-base insertions or deletions from a viral DNA molecule. They then showed that combining an insertion with a deletion restored function even though either one individually displayed loss of function. In this case, only the region between the insertion or deletion would be altered. By choosing a region of the gene that encoded a part of the protein not critical to function, this small change did not cause a change in phenotype.

When they combined a single deletion or two deletions near each other, the genetic message shifted, altering all of the amino acids after the deletion. When they made three deletions,

Hypothesis: *The genetic code is read in groups of three bases.*

Prediction: *If the genetic code is read in groups of three, then deletion of one or two bases would shift the reading frame after the deletion. Deletion of three bases, however, would produce a protein with a single amino acid deleted but no change downstream.*

Test: *Single-base deletion mutants are collected, each of which exhibits a mutant phenotype. Three of these deletions in a single region are combined to assess the effect of deletion of three bases.*

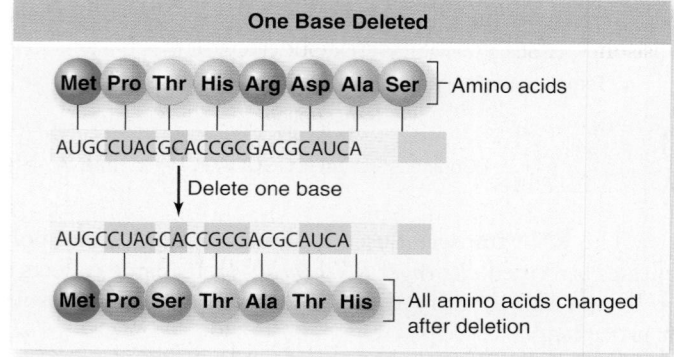

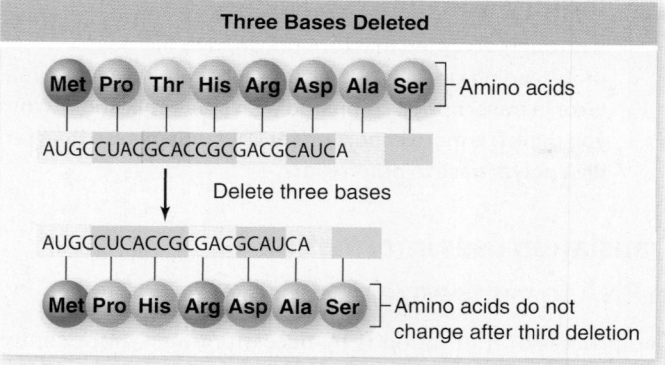

Result: *The combination of three deletions does not have the same drastic effect as the loss of one or two bases.*

Conclusion: *The genetic code is read in groups of three.*

Further Experiments: *If you also had mutants with one base additions, what would be the effect of combining a deletion and an addition?*

Figure 15.4 The genetic code is triplet.

however, the protein after the deletions was normal. They obtained the same results when they made additions to the DNA consisting of 1, 2, or 3 nt (nucleotides).

Thus, Crick and Brenner concluded that the genetic code is read in increments of three nucleotides (in other words, it is a triplet code), and that reading occurs continuously without punctuation between the 3-nt units (figure 15.4).

These experiments indicate the importance of the **reading frame** for the genetic message. Because there is no punctuation, the reading frame established by the first codon in the sequence determines how all subsequent codons are read. We now call the kinds of mutations that Crick and Brenner used **frameshift mutations** because they alter the reading frame of the genetic message.

Nirenberg and others deciphered the code

The determination of which of the 64 possible codons encoded each particular amino acids was one of the greatest triumphs of 20th-century biochemistry. Accomplishing this decryption required two main developments to succeed: (1) cell-free biochemical systems that would support protein synthesis from a defined RNA and (2) the ability to produce synthetic, defined RNAs that could be used in the cell-free system.

During a five-year period from 1961 to 1966, work performed primarily in Marshall Nirenberg's laboratory led to the elucidation of the genetic code. Nirenberg's group first showed that adding the synthetic RNA molecule polyU (an RNA molecule consisting of a string of uracil nucleotides) to their cell-free systems

produced the polypeptide polyphenylalanine (a string of phenylalanine amino acids). Therefore, UUU encodes phenylalanine.

Next they used enzymes to produce RNA polymers with more than one nucleotide. These polymers allowed them to infer the composition of many of the possible codons, but not the order of bases in each codon.

The researchers then were able to use enzymes to synthesize defined 3-base sequences that could be tested for binding to the protein-synthesis machinery. This so-called *triplet-binding assay* allowed them to identify 54 of the 64 possible triplets.

The organic chemist H. Gobind Khorana provided the final piece of the puzzle by using organic synthesis to produce artificial RNA molecules of defined sequence, and then examining what polypeptides they directed in cell-free systems. The combination of all of these methods allowed the determination of all 64 possible 3-nt sequences, and the full genetic code was determined (table 15.1).

The code is degenerate but specific

Some obvious features of the code jump out of table 15.1. First, 61 of the 64 possible codons are used to specify amino acids. Three codons, UAA, UGA, and UAG, are reserved for another function: they signal "stop" and are known as **stop codons.** The only other form of "punctuation" in the code is that AUG is used to signal "start" and is therefore the **start codon.** In this case the codon has a dual function because it also encodes the amino acid methionine (Met).

TABLE 15.1	The Genetic Code							
				SECOND LETTER				
First Letter	U		C		A		G		Third Letter
U	UUU	Phe Phenylalanine	UCU	Ser Serine	UAU	Tyr Tyrosine	UGU	Cys Cysteine	U
	UUC		UCC		UAC		UGC		C
	UUA	Leu Leucine	UCA		UAA	"Stop"	UGA	"Stop"	A
	UUG		UCG		UAG	"Stop"	UGG	Trp Tryptophan	G
C	CUU	Leu Leucine	CCU	Pro Proline	CAU	His Histidine	CGU	Arg Arginine	U
	CUC		CCC		CAC		CGC		C
	CUA		CCA		CAA	Gln Glutamine	CGA		A
	CUG		CCG		CAG		CGG		G
A	AUU	Ile Isoleucine	ACU	Thr Threonine	AAU	Asn Asparagine	AGU	Ser Serine	U
	AUC		ACC		AAC		AGC		C
	AUA		ACA		AAA	Lys Lysine	AGA	Arg Arginine	A
	AUG	Met Methionine; "Start"	ACG		AAG		AGG		G
G	GUU	Val Valine	GCU	Ala Alanine	GAU	Asp Aspartate	GGU	Gly Glycine	U
	GUC		GCC		GAC		GGC		C
	GUA		GCA		GAA	Glu Glutamate	GGA		A
	GUG		GCG		GAG		GGG		G

A codon consists of three nucleotides read in the sequence shown. For example, ACU codes for threonine. The first letter, A, is in the First Letter column; the second letter, C, is in the Second Letter column; and the third letter, U, is in the Third Letter column. Each of the mRNA codons is recognized by a corresponding anticodon sequence on a tRNA molecule. Many amino acids are specified by more than one codon. For example, threonine is specified by four codons, which differ only in the third nucleotide (ACU, ACC, ACA, and ACG).

Figure 15.5 Transgenic pig. The piglet on the right is a conventional piglet. The piglet on the left was engineered to express a gene from jellyfish that encodes green fluorescent protein. The color of this piglet's nose is due to expression of this introduced gene. Such transgenic animals indicate the universal nature of the genetic code.

You can see that 61 codons are more than enough to encode 20 amino acids. That leaves lots of extra codons. One way to deal with this abundance would be to use only 20 of the 61 codons, but this is not what cells do. In reality, all 61 codons are used, making the code **degenerate,** which means that some amino acids are specified by more than one codon. The reverse, however, in which a single codon would specify more than one amino acid, is never found.

This degeneracy is not uniform. Some amino acids have only one codon, and some have up to six. In addition, the degenerate base usually occurs in position 3 of a codon, such that the first two positions are the same, and two or four of the possible nucleotides at position 3 encode the same amino acid. (The nature of protein synthesis on ribosomes explains how this codon usage works, and it is discussed later.)

The code is practically universal, but not quite

The genetic code is the same in almost all organisms. The universality of the genetic code is among the strongest evidence that all living things share a common evolutionary heritage. Because the code is universal, genes can be transferred from one organism to another and can be successfully expressed in their new host (figure 15.5). This universality of gene expression is central to many of the advances of genetic engineering discussed in chapter 17.

In 1979, investigators began to determine the complete nucleotide sequences of the mitochondrial genomes in humans, cattle, and mice. It came as something of a shock when these investigators learned that the genetic code used by these mammalian mitochondria was not quite the same as the "universal code" that has become so familiar to biologists.

In the mitochondrial genomes, what should have been a stop codon, UGA, was instead read as the amino acid tryptophan; AUA was read as methionine rather than as isoleucine; and AGA and AGG were read as stop codons rather than as arginine. Furthermore, minor differences from the universal code have also been found in the genomes of chloroplasts and in ciliates (certain types of protists).

Thus, it appears that the genetic code is not quite universal. Some time ago, presumably after they began their endo-

symbiotic existence, mitochondria and chloroplasts began to read the code differently, particularly the portion associated with "stop" signals.

? Inquiry question

The genetic code is almost universal. Why do you think it is nearly universal?

Learning Outcomes Review 15.2

The genetic code was shown to be nucelotide base triplets with two forms of punctuation and no spaces: three bases code for an amino acid, and the groups of three are read in order. Sixty-one codons specify amino acids, one of which also codes for "start," and three codons indicate "stop," for 64 total. Because some amino acids are specified by more than one codon, the code is termed degenerate. All codons encode only one amino acid, however.

- **What would be the outcome if a codon specified more than one amino acid?**

15.3 Prokaryotic Transcription

Learning Outcomes

1. *Describe the transcription process in bacteria.*
2. *Differentiate features of initiation from those of elongation.*
3. *Define the unique features of prokaryotic transcription.*

We begin an examination of gene expression by describing the process of transcription in prokaryotes. The later description of eukaryotic transcription will concentrate on their differences from prokaryotes.

Figure 15.6 Bacterial RNA polymerase and transcription initiation. *a.* RNA polymerase has two forms: core polymerase and holoenzyme. *b.* The σ subunit of the holoenzyme recognizes promoter elements at –35 and –10 and binds to the DNA. The helix is opened at the –10 region, and transcription begins at the start site at +1.

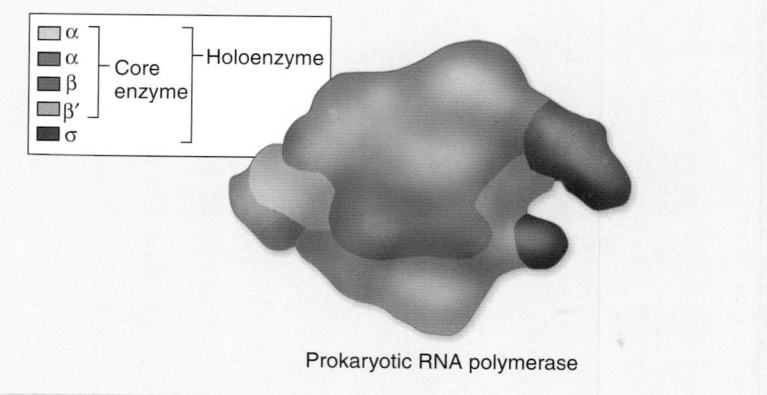

Prokaryotic RNA polymerase

a.

Prokaryotes have a single RNA polymerase

The single **RNA polymerase** of prokaryotes exists in two forms: the *core polymerase* and the *holoenzyme*. The core polymerase can synthesize RNA using a DNA template, but it cannot initiate synthesis accurately. The holoenzyme can accurately initiate synthesis.

The core polymerase is composed of four subunits: two identical α subunits, a β subunit, and a β′ subunit (figure 15.6*a*). The two α subunits help to hold the complex together and can bind to regulatory molecules. The active site of the enzyme is formed by the β and β′ subunits, which bind to the DNA template and the ribonucleotide triphosphate precursors.

The *holoenzyme*, which can properly initiate synthesis, is formed by the addition of a σ (sigma) subunit to the core polymerase (see figure 15.6*a*). Its ability to recognize specific signals in DNA allows RNA polymerase to locate the beginning of genes, which is critical to its function. Note that initiation of mRNA synthesis does not require a primer, in contrast to DNA replication.

Initiation occurs at promoters

Accurate initiation of transcription requires two sites in DNA: one called a **promoter** that forms a recognition and binding site for the RNA polymerase, and the actual **start site.** The polymerase also needs a signal to end transcription, which we call a **terminator.** We then refer to the region from promoter to terminator as a **transcription unit.**

The action of the polymerase moving along the DNA can be thought of as analogous to water flowing in a stream. We can speak of sites on the DNA as being "upstream" or "downstream" of the start site. We can also use this comparison to form a simple system for numbering bases in DNA to refer to positions in the transcription unit. The first base transcribed is called +**1**, and this numbering continues downstream until the last base is transcribed. Any bases upstream of the start site receive negative numbers, starting at −**1.**

The promoter is a short sequence found upstream of the start site and is therefore not transcribed by the polymerase. Two 6-base sequences are common to bacterial promoters: One

is located 35 nt upstream of the start site (−35), and the other is located 10 nt upstream of the start site (−10) (figure 15.6*b*). These two sites provide the promoter with asymmetry; they indicate not only the site of initiation, but also the direction of transcription.

The binding of RNA polymerase to the promoter is the first step in transcription. Promoter binding is controlled by the σ subunit of the RNA polymerase holoenzyme, which recognizes the −35 sequence in the promoter and positions the RNA polymerase at the correct start site, oriented to transcribe in the correct direction.

Once bound to the promoter, the RNA polymerase begins to unwind the DNA helix at the −10 site (see figure 15.6*b*). The polymerase covers a region of about 75 bp but only unwinds about 12–14 bp.

Inquiry question

? The prokaryotic promoter has two distinct elements that are not identical. How is this important to the initiation of transcription?

Elongation adds successive nucleotides

In prokaryotes, the transcription of the RNA chain usually starts with ATP or GTP. One of these forms the 5′ end of the chain, which grows in the 5′-to-3′ direction as ribonucleotides are added. As the RNA polymerase molecule leaves the promoter region, the σ factor is no longer required, although it may remain in association with the enzyme.

This process of leaving the promoter, called *clearance,* or *escape,* involves more than just synthesizing the first few nucleotides of the transcript and moving on, because the enzyme has made strong contacts to the DNA during initiation. It is necessary to break these contacts with the promoter region to be able to move progressively down the template. The enzyme goes through conformational changes during this clearance stage, and subsequently contacts less of the DNA than it does during the initial promoter binding.

The region containing the RNA polymerase, the DNA template, and the growing RNA transcript is called the **transcription bubble** because it contains a locally unwound

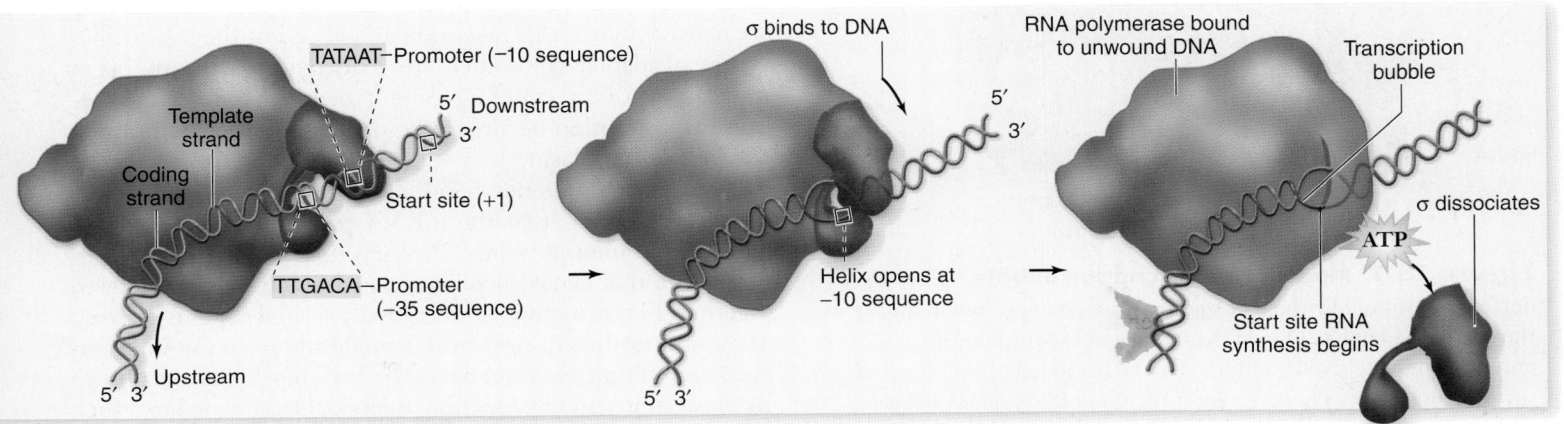

b.

"bubble" of DNA (figure 15.7). Within the bubble, the first 9 bases of the newly synthesized RNA strand temporarily form a helix with the template DNA strand. This stabilizes the positioning of the 3′ end of the RNA so it can interact with an incoming ribonucleotide triphosphate. The enzyme itself covers about 50 bp of DNA around this transcription bubble.

The transcription bubble created by RNA polymerase moves down the bacterial DNA at a constant rate, about 50 nt/sec, with the growing RNA strand protruding from the bubble. After the transcription bubble passes, the now-transcribed DNA is rewound as it leaves the bubble.

Termination occurs at specific sites

The end of a bacterial transcription unit is marked by terminator sequences that signal "stop" to the polymerase. Reaching these sequences causes the formation of phosphodiester bonds to cease, the RNA–DNA hybrid within the transcription bubble to dissociate, the RNA polymerase to release the DNA, and the DNA within the transcription bubble to rewind.

The simplest terminators consist of a series of G–C base-pairs followed by a series of A–T base-pairs. The RNA transcript of this stop region can form a double-stranded structure in the GC region called a *hairpin*, which is followed by four or more uracil (U) ribonucleotides (figure 15.8). Formation of the hairpin causes the RNA polymerase to pause,

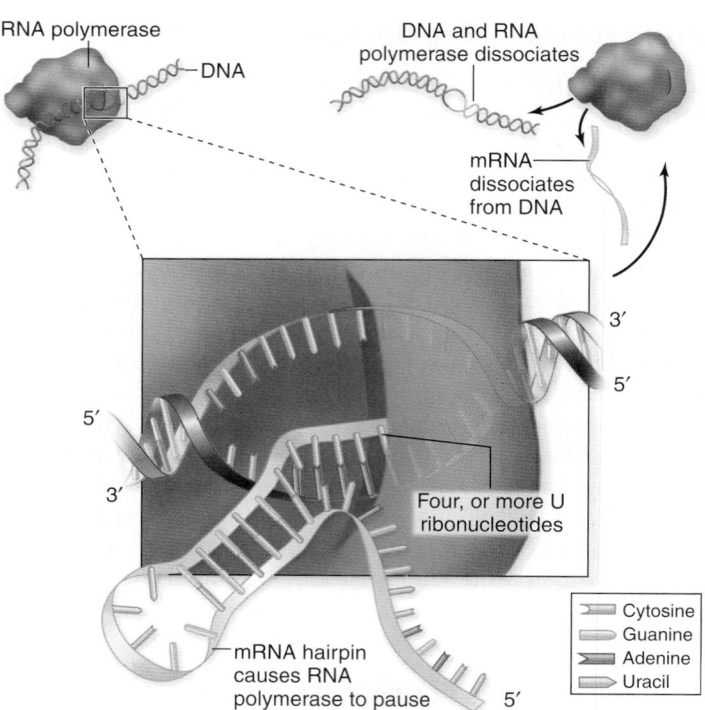

Figure 15.8 Bacterial transcription terminator. The self-complementary G–C region forms a double-stranded stem with a single-stranded loop called a hairpin. The stretch of U's forms a less stable RNA–DNA hybrid that falls off the enzyme.

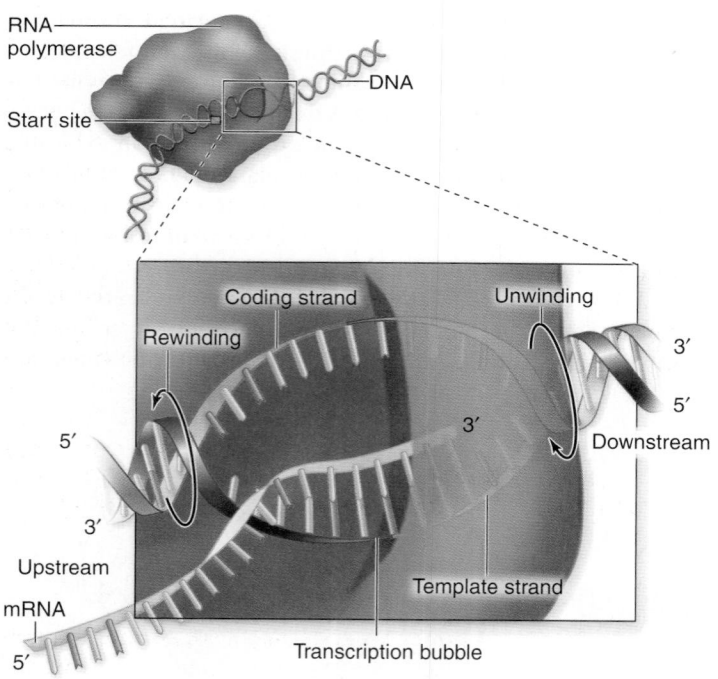

Figure 15.7 Model of a transcription bubble. The DNA duplex is unwound by the RNA polymerase complex, rewinding at the end of the bubble. One of the strands of DNA functions as a template, and nucleotide building blocks are added to the 3′ end of the growing RNA. There is a short region of RNA–DNA hybrid within the bubble.

placing it directly over the run of four uracils. The pairing of U with the DNA's A is the weakest of the four hybrid base-pairs, and it is not strong enough to hold the hybrid strands when the polymerase pauses. Instead, the RNA strand dissociates from the DNA within the transcription bubble, and transcription stops. A variety of protein factors also act at these terminators to aid in terminating transcription.

Prokaryotic transcription is coupled to translation

In prokaryotes, the mRNA produced by transcription begins to be translated before transcription is finished—that is, they are *coupled* (figure 15.9). As soon as a 5′ end of the mRNA becomes available, ribosomes are loaded onto this to begin translation. (This coupling cannot occur in eukaryotes because transcription occurs in the nucleus, and translation occurs in the cytoplasm.)

Another difference between prokaryotic and eukaryotic gene expression is that the mRNA produced in prokaryotes may contain multiple genes. Prokaryotic genes are often organized such that genes encoding related functions are clustered together. This grouping of functionally related genes is referred to as an **operon.** An operon is a single transcription unit that encodes multiple enzymes necessary for a biochemical pathway. By clustering genes by function, they can be regulated together, a topic that we return to in the next chapter.

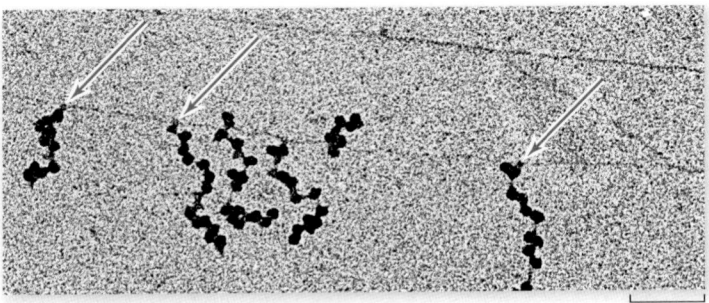

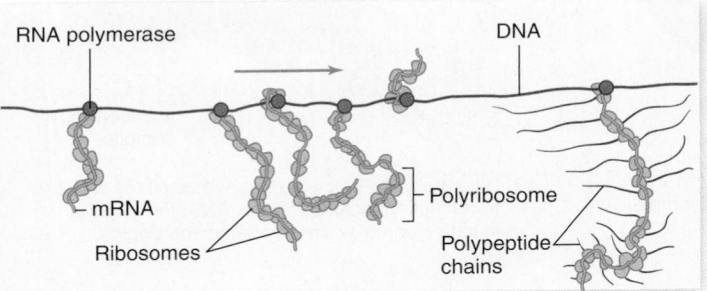

Figure 15.9 Transcription and translation are coupled in prokaryotes. In this micrograph of gene expression in *E. coli*, translation is occurring during transcription. The arrows point to RNA polymerase enzymes, and ribosomes are attached to the mRNAs extending from the polymerase. Polypeptides being synthesized by ribosomes, which are not visible in the micrograph, have been added to the last mRNA in the drawing.

Learning Outcomes Review 15.3

Transcription in bacteria is accomplished by RNA polymerase, which has two forms: a core polymerase and a holoenzyme. Initiation is accomplished by the holoenzyme form, which can accurately recognize promoter sequences. Elongation consists of RNA synthesis by the core enzyme, which adds RNA nucleotides in sequence until it reaches a terminator where synthesis stops, then the transcript is released. In prokaryotes, translation of the RNA transcript begins before transcription is finished, making the processes coupled.

■ *Yeast are unicellular organism like bacteria; would you expect them to have the same transcription/translation coupling?*

15.4 Eukaryotic Transcription

Learning Outcomes

1. List the different eukaryotic RNA polymerases.
2. Distinguish between the promoters of the RNA polymerases.
3. Define the processing that occurs to eukaryotic transcripts.

The basic mechanism of transcription by RNA polymerase is the same in eukaryotes as in prokaryotes; however, the details of the two processes differ enough that it is necessary to consider them separately. Here we concentrate only on how eukaryotic systems differ from prokaryotic systems, such as the bacterial system just discussed. All other features may be assumed to be the same.

Eukaryotes have three RNA polymerases

Unlike prokaryotes, which have a single RNA polymerase enzyme, eukaryotes have three different RNA polymerases, which are distinguished in both structure and function. The enzyme **RNA polymerase I** transcribes rRNA, **RNA polymerase II** transcribes mRNA and some small nuclear RNAs, and **RNA polymerase III** transcribes tRNA and some other small RNAs. Together, these three enzymes accomplish all transcription in the nucleus of eukaryotic cells.

Each polymerase has its own promoter

The existence of three different RNA polymerases requires different signals in the DNA to allow each polymerase to recognize where to begin transcription. Each polymerase recognizes a different promoter structure.

RNA polymerase I promoters

RNA polymerase I promoters at first puzzled biologists, because comparisons of rRNA genes between species showed no similarities outside the coding region. The current view is that these promoters are also specific for each species, and for this reason, cross-species comparisons do not yield similarities.

RNA polymerase II promoters

The RNA polymerase II promoters are the most complex of the three types, probably a reflection of the huge diversity of genes that are transcribed by this polymerase. When the first eukaryotic genes were isolated, many had a sequence called the **TATA box** upstream of the start site. This sequence was similar to the prokaryotic –10 sequence, and it was assumed that the TATA box was the primary promoter element. With the sequencing of entire genomes, many more genes have been analyzed, and this assumption has proved too simple. It has been replaced by the idea of a "core promoter" that can be composed of a number of different elements, including the TATA box. Additional control elements allow for tissue-specific and developmental time–specific expression (see chapter 16).

RNA polymerase III promoters

Promoters for RNA polymerase III also were a source of surprise for biologists in the early days of molecular biology who were examining the control of eukaryotic gene expression. A common technique for analyzing regulatory regions was to make successive deletions from the 5′ end of genes until enough was deleted to abolish specific transcription. The logic followed experiences with prokaryotes, in which the regulatory regions had been found at the 5′ end of genes. But in the case of tRNA genes, the 5′ deletions had no effect on

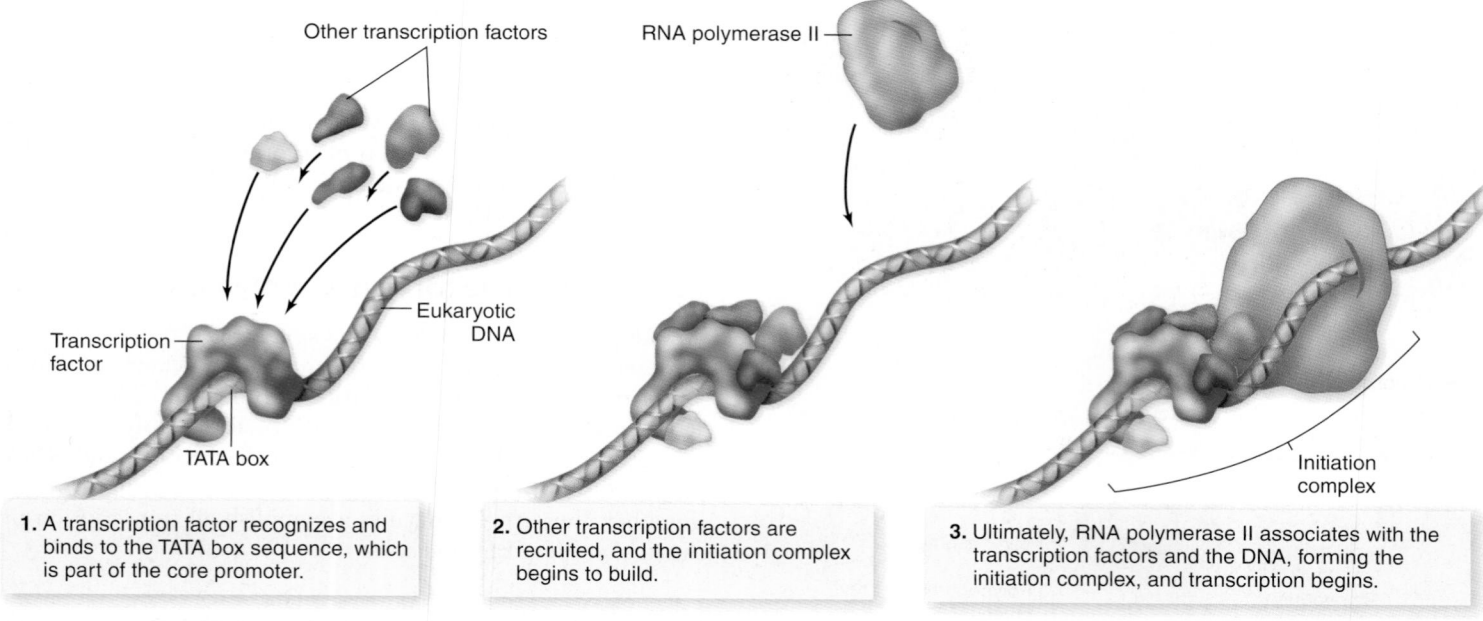

1. A transcription factor recognizes and binds to the TATA box sequence, which is part of the core promoter.

2. Other transcription factors are recruited, and the initiation complex begins to build.

3. Ultimately, RNA polymerase II associates with the transcription factors and the DNA, forming the initiation complex, and transcription begins.

Figure 15.10 Eukaryotic initiation complex. Unlike transcription in prokaryotic cells, in which the RNA polymerase recognizes and binds to the promoter, eukaryotic transcription requires the binding of transcription factors to the promoter before RNA polymerase II binds to the DNA. The association of transcription factors and RNA polymerase II at the promoter is called the initiation complex.

expression! The promoters were found to actually be internal to the gene itself. This has not proved to be the case for all polymerase III genes, but appears to be for most.

Initiation and termination differ from that in prokaryotes

The initiation of transcription at RNA polymerase II promoters is analogous to prokaryotic initiation but is more complex. Instead of a single factor allowing promoter recognition, eukaryotes use a host of **transcription factors.** These proteins are necessary to get the RNA polymerase II enzyme to a promoter and to initiate gene expression. A number of these transcription factors interact with RNA polymerase II to form an *initiation complex* at the promoter (figure 15.10). We explore this complex in detail in chapter 16 when we describe the control of gene expression.

The termination of transcription for RNA polymerase II also differs from that in prokaryotes. Although termination

sites exist, they are not as well defined as are prokaryotic terminators. The end of the mRNA is also not formed by RNA polymerase II because the primary transcript is modified after transcription.

Eukaryotic transcripts are modified

A primary difference between prokaryotes and eukaryotes is the fate of the transcript itself. Between transcription in the nucleus and export of a mature mRNA to the cytoplasm, a number of modifications occur to the initial transcripts made by RNA polymerase II. We call the RNA synthesized by RNA polymerase II the **primary transcript** and the final processed form the **mature mRNA.**

The 5′ cap

Eukaryotic transcripts have an unusual structure that is added to the 5′ end of mRNAs. The first base in the transcript is usually an adenine (A) or a guanine (G), and this is further modified by the addition of GTP to the 5′ PO_4 group, forming what is known as a **5′ cap** (figure 15.11). The G nucleotide in the cap is joined to the transcript by its 5′ end; the only such 5′-to-5′ bond found in nucleic acids. The G in the GTP is also modified by the addition of a methyl group, so it is often called a *methyl-G cap*. The cap is added while transcription is still in progress. This cap protects the 5′ end of the mRNA from degradation and is also involved in translation initiation.

Figure 15.11 Posttranscriptional modifications to 5′ and 3′ ends. Eukaryotic mRNA molecules are modified in the nucleus with the addition of a methylated GTP to the 5′ end of the transcript, called the 5′ cap, and a long chain of adenine residues to the 3′ end of the transcript, called the 3′ poly-A tail.

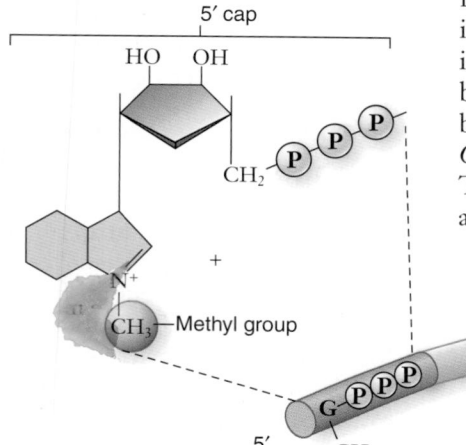

Evidence indicates that the normal pattern of splicing is important to an organism's function. It has been estimated that 15% of known human genetic disorders are due to altered splicing. Mutations in the signals for splicing can introduce new splice sites or can abolish normal patterns of splicing. (In chapter 16 we consider how alternative splicing can be used to regulate gene expression.)

Although many cases of alternative splicing have been documented, the recent completion of the reference sequence of the human genome, along with other large data sets of expressed sequences, now allow large-scale comparisons between sequences found in mRNAs and in the genome. Three different computer-based analyses have been performed, producing results that are in rough agreement. These initial genomic assessments indicate a range of 35 to 59% for human genes that exhibit some form of alternative splicing. If we pick the middle ground of around 40%, this result still vastly increases the number of potential proteins encoded by the 25,000 genes in the human genome.

It is important to note that these analyses are primarily computer-based, and the functions of the possible spliced products have been investigated for only a small part of the potentially spliced genes. These analyses, however, do explain how the 25,000 genes of the human genome can encode the more than 80,000 different mRNAs reported to exist in human cells. The emerging field of proteomics addresses the number and functioning of proteins encoded by the human genome.

Learning Outcomes Review 15.5

In prokaryotes, genes appear to be colinear with their protein products. Eukaryotic genes, by contrast, contain exon regions, which are expressed, and intron sequences, which interrupt the exons. The introns are removed by the spliceosome in a process that leaves the exons joined together. Alternative splicing can generate different mRNAs, and thus different proteins, from the same gene. Recent estimates are that as many as half of human genes may be alternatively spliced.

■ **What advantages would alternative splicing confer on an organism?**

15.6 The Structure of tRNA and Ribosomes

Learning Outcomes

1. **Explain why the tRNA charging reaction is critical to translation.**
2. **Identify the tRNA-binding sites in the ribosome.**

The ribosome is the key organelle in translation, but it also requires the participation of mRNA, tRNA and a host of other factors. Critical to this process is the interaction of the ribosomes with tRNA and mRNA. To understand this, we first examine the structure of the tRNA adapter molecule and the ribosome itself.

Aminoacyl-tRNA synthetases attach amino acids to tRNA

Each amino acid must be attached to a tRNA with the correct anticodon for protein synthesis to proceed. This covalent attachment is accomplished by the action of activating enzymes called **aminoacyl-tRNA synthetases.** One of these enzymes is present for each of the 20 common amino acids.

tRNA structure

Transfer RNA is a bifunctional molecule that must be able to interact with mRNA and with amino acids. The structure of tRNAs is highly conserved in all living systems, and it can be formed into a cloverleaf type of structure based on intramolecular base-pairing that produces double-stranded regions. This primary structure is then folded in space to form an L-shaped molecule that has two functional ends: the **acceptor stem** and the **anticodon loop** (figure 15.14).

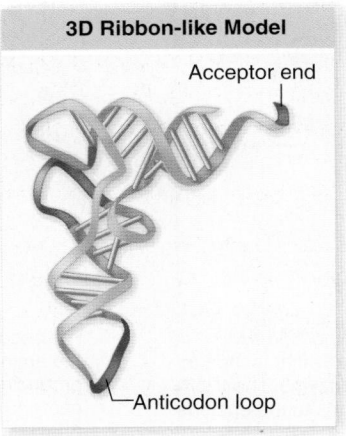

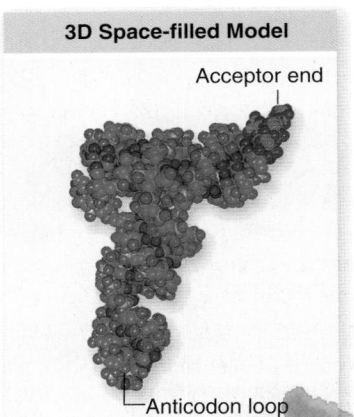

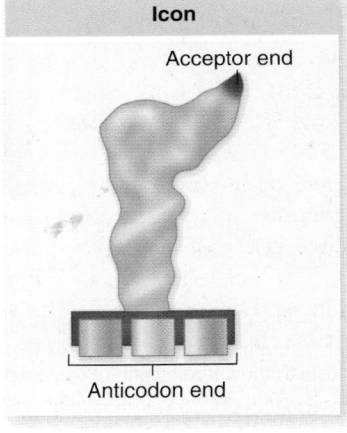

Figure 15.14 The structure of tRNA. Base-pairing within the molecule creates three stem and loop structures in a characteristic cloverleaf shape. The loop at the bottom of the cloverleaf contains the anticodon sequence, which can base-pair with codons in the mRNA. Amino acids are attached to the free, single-stranded —OH end of the acceptor stem. In its final three-dimensional structure, the loops of tRNA are folded into the final L-shaped structure.

The acceptor stem is the 3′ end of the molecule, which always ends in 5′ CCA 3′. The amino acid is attached to this end of the molecule. The anticodon loop is the bottom loop of the cloverleaf, and it can base-pair with codons in mRNA.

The charging reaction

The aminoacyl-tRNA synthetases must be able to recognize specific tRNA molecules as well as their corresponding amino acids. Although 61 codons code for amino acids, there are actually not 61 tRNAs in cells, although the number varies from species to species. Therefore, some aminoacyl-tRNA synthetases must be able to recognize more than one tRNA—but each recognizes only a single amino acid.

The reaction catalyzed by the enzymes is called the tRNA **charging reaction,** and the product is an amino acid joined to a tRNA, now called a *charged tRNA.* An ATP molecule provides energy for this endergonic reaction. The charged tRNA produced by the reaction is an activated intermediate that can undergo the peptide bond-forming reaction without an additional input of energy.

The charging reaction joins the acceptor stem to the carboxyl terminus of an amino acid (figure 15.15). Keeping this directionality in mind is critical to understanding the function of the ribosome, because each peptide bond will be formed between the amino group of one amino acid and the carboxyl group of another amino acid.

The correct attachment of amino acids to tRNAs is important because the ribosome does not verify this attachment. Ribosomes can only ensure that the codon–anticodon pairing is correct. In an elegant experiment, cysteine was converted chemically to alanine after the charging reaction, when the amino acid was already attached to tRNA. When this charged tRNA was used in an in vitro protein synthesis system, alanine was incorporated in the place of cysteine, showing that the ribosome cannot "proofread" the amino acids attached to tRNA.

In a very real sense, therefore, the charging reaction is the real translation step; amino acids are incorporated into a peptide based solely on the tRNA anticodon and its interaction with the mRNA.

The ribosome has multiple tRNA-binding sites

The synthesis of any biopolymer can be broken down into initiation, elongation, and termination—you have seen this division for DNA replication as well as for transcription. In the case of translation, or protein synthesis, all three of these steps take place on the ribosome, a large macromolecular assembly consisting of rRNA and proteins. Details of the process by which the two ribosome subunits are assembled during initiation are described shortly.

For the ribosome to function it must be able to bind to at least two charged tRNAs at once so that a peptide bond can be formed between their amino acids, as described in the previous overview. The bacterial ribosome contains three binding sites, summarized in figure 15.16:

- The **P site** (peptidyl) binds to the tRNA attached to the growing peptide chain.
- The **A site** (aminoacyl) binds to the tRNA carrying the next amino acid to be added.
- The **E site** (exit) binds the tRNA that carried the previous amino acid added (see figure 15.16).

Transfer RNAs move through these sites successively during the process of elongation. Relative to the mRNA, the sites are arranged 5′ to 3′ in the order E, P, and A. The incoming

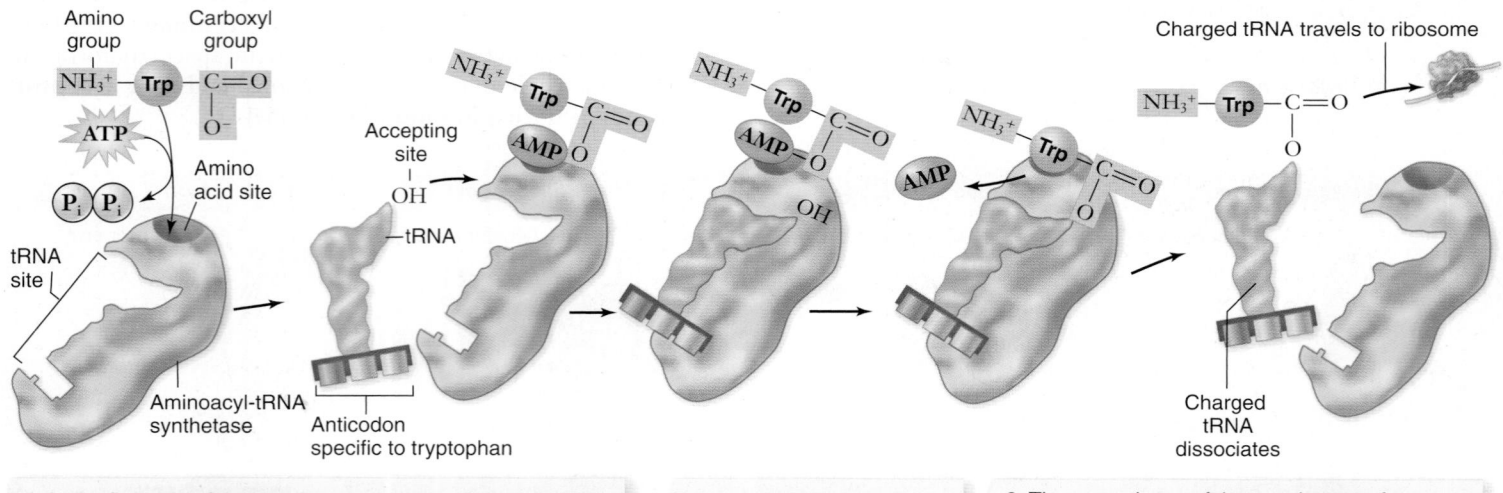

1. In the first step of the reaction, the amino acid is activated. The amino acid reacts with ATP to produce an intermediate with the carboxyl end of the amino acid attached to AMP. The two terminal phosphates (pyrophosphates) are cleaved from ATP in this reaction.

2. The amino acid-AMP complex remains bound to the enzyme. The tRNA next binds to the enzyme.

3. The second step of the reaction transfers the amino acid from AMP to the tRNA, producing a charged tRNA and AMP. The charged tRNA consists of a specific amino acid attached to the 3′ acceptor stem of its RNA.

Figure 15.15   tRNA charging reaction. There are 20 different aminoacyl-tRNA synthetase enzymes each specific for one amino acid, such as tryptophan (Trp). The enzyme must also recognize and bind to the tRNA molecules with anticodons specifying that amino acid, ACC for tryptophan. The reaction uses ATP and produces an activated intermediate that will not require further energy for peptide bond formation.

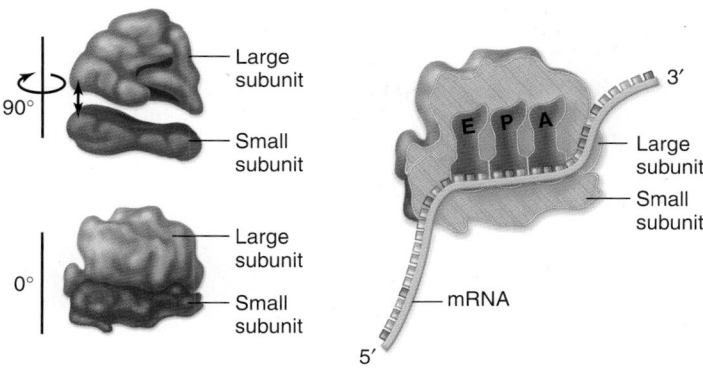

Figure 15.16 Ribosomes have two subunits.
Ribosome subunits come together and apart as part of a ribosome cycle. The smaller subunit fits into a depression on the surface of the larger one. Ribosomes have three tRNA-binding sites: aminoacyl site (A), peptidyl site (P), and empty site (E).

charged tRNAs enter the ribosome at the A site, transit through the P site, and then leave via the E site.

The ribosome has both decoding and enzymatic functions

The two functions of the ribosome involve decoding the transcribed message and forming peptide bonds. The decoding function resides primarily in the small subunit of the ribosome. The formation of peptide bonds requires the enzyme **peptidyl transferase,** which resides in the large subunit.

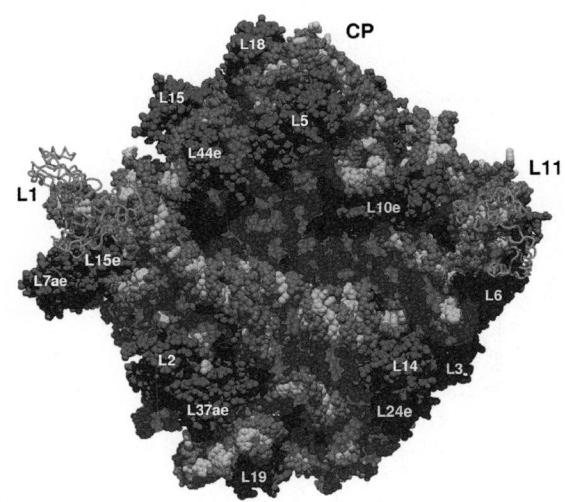

Figure 15.17 3-D structure of prokaryotic ribosome. The complete atomic structure of a prokaryotic large ribosomal subunit has been determined at 2.4-Å resolution. Bases of RNA are white, the polynucleotide backbone is red, and proteins are blue. The faces of each ribosomal subunit are lined with rRNA such that their interaction with tRNAs, amino acids, and mRNA all involve rRNA. Proteins are absent from the active site but abundant everywhere on the surface. The proteins stabilize the structure by interacting with adjacent RNA strands.

Our view of the ribosome has changed dramatically over time. Initially, molecular biologists assumed that the proteins in the ribosome carried out its function and that the rRNA was a structural scaffold necessary to hold the proteins in the correct position. Now this view has mostly been reversed; the ribosome is seen instead as rRNAs that are held in place by proteins. The faces of the two subunits that interact with each other are lined with rRNA, and the parts of both subunits that interact with mRNA, tRNA, and amino acids are also primarily rRNA (figure 15.17). It is now thought that the peptidyl transferase activity resides in an rRNA in the large subunit.

Learning Outcomes Review 15.6

Transfer RNA has two functional regions, one that bonds with an amino acid, and the other that can base-pair with mRNA. The tRNA charging reaction joins the carboxyl end of an amino acid to the 3′ acceptor stem of its tRNA; without charged tRNAs, translation cannot take place. This reaction is catalyzed by 20 different aminoacyl-tRNA synthetases, one for each amino acid. The ribosome has three different binding sites for tRNA, one for the tRNA adding to the growing peptide chain (P site), one for the next charged tRNA (A site), and one for the previous tRNA, which is now without an amino acid (E site). The ribosome can be thought of as having both a decoding function and an enzymatic function.

■ *What would be the effect on translation of a mutant tRNA that has an anticodon complementary to a STOP codon?*

15.7 The Process of Translation

Learning Outcomes

1. *Distinguish between translation initiation and elongation.*
2. *Explain the elongation cycle.*
3. *Compare translation on the RER and in the cytoplasm.*

The process of translation is one of the most complex and energy-expensive tasks that cells perform. An overview of the process, as you saw earlier, is perhaps deceptively simple: The mRNA is threaded through the ribosome, while tRNAs carrying amino acids bind to the ribosome, where they interact with mRNA by base-pairing with the mRNA's codons. The ribosome and tRNAs position the amino acids such that peptide bonds can be formed between each new amino acid and the growing polypeptide.

Initiation requires accessory factors

As mentioned earlier, the start codon is AUG, which also encodes the amino acid methionine. The ribosome usually uses the first AUG it encounters in an mRNA strand to signal the start of translation.

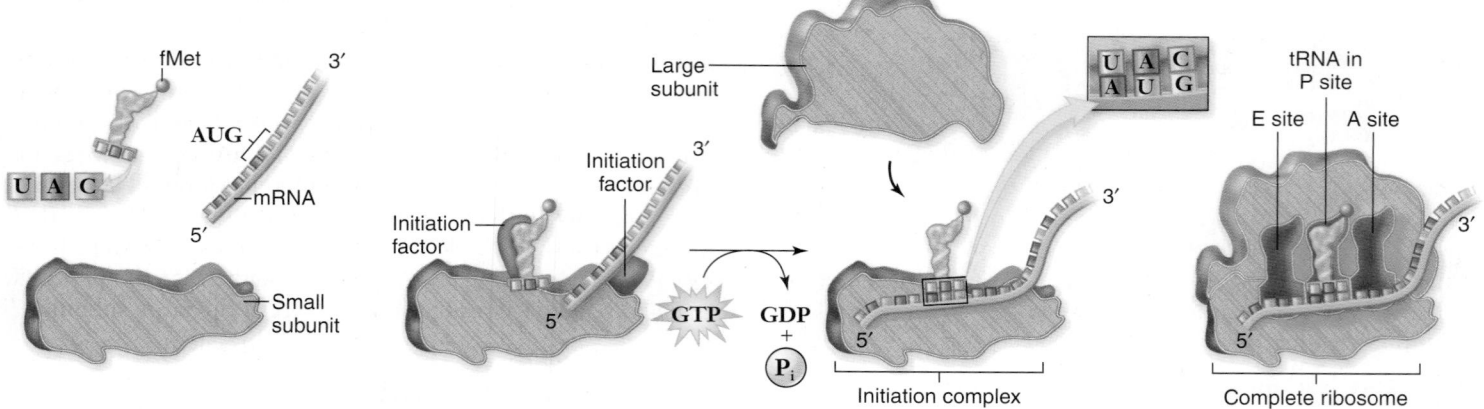

Figure 15.18 Initiation of translation. In prokaryotes, initiation factors play key roles in positioning the small ribosomal subunit, the initiator tRNA^fMet, and the mRNA. When the tRNA^fMet is positioned over the first AUG codon of the mRNA, the large ribosomal subunit binds, forming the E, P, and A sites where successive tRNA molecules bind to the ribosomes, and polypeptide synthesis begins. Ribosomal subunits are shown as a cutaway sectioned through the middle.

Prokaryotic initiation

In prokaryotes, the **initiation complex** includes a special **initiator tRNA** molecule charged with a chemically modified methionine, *N-formylmethionine*. The initiator tRNA is shown as tRNA^fMet. The initiation complex also includes the small ribosomal subunit and the mRNA strand (figure 15.18). The small subunit is positioned correctly on the mRNA due to a conserved sequence in the 5′ end of the mRNA called the **ribosome-binding sequence (RBS)** that is complementary to the 3′ end of a small subunit rRNA.

A number of initiation factors mediate this interaction of the ribosome, mRNA, and tRNA^fMet to form the initiation complex. These factors are involved in initiation only and are not part of the ribosome.

Once the complex of mRNA, initiator tRNA, and small ribosomal subunit is formed, the large subunit is added, and

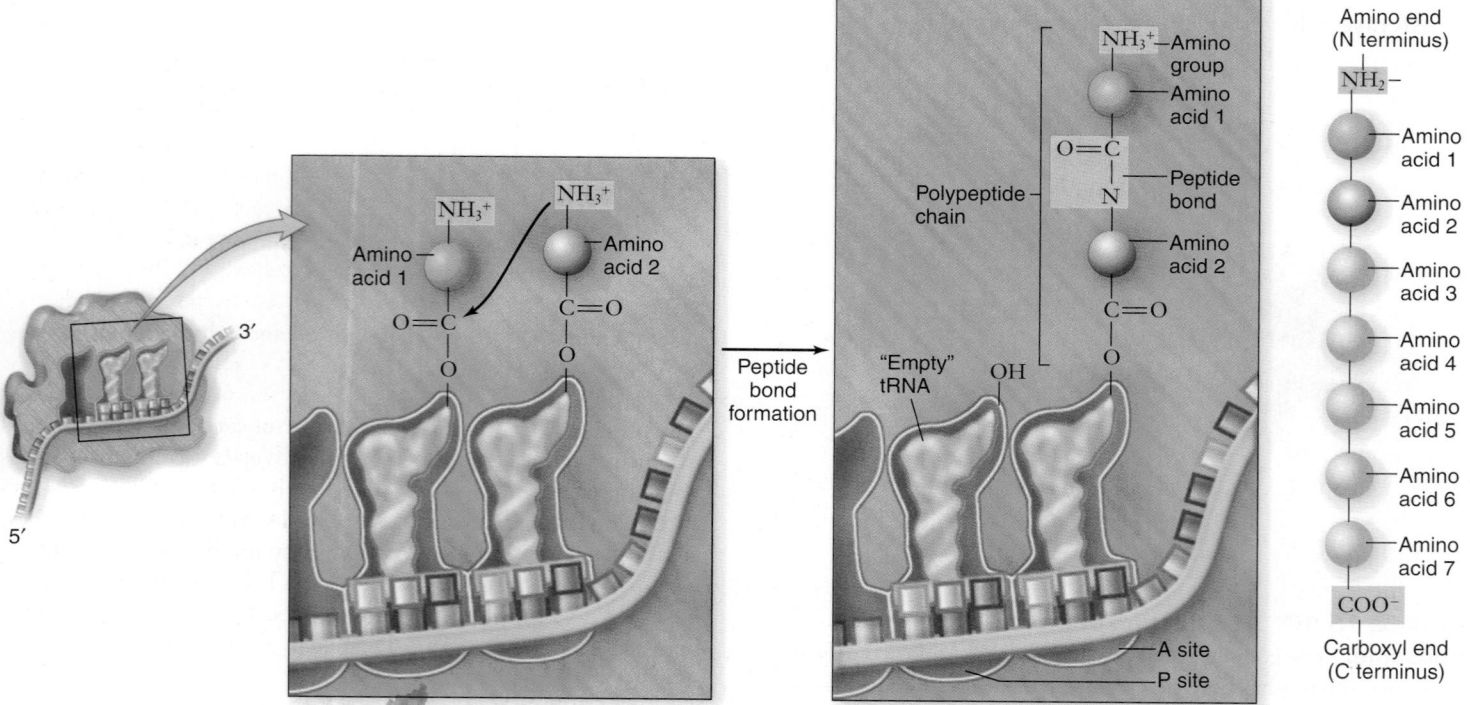

Figure 15.19 Peptide bond formation. Peptide bonds are formed between a "new" charged tRNA in the A site and the growing chain attached to the tRNA in the P site. The bond forms between the amino group of the new amino acid and the carboxyl group of the growing chain. This breaks the bond between the growing chain and its tRNA, transfering it to the A site as the new amino acid remains attached to its tRNA.

translation can begin. With the formation of the complete ribosome, the initiator tRNA is bound to the P site with the A site empty.

Eukaryotic initiation

Initiation in eukaryotes is similar, although it differs in two important ways. First, in eukaryotes, the initiating amino acid is methionine rather than *N*-formylmethionine. Second, the initiation complex is far more complicated than in prokaryotes, containing nine or more protein factors, many consisting of several subunits. Eukaryotic mRNAs also lack an RBS. The small subunit binds to the mRNA initially by binding to the 5′ cap of the mRNA.

Elongation adds successive amino acids

When the entire ribosome is assembled around the initiator tRNA and mRNA, the second charged tRNA can be brought to the ribosome and bind to the empty A site. This requires an **elongation factor** called **EF-Tu,** which binds to the charged tRNA and to GTP.

A peptide bond can then form between the amino acid of the initiator tRNA and the newly arrived charged tRNA in the A site. The geometry of this bond relative to the two charged tRNAs is critical to understanding the process. Remember that an amino acid is attached to a tRNA by its carboxyl terminus. The peptide bond is formed between the amino end of the incoming amino acid (in the A site) and the carboxyl end of the growing chain (in the P site) (figure 15.19).

The addition of successive amino acids is a series of events that occur in a cyclic fashion. Figure 15.20 shows the details of the elongation cycle.

1. **Matching tRNA anticodon with mRNA codon.** Each new charged tRNA comes to the ribosome bound to EF-Tu and GTP. The charged tRNA binds to the A site if its anticodon is complementary to the mRNA codon in the A site.

   After binding, GTP is hydrolyzed, and EF-Tu–GDP dissociates from the ribosome where it is recycled by another factor. This two-step binding and hydrolysis of GTP is thought to increase the accuracy of translation.

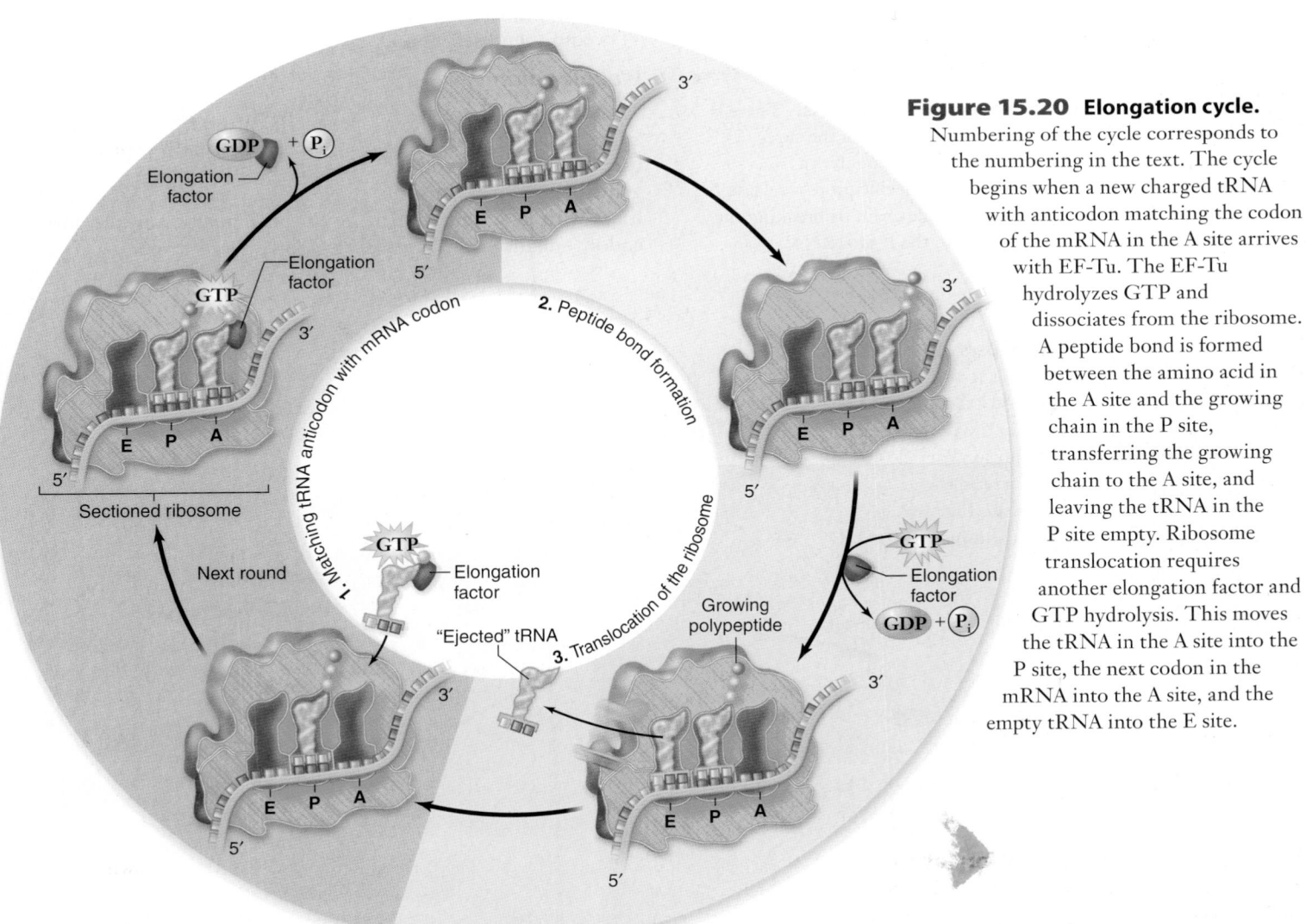

Figure 15.20 Elongation cycle. Numbering of the cycle corresponds to the numbering in the text. The cycle begins when a new charged tRNA with anticodon matching the codon of the mRNA in the A site arrives with EF-Tu. The EF-Tu hydrolyzes GTP and dissociates from the ribosome. A peptide bond is formed between the amino acid in the A site and the growing chain in the P site, transferring the growing chain to the A site, and leaving the tRNA in the P site empty. Ribosome translocation requires another elongation factor and GTP hydrolysis. This moves the tRNA in the A site into the P site, the next codon in the mRNA into the A site, and the empty tRNA into the E site.

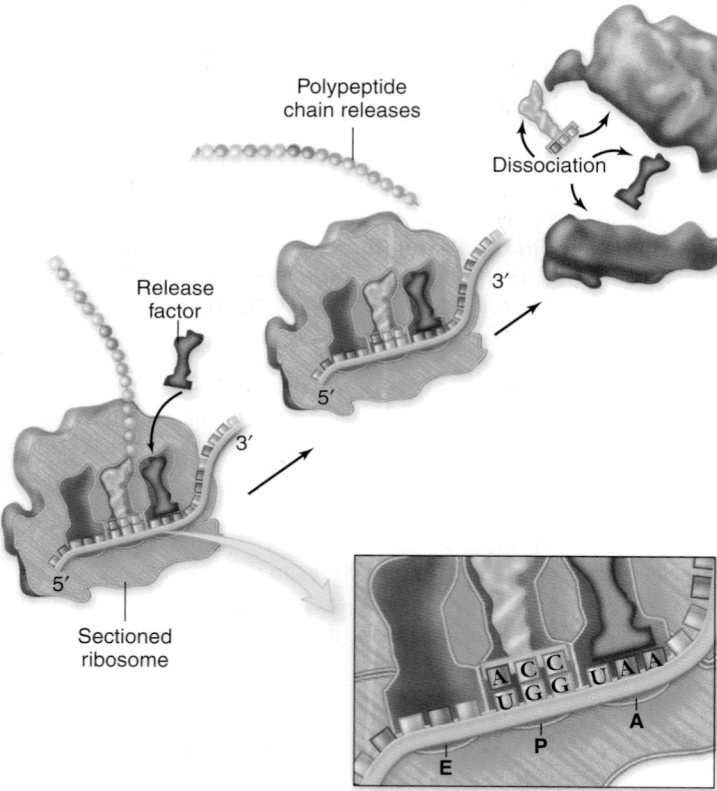

Figure 15.21 Termination of protein synthesis. There is no tRNA with an anticodon complementary to any of the three termination signal codons. When a ribosome encounters a termination codon, it stops translocating. A specific protein release factor facilitates the release of the polypeptide chain by breaking the covalent bond that links the polypeptide to the P site tRNA.

2. **Peptide bond formation.** Peptidyl transferase, located in the large subunit, catalyzes the formation of a peptide bond between the amino group of the amino acid in the A site and the carboxyl group of the growing chain. This also breaks the bond between the growing chain and the tRNA in the P site leaving it empty (no longer charged). The overall result of this is to transfer the growing chain to the tRNA in the A site.

3. **Translocation of the ribosome.** After the peptide bond has been formed, the ribosome moves relative to the mRNA and the tRNAs. The next codon in the mRNA shifts into the A site, and the tRNA with the growing chain moves to the P site. The uncharged tRNA formerly in the P site is now in the E site, and it will be ejected in the next cycle. This translocation step requires the accessory factor EF-G and the hydrolysis of another GTP.

This elongation cycle continues with each new amino acid added. The ribosome moves down the mRNA in a 5′-to-3′ direction, reading successive codons. The tRNAs move through the ribosome in the opposite direction, from the A site to the P site and finally the E site, before they are ejected as empty tRNAs, which can be charged with another amino acid and then used again.

Wobble pairing

As mentioned, there are fewer tRNAs than codons. This situation is easily rationalized because the pairing between the 3′ base of the codon and the 5′ base of the anticodon is less stringent than normal. In some tRNAs, the presence of modified bases with less accurate pairing in the 5′ position of the anticodon enhances this flexibility. This effect is referred to as

Figure 15.22 Synthesis of proteins on RER. Proteins that are synthesized on RER arrive at the ER because of sequences in the peptide itself. A signal sequence in the amino terminus of the polypeptide is recognized by the signal recognition particle (SRP). This complex docks with a receptor associated with a channel in the ER. The peptide passes through the channel into the lumen of the ER as it is synthesized.

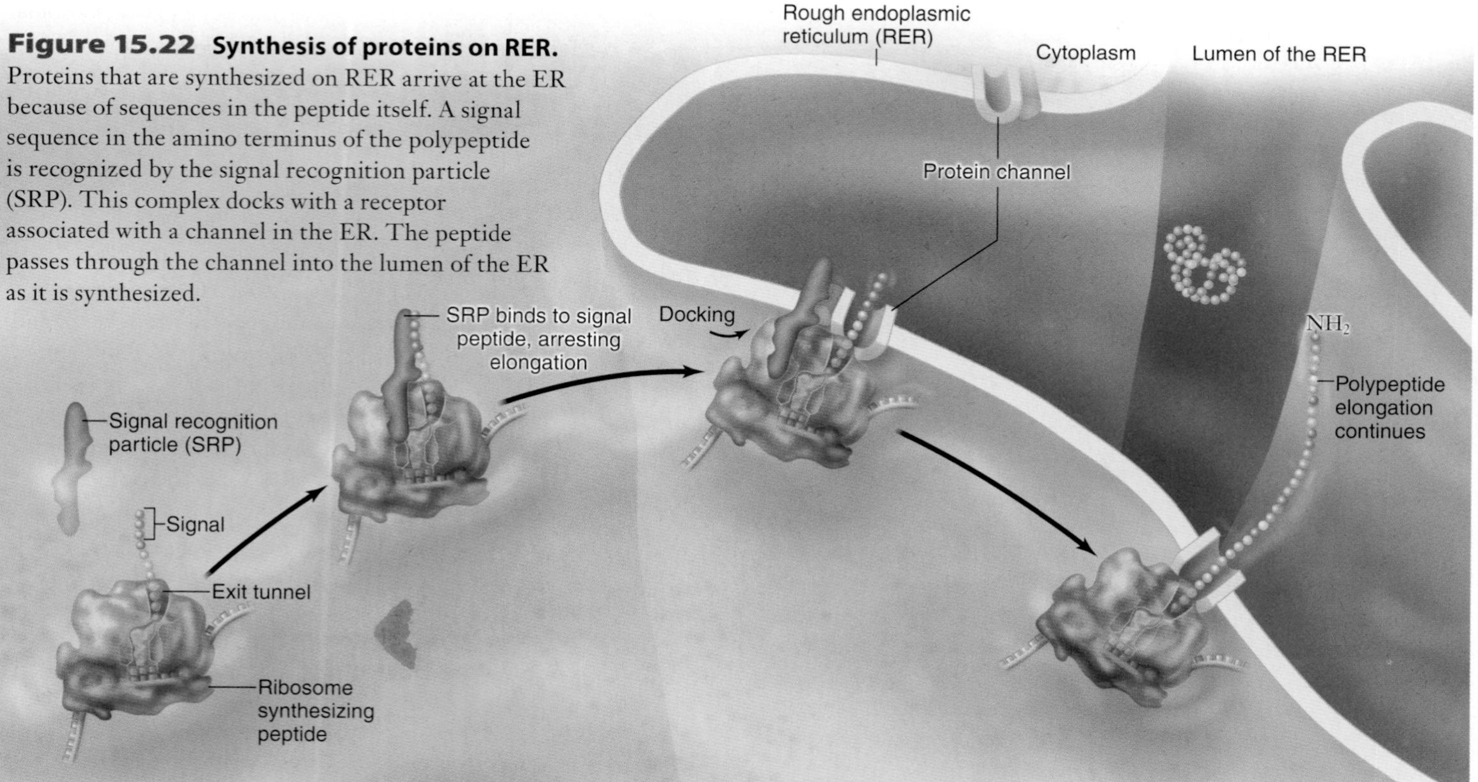

wobble pairing because these tRNAs can "wobble" a bit on the mRNA, so that a single tRNA can "read" more than one codon in the mRNA.

Inquiry question

? How is the wobble phenomenon related to the number of tRNAs and the degeneracy of the genetic code?

Termination requires accessory factors

Elongation continues in this fashion until a chain-terminating stop codon is reached (for example, UAA in figure 15.21). These stop codons do not bind to tRNA; instead, they are recognized by release factors, proteins that release the newly made poly-peptide from the ribosome.

Proteins may be targeted to the ER

In eukaryotes, translation can occur either in the cytoplasm or on the RER. Proteins that are translated on the RER are targeted there based on their own initial amino acid sequence. The ribosomes found on the RER are actively trans-lating and are not permanently bound to the ER.

A polypeptide that starts with a short series of amino acids called a **signal sequence** is specifically recognized and bound by a cytoplasmic complex of proteins called the *signal recognition particle (SRP)*. The complex of signal sequence and SRP is in turn recognized by a receptor protein in the ER membrane. The binding of the ER receptor to the signal sequence/SRP complex holds the ribosome engaged in translation of the protein on the ER membrane, a process called *docking* (figure 15.22).

As the protein is assembled, it passes through a channel formed by the docking complex and into the interior ER com-partment, the cisternal space. This is the basis for the docking metaphor—the ribosome is not actually bound to the ER itself, but with the newly synthesized protein entering the ER, the ribosome is like a boat tied to a dock with a rope.

The basic mechanism of protein translocation across membranes by the SRP and its receptor and channel complex has been conserved across all three cell types: eukaryotes, bac-teria, and archaea. Given that only eukaryotic cells have an en-domembrane system, this universality may seem curious; however, bacteria and archaea both export proteins through their plasma membrane, and the mechanism used is similar to the way in which eukaryotes move proteins into the cisternal space of the ER.

Once within the ER cisternal space, or lumen, the newly synthesized protein can be modified by the addition of sugars (glycosylation) and transported by vesicles to the Golgi appara-tus (see chapter 4). This is the beginning of the protein-trafficking pathway that can lead to other intracellular targets, to incorporation into the plasma membrane, or to release out-side of the cell itself.

Learning Outcomes Review 15.7

Translation initiation involves the interaction of the small ribosomal subunit with mRNA and a charged initiator tRNA. The elongation cycle involves bringing in new charged tRNAs to the ribosome's A site, forming peptide bonds between amino acids, and translocating the ribosome along the mRNA chain. The tRNAs transit through the ribosome from A to P to E sites during the process. In eukaryotes, signal sequences of a newly forming polypeptide may target it and its ribosome to be moved to the RER. Polypeptides formed on the RER enter the cisternal space rather than being released into the cytoplasm.

■ *What stages of translation require energy?*

15.8 Summarizing Gene Expression

Because of the complexity of the process of gene expression, it is worth stepping back to summarize some key points:

- The process of gene expression converts information in the genotype into the phenotype.
- A copy of the gene in the form of mRNA is produced by transcription, and the mRNA is used to direct the synthesis of a protein by translation.
- Both transcription and translation can be broken down into initiation, elongation, and termination cycles that produce their respective polymers. (The same is true for DNA replication.)
- Eukaryotic gene expression is much more complex than that of prokaryotes.

The nature of eukaryotic genes with their intron and exon components greatly complicates the process of gene expression by requiring additional steps between transcription and trans-lation. The production and processing of eukaryotic mRNAs also takes place in the nucleus, whereas translation takes place in the cytoplasm. This necessitates the transport of the mRNA through the nuclear pores to the cytoplasm before translation can take place. The entire eukaryotic process is summarized in figure 15.23.

A number of differences can be highlighted between gene expression in prokaryotes and in eukaryotes. Table 15.2 (on p. 298) summarizes these main points.

Learning Outcome Review 15.8

The greater complexity of eukaryotic gene expression is related to the functional organization of the cell, with DNA in the nucleus and ribosomes in the cytoplasm. The differences in gene expression between prokaryotes and eukaryotes is mainly in detail, but some differences have functional significance.

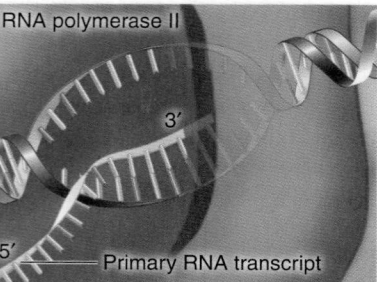

1. RNA polymerase II in the nucleus copies one strand of the DNA to produce the primary transcript.

RNA polymerase II

3′

5′ — Primary RNA transcript

Figure 15.23 An overview of gene expression in eukaryotes.

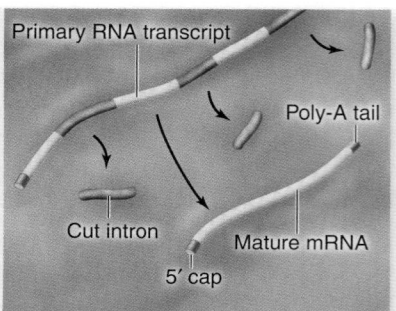

2. The primary transcript is processed by addition of a 5′ methyl-G cap, cleavage and polyadenylation of the 3′ end, and removal of introns. The mature mRNA is then exported through nuclear pores to the cytoplasm.

Primary RNA transcript
Poly-A tail
Cut intron
Mature mRNA
5′ cap

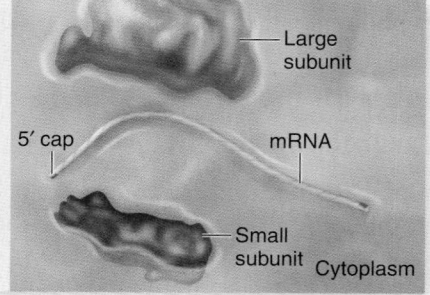

3. The 5′ cap of the mRNA associates with the small subunit of the ribosome. The initiator tRNA and large subunit are added to form an initiation complex.

Large subunit
5′ cap
mRNA
Small subunit
Cytoplasm

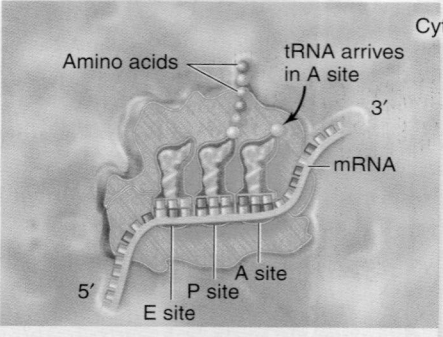

Cytoplasm
Amino acids
tRNA arrives in A site
3′
mRNA
A site
P site
E site
5′

4. The ribosome cycle begins with the growing peptide attached to the tRNA in the P site. The next charged tRNA binds to the A site with its anticodon complementary to the codon in the mRNA in this site.

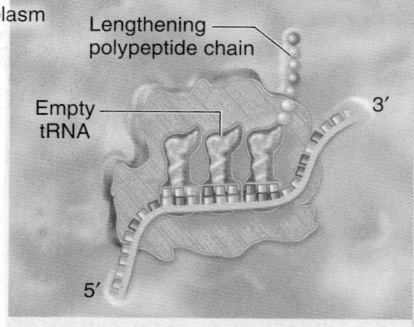

Lengthening polypeptide chain
Empty tRNA
3′
5′

5. Peptide bonds form between the amino terminus of the next amino acid and the carboxyl terminus of the growing peptide. This transfers the growing peptide to the tRNA in the A site, leaving the tRNA in the P site empty.

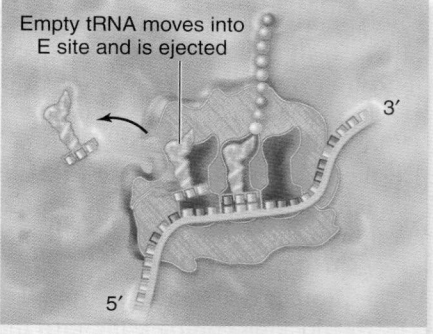

Empty tRNA moves into E site and is ejected
3′
5′

6. Ribosome translocation moves the ribosome relative to the mRNA and its bound tRNAs. This moves the growing chain into the P site, leaving the empty tRNA in the E site and the A site ready to bind the next charged tRNA.

TABLE 15.2	Differences Between Prokaryotic and Eukaryotic Gene Expression	
Characteristic	**Prokaryotes**	**Eukaryotes**
Introns	No introns, although some archaeal genes possess them.	Most genes contain introns.
Number of genes in mRNA	Several genes may be transcribed into a single mRNA molecule. Often these have related functions and form an operon, which helps coordinate regulation of biochemical pathways.	Only one gene per mRNA molecule; regulation of pathways accomplished in other ways.
Site of transcription and translation	No membrane-bounded nucleus, transcription and translation are coupled.	Transcription in nucleus; mRNA is transported to the cytoplasm for translation.
Initiation of translation	Begins at AUG codon preceded by special sequence that binds the ribosome.	Begins at AUG codon preceded by the 5′ cap (methylated GTP) that binds the ribosome.
Modification of mRNA after transcription	None; translation begins before transcription is completed. Transcription and translation are coupled.	A number of modifications while the mRNA is in the nucleus: Introns are removed and exons are spliced together; a 5′ cap is added; a poly-A tail is added.

15.9 Mutation: Altered Genes

Learning Outcomes

1. **Describe the effects of different point mutations.**
2. **Explain the nature of triplet repeat expansion.**
3. **List the different chromosomal mutations and their effects.**

One way to analyze the function of genes is to find or to induce mutations in a gene to see how this affects its function. In terms of the organism, however, inducing mutations is usually negative; most mutations have deleterious effects on the phenotype of the organism. In chapter 13, you saw how a number of genetic diseases, such as sickle cell anemia, are due to single base changes. We now consider mutations from the perspective of how the DNA itself is altered. Mutational changes range from the alteration of a single base to the loss of genetic material (deletion) to the loss of an entire chromosome. The change of a single base can result in changing a single amino acid in a protein, and this in turn can lead to a debilitating clinical phenotype. This is illustrated for the case of sickle cell anemia in figure 15.24. In the sickle cell allele, a single A is changed to a T resulting in a glutamic acid being replaced with a valine. The substitution of nonpolar valine causes the beta chains to aggregate into polymers, and this alters the shape of the cells, leading to the disease state.

Point mutations affect a single site in the DNA

A mutation that alters a single base is termed a **point mutation.** The mutation can be either the substitution of one base for another, or the deletion or addition of a single base (or a small number of bases).

Base substitution

The substitution of one base pair for another in DNA is called a **base substitution mutation.** Because of the degenerate nature of the genetic code, base substitution may or may not alter the amino acid encoded. If the new codon from the base substitution still encodes the same amino acid, we say the mutation is *silent* (figure 15.25b). When base substitution changes an amino acid in a protein, it is also called a **missense mutation** as the "sense" of the codon produced after transcription of the mutant gene will be altered (figure 15.25c). These fall into two classes, *transitions* and *transversions*. A transition does not change the type of bases in the base pair, that is, a pyrimidine is substituted for a pyrimidine, or purine for purine. In contrast, a transversion does change the type of bases in a base pair, that is, pyrimidine to purine or the reverse. A variety of human genetic diseases, including sickle cell anemia, are caused by base substitutions.

Nonsense mutations

A special category of base substitution arises when a base is changed such that the transcribed codon is converted to a stop codon (see figure 15.25d). We call these **nonsense mutations** because the mutation does not make "sense" to the translation apparatus. The stop codon results in premature termination of translation and leads to a truncated protein. How short the resulting protein is depends on where a stop codon has been introduced in the gene.

Frameshift mutations

The addition or deletion of a single base has much more profound consequences than does the substitution of one base for another. These mutations are called *frameshift mutations* because they alter the reading frame in the mRNA downstream of the mutation. This class of mutations was used by Crick and Brenner, as described earlier in the chapter, to infer the nature of the genetic code.

Changing the reading frame early in a gene, and thus in its mRNA transcript, means that the majority of the protein will be altered. Frameshifts also can cause premature termination of translation because 3 in 64 codons are stop codons, which represents a high probability in the sequence that has been randomized by the frameshift.

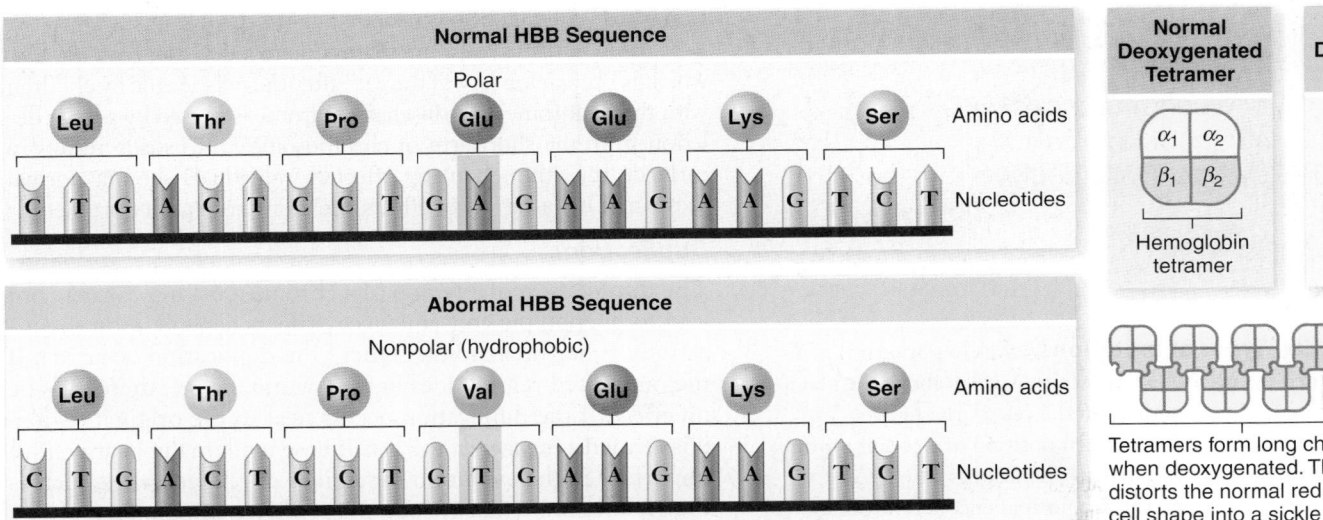
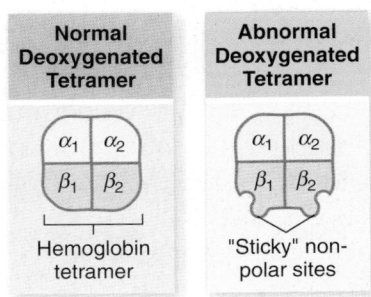
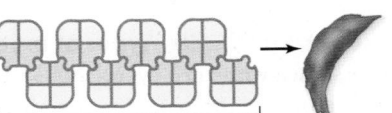

Figure 15.24 Sickle cell anemia is caused by an altered protein. Hemoglobin is composed of a tetramer of two α-globin and two β-globin chains. The sickle cell allele of the β-globin gene contains a single base change resulting in the substitution of Val for Glu. This creates a hydrophobic region on the surface of the protein that is "sticky" leading to their association into long chains that distort the shape of the red blood cells.

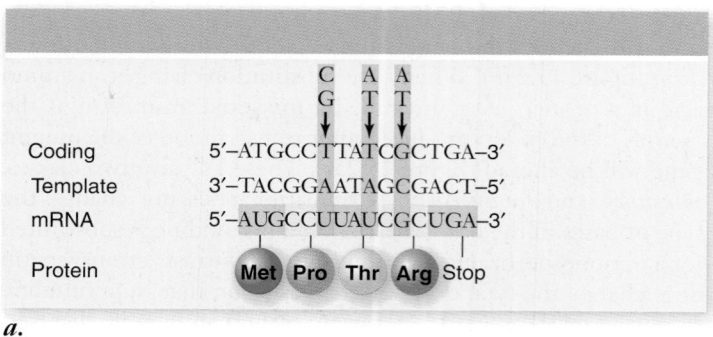

a.

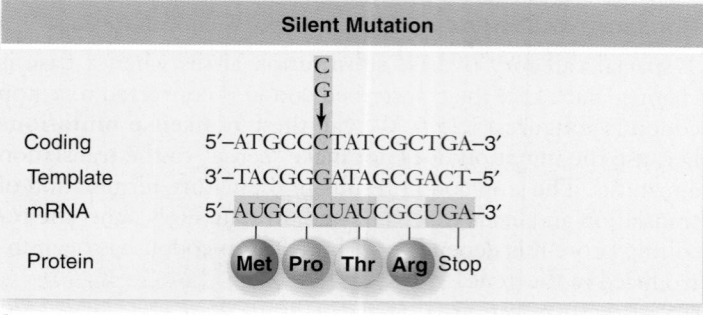

b.

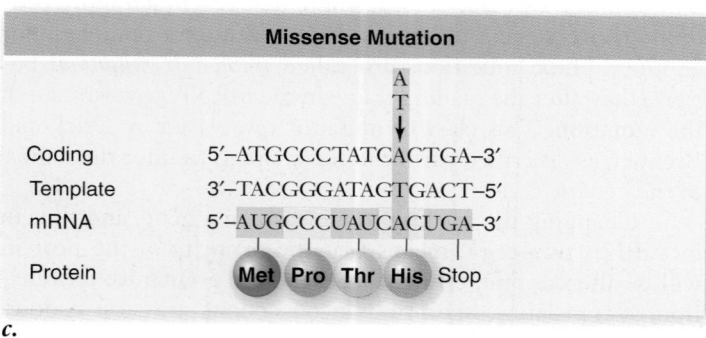

c.

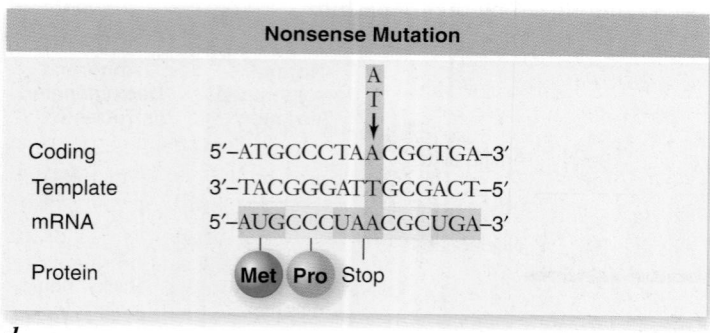

d.

Figure 15.25 **Types of mutations.** *a.* A hypothetical gene is shown with encoded mRNA and protein. Arrows above the gene indicate sites of mutations described in the rest of the figure. *b.* Silent mutation. A change in the third position of a codon is often silent due to degeneracy in the genetic code. In this case T/A to C/G mutation does not change the amino acid encoded (proline). *c.* Missesense mutation. The G/C to A/T mutation changes the amino acid encoded from arginine to histidine. *d.* Nonsense mutation. The T/A to A/T mutation produces a UAA stop codon in the mRNA.

Triplet repeat expansion mutations

Given the long history of molecular genetics, and the relatively short time that molecular analysis has been possible on humans, it is surprising that a new kind of mutation was discovered in humans. However, one of the first genes isolated that was associated with human disease, the gene for *Huntington disease*, provided a new kind of mutation. The gene for Huntington contains a triplet sequence of DNA that is repeated, and this repeat unit is expanded in the disease allele relative to the normal allele. Since this initial discovery, at least 20 other human genetic diseases appear to be due to this mechanism. The prevalence of this kind of mutation is unknown, but at present humans and mice are the only organisms in which they have been observed, implying that they may be limited to vertebrates, or even mammals. No such mutation has ever been found in *Drosophila* for example.

The expansion of the triplet can occur in the coding region or in noncoding transcribed DNA. In the case of Huntington disease, the repeat unit is actually in the coding region of the gene where the triplet encodes glutamine, and expansion results in a polyglutamine region in the protein. A number of other neurodegenerative disorders also show this kind of mutation. In the case of fragile-X syndrome, an inherited form of mental retardation, the repeat is in noncoding DNA.

Chromosomal mutations change the structure of chromosomes

Point mutations affect a single site in a chromosome, but more extensive changes can alter the structure of the chromosome itself, resulting in **chromosomal mutations**. Many human cancers are associated with chromosomal abnormalities, so these are of great clinical relevance. We briefly consider possible alterations to chromosomal structure, all of which are summarized in figure 15.26.

Deletions

A **deletion** is the loss of a portion of a chromosome. Frameshifts can be caused by one or more small deletions, but much larger regions of a chromosome may also be lost. If too much information is lost, the deletion is usually fatal to the organism.

One human syndrome that is due to a deletion is *cri-du-chat*, which is French for "cry of the cat" after the noise made by children with this syndrome. Cri-du-chat syndrome is caused by a large deletion from the short arm of chromosome 5. It usually results in early death, although many affected individuals show a normal lifespan. It has a variety of effects, including respiratory problems.

Duplications

The **duplication** of a region of a chromosome may or may not lead to phenotypic consequences. Effects depend upon the location of the "breakpoints" where the duplication occurred. If the duplicated region does not lie within a gene, there may be no effect. If the duplication occurs next to the original region, it is termed a *tandem duplication*. These tandem duplications are important in the evolution of families of related genes, such as the globin family that encode the protein hemoglobin.

Inversions

An **inversion** results when a segment of a chromosome is broken in two places, reversed, and put back together. An inversion

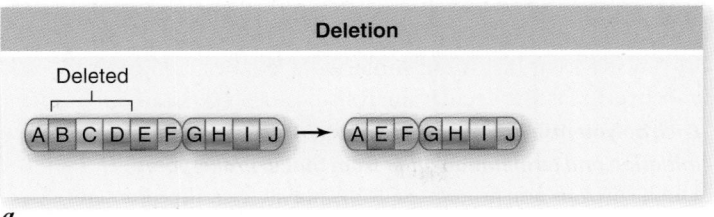

Deletion

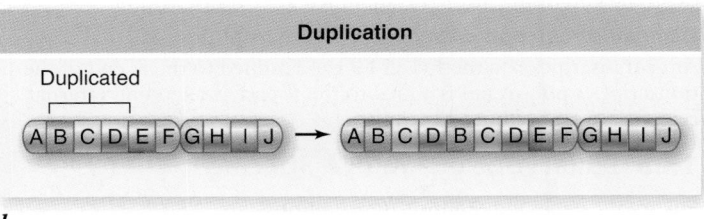

Duplication

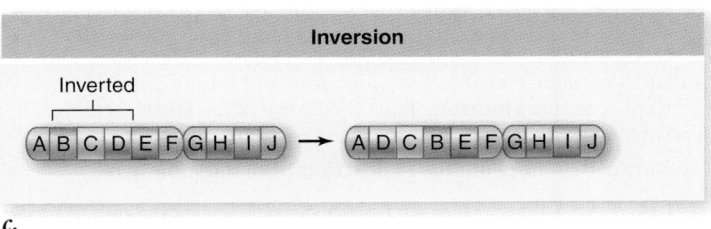

Inversion

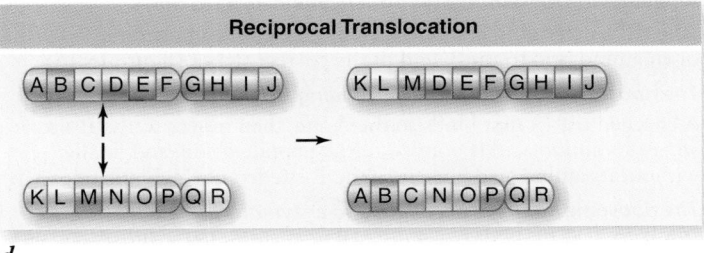

Reciprocal Translocation

d.

Figure 15.26 Chromosomal mutations. Larger-scale changes in chromosomes are also possible. Material can be deleted *(a)*, duplicated *(b)*, and inverted *(c)*. Translocations occur when one chromosome is broken and becomes part of another chromosome. This often occurs where both chromosomes are broken and exchange material, an event called a reciprocal translocation *(d)*.

may not have an effect on phenotype if the sites where the inversion occurs do not break within a gene. In fact, although humans all have the "same" genome, the order of genes in all individuals in a population is not precisely the same due to inversions that occur in different lineages.

Translocations

If a piece of one chromosome is broken off and joined to another chromosome, we call this a **translocation.** Translocations are complex because they can cause problems during meiosis, particularly when two different chromosomes try to pair with each other during meiosis I.

Translocations can also move genes from one chromosomal region to another in a manner that changes the expression of genes in the region involved. Two forms of leukemia have been shown to be associated with translocations that move oncogenes into regions of a chromosome where they are expressed inappropriately in blood cells.

Mutations are the starting point of evolution

If no changes occurred in genomes over time, then there could be no evolution. Too much change, however, is harmful to the individual with a greatly altered genome. Thus a delicate balance must exist between the amount of new variation that arises in a species and the health of individuals in the species. This topic is explored in more detail later in the book when we consider evolution and population genetics (chapter 20).

The larger scale alteration of chromosomes has also been important in evolution, although its role is poorly understood. It is clear that gene families arise by the duplication of an ancestral gene, followed by the functional divergence of the duplicated copies. It is also clear that even among closely related species, the number and arrangements of genes on chromosomes can differ. Large-scale rearrangements may have occurred.

Our view of the nature of genes has changed with new information

In this and the preceding chapters, we have seen multiple views of genes. Mendel used crosses to follow traits determined by what we now call genes. The behavior of these genes can be predicted based on the behavior of chromosomes during meiosis. Morgan and others learned to map the location of genes on chromosomes. These findings led to the view of genes as abstract entities that could be followed through generations and mapped to chromosomal locations like "beads on a string," with the beads being genes and the string the chromosome.

The original molecular analysis of genes led to the simple one-gene/one-polypeptide paradigm. This oversimplification was changed when geneticists observed the alternative splicing of eukaryotic genes, which can lead to multiple protein products from the same genetic information. Furthermore, some genes do not encode proteins at all, but only RNA, which can either be a part of the gene expression machinery (rRNA, tRNA, and other forms) or can itself act as an enzyme. Other stretches of DNA are important for regulating genes but are not expressed. All of these findings make a simple definition of genes difficult.

We are left with the rich complexity of the nature of genes, which defies simple definition. To truly understand the nature of genes we must consider both their molecular nature as well as their phenotypic expression. This brings us full circle, back to the relationship between genotype and phenotype, with a much greater appreciation for the complexity of this relationship.

Learning Outcomes Review 15.9

Point mutations (single-base changes, additions, or deletions) include missense mutations that cause substitution of one amino acid for another, nonsense mutations that halt transcription, and frameshift mutations that throw off the correct reading of codons. Triplet repeat expansion is the abnormal duplication of a codon with each round of cell division. Mutations affecting chromosomes include deletions, duplications, inversions, and translocations.

■ *Would an inversion or duplication always be expected to have a phenotype?*

15.1 The Nature of Genes

Garrod concluded that inherited disorders can involve specific enzymes.
Garrod found that alkaptonuria is due to an altered enzyme.

Beadle and Tatum showed that genes specify enzymes.
Neurospora mutants unable to synthesize arginine were found to lack specific enzymes. Beadle and Tatum advanced the "one gene/one polypeptide" hypothesis (figure 15.1).

The central dogma describes information flow in cells as DNA to RNA to protein (figure 15.2).
We call the DNA strand copied to mRNA the template (antisense) strand; the other the coding (sense) strand.

Transcription makes an RNA copy of DNA.

Translation uses information in RNA to synthesize proteins.
An adapter molecule, tRNA, is required to connect the information in mRNA into the sequence of amino acids.

RNA has multiple roles in gene expression.

15.2 The Genetic Code

The code is read in groups of three.
Crick and Brenner showed that the code is nonoverlapping and is read in groups of three. This finding established the concept of reading frame.

Nirenberg and others deciphered the code.
A codon consists of 3 nucleotides, so there are 64 possible codons. Three codons signal "stop," and one codon signals "start" and also encodes methionine. Thus 61 codons encode the 20 amino acids.

The code is degenerate but specific.
Many amino acids have more than one codon, but each codon specifies only a single amino acid.

The code is practically universal, but not quite.
In some mitochondrial and protist genomes, a STOP codon is read as an amino acid; otherwise the code is universal.

15.3 Prokaryotic Transcription

Prokaryotes have a single RNA polymerase.
Prokaryotic RNA polymerase exists in two forms: core polymerase, which can synthesize mRNA; and holoenzyme, core plus σ factor, which can accurately initiate synthesis (figure 15.6).

Initiation occurs at promoters.
Initiation requires a start site and a promoter. The promoter is upstream of the start site, and binding of RNA polymerase holoenzyme to its –35 region positions the polymerase properly.

Elongation adds successive nucleotides.
Transcription proceeds in the 5′-to-3′ direction. The transcription bubble contains RNA polymerase, the locally unwound DNA template, and the growing mRNA transcript (figure 15.7).

Termination occurs at specific sites.
Terminators consist of complementary sequences that form a double-stranded hairpin loop where the polymerase pauses (figure 15.8).

Prokaryotic transcription is coupled to translation.
Translation begins while mRNAs are still being transcribed.

15.4 Eukaryotic Transcription

Eukaryotes have three RNA polymerases.
RNA polymerase I transcribes rRNA; polymerase II transcribes mRNA and some snRNAs; polymerase III transcribes tRNA.

Each polymerase has its own promoter.

Initiation and termination differ from that in prokaryotes.
Unlike prokaryotic promoters, RNA polymerase II promoters require a host of transcription factors. Although termination sites exist, the end of the mRNA is modified after transcription.

Eukaryotic transcripts are modified (figure 15.11).
After transcription, a methyl-GTP cap is added to the 5′ end of the transcript. A poly-A tail is added to the 3′ end. Noncoding internal regions are also removed by splicing.

15.5 Eukaryotic pre-mRNA Splicing

Eukaryotic genes may contain interruptions.
Coding DNA (an exon) is interrupted by noncoding introns. These introns are removed by splicing (figure 15.13).

The spliceosome is the splicing organelle.
snRNPs recognize intron–exon junctions and recruit spliceosomes. The spliceosome ultimately joins the 3′ end of the first exon to the 5′ end of the next exon.

Splicing can produce multiple transcripts from the same gene.

15.6 The Structure of tRNA and Ribosomes

Aminoacyl-tRNA synthetases attach amino acids to tRNA.
The tRNA charging reaction attaches the carboxyl terminus of an amino acid to the 3′ end of the correct tRNA (figure 15.15).

The ribosome has multiple tRNA-binding sites (figure 15.16).
A charged tRNA first binds to the A site, then moves to the P site where its amino acid is bonded to the peptide chain, and finally, without its amino acid, moves to the E site from which it is released.

The ribosome has both decoding and enzymatic functions.
Ribosomes hold tRNAs and mRNA in position for a ribosomal enzyme to form peptide bonds.

15.7 The Process of Translation

Initiation requires accessory factors.
In prokaryotes, initiation-complex formation is aided by the ribosome-binding sequence (RBS) of mRNA, complementary to a small subunit. Eukaryotes use the 5′ cap for the same function.

Elongation adds successive amino acids (figure 15.20).
As the ribosome moves along the mRNA, new amino acids from charged tRNAs are added to the growing peptide (figure 15.19).

Termination requires accessory factors.
Stop codons are recognized by termination factors.

Proteins may be targeted to the ER.
In eukaryotes, proteins with a signal sequence in their amino terminus bind to the SRP, and this complex docks on the ER.
(15.8 Summary is omitted.)

15.9 Mutation: Altered Genes

Point mutations affect a single site in the DNA .
Base substitutions exchange one base for another, and frameshift mutations involve the addition or deletion of a base. Triplet repeat expansion mutations can cause genetic diseases.

Chromosomal mutations change the structure of chromosomes.
Chromosomal mutations include additions, deletions, inversions, or translocations.

Mutations are the starting point of evolution.
Our view of the nature of genes has changed with new information.

UNDERSTAND

1. The experiments with nutritional mutants in *Neurospora* by Beadle and Tatum provided evidence that
   a. bread mold can be grown in a lab on minimal media.
   b. X-rays can damage DNA.
   c. cells need enzymes.
   d. genes specify enzymes.

2. What is the *central dogma* of molecular biology?
   a. DNA is the genetic material.
   b. Information passes from DNA directly to protein.
   c. Information passes from DNA to RNA to protein.
   d. One gene encodes only one polypeptide.

3. In the genetic code, one codon
   a. consists of three bases.
   b. specifies a single amino acid.
   c. specifies more than one amino acid.
   d. both a & b

4. Eukaryotic transcription differs from prokaryotic in that
   a. eukaryotes have only one RNA polymerase.
   b. eukaryotes have three RNA polymerases.
   c. prokaryotes have three RNA polymerases.
   d. both a & c

5. An anticodon would be found on which of the following types of RNA?
   a. snRNA (small nuclear RNA)
   b. mRNA (messenger RNA)
   c. tRNA (transfer RNA)
   d. rRNA (ribosomal RNA)

6. RNA polymerase binds to a _____ to initiate _____.
   a. mRNA; translation
   b. promoter; transcription
   c. primer; transcription
   d. transcription factor; translation

7. During translation, the codon in mRNA is actually "read" by
   a. the A site in the ribosome.
   b. the P site in the ribosome.
   c. the anticodon in a tRNA.
   d. the anticodon in an amino acid.

APPLY

1. Which of the following functions as a "stop" signal for a prokaryotic RNA polymerase?
   a. A specific sequence of bases called a terminator
   b. The Poly-A site
   c. Addition of a 5′ cap
   d. A region of the mRNA that can base-pair to form a hairpin

2. The splicing process
   a. occurs in prokaryotes.
   b. joins introns together.
   c. can produce multiple mRNAs from the same transcript.
   d. only joins exons for each gene in one way.

3. During translation, the ribosome must move along the mRNA. This movement
   a. requires the ribosome to come apart into subunits.
   b. requires an accessory factor and energy.
   c. does not require energy, but requires the ribosome to change conformation.
   d. requires accessory factors and uses energy from peptide bond formation.

4. In comparing transcription in prokaryotes and eukaryotes the mRNAs
   a. differ in that eukaryotic mRNAs often encode more than one protein.
   b. differ in that prokaryotic mRNAs often encode more than one protein.
   c. are similar in that both are always colinear with their genes.
   d. are similar in that neither is colinear with their genes.

5. A nonsense mutation
   a. results in large scale change to a chromosome.
   b. will lead to the premature termination of transcription.
   c. will lead to the premature termination of translation.
   d. is the same as a transversion.

6. An inversion will
   a. necessarily cause a mutant phenotype.
   b. only cause a mutant phenotype if the inversion breakpoints fall within a gene.
   c. halt transcription in the inverted region because the chromosome is now backwards.
   d. interfere with translation of genes in the inverted region.

7. What is the relationship between mutations and evolution?
   a. Mutations make genes better.
   b. Mutations can create new alleles.
   c. Mutations happened early in evolution, but not now.
   d. There is no relationship between evolution and genetic mutations.

SYNTHESIZE

1. A template strand of DNA has the following sequence:
   3′ – CGTTACCCGAGCCGTACGATTAGG – 5′
   Use the sequence information to determine
   a. the predicted sequence of the mRNA for this gene.
   b. the predicted amino acid sequence of the protein.

2. Frameshift mutations often result in truncated proteins. Explain this observation based on the genetic code.

3. Describe how each of the following mutations will affect the final protein product (protein begins with START codon). Name the type of mutation.
   Original template strand:
   3′ – CGTTACCCGAGCCGTACGATTAGG – 5′
   a. 3′ – CGTTACCCGAGCCGTAACGATTAGG – 5′
   b. 3′ – CGTTACCCGATCCGTACGATTAGG – 5′
   c. 3′ – CGTTACCCGAGCCGTTCGATTAGG – 5′

4. There are a number of features that are unique to bacteria, and others that are unique to eukaryotes. Could any of these features offer the possibility to control gene expression in a way that is unique to either eukaryotes or bacteria?

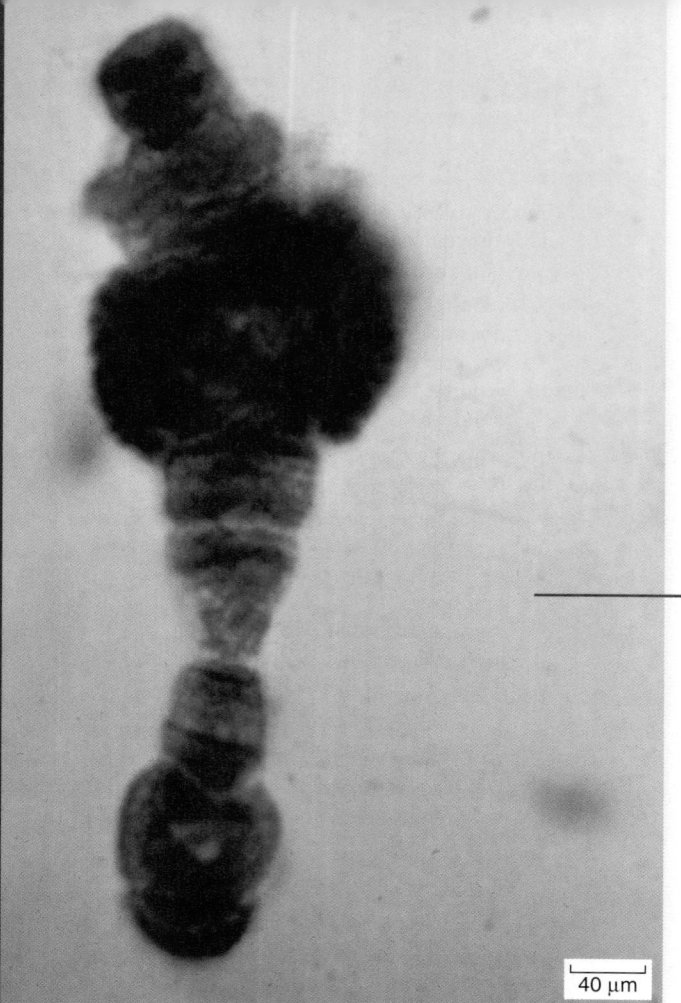

40 μm

Chapter **16**

Control of Gene Expression

Chapter Outline

16.1 Control of Gene Expression

16.2 Regulatory Proteins

16.3 Prokaryotic Regulation

16.4 Eukaryotic Regulation

16.5 Eukaryotic Chromatin Structure

16.6 Eukaryotic Posttranscriptional Regulation

16.7 Protein Degradation

Introduction

In a symphony, various instruments play their own parts at different times; the musical score determines which instruments play when. Similarly, in an organism, different genes are expressed at different times, with a "genetic score," written in regulatory regions of the DNA, determining which genes are active when. The picture shows the expanded "puff" of this Drosophila *chromosome, which represents genes that are being actively expressed. Gene expression and how it is controlled is our topic in this chapter.*

16.1 *Control of Gene Expression*

Learning Outcomes

1. *Identify the point at which control of gene expression usually occurs.*
2. *Describe the usual action of regulatory proteins.*
3. *List differences between control of gene expression in prokaryotes and that in eukaryotes.*

Control of gene expression is essential to all organisms. In prokaryotes, it allows the cell to take advantage of changing environmental conditions. In multicellular eukaryotes, it is critical for directing development and maintaining homeostasis.

Control usually occurs at the level of transcription initiation

You learned in the previous chapter that gene expression is the conversion of genotype to phenotype—the flow of information from DNA to produce functional proteins that control cellular activities. We could envision controlling this process at any point along the way, and in fact, examples of control occur at most steps. The most logical place to control this process, however, is at the beginning: production of mRNA from DNA by transcription.

Transcription itself could be controlled at any step, but again, the beginning is the most logical place. Although cells do not always behave in ways that conform to human logic, control of the initiation of transcription is common.

RNA polymerase is key to transcription, and it must have access to the DNA helix and must be capable of binding to the gene's promoter for transcription to begin. **Regulatory proteins** act by modulating the ability of RNA polymerase to bind to the promoter. This idea of controlling the access of RNA polymerase to a promoter is common to both prokaryotes and eukaryotes, but the details differ greatly, as you will see.

These regulatory proteins bind to specific nucleotide sequences on the DNA that are usually only 10–15 nt in length. (Even a large regulatory protein has a "footprint," or binding area, of only about 20 nt.) Hundreds of these regulatory sequences have been characterized, and each provides a binding site for a specific protein that is able to recognize the sequence. Binding of the protein either *blocks* transcription by getting in the way of RNA polymerase or *stimulates* transcription by facilitating the binding of RNA polymerase to the promoter.

Control strategies in prokaryotes are geared to adjust to environmental changes

Control of gene expression is accomplished very differently in prokaryotes than it is in eukaryotes. Prokaryotic cells have been shaped by evolution to grow and divide as rapidly as possible, enabling them to exploit transient resources. Proteins in prokaryotes turn over rapidly, allowing these organisms to respond quickly to changes in their external environment by changing patterns of gene expression.

In prokaryotes, the primary function of gene control is to adjust the cell's activities to its immediate environment. Changes in gene expression alter which enzymes are present in response to the quantity and type of available nutrients and the amount of oxygen. Almost all of these changes are fully reversible, allowing the cell to adjust its enzyme levels up or down in response to environment changes.

Control strategies in eukaryotes are aimed at maintaining homeostasis

The cells of multicellular organisms, in contrast, have been shaped by evolution to be protected from transient changes in their immediate environment. Most of them experience fairly constant conditions. Indeed, *homeostasis*—the maintenance of a constant internal environment—is considered by many to be the hallmark of multicellular organisms. Cells in such organisms respond to signals in their immediate environment (such as growth factors and hormones) by altering gene expression, and in doing so they participate in regulating the body as a whole.

Some of these changes in gene expression compensate for changes in the physiological condition of the body. Others mediate the decisions that actually produce the body, ensuring that the correct genes are expressed in the right cells at the right time during development. Later chapters deal with the details,

but for now we can simplify by saying that the growth and development of multicellular organisms entail a long series of biochemical reactions, each catalyzed by a specific enzyme. Once a particular developmental change has occurred, these enzymes cease to be active, lest they disrupt the events that must follow.

To produce this sequence of enzymes, genes are transcribed in a carefully prescribed order, each for a specified period of time, following a fixed genetic program that may even lead to programmed cell death **(apoptosis).** The one-time expression of the genes that guide a developmental program is fundamentally different from the reversible metabolic adjustments prokaryotic cells make in response to the environment. In all multicellular organisms, changes in gene expression within particular cells serve the needs of the whole organism, rather than the survival of individual cells.

Unicellular eukaryotes also use different control mechanisms from those of prokaryotes. All eukaryotes have a membrane-bounded nucleus, use similar mechanisms to condense DNA into chromosomes, and have the same gene expression machinery, all of which differ from those of prokaryotes.

Learning Outcomes Review 16.1

Gene expression is usually controlled at the level of transcription initiation. Regulatory proteins bind to specific DNA sequences and affect the binding of RNA polymerase to promoters. Individual protein may either prevent or stimulate transcription. In prokaryotes, regulation is focused on adjusting the cell's activities to the environment to ensure viability. In multicellular eukaryotes, regulation is geared to maintaining internal homeostasis, and even in unicellular forms, this control has mechanisms to deal with a bounded nucleus and multiple chromosomes.

■ *Would you expect the control of gene expression in a unicellular eukaryote like yeast to be more like that of humans or E. coli?*

16.2 Regulatory Proteins

Learning Outcomes

1. *Explain how proteins can interact with base pairs without unwinding the helix.*
2. *Describe the common features of DNA-binding motifs.*

The ability of certain proteins to bind to *specific* DNA regulatory sequences provides the basic tool of gene regulation—the key ability that makes transcriptional control possible. To understand how cells control gene expression, it is first necessary to gain a clear picture of this molecular recognition process.

Proteins can interact with DNA through the major groove

In the past, molecular biologists thought that the DNA helix had to unwind before proteins could distinguish one DNA sequence from another; only in this way, they reasoned, could regulatory proteins gain access to the hydrogen bonds between base-pairs. We now know it is unnecessary for the helix to unwind because proteins can bind to its outside surface, where the edges of the base-pairs are exposed.

Careful inspection of a DNA molecule reveals two helical grooves winding around the molecule, one deeper than the other. Within the deeper groove, called the **major groove**, the nucleotides' hydrogen bond donors and acceptors are accessible. The pattern created by these chemical groups is unique for each of the four possible base-pair arrangements, providing a ready way for a protein nestled in the groove to read the sequence of bases (figure 16.1).

DNA-binding domains interact with specific DNA sequences

Protein–DNA recognition is an area of active research; so far, the structures of over 30 regulatory proteins have been analyzed. Although each protein is unique in its fine details, the part of the protein that actually binds to the DNA is much less variable. Almost all of these proteins employ one of a small set of **DNA-binding motifs.** A motif, as described in chapter 3, is a form of three-dimensional substructure that is found in many proteins. These DNA-binding motifs share the property of interacting with specific sequences of bases, usually through the major groove of the DNA helix.

DNA-binding motifs are the key structure within the DNA-binding domain of these proteins. This domain is a functionally distinct part of the protein necessary to bind to DNA in a sequence-specific manner. Regulatory proteins also need to be able to interact with the transcription apparatus, which is accomplished by a different regulatory domain.

Note that two proteins that share the same DNA-binding domain do not necessarily bind to the same DNA sequence. The similarities in the DNA-binding motifs appear in their three-dimensional structure, and not in the specific contacts that they make with DNA.

Several common DNA-binding motifs are shared by many proteins

A limited number of common DNA-binding motifs are found in a wide variety of different proteins. Four of the best known are detailed in the following sections to give the sense of how DNA-binding proteins interact with DNA.

The helix-turn-helix motif

The most common DNA-binding motif is the **helix-turn-helix,** constructed from two α-helical segments of the protein linked by a short, nonhelical segment, the "turn" (figure 16.2a). As the first motif recognized, the helix-turn-helix motif has since been identified in hundreds of DNA-binding proteins.

A close look at the structure of a helix-turn-helix motif reveals how proteins containing such motifs interact with the major groove of DNA. The helical segments of the motif interact with one another, so that they are held at roughly right angles. When this motif is pressed against DNA, one of the helical

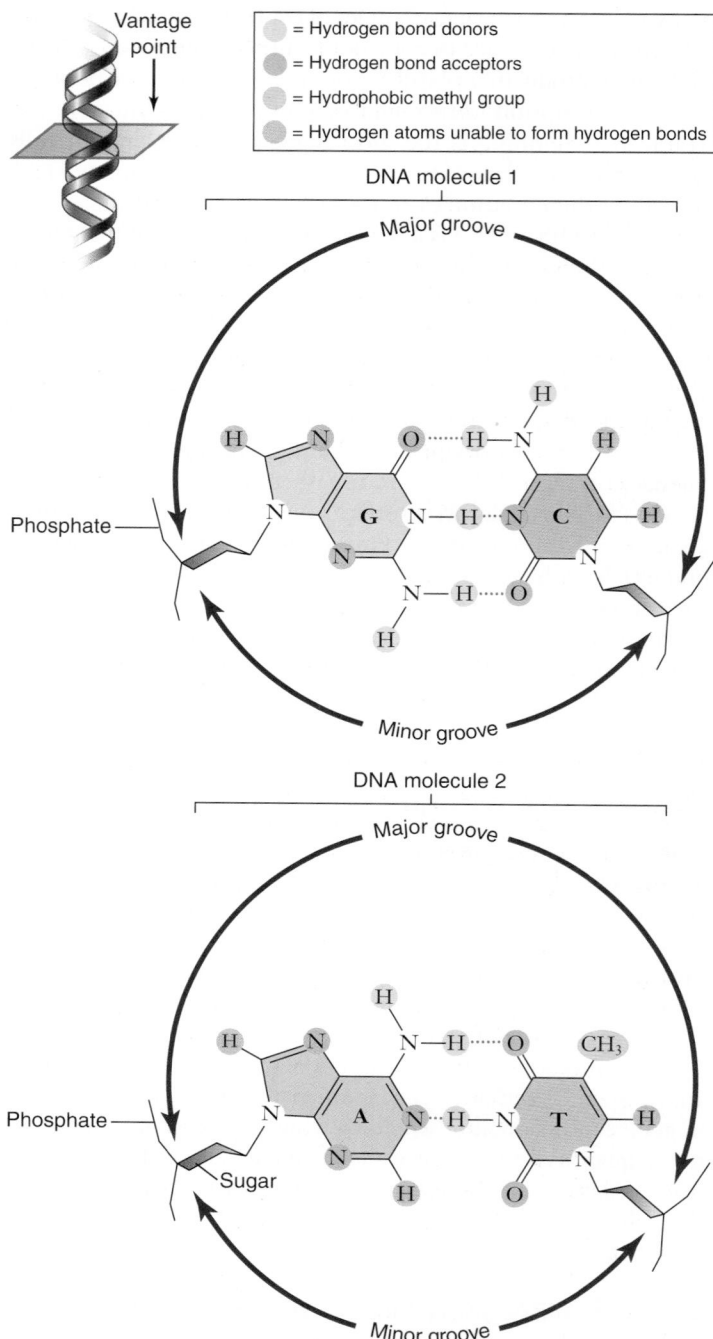

Figure 16.1 Reading the major groove of DNA. Looking down into the major groove of a DNA helix, we can see the edges of the bases protruding into the groove. Each of the four possible base-pair arrangements (two are shown here) extends a unique set of chemical groups into the groove, indicated in this diagram by differently colored circles. A regulatory protein can identify the base-pair arrangement by this characteristic signature.

segments (called the *recognition helix*) fits snugly in the major groove of the DNA molecule, and the other butts up against the outside of the DNA molecule, helping to ensure the proper positioning of the recognition helix.

Most DNA-regulatory sequences recognized by helix-turn-helix motifs occur in symmetrical pairs. Such sequences are bound by proteins containing two helix-turn-helix motifs separated by 3.4 nanometers (nm), the distance required for one turn of the DNA helix (see figure 16.2*a*). Having *two* protein–DNA-binding sites doubles the zone of contact between protein and DNA and greatly strengthens the bond between them.

The homeodomain motif

A special class of helix-turn-helix motifs, the **homeodomain,** plays a critical role in development in a wide variety of eukaryotic organisms, including humans. These motifs were discovered when researchers began to characterize a set of homeotic mutations in *Drosophila* (mutations that cause one body part to be replaced by another). They found that the mutant genes encoded regulatory proteins. Normally these proteins would initiate key stages of development by binding to developmental switch-point genes. More than 50 of these regulatory proteins have been analyzed, and they all contain a nearly identical sequence of 60 amino acids, which was termed the *homeodomain*. The most conserved part of the homeodomain contains a recognition helix of a helix-turn-helix motif. The rest of the homeodomain forms the other two helices of this motif.

The zinc finger motif

A different kind of DNA-binding motif uses one or more zinc atoms to coordinate its binding to DNA. Called **zinc fingers**, these motifs exist in several forms. In one form, a zinc atom links an α-helical segment to a β-sheet segment (see chapter 3) so that the helical segment fits into the major groove of DNA.

This sort of motif often occurs in clusters, the β sheets spacing the helical segments so that each helix contacts the major groove. The effect is like a hand wrapped around the DNA with the fingers lying in the major groove. The more zinc fingers in the cluster, the stronger the protein binds to the DNA.

The leucine zipper motif

In yet another DNA-binding motif, two different protein subunits cooperate to create a single DNA-binding site. This motif is created where a region on one subunit containing several hydrophobic amino acids (usually leucines) interacts with a similar region on the other subunit. This interaction holds the two subunits together at those regions, while the rest of the subunits remain separated. Called a **leucine zipper,** this structure has the shape of a Y, with the two arms of the Y being helical regions that fit into the major groove of DNA (figure 16.2*b*). Because the two subunits can contribute quite different helical regions to the motif, leucine zippers allow for great flexibility in controlling gene expression.

Learning Outcomes Review 16.2

A DNA helix exhibits a major groove and a minor groove; regulatory proteins interact with DNA by accessing bases along the major groove. These proteins all contain DNA-binding motifs, and they often include one or two α-helical segments. These motifs form the active part of the DNA-binding domain, and another domain of the protein interacts with the transcription apparatus.

■ **What would be the effect of a mutation in a helix-turn-helix protein that altered the spacing of the two helices?**

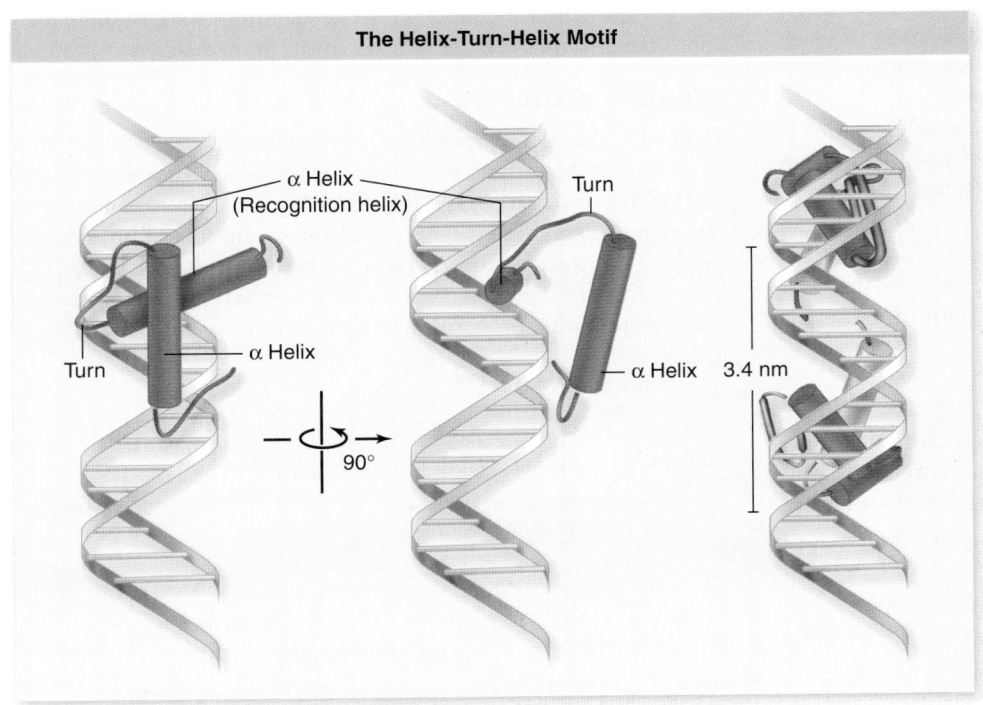

The Helix-Turn-Helix Motif

α Helix (Recognition helix)

Turn

α Helix

Turn

α Helix

3.4 nm

90°

a.

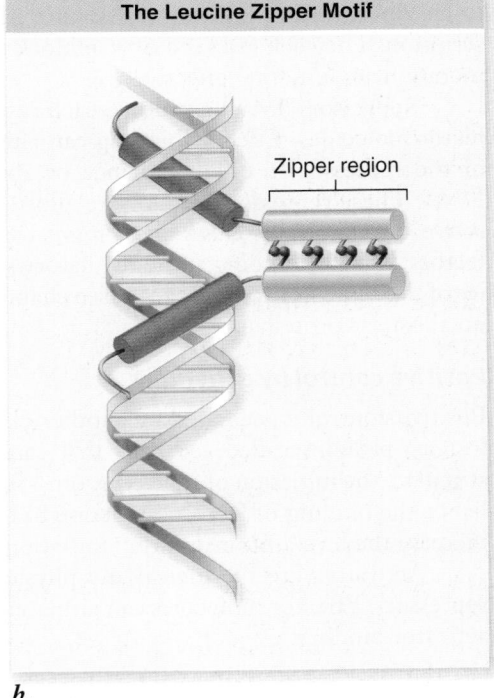

The Leucine Zipper Motif

Zipper region

b.

Figure 16.2 Major DNA-binding motifs. Two different DNA-binding motifs are pictured interacting with DNA. *a.* The helix-turn-helix motif binds to DNA using one α helix, the recognition helix, to interact with the major groove. The other helix positions the recognition helix. Proteins with this motif are usually dimers, with two identical subunits, each containing the DNA-binding motif. The two copies of the motif *(red)* are separated by 3.4 nm, precisely the spacing of one turn of the DNA helix. *b.* The leucine zipper acts to hold two subunits in a multisubunit protein together, thereby allowing α-helical regions to interact with DNA.

Prokaryotic Regulation

The details of regulation can be revealed by examining mechanisms used by prokaryotes to control the initiation of transcription. Prokaryotes and eukaryotes share some common themes, but they have some profound differences as well. Later on we discuss eukaryotic systems and concentrate on how they differ from the simpler prokaryotic systems.

Control of transcription can be either positive or negative

Control at the level of transcription initiation can be either positive or negative. **Positive control** increases the frequency of initiation, and **negative control** decreases the frequency of initiation. Each of these forms of control are mediated by regulatory proteins, but the proteins have opposite effects.

Negative control by repressors

Negative control is mediated by proteins called **repressors.** Repressors are proteins that bind to regulatory sites on DNA called **operators** to prevent or decrease the initiation of transcription. They act as a kind of roadblock to prevent the polymerase from initiating effectively.

Repressors do not act alone; each responds to specific effector molecules. Effector binding can alter the conformation of the repressor to either enhance or abolish its binding to DNA. These repressor proteins are allosteric proteins with an active site that binds DNA and a regulatory site that binds effectors. Effector binding at the regulatory site changes the ability of the repressor to bind DNA (see chapter 6 for more details on allosteric proteins).

Positive control by activators

Positive control is mediated by another class of regulatory, allosteric proteins called *activators* that can bind to DNA and stimulate the initiation of transcription. These activators enhance the binding of RNA polymerase to the promoter to increase the level of transcription initiation.

Activators are the logical and physical opposites of repressors. Effector molecules can either enhance or decrease activator binding.

Prokaryotes adjust gene expression in response to environmental conditions

Changes in the environments that bacteria and archaea encounter often result in changes in gene expression. In general, genes encoding proteins involved in catabolic pathways (breaking down molecules) respond oppositely from genes encoding proteins involved in anabolic pathways (building up molecules). In the discussion that follows, we describe enzymes in the catabolic pathway that transports and utilizes the sugar lactose. Later we describe the anabolic pathway that synthesizes the amino acid tryptophan.

As mentioned in the preceding chapter, prokaryotic genes are often organized into operons, multiple genes that are part of a single transcription unit having a single promoter. Genes that are involved in the same metabolic pathway are often organized in this fashion. The proteins necessary for the utilization of lactose are encoded by the *lac* **operon,** and the proteins necessary for the synthesis of tryptophan are encoded by the *trp* **operon.**

Induction and repression

If a bacterium encounters lactose, it begins to make the enzymes necessary to utilize lactose. When lactose is not present, however, there is no need to make these proteins. Thus, we say that the synthesis of the proteins is *induced* by the presence of lactose. **Induction** therefore occurs when enzymes for a certain pathway are produced in response to a substrate.

When tryptophan is available in the environment, a bacterium will not synthesize the enzymes necessary to make tryptophan. If tryptophan ceases to be available, then the bacterium begins to make these enzymes. **Repression** occurs when bacteria capable of making biosynthetic enzymes do not produce them. In the case of both induction and repression, the bacterium is adjusting to produce the enzymes that are optimal for its immediate environment.

Negative control

Knowing that gene expression is probably controlled at the level of initiation of transcription does not tell us whether that control is positive or negative. On the surface, repression may appear to be negative and induction positive; but in the case of both the *lac* and *trp* operons, control is negative by a repressor protein. The key is that the effector proteins have opposite effects on the repressor in induction with those seen in repression.

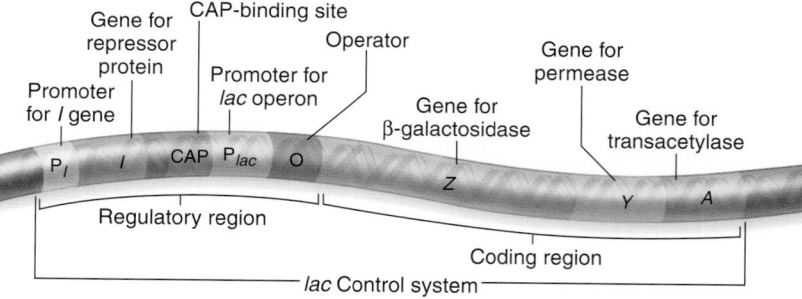

Figure 16.3 **The *lac* region of the *Escherichia coli* chromosome.** The *lac* operon consists of a promoter, an operator, and three genes (*lac Z, Y,* and *A*) that encode proteins required for the metabolism of lactose. In addition, there is a binding site for the catabolite activator protein (CAP), which affects RNA polymerase binding to the promoter. The *I* gene encodes the repressor protein, which can bind the operator and block transcription of the *lac* operon.

For either mechanism to work, the molecule in the environment, such as lactose or tryptophan, must produce the proper effect on the gene being regulated. In the case of *lac* induction, the presence of lactose must *prevent* a repressor protein from binding to its regulatory sequence. In the case of *trp* repression, by contrast, the presence of tryptophan must *cause* a repressor protein to bind to its regulatory sequence.

These responses are opposite because the needs of the cell are opposite in anabolic versus catabolic pathways. Each pathway is examined in detail in the following sections to show how protein–DNA interactions allow the cell to respond to environmental conditions.

The *lac* operon is negatively regulated by the *lac* repressor

The control of gene expression in the *lac* operon was elucidated by the pioneering work of Jaques Monod and François Jacob.

The *lac* operon consists of the genes that encode functions necessary to utilize lactose: β-galactosidase (*lacZ*), lactose permease (*lacY*), and lactose transacetylase (*lacA*), plus the regulatory regions necessary to control the expression of these genes (figure 16.3). In addition, the gene for the *lac* repressor (*lacI*) is linked to the rest of the *lac* operon and is thus considered part of the operon although it has its own promoter. The arrangement of the control regions upstream of the coding region is typical of most prokaryotic operons, although the linked repressor is not.

Action of the repressor

Initiation of transcription of the *lac* operon is controlled by the *lac* repressor. The repressor binds to the operator, which is adjacent to the promoter (figure 16.4a). This binding prevents RNA polymerase from binding to the promoter. This DNA binding is sensitive to the presence of lactose: The repressor binds DNA in the absence of lactose, but not in the presence of lactose.

Interaction of repressor and inducer

In the absence of lactose, the *lac* repressor binds to the operator, and the operon is repressed (see figure 16.4a). The effector that controls the DNA binding of the repressor is a metabolite of

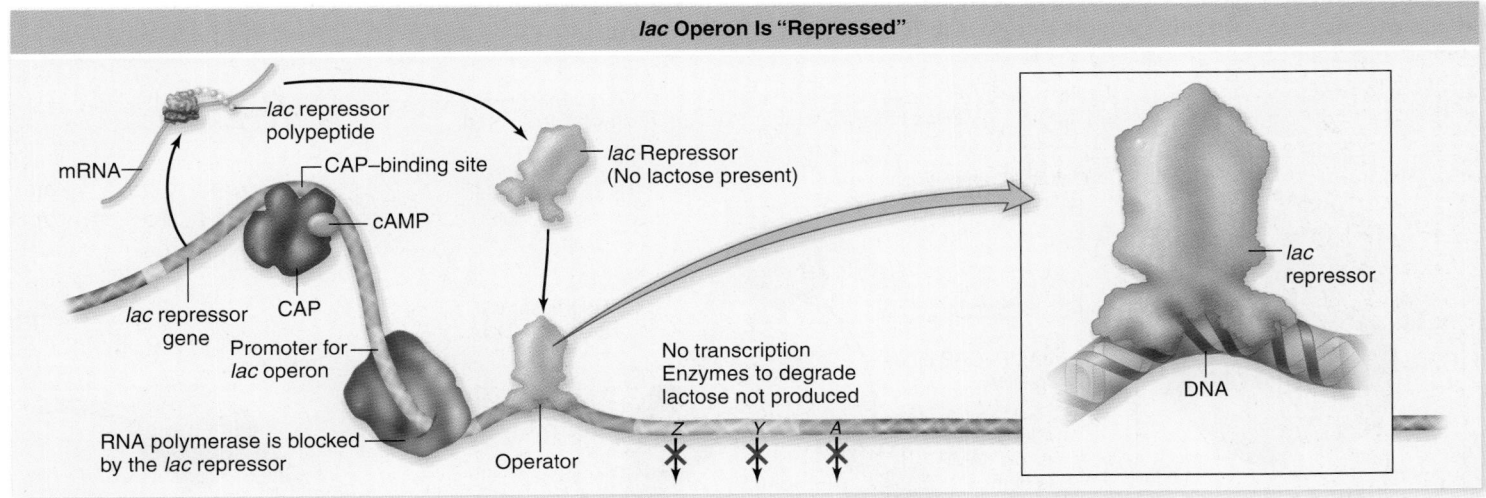

Figure 16.4 Induction of the *lac* operon. *a.* In the absence of lactose the *lac* repressor binds to DNA at the operator site, thus preventing transcription of the operon. When the repressor protein is bound to the operator site, the *lac* operon is shut down (repressed). *b.* The *lac* operon is transcribed (induced) when CAP is bound and when the repressor is not bound. Allolactose binding to the repressor alters the repressor's shape so it cannot bind to the operator site and block RNA polymerase activity.

lactose, allolactose, which is produced when lactose is available. Allolactose binds to the repressor, altering its conformation so that it no longer can bind to the operator (figure 16.4*b*). The operon is now induced. Since allolactose allows induction of the operon, it is usually called the inducer.

As the level of lactose falls, allolactose will no longer be available to bind to the repressor, allowing the repressor to bind to DNA again. Thus this system of negative control by the *lac* repressor and its inducer, allolactose, allows the cell to respond to changing levels of lactose in the environment.

Even in the absence of lactose, the *lac* operon is expressed at a very low level. When lactose becomes available, it is transported into the cell and enough allolactose is produced that induction of the operon can occur.

The presence of glucose prevents induction of the *lac* operon

Glucose repression is the preferential use of glucose in the presence of other sugars such as lactose. If bacteria are grown in the presence of both glucose and lactose, the *lac* operon is not induced. When the glucose is used up, the *lac* operon is induced, allowing lactose to be used as an energy source.

Despite the name *glucose repression*, this mechanism involves an activator protein that can stimulate transcription from multiple catabolic operons, including the *lac* operon. This activator, **catabolite activator protein (CAP),** is an allosteric protein with cAMP as an effector. This protein is also called **cAMP response protein (CRP)** because it binds cAMP, but we will use the name CAP to emphasize its role as a positive regulator. CAP alone does not bind to DNA, but binding of the effector cAMP to CAP changes its conformation such that it can bind to DNA (figure 16.5). The level of cAMP in cells is reduced in the presence of glucose so that no stimulation of transcription from CAP-responsive operons takes place.

The CAP–cAMP system was long thought to be the sole mechanism of glucose repression. But more recent research has indicated that the presence of glucose inhibits the transport of lactose into the cell. This deprives the cell of the *lac* operon inducer, allolactose, allowing the repressor to bind to the operator. This mechanism, called **inducer exclusion,** is now thought to be the main form of glucose repression of the *lac* operon.

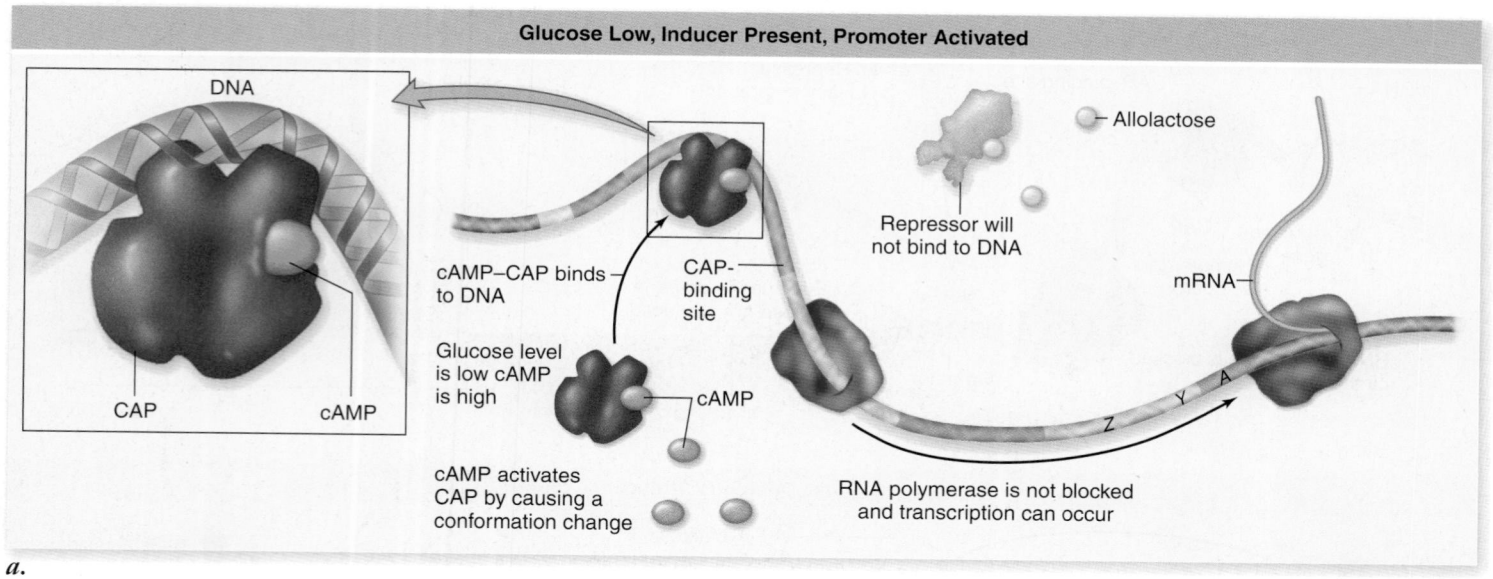

Glucose Low, Inducer Present, Promoter Activated

DNA

CAP — cAMP

cAMP–CAP binds to DNA

CAP-binding site

Glucose level is low cAMP is high

cAMP

cAMP activates CAP by causing a conformation change

Allolactose

Repressor will not bind to DNA

mRNA

Z Y A

RNA polymerase is not blocked and transcription can occur

a.

Figure 16.5 Effect of glucose on the *lac* operon. Expression of the *lac* operon is controlled by a negative regulator (repressor) and a positive regulator (CAP). The action of CAP is sensitive to glucose levels. *a.* For CAP to bind to DNA, it must bind to cAMP. When glucose levels are low, cAMP is abundant and binds to CAP. The CAP–cAMP complex causes the DNA to bend around it. This brings CAP into contact with RNA polymerase (not shown) making polymerase binding to the promoter more efficient. *b.* High glucose levels produce two effects: cAMP is scarce so CAP is unable to activate the promoter, and the transport of lactose is blocked (inducer exclusion).

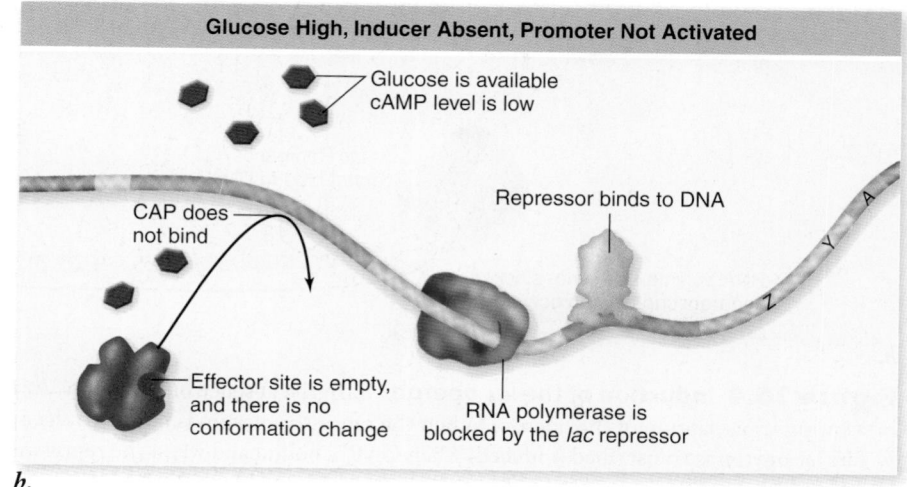

Glucose High, Inducer Absent, Promoter Not Activated

Glucose is available cAMP level is low

CAP does not bind

Repressor binds to DNA

Y A

Z

Effector site is empty, and there is no conformation change

RNA polymerase is blocked by the *lac* repressor

b.

Given that inducer exclusion occurs, the role of CAP in the absence of glucose seems superfluous. But in fact, the action of CAP–cAMP allows maximal expression of the operon in the absence of glucose. The positive control of CAP–cAMP is necessary because the promoter of the *lac* operon alone is not efficient in binding RNA polymerase. This inefficiency is overcome by the action of the positive control of the CAP–cAMP activator (see figure 16.5).

The *trp* operon is controlled by the *trp* repressor

Like the *lac* operon, the *trp* operon consists of a series of genes that encode enzymes involved in the same biochemical path-

way. In the case of the *trp* operon these enzymes are necessary for synthesizing tryptophan. The regulatory region that controls transcription of these genes is located upstream of the genes. The *trp* operon is controlled by a repressor encoded by a gene located outside the *trp* operon. The *trp* operon is continuously expressed in the absence of tryptophan and is not expressed in the presence of tryptophan.

The *trp* repressor is a helix-turn-helix protein that binds to the operator site located adjacent to the *trp* promoter (figure 16.6). This repressor behaves in a manner opposite to the *lac* repressor. In the absence of tryptophan, the *trp* repressor does not bind to its operator, allowing expression of the operon, and production of the enzymes necessary to make tryptophan.

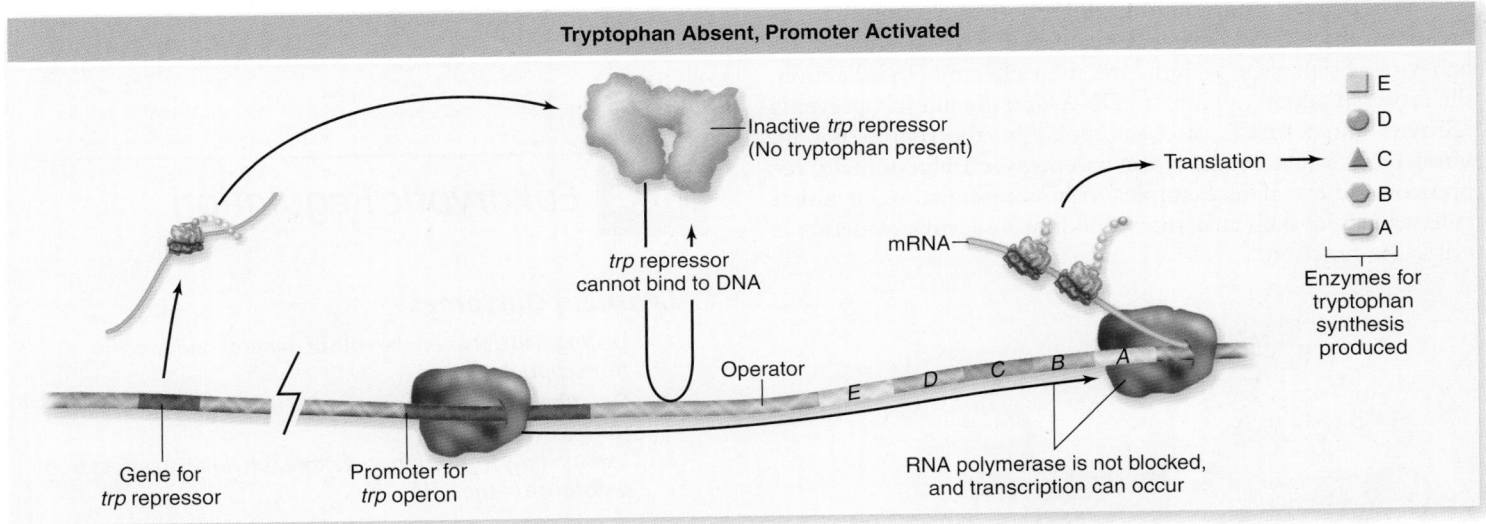

a.

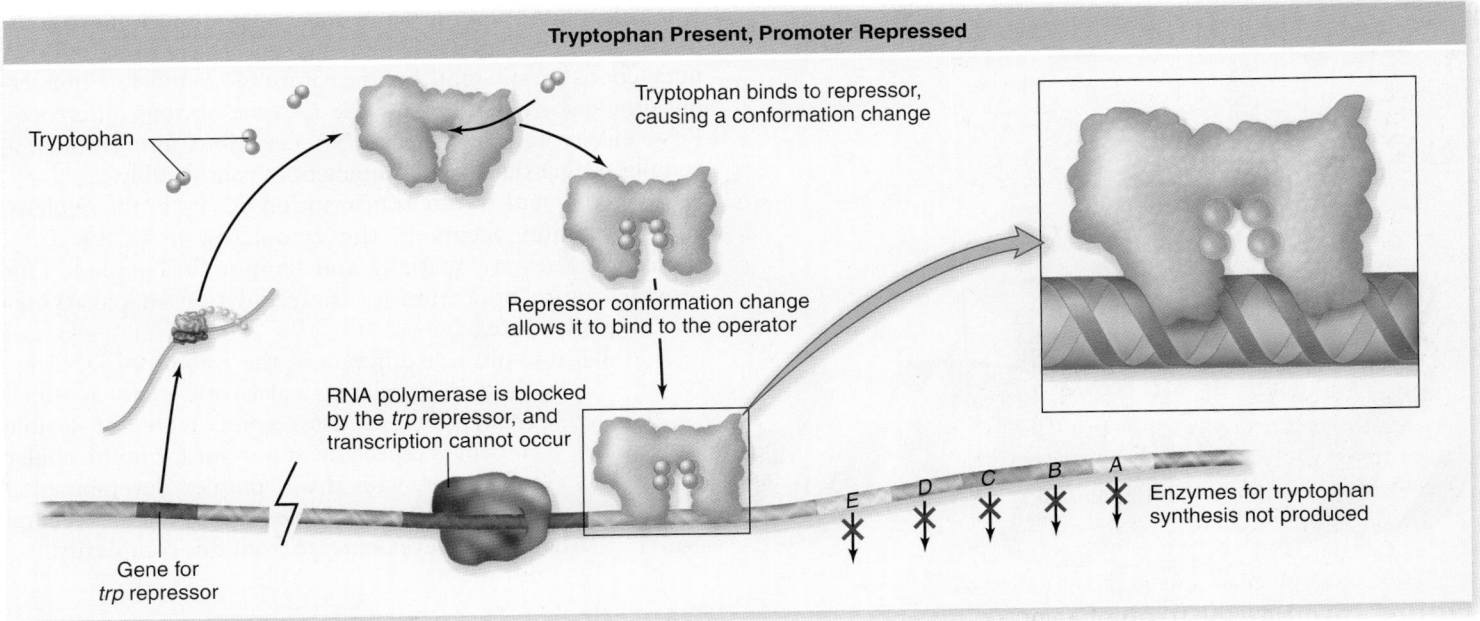

b.

Figure 16.6 How the *trp* operon is controlled. The tryptophan operon encodes the enzymes necessary to synthesize tryptophan. *a.* The tryptophan repressor alone cannot bind to DNA. The promoter is free to function, and RNA polymerase transcribes the operon. *b.* When tryptophan is present, it binds to the repressor, altering its conformation so it now binds DNA. The tryptophan–repressor complex binds tightly to the operator, preventing RNA polymerase from initiating transcription.

When levels of tryptophan rise, then tryptophan (the *corepressor*) binds to the repressor and alters its conformation, allowing it to bind to its operator. Binding of the repressor–corepressor complex to the operator prevents RNA polymerase from binding to the promoter. The actual change in repressor structure due to tryptophan binding is an alteration of the orientation of a pair of helix-turn-helix motifs that allows their recognition helices to fit into adjacent major grooves of the DNA (figure 16.7).

When tryptophan is present and bound to the repressor and this complex is bound to the operator, the operon is said to be *repressed*. As tryptophan levels fall, the repressor alone cannot bind to the operator, allowing expression of the operon. In this state, the operon is said to be **derepressed**, distinguishing this state from induction (see figure 16.6).

The key to understanding how both induction and repression can be due to negative regulation is knowledge of the behavior of repressor proteins and their effectors. In induction, the repressor alone can bind to DNA, and the inducer prevents DNA binding. In the case of repression, the repressor only binds DNA when bound to the corepressor. Induction and repression are excellent examples of how interactions of molecules can affect their structures, and how molecular structure is critical to function.

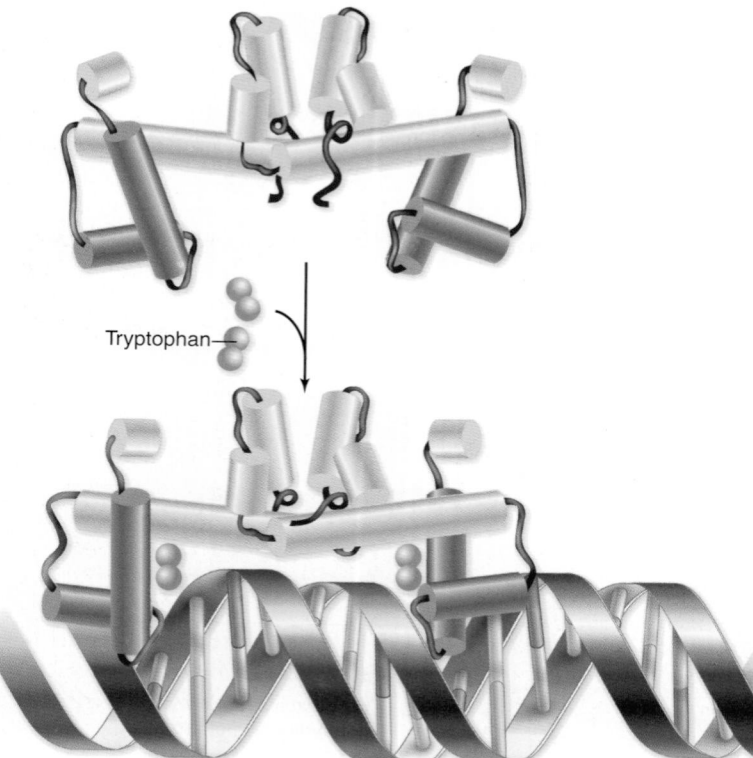

Figure 16.7 How the tryptophan repressor works. The binding of tryptophan to the repressor increases the distance between the two recognition helices in the repressor, allowing the repressor to fit snugly into two adjacent portions of the major groove in DNA.

Tryptophan

3.4 nm

16.4 Eukaryotic Regulation

The control of transcription in eukaryotes is much more complex than in prokaryotes. The basic concepts of protein–DNA interactions are still valid, but the nature and number of interacting proteins is much greater due to some obvious differences. First, eukaryotes have their DNA organized into chromatin, complicating protein–DNA interactions considerably.

Second, eukaryotic transcription occurs in the nucleus, and translation occurs in the cytoplasm; in prokaryotes, these processes are spatially and temporally coupled. This provides more opportunities for regulation in eukaryotes than in prokaryotes.

Because of these differences, the amount of DNA involved in regulating eukaryotic genes is much greater. The need for a fine degree of flexible control is especially important for multicellular eukaryotes, with their complex developmental programs and multiple tissue types. General themes, however, emerge from this complexity.

Transcription factors can be either general or specific

In the preceding chapter we introduced the concept of transcription factors. Eukaryotic transcription requires a variety of these protein factors, which fall into two categories: *general transcription factors* and *specific transcription factors*. General factors are necessary for the assembly of a transcription apparatus and recruitment of RNA polymerase II to a promoter. Specific factors increase the level of transcription in certain cell types or in response to signals.

General transcription factors

Transcription of RNA polymerase II templates (the majority being genes that encode protein products) requires more than just RNA polymerase II to initiate transcription. A host of **general transcription factors** are also necessary to establish productive initiation. These factors are required for transcription to occur, but they do not increase the rate above this basal rate.

General transcription factors are named with letter designations that follow the abbreviation TFII, for "transcription factor RNA polymerase II." The most important of these factors, TFIID, contains the TATA-binding protein that recognizes the TATA box sequence found in many eukaryotic promoters (figure 16.8).

Binding of TFIID is followed by binding of TFIIE, TFIIF, TFIIA, TFIIB, and TFIIH and a host of accessory factors called *transcription-associated factors*, TAFs. The *initiation complex* that results (figure 16.9) is clearly much more complex than the bacterial RNA polymerase holoenzyme binding to a promoter. And there is yet another level of complexity: The initiation complex, although capable of initiating synthesis at a basal level, does not achieve transcription at a high level without the participation of other, specific factors.

Specific transcription factors

Specific transcription factors act in a tissue- or time-dependent manner to stimulate higher levels of transcription than the basal level. The number and diversity of these factors are overwhelm-

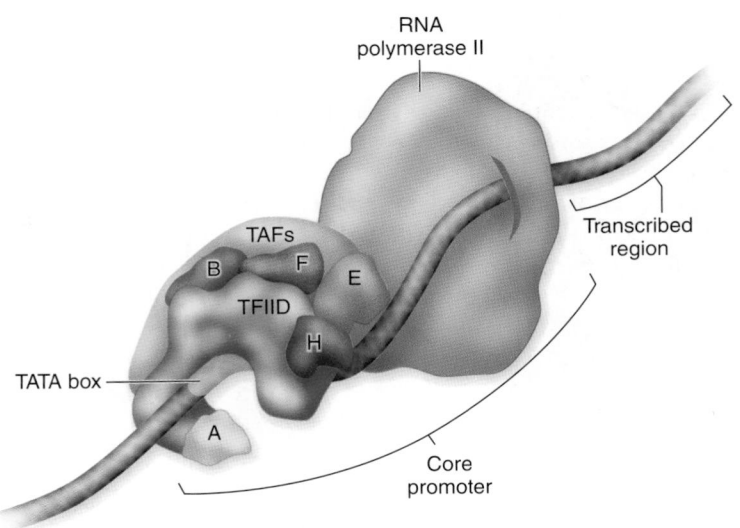

Figure 16.9 Formation of a eukaryotic initiation complex. The general transcription factor, TFIID, binds to the TATA box and is joined by the other general factors, TFIIE, TFIIF, TFIIA, TFIIB, and TFIIH. This complex is added to by a number of transcription-associated factors (TAFs) that together recruit the RNA pol II molecule to the core promoter.

ing. Some sense can be made of this proliferation of factors by concentrating on the DNA-binding motif, as opposed to the specific factors.

A key common theme that emerges from the study of these factors is that specific transcription factors, called *activators*, have a domain organization. Each factor consists of a DNA-binding domain and a separate activating domain that interacts with the transcription apparatus, and these domains are essentially independent in the protein. If the DNA-binding domains are "swapped" between different factors the binding specificity for the factors is switched without affecting their ability to activate transcription.

Promoters and enhancers are binding sites for transcription factors

Promoters, as mentioned in the preceding chapter, form the binding sites for general transcription factors. These factors then mediate the binding of RNA polymerase II to the promoter (and also the binding of RNA polymerases I and III to their specific promoters). In contrast, the holoenzyme portion of the RNA polymerase of prokaryotes can directly recognize a promoter and bind to it.

Enhancers were originally defined as DNA sequences necessary for high levels of transcription that can act independently of position or orientation. At first, this concept seemed counterintuitive, especially since molecular biologists had been conditioned by prokaryotic systems to expect control regions to be immediately upstream of the coding region. It turns out that enhancers are the binding site of

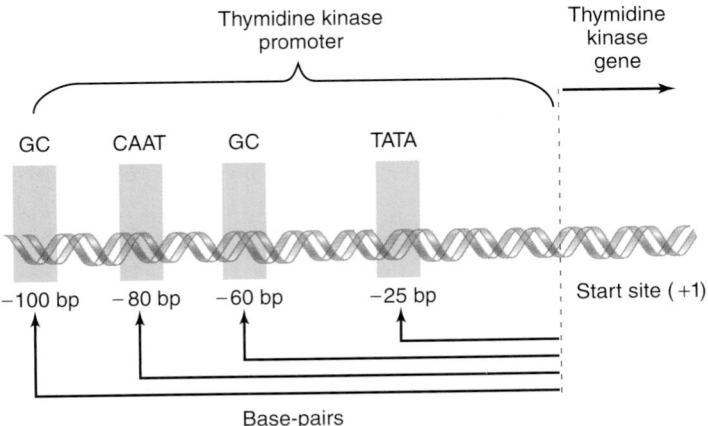

Figure 16.8 A eukaryotic promoter. This promoter is for the gene encoding the enzyme thymidine kinase. Formation of the transcription initiation complex begins with a general transcription factor binding to the TATA box. There are three other DNA sequences that direct the binding of other specific transcription factors.

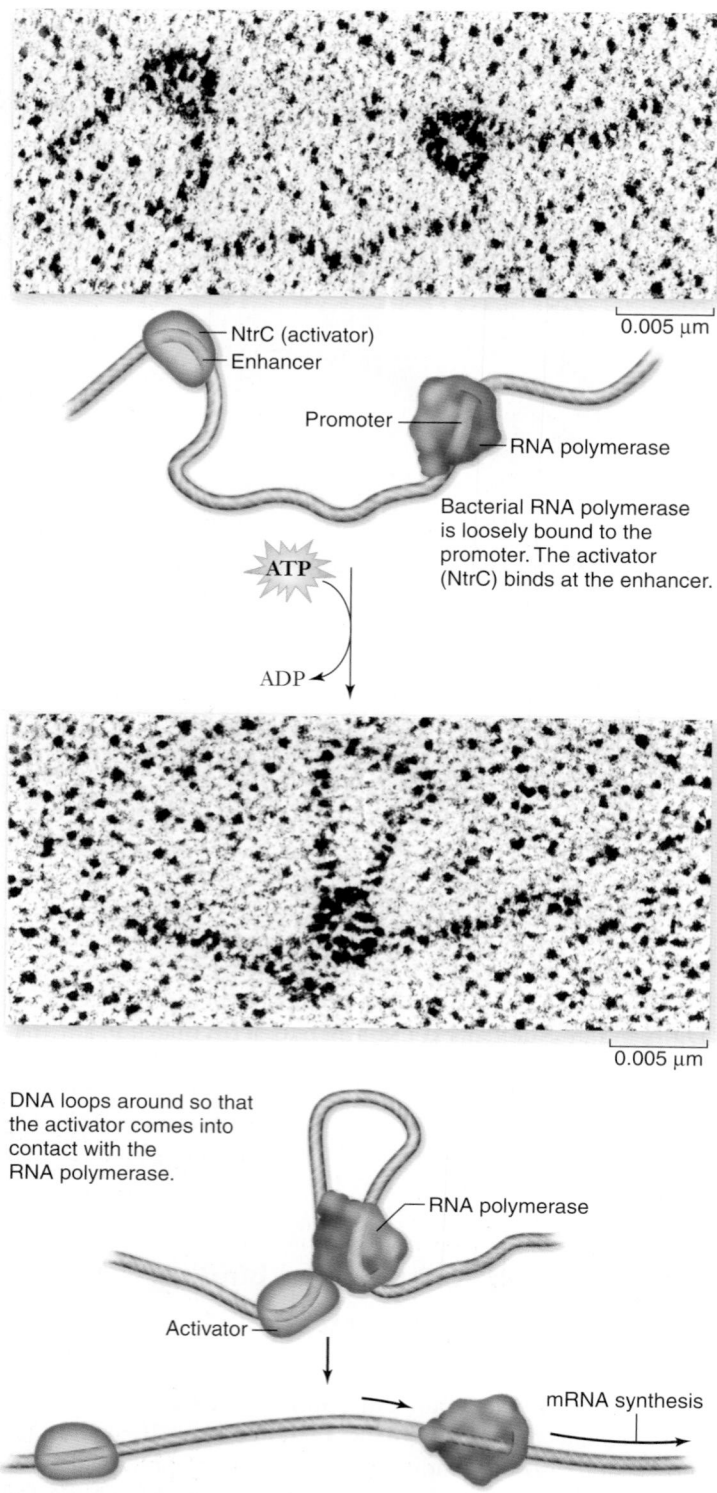

the specific transcription factors. The ability of enhancers to act over large distances was at first puzzling, but investigators now think this action is accomplished by DNA bending to form a loop, positioning the enhancer closer to the promoter.

Although more important in eukaryotic systems, this looping was first demonstrated using prokaryotic DNA-binding proteins (figure 16.10). The important point is that the linear distance separating two sites on the chromosome does not have to translate to great physical distance, because the flexibility of DNA allows bending and looping. An activator bound to an enhancer can thus be brought into contact with the transcription factors bound to a distant promoter (figure 16.11).

Coactivators and mediators link transcription factors to RNA polymerase II

Other factors specifically mediate the action of transcription factors. These *coactivators* and *mediators* are also necessary for activation of transcription by the transcription factor. They act by binding the transcription factor and then binding to another part of the transcription apparatus. Mediators are essential to the function of some transcription factors, but not all transcription

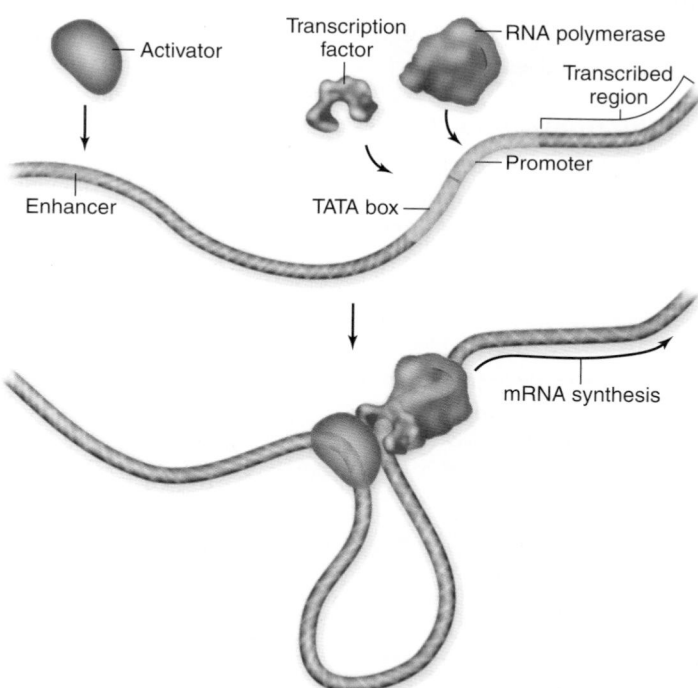

Figure 16.10 DNA looping caused by proteins. When the bacterial activator NtrC binds to an enhancer, it causes the DNA to loop over to a distant site where RNA polymerase is bound, thereby activating transcription. Although such enhancers are rare in prokaryotes, they are common in eukaryotes.

Figure 16.11 How enhancers work. The enhancer site is located far away from the gene being regulated. Binding of an activator (*gray*) to the enhancer allows the activator to interact with the transcription factors (*blue*) associated with RNA polymerase, stimulating transcription.

factors require them. The number of coactivators is much smaller than the number of transcription factors because the same coactivator can be used with multiple transcription factors.

The transcription complex brings things together

Although a few general principles apply to a broad range of situations, nearly every eukaryotic gene—or group of genes with coordinated regulation—represents a unique case. Virtually all genes that are transcribed by RNA polymerase II need the same suite of general factors to assemble an initiation complex, but the assembly of this complex and its ultimate level of transcription depend on specific transcription factors that in combination make up the **transcription complex** (figure 16.12).

The makeup of eukaryotic promoters, therefore, is either very simple, if we consider only what is needed for the initiation complex, or very complicated, if we consider all factors that may bind in a complex and affect transcription. This kind of combinatorial gene regulation leads to great flexibility because it can respond to the many signals a cell may receive affecting transcription, allowing integration of these signals.

Inquiry question

? How do eukaryotes coordinate the activation of many genes whose transcription must occur at the same time?

Learning Outcomes Review 16.4

In eukaryotes, initiation requires general transcription factors that bind to the promoter and recruit RNA polymerase II to form an initiation complex. General factors produce the basal level of transcription. Specific transcription factors, which bind to enhancer sequences, can increase the level of transcription. Enhancers can act at a distance because DNA can loop, bringing an enhancer and a promoter closer together. Additional coactivators and mediators link certain specific transcription factors to RNA polymerase II.

■ *What would be the effect of a mutation that results in the loss of a general transcription factor versus the loss of a specific factor?*

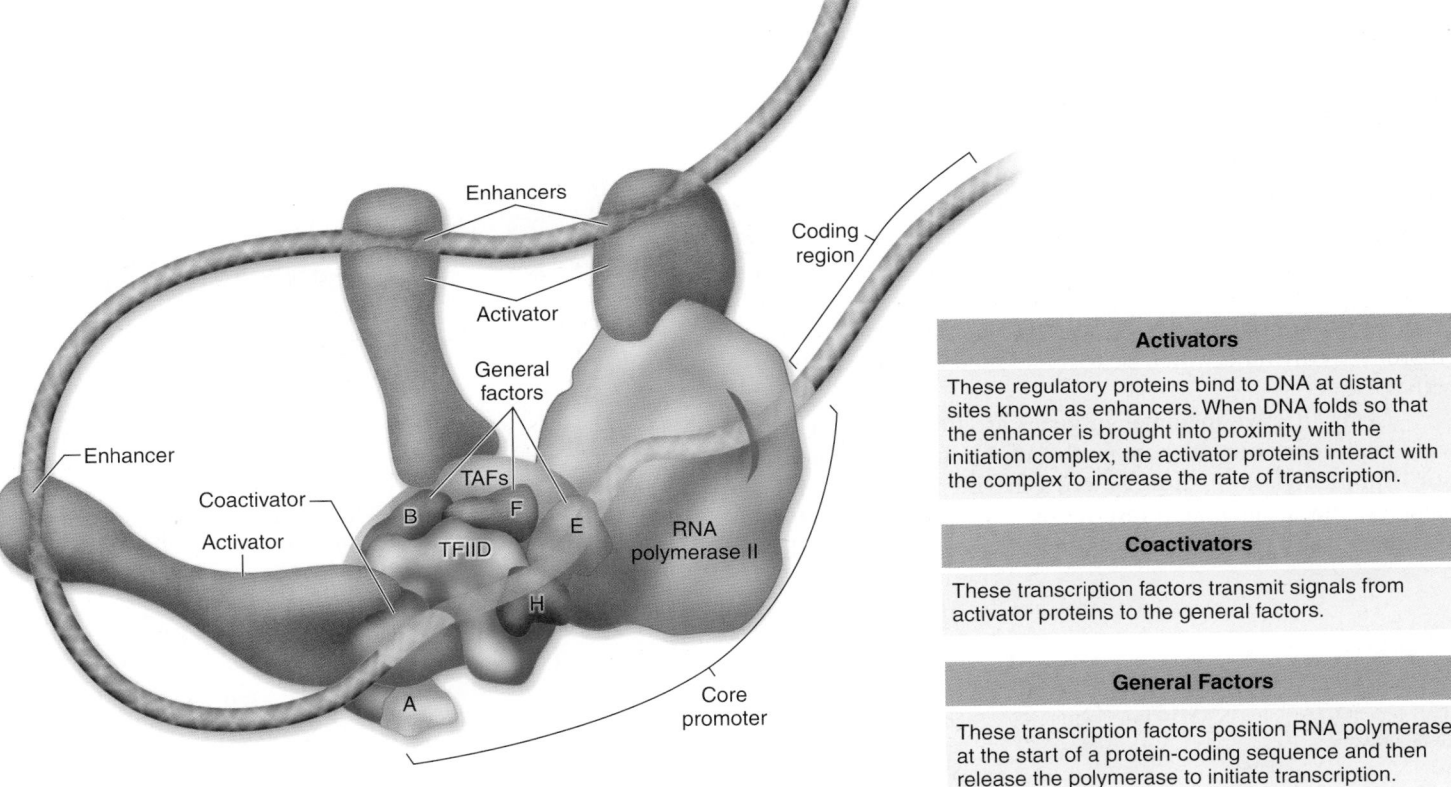

Activators

These regulatory proteins bind to DNA at distant sites known as enhancers. When DNA folds so that the enhancer is brought into proximity with the initiation complex, the activator proteins interact with the complex to increase the rate of transcription.

Coactivators

These transcription factors transmit signals from activator proteins to the general factors.

General Factors

These transcription factors position RNA polymerase at the start of a protein-coding sequence and then release the polymerase to initiate transcription.

Figure 16.12 Interactions of various factors within the transcription complex. All specific transcription factors bind to enhancer sequences that may be distant from the promoter. These proteins can then interact with the initiation complex by DNA looping to bring the factors into proximity with the initiation complex. As detailed in the text, some transcription factors, called activators, can directly interact with the RNA polymerase II or the initiation complex, whereas others require additional coactivators.

16.5 Eukaryotic Chromatin Structure

Learning Outcomes

1. *Describe how chromatin structure can affect gene expression.*
2. *Explain the function of chromatin remodeling complexes.*

Eukaryotes have the additional gene expression hurdle of possessing DNA that is packaged into chromatin. The packaging of DNA first into nucleosomes and then into higher order chromatin structures is now thought to be directly related to the control of gene expression.

Chromatin structure at its lowest level is the organization of DNA and histone proteins into *nucleosomes* (see chapter 10). These nucleosomes may block binding of transcription factors and RNA polymerase II at the promoter.

The higher order organization of chromatin, which is not completely understood, appears to depend on the state of the histones in nucleosomes. Histones can be modified to result in a greater condensation of chromatin, making promoters even less accessible for protein–DNA interactions. A chromatin remodeling complex exists that can make DNA more accessible.

Both DNA and histone proteins can be modified

Chemical *methylation* of the DNA was once thought to play a major role in gene regulation in vertebrate cells. The addition of a methyl group to cytosine creates 5-methylcytosine, but this change has no effect on its base-pairing with guanine (figure 16.13). Similarly, the addition of a methyl group to uracil produces thymine, which clearly does not affect base-pairing with adenine.

Many inactive mammalian genes are methylated, and it was tempting to conclude that methylation caused the inactivation. But methylation is now viewed as having a less direct role, blocking the accidental transcription of "turned-off" genes. Vertebrate cells apparently possess a protein that binds to clusters of 5-methylcytosine, preventing transcriptional activators from gaining access to the DNA. DNA methylation in vertebrates thus ensures that once a gene is turned off, it stays off.

The histone proteins that form the core of the nucleosome (chapter 10) can also be modified. This modification is correlated with active versus inactive regions of chromatin, similar to the methylation of DNA just described. Histones can also be methylated, and this alteration is generally found in inactive regions of chromatin. Finally, histones can be modified by the addition of an acetyl group, and this addition is correlated with active regions of chromatin.

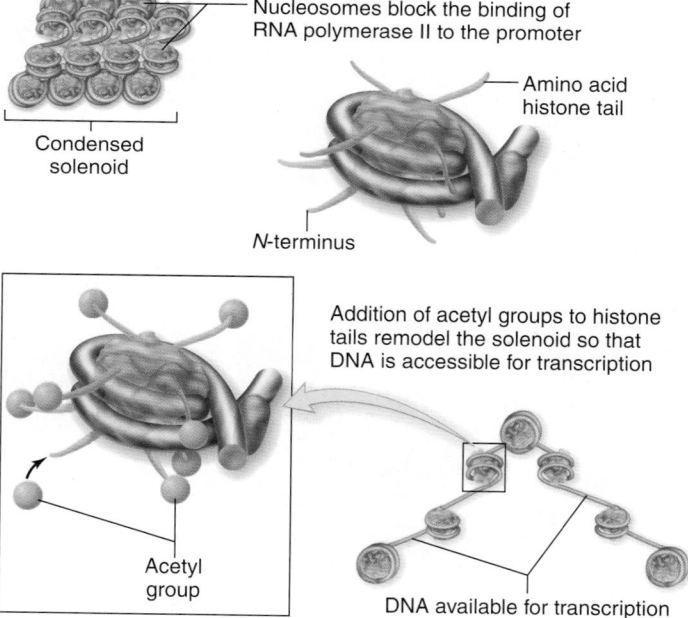

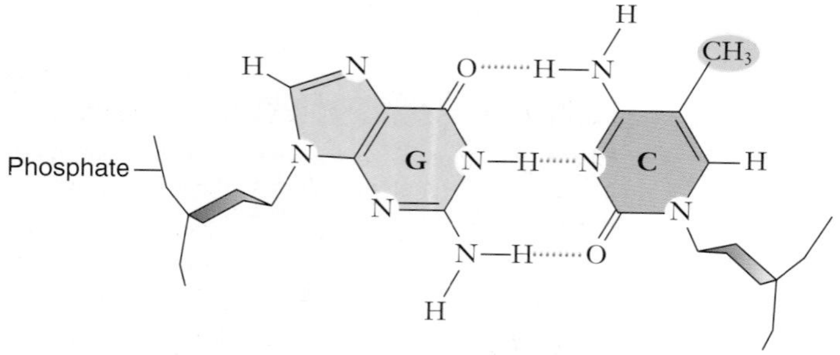

Figure 16.13 DNA methylation. Cytosine is methylated, creating 5-methylcytosine. Because the methyl group *(green)* is positioned to the side, it does not interfere with the hydrogen bonds of a G—C base-pair, but it can be recognized by proteins.

Some transcription activators alter chromatin structure

The control of eukaryotic transcription requires the presence of many different factors to activate transcription. Some activators seem to interact directly with the initiation complex or with coactivators that themselves interact with the initiation complex, as described earlier. Other cases are not so clear. The emerging consensus is that some coactivators have been shown to be histone acetylases. In these cases, it appears that transcription is increased by removing higher order chromatin structure that would prevent transcription (figure 16.14). Some corepressors have been shown to be histone deacetylases as well.

These observations have led to the suggestion that a "histone code" might exist, analogous to the genetic code.

Figure 16.14 Histone modification affects chromatin structure. DNA in eukaryotes is organized first into nucleosomes and then into higher order chromatin structures. The histones that make up the nucleosome core have amino tails that protrude. These amino tails can be modified by the addition of acetyl groups. The acetylation alters the structure of chromatin, making it accessible to the transcription apparatus.

This histone code is postulated to underlie the control of chromatin structure and, thus, of access of the transcription machinery to DNA.

Chromatin-remodeling complexes also change chromatin structure

The outline of how alterations to chromatin structure can regulate gene expression are beginning to emerge. A key discovery is the existence of so-called **chromatin-remodeling complexes.** These large complexes of proteins include enzymes that modify histones and DNA and that also change chromatin structure itself.

One class of these remodeling factors, ATP-dependent chromatin remodeling factors, function as molecular motors that affect DNA and histones. These ATP-dependent remodeling factors use energy from ATP to alter the relationships between histones and DNA. They can catalyze four different changes in histone/DNA binding (figure 16.15): 1) nucleosome sliding along DNA, which changes the position of a nucleosome on the DNA; 2) create a remodeled state where DNA is more accessible; 3) removal of nucleosomes from DNA; and 4) replacement of histones with variant histones. These functions all act to make DNA more accessible to regulatory proteins that in turn, affect gene expression.

Learning Outcomes Review 16.5

Eukaryotic DNA is packaged into chromatin, adding another structural challenge to transcription. Changes in chromatin structure correlate with modification of DNA and histones, and access to DNA by transcriptional regulators requires changes in chromatin structure. Some transcriptional activators modify histones by acetylation. Large chromatin-remodeling complexes include enzymes that alter the structure of chromatin, making DNA more accessible to regulatory proteins.

■ *Genes that are turned on in all cells are called "housekeeping" genes. Explain the idea behind this name.*

16.6 Eukaryotic Posttranscriptional Regulation

Learning Outcomes

1. *Explain how small RNAs can affect gene expression.*
2. *Differentiate between the different kinds of posttranscriptional regulation.*

The separation of transcription in the nucleus and translation in the cytoplasm in eukaryotes provides possible points of regulation that do not exist in prokaryotes. For many years we thought of this as "alternative" forms of regulation, but it now appears that they play a much more central role than previously suspected. In this section we will consider several of these mechanisms to control gene expression beginning with the exciting new area of regulation by small RNAs.

Small RNAs act after transcription to control gene expression

The study of development has lead to a number of important insights into the regulation of gene expression. A striking example is the discovery of small RNAs that affect gene expression. A mutant isolated in the worm *C. elegans* called *lin-4* was known to alter developmental timing, a so-called heterochronic mutant. Genetic studies had shown that this gene regulated another gene, *lin-14*. When the *lin-4* gene was isolated by Ambros, Lee, and Feinbaum in 1992, they showed that it did not encode a protein product. Instead, the *lin-4* gene encoded only two small RNA molecules, one of 22 nt and one of 61 nt. Further the 22 nt RNA was derived from the longer 61 nt RNA. Further work showed that this small RNA was complementary to a region in another heterochronic gene, *lin-14*. A model was developed where the *lin-4* RNA acted as a translational repressor of the *lin-14* mRNA

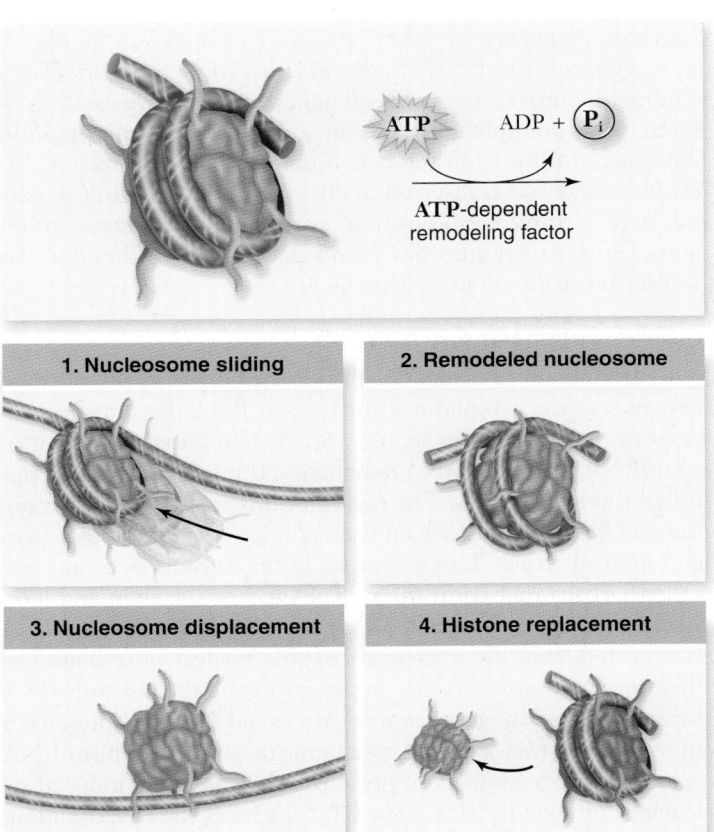

Figure 16.15 Function of ATP-dependent remodeling factors. ATP dependent remodeling factors use the energy from ATP to alter chromatin structure. They can *(1)* slide nucleosomes along DNA to reveal binding sites for proteins; *(2)* create a remodeled state of chromatin where the DNA is more accessible; *(3)* completely remove nucleosomes from DNA; and *(4)* replace histones in nucleosomes with variant histones.

ATP   ADP + Pᵢ

ATP-dependent remodeling factor

1. Nucleosome sliding

2. Remodeled nucleosome

3. Nucleosome displacement

4. Histone replacement

(figure 16.16). Although it was not called that at the time, this was the first identified micro RNA, or miRNA.

A completely different line of inquiry involved the use of double-stranded RNAs to turn off gene expression. This has been shown to act via another class of small RNA called small interfering RNAs, or siRNAs. These may be experimenatally introduced, derived from invading viruses, or even encoded in the genome. The use of siRNA to control gene expression re-

vealed the existence of cellular mechanisms for the control of gene expression via small RNAs.

Since its discovery, gene silencing by small RNAs has been a source of great interest for both its experimental uses, and as an explanation for posttranslational control of gene expression. As these small RNAs have been studied in a variety of systems, it has led to a proliferation of terms to describe them. Recent research has uncovered a wealth of new types of small RNAs, but we will confine ourselves to the two classes of miRNA and siRNA as these are well established and illustrate the RNA silencing machinery.

miRNA genes

The discovery of the role of miRNAs in gene expression initially appeared to be confined to nematodes as the *lin-4* gene did not have any obvious homologs in other systems. Seven years later, a second gene, *let-7*, was discovered in the same pathway in *C. elegans*. The *let-7* gene also encoded a 22 nt RNA that could influence translation. In this case, homologs for *let-7* were immediately found in both *Drosophila* and in humans.

As an increasing number of miRNAs were discovered in different organisms, miRNA gene discovery has turned to computer searching and high throughput methods such as microarrays and new high throughput sequencing. A database devoted to miRNAs currently lists 695 known human miRNA sequences.

Genes for miRNA are found in a variety of locations including the introns of expressed genes, and they are often clustered with multiple miRNAs in a single transcription unit. They are also found in regions of the genome that were previously considered transcriptionally silent. This finding is particularly exciting because other work looking at transcription across animal genomes has found that much we thought was transcriptionally silent, is actually not.

miRNA biogenesis and function

The production of a functional miRNA begins in the nucleus, and ends in the cytoplasm with a ~22 nt RNA that functions to repress gene expression (figure 16.17). The initial transcript of an miRNA gene is by RNA polymerase II producing a transcript called the Pri-miRNA. The region of this transcript containing the miRNA can fold back on itself and base-pair to form a stem and loop structure. This is cleaved in the nucleus by a nuclease called Drosha that trims the miRNA to just the stem and loop structure, which is now called the pre-miRNA. This pre-miRNA is exported from the nucleus through a nuclear pore bound to the protein exportin 5. Once in the cytoplasm the pre-miRNA is further cleaved by another nuclease called Dicer to produce a short double-stranded RNA containing the miRNA. The miRNA is loaded into a complex of proteins called an RNA induced silencing complex, or RISC. The RISC includes the RNA-binding protein Argonaute (Ago), which interacts with the miRNA. The complementary strand is either removed by a nuclease, or is removed during the loading process.

At this point, the RISC is targeted to repress the expression of other genes based on sequence complementarity to the miRNA. The complementary region is usually in the 3′ untranslated region of genes, and the result can be cleavage of the mRNA or inhibition of translation. It appears that in animals,

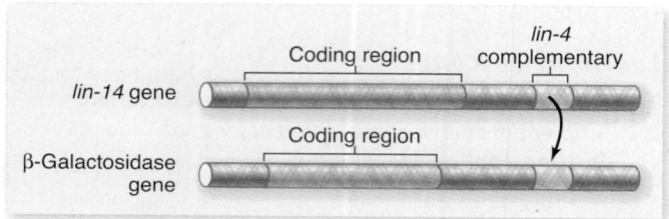
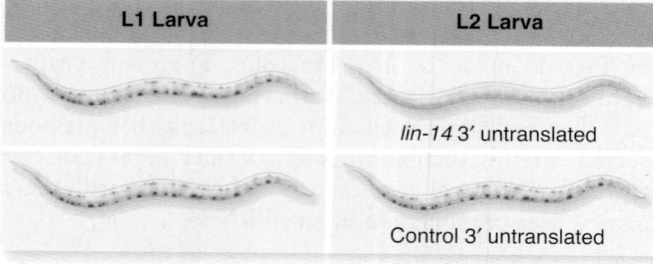
Figure 16.16 Control of *lin-14* gene expression. The *lin-14* gene is controlled by the *lin-4* gene. This is mediated by a region of the 3′ untranslated region of the *lin-14* mRNA that is complementary to *lin-4* miRNA.

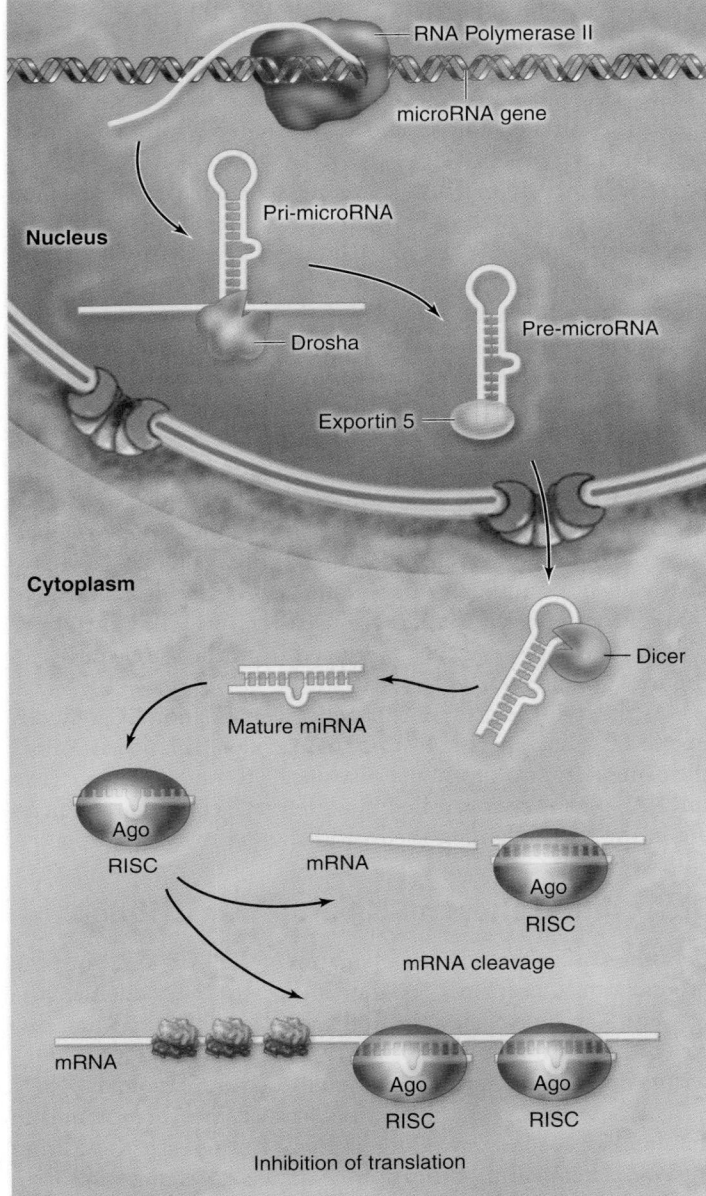

Figure 16.17 Biogenesis and function of miRNA. Genes for miRNAs are transcribed by RNA polymerase II to produce a Pri-miRNA. This is processed by the Drosha nuclease to produce the Pre-miRNA, which is exported from the nucleus bound to export factor Exportin 5. Once in the cytoplasm, the pre-miRNA is processed by Dicer nuclease to produce the mature miRNA. The miRNA is loaded into a RISC, which can act to either cleave target mRNAs, or to inhibit translation of target mRNAs.

the inhibition of translation is more common than the cleavage of the mRNA, although the precise mechanism of this inhibition is still unclear. In plants, the cleavage of the mRNA by the RISC is common and seems to be related to the more precise complementarity found between plant miRNAs and their targets compared to animal systems.

RNA interference

Small RNA mediated gene silencing has been known for a number of years. There has been some confusion created by observations in different systems leading to multiple names for similar phenomenon. Thus RNA interference, cosuppression, and posttranscriptional gene silencing all act through similar biochemical mechanisms. The term RNA interference is currently the most common and involves the production of siRNAs.

The production of siRNAs is similar to miRNAs except that they arise from a long double-stranded RNA (figure 16.18). This can be either a very long region of self complementarity, or from two complementary RNAs. These long double-stranded RNAs are processed by Dicer to yield multiple siRNAs that are loaded into an Ago containing RISC. The siRNAs usually have near-perfect complementarity to their target mRNAs, and the result is cleavage of the mRNA by the siRNA containing RISC.

The source of the double-stranded RNA to produce siRNAs can be either from the cell, or from outside the cell. From the cell itself, there are genes that produce RNAs with long regions of self-complementarity that fold back to produce a substrate for Dicer in the cytoplasm. They can also arise from repeated regions of the genome that contain transposable elements. Exogenous double-stranded RNAs can be introduced

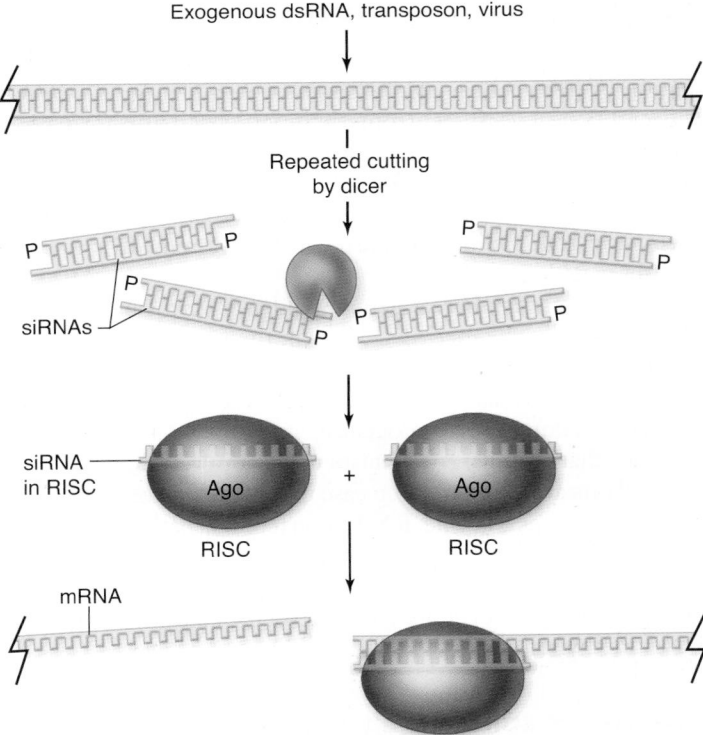

Figure 16.18 Biogenesis and function of siRNA. SiRNAs can arise from a variety of sources that all produce long double-stranded regions of RNA. The double-stranded RNA is processed by Dicer nuclease to produce a number of siRNAs that are each loaded onto their own RISC. The RISC then cleaves target mRNA.

experimentally, or by infection with a virus. The last origin for double-stranded RNAs may point to the evolution of the RNA silencing machinery as a form of antiviral defense.

Distinguishing miRNAs and siRNAs

The biogenesis of both miRNA and siRNA involves cleavage by Dicer, and incorporation into a RISC complex. The main thing that distinguishes these two types of molecules is their targets: miRNAs tend to repress genes different from their origin, while endogenous siRNAs tend to repress the genes they were derived from. Additionally siRNAs are used experimentally to turn off the expression of genes. This takes advantage of the cellular machinery to turn off a gene based with a double-stranded RNA corresponding to the gene of interest.

There are other differences between the two classes of small RNA. When multiple species are examined, miRNAs tend to be evolutionarily conserved while siRNAs do not. While the biogenesis is similar in terms of the nucleases involved, the actual structure of the double-stranded RNAs is not the same. The transcript of miRNA genes form stem-loop structures containing the miRNA while the double-stranded RNAs generating siRNAs may be bimolecular, or very long stem-loops. These longer double-stranded regions lead to multiple siRNAs while there is only a single miRNA generated from a pre-miRNA.

Small RNAs can mediate heterochromatin formation

RNA silencing pathways have also been implicated in the formation of heterochromatin in fission yeast, plants, and *Drosophila*. In fission yeast, centromeric heterochromatin formation is driven by siRNAs produced by the action of the Dicer nuclease. This heterochromatin formation also involves modification of histone proteins, and thus connects RNA interference with chromatin remodeling complexes in this system. It is not yet clear how widespread this is.

In *Drosophila*, there is genetic evidence for the involvement of the RNA interference machinery in the formation of heterochromatin. This is particularly clear in the germ line where a specific class of small RNA appears to be involved in silencing transposons during spermatogenesis and oogenesis. There is also evidence that a similar mechanism may act in vertebrates.

Plants are an interesting case in that they have a variety of small RNA species. The RNA interference pathway is more complex than in animals with multiple forms of Dicer nuclease proteins and Argonaute RNA binding proteins. One class of endogenous siRNA can lead to heterochromatin formation by DNA methylation and histone modification.

Alternative splicing can produce multiple proteins from one gene

As noted in the preceding chapter, splicing of pre-mRNA is one of the processes leading to mature mRNA. Many of these splicing events may produce different mRNAs from a single primary transcript by alternative splicing. This mechanism allows another level of control of gene expression.

Alternative splicing can change the splicing events that occur during different stages of development or in different tissues. An example of developmental differences is found in *Drosophila*, in which sex determination is the result of a complex series of alternative splicing events that differ in males and females.

An excellent example of tissue-specific alternative splicing in action is found in two different human organs: the thyroid gland and the hypothalamus. The thyroid gland is responsible for producing hormones that control processes such as metabolic rate. The hypothalamus, located in the brain, collects information from the body (for example, salt balance) and releases hormones that in turn regulate the release of hormones from other glands, such as the pituitary gland. (You'll learn more about these glands in chapter 46.)

These two organs produce two distinct hormones: *calcitonin* and *CGRP* (calcitonin gene-related peptide) as part of their function. Calcitonin controls calcium uptake and the balance of calcium in tissues such as bones and teeth. CGRP is involved in a number of neural and endocrine functions. Although these two hormones are used for very different physiological purposes, they are produced from the same transcript (figure 16.19).

The synthesis of one product versus another is determined by tissue-specific factors that regulate the processing of the primary transcript. In the case of calcitonin and CGRP, pre-mRNA splicing is controlled by different factors that are present in the thyroid and in the hypothalamus.

RNA editing alters mRNA after transcription

In some cases, the editing of mature mRNA transcripts can produce an altered mRNA that is not truly encoded in the genome—an unexpected possibility. RNA editing was first discovered as the insertion of uracil residues into some RNA transcripts in protozoa, and it was thought to be an anomaly.

RNA editing of a different sort has since been found in mammalian species, including humans. In this case, the editing involves chemical modification of a base to change its base-pairing properties, usually by deamination. For example, both deamination of cytosine to uracil and deamination of adenine to inosine have been observed (inosine pairs as G would during translation).

Apolipoprotein B

The human protein apolipoprotein B is involved in the transport of cholesterol and triglycerides. The gene that encodes this protein, *apoB*, is large and complex, consisting of 29 exons scattered across almost 50 kilobases (kb) of DNA.

The protein exists in two isoforms: a full-length APOB100 form and a truncated APOB48 form. The truncated form is due to an alteration of the mRNA that changes a codon for glutamine to one that is a stop codon. Furthermore, this editing occurs in a tissue-specific manner; the edited form appears only in the intestine, whereas the liver makes only the full-length form. The full-length APOB100 form is part of the low-density lipoprotein (LDL) particle that carries cholesterol. High levels of serum LDL are thought

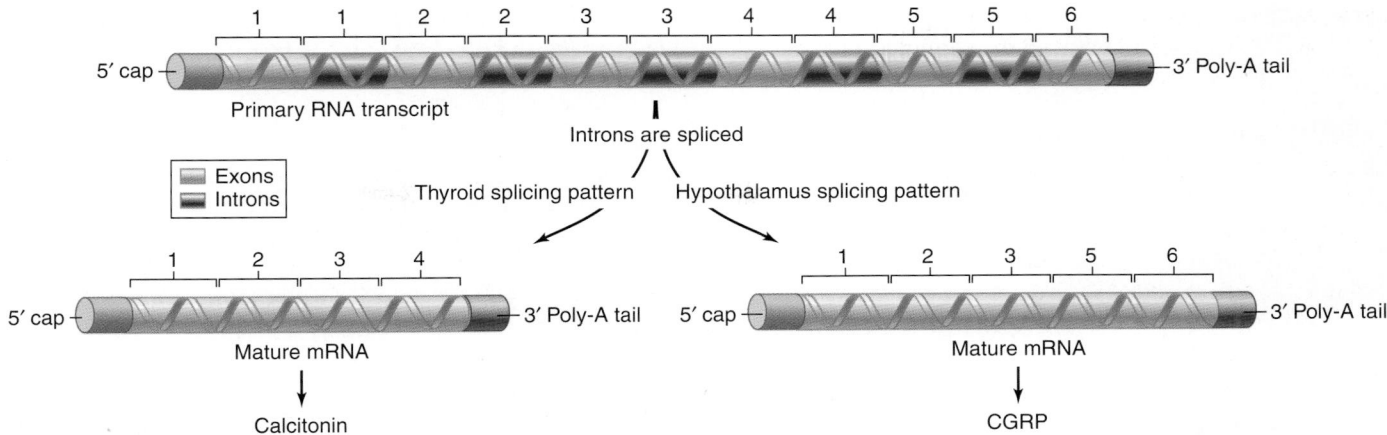

Figure 16.19 Alternative splicing. Many primary transcripts can be spliced in different ways to give rise to multiple mRNAs. In this example, in the thyroid the primary transcript is spliced to contain four exons encoding the protein calcitonin. In the hypothalamus the fourth exon, which contains the poly-A site used in the thyroid, is skipped and two additional exons are added to encode the protein calcitonin-gene-related peptide (CGRP).

to be a major predictor of atherosclerosis in humans. It does not appear that editing has any effect on the levels of the intestine-specific transcript.

The 5-HT serotonin receptor

RNA editing has also been observed in some brain receptors for opiates in humans. One of these receptors, the serotonin (5-HT) receptor, is edited at multiple sites to produce a total of 12 different isoforms of the protein.

It is unclear how widespread these forms of RNA editing are, but they are further evidence that the information encoded within genes is not the end of the story for protein production.

mRNA must be transported out of the nucleus for translation

Processed mRNA transcripts exit the nucleus through the nuclear pores (described in chapter 4). The passage of a transcript across the nuclear membrane is an active process that requires the transcript to be recognized by receptors lining the interior of the pores. Specific portions of the transcript, such as the poly-A tail, appear to play a role in this recognition.

There is little hard evidence that gene expression is regulated at this point, although it could be. On average, about 10% of primary transcripts consists of exons that will make up mRNA sequences, but only about 5% of the total mRNA produced as primary transcript ever reaches the cytoplasm. This observation suggests that about half of the exons in primary transcripts never leave the nucleus, but it is unclear whether the disappearance of this mRNA is selective.

Initiation of translation can be controlled

The translation of a processed mRNA transcript by ribosomes in the cytoplasm involves a complex of proteins called *translation factors*. In at least some cases, gene expression is regulated by modification of one or more of these factors. In other instances, **translation repressor proteins** shut down translation

by binding to the beginning of the transcript, so that it cannot attach to the ribosome.

In humans, the production of ferritin (an iron-storing protein) is normally shut off by a translation repressor protein called aconitase. Aconitase binds to a 30-nt sequence at the beginning of the ferritin mRNA, forming a stable loop to which ribosomes cannot bind. When iron enters the cell, the binding of iron to aconitase causes the aconitase to dissociate from the ferritin mRNA, freeing the mRNA to be translated and increasing ferritin production 100-fold.

The degradation of mRNA is controlled

Another aspect that affects gene expression is the stability of mRNA transcripts in the cell cytoplasm. Unlike prokaryotic mRNA transcripts, which typically have a half-life of about 3 min, eukaryotic mRNA transcripts are very stable. For example, β-globin gene transcripts have a half-life of over 10 hr, an eternity in the fast-moving metabolic life of a cell.

The transcripts encoding regulatory proteins and growth factors, however, are usually much less stable, with half-lives of less than 1 hr. What makes these particular transcripts so unstable? In many cases, they contain specific sequences near their 3' ends that make them targets for enzymes that degrade mRNA. A sequence of A and U nucleotides near the 3' poly-A tail of a transcript promotes removal of the tail, which destabilizes the mRNA.

Loss of the poly-A tail leads to rapid degradation by 3' to 5' RNA exonucleases. Another consequence of this loss is the stimulation of decapping enzymes that remove the 5' cap leading to degradation by 5' to 3' RNA exonucleases.

Other mRNA transcripts contain sequences near their 3' ends that are recognition sites for endonucleases, which cause these transcripts to be digested quickly. The short half-lives of the mRNA transcripts of many regulatory genes are critical to the function of those genes because they enable the levels of regulatory proteins in the cell to be altered rapidly.

A review of various methods of posttranscriptional control of gene expression is provided in figure 16.20.

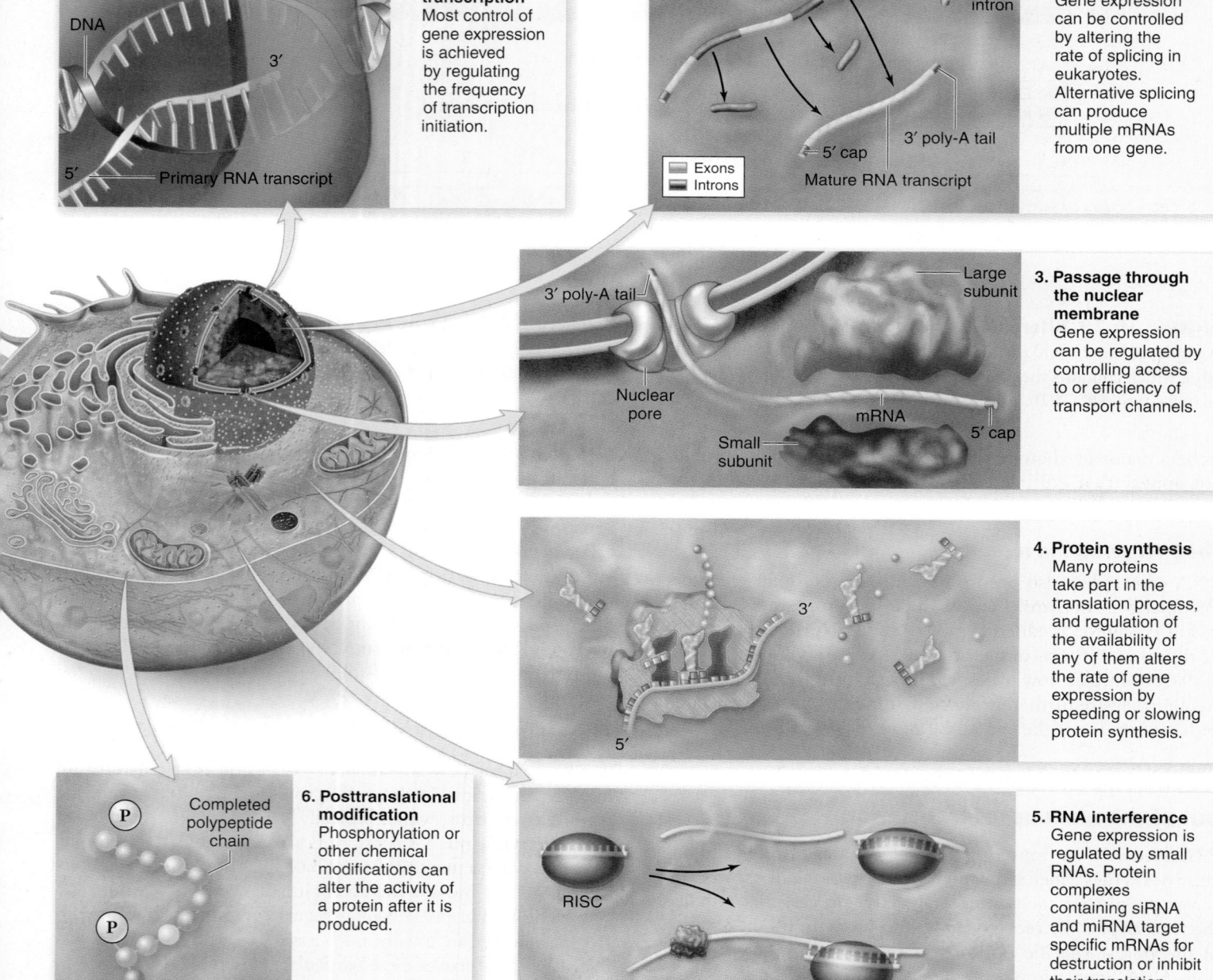

1. Initiation of transcription
Most control of gene expression is achieved by regulating the frequency of transcription initiation.

RNA polymerase II
DNA
3′
5′
Primary RNA transcript

2. RNA splicing
Gene expression can be controlled by altering the rate of splicing in eukaryotes. Alternative splicing can produce multiple mRNAs from one gene.

Cut intron
3′ poly-A tail
5′ cap
Mature RNA transcript
Exons
Introns

3. Passage through the nuclear membrane
Gene expression can be regulated by controlling access to or efficiency of transport channels.

3′ poly-A tail
Large subunit
Nuclear pore
mRNA
5′ cap
Small subunit

4. Protein synthesis
Many proteins take part in the translation process, and regulation of the availability of any of them alters the rate of gene expression by speeding or slowing protein synthesis.

3′
5′

6. Posttranslational modification
Phosphorylation or other chemical modifications can alter the activity of a protein after it is produced.

Completed polypeptide chain
P
P

5. RNA interference
Gene expression is regulated by small RNAs. Protein complexes containing siRNA and miRNA target specific mRNAs for destruction or inhibit their translation.

RISC

Figure 16.20 Mechanisms for control of gene expression in eukaryotes.

Learning Outcomes Review 16.6

Small RNAs control gene expression by either selective degradation of mRNA, inhibition of translation, or alteration of chromatin structure. Multiple mRNAs can be formed from a single gene via alternative splicing, which can be tissue- and developmentally specific. The sequence of an mRNA transcript can also be altered by RNA editing.

■ *How could the phenomenon of RNA interference be used in drug design?*

16.7 Protein Degradation

Learning Outcomes

1. Describe the role of ubiquitin in the degradation of proteins.
2. Explain the function of the proteasome.

If all of the proteins produced by a cell during its lifetime remained in the cell, serious problems would arise. Protein labeling studies in the 1970s indicated that eukaryotic cells turn over proteins in a controlled manner. That is, proteins are continually being synthesized and degraded. Although this protein turnover is not as rapid as in prokaryotes, it indicates that a system regulating protein turnover is important.

Proteins can become altered chemically, rendering them nonfunctional; in addition, the need for any particular protein may be transient. Proteins also do not always fold correctly, or they may become improperly folded over time. These changes can lead to loss of function or other chemical behaviors, such as aggregating into insoluble complexes. In fact, a number of neurodegenerative diseases, such as Alzheimer dementia, Parkinson disease, and mad cow disease, are related to proteins that aggregate, forming characteristic plaques in brain cells. Thus, in addition to normal turnover of proteins, cells need a mechanism to get rid of old, unused, and incorrectly folded proteins.

Enzymes called **proteases** can degrade proteins by breaking peptide bonds, converting a protein into its constituent amino acids. Although there is an obvious need for these enzymes, they clearly cannot be floating around in the cytoplasm active at all times.

One way that eukaryotic cells handle such problems is to confine destructive enzymes to a specific cellular compartment. You may recall from chapter 4 that lysosomes are vesicles that contain digestive enzymes, including proteases. Lysosomes are used to remove proteins and old or nonfunctional organelles, but this system is not specific for particular proteins. Cells need another regulated pathway to remove proteins that are old or unused, but leave the rest of cellular proteins intact.

Addition of ubiquitin marks proteins for destruction

Eukaryotic cells solve this problem by marking proteins for destruction, then selectively degrading them. The mark that cells use is the attachment of a **ubiquitin** molecule. Ubiquitin, so named because it is found in essentially all eukaryotic cells (that is, it is ubiquitous), is a 76–amino-acid protein that can exist as an isolated molecule or in longer chains that are attached to other proteins.

The longer chains are added to proteins in a stepwise fashion by an enzyme called *ubiquitin ligase* (figure 16.21). This reaction requires ATP and other proteins, and it takes place in a multistep, regulated process. Proteins that have a ubiquitin chain attached are called *polyubiquitinated*, and this state is a signal to the cell to destroy this protein.

Two basic categories of proteins become ubiquitinated: those that need to be removed because they are improperly folded or nonfunctional, and those that are produced and degraded in a controlled fashion by the cell. An example of the latter are the cyclin proteins that help to drive the cell cycle (chapter 10). When these proteins have fulfilled their role in active division of the cell, they become polyubiquitinated and are removed. In this way, a cell can control entry into cell division or maintain a nondividing state.

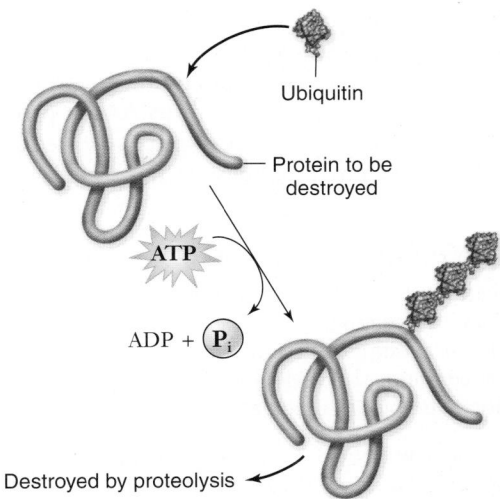

Figure 16.21 Ubiquitination of proteins. Proteins that are to be degraded are marked with ubiquitin. The enzyme ubiquitin ligase uses ATP to add ubiquitin to a protein. When a series of these have been added, the polyubiquitinated protein is destroyed.

The proteasome degrades polyubiquitinated proteins

The cellular organelle that degrades proteins marked with ubiquitin is the **proteasome,** a large cylindrical complex that proteins enter at one end and exit the other as amino acids or peptide fragments (figure 16.22).

The proteasome complex contains a central region that has protease activity and regulatory components at each end. Although not membrane-bounded, this organelle can be thought of as a form of compartmentalization on a very small scale. By using a two-step process, first to mark proteins for destruction, then to process them through a large complex, proteins to be degraded are isolated from the rest of the cytoplasm.

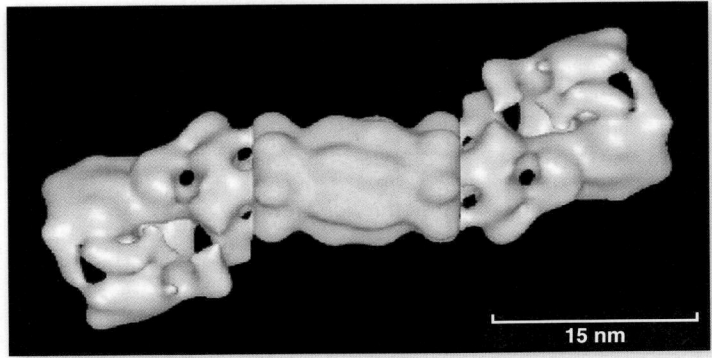

Figure 16.22 The *Drosophila* proteasome. The central complex contains the proteolytic activity, and the flanking regions act as regulators. Proteins enter one end of the cylinder and are cleaved to peptide fragments that exit the other end.

The process of ubiquitination followed by degradation by the proteasome is called the *ubiquitin–proteasome pathway*. It can be thought of as a cycle in that the ubiquitin added to proteins is not itself destroyed in the proteasome. As the proteins are degraded, the ubiquitin chain itself is simply cleaved back into ubiquitin units that can then be reused (figure 16.23).

Learning Outcomes Review 16.7

Control of protein degradation in eukaryotes involves addition of the protein ubiquitin, which marks the protein for destruction. The proteasome, a cylindrical complex with protease activity in its center, recognizes ubiquitinated proteins and breaks them down, much like a shredder destroys documents. Ubiquitin is recycled unchanged.

■ **If the ubiquitination process was not tightly controlled, what effect would this have on a cell?**

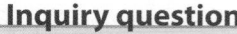

Inquiry question

? What are two reasons a cell would polyubiquitinate a polypeptide?

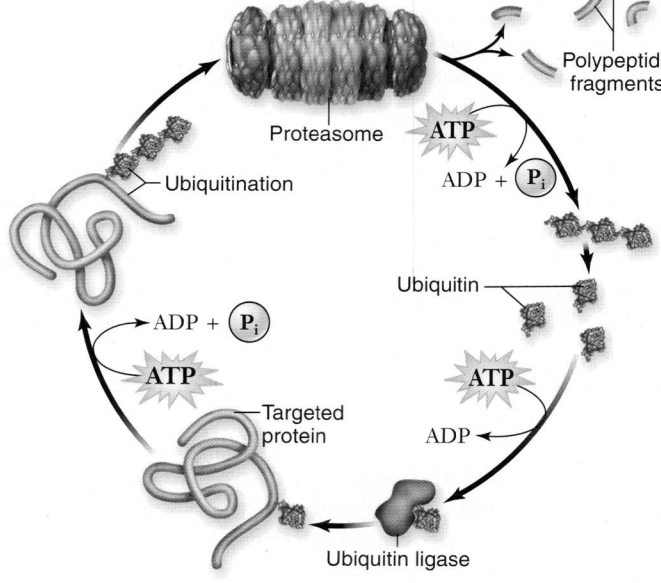

Figure 16.23 Degradation by the ubiquitin–proteasome pathway. Proteins are first ubiquitinated, then enter the proteasome to be degraded. In the proteasome, the polyubiquitin is removed and then is later "deubiquitinated" to produce single ubiquitin molecules that can be reused.

Chapter Review

16.1 Control of Gene Expression

Control usually occurs at the level of transcription initiation.
Transcription is controlled by regulatory proteins that modulate the ability of RNA polymerase to bind to the promoter. These may either block transcription or stimulate it.

Control strategies in prokaryotes are geared to adjust to environmental changes.

Control strategies in eukaryotes are aimed at maintaining homeostasis.

16.2 Regulatory Proteins

Proteins can interact with DNA through the major groove.
A DNA double helix exhibits a major groove and a minor groove; bases in the major groove are accessible to regulatory proteins.

DNA-binding domains interact with specific DNA sequences.
A region of the regulatory protein that can bind to the DNA is termed a DNA-binding motif (see figure 16.2).

Several common DNA-binding motifs are shared by many proteins.
Common motifs include the helix-turn-helix motif, the homeodomain motif, the zinc finger motif, and the leucine zipper.

16.3 Prokaryotic Regulation

Control of transcription can be either positive or negative.
Negative control is mediated by proteins called repressors that interfere with transcription. Positive control is mediated by a class of regulatory proteins called activators that stimulate transcription.

Prokaryotes adjust gene expression in response to environmental conditions.
The *lac* operon is induced in the presence of lactose; that is, the enzymes to utilize lactose are only produced when lactose is present. The *trp* operon is repressed; that is, the enzymes needed to produce tryptophan are turned off when tryptophan is present.

The lac operon is negatively regulated by the lac repressor.
The *lac* operon is induced when the effector (allolactose) binds to the repressor, altering its conformation such that it no longer binds DNA (see figure 16.4).

The presence of glucose prevents induction of the lac operon
Maximal expression of the *lac* operon requires positive control by catabolite activator protein (CAP) complexed with cAMP. When glucose is low, cAMP is high. Glucose repression involves both inducer exclusion, in which lactose is prevented from entering the cell, and the control of CAP function by the level of glucose.

The trp operon is controlled by the trp repressor.
The *trp* operon is repressed when tryptophan, acting as a corepressor, binds to the repressor, altering its conformation such that it can bind to DNA and turn off the operon. This prevents expression in the presence of excess *trp*.

16.4 Eukaryotic Regulation

Transcription factors can be either general or specific.

General transcription factors are needed to assemble the transcription apparatus and recruit RNA polymerase II at the promoter. Specific factors act in a tissue- or time-dependent manner to stimulate higher rates of transcription.

Promoters and enhancers are binding sites for transcription factors.

General factors bind to the promoter to recruit RNA polymerase. Specific factors bind to enhancers, which may be distant from the promoter but can be brought closer by DNA looping.

Coactivators and mediators link transcription factors to RNA polymerase II (see figure 16.12).

Some, but not all, transcription factors require a mediator. The number of coactivators is small because a single coactivator can be used with multiple transcription factors.

The transcription complex brings things together.

16.5 Eukaryotic Chromatin Structure

In eukaryotes, DNA is wrapped around proteins called histones, forming nucleosomes. These may block binding of transcription factors to promoters and enhancers.

Both DNA and histone proteins can be modified.

Methylation of DNA bases, primarily cytosine, correlates with genes that have been "turned off." Methylation is associated with inactive regions of chromatin.

Some transcription activators alter chromatin structure.

Acetylation of histones results in active regions of chromatin.

Chromatin-remodeling complexes also change chromatin structure.

Chromatin-remodeling complexes contain enzymes that move, reposition, and transfer nucleosomes.

16.6 Eukaryotic Posttranscriptional Regulation

Small RNAs act after transcription to control gene expression.

RNA interference is mediated by siRNAs formed by cleavage of double-stranded RNA by the Dicer nuclease. The siRNA is bound to a protein, Argonaute, in an RNA Induced Silencing Complex (RISC). The RISC can cleave mRNA or inhibit translation. Another class of small RNA, miRNA, is formed by the action of two nucleases, Drosha and Dicer, on RNA stem-and-loop structures. These also form a RISC that can either degrade mRNA or stop translation.

Small RNAs can mediate heterochromatin formation.

In fission yeast, *Drosophila*, and plants, RNA interference pathways lead to the formation of heterochromatin.

Alternative splicing can produce multiple proteins from one gene.

In response to tissue-specific factors, alternative splicing of pre-mRNA from one gene can result in multiple proteins.

RNA editing alters mRNA after transcription.

mRNA must be transported out of the nucleus for translation.

Initiation of translation can be controlled.

Translation factors may be modified to control initiation; translation repressor proteins can bind to the beginning of a transcript so that it cannot attach to the ribosome.

The degradation of mRNA is controlled.

An mRNA transcript is relatively stable, but it may carry targets for enzymes that degrade it more quickly as needed by the cell.

16.7 Protein Degradation

Addition of ubiquitin marks proteins for destruction.

In eukaryotes, proteins targeted for destruction have ubiquitin added to them as a marker.

The proteasome degrades polyubiquitinated proteins.

A cell organelle—the cylindrical proteasome—degrades ubiquitinated proteins that pass through it.

Review Questions

UNDERSTAND

1. In prokaryotes, control of gene expression usually occurs at the
   a. splicing of pre-mRNA into mature mRNA.
   b. initiation of translation.
   c. initiation of transcription.
   d. all of the above

2. Regulatory proteins interact with DNA by
   a. unwinding the helix and changing the pattern of base-pairing.
   b. binding to the sugar–phosphate backbone of the double helix.
   c. unwinding the helix and disrupting base-pairing.
   d. binding to the major groove of the double helix and interacting with base-pairs.

3. In *E. coli*, induction in the *lac* operon and repression in the *trp* operon are both examples of
   a. negative control by a repressor.
   b. positive control by a repressor.
   c. negative control by an activator.
   d. positive control by a repressor.

4. The *lac* operon is controlled by two main proteins. These proteins
   a. both act in a negative fashion.
   b. both act in a positive fashion.
   c. act in the opposite fashion, one negative and one positive.
   d. act at the level of translation.

5. In eukaryotes, binding of RNA polymerase to a promoter requires the action of
   a. specific transcription factors.
   b. general transcription factors.
   c. repressor proteins.
   d. inducer proteins.

6. In eukaryotes, the regulation of gene expression occurs
   a. only at the level of transcription.
   b. only at the level of translation.
   c. at the level of transcription initiation, or posttranscriptionally.
   d. only posttranscriptionally.

7. In the *trp* operon, the repressor binds to DNA
   a. in the absence of *trp*.
   b. in the presence of *trp*.
   c. in either the presence or absence of *trp*.
   d. only when *trp* is needed in the cell.

APPLY

1. The *lac* repressor, the *trp* repressor and CAP are all
   a. negative regulators of transcription.
   b. positive regulators of transcription.
   c. allosteric proteins that bind to DNA and an effector.
   d. proteins that can bind DNA or other proteins.

2. Specific transcription factors in eukaryotes interact with enhancers, which may be a long distance from the promoter. These transcription factors then
   a. alter the structure of the DNA between enhancer and promoter.
   b. do not interact with the transcription apparatus.
   c. can interact with the transcription apparatus via DNA looping.
   d. can interact with the transcription apparatus by removing the intervening DNA.

3. Repression in the *trp* operon and induction in the *lac* operon are both mechanisms that
   a. would only be possible with positive regulation.
   b. allow the cell to control the level of enzymes to fit environmental conditions.
   c. would only be possible with negative regulation.
   d. cause the cell to make the enzymes from these two operons all the time.

4. Regulation by small RNAs and alternative splicing are similar in that both
   a. act after transcription.
   b. act via RNA/protein complexes.
   c. regulate the transcription machinery.
   d. both a and b

5. Eukaryotic mRNAs differ from prokaryotic mRNAs in that they
   a. usually contain more than one gene.
   b. are colinear with the genes that encode them.
   c. are not colinear with the genes that encode them.
   d. both a and c

6. In the cell cycle, cyclin proteins are produced in concert with the cycle. This likely involves
   a. control of initiation of transcription of cyclin genes, and ubiquitination of cyclin proteins.
   b. alternative splicing of cyclin genes to produce different cyclin proteins.

   c. RNA editing to produce the different cyclin proteins.
   d. transcription/translation coupling.

7. A mechanism of control in *E. coli* not discussed in this chapter involves pausing of ribosomes allowing a transcription terminator to form in the mRNA. In eukaryotic fission yeast, this mechanism should
   a. be common since they are unicellular.
   b. not be common since they are unicellular.
   c. not occur as transcription occurs in the nucleus and translation in the cytoplasm.
   d. not occur due to possibility of alternative splicing.

SYNTHESIZE

1. You have isolated a series of mutants affecting regulation of the *lac* operon. All of these are constitutive, that is, they express the *lac* operon all the time. You also have both mutant and wild-type alleles for each mutant in all combinations, and on F′ plasmids, which can be introduced into cells to make the cell diploid for the relevant genes. How would you use these tools to determine which mutants affect DNA binding sites on DNA, and which affect proteins that bind to DNA?

2. Examples of positive and negative control of transcription can be found in the regulation of expression of the bacterial operons *lac* and *trp*. Use these two operon systems to describe the difference between positive and negative regulation.

3. What forms of eukaryotic control of gene expression are unique to eukaryotes? Could prokaryotes use the mechanisms, or are they due to differences in these cell types?

4. The number and type of proteins found in a cell can be influenced by genetic mutation and regulation of gene expression. Discuss how these two processes differ.

ONLINE RESOURCE

www.ravenbiology.com

Understand, Apply, and Synthesize—enhance your study with animations that bring concepts to life and practice tests to assess your understanding. Your instructor may also recommend the interactive eBook, individualized learning tools, and more.

Chapter

17

Biotechnology

Chapter Outline

17.1 DNA Manipulation

17.2 Molecular Cloning

17.3 DNA Analysis

17.4 Genetic Engineering

17.5 Medical Applications

17.6 Agricultural Applications

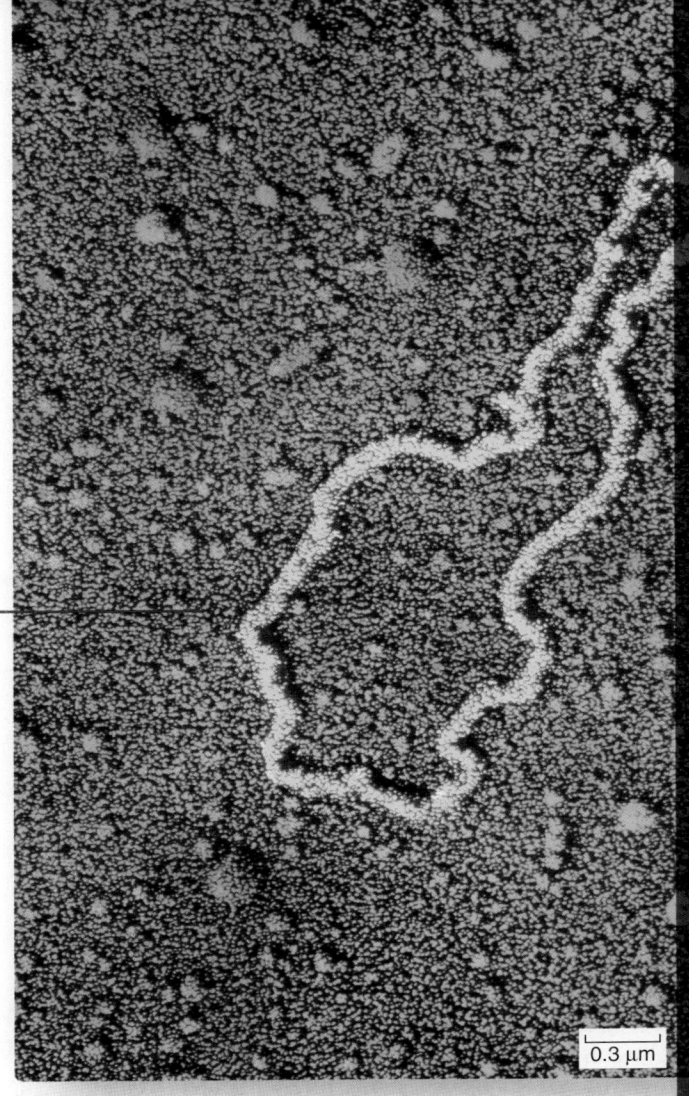

0.3 μm

Introduction

Over the past decades, the development of new and powerful techniques for studying and manipulating DNA has revolutionized biology. The knowledge gained in the last 25 years is greater than that accrued during the history of biology. Biotechnology also affects more aspects of everyday life than any other area of biology. From the food on your table to the future of medicine, biotechnology touches your life.

Biotechnology is the application of molecular biology principles to numerous aspects of life. The ability to isolate specific DNA sequences arose from the study and use of small DNA molecules found in bacteria, like the plasmid pictured here. In this chapter, we explore these technologies and consider how they apply to specific problems of practical importance.

17.1 DNA Manipulation

Learning Outcomes

1. *Relate endogenous roles of enzymes to their recombinant DNA applications.*
2. *Explain why DNA fragments can be separated with gel electrophoresis.*

The ability to directly isolate and manipulate genetic material was one of the most profound changes in the field of biology in the late 20th century. The construction of **recombinant DNA** molecules, that is, a single DNA molecule made from two different sources, began in the mid-1970s. The development of this technology, which has led to the entire field of biotechnology, is based on enzymes that can be used to manipulate DNA.

Restriction enzymes cleave DNA at specific sites

Enzymes called **restriction endonucleases** revolutionized molecular biology because of their ability to cleave DNA at specific sites. As described in chapter 14, nucleases are enzymes that degrade DNA, and many were known prior to the isolation of the first restriction enzyme (*Hin*dII) in 1970. If a DNA sequence were a rope, then restriction enzymes would be a knife that always cut that rope into specific pieces.

Discovery and significance of restriction endonucleases

This site-specific cleavage activity, long sought by molecular biologists, was discovered from basic research into why bacterial viruses can infect some cells but not others. This phenomenon was termed *host restriction*. The bacteria produce enzymes that can cleave the invading viral DNA at specific sequences. The host cells protect their own DNA from cleavage by modifying it at the cleavage sites; the restriction enzymes do not cleave that modified DNA. Since the initial discovery of these restriction endonucleases, hundreds more have been isolated that recognize and cleave different **restriction sites.**

The ability to cut DNA at specific places is significant in two ways: First, it allows physical maps to be constructed based on the positioning of cleavage sites for restriction enzymes. These restriction maps provide crucial data for identifying and working with DNA molecules.

Second, restriction endonuclease cleavage allows the creation of recombinant molecules. The ability to construct recombinant molecules is critical to research, because many steps in the process of cloning and manipulating DNA require the ability to combine molecules from different sources.

How restriction enzymes work

There are three types of restriction enzymes, but only type II cleaves at precise locations. Types I and III cleave with less precision and are not often used in cloning and manipulating DNA.

Type II enzymes allow creation of recombinant molecules; these enzymes recognize a specific DNA sequence, ranging from 4 bases to 12 bases, and cleave the DNA at a specific base within this sequence (figure 17.1).

The recognition sites for most type II enzymes are palindromes. A linguistic *palindrome* is a word or phrase that reads the same forward and in reverse, such as the sentence: "Madam I'm Adam." The palindromic DNA sequence reads the same from 5′ to 3′ on one strand as it does on the complementary strand (see figure 17.1).

Given this kind of sequence, cutting the DNA at the same base on either strand can lead to staggered cuts that produce "sticky ends." These short, unpaired sequences are the same for any DNA that is cut by this enzyme. Thus, these sticky ends allow DNAs from different sources to be easily joined together (see figure 17.1). While less common, some type II restriction enzymes, including *PvuII*, can cut both strands in the same position, producing blunt, not sticky, ends. Blunt cut ends can be joined with other blunt cut ends.

DNA ligase allows construction of recombinant molecules

Because the two ends of a DNA molecule cut by a type II restriction enzyme have complementary sequences, the pair can form a duplex. An enzyme is needed, however, to join the two fragments together to create a stable DNA molecule. The enzyme DNA ligase accomplishes this by catalyzing the formation of a phosphodiester bond between adjacent phosphate and hydroxyl groups of DNA nucleotides. The action of ligase is to seal nicks in one or both strands (see figure 17.1). This is the

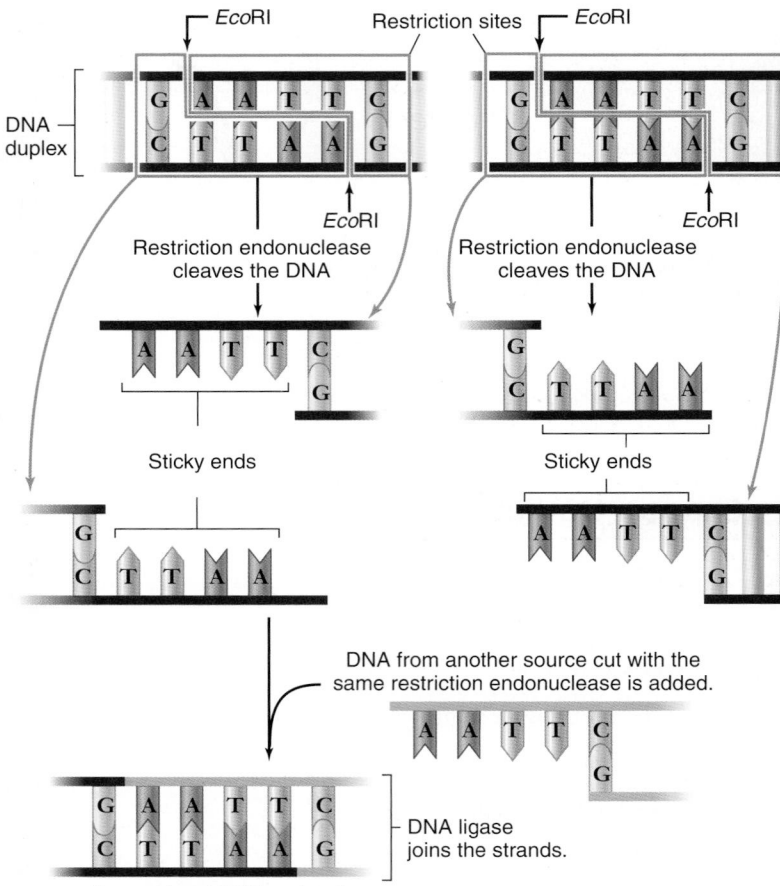

Figure 17.1 Many restriction endonucleases produce DNA fragments with "sticky ends." The restriction endonuclease *Eco*RI always cleaves the sequence 5′GAATTC3′ between G and A. Because the same sequence occurs on both strands, both are cut. However, the two sequences run in opposite directions on the two strands. As a result, single-stranded tails called "sticky ends" are produced that are complementary to each other. These complementary ends can then be joined to a fragment from another DNA that is cut with the same enzyme. These two molecules can then be joined by DNA ligase to produce a recombinant molecule.

same enzyme that joins Okazaki fragments on the lagging strand during DNA replication (see chapter 14).

Gel electrophoresis separates DNA fragments

The fragments produced by restriction enzymes would not be of much use if we could not also easily separate them for analysis. The most common separation technique used is gel electrophoresis. This technique takes advantage of the negative charge on DNA molecules by using an electrical field to provide the force necessary to separate DNA molecules based on size.

The gel, which is made of either agarose or polyacrylamide and spread thinly on supporting material, provides a three-dimensional matrix that separates molecules based on size (figure 17.2). The gel is submerged in a buffer solution containing ions that can carry current and is subjected to an electrical field.

The strong negative charges from the phosphate groups in the DNA backbone cause it to migrate toward the positive pole (figure 17.2*b*). The gel acts as a sieve to separate DNA molecules based on size: The larger the molecule, the slower it will move through the gel matrix. Over a given period, smaller molecules migrate farther than larger ones. The DNA in gels can be visualized using a fluorescent dye that binds to DNA (figure 17.2*c, d*).

Electrophoresis is one of the most important methods in the toolbox of modern molecular biology, with uses ranging from DNA fingerprinting to DNA sequencing, both of which are described later on.

Transformation allows introduction of foreign DNA into *E. coli*

The construction of recombinant molecules is the first step toward genetic engineering. It is also necessary to be able to reintroduce these molecules into cells. In chapter 14 you learned that Frederick Griffith demonstrated that genetic material could be transferred between bacterial cells. This process, called *transformation*, is a natural process in the cells that Griffith was studying.

The bacterium *E. coli*, used routinely in molecular biology laboratories, does not undergo natural transformation; but artificial transformation techniques have been developed to allow introduction of foreign DNA into *E. coli*. Through temperature shifts or an electical charge, the *E. coli* membrane becomes transiently permeable to the foreign DNA. In this way, recombinant molecules can be propagated in a cell that will make many copies of the constructed molecules.

In general, the introduction of DNA from an outside source into a cell is referred to as transformation. This process is important in *E. coli* for molecular cloning and the propagation of cloned DNA. Researchers also want to be able

---

Restriction Enzyme Digestion

DNA samples are cut with restriction enzymes in three different reactions producing different patterns of fragments.

Restriction endonuclease 1 cut site

Reaction 1

Short segment | Long segment

Restriction endonuclease 2 cut site

Reaction 2

Medium segment | Medium segment

Restriction endonuclease 3

Reaction 3

Long segment | Short segment

a.

Gel Electrophoresis

Samples from the restriction enzyme digests are introduced into the gel. Electric current is applied causing fragments to migrate through the gel.

Power source

Reaction 1 | Reaction 2 | Reaction 3

Mixture of DNA fragments of different sizes in solution placed at the top of "lanes" in the gel

Lane

Cathode

Gel

Anode

Buffer

b.

Visualizing Stained Gel

Gel is stained with a dye to allow the fragments to be visualized.

Longer fragments

Shorter fragments

c.

Electrophoresis in the Laboratory

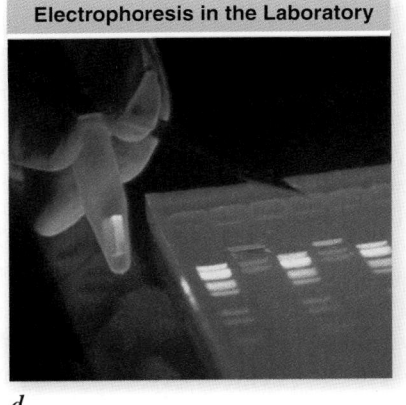

d.

Figure 17.2 Gel electrophoresis. *a.* Three restriction enzymes are used to cut DNA into specific pieces depending on each enzyme's recognition sequence. *b.* The fragments are loaded into a gel (agarose or polyacrylamide), and an electrical current is applied. The DNA fragments migrate through the gel based on size, with larger ones moving more slowly. *c.* This results in a pattern of fragments separated based on size, with the smaller fragments migrating farther than larger ones. *d.* The fragments can be visualized by staining with the dye ethidium bromide. When the gel is exposed to UV light, the DNA with bound dye fluoresces, appearing as pink bands in the gel. In the photograph, one band of DNA has been excised from the gel for further analysis and can be seen glowing in the tube the technician holds.

to reintroduce DNA into the original cells from which it was isolated. A transformed cell that can also be used to form all or part of an organism, is called a **transgenic** organism. Later in this chapter we explore the construction and uses of transgenic plants and animals.

Learning Outcomes Review 17.1

Restriction endonucleases are part of bacterial cells' strategies to fight viral infection. Type II endonucleases cleave DNA at specific sites. DNA ligase can be used to link together fragments following action of restriction endonucleases. Gel electrophoresis employs electrical charge to separate DNA fragments according to size. Foreign DNA can be introduced into *E. coli* through artificial transformation, and then propagation can produce cloned DNA.

■ **Compare and contrast the endogenous roles of EcoRI and ligase in E. coli with their use in a molecular biology lab.**

17.2 Molecular Cloning

Learning Outcomes

1. **Explain the role of a vector in molecular cloning.**
2. **Describe how a DNA library is constructed.**

The term **clone** refers to a genetically identical copy. The technique of propagating plants by growing a new plant from a cutting of a donor plant is an early method of cloning widely used in agriculture and horticulture. The topic of cloning entire organisms is discussed in chapter 19. For now, we explore the idea of molecular cloning.

Molecular cloning involves the isolation of a specific sequence of DNA, usually one that encodes a particular protein product. This is sometimes called *gene cloning*, but the term *molecular cloning* is more accurate.

Host–vector systems allow propagation of foreign DNA in bacteria

Although short sequences of DNA can be synthesized in vitro (in a test tube), the cloning of large unknown sequences requires propagation of recombinant DNA molecules in vivo (in a cell). The enzymes and methods described earlier allow biologists to produce, separate, and then introduce foreign DNA into cells.

The ability to propagate DNA in a host cell requires a **vector** (something to carry the recombinant DNA molecule) that can replicate in the host when it has been introduced. Such host–vector systems are crucial to molecular biology.

The most flexible and common host used for molecular cloning is the bacterium *E. coli*, but many other hosts are now possible. Investigators routinely reintroduce cloned eukaryotic DNA, using mammalian tissue culture cells, yeast cells, and insect cells as host systems. Each kind of host–vector system allows particular uses of the cloned DNA.

The two most commonly used vectors are plasmids and artificial chromosomes. *Plasmids* are small, circular extrachromosomal DNAs that are dispensable to the bacterial cell. Bacterial and eukaryotic artificial chromosomes are used to clone larger pieces of DNA.

Plasmid vectors

Plasmid vectors (small, circular chromosomes) are typically used to clone relatively small pieces of DNA, up to a maximum of about 10 kilobases (kb). A plasmid vector must have three components:

1. An *origin of replication* to allow it to be replicated in *E. coli* independently of the host chromosome,
2. A *selectable marker*, usually antibiotic resistance, and
3. *One or more unique restriction sites* where foreign DNA can be added.

The selectable marker allows the presence of the plasmid to be easily identified through genetic selection. For example, cells that contain a plasmid with an antibiotic resistance gene continue to live when plated on antibiotic-containing growth media, whereas cells that lack the plasmid will die (they are killed by the antibiotic).

A fragment of DNA is inserted by the techniques described into a region of the plasmid with restriction sites called the multiple-cloning site (MCS). This region contains a number of unique restriction sites such that when the plasmid is cut with the relevant restriction enzymes, a linear plasmid results. When DNA of interest is cut with the same restriction enzyme, it can then be ligated into this site. The plasmid is then introduced into cells by transformation (see figure 17.3).

This region of the vector often has been engineered to contain another gene that becomes inactivated, so-called *insertional inactivation*, because it is now interrupted by the inserted DNA. One of the first cloning vectors, pBR322, used another antibiotic resistance gene for insertional activation; resistance to one antibiotic and sensitivity to the other indicated the presence of inserted DNA.

More recent vectors use the gene for β-galactosidase, an enzyme that cleaves galactoside sugars such as lactose. When the enzyme cleaves the artificial substrate X-gal, a blue color is produced. In these plasmids, insertion of foreign DNA interrupts the β-galactosidase gene, preventing a functional enzyme from being produced. When transformed cells are plated on medium containing both antibiotic (to select for plasmid-containing cells) and X-gal, they remain white, whereas transformed cells with no inserted DNA are blue (see figure 17.3).

Artificial Chromosomes

The size of DNA molecules that can be cloned in plasmid vectors has limited the large-scale analysis of genomes. To deal

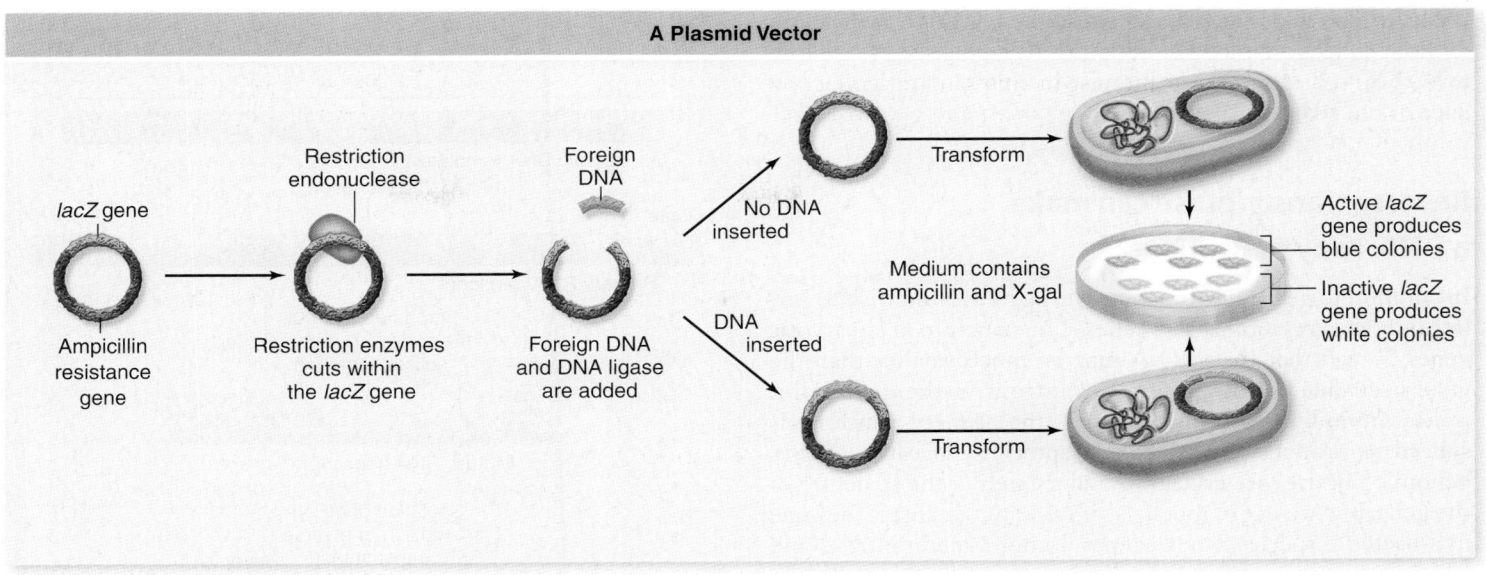

A Plasmid Vector

lacZ gene

Ampicillin resistance gene

Restriction endonuclease

Restriction enzymes cuts within the *lacZ* gene

Foreign DNA

Foreign DNA and DNA ligase are added

No DNA inserted

DNA inserted

Transform

Transform

Medium contains ampicillin and X-gal

Active *lacZ* gene produces blue colonies

Inactive *lacZ* gene produces white colonies

Figure 17.3 Molecular cloning with vectors. Plasmids are cut within the β-galactosidase gene (*lacZ*), and foreign DNA and DNA ligase are added. Foreign DNA inserted into *lacZ* interrupts the coding sequence, thus inactivating the gene. Plating cells on medium containing the antibiotic ampicillin selects for plasmid-containing cells. The medium also contains X-gal, and when *lacZ* is intact *(top)*, the expressed enzyme cleaves the X-gal, producing blue colonies. When *lacZ* is inactivated *(bottom)*, X-gal is not cleaved, and colonies remain white.

with this, geneticists decided to follow the strategy of cells and construct chromosomes, leading to the development of yeast artificial chromosomes (YACs) and bacterial artificial chromosomes (BACs). Progress has also been made on creating mammalian artificial chromosomes. Use of artificial chromosomes is described in the next chapter.

Inquiry question

? An investigator wishes to clone a 32-kb recombinant molecule. What do you think is the best vector to use?

DNA libraries contain the entire genome of an organism

The idea of molecular cloning depends on the ability to construct a representation of very complex mixtures in DNA, such as an entire genome, in a form that is easier to work with than the enormous chromosomes within a cell. If the huge DNA molecules in chromosomes can be converted into random fragments, and inserted into a vector such as plasmids, then when they are propagated in a host they will together represent the whole genome. This aggregate is termed a **DNA library,** a collection of DNAs in a vector that taken together represent the complex mixture of DNA (figure 17.4).

Conceptually the simplest possible kind of DNA library is a **genomic library**—a representation of the entire genome in a vector. This genome is randomly fragmented by partially digesting it with a restriction enzyme that cuts frequently. By not cutting the DNA to completion, not all sites are cleaved, and which sites are cleaved is random. The random fragments are

then inserted into a vector and introduced into host cells. Genomic libraries are usually constructed in bacterial artificial chromosomes (BACs).

A variety of different kinds of libraries can be made depending on the source DNA used. Any particular clone in the library contains only a single DNA, and all of them together make up the library. Keep in mind that unlike a library full of

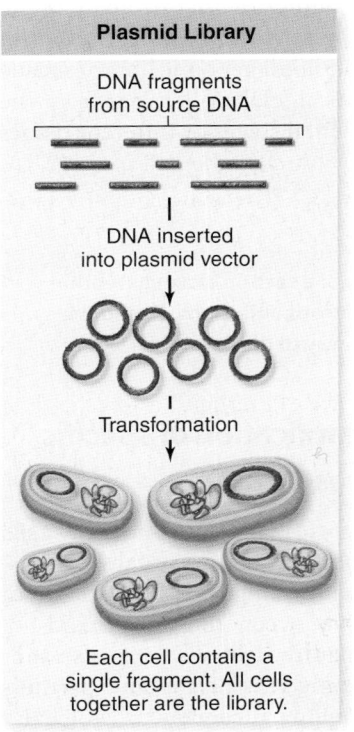

Plasmid Library

DNA fragments from source DNA

DNA inserted into plasmid vector

Transformation

Each cell contains a single fragment. All cells together are the library.

Figure 17.4 Creating DNA libraries.

books, which is organized and catalogued, a DNA library is a random collection of overlapping DNA fragments. We explore how to find a sequence of interest in this random collection later in the chapter.

Reverse transcriptase can make a DNA copy of RNA

In addition to genomic libraries, investigators often wish to isolate only the *expressed* part of genes. The structure of eukaryotic genes is such that the mRNA may be much smaller than the gene itself due to the presence of introns in the gene. After transcription by RNA polymerase II, the primary transcript is spliced to produce the mRNA (chapter 15). Because of this, genomic libraries are crucial to understanding the structure of the gene, but are not of much use if we want to express the gene in a bacterial species, whose genes do not contain introns and which has no mechanism for splicing.

A library of only expressed sequences represents a much smaller amount of DNA than the entire genome. The starting point for a cDNA library is isolated mRNA representing the genes expressed in a specific tissue at a specific developmental stage. Such a library of expressed sequences is made possible by the use of another enzyme: reverse transcriptase.

Reverse transcriptase was isolated from a class of viruses called retroviruses. The life cycle of a retrovirus requires making a DNA copy from its RNA genome. We can take advantage of the activity of the retrovirus enzyme to make DNA copies from isolated mRNA. DNA copies of mRNA are called **complementary DNA (cDNA)** (figure 17.5). A cDNA library is made by first isolating mRNA from genes being expressed and then using the reverse transcriptase enzyme to make cDNA from the mRNA. The cDNA is then used to make a library, as mentioned earlier. These cDNA libraries are extremely useful and are commonly made to represent the genes expressed in many different tissues or cells. While all genomic libraries made from an individual will be identical, cDNA libraries from the same cells at different developmental stages or different tissues will each be distinct.

Inquiry question

Suppose you wanted a copy of a section of a eukaryotic genome that included the introns and exons. Would the creation of cDNA be a good way to go about this?

Hybridization allows identification of specific DNAs in complex mixtures

The technique of **molecular hybridization** is commonly used to identify specific DNAs in complex mixtures such as libraries. Hybridization, also called annealing, takes advantage of the specificity of base-pairing between the two strands of DNA. If a DNA molecule is denatured, that is, the two strands are separated, the strands can only reassociate with partners that have the correct complementary sequence. Molecular biologists can take advantage of this feature experimentally to

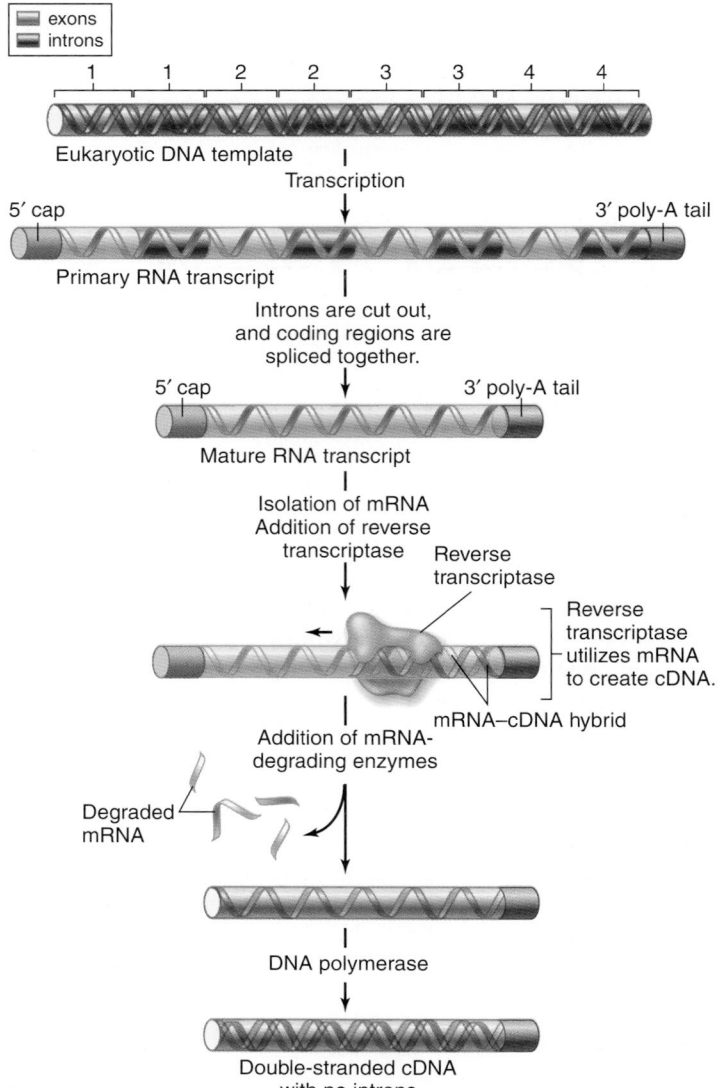

Figure 17.5 The formation of cDNA. A mature mRNA transcript is usually much smaller than the gene due to the loss of intron sequences by splicing. mRNA is isolated from the cytoplasm of a cell, which the enzyme reverse transcriptase uses as a template to make a DNA strand complementary to the mRNA. That newly made strand of DNA is the template for the enzyme DNA polymerase, which assembles a complementary DNA strand along it, producing cDNA—a double-stranded DNA version of the intron-free mRNA.

use a known, specific DNA molecule to find its partner in a complex mixture.

Any single-stranded nucleic acid (DNA or RNA) can be tagged with a radioactive label or with another detectable label, such as a fluorescent dye. This can then be used as a probe to identify its complement in a complex mixture of DNA or RNA. This renaturing is termed *hybridization* because the combination of labeled probe and unlabeled DNA form a hybrid molecule through base-pairing.

Probes have been made historically by a variety of techniques. One technique involved isolating a protein of interest and then chemically sequencing the protein. With the protein sequence in hand, the DNA sequence could be predicted using the genetic code. This information can then be used to make a synthetic DNA for use as a probe.

Specific clones can be isolated from a library

The isolation of a specific clone from the random collection that is a DNA library is akin to finding the proverbial needle in a haystack. It requires some information about the gene of interest. For example, many of the first genes isolated were those that are highly expressed in a specific cell type, such as the globin genes that encode the proteins found in the oxygen carrier hemoglobin.

Hybridization is the most common way of identifying a clone within a DNA library. This procedure is outlined for a DNA library in a plasmid vector in figure 17.6.

In the early days of molecular biology, individual investigators made their own DNA libraries, as is shown earlier in figure 17.4. Now, genomic and cDNA libraries are commercially available for a large number of organisms. Screening such a library involves growing the library on agar plates, making a replica of the library, and screening for the cloned sequence of interest.

Stage 1: Plating the library

Physically, the library is either a collection of bacterial viruses that each contain an inserted DNA, or bacterial cells that each harbor a plasmid or artificial chromosome with inserted DNA. To find a specific clone, the library needs to be represented in an organized fashion. Figure 17.6 shows this representation for a plasmid vector. The library of bacteria containing plasmids is grown on agar plates at a high density, but not so high that individual colonies cannot be distinguished.

Stage 2: Replicating the library

Once the library has been grown on plates, a replica can be made by laying a piece of filter paper on the plate; some of the viruses or cells in each colony will stick to the filter, and some will be left on the plate. The result is a copy of the library on a piece of filter paper. The DNA can be affixed to the filter paper by baking or by cross-linking it to the filter using UV light.

Stage 3: Screening the library

Once a replica of the library has been formed on a filter, a specific clone can be identified by hybridization. The probe, which represents the specific sequence of interest, is labeled with a radioactive nucleotide. The probe is then added to the filters with the library replicated on them. Film sensitive to radioactive emissions is then placed in contact with the filters; where radioactivity is present, a dark spot appears on the film. When the film is aligned with the original plate, the clone of interest can be identified (see figure 17.6).

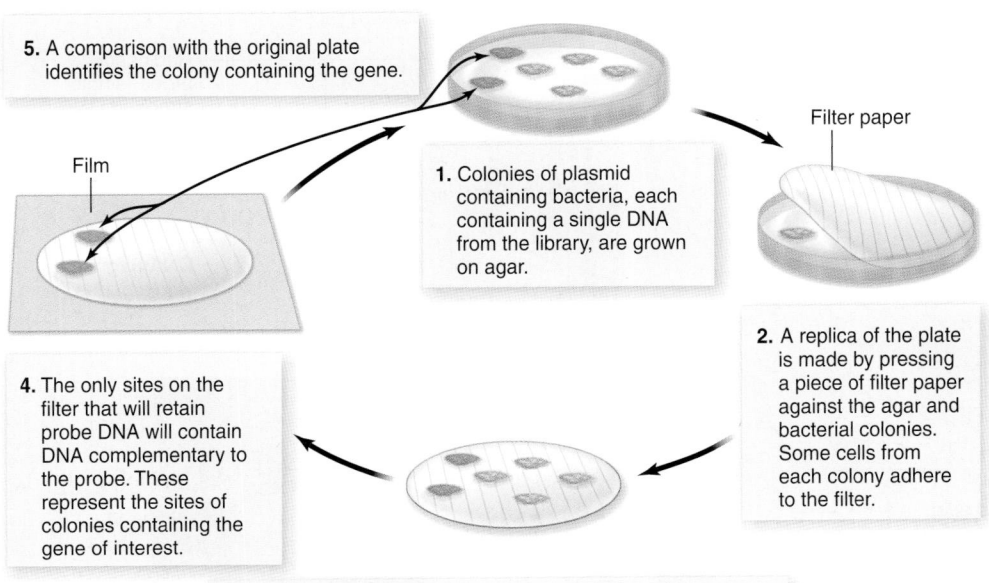

1. Colonies of plasmid containing bacteria, each containing a single DNA from the library, are grown on agar.

2. A replica of the plate is made by pressing a piece of filter paper against the agar and bacterial colonies. Some cells from each colony adhere to the filter.

3. The filter is washed with a solution to break the cells open and denature the DNA, which sticks to the filter at the site of each colony. The filter is incubated with a radioactively labeled probe that can form hybrids with complementary DNA in the gene of interest.

4. The only sites on the filter that will retain probe DNA will contain DNA complementary to the probe. These represent the sites of colonies containing the gene of interest.

5. A comparison with the original plate identifies the colony containing the gene.

Film

Filter paper

Figure 17.6 Screening a library using hybridization. This technique takes advantage of DNA's ability to be denatured and renatured, with complementary strands finding each other. Cells containing the library are plated on agar gel. A replica of the plates is made using special filter paper, nitrocellulose or nylon, which binds to single-stranded DNA. The filter paper with replica colonies is treated to lyse the cells and denature the DNA, producing a pattern of DNA bound to the filter that corresponds to the pattern of colonies. When a radioactive probe is added, it finds complementary DNA and forms hybrids at the site of colonies that contained the gene of interest.

1. Electrophoresis is performed, using radioactively labeled markers as a size guide in the first lane.

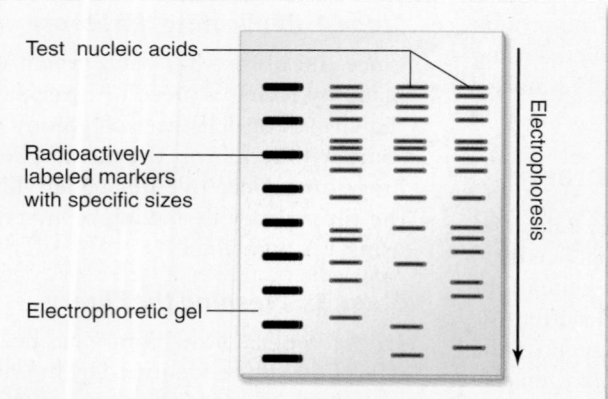

Test nucleic acids

Electrophoresis

Radioactively labeled markers with specific sizes

Electrophoretic gel

2. The gel is covered with a sheet of nitrocellulose and placed in a tray of buffer on top of a sponge. Alkaline chemicals in the buffer denature the DNA into single strands. The buffer wicks its way up through the gel and nitrocellulose into a stack of paper towels placed on top of the nitrocellulose.

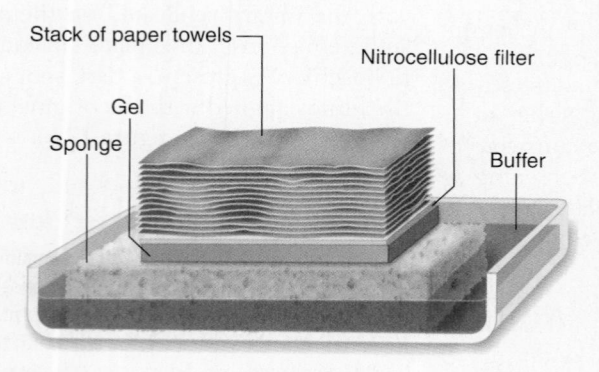

Stack of paper towels

Nitrocellulose filter

Gel

Sponge

Buffer

3. DNA in the gel is transferred, or "blotted," onto the nitrocellulose.

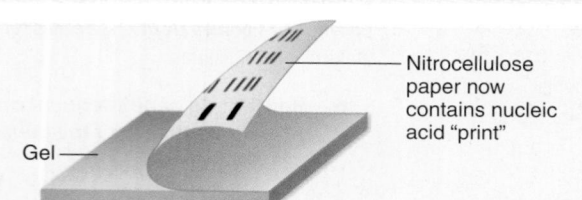

Nitrocellulose paper now contains nucleic acid "print"

Gel

4. Nitrocellulose with bound DNA is incubated with radioactively labeled nucleic acids and is then rinsed.

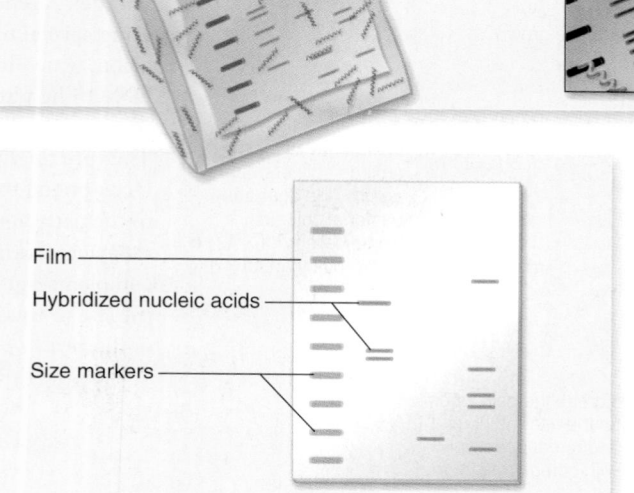

Sealed container

Radioactive probe (single-stranded DNA)

—AATGG—

—TTACC—

DNA fragments within bands

5. Photographic film is laid over the filter and is exposed only in areas that contain radioactivity (autoradiography). Bands on the film represent DNA in the gel that is complementary to the probe sequence.

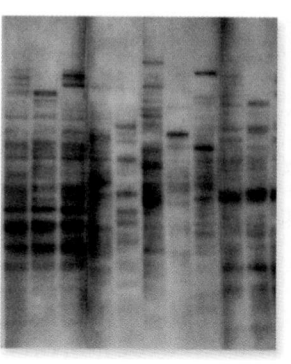

Film

Hybridized nucleic acids

Size markers

Figure 17.7 The Southern blot procedure. Edwin M. Southern developed this procedure in 1975 to enable DNA fragments of interest to be visualized in a complex sample containing many other fragments of similar size. In steps 1–3, the DNA is separated on a gel, and then transferred ("blotted") onto a solid support medium such as nitrocellulose paper or a nylon membrane. Sequences of interest can be detected by using a radioactively labeled probe. This probe (usually several hundred nucleotides in length) of single-stranded DNA (or an mRNA complementary to the gene of interest) is incubated with the filter containing the DNA fragments. All DNA fragments that contain nucleotide sequences complementary to the probe will form hybrids with the probe. Only a short segment of the probe and the complementary sequence are shown in panel 4. The fragments differ in size, with the smallest moving the farthest in the gel. The fragments of interest are then detected using photographic film. A representative image is shown in panel 5. The use of film for detection is being replaced by phosphor imagers, computer-controlled devices that have electronic sensors for light or radioactive emissions.

Learning Outcomes

1. *Explain the Southern blotting method of identifying genes.*
2. *Compare endogenous DNA replication with sequencing and with the polymerase chain reaction.*
3. *Explain how the yeast system is used to study protein–protein interactions.*

Molecular cloning provides specific DNA for further manipulation and analysis. The number of ways that DNA can be manipulated could fill the rest of this book, but for our purposes, we will highlight a few important methods of analysis and uses of molecular clones.

Restriction maps provide molecular "landmarks"

If you are new to a city, the easiest way to find your way around is to obtain a map and compare that map with your surroundings. In a similar fashion, molecular biologists need maps to analyze and compare cloned DNAs.

The first kind of physical maps were restriction maps that included the location and order of sites cut by the battery of restriction enzymes available. Initially, these maps were created by cutting the DNA with different enzymes, separating the fragments by gel electrophoresis, and analyzing the resulting patterns. Although this method is still in use, many restriction maps are now generated by computer searching of known DNA sequences for the sites cut by restriction enzymes.

Southern blotting reveals DNA differences

Once a gene has been cloned, it may be used as a probe to identify the same or a similar gene in DNA isolated from a cell or tissue (figure 17.7). In this procedure, called a **Southern blot,** DNA from the sample is cleaved into fragments with a restriction endonuclease, and the fragments are separated by gel electrophoresis. The double-stranded helix of each DNA fragment is then denatured into single strands by making the pH of the gel basic. Then the gel is "blotted" with a sheet of filter paper, transferring some of the DNA strands to the sheet.

Next, the filter is incubated with a labeled probe consisting of purified, single-stranded DNA corresponding to a specific gene (or mRNA transcribed from that gene). Any fragment that has a nucleotide sequence complementary to the probe's sequence hybridizes with the probe (see figure 17.7).

This kind of blotting technique has also been adapted for use with RNA and proteins. When mRNA is separated by electrophoresis, the technique is called a **Northern blot.** The methodology is the same except for the starting material (mRNA instead of DNA) and that no denaturation step is required. Proteins can also be separated by electrophoresis and blotted by a procedure called a **Western blot.** In this case both the electrophoresis and the detection step are different from Southern blotting. The detection, in this case, requires an antibody that can bind to one protein.

The names of these techniques all go back to the original investigator, the British biologist Edwin M. Southern; the Northern and Western blotting names were word play on Southern's name using the cardinal points of the compass.

RFLP analysis

In some cases, an investigator wants to do more than find a specific gene, but instead is looking for variation in the genes of different individuals. One powerful way to do this is by analyzing **restriction fragment length polymorphisms,** or **RFLPs,** using Southern blotting (figure 17.8).

Point mutations that change the sequence of DNA can eliminate sequences recognized by restriction enzymes or create new recognition sequences, changing the pattern of fragments seen in a Southern blot. Sequence repetitions may also occur between the restriction endonuclease sites, and differences in repeat number between individuals can also alter the length of the DNA fragments. These differences can all be detected with Southern blotting.

When a genetic disease has an associated RFLP, the RFLP can be used to diagnose the disease. Huntington disease, cystic fibrosis, and sickle cell anemia all have associated RFLPs that have been used as molecular markers for diagnosis.

DNA fingerprinting

RFLP analysis has been used in **DNA fingerprinting.** When a probe is made for DNA that is repetitive, it often detects a large number of fragments. These fragments are often not identical in different individuals. We say that the population is **polymorphic** for these molecular markers. These markers can be used as

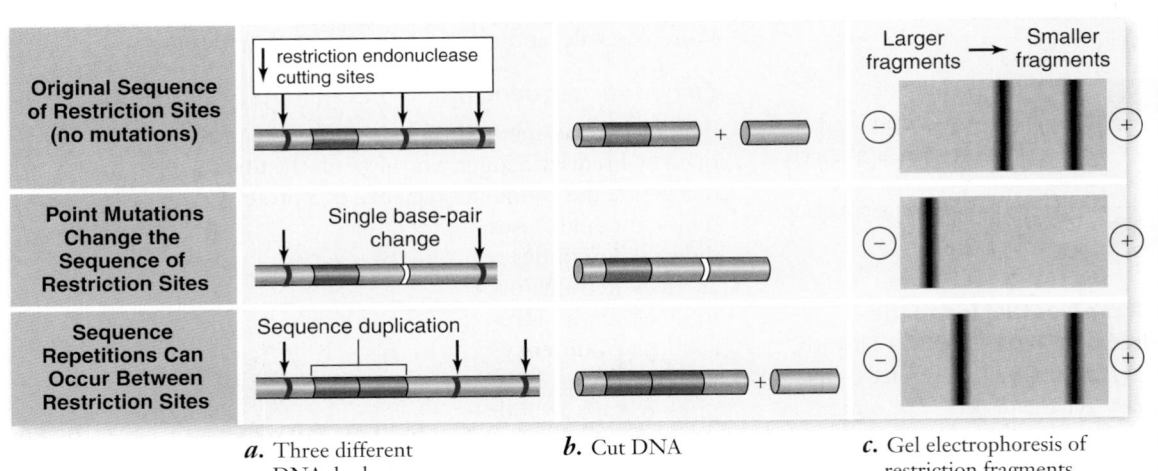

a. Three different DNA duplexes   *b.* Cut DNA   *c.* Gel electrophoresis of restriction fragments

Figure 17.8 Restriction fragment length polymorphism (RFLP) analysis. *a.* Three samples of DNA differ in their restriction sites due to a single base-pair substitution in one case and a sequence duplication in another case. *b.* When the samples are cut with a restriction endonuclease, different numbers and sizes of fragments are produced. *c.* Gel electrophoresis separates the fragments, and different banding patterns result.

DNA "fingerprints" in criminal investigations and other identification applications.

Figure 17.9 shows the DNA fingerprints a prosecuting attorney presented in a rape trial in 1987. They consist of autoradiographs, parallel bars on X-ray film. These bars can be thought of as being similar to the product price codes on consumer goods in that they may provide unique identification. Each bar represents the position of a DNA restriction endonuclease fragment produced by techniques similar to those described in figures 17.7 and 17.8. The long dark lane with many bars in figure 17.9 represents a standardized control.

Two different probes were used to identify the restriction fragments. A vaginal swab had been taken from the victim within hours of her attack; from it, semen was collected and its DNA analyzed for restriction endonuclease patterns.

Compare the restriction endonuclease patterns of the semen to that of blood from the suspect. You can see that the suspect's two patterns match that of the rapist (and are not at all like those of the victim). The suspect was Tommie Lee Andrews, and on November 6, 1987, the jury returned a verdict of guilty. Andrews became the first person in the United States to be convicted of a crime based on DNA evidence.

Since the Andrews verdict, DNA fingerprinting evidence is now a determining factor in at least forty percent of the criminal cases in the United States. Although some probes highlight profiles shared by many people, others are quite rare. Using several probes, the probability of identity can be calculated or identity can be ruled out. Laboratory analyses of DNA samples, however, must be carried out properly—sloppy procedures could lead to a wrongful conviction. After widely publicized instances of questionable lab procedures, national standards are being developed.

DNA fingerprinting is also used to identify human remains. After the September 11, 2001 attacks on the World Trade Centers in New York, DNA fingerprinting was the only option for identifying some of the victims of the attack. by 2005, 1585 of the 2792 people who were missing had been identified using DNA fingerprinting. Advances in forensic

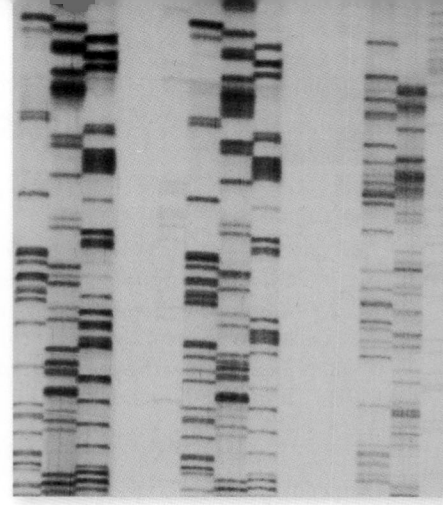

Figure 17.10 Ladder of fragments used in DNA sequencing. The photo shows the autoradiograph of the fragments generated by DNA-sequencing reactions. These fragments are generated by either organic reactions that cleave at specific bases or enzymatic reactions that terminate in specific bases. The gel can separate fragments that differ by a single base.

technology, including improved DNA isolation from very small amounts of tissue, have made it possible to identify additional individuals since 2005.

DNA sequencing provides information about genes and genomes

The ultimate level of analysis is determination of the actual sequence of bases in a DNA molecule. The development of sequencing technology has paralleled the advancement of molecular biology. As it became possible to determine the sequence of an entire genome relatively rapidly, the field of genomics emerged.

The basic idea used in DNA sequencing is to generate a set of nested fragments that each begin with the same sequence and end in a specific base. When this set of fragments is separated by high-resolution gel electrophoresis, the result is a "ladder" of fragments (figure 17.10) in which each band consists of fragments that end in a specific base. By starting with the shortest fragment, one can then read the sequence by moving up the ladder.

The problem then became how to generate the sets of fragments that end in specific bases. In the early days of sequencing, both a chemical method and an enzymatic method were utilized. The chemical method involved organic reactions specific for the different bases that made breaks in the DNA chains at specific bases. The enzymatic method used DNA polymerase to synthesize chains, but it also included in the reaction modified nucleotides that could be incorporated but not extended: so-called *chain terminators*. The enzymatic method has proved more versatile, and it is easier to adapt to different uses.

Enzymatic sequencing

The enzymatic method of sequencing was developed by Fredrick Sanger, who also was the first to determine the complete sequence of a protein. This method uses dideoxynucleotides as chain terminators in DNA synthesis reactions. A **dideoxynucleotide** has H in place of OH at both the 2′ position and at the 3′ position.

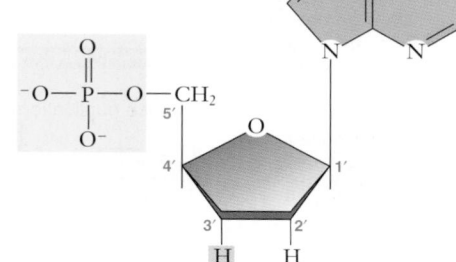

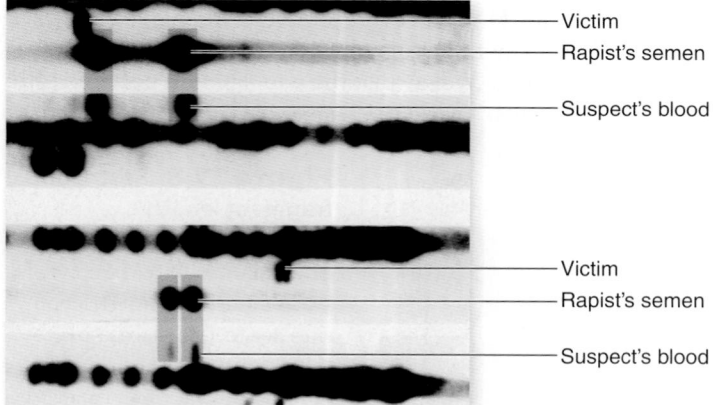

Figure 17.9 Two of the DNA profiles that led to the conviction of Tommie Lee Andrews for rape in 1987. The two DNA probes seen here were used to characterize DNA isolated from the victim, the semen left by the rapist, and the suspect. The dark channels are multiband controls. There is a clear match between the suspect's DNA and the DNA of the rapist's semen in these two profiles.

— Victim
— Rapist's semen
— Suspect's blood

— Victim
— Rapist's semen
— Suspect's blood

All DNA nucleotides lack —OH at the 2′ carbon of the sugar, but dideoxynucleotides have no 3′ —OH at which the enzyme can add new nucleotides. Thus the chain is terminated.

The experimenter must perform four separate reactions, each with a single dideoxynucleotide, to generate a set of fragments that terminate in specific bases. Thus all of the fragments produced in the A reaction incorporate dideoxy-adenosine and must end in A, and the same for the other three reactions with different terminators. When these fragments are separated by high-resolution gel electrophoresis, each reaction is run in a different track, or lane, to generate a pattern of nested fragments that can be read from the smallest fragment to fragments that are each longer by one base (figure 17.11*a*).

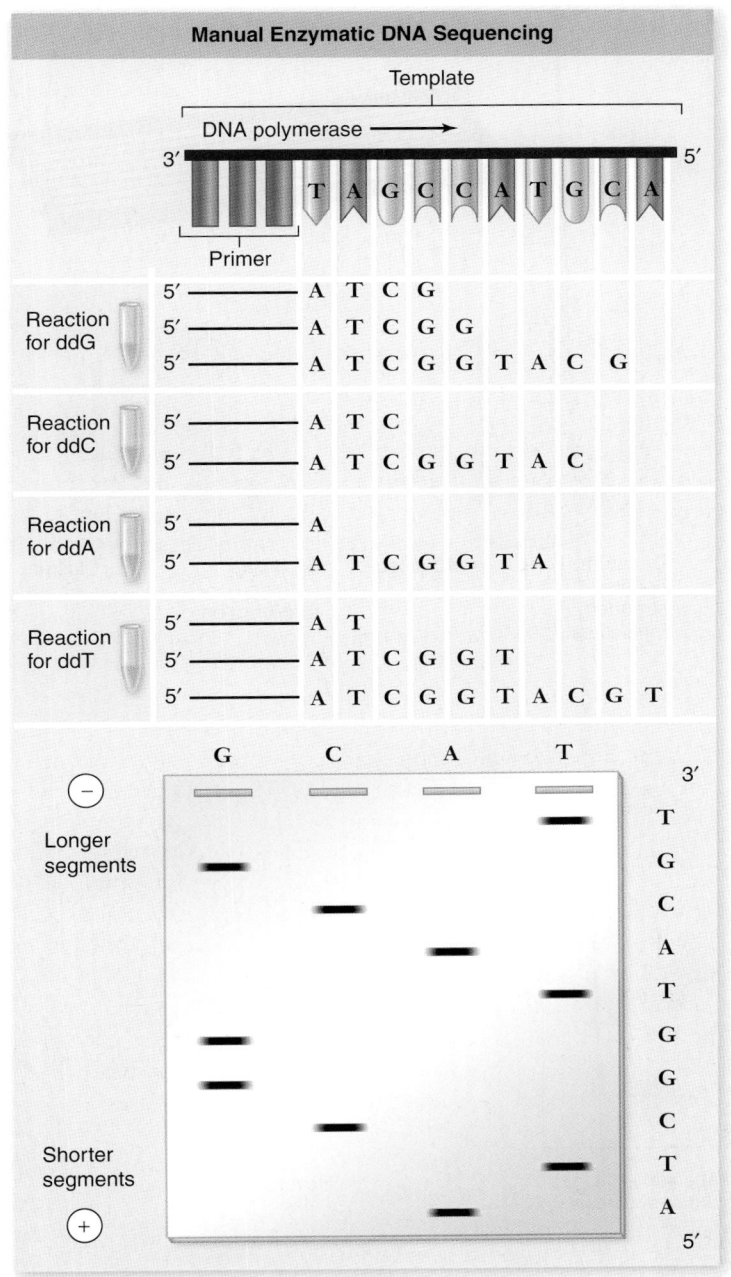

a.

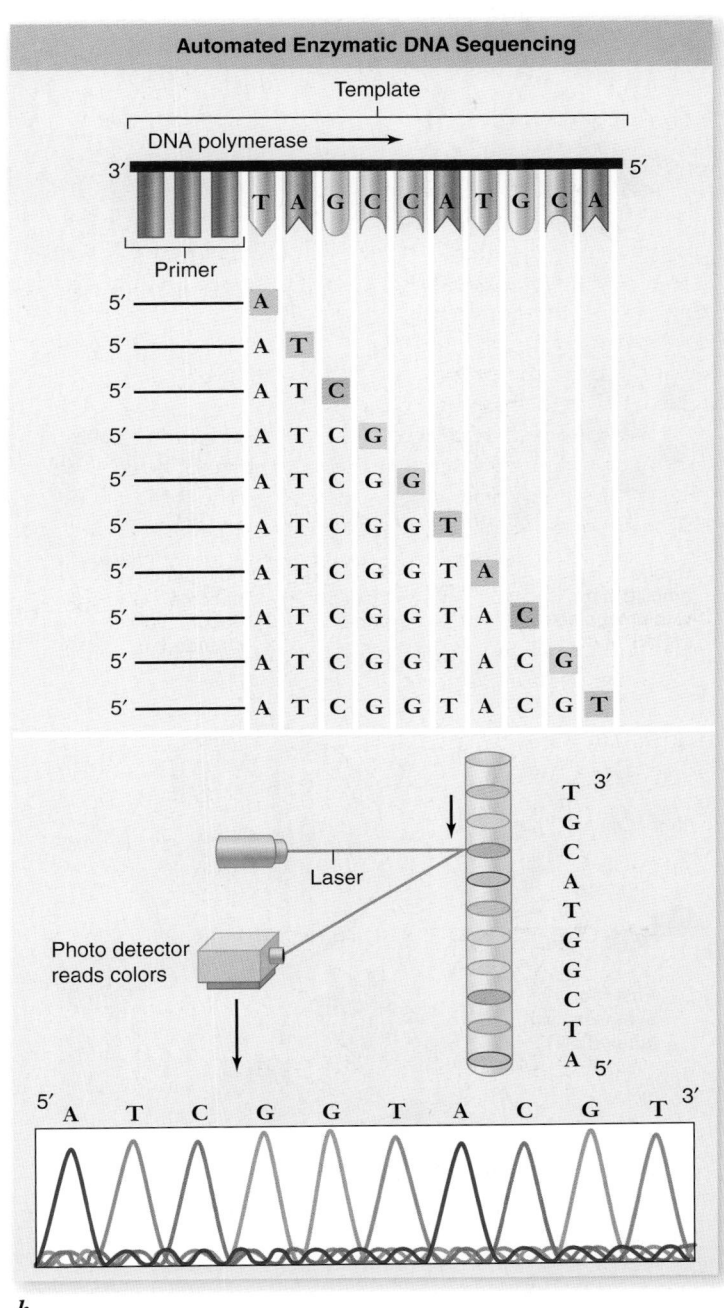

b.

Figure 17.11 Manual and automated enzymatic DNA sequencing. The sequence to be determined is shown at the top as a template strand for DNA polymerase with a primer attached. *a.* In the manual method, four reactions were done, one for each nucleotide. For example, the A tube would contain dATP, dGTP, dCTP, dTTP, and ddATP. This leads to fragments that end in A due to the dideoxy terminator. The fragments generated in each reaction are shown along with the results of gel electrophoresis. *b.* In automated sequencing, each ddNTP is labeled with a different color fluorescent dye, which allows the reaction to be done in a single tube. The fragments generated by the reactions are shown. When these are electrophoresed in a capillary tube, a laser at the bottom of the tube excites the dyes, and each will emit a different color that is detected by a photodetector.

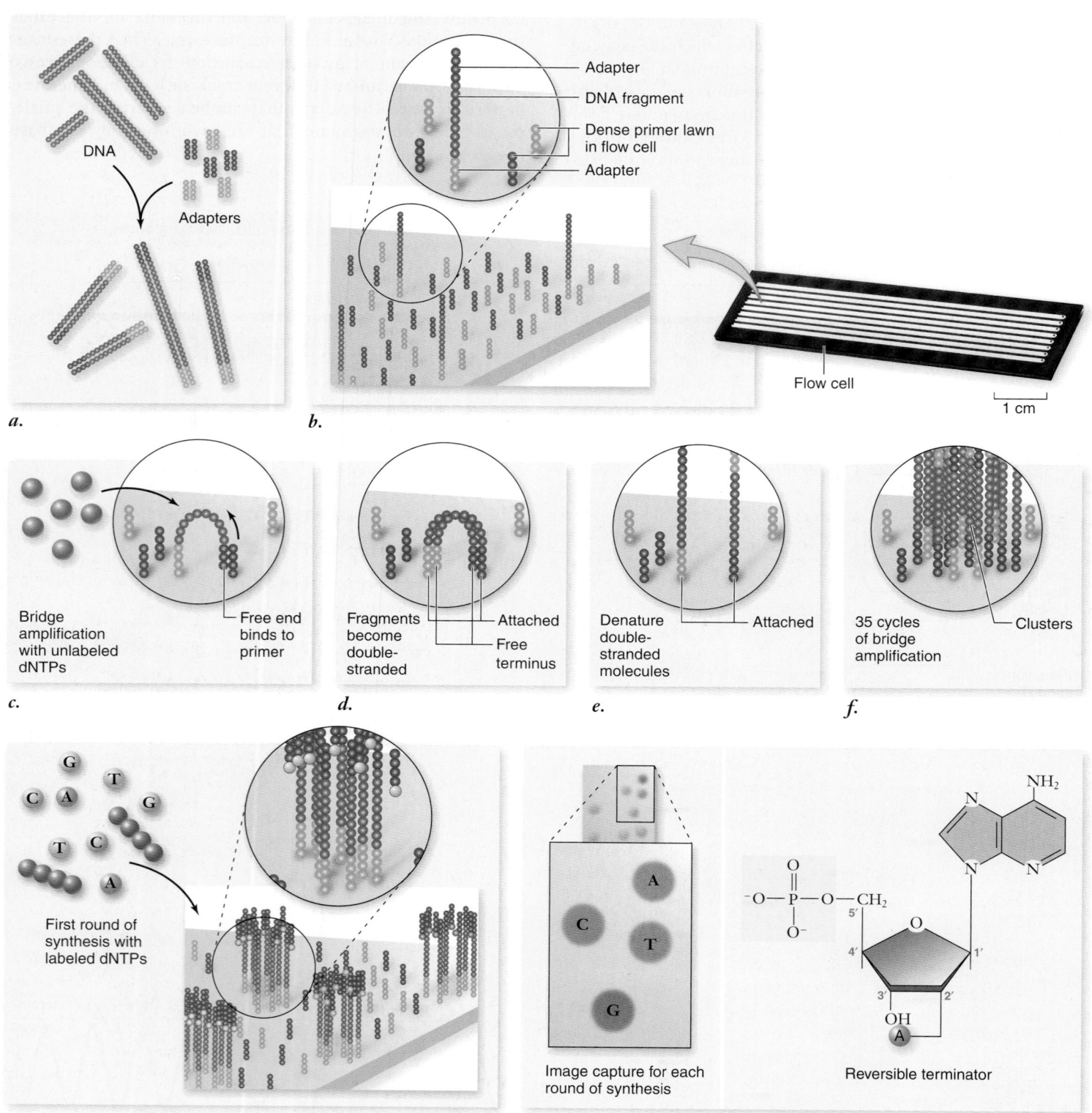

Figure 17.12 **New approach to sequencing.** DNA is cleaved into short fragments that will be sequenced. *a.* Adapters are added to the end of the DNA. *b.* DNA is denatured and the adapters bind to complementary primers in the flow cell. *c–f.* Individual fragments are amplified using dNTPs and polymerase. *g.* Fluorescently labeled dNTPs with cleavable dye that blocks the formation of additional phosphodiester bonds are added, and the first fluorescently labeled base is added. *h.* A CCD camera records the fluorescence pattern before the fluorescent dye is removed, and the next base is added to each DNA sequence.

Notice that since this is a DNA polymerase reaction, it requires a primer to begin synthesis. The vectors used for DNA sequencing have known regions next to the site where DNA is inserted. Short DNAs that are complementary to these regions are then synthesized and can be used as primers. This serves the dual purposes of providing a primer and ensuring that the first few bases sequenced are known because they are known in the vector itself. This allows the investigator to determine where the sequence of interest begins. As the sequence is generated, new primers can be designed near the end of the known sequence and DNA synthesized to use as a primer to extend the region sequenced in the next set of reactions.

Automated sequencing

The technique of enzymatic sequencing is very powerful, but it is also labor-intensive and takes a significant amount of time. It requires a series of enzymatic manipulations, time for electrophoresis, then time to expose the gel to film. At the end of this, a skilled researcher can read around 300 bases of sequence reliably. The development of automated techniques made sequencing a much more practical and less human-intensive procedure.

Automated sequencing machines use fluorescent dyes instead of a radioactive label and separate the products of the sequencing reactions using gels in thin capillary tubes instead of the large slab gels. The tubes run in front of a laser that excites the dyes, causing them to fluoresce. With a different colored dye for each base, a photodetector can determine the identity of each base by its color.

The data are assembled by a computer that generates a visual image consisting of different colored peaks; these are converted into the raw sequence data (figure 17.11b). The sequence data come directly from the electrophoresis, eliminating the time needed for exposing gels to film and for manual reading of the sequences. The use of different colored dyes also reduces handling and allows more sequence to be produced at one time.

With increases in the number of samples per run and the length of sequences able to be read, along with decreases in handling time, the amount of sequence information that can be generated is limited mainly by the number of machines that can be run at once.

New sequencing technology

For over 30 years, the basic chemistry of DNA sequencing did not change. Automation increased the speed of sequencing to the point that sequencing large eukaryotic genomes became possible. In the last few years, however, fundamentally new methods for sequencing have vastly accelerated the rate of sequence generation. Here we explore one new approach, which can generate 20 billion base pairs of sequence in a single run (figure 17.12). DNA is cleaved into smaller pieces, a few hundred base pairs, using a nebulizer—a device that converts the liquid to a very fine spray. Both ends are ligated to adapters that are complementary to specific primers. These DNA fragments are injected into a flow cell, which is like a microscope slide with seven channels, each containing a solid substrate with primers that complement the ligated ends of the DNA fragments. Millions of DNA fragments are placed in these channels, made single-stranded, and then amplified so there are clusters of fragments. Amplification works like DNA replication where a polymerase is added that recognizes the primer and starts copying. The fragments are again denatured to yield single-stranded molecules. They are now ready for sequencing. As with Sanger sequencing, deoxyribonucleotide triphosphates (dNTPs) have a fluorescent tag, but it can be removed. Four colors are used to distinguish each base. The fluorescent tag is reversibly attached to the 2′ position on the deoxyribose sugar and it blocks the 3′ OH so that only a single phosphodiester bond forms, but the blocking group can be removed after each round of DNA extension so the DNA strands continue to elongate. Very powerful charge-coupled device (CCD) cameras, once used exclusively by astronomers, record the pattern of fluorescence in the flow cell after each round of elongation. The technology works because a solid material holds the DNA fragments in place while they are being synthesized so that the repeated CCD images can be compiled and provide information about the sequence of each cluster of fragments. The amount of data generated each time another round of base pairs is added is enormous, so digital storage space and computational power to make sense of the data are the limiting factors.

The polymerase chain reaction accelerates the process of analysis

The next revolution in molecular biology was the development of the **polymerase chain reaction (PCR).** Kary Mullis developed PCR in 1983 while he was a staff chemist at the Cetus Corporation; in 1993, he was awarded the Nobel Prize in chemistry for his discovery.

The idea of the polymerase chain reaction is simple: Two primers are used that are complementary to the opposite strands of a DNA sequence, oriented toward each other. When DNA polymerase acts on these primers and the sequence of interest, the primers produce complementary strands, each containing the other primer. If this procedure is done cyclically, the result is a large quantity of a sequence corresponding to the DNA that lies between the two primers (figure 17.13).

The PCR procedure

Two developments turned this simple concept into a powerful technique. First, each cycle requires denaturing the DNA after each round of synthesis, which is easily done by raising the temperature; however, this destroys most polymerase enzymes. The solution was to isolate a DNA polymerase from a thermophilic, or heat-loving bacteria, *Thermus aquaticus*. This enzyme, called **Taq polymerase,** allows the reaction mixture to be repeatedly heated without destroying enzyme activity.

The second innovation was the development of machines with heating blocks that can be rapidly cycled over large temperature ranges with very accurate temperature control.

Thus each cycle of PCR involves three steps:

1. Denaturation (high temperature)
2. Annealing of primers (low temperature)
3. Synthesis (intermediate temperature)

Steps 1 to 3 are now repeated, and the two copies become four. It is not necessary to add any more polymerase, because the heating step does not harm Taq polymerase. Each complete cycle, which takes only 1–2 min, doubles the number of DNA molecules. After 20 cycles, a single fragment produces more than one million (2^{20}) copies!

In this way, the process of PCR allows the amplification of a single DNA fragment from a small amount of a complex mixture of DNA. This result is similar to what is isolated using molecular cloning, but in the case of PCR, the DNA cannot be reintroduced directly into a cell. The PCR product can be analyzed using electrophoresis, cloned into a vector for other manipulations, or directly sequenced. There are limitations on the size of the fragment that can be synthesized in this way, but it has been adapted for an amazing number of uses.

Applications of PCR

PCR, now fully automated, has revolutionized many aspects of science and medicine because it allows the investigation of minute samples of DNA. In criminal investigations, DNA fingerprints can now be prepared from the cells in a tiny speck of dried blood or from the tissue at the base of a single human hair. In medicine, physicians can detect genetic defects in very early embryos by collecting a single cell and amplifying its DNA. Due to its sensitivity, speed, and ease of use, technicians now routinely use PCR methods for these applications.

PCR has even been used to analyze mitochondrial DNA from the early human species *Homo neanderthalensis*. This application provides the first glimpse of data from extinct related species. The amplification of ancient DNA has been a controversial field because contamination with modern DNA is difficult to avoid. But it remains an active area of genetic research.

Protein interactions can be detected with the two-hybrid system

Protein–protein interactions form the basis of many biological structures. Just as human society is ultimately dependent on interactions between people, cells are dependent on interactions between proteins. This observation has led to the large-scale goal of determining all interactions among proteins in different cells. This goal once would have been a dream, but it is now becoming a reality. The yeast two-hybrid system is one of the workhorses of this kind of analysis (figure 17.14).

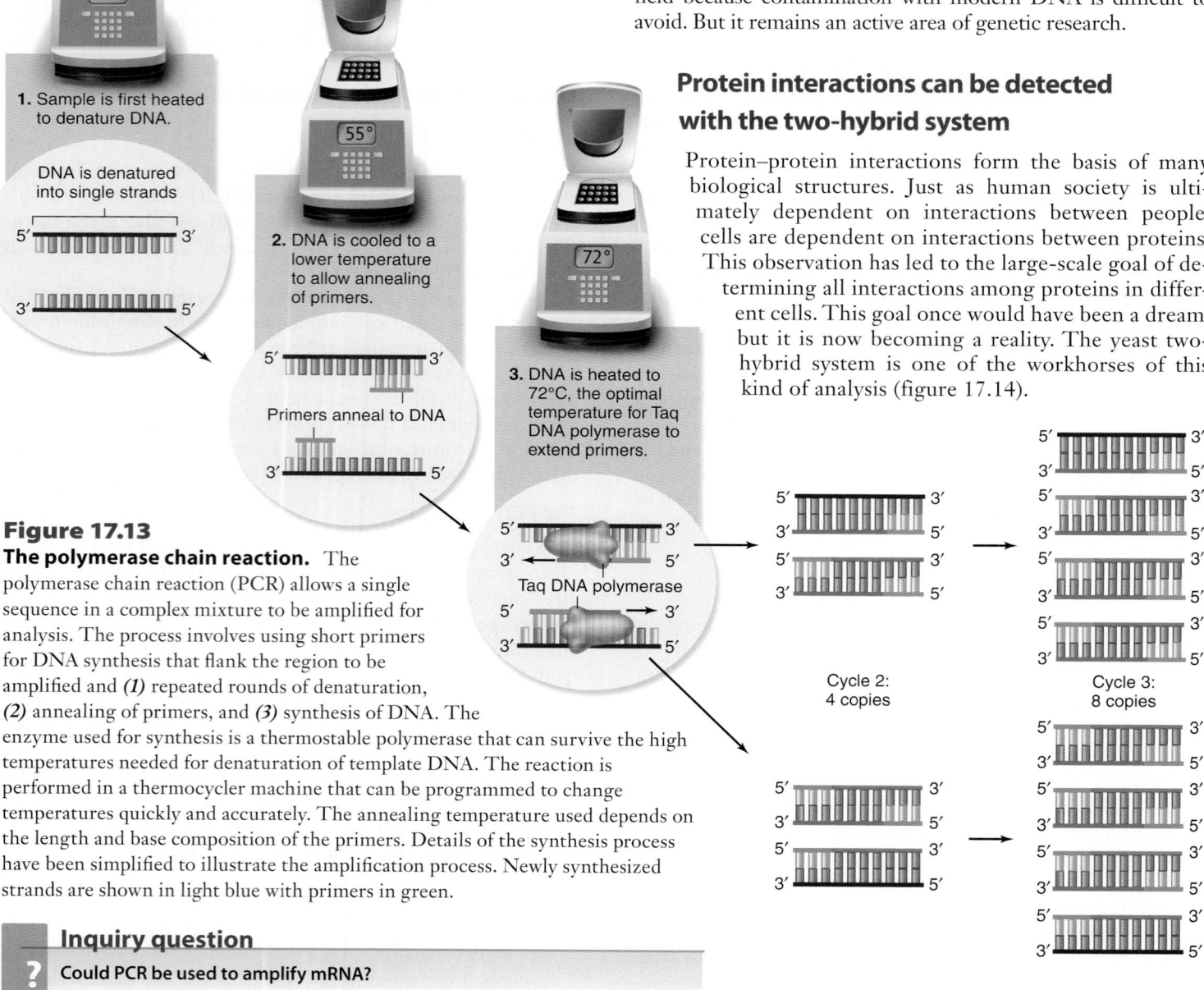

Figure 17.13
The polymerase chain reaction. The polymerase chain reaction (PCR) allows a single sequence in a complex mixture to be amplified for analysis. The process involves using short primers for DNA synthesis that flank the region to be amplified and *(1)* repeated rounds of denaturation, *(2)* annealing of primers, and *(3)* synthesis of DNA. The enzyme used for synthesis is a thermostable polymerase that can survive the high temperatures needed for denaturation of template DNA. The reaction is performed in a thermocycler machine that can be programmed to change temperatures quickly and accurately. The annealing temperature used depends on the length and base composition of the primers. Details of the synthesis process have been simplified to illustrate the amplification process. Newly synthesized strands are shown in light blue with primers in green.

Inquiry question

? Could PCR be used to amplify mRNA?

The yeast two-hybrid system integrates much of the technology discussed in this chapter. It takes advantage of one feature of eukaryotic gene regulation, namely that the structure of proteins that turn on eukaryotic gene expression, transcription factors, have a modular structure.

The *Gal4* gene of yeast encodes a transcriptional activator with modular structure consisting of a DNA-binding domain that binds sequences in *Gal4*-responsive promoters, and an activation domain that interacts with the transcription apparatus to turn on transcription. The system uses two vectors: one containing a fragment of the *Gal4* gene that encodes the DNA-binding domain, and another containing a fragment of the *Gal4* gene that encodes the transcription activation domain. Neither of these alone can activate transcription.

When cDNAs are inserted into each of these two vectors in the proper reading frame, they are expressed as a single protein consisting of the protein of interest and part of the Gal4 activator protein (see figure 17.13). These hybrid proteins are called *fusion proteins* since they are literally fused in the same polypeptide chain. The DNA-binding hybrid is called the *bait*, and the activating domain hybrid is called the *prey*.

These vectors are inserted into cells of different mating types that can be crossed. One of these vectors also contains a so-called *reporter gene* encoding a protein that can be assayed for enzymatic activity. The reporter gene is under control of a *Gal4*-responsive regulatory region, so that when active *Gal4* is present, the reporter gene is expressed and can be detected by an enzymatic assay.

The DNA-binding hybrid binds to DNA adjacent to the reporter gene. When the two proteins in bait and prey interact, the prey hybrid brings the activating domain into position to turn on gene expression from the reporter gene (see figure 17.13).

The beauty of this system is that it is both simple and flexible. It can be used with two known proteins or with a known protein in the bait vector and entire cDNA libraries in the prey vector. In the latter case, all of the possible interactions in a cell type can be mapped.

It is already clear that even more protein interactions occur in cells than anticipated. In the future these data will form the basis for understanding the networks of protein interactions that make up the normal activities of a cell.

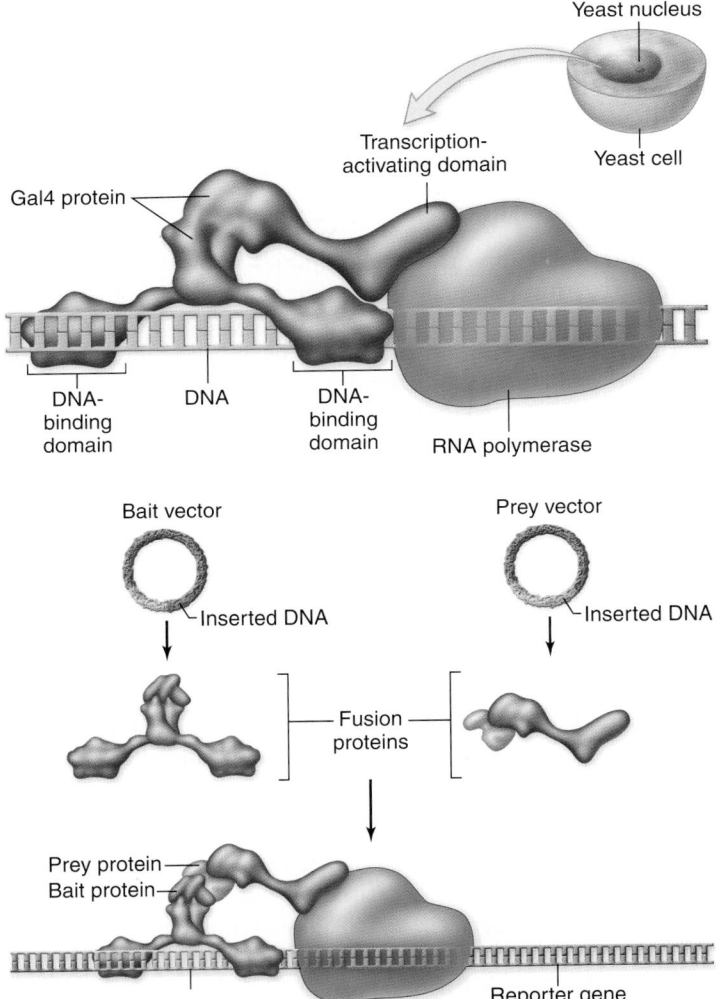

Figure 17.14 The yeast two-hybrid system detects interacting proteins. The Gal4 protein is a transcriptional activator *(top)*. The *Gal4* gene has been split and engineered into two different vectors such that one will encode only the DNA-binding domain (bait vector) and the other the transcription-activating domain (prey vector). When other genes are spliced into these vectors, they produce fusion proteins containing part of Gal4 and the proteins to be tested. If the proteins being tested interact, this will restore *Gal4* function and activate expression of a reporter gene.

Learning Outcomes Review 17.3

The Southern blotting technique allows identification of a target DNA by separating single-stranded DNA fragments and hybridizing fragments of interest with a labeled probe. In living cells, DNA polymerase is a key enzyme in replication. DNA sequencing uses a modified DNA polymerase reaction that contains chain terminators, allowing fragments to be ordered in sequence. The polymerase chain reaction (PCR) produces a large amount of a specific DNA from a small amount of starting material. The yeast system for detecting protein–protein interactions involves a bait protein, a prey protein, and a reporter gene.

■ ***What key component of PCR allows the rapid amplification of a sample?***

17.4 Genetic Engineering

Learning Outcome

1. *Describe three applications of cloning technology.*

The ability to clone individual genes for analysis ushered in an era of unprecedented advancement in research. At the time, these advancements were not accompanied by grand announcements of potential medical breakthroughs and other applications. The ability to truly genetically engineer any kind of cell

Figure 17.15

Construction of a knockout mouse. Steps in the construction of a knockout mouse. Some technical details have been omitted, but the basic concept is shown.

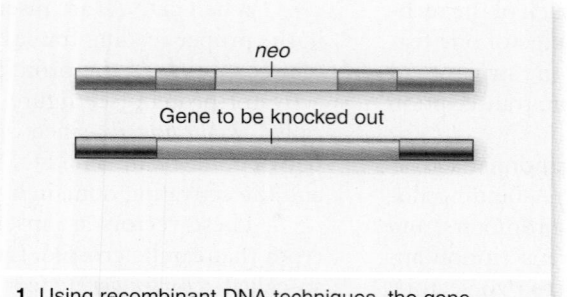

1. Using recombinant DNA techniques, the gene encoding resistance to *neomycin (neo)* is inserted into the gene of interest, disrupting it. The *neo* gene also confers resistance to the drug G418, which kills mouse cells. This construct is then introduced into ES cells.

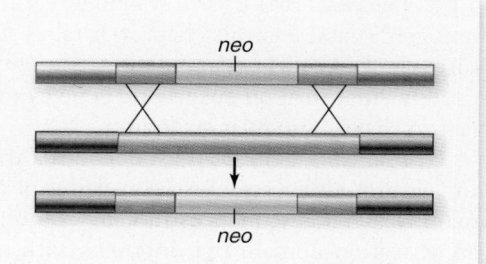

2. In some ES cells, the construct will recombine with the chromosomal copy of the gene to be knocked out. This replaces the chromosomal copy with the *neo* disrupted construct. This is the equivalent to a double crossover event in a genetic cross.

or organism was a long way off. But we are now approaching this ability, and it has generated much excitement as well as controversy.

Expression vectors allow production of specific gene products

A variety of specialized vectors have been constructed since the development of cloning technology. One very important type of vector are the **expression vectors.** These vectors contain the sequences necessary to drive expression of inserted DNA in a specific cell type, namely the correct sequences to permit transcription and translation of the sequences. The production of recombinant proteins in bacteria, for example, uses expression vectors with bacterial promoters and other control regions. The bacteria transformed by such vectors synthesize large amounts of the protein encoded by the inserted DNA. A number of pharmaceuticals have been produced in this way, the first of which was insulin, used to treat diabetes. (This type of application is discussed in more detail in the next section.)

Genes can be introduced across species barriers

The ability to reintroduce genes into an original host cell, or to introduce genes into another host, is true genetic engineering. An animal containing a gene that has been introduced without the use of conventional breeding is called a **transgenic animal.** We will explore a number of uses of transgenic animals in medicine and agriculture, but it is important to realize that their original use was for basic research.

The ability to engineer genes in context or out of context allows an experimenter to ask questions that could never be asked otherwise. A dramatic example was the use of the *eyeless* gene from mice in *Drosophila*. When this mouse gene was introduced into *Drosophila*, it was shown to be able to substitute for a *Drosophila* gene in organizing the formation of eyes. It could even cause the formation of eyes in incorrect locations when expressed in tissue that did not normally form eyes. This amazing result shows that the formation of the compound eye in an insect is not so different from the formation of the complex vertebrate eye. This example is discussed in more detail in chapter 25.

Cloned genes can be used to construct "knockout" mice

One of the most important technologies for research purposes is **in vitro mutagenesis**—the ability to create mutations at any site in a cloned gene to examine their effect on function. Rather than depending on mutations induced by chemical agents or radiation in intact organisms, which is time- and labor-intensive, the DNA itself is directly manipulated. The ultimate use of this approach is to be able to replace the wild-type gene with a mutant copy to test the function of the mutated gene. Developed first in yeast, this technique has now been extended to the mouse.

In mice, this technique has produced **knockout mice** in which a known gene is inactivated ("knocked out"). The effect of loss of this function is then assessed in the adult mouse, or if it is lethal, the stage of development at which function fails can be determined. The idea is simple, but the technology is quite complex. A streamlined description of the steps in this type of experiment are outlined as follows and illustrated in figure 17.15:

1. The cloned gene is disrupted by replacing it with a marker gene using recombinant DNA techniques. The marker gene codes for resistance to the antibiotic neomycin in bacteria, which allows mouse cells to survive when grown in a medium containing the related drug G418. The construction is done such that the marker gene is flanked by the DNA normally flanking the gene of interest in the chromosome.

2. The interrupted gene is introduced into **embryonic stem cells (ES cells).** These cells are derived from early embryos and can develop into different adult tissues. In these cells, the gene can recombine with the chromosomal copy of the gene based on the flanking DNA. This is the same kind of recombination used to map genes (chapter 13). The knockout gene with the drug resistance

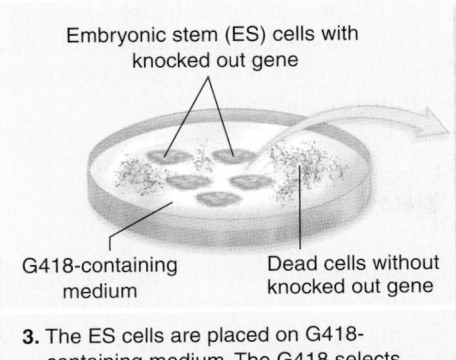

3. The ES cells are placed on G418-containing medium. The G418 selects cells that have had a replacement event, and now contain a copy of the knocked out gene.

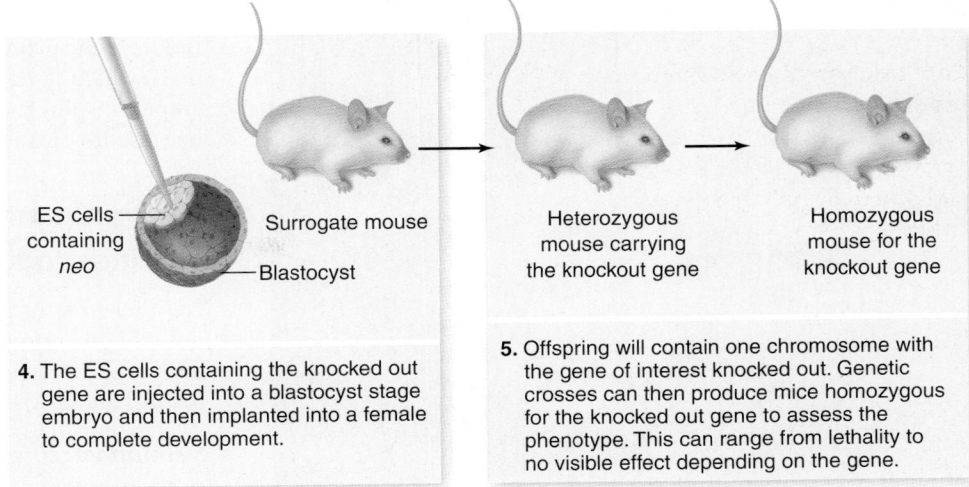

4. The ES cells containing the knocked out gene are injected into a blastocyst stage embryo and then implanted into a female to complete development.

5. Offspring will contain one chromosome with the gene of interest knocked out. Genetic crosses can then produce mice homozygous for the knocked out gene to assess the phenotype. This can range from lethality to no visible effect depending on the gene.

gene does not have an origin of replication, and thus it will be lost if no recombination occurs. Cells are grown in medium containing G418 to select for recombination events. (Only those containing the marker gene can grow in the presence of G418.)

3. The ES cells containing the knocked-out gene are injected into a blastocyst stage embryo, which is then implanted into a pseudopregnant female (one that has been mated with a vasectomized male and as a result has a receptive uterus). The pups from this female have one copy of the gene of interest knocked out. Transgenic animals can then be crossed to generate homozygous lines. These homozygous lines can be analyzed for phenotypes.

In conventional genetics, genes are identified based on mutants that show a particular phenotype. Molecular genetic techniques are then used to find the gene and isolate a molecular clone for analysis. The use of knockout mice is an example of **reverse genetics:** A cloned gene of unknown function is used to make a mutant that is deficient in that gene. A geneticist can then assess the effect on the entire organism of eliminating a single gene.

Sometimes this approach leads to surprises, such as happened when the gene for the p53 tumor suppressor was knocked out. Because this protein is found mutated in many human cancers and plays a key role in the regulation of the cell cycle (chapter 10), it was thought to be essential—the knockout was expected to be lethal. Instead, the mice were born normal; that is, development had proceeded normally. These mice do have a phenotype, however; they exhibit an increased incidence of tumors in a variety of tissues as they age.

Learning Outcome Review 17.4

Expression vectors that contain cloned genes allow the production of known proteins in different cells. This can be done for research purposes or to produce pharmaceuticals.

■ *Why is recombination an essential factor in creating a "knockout" mouse?*

Medical Applications

Learning Outcomes

1. *Explain how eukaryote proteins can be produced in bacterial cells.*
2. *Evaluate potential problems of gene therapy.*

The early days of genetic engineering led to a rash of startup companies, many of which are no longer in business. At the same time, all of the major pharmaceutical companies either began research in this area or actively sought to acquire smaller companies with promising technology. The number of applications of this technology are far too numerous to mention here, but we highlight a few; the section following discusses agricultural applications.

Human proteins can be produced in bacteria

The first and perhaps most obvious commercial application of genetic engineering was the introduction of genes that encode clinically important proteins into bacteria. Because bacterial cells can be grown cheaply in bulk, bacteria that incorporate recombinant genes can synthesize large amounts of the proteins those genes specify, assuming the inserted gene has been designed to be expressed in a bacterial cell. This method has been used to produce several forms of human insulin and the immune system protein interferon, as well as other commercially valuable proteins, such as human growth hormone (figure 17.16) and erythropoietin, which stimulates red blood cell production.

Among the medically important proteins now manufactured by these approaches are **atrial peptides,** small proteins that may provide a new way to treat high blood pressure and kidney failure. Another is **tissue plasminogen activator (TPA),** a human protein synthesized in minute amounts that causes blood clots to dissolve and that if used within the first

Figure 17.16 Genetically engineered mouse with human growth hormone. These two mice are from an inbred line and differ only in that the large one has one extra gene: the gene encoding human growth hormone. The gene was added to the mouse's genome and is now a stable part of the mouse's genetic endowment.

3 hr after an ischemic stroke (i.e., one that blocks blood to the brain) can prevent catastrophic disability.

A problem with this approach has been the difficulty of separating the desired protein from the others the bacteria make. The purification of proteins from such complex mixtures is both time-consuming and expensive, but it is still easier than isolating the proteins from bulk processing of the tissues of animals, which is how such proteins used to be obtained. For example, insulin was previously extracted from hog pancreases because hog insulin was similar to human insulin.

Recombinant DNA may simplify vaccine production

Another area of potential significance involves the use of genetic engineering to produce vaccines against communicable diseases. Two types of vaccines are under investigation: *subunit vaccines* and *DNA vaccines*.

Subunit vaccines

Subunit vaccines may be developed against viruses such as those that cause herpes and hepatitis. Genes encoding a part, or subunit, of the protein polysaccharide coat of the herpes simplex virus or hepatitis B virus are spliced into a fragment of the vaccinia (cowpox) virus genome (figure 17.17).

The vaccinia virus, which British physician Edward Jenner used more than 200 years ago in his pioneering vaccinations against smallpox, is now used as a vector to carry the herpes or hepatitis viral coat gene into cultured mammalian cells. These cells produce many copies of the recombinant vaccinia virus, which has the outside coat of a herpes or hepatitis virus. When this recombinant virus is injected into a mouse or rabbit, the immune system of the infected animal produces antibodies directed against the coat of the recombinant virus. The animal then develops an immunity to herpes or hepatitis virus.

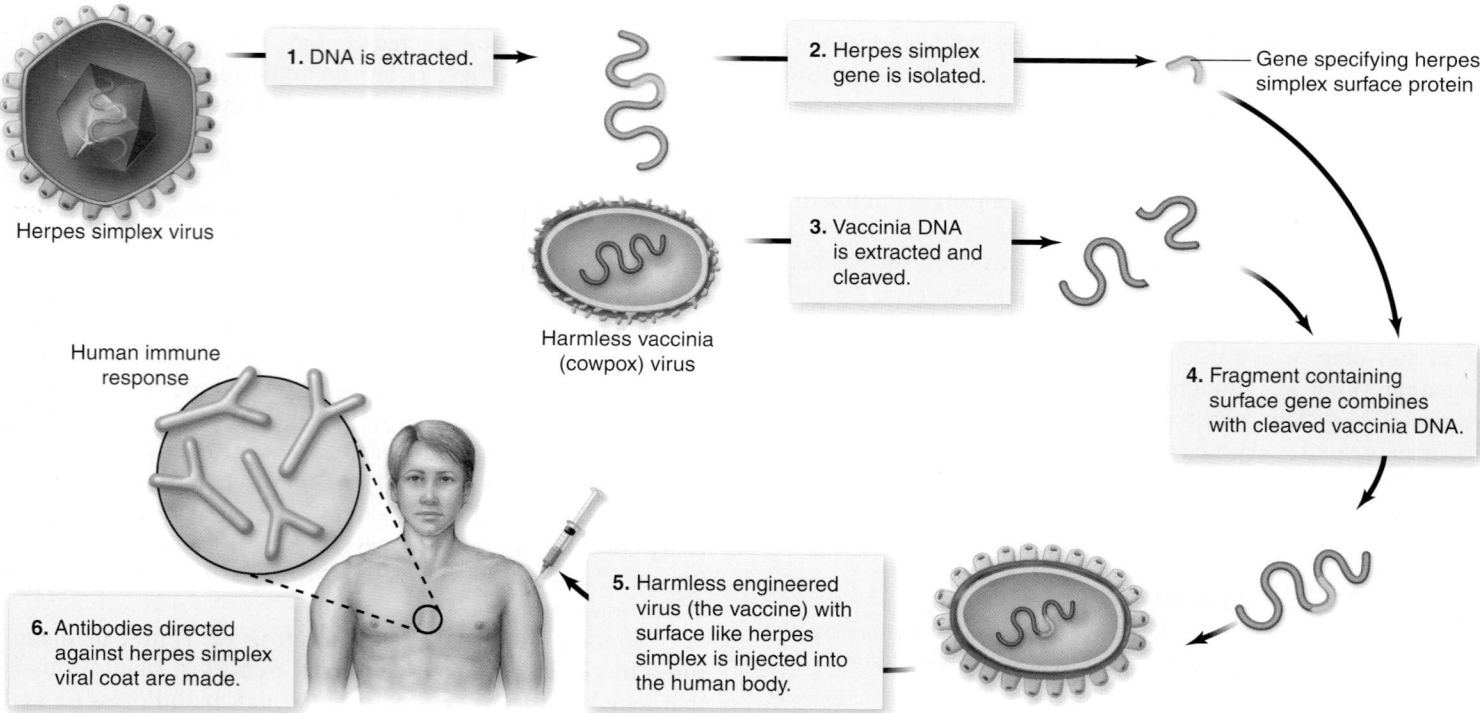

Figure 17.17 Strategy for constructing a subunit vaccine against herpes simplex. Recombinant DNA techniques can be used to construct vaccines for a single protein from a virus or bacterium. In this example, the protein is a surface protein from the herpes simplex virus.

Vaccines produced in this way are harmless because the vaccinia virus is benign, and only a small fragment of the DNA from the disease-causing virus is introduced via the recombinant virus.

The great attraction of this approach is that it does not depend on the nature of the viral disease. In the future, similar recombinant viruses may be used in humans to confer resistance to a wide variety of viral diseases.

DNA vaccines

In 1995, the first clinical trials began to test a novel new kind of **DNA vaccine,** one that depends not on antibodies but rather on the second arm of the body's immune defense, the so-called *cellular immune response*, in which blood cells known as killer T cells attack infected cells (chapter 52). The first DNA vaccines spliced an influenza virus gene encoding an internal nucleoprotein into a plasmid, which was then injected into mice. The mice developed a strong cellular immune response to influenza. Although new and controversial, the approach offers great promise.

Gene therapy can treat genetic diseases directly

In 1990, researchers first attempted to combat genetic defects by the transfer of human genes. When a hereditary disorder is the result of a single defective gene, an obvious way to cure the disorder would be to add a working copy of the gene. This approach is being used in an attempt to combat cystic fibrosis, and it offers the potential of treating muscular dystrophy and a variety of other disorders (table 17.1).

TABLE 17.1	Diseases Being Treated in Clinical Trials of Gene Therapy

Disease
Cancer (melanoma, renal cell, ovarian, neuroblastoma, brain, head and neck, lung, liver, breast, colon, prostate, mesothelioma, leukemia, lymphoma, multiple myeloma)
SCID (severe combined immunodeficiency)
Cystic fibrosis
Gaucher disease
Familial hypercholesterolemia
Hemophilia
Purine nucleoside phosphorylase deficiency
α_1-Antitrypsin deficiency
Fanconi anemia
Hunter syndrome
Chronic granulomatous disease
Rheumatoid arthritis
Peripheral vascular disease
Acquired immunodeficiency syndrome (AIDS)
Duchenne muscular dystrophy
Macular degeneration (wet variety)
Batten disease (neurological disorder)

Clinical trials for treating macular degeneration, a genetic eye disease, using an RNAi vector (see chapter 16) are promising. Individuals with a certain type of macular degeneration lose their sight because of the uncontrolled proliferation of blood vessels under the retina. For the patient, it is a lot like looking through a car windshield with broken wipers in the middle of a thunderstorm. RNAi gene therapy involves injection of double-stranded RNA coding for a gene necessary for blood vessel proliferation. The RNAi mechanism has the counterintuitive effect of supressing production of the protein needed for blood vessel development, preventing progression of the disease.

One disease that illustrates both the potential and the problems with gene therapy is **severe combined immunodeficiency disease (SCID).** This disease has multiple forms, including an X-linked form (X-SCID) and a form that lacks the enzyme adenosine deaminase (ADA-SCID).

Recent trials for both of these forms showed great initial promise, with patients exhibiting restoration of immune function. But then problems arose in the case of the X-SCID trial when a patient developed a rare form of leukemia. Since that time, two other patients have developed the same leukemia, and it appears to be due to the gene therapy itself. The vector used to introduce the X-SCID gene integrated into the genome next to a proto-oncogene called *LMO2* in all three cases. Activation of this gene can cause childhood leukemias.

The insertion of a gene during gene therapy has always been a random event, and it has been a concern that the insertion could inactivate an essential gene, or turn on a gene inappropriately. That effect had not been observed prior to the X-SCID trial, despite a large number of genes introduced into blood cells in particular. For leukemia to occur in 15% of the patients treated implies that some influence of the genetic background associated with X-SCID potentiates this development. This possibility is supported by the observation that the ADA-SCID patients treated have not been affected thus far.

On the positive side, 15 children treated successfully are still alive, 14 of them after more than four years, with functioning immune systems. On the negative side, three other children treated have developed leukemia.

When we understand the basis of the preferential integration in the case of X-SCID, it should be possible to overcome this unfortunate result. In the meantime, the investigators have halted the trial and are working on new vectors to reduce the possibility of this preferential integration.

Learning Outcomes Review 17.5

Recombinant DNA technology has allowed genes from eukaryotes, such as humans, to be isolated, inserted into vectors, and recombined into bacterial genomes, where the genes' products can be mass-produced. Gene therapy is the process of using genetic engineering to replace defective genes; however, in some cases unwanted effects result from random gene insertion.

- *What might be some undesirable effects of treating patients with human proteins manufactured in and isolated from other organisms?*

Perhaps no area of genetic engineering touches all of us so directly as the applications that are being used in agriculture today. Crops are being modified to resist disease, to be tolerant of herbicides, and for changes in nutritional and other content in a variety of ways. Plant systems are also being used to produce pharmaceuticals by "biopharming," and domesticated animals are being genetically modified to produce biologically active compounds.

The Ti plasmid can transform broadleaf plants

In plants, the primary experimental difficulty has been identifying a suitable vector for introducing recombinant DNA. Plant cells do not possess the many plasmids that bacteria have, so the choice of potential vectors is limited.

The Ti plasmid

The most successful results thus far have been obtained with the **Ti (tumor-inducing) plasmid** of the plant bacterium *Agrobacterium tumefaciens*, which normally infects broadleaf plants such as tomato, tobacco, and soybean. Part of the Ti plasmid integrates into the plant DNA, and researchers have succeeded in attaching other genes to this portion of the plasmid (figure 17.18). The characteristics of a number of plants have been altered using this technique, which should be valuable in improving crops and forests.

Among the features scientists would like to affect are resistance to disease, frost, and other forms of stress; nutritional balance and protein content; and herbicide resistance. All of these traits have either been modified or are being modified. Unfortunately, *Agrobacterium* normally does not infect cereal plants such as corn, rice, and wheat, but alternative methods can be used to introduce new genes into them.

Other methods of gene insertion

For cereal plants that are not normally infected by *Agrobacterium*, other methods have been used. One popular method, "the gene gun," uses bombardment with tiny gold or tungsten particles coated with DNA. This technique has the advantage of being usable for any species, but it does not allow as precise an engineering because the copy number of introduced genes is much harder to control.

Recently, modifications of the *Agrobacterium* system have allowed it to be used with cereal plants, so the gene gun technology may not be used much in the future. A new bacterium has also been manipulated to function like *Agrobacterium*, offering another potential alternative method of engineering cereal crops.

It is clear that genetic modification of crop plants of all sorts has become a mature technology, which should accelerate the production of a variety of transgenic crops.

Herbicide-resistant crops allow no-till planting

Recently, broadleaf plants have been genetically engineered to be resistant to **glyphosate,** a powerful, biodegradable herbicide that kills most actively growing plants (figure 17.19). Glyphosate works by inhibiting an enzyme called 5-enolpyruvyl-shikimate-3-phosphate (EPSP) synthetase, which plants require to produce aromatic amino acids.

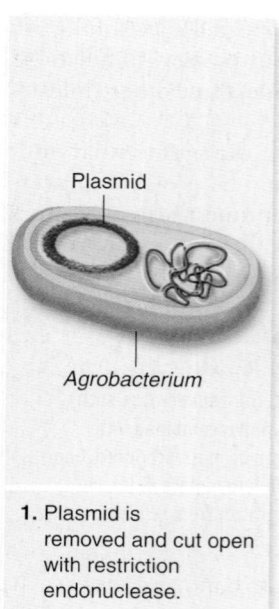

1. Plasmid is removed and cut open with restriction endonuclease.

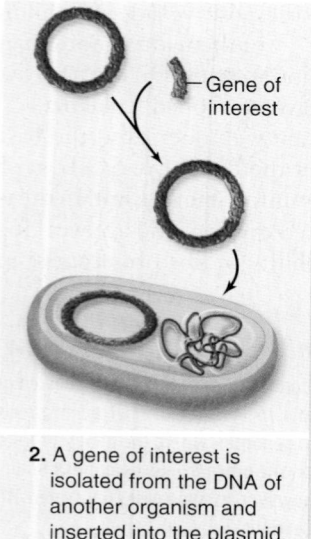

2. A gene of interest is isolated from the DNA of another organism and inserted into the plasmid. The plasmid is put back into the *Agrobacterium*.

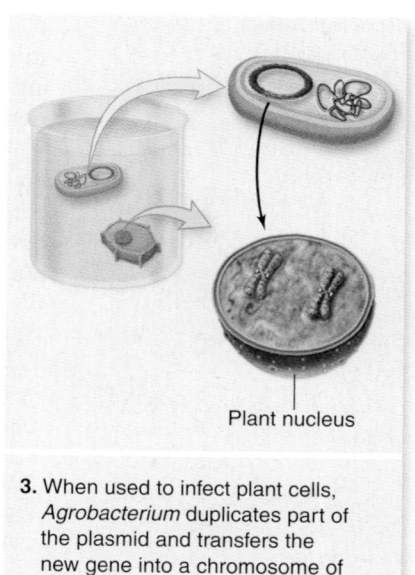

3. When used to infect plant cells, *Agrobacterium* duplicates part of the plasmid and transfers the new gene into a chromosome of the plant cell.

4. The plant cell divides, and each daughter cell receives the new gene. These cultured cells can be used to grow a new plant with the introduced gene.

Figure 17.18   The Ti plasmid. This *Agrobacterium tumefaciens* plasmid is used in plant genetic engineering.

Hypothesis: *Petunias can acquire tolerance to the herbicide glyphosate by overexpressing EPSP synthase.*

Prediction: *Transgenic petunia plants with a chimeric EPSP synthase gene with strong promoter will be glyphosate tolerant.*

Test:

1. *Use restriction enzymes and ligase to "paste" the cauliflower mosaic virus promoter (35S) to the EPSP synthase gene and insert the construct in Ti plasmids.*

2. *Transform Agrobacterium with the recombinant plasmid.*

3. *Infect petunia cells and regenerate plants. Regenerate uninfected plants as controls.*

4. *Challenge plants with glyphosate.*

Result: *Glyphosate kills control plants, but not transgenic plants.*

Conclusion: *Additional EPSP synthase provides glyphosate tolerance.*

Further Experiments: *The transgenic plants are tolerant, but not resistant (note bleaching at shoot tip). How could you determine if additional copies of the gene would increase tolerance? Can you think of any downsides to expressing too much EPSP synthase in petunia?*

Figure 17.19 Genetically engineered herbicide resistance.

Humans do not make aromatic amino acids; we get them from our diet, so we are unaffected by glyphosate. To make glyphosate-resistant plants, scientists used a Ti plasmid to insert extra copies of the EPSP synthetase gene into plants. These engineered plants produce 20 times the normal level of EPSP synthetase, enabling them to synthesize proteins and grow despite glyphosate's suppression of the enzyme. In later experiments, a bacterial form of the EPSP synthetase gene that differs from the plant form by a single nucleotide was introduced into plants via Ti plasmids; the bacterial enzyme is not inhibited by glyphosate (see figure 17.19).

These advances are of great interest to farmers because a crop resistant to glyphosate would not have to be weeded—the field could simply be treated with the herbicide. Because glyphosate is a broad-spectrum herbicide, farmers would no longer need to employ a variety of different herbicides, most of which kill only a few kinds of weeds. Furthermore, glyphosate breaks down readily in the environment, unlike many other herbicides commonly used in agriculture. A plasmid is actively being sought for the introduction of the EPSP synthetase gene into cereal plants, making them also glyphosate-resistant.

At this point four important crop plants have been modified to be glyphosate-resistant: maize (corn), cotton, soybeans, and canola. The use of glyphosate-resistant soy has been especially popular, accounting for 60% of the global area of GM (genetically modified) crops grown in nine countries worldwide. In the United States, 90% of soy currently grown is GM soy. Global variation in the use of GM crops has occurred, with the Americas, led by the United States, the largest adopter. The area currently with the largest growth in the use of GM crops is Asia, while Europe has been the slowest to move to their use.

Bt crops are resistant to some insect pests

Many commercially important plants are attacked by insects, and the usual defense against such attacks has been to apply insecticides. Over 40% of the chemical insecticides used today are targeted against boll weevils, bollworms, and other insects that eat cotton plants. Scientists have produced plants that are resistant to insect pests, removing the need to use many externally applied insecticides.

The approach is to insert into crop plants genes encoding proteins that are harmful to the insects that feed on the plants, but harmless to other organisms. The most commonly used protein is a toxin produced by the soil bacterium *Bacillus thuringiensis (Bt toxin)*. When insects ingest Bt toxin, endogenous enzymes convert it into an insect-specific toxin, causing paralysis and death. Because these enzymes are not found in other animals, the protein is harmless to them.

The same four crops that have been modified for herbicide resistance have also been modified for insect resistance using the Bt toxin. The use of Bt maize is the second most common GM crop globally, representing 14% of global area of GM crops in nine countries. The global distribution of these crops is also similar to the herbicide-resistant relatives.

Given the popularity of both of these types of crop modifications, it is not surprising that they have also been combined, so-called *stacked GM crops*, in both maize and cotton. Stacked crops now represent 9% of global area of GM crops.

Golden Rice shows potential of GM crops

One of the successes of GM crops is the development of Golden Rice. This rice has been genetically modified to produce β-carotene (provitamin A). The World Health Organization (WHO) estimates that vitamin A deficiency affects between 140 and 250 million preschool children worldwide. The deficiency is especially severe in developing countries where the major staple food is rice. Provitamin A in the diet can be converted by enzymes in the body to vitamin A, alleviating the deficiency.

Golden Rice is named for its distinctive color imparted by the presence of β-carotene in the endosperm (the outer layer of rice that has been milled). Rice does not normally make β-carotene in endosperm tissue, but does produce a precursor, geranyl geranyl diphosphate, that can be converted by three enzymes, phytoene synthase, phytoene desaturase, and lycopene β-cyclase, to β-carotene. These three genes were engineered to be expressed in endosperm and introduced into rice to complete the biosynthetic pathway producing β-carotene in endosperm (figure 17.20).

This is an interesting case of genetic engineering for two reasons. First, it introduces a new biochemical pathway in tissue of the transgenic plants. Second, it could not have been done by conventional breeding as no rice cultivar known produces these enzymes in endosperm. The original constructs used two genes from daffodil and one from a bacterium (see figure 17.20). There are many reasons to expect failure in the introduction of a biochemical pathway without disrupting normal metabolism. That the original form of Golden Rice makes significant amounts of β-carotene in an otherwise healthy plant is impressive. A second-generation version that makes much higher levels of β-carotene has also been produced by using the gene for phytoene synthase from maize in place of the original daffodil gene.

Golden Rice was originally constructed in a public facility in Switzerland and made available for free with no commercial entanglements. Since its inception, Golden Rice has been improved both by public groups and by industry scientists, and these improved versions are also being made available without commercial strings attached.

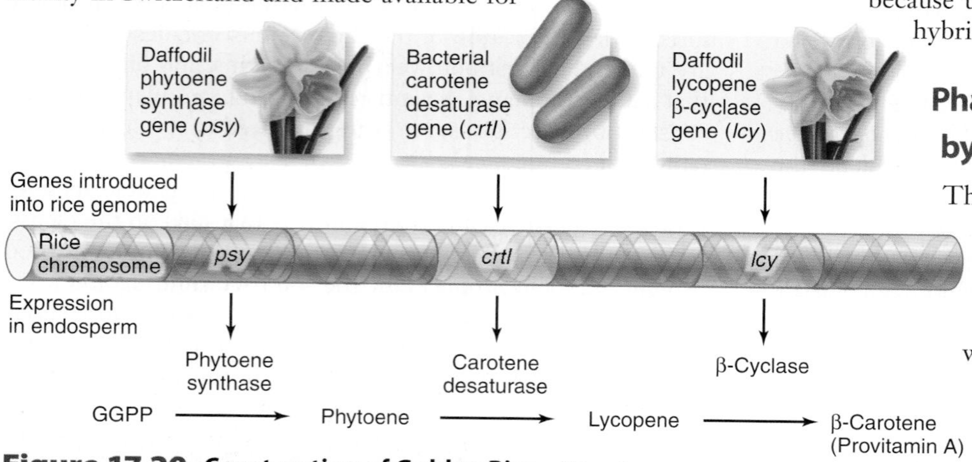

GM crops raise a number of social issues

The adoption of GM crops has been resisted in some places for a variety of reasons. Some people have wondered about the safety of these crops for human consumption, the likelihood of introduced genes moving into wild relatives, and the possible loss of biodiversity associated with these crops.

Powerful forces have aligned on opposing sides in this debate. On the side in favor of the use of GM crops are the multinational companies that are utilizing this technology to produce seeds for the various GM crops. On the other side are a variety of political organizations that are opposed to genetically modified foods. Scientists can be found on both sides of the controversy.

The controversy originally centered on the safety of introduced genes for human consumption. In the United States, this issue has been "settled" for the crops already mentioned, and a large amount of GM soy and maize is consumed in this country. Although some opponents still raise the issue of long-term use and allergic reactions, no negative effects have been documented so far. Existing crops will be monitored for adverse effects, and each new modification will require regulatory approval for human consumption.

Another contention has been the fear that genes might spread outside of the GM crops into wild relatives, a process called introgression. But at this point there is no indication of that happening. One study showed no evidence for the movement of genes from GM crops into native species in Mexico, despite earlier studies indicating significant movement of introduced genes.

This finding does not mean that such movement is impossible, but it does indicate that it seems not to have occurred at present. It is clear that this area requires more study. This issue will likely have to be considered on a case-by-case basis because the number of wild relatives and the ease of hybridization varies greatly among crop plants.

Pharmaceuticals can be produced by "biopharming"

The medicinal use of plants goes back as far as recorded history. In modern times, the pharmaceutical industry began by isolating biologically active compounds from plants. This approach began to change when in 1897, the Bayer company introduced acetyl salicylic acid, otherwise known as aspirin. This compound was a synthetic version of the compound salicylic acid, which was isolated from the bark of the white willow. The production of pharmaceuticals has since been dominated more by organic synthesis and less by the isolation of plant products.

One exception to this trend is cancer chemotherapeutic agents such as taxol, vinblastine, and vincristine, all of which were isolated from plant sources. In an interesting closing of

Figure 17.20 Construction of Golden Rice. Rice does not normally express the enzymes needed to synthesize β-carotene in endosperm. Three genes were added to the rice genome to allow expression of the pathway for β-carotene in endosperm. The source of the genes and the pathway for synthesis of β-carotene is shown. The result is Golden Rice, which contains enriched levels of β-carotene in endosperm.

the historical loop, the industry is now looking at using transgenic plants for the production of useful compounds.

The first human protein to be produced in plants was human serum albumin, which was produced in 1990 by both genetically engineered tobacco and potato plants. Since that time more than 20 proteins have been produced in transgenic plants. This first crop of transgenic pharmaceuticals are now in the regulatory pipeline.

Recombinant subunit vaccines

One promising aspect of plant genetic engineering is the production of recombinant subunit vaccines, which were discussed earlier. One of these, being produced in genetically modified potatoes, is a vaccine against Norwalk virus. Norwalk virus is not a common source of illness, but it reached the public consciousness when cruise ships were forced to cancel cruises due to outbreaks of the virus among passengers. The vaccine is now in clinical trials. A vaccine against rabies produced in transgenic spinach is also in clinical trials.

One obvious advantage of using plants for vaccine production is scalability. It has been estimated that 250 acres of greenhouse space could produce enough transgenic potato plants to supply Southeast Asia's need for hepatitis B vaccine.

Recombinant antibodies

Molecular cloning and immunology can be combined to produce antibodies in transgenic plants that are normally made by blood cells in vertebrates. The synthesis of monoclonal antibodies in plant systems is a promising use of transgenic plants.

A number of potentially therapeutic antibodies are being produced in plants, and some of these have reached clinical trial stage. One interesting example is an antibody against the bacterium responsible for dental caries, commonly known as tooth decay. It would make a visit to the dentist more pleasant to have a topical antibody applied instead of a drill.

Domesticated animals can also be genetically modified

Humans have been breeding and selecting domestic animals for thousands of years. With the advent of genetic engineering,

this process can be accelerated, and genes can be introduced from other species.

The production of transgenic livestock is in an early stage, and it is hard to predict where it will go. At this point, one of the uses of biotechnology is not to construct transgenic animals, but to use DNA markers to identify animals and to map genes that are involved in such traits as palatability in food animals, texture of hair or fur, and other features of animal products. Molecular techniques combined with the ability to clone domestic animals (chapter 19) could produce improved animals for economically desirable traits.

Transgenic animal technology has not been as successful as initially predicted. Early on, pigs were engineered to overproduce growth hormone in the hope that this would lead to increased and faster growth. These animals proved to have only slightly increased growth, and they had lower fat levels, which reduces flavor, as well as showing other deleterious effects. The main use thus far has been engineering animals to produce pharmaceuticals in milk—another example of the biopharming concept.

One interesting idea for transgenics is the EnviroPig. This animal has been engineered with the gene for phytase under the control of a salivary gland-specific promoter. The enzyme phytase breaks down phosphorus in the feed and can reduce phosphate excretion by up to 70%. Because phosphate is a major problem in pig waste, reducing its excretion could be a large environmental benefit.

As with GM crops, fears exist about the consumption of meat from transgenic animals. At this point, these fears do not seem to be based on sound science; nevertheless, every transgenic animal produced that is intended for consumption will need to be considered on a case-by-case basis.

Learning Outcomes Review 17.6

Genes can be introduced into plants using the bacterial Ti plasmid and techniques similar to those for bacteria. To date, herbicide resistance, pathogen protection, nutritional enhancement, and vaccine and drug production have been targets of agricultural genetic engineering. Controversy regarding the use of GM plants has centered on the potential of unforeseen effects on human health and on the environment.

■ *How might a recombinant gene for Bt toxin production "escape" from a crop plant and move into wild plants?*

Calvin and Hobbes   by Bill Watterson

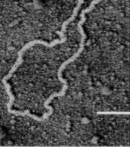

17.1 DNA Manipulation

Restriction enzymes cleave DNA at specific sites.

DNA molecules fragmented by known type II restriction endonucleases can be ordered into a physical map of DNA.

DNA ligase allows construction of recombinant molecules.

Just as in DNA replication, DNA ligase catalyzes formation of a phosphodiester bond between nucleotides, forming a recombinant molecule.

Gel electrophoresis separates DNA fragments.

An electric field applied to a gel matrix causes DNA to migrate through the matrix. Smaller fragments migrate farther than large fragments (figure 17.2).

Transformation allows introduction of foreign DNA into E. coli.

Artificial transformation techniques introduce foreign DNA into *E. coli* cells, which are then termed transgenic.

17.2 Molecular Cloning

Host–vector systems allow propagation of foreign DNA in bacteria.

Plasmids, and artificial chromosomes can be used as vectors. Foreign DNA is inserted using restriction enzymes and DNA ligase; once the vector is inside the host cell, it is replicated during the cell cycle.

DNA libraries contain the entire genome of an organism.

A DNA library is a complex mixture of DNAs collected into vectors. These libraries may be probed for a sequence of interest.

Reverse transcriptase can make a DNA copy of RNA.

A library can also be created for the expressed parts of the genome by isolating RNA and converting it to cDNA using the enzyme reverse transcriptase (figure 17.5).

Hybridization allows identification of specific DNAs in complex mixtures.

DNA can be reversibly denatured and renatured, resulting in single- and then double-stranded DNA. Renaturation of complementary strands from different sources is called hybridization. Known DNA can be labeled to identify complementary strands.

Specific clones can be isolated from a library.

Hybridization is the most common way to identify a gene of interest in a library.

17.3 DNA Analysis

Restriction maps provide molecular "landmarks."

The first physical maps of DNA molecules were based on the sites of restriction enzyme cleavage.

Southern blotting reveals DNA differences.

In Southern blotting, a complex mixture is separated by electrophoresis and transferred to filter paper. Specific sequences of DNA can then be identified by hybridization. Similar techniques can identify mRNA (Northern blot) and proteins (Western blot).

Restriction fragment length polymorphisms (RFLPs) identified by Southern blotting reveal individual differences in DNA. DNA fingerprinting uses probes to locate polymorphic DNA fragments.

DNA sequencing provides information about genes and genomes.

DNA sequencing uses chain-terminating reagents to identify the order of fragments and from this to infer the sequence of bases (figures 17.11, 17.12).

The polymerase chain reaction accelerates the process of analysis.

The polymerase chain reaction (PCR) amplifies a single small DNA fragment using two short primers that flank the region to be amplified. Cyclic replication is accomplished via heating and cooling; a key factor is Taq polymerase, which is not denatured at high temperature.

Protein interactions can be detected with the two-hybrid system.

The yeast two-hybrid system relies on fusion proteins and a reporter gene to study protein–protein interactions (figure 17.13).

17.4 Genetic Engineering

Expression vectors allow production of specific gene products.

Expression vectors contain the promoters and enhancers necessary to drive expression of the inserted DNA.

Genes can be introduced across species barriers.

Transgenic organisms can be constructed to express genes in a different species or to create mutations in genes to assess phenotype.

Cloned genes can be used to construct "knockout" mice.

In knockout mice, a gene is inactivated by replacing the wild-type version with a mutant copy (figure 17.15). In this way, the function of the gene can be analyzed and clarified.

17.5 Medical Applications

Human proteins can be produced in bacteria.

Bacterial production of human proteins such as insulin has allowed better results and has increased production to treat disease.

Recombinant DNA may simplify vaccine production.

Subunit vaccines produced in cultured cells have been shown to be effective in animals.

DNA vaccines, which alter the cellular immune response, are also promising. Both these approaches require further testing.

Gene therapy can treat genetic diseases directly.

Gene therapy involves inserting a normal gene to replace a defective one. Unfortunately, trials of two promising therapies had unintended and fatal consequences in 15% of patients.

17.6 Agricultural Applications

The Ti plasmid can transform broadleaf plants.

The tumor-inducing (Ti) plasmid from a plant bacterium is used to transfer genes into broad-leaf plants. A number of applications are currently in use.

Herbicide-resistant crops allow no-till planting.

Bt crops are resistant to some insect pests.

Golden Rice shows potential of GM crops.

GM crops raise a number of social issues.

Concerns about GM plants include unintended allergic reactions to proteins inserted from a different organism and spread of foreign genes into noncultivated plants in the environment.

Pharmaceuticals can be produced by "biopharming."

Domesticated animals can also be genetically modified.

To date, results with transgenic animals have been mixed.

Review Questions

UNDERSTAND

1. A recombinant DNA molecule is one that is
   a. produced through the process of crossing over that occurs in meiosis.
   b. constructed from DNA from different sources.
   c. constructed from novel combinations of DNA from the same source.
   d. produced through mitotic cell division.

2. What is the basis of separation of different DNA fragments by gel electrophoresis?
   a. The negative charge on DNA
   b. The size of the DNA fragments
   c. The sequence of the fragments
   d. The presence of a dye

3. The basic logic of enzymatic DNA sequencing is to produce
   a. a nested set of DNA fragments produced by restriction enzymes.
   b. a nested set of DNA fragments that each begin with different bases.
   c. primers to allow PCR amplification of the region between the primers.
   d. a nested set of DNA fragments that end with known bases.

4. A DNA library is
   a. an orderly array of all the genes within an organism.
   b. a collection of vectors.
   c. the collection of plasmids found within a single *E. coli*.
   d. a collection of DNA fragments representing the entire genome of an organism.

5. Molecular hybridization is used to
   a. generate cDNA from mRNA.
   b. introduce a vector into a bacterial cell.
   c. screen a DNA library.
   d. introduce mutations into genes.

6. How does the yeast two-hybrid system detect protein–protein interactions?
   a. Binding of fusion partners triggers a signal cascade that alters gene expression.
   b. Fusion partners are detected using radioactive probes of Western blots.
   c. Protein–protein binding of fusion partners triggers expression of a reporter gene.
   d. Protein–protein binding of fusion partners triggers expression of the *Gal4* gene.

7. In vitro mutagenesis is used to
   a. produce large quantities of mutant proteins.
   b. create mutations at specific sites within a gene.
   c. create random mutations within multiple genes.
   d. create organisms that carry foreign genes.

8. Insertion of a gene for a surface protein from a medically important virus such as herpes into a harmless virus is an example of
   a. a DNA vaccine.
   b. reverse genetics.
   c. gene therapy.
   d. a subunit vaccine.

9. What is a Ti plasmid?
   a. A vector that can transfer recombinant genes into plant genomes
   b. A vector that can be used to produce recombinant proteins in yeast
   c. A vector that is specific to cereal plants like rice and corn
   d. A vector that is specific to embryonic stem cells

APPLY

1. How is the gene for β-galactosidase used in the construction of a plasmid?
   a. The gene is a promoter that is sensitive to the presence of the sugar, galactose.
   b. It is an origin of replication.
   c. It is a cloning site.
   d. It is a marker for insertion of DNA.

2. Which of the following statements is accurate for DNA replication in your cells, but not PCR?
   a. DNA primers are required.
   b. DNA polymerase is stable at high temperatures.
   c. Ligase is essential.
   d. dNTPs are necessary.

3. What potential problems must be considered in creating a transgenic bacterium with the human insulin gene to produce insulin?
   a. Introns in the human gene will not be processed after transcription.
   b. The bacterial cell will be unable to post-translationally process the insulin peptide sequence.
   c. There is no way to get the bacterium to transcribe high levels of a human gene.
   d. Both a and b present problems.

SYNTHESIZE

1. Many human proteins, such as hemoglobin, are only functional as an assembly of multiple subunits. Assembly of these functional units occurs within the endoplasmic reticulum and Golgi apparatus of a eukaryotic cell. Discuss what limitations, if any exist to the large-scale production of genetically engineered hemoglobin.

2. Enzymatic sequencing of a short strand of DNA was completed using dideoxynucleotides. Use the gel shown to determine the sequence of that DNA.

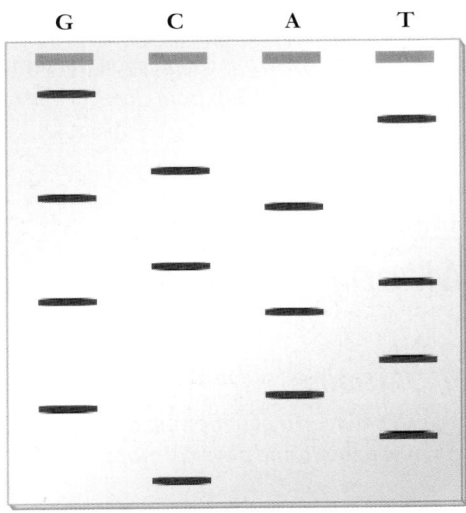

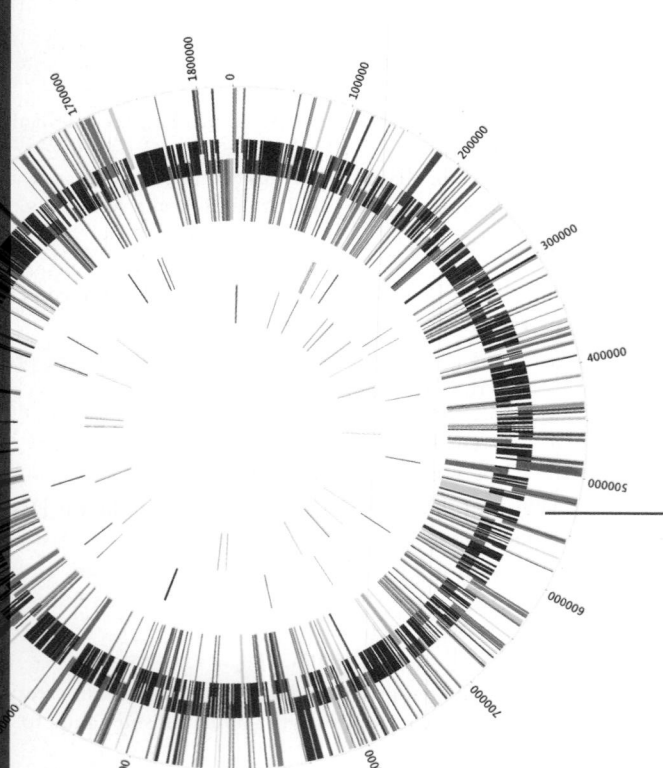

Genomics

Chapter Outline

18.1 Mapping Genomes

18.2 Whole-Genome Sequencing

18.3 Characterizing Genomes

18.4 Genomics and Proteomics

18.5 Applications of Genomics

Introduction

The pace of discovery in biology in the last 30 years has been like the exponential growth of a population. Starting with the isolation of the first genes in the mid-1970s, researchers had accomplished the first complete genome sequence by the mid-1990s—that of the bacterial species Haemophilus influenzae, *shown in the picture (genes with similar functions are shown in the same color). By the turn of the 21st century, the molecular biology community had completed a draft sequence of the human genome. Put another way, scientific accomplishments moved from cloning a single gene, to determining the sequence of a million base pairs in 20 years, then determining the sequence of a billion base pairs in another 5 years, and now sequencing 20 billion base pairs at one time. In the previous chapter you learned about the basic techniques of molecular biology. In this chapter you will see how those techniques have been applied to the analysis of whole genomes. This analysis integrates ideas from classical and molecular genetics with biotechnology, scaled and applied to whole genomes.*

18.1 Mapping Genomes

Learning Outcomes

1. *Distinguish between a genetic map and a physical map.*
2. *Explain how genetic and physical maps can be linked.*

We use maps to find our location, and depending on how accurately we wish to do this, we may use multiple maps with different resolutions. In genomics, we can locate a gene on a chromosome, in a subregion of a chromosome, and finally its precise location in the chromosome's DNA sequence. The DNA sequence level requires knowing the entire sequence of the genome, something that was once out of our reach technologically. Knowing the entire sequence is useless, however, without other kinds of maps; finding a single gene within the sequence of the human genome is like trying to find your house on a map of the world.

To overcome this difficulty, maps of genomes are constructed at different levels of resolution and using different kinds of information. We can distinguish between *genetic maps* and *physical maps*. **Genetic maps** are abstract maps that place the relative location of genes on chromosomes based on recombination frequency (see chapter 13). **Physical maps** use landmarks within DNA sequences, ranging from restriction sites (described in the preceding chapter) to the ultimate level of detail: the actual DNA sequence.

Different kinds of physical maps can be generated

To make sense of genome mapping, it is important to have physical landmarks on the genome that are at a lower level of resolution than the entire sequence. In fact, long before the Human Genome Project was even conceived, physical maps of DNA were needed as landmarks on cloned DNA. Two types of physical maps are (1) restriction maps, constructed using restriction enzymes and (2) chromosome-banding patterns, generated by cytological dye methods.

Restriction maps

Distances between "landmarks" on a physical map are measured in base-pairs (1000 base-pairs [bp] equal 1 kilobase, kb). It is not necessary to know the DNA sequence of a segment of DNA in order to create a physical map, or to know whether the DNA encompasses information for a specific gene.

The first physical maps were created by cutting genomic DNA with different restriction enzymes, both singly and with combinations of enzymes (figure 18.1). The analysis of the patterns of fragments generated were used to generate a map.

In terms of larger pieces of DNA, this process is repeated and then used to put the pieces back together, based on size and overlap, into a contiguous segment of the genome, called a **contig**. Coincidentally, the very first restriction enzymes to be isolated came from *Haemophilus*, which was also the first free-living genome to be completely sequenced.

Chromosome-banding patterns

Cytologists studying chromosomes with light microscopes found that by using different stains, they could produce reproducible patterns of bands on the chromosomes. In this way, they could identify all of the chromosomes and divide them into subregions based on banding pattern.

The use of different stains allows for the construction of a cytological map of the entire genome. These large-scale physical maps are like a map of an entire country, in that they encompass the whole genome, but at low resolution.

Cytological maps are used to characterize chromosomal abnormalities associated with human diseases, such as chronic myelogenous leukemia. In this disease, a reciprocal translocation occurs between chromosome 9 and chromosome 22 (figure 18.2a), resulting in an altered form of

1. Multiple copies of a segment of DNA are cut with restriction enzymes.

2. The fragments produced by enzyme A only, by enzyme B only, and by enzymes A and B together are run side-by-side on a gel, which separates them according to size.

3. The fragments are arranged so that the smaller ones produced by the simultaneous cut can be grouped to generate the larger ones produced by the individual enzymes.

4. A physical map is constructed.

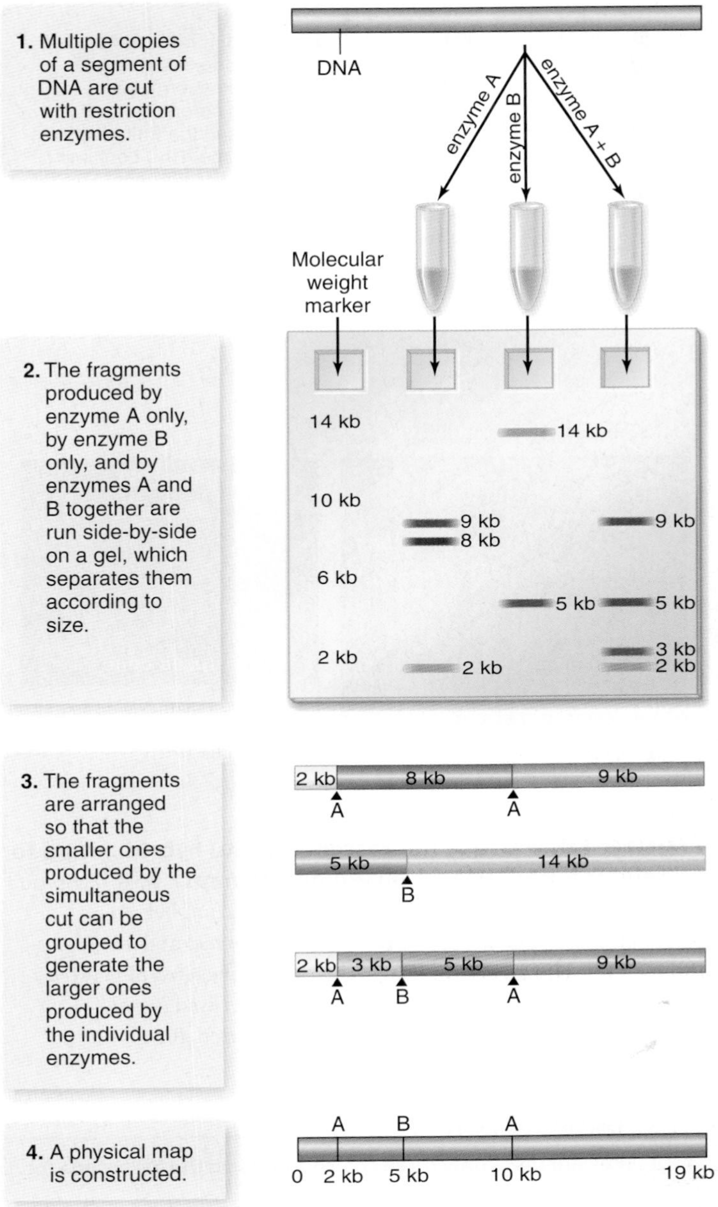

Figure 18.1 Restriction enzymes can be used to create a physical map. DNA is digested with two different restriction enzymes singly and in combination, then electrophoresed to separate the fragments. The location of sites can be deduced by comparing the sizes of fragments from the individual reactions with the combined reaction.

tyrosine kinase that is always turned on, causing white blood cell proliferation.

The use of hybridization with cloned DNA has added to the utility of chromosome-banding analysis. In this case, because the hybridization involves whole chromosomes, it is called *in situ hybridization*. It is done using fluorescently labeled probes, and so its complete name is **fluorescence in situ hybridization (FISH)** (figure 18.2b).

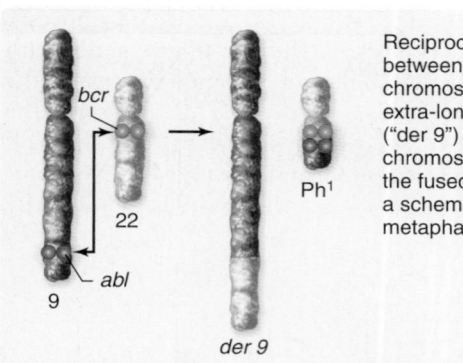

Reciprocal translocation between one 9 and one 22 chromosome forms an extra-long chromosome 9 ("der 9") and the Philadelphia chromosome (Ph¹) containing the fused *bcr-abl* gene. This is a schematic view representing metaphase chromosomes.

a.

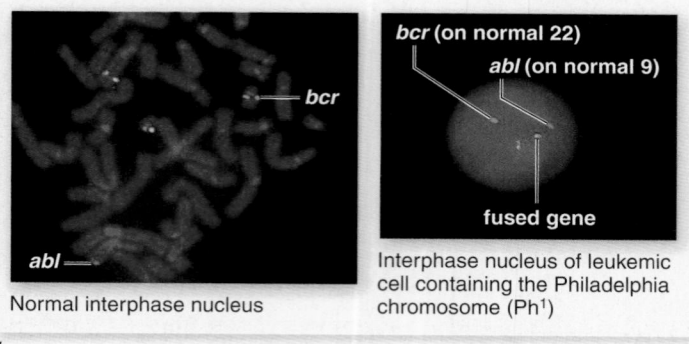

b.

Figure 18.2 Use of fluorescence in situ hybridization to correlate cloned DNA with cytological maps. *a.* Karyotype of human chromosomes showing the translocation between chromosomes 9 and 22. *b.* FISH using a *bcr* (*green*) and *abl* (*red*) probe. The yellow color indicates the fused genes (*red* plus *green* fluorescence combined). The *abl* gene and the fused *bcr-abl* gene both encode a tyrosine kinase, but the fused gene is always expressed.

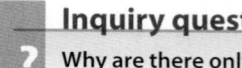

Inquiry question

? Why are there only three colored spots on the karyotype for two different genes?

Sequence-tagged sites provide a common language for physical maps

The construction of a physical map for a large genome requires the efforts of many laboratories in different locations. A variety of difficulties arose in comparing data from different labs, as well as integrating different types of landmarks used on physical and genetic maps.

In the early days of the Human Genome Project, this problem was addressed by the creation of a common molecular language that could be used to describe the different types of landmarks.

Defining common markers

Since all genetic information is ultimately based on DNA sequence, it was important for this common language to be

sequence-based, but not to require generating a large amount of sequence for any landmark. The solution was the **sequence-tagged site**, or **STS**. This site is a small stretch of DNA that is unique in the genome, that is, it only occurs once.

The boundary of the STS is defined by PCR primers, so the presence of the STS can be identified by PCR using any DNA as a template (see chapter 17). These sites need to be only 200–500 bp long, an amount of sequence that can be determined easily. The STS can contain any other kind of landmark—for example, part of a cloned gene that has been genetically mapped, or a restriction site that is polymorphic. Any marker that has been mapped can be converted to an STS by sequencing only 200–500 bp.

The use of STSs

As maps are generated, new STSs are identified and added to a database, that indicates the sequence of the STS, its location in the genome, and the PCR primers needed to identify it. Any researcher is then able to identify the presence or absence of any STS in the DNA that he or she is analyzing.

Fragments of DNA can be pieced together using STSs by identifying overlapping regions in fragments. Because of the high density of STSs in the human genome and the relative ease of identifying an STS in a DNA clone, investigators were able to develop physical maps on the huge scale of the 3.2-gigabase genome in the mid-1990s (figure 18.3). STSs provide a scaffold for assembling genome sequences.

Genetic maps provide a link to phenotypes

The first genetic (linkage) map was made in 1911 when Alfred Sturtevant mapped five genes in *Drosophila*. Distances on a genetic map reflect the frequency of recombination between genes and are measured in centimorgans (cM) in honor of the geneticist Thomas Hunt Morgan. One centimorgan corresponds to 1% recombination frequency between two loci. Over 14,000 genes have been mapped on the *Drosophila* genome.

Linkage mapping can be done without knowing the DNA sequence of a gene, as described in chapter 13. Computer programs make it possible to create a linkage map for a thousand genes at a time. But a few limitations to genetic maps still exist. One is that distances between genes determined by recombination frequencies do not directly correspond to physical distance on a chromosome. The conformation of DNA between genes varies, and this conformation can affect the frequency of recombination. Another limitation is that not all genes have obvious phenotypes that can be followed in segregating crosses.

The human genetic map is quite dense, with a marker roughly every 1 cM. This level of detail would have been unheard of 20 years ago, and it was made possible by development of molecular markers that do not cause a phenotype change.

The most common type of markers are short repeated sequences, called short tandem repeats, or STR loci, that differ in repeat length between individuals. These repeats are identified by using PCR to amplify the region containing the

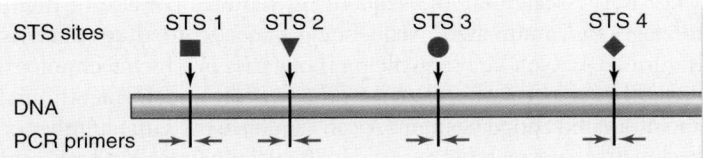

1. The location of 4 STSs in the genome is shown. PCR is used to amplify each STS from different clones in a library. Amplifying each STS by PCR generates a unique fragment that can be identified.

↓ PCR runs with four clones

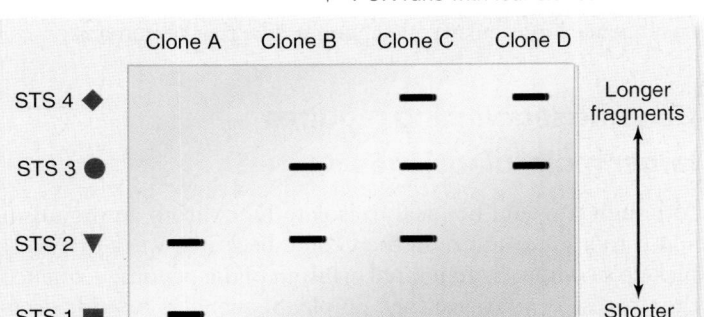

2. The products of the PCR reactions are separated by gel electrophoresis producing a different size fragment for each STS.

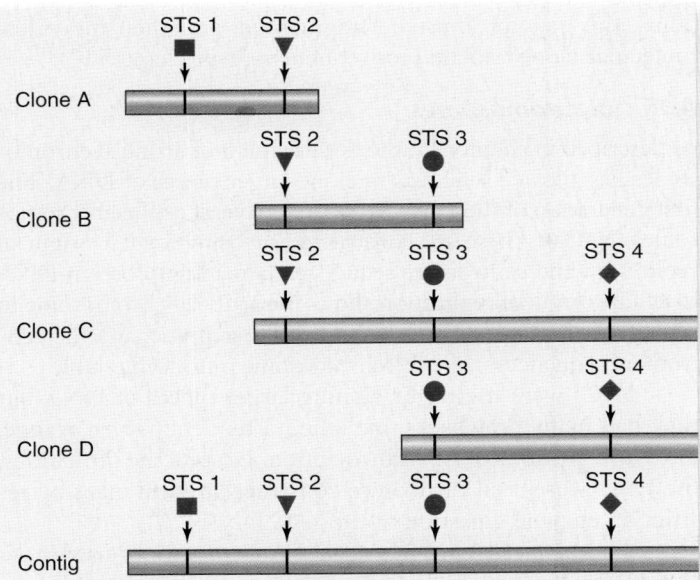

3. The presence or absence of each STS in the clones identifies regions of overlap. The final result is a contiguous sequence (contig) of overlapping clones.

Figure 18.3 Creating a physical map with sequence-tagged sites. The presence of landmarks called sequence-tagged sites, or STSs, in the human genome made it possible to begin creating a physical map large enough in scale to provide a foundation for sequencing the entire genome. *(1)* Primers *(green arrows)* that recognize unique STSs are added to cloned DNA, followed by DNA amplification via polymerase chain reaction (PCR). *(2)* PCR products are separated based on size on a DNA gel, and the STSs contained in each clone are identified. *(3)* Cloned DNA segments are aligned based on STSs to create a contig.

repeat, then analyzing the products using electrophoresis. Once a map is constructed using these markers, genes with alleles that cause a disease state can be mapped relative to the molecular landmarks. Thirteen of these STR loci form the basis for modern DNA fingerprinting developed by the FBI. The alleles for these 13 loci are what is cataloged in the Combined DNA Index System (CODIS) database used to identify criminal offenders.

Physical maps can be correlated with genetic maps

We need to be able to correlate genetic maps with physical maps, particularly genome sequences, to aid in finding physical sequences for genes that have been mapped genetically.

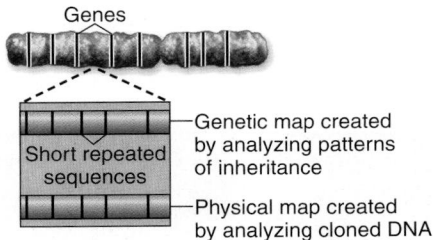

The problem in finding genes is that the resolution of genetic maps at present is not nearly as fine-grained as the genome sequence. Markers that are 1 cM apart may be as much as a million base pairs apart.

Since the markers used to construct genetic maps are now primarily molecular markers, they can be easily located within a genome sequence. Similarly, any gene that has been cloned can be placed within the genome sequence and can also be mapped genetically. This provides an automatic correlation between the two maps. The problem of finding genes that have been mapped genetically but not isolated as molecular clones lies in the nature of genetic maps. Distances measured on genetic maps are not uniform due to variation in recombination frequency along the chromosome. So 1 cM of genetic distance translates to different numbers of base-pairs in different regions.

Different kinds of maps are stored in databases so they can be aligned and viewed. The National Center for Biotechnology Information (NCBI) is a branch of the National Library of Medicine, and it serves as the U.S. repository for these data and more. Similar databases exist in Europe and Japan, and all are kept current. An enormous storehouse of information is available for use by biological researchers worldwide.

Learning Outcomes Review 18.1

Maps of genomes can by either physical maps or genetic maps. Physical maps include cytogenic maps of chromosome banding or restriction maps. Genetic maps are correlated with physical maps by using DNA markers such as sequence-tagged sites (STSs) unique to each genome.

■ *What accounts for the difference between the proximity of banding sites on a karyotype and the number of base-pairs separating the two sites?*

The ultimate physical map is the base-pair sequence of an entire genome. In the early days of molecular biology, all sequencing was done manually, and was therefore both time- and labor-intensive. As mentioned in chapter 17, the development of machines to automate this process increased the rate of sequence generation.

a.

b.

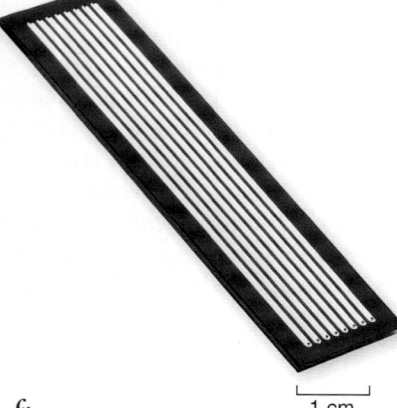

c.

1 cm

Figure 18.4 Automated sequencing. *a.* This Sanger sequence facility runs multiple automated sequencers, each processing 96 samples at a time. *b.* The development of new sequencing technologies permit sequencing that is orders of magnitude faster and that can be done in a very small space. *c.* Over 20 billion different DNA segments can be sequenced simultaneously in a flow cell the size of a microscope slide.

Large-scale genome sequencing requires the use of high-throughput automated sequencing and computer analysis (figure 18.4). Genome sequencing is one case in which technology drove the science, rather than the other way around. In a few hours, an automated Sanger sequencer can sequence the same number of base-pairs that a technician could manually sequence in a year—up to 50,000 bp. With the current generation of sequencing technology described in the previous chapter, the rate of sequence generation is now five orders of magnitude greater than when the human genome was sequenced with automated Sanger sequencers. Without the automation of sequencing, it would have been impossible to sequence large, eukaryotic genomes like that of humans.

Genome sequencing requires larger molecular clones

Although it would be ideal to isolate DNA from an organism, add it to a sequencer, and then come back in a week or two to pick up a computer-generated printout of the genome sequence, the process is not quite that simple. Sequencers provide accurate sequences for DNA segments up to 800 bp long. Even then, errors are possible. So, to reduce errors, each clone is sequenced 5–10 times.

Even with reliable sequence data in hand, each individual sequencing run produces a relatively small amount of sequence. Thus, the genome must be fragmented, and then individual molecular clones isolated for sequencing (see chapter 17).

Artificial chromosomes

As described in chapter 17, the development of artificial chromosomes has allowed scientists to clone larger pieces of DNA. The first generation of these new vectors were yeast artificial chromosomes (YACs). These are constructed by using a yeast origin of replication and centromere sequence, then adding foreign DNA to it. The origin of replication allows the artificial chromosome to replicate independently of the rest of the genome, and the centromere sequences make the chromosome mitotically stable.

YACs were useful for cloning larger pieces of DNA but they had many drawbacks, including a tendency to rearrange, or to lose portions of DNA by deletion. Despite the difficulties, the YACs were used early on to construct physical maps by restriction enzyme digestion of the YAC DNA.

The artificial chromosomes most commonly used now, particularly for large-scale sequencing, are made in *E. coli*. These bacterial artificial chromosomes (BACs) are a logical extension of the use of bacterial plasmids. BAC vectors accept DNA inserts between 100 and 200 kb long. The downside of BAC vectors is that, like the bacterial chromosome, they are maintained as a single copy whereas plasmid vectors exist at high copy numbers.

Human artificial chromosomes

Human artificial chromosomes can introduce large segments of human DNA into cultured cells. These artificial chromosomes are usually constructed by fragmentation of chromosomes with centromere sequence. Although circular, some can still segregate correctly during mitosis up to 98% of the time. Construction of linear human artificial chromosomes is not yet possible.

Whole-genome sequencing is approached in two ways: clone-by-clone and shotgun

Sequencing an entire genome is an enormous task. Two ways of approaching this challenge have been developed: one that approaches the sequencing one step at a time, and another that attempts to take on the whole thing at once and depends on computers to sort out the data. The two techniques grew out of competing projects to sequence the human genome.

Clone-by-clone sequencing

The cloning of large inserts in BACs facilitates the analysis of entire genomes. The strategy most commonly pursued is to construct a physical map first, and then use it to place the site of BAC clones for later sequencing.

Aligning large portions of a chromosome requires identifying regions that overlap between clones. This can be accomplished either by constructing restriction maps of each BAC clone, or by identifying STSs found in clones. If two BAC clones have the same STS, then they must overlap.

The alignment of a number of BAC clones results in a contiguous stretch of DNA called a *contig*. The individual BAC clones can then be sequenced 500 bp at a time to produce the sequence of the entire contig (figure 18.5*a*). This strategy of physical mapping followed by sequencing is called **clone-by-clone sequencing.**

Shotgun sequencing

The idea of **shotgun sequencing** is simply to randomly cut the DNA into small fragments, sequence all cloned fragments, and then use a computer to put together the overlaps (figure 18.5*b*). This terminology actually goes back to the early days of molecular cloning when the construction of a library of randomly cloned fragments was referred to as *shotgun cloning*. This approach is much less labor-intensive than the clone-by-clone method, but it requires much greater computer power to assemble the final sequence and very efficient algorithms to find overlaps.

Unlike the clone-by-clone approach, shotgun sequencing does not tie the sequence to any other information about the genome (figure 18.5*b*). Many investigators have used both clone-by-clone and shotgun-sequencing techniques, and such hybrid approaches are becoming the norm. This combination has the strength of tying the sequence to a physical map while greatly reducing the time involved.

Assembler programs compare multiple copies of sequenced regions in order to assemble a **consensus sequence,** that is, a sequence that is consistent across all copies. Although computer assemblers are incredibly powerful, final human analysis is required after both clone-by-clone and shotgun sequencing to determine when a genome sequence is sufficiently accurate to be useful to researchers.

The Human Genome Project used both sequencing methods

The vast scale of genomics ushered in a new way of doing biological research involving large teams. Although a single individual can isolate and manually sequence a molecular clone for

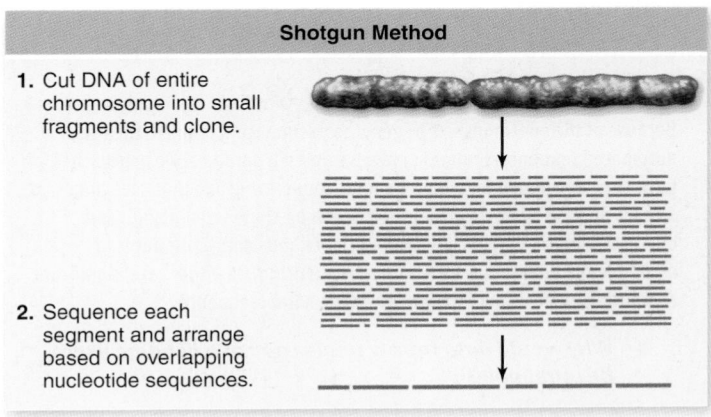

Figure 18.5 Comparison of sequencing methods. *a.* The clone-by-clone method uses large clones assembled into overlapping regions by STSs. Once assembled, these can be fragmented into smaller clones for sequencing. *b.* In the shotgun method the entire genome is fragmented into small clones and sequenced. Computer algorithms assemble the final DNA sequence based on overlapping nucleotide sequences.

a single gene, a huge genome like the human genome requires the collaborative efforts of hundreds of researchers.

The Human Genome Project originated in 1990 when a group of American scientists formed the International Human Genome Sequencing Consortium. The goal of this publicly funded effort was to use a clone-by-clone approach to sequence the human genome. Genetic and physical maps were used as scaffolding to sequence each chromosome.

In May, 1998, Craig Venter, whose research group had sequenced *Haemophilus influenzae*, announced his private company (Celera Genomics) would sequence the human genome. He proposed to shotgun-sequence the 3.2-gigabase genome in only two years. The Consortium rose to the challenge, and the race to sequence the human genome began. The upshot was a tie of sorts. On June 26, 2000, the groups jointly announced success, and each published its findings simultaneously in 2001. The Consortium's draft alone included 248 authors.

The draft sequence of the human genome was just the beginning. Gaps in the sequence are still being filled, and the map is constantly being refined. The most recent "finished" human sequence is down to only 260 gaps, a 400-fold reduction in gaps, and it now includes 99% of the euchromatic sequence, up from 95%. The reference sequence has an error rate of 1 per 100,000 bases. Newer sequencing technologies are being used to close the remaining gaps. A few individuals, including James Watson who codiscovered the structure of DNA, have now had their personal genomes sequenced. The cost for having one's genome sequenced is predicted to fall to $1000 in the next few years, raising many questions about genome privacy.

Research on the whole genome can move ahead. Now that the ultimate physical map is in place and is being integrated with the genetic map, diseases that result from changes in more than one gene, such as diabetes, can be addressed. Comparisons with other genomes are already changing our understanding of genome evolution (see chapter 24).

Learning Outcomes Review 18.2

Because of the enormous size of genomes, sequencing requires the use of automated sequencers running many samples in parallel. Two approaches have been developed for whole-genome sequencing: one that uses clones already aligned by physical mapping (clone-by-clone sequencing), and one that involves sequencing random clones and using a computer to assemble the final sequence (shotgun sequencing). In either case, significant computing power is necessary to assemble a final sequence.

■ *Why would data from a single copy of a genome likely be unreliable?*

18.3 Characterizing Genomes

Learning Outcomes

1. Describe the classes of DNA found in a genome.
2. Explain what an SNP is and why SNPs are helpful in characterizing genomes.

Automated sequencing technology has produced huge amounts of sequence data, eventually sequencing entire genomes. This has allowed researchers studying complex problems to move beyond approaches restricted to the analysis of individual genes. Sequencing projects in themselves are descriptive analyses that tells us nothing about the organization of genomes, let alone the function of gene products and how they may be interrelated. Additional research and evaluation has given us both answers and new puzzles.

The Human Genome Project found fewer genes than expected

For many years, geneticists had estimated the number of human genes to be around 100,000. This estimate, although based on some data, was really just a guess. Imagine researchers' surprise when the number turned out to be only around 25,000! This represents only about twice as many genes as *Drosophila* and fewer genes than rice (figure 18.6). Clearly the complexity of an organism is not a simple function of the number of genes in its genome.

Finding genes in sequence data requires computer searches

Once a genome has been sequenced, the next step is to determine which regions of the genome contain which genes, and what those genes do. A lot of information can be mined from the sequence data. Using markers from physical maps and information from genetic maps, it is possible to find the sequence of the small percentage of genes that are identified by mutations with an observable (phenotypic) effect. Genes can also be found by comparing expressed sequences to genomic sequences. The analysis of expressed sequences is discussed later in this section.

Locating starts and stops

Information in the nucleotide sequence itself can also be used in the search for genes. A protein-coding gene begins with a start codon, such as ATG, and it contains no stop

Figure 18.6 Size and complexity of genomes.
In general, eukaryotic genomes are larger and have more genes than prokaryotic genomes, although the size of the organism is not the determining factor. The mouse genome is nearly as large as the human genome, and the rice genome contains more genes than the human genome.

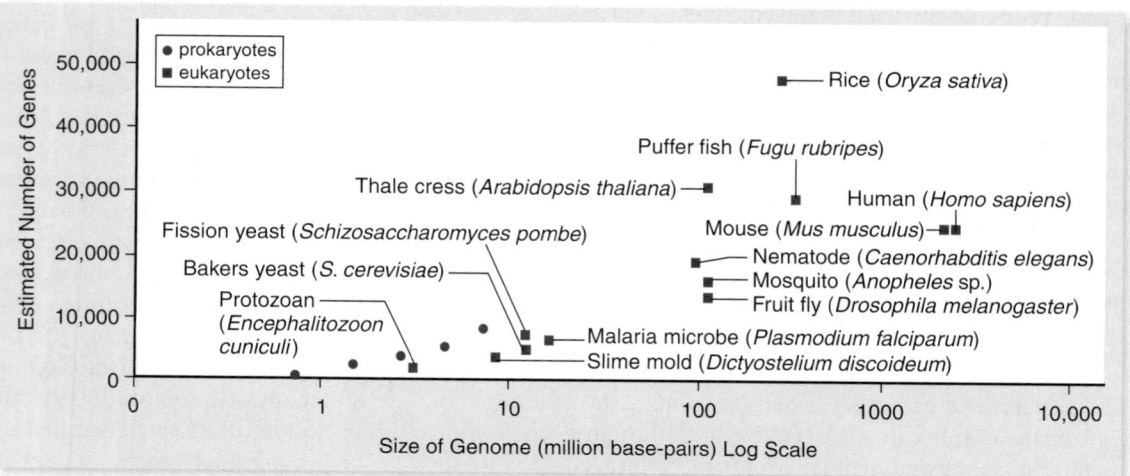

codons (TAA, TGA, or TAG) for a distance long enough to encode a protein. This coding region is referred to as an **open reading frame (ORF).** Although ORFs are likely to be genes, they may or may not actually be translated into a functional protein. Among putative genes, families of genes can be identified based on common domains. For example, genes in the HOX family have a conserved, 180-bp sequence called the homeobox, which encodes the homeodomain region of certain transcription factors. Sequences for potential genes need to be tested experimentally to determine whether they have a function.

The addition of information to the basic sequence information, like identifying ORFs, is called sequence **annotation.** This process is what converts simple sequence data into something that we can recognize based on landmarks such as regions that are transcribed and regions that are known or thought to encode proteins.

Inferring function across species: the BLAST algorithm

It is also possible to search genome databases for sequences that are homologous to known genes in other species. A researcher who has isolated a molecular clone for a gene of unknown function can search the database for similar sequences to infer function. The tool that makes this possible is a search algorithm called BLAST (which stands for Basic Local Alignment Search Tool). Using a networked computer, one can submit a sequence to the BLAST server and get back a reply with all possible similar sequences contained in the sequence database.

Using these techniques, sequences that are not part of ORFs have been identified that have been conserved over millions of years of evolution. These sequences may be important for the regulation of the genes contained in the genome.

Using computer programs to search for genes, to compare genomes, and to assemble genomes are only a few of the new genomics approaches falling under the heading of **bioinformatics.**

Genomes contain both coding and noncoding DNA

When genome sequences are analyzed, regions that encode proteins and other regions that do not encode proteins are revealed. For many years investigators had known of the latter, but they did not know the extent and nature of the noncoding DNA. We first consider the types of coding DNA that have been found, then move on to look at types of noncoding DNA.

Protein-encoding DNA in eukaryotes

Four different classes of protein-encoding genes are found in eukaryotic genomes, differing largely in gene copy number.

Single-copy genes. Many genes exist as single copies on a particular chromosome. Most mutations in these genes result in recessive Mendelian inheritance.

Segmental duplications. Sometimes whole blocks of genes are copied from one chromosome to another, resulting in *segmental duplication.* Blocks of similar genes in the same order are found throughout the human genome. Chromosome 19 seems to have been the biggest borrower, sharing blocks of genes with 16 other chromosomes.

Multigene families. As more has been learned about eukaryotic genomes, many genes have been found to exist as parts of *multigene families,* groups of related but distinctly different genes that often occur together in clusters. These genes appear to have arisen from a single ancestral gene that duplicated during an uneven meiotic crossover in which genes were added to one chromosome and subtracted from the other. These multigene families may include silent copies called *pseudogenes,* which are inactivated by mutation.

Tandem clusters. Identical copies of genes can also be found in *tandem clusters.* These genes are transcribed simultaneously, increasing the amount of mRNA available for protein production. Tandem clusters also include genes that do not encode proteins, such as clusters of rRNA genes.

Noncoding DNA in eukaryotes

One of the most notable characteristics is the amount of noncoding DNA they possess. The Human Genome Project has revealed a particularly startling picture. Each of your cells has about 6 feet of DNA stuffed into it, but of that, less than 1 inch is devoted to genes! Nearly 99% of the DNA in your cells is non-protein coding DNA.

True genes are scattered about the human genome in clumps among the much larger amount of noncoding DNA, like isolated oases in a desert. Seven major sorts of noncoding human DNA have been described. (Table 18.1 shows the composition of the human genome, including noncoding DNA.)

Noncoding DNA within genes. As discussed in chapter 15, a human gene is not simply a stretch of DNA, like the letters of a word. Instead, a human gene is made up of numerous fragments of protein-encoding information (exons) embedded within a much larger matrix of noncoding DNA (introns). Together, introns make up about 24% of the human genome and exons less than 1.5%.

Structural DNA. Some regions of the chromosomes remain highly condensed, tightly coiled, and untranscribed throughout the cell cycle. Called *constitutive heterochromatin,* these portions tend to be localized around the centromere or located near the ends of the chromosome, at the telomeres.

Simple sequence repeats. Scattered about chromosomes are **simple sequence repeats (SSRs).** An SSR is a 1- to 6-nt sequence such as CA or CGG, repeated like a broken record thousands and thousands of times. SSRs can arise from DNA replication errors. SSRs make up about 3% of the human genome.

Segmental duplications. Blocks of genomic sequences composed of from 10,000 to 300,000 bp have duplicated and moved either within a chromosome or to a nonhomologous chromosome.

TABLE 18.1 Classes of DNA Sequences Found in the Human Genome

Class	Estimated Frequency (%)	Description
Protein-encoding genes	1.5	Translated portions of the 25,000 genes scattered about the chromosomes
Introns	24	Noncoding DNA that constitutes the great majority of each human gene
Segmental duplications	5	Regions of the genome that have been duplicated
Pseudogenes (inactive genes)	2	Sequence that has characteristics of a gene but is not a functional gene
Structural DNA	20	Constitutive heterochromatin, localized near centromeres and telomeres
Simple sequence repeats	3	Stuttering repeats of a few nucleotides such as CGG, repeated thousands of times
Transposable elements	45	21%: Long interspersed elements (LINEs), which are active transposons 13%: Short interspersed elements (SINEs), which are active transposons 8%: Retrotransposons, which contain long terminal repeats (LTRs) at each end 3%: DNA transposon fossils
microRNA	0.03	Code for RNAs complementary to one or more mature mRNAs

Pseudogenes. These are inactive genes that may have lost function because of mutation.

Transposable elements. Fully 45% of the human genome consists of mobile bits of DNA called *transposable elements*. Some of these elements code for proteins, but many do not. Because of the significance of these elements, we describe them more fully in the following section.

microRNA genes. Hidden within the nonprotein-coding DNA lies an extraordinary mechanism for controlling gene expression and development. Compact regulatory RNAs have a much larger role in directing development in complex organisms than we imagined even a few years ago. Specifically, DNA that was once considered "junk" has been shown to encode microRNAs, or miRNAs, which are processed after transcription to lengths of 21 to 23 nt, but never translated. About 10,000 unique miRNAs have been identified that are complementary to one or more mature mRNAs.

Transposable elements: mobile DNA

Discovered by Barbara McClintock in 1950, **transposable elements,** also termed *transposons* and *mobile genetic elements*, are bits of DNA that are able to move from one location on a chromosome to another. Barbara McClintock received the 1983 Nobel Prize in physiology or medicine for discovery of these elements and their unexpected ability to change location.

Transposable elements move around in different ways. In some cases, the transposon is duplicated, and the duplicated DNA moves to a new place in the genome, so the number of copies of the transposon increases. Other types of transposons are excised without duplication and insert themselves elsewhere in the genome. The role of transposons in genome evolution is discussed in chapter 24.

Human chromosomes contain four sorts of transposable elements. Fully 21% of the genome consists of **long interspersed elements (LINEs).** These ancient and very successful elements are about 6000 bp long, and they contain all the equipment needed for transposition. LINEs encode a reverse transcriptase enzyme that can make a cDNA copy of the transcribed LINE RNA. The result is a double-stranded segment that can reinsert into the genome rather than undergo translation into a protein. Since these elements use an RNA intermediate, they are termed *retrotransposons*.

Short interspersed elements (SINEs) are similar to LINEs, but they cannot transpose without using the transposition machinery of LINEs. Nested within the genome's LINEs are over half a million copies of a SINE element called Alu (named for a restriction enzyme that cuts within the sequence). The Alu SINE is 300 bp and represents 10% of the human genome. Like a flea on a dog, Alu moves with the LINE it resides within. Just as a flea sometimes jumps to a different dog, so Alu sometimes uses the enzymes of its LINE to move to a new chromosome location. Alu can also jump right into genes, causing harmful mutations.

Two other sorts of transposable elements are also found in the human genome: 8% of the human genome is devoted to retrotransposons called **long terminal repeats (LTRs).** Although the transposition mechanism is a bit different from that of LINEs, LTRs also use reverse transcriptase to ensure that copies are double-stranded and can reintegrate into the genome.

Some 3% of the genome is devoted to dead transposons, elements that have lost the signals for replication and can no longer move.

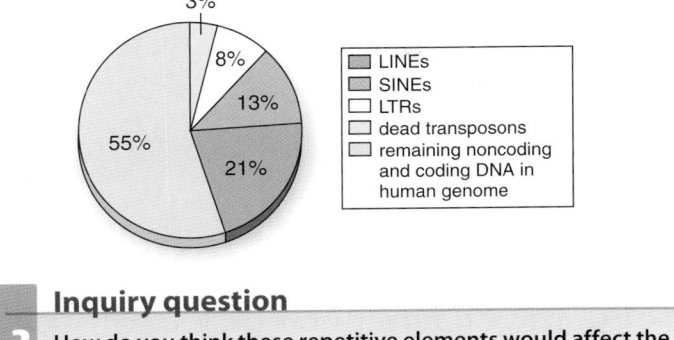

Inquiry question

? How do you think these repetitive elements would affect the determination of gene order?

Expressed sequence tags identify genes that are transcribed

Given the complexity of coding and noncoding DNA, it is important to be able to recognize regions of the genome that are actually expressed—that is, transcribed and then translated.

Because DNA is easier to work with than protein, one approach is to isolate mRNA, use this to make cDNA, then sequence one or both ends of as many cDNAs as possible. With automated sequencing, this task is not difficult, and these short sections of cDNA have been named **expressed sequence tags (ESTs).** An EST is another form of STS, and thus it can be included in physical maps. This technique does not tell us anything about the function of any particular EST, but it does provide one view, at the whole-genome level, of what genes are expressed, at least as mRNAs.

ESTs have been used to identify 87,000 cDNAs in different human tissues. About 80% of these cDNAs were previously unknown. You may wonder at this point how the estimated 25,000 genes of the human genome can result in 87,000 different cDNAs. The answer lies in the modularity of eukaryotic genes, which consist of exons interspersed with introns, as described in chapter 15.

Following transcription in eukaryotes, the introns are removed, and exons are spliced together. In some cells, some of the splice sites are skipped, and one or more exons is removed along with the introns. This process, called *alternative splicing* (figure 18.7), yields different proteins that can have different functions. Thus, the added complexity of proteins in the human genome comes not from additional genes, but from new ways to put existing parts of genes together.

SNPs are single-base differences between individuals

One fact becoming clear from analysis of the human genome is that a huge amount of genetic variation exists in our species. This information has practical use.

Single-nucleotide polymorphisms (SNPs) are sites where individuals differ by only a single nucleotide. To be classified as a polymorphism, an SNP must be present in at least 1% of the population. SNPs occur about every 100 to 300 bp in the 3 billion bp human genome. As of January 2009, 1.5 million nonredundant human SNPs had been identified, about 10% of the variation available. These SNPs are being used to look for associations between genes. We expect that the genetic recombination occurring during meiosis randomizes all but the most tightly linked genes. We call the tendency for genes *not* to be randomized **linkage disequilibrium.** This kind of association can be used to map genes.

The preliminary analysis of SNPs shows that many are in linkage disequilibrium. This unexpected result has led to the idea of genomic **haplotypes,** or regions of chromosomes that are not being exchanged by recombination. The existence of haplotypes allows the genetic characterization of genomic regions by describing a small number of SNPs (figure 18.8). If these haplotypes stand up to further analysis, they could greatly aid in mapping the genetic basis of disease. The Human Genome Project is now working on a haplotype map of the genome.

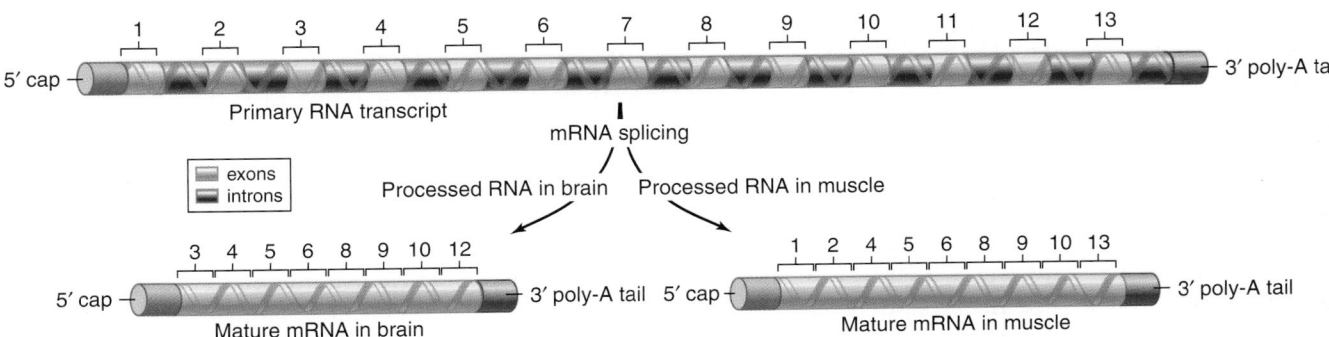

Figure 18.7 Alternative splicing can result in the production of different mRNAs from the same coding sequence. In some cells, exons can be excised along with neighboring introns, resulting in different proteins. Alternative splicing explains why 25,000 human genes can code for three to four times as many proteins.

Figure 18.8 Construction of a haplotype map. Single-nucleotide polymorphisms (SNPs) are single-base differences between individuals. Sections of DNA sequences from four individuals are shown in (*a*), with three SNPs indicated by arrows. *b.* These three SNPs are shown aligned along with 17 other SNPs from this chromosomal region. This represents a haplotype map for this region of the chromosome. Haplotypes are regions of the genome that are not exchanged by recombination during meiosis. *c.* Haplotypes can be identified using a small number of diagnostic SNPs that differ between the different haplotypes. In this case, 3 SNPs out of the 20 in this region are all that are needed to uniquely identify each haplotype. This greatly facilitates locating disease-causing genes, as haplotypes represent large regions of the genome that behave as a single site during meiosis.

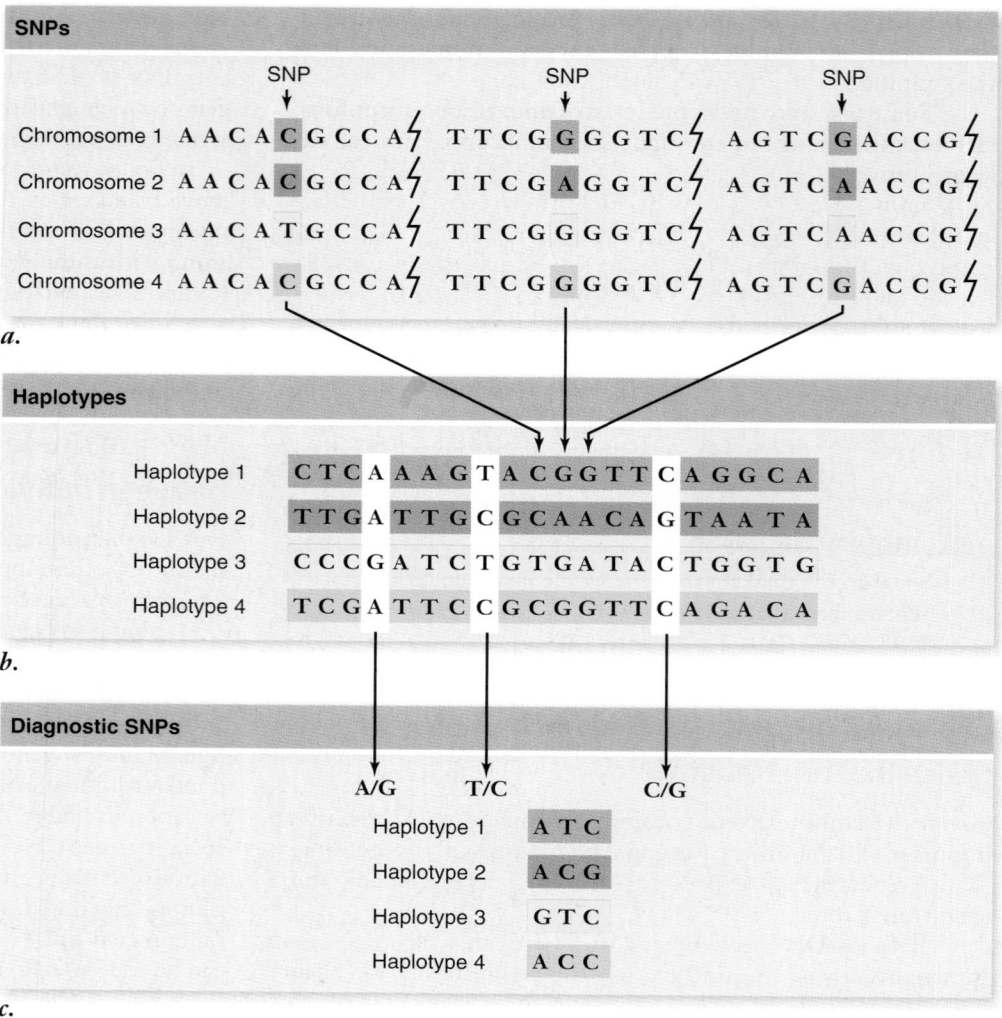

18.4 Genomics and Proteomics

Learning Outcomes

1. Describe the advances that have come from comparative genomics.
2. Distinguish between genomics and proteomics.

To fully understand how genes work, we need to characterize the proteins they produce. This information is essential to understanding cell biology, physiology, development, and evolution. In many ways, we continue to ask the same questions that Mendel asked, but at a much different level of organization.

Comparative genomics reveals conserved regions in genomes

With the large number of sequenced genomes, it is now possible to make comparisons at both the gene and genome level. The flood of information from different genomes has given rise to a new field: *comparative genomics*. One of the striking lessons learned from the sequence of the human genome is how very similar humans are to other organisms. More than half of the genes of *Drosophila* have human counterparts. Among mammals, the similarities are even greater. Humans have only 300 genes that have no counterpart in the mouse genome.

The use of comparative genomics to ask evolutionary questions is also a field of great promise. The comparison of the many prokaryotic genomes already indicates a greater degree of lateral gene transfer than was previously suspected. The latest round of animal genomes sequenced has included the chimpanzee, our closest living relative. The draft sequence of the chimp (*Pan troglodytes*) genome has just been completed, and comparisons between the chimp and human genome may allow us to unravel what makes us uniquely human.

The early returns from this sequencing effort confirm that our genomes differ by only 1.23% in terms of nucleotide substitutions. At first glance, the largest difference between our genomes actually appears to be in transposable elements. In humans, the SINEs have been threefold more active than in the chimp, but the chimp has acquired two elements that are not found in the human genome. The differences due to insertion and deletion of bases are fewer than substitutions but account for about 1.5% of the euchromatic sequence being unique in each genome.

Synteny allows comparison of unsequenced genomes

Similarities and differences between highly conserved genes can be investigated on a gene-by-gene basis between species. Genome science allows for a much larger scale approach to comparing genomes by taking advantage of synteny.

Synteny refers to the conserved arrangements of segments of DNA in related genomes. Physical mapping techniques can be used to look for synteny in genomes that have not been sequenced. Comparisons with the sequenced, syntenous segment in another species can be very helpful.

To illustrate this, consider rice, already sequenced, and its grain relatives maize, barley, and wheat, none of which have been fully sequenced. Even though these plants diverged more than 50 million years ago, the chromosomes of rice, corn, wheat, and other grass crops show extensive synteny (figure 18.9). In a genomic sense, "rice is wheat."

By understanding the rice genome at the level of its DNA sequence, identification and isolation of genes from grains with larger genomes should be much easier. DNA sequence analysis of cereal grains could be valuable for identifying genes associated with disease resistance, crop yield, nutritional quality, and growth capacity.

As mentioned earlier, the rice genome has more genes than the human genome. However, rice still has a much smaller genome than its grain relatives, which also represent a major food source for humans.

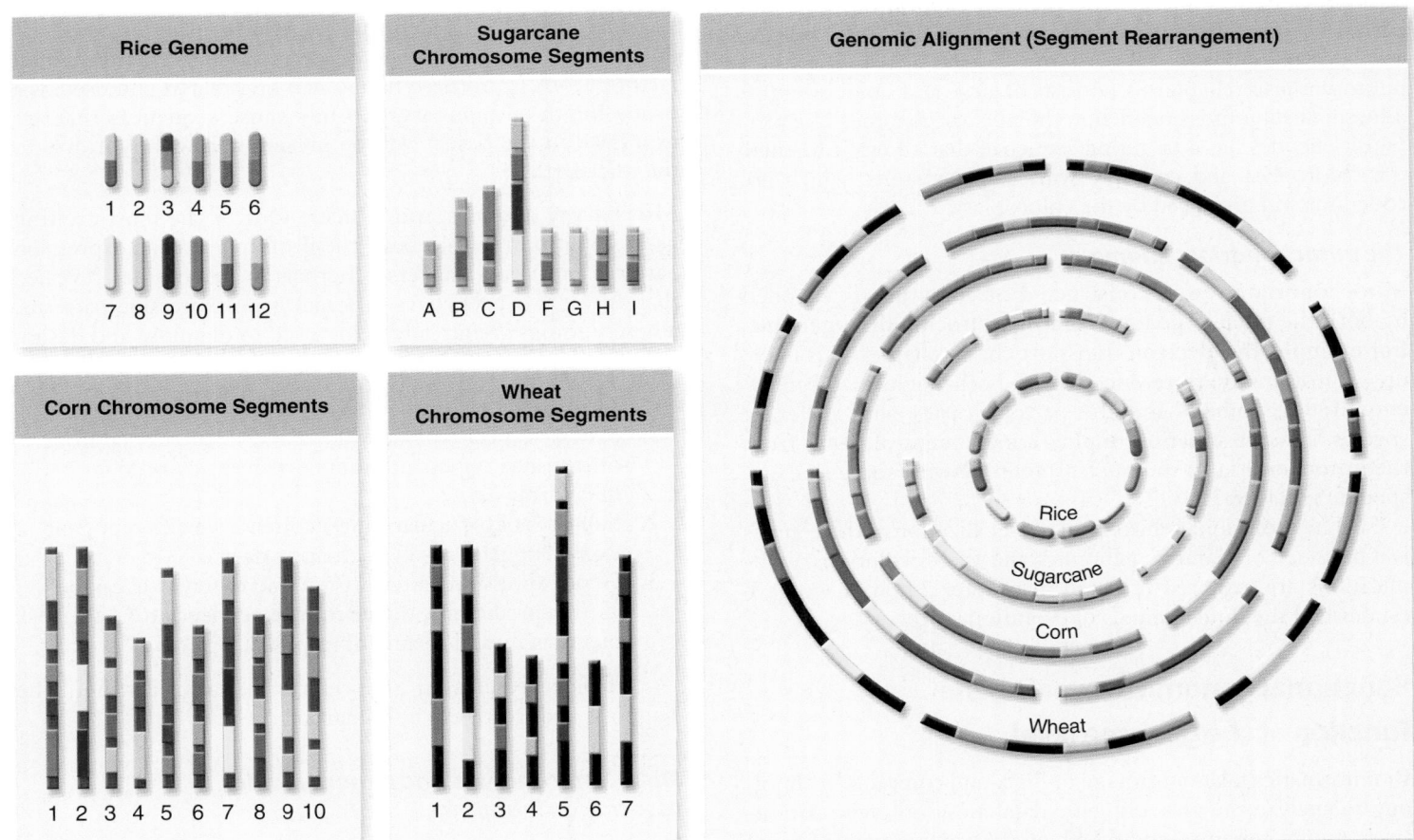

Figure 18.9 Grain genomes are rearrangements of similar chromosome segments. Shades of the same color represent pieces of DNA that are conserved among the different species but have been rearranged. By splitting the individual chromosomes of major grass species into segments and rearranging the segments, researchers have found that the genome components of rice, sugarcane, corn, and wheat are highly conserved. This implies that the order of the segments in the ancestral grass genome has been rearranged by recombination as the grasses have evolved.

Organelle genomes have exchanged genes with the nuclear genome

Mitochondria and chloroplasts are considered to be descendants of ancient bacterial cells living in eukaryotes as a result of endosymbiosis (chapter 4). Their genomes have been sequenced in some species, and they are most like prokaryotic genomes. The chloroplast genome, having about 100 genes, is minute compared with the rice genome, with 32,000 to 55,000 genes.

The chloroplast genome

The chloroplast, a plant organelle that functions in photosynthesis, can independently replicate in the plant cell because it has its own genome. The DNA in the chloroplasts of all land plants have about the same number of genes, and they are present in about the same order. In contrast to the evolution of the DNA in the plant cell nucleus, chloroplast DNA has evolved at a more conservative pace and therefore shows a more easily interpretable evolutionary pattern when scientists study DNA sequence similarities. Chloroplast DNA is also not subject to modification caused by transposable elements or to mutations due to recombination.

Over time, some genetic exchange appears to have occurred between the nuclear and chloroplast genomes. For example, Rubisco, the key enzyme in the Calvin cycle of photosynthesis (chapter 8), consists of large and small subunits. The small subunit is encoded in the nuclear genome. The protein it encodes has a targeting sequence that allows it to enter the chloroplast and combine with large subunits, which are coded for and produced by the chloroplast.

The mitochondrial genome

Mitochondria are also constructed of components encoded by both the nuclear genome and the mitochondrial genome. For example, the electron transport chain (chapter 7) is made up of proteins that are encoded by both nuclear and mitochondrial genomes—and the pattern varies with different species. This observation implies a movement of genes from the mitochondria to the nuclear genome with some lineage-specific variation.

The evolutionary history of the localization of these genes is a puzzle. Comparative genomics and their evolutionary implications are explored in detail in chapter 24, after we have established the fundamentals of evolutionary theory.

Functional genomics reveals gene function at the genome level

Bioinformatics takes advantage of high-end computer technology to analyze the growing gene databases, look for relationships among genomes, and then hypothesize functions of genes based on sequence. Genomics is now shifting gears and moving back to hypothesis-driven science, to **functional genomics,** the study of the function of genes and their products.

Like sequencing whole genomes, finding how these genomes work requires the efforts of a large team. For example,

an international community of researchers has come together with a plan to assign function to all of the 20,000–25,000 *Arabidopsis* genes by 2010 (Project 2010). One of the first steps is to determine when and where these genes are expressed. Each step beyond that will require additional improvements in technology.

DNA microarrays

The earlier description of ESTs indicated that we could locate sequences that are transcribed on our DNA maps—but this tells us nothing about when and where these genes are turned on. To be able to analyze gene expression at the whole-genome level requires a representation of the genome that can be manipulated experimentally. This has led to the creation of **DNA microarrays,** or "gene chips" (figure 18.10).

Preparation of a microarray To prepare a particular microarray, fragments of DNA are deposited on a microscope slide by a robot at indexed locations (i.e., an array). Silicon chips instead of slides can also be arrayed. These chips can then be used in hybridization experiments with labeled mRNA from different sources. This gives a high-level view of genes that are active and inactive in specific tissues.

Researchers are currently using a chip with 24,000 *Arabidopsis* genes on it to identify genes that are expressed developmentally in certain tissues or in response to environmental factors. RNA from these tissues can be isolated and used as a probe for these microarrays. Only those sequences that are expressed in the tissues will be present and will hybridize to the microarray.

Microarray analysis and cancer. One of the most exciting uses of microarrays has been the profiling of gene expression patterns in human cancers. Microarray analysis has revealed that different cancers have different gene expression patterns. These findings are already being used to diagnose and design specific treatments for particular cancers.

From a large body of data, several patterns emerge:

1. Specific cancer types can be reliably distinguished from other cancer types and from normal tissue based on microarray data.
2. Subtypes of particular cancers often have different gene expression patterns in microarray data.
3. Gene expression patterns from microarray data can be used to predict disease recurrence, tendency to metastasize, and treatment response.

This represents an important step forward in both the diagnosis and treatment of human cancers.

Microarray analysis and genome-wide association mapping

Genome-wide association (GWA) is an approach that compares SNPs throughout the genome between members in a population with and without a specific trait. The goal is to find a SNP that correlates with a specific trait as a way to map the trait. The dog genome exemplifies the value of GWA mapping. Using microarrays that distinguish between 15,000 SNP variants,

Hypothesis: *Flowers and leaves will express some of the same genes.*

Prediction: *When mRNAs isolated from* Arabidopsis *flowers and from leaves are used as probes on an* Arabidopsis *genome microarray, the two different probe sets will hybridize to both common and unique sequences.*

Test:

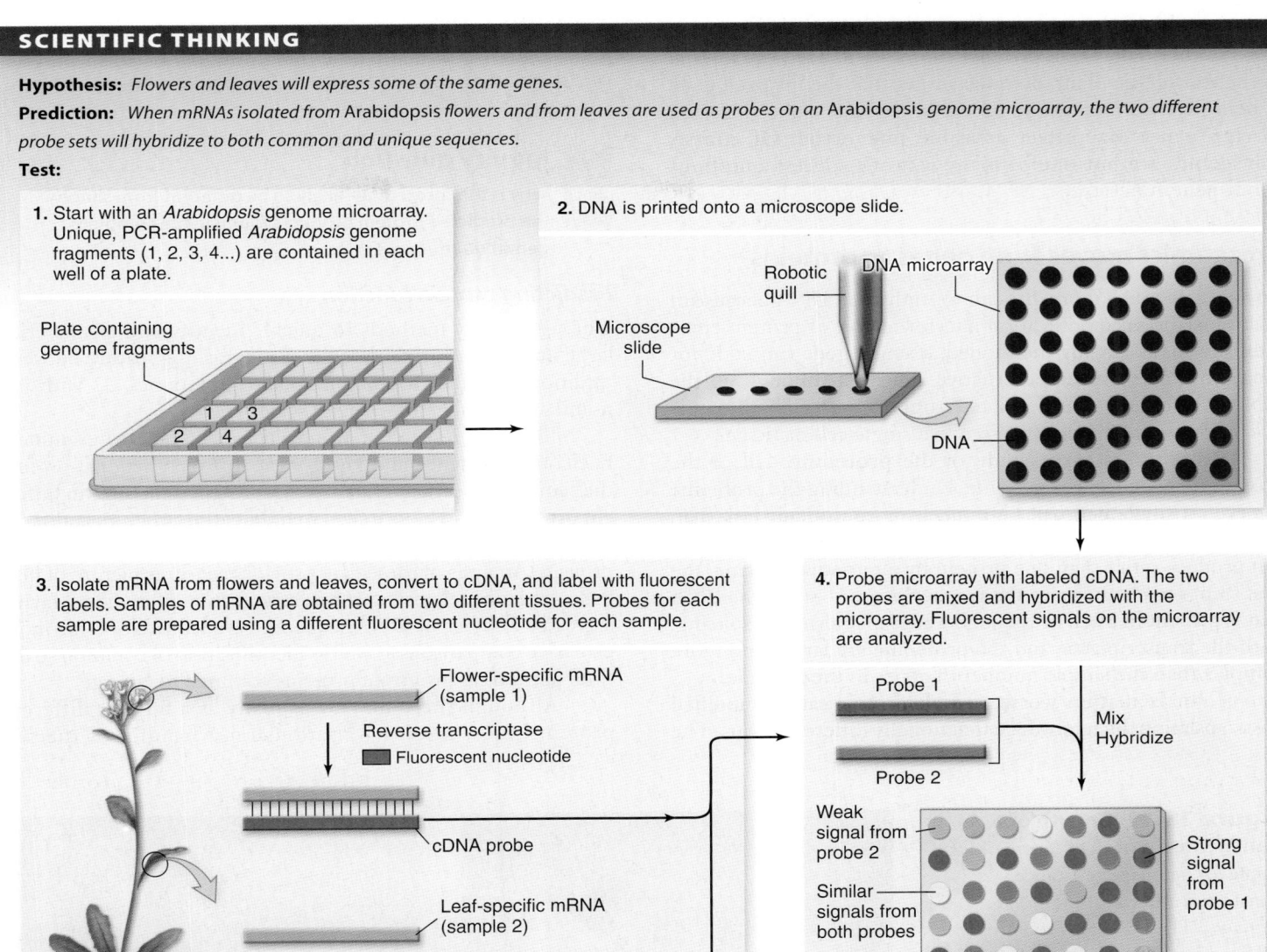

1. Start with an *Arabidopsis* genome microarray. Unique, PCR-amplified *Arabidopsis* genome fragments (1, 2, 3, 4...) are contained in each well of a plate.

Plate containing genome fragments

2. DNA is printed onto a microscope slide.

Robotic quill
DNA microarray
Microscope slide
DNA

3. Isolate mRNA from flowers and leaves, convert to cDNA, and label with fluorescent labels. Samples of mRNA are obtained from two different tissues. Probes for each sample are prepared using a different fluorescent nucleotide for each sample.

Flower-specific mRNA (sample 1)
Reverse transcriptase
Fluorescent nucleotide
cDNA probe
Leaf-specific mRNA (sample 2)
Reverse transcriptase
Different fluorescent nucleotide
cDNA probe

4. Probe microarray with labeled cDNA. The two probes are mixed and hybridized with the microarray. Fluorescent signals on the microarray are analyzed.

Probe 1
Probe 2
Mix Hybridize
Weak signal from probe 2
Similar signals from both probes
Strong signal from probe 2
Strong signal from probe 1
Weak signal from probe 1

Result: *Yellow spots represent sequences that hybridized to cDNA from both flowers and leaves. Red spots represent genes expressed only in flowers. Green spots represent genes expressed only in leaves.*

Conclusion: *Some* Arabidopsis *genes are expressed in both flowers and leaves, but there are genes expressed in flowers but not leaves and leaves but not flowers.*

Further Experiments: *How could you use microarrays to determine whether the genes expressed in both flowers and leaves are housekeeping genes or are unique to flowers and leaves?*

Figure 18.10 Microarrays.

disease alleles for a recessive trait can be mapped by comparing 20 purebred dogs exhibiting the disease with 20 healthy dogs.

Transgenics

How can we determine whether two genes from different species having similar sequences have the same function? And,

how can we be sure that a gene identified by an annotation program actually functions as a gene in the organism? One way to address these questions is through transgenics—the creation of organisms containing genes from other species (transgenic organisms).

The technology for creating transgenic organisms was discussed in chapter 17; it is illustrated for plants in figure 18.11. Different markers can be incorporated into the gene so that its protein product can be visualized or isolated in the transgenic plant, demonstrating that the inserted gene is being transcribed. In some cases, the transgene (inserted foreign gene) may affect a visible phenotype. Of course, transgenics are but one of many ways to address questions about gene function.

Proteomics moves from genes to proteins

Proteins are much more difficult to study than DNA because of posttranslational modification and formation of protein complexes. And, as already mentioned, a single gene can code for multiple proteins using alternative splicing. Although all the DNA in a genome can be isolated from a single cell, only a portion of the proteome is expressed in a single cell or tissue.

Proteomics is the study of the **proteome**—all of the proteins encoded by the genome. Understanding the proteome for even a single cell will be a much more difficult task than determining the sequence of a genome. Because a single gene can produce more than one protein by alternative splicing, the first step is to characterize the **transcriptome**—all of the RNA that is present in a cell or tissue. Because of alternative splicing, both the transcriptome and the proteome are larger and more complex than the simple number of genes in the genome.

To make matters worse, a single protein can be modified posttranslationally to produce functionally different forms. The function of a protein can also depend on its association with other proteins. Nonetheless, since proteins perform most of the major functions of cells, understanding their diversity is essential.

Inquiry question

? Why is the "proteome" likely to be different from simply the predicted protein products found in the complete genome sequence?

Predicting protein function

The use of new methods to quickly identify and characterize large numbers of proteins is the distinguishing feature between traditional protein biochemistry and proteomics. As with genomics, the challenge is one of scale.

Ideally, a researcher would like to be able to examine a nucleotide sequence and know what sort of functional protein the sequence specifies. Databases of protein structures in different organisms can be searched to predict the structure and function of genes known only by sequence, as identified in genome projects. Analysis of these data provides a clearer picture of how gene sequence relates to protein structure and function. Having a greater number of DNA sequences available allows for more extensive comparisons as well as identification of common structural patterns as groups of proteins continue to emerge.

Although there may be as many as a million different proteins, most are just variations on a handful of themes.

Figure 18.11 Growth of a transgenic plant. DNA containing a gene for herbicide resistance was transferred into wheat *(Triticum aestivum)*. The DNA also contains the *GUS* gene, which is used as a tag or label. The *GUS* gene produces an enzyme that catalyzes the conversion of a staining solution from clear to blue. *a.* Embryonic tissue just prior to insertion of foreign DNA. *b.* Following DNA transfer, callus cells containing the foreign DNA are indicated by color from the *GUS* gene *(blue spots)*. *c.* Shoot formation in the transgenic plants growing on a selective medium. Here, the gene for herbicide resistance in the transgenic plants allows growth on the selective medium containing the herbicide. *d.* Comparison of growth on the selection medium for transgenic plants bearing the herbicide resistance gene *(left)* and a nontransgenic plant *(right)*.

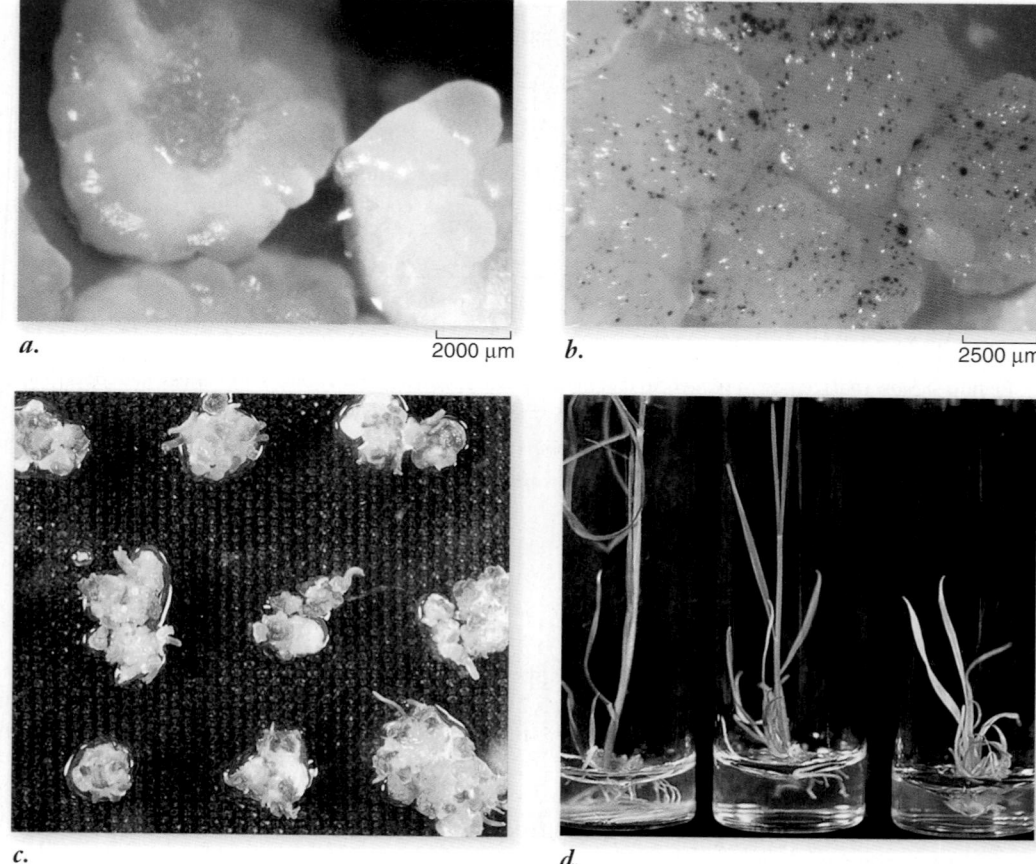

a.   2000 μm

b.   2500 μm

c.

d.

The same shared structural motifs—barrels, helices, molecular zippers—are found in the proteins of plants, insects, and humans (figure 18.12; also see chapter 3 for more information on protein motifs). The maximum number of distinct motifs has been estimated to be fewer than 5000. About 1000 of these motifs have already been cataloged. Efforts are now under way to detail the shapes of all the common motifs.

Protein microarrays

Protein microarrays, comparable to DNA microarrays, are being used to analyze large numbers of proteins simultaneously. Making a protein microarray starts with isolating the transcriptome of a cell or tissue. Then cDNAs are constructed and reproduced by cloning them into bacteria or viruses. Transcription and translation occur in the prokaryotic host, and micromolar quantities of protein are isolated and purified. These are then spotted onto glass slides.

Protein microarrays can be probed in at least three different ways. First, they can be screened with antibodies to specific proteins. Antibodies are labeled so that they can be detected, and the patterns on the protein array can be determined by computer analysis.

An array of proteins can also be screened with another protein to detect binding or other protein interactions. Thousands of interactions can be tested simultaneously. For example, calmodulin (which mediates Ca^{2+} function; see chapter 9) was labeled and used to probe a yeast proteome array with 5800 proteins. The screen revealed 39 proteins that bound calmodulin. Of those 39, 33 were previously unknown!

A third type of screen uses small molecules to assess whether they will bind to any of the proteins on the array. This approach shows promise for discovering new drugs that will inhibit proteins involved in disease.

Large-scale screens reveal protein–protein interactions

We often study proteins in isolation, compared with their normal cellular context. This approach is obviously artificial. One immediate goal of proteomics, therefore, is to map all the physical interactions between proteins in a cell. This is a daunting task that requires tools that can be automated, similarly to the way that genome sequencing was automated.

One approach is to use the yeast two-hybrid system discussed in the preceding chapter. This system can be automated once libraries of known cDNAs are available in each of the two vectors used. The use of two-hybrid screens has been applied to budding yeast to generate a map of all possible interacting proteins. This method is difficult to apply to more complex multicellular organisms, but in a technical tour-de-force, it has been applied to *Drosophila melanogaster* as well.

For vertebrates, the two-hybrid system is being applied more selectively, by concentrating on a biologically significant process, such as signal transduction. The technique can then be used to map all of the interacting proteins in a specific signaling pathway.

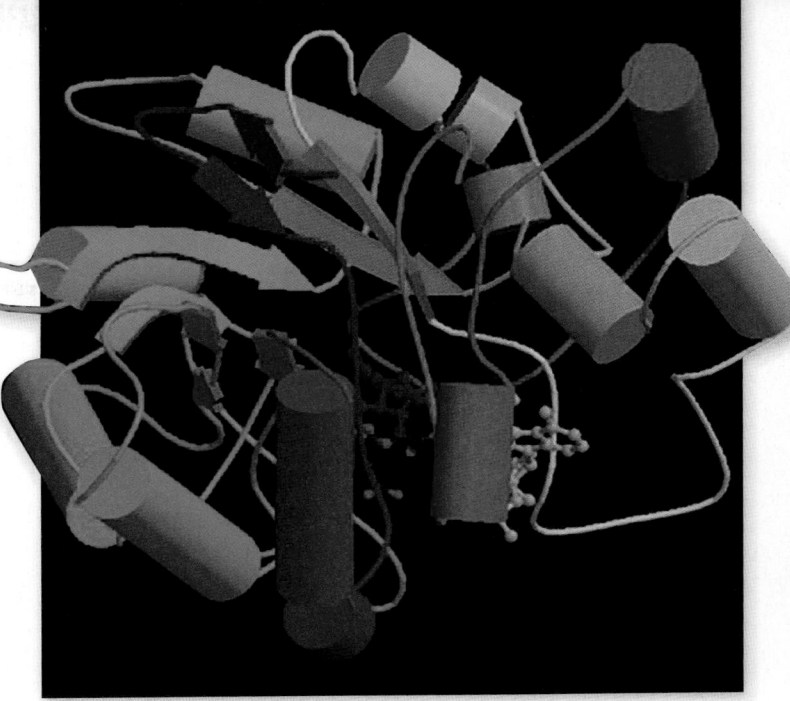

Figure 18.12 Computer-generated model of an enzyme. Searchable databases contain known protein structures, including human aldose reductase shown here. Secondary structural motifs are shown in different colors.

Inquiry question

? What is the relationship among genome, transcriptome, and proteome?

Learning Outcomes Review 18.4

Comparisons of different genomes allows geneticists to infer structural, functional, and evolutionary relationships between genes and proteins as well as relationships between species. Microarrays enable evaluation of gene expression for many genes at once. Proteomics involves similar analysis of all the proteins coded by a genome, that is, an organism's proteome. Because of alternative splicing, this task is much more complex.

■ *Why is establishment of a species' transcriptome an important step in studying its proteome?*

18.5 Applications of Genomics

Learning Outcomes

1. *List ways in which genomics could be applied to infectious disease research.*
2. *Explain how genomics could enhance crop production and nutritional yield.*
3. *Evaluate the issues of genome ownership and privacy.*

Space allows us to highlight only a few of the myriad applications of genomics to show the possibilities. The tools being developed truly represent a revolution in biology that will likely have a lasting influence on the way that we think about living systems.

Genomics can help to identify infectious diseases

The genomics revolution has yielded millions of new genes to be investigated. The potential of genomics to improve human health is enormous. Mutations in a single gene can explain some, but not most, hereditary diseases. With entire genomes to search, the probability of unraveling human, animal, and plant diseases is greatly improved.

Although proteomics will likely lead to new pharmaceuticals, the immediate effect of genomics is being seen in diagnostics. Both improved technology and gene discovery are enhancing the diagnosis of genetic abnormalities.

Diagnostics are also being used to identify individuals. For example, short tandem repeats (STRs), discovered through genomic research, were among the forensic diagnostic tools used to identify remains of victims of the September 11, 2001, terrorist attack on the World Trade Center in New York City.

The September 11 attacks were followed by an increased awareness and concern about biological weapons. Five people died and 17 more were infected with anthrax after envelopes containing anthrax spores were sent through the U.S. mail. A massive FBI investigation initially focused on the wrong individual, Steven J. Hatfill, a government scientist. Genome sequencing allowed exploration of possible sources of the deadly bacteria. A difference of only 10 bp between strains allowed the FBI to trace the source to a single vial of the bacteria used in a vaccine research program at U.S. Army Medical Research Institute for Infectious Diseases. By 2008, Hatfield was exonerated. Another researcher, Bruce E. Ivins, committed suicide just before being formally charged by the FBI with criminal activity in the 2001 anthrax attacks. Ivins had been working on vaccine development. In addition, substantial effort has been turned toward the use of genomic tools to distinguish between naturally occurring infections and intentional outbreaks of disease. The Centers for Disease Control and Prevention (CDC) have ranked bacteria and viruses that are likely targets for bioterrorism (table 18.2).

Genomics can help improve agricultural crops

Globally speaking, poor nutrition is the greatest impediment to human health. Much of the excitement about the rice genome project is based on its potential for improving the yield and nutritional quality of rice and other cereals worldwide. The development of Golden Rice (chapter 17) is an example of improved nutrition through genetic approaches. About one third of the world population obtains half its calories from rice (figure 18.13). In some regions, individuals consume up to 1.5 kg of rice daily. More than 500 million tons of rice is produced each year, but this may not be adequate to provide enough rice for the world in the future.

TABLE 18.2	High-Priority Pathogens for Genomic Research	
Pathogen	**Disease**	**Genome***
Variola major	Smallpox	Complete
Bacillus anthracis	Anthrax	Complete
Yersinia pestis	Plague	Complete
Clostridium botulinum	Botulism	In progress
Francisella tularensis	Tularemia	Complete
Filoviruses	Ebola and Marburg hemorrhagic fever	Both are complete
Arenaviruses	Lassa fever and Argentine hemorrhagic fever	Both are complete

*There are multiple strains of these viruses and bacteria. "Complete" indicates that at least one has been sequenced. For example, the Florida strain of anthrax was the first to be sequenced.

Due in large part to scientific advances in crop breeding and farming techniques, in the last 50 years world grain production has more than doubled, with an increase in cropland of only 1%. The world now farms a total area the size of South America, but without the scientific advances of the past 50 years, an area equal to the entire western hemisphere would need to be farmed to produce enough food for the world.

Unfortunately, water usage for crops has tripled in that time period, and quality farmland is being lost to soil erosion. Scientists are also concerned about the effects of global climate

Figure 18.13 Rice field. Most of the rice grown globally is directly consumed by humans and is the dietary mainstay of 2 billion people.

change on agriculture worldwide. Increasing the yield and quality of crops, especially on more marginal farmland, will depend on many factors—but genetic engineering, built on the findings of genomics projects, can contribute significantly to the solution.

Most crops grown in the United States produce less than half of their genetic potential because of environmental stresses (salt, water, and temperature), herbivores, and pathogens (figure 18.14). Identifying genes that can provide resistance to stress and pests is the focus of many current genomics research projects. Having access to entire genomic sequences will enhance the probability of identifying critical genes.

Genomics raises ethical issues over ownership of genomic information

Genome science is also a source of ethical challenges and dilemmas. One example is the issue of gene patents. Actually, it is the use of a gene, not the gene itself, that is patentable. For a patent to be granted for a gene's use, the product and its function must be known.

The public genome consortia, supported by federal funding, have been driven by the belief that the sequence of genomes should be freely available to all and should not be patented. Private companies patent gene functions, but they often make sequence data available with certain restrictions. The physical sciences have negotiated the landscape of public and for-profit research for decades, but this is relatively new territory for biologists.

Another ethical issue involves privacy. How sequence data are used is the focus of thoughtful and ongoing discussions. The Universal Declaration on the Human Genome and Human Rights states, "The human genome underlies the fundamental unity of all members of the human family, as well as the recognition of their inherent dignity and diversity. In a symbolic sense, it is the heritage of humanity."

Although we talk about "the" human genome, each of us has subtly different genomes that can be used to identify us. Genetic disorders such as cystic fibrosis and Huntington disease can already be identified by screening, but genomics will greatly increase the number of identifiable traits. The Genetic Information Nondiscrimination Act (GINA) was signed into law in 2008 to prevent discrimination based on genotype. Employers and health insurance companies may not request genetic tests or discriminate based on someone's genetic code. Life, disability, and long term care insurance are not covered by GINA. Members of the military are excluded from GINA's privacy protection. The U.S. Armed Forces require DNA samples from members of the military for possible casualty identification. The genome privacy debate continues.

Behavioral genomics is an area that is also rich with possibilities and dilemmas. Very few behavioral traits can be accounted for by single genes. Two genes have been associated with fragile-X mental retardation, and three with early-onset Alzheimer disease. Comparisons of multiple genomes will likely lead to the identification of multiple genes controlling a range of behaviors. Will this change the way we view acceptable behavior?

Figure 18.14 Corn crop productivity well below its genetic potential due to drought stress. Corn production can be limited by water deficiencies due to the drought that occurs during the growing season in dry climates. Global climate change may increase drought stress in areas where corn is the major crop.

Inquiry question

? As of February 2008 a draft version of the corn genome has been sequenced. How could you use information from the corn and rice genome sequences to try to improve drought tolerance in corn?

In Iceland, the parliament has voted to have a private company create a database from pooled medical, genetic, and genealogical information about all Icelanders, a particularly fascinating population from a genetic perspective. Because minimal migration or immigration has occurred there over the last 800 years, the information that can be mined from the Icelandic database is phenomenal. Ultimately, the value of that information has to be weighed, however, against any possible discrimination or stigmatization of individuals or groups.

Learning Outcomes Review 18.5

Genomics is one approach to better diagnosis, based on knowledge of infectious agents' genetic makeup; it also allows identification of individual disease strains. Genomics has enhanced DNA identification of remains. Agricultural crop yields and nutritional content could be improved if genes that confer disease resistance or increased synthesis can be identified.

■ *Suppose you produced an engineered form of potato that had twice the amount of protein. Would you seek a patent on this plant?*

18.1 Mapping Genomes

Different kinds of physical maps can be generated.

Physical genetic maps include fully sequenced genomes, restriction maps, and maps of chromosome banding patterns.

Sequence-tagged sites provide a common language for physical maps.

Any physical site can be used as a sequence-tagged site (STS), based on a small stretch of a unique DNA sequence that allows unambiguous identification of a fragment.

Genetic maps provide a link to phenotypes.

Short tandem repeats (STRs) are the most common type of markers for distinguishing regions of the genome and assessing its phenotypic effects.

Physical maps can be correlated with genetic maps.

Physical and genetic maps can be correlated. Any gene that can be cloned can be placed within the genome sequence and mapped. However, absolute correspondence of distances cannot be accomplished.

18.2 Whole-Genome Sequencing

Genome sequencing requires larger molecular clones.

Yeast artificial chromosomes (YACs) have allowed cloning of larger pieces of DNA, although their use has some drawbacks. Bacterial artificial chromosomes (BACs) are most commonly used now.

Whole-genome sequencing is approached in two ways: clone-by-clone and shotgun.

Clone-by-clone sequencing starts with known clones, often in BACs that can be aligned with each other.

Shotgun sequencing involves sequencing random clones, then using a computer to assemble the finished sequence.

The Human Genome Project used both sequencing methods.

By 2004, the "finished" sequence was announced, and it includes 99% of the euchromatic human DNA sequence.

18.3 Characterizing Genomes

The Human Genome Project found fewer genes than expected.

Although eukaryotic genomes are larger and have more genes than those of prokaryotes, the size of the organism is not always correlated with the size of the genome. The human genome contains only around 25,000 genes, fewer than found in rice.

Finding genes in sequence data requires computer searches.

In a sequenced genome, protein-coding genes are identified by looking for open-reading frames (ORFs). An ORF begins with a start codon and contains no stop codon for a distance long enough to encode a protein. Genes are then grouped based on conserved regions.

Genomes contain both coding and noncoding DNA.

Protein-encoding DNA includes single-copy genes, segmental duplications, multigene families, and tandem clusters. Noncoding DNA in eukaryotes makes up about 99% of DNA. Approximately 45% of the human genome is composed of mobile transposable elements, including LINEs, SINEs, and LTRs.

Expressed sequence tags identify genes that are transcribed.

The number and location of expressed genes can be estimated by sequencing the ends of randomly selected cDNAs to produce expressed sequence tags (ESTs).

SNPs are single-base differences between individuals.

Single-nucleotide difference between individuals are called single-nucleotide polymorphisms (SNPs). To be classified as a polymorphism, an SNP must be present in at least 1% of the population. At least 50,000 SNPs are currently known in coding regions.

Genomic haplotypes are regions of chromosomes that are not exchanged by recombination. These regions can be used to map genes by association (see figure 18.8).

18.4 Genomics and Proteomics

Comparative genomics reveals conserved regions in genomes.

More than half of the genes of *Drosophila* have human counterparts. The biggest difference between our genome and the chimpanzee genome is in transposable elements.

Synteny allows comparison of unsequenced genomes.

Synteny refers to the conserved arrangements of segments of DNA in related genomes (see figure 18.9). Many separate species have been found to have large regions of synteny.

Organelle genomes have exchanged genes with the nuclear genome.

Both chloroplasts and mitochondria contain components that indicate exchange of genetic material with the nuclear genome.

Functional genomics reveals gene function at the genome level.

Functional genomics uses high-end computer technology to analyze gene function and gene products. DNA microarrays allow the expression of all of the genes in a cell to be monitored at once (see figure 18.10).

Proteomics moves from genes to proteins.

Proteomics characterizes all of the proteins produced by a cell. The transcriptome is all the mRNAs present in a cell at a specific time. Protein microarrays can identify and characterize large numbers of proteins.

Large-scale screens reveal protein–protein interactions.

The yeast two-hybrid system is used to generate large-scale maps of interacting proteins; however, the scope of this task is daunting in humans, mice, and other vertebrates. Selective applications in specific areas, such as signal transduction, have been undertaken.

18.5 Applications of Genomics

Genomics can help to identify infectious diseases.

Genomics can help identify naturally occurring and intentional outbreaks of infectious diseases and tracing of disease strains.

Genomics can help improve agricultural crops.

Genomics can potentially increase the nutritional value of crops and alter their responses to environmental stresses, potentially helping to feed a growing population.

Genomics raises ethical issues over ownership of genomic information.

Questions regarding profit and ownership of genomic data provide ongoing challenges for the ethical use of scientific knowledge.

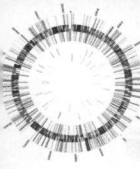

Review Questions

UNDERSTAND

1. A genetic map is based on the
   a. sequence of the DNA.
   b. relative position of genes on chromosomes.
   c. location of sites of restriction enzyme cleavage.
   d. banding pattern on a chromosome.

2. What is an STS?
   a. A unique sequence within the DNA that can be used for mapping
   b. A repeated sequence within the DNA that can be used for mapping
   c. An upstream element that allows for mapping of the 3′ region of a gene
   d. Both b and c

3. Which number represents the total number of genes in the human genome?
   a. 2500   b. 10,000
   c. 25,000   d. 100,000

4. An open reading frame (ORF) is distinguished by the presence of
   a. a stop codon.
   b. a start codon.
   c. a sequence of DNA long enough to encode a protein.
   d. All of the above

5. What is a BLAST search?
   a. A mechanism for aligning consensus regions during whole-genome sequencing
   b. A search for similar gene sequences from other species
   c. A method of screening a DNA library
   d. A method for identifying ORFs

6. Which of the following is *not* an example of a protein-encoding gene?
   a. Single-copy gene   b. Tandem clusters
   c. Pseudogene   d. Multigene family

7. What is a proteome?
   a. The collection of all genes encoding proteins
   b. The collection of all proteins encoded by the genome
   c. The collection of all proteins present in a cell
   d. The amino acid sequence of a protein

8. Which of the following is *not* an example of noncoding DNA?
   a. Promoter   b. Intron
   c. Pseudogene   d. Exon

APPLY

1. An artificial chromosome is useful because it
   a. produces more consistent results than a natural chromosome.
   b. allows for the isolation of larger DNA sequences.
   c. provides a high copy number of a DNA sequence.
   d. is linear.

2. Comparisons between genomes is made easier because of
   a. synteny.   b. haplotypes.
   c. transposons.   d. expressed sequence tags.

3. Which of the following techniques relies on prior knowledge of overlapping sequences?
   a. Yeast two-hybrid system
   b. Shotgun method of genome sequencing
   c. FISH
   d. Clone-by-clone method of genome sequencing

4. The duplication of a gene due to uneven meiotic crossing over is thought to lead to the production of a
   a. segmental duplication.   c. simple sequence repeat.
   b. tandem duplication.   d. multigene family.

5. What information can be obtained from a DNA microarray?
   a. The sequence of a particular gene.
   b. The presence of genes within a specific tissue.
   c. The pattern of gene expression.
   d. Differences between genomes.

6. Which of the following is true regarding microarray technology and cancer?
   a. A DNA microarray can determine the type of cancer.
   b. A DNA microarray can measure the response of a cancer to therapy.
   c. A DNA microarray can be used to predict whether the cancer will metastasize.
   d. All of the above

7. Which of the following techniques could be used to examine protein–protein interactions in a cell?
   a. Two-hybrid screens   c. Protein microarrays
   b. Protein structure databases   d. Both a and c

SYNTHESIZE

1. You are in the early stages of a genome-sequencing project. You have isolated a number of clones from a BAC library and mapped the inserts in these clones using STSs. Use the STSs to align the clones into a contiguous sequence of the genome (a contig).

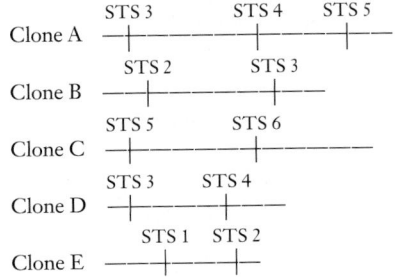

2. Genomic research can be used to determine if an outbreak of an infectious disease is natural or "intentional." Explain what a genomic researcher would be looking for in a suspected intentional outbreak of a disease like anthrax.

ONLINE RESOURCE

www.ravenbiology.com

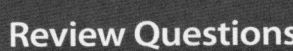

Understand, Apply, and Synthesize—enhance your study with animations that bring concepts to life and practice tests to assess your understanding. Your instructor may also recommend the interactive eBook, individualized learning tools, and more.

5.5 μm

Chapter

19

Cellular Mechanisms of Development

Chapter Outline

19.1   The Process of Development

19.2   Cell Division

19.3   Cell Differentiation

19.4   Nuclear Reprogramming

19.5   Pattern Formation

19.6   Morphogenesis

Introduction

Recent work with different kinds of stem cells, like those pictured, have captured the hopes and imagination of the public. For thousands of years, humans have wondered how organisms arise, grow, change, and mature. We are now in an era when long-standing questions may be answered, and new possibilities for regenerative medicine seem on the horizon.

We have explored gene expression from the perspective of individual cells, examining the diverse mechanisms cells employ to control the transcription of particular genes. Now we broaden our perspective and look at the unique challenge posed by the development of a single cell, the fertilized egg, into a multicellular organism. In the course of this developmental journey, a pattern of decisions about gene expression takes place that causes particular lines of cells to proceed along different paths, spinning an incredibly complex web of cause and effect. Yet, for all its complexity, this developmental program works with impressive precision. In this chapter, we explore the mechanisms of development at the cellular and molecular level.

19.1 The Process of Development

Development can be defined as the process of systematic, gene-directed changes through which an organism forms the successive stages of its life cycle. Development is a continuum, and explorations of development can be focused on any point along this continuum. The study of development plays a central role in unifying the understanding of both the similarities and diversity of life on Earth.

We can divide the overall process of development into four subprocesses:

■ **Cell Division.** A developing plant or animal begins as a fertilized egg, or zygote, that must undergo cell division to produce the new individual. In all cases early development involves extensive cell division, but in many cases it does not include much growth as the egg cell itself is quite large.

■ **Differentiation.** As cells divide, orchestrated changes in gene expression result in differences between cells that ultimately result in cell specialization. In differentiated cells, certain genes are expressed at particular times, but other genes may not be expressed at all.

- **Pattern Formation.** Cells in a developing embryo must become oriented to the body plan of the organism the embryo will become. Pattern formation involves cells' abilities to detect positional information that guides their ultimate fate.
- **Morphogenesis.** As development proceeds, the form of the body—its organs and anatomical features—is generated. Morphogenesis may involve cell death as well as cell division and differentiation.

Despite the overt differences between groups of plants and animals, most multicellular organisms develop according to molecular mechanisms that are fundamentally very similar. This observation suggests that these mechanisms evolved very early in the history of multicellular life.

19.2 Cell Division

Learning Outcomes

1. *Explain the importance of cell division to early development.*
2. *Describe the use of* C. elegans *to track cell lineages.*
3. *Distinguish differences in cell division between animals and plants.*

When a frog tadpole hatches out of its protective coats, it is roughly the same overall mass as the fertilized egg from which it came. Instead of being made up of just one cell, however, the tadpole consists of about a million cells, which are organized into tissues and organs with different functions. Thus, the very first process that must occur during embryogenesis is cell division.

Immediately following fertilization, the diploid zygote undergoes a period of rapid mitotic divisions that ultimately result in an early embryo comprised of dozens to thousands of diploid cells. In animal embryos, the timing and number of these divisions are species-specific and are controlled by a set of molecules that we examined in chapter 10: the *cyclins* and *cyclin-dependent kinases (Cdks)*. These molecules exert control over checkpoints in the cycle of mitosis.

Development begins with cell division

In animal embryos, the period of rapid cell division following fertilization is called **cleavage.** During cleavage, the enormous mass of the zygote is subdivided into a larger and larger number of smaller and smaller cells, called **blastomeres** (figure 19.1). Hence, cleavage is not accompanied by any increase in the overall size of the embryo. The G_1 and G_2 phases of the cell cycle, during which a cell increases its mass and size, are extremely shortened or eliminated during cleavage (figure 19.2).

Because of the absence of the two gap/growth phases, the rapid rate of mitotic divisions during cleavage is never again approached in the lifetime of any animal. For example, zebrafish blastomeres divide once every several minutes during cleavage, to create an embryo with a thousand cells in just under 3 hr! In contrast, cycling adult human intestinal epithelial cells divide on average only once every 19 hr. A comparison of the different patterns of cleavage can be found in chapter 54.

When external sources of nutrients become available—for example, during larval feeding stages or after implantation of mammalian embryos—daughter cells can increase in size following cytokinesis, and an overall increase in the size of the organism occurs as more cells are produced.

Every cell division is known in the development of *C. elegans*

One of the most completely described models of development is the tiny nematode *Caenorhabditis elegans*. Only about 1 mm long, the adult worm consists of 959 somatic cells.

Because *C. elegans* is transparent, individual cells can be followed as they divide. By observing them, researchers have learned how each of the cells that make up the adult worm is derived from the fertilized egg. As shown on the lineage map in figure 19.3*a*, the egg divides into two cells, and these daughter cells continue to divide. Each horizontal line on the map represents one round of cell division. The length of each vertical line represents the time between cell divisions, and the end of each vertical line represents one fully differentiated cell. In figure 19.3*b*, the major organs of the worm are color-coded to match the colors of the corresponding groups of cells on the lineage map.

Some of these differentiated cells, such as some cells that generate the worm's external cuticle, are "born" after only 8 rounds of cell division; other cuticle cells require as many as 14 rounds. The cells that make up the worm's pharynx, or feeding organ, are born after 9 to 11 rounds of division, whereas cells in the gonads require up to 17 divisions.

Exactly 302 nerve cells are destined for the worm's nervous system. Exactly 131 cells are programmed to die, mostly within minutes of their "birth." The fate of each cell is the same in every *C. elegans* individual, except for the cells that will become eggs and sperm.

Figure 19.1 Cleavage divisions in a frog embryo. *a.* The first cleavage division divides the egg into two large blastomeres. *b.* After two more divisions, four small blastomeres sit on top of four large blastomeres, each of which continues to divide to produce (*c*) a compact mass of cells.

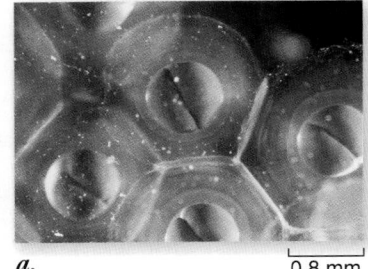
a.   0.8 mm

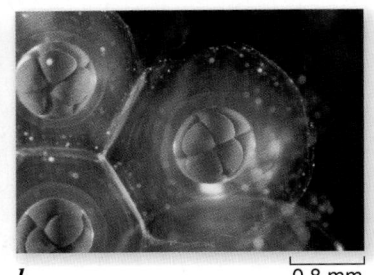
b.   0.8 mm

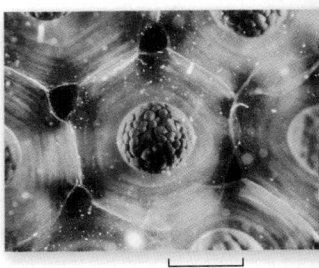
c.   0.8 mm

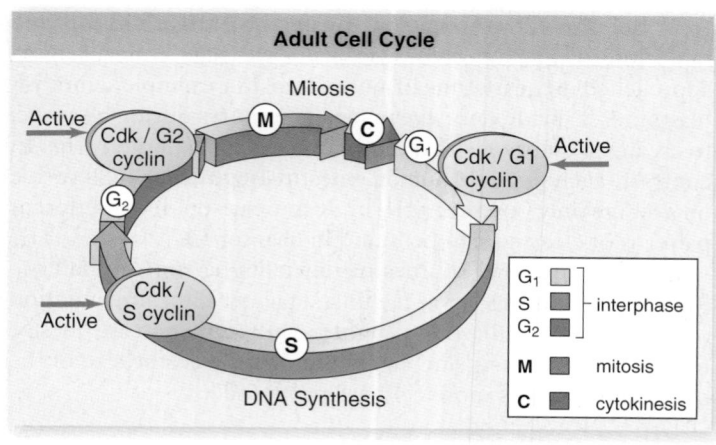

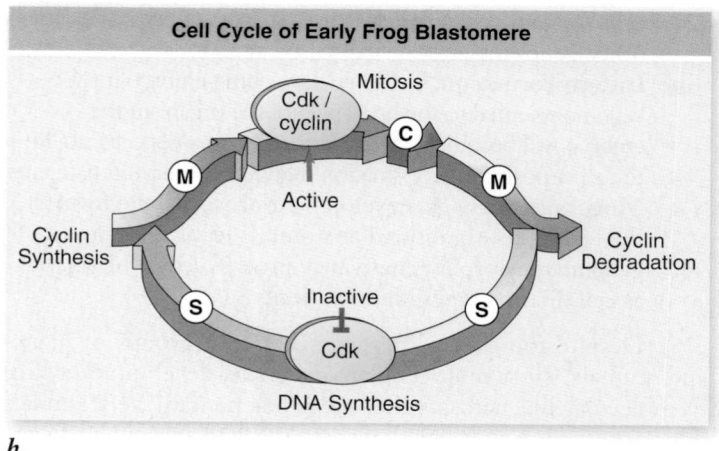

Figure 19.2 Cell cycle of adult cell and embryonic cell. In contrast to the cell cycle of adult somatic cells (*a*), the dividing cells of early frog embryos lack G_1 and G_2 stages (*b*), enabling the cleavage stage nuclei to rapidly cycle between DNA synthesis and mitosis. Large stores of cyclin mRNA are present in the unfertilized egg. Periodic degradation of cyclin proteins correlates with exiting from mitosis. Cyclin degradation and Cdk inactivation allow the cell to complete mitosis and initiate the next round of DNA synthesis.

Plant growth occurs in specific areas called meristems

A major difference between animals and plants is that most animals are mobile, at least in some phase of their life cycles, and therefore they can move away from unfavorable circumstances. Plants, in contrast, are anchored in position and must simply endure whatever environment they experience. Plants compen-

sate for this restriction by allowing development to accommodate local circumstances.

Instead of creating a body in which every part is specified to have a fixed size and location, a plant assembles its body throughout its life span from a few types of modules, such as leaves, roots, branch nodes, and flowers. Each module has a rigidly controlled structure and organization, but how the modules are utilized is quite flexible—they can be adjusted to environmental conditions.

Figure 19.3 Studying embryonic cell division and development in the nematode. Development in *C. elegans* has been mapped out such that the fate of each cell from the single egg cell has been determined. *a.* The lineage map shows the number of cell divisions from the egg, and the color coding links their placement in (*b*) the adult organism.

M. E. Challinor illustration. From Howard Hughes Medical Institute © as published in *From Egg to Adult*, 1992. Reprinted by permission.

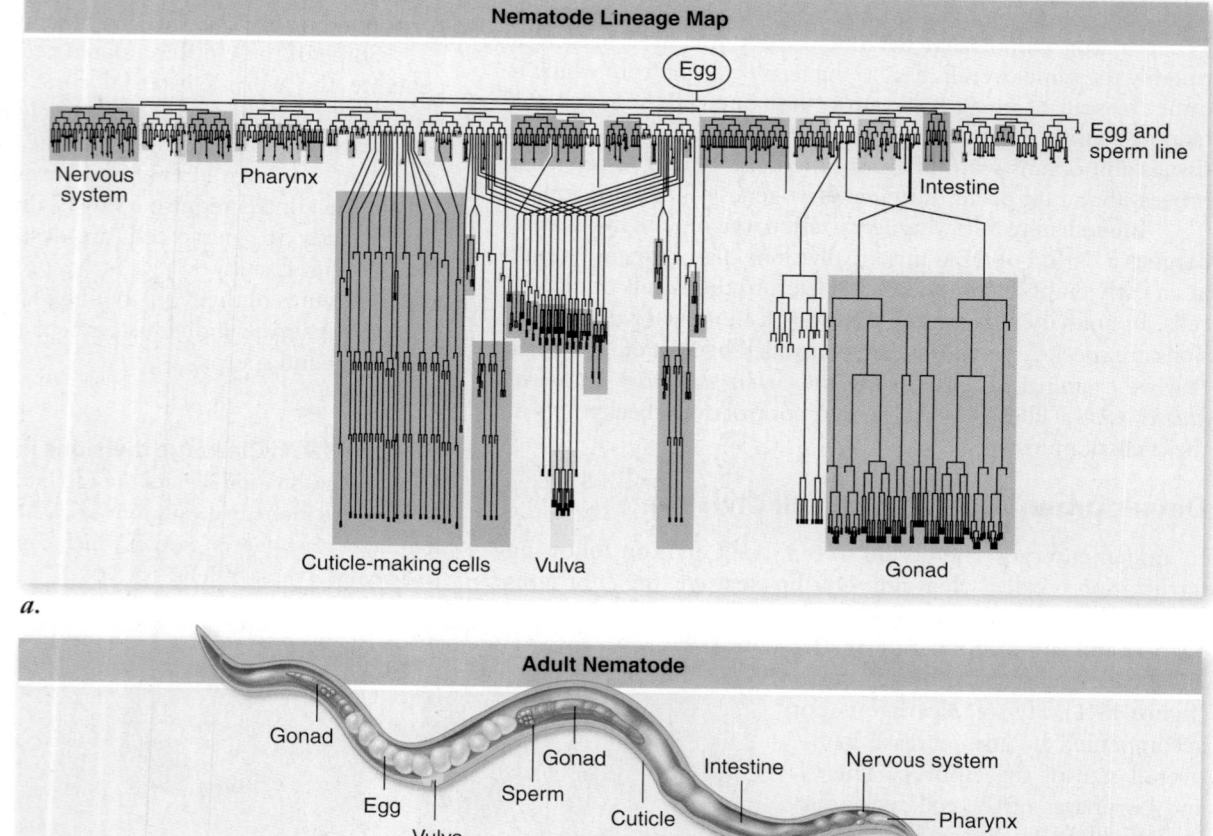

Plants develop by building their bodies outward, creating new parts from groups of stem cells that are contained in structures called **meristems.** As meristematic stem cells continually divide, they produce cells that can differentiate into the tissues of the plant.

This simple scheme indicates a need to control the process of cell division. We know that cell-cycle control genes are present in both yeast (fungi) and animal cells, implying that these are a eukaryotic innovation—and in fact, the plant cell cycle is regulated by the same mechanisms, namely through cyclins and cyclin-dependent kinases. In one experiment, overexpression of a Cdk inhibitor in transgenic *Arabidopsis thaliana* plants resulted in strong inhibition of cell division in leaf meristems, leading to significant changes in leaf size and shape.

Learning Outcomes Review 19.2

In animal embryos, a series of rapid cell divisions that skip the G_1 and G_2 phases convert the fertilized egg into many cells with no change in size. In the nematode *C. elegans,* every cell division leading to the adult form is known, and this pattern is invariant, allowing biologists to trace development in a cell-by-cell fashion. In plants, growth is restricted to specific areas called meristems, where undifferentiated stem cells are retained.

■ *How are early cell divisions in an embryo different from in an adult organism?*

19.3 Cell Differentiation

Learning Outcomes

1. *Describe the progressive nature of determination.*
2. *List the ways in which cells become committed to developmental pathways on the molecular level.*
3. *Differentiate between the different types of stem cells.*

In chapter 16, we examined the mechanisms that control eukaryotic gene expression. These processes are critical for the development of multicellular organisms, in which life functions are carried out by different tissues and organs. In the course of development, cells become different from one another because of the differential expression of subsets of genes—not only at different times, but in different locations of the growing embryo. We now explore some of the mechanisms that lead to differential gene expression during development.

Cells become determined prior to differentiation

A human body contains more than 210 major types of differentiated cells. These differentiated cells are distinguishable from one another by the particular proteins that they synthesize, their morphologies, and their specific functions. A molecular decision to become a particular type of differentiated cell occurs prior to any overt changes in the cell. This molecular decision-making process is called **cell determination,** and it commits a cell to a particular developmental pathway.

Tracking determination

Determination is often not visible in the cell and can only be "seen" by experiment. The standard experiment to test whether a cell or group of cells is determined is to move the donor cell(s) to a different location in a host (recipient) embryo. If the cells of the transplant develop into the same type of cell as they would have if left undisturbed, then they are judged to be already determined (figure 19.4).

Determination has a time course; it depends on a series of intrinsic or extrinsic events, or both. For example, a cell in the prospective brain region of an amphibian embryo at the early gastrula stage (see chapter 54) has not yet been determined; if transplanted elsewhere in the embryo, it will develop according to the site of transplant. By the late gastrula stage, however,

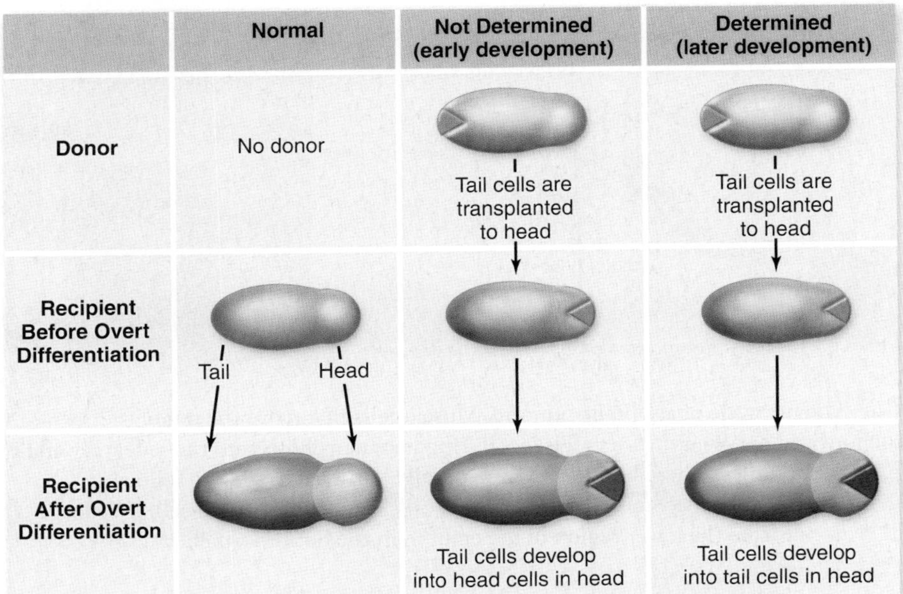

	Normal	Not Determined (early development)	Determined (later development)
Donor	No donor	Tail cells are transplanted to head	Tail cells are transplanted to head
Recipient Before Overt Differentiation	Tail　　Head		
Recipient After Overt Differentiation		Tail cells develop into head cells in head	Tail cells develop into tail cells in head

Figure 19.4 The standard test for determination. The gray ovals represent embryos at early stages of development. The cells to the right normally develop into head structures, whereas the cells to the left usually form tail structures. If prospective tail cells from an early embryo are transplanted to the opposite end of a host embryo, they develop according to their new position into head structures. These cells are not determined. At later stages of development, the tail cells are determined since they now develop into tail structures after transplantation into the opposite end of a host embryo!

additional cell interactions have occurred, determination has taken place, and the cell will develop as neural tissue no matter where it is transplanted.

Determination often takes place in stages, with a cell first becoming partially committed, acquiring positional labels that reflect its location in the embryo. These labels can have a great influence on how the pattern of the body subsequently develops. In a chicken embryo, tissue at the base of the leg bud normally gives rise to the thigh. If this tissue is transplanted to the tip of the identical-looking wing bud, which would normally give rise to the wing tip, the transplanted tissue will develop into a toe rather than a thigh. The tissue has already been determined as leg, but it is not yet committed to being a particular part of the leg. Therefore, it can be influenced by the positional signaling at the tip of the wing bud to form a tip (but in this case, a tip of leg).

The molecular basis of determination

Cells initiate developmental changes by using transcription factors to change patterns of gene expression. When genes encoding these transcription factors are activated, one of their effects is to reinforce their own activation. This rein-

forcement makes the developmental switch deterministic, initiating a chain of events that leads down a particular developmental pathway.

Cells in which a set of regulatory genes have been activated may not actually undergo differentiation until some time later, when other factors interact with the regulatory protein and cause it to activate still other genes. Nevertheless, once the initial "switch" is thrown, the cell is fully committed to its future developmental path.

Cells become committed to follow a particular developmental pathway in one of two ways:

1. via the differential inheritance of cytoplasmic determinants, which are maternally produced and deposited into the egg during oogenesis; or
2. via cell–cell interactions.

The first situation can be likened to a person's social status being determined by who his or her parents are and what he or she has inherited. In the second situation, the person's social standing is determined by interactions with his or her neighbors. Clearly both can be powerful factors in the development and maturation of that individual.

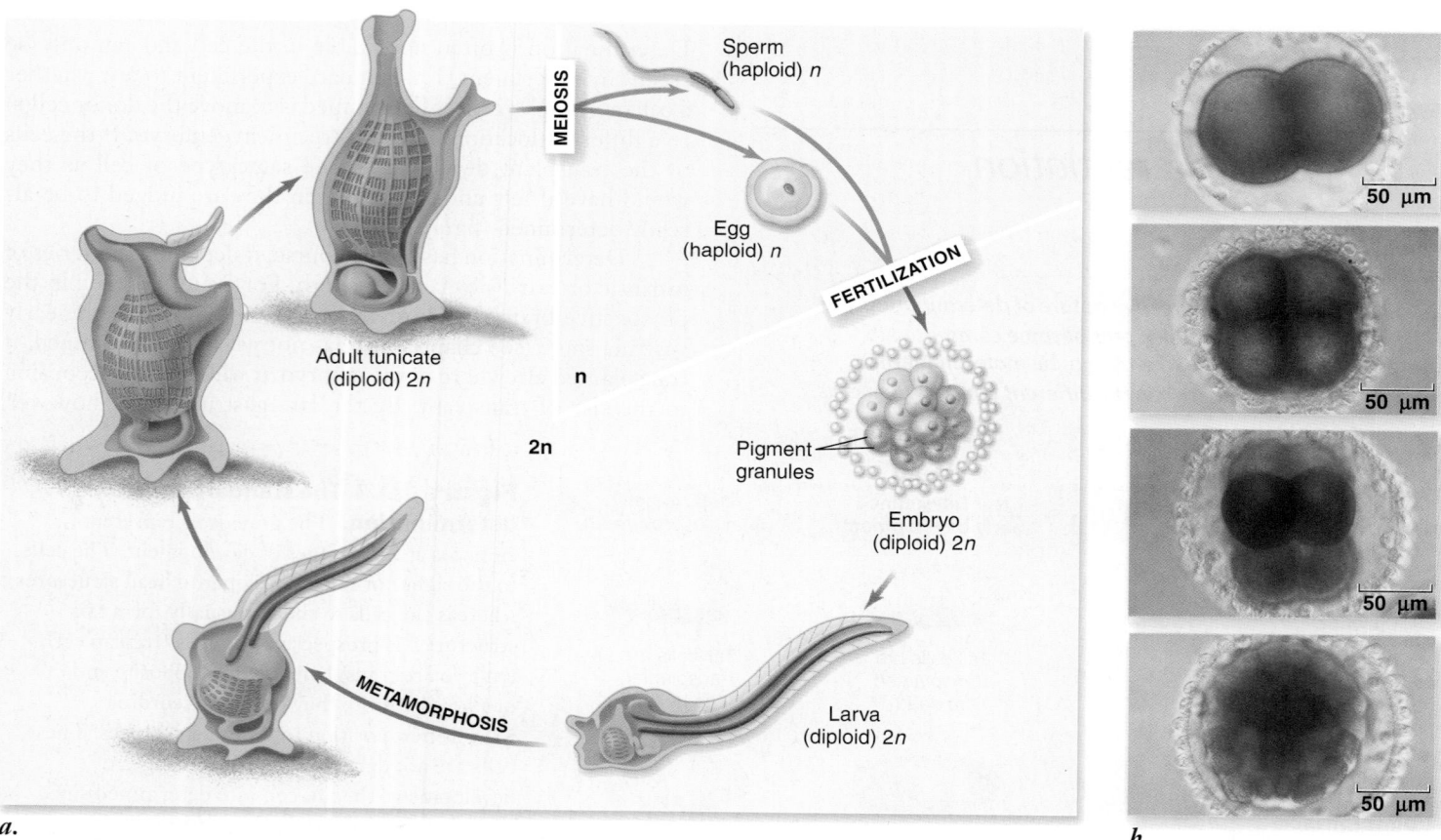

Figure 19.5 Muscle determinants in tunicates. *a.* The life cycle of a solitary tunicate. Muscle cells that move the tail of the swimming tadpole are arranged on either side of the notochord and nerve cord. The tail is lost during metamorphosis into the sedentary adult. *b.* The egg of the tunicate *Styela* contains bright yellow pigment granules. These become asymmetrically localized in the egg following fertilization, and cells that inherit the yellow granules during cleavage will become the larval muscle cells. Embryos at the 2-cell, 4-cell, 8-cell, and 64-cell stages are shown. The tadpole tail will grow out from the lower region of the embryo in the bottom panel.

Determination can be due to cytoplasmic determinants

Many invertebrate embryos provide good visual examples of cell determination through the differential inheritance of cytoplasmic determinants. Tunicates are marine invertebrates (see chapter 35), and most adults have simple, saclike bodies that are attached to the underlying substratum. Tunicates are placed in the phylum Chordata, however, due to the characteristics of their swimming, tadpolelike larval stage, which has a dorsal nerve cord and notochord (figure 19.5a). The muscles that move the tail develop on either side of the notochord.

In many tunicate species, colored pigment granules become asymmetrically localized in the egg following fertilization and subsequently segregate to the tail muscle cell progenitors during cleavage (figure 19.5b). When these pigment granules are shifted experimentally into other cells that normally do not develop into muscle, their fate is changed and they become muscle cells. Thus, the molecules that flip the switch for muscle development appear to be associated with the pigment granules.

The next step is to determine the identity of the molecules involved. Experiments indicate that the female parent provides the egg with mRNA encoded by the *macho-1* gene. The elimination of *macho-1* function leads to a loss of tail muscle in the tadpole, and the misexpression of *macho-1* mRNA leads to the formation of additional (ectopic) muscle cells from nonmuscle lineage cells. The *macho-1* gene product has been shown to be a transcription factor that can activate the expression of several muscle-specific genes.

Induction can lead to cell differentiation

In chapter 9, we examined a variety of ways by which cells communicate with one another. We can demonstrate the importance of cell–cell interactions in development by separating the cells of an early frog embryo and allowing them to develop independently.

Under these conditions, blastomeres from one pole of the embryo (the "animal pole") develop features of ectoderm, and blastomeres from the opposite pole of the embryo (the "vegetal pole") develop features of endoderm. None of the two separated groups of cells ever develop features characteristic of mesoderm, the third main cell type. If animal-pole cells and vegetal-pole cells are placed next to each other, however, some of the animal-pole cells develop as mesoderm. The interaction between the two cell types triggers a switch in the developmental path of these cells. This change in cell fate due to interaction with an adjacent cell is called **induction.** Signaling molecules act to alter gene expression in the target cells, in this case, some of the animal-pole cells.

Another example of inductive cell interactions is the formation of the notochord and mesenchyme, a specific tissue, in tunicate embryos. Muscle, notochord, and mesenchyme all arise from mesodermal cells that form at the vegetal margin of the 32-cell stage embryo. These prospective mesodermal cells receive signals from the underlying endodermal precursor cells that lead to the formation of notochord and mesenchyme (figure 19.6).

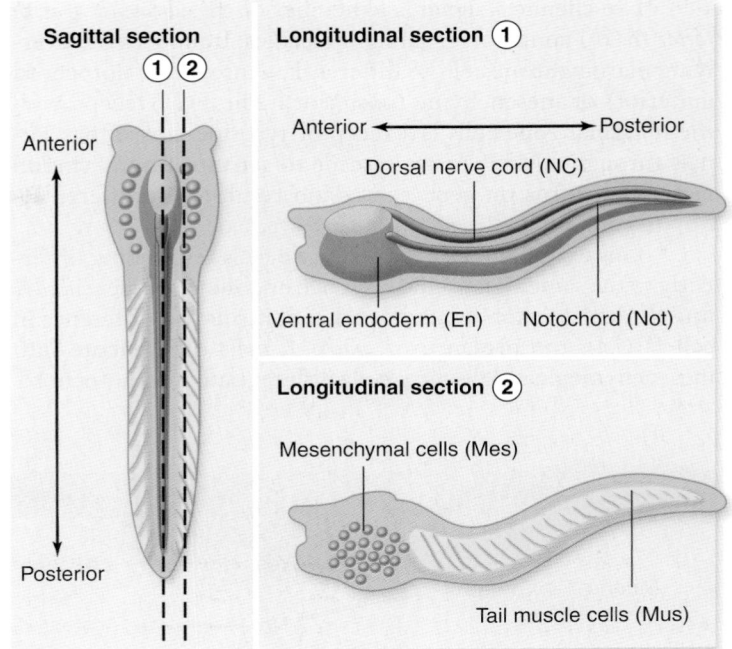

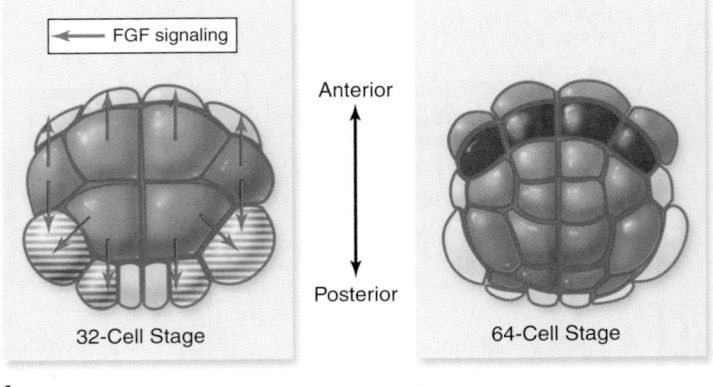

Figure 19.6 Inductive interactions contribute to cell fate specification in tunicate embryos. *a.* Internal structures of a tunicate larva. To the left is a sagittal section through the larva with dotted lines indicating two longitudinal sections. Section 1, through the midline of a tadpole, shows the dorsal nerve cord (NC), the underlying notochord (Not) and the ventral endoderm cells (En). Section 2, a more lateral section, shows the mesenchymal cells (Mes) and the tail muscle cells (Mus). *b.* View of the 32-cell stage looking up at the endoderm precursor cells. FGF secreted by these cells is indicated with light-green arrows. Only the surfaces of the marginal cells that directly border the endoderm precursor cells bind FGF signal molecules. Note that the posterior vegetal blastomeres also contain the *macho-1* determinants (red and white stripes). *c.* Cell fates have been fixed by the 64-cell stage. Colors are as in *(a)*. Cells on the anterior margin of the endoderm precursor cells become notochord and nerve cord, respectively, whereas cells that border the posterior margin of the endoderm cells become mesenchyme and muscle cells, respectively.

The chemical signal is a member of the *fibroblast growth factor (FGF)* family of signaling molecules. It induces the overlying marginal zone cells to differentiate into either notochord (anterior) or mesenchyme (posterior). The FGF receptor on the marginal zone cells is a receptor tyrosine kinase that signals through a MAP kinase cascade to activate a transcription factor that turns on gene expression resulting in differentiation (figure 19.7).

This example is also a case of two cells responding differently to the same signal. The presence or absence of the *macho-1* muscle determinant discussed earlier controls this difference in cell fate. In the presence of *macho-1*, cells differentiate into mesenchyme; in its absence, cells differentiate into notochord.

Thus, the combination of *macho-1* and FGF signaling leads to four different cell types (see figure 19.7)

Stem cells can divide and produce cells that differentiate

It is important, both during development, and even in the adult animal, to have cells set aside that can divide but are not determined for only a single cell fate. We call cells that are capable of continued division but that can also give rise to differentiated cells, **stem cells.** These cells can be characterized based on the degree to which they have become determined.

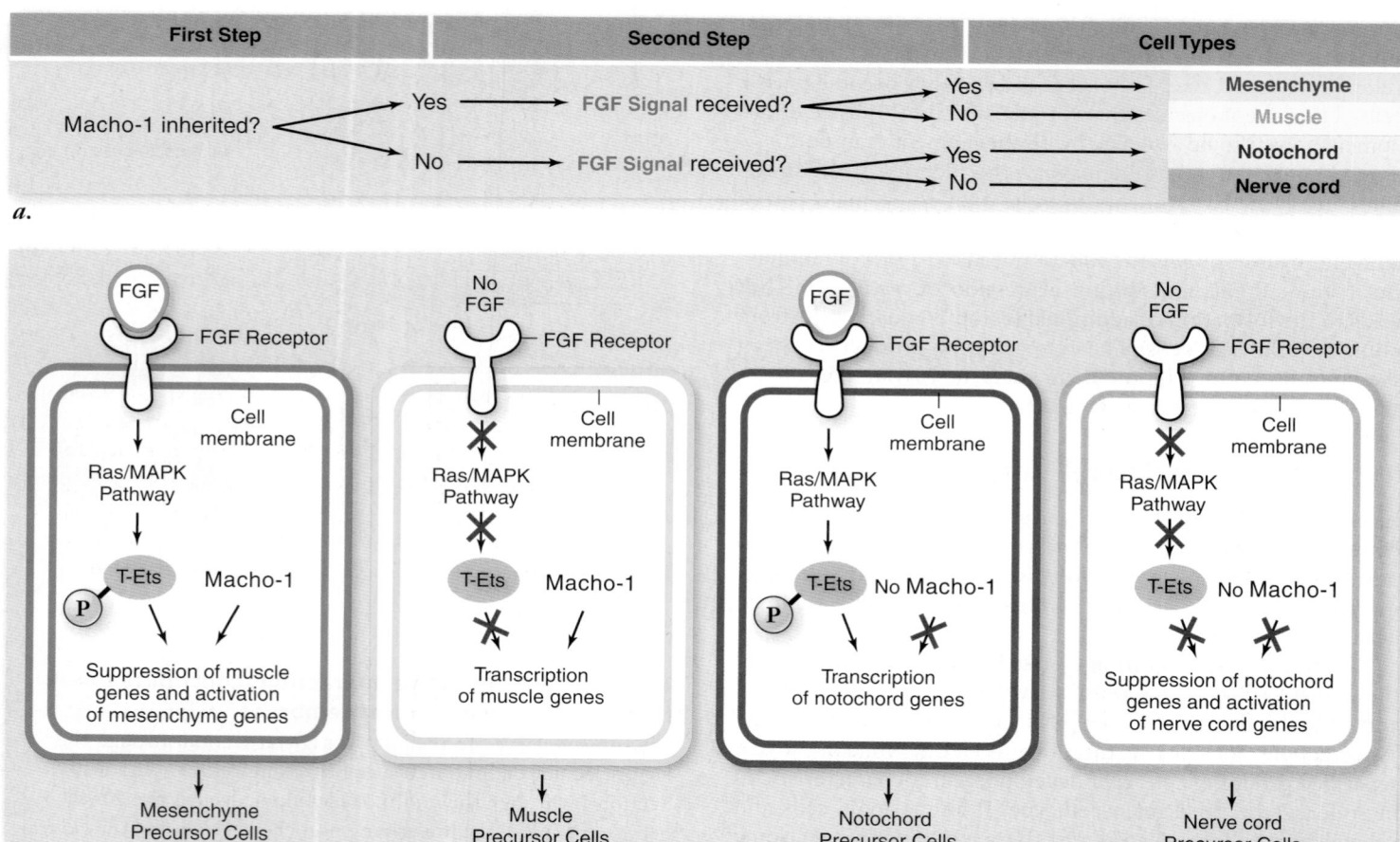

Figure 19.7 Model for cell fate specification by Macho-1 muscle determinant and FGF signaling. *a.* Two-step model of cell fate specification in vegetal marginal cells of the tunicate embryo. The first step is inheritance (or not) of muscle *macho-1* mRNA. The second step is FGF signaling from the underlying endoderm precursor cells. *b.* Posterior vegetal margin cells inherit *macho-1* mRNA. Signaling by FGF activates a Ras/MAP kinase pathway that produces the transcription factor T-Ets. Macho-1 protein and T-Ets suppress muscle-specific genes and turn on mesenchyme specific genes *(green cells)*. In cells with Macho-1 that do not receive the FGF signal, Macho-1 alone turns on muscle-specific cells *(yellow cells)*. Anterior vegetal margin cells do not inherit *macho-1* mRNA. If these cells receive the FGF signal, T-Ets turns on notochord-specific genes *(purple cells)*. In cells that lack Macho-1 and FGF, notochord-specific genes are suppressed and nerve cord-specific genes are activated *(gray cells)*.

Inquiry question

? What dictates whether Macho-1 acts as a transcriptional repressor or a transcriptional activator?

At one extreme, we call a cell that can give rise to any tissue in an organism **totipotent**. In mammals, the only cells that can give rise to both the embryo and the extraembryonic membranes are the zygote and early blastomeres from the first few cell divisions. Cells that can give rise to all of the cells in the organism's body are called **pluripotent**. A stem cell that can give rise to a limited number of cell types, such as the cells that give rise to the different blood cell types, are called **multipotent**. Then at the other extreme, **unipotent** stem cells give rise to only a single cell type, such as the cells that give rise to sperm cells in males.

Embryonic stem cells are pluripotent cells derived from embryos

A form of pluripotent stem cells that has been derived in the laboratory are called embryonic stem cells (ES cells). These cells are made from mammalian embryos that have undergone the cleavage stage of development to produce a ball of cells called a blastocyst. The blastocyst consists of an outer ball of cells, the trophectoderm, which will become the placenta, and the inner cell mass that will go on to form the embryo (see chapter 54 for details). Embryonic stem cells can be isolated from the inner cell mass and grown in culture (figure 19.8). In mice, these cells have been studied extensively and have been shown to be able to develop into any type of cell in the tissues of the adult. However, these cells cannot give rise to the extraembryonic tissues that arise during development, so they are pluripotent, but not totipotent.

Once these cells were found in mice, it was only a matter of time before human ES cells were derived as well. In 1998, the first human ES cells (hES cells) were isolated and grown in culture. While there are differences between human and mouse ES cells, there are also substantial similarities. These embryonic stem cells hold great promise for regenerative medicine based on their potential to produce any cell type as described below. These cells have also been the source of much controversy and ethical discussion due to their embryonic origin.

Differentiation in culture

In addition to their possible therapeutic uses, ES cells offer a way to study the differentiation process in culture. The manipulation of these cells by additions to the culture media will allow us to tease out the factors involved in differentiation at the level of the actual cell undergoing the process. Early attempts at assessing differentiation in culture was plagued by the culture conditions. The medium in early experiments contained fetal calf serum (common in tissue culture), which is ill-defined, and varies lot-to-lot. More recently, more defined culture conditions have been found that allow greater reproducibility in controlling differentiation in culture.

Using more defined media, ES cells have been used to recapitulate in culture the early events in mouse development. Thus mouse ES cells can be used to first give rise to ectoderm, endoderm, and mesoderm, then these three cell types will give rise to the different cells each germ layer is determined to become. This work is in early stages but is tremendously exciting as it offers the promise of understanding the molecular cues that are involved in the stepwise determination of different cell types.

In humans, ES cells have been used to give rise to a variety of cell types in culture. For example, human ES cells have been shown to give rise to different kinds of blood cells in culture. Work is underway to produce hematopoeitic stem cells in culture, which could be used to replace such cells in patients with diseases that affect blood cells. Human ES cells have also been used to produce cardiomyocytes in culture. These cells could be used to replace damaged heart tissue after heart attacks.

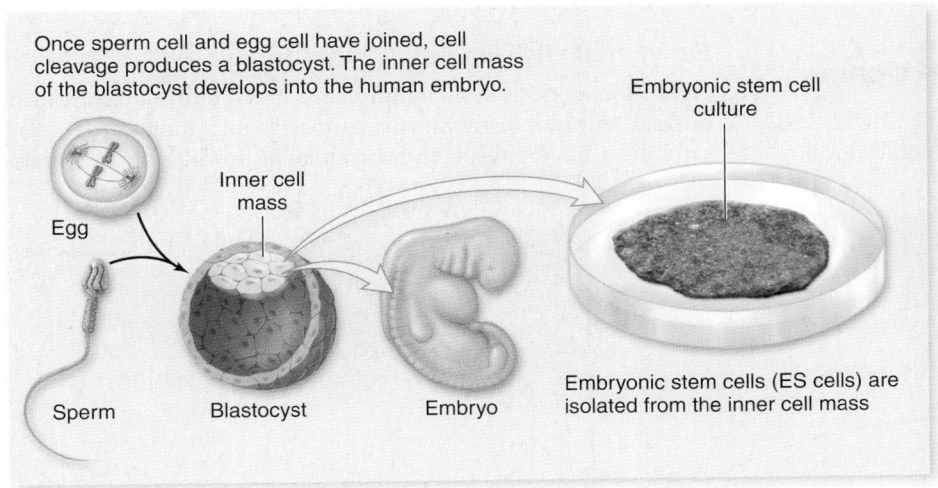
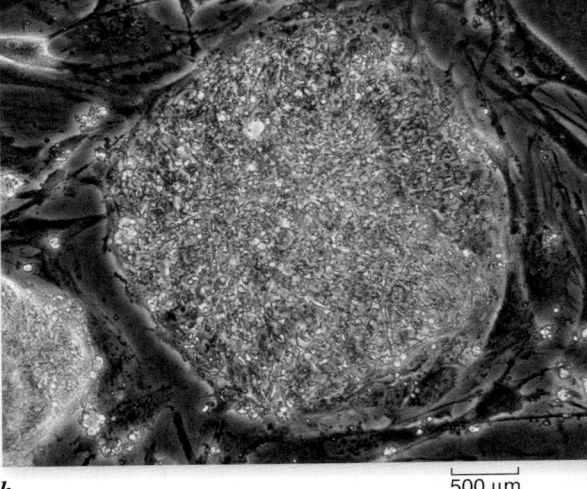

Once sperm cell and egg cell have joined, cell cleavage produces a blastocyst. The inner cell mass of the blastocyst develops into the human embryo.

Egg

Sperm

Inner cell mass

Blastocyst

Embryo

Embryonic stem cell culture

Embryonic stem cells (ES cells) are isolated from the inner cell mass

500 μm

a.

b.

Figure 19.8 Isolation of embryonic stem cells. *a.* Early cell divisions lead to the blastocyst stage that consists of an outer layer and an inner cell mass, which will go on to form the embryo. Embryonic stem cells (ES cells) can be isolated from this stage by disrupting the embryo and plating the cells. Stem cells removed from a six-day blastocyst can be established in culture and maintained indefinitely in an undifferentiated state. *b.* Human embryonic stem cells. This mass in the photograph is a colony of undifferentiated human embryonic stem cells being studied in the developmental biologist James Thomson's research lab at the University of Wisconsin–Madison.

19.4 Nuclear Reprogramming

Learning Outcomes

1. *Define nuclear reprogramming and describe ways in which it has been accomplished.*
2. *Differentiate between reproductive and therapeutic cloning.*

The study of the process of determination and differentiation leads quite naturally to questions about whether this process can be reversed. This is of interest both in terms of the experimental possibilities to understand the basic process, and the prospect of creating patient-specific populations of specific cell types to replace cells lost to disease or trauma. This has led to a fascinating path with many twists and turns that has accelerated in the recent past. We will briefly consider the history of this topic, then look at the most recent results available.

Reversal of determination has allowed cloning

Experiments carried out in the 1950s showed that single cells from fully differentiated tissue of an adult plant could develop into entire, mature plants. The cells of an early cleavage stage mammalian embryo are also totipotent. When mammalian embryos naturally split in two, identical twins result. If individual blastomeres are separated from one another, any one of them can produce a completely normal individual. In fact, this type of procedure has been used to produce sets of four or eight identical offspring in the commercial breeding of particularly valuable lines of cattle.

Early research in amphibians

An early question in developmental biology was whether the production of differentiated cells during development involved irreversible changes to cells. Experiments carried out in the 1950s by Briggs and King, and by John Gurdon in the 1960s and 1970s showed nuclei could be transplanted between cells. Using very fine pipettes (hollow glass tubes), these researchers sucked the nucleus out of a frog or toad egg and replaced the egg nucleus with a nucleus sucked out of a body cell taken from another individual.

The conclusions from these experiments are somewhat contradictory. On the one hand, cells do not appear to undergo any truly irreversible changes, such as loss of genes. On the other hand, the more differentiated the cell type, the less successful the nucleus in directing development when transplanted. This led to the concept of *nuclear reprogramming*, that is, a nucleus from a differentiated cell undergoes **epigenetic** changes that must be reversed to allow the nucleus to direct development. Epigenetic changes do not change a cell's DNA but are stable through cell divisions. The early work on amphibians showed that tadpoles' intestinal cell nuclei could be reprogrammed to produce viable adult frogs. These animals not only can be considered clones, but they show that tadpole nuclei can be completely reprogrammed. However, nuclei from adult differentiated cells could only be reprogrammed to produce tadpoles, but not viable, fertile adults. Thus this work showed that adult nuclei have remarkable developmental potential, but cannot be reprogrammed to be totipotent.

Early research in mammals

Given the work done in amphibians, much effort was put into nuclear transfer in mammals, primarily mice and cattle. Not only did this not result in reproducible production of cloned

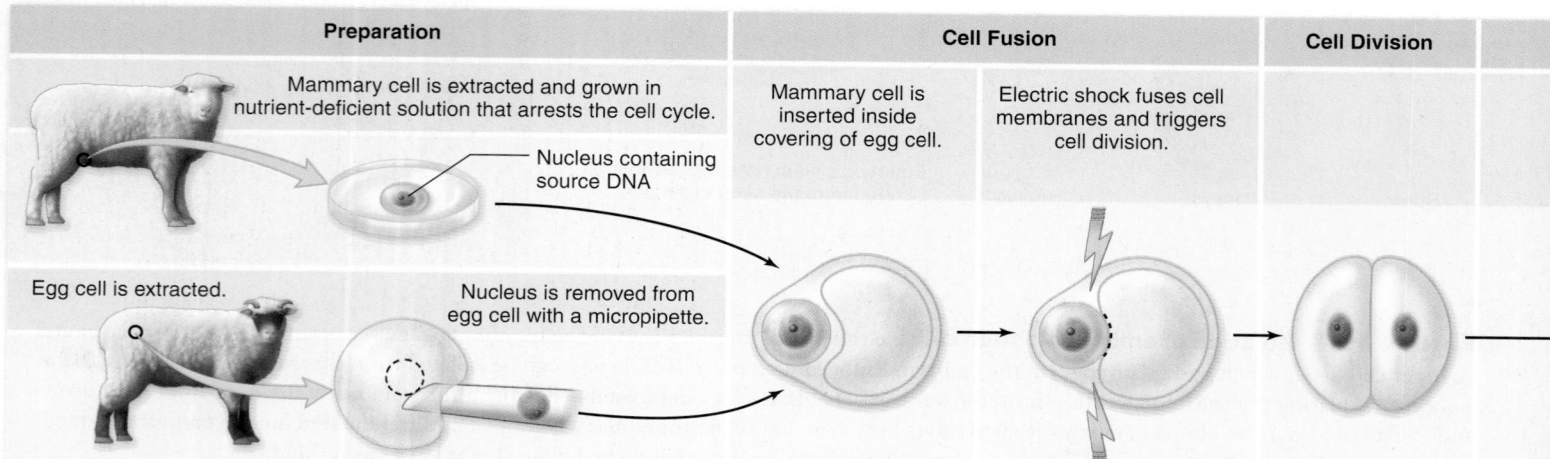

Preparation		Cell Fusion		Cell Division
Mammary cell is extracted and grown in nutrient-deficient solution that arrests the cell cycle.	Nucleus containing source DNA	Mammary cell is inserted inside covering of egg cell.	Electric shock fuses cell membranes and triggers cell division.	
Egg cell is extracted.	Nucleus is removed from egg cell with a micropipette.			

animals, but this work led to the discovery of imprinting through the production of embryos with only maternal or paternal input (see chapter 13 for more information on imprinting). These embryos never developed, and showed different kinds of defects depending on whether the maternal or paternal genome was the sole contributor.

Successful nuclear transplant in mammals

These results stood until a sheep was cloned using the nucleus from a cell of an early embryo in 1984. The key to this success was in picking a donor cell very early in development. This exciting result was soon replicated by others in a host of other organisms, including pigs and monkeys. Only early embryo cells seemed to work, however.

Geneticists at the Roslin Institute in Scotland reasoned that the egg and donated nucleus would need to be at the same stage of the cell cycle for successful development. To test this idea, they performed the following procedure (figure 19.9):

1. They removed differentiated mammary cells from the udder of a six-year-old sheep. The cells were grown in tissue culture, and then the concentration of serum nutrients was substantially reduced for five days, causing them to pause at the beginning of the cell cycle.
2. In parallel preparation, eggs obtained from a ewe were enucleated.
3. Mammary cells and egg cells were surgically combined in a process called **somatic cell nuclear transfer (SCNT)** in January of 1996. Mammary cells and eggs were fused to introduce the mammary nucleus into egg.
4. Twenty-nine of 277 fused couplets developed into embryos, which were then placed into the reproductive tracts of surrogate mothers.
5. A little over five months later, on July 5, 1996, one sheep gave birth to a lamb named Dolly, the first clone generated from a fully differentiated animal cell.

Dolly matured into an adult ewe, and she was able to reproduce the old-fashioned way, producing six lambs. Thus, Dolly established beyond all dispute that determination in animals is reversible—that with the right techniques, the nucleus of a fully differentiated cell *can* be reprogrammed to be totipotent.

Reproductive cloning has inherent problems

The term **reproductive cloning** refers to the process just described, in which scientists use SCNT to create an animal that is genetically identical to another animal. Since Dolly's birth in 1997, scientists have successfully cloned one or more cats, rabbits, rats, mice, cattle, goats, pigs, and mules. All of these procedures used some form of adult cell.

Low success rate and age-associated diseases

The efficiency in all reproductive cloning is quite low—only 3–5% of adult nuclei transferred to donor eggs result in live births. In addition, many clones that are born usually die soon thereafter of liver failure or infections. Many become oversized, a condition known as *large offspring syndrome (LOS)*. In 2003, three of four cloned piglets developed to adulthood, but all three suddenly died of heart failure at less than 6 months of age.

Dolly herself was euthanized at the relatively young age of six. Although she was put down because of virally induced lung cancer, she had been diagnosed with advanced-stage arthritis a year earlier. Thus, one difficulty in using genetic engineering and cloning to improve livestock is production of enough healthy animals.

Lack of imprinting

The reason for these problems lies in a phenomenon discussed in chapter 13: *genomic imprinting*. Imprinted genes are expressed differently depending on parental origin—that is, they are turned off in either egg or sperm, and this "setting" continues through development into the adult. Normal mammalian development depends on precise genomic imprinting.

The chemical reprogramming of the DNA, which occurs in adult reproductive tissue, takes months for sperm and years for eggs. During cloning, by contrast, the reprogramming of the donor DNA must occur within a few hours. The organization of the chromatin in a somatic cell is also quite different from that in a newly fertilized egg. Significant chromatin remodeling of the transferred donor nucleus must also occur if the cloned embryo is to survive. Cloning fails because there is likely not enough time in these few hours to get the remodeling and reprogramming jobs done properly.

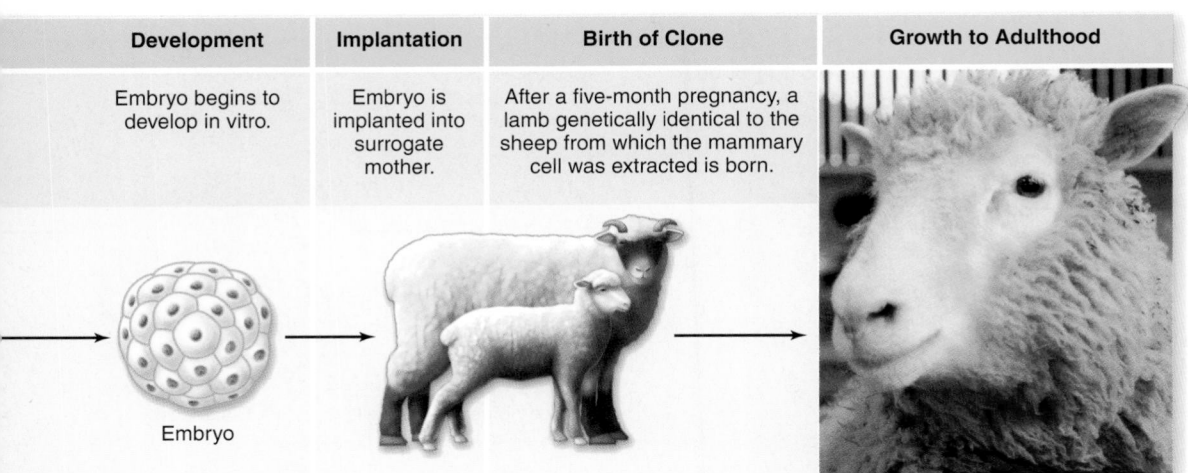

Development	Implantation	Birth of Clone	Growth to Adulthood
Embryo begins to develop in vitro.	Embryo is implanted into surrogate mother.	After a five-month pregnancy, a lamb genetically identical to the sheep from which the mammary cell was extracted is born.	

Embryo

Figure 19.9 Proof that determination in animals is reversible. Scientists combined a nucleus from an adult mammary cell with an enucleated egg cell to successfully clone a sheep, named Dolly, who grew to be a normal adult and bore healthy offspring. This experiment, the first successful cloning of an adult animal, shows that a differentiated adult cell can be used to drive all of development.

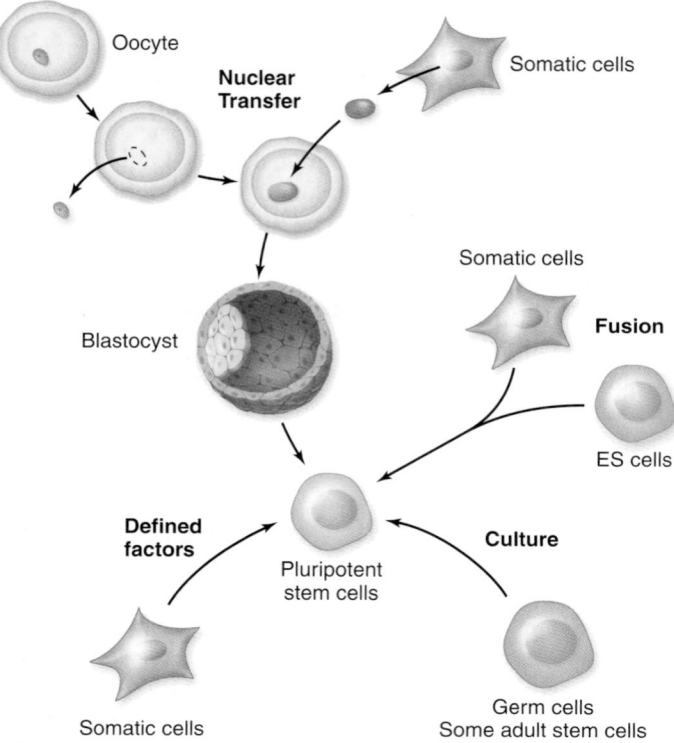

Figure 19.10 Methods to reprogram adult cell nuclei.
Cells taken from adult organisms can be reprogrammed to pluripotent cells in a number of different ways. Nuclei from somatic cells can be transplanted into oocytes as during cloning. Somatic cells can be fused to ES cells created by some other means. Germ cells, and some adult stem cells, after prolonged culture appear to be reprogrammed. Recent work has shown that somatic cells in culture can be reprogrammed by introduction of specific factors.

Nuclear reprogramming has been accomplished by use of defined factors

Stimulated by the discovery of ES cells and success in the reproductive cloning of mammals, much work has been put into trying to find ways to reprogram adult cells to become pluripotent cells without the use of embryos (figure 19.10). One approach was to fuse an ES cell to a differentiated cell.

These fusion experiments showed that the nucleus of the differentiated cell could be reprogrammed by exposure to ES cell cytoplasm. Of course, the resulting cells are tetraploid (4 copies of the genome), which limits their experimental and practical utility. Another line of research showed that primordial germ cells explanted into culture can give rise to cells that act similar to ES cells after extended time in culture. There are also reports that some adult stem cells become pluripotent cells with prolonged culture, but this is still controversial.

All of these different lines of inquiry showed that reprogramming of somatic nuclei was possible. The next obvious step was to reprogram nuclei using defined factors. While it was assumed that this was possible, it was not accomplished until 2006 when the genes for four different transcription factors, Oct4, Sox2, c-Myc, and Klf4 were introduced into fibroblast cells in culture. These cells were then selected for expression of a gene that is a target for Oct4 and Sox2, and these cells appear to be pluripotent. These were named induced pluripotent stem cells, or iPS cells. This protocol has been improved by selection for a different target gene, Nanog. These Nanog expressing iPS cells appear to be similar to ES cells in terms of developmental potential, as well as gene expression pattern.

This technology has now been used to construct ES cells from patients with the inherited neurological disorder spinal muscular atrophy. These ES cells will differentiate in culture into motor neurons that show the phenotype expected for the disease. The ability to derive disease specific stem cells will be an incredible advance for researchers studying such diseases. This will allow the creation of in vitro systems to study directly the cells affected by genetic diseases, and to screen for possible therapeutics.

Pluripotent cell types have potential for therapeutic applications. One way to solve the problem of graft rejection, such as in skin grafts in severe burn cases, is to produce patient-specific lines of embryonic stem cells. Early in 2001, a research team at Rockefeller University devised a way to accomplish this feat.

First, skin cells are isolated; then, using the same SCNT procedure that created Dolly, an embryo is assembled. After removing the nucleus from the skin cell, they insert it into an egg whose nucleus has already been removed. The egg with

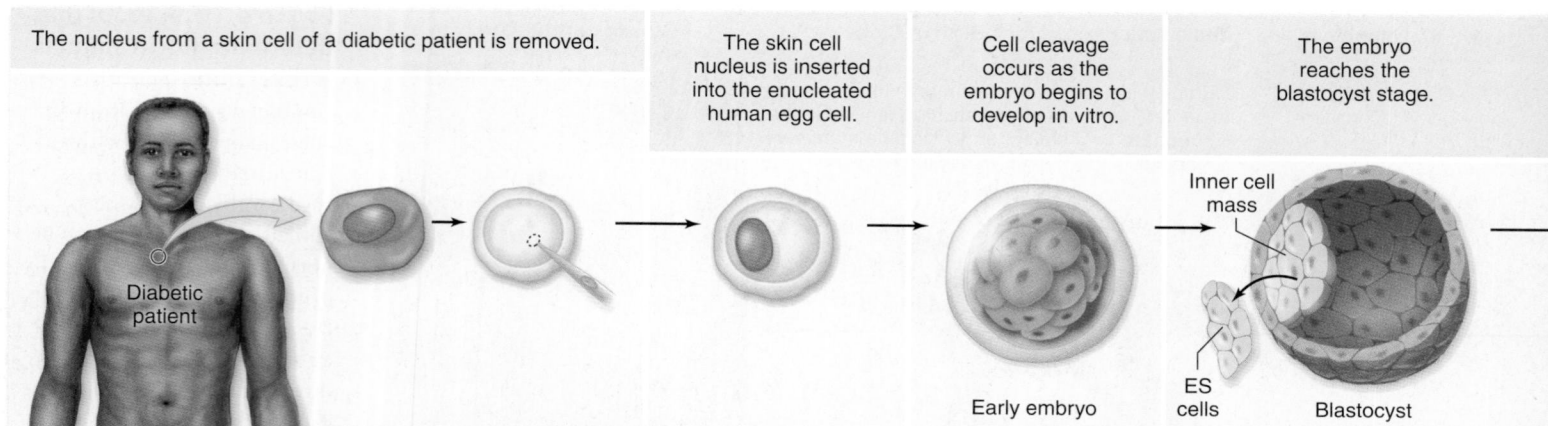

The nucleus from a skin cell of a diabetic patient is removed.

The skin cell nucleus is inserted into the enucleated human egg cell.

Cell cleavage occurs as the embryo begins to develop in vitro.

The embryo reaches the blastocyst stage.

Diabetic patient

Early embryo

Inner cell mass

ES cells

Blastocyst

its skin cell nucleus is allowed to form a blastocyst stage embryo. This artificial embryo is then destroyed, and its cells are used as embryonic stem cells for transfer to injured tissue (figure 19.11).

Using this procedure, termed **therapeutic cloning**, the researchers succeeded in converting cells from the tail of a mouse into the dopamine-producing cells of the brain that are lost in Parkinson disease. Therapeutic cloning successfully addresses the key problem that must be solved before stem cells can be used to repair human tissues damaged by heart attack, nerve injury, diabetes, or Parkinson disease—the problem of immune acceptance. Since stem cells are cloned from a person's own tissues in therapeutic cloning, they pass the immune system's "self" identity check, and the body readily accepts them.

These early attempts at therapeutic cloning may become obsolete before they are even refined with the work described above on iPS cells. The potential to produce pluripotent cells from adult skin cells removes the ethical problems of embryo destruction, and the practical problem of the requirement for oocytes for therapeutic cloning. However, these cell types are not without problems of their own. Two of the genes introduced to reprogram the nuclei of cells are oncogenes, and although these experiments have been reproduced without c-Myc, the efficiency is greatly reduced. These also require the introduction of new DNA, which can induce mutations by integration into the genome.

Learning Outcomes Review 19.4

Cloning has long been practiced in plants. In animals, cells from early-stage embryos are also totipotent, but attempts to use adult nuclei for cloning led to mixed results. The nucleus of a differentiated cell requires reprogramming to be totipotent. This appears to be necessary at least in part because of genomic imprinting. Nuclei may be reprogrammed by fusion with an embryonic stem cell, which produces a tetraploid cell, or through the introduction of four important transcription factors. That reprogramming is possible was shown by reproductive cloning via somatic cell nuclear transfer (SCNT). In therapeutic cloning, the goal is to produce replacement tissue using a patient's own cells.

■ *What changes must occur to produce a totipotent cell from a differentiated nucleus?*

Learning Outcomes

1. *Describe A/P axis formation in* Drosophila.
2. *Describe D/V axis formation in* Drosophila.
3. *Explain the importance of homeobox-containing genes in development.*

For cells in multicellular organisms to differentiate into appropriate cell types, they must gain information about their relative locations in the body. All multicellular organisms seem to use positional information to determine the basic pattern of body compartments and, thus, the overall architecture of the adult body. This positional information then leads to intrinsic changes in gene activity, so that cells ultimately adopt a fate appropriate for their location.

Pattern formation is an unfolding process. In the later stages, it may involve morphogenesis of organs (to be discussed later), but during the earliest events of development, the basic body plan is laid down, along with the establishment of the anterior–posterior (A/P, head-to-tail) axis and the dorsal–ventral (D/V, back-to-front) axis. Thus, pattern formation can be considered the process of taking a radially symmetrical cell and imposing two perpendicular axes to define the basic body plan, which in this way becomes bilaterally symmetrical. Developmental biologists use the term **polarity** to refer to the acquisition of axial differences in developing structures.

The fruit fly *Drosophila melanogaster* is the best understood animal in terms of the genetic control of early patterning. We will concentrate on the Drosophila system here, and later in chapter 54 we will examine axis formation in vertebrates in the context of their overall development.

A hierarchy of gene expression that begins with maternally expressed genes controls the development of *Drosophila*. To understand the details of these gene interactions, we first need to briefly review the stages of *Drosophila* development.

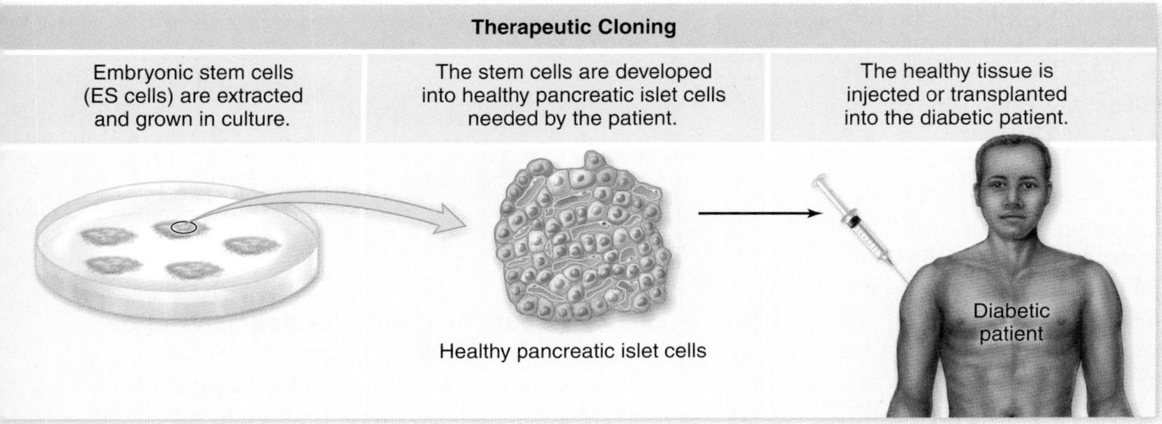

Therapeutic Cloning

| Embryonic stem cells (ES cells) are extracted and grown in culture. | The stem cells are developed into healthy pancreatic islet cells needed by the patient. | The healthy tissue is injected or transplanted into the diabetic patient. |

Healthy pancreatic islet cells

Diabetic patient

Figure 19.11 How human embryos might be used for therapeutic cloning. In therapeutic cloning, after initial stages to reproductive cloning, the embryo is broken apart and its embryonic stem cells are extracted. These are grown in culture and used to replace the diseased tissue of the individual who provided the DNA. This is useful only if the disease in question is not genetic as the stem cells are genetically identical to the patient.

Drosophila embryogenesis produces a segmented larva

Drosophila and many other insects produce two different kinds of bodies during their development: the first, a tubular eating machine called a **larva**, and the second, an adult flying sex machine with legs and wings. The passage from one body form to the other, called **metamorphosis**, involves a radical shift in development (figure 19.12). In this chapter, we concentrate on the process of going from a fertilized egg to a larva, which is termed *embryogenesis*.

Prefertilization maternal contribution

The development of an insect like *Drosophila* begins before fertilization, with the construction of the egg. Specialized *nurse cells* that help the egg grow move some of their own maternally encoded mRNAs into the maturing oocyte (figure 19.12a).

Following fertilization, the maternal mRNAs are transcribed into proteins, which initiate a cascade of sequential gene activations. Embryonic nuclei do not begin to function (that is, to direct new transcription of genes) until approximately 10 nuclear divisions have occurred. Therefore, the action of maternal, rather than zygotic, genes determines the initial course of *Drosophila* development.

Postfertilization events

After fertilization, 12 rounds of nuclear division without cytokinesis produce about 4000 nuclei, all within a single cytoplasm. All of the nuclei within this **syncytial blastoderm** (figure 19.12b) can freely communicate with one another, but nuclei located in different sectors of the egg encounter different maternal products.

Once the nuclei have spaced themselves evenly along the surface of the blastoderm, membranes grow between them to form the **cellular blastoderm.** Embryonic folding and primary tissue development soon follow, in a process fundamentally similar to that seen in vertebrate development. Within a day of fertilization, embryogenesis creates a segmented, tubular body—which is destined to hatch out of the protective coats of the egg as a larva.

Morphogen gradients form the basic body axes in *Drosophila*

Pattern formation in the early *Drosophila* embryo requires positional information encoded in labels that can be read by cells. The unraveling of this puzzle, work that earned the 1995 Nobel Prize for researchers Christiane Nüsslein-Volhard and Eric Wieschaus, is summarized in figure 19.13. We now know that two different genetic pathways control the establishment of A/P and D/V polarity in *Drosophila*.

Anterior–posterior axis

Formation of the A/P axis begins during maturation of the oocyte and is based on opposing gradients of two different proteins: **Bicoid** and **Nanos**. These protein gradients are established by an interesting mechanism.

Nurse cells in the ovary secrete maternally produced *bicoid* and *nanos* mRNAs into the maturing oocyte where they are differentially transported along microtubules to opposite poles of the oocyte (figure 19.14a). This differential transport comes

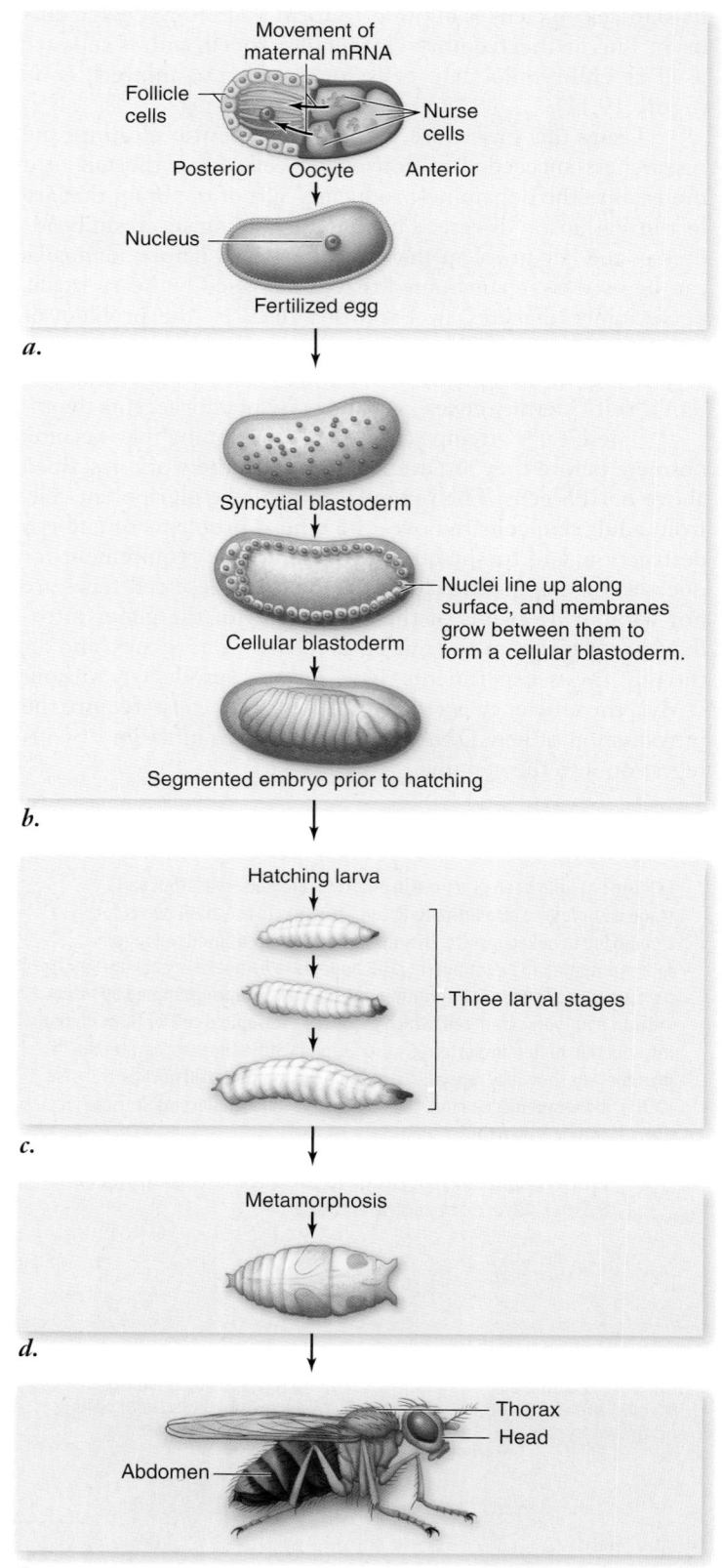

Figure 19.12 The path of fruit fly development. Major stages in the development of *Drosophila melanogaster* include formation of the *(a)* egg, *(b)* syncytial and cellular blastoderm, *(c)* larval instars, *(d)* pupa and metamorphosis into a *(e)* sexually mature adult.

Establishing the Polarity of the Embryo

Fertilization of the egg triggers the production of Bicoid protein from maternal RNA in the egg. The Bicoid protein diffuses through the egg, forming a gradient. This gradient determines the polarity of the embryo, with the head and thorax developing in the zone of high concentration (*green* fluorescent dye in antibodies that bind bicoid protein allows visualization of the gradient).

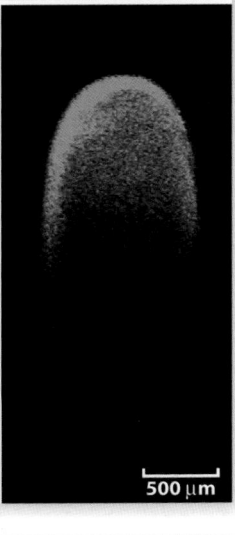

500 µm

Setting the Stage for Segmentation

About 2½ hours after fertilization, Bicoid protein turns on a series of brief signals from so-called gap genes. The gap proteins act to divide the embryo into large blocks. In this photo, fluorescent dyes in antibodies that bind to the gap proteins Krüppel (*orange*) and Hunchback (*green*) make the blocks visible; the region of overlap is yellow.

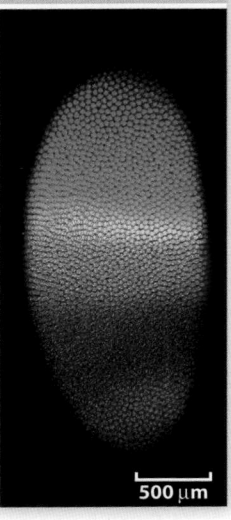

500 µm

Figure 19.13 Body organization in an early *Drosophila* embryo. In these fluorescent microscope images by 1995 Nobel laureate Christiane Nüsslein-Volhard and Sean Carroll, we watch a *Drosophila* egg pass through the early stages of development, in which the basic segmentation pattern of the embryo is established. The proteins in the photographs were made visible by binding fluorescent antibodies to each specific protein.

Laying Down the Fundamental Regions

About 0.5 hr later, the gap genes switch on the "pair-rule" genes, which are each expressed in seven stripes. This is shown for the pair-rule gene *hairy*. Some pair-rule genes are only required for even-numbered segments while others are only required for odd numbered segments.

500 µm

Forming the Segments

The final stage of segmentation occurs when a "segment-polarity" gene called *engrailed* divides each of the seven regions into halves, producing 14 narrow compartments. Each compartment corresponds to one segment of the future body. There are three head segments (H, *bottom right*), three thoracic segments (T, *upper right*), and eight abdominal segments (A, *from top right to bottom left*).

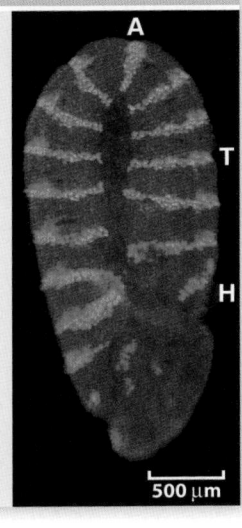

500 µm

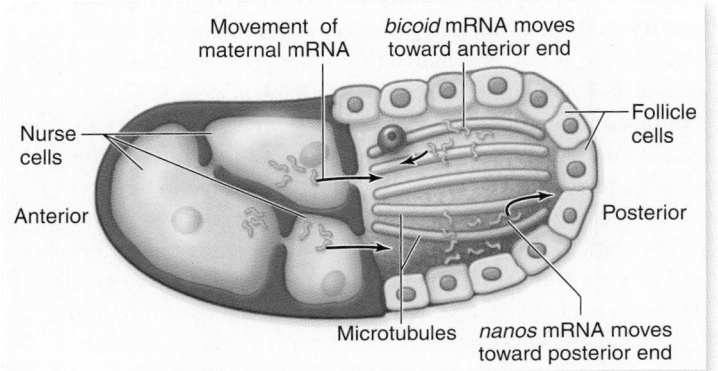

a.

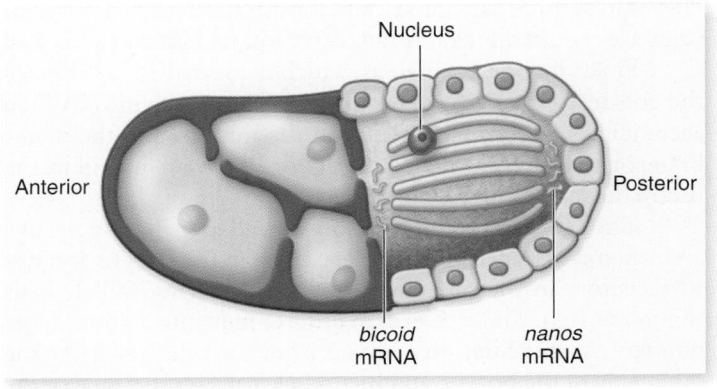

b.

Figure 19.14 Specifying the A/P axis in *Drosophila* embryos I. *a.* In the ovary, nurse cells secrete maternal mRNAs into the cytoplasm of the oocyte. Clusters of microtubules direct oocyte growth and maturation. Motor proteins travel along the microtubules transporting molecules in two directions. *Bicoid* mRNAs are transported toward the anterior pole of the oocyte, *nanos* mRNA is transported toward the posterior pole of the oocyte. *b.* A mature oocyte, showing localization of *bicoid* mRNAs to the anterior pole and *nanos* mRNAs to the posterior pole.

chapter **19** *Cellular Mechanisms of Development*

about due to the use of different motor proteins to move the two mRNAs. The *bicoid* mRNA then becomes anchored in the cytoplasm at the end of the oocyte closest to the nurse cells, and this end will develop into the anterior end of the embryo. *Nanos* mRNA becomes anchored to the opposite end of the oocyte, which will become the posterior end of the embryo. Thus, by the end of oogenesis, the *bicoid* and *nanos* mRNAs are already set to function as cytoplasmic determinants in the fertilized egg (figure 19.14*b*).

Following fertilization, translation of the anchored mRNA and diffusion of the proteins away from their respective sites of synthesis create opposing gradients of each protein: Highest levels of Bicoid protein are at the anterior pole of the embryo (figure 19.15*a*), and highest levels of the Nanos protein are at the posterior pole. Concentration gradients of soluble molecules can specify different cell fates along an axis, and proteins that act in this way, like Bicoid and Nanos, are called **morphogens.**

The Bicoid and Nanos proteins control the translation of two other maternal messages, *hunchback* and *caudal*, that encode transcription factors. **Hunchback** activates genes required for the formation of anterior structures, and **Caudal** activates genes required for the development of posterior (abdominal) structures. The *hunchback* and *caudal* mRNAs are evenly distributed across the egg (figure 19.15*b*), so how is it that proteins translated from these mRNAs become localized?

The answer is that Bicoid protein binds to and inhibits translation of *caudal* mRNA. Therefore, *caudal* is only translated in the posterior regions of the egg where Bicoid is absent. Similarly, Nanos protein binds to and prevents translation of the *hunchback* mRNA. As a result, *hunchback* is only translated in the anterior regions of the egg (figure 19.15*c*). Thus, shortly after fertilization, four protein gradients exist in the embryo: anterior–posterior gradients of Bicoid and Hunchback proteins, and posterior–anterior gradients of Nanos and Caudal proteins (figure 19.15*c*).

Dorsal–ventral axis

The dorsal–ventral axis in *Drosophila* is established by actions of the *dorsal* gene product. Once again the process begins in the ovary, when maternal transcripts of the *dorsal* gene are put into the oocyte. However, unlike *bicoid* or *nanos*, the *dorsal* mRNA does not become asymmetrically localized. Instead, a series of steps are required for Dorsal to carry out its function.

First, the oocyte nucleus, which is located to one side of the oocyte, synthesizes *gurken* mRNA. The *gurken* mRNA then accumulates in a crescent between the nucleus and the membrane on that side of the oocyte (figure 19.16*a*). This will be the future dorsal side of the embryo.

The Gurken protein is a soluble cell-signaling molecule, and when it is translated and released from the oocyte, it binds to receptors in the membranes of the overlying follicle cells (figure 19.16*b*). These cells then differentiate into a dorsal morphology. Meanwhile, no Gurken signal is released from the other side of the oocyte, and the follicle cells on that side of the oocyte adopt a ventral fate.

Following fertilization, a signaling molecule is differentially activated on the ventral surface of the embryo in a complex sequence of steps. This signaling molecule then binds to a membrane receptor in the ventral cells of the embryo and acti-

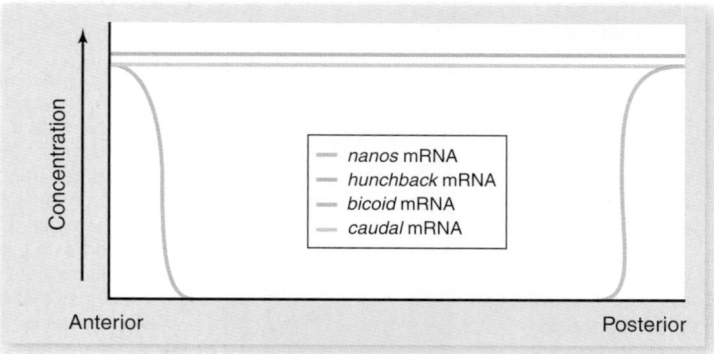

a. Oocyte mRNAs

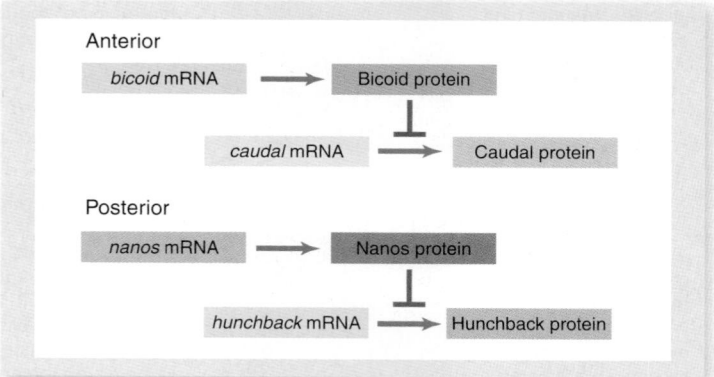

b. After fertilization

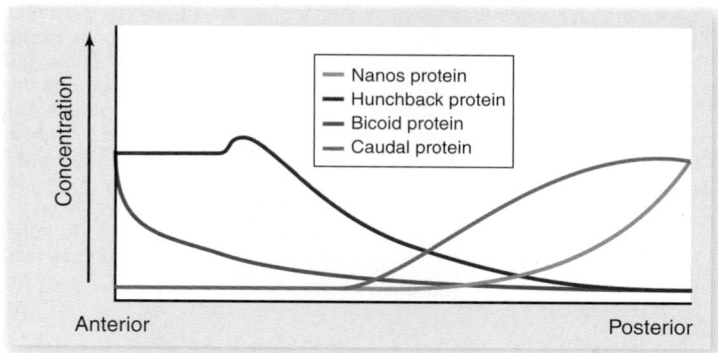

c. Early cleavage embryo proteins

Figure 19.15 Specifying the A/P axis in *Drosophila* embryos II. *a.* Unlike *bicoid* and *nanos*, *hunchback* and *caudal* mRNAs are evenly distributed throughout the cytoplasm of the oocyte. *b.* Following fertilization, *bicoid* and *nanos* mRNAs are translated into protein, making opposing gradients of each protein. Bicoid binds to and represses translation of *caudal* mRNAs (in anterior regions of the egg). Nanos binds to and represses translation of *hunchback* mRNAs (in posterior regions of the egg). *c.* Translation of *hunchback* mRNAs in anterior regions of the egg will create a Hunchback gradient that mirrors the Bicoid gradient. Translation of *caudal* mRNAs in posterior regions of the embryo will create a Caudal gradient that mirrors the Nanos gradient.

vates a signal transduction pathway in those cells. Activation of this pathway results in the selected transport of the Dorsal protein (which is everywhere) into ventral nuclei, forming a gradient along the D/V axis. The Dorsal protein levels are highest in the nuclei of ventral cells (figure 19.16*c*).

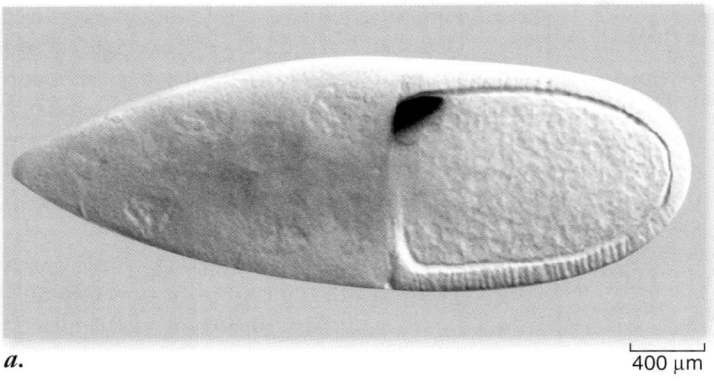

a.   400 μm

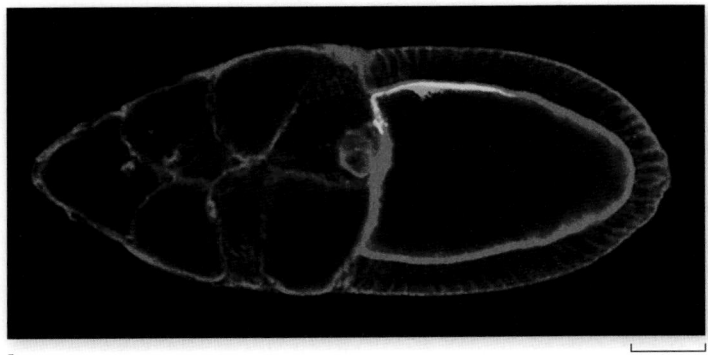

b.   400 μm

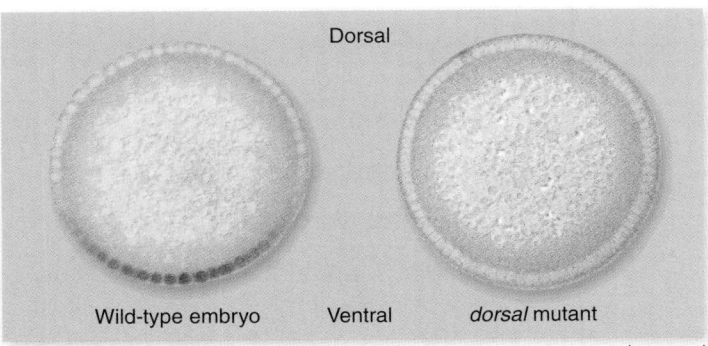

Dorsal

Wild-type embryo   Ventral   *dorsal* mutant

c.   100 μm

Figure 19.16 Specifying the D/V axis in *Drosophila* embryos. *a.* The *gurken* mRNA *(dark stain)* is concentrated between the oocyte nucleus (not visible) and the dorsal, anterior surface of the oocyte. *b.* In a more mature oocyte, Gurken protein *(yellow stain)* is secreted from the dorsal anterior surface of the oocyte, forming a gradient along the dorsal surface of the egg. Gurken then binds to membrane receptors in the overlying follicle cells. Double staining for actin *(red)* shows the cell boundaries of the oocyte, nurse cells, and follicle cells. *c.* For these images, cellular blastoderm stage embryos were cut in cross section to visualize the nuclei of cells around the perimeter of the embryos. Dorsal protein *(dark stain)* is localized in nuclei on the ventral surface of the blastoderm in a wild-type embryo *(left)*. The *dorsal* mutant on the right will not form ventral structures, and Dorsal is not present in ventral nuclei of this embryo.

The Dorsal protein is a transcription factor, and once it is transported into nuclei, it activates genes required for the proper development of ventral structures, simultaneously repressing genes that specify dorsal structures. Hence, the prod-

uct of the *dorsal* gene ultimately directs the development of ventral structures.

(Note that many *Drosophila* genes are named for the mutant phenotype that results from a loss of function in that gene. A lack of *dorsal* function produces dorsalized embryos with no ventral structures.)

Although profoundly different mechanisms are involved, the unifying factor controlling the establishment of both A/P and D/V polarity in *Drosophila* is that *bicoid*, *nanos*, *gurken*, and *dorsal* are all maternally expressed genes. The polarity of the future embryo in both instances is therefore laid down in the oocyte using information coming from the maternal genome.

The preceding discussion simplifies events, but the outline is clear: Polarity is established by the creation of morphogen gradients in the embryo based on maternal information in the egg. These gradients then drive the expression of the zygotic genes that will actually pattern the embryo. This reliance on a hierarchy of regulatory genes is a unifying theme for all of development.

The body plan is produced by sequential activation of genes

Let us now return to the process of pattern formation in *Drosophila* along the A/P axis. Determination of structures is accomplished by the sequential activation of three classes of **segmentation genes.** These genes create the hallmark segmented body plan of a fly, which consists of three fused head segments, three thoracic segments, and eight abdominal segments (see figure 19.12*e*).

To begin, Bicoid protein exerts its profound effect on the organization of the embryo by activating the translation and transcription of *hunchback* mRNA (which is the first mRNA to be transcribed after fertilization). *Hunchback* is a member of a group of nine genes called the **gap genes.** These genes map out the initial subdivision of the embryo along the A/P axis (see figure 19.13).

All of the gap genes encode transcription factors, which, in turn, activate the expression of eight or more **pair-rule genes.** Each of the pair-rule genes, such as *hairy*, produces seven distinct bands of protein, which appear as stripes when visualized with fluorescent reagents (see figure 19.13). These bands subdivide the broad gap regions and establish boundaries that divide the embryo into seven zones. When mutated, each of the pair-rule genes alters every other body segment.

All of the pair-rule genes also encode transcription factors, and they, in turn, regulate the expression of each other and of a group of nine or more **segment polarity genes.** The segment polarity genes are each expressed in 14 distinct bands of cells, which subdivide each of the seven zones specified by the pair-rule genes (see figure 19.13). The *engrailed* gene, for example, divides each of the seven zones established by *hairy* into anterior and posterior compartments. The segment polarity genes encode proteins that function in cell–cell signaling pathways. Thus, they function in inductive events—which occur *after* the syncytial blastoderm is divided into cells—to fix the anterior and posterior fates of cells within each segment.

In summary, within 3 hr after fertilization, a highly orchestrated cascade of segmentation gene activity transforms the broad gradients of the early embryo into a periodic, segmented

Figure 19.17 Mutations in homeotic genes. Three separate mutations in the bithorax complex caused this fruit fly to develop an additional second thoracic segment, with accompanying wings.

structure with A/P and D/V polarity. The activation of the segmentation genes depends on the free diffusion of maternally encoded morphogens, which is only possible within the syncytial blastoderm of the early *Drosophila* embryo.

Segment identity arises from the action of homeotic genes

With the basic body plan laid down, the next step is to give identity to the segments of the embryo. A highly interesting class of *Drosophila* mutants has provided the starting point for understanding the creation of segment identity.

In these mutants, a particular segment seems to have changed its identity—that is, it has characteristics of a different segment. In wild-type flies, a pair of legs emerges from each of the three tho-

racic segments, but only the second thoracic segment has wings. Mutations in the *Ultrabithorax* gene cause a fly to grow an extra pair of wings, as though it has two second thoracic segments (figure 19.17). Even more bizarre are mutations in *Antennapedia*, which cause legs to grow out of the head in place of antennae!

Thus, mutations in these genes lead to the appearance of perfectly normal body parts in inappropriate places. Such mutants are termed *homeotic mutants* because the transformed body part looks similar (homeotic) to another. The genes in which such mutants occur are therefore called **homeotic genes.**

Homeotic gene complexes

In the early 1950s, geneticist and Nobel laureate Edward Lewis discovered that several homeotic genes, including *Ultrabithorax*, map together on the third chromosome of *Drosophila* in a tight cluster called the **bithorax complex.** Mutations in these genes all affect body parts of the thoracic and abdominal segments, and Lewis concluded that the genes of the bithorax complex control the development of body parts in the rear half of the thorax and all of the abdomen.

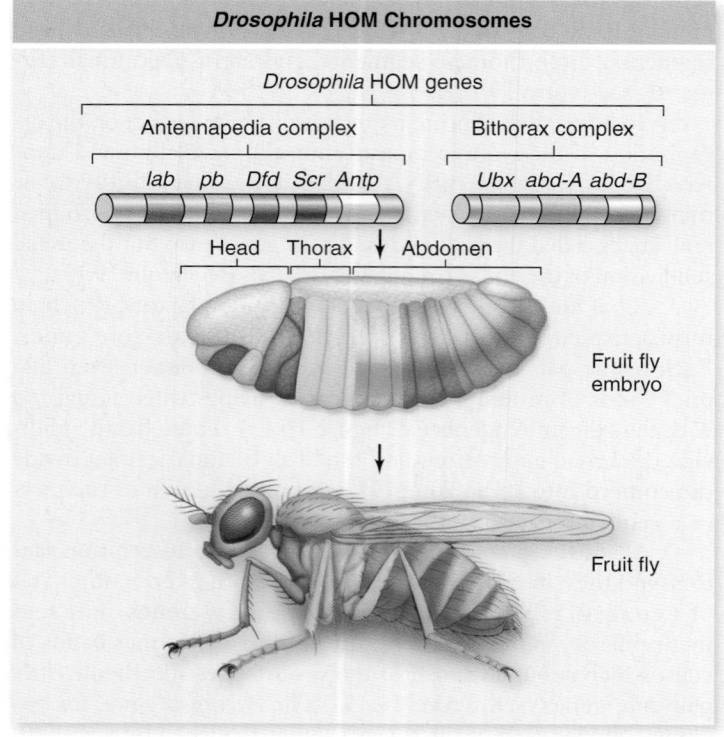

a.

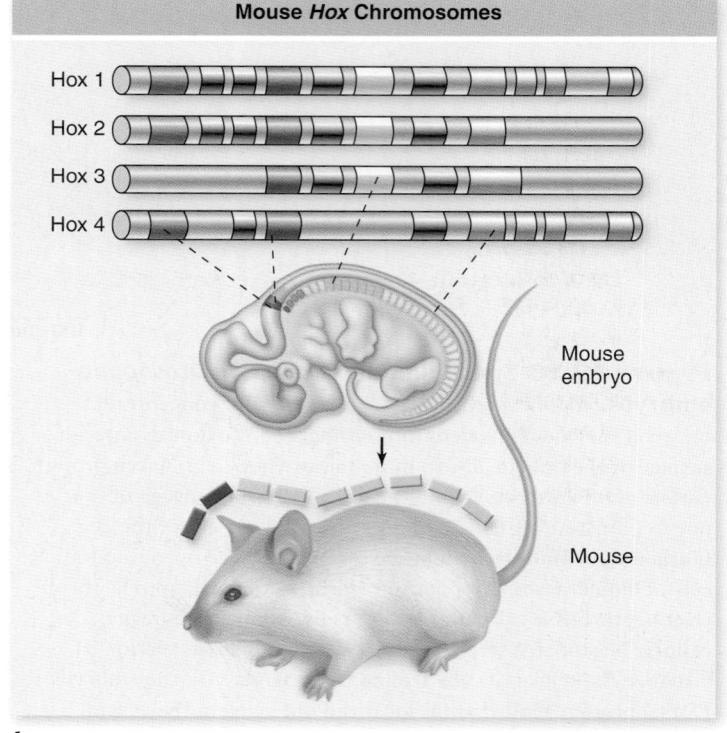

b.

Figure 19.18 A comparison of homeotic gene clusters in the fruit fly *Drosophila melanogaster* and the mouse *Mus musculus*. *a.* *Drosophila* homeotic genes. Called the homeotic gene complex, or HOM complex, the genes are grouped into two clusters: the Antennapedia complex (anterior) and the bithorax complex (posterior). *b.* The *Drosophila* HOM genes and the mouse *Hox* genes are related genes that control the regional differentiation of body parts in both animals. These genes are located on a single chromosome in the fly and on four separate chromosomes in mammals. In this illustration, the genes are color-coded to match the parts of the body along the A/P axis in which they are expressed. Note that the order of the genes along the chromosome(s) is mirrored by their pattern of expression in the embryo and in structures in the adult fly.

Interestingly, the order of the genes in the bithorax complex mirrors the order of the body parts they control, as though the genes are activated serially. Genes at the beginning of the cluster switch on development of the thorax; those in the middle control the anterior part of the abdomen; and those at the end affect the posterior tip of the abdomen.

A second cluster of homeotic genes, the **Antennapedia complex,** was discovered in 1980 by Thomas Kaufmann. The Antennapedia complex governs the anterior end of the fly, and the order of genes in this complex also corresponds to the order of segments they control (figure 19.18*a*).

The homeobox

An interesting relationship was discovered after the genes of the bithorax and Antennapedia complexes were cloned and sequenced. These genes all contain a conserved sequence of 180 nucleotides that codes for a 60-amino-acid, DNA-binding domain. Because this domain was found in all of the homeotic genes, it was named the *homeodomain*, and the DNA that encodes it is called the homeobox. Thus, the term ***Hox*** **gene** now refers to a homeobox-containing gene that specifies the identity of a body part. These genes function as transcription factors that bind DNA using their homeobox domain.

Clearly, the homeobox distinguishes portions of the genome that are devoted to pattern formation. How the *Hox* genes do this is the subject of much current research. Scientists believe that the ultimate targets of *Hox* gene function must be genes that control cell behaviors associated with organ morphogenesis.

Evolution of homeobox-containing genes

A large amount of research has been devoted to analyzing the clustered complexes of *Hox* genes in other organisms. These investigations have led to a fairly coherent view of homeotic gene evolution.

It is now clear that the *Drosophila* bithorax and Antennapedia complexes represent two parts of a single cluster of genes. In vertebrates, there are four copies of *Hox* gene clusters. As in *Drosophila*, the spatial domains of *Hox* gene expression correlate with the order of the genes on the chromosome (figure 19.18*b*). The existence of four *Hox* clusters in vertebrates is viewed by many as evidence that two duplication events of the entire genome have occurred in the vertebrate lineage.

This idea raises the issue of when the original cluster arose. To answer this question, researchers have turned to more primitive organisms, such as *Amphioxus* (now called *Branchiostoma*), a lancelet chordate (see chapter 35). The finding of only one cluster of *Hox* genes in *Amphioxus* implies that indeed there have been two duplications in the vertebrate lineage, at least of the *Hox* cluster. Given the single cluster in arthropods, this finding implies that the common ancestor to all animals with bilateral symmetry had a single *Hox* cluster as well.

The next logical step is to look at even more-primitive animals: the radially symmetrical cnidarians such as *Hydra* (see chapter 33). Thus far, *Hox* genes have been found in a number of cnidarian species, and recent sequence analyses suggest that cnidarian *Hox* genes are also arranged into clusters. Thus, the appearance of the ancestral *Hox* cluster likely preceded the divergence between radial and bilateral symmetries in animal evolution.

Pattern formation in plants is also under genetic control

The evolutionary split between plant and animal cell lineages occurred about 1.6 BYA, before the appearance of multicellular organisms with defined body plans. The implication is that multicellularity evolved independently in plants and animals. Because of the activity of meristems, additional modules can be added to plant bodies throughout their lifetimes. In addition, plant flowers and roots have a radial organization, in contrast to the bilateral symmetry of most animals. We may therefore expect that the genetic control of pattern formation in plants is fundamentally different from that of animals.

Although plants have homeobox-containing genes, they do not possess complexes of *Hox* genes similar to the ones that determine regional identity of developing structures in animals. Instead, the predominant homeotic gene family in plants appears to be the **MADS-box** genes.

MADS-box genes are a family of transcriptional regulators found in most eukaryotic organisms, including plants, animals, and fungi. The MADS-box is a conserved DNA-binding and dimerization domain, named after the first five genes to be discovered with this domain. Only a small number of *MADS*-box genes are found in animals, where their functions include the control of cell proliferation and tissue-specific gene expression in postmitotic muscle cells. They do not appear to play a role in the patterning of animal embryos.

In contrast, the number and functional diversity of *MADS*-box genes increased considerably during the evolution of land plants, and there are more than 100 *MADS*-box genes in the *Arabidopsis* genome. In flowering plants, the *MADS*-box genes dominate the control of development, regulating such processes as the transition from vegetative to reproductive growth, root development, and floral organ identity.

Although distinct from genes in the *Hox* clusters of animals, homeodomain-containing transcription factors in plants do have important developmental functions. One such example is the family of *knottedlike homeobox (knox)* genes, which are important regulators of shoot apical meristem development in both seed-bearing and nonseed-bearing plants. Mutations that affect expression of *knox* genes produce changes in leaf and petal shape, suggesting that these genes play an important role in generating leaf form.

Learning Outcomes Review 19.5

Pattern formation in animals involves the coordinated expression of a hierarchy of genes. Gradients of morphogens in *Drosophila* specify A/P and D/V axes, then lead to sequential activation of segmentation genes. Bicoid and Nanos protein gradients determine the A/P axis. The protein Dorsal determines the D/V axis, but activation requires a series of steps beginning with the oocyte's Gurken protein. The action of homeotic genes provide segment identity. These genes, which include a DNA-binding homeodomain sequence, are called *Hox* genes (for *homeobox* genes), and they are organized into clusters. Plants use a different set of developmental control genes called *MADS*-box genes.

■ *Why would you expect homeotic genes to be conserved across species evolution?*

19.6 *Morphogenesis*

Learning Outcomes

1. *Discuss the importance of cell shape changes and cell migration in development.*
2. *Explain how cell death can contribute to morphogenesis.*
3. *Describe the role of the extracellular matrix in cell migration.*

At the end of cleavage, the *Drosophila* embryo still has a relatively simple structure: It comprises several thousand identical-looking cells, which are present in a single layer surrounding a central yolky region. The next step in embryonic development is **morphogenesis**—the generation of ordered form and structure.

Morphogenesis is the product of changes in cell structure and cell behavior. Animals regulate the following processes to achieve morphogenesis:

- The number, timing, and orientation of cell divisions;
- Cell growth and expansion;
- Changes in cell shape;
- Cell migration; and
- Cell death.

Plant and animal cells are fundamentally different in that animal cells have flexible surfaces and can move, but plant cells are immotile and encased within stiff cellulose walls. Each cell in a plant is fixed into position when it is created. Thus, animal cells use cell migration extensively during development while plants use the other four mechanisms but lack cell migration. We consider the morphogenetic changes in animals first, and then those that occur in plants.

Cell division during development may result in unequal cytokinesis

The orientation of the mitotic spindle determines the plane of cell division in eukaryotic cells. The coordinated function of microtubules and their motor proteins determines the respective position of the mitotic spindle within a cell (see chapter 10). If the spindle is centrally located in the dividing cell, two equal-sized daughter cells will result. If the spindle is off to one side, one large daughter cell and one small daughter cell will result.

The great diversity of cleavage patterns in animal embryos is determined by differences in spindle placement. In many cases, the fate of a cell is determined by its relative placement in the embryo during cleavage. For example, in preimplantation mammalian embryos, cells on the outside of the embryo usually differentiate into trophectoderm cells, which form only extra-embryonic structures later in development (for example, a part of the placenta). In contrast, the embryo proper is derived from the inner cell mass, cells which, as the name implies, are in the interior of the embryo.

Cells change shape and size as morphogenesis proceeds

In animals, cell differentiation is often accompanied by profound changes in cell size and shape. For example, the large nerve cells that connect your spinal cord to the muscles in your big toe develop long processes called *axons* that span this entire distance. The cytoplasm of an axon contains microtubules, which are used for motor-driven transport of materials along the length of the axon.

As another example, muscle cells begin as *myoblasts*, undifferentiated muscle precursor cells. They eventually undergo conversion into the large, multinucleated *muscle fibers* that make up mammalian skeletal muscles. These changes begin with the expression of the *MyoD1* gene, which encodes a transcription factor that binds to the promoters of muscle-determining genes to initiate these changes.

Programmed cell death is a necessary part of development

Not every cell produced during development is destined to survive. For example, human embryos have webbed fingers and toes at an early stage of development. The cells that make up the webbing die in the normal course of morphogenesis. As another example, vertebrate embryos produce a very large number of neurons, ensuring that enough neurons are available to make the necessary synaptic connections, but over half of these neurons never make connections and die in an orderly way as the nervous system develops.

Unlike accidental cell deaths due to injury, these cell deaths are planned—and indeed required—for proper development and morphogenesis. Cells that die due to injury typically swell and burst, releasing their contents into the extracellular fluid. This form of cell death is called necrosis. In contrast, cells programmed to die shrivel and shrink in a process called apoptosis, which means "falling away," and their remains are taken up by surrounding cells.

Genetic control of apoptosis

Apoptosis occurs when a "death program" is activated. All animal cells appear to possess such programs. In *C. elegans*, the same 131 cells always die during development in a predictable and reproducible pattern.

Work on *C. elegans* showed that three genes are central to this process. Two (*ced-3* and *ced-4*) activate the death program itself; if either is mutant, those 131 cells do not die, and go on instead to form nervous tissue and other tissue. The third gene (*ced-9*) represses the death program encoded by the other two: All 1090 cells of the *C. elegans* embryo die in *ced-9* mutants. In *ced-9/ced-3* double mutants, all 1090 cells live, which suggests that *ced-9* inhibits cell death by functioning prior to *ced-3* in the apoptotic pathway (figure 19.19*a*).

The mechanism of apoptosis appears to have been highly conserved during the course of animal evolution. In human nerve cells, the *Apaf1* gene is similar to *ced-4* of *C. elegans* and activates the cell death program, and the human *bcl-2* gene acts

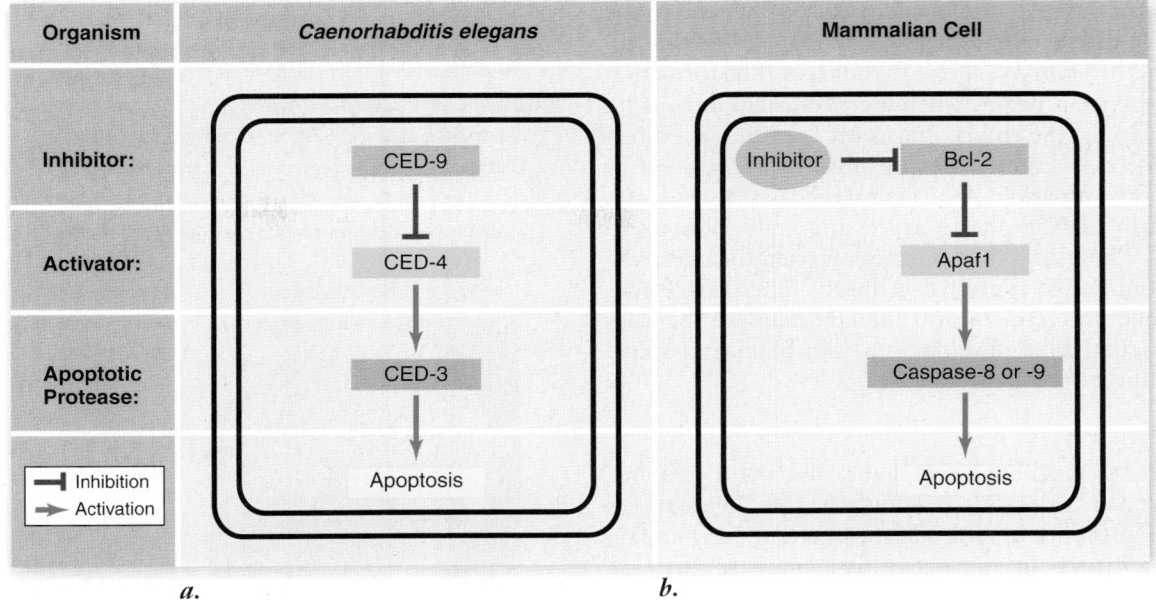

Organism	*Caenorhabditis elegans*	Mammalian Cell
Inhibitor:	CED-9	Inhibitor ⊣ Bcl-2
Activator:	CED-4	Apaf1
Apoptotic Protease:	CED-3	Caspase-8 or -9
	Apoptosis	Apoptosis

⊣ Inhibition
→ Activation

a.   *b.*

Figure 19.19 Programmed cell death pathway. Apoptosis, or programmed cell death, is necessary for the normal development of all animals. *a.* In the developing nematode, for example, two genes, *ced-3* and *ced-4*, code for proteins that cause the programmed cell death of 131 specific cells. In the other (surviving) cells of the developing nematode, the product of a third gene, *ced-9*, represses the death program encoded by *ced-3* and *ced-4*. *b.* The mammalian homologues of the apoptotic genes in *C. elegans* are *bcl-2* (*ced-9* homologue), *Apaf1* (*ced-4* homologue), and *caspase-8* or *-9* (*ced-3* homologues). In the absence of any cell survival factor, Bcl-2 is inhibited and apoptosis occurs. In the presence of nerve growth factor (NGF) and NGF receptor binding, Bcl-2 is activated, thereby inhibiting apoptosis.

similarly to *ced-9* to repress apoptosis. If a copy of the human *bcl-2* gene is transferred into a nematode with a defective *ced-9* gene, *bcl-2* suppresses the cell death program of *ced-3* and *ced-4*.

The mechanism of apoptosis

The product of the *C. elegans ced-4* gene is a protease that activates the product of the *ced-3* gene, which is also a protease. The human *Apaf1* gene is actually named for its role: *A*poptotic *p*rotease *a*ctivating *f*actor. It activates two proteases called caspases that have a role similar to the Ced-3 protease in *C. elegans* (figure 19.19*b*). When the final proteases are activated, they chew up proteins in important cellular structures such as the cytoskeleton and the nuclear lamina, leading to cell fragmentation.

The role of Ced-9/Bcl-2 is to inhibit this program. Specifically, it inhibits the activating protease, preventing the activation of the destructive proteases. The entire process is thus controlled by an inhibitor of the death program.

Both internal and external signals control the state of the Ced-9/Bcl-2 inhibitor. For example, in the human nervous system, neurons have a cytoplasmic inhibitor of Bcl-2 that allows the death program to proceed (see figure 19.19*b*). In the presence of nerve growth factor, a signal transduction pathway leads to the cytoplasmic inhibitor being inactivated, allowing Bcl-2 to inhibit apoptosis and the nerve cell to survive.

Cell migration gets the right cells to the right places

The migration of cells is important during many stages of animal development. The movement of cells involves both adhe-

sion and the loss of adhesion. Adhesion is necessary for cells to get "traction," but cells that are initially attached to others must lose this adhesion to be able to leave a site.

Cell movement also involves cell-to-substrate interactions, and the extracellular matrix may control the extent or route of cell migration. The central paradigm of morphogenetic cell movements in animals is a change in cell adhesiveness, which is mediated by changes in the composition of macromolecules in the plasma membranes of cells or in the extracellular matrix. Cell-to-cell interactions are often mediated through cadherins, but cell-to-substrate interactions often involve integrin-to-extracellular-matrix (ECM) interactions.

Cadherins

Cadherins are a large gene family, with over 80 members identified in humans. In the genomes of *Drosophila*, *C. elegans*, and humans, the cadherins can be sorted into several subfamilies that exist in all three genomes.

The cadherin proteins are all transmembrane proteins that share a common motif, the *cadherin domain*, a 110-amino-acid domain in the extracellular portion of the protein that mediates Ca^{2+}-dependent binding between like cadherins (homophilic binding).

Experiments in which cells are allowed to sort in vitro illustrate the function of cadherins. Cells with the same cadherins adhere specifically to one another, while not adhering to other cells with different cadherins. If cell populations with different cadherins are dispersed and then allowed to reaggregate, they sort into two populations of cells based on the nature of the cadherins on their surface.

An example of the action of cadherins can be seen in the development of the vertebrate nervous system. All surface ectoderm cells of the embryo express E-cadherin. The formation of the nervous system begins when a central strip of cells on the dorsal surface of the embryo turns off E-cadherin expression and turns on N-cadherin expression. In the process of **neurulation,** the formation of the neural tube (see chapter 54), the central strip of N-cadherin-expressing cells folds up to form the tube. The neural tube pinches off from the overlying cells, which continue to express E-cadherin. The surface cells outside the tube differentiate into the epidermis of the skin, whereas the neural tube develops into the brain and spinal cord of the embryo.

Integrins

In some tissues, such as connective tissue, much of the volume of the tissue is taken up by the spaces *between* cells. These spaces are filled with a network of molecules secreted by surrounding cells, termed a *matrix.* In connective tissue such as cartilage, long polysaccharide chains are covalently linked to proteins (proteoglycans), within which are embedded strands of fibrous protein (collagen, elastin, and fibronectin). Migrating cells traverse this matrix by binding to it with cell surface proteins called integrins.

Integrins are attached to actin filaments of the cytoskeleton and protrude out from the cell surface in pairs, like two hands. The "hands" grasp a specific component of the matrix, such as collagen or fibronectin, thus linking the cytoskeleton to the fibers of the matrix. In addition to providing an anchor, this binding can initiate changes within the cell, alter the growth of the cytoskeleton, and activate gene expression and the production of new proteins.

The process of **gastrulation** (described in detail in chapter 54), during which the hollow ball of animal embryonic cells folds in on itself to form a multilayered structure, depends on fibronectin–integrin interactions. For example, injection of antibodies against either fibronectin or integrins into salamander embryos blocks binding of cells to fibronectin in the ECM and inhibits gastrulation. The result is like a huge traffic jam following a major accident on a freeway: Cells (cars) keep coming, but they get backed up since they cannot get beyond the area of inhibition (accident site) (figure 19.20). Similarly, a targeted knockout of the fibronectin gene in mice resulted in gross defects in the migration, proliferation, and differentiation of embryonic mesoderm cells.

Thus, cell migration is largely a matter of changing patterns of cell adhesion. As a migrating cell travels, it continually extends projections that probe the nature of its environment. Tugged this way and that by different tentative attachments, the cell literally feels its way toward its ultimate target site.

In seed plants, the plane of cell division determines morphogenesis

The form of a plant body is largely determined by the plane in which cells divide. The first division of the fertilized egg in a flowering plant is off-center, so that one of the daughter

Hypothesis: *Fibronectin is required for cell migration during gastrulation.*

Prediction: *Blocking fibronectin with antifibronectin antibodies before gastrulation should prevent cell movement.*

Test: *Staged salamander embryos were injected either with antifibronectin antibody, or with preimmune serum as a control, prior to gastrulation. Cell movements were then monitored photographically.*

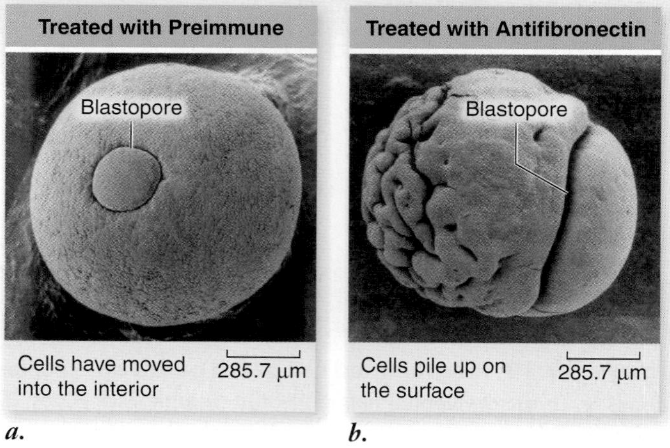

Treated with Preimmune

Blastopore

Cells have moved into the interior   285.7 μm

a.

Treated with Antifibronectin

Blastopore

Cells pile up on the surface   285.7 μm

b.

Result: *The experimental embryos injected with antifibronectin antibody show extremely aberrant gastrulation where cells pile up and do not enter the interior of the embryo. Control embryos gastrulate normally.*

Conclusion: *Fibronectin is required for cells to migrate into the interior of the embryo during gastrulation.*

Further Experiments: *How can this same system be used to analyze the role of fibronectin in other early morphogenetic events?*

Figure 19.20 Fibronectin is necessary for cell migration during gastrulation.

cells is small, with dense cytoplasm (figure 19.21*a*). That cell, the future embryo, begins to divide repeatedly, forming a ball of cells. The other daughter cell also divides repeatedly, forming an elongated structure called a *suspensor,* which links the embryo to the nutrient tissue of the seed. The suspensor also provides a route for nutrients to reach the developing embryo.

Just as many animal embryos acquire their initial axis as a cell mass formed during cleavage divisions, so the plant embryo forms its root–shoot axis at this time. Cells near the suspensor are destined to form a root, whereas those at the other end of the axis ultimately become a shoot, the aboveground portion of the plant.

The relative position of cells within the plant embryo is also a primary determinant of cell differentiation. The outermost cells in a plant embryo become epidermal cells. The bulk of the embryonic interior consists of ground tissue cells that eventually function in food and water storage. Finally, cells at the core of the embryo are destined to form the future vascular tissue (figure 19.21*b*). (Plant tissues and development are described in detail in chapters 36 and 37.)

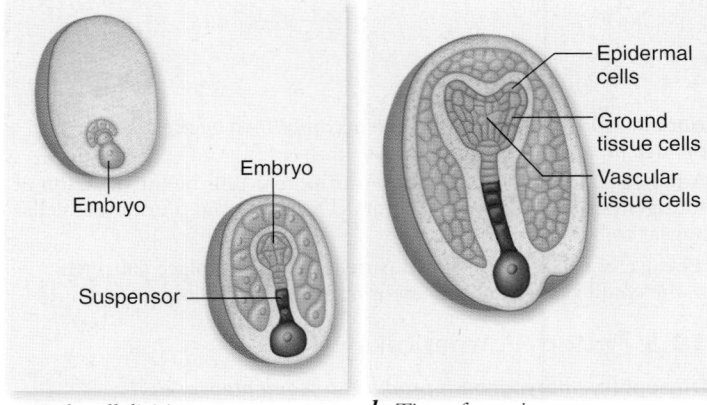

a. Early cell division

b. Tissue formation

Epidermal cells
Ground tissue cells
Vascular tissue cells

Embryo
Embryo
Suspensor

Shoot apical meristem
Seed wall
Cotyledons
Root apical meristem

c. Seed formation

d. Germination

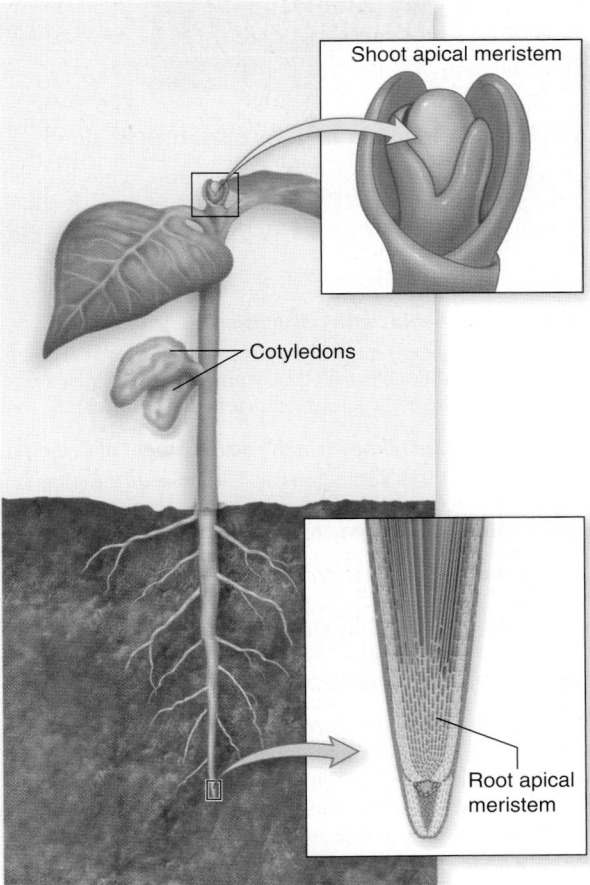

Shoot apical meristem
Cotyledons
Root apical meristem

e. Meristematic development and morphogenesis

Figure 19.21 **The path of plant development.** The developmental stages of *Arabidopsis thaliana* are *(a)* early embryonic cell division, *(b)* embryonic tissue formation, *(c)* seed formation, *(d)* germination, and *(e)* meristematic development and morphogenesis.

Soon after the three basic tissues form, a flowering plant embryo develops one or two seed leaves called *cotyledons*. At this point, development is arrested, and the embryo is either surrounded by nutritive tissue or has amassed stored food in its cotyledons (figure 19.21*c*). The resulting package, known as a *seed*, is resistant to drought and other unfavorable conditions.

A seed germinates in response to favorable changes in its environment. The embryo within the seed resumes development and grows rapidly, its roots extending downward and its leaf-bearing shoots extending upward (figure 19.21*d*). Plant development exhibits its great flexibility during the assembly of the modules that make up a plant body. Apical meristems at the root and shoot tips generate the large numbers of cells needed to form leaves, flowers, and all other components of the mature plant (figure 19.21*e*).

Growth within the developing flower is controlled by a cascade of transcription factors. A key member of this cascade is the *AINTEGUMENTA (ANT)* gene. Loss of ANT function reduces the number and size of floral organs, and inappropriate expression leads to larger floral organs.

Plant body form is also established by controlled changes in cell shape as cells expand osmotically after they form. Plant growth-regulating hormones and other factors influence the orientation of bundles of microtubules on the interior of the plasma membrane. These microtubules seem to guide cellulose deposition as the cell wall forms around the outside of a new cell. The orientation of the cellulose fibers, in turn, determines how the cell will elongate as it increases in volume due to osmosis, and so determines the cell's final shape.

Learning Outcomes Review 19.6

Morphogenesis is the generation of ordered form and structure. This process proceeds along with cell differentiation. The primary mechanisms of morphogenesis are cell shape change and cell migration. Apoptosis is programmed cell death that is a necessary part of morphogenesis. Cell migration in animals involves alternating changes in adhesion brought about by cadherins and integrins. In plants, which cannot move, cell division and cell expansion are the primary morphogenetic processes.

■ *Why is cell death important to morphogenesis?*

19.1 The Process of Development

Development is the sequence of systematic, gene-directed changes throughout a life cycle. The four subprocesses of development are growth, cell differentiation, pattern formation, and morphogenesis.

19.2 Cell Division

Development begins with cell division.

In animals, cleavage stage divisions divide the fertilized egg into numerous smaller cells called blastomeres. During cleavage the G_1 and G_2 phases of the cell cycle are shortened or eliminated (figure 19.2).

Every cell division is known in the development of C. elegans.

The lineage of 959 adult somatic *Caenorhabditis elegans* cells is invariant. Knowledge of the differentiation sequence and outcome allows study of developmental mechanisms.

Plant growth occurs in specific areas called meristems.

Plant growth continues throughout the life span from meristematic stem cells that can divide and differentiate into any plant tissue.

19.3 Cell Differentiation

Cells become determined prior to differentiation.

The process of determination commits a cell to a particular developmental pathway prior to its differentiation. This is not visible but can be tracked experimentally. Determination is due to differential inheritance of cytoplasmic factors or cell-to-cell interactions.

Determination can be due to cytoplasmic determinants.

In tunicates, determination of tail muscle cells depends on the presence of mRNA for the Macho-1 transcription factor, which is deposited in the egg cytoplasm during gamete formation.

Induction can lead to cell differentiation.

Induction occurs when one cell type produces signal molecules that induce gene expression in neighboring target cells.

In frogs, cells from animal and vegetal poles do not develop into mesoderm when isolated. In tunicates, signaling by the growth factor FGF induces mesoderm development.

Stem cells can divide and produce cells that differentiate.

Stem cells replace themselves by division and produce cells that differentiate. Totipotent stem cells can give rise to any cell type including extraembryonic tissues; pluripotent cells can give rise to all cells of an organism; and multipotent stem cells can give rise to many kinds of cells.

Embryonic stem cells are pluripotent cells derived from embryos.

Embryonic stem cells are derived from the inner cell mass of the blastocyst (figure 19.8). They can differentiate into any adult tissue in a mouse.

19.4 Nuclear Reprogramming

Reversal of determination has allowed cloning.

Cells undergo no irreversible changes during development. However, transplanted nuclei from older donors are less able to direct complete development. The cloning of the sheep Dolly showed that the nucleus of an adult cell can be reprogrammed to be totipotent (figure 19.9).

Reproductive cloning has inherent problems.

Reproductive cloning has a low success rate, and clones often develop age-associated diseases.

Nuclear reprogramming has been accomplished by use of defined factors.

Adult cells can be converted into pluripotent cells by introduction of four genes for transcription factors. These induced pluripotent cells appear to be similar to ES cells.

The use of cells cloned from a patient's cells to replace damaged tissue could avoid the problem of transplant rejection.

19.5 Pattern Formation

Drosophila embryogenesis produces a segmented larva.

The maternal contribution of mRNA along with the postfertilization events of cellular blastoderm formation produce a segmented embryo.

Morphogen gradients form the basic body axes in Drosophila.

Pattern formation produces two perpendicular axes in a bilaterally symmetrical organism. Positional information leads to changes in gene activity so cells adopt a fate appropriate for their location.

Formation of the anterior/posterior (A/P) axis is based on opposing gradients of morphogens, Bicoid and Nanos, synthesized from maternal mRNA (figures 19.14, 19.15).

The dorsal/ventral (D/V) axis is established by a gradient of the Dorsal transcription factor. Successive action of transcription factors divides the embryo into segments.

The body plan is produced by sequential activation of genes.

Segment identity arises from the action of homeotic genes.

Homeotic genes, called *Hox* genes because they contain a DNA sequence called the homeobox, give identity to embryo segments.

Hox genes are found in four clusters in vertebrates.

Pattern formation in plants is also under genetic control.

Plants have *MADS*-box genes that control the transition from vegetative to reproductive growth, root development, and floral organ identity.

19.6 Morphogenesis

Cell division during development may result in unequal cytokinesis.

Cells change shape and size as morphogenesis proceeds.

Depending on the orientation of the mitotic spindle, cells of equal or different sizes can arise. Morphogenesis involves changes in cell shape and size and cell migration.

Programmed cell death is a necessary part of development.

Apoptosis, the programmed death of cells, removes structures once they are no longer needed (figure 19.19).

Cell migration gets the right cells to the right places.

The migration of cells requires both adhesion and loss of adhesion between cells and their substrate.

Cell-to-cell interactions are often mediated by cadherin proteins, whereas cell-to-substrate interactions may involve integrin-to-extracellular-matrix interactions.

Integrins bind to fibers found in the extracellular matrix. This action can alter the cytoskeleton and activate gene expression.

In seed plants, the plane of cell division determines morphogenesis.

In plants, the primary morphogenetic processes are cell division, relative position of cells within the embryo, and changes in cell shape. Plant development stages begin with cell division and end with meristematic development and morphogenesis (figure 19.21).

Relative position of cells in the plant embryo is the main determinant of cell differentiation.

UNDERSTAND

1. During development, cells become
   a. differentiated before they become determined.
   b. determined before they become differentiated.
   c. determined by the loss of genetic material.
   d. differentiated by the loss of genetic material.

2. Determination can occur by
   a. the action of cytoplasmic determinants.
   b. induction by other cells.
   c. the loss of chromosomes during cell division.
   d. both a and b.

3. The rapid divisions that occur early in development are made possible by shortening
   a. M phase.
   b. S phase.
   c. G_1 and G_2 phases.
   d. all of the above.

4. A pluripotent cell is one that can
   a. become any cell type in an organism.
   b. produce an indefinite supply of a single cell type.
   c. produce a limited amount of a specific cell type.
   d. produce multiple cell types.

5. Plant meristems
   a. are only present during development.
   b. contain stem cells.
   c. undergo meiosis.
   d. all of the above

6. Pattern formation involves cells determining their position in the embryo. One mechanism that can accomplish this is
   a. the loss of genetic material.
   b. alterations of chromosome structure.
   c. gradients of morphogens.
   d. changes in the cell cycle.

7. The process of nuclear reprogramming
   a. is a normal part of pattern formation.
   b. reverses the changes that occur during differentiation.
   c. requires the introduction of new DNA.
   d. is not possible with mammalian cells.

APPLY

1. What is the common theme in cell determination by induction or cytoplasmic determinants?
   a. The activation of transcription factors
   b. The activation cell division
   c. A change in gene expression
   d. Both a and c

2. The process of reproductive cloning
   a. shows that nuclear reprogramming is possible.
   b. is very efficient in mammals.
   c. always produces adult animals that are identical to the donor.
   d. is both a and b.

3. Production of anterior–posterior and dorsal–ventral axes in the fruit fly *Drosophila*
   a. both use gradients of mRNA.
   b. are conceptually similar but mechanistically different.
   c. use the exact same mechanisms.
   d. both use gradients of protein.

4. For pattern formation to occur, the cells in the developing embryo must
   a. "know" their position in the embryo.
   b. be determined during the earliest divisions.
   c. differentiate as they are "born."
   d. must all be reprogrammed after each cell division.

5. The genes that encode the morphogen gradients in *Drosophila* were all identified in mutant screens. A mutation that removes the gradient necessary for the A/P morphogen gradient would be expected to
   a. affect the larvae but not the adult.
   b. affect the adult but not the larvae.
   c. be lethal and lead to an abnormal embryo.
   d. produce replacement of one adult structure with another.

6. What would be the likely result of a mutation of the *bcl-2* gene on the level of apoptosis?
   a. No change
   b. A decrease in apoptosis
   c. An increase in apoptosis
   d. An initial decrease, followed by a increase in apoptosis

7. *MADS*-box, and *Hox* genes are
   a. found only in plants and animals, respectively.
   b. found only in animals and plants, respectively.
   c. have similar roles in development in plants and animals, respectively.
   d. have similar roles in development in animals and plants, respectively.

SYNTHESIZE

1. The fate map for *C. elegans* (refer to figure 19.3) diagrams development of a multicellular organism from a single cell. Use this fate map to determine the number of cell divisions required to establish the population of cells that will become (a) the nervous system and (b) the gonads.

2. Carefully examine the *C. elegans* fate map in figure 19.3. Notice that some of the branchpoints (daughter cells) do *not* go on to produce more cells. What is the cellular mechanism underlying this pattern?

3. You have generated a set of mutant embryonic mouse cells. Predict the developmental consequences for each of the following mutations.
   a. Knockout mutation for N-cadherin
   b. Knockout mutation for integrin
   c. Deletion of the cytoplasmic domain of integrin

4. Assume you have the factors in hand necessary to reprogram an adult cell, and the factors necessary to induce differentiation to any cell type. How could these be used to replace a specific damaged tissue in a human patient?

ONLINE RESOURCE

www.ravenbiology.com

Understand, Apply, and Synthesize—enhance your study with animations that bring concepts to life and practice tests to assess your understanding. Your instructor may also recommend the interactive eBook, individualized learning tools, and more.

Chapter **36**

Plant Form

Chapter Outline

36.1 Organization of the Plant Body: An Overview

36.2 Plant Tissues

36.3 Roots: Anchoring and Absorption Structures

36.4 Stems: Support for Above-Ground Organs

36.5 Leaves: Photosynthetic Organs

Part **VI** Plant Form and Function

Introduction

Although the similarities among a cactus, an orchid, and a hardwood tree might not be obvious at first sight, most plants have a basic unity of structure. This unity is reflected in how the plants are constructed; in how they grow, manufacture, and transport their food; and in how their development is regulated. This chapter addresses the question of how a vascular plant is "built." We will focus on the cells, tissues, and organs that compose the adult plant body. The roots and shoots that give the adult plant its distinct above- and below-ground architecture are the final product of a basic body plan first established during embryogenesis, a process we will explore in detail in this chapter.

Learning Outcomes

1. *Distinguish between the functions of roots and shoots.*
2. *Name the three types of tissues in a plant.*
3. *Compare primary growth and secondary growth.*

As you learned in chapter 30, the plant kingdom has great diversity, not only among its many phyla but even within species. The earliest vascular plants, many of which are extinct, did not have a clear differentiation of the plant body into specialized organs such as roots and leaves.

Among modern vascular plants, the presence of these organs reflects increasing specialization, particularly in relation to the demands of a terrestrial existence. Obtaining water, for example, is a major challenge, and roots are adapted for water absorption from the soil. Leaves, roots, branches, and flowers all exhibit variations in size and number from plant to plant. Development of the form and structure of these parts may be precisely controlled, but some aspects of leaf, stem, and root development are quite flexible. This chapter emphasizes the unifying aspects of plant form, using the flowering plants as a model.

Vascular plants have roots and shoots

A vascular plant consists of a root system and a shoot system (figure 36.1). Roots and shoots grow at their tips, which are called apices (singular, **apex**).

The **root system** anchors the plant and penetrates the soil, from which it absorbs water and ions crucial for the plant's nutrition. Root systems are often extensive, and growing roots can exert great force to move matter as they elongate and expand. Roots developed later than the shoot system as an adaptation to living on land.

The **shoot system** consists of the stems and their leaves. Stems serve as a scaffold for positioning the leaves, the principal sites of photosynthesis. The arrangement, size, and other features of the leaves are critically important in the plant's production of food. Flowers, other reproductive organs, and ultimately, fruits and seeds are also formed on the shoot (flower morphology and plant reproduction is covered in chapter 42).

The iterative (repeating) unit of the vegetative shoot consists of the internode, node, leaf, and axillary bud, but not reproductive structures. An axillary bud is a lateral shoot apex that allows the plant to branch or replace the main shoot if it is eaten by an herbivore. A vegetative axillary bud has the capacity to reiterate the development of the primary shoot. When the plant has shifted to the reproductive phase of development, these axillary buds may produce flowers or floral shoots.

Roots and shoots are composed of three types of tissues

Roots, shoots, and leaves all contain three basic types of tissues: dermal, ground, and vascular tissue. Because each of these tissues extend through the root and shoot systems, they are called **tissue systems.**

Plant cell types can be distinguished by the size of their vacuoles, whether they are living or not at maturity, and by the thickness of secretions found in their cellulose cell walls, a distinguishing feature of plant cells (see chapter 4 to review cell structure). Some cells have only a primary cell wall of cellulose, synthesized by the protoplast near the cell membrane. Microtubules align within the cell and determine the orientation of the cellulose fibers (figure 36.2a). Cells that support the plant

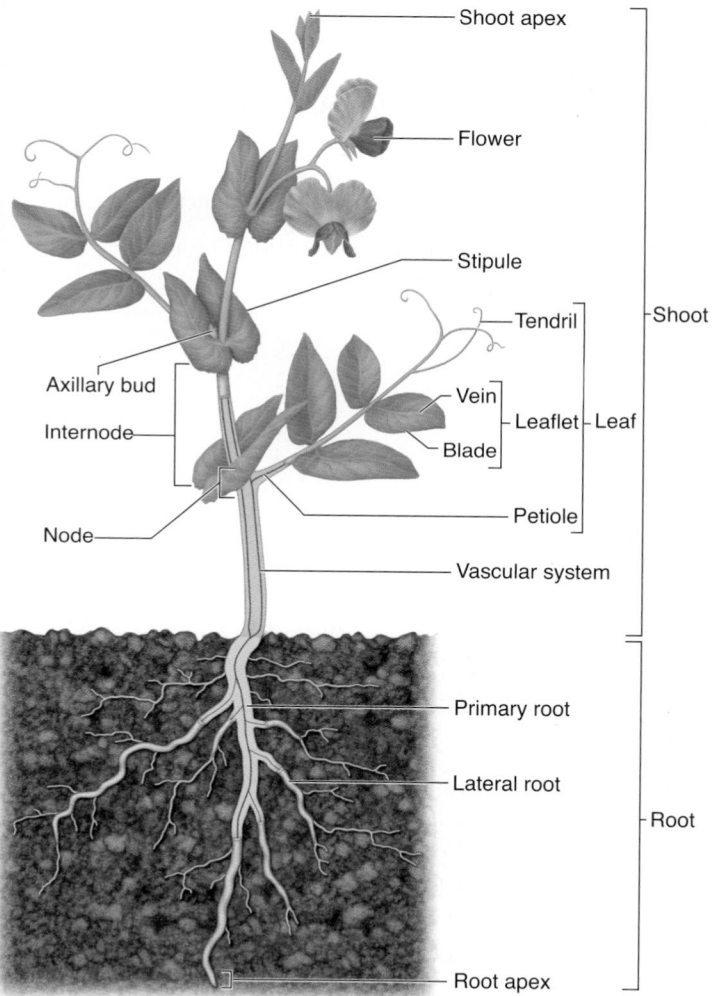

Figure 36.1 Diagram of a plant body. Branching root and shoot systems create the plant's architecture. Each root and shoot has an apex that extends growth. Leaves are initiated at the nodes of the shoot, which also contain axillary buds that can remain dormant, grow to form lateral branches, or make flowers. A leaf can be a simple blade or consist of multiple parts as shown here. Roots, shoots, and leaves are all connected with vascular (conducting) tissue.

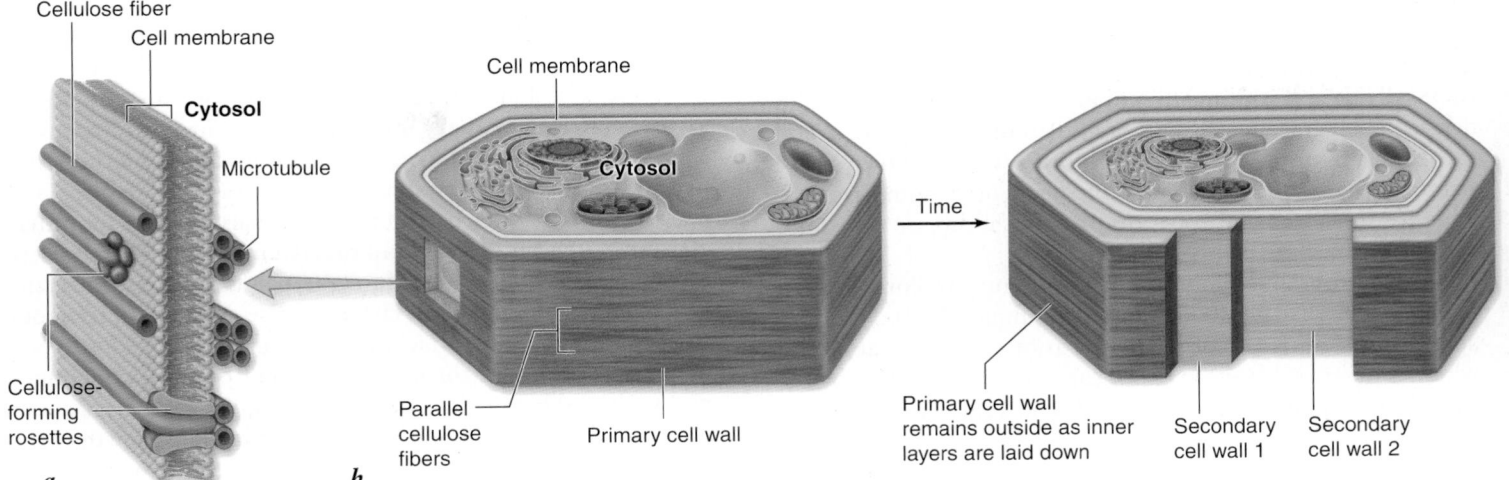

Figure 36.2 Synthesis of a plant cell wall. *a.* Cellulose is a glucose polymer that is produced at the cellulose-forming rosettes in the cell membrane to form the cell wall. Cellulose fibers are laid down parallel to microtubules inside the cell membrane. Additional substances that strengthen and waterproof the cell wall are added to the cell wall in some cell types. *b.* Some cells extrude additional layers of cellulose, increasing the mechanical strength of the wall. Because new cellulose is produced at the cell, the oldest layers of cellulose are on the outside of the cell wall. All cells have a primary cell wall. Additional layers of cellulose and lignin contribute to the secondary cell wall.

body have more heavily reinforced cell walls with multiple layers of cellulose. Cellulose layers are laid down at angles to adjacent layers like plywood; this enhances the strength of the cell wall (figure 36.2*b*).

Plant cells contribute to three tissue systems. **Dermal tissue,** primarily *epidermis*, is one cell layer thick in most plants, and it forms an outer protective covering for the plant. **Ground tissue** cells function in storage, photosynthesis, and secretion, in addition to forming fibers that support and protect plants. **Vascular tissue** conducts fluids and dissolved substances throughout the plant body. Each of these tissues and their many functions are described in more detail in later sections.

Meristems elaborate the body plan throughout the plant's life

When a seed sprouts, only a tiny portion of the adult plant exists. Although embryo cells can undergo division and differentiation to form many cell types, the fate of most adult cells is more restricted. Further development of the plant body depends on the activities of *meristems*, specialized cells found in shoot and root apices, as well as other parts of the plant.

Overview of meristems

Meristems are clumps of small cells with dense cytoplasm and proportionately large nuclei that act as stem cells do in animals. That is, one cell divides to give rise to two cells, of which one remains meristematic, while the other undergoes differentiation and contributes to the plant body (figure 36.3). In this way, the population of meristem cells is continually renewed. Molecular genetic evidence supports the hypothesis that animal stem cells and plant meristem cells may also share some common pathways of gene expression. Extension of both root

and shoot takes place as a result of repeated cell divisions and subsequent elongation of the cells produced by the **apical meristems.** In some vascular plants, including shrubs and most trees, **lateral meristems** produce an increase in root and shoot diameter.

Figure 36.3 Meristem cell division. Plant meristems consist of cells that divide to give rise to a differentiating daughter cell and a cell that persists as a meristem cell.

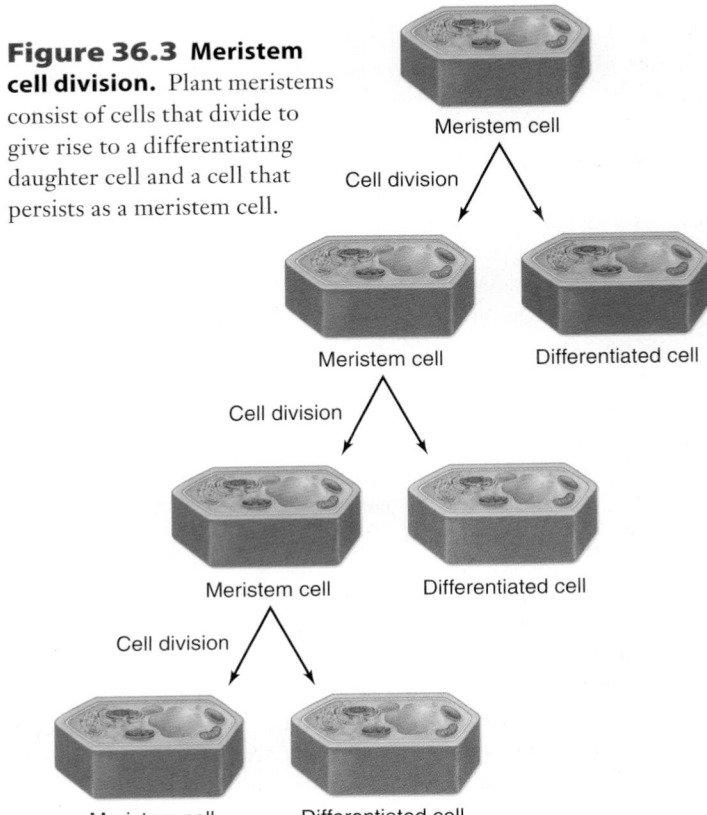

Apical meristems

Apical meristems are located at the tips of stems and roots (figure 36.4). During periods of growth, the cells of apical meristems divide and continually add more cells at the tips. Tissues derived from apical meristems are called **primary tissues,** and the extension of the root and stem forms what is known as the **primary plant body.** The primary plant body comprises the young, soft shoots and roots of a tree or shrub, or the entire plant body in some plants.

Both root and shoot apical meristems are composed of delicate cells that need protection (see figure 36.4). The root apical meristem is protected by the root cap, the anatomy of which is described later on. Root cap cells are produced by the root meristem and are sloughed off and replaced as the root moves through the soil. In contrast, leaf primordia shelter the growing shoot apical meristem, which is particularly susceptible to desiccation because of its exposure to air and sun.

The apical meristem gives rise to the three tissue systems by first initiating **primary meristems.** The three primary meristems are the **protoderm,** which forms the epidermis; the **procambium,** which produces primary vascular tissues (primary xylem for water transport and primary phloem for nutrient transport); and the **ground meristem,** which differentiates further into ground tissue. In some plants, such as horsetails and corn, **intercalary meristems** arise in stem internodes (spaces between leaf attachments), adding to the internode lengths. If you walk through a cornfield on a quiet summer night when the corn is about knee high, you may hear a soft popping sound. This sound is caused by the rapid growth of the intercalary meristems. The amount of stem elongation that occurs in a very short time is quite surprising.

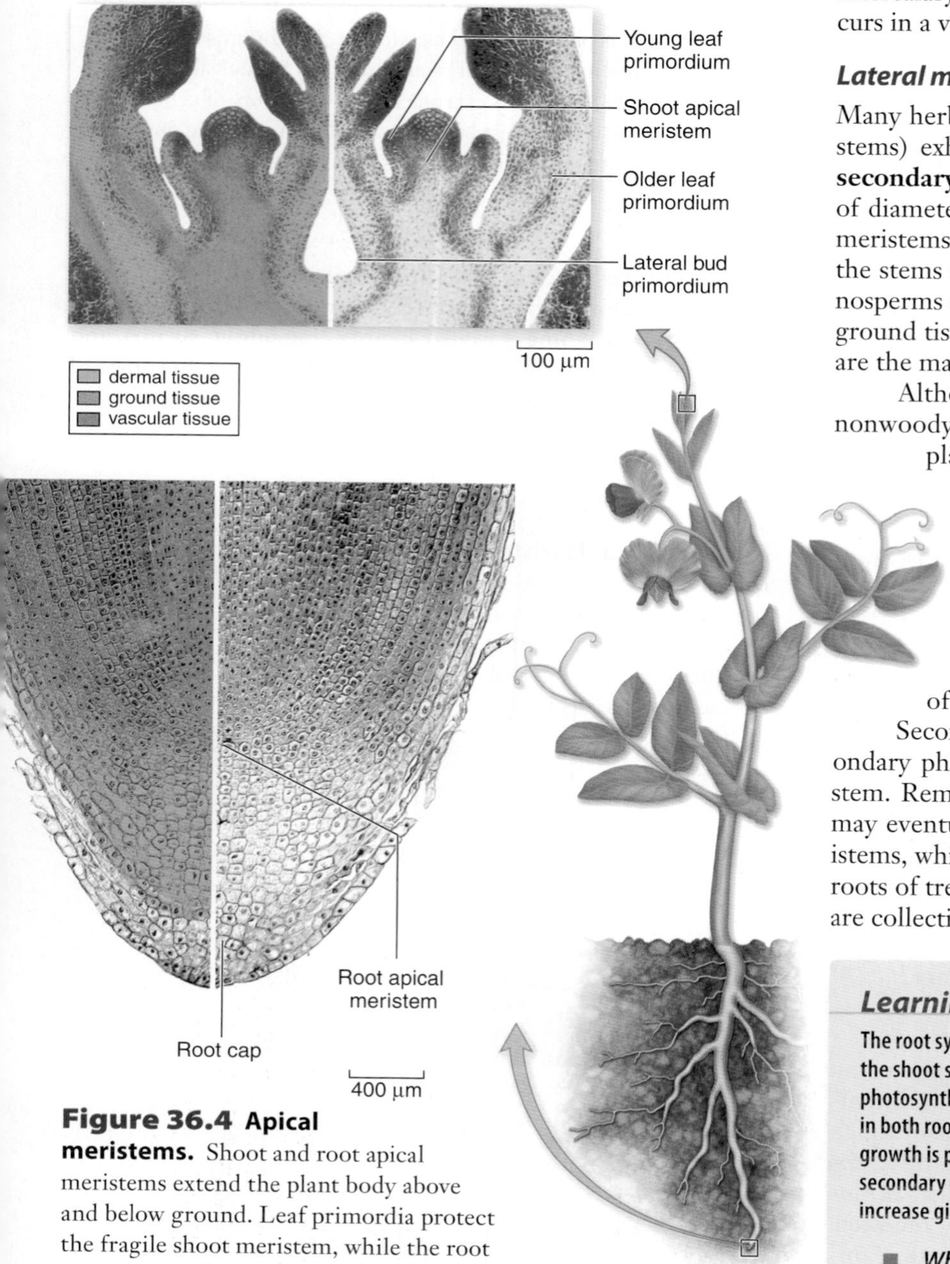

Lateral meristems

Many herbaceous plants (that is, plants with fleshy, not woody stems) exhibit only primary growth, but others also exhibit **secondary growth,** which may result in a substantial increase of diameter. Secondary growth is accomplished by the lateral meristems—peripheral cylinders of meristematic tissue within the stems and roots that increase the girth (diameter) of gymnosperms and most angiosperms. Lateral meristems form from ground tissue that is derived from apical meristems. Monocots are the major exception (figure 36.5).

Although secondary growth increases girth in many nonwoody plants, its effects are most dramatic in woody plants, which have two lateral meristems. Within the bark of a woody stem is the **cork cambium**—a lateral meristem that contributes to the outer bark of the tree. Just beneath the bark is the **vascular cambium**—a lateral meristem that produces secondary vascular tissue. The vascular cambium forms between the xylem and phloem in vascular bundles, adding secondary vascular tissue to both of its sides.

Secondary xylem is the main component of wood. Secondary phloem is very close to the outer surface of a woody stem. Removing the bark of a tree damages the phloem and may eventually kill the tree. Tissues formed from lateral meristems, which comprise most of the trunk, branches, and older roots of trees and shrubs, are known as **secondary tissues** and are collectively called the **secondary plant body.**

- dermal tissue
- ground tissue
- vascular tissue

Young leaf primordium

Shoot apical meristem

Older leaf primordium

Lateral bud primordium

100 μm

Root apical meristem

Root cap

400 μm

Figure 36.4 Apical meristems. Shoot and root apical meristems extend the plant body above and below ground. Leaf primordia protect the fragile shoot meristem, while the root meristem produces a protective root cap in addition to new root tissue.

Learning Outcomes Review 36.1

The root system anchors plants and absorbs water and nutrients, whereas the shoot system, consisting of stems, leaves, and flowers carries out photosynthesis and sexual reproduction. The three general types of tissue in both roots and shoots are dermal, ground, and vascular tissue. Primary growth is produced by apical meristems at the tips of roots and shoots; secondary growth is produced by lateral meristems that are peripheral and increase girth.

■ *Why are both primary and secondary growth necessary in a woody plant?*

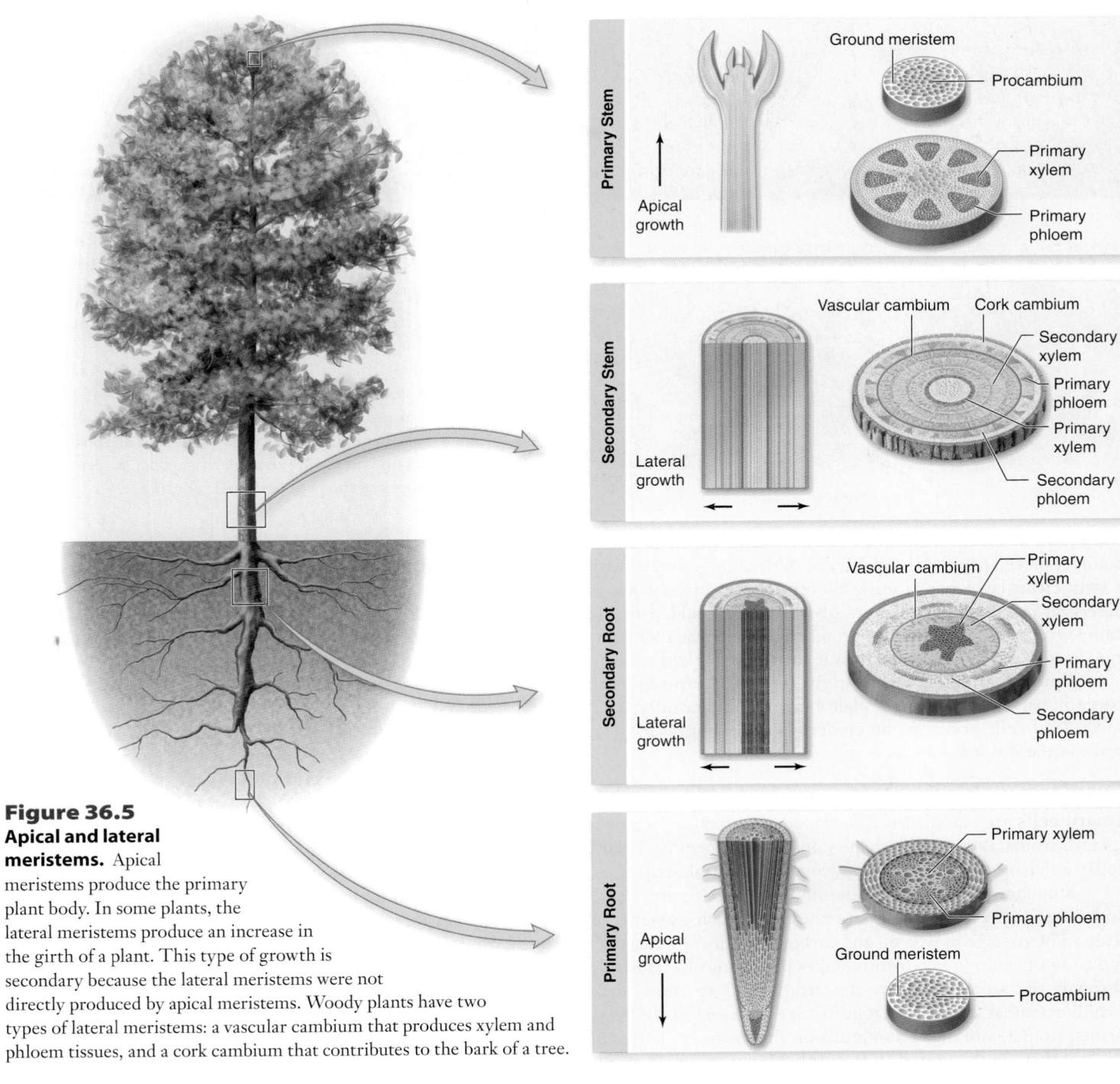

Figure 36.5
Apical and lateral meristems. Apical meristems produce the primary plant body. In some plants, the lateral meristems produce an increase in the girth of a plant. This type of growth is secondary because the lateral meristems were not directly produced by apical meristems. Woody plants have two types of lateral meristems: a vascular cambium that produces xylem and phloem tissues, and a cork cambium that contributes to the bark of a tree.

36.2 Plant Tissues

Learning Outcomes

1. Describe the functions of dermal, ground, and vascular tissues.
2. Name the three cell types found in ground tissue and their functions.
3. Distinguish between xylem and phloem.

Three main categories of tissue can be distinguished in the plant body. These are (1) *dermal tissue* on external surfaces that serves a protective function; (2) *ground tissue* that forms several different internal tissue types and that can participate in photosynthesis, serve a storage function, or provide structural support; and (3) *vascular tissue* that conducts water and nutrients.

Dermal tissue forms a protective interface with the environment

Dermal tissue derived from an embryo or apical meristem forms **epidermis.** This tissue is one cell layer thick in most

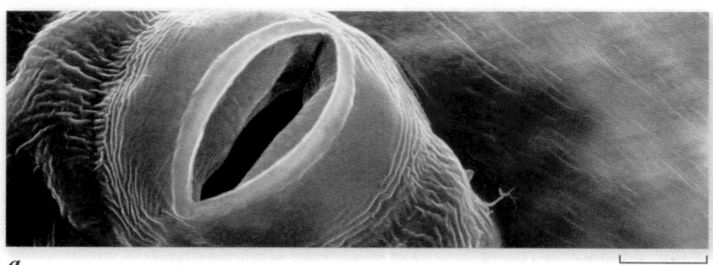

a.

4 μm

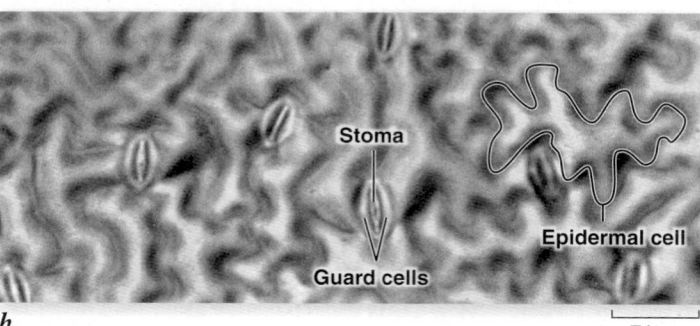

Stoma

Epidermal cell

Guard cells

b.

71 μm

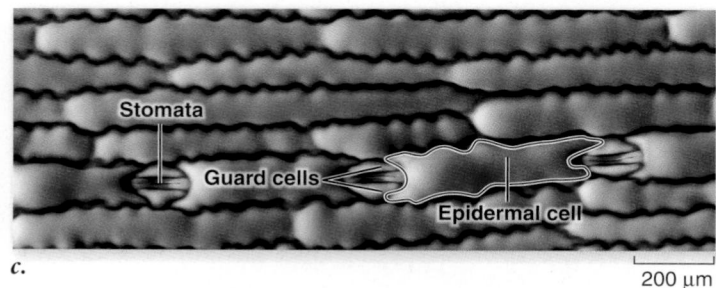

Stomata

Guard cells

Epidermal cell

c.

200 μm

Figure 36.6 Stomata. *a.* A stoma is the space between two guard cells that regulate the size of the opening. Stomata are evenly distributed within the epidermis of monocots and eudicots, but the patterning is quite different. *b.* A pea (eudicot) leaf with a random arrangement of stomata. *c.* A maize (corn, a monocot) leaf with stomata evenly spaced in rows. These photomicrographs also show the variety of cell shapes in plants. Some plant cells are boxlike, as seen in maize *(c)*, and others are irregularly shaped, as seen in the jigsaw puzzle shapes of the pea epidermal cells, *(b)*.

plants and forms the outer protective covering of the plant. In young, exposed parts of the plant, the epidermis is covered with a fatty **cutin** layer constituting the **cuticle;** in plants such as desert succulents, several layers of wax may be added to the cuticle to limit water loss and protect against ultraviolet damage. In some cases, the dermal tissue forms the bark of trees.

Epidermal cells, which originate from the protoderm, cover all parts of the primary plant body. A number of types of specialized cells occur in the epidermis, including *guard cells, trichomes,* and *root hairs.*

Guard cells

Guard cells are paired, sausage-shaped cells flanking a stoma (plural, stomata), a mouth-shaped epidermal opening. Guard cells, unlike other epidermal cells, contain chloroplasts.

Stomata occur in the epidermis of leaves (figure 36.6a) and sometimes on other parts of the plant, such as stems or fruits. The passage of oxygen and carbon dioxide, as well as the diffusion of water in vapor form, takes place almost exclusively through the stomata. There are from 1000 to more than 1 million stomata per square centimeter of leaf surface. In many plants, stomata are more numerous on the lower epidermis of the leaf than on the upper—a factor that helps minimize water loss. Some plants have stomata only on the lower epidermis, and a few, such as water lilies, have them only on the upper epidermis to maximize gas exchange.

Guard cell formation is the result of an asymmetrical cell division producing a guard cell and a subsidiary cell that aids in the opening and closing of the stoma. The patterning of these asymmetrical divisions that results in stomatal distribution has intrigued developmental biologists (figure 36.6b, c).

Research on mutants that get "confused" about where to position stomata is providing information on the timing of stomatal initiation and the kind of intercellular communication that triggers guard cell formation. For example, the *too many mouths (tmm)* mutation that occurs in *Arabidopsis* disrupts the normal pattern of cell division that spatially separates stomata

(figure 36.7). Investigations of this and other stomatal patterning genes revealed a coordinated network of cell–cell communication (see chapter 9) that informs cells of their position relative to other cells and determines cell fate. The *TMM* gene encodes a membrane-bound receptor that is part of a signaling pathway controlling asymmetrical cell division.

Trichomes

Trichomes are cellular or multicellular hairlike outgrowths of the epidermis (figure 36.8). They occur frequently on stems, leaves, and reproductive organs. A "fuzzy" or "woolly" leaf is covered with trichomes that can be seen clearly with a microscope under low magnification. Trichomes keep leaf surfaces cool and reduce evaporation by covering stomatal openings. They also protect leaves from high light intensities and ultraviolet radiation and can buffer against temperature fluctuations. Trichomes can vary greatly in form; some consist of a single cell; others are multicellular. Some are glandular, often secreting sticky or toxic substances to deter herbivory.

Figure 36.7 The too many mouths stomatal mutant. This *Arabidopsis* mutant plant lacks an essential signal for spacing stomata. Usually a differentiating guard cell pair inhibits differentiation of a nearby cell into a guard cell.

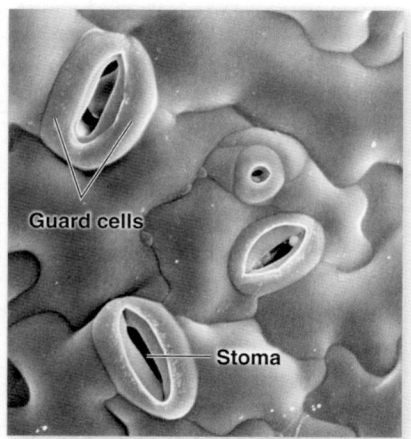

Guard cells

Stoma

272 μm

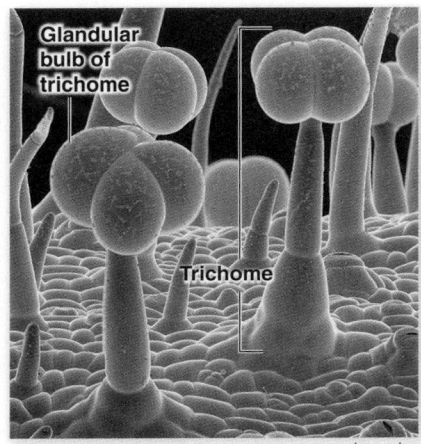

Figure 36.8 **Trichomes.** The trichomes with tan, bulbous tips on this tomato plant are glandular trichomes. These trichomes secrete substances that can literally glue insects to the trichome.

34.62 μm

1,667 μm

Figure 36.10 Root hairs. Root hair cells are a type of epidermal cell that increase the surface area of the root to enhance water and mineral uptake.

Genes that regulate trichome development have been identified, including *GLABROUS3 (GL3)* (figure 36.9). When trichome-initiating proteins, like GL3, reach a threshold level compared with trichome-inhibiting proteins, an epidermal cell becomes a trichome. Signals from this trichome cell now prevent neighbor cells from expressing trichome-promoting genes (see figure 36.9).

Root hairs

Root hairs, which are tubular extensions of individual epidermal cells, occur in a zone just behind the tips of young, growing roots (figure 36.10). Because a root hair is simply an extension of an epidermal cell and not a separate cell, no cross-wall isolates the hair from the rest of the cell. Root hairs keep the root in intimate contact with the surrounding soil particles and greatly increase the root's surface area and efficiency of absorption.

As a root grows, the extent of the root hair zone remains roughly constant as root hairs at the older end slough off while new ones are produced at the apex. Most of the absorption of water and minerals occurs through root hairs, especially in herbaceous plants. Root hairs should not be confused with lateral roots, which are multicellular structures and originate deep within the root. Root hairs are not found when the dermal tissue system is extended by the cork cambium, which contributes to the periderm (outer bark) of a tree trunk or root. The epidermis gets stretched and broken with the radial expansion of the axis by the vascular cambium

The first land plants lacked roots, which later evolved from shoots. Given this common ancestry, it is not surprising that some of the genes needed for trichome and stomatal

Figure 36.9 Trichome patterning. Mutants have revealed genes involved in regulating the spacing and development of trichomes in *Arabidopsis. **a.** Wild type. **b.** glaborous3* mutant, which fails to initiate trichome development. **c.** When there is sufficient GL3 in a cell and the levels of trichome-inhibiting proteins are sufficiently low, that cell will develop a trichome. Once a cell begins trichome initiation, it signals neighboring cells and inhibits their ability to develop trichomes.

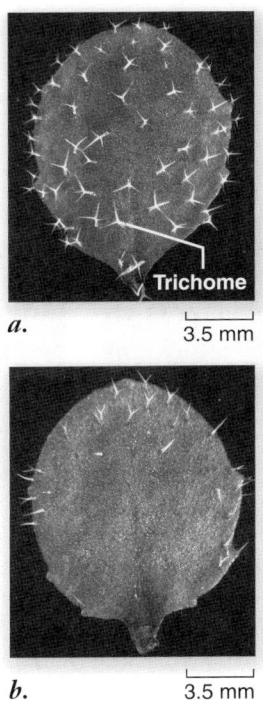

a. 3.5 mm

b. 3.5 mm

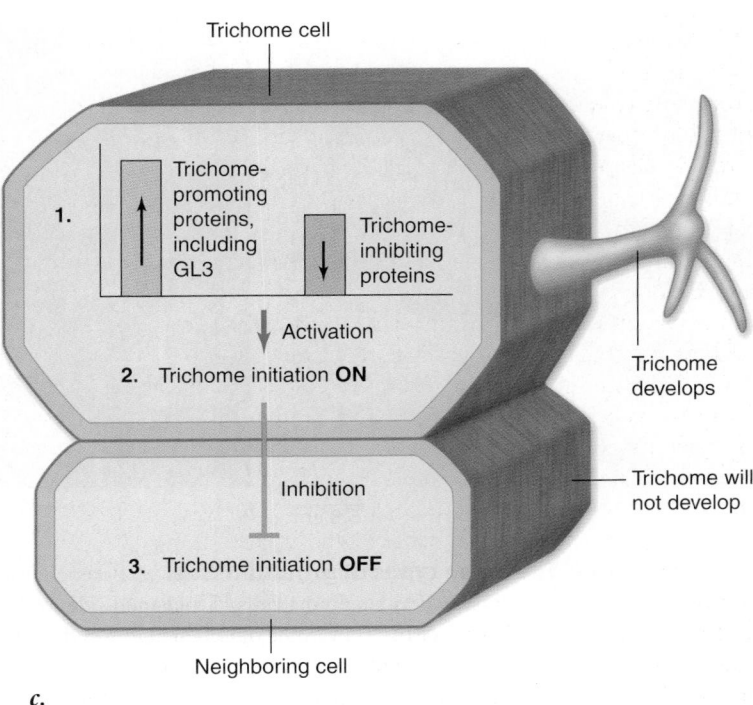

c.

differentiation in shoot epidermal cells also play a role in root hair development.

Inquiry question

? Identify three dermal tissue traits that are adaptive for a terrestrial lifestyle and explain why these traits are advantageous.

Ground tissue cells perform many functions, including storage, photosynthesis, and support

Ground tissue consists primarily of thin-walled *parenchyma cells* that function in storage, photosynthesis, and secretion. Other ground tissue, composed of *collenchyma cells* and *sclerenchyma cells*, provide support and protection.

Parenchyma

Parenchyma cells are the most common type of plant cell. They have large vacuoles, thin walls, and are initially (but briefly) more or less spherical. These cells, which have living protoplasts, push up against each other shortly after they are produced, however, and assume other shapes, often ending up with 11 to 17 sides.

Parenchyma cells may live for many years; they function in storage of food and water, photosynthesis, and secretion. They are the most abundant cells of primary tissues and may also occur, to a much lesser extent, in secondary tissues (figure 36.11*a*). Most parenchyma cells have only primary walls, which are walls laid down while the cells are still maturing. Parenchyma are less specialized than other plant cells, although many variations occur with special functions, such as nectar and resin secretion or storage of latex, proteins, and metabolic wastes.

Parenchyma cells have functional nuclei and are capable of dividing, and they usually remain alive after they mature; in some plants (for example, cacti), they may live to be over 100 years old. The majority of cells in fruits such as apples are parenchyma. Some parenchyma contain chloroplasts, especially in leaves and in the outer parts of herbaceous stems. Such photosynthetic parenchyma tissue is called *chlorenchyma*.

Collenchyma

If celery "strings" have ever been caught between your teeth, you are familiar with tough, flexible **collenchyma cells.** Like parenchyma cells, collenchyma cells have living protoplasts and may live for many years. These cells, which are usually a little longer than wide, have walls that vary in thickness (figure 36.11*b*).

Flexible collenchyma cells provide support for plant organs, allowing them to bend without breaking. They often form strands or continuous cylinders beneath the epidermis of stems or leaf petioles (stalks) and along the veins in leaves. Strands of collenchyma provide much of the support for stems in the primary plant body.

Sclerenchyma

Sclerenchyma cells have tough, thick walls. Unlike collenchyma and parenchyma, they usually lack living protoplasts at maturity. Their secondary cell walls are often impregnated with **lignin,** a highly branched polymer that makes cell walls more rigid; for example, lignin is an important component in wood. Cell walls containing lignin are said to be *lignified*. Lignin is common in the walls of plant cells that have a structural or mechanical function. Some kinds of cells have lignin deposited in primary as well as secondary cell walls.

Sclerenchyma is present in two general types: fibers and sclereids. *Fibers* are long, slender cells that are usually grouped

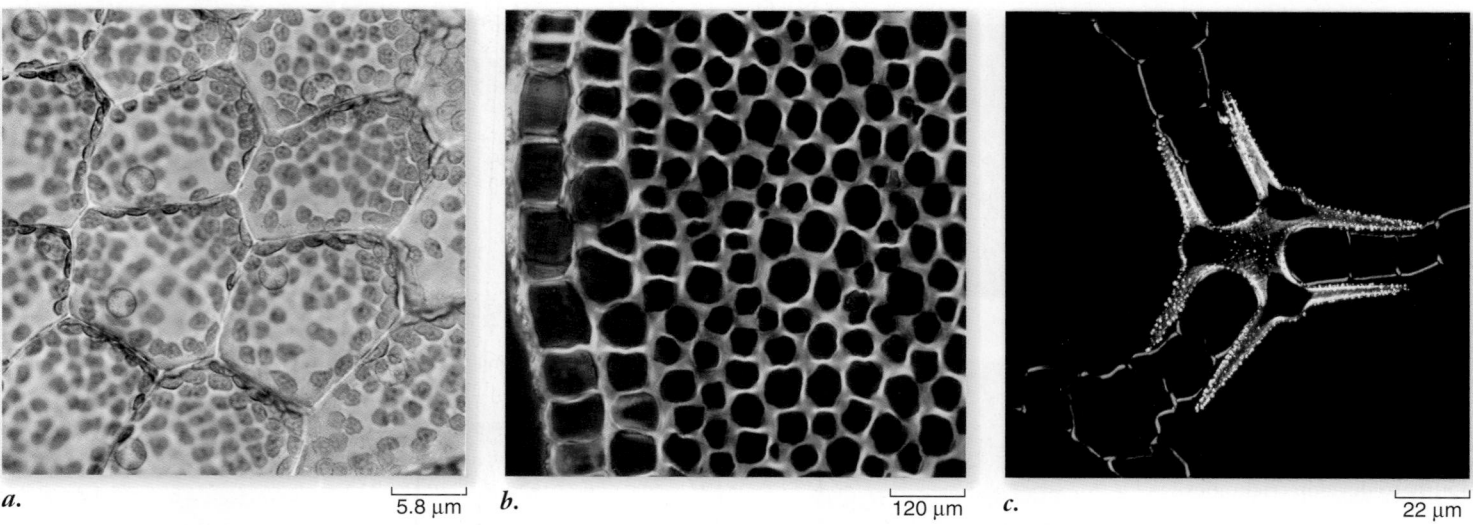

a.   5.8 μm   *b.*   120 μm   *c.*   22 μm

Figure 36.11 The three types of ground tissue. *a.* Parenchyma cells. Only primary cell walls are seen in this cross section of parenchyma cells from grass. *b.* Collenchyma cells. Thickened side walls are seen in this cross section of collenchyma cells from a young branch of elderberry *(Sambucus).* In other kinds of collenchyma cells, the thickened areas may occur at the corners of the cells or in other kinds of strips. *c.* Sclereids. Clusters of sclereids ("stone cells"), stained red in this preparation. The surrounding thin-walled cells, stained green, are parenchyma. Sclereids are one type of sclerenchyma tissue, which also contains fibers.

together in strands. Linen, for example, is woven from strands of sclerenchyma fibers that occur in the phloem of flax (*Linum* spp.) plants. *Sclereids* are variable in shape but often branched. They may occur singly or in groups; they are not elongated, but may have many different forms, including that of a star. The gritty texture of a pear is caused by groups of sclereids that occur throughout the soft flesh of the fruit (figure 36.11*c*). Sclereids are also found in hard seed coats. Both of these tough, thick-walled cell types serve to strengthen the tissues in which they occur.

Vascular tissue conducts water and nutrients throughout the plant

Vascular tissue, as mentioned earlier, includes two kinds of conducting tissues: (1) *xylem*, which conducts water and dissolved minerals, and (2) *phloem*, which conducts a solution of carbohydrates—mainly sucrose—used by plants for food. The phloem also transports hormones, amino acids, and other substances that are necessary for plant growth. Xylem and phloem differ in structure as well as in function.

Xylem

Xylem, the principal water-conducting tissue of plants, usually contains a combination of *vessels*, which are continuous tubes formed from dead, hollow, cylindrical cells arranged end-to-end, and *tracheids*, which are dead cells that taper at the ends and overlap one another (figure 36.12). Primary xylem is derived from the procambium produced by the apical meristem. Secondary xylem is formed by the vascular cambium, a lateral meristem. Wood consists of accumulated secondary xylem.

In some plants (but not flowering plants), tracheids are the only water-conducting cells present; water passes in an unbroken stream through the xylem from the roots up through the shoot and into the leaves. When the water reaches the leaves, much of it diffuses in the form of water vapor into the intercellular spaces and out of the leaves into the surrounding air, mainly through the stomata. This diffusion of water vapor from a plant is known as **transpiration** (see chapter 38). In addition to conducting water, dissolved minerals, and inorganic ions such as nitrates and phosphates throughout the plant, xylem supplies support for the plant body.

Vessel members tend to be shorter and wider than tracheids. When viewed with a microscope, they resemble beverage cans with both ends removed. Both vessel members and tracheids have thick, lignified secondary walls and no living protoplasts at maturity. Lignin is produced by the cell and secreted to strengthen the cellulose cell walls before the protoplast dies, leaving only the cell wall.

Tracheids contain *pits*, which are small, mostly rounded-to-elliptical areas where no secondary wall material has been deposited. The pits of adjacent cells occur opposite one another; the continuous stream of water flows through these pits from tracheid to tracheid. In contrast, vessel members, which are joined end to end, may be almost completely open or may have bars or strips of wall material across the open ends (see figure 36.12). Vessels appear to conduct water more efficiently than do the overlapping strands of tracheids. We know this partly because vessel members have evolved from tracheids independently in several groups of plants, suggesting that they are favored by natural selection.

In addition to conducting cells, xylem typically includes fibers and parenchyma cells (ground tissue cells). It is probable that some types of fibers have evolved from tracheids, becoming specialized for strengthening rather than conducting. The parenchyma cells, which are usually produced in horizontal

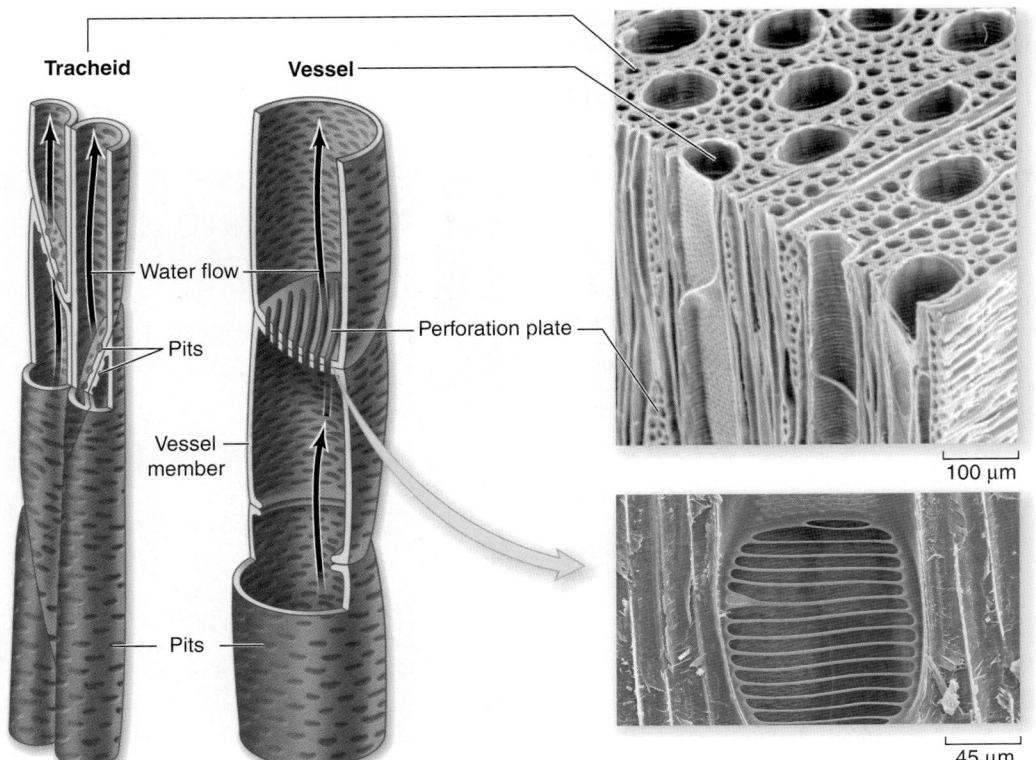

Figure 36.12 Comparison between tracheids and vessel members. In tracheids, the water passes from cell to cell by means of pits. In vessel members, water moves by way of perforation plates (as seen in the photomicrograph in this figure). In gymnosperm wood, tracheids both conduct water and provide support; in most kinds of angiosperms, vessels are present in addition to tracheids. These two types of cells conduct water, and fibers provide additional support. The wood of red maple, *Acer rubrum*, contains both tracheids and vessels as seen in the electron micrographs in this figure.

Tracheid — Vessel — Water flow — Pits — Perforation plate — Vessel member — Pits

100 µm

45 µm

rows called *rays* by special *ray initials* of the vascular cambium, function in lateral conduction and food storage. (An *initial* is another term for a meristematic cell. It divides to produce another initial and a cell that differentiates.)

In cross sections of woody stems and roots, the rays can be seen radiating out from the center of the xylem like the spokes of a wheel. Fibers are abundant in some kinds of wood, such as oak (*Quercus* spp.), and the wood is correspondingly dense and heavy. The arrangements of these and other kinds of cells in the xylem make it possible to identify most plant genera and many species from their wood alone.

Over 2000 years ago paper as we recognize it today was made in China by mashing herbaceous plants in water and separating out a thin layer of phloem fibers on a screen. Not until the third century of the common era did the secret of making paper make its way out of China. Today the ever-growing demand for paper is met by extracting xylem fibers from wood, including spruce, that is relatively soft, having fewer ray fibers than oak. The lignin-rich cell walls yield brown paper that is often bleached. In addition, tissues from many other plants have been developed as sources of paper, including kenaf and hemp. United States paper currency is 75% cotton and 25% flax.

Phloem

Phloem, which is located toward the outer part of roots and stems, is the principal food-conducting tissue in vascular plants. If a plant is *girdled* (by removing a substantial strip of bark down to the vascular cambium around the entire circumference), the plant eventually dies from starvation of the roots.

Food conduction in phloem is carried out through two kinds of elongated cells: sieve cells and sieve-tube members. Gymnosperms, ferns, and horsetails have only sieve cells; most angiosperms have sieve-tube members. Both types of cells have clusters of pores known as sieve areas because the cell walls resemble sieves. Sieve areas are more abundant on the overlapping ends of the cells and connect the protoplasts of adjoining sieve cells and sieve-tube members. Both of these types of cells

are living, but most sieve cells and all sieve-tube members lack a nucleus at maturity.

In sieve-tube members, some sieve areas have larger pores and are called sieve plates (figure 36.13). Sieve-tube members occur end to end, forming longitudinal series called sieve tubes. Sieve cells are less specialized than sieve-tube members, and the pores in all of their sieve areas are roughly of the same diameter. Sieve-tube members are more specialized, and presumably, more efficient than sieve cells.

Each sieve-tube member is associated with an adjacent, specialized parenchyma cell known as a *companion cell*. Companion cells apparently carry out some of the metabolic functions needed to maintain the associated sieve-tube member. In angiosperms, a common initial cell divides asymmetrically to produce a sieve-tube member cell and its companion cell. Companion cells have all the components of normal parenchyma cells, including nuclei, and numerous plasmodesmata (cytoplasmic connections between adjacent cells) connect their cytoplasm with that of the associated sieve-tube members.

Sieve cells in nonflowering plants have albuminous cells that function as companion cells. Unlike a companion cell, an albuminous cell is not necessarily derived from the same mother cell as its associated sieve cell. Fibers and parenchyma cells are often abundant in phloem.

Learning Outcomes Review 36.2

Dermal tissue protects a plant from its environment and contains specialized cells such as guard cells, trichomes, and root hairs. Ground tissue serves several functions, including storage (parenchyma cells), photosynthesis (specialized parenchyma called chlorenchyma), and structural support (collenchyma and sclerenchyma). Vascular tissue carries water through the xylem (primarily vessels) and nutrients through the phloem (primarily sieve-tube members).

■ **Contrast the structure and function of mature vessels and sieve-tube members.**

Figure 36.13 A sieve-tube member.

a. Sieve-tube member cells are stacked, with sieve plates forming the connection. The narrow cell with the nucleus at the right of the sieve-tube member is a companion cell. This cell nourishes the sieve-tube members, which have plasma membranes, but no nuclei.
b. Looking down into sieve plates in squash phloem reveals the perforations through which sucrose and hormones move.

© Dr. Richard Kessel & Dr. Gene Shih/Visuals Unlimited

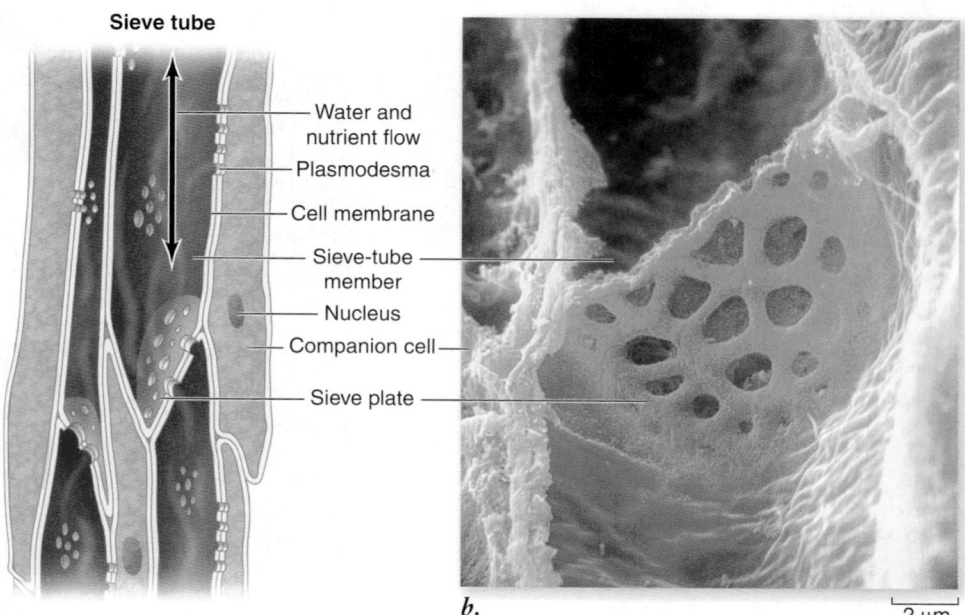

Sieve tube

- Water and nutrient flow
- Plasmodesma
- Cell membrane
- Sieve-tube member
- Nucleus
- Companion cell
- Sieve plate

2 µm

a. *b.*

36.3 Roots: Anchoring and Absorption Structures

Learning Outcomes

1. Describe the four regions of a typical root.
2. Explain the function of root hairs.
3. Describe functions of modified roots.

Roots have a simpler pattern of organization and development than stems, and we will consider them first. Keep in mind, however, that roots evolved after shoots and are a major innovation for terrestrial living.

Roots are adapted for growing underground and absorbing water and solutes

Four regions are commonly recognized in developing roots: the *root cap*, the *zone of cell division*, the *zone of elongation*, and the *zone of maturation* (figure 36.14). In these last three zones, the boundaries are not clearly defined.

When apical initials divide, daughter cells that end up on the tip end of the root become root cap cells. Cells that divide in the opposite direction pass through the three other zones before they finish differentiating. As you consider the different zones, visualize the tip of the root moving deeper into the soil, actively growing. This counters the static image of a root that diagrams and photos convey.

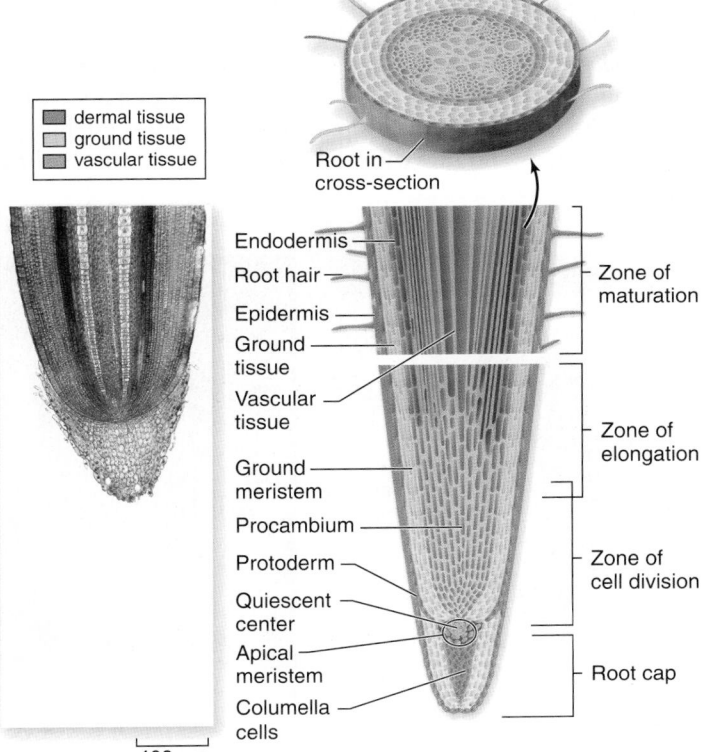

dermal tissue
ground tissue
vascular tissue

Root in cross-section

Endodermis
Root hair
Epidermis
Ground tissue
Vascular tissue
Ground meristem
Procambium
Protoderm
Quiescent center
Apical meristem
Columella cells

Zone of maturation

Zone of elongation

Zone of cell division

Root cap

400 μm

Figure 36.14 Root structure. A root tip in corn, *Zea mays.*

The root cap

The **root cap** has no equivalent in stems. It is composed of two types of cells: the inner *columella cells* (they look like columns), and the outer, lateral *root cap cells*, which are continuously replenished by the root apical meristem. In some plants with larger roots, the root cap is quite obvious. Its main function is to protect the delicate tissues behind it as growth extends the root through mostly abrasive soil particles.

Golgi bodies in the outer root cap cells secrete and release a slimy substance that passes through the cell walls to the outside. The root cap cells, which have an average life of less than a week, are constantly being replaced from the inside, forming a mucilaginous lubricant that eases the root through the soil. The slimy mass also provides a medium for the growth of beneficial nitrogen-fixing bacteria in the roots of plants such as legumes. A new root cap is produced when an existing one is artificially or accidentally removed from a root.

The root cap also functions in the perception of gravity. The columella cells are highly specialized, with the endoplasmic reticulum in the periphery and the nucleus located at either the middle or the top of the cell. They contain no large vacuoles. Columella cells contain *amyloplasts* (plastids with starch grains) that collect on the sides of cells facing the pull of gravity. When a potted plant is placed on its side, the amyloplasts drift or tumble down to the side nearest the source of gravity, and the root bends in that direction.

Lasers have been used to ablate (kill) individual columella cells in *Arabidopsis*. It turns out that only two columella cells are sufficient for gravity sensing! The precise nature of the gravitational response is unknown, but some evidence indicates that calcium ions in the amyloplasts influence the distribution of growth hormones (auxin in this case) in the cells. Multiple signaling mechanisms may exist, because bending has been observed in the absence of auxin. A current hypothesis is that an electrical signal moves from the columella cell to cells in the elongation zone (the region closest to the zone of cell division).

The zone of cell division

The apical meristem is located in the center of the root tip in the area protected by the root cap. Most of the activity in this **zone of cell division** takes place toward the edges of the meristem, where the cells divide every 12 to 36 hours, often coordinately, reaching a peak of division once or twice a day.

Most of the cells are essentially cuboidal, with small vacuoles and proportionately large, centrally located nuclei. These rapidly dividing cells are daughter cells of the apical meristem. A group of cells in the center of the root apical meristem, termed the *quiescent center*, divide only very infrequently. The presence of the quiescent center makes sense if you think about a solid ball expanding—the outer surface would have to increase far more rapidly than the very center.

The apical meristem daughter cells soon subdivide into the three primary tissues previously discussed: protoderm, procambium, and ground meristem. Genes have been identified in the relatively simple root of *Arabidopsis* that regulate the patterning of these tissue systems. The patterning of these cells begins in this zone, but the anatomical and morphological expression of this patterning is not fully revealed until the cells reach the zone of maturation.

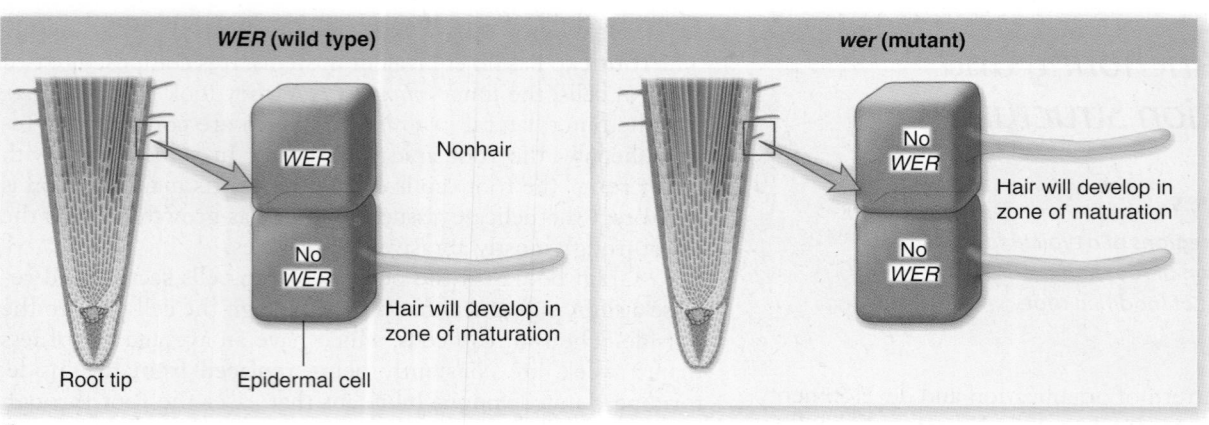
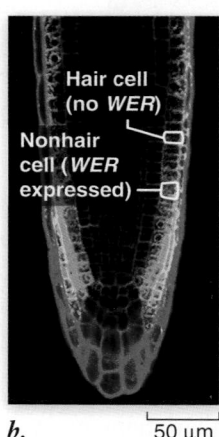

a.

b.
50 μm

Figure 36.15 Tissue-specific gene expression. *a.* The *WEREWOLF* gene of *Arabidopsis* is expressed in some, but not all, epidermal cells and suppresses root hair development. The *wer* mutant is covered with root hairs. *b.* The *WER* promoter was attached to a gene coding for a green fluorescent protein and used to make a transgenic plant. The green fluorescence shows the nonhair epidermal cells where the gene is expressed. The red visually indicates cell boundaries because cell walls autofluoresce.

For example, the *WEREWOLF (WER)* gene is required for the patterning of the two root epidermal cell types, those with and those without root hairs (figure 36.15). Plants with the *wer* mutation have an excess of root hairs because *WER* is needed to prevent root hair development in nonhair epidermal cells. Similarly, the *SCARECROW (SCR)* gene is necessary in ground cell differentiation (figure 36.16). A ground meristem cell undergoes an asymmetrical cell division that gives rise to two nested cylinders of cells from one if *SCR* is present. The outer cell layer becomes ground tissue and serves a storage function. The inner cell layer forms the endodermis, which regulates the intercellular flow of water and solutes into the vascular core of the root (see figure 36.5). The *scr* mutant, in contrast, forms a single layer of cells that have both endodermal and ground cell traits.

SCR illustrates the importance of the orientation of cell division. If a cell's relative position changes because of a mistake in cell division or the ablation of another cell, the cell develops according to its new position. The fate of most plant cells is determined by their position relative to other cells.

The zone of elongation

In the **zone of elongation,** roots lengthen because the cells produced by the primary meristems become several times longer than wide, and their width also increases slightly. The small vacuoles present merge and grow until they occupy 90% or more of the volume of each cell. No further increase in cell size occurs above the zone of elongation. The mature parts of the root, except for increasing in girth, remain stationary for the life of the plant.

The zone of maturation

The cells that have elongated in the zone of elongation become differentiated into specific cell types in the **zone of maturation** (see figure 36.14). The cells of the root surface cylinder mature into *epidermal cells*, which have a very thin cuticle, and include both root hair and nonhair cells. Although the root hairs are not visible until this stage of development, their fate was established much earlier, as you saw with the expression patterns of *WER* (see figure 36.15).

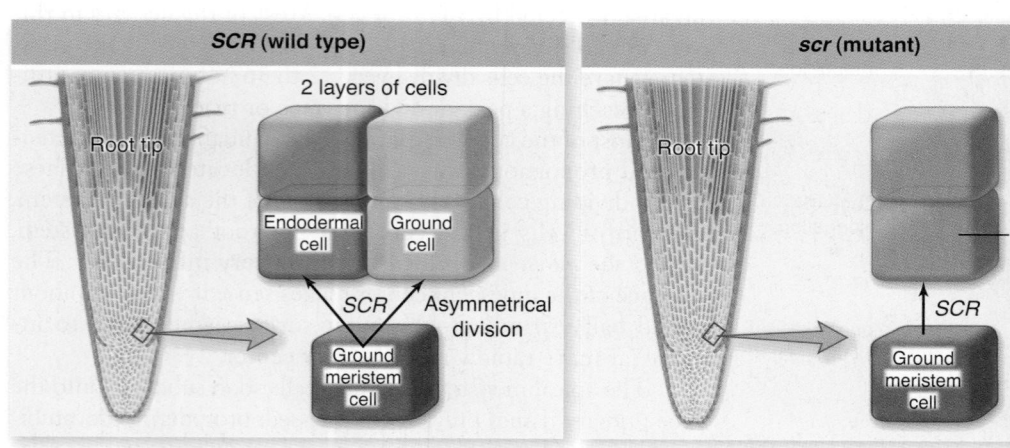
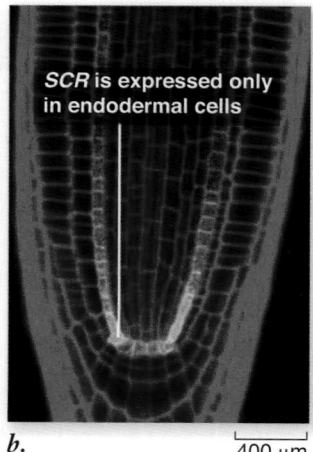

a.

b.
400 μm

Figure 36.16 Scarecrow regulates asymmetrical cell division. *a.* *SCR* is needed for an asymmetrical cell division leading to the differentiation of daughter cells into endodermal and ground cells. *b.* The *SCR* promoter was attached to a gene coding for a green fluorescent protein to find out exactly where in the wild type root *SCR* is expressed. *SCR* is only expressed in the endodermal cells, not the ground cells.

Root hairs can number over 37,000 cm² of root surface and many billions per plant; they greatly increase the surface area and therefore the absorptive capacity of the root. Symbiotic bacteria that fix atmospheric nitrogen into a form usable by legumes enter the plant via root hairs and "instruct" the plant to create a nitrogen-fixing nodule around it (see chapter 39).

Parenchyma cells are produced by the ground meristem immediately to the interior of the epidermis. This tissue, called the **cortex,** may be many cell layers wide and functions in food storage. As just described, the inner boundary of the cortex differentiates into a single-layered cylinder of **endodermis,** after an asymmetrical cell division regulated by *SCR* (see figures 36.16 and 36.17). Endodermal primary walls are impregnated with *suberin,* a fatty substance that is impervious to water. The suberin is produced in bands, called **Casparian strips,** that surround each

adjacent endodermal cell wall perpendicular to the root's surface (see figure 36.17). These strips block transport between cells. The two surfaces that are parallel to the root surface are the only way into the vascular tissue of the root, and the plasma membranes control what passes through. Plants with a *scr* mutation lack this waterproof Casparian strip.

All the tissues interior to the endodermis are collectively referred to as the **stele.** Immediately adjacent and interior to the endodermis is a cylinder of parenchyma cells known as the **pericycle.** Pericycle cells divide, even after they mature. They can give rise to lateral (branch) roots or, in eudicots, to the two lateral meristems, the vascular cambium and the cork cambium.

The water-conducting cells of the primary xylem are differentiated as a solid core in the center of young eudicot roots. In a cross section of a eudicot root, the central core of primary xylem often is somewhat star-shaped, having from two to several radiating arms that point toward the pericycle (see figure 36.17). In monocot (and a few eudicot) roots, the primary xylem is in discrete vascular bundles arranged in a ring, which surrounds

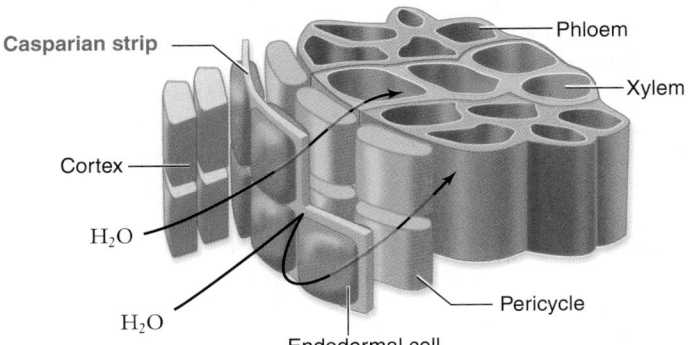

Casparian strip
Cortex
H₂O
H₂O
Endodermal cell
Phloem
Xylem
Pericycle

Figure 36.17 Cross sections of the zone of maturation of roots. Both monocot and eudicot roots have a Casparian strip as seen in the cross section of greenbriar *(Smilax),* a monocot, and buttercup *(Ranunculus),* a eudicot. The Casparian strip is a water-proofing band that forces water and minerals to pass through the plasma membranes, rather than through the spaces in the cell walls.

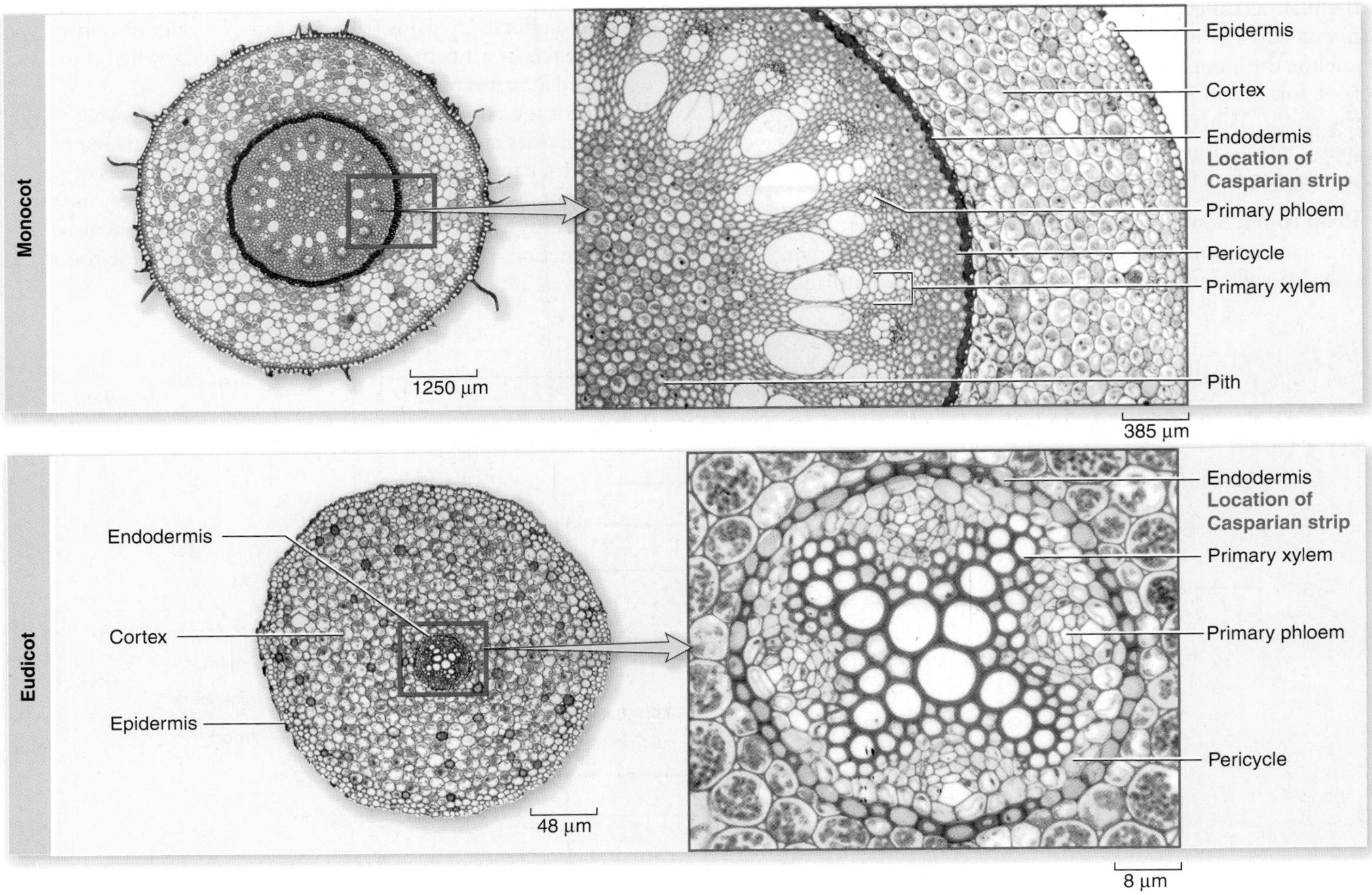

Monocot

1250 µm

Epidermis
Cortex
Endodermis
Location of Casparian strip
Primary phloem
Pericycle
Primary xylem
Pith

385 µm

Eudicot

Endodermis
Cortex
Epidermis

48 µm

Endodermis
Location of Casparian strip
Primary xylem
Primary phloem
Pericycle

8 µm

parenchyma cells, called *pith*, at the very center of the root (see figure 36.17). Primary phloem, composed of cells involved in food conduction, is differentiated in discrete groups of cells adjacent to the xylem in both eudicot and monocot roots.

In eudicots and other plants with secondary growth, part of the pericycle and the parenchyma cells between the phloem patches and the xylem become the root vascular cambium, which starts producing secondary xylem to the inside and secondary phloem to the outside. Eventually, the secondary tissues acquire the form of concentric cylinders. The primary phloem, cortex, and epidermis become crushed and are sloughed off as more secondary tissues are added.

In the pericycle of woody plants, the cork cambium contributes to the outer bark, which will be discussed in more detail when we look at stems. In the case of secondary growth in eudicot roots, everything outside the stele is lost and replaced with bark. Figure 36.18 summarizes the process of differentiation that occurs in plant tissue.

Modified roots accomplish specialized functions

Most plants produce either a taproot system, characterized by a single large root with smaller branch roots, or a fibrous root system, composed of many smaller roots of similar diameter. Some plants, however, have intriguing root modifications with specific functions in addition to those of anchorage and absorption.

Not all roots are produced by preexisting roots. Any root that arises along a stem or in some place other than the root of the plant is called an **adventitious root.** For example, climbing plants such as ivy produce roots from their stems; these can anchor the stems to tree trunks or to a brick wall. Adventitious root formation in ivy depends on the developmental stage of the shoot. When the shoot enters the adult phase of development, it is no longer capable of initiating these roots. Below we investigate functions of modified roots.

Prop roots. Some monocots, such as corn, produce thick adventitious roots from the lower parts of the stem. These so-called prop roots grow down to the ground and brace the plants against wind (figure 36.19*a*). Adventious roots are common in wetland plants, allowing them to tolerate wet conditions.

Aerial roots. Plants such as epiphytic orchids, which are attached to tree branches and grow unconnected to the ground (but are not parasites), have roots that extend into the air (figure 36.19*b*). Some aerial roots have an epidermis that is several cell layers thick, an adaptation to reduce water loss. These aerial roots may also be green and photosynthetic, as in the vanilla orchid (*Vanilla planifolia).*

Pneumatophores. Some plants that grow in swamps and other wet places may produce spongy outgrowths called *pneumatophores* from their underwater roots (figure 36.19*c*). The pneumatophores commonly extend several centimeters above water, facilitating oxygen uptake in the roots beneath (figure 36.19*c*).

Contractile roots. The roots from the bulbs of lilies and from several other plants, such as dandelions, contract by spiraling to pull the plant a little deeper into the soil each year, until they reach an area of relatively stable temperature. The roots may contract to one-third their original length as they spiral like a corkscrew due to cellular thickening and constricting.

Parasitic roots. The stems of certain plants that lack chlorophyll, such as dodder (*Cuscuta* spp.), produce peglike roots called *haustoria* that penetrate the host plants around which they are twined. The haustoria establish contact with the conducting tissues of the host and effectively parasitize their host. Dodder not only weakens plants but can also spread disease when it grows and attaches to several plants.

Food storage roots. The xylem of branch roots of sweet potatoes and similar plants produce at intervals many extra parenchyma cells that store large quantities of carbohydrates. Carrots, beets, parsnips, radishes, and turnips have combinations of stem and root that also function in food storage. Cross sections of these roots reveal multiple rings of secondary growth.

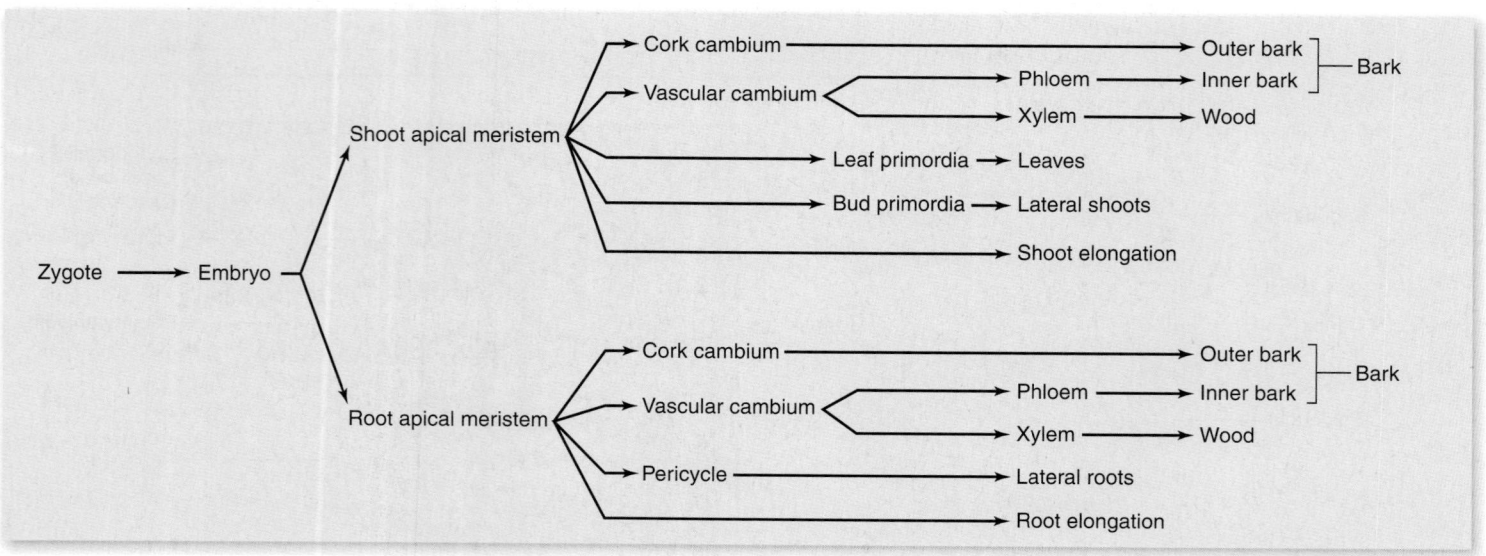

Figure 36.18 Stages in the differentiation of plant tissues.

a.

b.

c.

d.

e.

Figure 36.19 Five types of modified roots. *a.* Maize (corn) prop roots originate from the stem and keep the plant upright. *b.* Epiphytic orchids attach to trees far above the tropical soil. Their roots are adapted to obtain water from the air rather than the soil. *c.* Pneumatophores *(foreground)* are spongy outgrowths from the roots below. *d.* A water storage root weighing over 25 kg (60 pounds). *e.* Buttress roots of a tropical fig tree.

Water storage roots. Some members of the pumpkin family (Cucurbitaceae), especially those that grow in arid regions, may produce water storage roots weighing 50 kg or more (figure 36.19*d*).

Buttress roots. Certain species of fig and other tropical trees produce huge buttress roots toward the base of the trunk, which provide considerable stability (figure 36.19*e*).

Learning Outcomes Review 36.3

The root cap protects the root apical meristem and helps to sense gravity. New cells formed in the zone of cell division grow in length in the zone of elongation. Cells differentiate in the zone of maturation, and root hairs appear here. Root hairs greatly increase the absorptive surface area of roots. Modified roots allow plants to carry out many additional functions, including bracing, aeration, and storage of nutrients and water.

■ *Why do you suppose root hairs are not formed in the region of elongation?*

36.4 Stems: Support for Above-Ground Organs

Learning Outcomes

1. *List the potential products of an axillary bud.*
2. *Differentiate between cross sections of a monocot stem and a eudicot stem.*
3. *Describe three functions of modified stems.*

The supporting structure of a vascular plant's shoot system is the mass of stems that extend from the root system below ground into the air, often reaching great height. Stiff stems capable of rising upward against gravity are an ancient adaptation that allowed plants to move into terrestrial ecosystems.

Stems carry leaves and flowers and support the plant's weight

Like roots, stems contain the three types of plant tissue. Stems also undergo growth from cell division in apical and lateral meristems. The stem may be thought of as an axis from which other stems or organs grow. The shoot apical meristems are capable of producing these new stems and organs.

External stem structure

The shoot apical meristem initiates stem tissue and intermittently produces bulges (primordia) that are capable of developing into leaves, other shoots, or even flowers (figure 36.20).

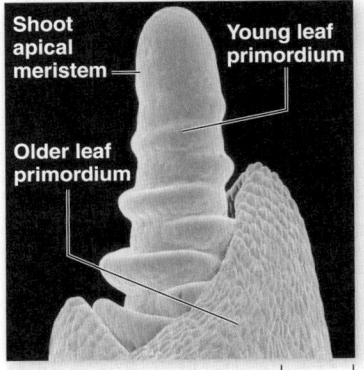

Shoot apical meristem

Young leaf primordium

Older leaf primordium

67 μm

Figure 36.20 A shoot apex. Scanning electron micrograph of the apical meristem of wheat *(Triticum).*

Leaves may be arranged in a spiral around the stem, or they may be in pairs opposite or alternate to one another; they also may occur in whorls (circles) of three or more (figure 36.21). The spiral arrangement is the most common, and for reasons still not understood, sequential leaves tend to be placed 137.5° apart. This angle relates to the golden mean, a mathematical ratio found in nature. The angle of coiling in shells of some gastropods is the same. The golden mean has been used in classical architecture (the Greek Parthenon wall dimensions), and even in modern art (for example, in paintings by Mondrian). In plants, this pattern of leaf arrangement, called **phyllotaxy,** may optimize the exposure of leaves to the sun.

The region or area of leaf attachment to the stem is called a **node;** the area of stem between two nodes is called an **internode.** A leaf usually has a flattened blade and sometimes a petiole (stalk). The angle between a leaf's petiole (or blade) and the stem is called an **axil.** An **axillary bud** is produced in each axil. This bud is a product of the primary shoot apical meristem, and it is itself a shoot apical meristem. Axillary buds frequently develop into branches with leaves or may form flowers.

Neither monocots nor herbaceous eudicot stems produce a cork cambium. The stems in these plants are usually green and photosynthetic, with at least the outer cells of the cortex containing chloroplasts. Herbaceous stems commonly have stomata, and may have various types of trichomes (hairs).

Woody stems can persist over a number of years and develop distinctive markings in addition to the original organs that form (figure 36.22). Terminal buds usually extend the length of the shoot system during the growing season. Some buds, such as those of geraniums, are unprotected, but most buds of woody plants have protective winter bud scales that drop off, leaving tiny bud scale scars as the buds expand.

Some twigs have tiny scars of a different origin. A pair of butterfly-like appendages called *stipules* (part of the leaf) develop at the base of some leaves. The stipules can fall off and leave stipule *scars*. When the leaves of deciduous trees drop in the fall, they leave leaf scars with tiny bundle scars, marking where vascular connections were. The shapes, sizes, and other features of leaf scars can be distinctive enough to identify deciduous plants in winter, when they lack leaves (see figure 36.22).

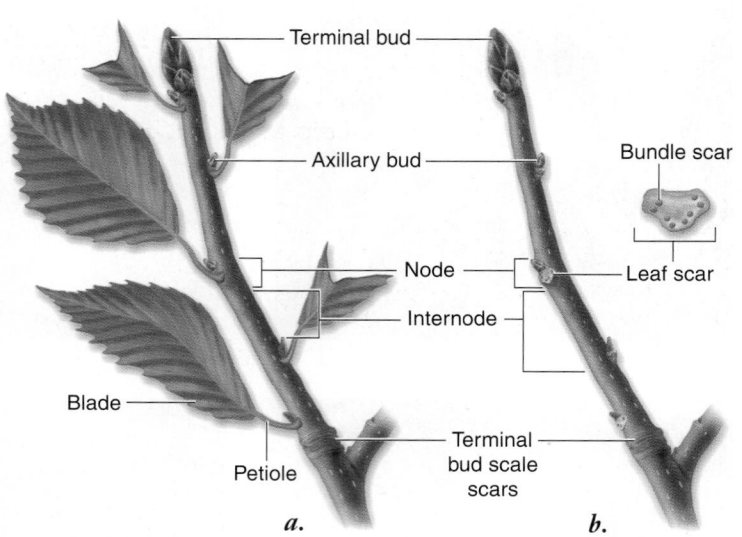

Figure 36.22 A woody twig. *a.* In summer. *b.* In winter.

Internal stem structure

A major distinguishing feature between monocot and eudicot stems is the organization of the vascular tissue system (figure 36.23). Most monocot vascular bundles are scattered throughout the ground tissue system, whereas eudicot vascular tissue is arranged in a ring with internal ground tissue *(pith)* and external ground tissues *(cortex)*. The arrangement of vascular tissue is directly related to the ability of the stem to undergo

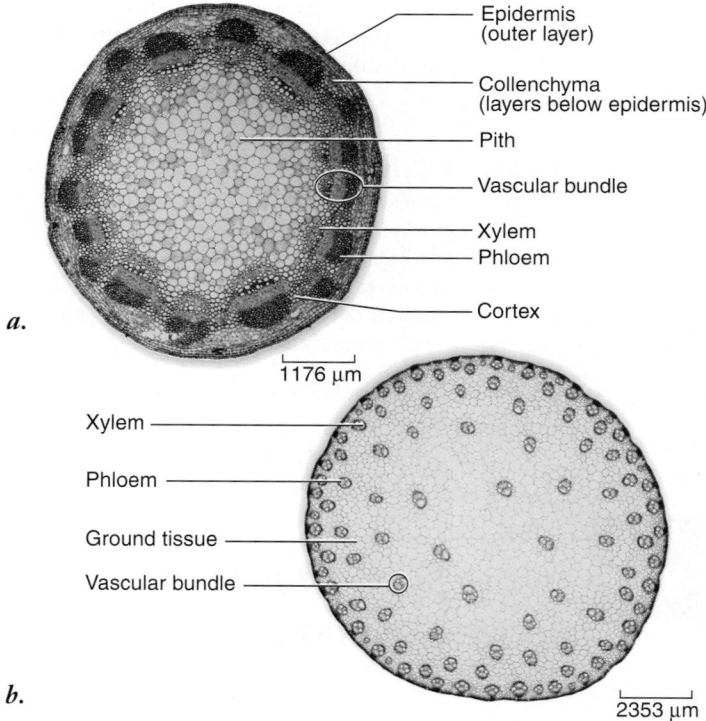

Figure 36.23 Stems. Transverse sections of a young stem in *(a)* a eudicot, the common sunflower (*Helianthus annuus*), in which the vascular bundles are arranged around the outside of the stem; and *(b)* a monocot, corn (*Zea mays*), with characteristically scattered vascular bundles.

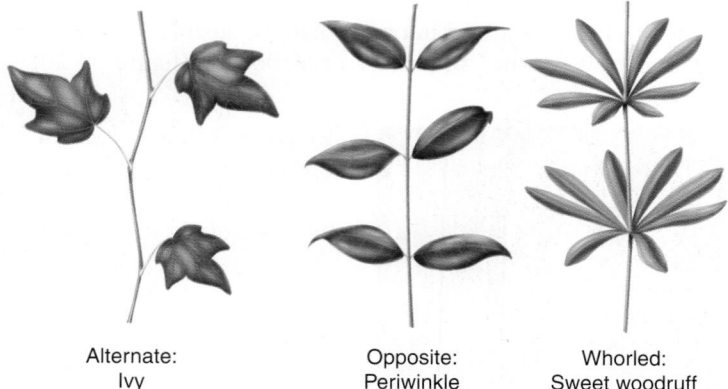

Alternate: Ivy   Opposite: Periwinkle   Whorled: Sweet woodruff

Figure 36.21 Types of leaf arrangements. The three common types of leaf arrangements are alternate, opposite, and whorled.

secondary growth. In eudicots, a vascular cambium may develop between the primary xylem and primary phloem (figure 36.24). In many ways, this is a connect-the-dots game in which the vascular cambium connects the ring of primary vascular bundles. There is no logical way to connect primary monocot vascular tissue that would allow a uniform increase in girth. Lacking a vascular cambium, therefore, monocots do not have secondary growth.

Rings in the stump of a tree reveal annual patterns of vascular cambium growth; cell size varies, depending on growth

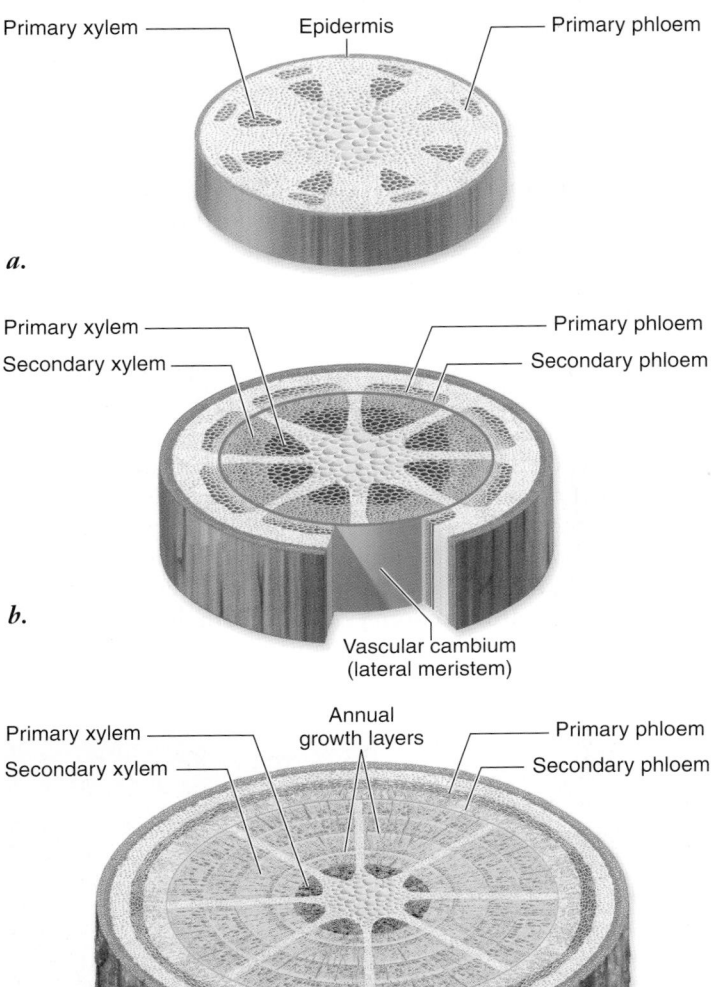

Figure 36.24 Secondary growth. *a.* Before secondary growth begins in eudicot stems, primary tissues continue to elongate as the apical meristems produce primary growth. *b.* As secondary growth begins, the vascular cambium produces secondary tissues, and the stem's diameter increases. *c.* In this four-year-old stem, the secondary tissues continue to widen, and the trunk has become thick and woody. Note that the vascular cambium forms a cylinder that runs axially (up and down) in the roots and shoots that have them.

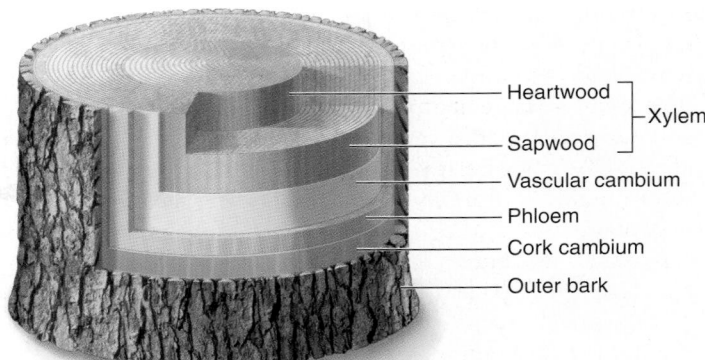

Figure 36.25 Tree stump. The vascular cambium produces rings of xylem (sapwood and nonconducting heartwood) and phloem, and the cork cambium produces the cork.

conditions (figure 36.25). Large cells form under favorable conditions such as abundant rainfalls. Rings of smaller cells mark the seasons where growth is limited. In woody eudicots and gymnosperms, a second cambium, the cork cambium, arises in the outer cortex (occasionally in the epidermis or phloem); it produces boxlike cork cells to the outside and also may produce parenchyma-like phelloderm cells to the inside (figure 36.26).

The cork cambium, cork, and phelloderm are collectively referred to as the *periderm* (see figure 36.26). Cork tissues, the cells of which become impregnated with water-repellent suberin shortly after they are formed and which then die, constitute the *outer bark*. The cork tissue cuts off water and food to the epidermis, which dies and sloughs off. In young stems, gas exchange between stem tissues and the air takes place through stomata, but as the cork cambium produces cork, it also produces patches of unsuberized cells beneath the stomata. These unsuberized cells, which permit gas exchange to continue, are called *lenticels* (figure 36.27).

Modified stems carry out vegetative propagation and store nutrients

Although most stems grow erect, some have modifications that serve special purposes, including natural vegetative propagation. In fact, the widespread artificial vegetative propagation of plants,

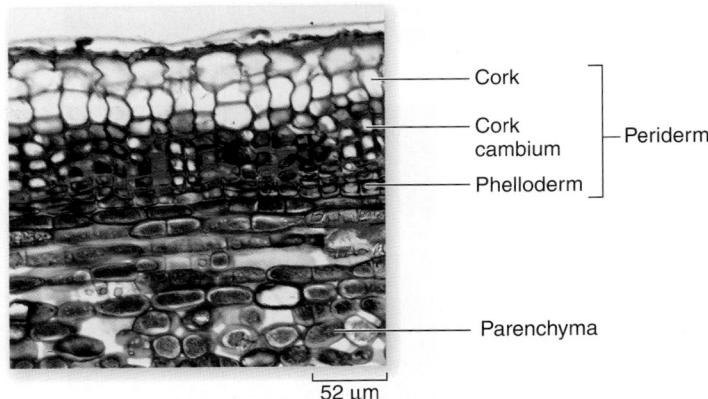

Figure 36.26 Section of periderm. An early stage in the development of periderm in cottonwood, *Populus* sp.

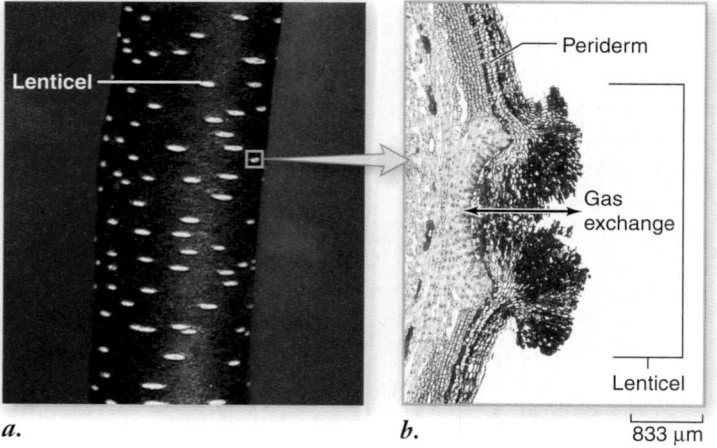

a.   b.   833 µm

Figure 36.27 Lenticels. *a.* Lenticels, the numerous small, pale, raised areas shown here on cherry tree bark *(Prunus cerasifera)*, allow gas exchange between the external atmosphere and the living tissues immediately beneath the bark of woody plants. *b.* Transverse section through a lenticel in a stem of elderberry, *Sambucus canadensis.*

both commercial and private, frequently involves cutting modified stems into segments, which are then planted, producing new plants. As you become acquainted with the following modified stems, keep in mind that stems have leaves at nodes, with internodes between the nodes, and buds in the axils of the leaves, whereas roots have no leaves, nodes, or axillary buds.

Bulbs. Onions, lilies, and tulips have swollen underground stems that are really large buds with adventitious roots at the base (figure 36.28*a*). Most of a bulb consists of fleshy leaves attached to a small, knoblike stem. For most bulbs,

next year's foliage comes from the tip of the shoot apex, protected by storage leaves from the previous year

Corms. Crocuses, gladioluses, and other popular garden plants produce corms that superficially resemble bulbs. Cutting a corm in half, however, reveals no fleshy leaves. Instead, almost all of a corm consists of stem, with a few papery, brown nonfunctional leaves on the outside, and adventitious roots below.

Rhizomes. Perennial grasses, ferns, bearded iris, and many other plants produce rhizomes, which typically are horizontal stems that grow underground, often close to the surface (figure 36.28*b*). Each node has an inconspicuous scalelike leaf with an axillary bud; much larger photosynthetic leaves may be produced at the rhizome tip. Adventitious roots are produced throughout the length of the rhizome, mainly on the lower surface.

Runners and stolons. Strawberry plants produce horizontal stems with long internodes that unlike rhizomes, usually grow along the surface of the ground. Several runners may radiate out from a single plant (figure 36.28*c*). Some biologists use the term *stolon* synonymously with runner; others reserve the term *stolon* for a stem with long internodes (but no roots) that grows underground, as seen in potato plants *(Solanum* sp.). A potato itself, however, is another type of modified stem—a tuber.

Tubers. In potato plants, carbohydrates may accumulate at the tips of rhizomes, which swell, becoming tubers; the rhizomes die after the tubers mature (figure 36.28*d*). The "eyes" of a potato are axillary buds formed in the axils of scalelike leaves. These leaves, which are present when the potato is starting to form, soon drop off; the tiny ridge adjacent to each "eye" of a mature potato is a leaf scar.

Figure 36.28 Types of modified stems. *a.* Bulb. *b.* Adventitious roots. *c.* Runner. d. Stolon. *e.* Tendril. *f.* Cladophyll.

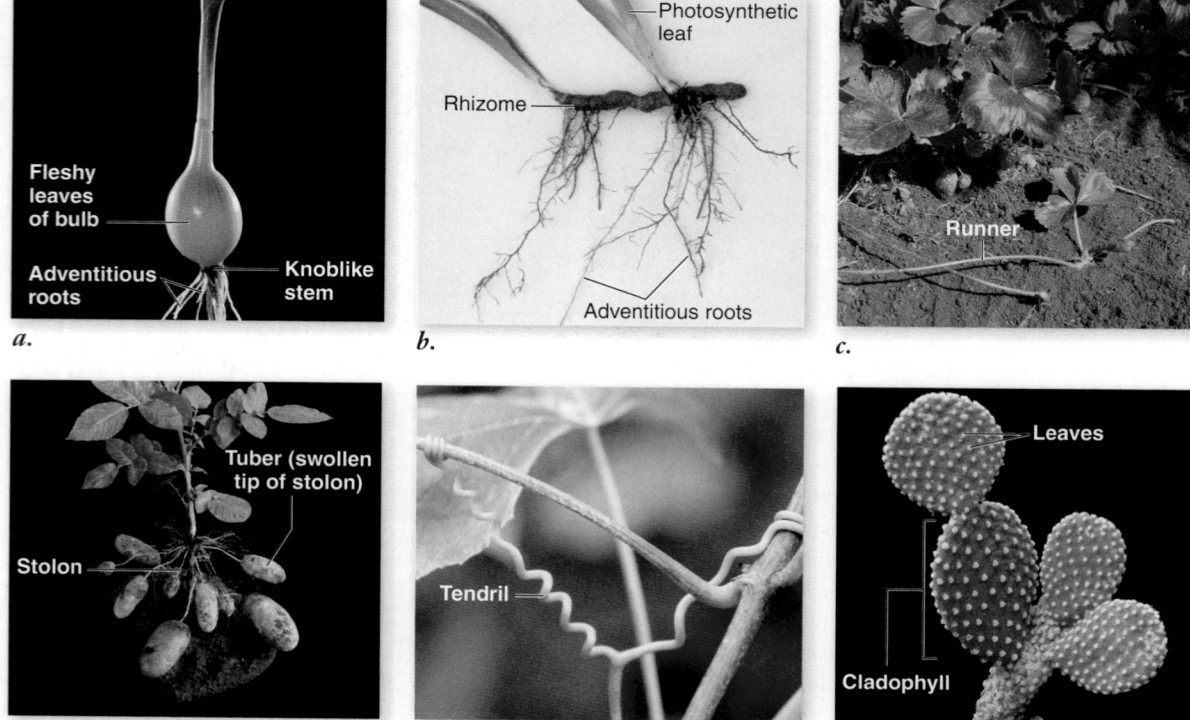

a.   b.   c.

d.   e.   f.

Crop potatoes are not grown from seeds produced by potato flowers, but propagated vegetatively from "seed potatoes." A tuber is cut up into pieces that contain at least one eye, and these pieces are planted. The eye then grows into a new potato plant.

Tendrils. Many climbing plants, such as grapes and English ivy, produce modified stems known as tendrils that twine around supports and aid in climbing (figure 36.28e). Some other tendrils, such as those of peas and pumpkins, are actually modified leaves or leaflets.

Cladophylls. Cacti and several other plants produce flattened, photosynthetic stems called cladophylls that resemble leaves (figure 36.28f). In cacti, the real leaves are modified as spines (see the following section).

Learning Outcomes Review 36.4

Shoots grow from apical and lateral meristems. Auxilliary buds may develop into branches, flowers, or leaves. In monocots, vascular tissue is evenly spaced throughout the stem ground tissue; in eudicots, vascular tissue is arranged in a ring with inner and outer ground tissues. Some plants produce modified stems for support, vegetative reproduction, or nutrient storage.

■ *Why don't stems produce the equivalent of root caps?*

36.5 Leaves: Photosynthetic Organs

Learning Outcomes

1. *Distinguish between a simple and a compound leaf.*
2. *Compare the mesophyll of a monocot leaf with that of a eudicot leaf.*

Leaves, which are initiated as primordia by the apical meristems (see figure 36.20), are vital to life as we know it because they are the principal sites of photosynthesis on land, providing the base of the food chain. Leaves expand by cell enlargement and cell division. Like arms and legs in humans, they are determinate structures, which means their growth stops at maturity. Because leaves are crucial to a plant, features such as their arrangement, form, size, and internal structure are highly significant and can differ greatly. Different patterns have adaptive value in different environments.

Leaves are an extension of the shoot apical meristem and stem development. When they first emerge as primordia, they are not committed to being leaves. Experiments in which very young leaf primordia are isolated from fern and coleus plants and grown in culture have demonstrated this feature: If the primordia are young enough, they will form an entire shoot rather than a leaf. The positioning of leaf primordia and the initial cell divisions occur before those cells are committed to the leaf developmental pathway.

External leaf structure reflects vascular morphology

Leaves fall into two different morphological groups, which may reflect differences in evolutionary origin. A **microphyll** is a leaf with one vein branching from the vascular cylinder of the stem and not extending the full length of the leaf; microphylls are mostly small and are associated primarily with the phylum Lycophyta (see chapter 30). Most plants have leaves called **megaphylls,** which have several to many veins.

Most eudicot leaves have a flattened **blade** and a slender stalk, the **petiole.** The flattening of the leaf blade reflects a shift from radial symmetry to dorsal–ventral (top–bottom) symmetry. Leaf flattening increases the photosynthetic surface. Plant biologists are just beginning to understand how this shift occurs by analyzing mutants lacking distinct tops and bottoms (figure 36.29).

In addition, leaves may have a pair of **stipules,** which are outgrowths at the base of the petiole. The stipules, which may be leaf-like or modified as spines (as in the black locust, *Robinia pseudo-acacia*) or glands (as in the purple-leaf plum tree *Prunus cerasifera*), vary considerably in size from the microscopic to almost half the size of the leaf blade. Grasses and other monocot leaves usually lack a petiole; these leaves tend to sheathe the stem toward the base.

Veins (a term used for the vascular bundles in leaves) consist of both xylem and phloem and are distributed

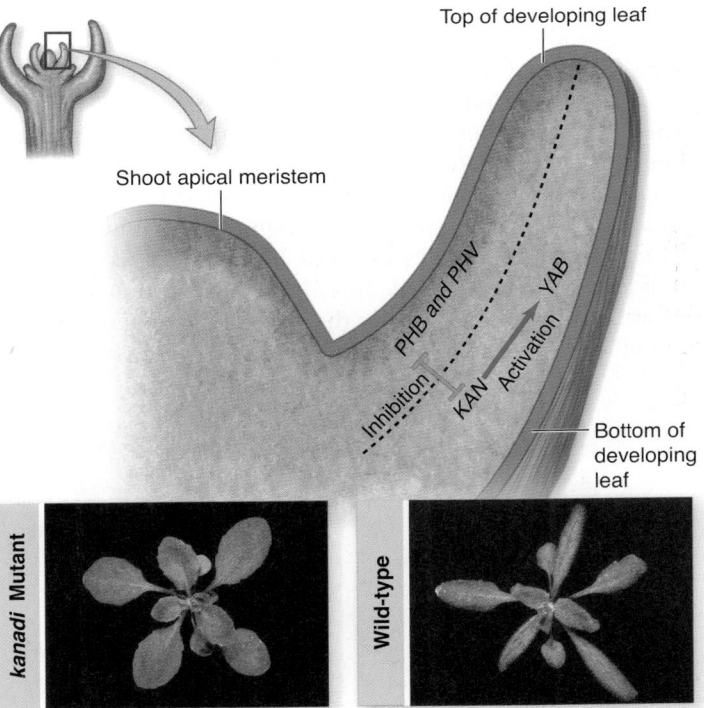

Figure 36.29 Establishing top and bottom in leaves.
Several genes, including *PHABULOSA (PHB)*, *PHAVOLUTA (PHV)*, *KANADI (KAN)*, and *YABBY (YAB)* make a flattened *Arabidopsis* leaf with a distinct upper and lower surface. *PHB* and *PHV* RNAs are restricted to the top; *KAN* and *YAB* are expressed in the bottom cells of a leaf. PHB and KAN have an antagonistic relationship, restricting expression of each to separate leaf regions. *KAN* leads to *YABBY* expression and lower leaf development. Without *KAN*, both sides of the leaf develop like the top portion.

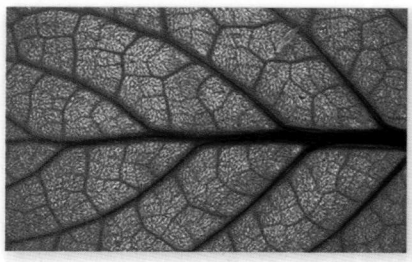

a.

b.

Figure 36.30
Eudicot and monocot leaves. *a.* The leaves of eudicots, such as this African violet relative from Sri Lanka, have netted, or reticulate, veins. *b.* Those of monocots, such as this cabbage palmetto, have parallel veins. The eudicot leaf has been cleared with chemicals and stained with a red dye to make the veins show more clearly.

throughout the leaf blades. The main veins are parallel in most monocot leaves; the veins of eudicots, on the other hand, form an often intricate network (figure 36.30).

Leaf blades come in a variety of forms, from oval to deeply lobed to having separate leaflets. In **simple leaves** (figure 36.31*a*), such as those of lilacs or birch trees, the blades are undivided, but simple leaves may have teeth, indentations, or lobes of various sizes, as in the leaves of maples and oaks.

In **compound leaves** (figure 36.31*b*), such as those of ashes, box elders, and walnuts, the blade is divided into *leaflets*. The relationship between the development of compound and simple leaves is an open question. Two explanations are being debated: (1) A compound leaf is a highly lobed simple leaf, or (2) a compound leaf utilizes a shoot development program, and each leaflet was once a leaf. To address this question, researchers are using single mutations that are known to convert compound leaves to simple leaves (figure 36.32).

a.   *b.*

Figure 36.31 Simple versus compound leaves.
a. A simple leaf, its margin deeply lobed, from the oak tree (*Quercus robur*). *b.* A pinnately compound leaf, from a black walnut (*Juglans nigra*). A compound leaf is associated with a single lateral bud, located where the petiole is attached to the stem.

SCIENTIFIC THINKING

Hypothesis: *The gene UNIFOLIATA (UNI) is necessary for compound leaf development in garden pea, Pisum sativum.*

Prediction: *Developing leaf primordia of a wild-type pea plant will express the UNI gene while uni mutant plants will not express the gene.*

Test: *Cut thin sections of wild-type and mutant pea shoots and place them on a microscope slide. Test for the presence of UNI RNA using a color-labeled, single-stranded DNA probe that will hybridize (bind) only the UNI RNA. View the labeled sections under a microscope.*

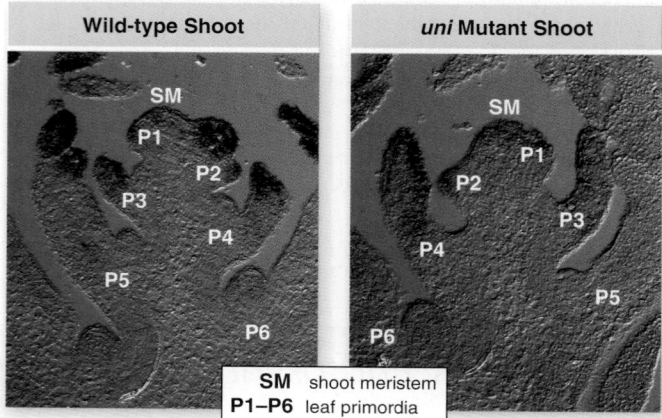

| **SM** | shoot meristem |
| **P1–P6** | leaf primordia |

Result: *UNI RNA was found in the wild-type and also in mutant leaves, but at lower levels.*

Conclusion: *The mutant uni gene is transcribed but at lower levels than the wild-type gene. Thus the prediction was incorrect.*

Further Experiments: *Although the uni gene is expressed, compound leaves do not develop. Refine the hypothesis and propose an experiment to test the revised hypothesis.*

Figure 36.32 Genetic regulation of leaf development.

Internal leaf structure regulates gas exchange and evaporation

The entire surface of a leaf is covered by a transparent epidermis, and most of these epidermal cells have no chloroplasts. As described earlier, the epidermis has a waxy cuticle, and different types of glands and trichomes may be present. Also, the lower epidermis (and occasionally the upper epidermis) of most leaves contains numerous slitlike or mouth-shaped stomata flanked by guard cells (figure 36.33).

The tissue between the upper and lower epidermis is called **mesophyll.** Mesophyll is interspersed with veins of various sizes.

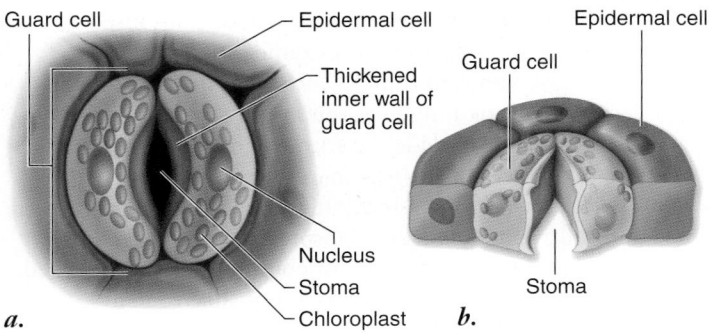

Figure 36.33 A stoma. *a.* Surface view. *b.* View in cross section.

Most eudicot leaves have two distinct types of mesophyll. Closest to the upper epidermis are one to several (usually two) rows of tightly packed, barrel-shaped to cylindrical chlorenchyma cells (parenchyma with chloroplasts) that constitute the palisade mesophyll (figure 36.34). Some plants, including species of *Eucalyptus*, have leaves that hang down, rather than extend horizontally. They have palisade mesophyll on both sides of the leaf.

Nearly all eudicot leaves have loosely arranged spongy mesophyll cells between the palisade mesophyll and the lower epidermis, with many air spaces throughout the tissue. The interconnected intercellular spaces, along with the stomata, function in gas exchange and the passage of water vapor from the leaves.

The mesophyll of monocot leaves often is not differentiated into palisade and spongy layers, and there is often little distinction between the upper and lower epidermis. Instead, cells surrounding the vascular tissue are distinctive and are the site of carbon fixation. This anatomical difference often correlates with a modified photosynthetic pathway, C_4 *photosynthesis*, that maximizes the amount of CO_2 relative to O_2 to reduce energy loss through photorespiration (see chapter 9). The anatomy of a leaf directly relates to its juggling act of balancing water loss, gas exchange, and transport of photosynthetic products to the rest of the plant.

Modified leaves are highly versatile organs

As plants colonized a wide variety of environments, from deserts to lakes to tropical rain forests, plant organ modifications arose that would adapt the plants to their specific habitats. Leaves, in particular, have evolved some remarkable adaptations. A brief discussion of a few of these modifications follows:

Floral leaves (bracts). Poinsettias and dogwoods have relatively inconspicuous, small, greenish yellow flowers. However, both plants produce large modified leaves called *bracts* (mostly colored red in poinsettias and white or pink in dogwoods). These bracts surround the true flowers and perform the same function as showy petals. In other plants, however, bracts can be quite small and inconspicuous.

Spines. The leaves of many cacti and other plants are modified as *spines* (see figure 36.28f). In cacti, having less leaf surface reduces water loss, and the sharp spines also may deter predators. Spines should not be confused with *thorns*, such as those on the honey locust (*Gleditsia triacanthos*), which are modified stems, or with the prickles on raspberries, which are simply outgrowths from the epidermis or the cortex just beneath it.

Reproductive leaves. Several plants, notably *Kalanchoë*, produce tiny but complete plantlets along their margins. Each plantlet, when separated from the leaf, is capable of growing independently into a full-sized plant. The walking fern (*Asplenium rhizophyllum*) produces new plantlets at the tips of its fronds. Although many species can regenerate a whole plant from isolated leaf tissue, this in vivo regeneration is found among just a few species.

Window leaves. Several genera of plants growing in arid regions produce succulent, cone-shaped leaves with transparent tips. The leaves often become mostly buried

Figure 36.34 A leaf in cross section. Transection of a leaf showing the arrangement of palisade and spongy mesophyll, a vascular bundle or vein, and the epidermis with paired guard cells flanking the stoma.

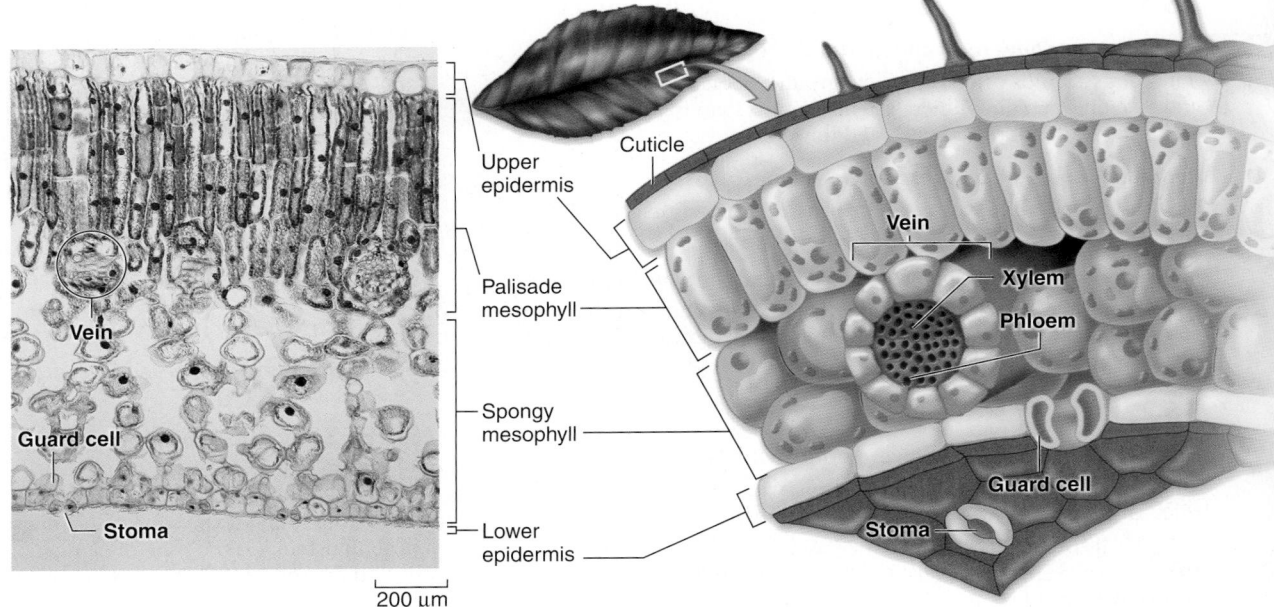

200 μm

in sand blown by the wind, but the transparent tips, which have a thick epidermis and cuticle, admit light to the hollow interiors. This strategy allows photosynthesis to take place beneath the surface of the ground.

Shade leaves. Leaves produced in the shade, where they receive little sunlight, tend to be larger in surface area, but thinner and with less mesophyll than leaves on the same tree receiving more direct light. This plasticity in development is remarkable. Environmental signals can have a major effect on development.

Insectivorous leaves. Almost 200 species of flowering plants are known to have leaves that trap insects; some plants digest the insects' soft parts. Plants with insectivorous leaves often grow in acid swamps that are deficient in needed elements or contain elements in forms not readily available to the plants; this inhibits the plants' capacities to maintain metabolic processes needed for their growth and reproduction. Their needs are met, however, by the supplementary absorption of nutrients from the animal kingdom.

Pitcher plants (for example, *Sarracenia*, *Darlingtonia*, or *Nepenthes* spp.) have cone-shaped leaves in which rainwater can accumulate. The insides of the leaves are very smooth, but stiff, downward-pointing hairs line the rim. An insect falling into such a leaf finds it very difficult to escape and eventually drowns. The leaf absorbs the nutrients released when bacteria, and in most species the plant's own digestive enzymes, decompose the insect bodies. Other plants, such as sundews (*Drosera*), have

glands that secrete sticky mucilage that traps insects, which are then digested by enzymes.

The Venus flytrap (*Dionaea muscipula*) produces leaves that look hinged at the midrib. When tiny trigger hairs on the leaf blade are stimulated by a moving insect, the two halves of the leaf snap shut, and digestive enzymes break down the soft parts of the trapped insect into nutrients that can be absorbed through the leaf surface. Nitrogen is the most common nutrient needed. Curiously, the Venus flytrap cannot survive in a nitrogen-rich environment, perhaps as a result of a biochemical trade-off during the intricate evolutionary process that developed its ability to capture and digest insects.

Learning Outcomes Review 36.5

Leaves come in a range of forms. A simple leaf is undivided, whereas a compound leaf has a number of separate leaflets. Pinnate leaves have a central rib like a feather; palmate leaves have several ribs radiating from a central point, like the palm of the hand. Monocots typically produce leaves with parallel veins, while those of eudicots are netted. Mesophyll cells carry out photosynthesis; in monocots, mesophyll is undifferentiated, whereas in eudicots it is divided into palisade and spongy mesophyll. Leaves may be modified for reproduction, protection, water conservation, uptake of nutrients, and even as traps for insects.

■ *Why would a plant with vertically oriented leaves produce palisade, but not spongy mesophyll cells?*

Chapter Review

36.1 Organization of the Plant Body: An Overview

Vascular plants have roots and shoots.
The root system is primarily below ground; roots anchor the plant and take up water and minerals. The shoot system is above ground and provides support for leaves and flowers.

Roots and shoots are composed of three types of tissues.
The three types of tissues are dermal tissue, ground tissue, and vascular tissue.

Meristems elaborate the body plan throughout the plant's life.
Apical meristems are located on the tips of stems and near the tips of roots. Lateral meristems are found in plants that exhibit secondary growth. They add to the diameter of a stem or root.

36.2 Plant Tissues

Dermal tissue forms a protective interface with the environment.
Dermal tissue is primarily the epidermis, which is usually one cell thick and is covered with a fatty or waxy cuticle to retard water loss. Guard cells in the epidermis control water loss through stomata. Root hairs are epidermal cell structures that help increase the absorptive area of roots.

Ground tissue cells perform many functions, including storage, photosynthesis, and support.
Ground tissue is mainly composed of parenchyma cells, which function in storage, photosynthesis, and secretion. Collenchyma cells provide flexible support, and sclerenchyma cells provide rigid support.

Vascular tissue conducts water and nutrients throughout the plant.
Xylem tissue conducts water through dead cells called tracheids and vessel elements.

Phloem tissue conducts nutrients such as dissolved sucrose through living cells called sieve-tube members and sieve cells.

36.3 Roots: Anchoring and Absorption Structures

Roots evolved after shoots and are a major innovation for terrestrial living.

Roots are adapted for growing underground and absorbing water and solutes.
Developing roots exhibit four regions: (1) the root cap, which protects the root; (2) the zone of cell division, which contains the apical meristem; (3) the zone of elongation, which extends the root through the soil; and (4) the zone of maturation, in which cells become differentiated.

Modified roots accomplish specialized functions.

Most plants produce either a taproot system containing a single large root with smaller branch roots, or a fibrous root system composed of many small roots.

Adventitious roots may be modified for support, stability, acquisition of oxygen, storage of water and food, or parasitism of a host plant.

36.4 Stems: Support for Above-Ground Organs

Stems carry leaves and flowers and support the plant's weight.

Leaves are attached to stems at nodes. The axil is the area between the leaf and stem, and an axillary bud develops in axils of eudicots.

The vascular bundles in stems of monocots are randomly scattered, whereas in eudicots the bundles are arranged in a ring.

Vascular cambium develops between the inner xylem and the outer phloem, allowing for secondary growth.

Modified stems carry out vegetative propagation and store nutrients.

Bulbs, corms, rhizomes, runners and stolons, tubers, tendrils, and cladophylls are examples of modified stems. The tubers of potatoes are both a food source and a means of propagating new plants.

36.5 Leaves: Photosynthetic Organs

Leaves are the principle sites of photosynthesis. Leaf features such as their arrangement, form, size, and internal structure can be highly variable across environments.

External leaf structure reflects vascular morphology.

Vascular bundles are parallel in monocots, but form a network in eudicots. The leaves of most eudicots have a flattened blade and a slender petiole; monocots usually do not have a petiole.

Leaf blades may be simple or compound (divided into leaflets). Leaves may also be pinnate (with a central rib, like a feather) or palmate (with ribs radiating from a central point).

Internal leaf structure regulates gas exchange and evaporation.

The tissues of the leaf include the epidermis with guard cells, vascular tissue, and mesophyll in which photosynthesis takes place.

In eudicot leaves with a horizontal orientation, the mesophyll is partitioned into palisade cells near the upper surface and spongy cells near the lower surface.

The mesophyll of monocot leaves is often not differentiated.

Modified leaves are highly versatile organs.

Leaves are highly variable in form and are adapted to serve many different functions. Leaves may be modified for reproduction, protection, storage, mineral uptake, or even as insect traps in carnivorous plants.

Review Questions

UNDERSTAND

1. Which cells lack living protoplasts at maturity?
   - a. Parenchyma
   - b. Companion
   - c. Collenchyma
   - d. Sclerenchyma

2. The food-conducting cells in an oak tree are called
   - a. tracheids.
   - b. vessels.
   - c. companion cells.
   - d. sieve-tube members.

3. Root hairs form in the zone of
   - a. cell division.
   - b. elongation.
   - c. maturation.
   - d. more than one of the above

4. Roots differ from stems because roots lack
   - a. vessel elements.
   - b. nodes.
   - c. an epidermis.
   - d. ground tissue.

5. A plant that produces two axillary buds at a node is said to have what type of leaf arrangement?
   - a. Opposite
   - b. Alternate
   - c. Whorled
   - d. Palmate

6. Unlike eudicot stems, monocot stems lack
   - a. vascular bundles.
   - b. parenchyma.
   - c. pith.
   - d. epidermis.

7. The function of guard cells is to
   - a. allow carbon dioxide uptake.
   - b. repel insects and other herbivores.
   - c. support leaf tissue.
   - d. allow water uptake.

8. Palisade and spongy parenchyma are typically found in the mesophyll of
   - a. monocots.
   - b. eudicots.
   - c. monocots and eudicots.
   - d. neither monocots or eudicots

9. In vascular plants, one difference between root and shoot systems is that:
   - a. root systems cannot undergo secondary growth.
   - b. root systems undergo secondary growth, but do not form bark.
   - c. root systems contain pronounced zones of cell elongation, whereas shoot systems do not.
   - d. root systems can store food reserves, whereas stem structures do not.

10. Which of the following statements is not true of the stems of vascular plants?
    - a. Stems are composed of repeating segments, including nodes and internodes.
    - b. Primary growth only occurs at the shoot apical meristem.
    - c. Vascular tissues may be arranged on the outside of the stem or scattered throughout the stem.
    - d. Stems can contain stomata.

11. Which of the following plant cell type is mismatched to its function?
    - a. Xylem—conducts mineral nutrients
    - b. Phloem—serves as part of the bark
    - c. Trichomes—reduces evaporation
    - d. Collenchyma—performs photosynthesis

1. Fifteen years ago, your parents hung a swing from the lower branch of a large tree growing in your yard. When you go and sit in it today, you realize it is exactly the same height off the ground as it was when you first sat in it 15 years ago. The reason the swing is not higher off the ground as the tree has grown is that
   a. the tree trunk lacks secondary growth.
   b. the tree trunk is part of the primary growth system of the plant, but elongation is no longer occurring in that part of the tree.
   c. trees lack apical meristems and so do not get taller.
   d. you are hallucinating, because it is impossible for the swing not to have been raised off the ground as the tree grew.

2. A unique feature of plants is indeterminate growth. Indeterminate growth is possible because
   a. meristematic regions for primary growth occur throughout the entire plant body.
   b. all cell types in a plant often give rise to meristematic tissue.
   c. meristematic cells continually replace themselves.
   d. all cells in a plant continue to divide indefinitely.

3. If you were to relocate the pericycle of a plant root to the epidermal layer, how would it affect root growth?
   a. Secondary growth in the mature region of the root would not occur.
   b. The root apical meristem would produce vascular tissue in place of dermal tissue.
   c. Nothing would change because the pericycle is normally located near the epidermal layer of the root.
   d. Lateral roots would grow from the outer region of the root and fail to connect with the vascular tissue.

4. Many vegetables are grown today through hydroponics, in which the plant roots exist primarily in an aqueous solution. Which of the following root structures is no longer beneficial in hydroponics?
   a. Epidermis   c. Root cap
   b. Xylem   d. Bark

5. When you peel your potatoes for dinner, you are removing the majority of their
   a. dermal tissue.
   b. vascular tissue.
   c. ground tissue.
   d. Only (a) and (b) are removed with the peel.
   e. All of these are removed with the peel.

6. You can determine the age of an oak tree by counting the annual rings of _____ formed by the _____.
   a. primary xylem; apical meristem
   b. secondary phloem; vascular cambium
   c. dermal tissue; cork cambium
   d. secondary xylem; vascular cambium

7. Root hairs and lateral roots are similar in each respect except
   a. both increase the absorptive surface area of the root system.
   b. both are generally long-lived.
   c. both are multicellular.
   d. (b) and (c).

8. Plant organs form by
   a. cell division in gamete tissue.
   b. cell division in meristematic tissue.
   c. cell migration into the appropriate position in the tissue.
   d. eliminating chromosomes in the precursor cells.

9. Which is the correct sequence of cell types encountered in an oak tree, moving from the center of the tree out?
   a. Pith, secondary xylem, primary xylem, vascular cambium, primary phloem, secondary phloem, cork cambium, cork.
   b. Pith, primary xylem, secondary xylem, vascular cambium, secondary phloem, primary phloem, cork cambium, cork
   c. Pith, primary xylem, secondary xylem, vascular cambium, secondary phloem, primary phloem, cork, cork cambium
   d. Pith, primary phloem secondary phloem, vascular cambium, secondary xylem, primary xylem, cork cambium, cork.

10. You've just bought a house with a great view of the mountains, but you have a neighbor who planted a bunch of trees that are now blocking your view. In an attempt to ultimately remove the trees and remain unlinked to the deed, you begin training several porcupines to enter the yard under the cover of night and perform a stealth operation. In order to most effectively kill the trees, you should train the porcupines to completely remove
    a. the vascular cambium.
    b. the cork.
    c. the cork cambium.
    d. the primary phloem.

SYNTHESIZE

1. If you were given an unfamiliar vegetable, how could you tell if it was a root or a stem, based on its external features and a microscopic examination of its cross section?

2. Potato tubers harvested from wet soil often have large lenticels. What is the adaptive significance of this?

3. Plant organs undergo many modifications to deal with environmental challenges. Design an imaginary, modified root, shoot, or leaf, and make a case for why it is the best example of a modified plant organ.

4. You have identified a mutant maize plant that cannot differentiate vessel cells. How would this affect the functioning of the plant?

5. Increasing human population on the planet is stretching our ability to produce sufficient food to support the world's population. If you could engineer the perfect crop plant, what features might it possess?

ONLINE RESOURCE

www.ravenbiology.com

Understand, Apply, and Synthesize—enhance your study with animations that bring concepts to life and practice tests to assess your understanding. Your instructor may also recommend the interactive eBook, individualized learning tools, and more.

Chapter 37

Vegetative Plant Development

Chapter Outline

37.1 Embryo Development

37.2 Seeds

37.3 Fruits

37.4 Germination

Introduction

How does a fertilized egg develop into a complex adult plant body? Because plant cells cannot move, the timing and directionality of each cell division must be carefully orchestrated. Cells need information about their location relative to other cells so that cell specialization is coordinated. The developing embryo is quite fragile, and numerous protective structures have evolved since plants first colonized land.

Only a portion of the plant has actually formed when its seedling first emerges from the soil. New plant organs develop throughout the plant's life.

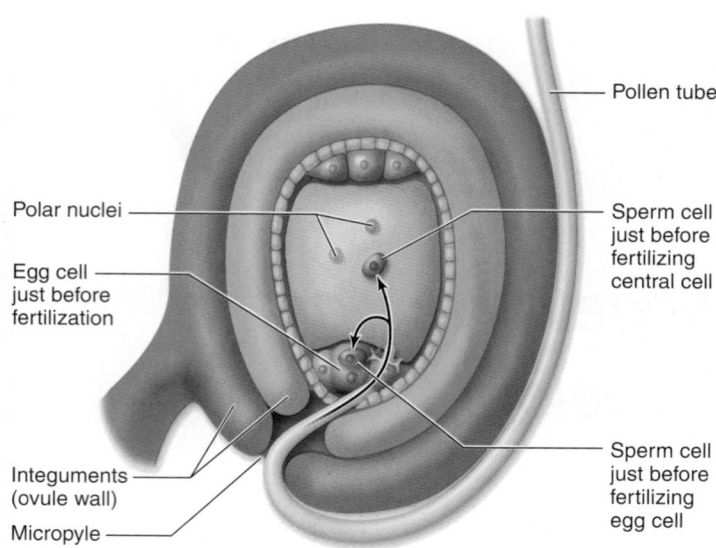

Figure 37.1 **Fertilization triggers embryogenesis.** The egg cell, within the embryo sac, is fertilized by one sperm cell released from the pollen tube. The second sperm cell fertilizes the central cell and initiates endosperm development. This diagram shows sperm just before fertilization.

Learning Outcomes

1. *Name the two axes of the plant body that are established during embryonic development.*
2. *List the three tissue systems that develop in an embryo.*
3. *Describe the three critical events that must accompany seed development.*

Embryo development begins once the egg cell is fertilized. As described briefly in chapter 30, the growing pollen tube from a pollen grain enters the angiosperm embryo sac through one of the synergids, releasing two sperm cells (figure 37.1). One sperm cell fertilizes the central cell with its polar nuclei, and the resulting cell division produces a nutrient source, the **endosperm,** for the embryo. The other sperm cell fertilizes the egg to produce a zygote, and cell division soon follows, creating the **embryo.**

A single cell divides to produce a three-dimensional body plan

The first division of the zygote (fertilized egg) in a flowering plant is asymmetrical and generates cells with two different fates (figure 37.2). One daughter cell is small, with dense cytoplasm. That cell, which is destined to become the embryo, begins to divide repeatedly in different planes, forming a ball of cells. The other, larger daughter cell divides repeatedly, forming an elongated structure called a **suspensor,** which links the embryo to the nutrient tissue of the seed. The suspensor also provides a route for nutrients to reach the developing embryo. The root–shoot axis also forms at this time; cells near the sus-

pensor are destined to form a root, while those at the other end of the axis ultimately become a shoot.

Investigating mechanisms for establishing asymmetry in plant embryo development is difficult because the zygote is embedded within the female gametophyte, which is surrounded by sporophyte tissue (ovule and carpel tissue) (see chapter 30). To understand the cell biology of the first asymmetrical division of zygotes, biologists have studied the brown alga *Fucus*. We must be cautious about inferring too much about angiosperm asymmetrical divisions from the brown algae because the last common ancestor of brown algae and the angiosperm line was a single-celled organism. Nevertheless,

Figure 37.2 **Stages of development in an angiosperm embryo.** The very first cell division is asymmetrical. Differentiation begins almost immediately after fertilization.

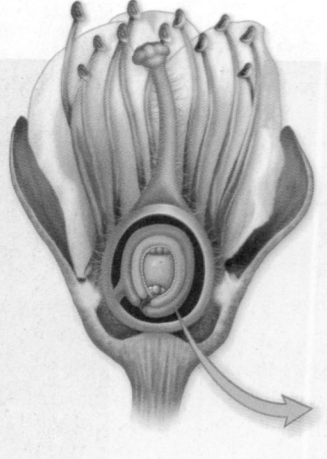

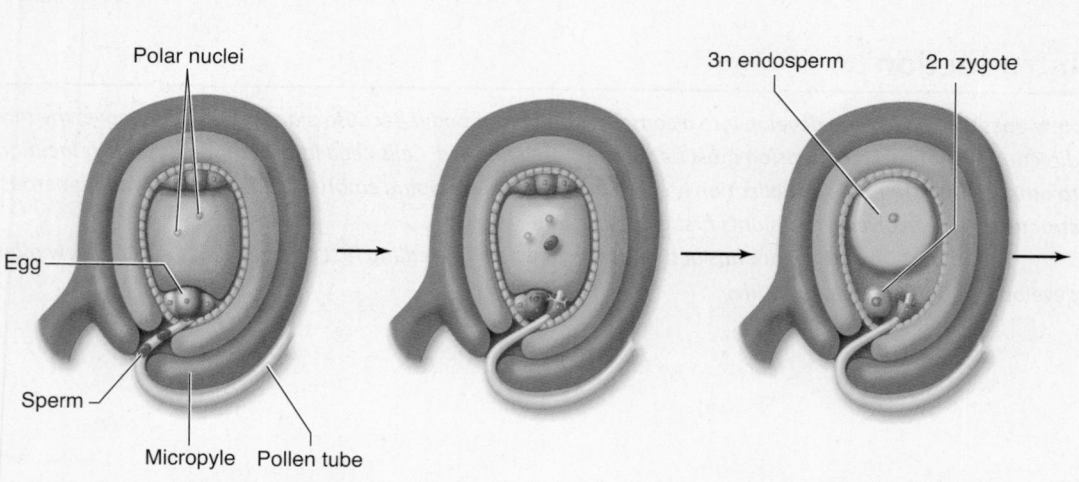

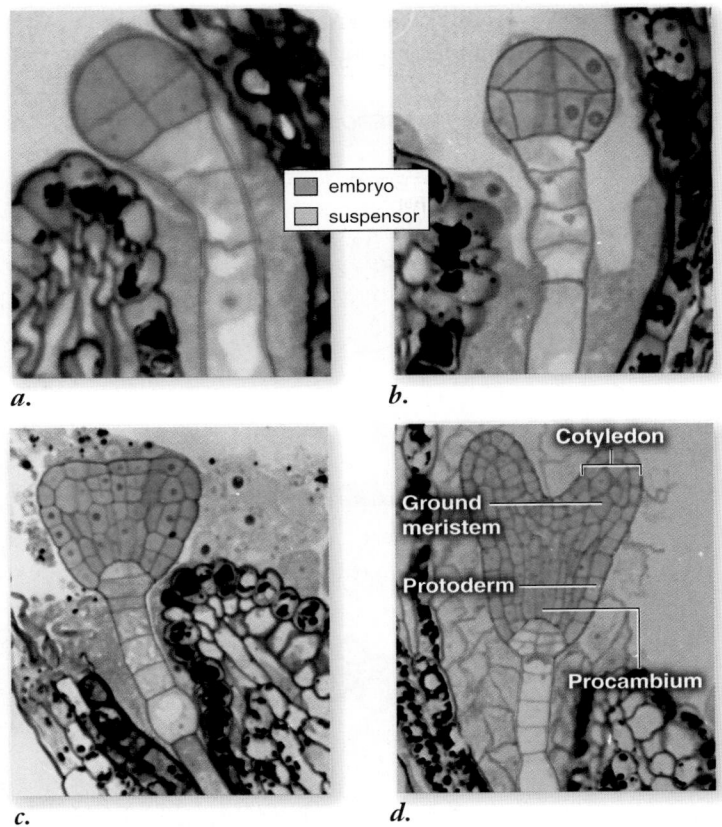

a.

b.

embryo
suspensor

Cotyledon

Ground
meristem

Protoderm

Procambium

c.

d.

Figure 37.6 Early developmental stages of *Arabidopsis thaliana*. *a.* Early cell division has produced the embryo and suspensor. *b.* Globular stage results from cell divisions along both the root–shoot and radial axes. Cell differentiation, including establishment of the root and shoot apical meristems occurs at this stage. *c, d.* Heart-shaped stage. The cotyledons (seed leaves) are now visible, and the three tissue systems continue to differentiate.

Figure 37.7 *SHOOTMERISTEMLESS* is needed for shoot formation. Shoot-specific genes specify formation of the shoot apical meristem, but are not necessary for root development. The *stm* mutant of *Arabidopsis* (shown on top) has a normal root meristem but fails to produce a shoot meristem between its two cotyledons. The *STM* wild type is shown below the *stm* mutant for comparison.

Root formation requires the *HOBBIT* gene in *Arabidopsis* (figure 37.8). The *hobbit* mutants form shoot meristems, but no root meristems form. Cell divisions in *hobbit* roots occur in the wrong directions. Plants with a *hobbit* mutation accumulate a biochemical repressor of genes that are induced by auxin (a plant hormone). Based on the mutant phenotype, *HOBBIT* appears to repress the production of the repressor of auxin-induced genes. Or, more simply stated, HOBBIT protein allows auxin to induce the expression of a gene or genes needed for correct cell division to make a root meristem. Auxin is one of seven classes of hormones that regulate plant development and

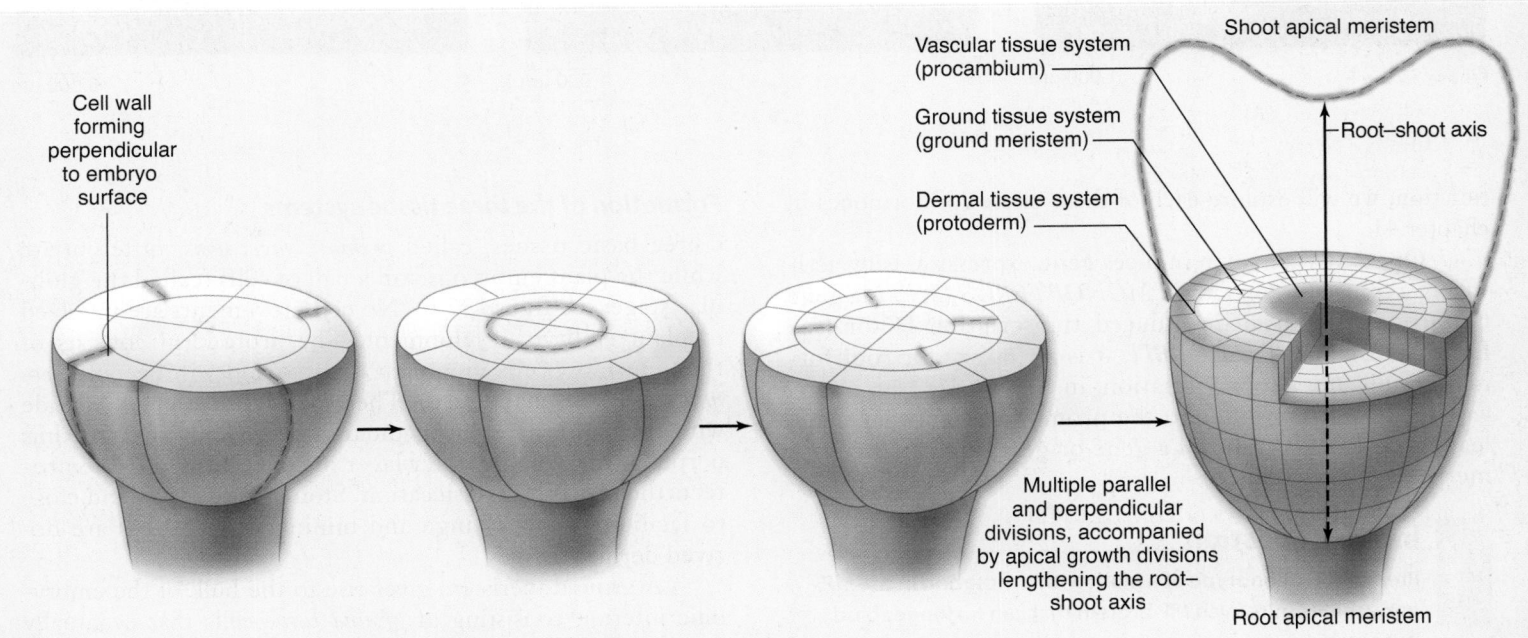

Cell wall forming perpendicular to embryo surface

Vascular tissue system (procambium)

Ground tissue system (ground meristem)

Dermal tissue system (protoderm)

Shoot apical meristem

Root–shoot axis

Multiple parallel and perpendicular divisions, accompanied by apical growth divisions lengthening the root–shoot axis

Root apical meristem

Figure 37.8 Genetic control of embryonic root development in *Arabidopsis*. *a.* HOBBIT represses the repression of the auxin response, allowing auxin-induced root development to occur. *b.* MONOPTEROS cannot act as a transcription factor when it is bound by a repressor. Auxin releases the repressor from MONOPTEROS, which then activates transcription of a root development gene. *c.* A wild-type seedling depends on auxin-induced genes for normal root initiation during embryogenesis. *d.* The *hobbit* seedling has a stub rather than a root because abnormal cell divisions prevent root meristem formation. *e.* The *monopteros* seedling also fails to develop a root.

Inquiry question

? Referring to part *(e)* of figure 37.8, explain why this mutant fails to develop an embryonic root.

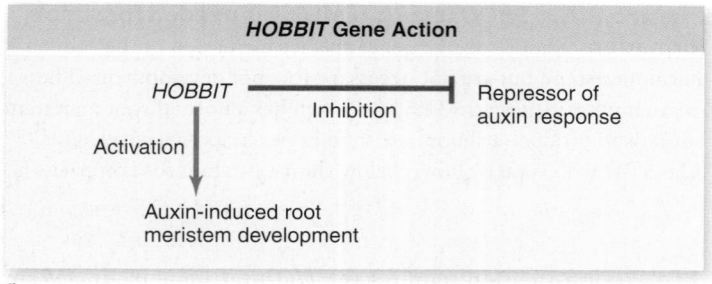

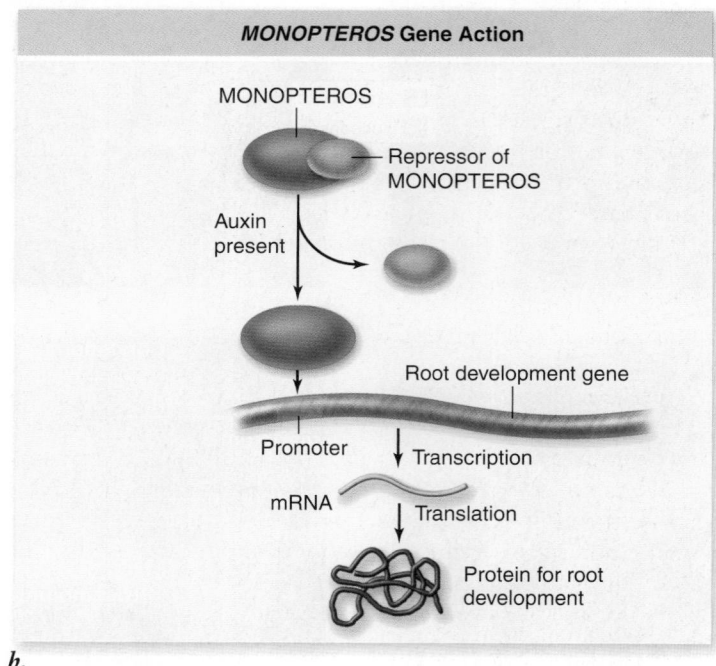

a.

b.

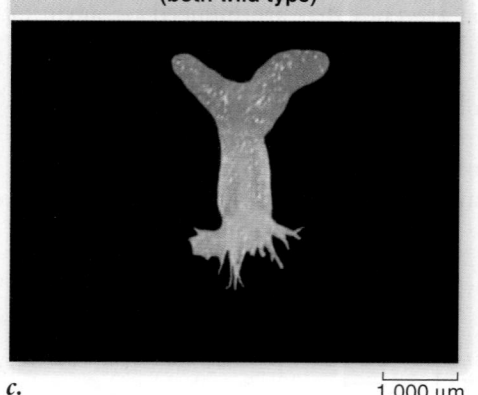

c.   1,000 μm

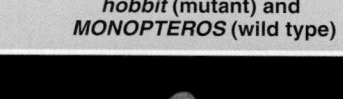
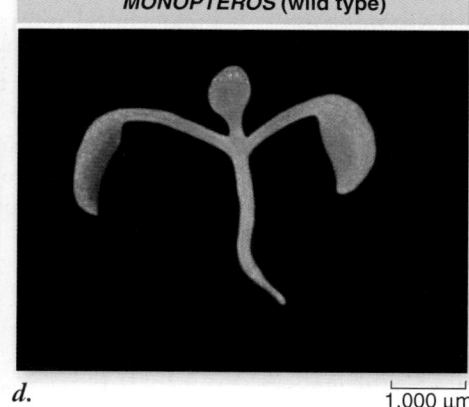

d.   1,000 μm

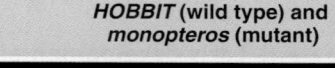
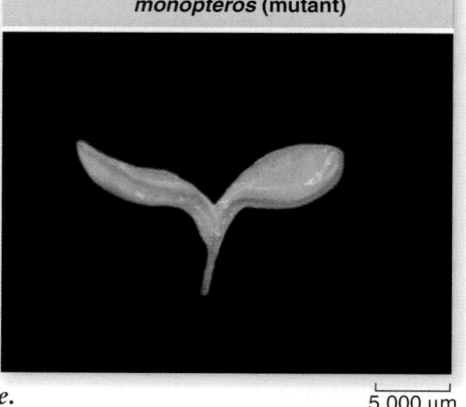

e.   5,000 μm

function; we will explore each of these classes of hormones in chapter 41.

One way that auxin induces gene expression is by activating a transcription factor. *MONOPTEROS (MP)* is a gene that codes for an auxin-induced transcription factor (see figure 37.8), and like *HOBBIT*, it is necessary for root formation, but not shoot formation, in *Arabidopsis*. Once activated, MP protein binds to the promoter of another gene, leading to transcription of a gene or genes needed for root meristem formation.

Inquiry question

? Predict the phenotype of a plant with a mutation in the *MP* gene that results in an MP protein that can no longer bind its repressor.

Formation of the three tissue systems

Three basic tissues, called *primary meristems*, differentiate while the plant embryo is still a ball of cells (called the globular stage; see figure 37.6). No cell movements are involved in plant embryo development. The protoderm consists of the outermost cells in a plant embryo and will become *dermal tissue* (see chapter 36). These cells almost always divide with their cell plate perpendicular to the body surface, thus perpetuating a single outer layer of cells. Dermal tissue protects the plant from desiccation. Stomata that open and close to facilitate gas exchange and minimize water loss are derived dermal tissue.

A ground meristem gives rise to the bulk of the embryonic interior, consisting of *ground tissue* cells that eventually function in food and water storage.

Finally, procambium at the core of the embryo will form the future *vascular tissue*, which is responsible for water and nutrient transport.

Cell fates are generally more limited after embryogenesis, however, when embryo-specific genes are not expressed. For example, the *LEAFY COTYLEDON* gene in *Arabidopsis* is active in early and late embryo development, and it may be responsible for maintaining an embryonic environment. It is possible to turn this gene on later in development using recombinant DNA techniques described in chapter 16. When it is turned on, embryos can form on leaves!

Morphogenesis

The globular stage gives rise to a heart-shaped embryo with two bulges in one group of angiosperms (the eudicots, such as *A. thaliana* in figure 37.6c, d), and a ball with a bulge on a single side in another group (the monocots). These bulges are **cotyledons** ("first leaves") and are produced by the embryonic cells, and not by the shoot apical meristem that begins forming during the globular stage. This process, called morphogenesis (generation of form), results from changes in planes and rates of cell division (see figure 37.5).

Because plant cells cannot move, the form of a plant body is largely determined by the plane in which its cells divide. It is

also controlled by changes in cell shape as cells expand osmotically after they form (figure 37.9). The position of the cell plate determines the direction of division, and both microtubules and actin play a role in establishing the cell plate's position. Plant hormones and other factors influence the orientation of bundles of microtubules on the interior of the plasma membrane. These microtubules also guide cellulose deposition as the cell wall forms around the outside of a new cell (see figure 36.2) where four of the six sides are reinforced more heavily with cellulose; the cell tends to expand and grow in the direction of the two sides having less reinforcement (figure 37.9b).

Much is being learned about morphogenesis at the cellular level from mutants that are able to divide, but cannot control their plane of cell division or the direction of cell expansion. The lack of root meristem development in *hobbit* mutants is just one such example. As the procambium begins differentiating in the root, a critical division parallel to the root's surface is regulated by the gene *WOODEN LEG* (*WOL*, figure 37.10). Without that division, the cylinder of cells that would form phloem is missing. Only xylem forms in the vascular tissue system, giving the root a "wooden leg."

Early in embryonic development, most cells can give rise to a wide range of cell and organ types, including leaves. As development proceeds, the cells with multiple potentials are mainly restricted to the meristem regions. Many meristems have been established by the time embryogenesis ends and the seed becomes dormant. After germination, apical meristems continue adding cells to the growing root and shoot tips. Apical meristem cells of corn, for example, divide every 12 hours, producing half a million cells per day in an actively growing corn plant. Lateral meristems can cause an increase in the girth of some plants, while intercalary meristems in the stems of grasses allow for elongation.

Food reserves form during embryogenesis

While the embryo is developing, three other critical events are occurring in angiosperms: (1) development of a food supply, (2) development of the seed coat, and (3) development of the

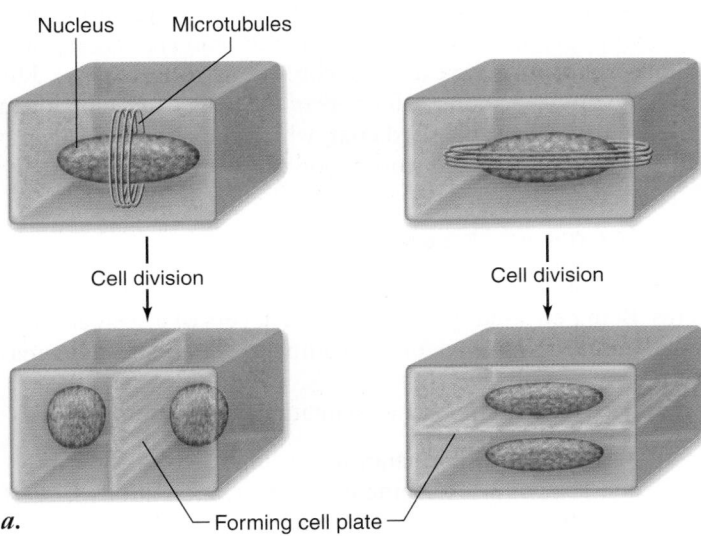

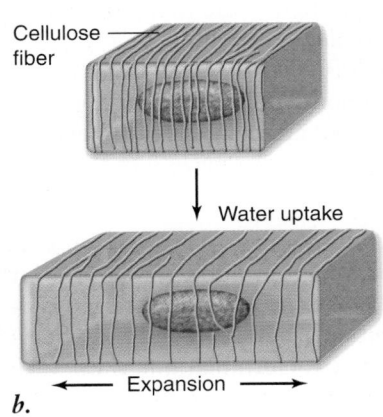

Figure 37.9 Cell division and expansion.
a. Orientation of microtubules determines the orientation of cell plate formation and thus the new cell wall. *b.* Not all sides of a plant cell have the same amount of cellulose reinforcement. With water uptake, cells expand in directions that have the least amount of cell wall reinforcement.

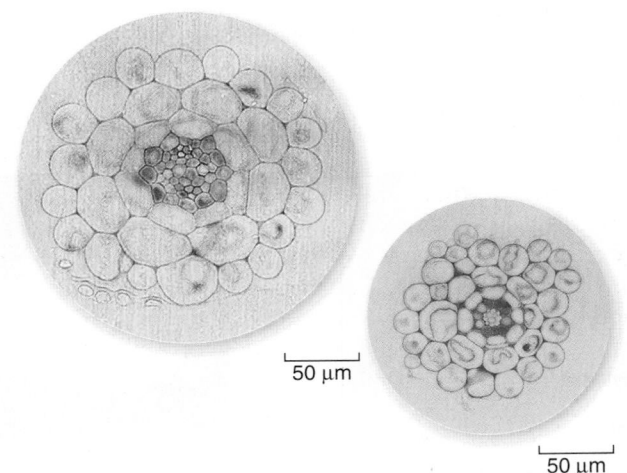

Figure 37.10 *WOODEN LEG* is needed for phloem development. The *wol* mutant (right) has less vascular tissue than wild-type *Arabidopsis* (left), but all of it is xylem.

fruit surrounding the seed. Nutritional reserves support the embryo during germination, while it gains photosynthetic capacity. In angiosperms, double fertilization produces endosperm for nutrition; in gymnosperms, the megagametophyte is the food source (see chapter 30). The seed coat is the result of the differentiation of ovule tissue (from the parental sporophyte) to form a hard, protective covering around the embryo. The seed then enters a dormant phase, signaling the end of embryogenesis. In angiosperms, the fruit develops from the carpel wall surrounding the ovule. Seed development and germination, as well as fruit development, are addressed later in this chapter. In this section, we focus on nutrient reserves.

Throughout embryogenesis, starch, lipids, and proteins are synthesized. The seed storage proteins are so abundant that the genes coding for them were the first cloning targets for plant molecular biologists. Providing nutritional resources is part of the evolutionary trend toward enhancing embryo survival.

The sporophyte transfers nutrients via the suspensor in angiosperms. (In gymnosperms, the suspensor serves only to push the embryo closer to the megagametophytic nutrient source.) This happens concurrently with the development of the endosperm, which is present only in angiosperms (although double fertilization has been observed in the gymnosperm *Ephedra*). Endosperm formation may be extensive or minimal.

Endosperm in coconut includes the "milk," a liquid. In corn, the endosperm is solid. In popping corn it expands with heat to form the white edible part of popped corn. In peas and beans, the endosperm is used up during embryo development, and nutrients are stored in thick, fleshy cotyledons (figure 37.11).

Because the photosynthetic machinery is built in response to light, it is critical that seeds have stored nutrients to aid in germination until the growing sporophyte can photosynthesize. A seed buried too deeply in the soil will use up all its reserves in cellular respiration before reaching the surface and sunlight.

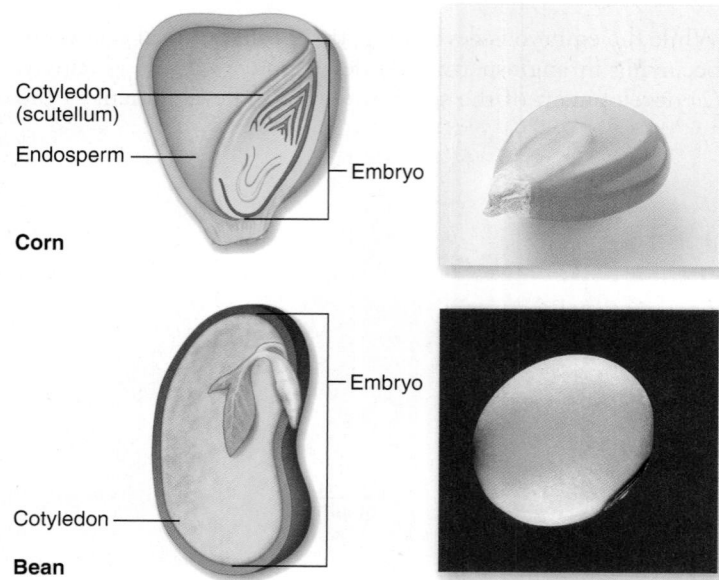

Figure 37.11 Endosperm in maize and bean. The maize kernel has endosperm that is still present at maturity, but the endosperm in the bean has disappeared. The bean embryo's cotyledons take over food storage functions.

Learning Outcomes Review 37.1

The root-shoot axis and the radial axis form during plant embryogenesis. The three tissues formed in an embryo are the protoderm, ground meristem, and procambium, which give rise to the three adults tissues. While the embryo is being formed, a food supply is being established for the embryo in the form of endosperm; a seed coat is forming from ovule tissues; and the fruit is developing from the carpel wall.

■ *How does the nutritive tissue of a gymnosperm seed differ from that of an angiosperm seed?*

37.2 Seeds

Learning Outcomes

1. Describe four ways in which seeds help to ensure the survival of a plant's offspring.
2. List environmental conditions that can lead to seed germination in some plants.

Early in the development of an angiosperm embryo, a profoundly important event occurs: The embryo stops developing. In many plants, development of the embryo is arrested soon after the meristems and cotyledons differentiate. The integuments—the outer cell layers of the ovule—develop into a relatively impermeable **seed coat,** which encloses the seed with its dormant embryo and stored food (figure 37.12).

Seeds protect the embryo

The seed is a vehicle for dispersing the embryo to distant sites. Being encased in the protective layers of a seed allows a plant embryo to survive in environments that might kill a mature plant.

Seeds are an important adaptation in at least four ways:

1. Seeds maintain dormancy under unfavorable conditions and postpone development until better conditions arise. If conditions are marginal, a plant can "afford" to have some seeds germinate, because some of those that germinate may survive, while others remain dormant.
2. Seeds afford maximum protection to the young plant at its most vulnerable stage of development.
3. Seeds contain stored food that allows a young plant to grow and develop before photosynthetic activity begins.
4. Perhaps most important, seeds are adapted for dispersal, facilitating the migration of plant genotypes into new habitats.

A mature seed contains only about 5 to 20% water. Under these conditions, the seed and the young plant within it are very stable; its arrested growth is primarily due to the progressive and severe desiccation of the embryo and the associated reduction in metabolic activity. Germination cannot take place until water and oxygen reach the embryo. Seeds of some

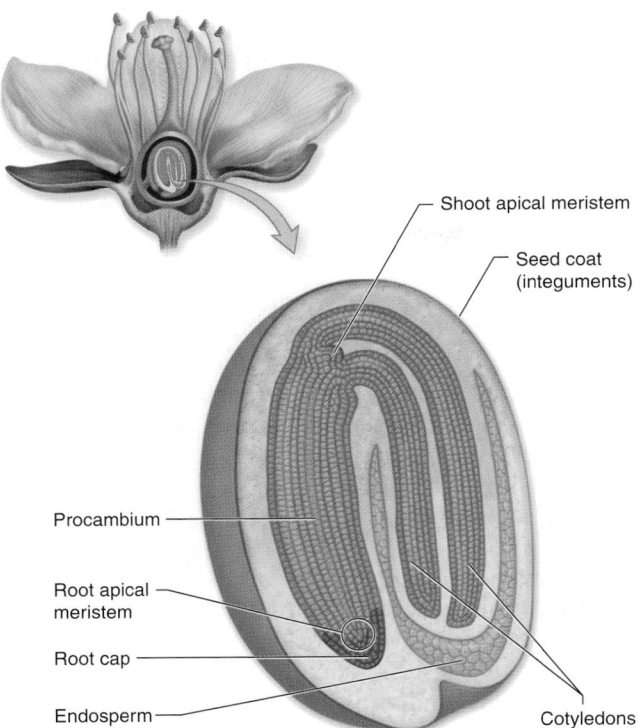

Figure 37.12 Seed development. The integuments of this mature angiosperm ovule are forming the seed coat. Note that the two cotyledons have grown into a bent shape to accommodate the tight confines of the seed. In some embryos, the shoot apical meristem will have already initiated a few leaf primordia as well.

Inquiry question

? Is this embryo a monocot or a eudicot?

plants have been known to remain viable for hundreds and, in rare instances, thousands of years.

Specialized seed adaptations improve survival

Specific adaptations often help ensure that seeds will germinate only under appropriate conditions. Sometimes, seeds lie within tough cones that do not open until they are exposed to the heat of a fire (figure 37.13). This strategy causes the seed to germinate in an open, fire-cleared habitat where nutrients are relatively abundant, having been released from plants burned in the fire.

Seeds of other plants germinate only when inhibitory chemicals leach from their seed coats, thus guaranteeing their germination when sufficient water is available. Still other seeds germinate only after they pass through the intestines of birds or mammals or are regurgitated by them, which both weakens the seed coats and ensures dispersal. Sometimes seeds of plants thought to be extinct in a particular area may germinate under unique or improved environmental circumstances, and the plants may then reestablish themselves.

a.

b.

Figure 37.13 Fire induces seed release in some pines. Fire can destroy adult jack pines, but stimulate growth of the next generation. *a.* The cones of a jack pine are tightly sealed and cannot release the seeds protected by the scales. *b.* High temperatures lead to the release of the seeds.

Learning Outcomes Review 37.2

The seed coat originates from the integuments and encloses the embryo and stored nutrients. The four advantages conferred by seeds are dormancy, protection of the embryo, nourishment, and a method of dispersal. Fire, heavy rains, or passage through an animal's digestive tract may be required for germination in some species.

■ *What type of seed dormancy would you expect to find in trees living in climates with cold winters?*

37.3 Fruits

Learning Outcomes

1. *Identify the structures from which fruits develop.*
2. *Distinguish among berries, legumes, drupes, and samaras.*

Survival of angiosperm embryos depends on fruit development as well as seed development. Fruits are most simply defined as mature ovaries (carpels). During seed formation,

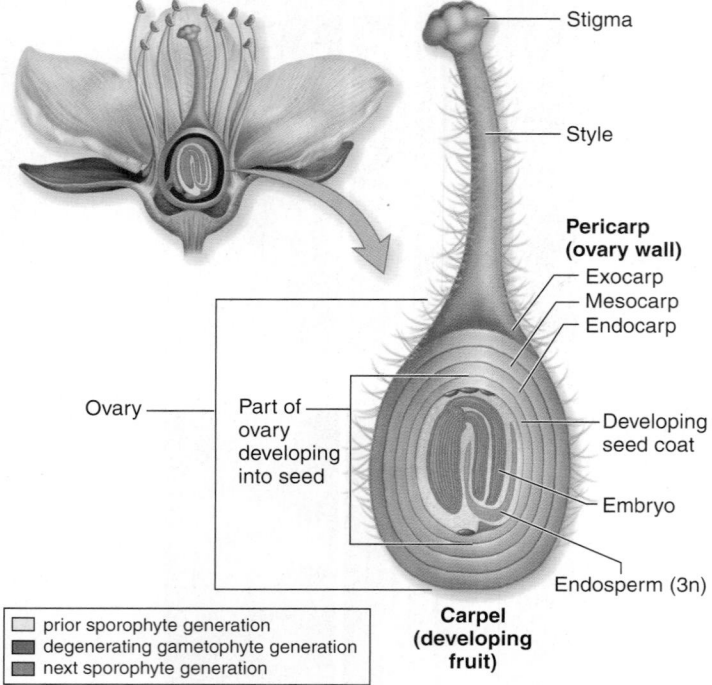

Figure 37.14 Fruit development. The carpel (specifically the ovary) wall is composed of three layers: the exocarp, mesocarp, and endocarp. One, some, or all of these layers develops to contribute to the recognized fruit in different species. The seed matures within this developing fruit.

Inquiry question

? Three generations are represented in this diagram. Label the ploidy levels of the tissues of different generations shown here.

the flower ovary begins to develop into fruit (figure 37.14). In some cases, pollen landing on the stigma can initiate fruit development, but more frequently the coordination of fruit, seed coat, embryo, and endosperm development follow fertilization.

It is possible for fruits to develop without seed development. Commercial bananas for example have aborted seed development, but do produce mature, edible ovaries. Bananas are propagated asexually since no embryo develops.

Fruits are adapted for dispersal

Fruits form in many ways and exhibit a wide array of adaptations for dispersal. Three layers of ovary wall, also called the *pericarp*, can have distinct fates, which account for the diversity of fruit types from fleshy to dry and hard. The differences among some of the fruit types are shown in figure 37.15.

Developmentally, fruits are fascinating organs that contain three genotypes in one package. The fruit and seed coat are from the prior sporophyte generation. Remnants of the gametophyte generation that produced the egg are found in the de-

veloping seed, and the embryo represents the next sporophyte generation (see figure 37.14).

Fruits allow angiosperms to colonize large areas

Aside from the many ways fruits can form, they also exhibit a wide array of specialized dispersal methods. Fruits with fleshy coverings, often shiny black or bright blue or red, normally are dispersed by birds or other vertebrates (figure 37.16a). Like red flowers, red fruits signal an abundant food supply. By feeding on these fruits, birds and other animals may carry seeds from place to place and thus transfer plants from one suitable habitat to another. Such seeds require a hard seed coat to resist stomach acids and digestive enzymes.

Fruits with hooked spines, such as those of burrs (figure 37.16b), are typical of several genera of plants that occur in the northern deciduous forests. Such fruits are often disseminated by mammals, including humans, when they hitch a ride on fur or clothing. Squirrels and similar mammals disperse and bury fruits such as acorns and other nuts. Some of these sprout when conditions become favorable, such as after the spring thaw.

Other fruits, including those of maples, elms, and ashes, have wings that aid in their distribution by the wind. Orchids have minute, dustlike seeds, which are likewise blown away by the wind. The dandelion provides another familiar example of a fruit type that is wind-dispersed (figure 37.16c), and the dispersal of seeds from plants such as milkweeds, willows, and cottonwoods is similar. Water dispersal adaptations include air-filled chambers surrounded by impermeable membranes to prevent the entrance of H_2O.

Coconuts and other plants that characteristically occur on or near beaches are regularly spread throughout a region by floating in water (figure 37.16d). This sort of dispersal is especially important in the colonization of distant island groups, such as the Hawaiian Islands.

It has been calculated that the seeds of about 175 angiosperms, nearly one-third from North America, must have reached Hawaii to have evolved into the roughly 970 species found there today. Some of these seeds blew through the air, others were transported on the feathers or in the guts of birds, and still others floated across the Pacific. Although the distances are rarely as great as the distance between Hawaii and the mainland, dispersal is just as important for mainland plant species that have discontinuous habitats, such as mountaintops, marshes, or north-facing cliffs.

Learning Outcomes Review 37.3

As a seed develops, the pericarp layers of the ovary wall develop into the fruit. A berry has a fleshy pericarp; a legume has a dry pericarp that opens to release seeds; the outer layers of a drupe pericarp are fleshy; and a samara is a dry structure with a wing. Animals often distribute the seeds of fleshy fruits and fruits with spines or hooks. Wind disperses lightweight seeds and samara forms.

■ *What features of fruits might encourage animals to eat them?*

True Berries

The entire pericarp is fleshy, although there may be a thin skin. Berries have multiple seeds in either one or more ovaries. The tomato flower had four carpels that fused. Each carpel contains multiple ovules that develop into seeds.

Outer pericarp
Fused carpels
Seed

Drupes

Single seed enclosed in a hard pit; peaches, plums, cherries. Each layer of the pericarp has a different structure and function, with the endocarp forming the pit.

Pericarp
Exocarp (skin)
Mesocarp
Endocarp (pit)
Seed

Aggregate Fruits

Derived from many ovaries of a single flower; strawberries, blackberries. Unlike tomato, these ovaries are not fused and covered by a continuous pericarp.

Sepals of a single flower
Ovary
Seed

Legumes

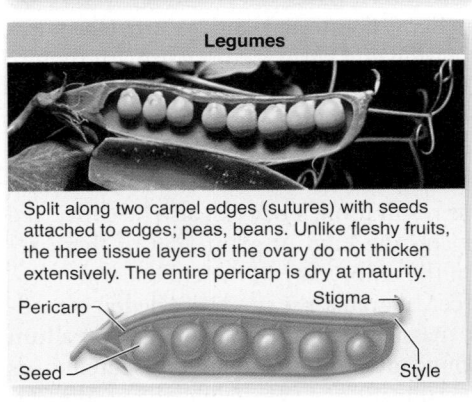

Split along two carpel edges (sutures) with seeds attached to edges; peas, beans. Unlike fleshy fruits, the three tissue layers of the ovary do not thicken extensively. The entire pericarp is dry at maturity.

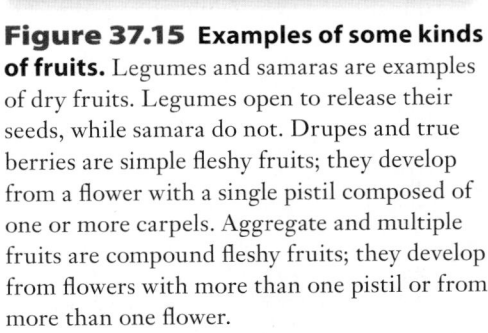

Pericarp
Stigma
Seed
Style

Figure 37.15 Examples of some kinds of fruits. Legumes and samaras are examples of dry fruits. Legumes open to release their seeds, while samara do not. Drupes and true berries are simple fleshy fruits; they develop from a flower with a single pistil composed of one or more carpels. Aggregate and multiple fruits are compound fleshy fruits; they develop from flowers with more than one pistil or from more than one flower.

Samaras

Not split and with a wing formed from the outer tissues; maples, elms, ashes.

Pericarp
Seed

Multiple Fruits

Individual flowers form fruits around a single stem. The fruits fuse as seen with pineapple.

Main stem
Pericarp of individual flower

a.

b.

c.

d.

Figure 37.16 Animal-dispersed fruits. *a.* The bright red berries of this honeysuckle, *Lonicera hispidula*, are highly attractive to birds. After eating the fruits, birds may carry the seeds they contain for great distances either internally or, because of their sticky pulp, stuck to their feet or other body parts. *b.* You will know if you have ever stepped on the fruits of *Cenchrus incertus;* their spines adhere readily to any passing animal. *c.* False dandelion, *Pyrrhopappus carolinianus*, has "parachutes" that widely disperse the fruits in the wind, much to the gardener's despair. *d.* This fruit of the coconut palm, *Cocos nucifera*, is sprouting on a sandy beach. Coconuts, one of the most useful fruits for humans in the tropics, have become established on other islands by drifting there on the waves.

Learning Outcomes

1. **Describe the events that occur during seed germination.**
2. **Contrast the pattern of shoot emergence in bean (dicot) with that in maize (monocot).**

When conditions are satisfactory, the embryo emerges from its previously desiccated state, utilizes food reserves, and resumes growth. Although **germination** is a process characterized by several stages, it is often defined as the emergence of the **radicle** (first root) through the seed coat.

External signals and conditions trigger germination

Germination begins when a seed absorbs water and its metabolism resumes. The amount of water a seed can absorb is phenomenal, and osmotic pressure creates a force strong enough to break the seed coat. At this point, it is important that oxygen be available to the developing embryo because plants, like animals, require oxygen for cellular respiration. Few plants produce seeds that germinate successfully under water, although some, such as rice, have evolved a tolerance to anaerobic conditions.

Even though a dormant seed may have imbibed a full supply of water and may be respiring, synthesizing proteins and RNA, and apparently carrying on normal metabolism, it may fail to germinate without an additional signal from the environment. This signal may be light of the correct wavelength and intensity, a series of cold days, or simply the passage of time at temperatures appropriate for germination. The seeds of many plants will not germinate unless they have been **stratified**—held for periods of time at low temperatures. This phenomenon prevents the seeds of plants that grow in seasonally cold areas from germinating until they have passed the winter, thus protecting their tender seedlings from harsh, cold conditions.

Germination can occur over a wide temperature range (5° to 30°C), although certain species may have relatively narrow optimum ranges. Some seeds will not germinate even under the best conditions. In some species, a significant fraction of a season's seeds remain dormant for an indeterminate length of time, providing a gene pool of great evolutionary significance to the future plant population. The presence of ungerminated seeds in the soil of an area is referred to as the **seed bank.**

Nutrient reserves sustain the growing seedling

Germination occurs when all internal and external requirements are met. Germination and early seedling growth require the utilization of metabolic reserves stored as starch in amyloplasts (colorless plastids) and protein bodies. Fats and oils, also stored, in some kinds of seeds, can readily be digested during germination to produce glycerol and fatty acids, which yield energy through cellular respiration. They can also be converted to glucose. Depending on the kind of plant, any of these reserves may be stored in the embryo or in the endosperm.

In the kernels of cereal grains, the single cotyledon is modified into a relatively massive structure called the **scutellum** (figure 37.17). The abundant food stored in the scutellum is used up first during germination. Later, while the seedling is

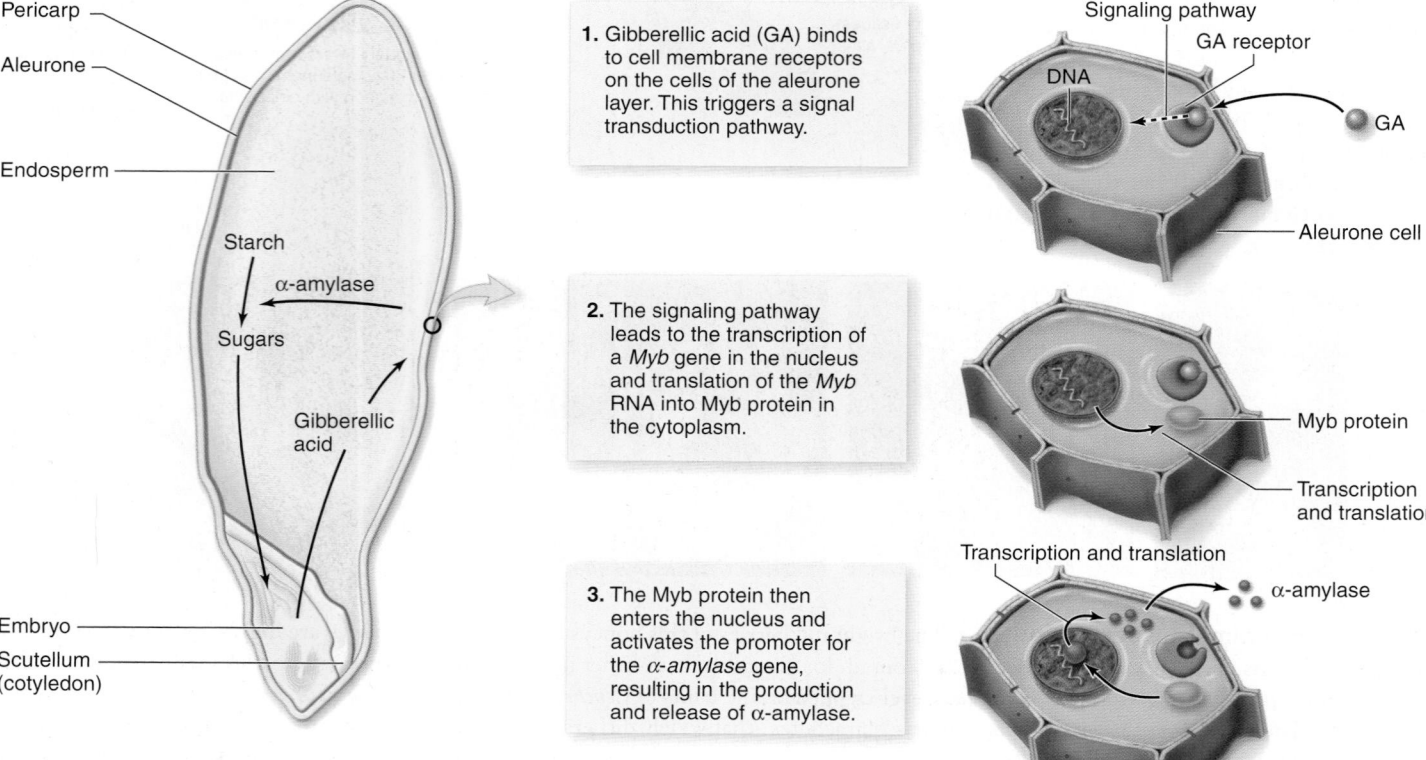

1. Gibberellic acid (GA) binds to cell membrane receptors on the cells of the aleurone layer. This triggers a signal transduction pathway.

2. The signaling pathway leads to the transcription of a *Myb* gene in the nucleus and translation of the *Myb* RNA into Myb protein in the cytoplasm.

3. The Myb protein then enters the nucleus and activates the promoter for the *α-amylase* gene, resulting in the production and release of α-amylase.

Pericarp
Aleurone
Endosperm
Starch
α-amylase
Sugars
Gibberellic acid
Embryo
Scutellum (cotyledon)

Signaling pathway
GA receptor
DNA
GA
Aleurone cell
Myb protein
Transcription and translation
Transcription and translation
α-amylase

Figure 37.17 Hormonal regulation of seedling growth.

becoming established, the scutellum serves as a nutrient conduit from the endosperm to the rest of the embryo.

The utilization of stored starch by germinating plants is one of the best examples of how hormones modulate plant development (see figure 37.17). The embryo produces gibberellic acid, a hormone, that signals the outer layer of the endosperm, called the **aleurone,** to produce α-amylase. This enzyme is responsible for breaking down the endosperm's starch, primarily amylose, into sugars that are passed by the scutellum to the embryo. Abscisic acid, another plant hormone, which is important in establishing dormancy, can inhibit starch breakdown. Abscisic acid levels may be reduced when a seed beginning to germinate absorbs water. (The action of plant hormones is covered in chapter 41.)

The seedling becomes oriented in the environment, and photosynthesis begins

As the sporophyte pushes through the seed coat, it orients with the environment so that the root grows down and the shoot grows up. New growth comes from delicate meristems that are protected from environmental rigors. The shoot becomes photosynthetic, and the postembryonic phase of growth and development is under way. Figure 37.18 shows the process of germination and subsequent development of the plant body in eudicots and monocots.

The emerging shoot and root tips are protected by additional tissue layers in the monocots—the *coleoptile* surrounding the shoot, and the *coleorhiza* surrounding the radicle. Other

protective strategies include having a bent shoot emerge so tissues with more rugged cell walls push through the soil.

The emergence of the embryonic root and shoot from the seed during germination varies widely from species to species. In most plants, the root emerges before the shoot appears and anchors the young seedling in the soil (see figure 37.18). In plants such as peas, the cotyledons may be held below ground; in other plants, such as beans, radishes, and onions, the cotyledons are held above ground. The cotyledons may become green and contribute to the nutrition of the seedling as it becomes established, or they may shrivel relatively quickly. The period from the germination of the seed to the establishment of the young plant is critical for the plant's survival; the seedling is unusually susceptible to disease and drought during this period. Soil composition and pH can also affect the survival of a newly germinated plant (figure 37.19).

Learning Outcomes Review 37.4

During germination, the seed and embryo take up water, increase respiration, and synthesize protein and RNA. Metabolic reserves in seeds include starch, fats, and oils. During seedling emergence, the cotyledons and seed coat may be pulled out of the ground and become photosynthetic, as they do in dicots such as beans. Alternatively, the cotyledon and seed coat may remain in the ground, as they do in monocots such as maize.

■ *What might be an advantage of retaining a seed in the ground during seedling emergence?*

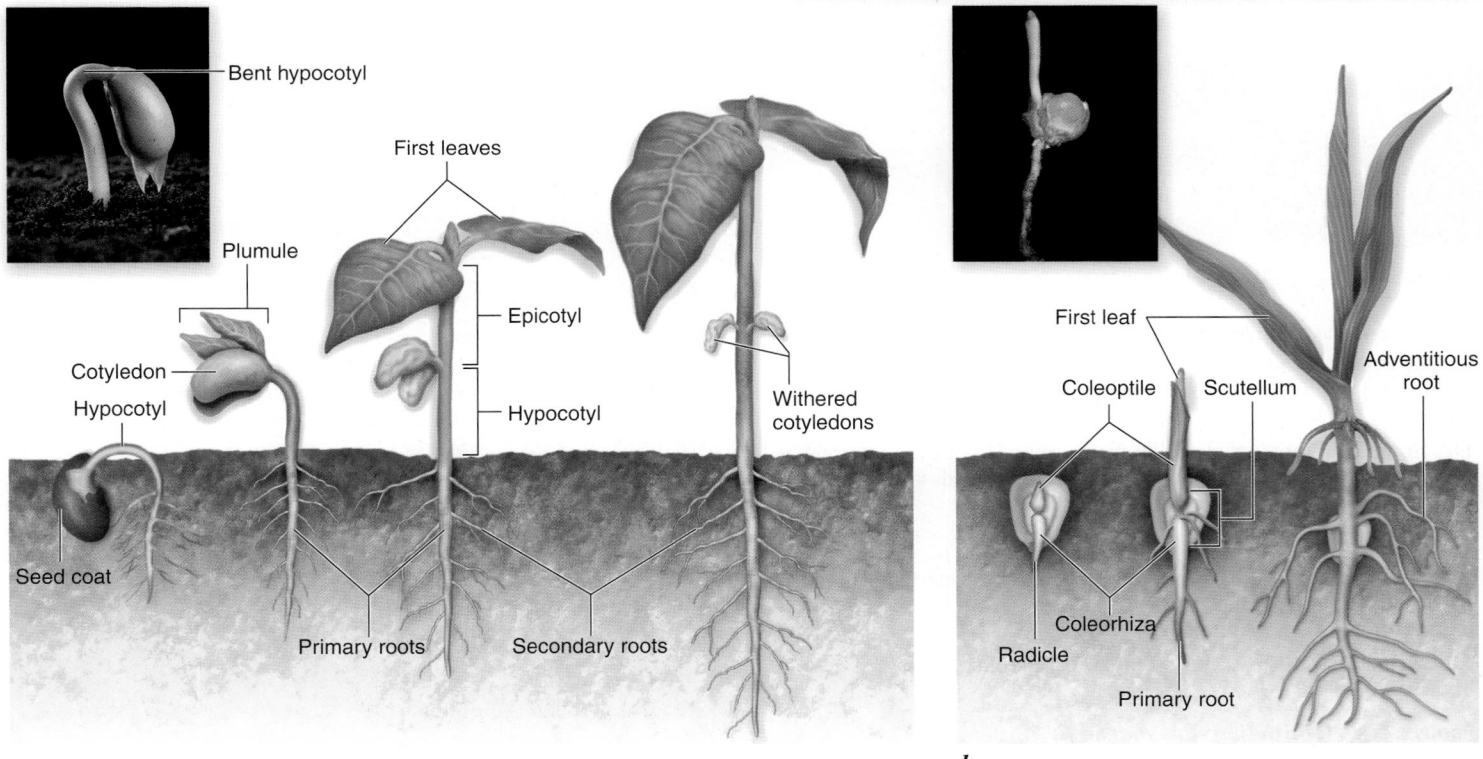

a.   *b.*

Figure 37.18 Germination. The stages shown are for *(a)* a eudicot, the common bean (*Phaseolus vulgaris*), and *(b)* a monocot, maize (*Zea mays*). Note that the bending of the hypocotyl (region below the cotyledons) protects the delicate bean shoot apex as it emerges through the soil. Maize radicles are protected by a protective layer of tissue called the coleorhiza, in addition to the root cap found in both bean and maize. A sheath of cells called the coleoptile, rather than a hypocotyl tissue, protects the emerging maize shoot tip.

Hypothesis: *Glandular trichomes prevent leafhoppers from feeding and reproducing on alfalfa plants.*

Prediction: *Rates of leafhopper survival and reproduction will be lower on plants with glandular trichomes than on those without glandular trichomes.*

Test: *Place alfalfa variety that produces glandular trichomes in a cage and a variety that lacks glandular trichomes in another cage. Place the same number of leafhoppers in each cage. Return after a period of time and count the number of live leafhoppers in each cage.*

The same number of leafhoppers are placed in each cage with alfalfa plants.

After a period of time, more leafhoppers are present on the alfalfa plants that lack trichomes.

Result: *There are fewer live leafhoppers in the cage with the trichome-bearing plant.*

Conclusion: *The hypothesis is supported. The survival and reproduction rate of leafhoppers on plants with trichomes was lower than that on plants lacking trichomes.*

Further Experiments: *Design an experiment to determine if trichomes in general or just glandular trichomes can deter leafhoppers.*

Figure 37.19 Glandular trichomes can protect plants from insects.

Chapter Review

37.1 Embryo Development

A single cell divides to produce a three-dimensional body plan.

An angiosperm zygote divides to produce an embryo surrounded by endosperm (see figure 37.1). In early divisions, the root-shoot axis and radial axis become established.

Developmental mutants in model plants reveal what can go wrong, allowing inferences about how development proceeds under normal conditions.

A simple body plan emerges during embryogenesis.

Shoot and root apical meristems develop, and protoderm, ground meristem, and procambium differentiate; these will become the three types of tissue in an adult plant.

Morphogenesis creates a three-dimensional embryo that includes one or two cotyledons.

Food reserves form during embryogenesis.

While the embryo is being formed, a food supply is being established for the embryo. In angiosperms, this consists of the endosperm produced by double fertilization; in gymnosperms, the megagametophyte is the food source. In addition, a seed coat forms, and the fruit develops.

37.2 Seeds (see figure 37.12)

Seeds protect the embryo.

Seeds help to ensure the survival of the next generation by maintaining dormancy during unfavorable conditions, protecting the embryo, providing food for the embryo, and providing a means for dispersal.

Specialized seed adaptations improve survival.

Before a seed germinates, its seed coat must become permeable so that water and oxygen can reach the embryo. Adaptations have evolved to ensure germination under appropriate survival conditions. In certain gymnosperms, seeds may be released from cones after a fire. Alternatively, seeds may require passage through a digestive tract, freeze–thaw cycles, or abundant moisture.

37.3 Fruits (see figure 37.14)

Fruits are adapted for dispersal.

In angiosperms, a fruit is a mature ovary. Fruit development is coordinated with embryo, endosperm, and seed coat development.

Angiosperms produce many types of fruit, which vary depending on the fate of the pericarp (carpel wall). Fruits can be dry or fleshy, and they can be simple (single carpel), aggregate (multiple carpels), or multiple (multiple flowers).

A fruit is genetically unique because it contains tissues from the parent sporophyte (the seed coat and fruit tissue), the gametophyte (remnants in the developing seed) and the offspring sporophyte (the embryo).

Fruits allow angiosperms to colonize large areas.

Fruits exhibit a wide array of dispersal mechanisms. They may be ingested and transported by animals, buried in caches by herbivores, carried away by birds and mammals, blown by the wind, or float away on water.

37.4 Germination

Seed germination is defined as the emergence of the radical through the seed coat.

External signals and conditions trigger germination.

A seed must imbibe water in order to germinate. Abundant oxygen is necessary to support the high metabolic rate of a germinating seed.

Environmental signals are often needed for germination. Examples include light of a certain wavelength, an appropriate temperature, and stratification (a period of chilling).

Nutrient reserves sustain the growing seedling.

Germination is a high-energy process, requiring stored nutrients such as starch, fats, and oils.

The endosperm acts as a starch reserve. Utilization of stored starch begins when the embryo produces the plant hormone gibberellic acid, which in turn stimulates production of an amylase to break down amylose. Starch metabolism can be inhibited by abscisic acid, a plant hormone that has a role in dormancy.

The seedling becomes oriented in the environment, and photosynthesis begins.

In most plants, the root emerges before the shoot appears, anchoring the young seedling.

In many eudicots, the shoot is bent as it emerges from the soil, protecting the growing tip (see figure 37.18). Monocots produce additional tissues to protect emerging shoots and roots.

During seedling emergence in dicots such as beans, the cotyledons are often pulled up with the growing shoot. In monocots such as corn, the cotyledon remains underground.

A seedling enters the postembryonic phase of growth and development when the emerging shoot becomes photosynthetic.

Review Questions

UNDERSTAND

1. After the first mitotic division of the zygote, the larger of the two cells becomes the
   a. embryo.
   b. endosperm.
   c. suspensor.
   d. micropyle.

2. Endosperm is produced by the union of
   a. a central cell with a sperm cell.
   b. a sperm cell with a synergid cell.
   c. an egg cell with a sperm cell.
   d. a suspensor with an egg cell.

3. During the globular stage of embryo development, apical meristems establish the
   a. embryo–suspensor axis.
   b. inner–outer axis.
   c. embryo–endosperm axis.
   d. root–shoot axis.

4. Which of the following is not a primary meristem?
   a. Cork cambium
   b. Ground meristem
   c. Procambium
   d. Protoderm

5. The integuments of an ovule will develop into the
   a. embryo.
   b. endosperm.
   c. fruit.
   d. seed coat.

6. An example of a drupe is a
   a. strawberry.
   b. plum.
   c. bean.
   d. pineapple.

7. The pericarp is the
   a. ovary wall.
   b. developing seed coat.
   c. ovary.
   d. mature endosperm.

8. During seed germination, this hormone produces the signal for the aleurone to begin starch breakdown.
   a. Abscisic acid
   b. Ethylene
   c. Gibberellic acid
   d. Auxin

9. The shoot tip of an emerging maize seedling is protected by
   a. hypocotyl.
   b. epicotyl.
   c. coleoptile.
   d. plumule.

APPLY

1. A plant lacking the *WOODEN LEG* gene will likely
   a. be incapable of transporting water to its leaves.
   b. lack xylem and phloem.
   c. be incapable of transporting photosynthate.
   d. all of the above

2. Explore how plant development changes if the functions of the genes *SHOOTMERISTEMLESS (STM)* and *MONOPTEROUS (MP)* were reversed?
   a. The embryo–suspensor axis would be reversed.
   b. The embryo–suspensor axis would be duplicated.
   c. The root–shoot axis would be reversed.
   d. The root–shoot axis would be duplicated.

3. How would a loss-of-function mutation in the α-amylase gene affect seed germination?
   a. The seed could not imbibe water.
   b. The embryo would starve.
   c. The seed coat would not rupture.
   d. The seed would germinate prematurely.

4. Fruits are complex organs that are specialized for dispersal of seeds. Which of the following plant tissues does *not* contribute to mature fruit?
    a. Sporophytic tissue from the previous generation
    b. Gametophytic tissue from the previous generation
    c. Sporophytic tissue from the next generation
    d. Gametophytic tissue from the next generation

5. Loss-of-function mutations in the *suspensor* gene in *Arabidopsis* lead to the development of two embryos in a seed. After analyzing the expression of this gene in early wild-type embryos, you find high levels of mRNA transcribed from the *suspensor* gene in the developing suspensor cells. What is the likely function of the suspensor protein?
    a. Suspensor protein likely stimulates development of the embryonic tissue.
    b. Suspensor protein likely stimulates development of the suspensor tissue.
    c. Suspensor protein likely inhibits embryonic development in the suspensor.
    d. Suspensor protein likely inhibits suspensor development in the embryo.

SYNTHESIZE

1. Design an experiment to determine whether light or gravity is more important in determining the orientation of the rhizoid during zygote development in *Fucus*.

2. In gymnosperms, the nutritive tissue in the seed is megagametophyte tissue. It is a product of meiosis. A major evolutionary advance in the angiosperms is that the nutritive tissue is endosperm, a triploid product of fertilization. Why do you suppose endosperm is a richer source of nutrition than megagametophyte tissue?

3. As you are eating an apple one day, you decide that you'd like to save the seeds and plant them. You do so, but they fail to germinate. Discuss all possible reasons that the seeds did not germinate and strategies you could try to improve your chances of success.

ONLINE RESOURCE

www.ravenbiology.com

Understand, Apply, and Synthesize—enhance your study with animations that bring concepts to life and practice tests to assess your understanding. Your instructor may also recommend the interactive eBook, individualized learning tools, and more.

Chapter **38**

Transport in Plants

Chapter Outline

38.1 Transport Mechanisms

38.2 Water and Mineral Absorption

38.3 Xylem Transport

38.4 The Rate of Transpiration

38.5 Water-Stress Responses

38.6 Phloem Transport

Introduction

Terrestrial plants face two major challenges: maintaining water and nutrient balance, and providing sufficient structural support for upright growth. The vascular system transports water, minerals, and organic molecules over great distances. Whereas the secondary growth of vascular tissue allows trees to achieve great heights, water balance alone keeps herbaceous plants upright. Think of a plant cell as a water balloon pressing against the insides of a soft-sided box, with many other balloon/box cells stacked on top. If the balloon springs a leak, the support is gone, and the box can collapse. How water, minerals, and organic molecules move between the roots and shoots of small and tall plants is the topic of this chapter.

How does water get from the roots to the top of a 10-story-high tree? Throughout human existence, curious people have wondered about this question. Plants lack muscle tissue or a circulatory system like animals have to pump fluid throughout a plant's body. Nevertheless, water moves through the cell wall spaces between the protoplasts of cells, through plasmodesmata (connections between cells), through plasma membranes, and through the interconnected, conducting elements extending throughout a plant (figure 38.1). Water first enters the roots and then moves to the xylem, the innermost vascular tissue of plants. Water rises through the xylem because of a combination of factors, and most of that water exits through the stomata in the leaves (figure 38.2).

Local changes result in long-distance movement of materials

The greatest distances traveled by water molecules and dissolved minerals are in the xylem. Once water enters the xylem of a redwood, for example, it can move upward as much as 100 m. Most of the force is "pulling" caused by transpiration—evaporation from thin films of water in the stomata. This pulling occurs because water molecules stick to each other (cohesion) and to the walls of the tracheid or xylem vessel (ad-

hesion). The result is an unusually stable column of liquid reaching great heights.

The movement of water at the cellular level plays a significant role in bulk water transport in the plant as well, although over much shorter distances. Although water can diffuse through plasma membranes, charged ions and organic compounds, including sucrose, depend on protein transporters to cross membranes through facilitated diffusion or active transport (see figure 38.1 and chapter 5). ATP-dependent hydrogen ion pumps often fuel active transport. They create a hydrogen ion gradient across a membrane. This hydrogen ion gradient can be used in a variety of ways, including transporting sucrose (see figure 38.1). Unequal concentrations of solutes (for example, ions and organic molecules), drive osmosis as you saw in chapter 5. Using a quantitative approach to osmosis you can predict which way water will move.

Water potential regulates movement of water through the plant

Plant biologists explain the forces that act on water within a plant in terms of potentials. *Potentials* are a way of representing free energy (the potential to do work; see chapter 5). **Water potential,** abbreviated by the Greek letter psi with a subscript W (Ψ_w), is used to predict which way water will move. The key is to remember that water will move from a cell or solution with higher water potential to a cell or solution with lower water potential. Water potential is measured in units of pressure called **megapascals (MPa).** If you turn on your kitchen or bathroom faucet full blast, the water pressure should be between 0.2 and 0.3 MPa (30 to 45 psi).

Movement of water by osmosis

If a single plant cell is placed into water, then the concentration of solutes inside the cell is greater than that of the external

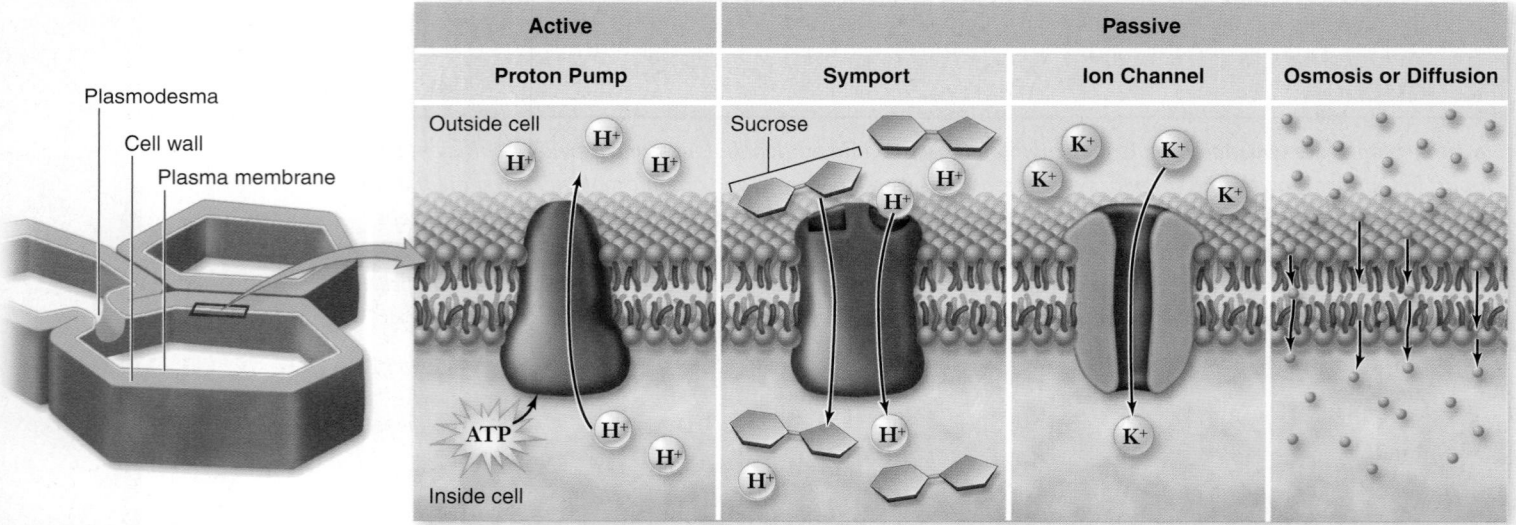

Figure 38.1 Transport between cells. Water, minerals, and organic molecules can diffuse across membranes, be actively or passively transported by membrane-bound transporters, or move through plasmodesmata. Details of membrane transport are found in chapter 5.

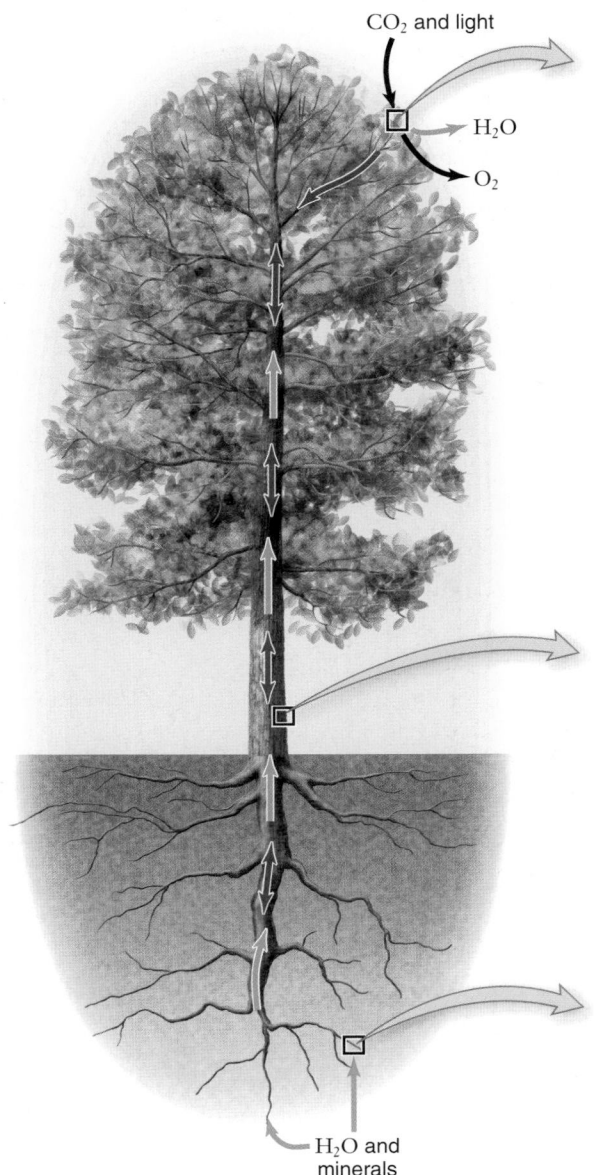

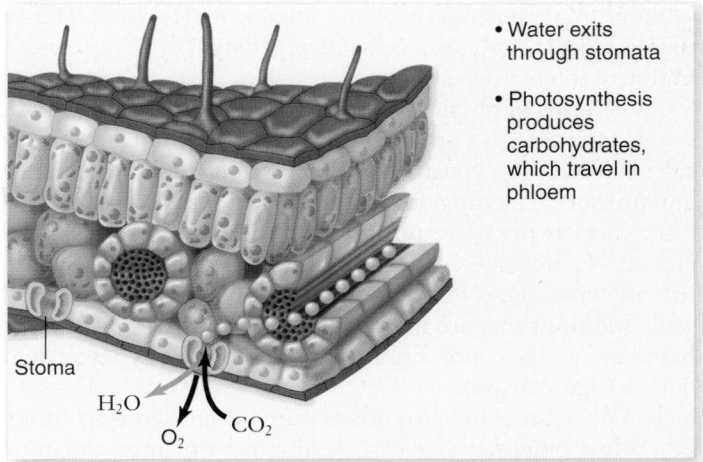

- Water exits through stomata
- Photosynthesis produces carbohydrates, which travel in phloem

Stoma

H_2O

O_2 CO_2

CO_2 and light

H_2O

O_2

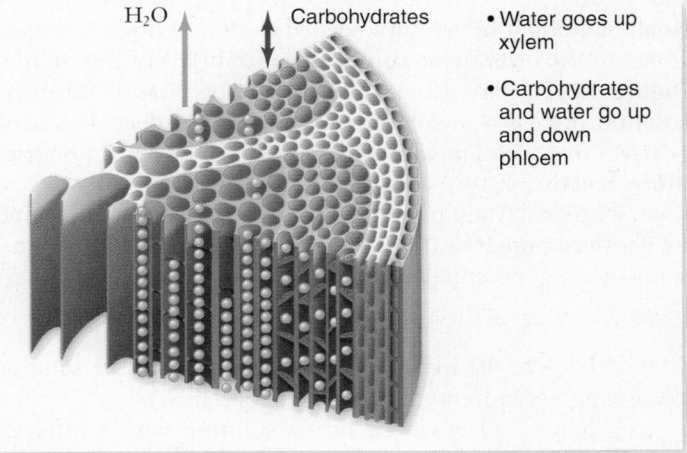

H_2O Carbohydrates

- Water goes up xylem
- Carbohydrates and water go up and down phloem

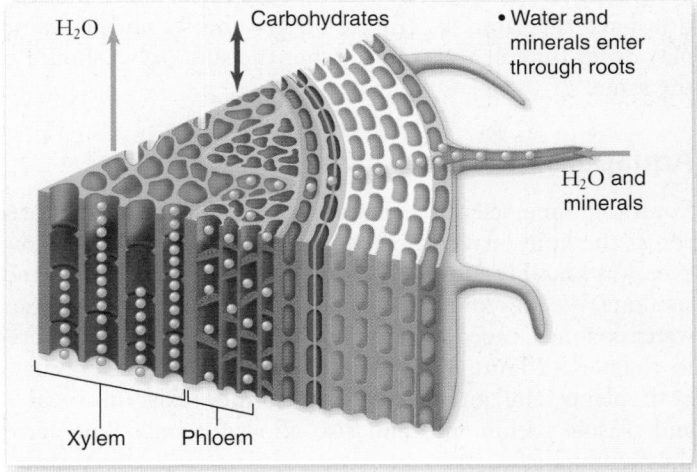

H_2O Carbohydrates

- Water and minerals enter through roots

H_2O and minerals

Xylem   Phloem

H_2O and minerals

Figure 38.2 Water and mineral movement through a plant. This diagram illustrates the path of water and inorganic materials as they move into, through, and out of the plant body.

solution, and water moves into the cell by the process of **osmosis,** which you may recall from the discussion of membranes in chapter 5. The cell expands and presses against the cell wall, making it *turgid,* or swollen, because of the cell's increased turgor pressure. By contrast, if the cell is placed into a solution with a very high concentration of sucrose, water leaves the cell and turgor pressure drops. The cell membrane pulls away from the cell wall as the volume of the cell shrinks. This

process is called **plasmolysis,** and if the cell loses too much water it will die. Even a tiny change in cell volume causes large changes in turgor pressure. When the turgor pressure falls to zero, most plants will wilt.

Calculation of water potential

A change in turgor pressure can be predicted more accurately by calculating the water potential of the cell and the surrounding solution. Water potential has two components: (1) physical forces, such as pressure on a plant cell wall or gravity, and (2) the concentration of solute in each solution.

In terms of physical forces, the contribution of gravity to water potential is so small that it is generally not included in calculations unless you are considering a very tall tree. The turgor pressure, resulting from pressure against the cell wall, is referred to as **pressure potential (Ψ_p)**. As turgor pressure increases, Ψ_p increases. A beaker of water containing dissolved sucrose, however, is not bounded by a cell membrane or a cell wall. Solutions that are not contained within a vessel or membrane cannot have turgor pressure, and they always have a Ψ_p of 0 MPa (figure 38.3a).

Water potential also arises from an uneven distribution of a solute on either side of a membrane, which results in osmosis. Applying pressure on the side of the membrane that has the greater concentration of solute prevents osmosis. The smallest amount of pressure needed to stop osmosis is proportional to the osmotic or **solute potential (Ψ_s)** of the solution (figure 38.3b). Pure water has a solute potential of zero. As a solution increases in solute concentration, it decreases in Ψ_s (< 0 MPa). A solution with a higher solute concentration has a more negative Ψ_s.

The total water potential (Ψ_w) of a plant cell is the sum of its pressure potential (Ψ_p) and solute potential (Ψ_s); it represents the total potential energy of the water in the cell:

$$\Psi_w = \Psi_p + \Psi_s$$

When the Ψ_w inside the cell equals that of the solution, there is no net movement of water (figure 38.3c).

When a cell is placed into a solution with a different Ψ_w, the tendency is for water to move in the direction that eventually results in equilibrium—both the cell and the solution have the same Ψ_w (figure 38.4). The Ψ_p and Ψ_s values may differ for cell and solution, but the sum (=Ψ_w) should be the same.

Aquaporins enhance osmosis

For a long time, scientists did not understand how water moved across the lipid bilayer of the plasma membrane. Water, however, was found to move more rapidly than predicted by osmosis alone. We now know that osmosis is enhanced by membrane water channels called aquaporins, which you first encountered in chapter 5 (figure 38.5). These transport channels occur in both plants and animals; in plants, they exist in vacuoles and plasma membranes and also allow for bulk flow across the membrane.

At least 30 different genes code for aquaporin-like proteins in *Arabidopsis*. Aquaporins speed up osmosis, but they do not change the direction of water movement. They are important in maintaining water balance within a cell and in moving water into the xylem.

Water potential and pressure gradients form a foundation for understanding local and long-distance transport in plants. The remaining sections of this chapter explore transport within and among different tissues and organs of the plant in more depth.

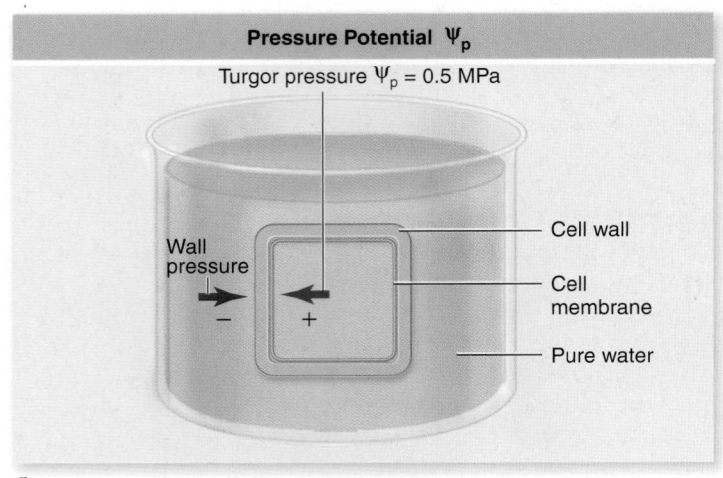

a.

b.

$$\Psi = \Psi_s + \Psi_p$$
$$\Psi_{cell} = -0.7 \text{ MPa} + 0.5 \text{ MPa} = -0.2 \text{ MPa}$$
$$\Psi_{solution} = -0.2 \text{ MPa (solution has no pressure potential)}$$

c.

Figure 38.3 Determining water potential. *a.* Cell walls exert pressure in the opposite direction of cell turgor pressure. *b.* Using the given solute potentials, predict the direction of water movement based only on solute potential. *c.* Total water potential is the sum of Ψ_s and Ψ_p. Since the water potential inside the cell equals that of the solution, there is no net movement of water.

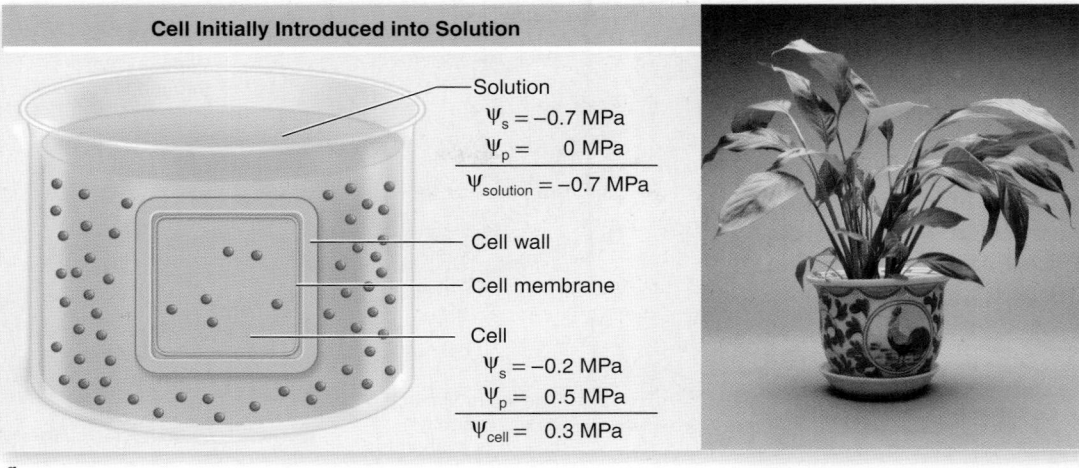

Cell Initially Introduced into Solution

Solution
$\Psi_s = -0.7$ MPa
$\Psi_p = \ \ \ 0$ MPa
$\overline{\Psi_{solution} = -0.7 \text{ MPa}}$

Cell wall
Cell membrane
Cell
$\Psi_s = -0.2$ MPa
$\Psi_p = \ \ 0.5$ MPa
$\overline{\Psi_{cell} = \ \ 0.3 \text{ MPa}}$

a.

Cell at Equilibrium Is Plasmolyzed

$\Psi_{cell} = \ \Psi_{solution} = -0.7$ MPa

Cell
$\Psi_p = 0$
-0.7 MPa $=$
$\Psi_s + 0$ MPa
$\Psi_s = -0.7$
Cell membrane
Cell wall

b.

Figure 38.4 Water potential at equilibrium.
a. This cell initially had a larger Ψ_w than the solution surrounding it. *b.* At osmotic equilibrium, the Ψ_w of the cell and the solution should be the same. We assume that the cell is in a very large volume of solution of constant concentration. The final Ψ_w of the cell should therefore equal the initial Ψ_w of the solution. When a cell is plasmolyzed, $\Psi_p = 0$. As the cell loses water, the cell's solution becomes concentrated.

Inquiry question

? What would Ψ_w, Ψ_s, and Ψ_p of the cell in (a) be at equilibrium if it had been placed in a solution with a Ψ_s of −0.5?

Cell wall and exterior

Diffusion

Bulk flow

Cell membrane

Aquaporin

Cytoplasm

Water molecules

Figure 38.5 Aquaporins. Aquaporins are water-selective pores in the plasma membrane that increase the rate of osmosis because they allow bulk flow across the membrane. They do not alter the direction of water movement, however.

Learning Outcomes Review 38.1

Transpiration is the evaporation of thin films of water from the stomata, exerting a lifting force on water in the xylem. Water potential is the sum of the pressure potential and the solute potential; water moves from an area of high water potential to an area of low water potential. This difference moves water from the soil into roots, and from the roots to the rest of the plant body. The vapor pressure gradient between the inside and the outside of a leaf drives transpiration.

■ *Explain how physical pressure and solute concentration contribute to water potential.*

38.2 *Water and Mineral Absorption*

Learning Outcomes

1. *Explain the function of root hairs.*
2. *List the three water transport routes through plants.*
3. *Describe the function of Casparian strips.*

Most of the water absorbed by the plant comes in through the region of the root with root hairs (figures 38.6 and 38.7). As you learned in chapter 36, root hairs are extensions of root epidermal cells located just behind the tips of growing roots.

Surface area for the absorption of water and minerals is further increased in many species of plants by interacting with mycorrhizal fungi. These fungi extend the absorptive net far beyond that of root hairs and are particularly helpful in the uptake of phosphorous in the soil. Mycorrhizae are discussed in detail in chapter 31.

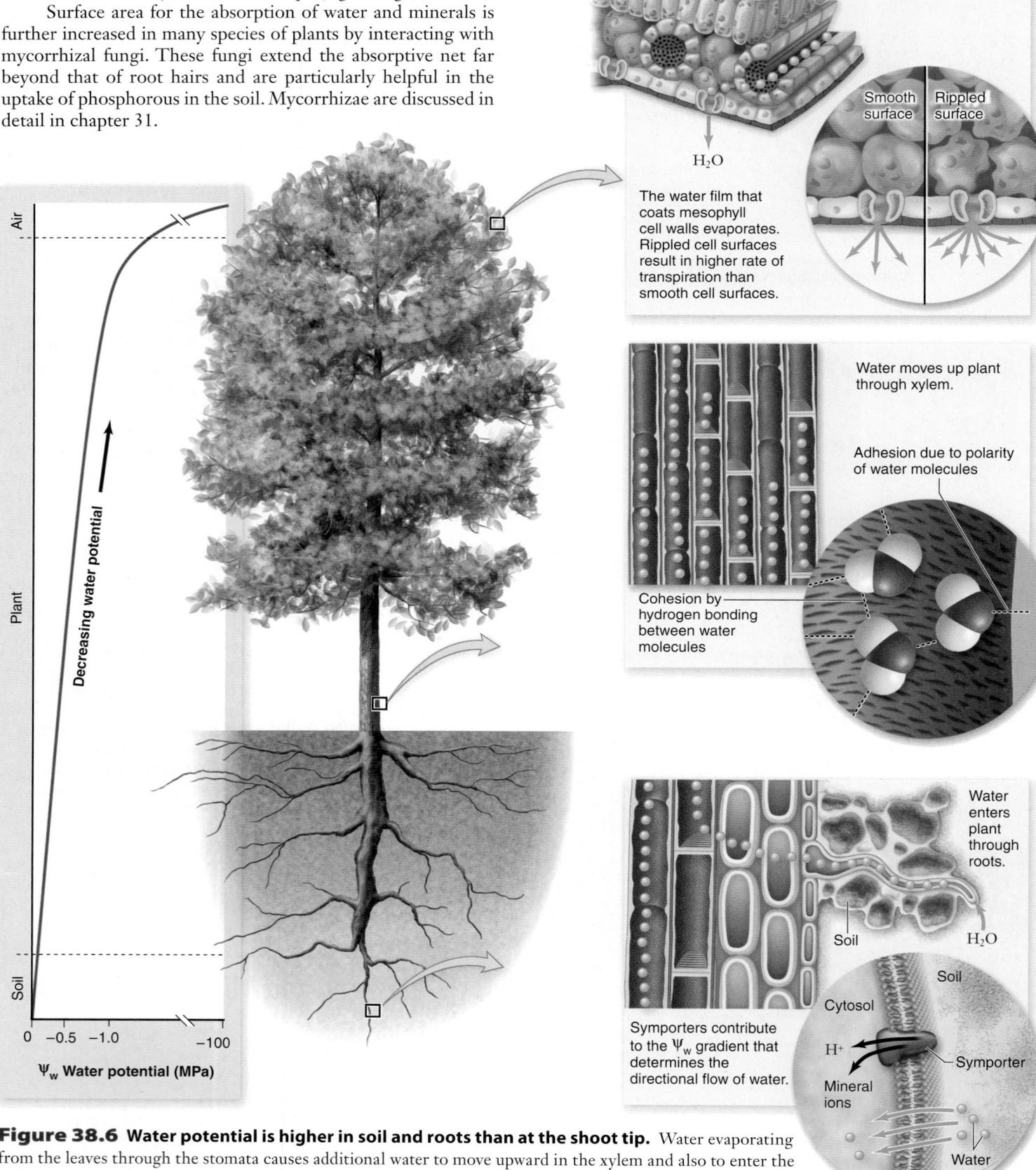

Water exits plant through stomata.

H_2O

The water film that coats mesophyll cell walls evaporates. Rippled cell surfaces result in higher rate of transpiration than smooth cell surfaces.

Smooth surface | Rippled surface

Water moves up plant through xylem.

Adhesion due to polarity of water molecules

Cohesion by hydrogen bonding between water molecules

Water enters plant through roots.

Soil | H_2O

Soil

Cytosol

H^+

Symporter

Mineral ions

Water

Symporters contribute to the Ψ_w gradient that determines the directional flow of water.

Air

Plant

Soil

Decreasing water potential

0   −0.5   −1.0   −100

Ψ_w **Water potential (MPa)**

Figure 38.6 Water potential is higher in soil and roots than at the shoot tip. Water evaporating from the leaves through the stomata causes additional water to move upward in the xylem and also to enter the plant through the roots. Water potential drops substantially in the leaves due to transpiration.

Figure 38.7 Water and minerals move into roots in regions rich with root hairs.

Once absorbed through root hairs, water and minerals must move across cell layers until they reach the vascular tissues; water and dissolved ions then enter the xylem and move throughout the plant.

Three transport routes exist through cells

Water and minerals can follow three pathways to the vascular tissue of the root (figure 38.8). The **apoplast route** includes movement through the cell walls and the space between cells. Transport through the apoplast avoids membrane transport. The **symplast route** is the continuum of cytoplasm between cells connected by plasmodesmata. Once molecules are inside a cell, they can move between cells through plasmodesmata without crossing a plasma membrane. The **transmembrane route** involves membrane transport between cells and also across the membranes of vacuoles within cells. This route permits each cell the greatest amount of control over what substances enter and leave. These three routes are not exclusive, and molecules can change pathways at any time, until reaching the endodermis of the root.

Transport through the endodermis is selective

Eventually, on their journey inward, molecules reach the endodermis. Any further passage through the cell walls is blocked by the Casparian strips. As described in chapter 36, all cells in the cylinder of endodermis have connecting walls embedded with the waterproof material suberin (figure 38.9). Molecules must pass through the plasma membranes and protoplasts of the endodermal cells to reach the xylem. The endodermis, with its unique structure, along with the cortex and epidermis, controls water and nutrient flow to the xylem to regulate water potential and helps limit leakage of water out of the root.

Because the mineral ion concentration in the soil water is usually much lower than it is in the plant, an expenditure of energy (supplied by ATP) is required for these ions to accumulate in root cells. The plasma membranes of endodermal cells contain a variety of protein transport channels, through which proton pumps transport specific ions against even larger concentration gradients (refer to figure 38.1). Once inside the vascular stele, the ions, which are plant nutrients, are transported via the xylem throughout the plant.

Learning Outcomes Review 38.2

Water and minerals move into the plant from the soil, particularly in the region rich with root hairs. The three water transport routes are the apoplast route through the cells walls, the symplast route through plasmodesmata, and the transmembrane route across cell and vacuole membranes. Casparian strips force water and nutrients to move through the cell membranes of the endodermis, allowing selective control.

■ *What qualities of the cell membrane allow it to act as a selective barrier?*

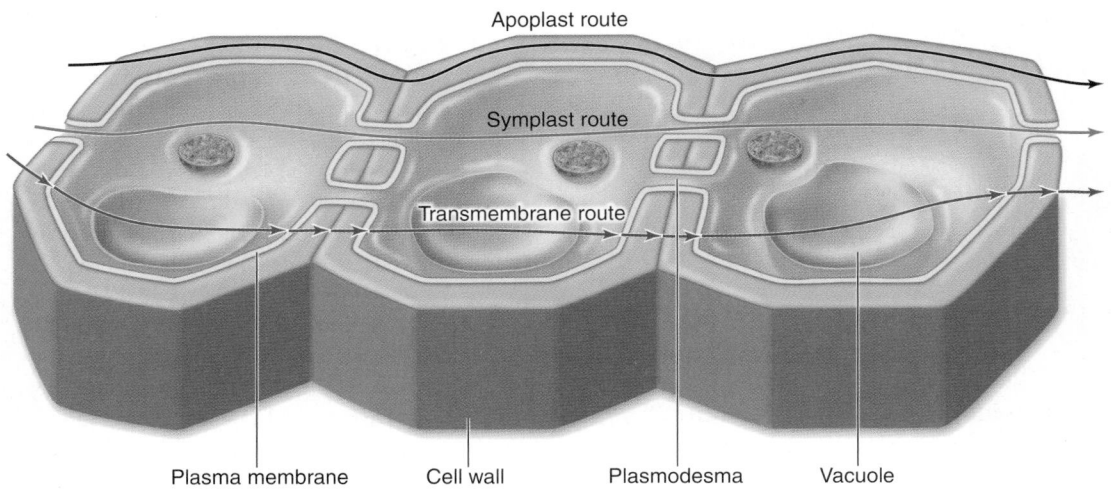

Figure 38.8 Transport routes between cells.

 Inquiry question

Which route would be the fastest for water movement? Would this always be the best way to move nutrients into the plant?

Apoplast route

Symplast route

Transmembrane route

Plasma membrane   Cell wall   Plasmodesma   Vacuole

Learning Outcomes

1. **Describe the environmental conditions in which guttation occurs.**
2. **List the properties of water that cause it to have a high tensile strength.**
3. **Explain how cavitation interrupts water flow.**

The aqueous solution that passes through the membranes of endodermal cells enters the plant's vascular tissues and moves into the tracheids and vessel members of the xylem. As ions are actively pumped into the root or move via facilitated diffusion, their presence increases the water potential and increases turgor pressure in the roots due to osmosis.

Root pressure is present even when transpiration is low or not occurring

Root pressure, which often occurs at night, is caused by the continued accumulation of ions in the roots at times when transpiration from the leaves is very low or absent. This accumula-
tion results in an increasingly high ion concentration within the cells, which in turn causes more water to enter the root hair cells by osmosis. Ion transport further decreases the Ψ_s of the roots. The result is movement of water into the plant and up the xylem columns despite the absence of transpiration.

Under certain circumstances, root pressure is so strong that water will ooze out of a cut plant stem for hours or even days. When root pressure is very high, it can force water up to the leaves, where it may be lost in a liquid form through a process known as **guttation.** Guttation cannot move water up great heights or at rapid speeds. It does not take place through the stomata, but instead occurs through special groups of cells located near the ends of small veins that function only in this process. Guttation produces what is more commonly called dew on leaves.

Root pressure alone, however, is insufficient to explain xylem transport. Transpiration provides the main force for moving water and ionic solutes from roots to leaves.

A water potential gradient from roots to shoots enables transport

Water potential regulates the movement of water through a whole plant, as well as across cell membranes. Roots are the entry point. Water moves from the soil into the plant only if water potential of the soil is greater than in the root. Too much fertilizer or drought conditions lower the Ψ_w of the soil and limit water flow into the plant. Water in a plant moves along a Ψ_w gradient from the soil (where the Ψ_w may be close to zero under wet conditions) to successively more negative water potentials in the roots, stems, leaves, and atmosphere (see figure 38.6).

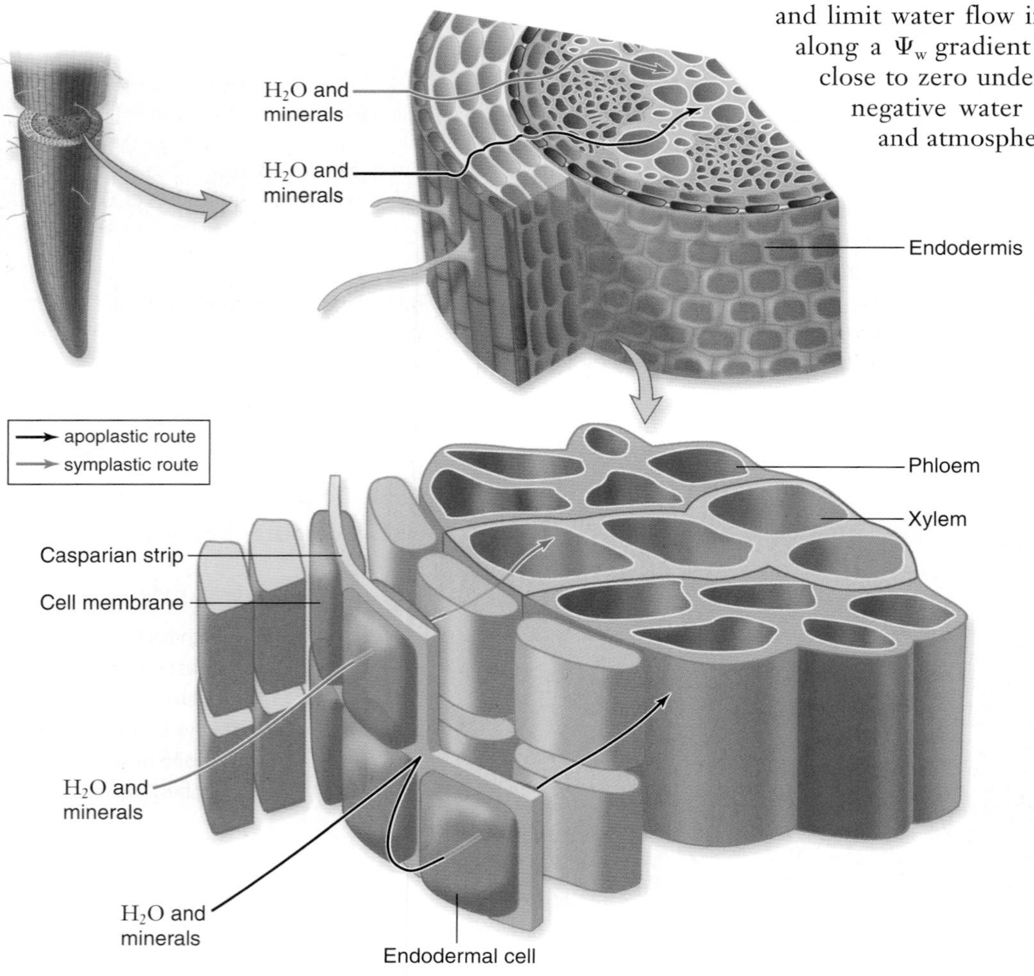

apoplastic route
symplastic route

H₂O and minerals
H₂O and minerals
Endodermis
Phloem
Xylem
Casparian strip
Cell membrane
H₂O and minerals
H₂O and minerals
Endodermal cell

Figure 38.9 The pathways of mineral transport in roots. Minerals are absorbed at the surface of the root. In passing through the cortex, they must either follow the cell walls and the spaces between them or go directly through the plasma membranes and the protoplasts of the cells, passing from one cell to the next by way of the plasmodesmata. When they reach the endodermis, however, their further passage through the cell walls is blocked by the Casparian strips, and they must pass through the membrane and protoplast of an endodermal cell before they can reach the xylem.

Evaporation of water in a leaf creates negative pressure or tension in the xylem, which literally pulls water up the stem from the roots. The strong pressure gradient between leaves and the atmosphere cannot be explained by evaporation alone. As water diffuses from the xylem of tiny, branching veins in a leaf, it forms a thin film along mesophyll cell walls. If the surface of the air–water interface is fairly smooth (flat), the water potential is higher than if the surface becomes rippled.

The driving force for transpiration is the humidity gradient from 100% relative humidity inside the leaf to much less than 100% relative humidity outside the stomata. Molecules diffusing from the xylem replace evaporating water molecules. As the rate of evaporation increases, diffusion cannot replace all the water molecules. The film is pulled back into the cell walls and becomes rippled rather than smooth. The change increases the pull on the column of water in the xylem, and concurrently increases the rate of transpiration.

Vessels and tracheids accommodate bulk flow

Water has an inherent **tensile strength** that arises from the cohesion of its molecules, their tendency to form hydrogen bonds with one another (see chapter 2). These two factors are the basis of the cohesion–tension theory of the bulk flow of water in the xylem. The tensile strength of a column of water varies inversely with the diameter of the column; that is, the smaller the diameter of the column, the greater the tensile strength. Because plant tracheids and vessels are tiny in diameter, the cohesive force of water is stronger than the pull of gravity. The water molecules also adhere to the sides of the tracheid or xylem vessels, further stabilizing the long column of water.

Given that a narrower column of water has greater tensile strength, it is intriguing that vessels, having diameters that are larger than tracheids, are found in so many plants. The difference in diameter has a larger effect on the mass of water in the column than on the tensile strength of the column. The volume of liquid moving in a column per second is proportional to r^4, where r is the radius of the column, at constant pressure. A twofold increase in radius would result in a 16-fold increase in the volume of liquid moving through the column. Given equal cross-sectional areas of xylem, a plant with larger-diameter vessels can move more water up its stems than a plant with narrower tracheids.

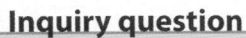

Inquiry question

? If a mutation increased the radius of a xylem vessel threefold, how would the movement of water through the plant be affected?

The effect of cavitation

Tensile strength depends on the continuity of the water column; air bubbles introduced into the column when a vessel is broken or cut would cause the continuity and the cohesion to fail. A gas-filled bubble can expand and block the tracheid or vessel, a process called **cavitation**. Cavitation stops water transport and can lead to dehydration and death of part or all of a plant (figure 38.10).

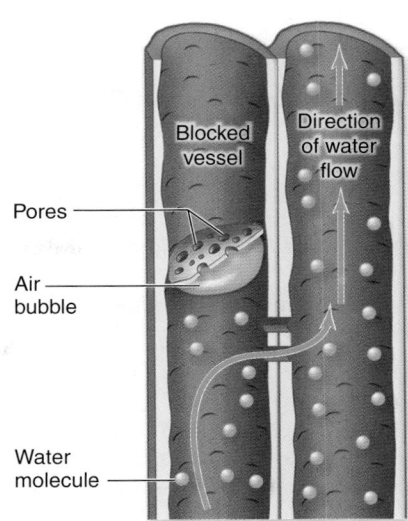

Figure 38.10 Cavitation. An air bubble can break the tensile strength of the water column. Bubbles are larger than pits and can block transport to the next tracheid or vessel. Water drains to surrounding tracheids or vessels.

Anatomical adaptations can compensate for the problem of cavitation, including the presence of alternative pathways that can be used if one path is blocked. Individual tracheids and vessel members are connected to other tracheids or vessels by pits in their walls, and air bubbles are generally larger than these openings. In this way, bubbles cannot pass through the pits to further block transport. Freezing or deformation of cells can also cause small bubbles of air to form within xylem cells, especially with seasonal temperature changes. Cavitation is one reason older xylem often stops conducting water.

Mineral transport

Tracheids and vessels are essential for the bulk transport of minerals. Ultimately, the minerals that are actively transported into the roots are removed and relocated through the xylem to other metabolically active parts of the plant. Phosphorus, potassium, nitrogen, and sometimes iron may be abundant in the xylem during certain seasons. In many plants, this pattern of ionic concentration helps conserve these essential nutrients, which may move from mature deciduous parts such as leaves and twigs to areas of active growth, namely meristem regions.

Keep in mind that minerals that are relocated via the xylem must move with the generally upward flow through the xylem. Not all minerals can reenter the xylem conduit once they leave. Calcium, an essential nutrient, cannot be transported elsewhere once it has been deposited in a particular plant part. But some other nutrients can be transported in the phloem.

Learning Outcomes Review 38.3

Guttation occurs when root pressure is high but transpiration is low. It commonly occurs at night in temperate climates when the air is cool and the humidity is high. Water's high tensile strength results from the cohesiveness of water molecules for each other and adhesiveness to the walls of cells in the xylem; both of these are effects of hydrogen bonding. Cavitation, which stops water movement, results from a bubble in the water transport system that breaks cohesion.

■ **What controls the rate of transpiration when the humidity is low?**

■ **What happens to minerals once they leave the xylem?**

The Rate of Transpiration

More than 90% of the water taken in by the roots of a plant is ultimately lost to the atmosphere. Water moves from the tips of veins into mesophyll cells, and from the surface of these cells it evaporates into pockets of air in the leaf. As discussed in chapter 36, these intercellular spaces are in contact with the air outside the leaf by way of the stomata.

Stomata open and close to balance H_2O and CO_2 needs

Water is essential for plant metabolism, but it is continuously being lost to the atmosphere. At the same time, photosynthesis requires a supply of CO_2 entering the chlorenchyma cells from the atmosphere. Plants therefore face two somewhat conflicting requirements: the need to minimize the loss of water to the atmosphere and the need to admit carbon dioxide. Structural features such as stomata and the cuticle have evolved in response to one or both of these requirements.

The rate of transpiration depends on weather conditions, including humidity and the time of day. As stated earlier, transpiration from the leaves decreases at night, when stomata are closed and the vapor pressure gradient between the leaf and the atmosphere is less. During the day, sunlight increases the temperature of the leaf, while transpiration cools the leaf through evaporative cooling.

On a short-term basis, closing the stomata can control water loss. This occurs in many plants when they are subjected to water stress. But the stomata must be open at least part of the time so that CO_2 can enter. As CO_2 enters the intercellular spaces, it dissolves in water before entering the plant's cells where it is used in photosynthesis. The gas dissolves mainly in water on the walls of the intercellular spaces below the stomata. The continuous stream of water that reaches the leaves from the roots keeps these walls moist.

Turgor pressure in guard cells causes stomata to open and close

The two sausage-shaped guard cells on each side of a stoma stand out from other epidermal cells not only because of their shape, but also because they are the only epidermal cells containing chloroplasts. Their distinctive wall construction, which is thicker on the inside and thinner elsewhere, results in a bulging out and bowing when they become turgid.

You can make a model of this for yourself by taking two elongated balloons, tying the closed ends together, and inflating both balloons slightly. When you hold the two open ends together, there should be very little space between the two balloons. Now wrap duct tape around both balloons as shown in figure 38.11 (without releasing any air) and inflate each one a bit more. Hold the open ends together again. You should now be holding a roughly doughnut-shaped pair of "guard cells" with a "stoma" in the middle. Real guard cells rely on the influx and efflux of water, rather than air, to open and shut.

Turgor in guard cells results from the active uptake of potassium (K^+), chloride (Cl^-), and malate. As solute concentration increases, water potential decreases in the guard cells, and water enters osmotically. As a result, these cells accumulate water and become turgid, opening the stomata (figure 38.12). The energy required to move the ions across the guard cell membranes comes from the ATP-driven H^+ pump shown in figure 38.1.

The guard cells of many plant species regularly become turgid in the morning, when photosynthesis occurs, and lose turgor in the evening, regardless of the availability of water. During the course of a day, sucrose accumulates in the photosynthetic guard cells. The active pumping of sucrose out of guard cells in the evening may lead to loss of turgor and close the guard cell.

Figure 38.11 Unequal cell wall thickenings on guard cells result in the opening of stomata when the guard cells expand.

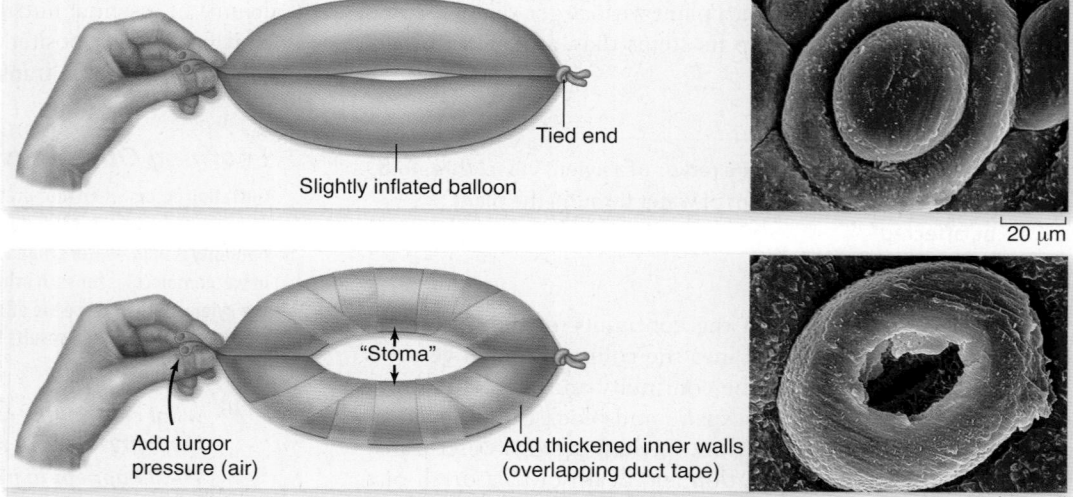

Tied end

Slightly inflated balloon

20 µm

"Stoma"

Add turgor pressure (air)

Add thickened inner walls (overlapping duct tape)

20 µm

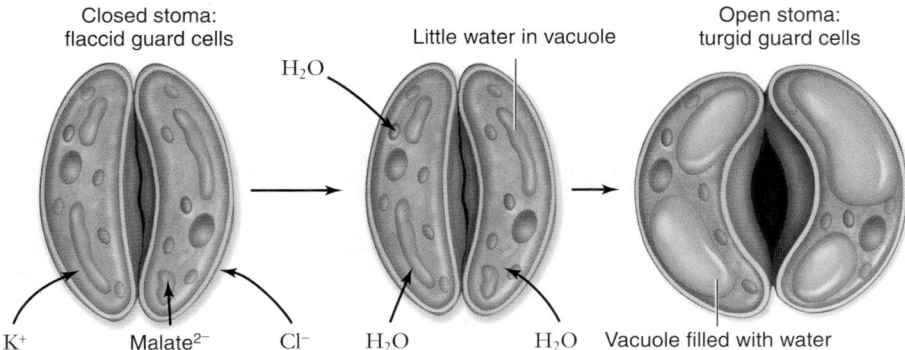

Figure 38.12 How a stoma opens. When H+ ions are pumped from guard cells, K+ and Cl- ions move in, and the guard cell turgor pressure increases as water enters by osmosis. The increased turgor pressure causes the guard cells to bulge, with the thick walls on the inner side causing each guard cell to bow outward, thereby opening the stoma.

Environmental factors affect transpiration rates

Transpiration rates increase with temperature and wind velocity because water molecules evaporate more quickly. As humidity increases, the water potential difference between the leaf and the atmosphere decreases, but even at 95% relative humidity in the atmosphere, the vapor pressure gradient can sustain full transpiration. On a catastrophic level, when a whole plant wilts because insufficient water is available, the guard cells may lose turgor, and as a result, the stomata may close. Fluctuations in transpiration rate are tempered by opening or closing stomata.

Experimental evidence has indicated that several pathways regulate stomatal opening and closing. **Abscisic acid (ABA),** a plant hormone discussed in chapter 41, plays a primary role in allowing K+ to pass rapidly out of guard cells, causing the stomata to close in response to drought. ABA binds to receptor sites in the plasma membranes of guard cells, triggering a signaling pathway that opens K+, Cl−, and malate ion channels. Turgor pressure decreases as water loss follows, and the guard cells close (figure 38.13).

CO_2 concentration, light, and temperature also affect stomatal opening. When CO_2 concentrations are high, the guard cells of many plant species are triggered to decrease the stomatal opening. Additional CO_2 is not needed at such times, and water is conserved when the guard cells are closed.

Blue light regulates stomatal opening. This helps increase turgor to open the stomata when sunlight increases the evaporative cooling demands. K+ transport against a concentration gradient is promoted by light. Blue light in particular triggers proton (H+) transport, creating a proton gradient that drives the opening of K+ channels.

The stomata may close when the temperature exceeds 30° to 34°C and water relations are unfavorable. To ensure sufficient gas exchange, these stomata open when it is dark and the temperature has dropped. Some plants are able to collect CO_2 at night in a modified form to be utilized in photosynthesis during daylight hours. In chapter 9, you learned about Crassulacean acid metabolism (CAM), which occurs in succulent plants such as cacti. In this process, stomata open and CO_2 is taken in at night and stored in organic compounds. These compounds are decarboxylated during the day, providing a source of CO_2 for fixation when stomata are closed. CAM plants are able to conserve water in dry environments.

Learning Outcomes Review 38.4

When guard cells of the stomata actively take up ions, their water potential decreases and they take up water by osmosis. When they become turgid they change shape, creating an opening in the stoma. Stomata close when a plant is under water stress, but they open when carbon dioxide is needed and transpiration does not cause excess water loss. Transpiration rates increase with high wind velocity, high temperatures, and low humidity.

■ *Why is it critical that carbon dioxide dissolve in water upon entering plants?*

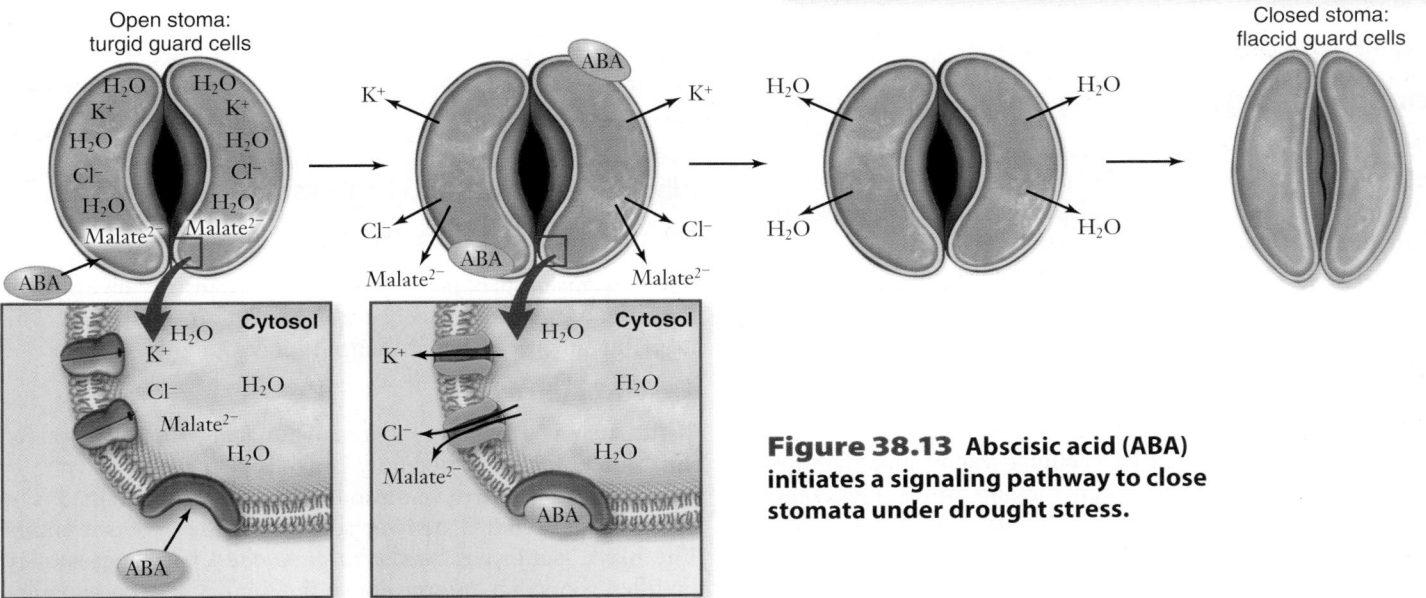

Figure 38.13 Abscisic acid (ABA) initiates a signaling pathway to close stomata under drought stress.

Water-Stress Responses

Learning Outcomes

1. **List three drought adaptations in plants.**
2. **Describe the negative effects of flooding on plant growth.**
3. **Outline three ways in which a plant may deal with a salty environment.**

Because plants cannot simply move on when water availability or salt concentrations change, adaptations have evolved to allow plants to cope with environmental fluctuations, including drought, flooding, and changing salinity.

Plant adaptations to drought include strategies to limit water loss

Many mechanisms for controlling the rate of water loss have evolved in plants. Regulating the opening and closing of stomata provides an immediate response. Morphological adaptations provide longer term solutions to drought periods. For example, for some plants dormancy occurs during dry times of the year; another mechanism involves loss of leaves, limiting transpiration. Deciduous plants are common in areas that periodically experience severe drought. In a broad sense, annual plants conserve water when conditions are unfavorable simply by going into "dormancy" as seeds.

Thick, hard leaves often with relatively few stomata—and frequently with stomata only on the lower side of the leaf—lose water far more slowly than large, pliable leaves with abundant stomata. Leaves covered with masses of wooly-looking trichomes (hairs) reflect more sunlight and thereby reduce the heat load on the leaf and the demand for transpiration for evaporative cooling.

Plants in arid or semiarid habitats often have their stomata in crypts or pits in the leaf surface (figure 38.14). Within these depressions, the water surface tensions are altered, reducing the rate of water loss.

Plant responses to flooding include short-term hormonal changes and long-term adaptations

Plants can also receive too much water, in which case they ultimately "drown." Flooding rapidly depletes available oxygen in the soil and interferes with the transport of minerals and carbohydrates in the roots. Abnormal growth often results. Hormone levels change in flooded plants; ethylene, a hormone associated with suppression of root elongation, increases, while gibberellins and cytokinins, which enhance growth of new roots, usually decrease (see chapter 41). Hormonal changes contribute to the abnormal growth patterns.

Oxygen deprivation is among the most significant problems because it leads to decreased cellular respiration. Standing water has much less oxygen than moving water. Generally, standing-water flooding is more harmful to a plant (riptides excluded). Flooding that occurs when a plant is dormant is much less harmful than flooding when it is growing actively.

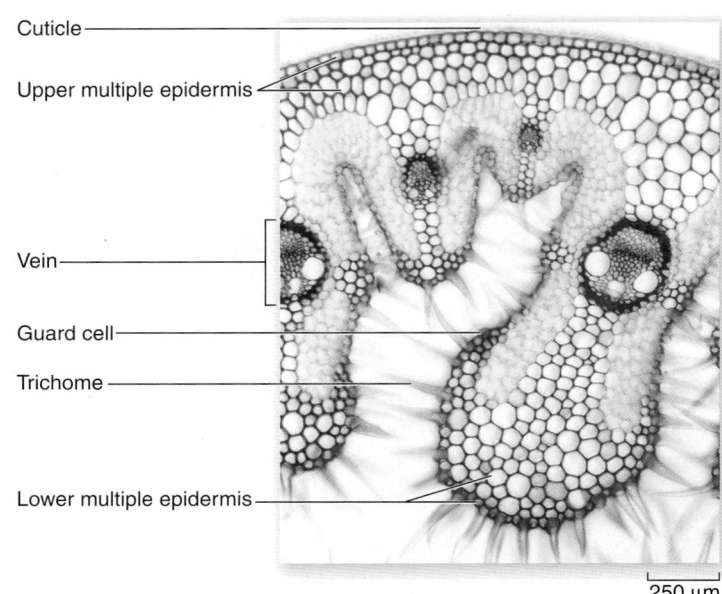

Figure 38.14 Anatomical protection from drought in leaves. Deeply embedded stomata, extensive trichomes, and multiple layers of epidermis minimize water loss in this leaf, shown in cross section.

Physical changes that occur in the roots as a result of oxygen deprivation may halt the flow of water through the plant. Paradoxically, even though the roots of a plant may be standing in water, its leaves may be drying out. Plants can respond to flooded conditions by forming larger lenticels (which facilitate gas exchange) and adventitious roots that reach above flood level for gas exchange.

Whereas some plants survive occasional flooding, others have adapted to living in fresh water. One of the most frequent adaptations among plants to growing in water is the formation of **aerenchyma,** loose parenchymal tissue with large air spaces in it (figure 38.15). Aerenchyma is very prominent in water lilies and many other aquatic plants. Oxygen may be transported from the parts of the plant above water to those below by way of passages in the aerenchyma. This supply of oxygen allows oxidative respiration to take place even in the submerged portions of the plant.

Some plants normally form aerenchyma, whereas others, subject to periodic flooding, can form it when necessary. In corn, increased ethylene due to flooding induces aerenchyma formation.

Plant adaptations to high salt concentration include elimination methods

The algal ancestors of plants adapted to a freshwater environment from a saltwater environment before the "move" onto land. This adaptation involved a major change in controlling salt balance.

Growth in salt water

Plants such as mangroves that grow in areas normally flooded with salt water must not only provide a supply of oxygen to their submerged parts, but also control their salt balance. The salt must be excluded, actively secreted, or diluted as it enters. The black mangrove (*Avicennia germinans*) has long, spongy, air-filled roots that emerge above the mud. These roots, called

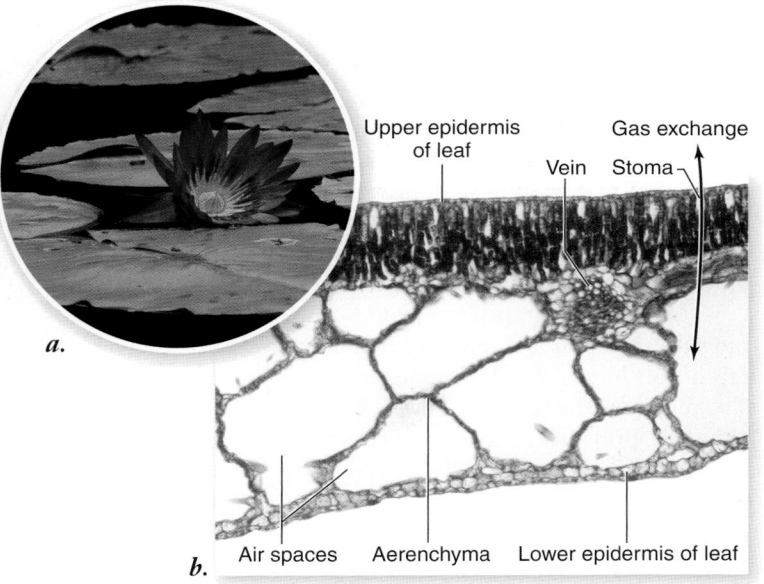

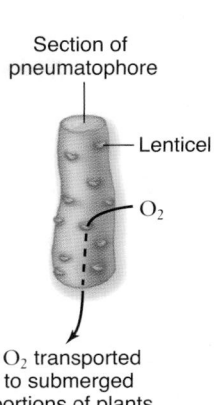

Figure 38.15 Aerenchyma. This tissue facilitates gas exchange in aquatic plants. ***a.*** Water lilies float on the surface of ponds, collecting oxygen and then transporting it to submerged portions of the plant. ***b.*** Large air spaces in the leaves of the water lily add buoyancy. The specialized parenchyma tissue that forms these open spaces is called aerenchyma. Gas exchange occurs through stomata found only on the upper surface of the leaf.

pneumatophores (see chapter 36), have large lenticels on their above-water portions through which oxygen enters; it is then transported to the submerged roots (figure 38.16). In addition, the succulent leaves of some mangrove species contain large quantities of water, which dilute the salt that reaches them. Many plants that grow in such conditions also either secrete large quantities of salt or block salt uptake at the root level.

Growth in saline soil

Soil salinity is increasing, often caused by salt accumulation from irrigation. Currently 23% of the world's cultivated land has high levels of saline that reduce crop yield. The low water potential of saline soils results in water-stressed crops. Some plants, called **halophytes** (salt lovers), can tolerate soils with high salt concentrations. Mechanisms for salt tolerance are being studied with the goal of breeding more salt-tolerant plants. Some halophytes produce high concentrations of organic molecules within their roots to alter the water potential gradient between the soil and the root so that water flows into the root.

Learning Outcomes Review 38.5

Adaptations to drought include dormancy, leaf loss, leaves that minimize water loss, and stomata that lie in depressions. When plants are exposed to flooding, oxygen deprivation leads to lower cellular respiration rates, impedance of mineral and carbohydrate transport, and changes in hormone levels. If a plant is exposed to a salty environment, it may exclude the salt from uptake, secrete it after it has been taken up, or dilute it.

■ *Why are flooded plants in danger of oxygen deprivation when photosynthesis produces oxygen?*

Figure 38.16 How mangroves get oxygen to their submerged parts. The black mangrove (*Avicennia germinans*) grows in areas that are commonly flooded, and much of each plant is usually submerged. However, modified roots called pneumatophores supply the submerged portions of the plant with oxygen because these roots emerge above the water and have large lenticels. Oxygen diffuses into the roots through the lenticels, passes into the abundant aerenchyma, and moves to the rest of the plant.

38.6 Phloem Transport

Learning Outcomes

1. *Define translocation.*
2. *List the substances found in plant sap.*
3. *Explain the pressure-flow hypothesis.*

Most carbohydrates manufactured in leaves and other green parts are distributed through the phloem to the rest of the plant. This process, known as translocation, provides suitable carbohydrate building blocks for the roots and other actively growing regions of the plant. Carbohydrates concentrated in storage organs such as tubers, often in the form of starch, are also converted into transportable molecules, such as sucrose, and moved through the phloem. In this section we discuss the ways by which carbohydrate- and nutrient-rich fluid, termed **sap**, is moved through the plant body.

Organic molecules are transported up and down the plant

The movement of sugars and other substances can be followed in phloem using radioactive labels (figure 38.17). Radioactive carbon dioxide ($^{14}CO_2$) can be incorporated into glucose as a result of photosynthesis. Glucose molecules are used to make the disaccharide sucrose, which is transported in the phloem. Such studies have shown that sucrose moves both up and down in the phloem.

Hypothesis: *As pea embryos develop in a pod, sugars will be transported through the phloem to the developing embryos.*

Prediction: *Radioactively labeled sugars will accumulate in developing pea embryos.*

Test: *Expose a healthy pea leaf to radioactive carbon dioxide ($^{14}CO_2$). Place photographic film over the entire plant at 1 and 12 hours after treatment and develop film.*

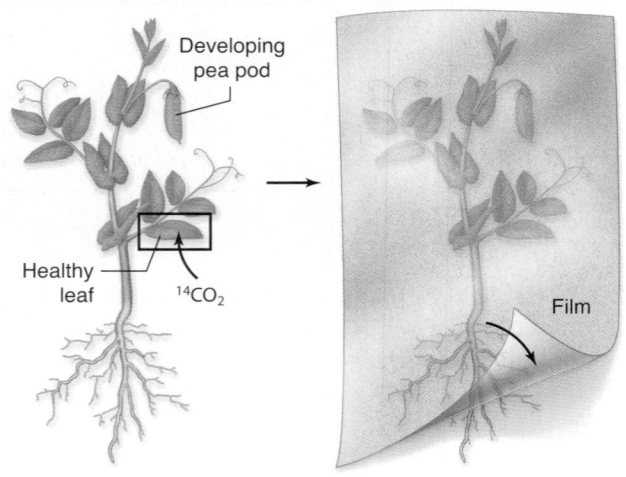

Result: *After 1 hour the radioactivity is concentrated near the application site. After 12 hours the radioactivity is concentrated in the developing embryo.*

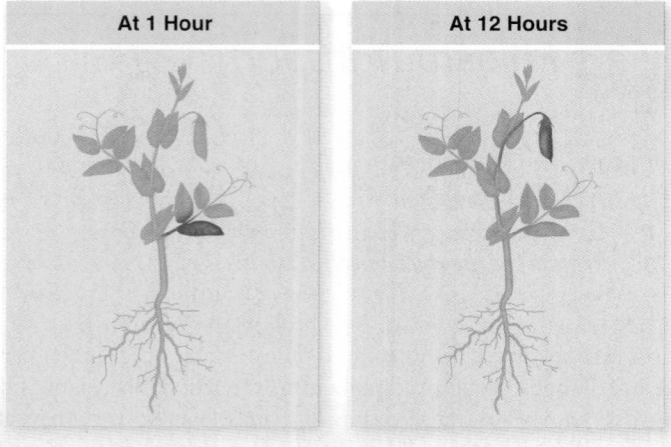

At 1 Hour	At 12 Hours

Conclusion: *The $^{14}CO_2$ is incorporated into sugars during photosynthesis and transported to the developing embryo in the pod.*

Further Experiments: *Carrots take two years to flower. During the first season an underground root, the 'carrot', develops and sugars are stored to be used for reproduction the next year. How could you test the hypothesis that sugars are transported to the developing storage root during the first season of growth for a carrot plant?*

Figure 38.17 Sucrose flow in phloem during fruit development.

Aphids, a group of insects that extract plant sap for food, have been valuable tools in understanding translocation. Aphids thrust their stylets (piercing mouthparts) into phloem cells of leaves and stems to obtain the abundant sugars there. When a feeding aphid is removed by cutting its stylet, the liquid from the phloem continues to flow through the detached mouthpart and is thus available in pure form for analysis (figure 38.18). The liquid in the phloem, when evaporated, contains 10 to 25% of dry-weight matter, almost all of which is sucrose. Using aphids to obtain the critical samples and radioactive tracers to mark them, plant biologists have demonstrated that substances in phloem can move remarkably fast, as much as 50 to 100 cm/h.

Phloem also transports plant hormones, and as will be explored in chapter 41, environmental signals can result in the rapid translocation of hormones in the plant. Recent evidence also indicates that mRNA can move through the phloem, providing a previously unknown mechanism for long-distance communication among cells. In addition, phloem carries other molecules, such as a variety of sugars, amino acids, organic acids, proteins, and ions.

Turgor pressure differences drive phloem transport

The most widely accepted model of how carbohydrates in solution move through the phloem has been called the **pressure–flow theory.** Dissolved carbohydrates flow from a *source* and are released at a *sink*, where they are utilized. Carbohydrate sources include photosynthetic tissues, such as the mesophyll of leaves. Food-storage tissues, such as the cortex of roots, can be either sources

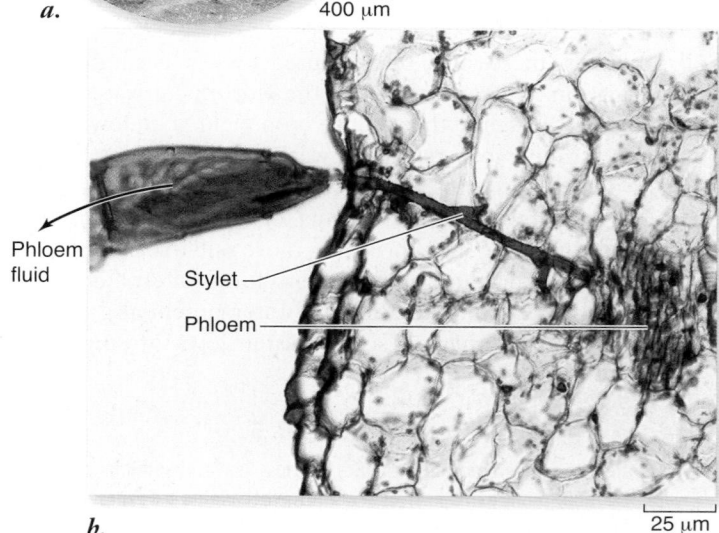

Figure 38.18 Feeding on phloem. *a.* Aphids, including this individual shown on the edge of a leaf, feed on the food-rich contents of the phloem, which they extract through (*b*) their piercing mouthparts, called stylets. When an aphid is separated from its stylet and the cut stylet is left in the plant, the phloem fluid oozes out of it and can then be collected and analyzed.

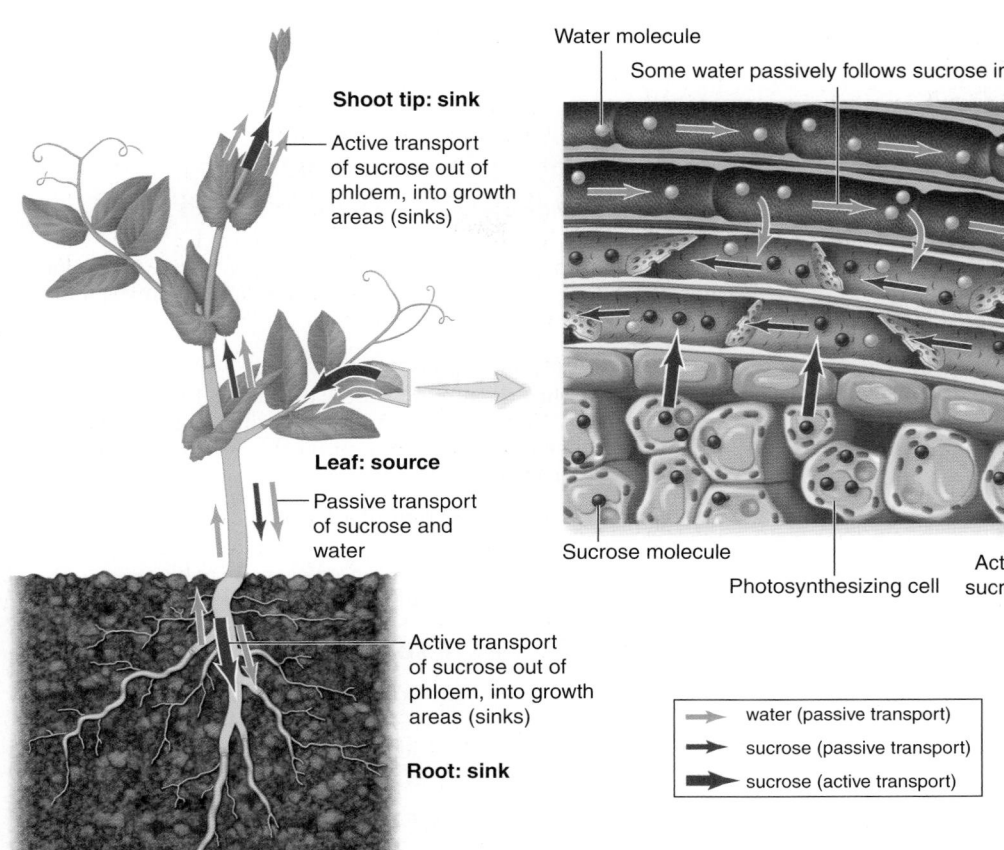

Shoot tip: sink

Active transport of sucrose out of phloem, into growth areas (sinks)

Leaf: source

Passive transport of sucrose and water

Active transport of sucrose out of phloem, into growth areas (sinks)

Root: sink

Water molecule

Some water passively follows sucrose into phloem

Xylem

Phloem

Sucrose molecule

Photosynthesizing cell

Active transport of sucrose into phloem

→ water (passive transport)

→ sucrose (passive transport)

→ sucrose (active transport)

Figure 38.19
Diagram of mass flow.
In this diagram, *red* dots represent sucrose molecules and *blue* dots symbolize water molecules. After moving from the mesophyll cells of a leaf or another part of the plant into the conducting cells of the phloem, the sucrose molecules are transported to other parts of the plant by mass flow and unloaded where they are required.

or sinks. Sinks also occur at the growing tips of roots and stems and in developing fruits. Also, because sources and sinks can change through time as needs change, the direction of phloem flow can change.

In a process known as **phloem loading,** carbohydrates (mostly sucrose) enter the sieve tubes in the smallest veins at the source. Some sucrose travels from mesophyll cells to the companion and sieve cells via the symplast (see figure 38.8). Much of the sucrose arrives at the sieve cell through apoplastic transport and is moved across the membrane via a sucrose and H^+ symporter (see chapter 5). This energy-requiring step is driven by a proton pump (see figure 38.1). Companion cells and parenchyma cells adjacent to the sieve tubes provide the ATP energy to drive this transport. Unlike vessels and tracheids, sieve cells must be alive to participate in active transport.

Bulk flow occurs in the sieve tubes without additional energy requirements. Because of the difference between the water potential in the sieve tubes and in the nearby xylem cells, water flows into the sieve tubes by osmosis. Turgor pressure in the sieve tubes thus increases, and this pressure drives the fluid throughout the plant's system of sieve tubes. At the sink, sucrose and hormones are actively removed from the sieve tubes,

and water follows by osmosis. The turgor pressure at the sink drops, causing a mass flow from the stronger pressure at the source to the weaker pressure at the sink (figure 38.19). Most of the water at the sink then diffuses back into the xylem, where it may either be recirculated or lost through transpiration.

Transport of sucrose and other carbohydrates within sieve tubes does not require energy. But the pressure needed to drive the movement is created through energy-dependent loading and unloading of these substances from the sieve tubes.

Learning Outcomes Review 38.6

Translocation is the movement of dissolved carbohydrates and other substances from one part of the plant to another through the phloem. Sap in the phloem contains sucrose and other sugars, hormones, mRNA, amino acids, organic acids, proteins, and ions. According to the pressure-flow hypothesis, carbohydrates are loaded into sieve tubes, creating a difference in water potential. As a result, water enters the tubes and creates pressure to move fluid through the phloem.

■ *What is the key difference between the fluid in xylem and the fluid in phloem?*

38.1 Transport Mechanisms (see figure 38.2)

Local changes result in long-distance movement of materials.

Properties of water, osmosis, and cellular activities predict the directions of water movement.

Water potential regulates movement of water through the plant (see figures 38.3 and 38.4).

The major force for water transport in a plant is the pulling of water by transpiration. Cohesion, adhesion, and osmosis all contribute to water movement.

Water potential is the sum of pressure potential and solute potential. Water moves from an area of high water potential to an area of low water potential.

Aquaporins enhance osmosis (see figure 38.5).

Aquaporins are water channels in plasma membranes that allow water to move across the membrane more quickly.

38.2 Water and Mineral Absorption

Root hairs and mycorrhizal fungi can increase the surface area for absorption of water and minerals.

Three transport routes exist through cells.

The apoplast route is through cell walls and spaces between cells. The symplast route is through the cytoplasm and between cells via plasmodesmata. The transmembrane route is also through the cytoplasm, but across membranes, where entry and exit of substances can be controlled.

Transport through the endodermis is selective.

Casparian strips in the endoderm force water and nutrients to move across the cell membranes, allowing selective flow of water and nutrients to the xylem.

38.3 Xylem Transport

Root pressure is present even when transpiration is low or not occurring.

Root pressure results from the active transport of ions into the root cells, which causes water to move in through osmosis. Guttation occurs when water is forced out of a plant as a result of high root pressure.

Water has a high tensile strength due to its cohesive and adhesive properties, which are related to hydrogen bonding.

A water potential gradient from roots to shoots enables transport.

Water moves into plants when the soil water potential is greater than that of roots. Evaporation of water from leaves creates a negative water potential that pulls water upward through the xylem.

Vessels and tracheids accommodate bulk flow.

The volume of water that can be transported by a xylem vessel or tracheid is a function of its diameter. As diameter decreases, tensile strength increases; however, a larger volume of water can be transported through a tube with a larger radius.

Cavitation occurs when a gas bubble forms in a water column and water movement ceases.

38.4 The Rate of Transpiration

Stomata open and close to balance H_2O and CO_2 needs.

More than 90% of the water absorbed by the roots is lost by evaporation through stomata. Stomata must open to take up carbon dioxide for photosynthesis and to allow evaporation for transpiration and cooling for the leaf (see figure 39.12).

Turgor pressure in guard cells causes stomata to open and close.

Stomata open when the turgor pressure of guard cells increases due to the uptake of ions. The turgid guard cells change shape and create an opening between them. Stomata close when guard cells lose turgor pressure and become flaccid.

Environmental factors affect transpiration rates.

Transpiration rates increase as temperature and wind velocity increase and as humidity decreases. Stomata close at high temperatures or when carbon dioxide concentrations increase.

38.5 Water-Stress Responses

Plant adaptations to drought include strategies to limit water loss.

Plant adaptations to minimize water loss include closing stomata, becoming dormant, altering leaf characteristics to minimize water loss, and losing leaves.

Plant responses to flooding include short-term hormonal changes and long-term adaptations.

Flooding reduces oxygen availability for cellular respiration, results in abnormal growth, and reduces the efficiency of transport mechanisms.

Plants adapted to wet environments exhibit a variety of strategies, including lenticels, adventitious roots such as pneumatophores, and aerenchyma tissue to ensure oxygen for submerged parts.

Plant adaptations to high salt concentration include elimination methods.

Plants found in saline waters may exclude, secrete, or dilute salts that have been taken up.

Halophytes can take up water from saline soils by decreasing the water potential of their roots with high concentrations of organic molecules.

39.6 Phloem Transport

Organic molecules are transported up and down the plant.

Movement of organic nutrients from leaves to other parts of the plant through the phloem is called translocation.

The sap that moves through phloem contains sugars, plant hormones, mRNA, and other substances. Carbohydrates must be actively transported into the sieve tubes.

Turgor pressure differences drive phloem transport.

At the carbohydrate source, such as a photosynthetic leaf, active transport of sugars into the phloem causes a reduction in water potential.

As water moves into the phloem, turgor pressure drives the contents to a sink, such as a nonphotosynthetic tissue, where the sugar is unloaded.

UNDERSTAND

1. Which of the following is an active transport mechanism?
   a. Proton pump   c. Symport
   b. Ion channel   d. Osmosis

2. The water potential of a plant cell is the
   a. sum of the membrane potential and gravity.
   b. difference between membrane potential and gravity.
   c. sum of the pressure potential and solute potential.
   d. difference between pressure potential and solute potential.

3. Hydrogen bonding between water molecules results in
   a. submersion.   c. evaporation.
   b. adhesion.   d. cohesion.

4. Water movement through cell walls is
   a. apoplastic.   c. both a and b
   b. symplastic.   d. neither a nor b

5. Casparian strips are found in the root
   a. cortex.   c. endodermis.
   b. dermal tissue.   d. xylem.

6. The formation of an air bubble is the xylem is called
   a. agitation.   c. adhesion.
   b. cohesion.   d. cavitation.

7. Guttation is most likely to be observed on
   a. cold winter day.   c. warm sunny day.
   b. cool summer night.   d. warm cloudy day.

8. Stomata open when guard cells
   a. take up potassium.   c. take up sugars.
   b. lose potassium.   d. lose sugars.

9. Which of the following is not an adaptation to a high saline environment?
   a. Secretion of salts
   b. Lowering of root water potential
   c. Exclusion of salt
   d. Production of pneumatophores

10. A plant must expend energy to drive
   a. transpiration.
   b. translocation.
   c. both transpiration and translocation.
   d. neither transpiration nor translocation.

APPLY

1. Which of the following statements is inaccurate?
   a. Water moves to areas of low water potential.
   b. Xylem transports materials up the plant while phloem transports materials down the plant.
   c. Water movement in the xylem is largely due to the cohesive and adhesive properties of water.
   d. Water movement across membranes is often due to differences in solute concentrations.

2. If you could override the control mechanisms that open stomata and force them to remain closed, what would you expect to happen to the plant?
   a. Sugar synthesis would likely slow down.
   b. Water transport would likely slow down.
   c. Both a and b could be the result of keeping stomata closed.
   d. Neither a nor b would be the result of keeping stomata closed.

3. What will happen if a cell with a solute potential of –0.4 MPa and a pressure potential of 0.2 MPa is placed in a chamber filled with pure water that is pressurized with 0.5 MPa?
   a. Water will flow out of the cell.
   b. Water will flow into the cell.
   c. The cell will be crushed.
   d. The cell will explode.

4. If you were able to remove the aquaporins from cell membranes, which of the following would be the likely consequence?
   a. Water would no longer move across membranes.
   b. Plants would no longer be able to control the direction of water movement across membranes.
   c. The potassium symport would no longer function.
   d. Turgor pressor would increase.

5. What would be the consequence of removing the Casparian strip?
   a. Water and mineral nutrients would not be able to reach the xylem.
   b. There would be less selectivity as to what passed into the xylem.
   c. Water and mineral nutrients would be lost from the xylem back into the soil.
   d. Water and mineral nutrients would no longer be able to pass through the cell walls of the endodermis.

SYNTHESIZE

1. If you fertilize your houseplant too often, you may find that it looks wilted even when the soil is wet. Explain what has happened in terms of water potential.

2. How could you detect a plant with a mutation in a gene for an important aquaporin protein?

3. Contrast water transport mechanisms in plants with those in animals.

4. Measurements of tree trunk diameters indicate that the trunk shrinks during the day, with shrinkage occurring in the upper part of the trunk before it occurs in the lower part. Explain how these observations support the hypothesis that water is pulled through the trunk as a result of transpiration.

5. A carrot is a biennial plant. In the first year of growth, the seed germinates and produces a plant with a thick storage root. In the second year, a shoot emerges from the storage root and produces a flower stalk. Following fertilization, seeds are formed to start the life cycle again. Draw a carrot plant during the spring, summer, and fall of the two years of its life cycle and indicate the carbohydrate sources and sinks in each season.

ONLINE RESOURCE

www.ravenbiology.com

Understand, Apply, and Synthesize—enhance your study with animations that bring concepts to life and practice tests to assess your understanding. Your instructor may also recommend the interactive eBook, individualized learning tools, and more.

Chapter **39**

Plant Nutrition and Soils

Chapter Outline

39.1 Soils: The Substrates on Which Plants Depend

39.2 Plant Nutrients

39.3 Special Nutritional Strategies

39.4 Carbon–Nitrogen Balance and Global Change

39.5 Phytoremediation

Introduction

Vast energy inputs are required for the building and ongoing growth of a plant. In this chapter, you'll learn what inputs, besides energy from the Sun, a plant needs to survive. Plants, like animals, need various nutrients to remain healthy. The lack of an important nutrient may slow a plant's growth or make the plant more susceptible to disease or even death. Plants acquire these nutrients mainly through photosynthesis and from the soil. In addition to contributing nutrients, the soil hosts bacteria and fungi that aid plants in obtaining nutrients in a usable form. Getting sufficient nitrogen is particularly problematic because plants cannot directly convert atmospheric nitrogen into amino acids. A few plants are able to capture animals and secrete digestive juices to make nitrogen available for absorption.

39.1 Soils: The Substrates on Which Plants Depend

Learning Outcomes

1. *List the three main components of topsoil.*
2. *Explain how the charge of soil particles can affect the relative balance of positively and negatively charged molecules and ions in the soil water.*
3. *Describe cultivation approaches that can reduce soil erosion.*

Much of the activity that supports plant life is hidden within the soil. **Soil** is the highly weathered outer layer of the Earth's crust. It is composed of a mixture of ingredients, which may include sand, rocks of various sizes, clay, silt, humus (partially decomposed organic matter), and various other forms of mineral and organic matter. Pore spaces containing water and air occur between the particles of soil.

Soil is composed of minerals, organic matter, water, air, and organisms

The mineral fraction of soils varies according to the composition of the rocks. The Earth's crust includes about 92 naturally occurring elements (see chapter 2). Most elements are found in the form of inorganic compounds called *minerals;* most rocks consist of several different minerals.

The soil is also full of microorganisms that break down and recycle organic debris. For example, about 5 metric tons of carbon is tied up in the organisms present in the soil under a hectare of wheat land in England—an amount that approximately equals the weight of 100 sheep!

Most roots are found in **topsoil** (figure 39.1), which is a mixture of mineral particles of varying size (most less than 2 mm in diameter), living organisms, and **humus.** Topsoils are characterized by their relative amounts of sand, silt, and clay. Soil composition determines the degree of water and nutrient binding to soil particles. Sand binds molecules minimally, but clay adsorbs (binds) water and nutrients quite tightly.

Water and mineral availability is determined by soil characteristics

Only minerals that are dissolved in water in the spaces or pores among soil particles are available for uptake by roots. Both mineral and organic soil particles tend to have negative charges, so they attract positively charged molecules and ions. The negatively charged anions stay in solution, creating a charge gradient between the soil solution and the root cells, so that positive ions would normally tend to move out of the cells. Proton pumps move H^+ out of the root to form a strong membrane potential ($\approx$ –160 mV). The strong electrochemical gradient then causes K^+ and other ions to enter via ion channels. Some ions, especially anions, use cotransporters (figure 39.2). The membrane potential maintained by the root, as well as the water potential difference inside and outside the root, affects root transport. (Water potential is described in chapter 38.)

About half of the total soil volume is occupied by pores, which may be filled with air or water, depending on moisture

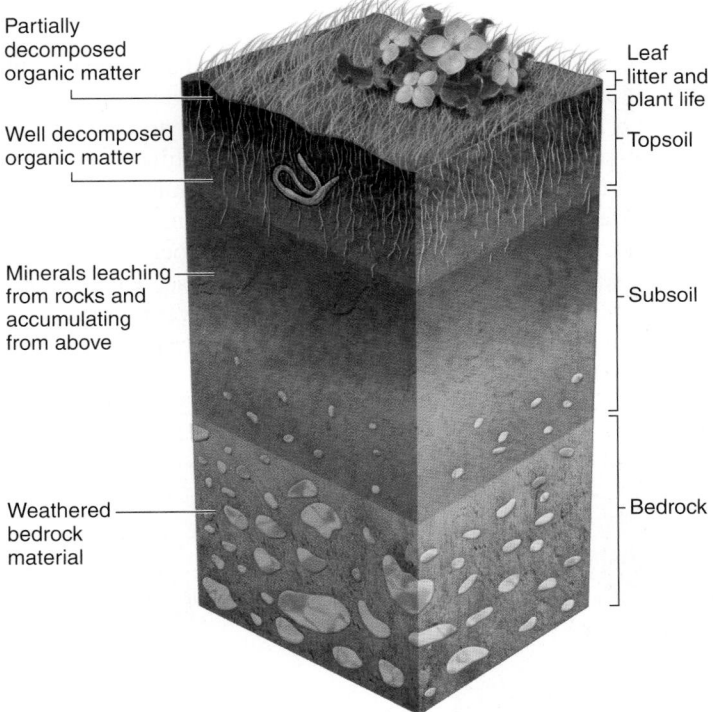

Figure 39.1 Most roots grow in the topsoil. Leaf litter and animal remains cover the uppermost layer in soil called topsoil. Topsoil contains organic matter, such as roots, small animals, humus, and mineral particles of various sizes. Subsoil lies underneath the topsoil and contains larger mineral particles and relatively little organic matter. Beneath the subsoil are layers of bedrock, the raw material from which soil is formed over time and through weathering.

Partially decomposed organic matter

Well decomposed organic matter

Minerals leaching from rocks and accumulating from above

Weathered bedrock material

Leaf litter and plant life

Topsoil

Subsoil

Bedrock

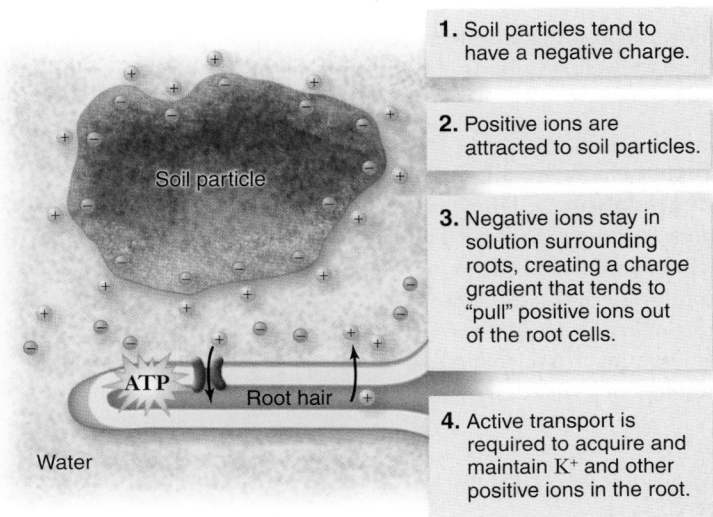

Figure 39.2 Role of soil charge in transport. Active transport is required to move positively charged ions into a root hair.

1. Soil particles tend to have a negative charge.
2. Positive ions are attracted to soil particles.
3. Negative ions stay in solution surrounding roots, creating a charge gradient that tends to "pull" positive ions out of the root cells.
4. Active transport is required to acquire and maintain K^+ and other positive ions in the root.

Soil particle

ATP

Root hair

Water

Figure 39.3 Water and air fill pores among soil particles. *a.* Without some space for air circulation in the soil, roots cannot respire. *b.* A balance of air and water in the soil is essential for root growth. *c.* Too little water decreases the soil water potential and prevents transpiration in plants.

conditions (figure 39.3). Some of the soil water is unavailable to plants. In sandy soil, for example, a substantial amount of water drains away immediately due to gravity. Another fraction of the water is held in small soil pores, which are generally less than about 50 μm in diameter. This water is readily available to plants. When this water is depleted through evaporation or root uptake, the plant wilts and will eventually die unless more water is added to the soil. However, as plants deplete water near the roots, the soil water potential decreases. This helps to move more water toward the roots since the soil water further away has a higher water potential.

Soils have widely varying composition, and any particular soil may provide more or fewer plant nutrients. In addition, the soil's acidity and salinity, described shortly, can affect the availability of nutrients and water.

Cultivation can result in soil loss and nutrient depletion

When topsoil is lost because of erosion or poor landscaping, both the water-holding capacity and the nutrient relationships of the soil are adversely affected. Up to 50 billion tons of topsoil have been lost from fields in the United States in a single year.

Whenever the vegetative cover of soil is disrupted, such as by plowing and harvesting, erosion by water and wind increases—sometimes dramatically, as was the case in the 1930s in the southwestern Great Plains of the United States. This region became known as the "Dust Bowl" when a combination of poor farming practices and several years of drought made the soil particularly susceptible to wind erosion (figure 39.4*a*).

New approaches to cultivation are aimed at reducing soil loss. Intercropping (mixing crops in a field), conservation tillage, and not plowing fall crop detritis under (no-till) are all erosion-prevention measures. Conservation tillage includes minimal till and even no-till approaches to farming.

Overuse of fertilizers in agriculture, lawns, and gardens can cause significant water pollution and its associated negative effects, such as overgrowth of algae in lakes (see chapter 58). Maintaining nutrient levels in the soil and preventing nutrient runoff into lakes, streams, and rivers improves crop growth and minimizes ecosystem damage.

Figure 39.4 Soil degradation. *a.* Drought and poor farming practices led to wind erosion of farmland in the southwestern Great Plains of the United States in the 1930s. *b.* Draining marshland in Iraq resulted in a salty desert.

a.

b.

One approach, site-specific farming, uses variable-rate fertilizer applicators guided by a computer and the global positioning system (GPS). Variable-rate application relies on information about local soil nutrient levels, based on analysis of soil samples. Another approach, integrated nutrient management, maximizes nutritional inputs using "green manure" (such as alfalfa tilled back into the soil), animal manure, and inorganic fertilizers. Green manures and animal manure have the advantage of releasing nutrients slowly as they are broken down by decomposer organisms, so that nutrients may be utilized before leaching away. Sustainable agriculture integrates these conservation approaches.

pH and salinity affect water and mineral availability

Anything that alters water pressure differences or ionic gradient balance between soil and roots can affect the ability of plants to absorb water and nutrients. Acid soils (having low pH) and saline soils (high in salts) can present problems for plant growth.

Acid soils

The pH of a soil affects the release of minerals from weathering rock. For example, at low pH aluminum, which is toxic to many plants, is released from rocks. Furthermore, aluminum can also combine with other nutrients and make them inaccessible to plants.

Most plants grow best at a neutral pH, but about 26% of the world's arable land is acidic. In the tropical Americas, 68% of the soil is acidic. Aluminum toxicity in acid soils in Colombian fields can reduce maize (corn) yield fourfold (figure 39.5).

Breeding efforts in Colombia are producing aluminum-tolerant plants, and crop yields have increased 33%. In a few test fields, the yield increases have been as high as 70% compared with that for nontolerant plants. The ability of plants to take up toxic metals can also be employed to clean up polluted soil, a topic explored later in this chapter.

Salinity

The accumulation of salt ions, usually Na^+ and Cl^-, in soil alters water potential, leading to the loss of turgor in plants. Approximately 23% of all arable land has salinity levels that limit plant growth. Saline soil is most common in dry areas where salts are introduced through irrigation. In such areas, precipitation is insufficient to remove the salts, which gradually accumulate in the soil.

One of the more dramatic examples of soil salinity occurs in the "cradle of civilization," Mesopotamia. The region once called the Fertile Crescent for its abundant agriculture is now largely a desert. Desertification was accelerated in southern Iraq. In the 1990s, most of 20,000 km² of marshlands was drained by redirecting water flow with dams, turning the marshes into a salty desert (see figure 39.4b). The dams were destroyed later, allowing water to enter the marshlands once again. Recovery of the marshlands is not guaranteed, but in areas where the entering water has lowered the salinity there is hope.

SCIENTIFIC THINKING

Hypothesis: *Acidic or basic soils inhibit the growth of corn plants.*

Prediction: *Plants grown in soil with neutral pH will be more vigorous than those grown at high or low pH.*

Test: *Sow equal numbers of corn kernels in identical pots with soil adjusted to pH values of 6.0, 7.0, and 8.0. Allow plants to grow and, after 16 weeks, measure the biomass.*

Put potting soil in three pots and adjust pH.

Grow plants for 16 weeks.

At 16 weeks, wash soil off roots, dry plants, and weigh.

Result: *Corn plant biomass is highest in pots with pH 7.0 soil and lowest in pH 6.0 soil.*

Conclusion: *The hypothesis is supported. Soil pH influences plant growth. Among the pH levels tested, the best for plant growth was 7.0. Acidic soil resulted in the lowest growth.*

Further Experiments: *How could you test the hypothesis that soil pH affects mineral uptake and that changes in mineral uptake were responsible for differences in plant growth?*

Figure 39.5 Soil pH affects plant growth.

Learning Outcomes Review 39.1

Topsoil is composed of mineral particles, living organisms, and humus. Roots use proton pumps to move protons (H^+) out of the root and into the soil. The result is an electrochemical gradient that causes positive mineral ions to enter the root through ion channels. The loss of topsoil by erosion can be reduced by intercropping, planting crop mixtures, conservation tillage, and no-till farming.

■ *In what way would alkaline soil affect plant nutrition?*

39.2 Plant Nutrients

Learning Outcomes

1. *Distinguish between macronutrients and micronutrients.*
2. *Explain how scientists determine the nutritional needs of plants.*
3. *Describe the goal of food fortification research.*

The major source of plant nutrition is the fixation of atmospheric carbon dioxide (CO_2) into simple sugars using the energy of the Sun. CO_2 enters through the stomata; oxygen (O_2) is a waste product of photosynthesis and an atmospheric component that also moves through the stomata. Oxygen is used in cellular respiration to support growth and maintenance in the plant.

CO_2 and light energy are not sufficient, however, for the synthesis of all the molecules a plant needs. Plants require a number of inorganic nutrients as well. Some of these are **macronutrients,** which plants need in relatively large amounts, and others are **micronutrients,** required in trace amounts (table 39.1).

Plants require nine macronutrients and seven micronutrients

The nine macronutrients are carbon, oxygen, and hydrogen—the three elements found in all organic compounds—plus nitrogen (essential for amino acids), potassium, calcium, magnesium (the

TABLE 39.1	Essential Nutrients in Plants			
Element	**Principal Form in Which Element Is Absorbed**	**Approximate Percent of Dry Weight**	**Examples of Important Functions**	
MACRONUTRIENTS				
Carbon	CO_2	44	Major component of organic molecules	
Oxygen	O_2, H_2O	44	Major component of organic molecules	
Hydrogen	H_2O	6	Major component of organic molecules	
Nitrogen	NO_3^-, NH_4^+	1–4	Component of amino acids, proteins, nucleotides, nucleic acids, chlorophyll, coenzymes, enzymes	
Potassium	K^+	0.5–6	Protein synthesis, operation of stomata	
Calcium	Ca^{2+}	0.2–3.5	Component of cell walls, maintenance of membrane structure and permeability; activates some enzymes	
Magnesium	Mg^{2+}	0.1–0.8	Component of chlorophyll molecule, activates many enzymes	
Phosphorus	$H_2PO_4^-$, HPO_4^-	0.1–0.8	Component of ADP and ATP, nucleic acids, phospholipids, several coenzymes	
Sulfur	SO_4^{2-}	0.05–1	Components of some amino acids and proteins, coenzyme A	
MICRONUTRIENTS (CONCENTRATIONS in ppm)				
Chlorine	Cl^-	100–10,000	Osmosis and ionic balance	
Iron	Fe^{2+}, Fe^{3+}	25–300	Chlorophyll synthesis, cytochromes, nitrogenase	
Manganese	Mn^{2+}	15–800	Activator of certain enzymes	
Zinc	Zn^{2+}	15–100	Activator of many enzymes; active in formation of chlorophyll	
Boron	BO_3^-, $B_4O_7^-$, or $H_2BO_3^-$	5–75	Possibly involved in carbohydrate transport, nucleic acid synthesis	
Copper	Cu^2 or Cu^+	4–30	Activator or component of certain enzymes	
Molybdenum	MoO_4^-	0.1–5	Nitrogen fixation, nitrate reduction	

a.   b.   c.   d.

Figure 39.6 Mineral deficiencies in plants. *a.* Leaves of a healthy wheat plant. *b.* Chlorine-deficient plants with necrotic leaves (leaves with patches of dead tissue). *c.* Copper-deficient plant with dry, bent leaf tips. *d.* Zinc-deficient plant with stunted growth and chlorosis (loss of chlorophyll) in patches on leaves. The agricultural implications of deficiencies such as these are obvious; a trained observer can determine the nutrient deficiencies affecting a plant simply by inspecting it.

center of the chlorophyll molecule), phosphorus, and sulfur. Each of these nutrients approaches or, in the case of carbon, may greatly exceed 1% of the dry weight of a healthy plant.

The seven micronutrient elements—chlorine, iron, manganese, zinc, boron, copper, and molybdenum—constitute from less than one to several hundred parts per million in most plants. A deficiency of any one can have severe effects on plant growth (figure 39.6). The macronutrients were generally discovered in the last century, but the micronutrients have been detected much more recently as technology developed to identify and work with such small quantities.

Nutritional requirements are assessed by growing plants in hydroponic cultures in which the plant roots are suspended in aerated water containing nutrients. For the purposes of testing, the solutions contain all the necessary nutrients in the right proportions, but with certain known or suspected nutrients left out. The plants are then allowed to grow and are studied for altered growth patterns and leaf coloration that might indicate a need for the missing element (figure 39.7). To give an idea of how small the needed quantities of micronutrients may be, the standard dose of molybdenum added to seriously deficient soils in Australia amounts to about 34 g (about one handful) per hectare (a square 100 meters on a side—about 2.5 acres), once every 10 years!

Most plants grow satisfactorily in hydroponic cultures, if the roots are properly aerated. The method, although expensive, is occasionally practical for commercial purposes (figure 39.8). Analytical chemistry has made it much easier to test plant material for levels of different molecules.

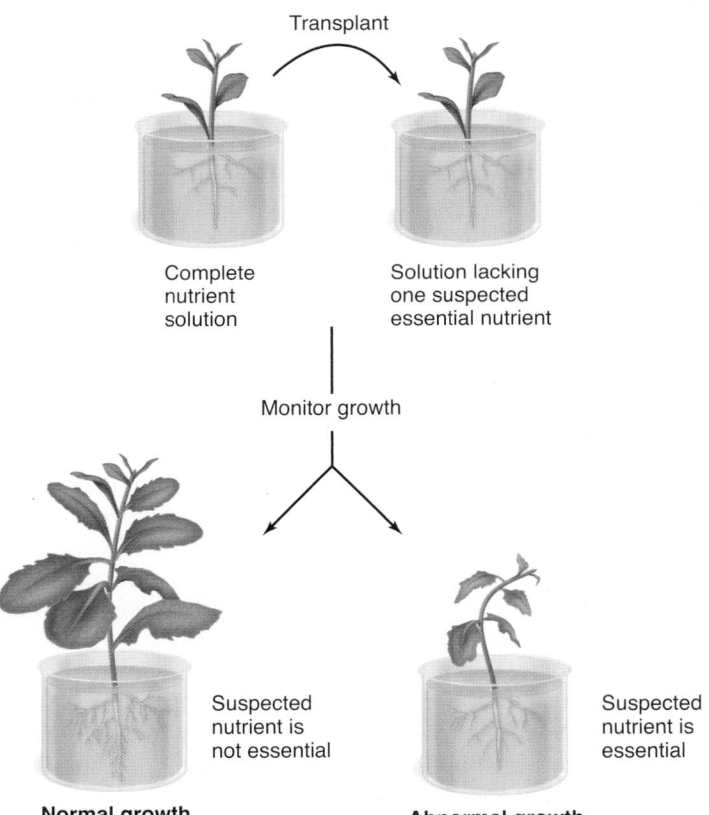

Figure 39.7 Identifying nutritional requirements of plants. A seedling is first grown in a complete nutrient solution. The seedling is then transplanted to a solution that lacks one nutrient thought to be essential. The growth of the seedling is studied for the presence of symptoms indicative of abnormal growth, such as discolored leaves or stunting. If the seedling's growth is normal, the nutrient that was left out may not be essential; if the seedling's growth is abnormal, the nutrient that is lacking is essential for growth.

Figure 39.8 Hydroponics. Soil provides nutrients and support, but both of these functions can be replaced in hydroponic systems. Here, tomato plants are suspended in the air, and the roots rotate through a nutrient bath.

Food security is related to crop productivity and nutrient levels

Nutrient levels and crop productivity are a significant human concern. **Food security,** avoiding starvation, is a global issue. Increasing the nutritional value of crop species, especially in developing countries, could have tremendous human health benefits.

Food fortification is an active area of research focused on ways to increase plants' uptake of minerals and the storage of minerals in roots and shoots for later human consumption. Phosphate uptake can be increased, for example, if it is more soluble in the soil. Some plants have been genetically modified to secrete citrate, an organic acid that solubilizes phosphate. As an added benefit, the citrate binds to aluminum, which can be toxic to plants and animals, and thus limits the uptake of aluminum into plants.

For other nutrients, such as iron, manganese, and zinc, plasma membrane transport is a limiting factor. Genes coding for these plasma membrane transporters have been cloned in other species and are being incorporated into crop plants. Eventually, breakfast cereals may be fortified with additional nutrients while the grains are growing in the field, as opposed to when they are processed in the factory.

Learning Outcomes Review 39.2

Plants require nine macronutrients in relatively large amounts and seven micronutrients in trace amounts. Plants are grown in controlled hydroponic solutions to determine which nutrients are required for growth. Scientists are studying ways to enhance the nutritional composition of food crops through enhancing nutrient uptake and storage. These methods of food fortification may enhance food security, the avoidance of human starvation.

■ *Why would a lack of magnesium in the soil limit food production?*

39.3 *Special Nutritional Strategies*

Learning Outcomes

1. *Explain the significance of nitrogen-fixing bacteria for plant nutrition.*
2. *Explain how mycorrhizal fungi benefit plants.*
3. *Describe the benefit gained by carnivorous plants when they capture insects.*

In some species, scarce nutrients have been obtained through the evolution of mutualistic associations with other organisms, parasitism, or even predation. One example is the requirement for nitrogen: Plants need ammonia (NH_3) or nitrate (NO_3^-) to build amino acids, but most of the nitrogen in the atmosphere is in the form of gaseous nitrogen (N_2). Plants lack the bio-

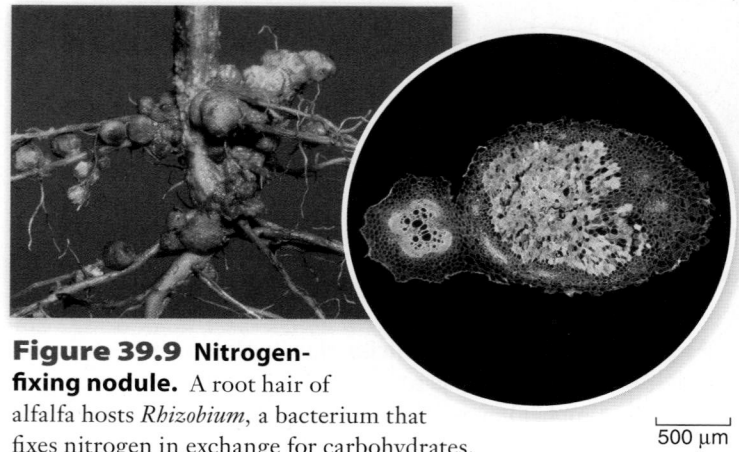

Figure 39.9 Nitrogen-fixing nodule. A root hair of alfalfa hosts *Rhizobium*, a bacterium that fixes nitrogen in exchange for carbohydrates.

500 μm

chemical pathways (including the enzyme nitrogenase) necessary to convert gaseous nitrogen to ammonia, but some bacteria have this capacity.

Bacteria living in close association with roots can provide nitrogen

Symbiotic relationships have evolved between some plant groups and bacteria that can convert gaseous nitrogen. Some of these bacteria live in close association with the roots of plants. Others end up being housed in tissues the plant grows especially for this purpose, called **nodules** (figure 39.9). Legumes and a few other plants can form root nodules. Hosting these bacteria costs the plant energy, but is well worth it when the soil lacks nitrogen compounds. To conserve energy, legume root hairs do not respond to bacterial signals when nitrogen levels are high.

Nitrogen fixation is the most energetically expensive reaction known to occur in any cell. Why should it be so difficult to add H_2 to N_2? The answer lies in the strength of the triple bond in N_2. Nitrogenase requires 16 ATPs to make two molecules of NH_3. Making NH_3 without nitrogenase requires a contained system maintained at 450°C and 500 atm pressure—far beyond the maximums under which plants can survive.

Rhizobium bacteria require oxygen and carbohydrates to support their energetically expensive lifestyle as nitrogen fixers. Carbohydrates are supplied through the vascular tissue of the plant, and leghemoglobin, which is structurally similar to animal hemoglobin, is produced by the plant to regulate oxygen availability to the bacteria. Without oxygen, the bacteria die; within the bacteria, however, nitrogenase has to be isolated from oxygen, which inhibits its activity. Leghemoglobin binds oxygen and controls its availability within the nodule to optimize both nitrogenase activity and cellular respiration.

Just how do legumes and nitrogen-fixing *Rhizobium* bacteria get together (figure 39.10)? Extensive signaling between the bacterium and the legume not only lets each organism know the other is present, but also checks whether the bacterium is the correct species for the specific legume. These highly evolved symbiotic relationships depend on exact species matches. Soybean and garden peas are both legumes, but each requires its own species of symbiotic *Rhizobium*.

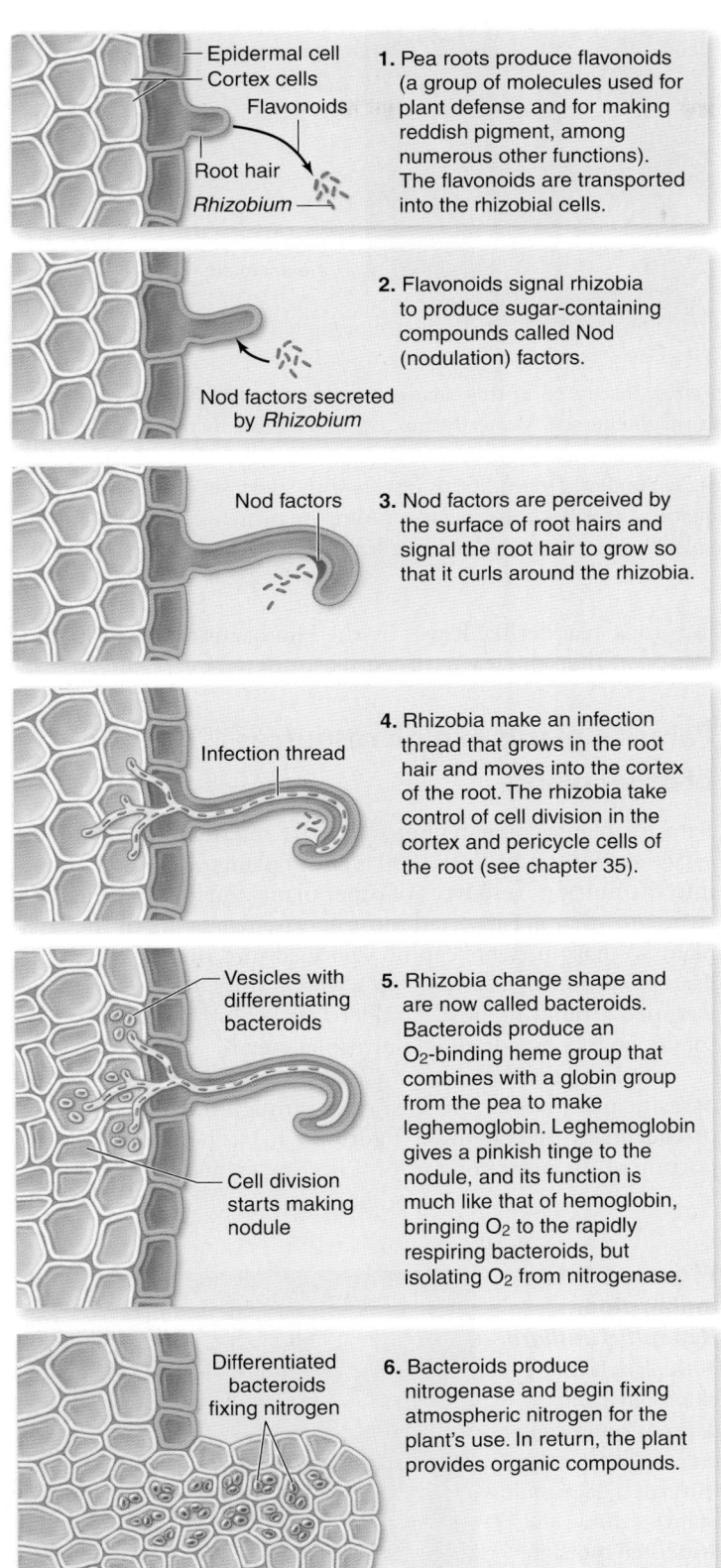

1. Pea roots produce flavonoids (a group of molecules used for plant defense and for making reddish pigment, among numerous other functions). The flavonoids are transported into the rhizobial cells.

- Epidermal cell
- Cortex cells
- Flavonoids
- Root hair
- *Rhizobium*

2. Flavonoids signal rhizobia to produce sugar-containing compounds called Nod (nodulation) factors.

Nod factors secreted by *Rhizobium*

3. Nod factors are perceived by the surface of root hairs and signal the root hair to grow so that it curls around the rhizobia.

Nod factors

4. Rhizobia make an infection thread that grows in the root hair and moves into the cortex of the root. The rhizobia take control of cell division in the cortex and pericycle cells of the root (see chapter 35).

Infection thread

5. Rhizobia change shape and are now called bacteroids. Bacteroids produce an O_2-binding heme group that combines with a globin group from the pea to make leghemoglobin. Leghemoglobin gives a pinkish tinge to the nodule, and its function is much like that of hemoglobin, bringing O_2 to the rapidly respiring bacteroids, but isolating O_2 from nitrogenase.

- Vesicles with differentiating bacteroids
- Cell division starts making nodule

6. Bacteroids produce nitrogenase and begin fixing atmospheric nitrogen for the plant's use. In return, the plant provides organic compounds.

- Differentiated bacteroids fixing nitrogen
- Mature nodule

Figure 39.10 *Rhizobium* **induced nodule formation.**

Mycorrhizae aid a large portion of terrestrial plants

Nitrogen is not the only nutrient that is difficult for plants to obtain without assistance. Whereas symbiotic relationships with nitrogen-fixing bacteria are generally limited to some legume species, symbiotic associations with mycorrhizal fungi, described in chapter 31, are found in about 90% of vascular plants. Mycorrhizae play a significant role in enhancing phosphorus transfer to the plant, and the uptake of some of the micronutrients is also facilitated. Functionally, the mycorrhizae extend the surface area available for nutrient uptake substantially.

Fungi most likely aided early rootless plants in colonizing land. Evidence now indicates that the signaling pathways that lead to plant symbiosis with some mycorrhizae may have been exploited to bring about the *Rhizobium*–legume symbiosis.

Carnivorous plants trap and digest animals to extract additional nutrients

Some plants are able to obtain nitrogen directly from other organisms, just as animals do. These carnivorous plants often grow in acidic soils, such as bogs, that lack organic nitrogen. By capturing and digesting small animals, primarily insects, directly, such plants obtain adequate nitrogen supplies and are able to grow in these seemingly unfavorable environments. Carnivorous plants have modified leaves adapted for luring and trapping prey. The plants often digest their prey with enzymes secreted from specialized types of glands.

Pitcher plants (*Nepenthes* spp.) attract insects by the bright, flowerlike colors within their pitcher-shaped leaves, by scents, and perhaps also by sugar-rich secretions (figure 39.11*a*). Once inside the pitcher, insects slide down into the cavity of the leaf, which is filled with water and digestive enzymes. This passive mechanism provides pitcher plants with a steady supply of nitrogen.

The Venus flytrap *(Dionaea muscipula)* grows in the bogs of coastal North and South Carolina. Three sensitive hairs on a leaf that, when touched, trigger the two halves of the leaf to snap together in about 100 ms (figure 39.11*b*). The speed of trap closing has puzzled biologists as far back as Darwin. Turgor pressure changes can account for the movement; the speed, however, depends on the curved geometry of the leaf, which can snap between convex and concave shapes.

Once the Venus flytrap enfolds prey within a leaf, enzymes secreted from the leaf surfaces digest the prey. These flytraps use a growth mechanism to close, not just a decrease in turgor pressure. The cells on the outer leaf surface irreversibly increase in size each time the trap shuts. As a result, they can only open and close a limited number of times.

In the sundews (*Drosera* spp.), another carnivorous group, glandular trichomes secrete both sticky mucilage, which traps small animals, and digestive enzymes; they do not close rapidly (figure 39.11*c*). Venus flytraps and the sundews share a common ancestor that lacked the snap-trap mechanism characteristic of the flytrap lineage (figure 39.12).

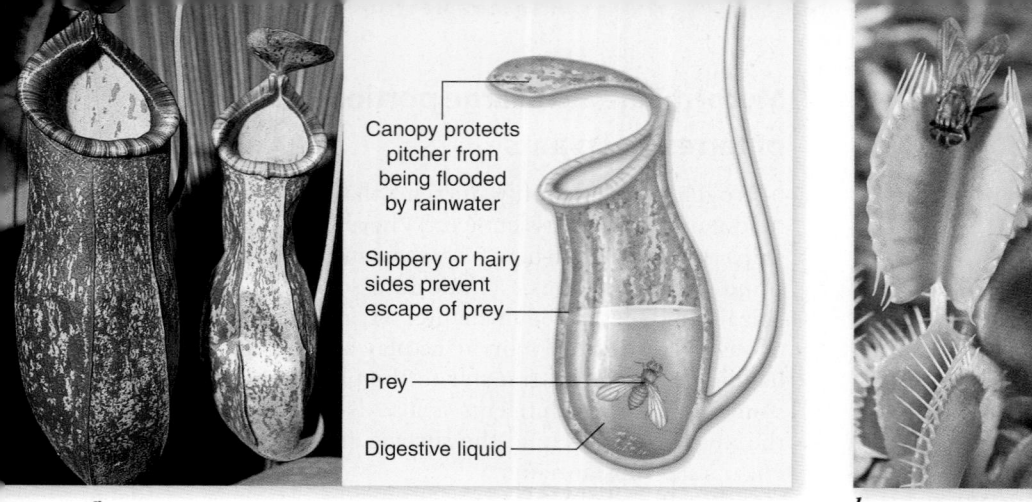

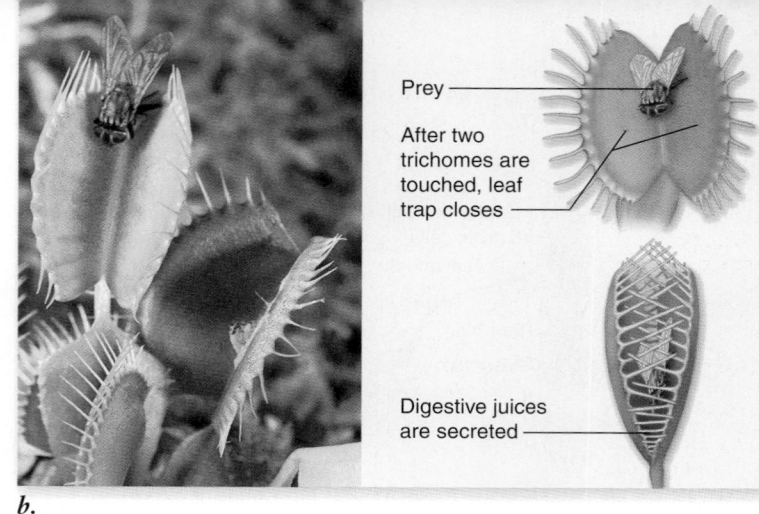

a.

b.

Figure 39.11 Nutritional adaptations. *a.* Asian pitcher plant, *Nepenthes*. Insects enter this carnivorous plant and are trapped and digested. Complex communities of invertebrate animals and protists inhabit the pitchers. *b.* Venus flytrap, *Dionaea*. If this fly touches two of the trichomes (hairs) on this modified leaf in a short time span, the trap will close. The plant will secrete digestive enzymes that release nitrogen compounds from the fly, which will then be absorbed by the flytrap. *c.* Sundew, *Drosera*, traps insects with sticky secretions and then excretes digestive enzymes to obtain nutrients from the insect's body. *d.* Aquatic waterwheel, *Aldrovanda*. This close relative of the Venus flytrap snaps shut to capture and digest small aquatic animals. This aquatic plant's ancestor was a land dweller.

Aldrovanda vesicular, the aquatic waterwheel, is a closer relative of the flytraps. The waterwheel is a rootless plant that uses trigger hairs and a snap-trap mechanism like that of the Venus flytrap to capture and digest small animals (figure 39.11*d*). Molecular phylogenetic studies indicate that Venus flytraps are sister species with sundews, forming a sister clade. It appears that the snap-trap mechanism evolved only once in descendants of a sundew ancestor. Therefore, the waterwheel's common ancestor must have been a terrestrial plant that made its way back into the water.

Bladderworts (*Utricularia*) are aquatic, but appear to have different origins from the waterwheel, as well as a different mechanism for trapping organisms. Small animals are swept into their bladderlike leaves by the rapid action of a springlike trapdoor; then the leaves digest these animals.

Parasitic plants exploit resources of other plants

Parasitic plants come in photosynthetic and nonphotosynthetic varieties. In total, at least 3000 types of plants are known to tap into the nutrient resources of other plants. Adaptations include structures that are inserted into the vascular tissue of the host plant so that nutrients can be siphoned into the parasite. One example is dodder (*Cuscuta* spp.), which looks like brown twine wrapped around its host. Dodder lacks chlorophyll and relies totally on its host for all its nutritional needs.

Indian pipe, *Hypopitys uniflora*, also lacks chlorophyll. This parasitic plant hooks into host trees through the fungal hyphae of the host's mycorrhizae (figure 39.13). The above-ground portion of the plant consists of flowering stems.

Figure 39.12 Phylogenetic relationships among carnivorous plants. The snap-trap mechanism was acquired by a common ancestor of the Venus flytrap and the aquatic waterwheel. Pitcher plants are not related to this clade.

Figure 39.13 Indian pipe, *Hypopitys uniflora*. This plant lacks chlorophyll and depends completely on nutrient transfer through the invasion of mycorrhizae and associated roots of other plants. Indian pipes are frequently found in northeastern United States forests.

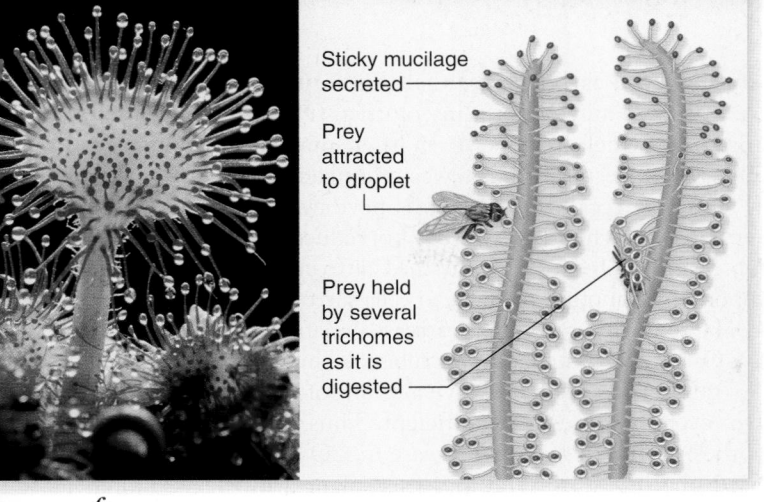

Sticky mucilage secreted

Prey attracted to droplet

Prey held by several trichomes as it is digested

c.

Prey

d.

Learning Outcomes Review 39.3

Certain types of plants, such as legumes, produce root nodules in which nitrogen-fixing bacteria grow. These bacteria provide nitrogen compounds that the plant can use for growth. Mycorrhizal fungi live in association with plant roots and are important for phosphorus uptake. Carnivorous plants typically live in low-nitrogen soils and obtain nitrogen from the insects they capture and digest.

- **Why is nitrogen a critical macronutrient for plant growth and reproduction?**

39.4 Carbon–Nitrogen Balance and Global Change

Learning Outcomes

1. **Describe the predicted effect of increased atmospheric carbon dioxide on the rate of photosynthesis in C_3 plants.**
2. **Explain the main effect on herbivores of a higher carbon:nitrogen ratio in plants.**
3. **Discuss why respiration rates increase with warmer temperatures.**

The Intergovernmental Panel on Climate Change (IPCC), established by the United Nations and the World Meteorological Organization, has concluded that CO_2 is probably at its highest concentration in the atmosphere in at least 20 million years. In only the last 250 years, atmospheric CO_2 has increased 31%, which correlates with increases in many human activities, including the burning of fossil fuels.

The long-term effects of elevated CO_2 are complex and are not fully understood, but are associated with increased temperatures. The IPCC predicts the average global surface temperatures will continue to increase to between 1.4°C and 5.8°C above 1990 levels, by 2100. Chapter 59 explores the causal link between elevated CO_2 and global warming. Here, we consider how increased CO_2 may alter nutrient balance within plants, specifically the carbon and nitrogen balance.

The ratio of carbon to nitrogen in a plant is important for both plant health and the health of herbivores. Altering this ratio could alter plant–pest interactions as well as affect human nutrition.

Elevated CO_2 levels can alter photosynthesis and carbon levels in plants

First, we investigate the relationship between photosynthesis and the relative concentration of atmospheric CO_2. The two questions to be addressed in this section are (1) Does elevated CO_2 increase the rate of photosynthesis? and (2) Will elevated levels of CO_2 change the ratio of carbohydrates and proteins in plants?

The rate of photosynthesis

The Calvin cycle of photosynthesis fixes atmospheric CO_2 into sugar (see chapter 8). The first step of the Calvin cycle stars the most abundant protein on Earth, ribulose 1,5-bisphosphate carboxylase/oxygenase (rubisco). The active site of this enzyme can bind either CO_2 or O_2, and it catalyzes the addition of either molecule to a five-carbon molecule, ribulose 1,5-bisphosphate (RuBP) (figure 39.14). CO_2 is used to

Figure 39.14 Photorespiration.

CO_2 and O_2 compete for the same site on the enzyme that catalyzes the first step in the Calvin cycle. If CO_2 binds, a three-carbon sugar is produced that can make glucose and sucrose. If O_2 binds, photorespiration occurs, and energy is used to break down a five-carbon molecule without yielding any useful product. As the ratio of CO_2 to O_2 increases, the Calvin cycle can produce more sugar.

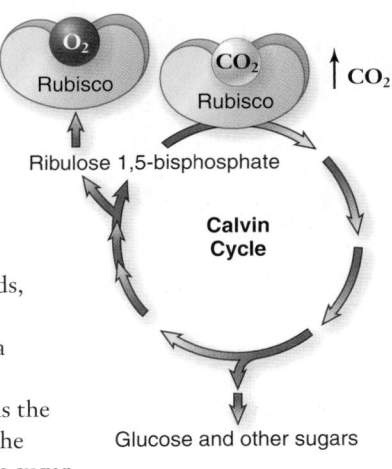

Photorespiration (no sugars)

Ribulose 1,5-bisphosphate

Calvin Cycle

Glucose and other sugars

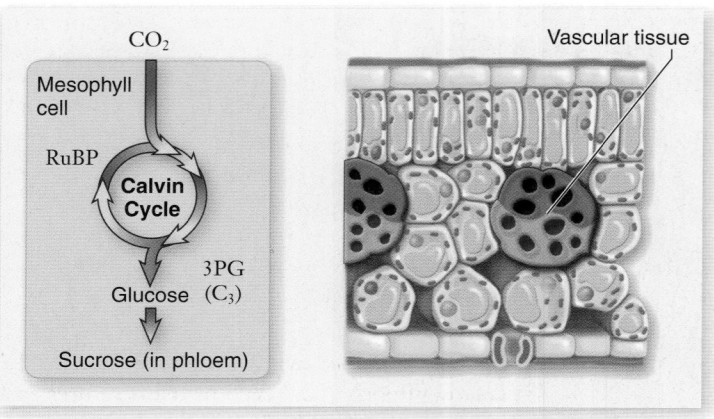

a. C₃ leaf

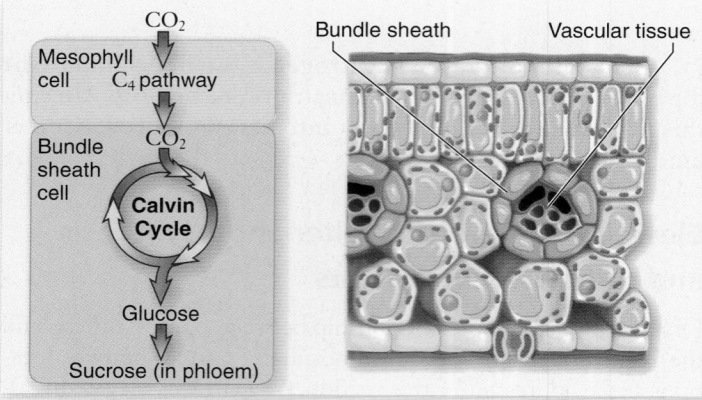

b. C₄ leaf (Kranz anatomy)

Figure 39.15 C₄ plants reduce photorespiration by limiting the Calvin cycle to cells surrounding the vascular tissue, where O_2 levels are reduced. *a.* C₃ photosynthesis occurs in the mesophyll cells. *b.* C₄ photosynthesis uses an extra biochemical pathway to shuttle carbon deep within the leaf.

produce a three-carbon sugar that can in turn be used to synthesize glucose and sucrose; in contrast, O_2 is used in photorespiration, which results in neither nutrient nor energy storage. Photorespiration is a wasteful process.

You may recall that C₄ plants have evolved a novel anatomical and biochemical strategy to reduce photorespiration (figure 39.15). CO_2 does not enter the Calvin cycle until it has been transported via another pathway to cells surrounding the vascular tissue. Here the level of CO_2 is increased relative to O_2 levels, and thus CO_2 has less competition for rubisco's binding site.

In C₃ plants, as the relative amount of CO_2 increases, the Calvin cycle becomes more efficient. Thus, it is reasonable to hypothesize that the global increase in CO_2 should lead to increased photosynthesis and increased plant growth. Assuming that nutrient availability in the soil remains the same, the more rapidly growing plants should have lower levels of nitrogen-containing compounds, such as proteins, and also lower levels of minerals obtained from the soil. The ratio of carbon to nitrogen should increase. Long-term studies of plants grown under elevated CO_2 confirm this prediction.

The optimal way to determine how CO_2 concentrations affect plant nutrition is to grow plants in an environment in which CO_2 levels can be precisely controlled. Experiments with potted plants in growth chambers are one approach, but far more information can be obtained in natural areas enriched with CO_2, called Free Air CO_2 Enrichment (FACE) studies. For example, the Duke Experimental Forest has rings of towers that release CO_2 toward the center of the ring (figure 39.16). These rings are 30 m in diameter and allow studies to be conducted at the ecosystem level. Such facilities allow for long-term studies of the effects of altered atmospheric conditions on ecosystems.

a.

b.

Figure 39.16 Experimentally elevating CO₂. CO₂ rings in the Duke Experimental Forest FACE site provide ecosystem-level comparisons of plants grown in ambient and elevated CO_2 environments. *a.* Each ring is 30 m in diameter. *b.* Towers surrounding the rings blow CO_2 inward under closely monitored conditions.

Extensive studies have yielded complex results. Potatoes grown in a European facility had a 40% higher photosynthetic rate when the concentration of CO_2 was approximately doubled. Potted plants often show an initial increase in photosynthesis, followed by a decrease over time that is associated with lower levels of rubisco production. Different species of plants in a Florida oak-shrub system showed different responses to elevated CO_2 levels, while over three years in the Duke Experimental Forest, plants achieved more biomass in the CO_2 enclosures than outside the enclosures, if the soil contained sufficient nitrogen availability to support enhanced growth. C_3 plants show a greater increase in biomass than C_4 plants, and nitrogen fixing legumes, especially soybean, had larger increases in biomass than plants depending on nitrogen from the soil. In general, increased CO_2 corresponds to some increase in biomass, but also to an increase in the carbon:nitrogen ratio.

The ratio of proteins and carbohydrates

You learned earlier in this chapter that nitrogen availability limits plant growth. As CO_2 levels increase, relatively less nitrogen and other macronutrients are found in leaves. Legumes, because of their nitrogen-fixing ability, have less of a decrease in nitrogen under elevated CO_2 conditions. In that event, herbivores need to eat more biomass to obtain adequate nutrients, particularly protein. This situation would be of significant concern in agriculture, and it could affect human health. Insect infestations could be more devastating if each herbivore consumed more biomass. Protein deficiencies in human diets could result from decreased nitrogen in crops.

The relative decreases in nitrogen in some plants is greater than would be predicted by an increase in CO_2 fixation alone. The additional decrease in nitrogen incorporation into proteins has been accounted for by a decrease in photorespiration in plants using NO_3^- as their primary nitrogen source, but not in plants using ammonia. It is possible that energy-wasting photorespiration may actually be necessary for nitrogen to be incorporated into proteins in some plants.

This example illustrates how interdependent the biochemical pathways are that regulate carbon and nitrogen levels. Although global change is an ecosystem-level problem, predictions about long-term effects hinge on understanding the physiological complexities of plant nutrition—an area of active research.

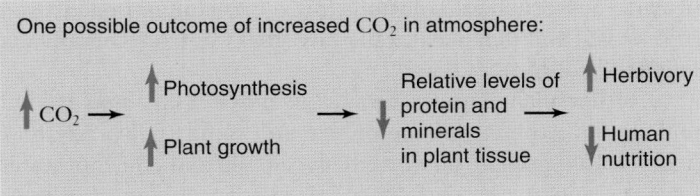

One possible outcome of increased CO_2 in atmosphere:

↑CO_2 → ↑Photosynthesis ↑Plant growth → ↓Relative levels of protein and minerals in plant tissue → ↑Herbivory ↓Human nutrition

Elevated temperature can affect respiration and carbon levels in plants

As much as half of all the carbohydrates produced from photosynthesis each day can be used in plant respiration that same day. The amount of carbohydrate available for respiration may be affected by atmospheric CO_2 and photosynthesis, as just discussed. Further-

more, the anticipated rise in temperature over the next century may affect the rate of respiration in other ways. Altered respiration rates can affect overall nutrient balance and plant growth.

Inquiry question

? Why is plant respiration affected by both short-term and long-term temperature changes?

Biologists have known for a long time that respiration rates are temperature-sensitive in a broad range of plant species. Why does respiration rate change with temperature? One important factor is the effect of temperature on enzyme activity (see chapter 3). This effect is particularly important at very low temperatures and also very high temperatures that lead to protein denaturation.

Many responses of respiration rate to temperature change may be short-term, rather than long-term. Growing evidence indicates that respiration rate acclimates to a temperature increase over time, especially in leaves and roots that develop after the temperature shift. Over a long period at an elevated temperature, a plant could end up respiring at the same rate at which it had previously respired at a lower temperature.

Learning Outcomes Review 39.4

As atmospheric carbon dioxide increases, the rate of photosynthesis and the carbon:nitrogen ratio in plants are expected to increase as long as available soil nutrients do not change. A higher than normal carbon:nitrogen ratio would require herbivores to eat more biomass to meet their protein needs, which could, in turn, affect human health. As temperature increases, enzyme activity increases, accelerating the rate of respiration and breakdown of carbohydrates.

■ *What strategies could help keep the carbon:nitrogen ratio in crop plants lower?*

39.5 *Phytoremediation*

Learning Outcomes

1. *Define phytoremediation.*
2. *Explain how poplar trees have been used for phytoremediation.*
3. *Describe an advantage and a disadvantage of phytoremediation.*

Some root cell membrane channels and transporters lack absolute specificity and can take up heavy metals like aluminum and other toxins. Although in most cases uptake of toxins is lethal or growth-limiting, some plants have evolved the ability to sequester or release these compounds into the atmosphere. These plants have potential for **phytoremediation,** the use of plants to concentrate or breakdown pollutants (figure 39.17).

Phytoremediation can work in a number of ways with both aquatic and soil pollutants. Plants may secrete a substance from

Figure 39.17
Phytoremediation.

Plants can use the same mechanisms to remove both nutrients and toxins from the soil. *a.* TCE (trichloroethylene) can be taken up by plants and degraded into CO_2 and chlorine before being released into the atmosphere. This process is called *phytodegradation*. Some of the TCE moves so rapidly through the xylem that it is not degraded before it is released through the stomata as a gas in a process called *phytovolatilization*. *b.* Other toxins, including heavy metals such as lead, can be taken up by plants, but not degraded. Such *phytoaccumulation* is particularly effective in removing toxins if they are stored in the shoot, where they can more easily be harvested.

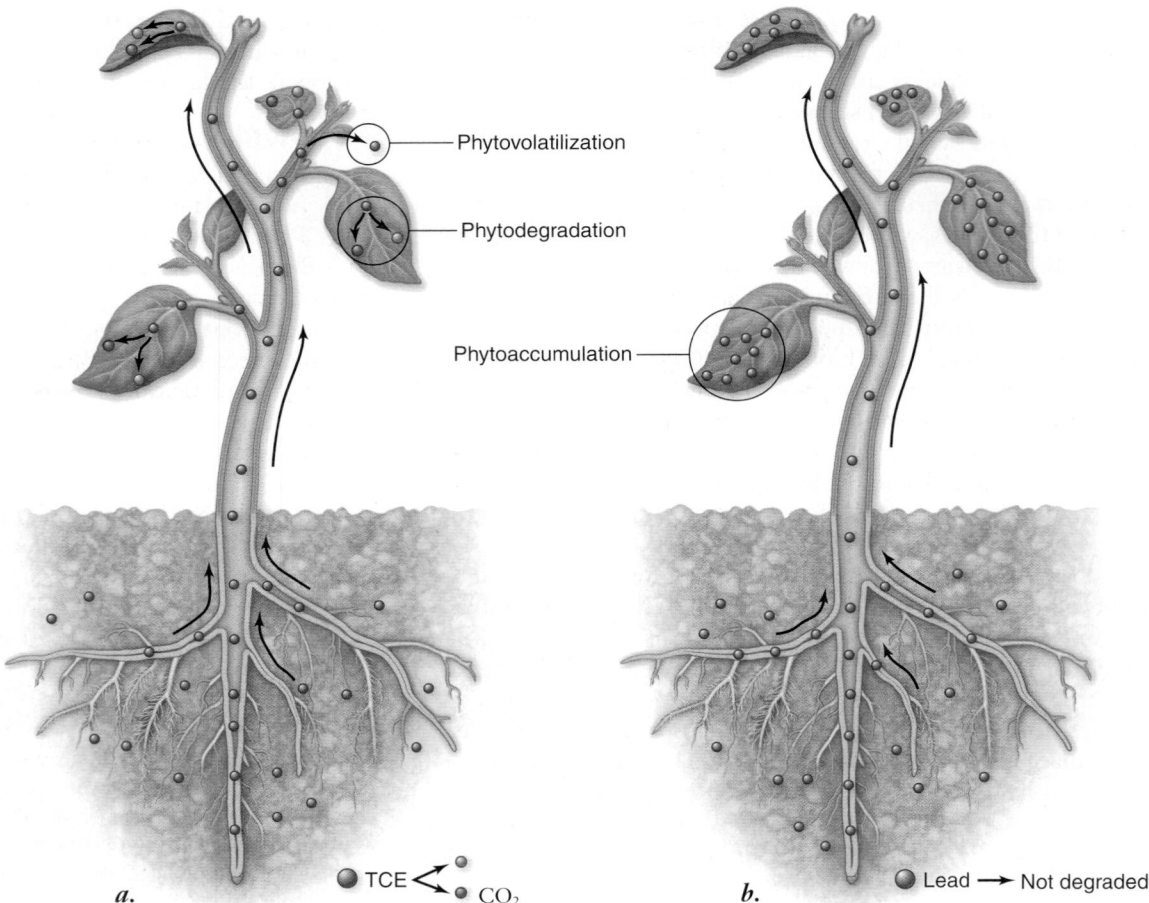

Phytovolatilization

Phytodegradation

Phytoaccumulation

a. TCE → CO_2

b. Lead → Not degraded

their roots that breaks down the contaminant. More often, the harmful chemical enters the roots and is preferably transported to the shoot system, making it easier to remove the chemical from the site. Some substances are simply stored by the plant; later, the plant material is harvested, dried, and removed to a storage site.

For example, after the nuclear reactor disaster at Chernobyl in northern Ukraine, sunflowers effectively removed radioactive cesium from nearby lakes. The plants were floated in foam supports on the surface of the lakes and later collected. Because up to 85% of the weight of herbaceous plants can be water, drying down phytoremediators can restrict toxins like radioactive cesium to a small area.

In this section, we will explore several examples of soil phytoremediation.

Trichloroethylene may be removed by poplar trees

Trichloroethylene (TCE) is a volatile solvent that has been widely used as spot remover in the dry-cleaning industry, for degreasing engine turbines, as an ingredient in paints and cosmetics, and even as an anesthetic in human and veterinary medicine. Unfortunately, TCE is also a confirmed carcinogen, and chronic exposure can damage the liver.

In 1980, the Environmental Protection Agency (EPA) established a Superfund to clean up contamination in the United States. Forty percent of all sites funded by the Superfund include TCE contamination. How can we clean up 1900 hectares of soil in a Marine Corps Air Station in Orange County, California, that contain TCE once used to clean fighter jets? Landfills can isolate, but not eliminate, this volatile substance. Burning eliminates it from the site, but may release harmful substances into the atmosphere. A promising approach is to use plants to remove TCE from the soil.

Plants may take up a toxin from soil, allowing the toxin to be removed and concentrated elsewhere; but an even more successful strategy is for the plant to break down the contaminant into nontoxic by-products. Poplar trees (genus *Populus*) may provide just such a solution for TCE-contaminated sites (figure 39.18). Poplars naturally take up TCE from the soil and metabolize it into CO_2 and chlorine.

Other plant species can break down TCE as well, but poplars have the advantage of size and rapid transpiration. A five-year-old poplar can move between 100 and 200 L of water from its roots out through its leaves in a day. A plant that transpires less would not be able to remove as much TCE in a day.

Figure 39.18
Phytoremediation for TCE.
The U.S. Air Force is testing phytoremediation technology to clean up TCE at a former Air Force base in Fort Worth, Texas.

Although removing TCE with poplar trees sounds like the perfect solution, this method has some limitations. Not all the TCE is metabolized, and given the rapid rate of transpiration in the poplar, some of the TCE enters the atmosphere via the leaves. Once in the air, TCE has a half-life of 9 hours (half of it will break down into smaller molecules every 9 hours). Clearly, more risk assessment is needed before poplars are planted on every TCE-containing Superfund site.

The TCE that remains in the plant is metabolized quickly, and it is possible that the wood could be used after remediation is complete. It has been suggested that any remaining TCE would be eliminated if the wood were processed to make paper. Genetically modified poplars have been shown to metabolize about four times as much TCE as nonmodified poplars, so perhaps greater metabolic rates can be obtained.

As with any phytoremediation plan, it is critically necessary to estimate how much of a contaminant can be removed from a site by plants, and arriving at this estimate can be difficult. Possible risks, particularly when genetic modification is involved, must be weighed against the dangers posed by the contaminant.

Trinitrotoluene can be removed in limited amounts

In addition to volatile chemicals such as TCE, phytoremediation also holds promise for dealing with other environmental contaminants, including the explosive trinitrotoluene (TNT) and heavy metals. TNT is a solid, yellow material that was used widely in grenades and bombs until 1980. Contamination is found around factories that made TNT.

In some places, there is enough TNT in the soil to detonate, and thus incineration is not a viable option for removing TNT from most sites. Another issue is that TNT can seep into the groundwater; this is a matter of concern because TNT is carcinogenic and associated with liver disease.

TNT tends to stay near the top of the soil and to wash away quickly. Bean *(Phaseolus vulgaris)*, poplar, and the aquatic parrot feather *(Myriophyllum spicatum)* can take up and degrade low levels of TNT, but at higher concentrations, TNT is toxic to these plants.

Heavy metals can be successfully removed at lower cost

Heavy metals, including arsenic, cadmium, and lead, persist in soils and are toxic to animals in even small quantities. Many plants are also susceptible to heavy-metal toxicity, but species near mines have evolved strategies to partition certain heavy metals from the rest of the plant (see figure 39.17*b*).

Four hundred species of plants have been identified that have the ability to hyperaccumulate toxic metals from the soil. For example, *Brassica juncea* (a relative of broccoli and mustard plants) is especially effective at hyperaccumulating lead in the shoots of the plant. Unfortunately, *B. juncea* is a small, slow-growing plant, and eventually it becomes saturated with lead.

How would lead or cadmium travel from the soil into the leaves of a plant? There are some hints that root cell membranes may contain metal transporters that load the metal in the soil

into the xylem. Citrate, mentioned earlier, can increase the rate of metal transport in xylem. The metals are sequestered inside vacuoles in the leaves. Trichomes, which are modified leaf epidermal cells, can sequester both lead and cadmium.

These hyperaccumulating plants are not a panacea for metal-contaminated soil because of concern that animals might move into the site and graze on lead- or cadmium-enriched plants. Harvesting and consolidating dried plant material is not a simple matter, but still phytoremediation is a promising technique. Estimated costs for phytoremediation are 50 to 80% lower than cleanup strategies that involve digging and dumping the contaminated soil elsewhere.

Phytoremediation may be a solution to the contamination resulting from a 1998 accident at the Aznalcóllar mine in Spain. A dam that contained the sludge from the mining operation broke, releasing 5 million cubic meters of sludge, composed of arsenic, cadmium, lead, and zinc, over 4300 hectares of land (figure 39.19). Much of the sludge was physically removed

a.

b.

c.

Figure 39.19 Aznalcóllar mine spill. *a.* When the dike of a holding lagoon for mine waste broke, 5 million cubic meters of black sludge containing heavy metals was released into a national park and the Guadiamar River. *b.* Large amounts of sludge were removed mechanically. *c.* Phytoremediation appears to be a promising solution for treating the remaining heavy metals.

and dumped into an open mine pit. Phytoremediation solutions are being sought for the remaining contaminated soil.

Since the original spill, three plant species with the potential to hyperaccumulate some of the metals have begun growing in the area. These plants are fairly large and can accumulate a substantial amount of metal. They offer the advantage of being native species, thus reducing the dangers associated with introducing a nonnative, potentially invasive species to clean up the spill.

Learning Outcomes Review 39.5

Phytoremediation is the use of plants to concentrate or break down pollutants. Poplar trees can take up the soil contaminant trichloroethylene and break it down into nontoxic by-products. Compared with the alternative of removing contaminated soil, phytoremediation is less costly. A disadvantage is that animals could be harmed if they graze in an area where plants have taken up high levels of toxic compounds.

■ **How could animals be protected from ingesting plants used for phytoremediation?**

Chapter Review

39.1 Soils: The Substrates on Which Plants Depend

Soil is composed of minerals, organic matter, water, air, and organisms.

Topsoil is a mixture of mineral particles, living organisms, and humus, which is partially decayed organic material. Microorganisms in the soil are important for nutrient recycling.

Water and mineral availability is determined by soil characteristics.

Minerals and organic soil particles are typically negatively charged so they draw positively charged ions away from the roots. Therefore, active transport of positively charged ions into the roots is required. Proton pumps in roots pump out H^+, creating an electrochemical gradient that draws mineral ions into the roots.

Approximately one-half the soil volume is made up of pores filled with air or water. Water added to the soil may drain through or be held in the pores, where it is available for root uptake.

Cultivation can result in soil loss and nutrient depletion.

Loss of topsoil through soil erosion results in reduced water-holding capacity and nutrient availability. Cultivation practices have been developed to reduce soil erosion.

Overuse of fertilizers, pesticides, and herbicides causes water pollution.

pH and salinity affect water and mineral availability.

Acidic soils release minerals, such as aluminum, at levels that are toxic to plants.

Saline soils alter water potential, leading to a loss of water and turgor in plants. Saline soils are common where irrigation is practiced.

39.2 Plant Nutrients

Plants require nine macronutrients and seven micronutrients.

The nine macronutrients required by plants are carbon, oxygen, hydrogen, nitrogen, potassium, calcium, magnesium, phosphorus, and sulfur. The eight micronutrients are chlorine, iron, manganese, zinc, boron, copper, molybdenum, and nickel.

Food security is related to crop productivity and nutrient levels.

Plant breeding efforts to increase nutrient levels in food crops aim to provide health benefits and improve food security.

39.3 Special Nutritional Strategies

Bacteria living in close association with roots can provide nitrogen.

Some plants, such as legumes, have a symbiotic relationship with nitrogen-fixing bacteria to obtain the nitrogen needed for protein synthesis. In exchange, the plants provide carbohydrates to the bacteria.

Mycorrhizae aid a large portion of terrestrial plants.

More than 90% of plants live in symbiotic association with mycorrhizal fungi. By extending the surface area of the root system, these fungi facilitate the uptake of phosphorus and micronutrients.

Carnivorous plants trap and digest animals to extract additional nutrients.

Some plants that live in acidic, nitrogen-poor environments obtain mineral nutrients by capturing and digesting small animals such as insects.

Parasitic plants exploit resources of other plants.

Some parasitic plants produce chlorophyll, while others do not. They tap into host plants to obtain nutrients, including carbohydrates.

39.4 Carbon–Nitrogen Balance and Global Change

Elevated CO_2 levels can alter photosynthesis and carbon levels in plants.

As CO_2 concentrations increase, the rate of photosynthesis increases and consequently biomass increases; however, the plant tissue that is produced is high in carbon relative to nitrogen, with a shift toward more carbohydrate and less protein.

As nutritional value decreases, more plant matter must be consumed to obtain the same amount of nutrients; the result is greater plant loss by herbivory.

Elevated temperature can affect respiration and carbon levels in plants.

The rate of enzyme reactions increases with ambient temperatures, increasing respiration. Because respiration breaks down carbohydrates, higher temperatures could cause additional changes in plant nutrient balance.

39.5 Phytoremediation

Phytoremediation utilizes plants to remove toxic contaminants from soil or water.

Trichloroethylene may be removed by poplar trees.

Poplar trees have been used to remove trichloroethylene from the soil and convert it to nontoxic carbon dioxide and chlorine compounds.

Trinitrotoluene can be removed in limited amounts.

Some plants can take up low levels of trinitrotoluene (TNT) in the soil and degrade it. However, high levels are toxic to the plants.

Heavy metals can be successfully removed at lower cost.

Plants may accumulate high levels of contaminants in their shoots and store them there. The plants can be harvested and removed. If animals feed on these plants, however, they may be exposed to high concentrations of toxic compounds.

Phytoremediation is less expensive than removing contaminated soils.

Review Questions

UNDERSTAND

1. Which of the following is not found in topsoil?
   a. Humus   c. Bacteria
   b. Bedrock   d. Air

2. Mineral soil particles are typically
   a. negatively charged.
   b. positively charged.
   c. neutral.

3. What proportion of the soil volume is occupied by air and water?
   a. 10%   d. 75%
   b. 25%   e. 90%
   c. 50%

4. Which of the following is a micronutrient?
   a. Nitrogen   c. Phosphorus
   b. Calcium   d. Iron

5. The nodules of legume roots contain nitrogen-fixing
   a. bacteria.   c. algae.
   b. fungi.   d. plants.

6. Photorespiration occurs when
   a. glucose interacts with carbon dioxide.
   b. rubisco binds with oxygen.
   c. RuBP is converted to a sugar.
   d. the Sun provides energy for the breakdown of sugar.

7. In a C_4 plant, the Calvin cycle occurs in
   a. the epidermis.   c. bundle sheath cells.
   b. vascular tissue.   d. mesophyll cells.

8. One potential problem with using poplars to remove TCE from soils is that
   a. some TCE enters the atmosphere via the transpiration stream.
   b. poplar trees grow slowly.
   c. most TCE will wash away from the soil before it is removed.
   d. TCE interferes with chlorophyll production.

APPLY

1. You are performing an experiment to determine the nutrient requirements for a newly discovered plant and find that for some reason your plants die if you leave boron out of the growth medium but do fine with as low as 5 ppm in solution. This suggests that boron is
   a. an essential macronutrient.
   b. a nonessential micronutrient.
   c. an essential micronutrient.
   d. a nonessential macronutrient.

2. If you wanted to conduct an experiment to determine the effects of varying levels of macronutrients on plant growth and did so in your small greenhouse at home, which of the following macronutrients would be the most difficult to regulate?
   a. Carbon   c. Potassium
   b. Nitrogen   d. Phosphorus

3. Which of the following would decrease nitrogen availability for a pea plant?
   a. Inability of the plant to produce flavonoids
   b. Formation of Nod factors
   c. Presence of oxygen in the soil
   d. Production of leghemoglobin

4. Which of the following might you do to increase nutrient uptake by crop plants?
   a. Decrease the solubility of nutrients
   b. Create nutrients as positive ions
   c. Frequently plow the soil
   d. Genetically modify plants to increase the density of plasma membrane transporters in root cells

5. If you were to eat one ton (1000 kg) of potatoes, calculate approximately how much of the following minerals would you eat?
   a. Copper between 4–30 ppm
   b. Zinc between 15–100 ppm
   c. Potassium between 0.5 and 6%
   d. Iron between 25–300 ppm

SYNTHESIZE

1. A common farming practice involves fumigating the soil to kill harmful fungi. Fumigants may not be selective, though, so they may kill most microorganisms in the soil. What short-term and long-term effects might fumigation have on the soil?

2. Describe an experiment to determine the amount of boron needed for the normal growth of tomato seedlings.

3. Growers of commercial crops in greenhouses often use supplemental carbon dioxide to enhance plant growth. What other inputs do you suppose they must provide to maximize plant growth?

ONLINE RESOURCE

www.ravenbiology.com

Understand, Apply, and Synthesize—enhance your study with animations that bring concepts to life and practice tests to assess your understanding. Your instructor may also recommend the interactive eBook, individualized learning tools, and more.

Chapter 40

Plant Defense Responses

Chapter Outline

40.1   Physical Defenses

40.2   Chemical Defenses

40.3   Animals That Protect Plants

40.4   Systemic Responses to Invaders

Introduction

Plants are constantly under attack by viruses, bacteria, fungi, animals, and even other plants. An amazing array of defense mechanisms has evolved to block or temper an invasion. Many plant–pest relationships undergo coevolution, with the plant winning sometimes and the pest winning with a new offensive adaptation at other times. The first line of plant defense is thick cell walls covered with a strong cuticle. Bark, thorns, and even trichomes can deter a hungry insect. When that first line of defense fails, a chemical arsenal of toxins is waiting. Many of these molecules have no effect on the plant. Some are modified by microbes in the intestine of an herbivore into a poisonous compound. Maintaining a toxin arsenal is energy-intensive; so, an alternative means of defense uses induced responses to protect and prevent future attacks.

40.1 Physical Defenses

Learning Outcomes

1. *Identify the compounds produced by the epidermis to protect against invasion.*
2. *Outline the steps taken by a fungus to invade a plant leaf.*
3. *Describe two beneficial associations between plants and microorganisms.*

There are no tornado shelters for trees. Storms and changing environmental conditions can be life-threatening to plants. Structurally, trees can often withstand high winds and the weight of ice and snow, but there are limits. Winds can uproot a tree, or snap the main shoot off a small plant. Axillary buds give many plants a second chance as they grow out and replace the lost shoot (figure 40.1).

Although abiotic factors such as weather constitute genuine threats to a plant, even greater daily threats exist in the form of viruses, bacteria, fungi, animals, and other plants. These enemies can tap into the nutrient resources of plants or use

Figure 40.1 Shoots in reserve. Axillary shoots give plants a second chance when the terminal shoot breaks off, as is the case with this storm-felled tree.

their DNA-replicating mechanisms to self-replicate. Some invaders kill the plant cells immediately, leading to necrosis (brown, dead tissue). Certain insects may tap into the phloem of a plant seeking carbohydrates, but leave behind a hitchhiking virus or bacterium.

The threat of these attackers is reduced when they have natural predators themselves. One of the greatest problems with nonnative invasive species, such as the alfalfa plant bug (figure 40.2), is the lack of natural predators in the new environment.

Dermal tissue provides first-line defense

The first defense all plants have is the dermal tissue system (see chapter 36). Epidermal cells throughout the plant secrete wax, which is a mixture of hydrophobic lipids. Layers of lipid material protect exposed plant surfaces from water loss and attack. Aboveground plant parts are also covered with cutin, a macromolecule consisting of long-chain fatty acids linked together. **Suberin,** another version of linked fatty acid chains, is found in cell walls of subterranean plant organs; suberin forms the water-impermeable Casparian strips of roots. Silica inclusions, trichomes, bark, and even thorns can also protect the nutrient-rich plant interior.

Figure 40.2 Alfalfa plant bug. This invasive species is an agricultural problem because it arrived in the United States without any natural predators and feeds on alfalfa.

Invaders can penetrate dermal defenses

Unfortunately, these exterior defenses can be penetrated in many ways. Mechanical wounds leave an open passageway through which microbial organisms can enter. Parasitic nematodes use their sharp mouthparts to get through the plant cell walls. Their actions either trigger the plant cells to divide, forming a tumorous growth, or, in species that attach to a single plant cell, cause the cell to enlarge and transfer carbohydrates from the plant to the hungry nematode (figure 40.3). In some cases, the wounding makes it

a.   *b.*

Figure 40.3 Nematodes attack the roots of crop plants. *a.* A nematode breaks through the epidermis of the root. *b.* Root-knot nematodes form tumors on roots.

Hypothesis: *Nematodes increase the severity of a potato wilt fungal disease by wounding roots and allowing the fungus to penetrate root tissue.*

Prediction: *Leaf wilt will be more severe when the root system is exposed to both the nematode and the fungus than when the root system is exposed to neither or either separately.*

Test: *Establish four treatments with four plants in each treatment group. Add the nematodes and the fungal pathogen to the soil of plants in group 1. Group 2 will only have fungus. Group 3 will have only nematodes, and group 4 will be untreated. Allow plants to grow for 42 days and record the extent of leaf wilt on each plant.*

Nematodes and fungus
(severe effect)

Fungus
(moderate effect)

Nematodes
(moderate effect)

Untreated (control)
(no effect)

Result: *Plants that are coinfected with the nematodes and fungus have more severe wilting than plants treated with nematodes or fungus alone. Control plants do not wilt.*

Conclusion: *Nematodes increase the severity of the wilting infection.*

Further Experiments: *Design an experiment to test the hypothesis that increased fungal wilt symptoms are the result of damage to the roots by the nematode, making it easier for the fungus to enter the plant. Could you mechanically wound the roots instead of exposing them to nematodes?*

Figure 40.4 Nematodes increase susceptibility of plant to fungal infection.

easier for other pathogens, including fungi, to infect the plant (figure 40.4). In some cases simply having bacteria on the leaf surface can increase the risk of frost damage. The bacteria function as sites for ice nucleation; the resulting ice crystals severely damage the leaves.

Fungi strategically seek out the weak spot in the dermal system, the stomatal openings, to enter the plant. Some fungi have coevolved with a monocot that has evenly spaced stomata. These fungi appear to be able to measure distance to locate these evenly spaced stomatal openings and invade the plant. Figure 40.5 shows the phases of fungal invasion, which can include the following:

1. Windblown spores land on leaves. A germ tube emerges from the spore. Host recognition is necessary for spore germination.
2. The spore germinates and forms an adhesion pad, allowing it to stick to the leaf.
3. Hyphae grow through cell walls and press against the cell membrane.
4. Hyphae differentiate into specialized structures called haustoria. They expand, surrounded by cell membrane, and nutrient transfer begins.

Bacteria and fungi can also be beneficial to plants

Mutualistic and parasitic relationships are often just opposite sides of the evolutionary coin. A parasitic relationship can evolve to become mutalistic, and a mutualistic relationship

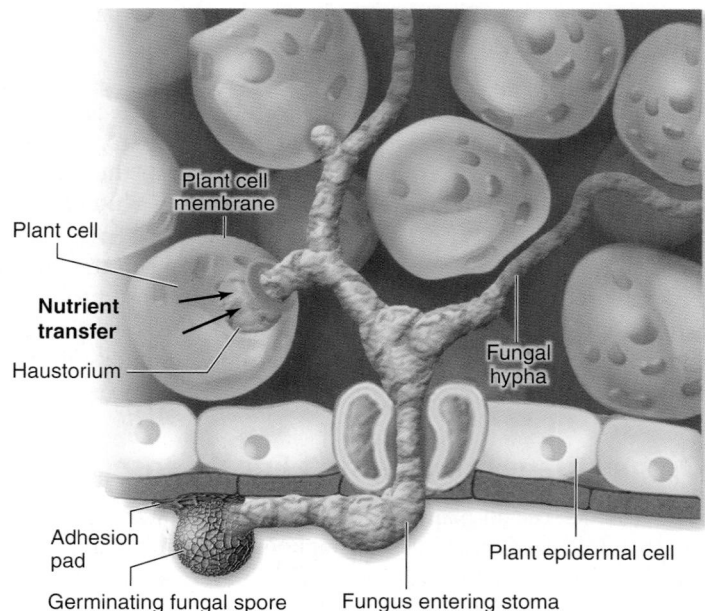

Figure 40.5 Fungi sneak in through stomata. Fungal hyphae penetrate cell walls, but not plasma membranes. The close contact between the fungal hyphae and the plant plasma membrane allows for ready transfer of plant nutrients to the fungus.

can transform into a parasitic one. In chapters 31 and 39, you saw how mycorrhizal fungi use a mechanism similar to the one just described to the mutual benefit of both the plant and the fungus. In the case of the relationship between legumes and nitrogen-fixing bacteria, the *Rhizobium* bacteria seeks out a root hair, infects it along with other tissues, and forms a root nodule. Other soil bacteria can also enhance plant growth, and are called plant growth-promoting rhizobacteria (PGPR). The term *rhizobacteria* refers to bacteria that live around the root system and often benefit from root exudates. In return they provide substances that support plant growth. *Azospirillum* spp., for example, provide gibberellins, which are growth hormones, for rice plants when the bacteria are living in close proximity to the root system. PGPR can also limit the growth of pathogenic soil bacteria.

Learning Outcomes Review 40.1

Epidermal cells secrete protective compounds, including wax and suberin. Fungal spores may germinate and stick to plant leaves; hyphae enter the leaf through stomata, and produce haustoria to take up plant nutrients. Mutualistic partners with plants include mycorrhizal fungi that assist with nutrient absorption and nitrogen-fixing bacteria that provide nutrients.

■ *Why would protective substances on leaves include lipid-based compounds?*

40.2 Chemical Defenses

Learning Outcomes

1. Describe the role of secondary metabolites in plant defense.
2. Define alleleopathy.
3. List three examples of the medicinal value of secondary metabolites.

Many plants are filled with toxins that kill herbivores or, at the very least, make them quite ill. One example is the production of cyanide, (HCN). Over 3000 species of plants produce cyanide-containing compounds called *cyanogenic glycosides* that break down into cyanide when cells are damaged. Cyanide stops electron transport, blocking cellular respiration.

Cassava (genus *Manihot*), a major food staple for many Africans, is filled with cyanogenic glycosides (specifically, manihotoxins) in the outer layers of the edible root. Unless these outer layers are scrubbed off, the cumulative effect of eating primarily cassava can be deadly.

Some toxins are unique to plants, but others are found in plants, vertebrates, and invertebrates and are called **defensins.** Defensins are small, cysteine-rich peptides with antimicrobial activity. The conservation of defensins in animals and plants reveals the ancient origins of innate immunity. Between 15 and 50 defensin genes have been identified in plant genomes, and over 317 defensin-like genes exist in the *Arabidopsis* genome. The exact mechanisms are being worked out, but in some cases plant defensins inhibit protein synthesis. When expression of defensin genes is suppressed in plants, they are more susceptible to bacterial and fungal infections. In addition to toxins that kill, plants can produce chemical compounds that make potential herbivores ill or that repel them with strong flavors or odors.

Plants maintain chemical arsenals

How did the biosynthetic pathways that produce these toxins evolve? Growing evidence indicates that the metabolic pathways needed to sustain life in plants have taken some evolutionary side trips, leading to the production of a stockpile of chemicals known as **secondary metabolites.** Many of these secondary metabolites affect herbivores as well as humans (table 40.1).

Alkaloids, including caffeine, nicotine, cocaine, and morphine, can affect multiple cellular processes; if a plant cannot kill its attackers, it can overstimulate them with caffeine or sedate them with morphine. For example, the tobacco hornworm (*Manduca sexta*) can level a field of tobacco (figure 40.6); however, wild species of tobacco appear to have elevated levels of nicotine that are lethal to tobacco hornworms.

Tannins bind to proteins and inactivate them. For example, some act by blocking enzymes that digest proteins, which reduces the nutritional value of the plant tissue. An insect that gets sick from a strong dose of tannins is likely to associate the flavor with illness and to avoid having that type of plant for lunch another time. Small doses of tannins and most other secondary metabolites are unlikely to cause any major digestive difficulties in larger animals, including humans. Animals, including humans, can avoid many of the cumulative toxic effects of secondary metabolites by eating a varied diet.

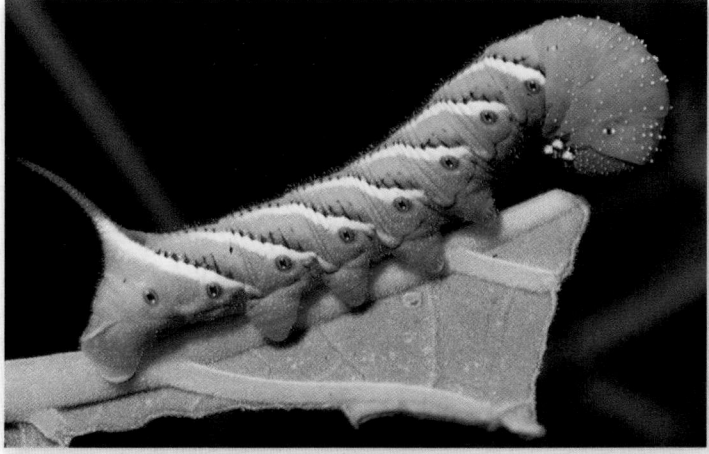

Figure 40.6 Herbivores can kill plants. Tobacco hornworms, *Manduca sexta*, consume huge amounts of tobacco leaf tissue, as well as tomato leaves.

TABLE 40.1 Secondary Metabolites

Compound	Source	Structure	Effect on Humans
Manihotoxin (cyanogenic glycoside)	Cassava, *Manihot esculenta*		Metabolized to release lethal cyanide
Genistein (phytoestrogen)	Soybean, *Glycine max*		Estrogen mimic
Taxol (terpenoid)	Pacific yew, *Taxus brevifolia*		Anticancer drug
Quinine (alkaloid)	Quinine bark, *Cinchona officinalis*		Antimalarial drug
Morphine (alkaloid)	Opium poppy, *Papaver somniferum*		Narcotic pain killer

Plant oils, particularly those found in plants of the mint family, which includes peppermint, sage, pennyroyal, and many others, repel insects with their strong odors. At high concentrations, some of these oils can also be toxic if ingested.

Why don't the toxins kill the plant? One strategy is for a plant to sequester a toxin in a membrane-bound structure, so that it does not come into contact with the cell's metabolic processes. The second solution is for the plant to produce a compound that is not toxic unless it is metabolized, often by microorganisms, in the intestine of an animal. Cyanogenic glycosides are a good example of the latter solution. The plant produces a sugar-bound cyanide compound that does not affect electron transport chains. Once an animal ingests cyanogenic glycoside, the compound is enzymatically broken down, releasing the toxic hydrogen cyanide.

Coevolution has led to defenses against some plant toxins. A tropical butterfly, *Helioconius sara*, can sequester the cyanogenic glycosides it ingests from its sole food source, the passion vine. Even more intriguing is a biochemical pathway that allows the butterfly to safely break down cyanogenic glycosides and use the released nitrogen in its own protein metabolism.

Plants can poison other plants

Some chemical toxins protect plants from other plants. **Allelopathy** occurs when a chemical compound secreted by the roots of one plant blocks the germination of nearby seeds or inhibits the growth of a neighboring plant. This strategy minimizes shading and competition for nutrients, while it maximizes the ability of a plant to use radiant sunlight for photosynthesis. Allelopathy works with both a plant's own species and different species. Black walnut trees (*Juglans nigra*) are a good example. Very little vegetation will grow under a black walnut tree because of allelopathy (figure 40.7).

Figure 40.7 Black walnuts are allelopaths. Seedlings die when their roots come in contact with the root secretions of a black walnut tree.

Humans are susceptible to plant toxins

Not only have humans been inadvertently poisoned by plants, but throughout much of human history, they have also been intentionally poisoned by other humans using plant products. Socrates, an important Greek philosopher who lived 2400 years ago, was sentenced to death in Athens, and he died after he drank a hemlock extract containing an alkaloid that paralyzes motor nerve endings.

Ricin, an alkaloid found in castor beans (*Ricinus communis*), is six times more lethal than cyanide and twice as lethal as cobra venom. A single seed from the plant, which is still grown in flower gardens, can kill a young child if ingested. Death occurs because ricin functions as a ribosome-binding protein that changes the structure of rRNA, thus inhibiting translation (figure 40.8).

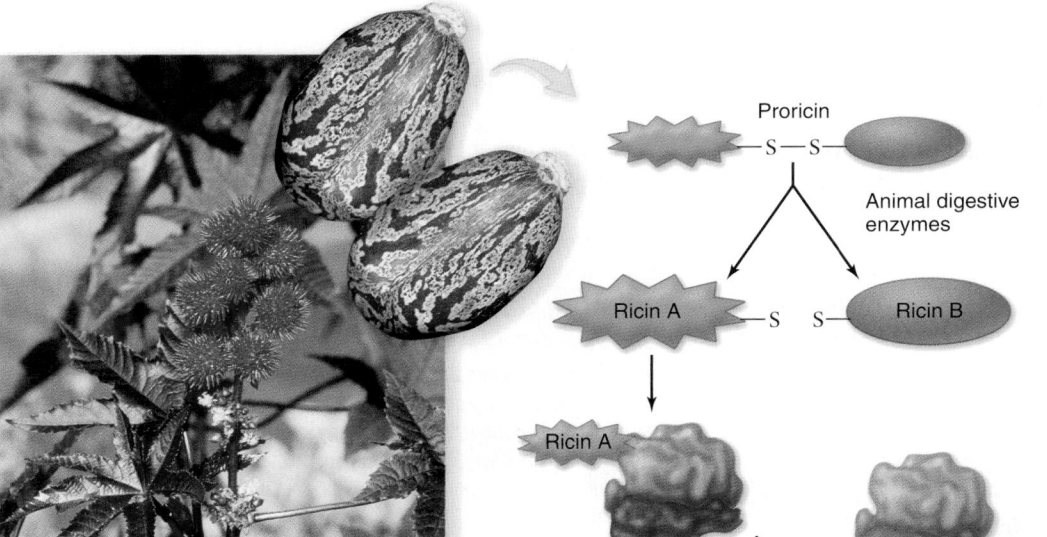

Proricin

Animal digestive enzymes

Ricin A

Ricin B

Ricin A

Ribosome

Inactivated ribosome

Figure 40.8 Ricin from castor beans blocks translation. When the ricin A subunit is released from proricin, it binds to rRNA in ribosomes and prevents mRNA from being translated into protein.

Ricin is found in the endosperm of the seed as a hetero-dimer composed of ricin A and ricin B, joined by a single disulfide bond. This heterodimer (proricin) is nontoxic, but when the disulfide bond is broken in humans or other animals, ricin A targets the GAGA sequence of the 28s rRNA of the ribosome. A single ricin molecule can inactivate 1500 ribosomes per minute, blocking translation of proteins.

In 1978, Bulgarian expatriate and dissident Georgi Markov was about to board a bus in London on his way to work at the BBC when he felt a sharp stabbing pain in his thigh. A man near him picked up an umbrella from the ground and hurriedly left. Markov had been injected via a mechanism in the umbrella tip with a pinhead-sized metal sphere containing 0.2 mg of ricin. He died four days later. After the collapse of the Soviet Union, former KGB officers revealed that the KGB had set up the assassination at the behest of the Bulgarian Communist Party leadership.

Inquiry question

? Explain how ricin led to Markov's death.

Secondary metabolites may have medicinal value

Major research efforts on plant secondary metabolites are in progress because of their potential benefits, as well as dangers, to human health (see table 40.1).

Soy and phytoestrogens

One example of the benefits and dangers is the presence of **phytoestrogens,** compounds very similar to the human hormone estrogen, in soybean products. In soybean plants, genistein is one of the major phytoestrogens.

Comparative studies between Asian populations that consume large amounts of soy foods and populations with lower dietary intake of soy products are raising intriguing questions and some conflicting results. For example, the lower rate of prostate cancer in Asian males might be accounted for by the down-regulation of androgen and estrogen receptors by a phytoestrogen. Soy is being marketed as a means for minimizing menopausal symptoms caused by declining estrogen levels in older women.

In humans, dietary phytoestrogens cross the placenta and can be found in the amniotic fluid during the second trimester of pregnancy. Questions have been raised about the effect of phytoestrogens on developing fetuses and even on babies who consume soy-based formula because of allergies to cow's milk formula. Because hormonal signaling is so complex, much more research is needed to fully understand how or even if phytoestrogens affect human physiology and development.

Taxol and breast cancer

Taxol, a secondary metabolite found in the Pacific yew (*Taxus brevifolia*), is effective in fighting cancer, especially breast cancer. The discovery of taxol's pharmaceutical value raised an environmental challenge. The very existence of the Pacific yew was being threatened as the shrubs were destroyed so that taxol could be extracted. Fortunately, it became possible to synthesize taxol in the laboratory.

Taxol is not an isolated case of drug discovery in plants. The hidden pharmaceutical value of many plants may lead to increased conservation efforts to protect plants that have the potential to make contributions toward human health. Although the plant pharmaceutical industry is growing, it is certainly not a new field. Until recent times, almost all medicines used by humans came from plants.

Quinine and malaria

In the 1600s, the Incas of Peru were treating malaria with a drink made from the bark of *Cinchona* trees. Malaria is caused by four types of human malaria parasites in the genus *Plasmodium*, which are carried by female *Anopheles* mosquitoes. *Plasmodium falciparum* is the most lethal of the four types. Symptoms include severe fevers and vomiting. The parasite feeds on red blood cells, and death can result from anemia or blocking of blood flow to the brain.

By 1820, the active ingredient in the bark of *Cinchona* trees, **quinine,** had been identified (see table 40.1). In the 19th century, British soldiers in India used quinine-containing "tonic water" to fight malaria. They masked the bitter taste of quinine with gin, creating the first gin and tonic drinks. In 1944, Robert Woodward and William Doering synthesized quinine. Now several other synthetic drugs are available to treat malaria.

Exactly how quinine and synthetic versions of this drug family work has puzzled researchers for a long time. Quinine can affect DNA replication, and also, when *P. falciparum* breaks down hemoglobin from red blood cells in its digestive vacuole, an intermediary toxic form of heme is released. Quinine may interfere with the subsequent polymerization of these hemes, leading to a build up of toxic hemes that poison the parasite.

Unfortunately, even today malaria is a major threat to human health, causing over a million deaths per year. Ninety percent of these deaths occur in sub-Saharan Africa. An estimated 300,000,000 individuals are infected. *P. falciparum* strains have acquired resistance to synthetic drugs, and quinine is once again the drug of choice in some cases.

Herbal remedies have been used for centuries in most cultures. A resurgence of interest in plant-based remedies is resulting in a growing and unregulated industry. Although herbal remedies have great promise, we need to be aware that each plant contains many secondary metabolites, many of which have evolved to cause harm to herbivores including humans.

Learning Outcomes Review 40.2

Plants accumulate secondary metabolites that can poison or otherwise harm herbivores. Plants also secrete chemicals that inhibit the growth of neighboring plants, a process termed allelopathy. Secondary metabolites may also have beneficial uses, such as phytoestrogens from soy, which may reduce menopausal symptoms in women; taxol from the Pacific yew, which acts as an anticancer agent; and quinine from *Cinchona* trees, which helps treat malaria.

■ *In what ways would a drug prepared from a whole plant differ from a drug prepared from an isolated chemical compound?*

40.3 Animals That Protect Plants

Learning Outcomes

1. Describe the benefit Acacia trees receive from ants that live in them.
2. Explain how some plants use parasitoid wasps to destroy caterpillars.

Figure 40.9 Ants attacking a katydid to protect "their" *Acacia.* Through coevolution, ants are sheltered by acacia trees and attack otherwise harmful herbivores.

Not only do individual species and their traits evolve over time, but so do relationships between species. For example, evolution of chemicals to deter herbivores may often be accompanied over time by adaptation on the part of herbivores to withstand these chemicals. This evolutionary pattern is called coevolution. Here we consider two cases of mutualism that coevolved between animal and plant species.

Acacia trees and ants. Several species of ants provide small armies to protect some species of *Acacia* trees from other herbivores. These stinging ants may inhabit an enlarged thorn of the tree; they attack other insects (figure 40.9) and sometimes small mammals and epiphytic plants. Some of the *Acacia* species provide their ants with sugar in nectaries located away from the flowers, and even with lipid food bodies at the tips of leaves.

The only problem with ants chasing away other insects is that acacia trees depend on bees to pollinate their flowers. What keeps the ants from swarming and stinging a bee that stops by to pollinate? Evidence indicates that when a flower opens on an acacia tree, it produces some type of chemical ant deterrent that does not deter the bees. This chemical has not yet been identified.

Parasitoid wasps, caterpillars, and leaves. Caterpillars fill up on leaf tissue before they metamorphose into a moth or a butterfly. In some cases, proteinase inhibitors in leaves are sufficient to deter very hungry caterpillars. But some plants have developed another strategy: As the caterpillar chews away, a wound response in the plant leads to the release of a volatile compound. This compound wafts through the air, and if a female parasitoid wasp happens to be in the neighborhood, it is immediately attracted to the source. Parasitoid wasps are so named because they are parasitic on caterpillars. The wasp lays her fertilized eggs in the body of the caterpillar that is feeding on the leaf of the plant. These eggs hatch, and the emerging larvae kill and eat the caterpillar (figure 40.10).

Learning Outcomes Review 40.3

Mutualism is an interaction between species that is beneficial to both. Ants protect *Acacia* by attacking feeding herbivores. Parasitoid wasps are attracted by compounds released from plant tissues damaged by feeding caterpillars; they lay eggs in the caterpillars, which later are killed by the emerging larvae.

- **Would you expect that wasps kill all the caterpillars? Explain.**

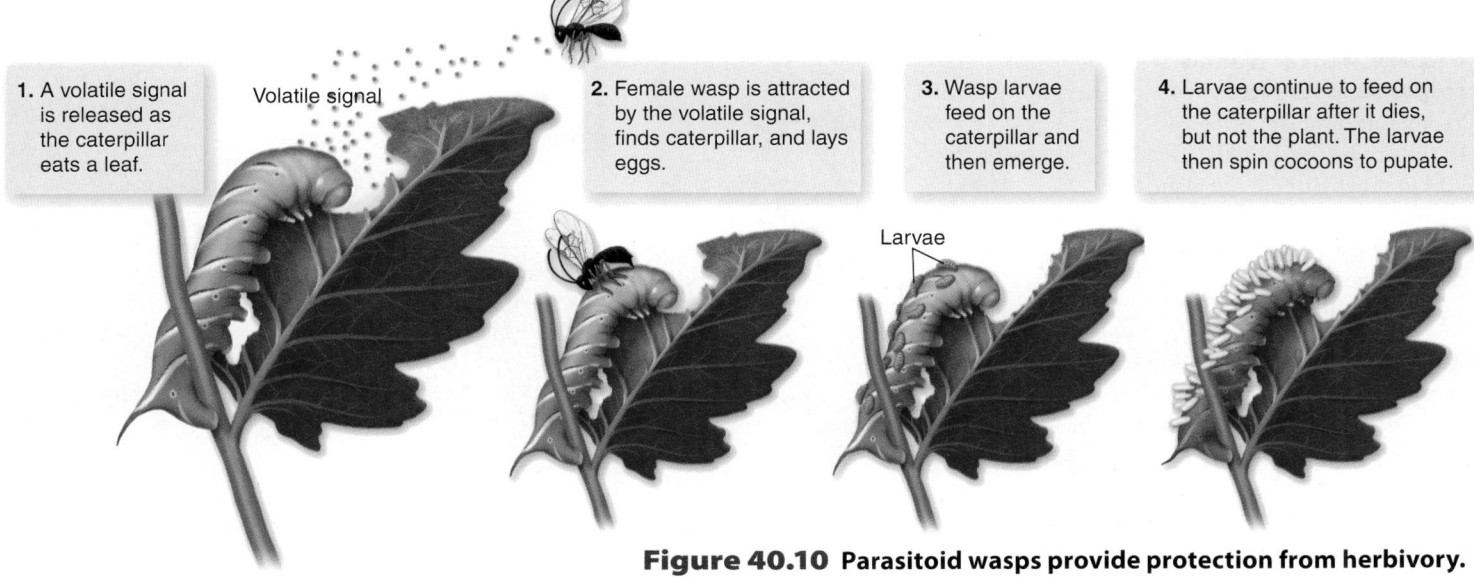

1. A volatile signal is released as the caterpillar eats a leaf.

Volatile signal

2. Female wasp is attracted by the volatile signal, finds caterpillar, and lays eggs.

3. Wasp larvae feed on the caterpillar and then emerge.

4. Larvae continue to feed on the caterpillar after it dies, but not the plant. The larvae then spin cocoons to pupate.

Larvae

Figure 40.10 Parasitoid wasps provide protection from herbivory.

So far, we have focused mainly on static plant responses to threats. Most of the deterrent chemicals such as toxins are maintained at steady-state levels. In addition, the morphological structures such as thorns or trichomes that help defend plants are part of the normal developmental program. Because these defenses are maintained whether an herbivore or other invader is present or not, they have an energetic downside. By contrast, resources could be conserved if the response to being under siege was inducible—that is, if the defense response could be launched only when a threat had been recognized. In this section, we explore these inducible defense mechanisms.

Wound responses protect plants from herbivores

As you just learned from the example of the parasitoid wasp, a **wound response** may occur when a leaf is chewed or injured. One induced outcome is the rapid production of proteinase inhibitors. These chemical toxins do not exist in the stockpile of defenses, but instead are produced in response to wounding.

Proteinase inhibitors bind to digestive enzymes in the gut of the herbivore. The proteinase inhibitors are produced throughout the plant, and not just at the wound site. How are cells in distant parts of the plant signaled to produce proteinase inhibitors? In tomato plants, the following sequence of events is responsible for this systemic response (figure 40.11):

1. Wounded leaves produce an 18-amino-acid peptide called **systemin** from a larger precursor protein.

2. Systemin moves through the apoplast (the space between cell walls) of the wounded tissue and into the nearby phloem. This small peptide-signaling molecule then moves throughout the plant in the phloem.
3. Cells with a systemin receptor bind the systemin, which leads to the production of **jasmonic acid.**
4. Jasmonic acid activates the transcription of defense genes, including the production of a proteinase inhibitor.

Although we know the most about the signaling pathway involving jasmonic acid, other molecules are involved in wound response as well. **Salicylic acid,** which is found in the bark of plants such as the white willow (*Salix alba*) is one example. Cell fragments also appear to be important signals for triggering an induced response, as is discussed shortly.

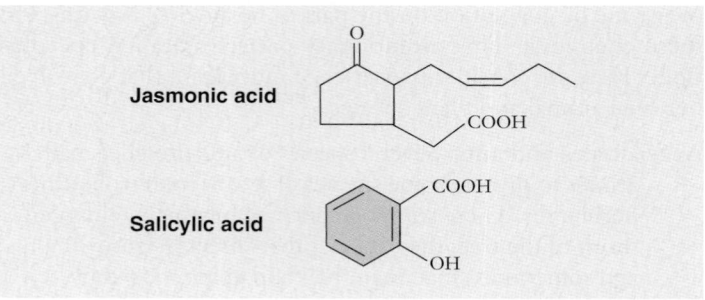

Mechanical damage separate from herbivore attack also elicits wound responses, which presents a challenge in designing plant experiments that involve cutting or otherwise mechanically damaging the tissue. Experimental controls, which should be cut or manipulated in the same way but without the test treatment, are especially important to ensure that any changes observed are not due only to the wound response.

Defense responses can be pathogen-specific

Wound responses are independent of the type of herbivore or other agent causing the damage, but other responses are triggered by a specific pathogen that carries a specific allele in its genome.

Figure 40.11 **Wound response in tomato.**
Wounding a tomato leaf leads to the production of jasmonic acid in other parts of the plant. Jasmonic acid initiates a signaling pathway that turns on genes needed to synthesize a proteinase inhibitor.

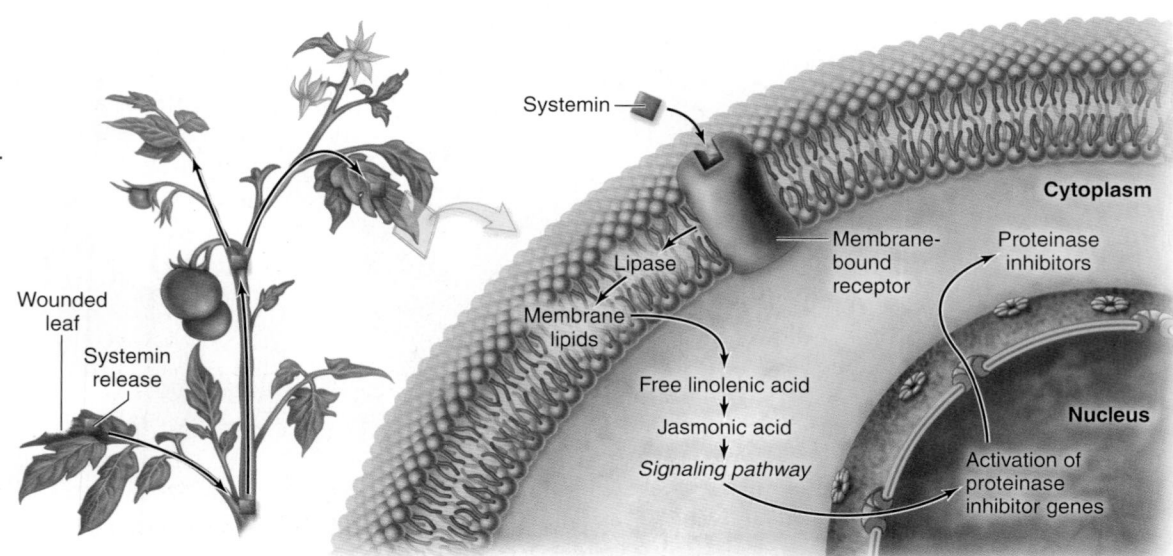

Pathogen recognition

Half a century ago, the geneticist H. H. Flor proposed the existence of a plant resistance gene *(R)*, the product of which interacts with the product of an avirulence gene *(avr)* carried by a pathogen. *Avirulent* means not virulent (disease-causing). An **avirulent pathogen** is one that can utilize host resources for its own use and reproduction without causing severe damage or death. The product of this pathogen's avr protein interacts with the plant's R protein to signal the pathogen's presence. In this way, the plant under attack can mount defenses, thus ensuring that the pathogen remains avirulent. If the pathogen's avr protein is not recognized by the plant, disease symptoms appear.

Flor's proposal is called the **gene-for-gene hypothesis** (figure 40.12), and several pairs of *avr* and *R* genes have been cloned in different species pathogenized by microbes, fungi, and even insects in one case. This research has been motivated partially by the agronomic benefit of identifying genes that can be added via gene technology to crop plants to protect them from invaders.

The *avr/R* gene interaction is an example of ongoing coevolution. An avirulent invader can be detected and recognized. Mutations arising in the avirulent pathogen can result in a virulent pathogen that overcomes a plant's defenses and kills it—often leading to the pathogen's demise as well.

Specific defenses and the hypersensitive response

Much is now known about the signal transduction pathways that follow the recognition of the pathogen by the *R* gene product. These pathways lead to the triggering of the **hypersensitive response (HR),** which leads to rapid cell death around the source of the invasion and also to a longer term, whole-plant resistance (figures 40.12 and 40.13). A gene-for-gene response does not always occur, but plants still have defense responses to pathogens in general as well as to mechanical wounding. Some of the response pathways may be similar. Also, fragments of cell wall carbohydrates may serve as recognition and signaling molecules.

When a plant is attacked and a gene-for-gene recognition occurs, the HR leads to very rapid cell death around the site of attack. This seals off the wounded tissue to prevent the pathogen or pest from moving into the rest of the plant. Hydrogen peroxide and nitric oxide are produced and may signal a cascade of bio-chemical events resulting in the localized death of host cells. These chemicals may also have negative effects on the pathogen, although protective mechanisms have coevolved in some pathogens.

Other antimicrobial agents produced include the **phytoalexins,** which are antimicrobial chemical defense agents. A variety of pathogenesis-related genes *(PR* genes) are also expressed, and their proteins can function as either antimicrobial agents or signals for other events that protect the plant.

In the case of virulent invaders for which there is no *R* recognition, changes in local cell walls at least partially block the pathogen or pest from moving further into the plant. In this case, an HR does not occur, and the local plant cells do not die.

Long-term protection

In addition to the HR or other local responses, plants are capable of a systemic response to a pathogen or pest attack, called a **systemic acquired resistance (SAR)** (see figure 40.12). Several pathways lead to broad-ranging resistance that lasts for a period of days.

The long-distance signal that induces SAR is likely salicylic acid, rather than systemin, which is the long-distance signal in wound responses. At the cellular level, jasmonic acid (which was mentioned earlier in the context of the wound response pathways) is involved in SAR signaling. SAR allows the plant to respond more quickly if it is attacked again. This response, however, is not the same as the human or mammalian immune response, in which antibodies (proteins) that recognize specific antigens (foreign proteins) persist in the body. SAR is neither as specific nor as long-lasting.

Learning Outcomes Review 40.4

A wounded leaf initiates a signaling chain that stimulates production of proteinase inhibitors. When a plant has a resistance gene with a product that recognizes the product of an avirulence gene in the pathogen, the plant carries out a defense response; this recognition is called the gene-for-gene hypothesis. Systemic acquired resistance is a temporary broad form of resistance that may be induced by exposure to a pathogen.

■ *How does local cell death help preserve a plant under attack by a pathogen?*

---

1. Pathogen enters cell.

2. Proteins are released into cell by pathogen.

3. *R* gene products from the plant cell bind to *avr* gene products.

4. If binding occurs, the *R* gene product is activated, triggering a protective hypersensitive response. If no binding occurs, the plant succumbs to disease.

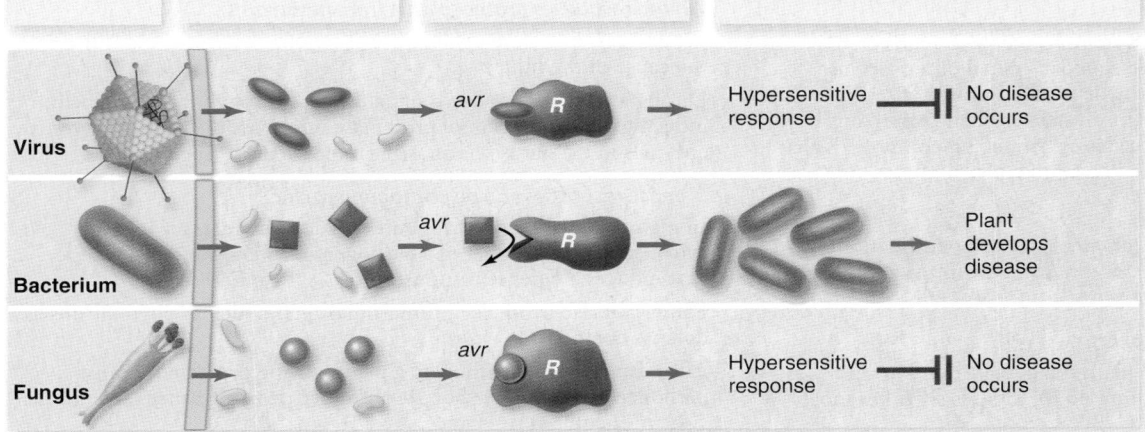

Figure 40.12 Gene-for-gene hypothesis. Flor proposed that pathogens have an avirulence *(avr)* gene that recognizes the product of a plant resistance gene *(R).* If the virus, bacterium, fungus, or insect has an *avr* gene product that matches the *R* gene product, a defense response will occur.

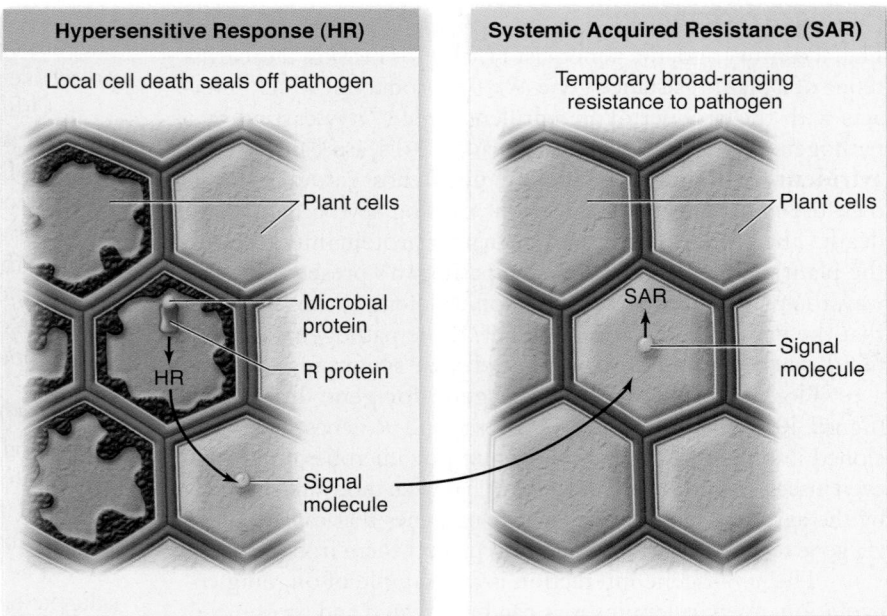

Hypersensitive Response (HR)

Local cell death seals off pathogen

Plant cells

Microbial protein

R protein

HR

Signal molecule

Systemic Acquired Resistance (SAR)

Temporary broad-ranging resistance to pathogen

Plant cells

SAR

Signal molecule

Figure 40.13 Plant defense responses.
In the gene-for-gene response, a cascade of events is triggered, leading to local cell death (HR) and to the production of a mobile signal that provides longer term resistance in the rest of the plant (SAR).

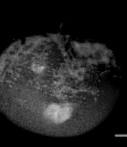

Chapter Review

40.1 Physical Defenses

Pathogens can harm plants in many ways, including exploiting nutrient resources and taking over DNA replication machinery.

Dermal tissue provides first-line defense.

Dermal tissues are covered with lipids such as cutin and suberin, which reduce water loss and prevent attack. Morphological features such as trichomes, bark, and thorns protect some plants.

Invaders can penetrate dermal defenses.

In spite of defense mechanisms, invaders can cause damage by piercing plants, eating plant parts, or entering the plant through the stomata.

Bacteria and fungi can also be beneficial to plants.

Mycorrhizal fungi form beneficial relationships with plants by enhancing uptake of water and minerals. Nitrogen-fixing bacteria provide nitrogen to plants in a usable form.

40.2 Chemical Defenses

Plants maintain chemical arsenals.

Plants may produce and stockpile secondary metabolites such as alkaloids, tannins, and oils that provide protection from predators (see table 40.1). Plants protect themselves from their own toxins either by sequestering them in vesicles or producing compounds that are not toxic until they are ingested by a predator.

Plants can poison other plants.

Allelopathic plants secrete chemicals to block seed germination or inhibit growth of nearby plants. This strategy minimizes competition for resources such as light and nutrients.

Humans are susceptible to plant toxins.

Ricin is an example of a powerful plant toxin. It is found in the endosperm of castor beans (see figure 40.8). Ricin is six times more lethal than cyanide.

Secondary metabolites may have medicinal value.

Plant secondary metabolites such as phytoestrogens, taxol, and quinine have pharmaceutical value for humans. Many other plant-based remedies have been used for centuries in human cultures.

40.3 Animals That Protect Plants

Mutualistic associations are beneficial to both the plant and animal partners. One example is the relationship between acacia trees and ants, in which ants protect the trees from herbivores.

Another example is the association between certain plants, caterpillars, and parasitoid wasps. When chewed or damaged, the leaves release compounds that attract the wasps, which lay their eggs in the caterpillars. The wasps' larvae feed on the caterpillar, killing it (see figure 40.10).

40.4 Systemic Responses to Invaders

Plants avoid an unnecessary expenditure of energy if they produce defense mechanisms only when needed.

Wound responses protect plants from herbivores.

Wound responses are generalized reactions that occur regardless of the cause of the injury.

During a wound response, a signal spreads throughout the phloem, inducing the production of proteinase inhibitors that bind to digestive enzymes in the gut of the animal eating the plant (see figure 40.11).

Defense responses can be pathogen-specific.

In many plants, the plant *R* gene product may interact with an avirulence gene product of a pathogen in a gene-for-gene reaction that induces a defense response.

Plants can also produce antimicrobial agents such as phytoalexins as defense compounds.

After exposure to a pathogen, a plant may be protected against pathogen attack in the short-term future through a mechanism called systemic acquired resistance.

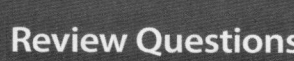

Review Questions

UNDERSTAND

1. Nonnative invasive species are often a threat to native species because they
   a. typically grow larger than other plants.
   b. are not susceptible to any diseases.
   c. are parasitic.
   d. do not have natural enemies in their new location.

2. Fungal pathogens transfer nutrients across a plant cell membrane using
   a. an adhesion pad.   c. guard cells.
   b. a haustorium.   d. tumors.

3. Casparian strips in roots contain _____, which helps to defend against invaders.
   a. wax   b. suberin
   c. cutin   d. cuticle

4. Which of the following is not a secondary metabolite?
   a. Caffeine   c. Taxol
   b. Morphine   d. Glucose

5. Parasitoid wasps protect plants from caterpillars by
   a. stinging them.   c. eating them.
   b. repelling them.   d. enclosing them in a capsule.

6. In response to wounding, a tomato plant first produces a peptide called
   a. systemin.   c. ricin.
   b. jasmonic acid.   d. salicylic acid.

7. When a cell undergoes a hypersensitive response, it
   a. builds cell walls quickly.
   b. releases defense response molecules from its vacuole.
   c. dies rapidly.
   d. destroys avirulence gene products.

8. The wound response products that bind to digestive enzymes in herbivores are
   a. proteinase inhibitors.   c. lipase inhibitors.
   b. proteinase promoters.   d. lipase promoters.

9. If a plant has been attacked by a pathogen, then it is likely to be able to respond more quickly to a subsequent attack due to a mechanism called
   a. basal defense.
   b. induced hypersensitive response.
   c. antimicrobial pathogen resistance.
   d. systemic acquired resistance.

APPLY

1. Some plants have developed a mutualistic relationship with parasitoid wasps. This mutualistic relationship would not occur if
   a. the plant quit producing nectar for the wasp.
   b. the wasp ceased to live on the plant.
   c. the plant quit producing volatile compounds that attract the wasp.
   d. the plant attracted too many caterpillars.

2. Both plant and animal immune systems can
   a. develop memory of past pathogens to more effectively deal with subsequent infections.
   b. initiate expression of proteins to help fight the infection.

   c. kill their own cells to prevent spread of the infection.
   d. all of the above

3. Your friend informs you that it is highly likely all of the plants in your yard are "infected" with some kind of fungi or bacteria. The plants look perfectly healthy to you at this time. The most prudent thing for you to do would be:
   a. Remove all your plants because they are likely to die.
   b. Spray your plants with chemicals to remove all bacteria and fungi.
   c. Remove all your plants and replace the soil.
   d. Do nothing because many of these bacteria and fungi may be beneficial.

4. Some plants are recognized by fungal pathogens on the basis of their stomatal pores. Which of the following would provide these plants immunity from fungal infection?
   a. Removing all of the stomata from the plant
   b. Changing the spacing of stomatal pores in these plants
   c. Reinforcing the cell wall in the guard cells of stomatal pores
   d. Increasing the number of trichomes on the surfaces

5. You decide to plant a garden with a beautiful black walnut at one end and a majestic white oak at the other end. You are quite disappointed, however, when none of the seeds you plant around the walnut tree grow. What might explain this observation?
   a. The walnut tree filters out too much light, so the seeds fail to germinate.
   b. The roots of the walnut tree deplete all of the nutrients from the soil, so the new seedlings starve.
   c. The walnut tree produces chemical toxins that prevent seed germination.

6. If a pathogen contains an *avr* gene not recognized by a plant, the plant will most likely
   a. develop a disease.
   b. eliminate the pathogen because it is unrecognized.
   c. develop proteinase inhibitors.
   d. develop a different *R* gene.

SYNTHESIZE

1. During the domestication of crops, humans have intentionally or inadvertently selected for lower levels of toxic compounds. Explain why each of these two types of selection would have occurred.

2. Parasitoid wasps seem like an effective method to control caterpillars. Discuss some limitations of this strategy. That is, outline some scenarios in which a plant might not be effectively protected by the wasps.

3. Systemin is transported through the phloem of a tomato plant to induce a wound response to herbivores. However, the direction of phloem movement is always from source to sink. Explain how the sites that receive the wound signal may vary with stages of the plant's life cycle.

ONLINE RESOURCE

www.ravenbiology.com

Understand, Apply, and Synthesize—enhance your study with animations that bring concepts to life and practice tests to assess your understanding. Your instructor may also recommend the interactive eBook, individualized learning tools, and more.

Chapter 41

Sensory Systems in Plants

Chapter Outline

41.1 Responses to Light

41.2 Responses to Gravity

41.3 Responses to Mechanical Stimuli

41.4 Responses to Water and Temperature

41.5 Hormones and Sensory Systems

Introduction

All organisms sense and interact with their environments. This is particularly true of plants. Plant survival and growth are critically influenced by abiotic factors, including water, wind, and light. The effect of the local environment on plant growth also accounts for much of the variation in adult form within a species. In this chapter, we explore how a plant senses such factors and transduces these signals to elicit an optimal physiological, growth, or developmental response. Although responses can be observed on a macroscopic scale, the mechanism of response occurs at the level of the cell. Signals are perceived when they interact with a receptor molecule, causing a shape change and altering the receptor's ability to interact with signaling molecules. Hormones play an important role in the internal signaling that brings about environmental responses and are keyed in many ways to the environment.

In chapter 8 we covered the details of photosynthesis, the process by which plants convert light energy into chemical bond energy. We described pigments, molecules that are capable of absorbing light energy; you learned that chlorophylls are the primary pigment molecules of photosynthesis. Plants contain other pigments as well, and one of the functions of these other pigments is to detect light and to mediate plants' response to light by passing on information.

Several environmental factors, including light, can initiate seed germination, flowering, and other critical developmental events in the life of a plant. **Photomorphogenesis** is the term used for nondirectional, light-triggered development. It can result in complex changes in form, including flowering.

Unlike photomorphogenesis, phototropisms are directional growth responses to light. Both photomorphogenesis and phototropisms compensate for the plant's inability to walk away from unfavorable environmental conditions.

P_{fr} facilitates expression of light-response genes

Phytochrome is present in all groups of plants and in a few genera of green algae, but not in other protists, bacteria, or fungi. Phytochrome systems probably evolved among the green algae and were present in the common ancestor of the plants.

The phytochrome molecule exists in two interconvertible forms: The first form, P_r, absorbs red light at 660 nm wavelength; the second, P_{fr}, absorbs far-red light at 730 nm. Sunlight has more red than far-red light. P_r is biologically inactive; it is converted into P_{fr}, the active form, when red photons are present. P_{fr} is converted back into P_r when far-red photons are available. In other words, biological reactions that are affected by phytochrome occur when P_{fr} is present. When most of the P_{fr} has been replaced by P_r, the reaction will not occur (figure 41.1).

The pigment-containing protein **phytochrome (P)** consists of two parts: a smaller part that is sensitive to light, called the *chromophore*, and a larger portion called the *apoprotein* (figure 41.2). The apoprotein facilitates expression of light-response genes. Over 2500 genes, 10% of the *Arabidopsis* genome, are involved in biological responses that begin with a conformational change in one of the phytochromes in response to red light. Phytochromes are involved in numerous signaling pathways that lead to gene expression. Some pathways also involve protein kinases or G proteins (described in chapter 9).

Phytochrome is found in the cytoplasm, but enters the nucleus to facilitate transcription of light response genes. When P_r is converted to P_{fr}, it can move into the nucleus. Once in the nucleus, P_{fr} binds with other proteins that form a transcription complex, leading to the expression of light-

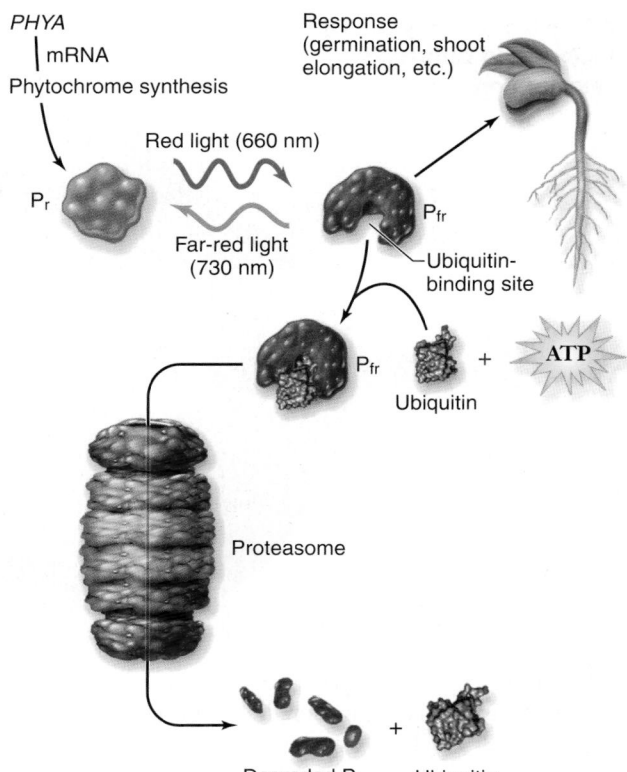

Figure 41.1 **How phytochrome works.** *PHYA* is one of the five *Arabidopsis* phytochrome genes. When exposed to red light, P_r changes to P_{fr}, the active form that elicits a response in plants. P_{fr} is converted to P_r when exposed to far-red light. The amount of P_{fr} is regulated by protein degradation. The protein ubiquitin tags P_{fr} for degradation in the proteasome.

regulated genes (figure 41.3). Phytochrome's protein-binding site (see figure 41.2) is essential for interactions with transcription factors.

Phytochrome also works through protein kinase-signaling pathways. When phytochrome converts to the P_{fr} form, the protein kinase domain of the apoprotien may phosphorylate a serine and the amino (N) terminus of the phytochrome itself

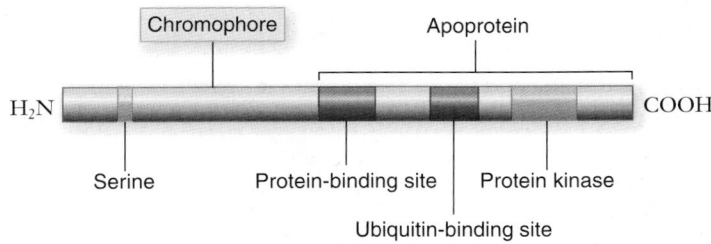

Figure 41.2 **Phytochrome.** Different parts of the phytochrome molecule have distinct roles in light regulation of growth and development. Phytochrome changes conformation when the chromophore responds to relative amounts of red far-red light. The shape change affects the ability of ph to bind to other proteins that participate in the sign The ubiquitin-binding sites allow for degradatio kinase domain allows for further signaling vi

Figure 41.3 P$_{fr}$ enters the nucleus and regulates gene expression.

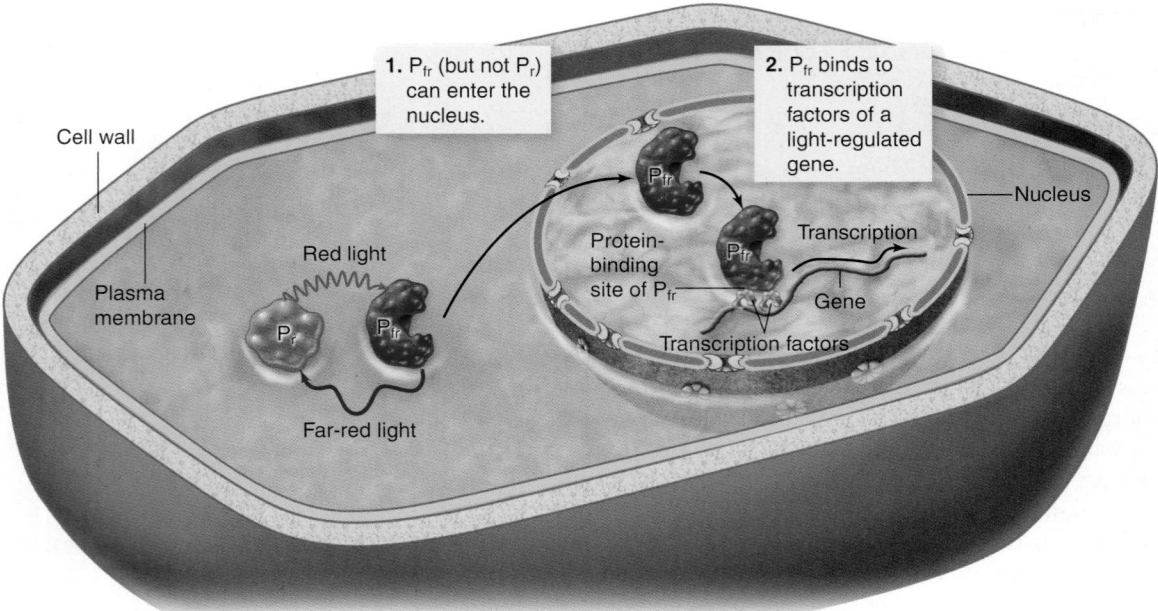

1. P$_{fr}$ (but not P$_r$) can enter the nucleus.

2. P$_{fr}$ binds to transcription factors of a light-regulated gene.

Cell wall

Plasma membrane

Red light

P$_r$

P$_{fr}$

Far-red light

Nucleus

Transcription

Protein-binding site of P$_{fr}$

P$_{fr}$

P$_{fr}$

Gene

Transcription factors

(autophosphorylation), or it may phosphorylate the serine of another protein involved in light signaling (figure 41.4). Phosphorylation initiates a signaling cascade that can activate transcription factors and lead to the transcription of light-regulated genes.

Although phytochrome is involved in multiple signaling pathways, it does not directly initiate the expression of that 10% of the *Arabidopsis* plant genome. Rather, phytochrome initiates expression of master regulatory genes that manage the complex interactions leading to photomorphogenesis and phototropisms. Gene expression is just the first step, with hormones playing important roles as well.

Inquiry question

? You are given seed of a plant with a mutation in the protein kinase domain of phytochrome. Would you expect to see any red-light–mediated responses when you germinate the seed? Explain your answer.

Chlorophyll also absorbs red light, but it is not a receptor like phytochrome. Unlike receptors that transduce information, chlorophyll transduces energy.

The amount of P$_{fr}$ is also regulated by degradation. Ubiquitin is a protein that tags P$_{fr}$ for transport to the **proteasome,** a protein shredder composed of 28 proteins. The proteasome has a channel in the center, and as proteins pass through, they are clipped into amino acids that can be used to build other proteins as described in chapter 16. The process of tagging and recycling P$_{fr}$ is precisely regulated to maintain needed amounts of phytochrome in the cell.

Although we often refer to phytochrome as a single molecule here, several different phytochromes have been identified that appear to have specific functions. In *Arabidopsis* five forms of phytochrome, PHYA to PHYE, have been characterized, each playing overlapping but distinct roles in the light regulation of growth and development.

Figure 41.4 The kinase domain of P$_{fr}$ phosphorylates P$_{fr}$, leading directly or indirectly to light-regulated gene expression. In this example, signaling leads to the release of a transcription factor from a protein

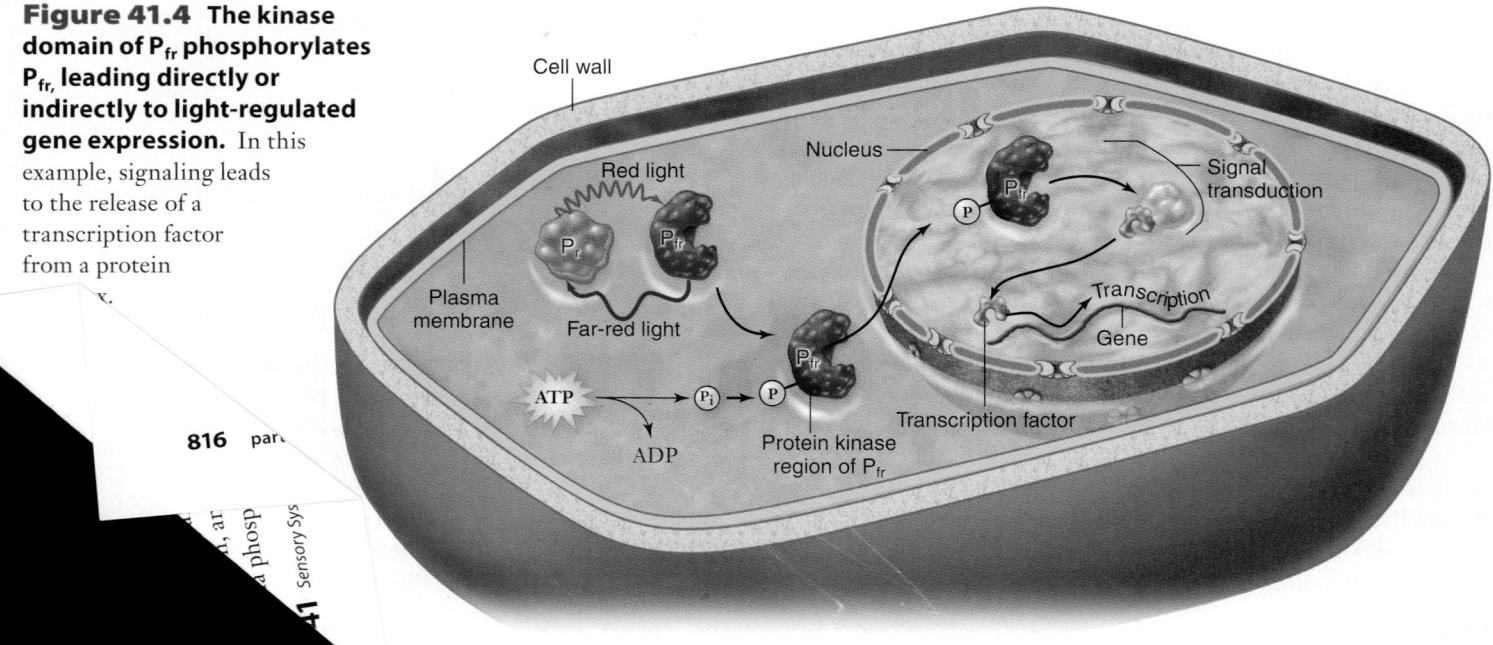

Cell wall

Red light

Nucleus

Signal transduction

P$_r$

P$_{fr}$

P

P$_{fr}$

Plasma membrane

Far-red light

Transcription

Gene

ATP

P$_i$ → P

P$_{fr}$

Transcription factor

ADP

Protein kinase region of P$_{fr}$

Sensory Sys
phosp
41

Many growth responses are linked to phytochrome action

Phytochrome is involved in a number of plant growth responses, including seed germination, shoot elongation, and detection of plant spacing.

Seed germination

Seed germination is inhibited by far-red light and stimulated by red light in many plants. Because chlorophyll absorbs red light strongly but does not absorb far-red light, light filtered through the green leaves of canopy trees above a seed contains a reduced amount of red light. The far-red light inhibits seed germination by converting P_{fr} into the biologically inactive P_r form.

Consequently, seeds on the ground under deciduous plants, which lose their leaves in winter, are more apt to germinate in the spring after the leaves have decomposed and the seeds are exposed to direct sunlight and a greater amount of red light. This adaptation greatly improves the chances that seedlings will become established before leaves on taller plants shade the seedlings and reduce sunlight available for photosynthesis.

Shoot elongation

Elongation of the shoot in an etiolated seedling (one that is pale and slender from having been kept in the dark) is caused by a lack of red light. The morphology of such plants becomes normal when they are exposed to red light, increasing the amount of P_{fr}.

Etiolation is an energy conservation strategy to help plants growing in the dark reach the light before they die. They don't green up until light becomes available, and they divert energy to internode elongation. This strategy is useful for seedlings when they have sprouted underground or under leaf cover.

The de-etiolated (*det2*) *Arabidopsis* mutant has a poor etiolation response; seedlings fail to elongate in the dark (figure 41.5). The *det2* mutants are defective in an enzyme necessary for biosynthesis of a brassinosteroid hormone, leading researchers to propose that brassinosteroids play a role in plant responses to light through phytochrome. (Brassinosteroids and other hormones are discussed later in this chapter.)

Detection of plant spacing

Red and far-red light also signal plant spacing. Again, leaf shading increases the amount of far-red light relative to red light. Plants somehow measure the amount of far-red light bounced back to them from neighboring plants. The closer together plants are, the more far-red relative to red light they perceive and the more likely they are to grow tall, a strategy for outcompeting others for sunshine. If their perception is distorted by putting a light-blocking collar around the stem, the elongation response no longer occurs.

Light affects directional growth

Phototropisms, directional growth responses, contribute to the variety of overall plant shape we see within a species as shoots grow toward light. Tropisms are particularly intriguing because they challenge us to connect environmental signals with cellular perception of the signal, transduction into biochemical pathways, and ultimately an altered growth response.

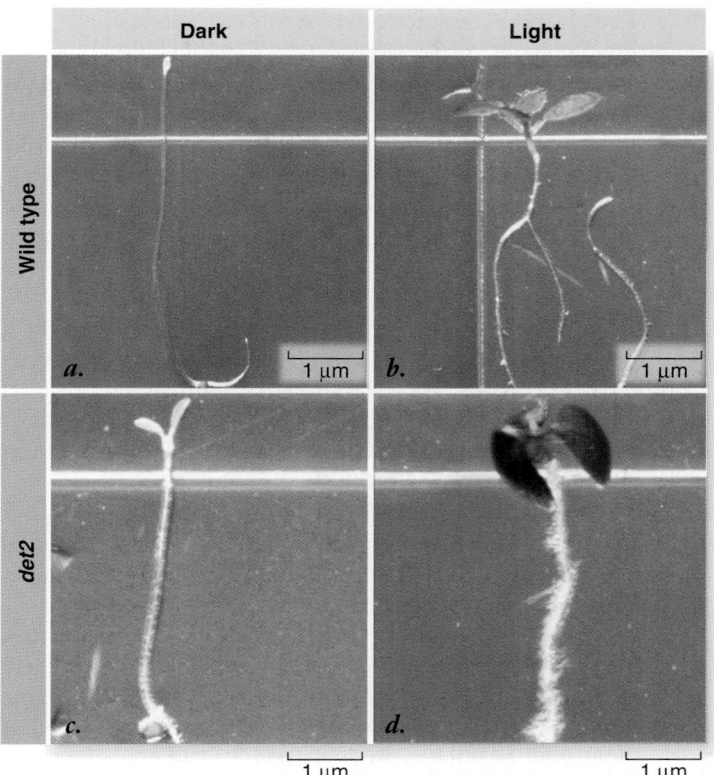

Figure 41.5 **Etiolation is regulated by light and the** *det2* **gene in** *Arabidopsis*. *det2* is needed for etiolation in dark grown plants.

Positive phototropism in stems

Phototropic responses include the bending of growing stems and other plant parts toward sources of light with blue wavelengths (460-nm range) (figure 41.6). In general, stems are positively phototropic, growing toward a light source, but most roots do not respond to light, or in exceptional cases, exhibit only a weak negative phototropic response.

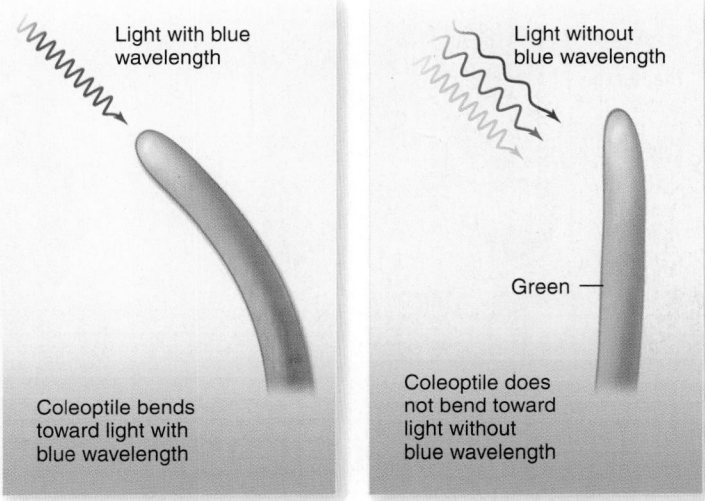

Figure 41.6 **Phototropism.** Oat coleoptiles growing toward light with blue wavelengths. Colors indicate the color of light shining on coleoptiles. Arrows indicate the direction of light.

The phototropic reactions of stems are clearly of adaptive value, giving plants greater exposure to available light. They are also important in determining the development of plant organs and, therefore, the appearance of the plant. Individual leaves may also display phototropic responses; the position of leaves is important to the photosynthetic efficiency of the plant. A plant hormone called *auxin*, discussed in a later section, is probably involved in most, if not all, of the phototropic growth responses of plants.

Blue-light receptors

The recent identification of blue-light receptors in plants is leading to exciting discoveries of how the light signal can ultimately be connected with a phototropic response. A blue-light receptor **phototropin 1 (PHOT1)** was identified through the characterization of a nonphotototropic mutant.

The phot1 protein has two light-sensing regions, and they change conformation in response to blue light. This change activates another region of the protein that is a kinase. Both PHOT1 and a similar receptor, PHOT2, are receptor kinases unique to plants. A portion of PHOT1 is a kinase that autophosphorylates (figure 41.7). Currently, only the early steps in this signal transduction are understood. It will be intriguing to watch the story of the phot1 signal transduction pathway unfold, leading to an explanation of how plants grow toward the light.

Circadian clocks are independent of light but are entrained by light

Although shorter and much longer naturally occurring rhythms also exist, **circadian rhythms** ("around the day") are particularly common and widespread among eukaryotic organisms. They relate the day–night cycle on Earth, although they are not exactly 24 hr in duration.

Jean de Mairan, a French astronomer, first identified circadian rhythms in 1729. He studied the sensitive plant (*Mimosa pudica*), which closes its leaflets and leaves at night. When de Mairan put the plants in total darkness, they continued "sleeping" and "waking" just as they had when exposed to night and day. This is one of four characteristics of a circadian rhythm—it must continue to run in the absence of external inputs. Plants with a circadian rhythm do not actually have to be experiencing a pattern of daylight and darkness for their cycle to occur.

In addition, a circadian rhythm must be about 24 hr in duration, and the cycle can be reset or entrained. Although plants kept in darkness will continue the circadian cycle, the cycle's period may gradually move away from the actual day–night cycle, becoming desynchronized. In the natural environment, the cycle is entrained to a daily cycle through the action of phytochrome and blue-light photoreceptors.

Other eukaryotes, including humans, have circadian rhythms, and perhaps you have experienced jet lag when you traveled by airplane across a few time zones. Recovery from jet lag involves entrainment to the new time zone.

Another characteristic of a circadian cycle is that the clock can compensate for differences in temperature, so that the duration remains unchanged. This characteristic is unique, considering what we know about biochemical reactions, because most rates of reactions vary significantly based on temperature. Circadian clocks exist in many organisms, and they appear to have evolved independently multiple times.

The reversible circadian rhythm changes in leaf movements are typically brought about by alteration of cells' turgor pressure; we describe these changes in a later section.

Learning Outcomes Review 41.1

Plants grow and develop in response to environmental signals. Phytochrome, a red-light receptor, transduces information, while chlorophyll transduces energy. Phytochrome influences seed germination, shoot elongation, and other growth. Phototropism is directional growth in response to light and is controlled by a blue-light receptor. Circadian rhythms are 24-hr cycles entrained to the day–night cycle.

■ **Why would it be an advantage to have both phytochromes and chlorophylls as pigments?**

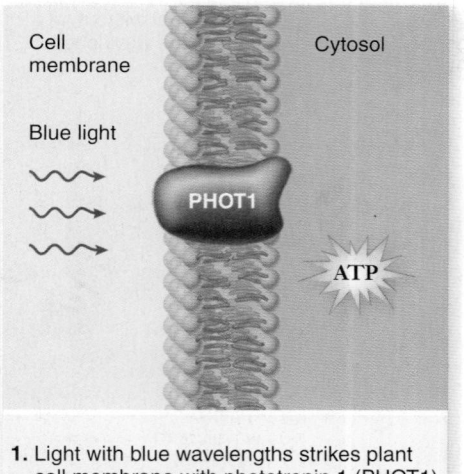

1. Light with blue wavelengths strikes plant cell membrane with phototropin 1 (PHOT1).

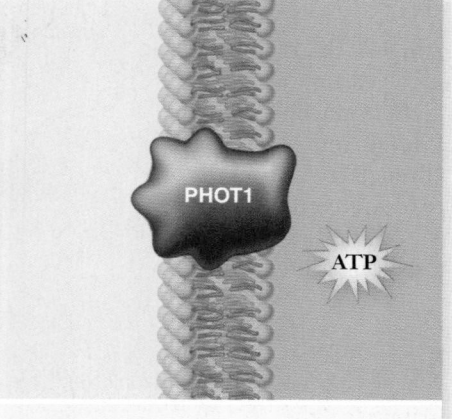

2. Blue light is absorbed by PHOT1, causing a change in conformation.

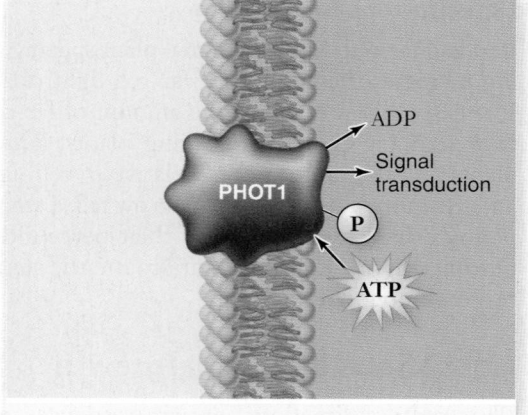

3. This conformational change results in autophosphorylation, triggering a signal transduction.

Figure 41.7 Blue-light receptor. Blue light activates the light-sensing region of PHOT1, which in turn stimulates the kinase region of PHOT1 to autophosphorylate. This is just the first step in a signal transduction pathway that leads to phototropic growth.

Responses to Gravity

When a potted plant is tipped over and left in place, the shoot bends and grows upward. The same thing happens when a storm pushes plants over in a field. These are examples of **gravitropism,** the response of a plant to the gravitational field of the Earth (figure 41.8; see also chapter opener). Because plants also grow in response to light, separating out phototropic effects is important in the study of gravitropism.

Plants align with the gravitational field: An overview

Gravitropic responses are present at germination, when the root grows down and the shoot grows up. Why does a shoot have a negative gravitropic response (growth away from gravity), while a root has a positive one? Auxins play a primary role in gravitropic responses, but they may not be the only way gravitational information is sent through the plant.

The opportunity to experiment on the Space Shuttle in a gravity-free environment has accelerated research in this area. Analysis of gravitropic mutants is also adding to our understanding of gravitropism. Investigators propose that four general steps lead to a gravitropic response:

1. Gravity is perceived by the cell.
2. A mechanical signal is transduced into a physiological signal in the cell that perceives gravity.
3. The physiological signal is transduced inside the cell and externally to other cells.
4. Differential cell elongation occurs, affecting cells in the "up" and "down" sides of the root or shoot.

Figure 41.8 Plant response to gravity. This plant was placed horizontally and allowed to grow for seven days. Note the negative gravitational response of the shoot.

Currently researchers are debating the steps involved in perception of gravity. In shoots, gravity is sensed along the length of the stem in the endodermal cells that surround the vascular tissue (figure 41.9a), and signaling occurs toward the outer epidermal cells. In roots, the cap is the site of gravity perception, and a signal must trigger differential cell elongation and division in the elongation zone (figure 41.9b).

In both shoots and roots, amyloplasts, plastids that contain starch, sink toward the center of the gravitational field and thus may be involved in sensing gravity. Amyloplasts interact with the cytoskeleton. Auxin evidently plays a role in transmitting a signal from the gravity-sensing cells that contain amyloplasts and the site where growth occurs. The link between amyloplasts and auxin is not fully understood.

Stems bend away from a center of gravity

Increased auxin concentration on the lower side in stems causes the cells in that area to grow more than the cells on the upper side. The result is a bending upward of the stem against the

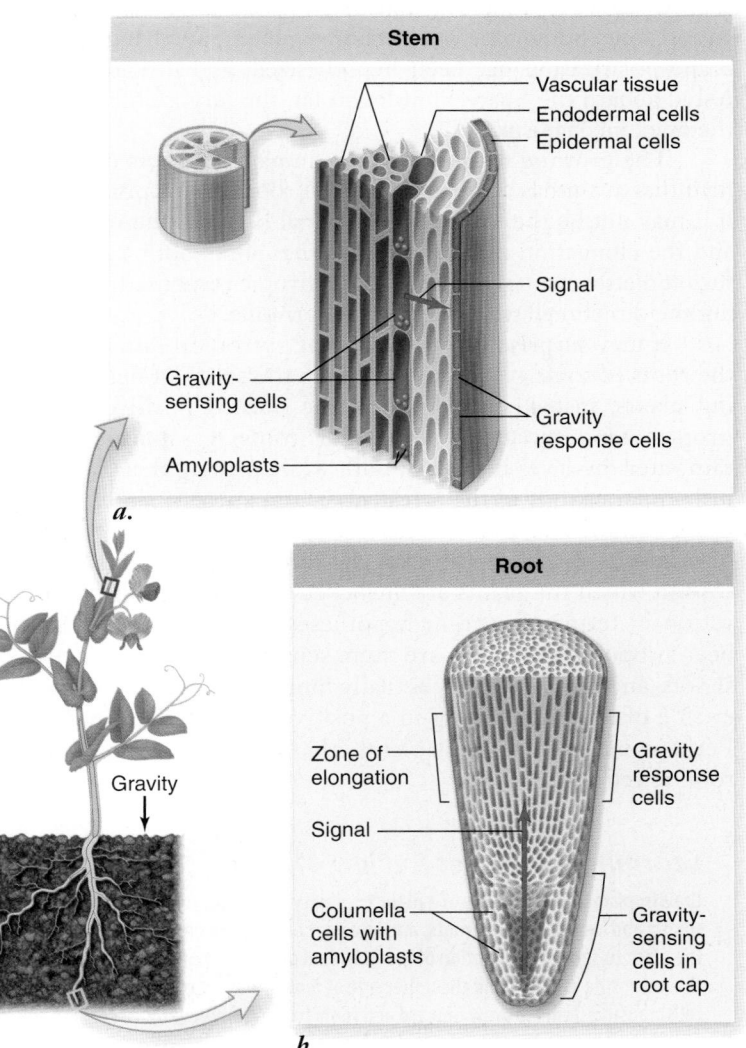

Figure 41.9 Sites of gravity sensing and response in roots and shoots.

force of gravity—in other words, a *negative gravitropic response*. Such differences in hormone concentration have not been as well documented in roots. Nevertheless, the upper sides of roots oriented horizontally grow more rapidly than the lower sides, causing the root ultimately to grow downward; this phenomenon is known as *positive gravitropic response*.

Two *Arabidopsis* mutants, *scarecrow (scr)* and *short root (shr)*, were initially identified by aberrant root phenotypes, but they also affect shoot gravitropism (figure 41.10). Both genes are needed for normal endodermal development (see figure 36.16). Without a fully functional endodermis, stems lack a normal gravitropic response. These endodermal cells carry amyloplasts in the stems, and in the mutants, stem endodermis fails to differentiate and produce gravity-sensing amyloplasts.

Roots bend toward a center of gravity

In roots, the gravity-sensing cells are located in the root cap, and the cells that actually undergo asymmetrical growth are in the distal elongation zone, which is closest to the root cap. How the information is transferred over this distance is an intriguing question. Auxin may be involved, but when auxin transport is suppressed, a gravitropic response still occurs in the distal elongation zone. Some type of electrical signaling involving membrane polarization has been hypothesized, and this idea was tested aboard the Space Shuttle. So far, the jury is still out on the exact mechanism.

The growing number of auxin mutants in roots do confirm that auxin has an essential role in root gravitropism, even if it may not be the long-distance signal between the root cap and the elongation zone. Mutations that affect both auxin influx and efflux can eliminate the gravitropic response by altering the directional transport of this hormone.

It may surprise you to learn that in tropical rain forests, the roots of some plants may grow up the stems of neighboring plants, instead of exhibiting the normal positive gravitropic responses typical of other roots. It appears that rainwater dissolves nutrients, both while passing through the lush upper canopy of the forest, and subsequently while trickling down the tree trunks. This water is a more reliable source of nutrients for the roots than the nutrient-poor rain forest soils in which the plants are anchored. Explaining this observation in terms of current hypotheses is a challenge. It has been proposed that roots are more sensitive to auxin than are shoots, and that auxin may actually inhibit growth on the lower side of a root, resulting in a positive gravitropic response. Perhaps in these tropical plants, the sensitivity to auxin in roots is reduced.

Learning Outcomes Review 41.2

Gravitropism is the response of a plant to gravity. In endodermis cells of shoots and root cap cells of roots, amyloplasts settle to the bottom, allowing the plant to sense the direction of gravitational pull. In response, cells on the lower side of stems and the upper side of roots grow faster than other cells, causing stems to grow upward and roots to grow downward.

■ **What would happen to a plant growing under weightless conditions, such as in an orbiting spacecraft?**

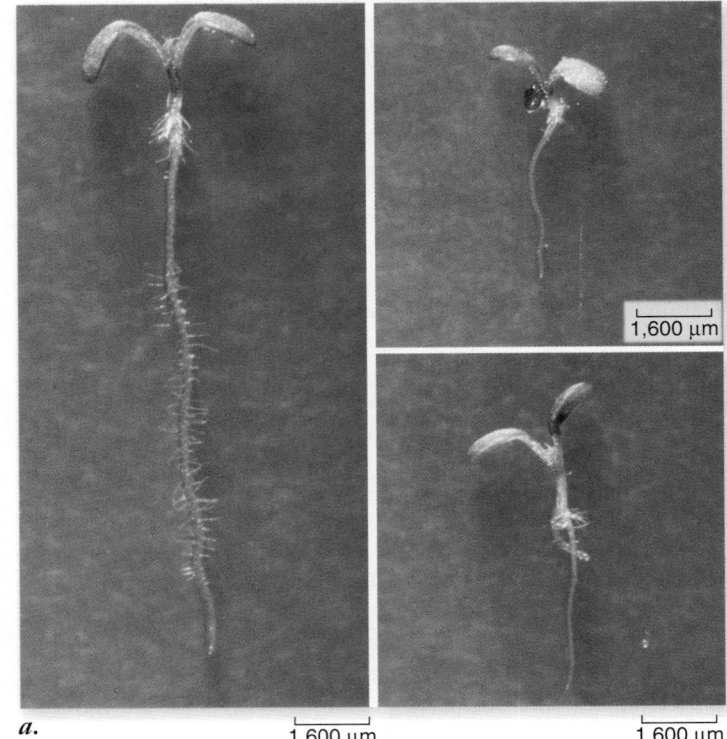

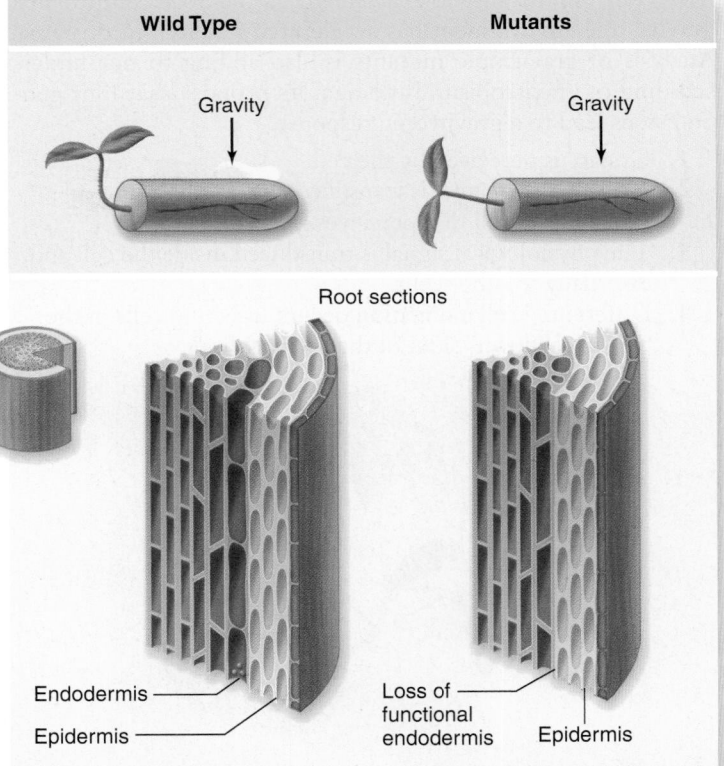

Figure 41.10 Amyloplasts in stem endoderm is needed for gravitropism. *a.* The *scr* and *shr* mutants of *Arabidopsis* have abnormal root development because they lack a fully differentiated endodermal layer. *b.* The endodermal defect extends into the stem, eliminating the positive gravitropic response of wild-type stems.

Plants respond to touch and other mechanical stimuli in different ways, depending on the species and the type of stimulus. In some cases, plants permanently change form in response to mechanical stresses, a process termed **thigmomorphogenesis.** This change can be seen in trees growing where an almost constant wind blows from one direction. Other responses are reversible and occur in the short term, as when mimosa leaves droop in response to touch. These responses are not tropisms, but rather turgor movements that come about due to changes in the internal water pressure of cells.

Touch can trigger irreversible growth responses

A **thigmotropism** is directional growth of a plant or plant part in response to contact with an object, animal, other plant, or even the wind. Thigmonastic responses are very similar to thigmotropisms, except that the direction of the growth response is the same regardless of the direction of the stimulus.

Tall, slender plants are more likely to snap during a wind or rain storm than are plants with short, wide internodes. Environmental signals such as regularly occurring winds or the rubbing of one plant against another are sufficient to induce morphogenetic change leading to thicker, shorter internodes. In some cases, even repeated touching of a plant with a finger is enough to cause a change in plant growth.

Tendrils are modified stems that some species use to anchor themselves in the environment (figure 41.11). When a tendril makes contact with an object, specialized epidermal cells perceive the contact and promote uneven growth, causing the tendril to curl around the object, sometimes within only 3 to 10 min. Two hormones, auxin and ethylene, appear to be involved in tendril movements, and they can induce coiling even in the absence of any contact stimulus. Curiously, the tendrils of some species coil toward the site of the stimulus (thigmotropic growth), while those of other species may always coil clockwise, regardless of the side of the tendril that makes contact with an object. In some other plants, such as clematis, bindweed, and dodder, leaf petioles or unmodified stems twine around other stems or solid objects.

Perhaps the most dramatic touch response is the snapping of a Venus flytrap. As discussed in chapter 39, the modified leaves of the flytrap close in response to a touch stimulus, trapping insects or other potential sources of protein. A flytrap can shut in a mere 0.5 sec. The enlarged epidermal or mesophyll cells of the flytrap cause the trap to close. The speed

Figure 41.11 Thigmotropism. The thigmotropic response of these twining stems causes them to coil around the object with which they have come in contact.

of trap closure is enhanced by the shape of the leaf, which flips between a concave and convex form.

What is particularly amazing about this response is that the outer cells actually grow. The cell walls may soften in response to an electrical signal that moves through the leaf when the trigger hairs are touched, and the high pressure (turgor) of the water inside the cells pushes against the softened walls to enlarge the cell. This growth mechanism is distinct from other turgor movements (to be discussed shortly) because the water is already within the cell, not transferred into it in response to the electrical signal.

If digestible prey is caught, the trap will open about 24 hr later through the growth of inner cells of the flytrap. This growth response can only be triggered about four times before the leaf dies, presumably because so much energy is required for the individual flytrap to do this trick.

Arabidopsis is proving valuable as a model system to explore plant responses to touch. A gene has been identified that is expressed in 100-fold higher levels 10 to 30 min after touch. The gene codes for a calmodulin-like protein that binds Ca^{2+}, which is involved in a number of plant physiological processes. Given the value of a molecular genetics approach in dissecting the pathways leading from an environmental signal to a growth response, the touch gene provides a promising first step in understanding how plants respond to touch.

Reversible responses to touch and other stimuli involve turgor pressure

Unlike tropisms, some touch-induced plant movements are not based on growth responses, but instead result from reversible changes in the turgor pressure of specific cells. Turgor, as described in chapter 38, is pressure within a living cell resulting from diffusion of water into it. If water leaves turgid cells, the cells may collapse, causing plant movement; conversely, water

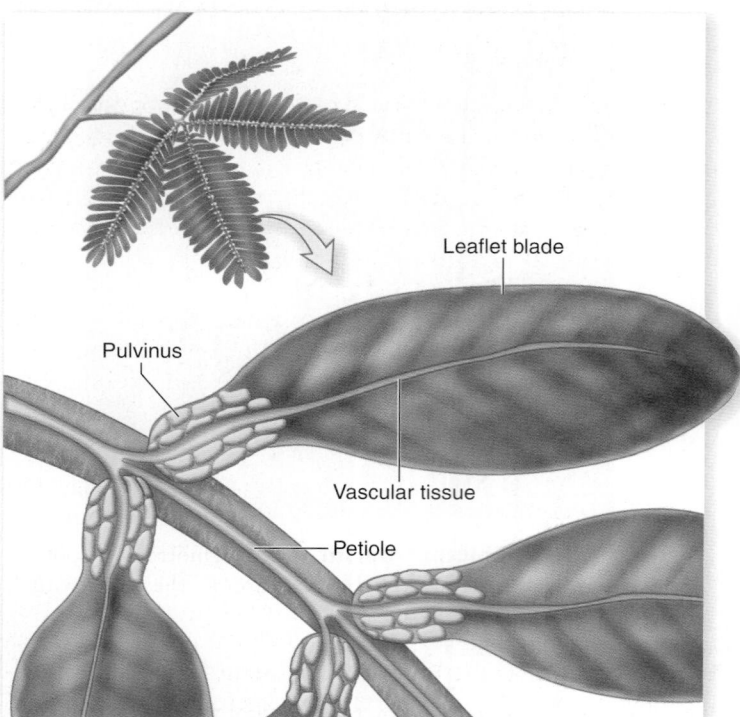

a.

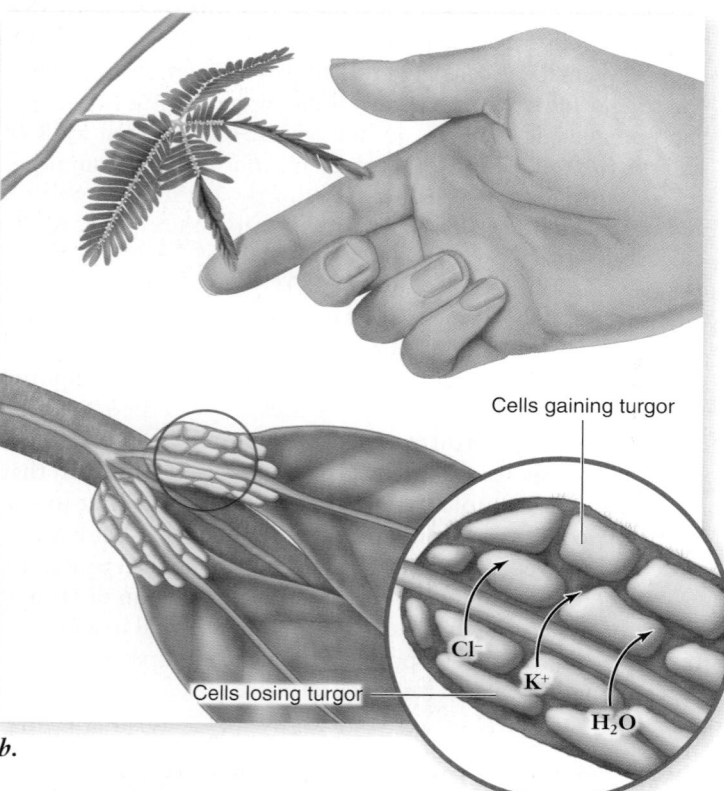

b.

Figure 41.12 Sensitive plant (*Mimosa pudica*).

a. The blades of *Mimosa* leaves are divided into numerous leaflets; at the base of each leaflet is a swollen structure called a pulvinus. *b.* Changes in turgor cause leaflets to fold in response to a stimulus. When leaves are touched (center two leaves), ions move to the outer side of the pulvinus, water follows by osmosis, and the decreased interior turgor pressure leads to folding.

Figure 41.13 Heliotropism. These sunflowers track the movement of the Sun every day.

entering a limp cell may also cause movement as the cell once more becomes turgid.

Many plants, including those of the legume family (Fabaceae), exhibit leaf movements in response to touch or other stimuli. After exposure to a stimulus, the changes in leaf orientation are mostly associated with rapid turgor pressure changes in pulvini (singular, *pulvinus*), two-sided multicellular swellings located at the base of each leaf or leaflet. When leaves with pulvini, such as those of the sensitive plant (*Mimosa pudica*), are stimulated by wind, heat, touch, or in some instances, intense light, an electrical signal is generated. The electrical signal is translated into a chemical signal, with potassium ions being pumped from the cells in one-half of a pulvinus to the intercellular spaces in the other half, leading to the rapid osmosis of water to one side of the pulvinus.

The loss of turgor in half of the pulvinus causes the leaf to "fold." The movements of the leaves and leaflets of a sensitive plant are especially rapid; the folding occurs within a second or two after the leaves are touched (figure 41.12). Over a span of about 15 to 30 min after the leaves and leaflets have folded, water usually diffuses back into the same cells from which it left, and the leaf returns to its original position.

Some turgor movements are triggered by light. For example, the leaves of some plants may track the Sun, with their blades oriented at right angles to it; how their orientation is directed, however, is poorly understood. Such leaves can move quite rapidly (as much as 15 degrees an hour). This movement maximizes photosynthesis and is analogous to solar panels designed to track the Sun (figure 41.13).

Some of the most familiar reversible changes due to turgor pressure are the circadian rhythms seen in leaves and flowers that open during the day and close at night, or vice versa. For example, the flowers of four o'clocks open in the afternoon, and evening primrose petals open at night. As described earlier, sensitive plant leaves also close at night. Bean leaves are horizontal during the day when their pulvini are turgid, but become more or less vertical at night as the pulvini lose turgor (figure 41.14). These sleep movements reduce water loss from transpiration during the night, but maximize photosynthetic surface area during the day.

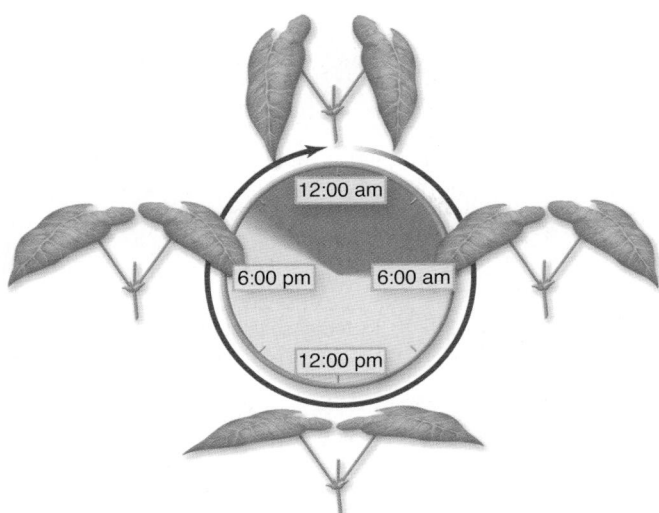

Figure 41.14 Sleep movements in bean leaves. In the bean plant, leaf blades are oriented horizontally during the day and vertically at night.

Learning Outcomes Review 41.3

Thigmomorphogenesis is a change in growth form in response to a mechanical stress (physical contact or wind). Thigmotropism is directional growth, whereas a thigmonastic response has no directionality. A tropism is an irreversible growth response; a touch-induced plant movement, such as exhibited by *Mimosa pudica,* is reversible and is based on changes in turgor pressure.

■ **What would be some advantages of having leaves that fold when stimulated?**

41.4 Responses to Water and Temperature

Learning Outcomes

1. *List the environmental factors that can lead to dormancy.*
2. *Explain why seed dormancy is an important evolutionary innovation.*
3. *Identify the types of biological molecules that are most directly affected by low and high temperatures.*

Sometimes, modifying the direction of growth is not enough to protect a plant from harsh conditions. The ability to cease growth and go into a dormant stage when conditions become unfavorable, such as during seasonal changes in temperate climates, provides a survival advantage. The extreme example is seed dormancy, but there are intermediate approaches to waiting out the bad times as well.

Plants also have developed adaptations to more short-term fluctuations in temperature, such as might occur during a heat wave or cold snap. These strategies include changes in membrane composition and the production of heat shock proteins.

Dormancy is a response to water, temperature, and light

In temperate regions, we generally associate dormancy with winter, when freezing temperatures and the accompanying unavailability of water make it impossible for most plants to grow. During this season, buds of deciduous trees and shrubs remain dormant, and apical meristems remain well protected inside enfolding scales. Perennial herbs spend the winter underground, existing as stout stems or roots packed with stored food. Many other kinds of plants, including most annuals, pass the winter as seeds. Often dormancy begins with the dropping of leaves, which you have probably seen occur in deciduous trees in the autumn.

Organ abscission

Deciduous leaves are often shed as the plant enters dormancy. The process by which leaves or petals are shed is called **abscission.**

Abscission can be useful even before dormancy is established. For example, shaded leaves that are no longer photosynthetically productive can be shed. Petals, which are modified leaves, may senesce once pollination occurs. Orchid flowers remain fresh for long periods of time, even in a florist shop; however, once pollination occurs, a hormonal change is triggered that leads to petal senescence. This strategy makes sense in terms of allocation of energy resources because the petals are no longer necessary to attract a pollinator. One advantage of organ abscission, therefore, is that nutrient sinks can be discarded, conserving resources.

On a larger scale, deciduous plants in temperate areas produce new leaves in the spring and then lose them in the fall. In the tropics, however, the production and subsequent loss of leaves in some species is correlated with wet and dry seasons. Evergreen plants, such as most conifers, usually have a complete change of leaves every two to seven years, periodically losing some but not all of their leaves.

Abscission involves changes that take place in an *abscission zone* at the base of the petiole (figure 41.15). Young leaves produce

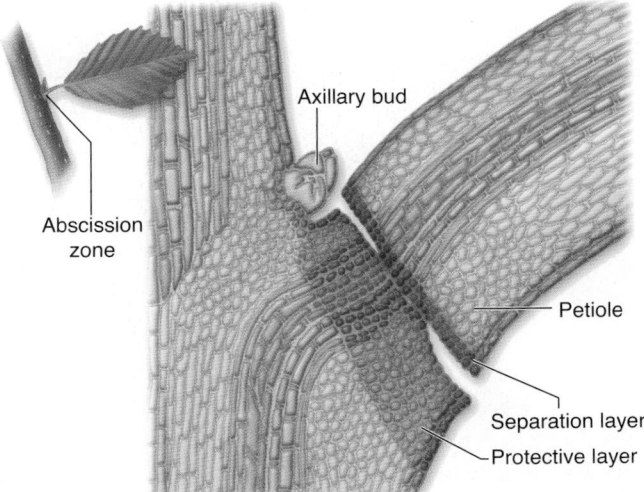

Figure 41.15 Leaf abscission. Hormonal changes in the leaf's abscission zone cause abscission. Two layers of cells in the abscission zone differentiate into a protective layer and a separation layer. As pectins in the separation layer break down, wind and rain can easily separate the leaf from the stem.

hormones (especially cytokinins) that inhibit the development of specialized layers of cells in this zone. Hormonal changes take place as the leaf ages, however, and two layers of cells become differentiated. A *protective layer*, which may be several cells wide, develops on the stem side of the petiole base. These cells become impregnated with suberin, which you may recall is a fatty substance impervious to moisture. A *separation layer* develops on the leaf-blade side; the cells of the separation layer sometimes divide, swell, and become gelatinous.

When temperatures drop, when the duration and intensity of light diminishes, or when other environmental changes occur, enzymes break down the pectins in the middle lamellae of the separation cells. Wind and rain can then easily separate the leaf from the stem. Left behind is a sealed leaf scar that is protected from invasion by bacteria and other disease organisms.

As the abscission zone develops, the green chlorophyll pigments present in the leaf break down, revealing the yellows and oranges of other pigments, such as carotenoids, that previously had been masked by the intense green colors. At the same time, water-soluble red or blue pigments called *anthocyanins* and *betacyanins* may also accumulate in the vacuoles of the leaf cells—all contributing to an array of fall colors in leaves (figure 41.16).

Seed dormancy

The extraordinary evolutionary innovation of the seed plants is the dormant seed that allows plant offspring to wait until conditions for germination are optimal. Sometimes the seeds can endure a wait of hundreds of years (figure 41.17). In seasonally dry climates, seed dormancy occurs primarily during the dry season, often the summer. Rainfalls trigger germination when conditions for survival are more favorable.

Annual plants occur frequently in areas of seasonal drought. Seeds are ideal for allowing annual plants to bypass the dry season, when there is insufficient water for growth.

Figure 41.16 **Leaf color changes during abscission.**

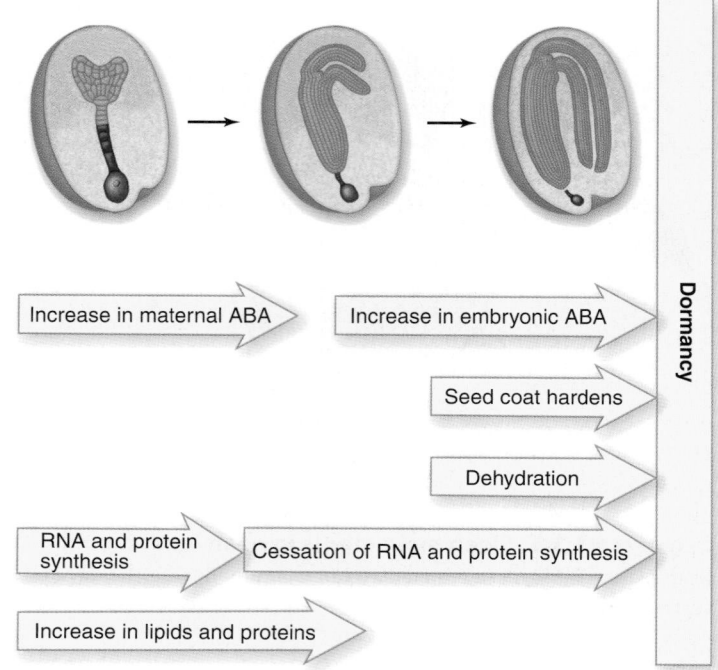

Figure 41.17 **Seed dormancy.** Accumulating food reserves, forming a protective seed coat, and dehydration are essential steps leading to dormancy. Abscisic acid (ABA) from both maternal and embryonic tissue is necessary for dormancy.

When it rains, these seeds can germinate, and the plants can grow rapidly, having adapted to the relatively short periods when water is available.

Chapter 37 covered some of the mechanisms involved in breaking seed dormancy and allowing germination under favorable circumstances. These include water leaching away the chemicals that inhibit germination or mechanically cracking the seed coats due to osmotic swelling, a procedure particularly suitable for promoting growth in seasonally dry areas.

Seeds may remain dormant for a surprisingly long time. Many legumes have tough seeds that are virtually impermeable to water and oxygen. These seeds often last decades and even longer without special care; they will eventually germinate when their seed coats have been cracked and water is available. Seeds that are thousands of years old have been successfully germinated!

Favorable temperatures, day length, and amounts of water can release buds, underground stems and roots, and seeds from a dormant state. Requirements vary among species. For example, some weed seeds germinate in cooler parts of the year and are inhibited from germinating by warmer temperatures. Day length differences can have dramatic effects on dormancy. For example, tree dormancy is common in temperate climates when the days are short, but is unusual in tropical trees growing near the equator, where day length remains about the same regardless of season.

Plants can survive temperature extremes

Sometimes temperatures change rapidly, and dormancy is not possible. How do plants survive temperature extremes? A number of adaptations, including some rapid response strategies, help plants overcome sudden chilling or extreme heat.

Chilling

Knowing the lipid composition of a plant's membranes can help predict whether the plant will be sensitive or resistant to chilling. Saturated lipids solidify at a higher temperature because they pack together more closely (see chapter 5), so the more unsaturated the membrane lipids are, the more resistant the plant is to chilling. *Arabidopsis* plants genetically modified to contain a higher percentage of saturated fatty acids have proved to be more sensitive to chilling.

When chilling occurs, the enzyme desaturase converts the single bonds in the saturated lipids to double bonds. This process lowers the temperature at which the membrane becomes rigid and cannot function properly.

Even highly unsaturated membranes are not enough to protect plants from freezing temperatures. At freezing, ice crystals form and the cells die from dehydration—not enough liquid water is available for metabolism. Some plants, however, have the ability to undergo deep supercooling and survive temperatures as low as –40°C. Supercooling occurs when ice crystal formation is limited, and the crystals occur in extracellular spaces where they cannot damage cell organelles. Furthermore, the cells of these plants must be able to withstand gradual dehydration.

Acquiring tolerance to chilling or freezing as the temperature drops can be explained by increased solute concentration. In addition, antifreeze proteins prevent ice crystals from forming. Ice crystals can also form (nucleate) around bacteria naturally found on the leaf surface. Some bacteria have been genetically engineered so that they do not nucleate ice crystals. Spraying leaves with these modified bacteria can provide frost tolerance in some crops.

High temperatures

High temperatures can be harmful because proteins denature and lose their function when heated. If temperatures suddenly rise 5° to 10°C, heat shock proteins (HSPs) are produced. These proteins can stabilize other proteins so that they don't unfold or misfold at higher temperatures. In some cases, HSPs induced by temperature increases can also protect plants from other stresses, including chilling.

Plants can survive otherwise lethal temperatures if they are gradually exposed to increasing temperature. These plants have *acquired thermotolerance*. More is being learned about temperature acclimation by isolating mutants that fail to acquire thermotolerance, including the aptly named *hot* mutants in *Arabidopsis*. One of the *HOT* genes codes for an HSP. Characterization of other *HOT* genes indicates that thermotolerance requires more than the synthesis of HSPs; some *HOT* genes stabilize membranes and are necessary for protein activity.

Learning Outcomes Review 41.4

Seasonal changes, such as reduction in temperature, light, and water availability, may lead to plant dormancy; in deciduous trees, leaf abscission is part of entering dormancy. Seed dormancy prevents germination until growth conditions are optimal. At low temperatures, lipids in membranes begin to solidify and ice crystals may form in tissues; at high temperatures, proteins denature.

■ **Why is it advantageous for broadleaf trees to drop leaves in autumn, when they must grow them again in spring?**

Learning Outcomes

1. *Discuss properties of hormones.*
2. *Compare auxins with cytokinins.*
3. *Describe the major roles of abscisic acid.*

Sensory responses that alter morphology rely on complex physiological networks. Many internal signaling pathways involve plant hormones, which are the focus of this section. Hormones are involved in responses to the environment, as well as in internally regulated development (see chapter 37).

The hormones that guide growth are keyed to the environment

Hormones are chemical substances produced in small, often minute quantities in one part of an organism and then transported to another part where they bring about physiological or developmental responses. How hormones act in a particular instance is influenced both by the hormone and the tissue that receives the message.

In animals, hormones are usually produced at definite sites, most commonly in organs such as glands. In plants, hormones are not produced in specialized tissues but, instead, in tissues that also carry out other, usually more obvious functions. Seven major kinds of plant hormones have been identified: auxin, cytokinins, gibberellins, brassinosteroids, oligosaccharins, ethylene, and abscisic acid (table 41.1). Current research is focused on the biosynthesis of hormones and on characterizing the hormone receptors involved in signal transduction pathways. Much of the molecular basis of hormone function remains enigmatic.

Because hormones are involved in so many aspects of plant function and development, we have chosen to integrate examples of hormone activity with specific aspects of plant biology throughout the text. In this section, our goal is to give a brief overview of these hormones.

Auxin allows elongation and organizes the body plan

More than a century ago, an organic substance known as **auxin** was the first plant hormone to be discovered. Auxin increases the plasticity of plant cell walls and is involved in elongation of stems. Cells can enlarge in response to changes in turgor pressure, but cell walls must be fairly plastic for this expansion to occur. Auxin plays a role in softening cell walls. The discovery of auxin and its role in plant growth is an elegant example of thoughtful experimental design and is recounted here for that reason.

Discovery of auxin

Later in life, the great evolutionist Charles Darwin became increasingly devoted to the study of plants. In 1881, he and his

TABLE 41.1 Functions of the Major Plant Hormones

Hormone		Major Functions	Where Produced or Found in Plant
Auxins		Promotion of stem elongation and growth; formation of adventitious roots; inhibition of leaf abscission; promotion of cell division (with cytokinins); inducement of ethylene production; promotion of lateral bud dormancy	Apical meristems; other immature parts of plants
Cytokinins		Stimulation of cell division, but only in the presence of auxin; promotion of chloroplast development; delay of leaf aging; promotion of bud formation	Root apical meristems; immature fruits
Gibberellins		Promotion of stem elongation; stimulation of enzyme production in germinating seeds	Roots and shoot tips; young leaves; seeds
Brassinosteroids		Overlapping functions with auxins and gibberellins	Pollen, immature seeds, shoots, leaves
Oligosaccharins		Pathogen defense, possibly reproductive development	Cell walls
Ethylene		Control of leaf, flower, and fruit abscission; promotion of fruit ripening	Roots, shoot apical meristems; leaf nodes; aging flowers; ripening fruits
Abscisic acid		Inhibition of bud growth; control of stomatal closure; some control of seed dormancy; inhibition of effects of other hormones	Leaves, fruits, root caps, seeds

son Francis published a book called *The Power of Movement of Plants*. In this book, the Darwins reported their systematic experiments on the response of growing plants to light—the responses that came to be known as phototropisms. They used germinating oat and canary grass seedlings in their experiments and made many observations in this field.

Charles and Francis Darwin knew that if light came primarily from one direction, seedlings would bend strongly toward it. If they covered the tip of a shoot with a thin glass tube, the shoot would bend as if it were not covered. However, if they used a metal foil cap to exclude light from the plant tip, the shoot would not bend (figure 41.18). They also found that using an opaque collar to exclude light from the stem below the tip did not keep the area above the collar from bending.

In explaining these unexpected findings, the Darwins hypothesized that when the shoots were illuminated from one side, they bent toward the light in response to an "influence" that was transmitted downward from its source at the tip of the shoot.

For some 30 years, the Darwins' perceptive experiments remained the sole source of information about this interesting phenomenon. Then the Danish plant physiologist Peter Boysen-Jensen and the Hungarian plant physiologist Arpad Paal independently demonstrated that the substance causing the shoots to bend was a chemical. They showed that if the tip of a germinating grass seedling was cut off and then replaced, with a small block of agar separating it from the rest of the seedling, the seedling would still grow as if there had been no change. Something evidently was passing from the tip of the seedling through the agar into the region where the bending occurred.

On the basis of these observations under conditions of either uniform illumination or darkness, Paal suggested that an unknown substance continually moves down from the tips of grass seedlings and promotes growth on all sides. Such a light pattern would not, of course, cause the shoot to bend.

Inquiry question

? Propose a mechanism to explain how seedlings could bend in the light using what Paal discovered.

Then, in 1926, the Dutch plant physiologist Frits Went carried Paal's experiments a step further. Went cut off the tips of oat seedlings that had been illuminated normally and set these tips on agar. He then took oat seedlings that had been grown in the dark and cut off their tips in a similar way. Finally, Went cut tiny blocks from the agar on which the tips of the light-grown seedlings had been placed and placed them off-center on the tops of the decapitated dark-grown seedlings (figure 41.19). Even though these seedlings had not been exposed to the light themselves, they bent away from the side on which the agar blocks were placed.

As an experimental control, Went put blocks of pure agar on the decapitated stem tips and noted either no effect or a slight bending toward the side where the agar blocks were placed. Finally, Went cut sections out of the lower portions of the light-grown seedlings. He placed these sections on the tips of decapitated, dark-green oat seedlings and again observed no effect.

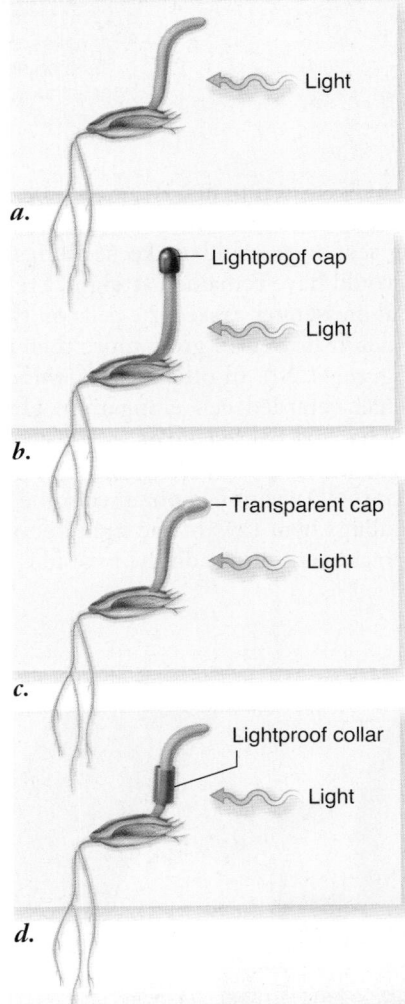

Hypothesis: *The shoot tip of a plant detects the direction of light.*

Prediction: *The shoot tip of a grass seedling will grow toward a unidirectional light source if it is not covered.*

Test: *Make four treatment groups, including (1) untreated seedling, (2) tip covered with lightproof cap, (3) tip covered with transparent cap, and (4) lightproof collar placed below tip.*

a.

Light

b.

Lightproof cap

Light

c.

Transparent cap

Light

d.

Lightproof collar

Light

Result: *a. Young grass seedlings normally bend toward the light. b. The bending did not occur when the tip of a seedling was covered with a lightproof cap. c. Bending did occur when it was covered with a transparent one. d. When a collar was placed below the tip, the characteristic light response took place.*

Conclusion: *In response to light, an "influence" that caused bending was transmitted from the tip of the seedling to the area below, where bending normally occurs.*

Further Experiments: *How could you determine if the light response in a shoot tip requires the movement of a signal from one side of the shoot to the other? (Hint: See Went's experiment in figure 41.19).*

Figure 41.18 Shoot tips perceive unidirectional light.

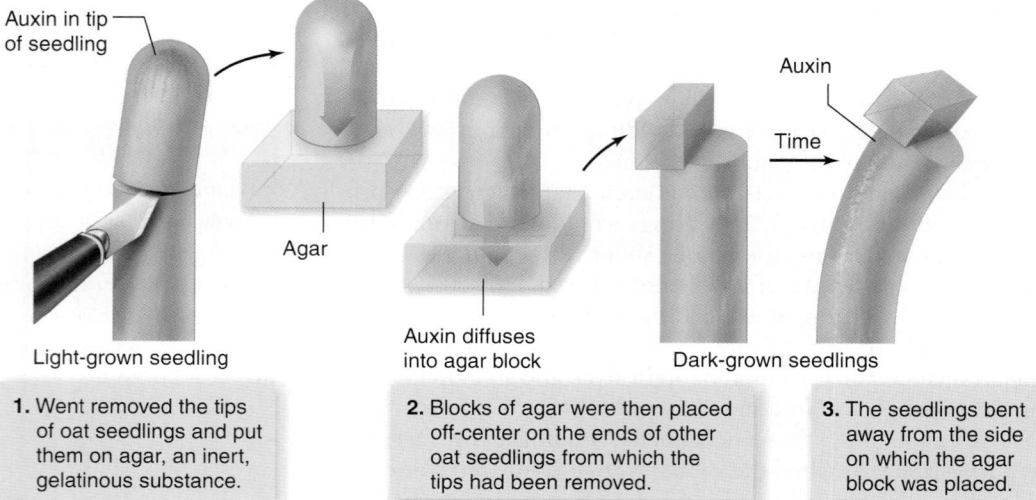

Figure 41.19 Frits Went's experiment. Went concluded that a substance he named *auxin* promoted the elongation of the cells and that it accumulated on the side of an oat seedling away from the light.

Auxin in tip of seedling

Light-grown seedling

Agar

Auxin diffuses into agar block

Auxin

Time

Dark-grown seedlings

1. Went removed the tips of oat seedlings and put them on agar, an inert, gelatinous substance.

2. Blocks of agar were then placed off-center on the ends of other oat seedlings from which the tips had been removed.

3. The seedlings bent away from the side on which the agar block was placed.

As a result of his experiments, Went was able to show that the substance that had diffused into the agar from the tips of light-grown oat seedlings could make seedlings bend when they otherwise would have remained straight. He also showed that this chemical messenger caused the cells on the side of the seedling into which it flowed to grow more than those on the opposite side (figure 41.20). In other words, the chemical enhanced rather than retarded cell elongation. He named the substance that he had discovered *auxin*.

Went's experiments provided a basis for understanding the responses that the Darwins had obtained some 45 years earlier. The oat seedlings bent toward the light because of differences in the auxin concentrations on the two sides of the shoot.

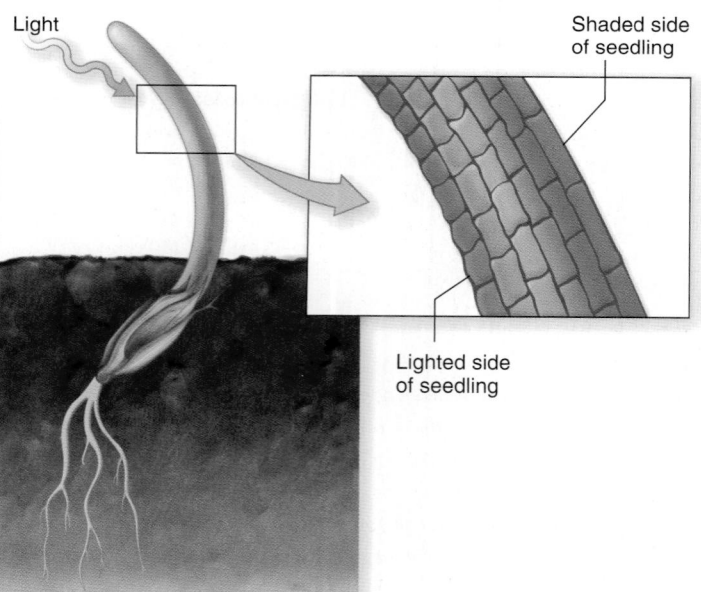

Light

Shaded side of seedling

Lighted side of seedling

Figure 41.20 Auxin causes cells on the dark side to elongate. Plant cells that are in the shade have more auxin and grow faster than cells on the lighted side, causing the plant to bend toward light. Further experiments showed exactly why there is more auxin on the shaded side of a plant.

The side of the shoot that was in the shade had more auxin, and its cells therefore elongated more than those on the lighted side, bending the plant toward the light.

The effects of auxin

Auxin acts to adapt the plant to its environment in a highly advantageous way by promoting growth and elongation. Environmental signals directly influence the distribution of auxin in the plant. How does the environment—specifically, light—exert this influence? Theoretically, light might destroy the auxin, might decrease the cells' sensitivity to auxin, or might cause the auxin molecules to migrate away from the light into the shaded portion of the shoot. This last possibility has proved to be the case.

In a simple but effective experiment, Winslow Briggs inserted a thin sheet of transparent mica vertically between the half of the shoot oriented toward the light and the half of the shoot oriented away from it (figure 41.21). He found that light from one side does not cause a shoot with such a barrier to bend. When Briggs examined the illuminated plant, he found equal auxin levels on both the light and dark sides of the barrier. He concluded that a normal plant's response to light from one direction involves auxin migrating from the light side to the dark side, and that the mica barrier prevented a response by blocking the migration of auxin.

The effects of auxin are numerous and varied. Auxin promotes the activity of the vascular cambium and the vascular tissues. Also, auxin is present in pollen in large quantities and plays a key role in the development of fruits. Synthetic auxins are used commercially for the same purpose. Fruits will normally not develop if fertilization has not occurred and seeds are not present, but frequently they will develop if auxin is applied. Pollination may trigger auxin release in some species, leading to fruit development even before fertilization has taken place.

How auxin works

In spite of this long history of research, auxin's molecular basis of action has been an enigma. The chemical structure of the most common auxin, **indoleacetic acid (IAA),** resembles that of the amino acid tryptophan, from which it is probably

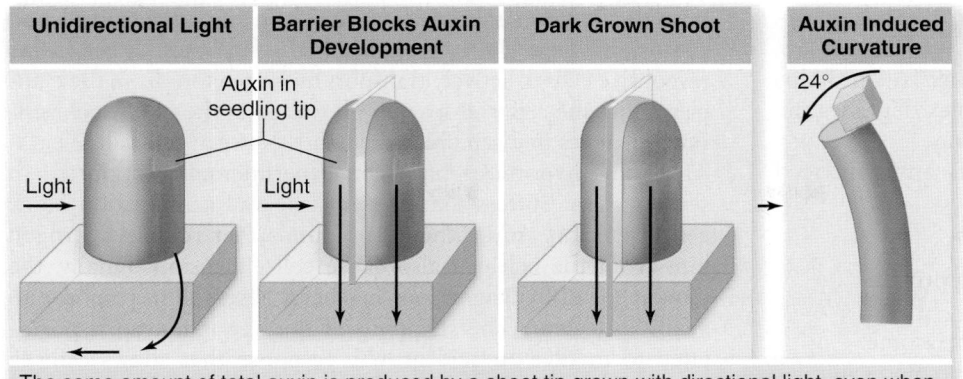

Figure 41.21 Phototropism and auxin: The Winslow Briggs experiments. Directional light causes the accumulation of auxin in the dark side of the shoot tip, which can move down the stem. Barriers inserted in the tip revealed that light affects auxin displacement rather than rate of auxin production.

The same amount of total auxin is produced by a shoot tip grown with directional light, even when a barrier divides the shoot tip, and a shoot tip grown in the dark. All three blocks of agar cause the same amount of curvature in a tipless shoot.

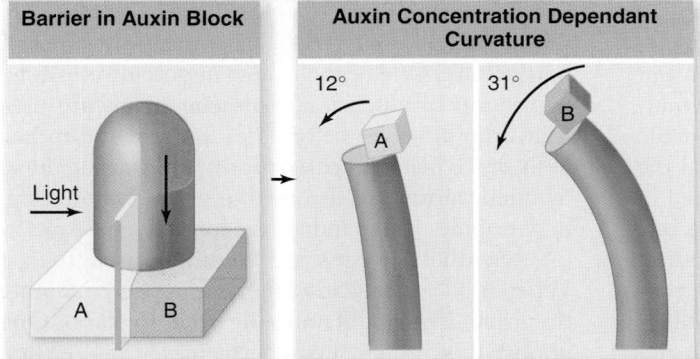

Separating the base of the shoot tip and the agar block results in two agar blocks with different concentrations of auxin that produce different degrees of curvature in tipless shoots.

synthesized by plants (figure 41.22). Although other forms of auxin exist, IAA is the most common natural auxin.

An auxin-binding protein (ABP1) was identified two decades ago. ABP1 is found in the cytoplasm and its role in auxin response is still unclear. Mutants that lack ABP1 do not make it past embryogenesis because cell elongation is inhibited and the basic body plan described in chapter 36 is not organized. But, the *abp1* mutant cells divide, which indicates that part of the auxin pathway is still functioning.

More recently, two families of proteins that mediate rapid, auxin-induced changes in gene expression have been identified: the auxin response factors (ARFs) and the Aux/IAA proteins. Transcription can be either enhanced or suppressed by ARFs, which are known to bind DNA. The Aux/IAA pro-

teins function a bit earlier in the auxin response pathway and have been shown to bind to and repress proteins that activate the expression of *ARF* genes.

ARF genes are activated when Aux/IAA proteins are degraded by ubiquitin tagging and protein degradation in the proteasome. Auxin binding to ARF protein is not sufficient to initiate gene expression in response to auxin signaling because of Aux/IAA repression of ARF activity. How then does a plant sense auxin and degrade Aux/IAA proteins?

The identification of the elusive auxin receptor in 2005 hints at how plants sense and respond to auxin. Auxin binds directly to a protein called the transport inhibitor response protein 1 (TIR1). TIR1 is the enigmatic auxin receptor. It is part of a protein complex known as SCF which is found

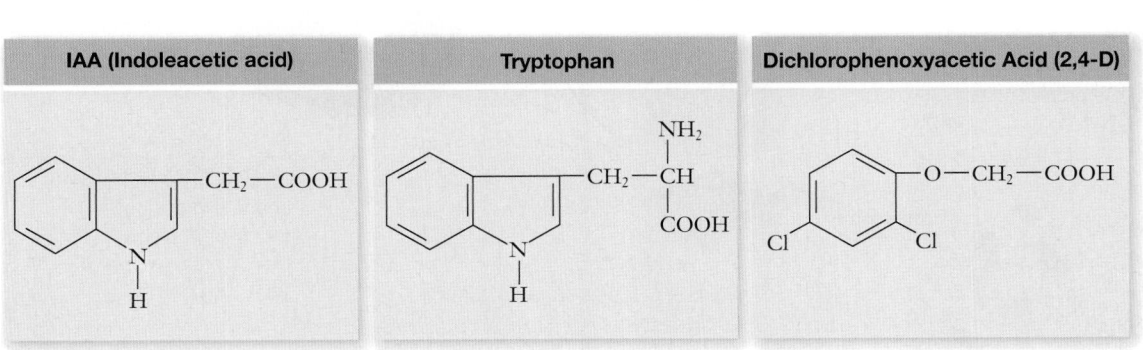

Figure 41.22 Auxins.
a. Indoleacetic acid (IAA), the principal naturally occurring auxin.
b. Tryptophan, the amino acid from which plants probably synthesize IAA.
c. Dichlorophenoxyacetic acid (2,4-D), a synthetic auxin, is a widely used herbicide.

throughout eukaryotes. SCF is shorthand for the three polypeptide subunits found in the complex: *Skp, Cullin,* and *F-box.* Auxin binds to TIR1 in the SCF complex if Aux/IAA proteins are present. Once auxin binds, the SCF complex degrades the Aux/IAA proteins through the ubiquitin pathway.

Five steps lead from auxin perception to auxin-induced gene expression (figure 41.23):

1. Auxin binds TIR1 in the SCF complex.
2. The activated SCF complex tags Aux/IAA proteins with ubiquitin.
3. Aux/IAA proteins are degraded in the proteasome.
4. Aux/IAA proteins are no longer available to bind and repress ARF (auxin response factor) transcriptional activators.
5. ARF transcription factors facilitate transcription of auxin-response genes.

Unlike with animal hormones, a specific signal is not sent to specific cells, eliciting a predictable response. Most likely, multiple auxin perception sites are present. Auxin is also unique among the plant hormones in that it is transported toward the base of the plant. Two families of genes have been identified in *Arabidopsis* that are involved in auxin transport. For example, one family of proteins (the PINs) are involved in the top-to-bottom transport of auxin, while two other proteins function in the root tip to regulate the growth response to gravity, described earlier.

One of the direct effects of auxin is an increase in the plasticity of the plant cell wall, but this effect works only on young cell walls lacking extensive secondary cell wall formation and may or may not involve rapid changes in gene expression. The **acid growth hypothesis** provides a model linking auxin to cell wall expansion (figure 41.24). According to this hypothesis, auxin causes responsive cells to actively transport hydrogen ions from the cytoplasm into the cell wall space. This decreases the pH, which activates enzymes that can break the bonds between cell wall fibers.

This hypothesis has been experimentally supported in several ways. Buffers that prevent cell wall acidification block cell expansion. And, other compounds that release hydrogen ions from the cell can also cause cell expansion. Finally, the movement of hydrogen ions has been observed in response to auxin treatment. The snapping of the Venus flytrap is postulated to involve an acid growth response that allows cells to grow in just 0.5 sec and close the trap.

Synthetic auxins

Synthetic auxins, such as *naphthalene acetic acid (NAA)* and **indolebutyric acid (IBA),** have many uses in agriculture and horticulture. One of their most important uses is based on their prevention of abscission. Synthetic auxins are used to prevent fruit drop in apples before they are ripe and to hold berries on holly that is being prepared for shipping during the winter season. Synthetic auxins are also used to promote flowering and fruiting in pineapples and to induce the formation of roots in cuttings.

Synthetic auxins are routinely used to control weeds. When used as herbicides, they are applied in higher concentrations than IAA would normally occur in plants. One of the most important synthetic auxin herbicides is *2,4-dichlorophenoxyacetic acid,* usually known as **2,4-D** (see figure 41.22*c*). It kills weeds in grass lawns by selectively eliminating broad-leaved dicots. The stems of the dicot weeds cease all axial growth.

Figure 41.23 Auxin regulation of gene expression. Auxin activates a ubiquitination pathway that releases ARF transcription factors from repression by Aux/IAA proteins. The result is auxin-induced gene expression.

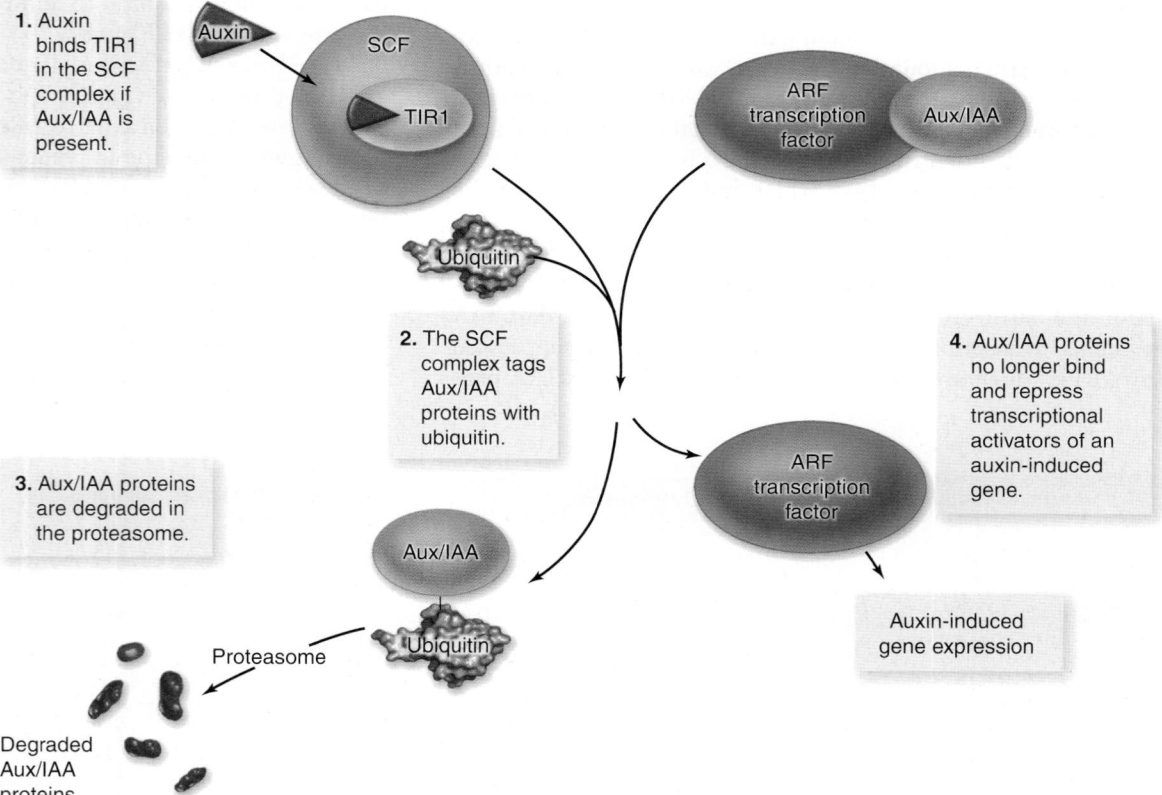

1. Auxin binds TIR1 in the SCF complex if Aux/IAA is present.

2. The SCF complex tags Aux/IAA proteins with ubiquitin.

3. Aux/IAA proteins are degraded in the proteasome.

4. Aux/IAA proteins no longer bind and repress transcriptional activators of an auxin-induced gene.

Auxin-induced gene expression

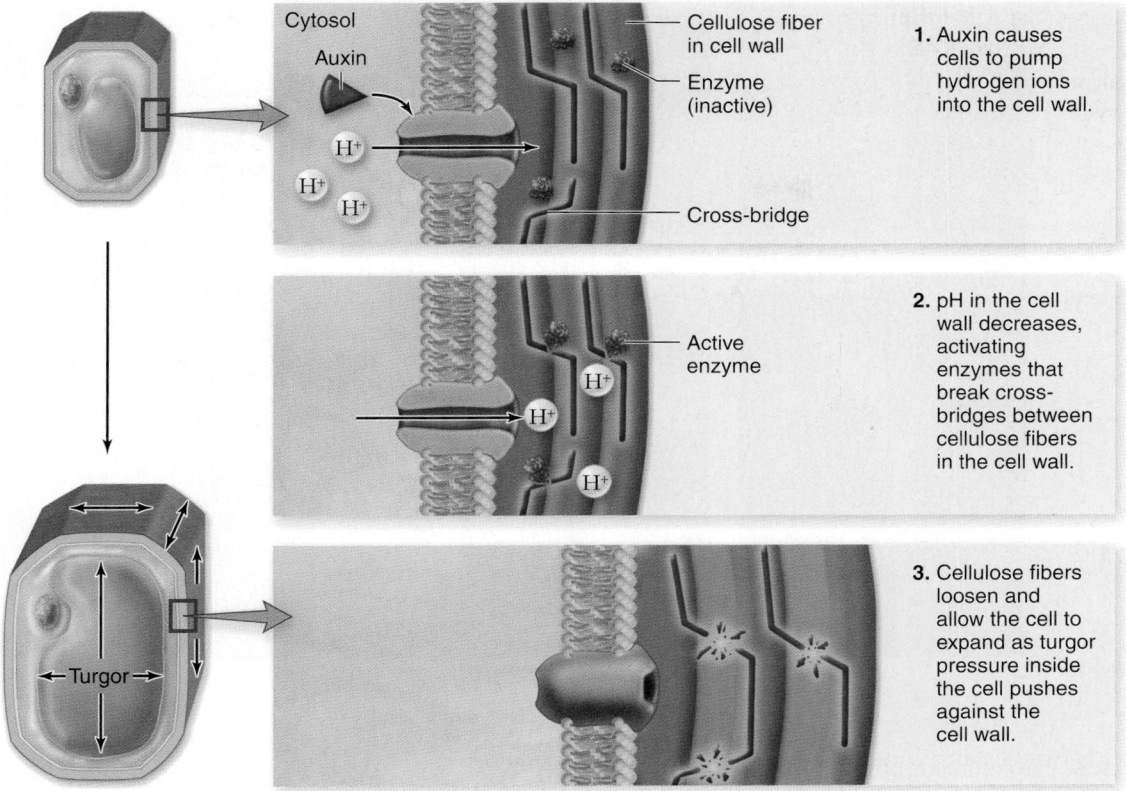

Figure 41.24 Acid growth hypothesis. Auxin stimulates the release of hydrogen ions from the target cells, which alters the pH of the cell wall. This optimizes the activity of enzymes that break bonds in the cell wall, allowing the wall to expand.

Cytosol
Auxin

Cellulose fiber in cell wall
Enzyme (inactive)

1. Auxin causes cells to pump hydrogen ions into the cell wall.

H+

Cross-bridge

Active enzyme

2. pH in the cell wall decreases, activating enzymes that break cross-bridges between cellulose fibers in the cell wall.

3. Cellulose fibers loosen and allow the cell to expand as turgor pressure inside the cell pushes against the cell wall.

Turgor

The herbicide 2,4,5-trichlorophenoxyacetic acid, better known as 2,4,5-T, is closely related to 2,4-D. 2,4,5-T was widely used as a broad-spectrum herbicide to kill weeds and the seedlings of woody plants. It became notorious during the Vietnam War as a component of a jungle defoliant known as Agent Orange. When 2,4,5-T is manufactured, it is unavoidably contaminated with minute amounts of dioxin. Dioxin, in doses as low as a few parts per billion, has produced liver and lung diseases, leukemia, miscarriages, birth defects, and even death in laboratory animals. This chemical was banned in 1979 for most uses in the United States.

Cytokinins stimulate cell division and differentiation

Cytokinins comprise another group of naturally occurring growth hormones in plants. Studies by Gottlieb Haberlandt of Austria around 1913 demonstrated the existence of an unknown chemical in various tissues of vascular plants that, when applied to cut potato tubers, would cause parenchyma cells to become meristematic, and would induce the differentiation of a cork cambium. In other research, coconut milk, subsequently found to contain cytokinins was used to promote the differentiation of organs in masses of plant tissue growing in culture. Subsequent studies have focused on the role cytokinins play in the differentiation of tissues from callus.

A *cytokinin* is a plant hormone that, in combination with auxin, stimulates cell division and differentiation. Most cytokinins are produced in the root apical meristems and transported throughout the plant. Developing fruits are also important sites of cytokinin synthesis. In mosses, cytokinins cause the formation of vegetative buds on the gametophyte. In all plants, cytokinins, working with other hormones, seem to regulate growth patterns.

Cytokinins are purines that appear to be derivatives of adenine (figure 41.25). Other chemically diverse molecules, not known to occur naturally, have effects similar to those of cytokinins. Cytokinins promote the growth of lateral buds into

Kinetin	6-Benzylamino Purine (BAP)	Adenine
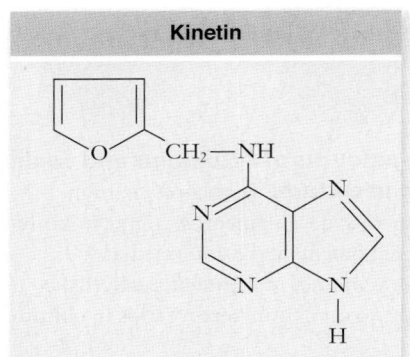	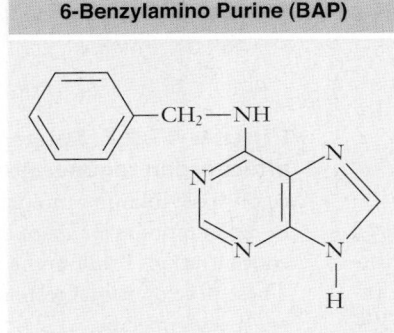	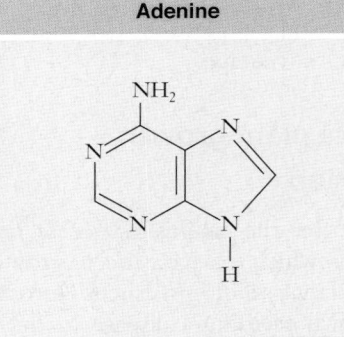

Figure 41.25 Some cytokinins. Two commonly used synthetic cytokinins: kinetin and 6-benzylamino purine. Note their resemblance to the purine base adenine.

Figure 41.26 Cytokinins stimulate lateral bud growth.
a. When the apical meristem of a plant is intact, auxin from the apical bud will inhibit the growth of lateral buds.
b. When the apical bud is removed, cytokinins are able to induce the growth of lateral buds into branches.
c. When the apical bud is removed and auxin is added to the cut surface, lateral bud outgrowth is suppressed.

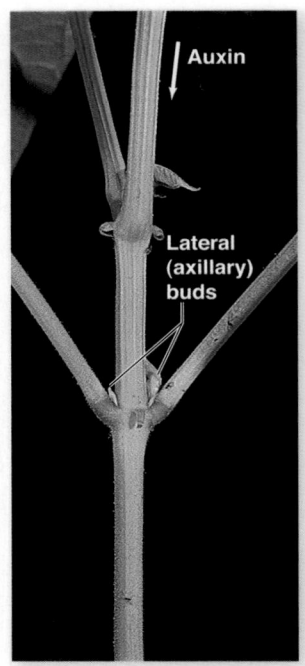

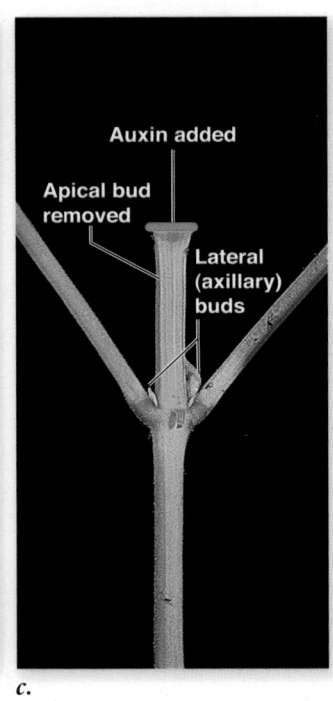

a.   *b.*   *c.*

branches (figure 41.26). Conversely, cytokinins inhibit the formation of lateral roots, while auxins promote their formation.

As a consequence of these relationships, the balance between cytokinins and auxin, along with many other factors, determines the form of a plant. In addition, the application of cytokinins to leaves detached from a plant retards their yellowing. Therefore, they function as antiaging hormones.

The action of cytokinins, like that of other hormones, has been studied in terms of its effects on the growth and differentiation of masses of tissue growing in defined media. Plant tissue can form shoots, roots, or an undifferentiated mass, depending on the relative amounts of auxin and cytokinin (figure 41.27).

In the early cell-growth experiments in culture, coconut milk was an essential factor. Eventually, researchers discovered that coconut milk is not only rich in amino acids and other reduced nitrogen compounds required for growth, but it also contains cytokinins. Cytokinins apparently promote the synthesis or activation of proteins specifically required for cytokinesis.

Cytokinins have also been used against plants by pathogens. The bacterium *Agrobacterium*, for example, introduces genes into the plant genome that increase the rate of cytokinin, as well as auxin, production. This causes massive cell division and the formation of a tumor called *crown gall* (figure 41.28). How these hormone–biosynthesis genes ended up in a bacterium is an intriguing evolutionary question. Coevolution does not always work to a plant's advantage.

Gibberellins enhance plant growth and nutrient utilization

Gibberellins are named after the fungus *Gibberella fujikuroi*, which causes rice plants, on which it is parasitic, to grow abnormally tall. The Japanese plant pathologist Eiichi Kurosawa investigated bakanae ("foolish seedling") disease in the 1920s.

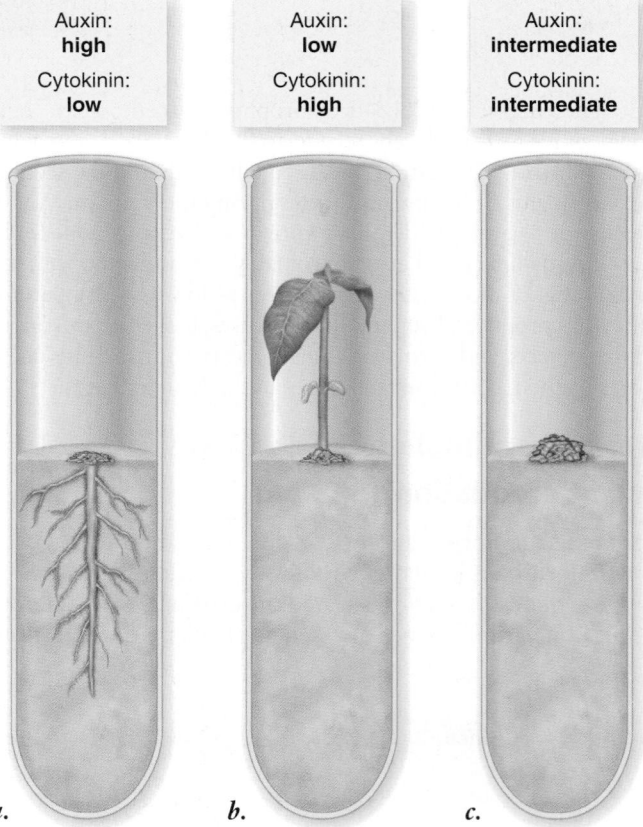

| Auxin: **high** Cytokinin: **low** | Auxin: **low** Cytokinin: **high** | Auxin: **intermediate** Cytokinin: **intermediate** |

a.   *b.*   *c.*

Figure 41.27 Relative amounts of cytokinins and auxin affect organ regeneration in culture. In tobacco, *a.* high auxin-to-cytokinin ratios favor root development; *b.* high cytokinin-to-auxin ratios favor shoot development; and *c.* intermediate concentrations result in the formation of undifferentiated cells. These developmental responses to cytokinin–auxin ratios in culture are species-specific.

Figure 41.28 Crown gall tumor. Sometimes cytokinins can be used against the plant by a pathogen. In this case, *Agrobacterium tumefaciens* (a bacterium) has incorporated a piece of its DNA into the plant genome. This DNA contains genes coding for enzymes necessary for cytokinin and auxin biosynthesis. The increased levels of these hormones in the plant cause massive cell division and the formation of a tumor.

He grew *Gibberella* in culture and obtained a substance that, when applied to rice plants, produced bakanae. This substance was isolated and its structural formula identified by Japanese chemists in 1939. British chemists reconfirmed the formula in 1954.

Although such chemicals were first thought to be only a curiosity, they have since turned out to belong to a large class of more than 100 naturally occurring plant hormones. All are acidic and are usually abbreviated GA (for gibberellic acid), with a different subscript (GA_1, GA_2, and so forth) to distinguish each one.

Gibberellins, which are synthesized in the apical portions of stems and roots, have important effects on stem elongation. The elongation effect is enhanced if auxin is also present. The application of gibberellins to certain dwarf mutants is known to restore normal growth and development in many plants (figure 41.29). Some dwarf mutants produce insufficient amounts of gibberellin and respond to GA applications; others lack the ability to respond to gibberellin.

The large number of gibberellins are all part of a complex biosynthetic pathway that has been unraveled using gibberellin-deficient mutants in maize (corn). Although many of these gibberellins are intermediate forms in the production of GA_1, recent work shows that some forms may have specific biological roles.

In chapter 37, we noted the role of gibberellins in stimulating the production of α-amylase and other hydrolytic enzymes needed for utilization of food resources during germination and establishment of cereal seedlings. How is transcription of the genes encoding these enzymes regulated?

Figure 41.29 Effects of gibberellins. This rapid-cycling member of the mustard family *(Brassica rapa)* will "bolt" and flower because of increased gibberellin levels. Mutants such as the rosette mutant (left) are defective in producing gibberellins. They can be rescued by applying gibberellins to the shoot tip (right). Other mutants have been identified that are defective in perceiving gibberellins, and they will not respond to gibberellin applications.

GA is used as a signal from the embryo that turns on transcription of one or more genes encoding hydrolytic enzymes in the aleurone layer. The GA receptor has been identified. When GA binds to its receptor, it frees GA-dependent transcription factors from a repressor. These transcription factors can now directly affect gene expression (figure 41.30). Synthesis of DNA does not seem to occur during the early stages of seed germination, but it becomes important when the radicle has grown through the seed coats.

Gibberellins also affect a number of other aspects of plant growth and development. In some cases, GAs hasten seed

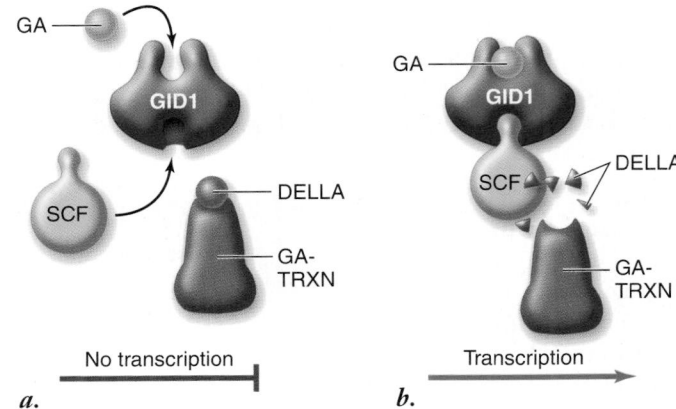

Figure 41.30 Gibberellins activate gibberellin-dependent transcription factors (GA-TRXN). *a.* GA-TRXN cannot bind to a promotor when they are bound to DELLA proteins. *b.* GA activates a protein complex that degrades DELLA proteins, freeing GA-TRXN to bind to a promoter, inducing gene transcription.

Figure 41.31 Applications of gibberellins increase the space between grapes. Larger grapes (right) develop because there is more room between individual grapes.

germination, apparently by substituting for the effects of cold or light requirements. Gibberellins are used commercially to increase space between grape flowers by extending internode length, so that the fruits have more room to grow. The result is a larger bunch of grapes containing larger individual fruits (figure 41.31).

Although gibberellins function endogenously as hormones, they also function as pheromones in ferns. In ferns, gibberellin-like compounds released from one gametophyte can trigger the development of male reproductive structures on a neighboring gametophyte.

Brassinosteroids are structurally similar to animal hormones

Although plant biologists have known about *brassinosteroids* for 30 years, it is only recently that they have claimed their place as a class of plant hormones. They were first discovered in *Brassica* spp. pollen, hence the name. Their historical absence in discussions of hormones may be partially due to their functional overlap with other plant hormones, especially auxins and gibberellins. Additive effects among these three classes have been reported.

The application of molecular genetics to the study of brassinosteroids has advanced our understanding of how they are made and, to some extent, how they function in signal transduction pathways. What is particularly intriguing about brassinosteroids is their similarity to animal steroid hormones (figure 41.32). One of the genes coding for an enzyme in the brassinosteroid biosynthetic pathway has significant similarity to an enzyme used in the synthesis of testosterone and related steroids. Brassinosteroids have also been identified in algae, and they appear to be ubiquitous among the plants. It is plausible that their evolutionary origin predated the plant–animal split.

Brassinosteroids have a broad spectrum of physiological effects—elongation, cell division, bending of stems, vascular tissue development, delayed senescence, membrane polarization, and reproductive development. Environmental signals can trigger brassinosteroid actions. Mutants have been identified that alter the response to a brassinosteroid, but signal transduction pathways remain to be uncovered. From an evolutionary perspective, it will be quite interesting to see how these pathways compare with animal steroid signal transduction pathways.

Oligosaccharins act as defense-signaling molecules

Plant cell walls are composed not only of cellulose but also of numerous complex carbohydrates called *oligosaccharides*. Some evidence indicates that these cell wall components (when degraded by pathogens) function as signaling molecules as well as structural wall components. Oligosaccharides that are proposed to have a hormone-like function are called *oligosaccharins*.

Oligosaccharins can be released from the cell wall by enzymes secreted by pathogens. These carbohydrates are believed to signal defense responses, such as the hypersensitive response (HR) discussed in chapter 40.

Another oligosaccharin has been shown to inhibit auxin-stimulated elongation of pea stems. These molecules are active at concentrations one to two orders of magnitude less than those of the traditional plant hormones; you have seen how

Figure 41.32 Brassinosteroids.

Brassinolide and other brassinosteroids have structural similarities to animal steroid hormones. Cortisol, testosterone, and estradiol (not shown) are animal steroid hormones.

Plant	Animal	
Brassinolide	Cortisol	Testosterone

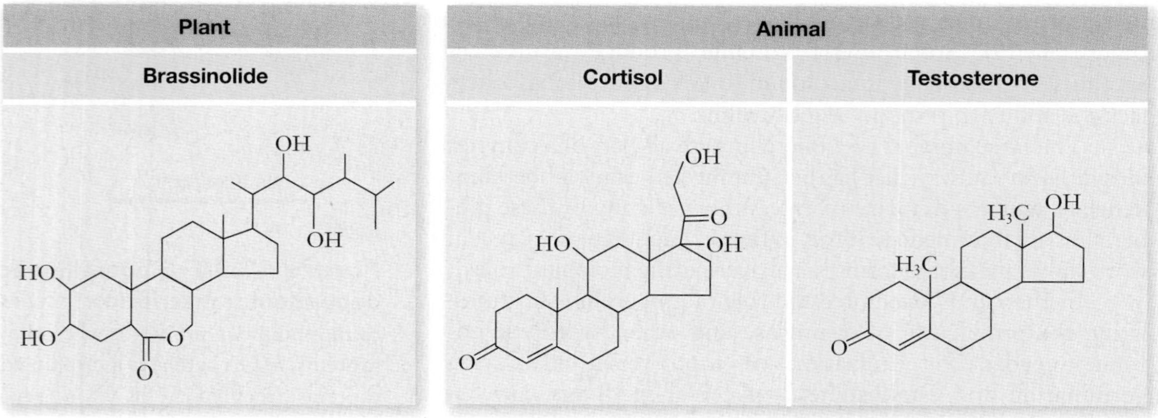

auxin and cytokinin ratios can affect organogenesis in culture (see figure 41.27).

Oligosaccharins also affect the phenotype of regenerated tobacco tissue, inhibiting root formation and stimulating flower production in tissues that are competent to regenerate flowers. How the culture results translate to in vivo systems remains an open question.

Ethylene induces fruit ripening and aids plant defenses

Long before its role as a plant hormone was appreciated, the simple, gaseous hydrocarbon *ethylene* (H_2C—CH_2) was known to defoliate plants when it leaked from gaslights in old-fashioned streetlamps. Ethylene is, however, a natural product of plant metabolism that, in minute amounts, interacts with other plant hormones.

When auxin is transported down from the apical meristem of the stem, it stimulates the production of ethylene in the tissues around the lateral buds and thus retards their growth. Ethylene also suppresses stem and root elongation, probably in a similar way. An ethylene receptor has been identified and characterized, and it appears to have evolved early in the evolution of photosynthetic organisms, sharing features with environmental-sensing proteins identified in bacteria.

Ethylene plays a major role in fruit development. At first, auxin, which is produced in significant amounts in pollinated flowers and developing fruits, stimulates ethylene production; this, in turn, hastens fruit ripening. Complex carbohydrates are broken down into simple sugars, chlorophylls are broken down, cell walls become soft, and the volatile compounds associated with flavor and scent in ripe fruits are produced.

One of the first observations that led to the recognition of ethylene as a plant hormone was the premature ripening in bananas produced by gases coming from oranges. Such relationships have led to major commercial uses of ethylene. For example, tomatoes are often picked green and artificially ripened later by the application of ethylene. Ethylene is widely used to speed the ripening of lemons and oranges as well. Carbon dioxide has the opposite effect of arresting ripening; fruits are often shipped in an atmosphere of carbon dioxide.

Also, a biotechnology solution has been developed in which one of the genes necessary for ethylene biosynthesis has been cloned, and its antisense copy inserted into the tomato genome (figure 41.33). The antisense copy of the gene is a nucleotide sequence that is complementary to the sense copy of the gene. In this transgenic plant, both the sense and antisense

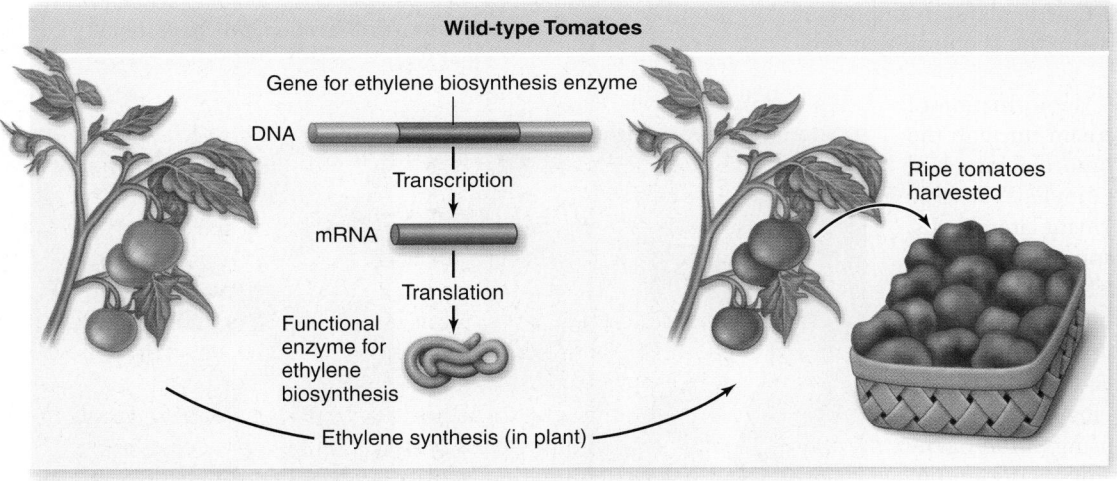

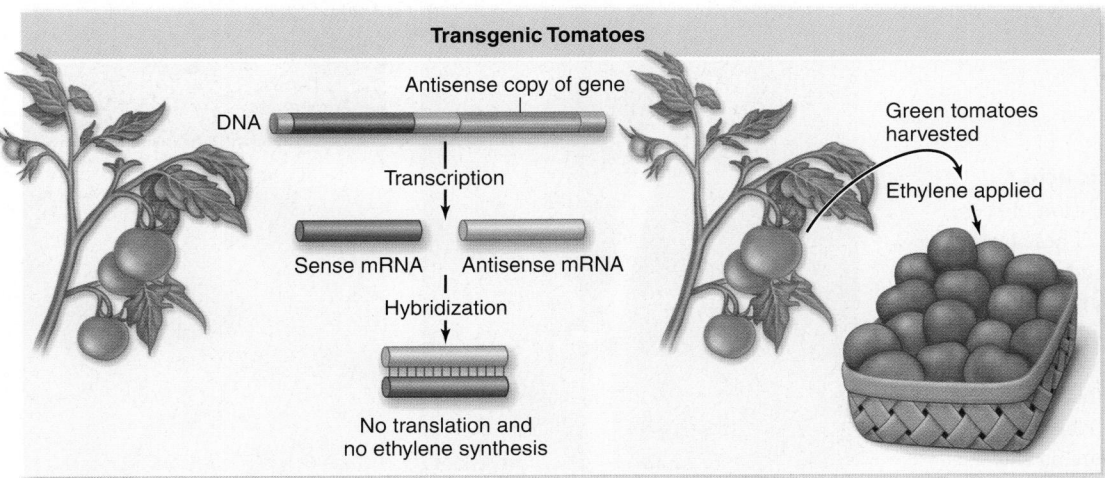

Figure 41.33 Genetic regulation of fruit ripening. An antisense copy of the gene for ethylene biosynthesis prevents the formation of ethylene and subsequent ripening of transgenic fruit. The antisense strand is complementary to the sequence for the ethylene biosynthesis gene. After transcription, the antisense mRNA pairs with the sense mRNA, and the double-stranded mRNA cannot be translated into a functional protein. Ethylene is not produced, and the fruit does not ripen. The fruit is sturdier for shipping in its unripened form and can be ripened later with exposure to ethylene. Thus, while wild-type tomatoes may already be rotten and damaged by the time they reach stores, transgenic tomatoes stay fresh longer.

sequences for the ethylene biosynthesis gene are transcribed. The sense and antisense mRNA sequences then pair with each other. This pairing blocks translation, which requires single-stranded RNA; as a result, ethylene is not synthesized, and the transgenic tomatoes do not ripen. In this way, the sturdy green tomatoes can be shipped without ripening and rotting. Exposing these tomatoes to ethylene later induces them to ripen.

Studies have shown that ethylene plays an important ecological role. Ethylene production increases rapidly when a plant is exposed to ozone and other toxic chemicals, temperature extremes, drought, attack by pathogens or herbivores, and other stresses. The increased production of ethylene that occurs can accelerate the loss of leaves or fruits that have been damaged by these stresses. Some of the damage associated with exposure to ozone is due to the ethylene produced by the plants.

The production of ethylene by plants attacked by herbivores or infected with pathogens may be a signal to activate the defense mechanisms of the plants and may include the production of molecules toxic to the pests.

Abscisic acid suppresses growth and induces dormancy

Abscisic acid appears to be synthesized mainly in mature green leaves, fruits, and root caps. The hormone earned its name because applications of it appear to stimulate fruit abscission in cotton, but there is little evidence that it plays an important role in this process. Ethylene is actually the chemical that promotes senescence and abscission.

Abscisic acid probably induces the formation of winter buds—dormant buds that remain through the winter. The conversion of leaf primordia into bud scales follows (figure 41.34a). Like ethylene, abscisic acid may also suppress growth of dormant lateral buds. It appears that abscisic acid, by suppressing growth and elongation of buds, can counteract some of the effects of gibberellins; it also promotes senescence by counteracting auxin.

Abscisic acid plays a role in seed dormancy and is antagonistic to gibberellins during germination. Abscisic acid levels in seeds rise during embryogenesis (see figure 41.17). As maize embryos develop in the kernels on the cob, abscisic acid is necessary to induce dormancy and prevent precocious germination, called vivipary (figure 41.34b). It is also important in controlling the opening and closing of stomata (figure 41.34c).

Found to occur in all groups of plants, abscisic acid apparently has been functioning as a growth-regulating substance since early in the evolution of the plant kingdom. Relatively little is known about the exact nature of its physiological and biochemical effects, but these effects are very rapid—often taking place within a minute or two—and therefore they must be at least partly independent of gene expression.

All of the genes have been sequenced in *Arabidopsis*, making it easier to identify which genes are transcribed in response to abscisic acid. Abscisic acid levels become greatly elevated when the plant is subject to stress, especially drought. Like other plant hormones, abscisic acid will probably prove to have valuable commercial applications when its mode of action is better understood.

Learning Outcomes Review 41.5

Hormones are chemicals produced in small quantities in one region of the plant and then transported to another region, where they cause a physiological or developmental response. Both auxins and cytokinins are produced in meristems and promote growth; however, auxins stimulate growth by cell elongation, while cytokinins stimulate cell division. In contrast, abscisic acid inhibits growth and promotes dormancy.

■ *What methods could you use to test whether abscisic acid produced in root caps can affect bud growth in stems?*

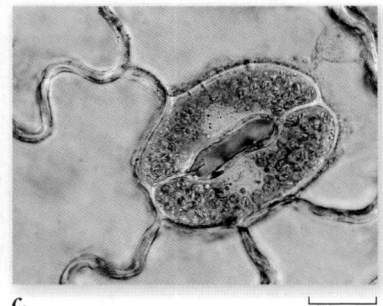

Figure 41.34 Effects of abscisic acid.
a. Abscisic acid plays a role in the formation of these winter buds of an American basswood. These buds will remain dormant for the winter, and bud scales—modified leaves—will protect the buds from desiccation. *b.* In addition to bud dormancy, abscisic acid is necessary for dormancy in seeds. This viviparous mutant in maize is deficient in abscisic acid, and the embryos begin germinating on the developing cob. *c.* Abscisic acid also affects the closing of stomata by influencing the movement of potassium ions out of guard cells.

41.1 Responses to Light

P_{fr} facilitates expression of light response genes (figure 41.1)

Phytochrome exists as two interconvertible forms. The inactive form, P_r, absorbs red light and is converted to the active form, P_{fr}. P_{fr} absorbs far-red light and is converted to the inactive form, P_r. P_{fr} enters the nucleus and binds with other proteins to form a transcription complex, leading to expression of light-regulated genes. It can also activate a cascade of transcription factors.

Many growth responses are linked to phytochrome action.

P_{fr} is involved in seed germination, shoot elongation, and detection of plant spacing. Far-red light inhibits germination by inactivating P_{fr}, and red light stimulates it by activating P_r.

Crowded plants receive a greater proportion of far-red light, which is reflected from neighboring plants. The plants respond by growing taller to compete more effectively for sunlight.

Light affects directional growth.

Phototropisms are directional growth responses of stems toward blue light. Blue-light receptors such as phototropin 1 are a recent discovery.

Circadian clocks are independent of light but are entrained by light.

Circadian rhythms entrain to the daily cycle through the action of phytochrome and blue-light photoreceptors. In the absence of light, the cycle's period may become desynchronized, but it resets when light is available.

41.2 Responses to Gravity

Plants align with the gravitational field: An overview.

Gravitropism is the growth response to a gravitational field.

Certain cells in plants perceive gravity when amyloplasts are pulled downward. Following the detection of gravity, a physiological signal causes cell elongation in other cells. The hormone auxin is believed to transmit the signal.

Stems bend away from a center of gravity.

Shoots bend away from gravity, so they exhibit negative gravitropism. When auxin accumulates on the lower side of the stem, those cells elongate, causing the stem to bend upward.

Roots bend toward a center of gravity.

Roots bend toward gravity, so they exhibit positive gravitropism. If the root cap is horizontally oriented, the cells on the upper side of the root become elongated, causing the root to grow downward.

41.3 Responses to Mechanical Stimuli

Touch can trigger irreversible growth responses.

Thigmotropism is a permanent directional growth of a plant toward or away from a physical stimulus. It results in thigmomorphogenesis, a change in growth form.

Thigmonastic responses are independent of the direction of the stimulus and are usually produced by changes in turgor pressure.

Reversible responses to touch and other stimuli involve turgor pressure.

Touch-induced responses result from changes in turgor pressure. A stimulus causes an electrical signal, which results in a loss of potassium ions and water from cells of the pulvini. The loss of turgor causes the leaves to move.

Light can induce changes in turgor pressure, resulting in leaf tracking of sunlight, flower opening, and leaf sleep movements.

41.4 Responses to Water and Temperature

Dormancy is a response to water, temperature, and light.

Dormancy is the cessation of growth that occurs when a plant is exposed to environmental stress. Seasonal leaf abscission occurs in deciduous trees in the fall. Seed dormancy suspends germination until environmental conditions are optimal.

Plants can survive temperature extremes.

Plants respond to cold temperatures by increasing unsaturated lipids in membranes, limiting ice crystal formation to extracellular spaces, and producing antifreeze proteins.

When exposed to rapid increases in temperature, plants produce heat shock proteins, which help to stabilize other proteins.

41.5 Hormones and Sensory Systems

The hormones that guide growth are keyed to the environment.

Hormones are produced in small quantities in one part of a plant and then transported to another, where they bring about physiological or developmental responses.

Auxin allows elongation and organizes the body plan.

Auxins are produced in apical meristems and immature parts of a plant. They affect DNA transcription by binding to proteins. Auxins promote stem elongation, adventitious root formation, cell division, and lateral bud dormancy. They also inhibit leaf abscission and induce ethylene production.

Cytokinins stimulate cell division and differentiation.

Cytokinins are purines produced in root apical meristems and immature fruits. They promote mitosis, chloroplast development, and bud formation. Cytokinins also delay leaf aging.

Gibberellins enhance plant growth and nutrient utilization.

Gibberellins are produced by root and shoot tips, young leaves, and seeds. They promote the elongation of stems and the production of enzymes in germinating seeds. In ferns, gibberellins function as pheromones.

Brassinosteroids are structurally similar to animal hormones.

Brassinosteroids are steroids produced in pollen, immature seeds, shoots, and leaves. They produce a broad spectrum of effects related to growth, senescence, and reproductive development.

Oligosaccharins act as defense-signaling molecules.

Pathogens secrete enzymes that release oligosaccharins from cell walls; these molecules induce pathogen defense responses. Oligosaccharins can also inhibit auxin-stimulated elongation, inhibit root formation, and stimulate flower production.

Ethylene induces fruit ripening and aids plant defenses.

Roots, shoot apical meristems, aging flowers, and ripening fruits produce ethylene, a gas that controls leaf, flower, and fruit abscission, promotes fruit ripening, and suppresses stem and root elongation. Ethylene may activate a defense response to attacks by pathogens and herbivores.

Abscisic acid suppresses growth and induces dormancy.

Mature green leaves, fruits, root caps, and seeds produce abscisic acid. Abscisic acid inhibits bud growth and the effects of other hormones, induces seed dormancy, and controls stomatal closure.

UNDERSTAND

1. Which of the following is stimulated by blue light?

   a. Seed germination
   b. Detection of plant spacing
   c. Phototropism
   d. Shoot elongation

2. Stems and roots, respectively, exhibit

   a. a positive phototropic response and no phototropic response.
   b. a negative phototropic response and no phototropic response.
   c. no phototropic response and a positive phototropic response.
   d. no phototropic response and a negative phototropic response.

3. In stems, gravity is detected by cells of the

   a. epidermis.   c. periderm.
   b. cortex.   d. endodermis.

4. Chilling most directly affects

   a. nuclear proteins.   c. the cytoskeleton.
   b. vacuolar inclusions.   d. membrane lipids.

5. Which of the following does not happen as a seed approaches a state of dormancy?

   a. The seed loses water.
   b. Abscisic acid levels in the embryo decrease.
   c. The seed coat hardens.
   d. Protein synthesis stops.

6. Dwarf mutants can sometimes be induced to grow normally by applying

   a. auxin.   c. ethylene.
   b. abscisic acid.   d. gibberellin.

APPLY

1. If you exposed seeds to a series of red-light versus far-red-light treatments, which of the following exposure treatments would result in seed germination?

   a. Red; far-red
   b. Far-red; red
   c. Red; far-red; red; far-red; red; far-red; red; far-red
   d. None of the above

2. If you were to plant a de-etiolated (det2) mutant *Arabidopsis* seed and keep it in a dark box, what would you expect to happen?

   a. The seed would germinate normally, but the plant would not become tall and spindly while it sought a light source.
   b. The seed would fail to germinate because it would not have light.
   c. The seed would germinate, and the plant would become tall and spindly while it sought a light source.
   d. The seed would germinate, and the plant would immediately die because it could not make sugar in the dark.

3. When Charles and Francis Darwin investigated phototropisms in plants, they discovered that

   a. auxin was responsible for light-dependent growth.
   b. light was detected at the shoot tip of a plant.
   c. light was detected below the shoot tip of a plant.
   d. only red light stimulated phototropism.

4. Auxin promotes a plant to grow toward a light source by

   a. increasing the rate of cell division on the shaded side of the stem.
   b. shortening the cells on the light side of the stem.
   c. causing cells on the shaded side of the stem to elongate.
   d. decreasing the rate of cell division on the light side of the stem.

5. You have come up with a brilliant idea to stretch your grocery budget by buying green fruit in bulk and then storing it in a bag that you have blown up like a balloon. As you need fruit, you would take it out of the bag, and it would miraculously ripen. How would this work?

   a. The bag would block light from reaching the fruit, so it would not ripen.
   b. The bag would keep the fruit cool, so it would not ripen.
   c. The high CO_2 levels in the bag would prevent ripening.
   d. The high O_2 levels in the bag would prevent ripening.

6. Gibberellins are used to increase productivity in grapes because they

   a. cause fruits to be larger by promoting cell division within the fruit.
   b. increase the internode length so the fruits have more room to grow.
   c. increase the number of flowers produced, thus increasing the number of fruits.
   d. do all of the above.

7. Which of the following might not be observed in a plant that is grown on the Space Shuttle in space?

   a. Phototropism   c. Circadian rhythms
   b. Photomorphogenesis d. Gravitropism

SYNTHESIZE

1. If you buy a bag of potatoes and leave them in a dark cupboard for too long, they will begin to form long white sprouts with tiny leaves. Name this process and explain why the potatoes are behaving as they are.

2. Find the discussion of taxis in this book. Compare and contrast tropism with taxis.

3. The current model for gravitropism suggests that the accumulation of amyloplasts on the bottom of a cell allows the cell to sense gravity. Suggest a plausible mechanism for the sensing of gravity that does not involve the settling out of particles.

4. Farmers who grow crops that are planted as seedlings may prepare them for their transition from the greenhouse to the field by brushing them gently every day for a few weeks. Why is this beneficial?

ONLINE RESOURCE

www.ravenbiology.com

Understand, Apply, and Synthesize—enhance your study with animations that bring concepts to life and practice tests to assess your understanding. Your instructor may also recommend the interactive eBook, individualized learning tools, and more.

Chapter 42

Plant Reproduction

Chapter Outline

42.1   Reproductive Development

42.2   Flower Production

42.3   Structure and Evolution of Flowers

42.4   Pollination and Fertilization

42.5   Asexual Reproduction

42.6   Plant Life Spans

Introduction

The remarkable evolutionary success of flowering plants can be linked to their novel reproductive strategies. In this chapter, we explore the reproductive strategies of the angiosperms and how their unique features—flowers and fruits—have contributed to their success. This is, in part, a story of coevolution between plants and animals that ensures greater genetic diversity by dispersing plant gametes widely. In a stable environment, however, there are advantages to maintaining the status quo genetically; asexual reproduction, for example, is a strategy that produces cloned individuals. An unusual twist to sexual reproduction in some flowering plants is that senescence and death of the parent plant immediately follow.

In chapter 30, we noted that angiosperms represent an evolutionary innovation with their production of flowers and fruits. In chapter 37, we outlined the development of form, or morphogenesis, which a germinating seed undergoes to become a vegetative plant. In this section, we describe the additional changes that occur in a vegetative plant to produce the elaborate structures associated with flowering (figure 42.1).

Plants go through developmental changes leading to reproductive maturity just as many animals do. This shift from juvenile to adult development is seen in the metamorphosis of a tadpole to an adult frog or a caterpillar to a butterfly that can then reproduce. Plants undergo a similar metamorphosis that leads to the production of a flower. Unlike the juvenile frog, which loses its tail, plants just keep adding structures to existing structures with their meristems.

Carefully regulated processes determine when and where flowers will form. Moreover, plants must often gain competence to respond to internal or external signals regulating flowering. Once plants are competent to reproduce, a combination of factors—including light, temperature, and both promotive and inhibitory internal signals—determines when a flower is produced (figure 42.2). These signals turn on genes that specify formation of the floral organs—sepals, petals, stamens, and carpels. Once cells have instructions to become a specific floral organ, yet another developmental cascade leads to the three-dimensional construction of flower parts. We describe details of this process in the following sections.

The transition to flowering competence is termed phase change

At germination, most plants are incapable of producing a flower, even if all the environmental cues are optimal. Internal developmental changes allow plants to obtain competence to respond to external or internal signals (or both) that trigger flower formation. This transition is referred to as **phase change.**

Phase change can be morphologically obvious or very subtle. Take a look at an oak tree in the winter: Leaves will still be clinging to the lower branches until spring when the new buds push them off, but leaves on the upper branches will have fallen earlier (figure 42.3a). Those lower branches were initiated by a juvenile meristem. The fact that they did not respond to environmental cues and drop their leaves indicates that they are juvenile branches and have not made a phase change. Although the lower branches are older, their juvenile state was established when they were initiated and will not change.

Ivy also has distinct juvenile and adult phases of growth (figure 42.3b). Stem tissue produced by a juvenile meristem initiates adventitious roots that can cling to walls. If you look at very old brick buildings covered with ivy, you will notice that the uppermost branches are falling off because they have transitioned to the adult phase of growth and have lost the ability to produce adventitious roots.

It is important to note that even though a plant has reached the adult stage of development, it may or may not produce reproductive structures. Other factors may be necessary to trigger flowering.

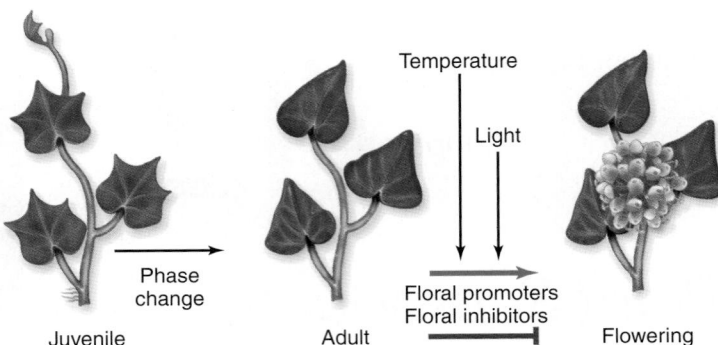

Figure 42.2 Factors involved in initiating flowering. This model depicts the environmentally cued and internally processed events that result in a shoot meristem initiating flowers. During phase change, the plant acquires competence to respond to flowering signals.

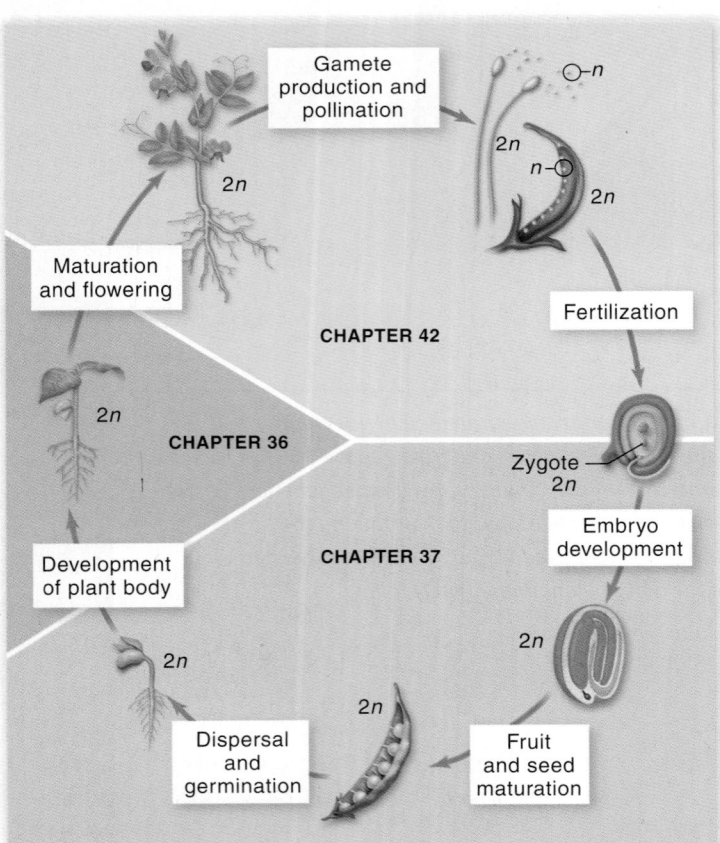

Figure 42.1 Life cycle of a flowering plant (Angiosperm).

a.

b.

Figure 42.3 Phase change.
a. The lower branches of this oak tree represent the juvenile phase of development; they cling to their leaves in the winter. The lower leaves are not able to form an abscission layer and break off the tree in the fall. Such visible changes are marks of phase change, but the real test is whether the plant is able to flower. *b.* Juvenile ivy (right) makes adventitious roots and has an alternating leaf phyllotaxy. Mature ivy (left) lacks adventitious roots, has spiral phyllotaxy, and can make flowers.

Mutations have clarified how phase change is controlled

Generally it is easier to get a plant to revert from an adult to juvenile state than to induce phase change experimentally. Applications of the plant hormone gibberellin and severe pruning can cause reversion. In the latter case, new vegetative growth occurs, as when certain shrubs are cut back and put out lush new growth in response.

The *embryonic flower (emf)* mutant of *Arabidopsis* flowers almost immediately (figure 42.4), which is consistent with the hypothesis that the wild-type allele suppresses flowering. As the wild-type plant matures, *EMF* expression decreases. This finding suggests that flowering is the default state, and that mechanisms have evolved to delay flowering. This delay presumably allows the plant to store more energy to be allocated for reproduction.

An example of inducing the juvenile-to-adult transition comes from overexpressing a gene necessary for flowering that is found in many species. This gene, *LEAFY (LFY)*, was cloned in *Arabidopsis*, and its promoter was replaced with a viral promoter that results in constant, high levels of *LFY* transcription. *LFY* with its viral promoter was then introduced into cultured aspen cells that were used to regenerate plants. When *LFY* is overexpressed in aspen, flowering occurs in weeks instead of years (figure 42.5).

Phase change requires both a sufficiently strong promotive signal and the ability to perceive the signal. Phase change can result in the production of receptors in the shoot to perceive a signal of a certain intensity. Alternatively an increase of promotive signal(s) or a decrease of inhibitory signal(s) can trigger phase change.

Figure 42.4 Embryonic flower *(EMF)* prevents early flowering. Mutant plants that lack EMF protein flower as soon as they germinate. The flowers have malformed carpels and other defective floral structures close to the roots.

Carpel-like structure

Roots

Phase change, as we said earlier, results in an adult plant, but not necessarily a flowering plant. The ability to reproduce is distinct from actual reproductive development. Flower production depends on a number of factors, which we explore next.

Learning Outcomes Review 42.1

In a flowering plant life cycle, fertilization produces an embryo in a seed. The embryo develops into a plant that eventually flowers, and the flowers once again produce gametes. Phase change is the transition from vegetative to reproductive growth. In *Arabidopsis*, expression of the embryonic flower mutant *(emf)* or overexpression of the *LEAFY* gene *(LFY)* result in early flowering.

■ *In evolutionary terms, why is flower production the default state in plants?*

Normal Flowering

Accelerated Flowering

a.

b.

Figure 42.5 Overexpression of a flowering gene can accelerate phase change. *a.* Normally, an aspen tree grows for several years before producing flowers (see inset). *b.* Overexpression of the *Arabidopsis* flowering gene, *LFY*, causes rapid flowering in a transgenic aspen (see inset).

Four genetically regulated pathways to flowering have been identified: (1) the light-dependent pathway, (2) the temperature-dependent pathway, (3) the gibberellin-dependent pathway, and (4) the autonomous pathway.

Plants can rely primarily on one pathway, but all four pathways can be present.

The environment can promote or repress flowering, and in some cases, it can be relatively neutral. For example, increasing light duration can be a signal that long summer days have arrived in a temperate climate and that conditions are favorable for reproduction. In other cases, plants depend on light to accumulate sufficient amounts of sucrose to fuel reproduction, but flower independently of day length.

Temperature can also be used as a signal. **Vernalization,** the requirement for a period of chilling of seeds or shoots for flowering, affects the temperature-dependent pathway. Assuming that regulation of reproduction first arose in more constant tropical environments, many of the day-length and temperature controls would have evolved as plants colonized more temperate climates. Plants with a vernalization requirement flower after, not during, a cold winter, enhancing reproductive success. The existence of redundant pathways to flowering helps ensure new generations.

The light-dependent pathway is geared to the photoperiod

Flowering requires much energy accumulated via photosynthesis. Thus, all plants require light for flowering, but this is distinct from the **photoperiodic,** or light-dependent, flowering pathway. Aspects of growth and development in most plants are keyed to changes in the proportion of light to dark in the daily 24-hr cycle (day length).

Sensitivity to the photoperiod provides a mechanism for organisms to respond to seasonal changes in the relative length of day and night. Day length changes with the seasons; the farther a region is from the equator, the greater the variation in day length.

Short-day and long-day plants

The flowering responses of plants to day length fall into several basic categories. In short-day plants, flowering is initiated when daylight becomes shorter than a critical length (figure 42.6). In **long-day plants,** flowering begins when daylight becomes longer. Other plants, such as snapdragons, roses, and many native to the tropics, flower when mature

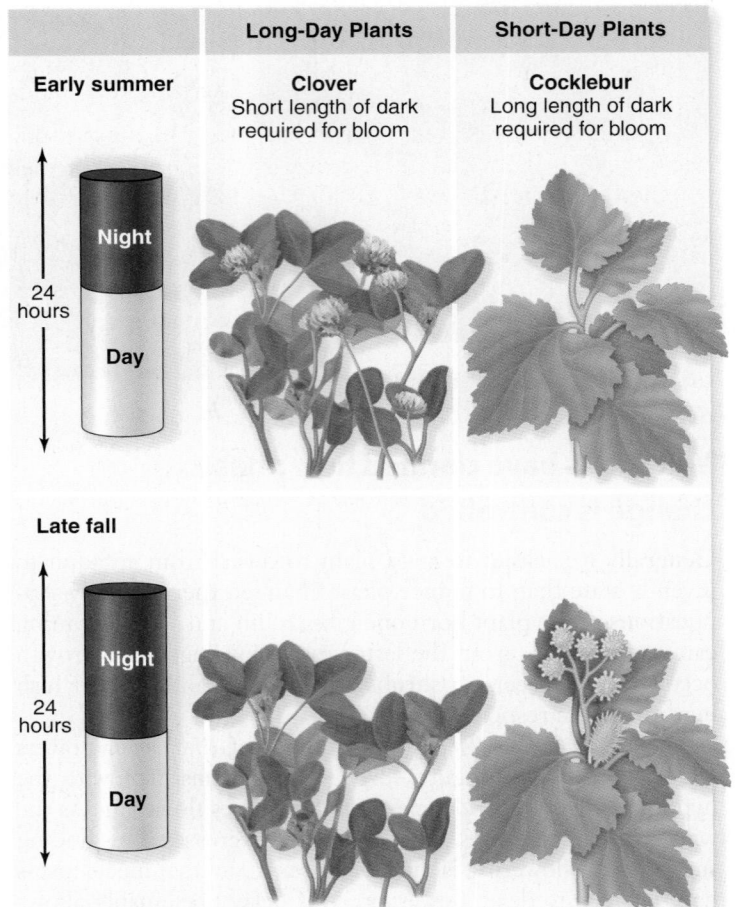

Figure 42.6 How flowering responds to day length.
a. Clover (center panels) is a long-day plant that is stimulated by short nights to flower in the spring. Cocklebur (right-hand panels) is a short-day plant that, throughout its natural distribution in the northern hemisphere, is stimulated by long nights to flower in the fall. *b.* If the long night of late fall is artificially interrupted by a flash of light, the cocklebur will not flower, and the clover will. Although the terms *long-day* and *short-day* refer to the length of day, in each case, it is the duration of uninterrupted darkness that determines when flowering will occur.

regardless of day length, as long as they have received enough light for normal growth. These are referred to as day-neutral plants. Still other plants, including ivy, have two critical photoperiods; they will not flower if the days are too long, and they also will not flower if the days are too short.

Although plants are referred to as long-day or short-day plants, it is actually the amount of darkness that determines whether a plant flowers. In obligate long- or short-day species, there is a sharp distinction between short and long nights, respectively. Flowering occurs in obligate long-day plants when the night length is less than the maximal amount of required darkness (critical night length) for that species. For obligate short-day plants, the amount of darkness must exceed the critical night length for the species.

In other long- or short-day plants, flowering occurs more rapidly or slowly depending on the length of day. These plants, which rely on other flowering pathways as well, are called **facultative long- or short-day** plants because the photoperiodic requirement is not absolute. The garden pea is an example of a facultative long-day plant.

Advantages of photoperiodic control of flowering

Using light as a cue permits plants to flower when abiotic environmental conditions are optimal, pollinators are available, and competition for resources with other plants may be less. For example, the spring herbaceous plants termed *ephemerals* flower in the woods before the tree canopy leafs out and blocks the sunlight necessary for photosynthesis. An example is the trailing arbutus *(Epigaea repens)* of the Northeast woods, which is also known as mayflower because of the time of year in which it blooms.

At middle latitudes, most long-day plants flower in the spring and early summer; examples of such plants include clover, irises, lettuce, spinach, and hollyhocks. Short-day plants usually flower in late summer and fall; these include chrysanthemums, goldenrods, poinsettias, soybeans, and many weeds, such as ragweed. Commercial plant growers use these responses to day length to bring plants into flower at specific times. For example, photoperiod is manipulated in greenhouses so that poinsettias flower just in time for the winter holidays (figure 42.7). The geographic distribution of certain plants may be determined by their flowering responses to day length.

The mechanics of light signaling

Photoperiod is perceived by several different forms of phytochrome and also by a blue-light–sensitive molecule (cryptochrome). Another type of blue-light–sensitive molecule (phototropin) was discussed in chapter 41. Phototropin affects photomorphogenesis, and cryptochrome affects photoperiodic responses.

The conformational change in a phytochrome or cryptochrome light-receptor molecule triggers a cascade of events that leads to the production of a flower. There is a link between light and the circadian rhythm regulated by an internal clock that facilitates or inhibits flowering. At a molecular level, the gaps in information about how light signaling and flower production are related are rapidly being filled in, and the control mechanisms have been found to be quite complex.

Figure 42.7 Flowering time can be altered.
Manipulation of photoperiod in greenhouses ensures that short-day poinsettias flower in time for the winter holidays. Even after flowering is induced, many developmental events must occur in order to produce species-specific flowers.

Photoperiodic Regulation of Transcription of the *CO* Gene. *Arabidopsis*, which as you know is commonly used in plant studies, is a facultative long-day plant that flowers in response to both far-red and blue light. Phytochrome and cryptochrome, the red- and blue-light receptors, respectively, regulate flowering via the gene *CONSTANS (CO)*. Precise levels of CO protein are maintained in accordance with the circadian clock, and phytochrome regulates the transcription of *CO*. Levels of *CO* mRNA are low at night and increase at daybreak. In addition, CO protein levels are modulated through the action of cryptochrome. CO is an important protein because it links the perception of day length with the production of a signal that moves from the leaves to the shoot where a change in gene transcription leads to the production of flowers.

Inquiry question

? If levels of *CO* mRNA follow a circadian pattern, how could you determine whether protein levels are modulated by a mechanism other than transcription? Why would an additional level of control even be necessary?

The importance of posttranslational regulation of *CO* activity became apparent through studies of transgenic *Arabidopsis* plants. These plants contain a *CO* gene fused to a viral promoter that is always on and produces high levels of *CO* mRNA regardless of whether it is day or night. The regulation of *CO* gene expression by phytochrome A is therefore eliminated when this viral promoter is fused to the gene. Curiously, CO protein levels still follow a circadian pattern.

Although CO protein is produced day and night, levels of CO are lower at night because of targeted protein degradation. Ubiquitin tags the CO protein, and it is degraded by the proteasome as was described in chapter 41 for phytochrome degradation. Blue light acting via cryptochrome stabilizes CO during the day and protects it from ubiquitination and subsequent degradation.

***CO* and *LFY* Expression.** CO is a transcription factor that turns on other genes, which results in the expression of *LFY*. As discussed in connection with phase change earlier in this section, *LFY* is one of the key genes that "tells" a meristem to switch over to flowering. We will see that other pathways also converge on this important gene. Genes that are regulated by *LFY* are discussed later in this chapter.

Florigen—The elusive flowering hormone

Long before any genes regulating flowering were cloned, a flowering hormone called florigen was postulated to trigger flower production. A considerable amount of evidence demonstrates the existence of substances that promote flowering and substances that inhibit it. Grafting experiments have shown that these substances can move from leaves to shoots. The complexity of their interactions, as well as the fact that multiple chemical messengers are evidently involved, has made this scientifically and commercially interesting search very difficult. The existence of a flowering hormone remains strictly hypothetical even after a scientific quest of 50 years.

One intriguing possibility is that CO protein is a graft-transmissible flowering signal or that it affects such a signal. CO has been found in the phloem that moves throughout the plant body. When *co* mutant shoots are grafted to stocks that produce CO, flowering occurs. Because CO is found in the phloem, it is possible that this is the protein that moves in the grafted plant to cause flowering. Equally likely, however, is the possibility that CO directly or indirectly affects a separate graft-transmissible factor that is essential for flowering.

The temperature-dependent pathway is linked to cold

Cold temperatures can accelerate or permit flowering in many species. As with light, this environmental connection ensures that plants flower at more optimal times.

Some plants require a period of chilling before flowering, called *vernalization*. This phenomenon was discovered in the 1930s by the Ukrainian scientist T. D. Lysenko while trying to solve the problem of winter wheat rotting in the fields. Because winter wheat would not flower without a period of chilling, Lysenko chilled the seeds and then planted them in the spring. The seeds successfully sprouted, grew, and produced grain.

Although this discovery was scientifically significant, Lysenko erroneously concluded that he had converted one species, winter wheat, to another, spring wheat, by simply altering the environment. Lysenko's point of view was supported by the communist philosophy of the time, which held that people could easily manipulate nature to increase production. Unfortunately, this philosophy led to a great many problems, including mistreatment of legitimate geneticists in the former Soviet Union. In addition, genetics and Darwinian evolution were suspect in the Soviet Union until the mid-1960s.

Vernalization is necessary for some seeds or plants in later stages of development. Analysis of mutants in *Arabidopsis* and pea plants indicate that vernalization is a separate flowering pathway.

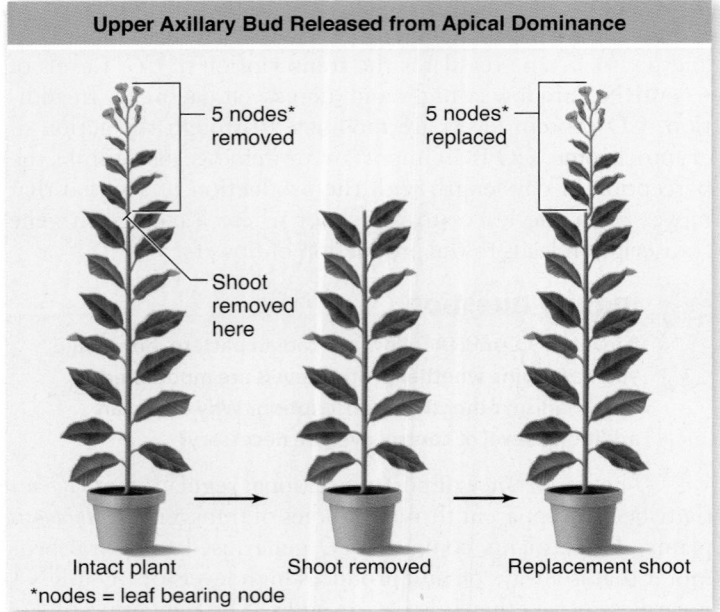

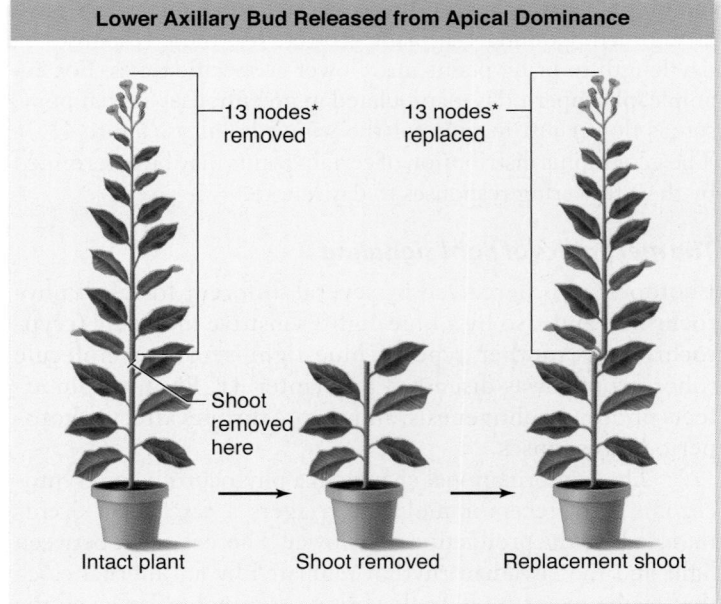

Figure 42.8 Plants can "count." When axillary buds of flowering, day-neutral tobacco plants are released from apical dominance by removing the main shoot, they replace the number of nodes that were initiated by the main shoot.

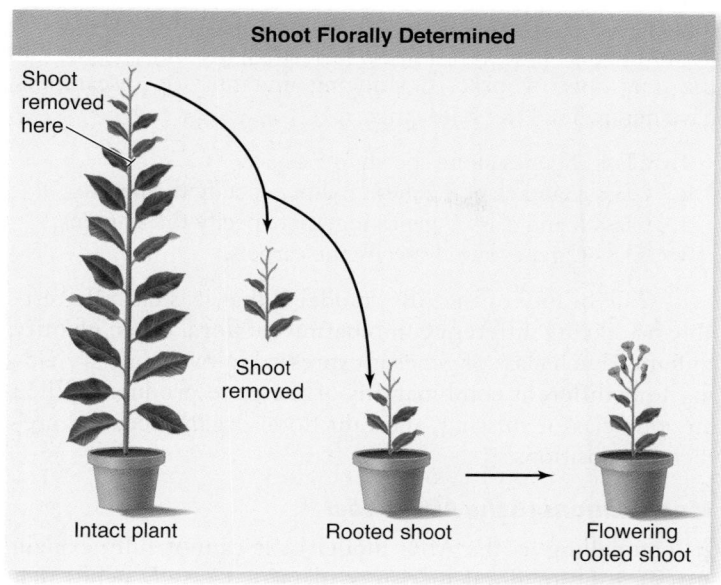

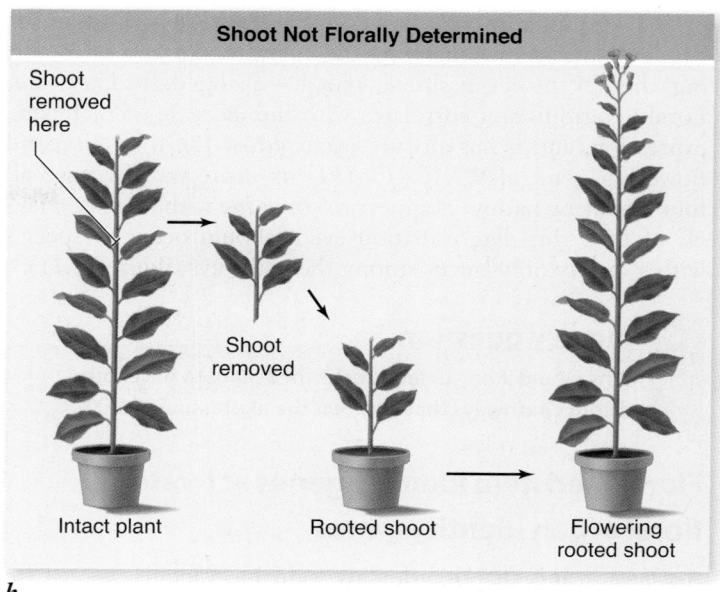

a. *b.*

Figure 42.9 Plants can "remember." At a certain point in the flowering process, shoots become committed to making a flower. This is called floral determination. *a.* Florally determined shoots "remember" their position when rooted in a pot. That is, they produce the same number of nodes that they would have if they had grown out on the plant, and then they flower. *b.* Shoots that are not yet florally determined cannot remember how many nodes they have left, so they start counting again. That is, they develop like a seedling and then flower.

The gibberellin-dependent pathway requires an increased hormone level

In *Arabidopsis* and some other species, decreased levels of gibberellins delay flowering. Thus the gibberellin pathway is proposed to promote flowering. It is known that gibberellins enhance the expression of *LFY*. Gibberellin actually binds the promoter of the *LFY* gene, so its effect on flowering is direct.

The autonomous pathway is independent of environmental cues

The autonomous pathway to flowering does not depend on external cues except for basic nutrition. Presumably, this was the first pathway to evolve. Day-neutral plants often depend primarily on the autonomous pathway, which allows plants to "count" and "remember."

As an example, a field of day-neutral tobacco plants will produce a uniform number of nodes before flowering. If the shoots of these plants are removed at different positions, axillary buds will grow out and produce the same number of nodes as the removed portion of the shoot (figure 42.8). The upper axillary buds of flowering tobacco will remember their position when rooted or grafted. The terminal shoot tip becomes committed, or determined, to flower about four nodes before it actually initiates a flower (figure 42.9). In some other species, this commitment is less stable or it occurs later.

How do shoots "know" where they are and at some point "remember" that information? It has become clear that inhibitory signals are sent from the roots. When bottomless pots are continuously placed over a growing tobacco plant and filled with soil, flowering is delayed by the formation of adventitious roots (figure 42.10). Control experiments with leaf removal show that the addition of roots, and not the loss of leaves, delays flowering. A balance between floral promoting and inhibiting signals may regulate when flowering occurs in the autonomous pathway and the other pathways as well.

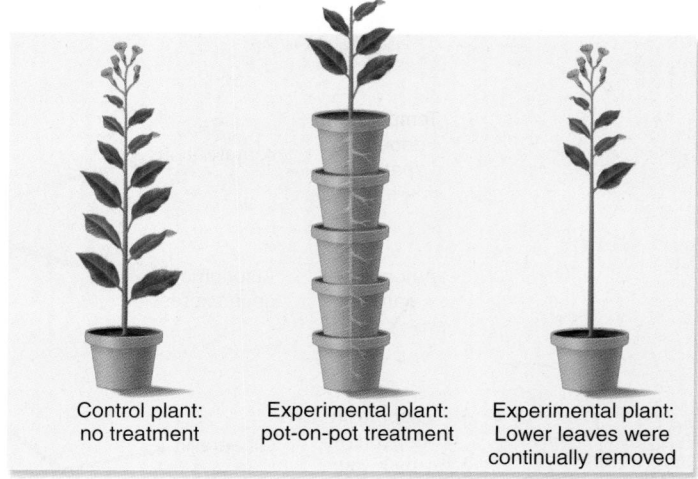

Figure 42.10 Roots can inhibit flowering. Adventitious roots formed as bottomless pots were continuously placed over growing tobacco plants, delaying flowering. The delay in flowering is caused by the roots, not by the loss of the leaves. This was shown by removing leaves on plants at the same time and in the same position as leaves on experimental plants that became buried as pots were added.

Determination for flowering is tested at the organ or whole-plant level by changing the environment and ascertaining whether the developmental fate has changed. In *Arabidopsis*, floral determination correlates with the increase of *LFY* gene expression, and it has already occurred by the time a second flowering gene, *APETALA1 (AP1)*, is expressed. Because all four flowering pathways appear to converge with increased levels of *LFY*, this determination event should occur in species with a variety of balances among the pathways (figure 42.11).

Inquiry question

? Why would it be advantageous for a plant to have four distinct pathways that all affect the expression of *LFY*?

Floral meristem identity genes activate floral organ identity genes

Arabidopsis and snapdragons are valuable model systems for identifying flowering genes and understanding their interactions. The four flowering pathways discussed earlier in this section lead to an adult meristem becoming a floral meristem by either activating or repressing the inhibition of floral meristem identity genes (see figure 42.11). Two of the key floral meristem identity genes are *LFY* and *AP1*. These genes establish the meristem as a flower meristem. They then turn on floral organ identity genes. The floral organ identity genes define four concentric whorls, moving inward in the floral meristem, as sepal, petal, stamen, and carpel.

The ABC model

To explain how three classes of floral organ identity genes could specify four distinct organ types, the ABC model was developed

(figure 42.12). The ABC model proposes that three classes of organ identity genes (*A*, *B*, and *C*) specify the floral organs in the four floral whorls. By studying mutants, the researchers have determined the following:

1. Class *A* genes alone specify the sepals.
2. Class *A* and class *B* genes together specify the petals.
3. Class *B* and class *C* genes together specify the stamens.
4. Class *C* genes alone specify the carpels.

The beauty of the ABC model is that it is entirely testable by making different combinations of floral organ identity mutants. Each class of genes is expressed in two whorls, yielding four different combinations of the gene products. When any one class is missing, aberrant floral organs occur in predictable positions.

Modifications to the ABC model

As compelling as the ABC model is, it cannot fully explain specification of floral meristem identity. Class *D* genes that are essential for carpel formation have been identified, but even this discovery did not explain why a plant lacking *A*, *B*, and *C* gene function produced four whorls of sepals rather than four whorls of leaves. Floral parts are thought to have evolved from leaves; therefore, if the floral organ identity genes are removed, whorls of leaves, rather than sepals, would be predicted.

The answer to this puzzle is found in the more recently discovered class *E* genes, *SEPALATA1 (SEP1)* through *SEPALATA4 (SEP4)*. The triple mutant *sep1 sep2 sep3* and the *sep4* mutant both produce four whorls of leaves. The proteins encoded by the *SEP* genes can interact with class A, B, and C proteins and possibly affect transcription of genes needed for the development of floral organs. Identification of the *SEP*

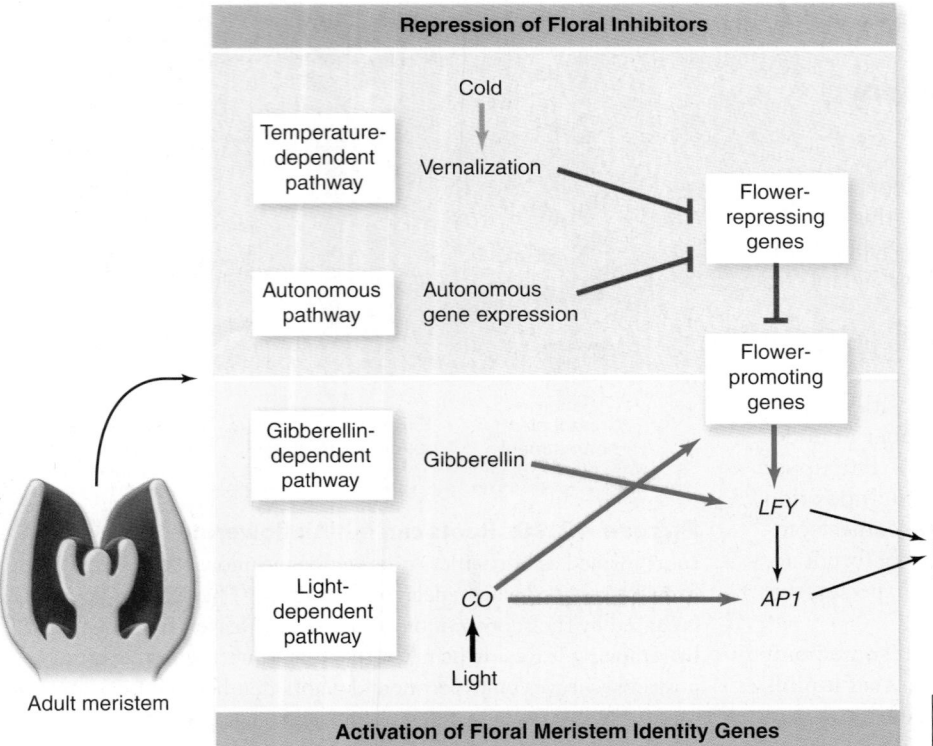

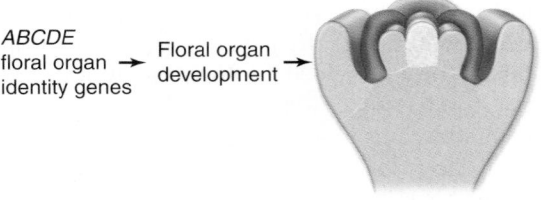

Figure 42.11 Model for flowering. The temperature-dependent, gibberellin-dependent, and light-dependent flowering pathways promote the formation of floral meristems from adult meristems by repressing floral inhibitors and activating floral meristem identity genes.

Inquiry question

? Would you expect plants to flower at a different time if there were no flower-repressing genes and the vernalization and autonomous pathway genes induced expression of flower-promoting genes?

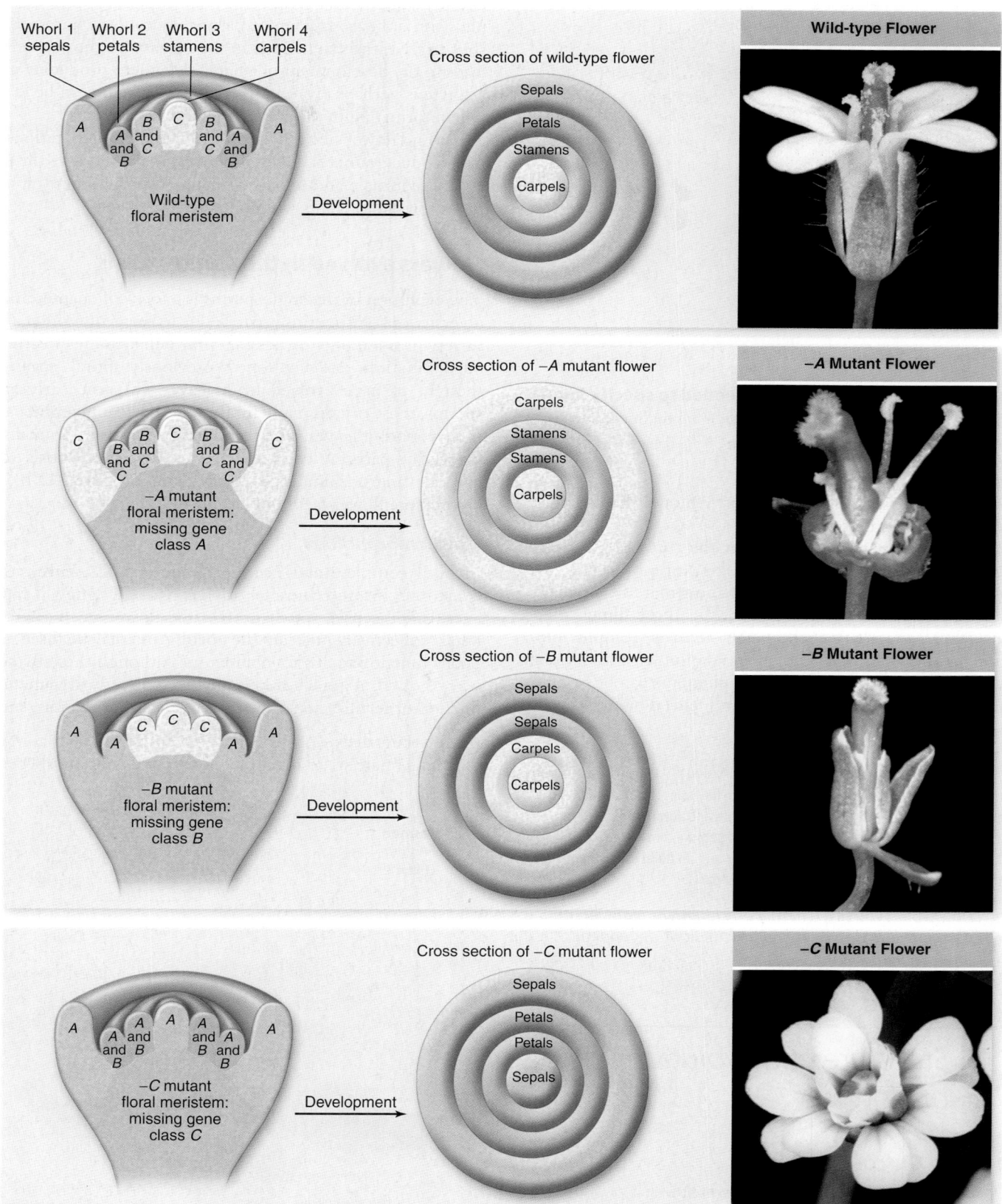

Figure 42.12 ABC model for floral organ specification. Letters labeling whorls indicate which gene classes are active. When *A* function is lost (–*A*), *C* expands to the first and second whorls. When *B* function is lost (–*B*), The outer twowhorls have just *A* function, and both inner two whorls have just *C* function; none of the whorls have dual gene function. When *C* function is lost (–*C*), *A* expands into the inner two whorls. These new combinations of gene expression patterns alter which floral structures form in each whorl.

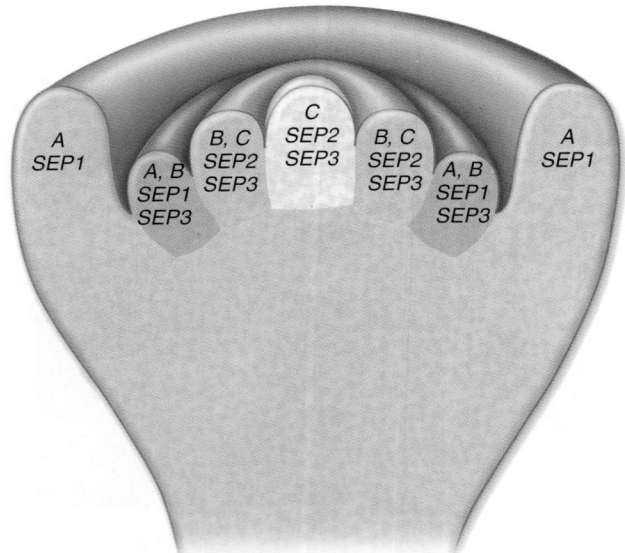

Figure 42.13 **Class *E* genes are needed to specify floral organ identity.** When all three *SEP* genes are mutated, four whorls of leaves are produced.

genes lead to a new floral organ identity model that includes these class *E* genes (figure 42.13).

It is important to recognize that the *ABCDE* genes are actually only the beginning of the making of a flower. These organ identity genes are transcription factors that turn on many more genes that actually give rise to the three-dimensional flower. Other genes "paint" the petals—that is, complex biochemical pathways lead to the accumulation of anthocyanin pigments in petal cell vacuoles. These pigments can be orange, red, or purple, and the actual color is influenced by pH as well.

Learning Outcomes Review 42.2

Four pathways have been identified that lead to flowering: light-dependent, temperature-dependent, gibberellin-dependent, and autonomous. Floral determination marks the point at which shoots become committed to making flowers. Floral meristem identity genes turn on floral organ identity genes, which control the development of flower parts.

■ *How would you test whether day length or night length determines flowering in plants with light-dependent flowering pathways?*

42.3 Structure and Evolution of Flowers

Learning Outcomes

1. *List the parts of a typical angiosperm flower.*
2. *Distinguish between bilateral symmetry and radial symmetry.*
3. *Differentiate between microgametophytes and megagametophytes.*

The complex and elegant process that gives rise to the reproductive structure called the flower is often compared with metamorphosis in animals. It is indeed a metamorphosis, but the subtle shift from mitosis to meiosis in the megaspore mother cell that leads to the development of a haploid, gamete-producing gametophyte is perhaps even more critical. The same can be said for pollen formation in the anther of the stamen.

The flower not only houses the haploid generations that will produce gametes, but it also functions to increase the probability that male and female gametes from different (or sometimes the same) plants will unite.

Flowers evolved in the angiosperms

The evolution of the angiosperms is a focus of chapter 30. The diversity of angiosperms is partly due to the evolution of a great variety of floral phenotypes that may enhance the effectiveness of pollination. As mentioned previously, floral organs are thought to have evolved from leaves. In some early angiosperms, these organs maintain the spiral developmental pattern often found in leaves. The trend has been toward four distinct whorls of parts. A complete flower has four whorls (calyx, corolla, androecium, and gynoecium) (figure 42.14). An incomplete flower lacks one or more of the whorls.

Flower morphology

In both complete and incomplete flowers, the **calyx** usually constitutes the outermost whorl; it consists of flattened appendages, called sepals, which protect the flower in the bud. The petals collectively make up the **corolla** and may be fused. Many petals function to attract pollinators. Although these two outer whorls of floral organs are not involved directly in gamete production or fertilization, they can enhance reproductive success.

Male structures. Androecium is a collective term for all the **stamens** (male structures) of a flower. Stamens are specialized

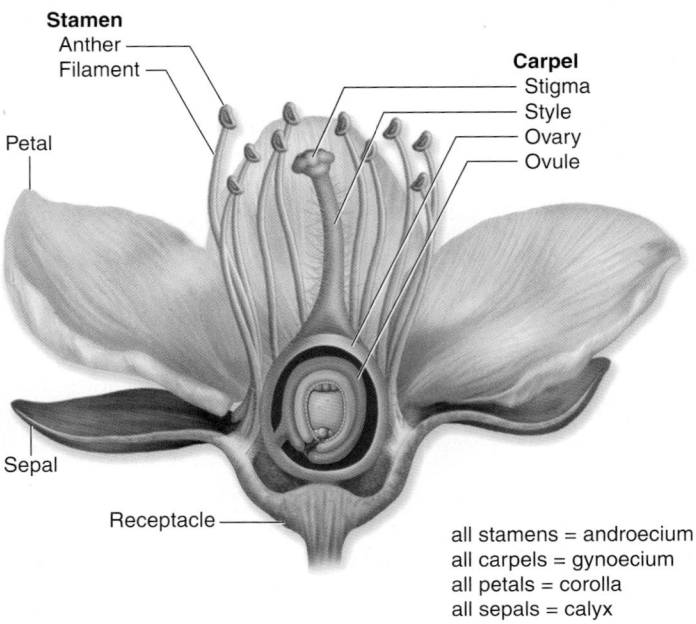

all stamens = androecium
all carpels = gynoecium
all petals = corolla
all sepals = calyx

Figure 42.14 **A complete angiosperm flower.**

structures that bear the angiosperm microsporangia. Similar structures bear the microsporangia in the pollen cones of gymnosperms. Most living angiosperms have stamens with filaments ("stalks") that are slender and often threadlike; four microsporangia are evident at the apex in a swollen portion, the **anther.** Some of the more primitive angiosperms have stamens that are flattened and leaflike, with the sporangia produced from the upper or lower surface.

Female structures. The gynoecium is a collective term for all the female parts of a flower. In most flowers, the gynoecium, which is unique to angiosperms, consists of a single carpel or two or more fused carpels. Single or fused carpels are often referred to as simple or compound pistils, respectively. Most flowers with which we are familiar—for example, those of tomatoes and oranges—have a compound pistil. Other, less specialized flowers—for example, buttercups and stonecups—may have several to many separate, simple pistils, each formed from a single carpel.

Ovules (which develop into seeds) are produced in the pistil's swollen lower portion, the **ovary,** which usually narrows at the top into a slender, necklike style with a pollen-receptive stigma at its apex. Sometimes the stigma is divided, with the number of stigma branches indicating how many carpels compose the particular pistil.

Carpels are essentially rolled floral leaves with ovules along the margins. It is possible that the first carpels were leaf blades that folded longitudinally; the leaf margins, which had hairs, did not actually fuse until the fruit developed, but the hairs interlocked and were receptive to pollen. In the course of evolution, evidence indicates that the hairs became localized into a stigma; a style was formed; and the fusing of the carpel margins ultimately resulted in a pistil. In many modern flowering plants, the carpels have become highly modified and are not visually distinguishable from one another unless the pistil is cut open.

Trends of floral specialization

Two major evolutionary trends led to the wide diversity of modern flowering plants: (1) Separate floral parts have grouped together, or fused, and (2) floral parts have been lost or reduced (figure 42.15).

In the more advanced angiosperms, the number of parts in each whorl has often been reduced from many to few. The spiral patterns of attachment of all floral parts in primitive an-

Figure 42.16
Bilateral symmetry in an orchid.
Although more basal flowers are usually radially symmetrical, flowers of many derived groups, such as the orchid family (Orchidaceae), are bilaterally symmetrical.

giosperms have, in the course of evolution, given way to a single whorl at each level. The central axis of many flowers has shortened, and the whorls are close to one another. In some evolutionary lines, the members of one or more whorls have fused with one another, sometimes joining into a tube. In other kinds of flowering plants, different whorls may be fused together.

Whole whorls may even be lost from the flower, which may lack sepals, petals, stamens, carpels, or various combinations of these structures. Modifications often relate to pollination mechanisms, and in plants such as the grasses, wind has replaced animals for pollen dispersal.

Trends in floral symmetry

Other trends in floral evolution have affected the symmetry of the flower. Primitive flowers such as those of buttercups are radially symmetrical; that is, one could draw a line anywhere through the center and have two roughly equal halves. Flowers of many advanced groups are bilaterally symmetrical; they are divisible into two equal parts along only a single plane. Examples of such flowers are snapdragons, mints, and orchids (figure 42.16). Bilaterally symmetrical flowers are also common among violets and peas. In these groups, they are often associated with advanced and highly precise pollination systems.

Bilateral symmetry has arisen independently many times. In snapdragons, the *CYCLOIDIA* gene regulates floral symmetry, and in its absence flowers are more radial (figure 42.17).

Figure 42.15
Trends in floral specialization. Wild geranium, *Geranium maculatum*, a typical eudicot. The petals are reduced to five each, the stamens to ten, compared with early angiosperms.

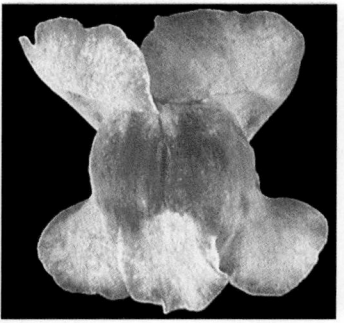

a.   *b.*

Figure 42.17 Genetic regulation of asymmetry in flowers. *a.* Snapdragon flowers normally have bilateral symmetry. *b.* The *CYCLOIDIA* gene regulates floral symmetry, and *cycloidia* mutant snapdragons have radially symmetrical flowers.

Here the experimental alteration of a single gene is sufficient to cause a dramatic change in morphology. Whether the same gene or functionally similar genes arose naturally in parallel in other species is an open question.

The human influence on flower morphology

Although much floral diversity is the result of natural selection related to pollination, it is important to recognize the effect breeding (artificial selection) has on flower morphology. Humans have selected for practical or aesthetic traits that may have little adaptive value to species in the wild. For example, maize (corn) has been bred to satisfy the human palate. Human intervention ensures the reproductive success of each generation; however, in a natural setting, modern corn would not have the same protection from herbivores as its ancestors, and the fruit dispersal mechanism would be quite different.

Gametes are produced in the gametophytes of flowers

Reproductive success depends on uniting the gametes (egg and sperm) found in the embryo sacs and pollen grains of flowers. As you learned in chapter 30, plant sexual life cycles are characterized by an *alternation of generations*, in which a diploid sporophyte generation gives rise to a haploid gametophyte generation. In angiosperms, the gametophyte generation is very small and is completely enclosed within the tissues of the parent sporophyte. The male gametophytes, or microgametophytes, are **pollen grains.** The female gametophyte, or megagametophyte, is the **embryo sac.** Pollen grains and the embryo sac both are produced in separate, specialized structures of the angiosperm flower.

Like animals, angiosperms have separate structures for producing male and female gametes (figure 42.18), but the reproductive organs of angiosperms are different from those of animals in two ways. First, both male and female structures usually occur together in the same individual flower. Second, angiosperm reproductive structures are not permanent parts of the adult individual. Angiosperm flowers and reproductive organs develop seasonally, at times of the year most favorable for pollination. In some cases, reproductive structures are produced only once, and the parent plant dies. And, as you learned earlier in this chapter, the germ line in angiosperms is not set aside early on, but forms quite late during phase change.

Pollen formation

Anthers contain four microsporangia, which produce microspore mother cells *(2n)*. Microspore mother cells produce microspores *(n)* through meiotic cell division. The microspores, through mitosis and wall differentiation, become pollen. Inside each pollen grain is a generative cell; this cell later divides to produce two sperm cells.

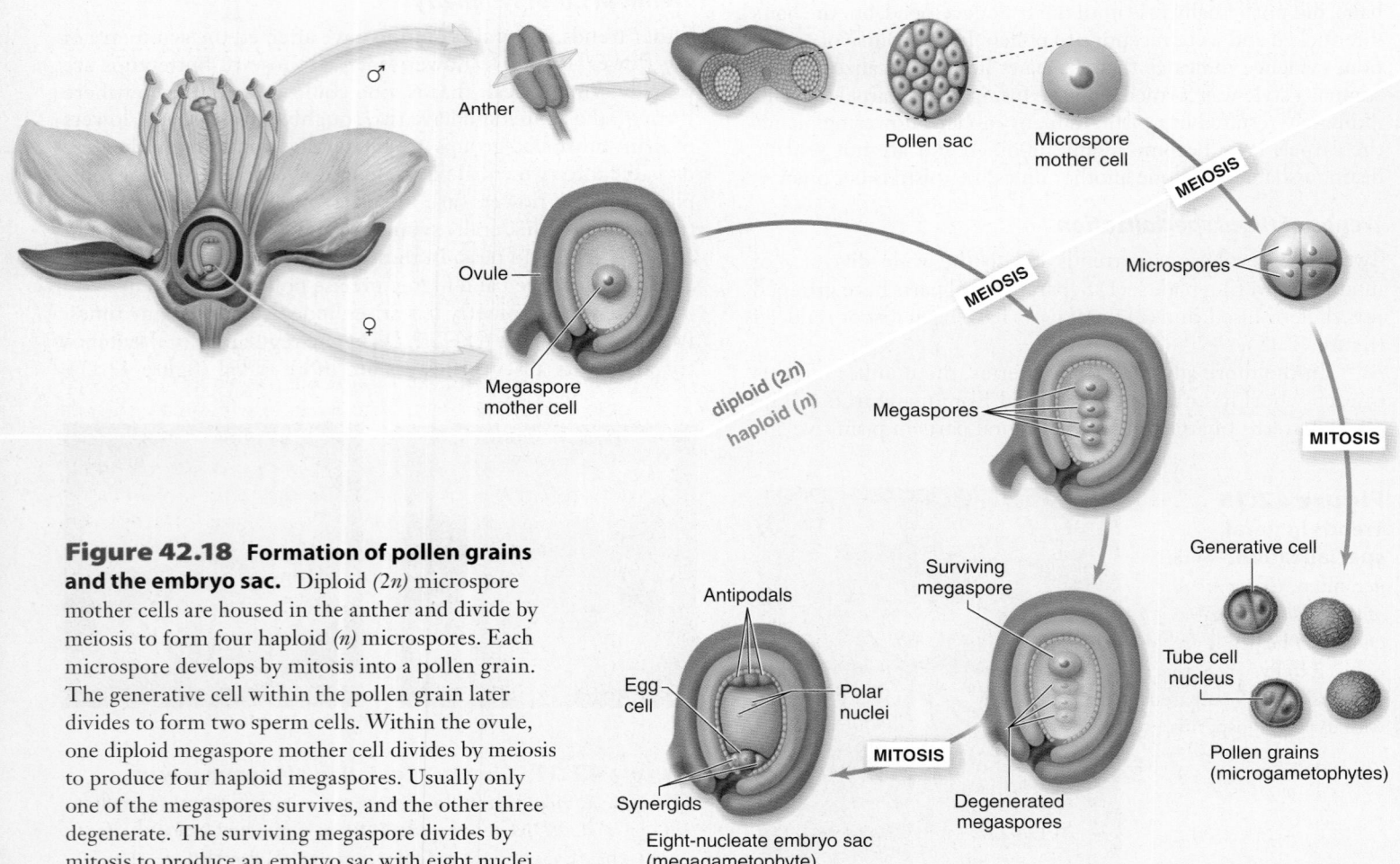

Figure 42.18 Formation of pollen grains and the embryo sac. Diploid *(2n)* microspore mother cells are housed in the anther and divide by meiosis to form four haploid *(n)* microspores. Each microspore develops by mitosis into a pollen grain. The generative cell within the pollen grain later divides to form two sperm cells. Within the ovule, one diploid megaspore mother cell divides by meiosis to produce four haploid megaspores. Usually only one of the megaspores survives, and the other three degenerate. The surviving megaspore divides by mitosis to produce an embryo sac with eight nuclei.

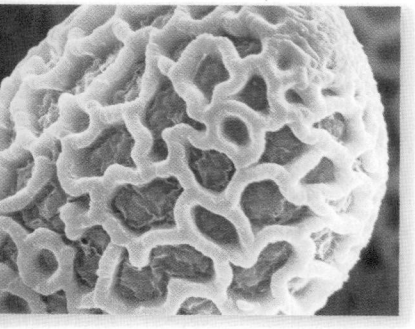

a.   *b.*

Figure 42.19   Pollen grains. *a.* In the Easter lily, *Lilium candidum*, the pollen tube emerges from the pollen grain through the groove or furrow that occurs on one side of the grain. *b.* In a plant of the sunflower family, *Hyoseris longiloba*, three pores are hidden among the ornamentation of the pollen grain. The pollen tube may grow out through any one of them.

Pollen grain shapes are specialized for specific flower species. As discussed in more detail later in this section, fertilization requires that the pollen grain grow a tube that penetrates the style until it encounters the ovary. Most pollen grains have a furrow or pore from which this pollen tube emerges; some grains have three furrows (figure 42.19).

Embryo sac formation

Eggs develop in the ovules of the angiosperm flower. Within each ovule is a megaspore mother cell. Just as in pollen production, the megaspore mother cell undergoes meiosis to produce four haploid megaspores. In most plants, however, only one of these megaspores survives; the rest are absorbed by the ovule. The lone remaining megaspore enlarges and undergoes repeated mitotic divisions to produce eight haploid nuclei that are enclosed within a seven-celled embryo sac.

Within the embryo sac, the eight nuclei are arranged in precise positions. One nucleus is located near the opening of the embryo sac in the egg cell. Two others are located together in a single cell in the middle of the embryo sac; these are called *polar nuclei*. Two more nuclei are contained in individual cells called synergids that flank the egg cell; the other three nuclei reside in cells called the antipodals, located at the end of the sac, opposite the egg cell (figure 42.20).

The first step in uniting the two sperm cells in the pollen grain with the egg and polar nuclei is the germination of pollen on the stigma of the carpel and its growth toward the embryo sac.

Learning Outcomes Review 42.3

An angiosperm flower consists of four concentric whorls: calyx, corolla, androecium, and gynoecium. Bilaterally symmetrical flowers are divisible into two equal parts along only a single plane; radially symmetrical flowers can be divided equally on any plane. The microspore mother cells in flowers undergo meiosis to produce microspores, which undergo mitosis to produce microgametophytes (pollen grains). Megaspore mother cells undergo a similar process to produce megaspores, which result in megagametophytes (embryo sacs).

■   *What is the main evolutionary advantage of the flower?*

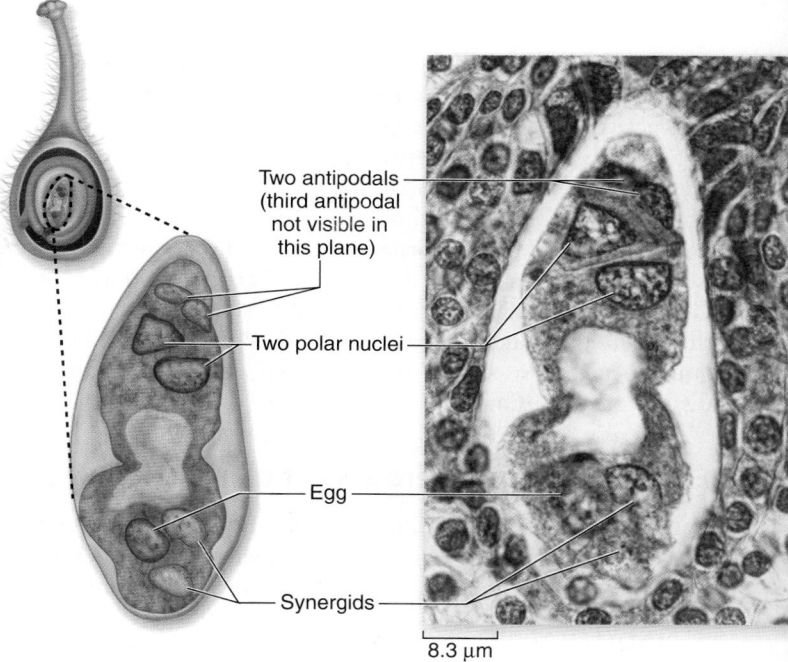

Two antipodals (third antipodal not visible in this plane)

Two polar nuclei

Egg

Synergids

8.3 μm

Figure 42.20   A mature embryo sac of a lily.   Eight nuclei are produced by mitotic divisions of the haploid megaspore. One is in the egg, two are polar nuclei, two occur in synergid cells, and three are in antipodal cells. The micrograph is falsely colored.

42.4   Pollination and Fertilization

Learning Outcomes

1.   **Discuss conditions under which self-pollination may be favored.**
2.   **Describe three evolutionary strategies that promote outcrossing.**
3.   **List the products of double fertilization.**

Pollination is the process by which pollen is placed on the stigma. Pollen may be carried to the flower by wind or by animals, or it may originate within the individual flower itself. When pollen from a flower's anther pollinates the same flower's stigma, the process is called *self-pollination*. When pollen from the anther of one flower pollinates the stigma of a different flower, the process is termed *cross-pollination*, or *outcrossing*.

As you just learned, pollination in angiosperms does not involve direct contact between the pollen grain and the ovule. When pollen reaches the stigma, it germinates, and a pollen tube grows down, carrying the sperm nuclei to the embryo sac. After double fertilization takes place, development of the embryo and endosperm begins. The seed matures within the ripening fruit; eventually, the germination of the seed initiates another life cycle.

Successful pollination in many angiosperms depends on the regular attraction of **pollinators,** such as insects, birds, and other animals, which transfer pollen between plants of the same species. When animals disperse pollen, they perform the same function for flowering plants that they do for themselves when they actively search out mates.

The relationship between plant and pollinator can be quite intricate. Mutations in either partner can block reproduction. If a plant flowers at the "wrong" time, the pollinator may not be available. If the morphology of the flower or pollinator is altered, the result may be physical barriers to pollination. Clearly, floral morphology has coevolved with pollinators, and the result is a much more complex and diverse morphology, going beyond the simple initiation and development of four distinct whorls of organs.

Early seed plants were wind-pollinated

Early seed plants were pollinated passively, by the action of the wind. As in present-day conifers, great quantities of pollen were shed and blown about, occasionally reaching the vicinity of the ovules of the same species.

Individual plants of any wind-pollinated species must grow relatively close to one another for such a system to operate efficiently. Otherwise, the chance that any pollen will arrive at an appropriate destination is very small. The vast majority of windblown pollen travels less than 100 m. This short distance is significant compared with the long distances pollen is routinely carried by certain insects, birds, and other animals.

Flowers and animal pollinators have coevolved

The spreading of pollen from plant to plant by pollinators visiting flowers of an angiosperm species has played an important role in the evolutionary success of the group. It now seems clear that the earliest angiosperms, and perhaps their ancestors also, were insect-pollinated, and the coevolution of insects and plants has been important for both groups for over 100 million years. Such interactions have also been important in bringing about increased floral specialization. As flowers become increasingly specialized, so do their relationships with particular groups of insects and other animals.

Bees

Among insect-pollinated angiosperms, the most numerous groups are those pollinated by bees (figure 42.21). Like most insects, bees initially locate sources of food by odor and then orient themselves on the flower or group of flowers by its shape, color, and texture.

Flowers that bees characteristically visit are often blue or yellow. Many have stripes or lines of dots that indicate the location of the nectaries, which often occur within the throats of specialized flowers. Some bees collect nectar, which is used as a source of food for adult bees and occasionally for larvae. Most of the approximately 20,000 species of bees visit flowers to obtain pollen, which is used to provide food in cells where bee larvae complete their development.

Except for a few hundred species of social and semisocial bees and about 1000 species that are parasitic in the nests of other bees, the great majority of bees—at least 18,000 species—are solitary. Solitary bees in temperate regions characteristically

Figure 42.21   Pollination by a bumblebee. As this bumblebee, *Bombus* sp., collects nectar, pollen sticks to its body. The pollen will be distributed to the next plant the bee visits.

produce only a single generation in the course of a year. Often, they are active as adults for as little as a few weeks a year.

Solitary bees often use the flowers of a particular group of plants almost exclusively as sources of their larval food. The highly constant relationships of such bees with those flowers may lead to modifications, over time, in both the flowers and the bees. For example, the time of day when the flowers open may correlate with the time when the bees appear; the mouthparts of the bees may become elongated in relation to tubular flowers; or the bees' pollen-collecting apparatuses may be adapted to the anthers of the plants that they normally visit. When such relationships are established, they provide both an efficient mechanism of pollination for the flowers and a constant source of food for the bees that "specialize" on them.

Insects other than bees

Among flower-visiting insects other than bees, a few groups are especially prominent. Flowers such as phlox, which are visited regularly by butterflies, often have flat "landing platforms" on which butterflies perch. They also tend to have long, slender floral tubes filled with nectar that is accessible to the long, coiled proboscis characteristic of Lepidoptera, the order of insects that includes butterflies and moths.

Flowers such as jimsonweed (*Datura stramonium*), evening primrose (*Oenothera biennis*), and others visited regularly by moths are often white, yellow, or some other pale color; they also tend to be heavily scented, making the flowers easy to locate at night (figure 42.22).

Birds

Several interesting groups of plants are regularly visited and pollinated by birds, especially the hummingbirds of North and South America and the sunbirds of Africa (figure 42.23). Such plants must produce large amounts of nectar because birds will not continue to visit flowers if they do not find enough food to

Hypothesis: *Moths are more effective than bumblebees at moving pollen long distances.*

Prediction: *The pollen donors of seeds of wild plants are more widely distributed if moths carried the pollen than if bees carried it.*

Test: *Locate a large natural patch of the wild plant. Make sure that both moths and bees are abundant and that the plants are variable for a genetically controlled trait. In this case, assume the population contains some purple-flowered plants (a dominant trait) and some with white flowers (a recessive trait). Remove all the flowers from the purple-flowered plants except those at the edge of the population. Find a white-flowered plant at the center of the population to use as the test plant. Cover some flowers during the day and uncover them in the evening so moths, but not bees, can pollinate them. With other flowers, cover in the evening but not during the day, so bees, but not moths, can pollinate them. Collect seeds from each set of flowers and grow the plants. For each treatment, count the number of plants that produce purple flowers. These will have pollen donors that were a long distance from the test plant.*

Cover some flowers during the day and others in the evening. Count the number of purple flowered plants obtained from each treatment.

Result: *Seeds produced by bee pollination produced the same number of plants with purple flowers as those produced by moth pollination.*

Conclusion: *The hypothesis is not supported. Bees carry pollen as far as moths do.*

Further Experiments: *Growing plants from seed to check for flower color is very time-consuming. Propose another way to determine the source of the pollen in this experiment.*

Figure 42.22 Bees and moths as pollinators.

maintain themselves. But flowers producing large amounts of nectar have no advantage in being visited by insects, because an insect could obtain its energy requirements at a single flower and would not cross-pollinate the flower. How are these different selective forces balanced in flowers that are "specialized" for hummingbirds and sunbirds?

The answer involves the evolution of flower color. Ultraviolet light is highly visible to insects. Carotenoids, the yellow

Figure 42.23 Hummingbirds and flowers. A long-tailed hermit hummingbird *(Phaethornis superciliosus)* extracts nectar from the flowers of *Heliconia imbricata* in the forests of Costa Rica. Note the pollen on the bird's beak. Hummingbirds of this group obtain nectar primarily from long, curved flowers that more or less match the length and shape of their beaks.

or orange pigments we described in chapter 8 in the context of photosynthesis, are responsible for the colors of many flowers, including sunflowers and mustard. Carotenoids reflect both in the yellow range and in the ultraviolet range, the mixture resulting in a distinctive color called "bee's purple." Such yellow flowers may also be marked in distinctive ways normally invisible to us, but highly visible to bees and other insects (figure 42.24). These markings can be in the form of a bull's-eye or a landing strip.

a. *b.*

Figure 42.24 How a bee sees a flower. *a.* The yellow flower of *Ludwigia peruviana* (Peruvian primrose) photographed in normal light and *(b)* with a filter that selectively transmits ultraviolet light. The outer sections of the petals reflect both yellow and ultraviolet, a mixture of colors called "bee's purple"; the inner portions of the petals reflect yellow only and therefore appear dark in the photograph that emphasizes ultraviolet reflection. To a bee, this flower appears as if it has a conspicuous central bull's-eye.

Figure 42.25 Staminate and pistillate flowers of a birch, *Betula* sp. Birches are monoecious; their staminate flowers hang down in long, yellowish tassels, and their pistillate flowers mature into clusters of small, brownish, conelike structures.

In contrast, red does not stand out as a distinct color to most insects, but it is a very conspicuous color to birds. To most insects, the red upper leaves of poinsettias look just like the other leaves of the plant. Consequently, even though the flowers produce abundant supplies of nectar and attract humming-birds, insects tend to bypass them. Thus, the red color both signals to birds the presence of abundant nectar and makes that nectar as inconspicuous as possible to insects. Red is also seen again in fruits that are dispersed by birds (see chapter 37).

Other animal pollinators

Other animals, including bats and small rodents, may aid in pollination. The signals here are also species-specific. As an example, the saguaro cactus (*Carnegeia gigantea*) of the Sonoran desert is pollinated by bats that feed on nectar at night, as well as by birds and insects.

These animals may also assist in dispersing the seeds and fruits that result from pollination. Monkeys are attracted to orange and yellow, and thus can be effective in dispersing fruits of this color in their habitats.

Some flowering plants continue to use wind pollination

A number of groups of angiosperms are wind-pollinated—a characteristic of early seed plants. Among these groups are oaks, birches, cottonwoods, grasses, sedges, and nettles. The flowers of these plants are small, greenish, and odorless; their corollas are reduced or absent (figures 42.25 and 42.26). Such flowers often are grouped together in fairly large numbers

and may hang down in tassels that wave about in the wind and shed pollen freely.

Many wind-pollinated plants have stamen- and carpel-containing flowers separated between individuals or physically separated on a single individual. Maize is a good example, with pollen-producing tassels at the top of the plant and axillary shoots with female flowers lower down. Separation of pollen-producing and ovule-bearing flowers is a strategy that greatly promotes outcrossing, since pollen from one flower must land on a different flower for fertilization to have any chance of occurring. Some wind-pollinated plants, especially trees and shrubs, flower in the spring, before the development of their leaves can interfere with the wind-borne pollen. Wind-pollinated species do not depend on the presence of a pollinator for species survival, which may be another survival advantage.

Self-pollination is favored in stable environments

Thus far we have considered examples of pollination that tend to lead to outcrossing, which is as highly advantageous for plants and for eukaryotic organisms generally. Nevertheless, self-pollination also occurs among angiosperms, particularly in temperate regions. Most self-pollinating plants have small, relatively inconspicuous flowers that shed pollen directly onto the stigma, sometimes even before the bud opens.

You might logically ask why many self-pollinated plant species have survived if outcrossing is as important genetically

Figure 42.26 Wind-pollinated flowers. The large yellow anthers, dangling on very slender filaments, are hanging out, about to shed their pollen to the wind. Later, these flowers will become pistillate, with long, feathery stigmas—well suited for trapping windblown pollen—sticking far out of them. Many grasses, like this one, are therefore dichogamous.

for plants as it is for animals. Biologists propose two basic reasons for the frequent occurrence of self-pollinated angiosperms:

1. Self-pollination is ecologically advantageous under certain circumstances because self-pollinators do not need to be visited by animals to produce seed. As a result, self-pollinated plants expend less energy in producing pollinator attractants and can grow in areas where the kinds of insects or other animals that might visit them are absent or very scarce—as in the Arctic or at high elevations.

2. In genetic terms, self-pollination produces progenies that are more uniform than those that result from outcrossing. Remember that because meiosis is involved, recombination still takes place, as described in chapter 11—and therefore the offspring will not be identical to the parent. However, such progenies may contain high proportions of individuals well-adapted to particular habitats.

Self-pollination in normally outcrossing species tends to produce large numbers of ill-adapted individuals because it brings together deleterious recessive alleles—but some of these combinations may be highly advantageous in particular habitats. In these habitats, it may be advantageous for the plant to continue self-pollinating indefinitely.

Several evolutionary strategies promote outcrossing

Outcrossing, as we have stressed, is critically important for the adaptation and evolution of all eukaryotic organisms, with a few exceptions. Often, flowers contain both stamens and pistils,

which increases the likelihood of self-pollination. One general strategy to promote outcrossing, therefore, is to separate stamens and pistils. Another strategy involves self-incompatibility that prevents self-fertilization.

Separation of male and female structures in space or in time

In a number of species—for example, willows and some mulberries—staminate and pistillate flowers may occur on separate plants. Such plants, which produce only ovules or only pollen, are called dioecious, meaning "two houses." These plants clearly cannot self-pollinate and must rely exclusively on outcrossing. In other kinds of plants, such as oaks, birches, corn (maize), and pumpkins, separate male and female flowers may both be produced on the same plant. Such plants are called **monoecious,** meaning "one house" (see figure 42.25). In monoecious plants, the separation of pistillate and staminate flowers, which may mature at different times, greatly enhances the probability of outcrossing.

Even if, as usually is the case, functional stamens and pistils are both present in each flower of a particular plant species, these organs may reach maturity at different times. Plants in which this occurs are called **dichogamous.** If the stamens mature first, shedding their pollen before the stigmas are receptive, the flower is effectively staminate at that time. Once the stamens have finished shedding pollen, the stigma or stigmas may become receptive, and the flower may become essentially pistillate (see figures 42.26 and 42.27). This separation in time has the same effect as if individuals were dioecious; the outcrossing rate is thereby significantly increased.

Many flowers are constructed such that the stamens and stigmas do not come in contact with each other. With this

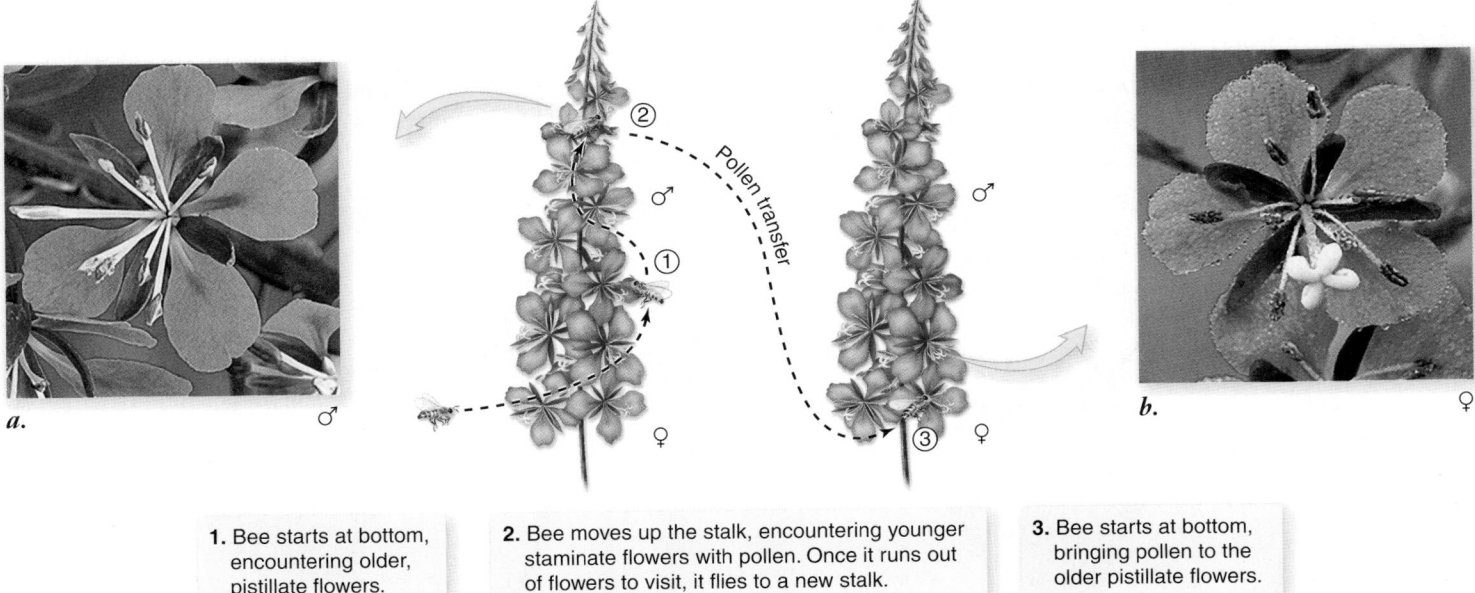

1. Bee starts at bottom, encountering older, pistillate flowers.

2. Bee moves up the stalk, encountering younger staminate flowers with pollen. Once it runs out of flowers to visit, it flies to a new stalk.

3. Bee starts at bottom, bringing pollen to the older pistillate flowers.

Figure 42.27 Dichogamy, as illustrated by the flowers of fireweed, *Epilobium angustifolium.* More than 200 years ago (in the 1790s) fireweed, which is outcrossing, was one of the first plant species to have its process of pollination described. First, the anthers shed pollen, and then the style elongates above the stamens while the four lobes of the stigma curl back and become receptive. Consequently, the flowers are functionally staminate at first, becoming pistillate about two days later. The flowers open progressively up the stem, so that the lowest are visited first, promoting outcrossing. Working up the stem, the bees encounter pollen-shedding, staminate-phase flowers and become covered with pollen, which they then carry to the lower, functionally pistillate flowers of another plant. Shown here are flowers in (*a*) the staminate phase and (*b*) the pistillate phase.

    chapter **42** *Plant Reproduction* **855**

arrangement, the natural tendency is for the pollen to be transferred to the stigma of another flower, rather than to the stigma of its own flower, thereby promoting outcrossing.

Self-incompatibility

Even when a flower's stamens and stigma mature at the same time, genetic self-incompatibility, which is widespread in flowering plants, increases outcrossing. Self-incompatibility results when the pollen and stigma recognize each other as being genetically related, and pollen tube growth is blocked (figure 42.28).

Self-incompatibility is controlled by the *S* (self-incompatibility) locus. Many alleles at the *S* locus regulate recognition responses between pollen and stigma. Researchers have identified two types of self-incompatibility. *Gametophytic self-incompatibility* depends on the haploid *S* locus of the pollen and the diploid *S* locus of the stigma. If either of the *S* alleles in the stigma matches the pollen's *S* allele, pollen tube growth stops before it reaches the embryo sac. Petunias exhibit gametophytic self-incompatibility.

In *sporophytic self-incompatibility*, as occurs in broccoli, both *S* alleles of the pollen parent, not just the *S* allele of the pollen itself, are important. If the alleles in the stigma match either of the pollen parent's *S* alleles, the haploid pollen will not germinate.

Pollen-recognition mechanisms may have originated in a common ancestor of the gymnosperms. Fossils with pollen tubes from the Carboniferous period are consistent with the hypothesis that they had highly evolved pollen-recognition systems.

Angiosperms undergo double fertilization

Fertilization in angiosperms is a complex, somewhat unusual process in which two sperm cells are utilized in a unique process called double fertilization. Double fertilization results in two key developments: (1) the fertilization of the egg, and (2) the formation of a nutrient substance called endosperm that nourishes the embryo.

Once a pollen grain has been spread by wind, by animals, or through self-pollination, it adheres to the sticky, sugary substance that covers the stigma and begins to grow a pollen tube that pierces the style (figure 42.29). The pollen tube, nourished by the sugary substance, grows until it reaches the ovule in the ovary. Meanwhile, the generative cell within the pollen grain tube cell divides to form two sperm cells.

The pollen tube eventually reaches the embryo sac in the ovule. At the entry to the embryo sac, one of the nuclei flanking the egg cell degenerates, and the pollen tube enters that cell. The tip of the pollen tube bursts and releases the two sperm cells. One of the sperm cells fertilizes the egg cell, forming a zygote. The other sperm cell fuses with the two polar nuclei located at the center of the embryo sac, forming the triploid ($3n$) primary endosperm nucleus. The primary endosperm nucleus eventually develops into the endosperm (food supply).

Once fertilization is complete, the embryo develops as its cells divide numerous times. Meanwhile, protective tissues

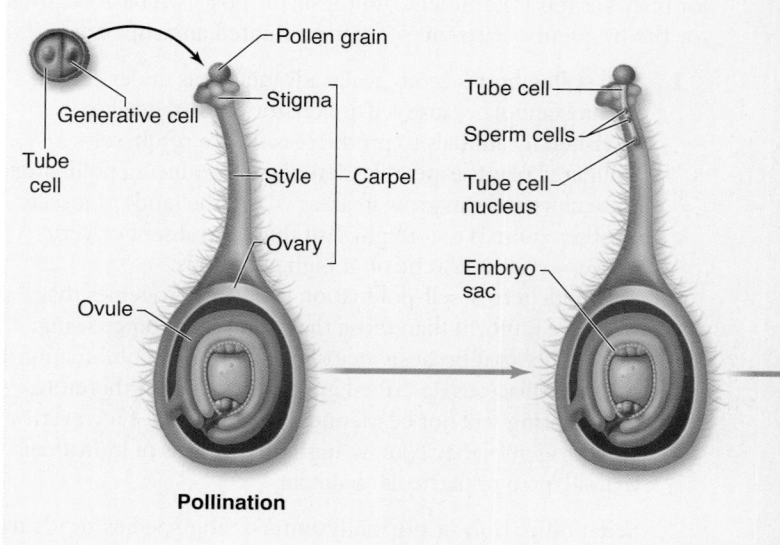

Pollination

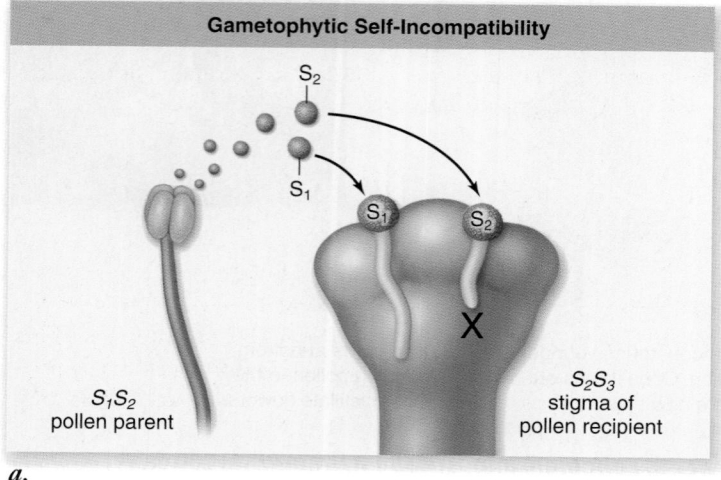

a.

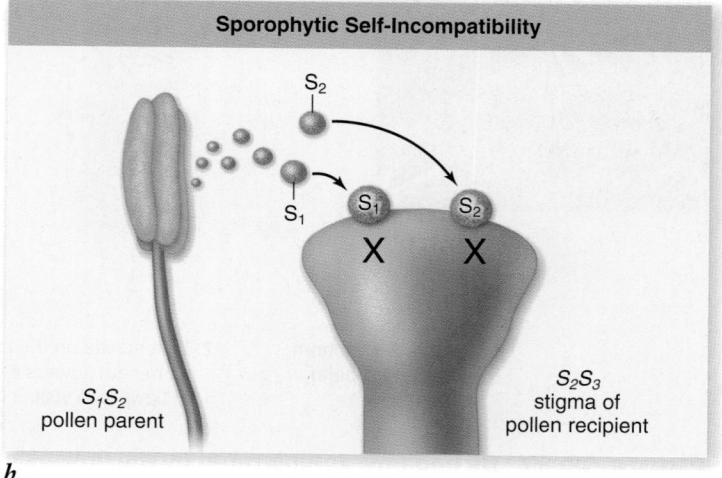

b.

Figure 42.28 Genetic control can block self-pollination. *a.* Gametophytic self-incompatibility is determined by the haploid pollen genotype. *b.* Sporophytic self-incompatibility recognizes the genotype of the diploid pollen parent, not just the haploid pollen genotype. The pollen contains proteins produced by the S_1S_2 parent. In both cases, the recognition is based on the *S* locus, which has many different alleles. The subscript numbers indicate the *S* allele genotype. In gametophytic self-incompatibility, the block comes after pollen tube germination. In sporophytic self-incompatibility, the pollen tube fails to germinate.

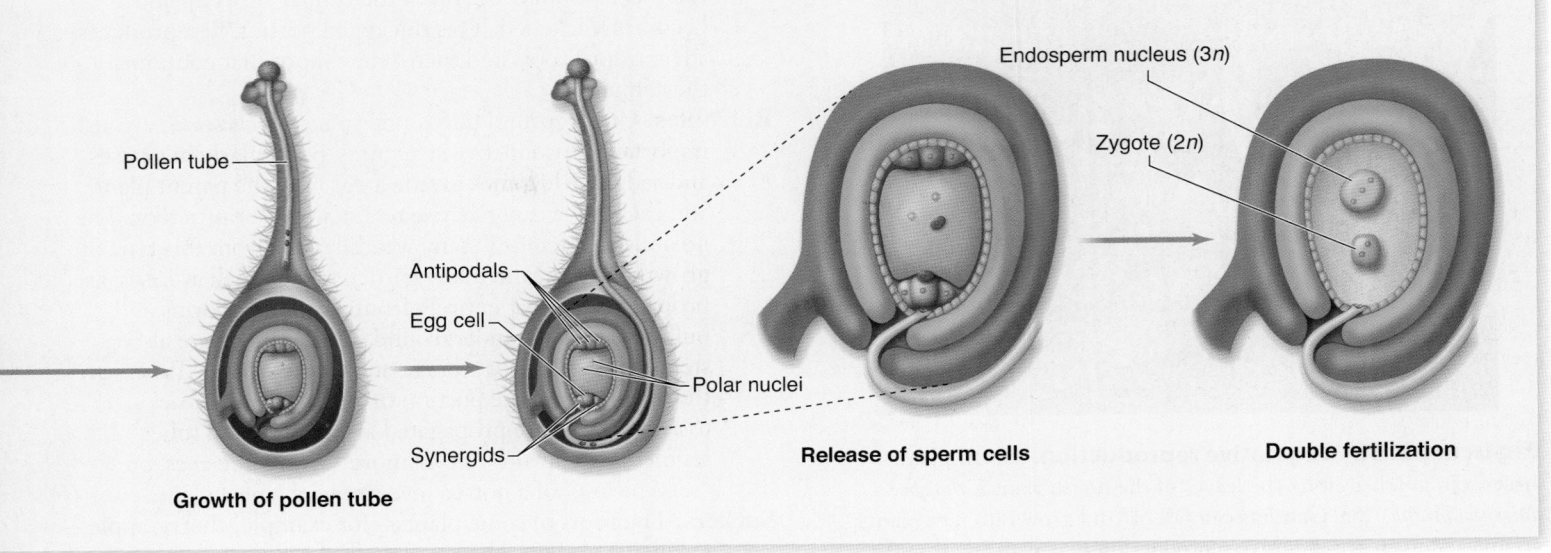

Figure 42.29 The formation of the pollen tube and double fertilization. When pollen lands on the stigma of a flower, the pollen tube cell grows toward the embryo sac, forming a pollen tube. While the pollen tube is growing, the generative cell divides to form two sperm cells. When the pollen tube reaches the embryo sac, it enters one of the synergids and releases the sperm cells. In a process called double fertilization, one sperm cell nucleus fuses with the egg cell to form the diploid *(2n)* zygote, and the other sperm cell nucleus fuses with the two polar nuclei to form the triploid *(3n)* endosperm nucleus.

enclose the embryo, resulting in the formation of the seed. The seed, in turn, is enclosed in another structure, called the fruit. These typical angiosperm structures evolved in response to the need for seeds to be dispersed over long distances to ensure genetic variability.

Learning Outcomes Review 42.4

Self-pollination may be favored when pollinators are absent or when plants are adapted to a stable environment, and therefore uniform offspring are advantageous. Mechanisms to promote outcrossing include the production of separate male and female flowers, maturation of male flowers at a different time than female flowers, and genetically controlled self-incompatibility. Double fertilization produces a diploid embryo and triploid endosperm that provides nutrition.

■ *Are all offspring of a self-pollinating plant identical?*

42.5 *Asexual Reproduction*

Learning Outcomes

1. *Define apomixis.*
2. *List examples of plant parts involved in vegetative reproduction.*
3. *Outline the steps involved in protoplast regeneration.*

Self-pollination reduces genetic variability, but asexual reproduction results in genetically identical individuals because only mitotic cell divisions occur. In the absence of meiosis, individuals that are highly adapted to a relatively unchanging environment persist for the same reasons that self-pollination is favored. Should conditions change dramatically, there will be less variation in the population for natural selection to act on, and the species may be less likely to survive.

Asexual reproduction is also used in agriculture and horticulture to propagate a particularly desirable plant with traits that would be altered by sexual reproduction or even by self-pollination. Most roses and potatoes, for example, are vegetatively (asexually) propagated.

Apomixis involves development of diploid embryos

In certain plants, including some citruses, certain grasses (such as Kentucky bluegrass), and dandelions, the embryos in the seeds may be produced asexually from the parent plant. This kind of asexual reproduction is known as apomixis. Seeds produced in this way give rise to individuals that are genetically identical to their parents.

Although these plants reproduce by cloning diploid cells in the ovule, they also gain the advantage of seed dispersal, an adaptation usually associated with sexual reproduction. Asexual reproduction in plants is far more common in harsh or marginal environments, where there is little leeway for variation. For example, a greater proportion of asexual plants occur in the Arctic than in temperate regions.

Figure 42.30 Vegetative reproduction. Small plants arise from notches along the leaves of the house plant *Kalanchoë daigremontiana*. The plantlets can fall off and grow into new plants, an unusual form of vegetative reproduction.

In vegetative reproduction, new plants arise from nonreproductive tissues

In a very common form of asexual reproduction called vegetative reproduction, new plant individuals are simply cloned from parts of adults (figure 42.30). The forms of vegetative reproduction in plants are many and varied.

Runners or stolons. Some plants reproduce by means of *runners* (also called stolons)—long, slender stems that grow along the surface of the soil. In the cultivated strawberry, for example, leaves, flowers, and roots are produced at every other node on the runner. Just beyond each second node, the tip of the runner turns up and becomes thickened. This thickened portion first produces adventitious roots and then a new shoot that continues the runner.

Rhizomes. Underground horizontal stems, or *rhizomes*, are also important reproductive structures, particularly in grasses and sedges. Rhizomes invade areas near the parent plant, and each node can give rise to a new flowering shoot. The noxious character of many weeds results from this type of growth pattern, and many garden plants, such as irises, are propagated almost entirely from rhizomes. Corms and bulbs are vertical underground stems. Tubers are also stems specialized for storage and reproduction. Tubers are the terminal storage portion of a rhizome. Potatoes (*Solanum* spp.) are propagated artificially from tuber segments, each with one or more "eyes." The eyes, or "seed pieces," of a potato give rise to the new plant.

Suckers. The roots of some plants—for example, cherry, apple, raspberry, and blackberry—produce *suckers*, or sprouts, which give rise to new plants. Commercial varieties of banana do not produce seeds and are propagated by suckers that develop from buds on underground stems. When the root of a dandelion is broken, as it may be if one attempts to pull it from the ground, each root fragment may give rise to a new plant.

Adventitious plantlets. In a few plant species, even the leaves are reproductive. One example is the houseplant *Kalanchoë daigremontiana* (see figure 42.30), familiar to many people as the "maternity plant," or "mother of thousands." The common names of this plant are based on the fact that numerous plantlets arise from meristematic tissue located in notches along the leaves. The maternity plant is ordinarily propagated by means of these small plants, which, when they mature, drop to the soil and take root.

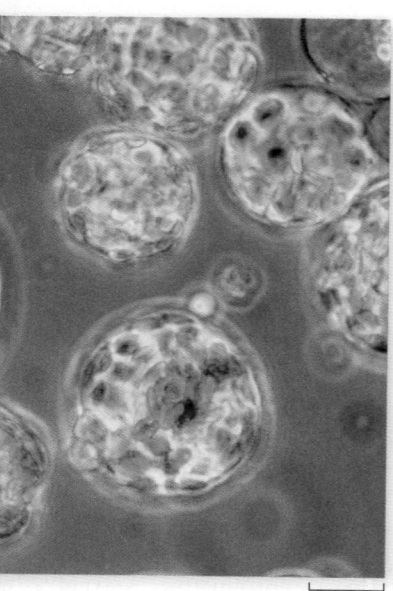
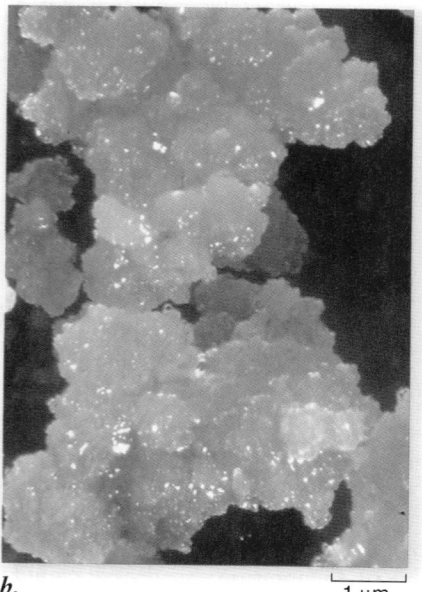
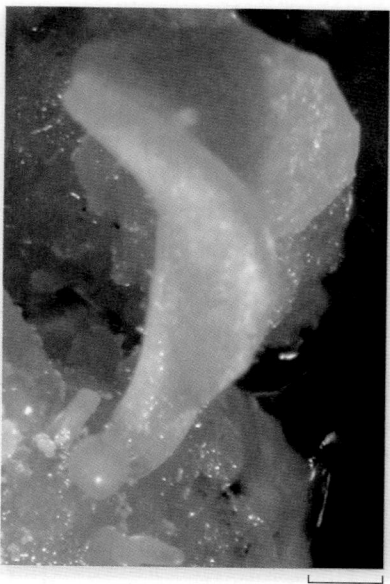

a.   100 μm   *b.*   1 μm   *c.*   1 μm   *d.*   1 μm

Figure 42.31 Protoplast regeneration. Different stages in the recovery of intact plants from single plant protoplasts of evening primrose. *a.* Individual plant protoplasts. *b.* Regeneration of the cell wall and the beginning of cell division. *c.* Production of somatic cell embryos from the callus. *d.* Recovery of a plantlet from the somatic cell embryo in culture. The plant can later be rooted in soil.

Plants can be cloned from isolated cells in the laboratory

Whole plants can be cloned by regenerating plant cells or tissues on nutrient medium with growth hormones. This is another form of asexual reproduction. Cultured leaf, stem, and root tissues can undergo organogenesis in culture and form roots and shoots. In some cases, individual cells can also give rise to whole plants in culture.

Individual cells can be isolated from tissues with enzymes that break down cell walls, leaving behind the *protoplast*, a plant cell enclosed only by a plasma membrane. Plant cells have greater developmental plasticity than most vertebrate animal cells, and many, but not all, cell types in plants maintain the ability to generate organs or an entire organism in culture. Consider the limited number of adult stem cells in vertebrates and the challenges associated with cloning discussed in chapter 19.

When single plant cells are cultured, wall regeneration takes place. Cell division follows to form a *callus*, an undifferentiated mass of cells (figure 42.31). Once a callus is formed, whole plants can be produced in culture. Whole-plant development can go through an embryonic stage or can start with the formation of a shoot or root.

Tissue culture has many agricultural and horticultural applications. Virus-free raspberries and sugarcane can be propagated by culturing meristems, which are generally free of viruses, even in an infected plant. As with other forms of asexual reproduction, genetically identical individuals can be propagated.

a.   *b.*

Figure 42.32 Annual and perennial plants. Plants live for very different lengths of time. *a.* Desert annuals complete their entire life span in a few weeks, flowering just once. *b.* Some trees, such as the giant redwood (*Sequoiadendron giganteum*), which occurs in scattered groves along the western slopes of the Sierra Nevada in California, live 2000 years or more, and flower year after year.

Learning Outcomes Review 42.5

In apomixis, embryos are produced by mitosis rather than fertilization; in contrast, asexual vegetative reproduction occurs from vegetative plant parts. Examples include runners, stolons, rhizomes, suckers, and adventitious plant parts. In the laboratory, protoplasts are produced by isolating cells and removing the cell walls. Inducing mitosis results in a cluster of undifferentiated cells called a callus, which can then be stimulated to differentiate into a plant.

■ *Under what conditions would vegetative reproduction benefit survival?*

42.6   Plant Life Spans

Learning Outcomes

1. *Distinguish between herbaceous and woody perennials.*
2. *Define perennial and annual plants.*
3. *Describe the life cycle of a biennial plant.*

Once established, plants live for highly variable periods of time, depending on the species. Life span may or may not correlate with reproductive strategy. Woody plants, which have extensive secondary growth, nearly always live longer than herbaceous plants, which have limited or no secondary growth. Bristlecone pine, for example, can live upward of 4000 years.

Some herbaceous plants send new stems above the ground every year, producing them from woody underground structures. Others germinate and grow, flowering just once before they die. Shorter-lived plants rarely become very woody because there is not enough time for secondary tissues to accumulate. Depending on the length of their life cycles, herbaceous plants may be annual, biennial, or perennial, whereas woody plants are generally perennial (figure 42.32).

Determining life span is even more complicated for clonally reproducing organisms. Aspen trees (*Populus tremuloides*) form huge clones from asexual reproduction of their roots. Collectively, an aspen clone may form the largest "organism" on Earth. Other asexually reproducing plants may cover less territory but live for thousands of years. Creosote bushes (*Larrea tridentata*) in the Mojave Desert have been identified that are up to 12,000 years old!

Perennial plants live for many years

Perennial plants continue to grow year after year and may be herbaceous (as are many woodland, wetland, and prairie wildflowers), or woody (as are trees and shrubs). The majority of vascular plant species are perennials. Perennial plants in general are able to flower and produce seeds and fruit for an indefinite number of growing seasons.

Herbaceous perennials rarely experience any secondary growth in their stems; the stems die each year after a period of relatively rapid growth and food accumulation. Food is often stored in the plants' roots or underground stems, which can become quite large in comparison with their less substantial aboveground counterparts.

Trees and shrubs generally flower repeatedly, but there are exceptions. Bamboo lives for many seasons as a nonreproducing plant, but senesces and dies after flowering. The same is true for at least one tropical tree *(Tachigali versicolor)*, which achieves great heights before flowering and senescing. Considering the tremendous amount of energy that goes into the growth of a tree, this particular reproductive strategy is quite curious.

Trees and shrubs are either *deciduous*, with all the leaves falling at one particular time of year and the plants remaining bare for a period, or *evergreen*, with the leaves dropping throughout the year and the plants never appearing completely bare. In northern temperate regions, conifers are the most familiar evergreens, but in tropical and subtropical regions, most angiosperms are evergreen, except where there is severe seasonal drought. In these areas, many angiosperms are deciduous, losing their leaves during the drought and thus conserving water.

Annual plants grow, reproduce, and die in a single year

Annual plants grow, flower, and form fruits and seeds within one growing season and die when the process is complete. Many crop plants are annuals, including corn, wheat, and soybeans. Annuals generally grow rapidly under favorable conditions and in proportion to the availability of water or nutrients. The lateral meristems of some annuals, such as sunflowers or giant ragweed, do produce some secondary tissues for support, but most annuals are entirely herbaceous.

Annuals typically die after flowering once; the developing flowers or embryos use hormonal signaling to reallocate nutrients, so the parent plant literally starves to death. This can be demonstrated by comparing a population of bean plants in which the beans are continually picked with a population in which the beans are left on the plant. The frequently picked population will continue to grow and yield beans much longer than the untouched population. The process that leads to the death of a plant is called **senescence.**

Biennial plants follow a two-year life cycle

Biennial plants, which are much less common than annuals, have life cycles that take two years to complete. During the first year, biennials store the products of photosynthesis in underground storage organs. During the second year of growth, flowering stems are produced using energy stored in the underground parts of the plant. Certain crop plants, including carrots, cabbage, and beets, are biennials, but these plants generally are harvested for food during their first season, before they flower. They are grown for their leaves or roots, not for their fruits or seeds.

Wild biennials include evening primroses, Queen Anne's lace *(Daucus carota)*, and mullein *(Verbascum thapsis)*. Many plants that are considered biennials actually do not flower until they are three or more years of age, but all biennial plants flower only once before they die.

Learning Outcomes Review 42.6

Woody perennials produce secondary growth, but herbaceous perennials typically do not. Perennial plants continue to grow year after year, whereas annual plants die after one growing season. During the first year of a biennial plant life cycle, food is produced and stored in underground storage organs. During the second year of growth, the stored energy is used to produce flowering stems.

■ *What are the advantages and disadvantages of a biennial life cycle compared to an annual cycle?*

Chapter Review

42.1 Reproductive Development

Plant life cycles are characterized by an alternation of generations.

The transition to flowering competence is termed phase change.
Phase change prepares a plant to respond to external and internal signals to begin flowering. External factors include light and temperature, and internal factors include hormone production.

Mutations have clarified how phase change is controlled.
In experiments with *Arabidopsis*, plants that flower earlier than normal result from mutations in phase change genes. The implication is that mechanisms have evolved to delay flowering.

42.2 Flower Production

Four genetically regulated pathways to flowering have been identified. The balance between floral-promoting and floral-inhibiting signals regulates flowering.

The light-dependent pathway is geared to the photoperiod.
The light-dependent pathway induces flowering based on the length of the dark period a plant experiences during 24 hr. Plants may be short-day, long-day, or day-neutral, depending on their flowering response.

The temperature-dependent pathway is linked to cold.
Some plants require vernalization, or exposure of seeds or plants to chilling in order to induce flowering.

The gibberellin-dependent pathway requires an increased hormone level.
Decreased levels of gibberellins delay flowering in plants with this pathway. Gibberellins likely affect phase-change gene expression.

The autonomous pathway is independent of environmental cues.
The autonomous pathway is typical of day-neutral plants. A balance between floral-promoting and floral-inhibiting signals controls flower development.

Floral meristem identity genes activate floral organ identity genes.

Once floral organ identity genes are turned on, the four floral organs develop according to the ABC model. Class *A* genes alone specify sepals, classes *A* and *B* together specify petals, classes *B* and *C* specify stamens, and class *C* genes alone specify carpels.

42.3 Structure and Evolution of Flowers

Flowers evolved in the angiosperms.

Floral organs are believed to have evolved from leaves.

Complete flowers have four whorls corresponding to the four floral organs: the calyx, corolla, androecium, and gynoecium. Incomplete flowers lack one or more of the whorls.

Angiosperms may have radially or bilaterally symmetrical flowers.

Gametes are produced in the gametophytes of flowers.

Meiosis in the anthers produces microspores, which undergo mitosis to produce pollen grains, which are the male gametophytes or microgametophytes.

Each pollen grain contains the generative cell that later divides to produce two sperm cells and a tube cell.

Meiosis in the ovules produces megaspores, which undergo mitosis to produce embryo sacs, which are the female gametophytes or megagametophytes.

The embryo sac contains seven cells, one of which is the egg cell and one of which contains two polar nuclei. The latter cell develops into triploid endosperm after fertilization.

42.4 Pollination and Fertilization

Early seed plants were wind-pollinated.

Wind-pollination is a passive process and does not carry pollen over long distances. Consequently, plants must be relatively close together to ensure that pollination occurs.

Flowers and animal pollinators have coevolved.

Animal pollinators provide an efficient transfer of pollen that may cover long distances. Animal-pollinated flowers produce odors and visual cues to guide pollinators.

Some flowering plants continue to use wind pollination.

Many wind-pollinated plant species have male and female flowers on separate individuals or on separate parts of each individual. The flowers are grouped in large numbers and exposed to the wind.

Self-pollination is favored in stable environments.

Plants adapted to a stable environment benefit from having uniform progeny that are likely to be more successful than those arising from cross-pollination. Offspring from self-pollination are not genetically identical, however.

Self pollination is also favored where animal pollinators are scarce.

Several evolutionary strategies promote outcrossing.

Outcrossing is promoted in plants in which male and female flowers are physically separated on the same plant or on different plants, or in which the two flowers mature on a different schedule.

Self-incompatibility prevents self-fertilization by preventing pollen tube growth.

Angiosperms undergo double fertilization.

Double fertilization produces a diploid zygote and triploid endosperm that provides nourishment to the zygote.

42.5 Asexual Reproduction

Asexual reproduction results in genetically identical individuals because progeny are produced by mitosis.

Apomixis involves development of diploid embryos.

Apomixis is the production of embryos by mitosis rather than fertilization. These embryos develop in seeds.

In vegetative reproduction, new plants arise from nonreproductive tissues.

Vegetative parts such as runners, rhizomes, suckers, and adventitious plantlets may give rise to new individual clones.

Plants can be cloned from isolated cells in the laboratory.

Stripping away the cell wall produces a protoplast, which can then be induced to undergo mitosis to produce a callus. With the proper treatments, the callus can differentiate into a complete plant.

42.6 Plant Life Spans

Perennial plants live for many years.

Perennials live for years, although they may undergo dormancy.

Annual plants grow, reproduce, and die in a single year.

Many crop plants are annuals and require replanting every year, such as corn, wheat, and soy beans.

Biennial plants follow a two-year life cycle.

During the first year, biennials grow and store nutrients. In the second year, they produce flowers and seeds. Biennial crop plants are often harvested during the first year, such as carrots.

Review Questions

UNDERSTAND

1. Morphogenesis is the development of
   a. growth form.
   b. reproductive structures.
   c. a phase change.
   d. meristems.

2. Vernalization induces flowering following exposure to
   a. water.
   b. drought.
   c. cold.
   d. heat.

3. Photoperiod is perceived by
   a. phytochrome and cryptochrome.
   b. phytochrome and chlorophyll.
   c. cryptochrome and chlorophyll.
   d. phytochrome, cryptochrome, and chlorophyll.

4. Which of the following is not a component of a flower?
   a. Sepal
   b. Stamen
   c. Carpel
   d. Bract

5. Megaspores are produced in

    a. anthers by mitosis.   c. ovules by mitosis.

    b. anthers by meiosis.   d. ovules by meiosis.

6. A stamen contains a

    a. style.   c. filament.

    b. stigma.   d. carpel.

7. Unlike bee-pollinated flowers, bird-pollinated flowers

    a. produce a strong fragrance.

    b. contain a landing pad.

    c. produce a bull's-eye pattern.

    d. are red.

8. Asexual reproduction is likely to be most common in which ecosystem?

    a. Tropical rainforest   c. Arctic tundra

    b. Temperate grassland   d. Deciduous forest

9. Protoplasts are plant cells that lack

    a. nuclei.   c. plasma membranes.

    b. cell walls.   d. protoplasm.

10. Perennial plants are

    a. always herbaceous.

    b. always woody.

    c. either herbaceous or woody.

    d. neither herbaceous nor woody.

11. Senescence refers to

    a. plant death.   d. the accumulation of

    b. reproductive growth.   storage reserves.

    c. pollination.

APPLY

1. Under which of the following conditions would pollen from an S_2S_5 plant successfully pollinate an S_1S_5 flower?

    a. Using pollen from a carpelate flower to fertilize a staminate flower would be successful.

    b. If the plants used gametophytic self-incompatibility, half of the pollen would be successful.

    c. If the plants used sporophytic self-incompatibility, half of the pollen would be successful.

    d. Pollen from an S_2S_5 plant can never pollinate an S_1S_5 flower.

2. Your roommate is taking biology with you this semester and thinks he understands short- and long-day plants. He purchases one plant of each type and decides to see the difference himself by first trying to cause the short-day plant to flower. He places both plants under the same conditions and exposes each to a regimen of 10-hr days, expecting that the short-day plant will flower, and the long-day plant will not. You play a trick on your roommate and reverse the outcome. Specifically, what did you have to do?

    a. Lengthen the time each is exposed to light

    b. Shorten the time each is exposed to light

    c. Quickly expose the plants to light during the middle of the night

    d. None of the above

3. In Iowa, a company called Team Corn works to ensure that fields of seed corn outcross so that hybrid vigor can be maintained. They do this by removing the staminate (that is, pollen-producing) flowers from the corn plants. In an attempt to put Team Corn out of business, you would like to develop genetically engineered corn plants that

    a. contain Z genes to prevent germination of pollen on the stigmatic surface.

    b. contain S genes to stop pollen tube growth during self-fertilization.

    c. express B-type homeotic genes throughout developing flowers.

    d. express A-type homeotic genes throughout developing flowers.

4. Monoecious plants such as corn have either staminate or carpelate flowers. Knowing what you do about the molecular mechanisms of floral development, which of the following might explain the development of single-sex flowers?

    a. Expression of B-type genes in the presumptive carpel whorl will generate staminate flowers.

    b. Loss of A-type genes in the presumptive petal whorl will allow C-type and B-type genes to produce stamens instead of petals in that whorl.

    c. Restricting B-type gene expression to the presumptive petal whorl will generate carpelate flowers.

    d. All of these are correct.

5. One of the most notable differences between gamete formation in most animals and gamete formation in plants is that

    a. plants produce gametes in somatic tissue, whereas animals produce gametes in germ tissue.

    b. plants produce gametes by mitosis, whereas animals produce gametes by meiosis.

    c. plants produce only one of each gamete, but animals produce many gametes.

    d. plants produce gametes that are diploid, but animals produce gametes that are haploid.

SYNTHESIZE

1. A commercial greenhouse in a remote location produces poinsettias. However, after a highway is built near the greenhouse, the poinsettias fail to flower. Explain what has happened.

2. If you live in a north temperate region, explain why it is advantageous to grow spinach for your salad in early spring rather than during the summer.

3. In wild columbine, flower morphology encourages cross-pollination. However, during the middle of the receptive period of the stigma, self-pollination can occur if the flower was not previously pollinated. If cross-pollination occurs after self-pollination, then that pollen reaches the base of the style before the self-pollen. Discuss the adaptive significance of this reproduction strategy.

4. In most parts of the world, commercial potato crops are produced asexually by planting tubers. However, in some regions of the world, such as Southeast Asia and the Andes, some potatoes are grown from true seeds. Discuss the advantages and disadvantages of growing potatoes from true seed.

ONLINE RESOURCE

www.ravenbiology.com

connect BIOLOGY

Understand, Apply, and Synthesize—enhance your study with animations that bring concepts to life and practice tests to assess your understanding. Your instructor may also recommend the interactive eBook, individualized learning tools, and more.

Chapter *43*

The Animal Body and Principles of Regulation

Chapter Outline

43.1   Organization of the Vertebrate Body

43.2   Epithelial Tissue

43.3   Connective Tissue

43.4   Muscle Tissue

43.5   Nerve Tissue

43.6   Overview of Vertebrate Organ Systems

43.7   Homeostasis

43.8   Regulating Body Temperature

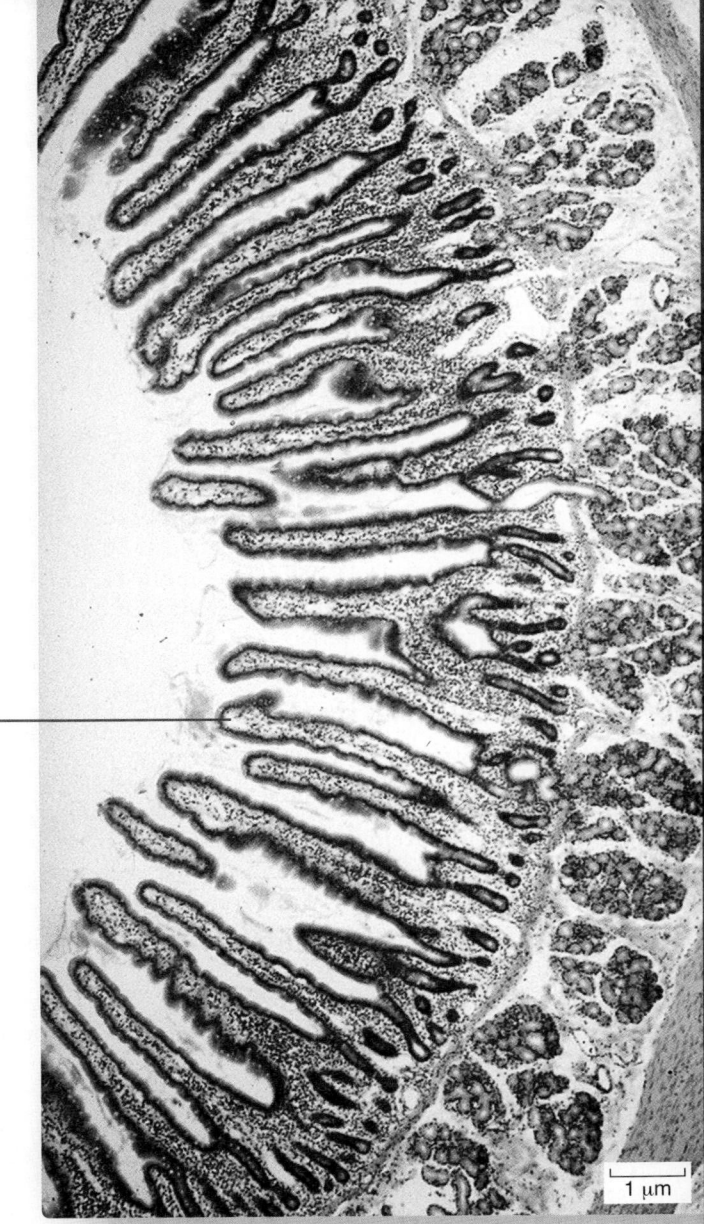

1 μm

Part **VII** Animal Form and Function

Introduction

When people think of animals, they may think of pet dogs and cats, the animals in a zoo, on a farm, in an aquarium, or wild living outdoors. When thinking about the diversity of animals, people may picture the differences between the predatory lions and tigers and the herbivorous deer and antelope, or between a dangerous shark and a playful dolphin. Despite the differences among these animals, they are all vertebrates. All vertebrates share the same basic body plan, with similar tissues and organs that operate in much the same way. The micrograph shows a portion of the duodenum, part of the digestive system, which is made up of multiple types of tissues. In this chapter, we begin a detailed consideration of the biology of the vertebrates and the fascinating structure and function of their bodies. We conclude this chapter by exploring the principles involved in regulation and control of complex functional systems.

Organization of the Vertebrate Body

Learning Outcomes

1. List the levels of organization in the vertebrate body.
2. Identify the tissue types found in vertebrates.
3. Describe how body cavities are organized.

The vertebrate body has four levels of organization: (1) cells, (2) tissues, (3) organs, and (4) organ systems. Like those of all animals, the bodies of vertebrates are composed of different cell types. Depending on the group, between 50 and several hundred different kinds of cells contribute to the adult vertebrate body. Humans have 210 different types of cells.

Tissues are groups of cells of a single type and function

Groups of cells that are similar in structure and function are organized into *tissues*. Early in development, the cells of the growing embryo differentiate into the three fundamental embryonic tissues, called **germ layers.** From the innermost to the outermost layers, these are the *endoderm*, *mesoderm*, and *ectoderm*. Each germ layer, in turn, differentiates into the scores of different cell types and tissues that are characteristic of the vertebrate body.

In adult vertebrates, there are four principal kinds of tissues, or **primary tissues:** (1) **epithelial**, (2) **connective,** (3) **muscle,** and (4) **nerve tissue.** Each type is discussed in separate sections of this chapter.

Organs and organ systems provide specialized functions

Organs are body structures composed of several different types of tissues that form a structural and functional unit (figure 43.1). One example is the heart, which contains cardiac muscle, connective tissue, and epithelial tissue. Nerve tissue connects the brain and spinal cord to the heart and helps regulate the heartbeat.

An **organ system** is a group of organs that cooperate to perform the major activities of the body. For example, the circulatory system is composed of the heart and blood vessels (arteries, capillaries, and veins) (see chapter 50). These organs cooperate in the transport of blood and help distribute substances about the body. The vertebrate body contains 11 principal organ systems.

The general body plan of vertebrates is a tube within a tube, with internal support

The bodies of all vertebrates have the same general architecture. The body plan is essentially a tube suspended within a tube. The inner tube is the digestive tract, a long tube that travels from the mouth to the anus. An internal skeleton made of jointed bones or cartilage that grows as the body grows supports the outer tube, which forms the main vertebrate body. The outermost layer of the vertebrate body is the integument, or skin, and its many accessory organs and parts—hair, feathers, scales, and sweat glands.

Vertebrates have both dorsal and ventral body cavities

Inside the main vertebrate body are two identifiable cavities. The *dorsal body cavity* forms within a bony skull and a column of bones, the vertebrae. The skull surrounds the brain, and within the stacked vertebrae is a channel that contains the spinal cord.

The *ventral body cavity* is much larger and extends anteriorly from the area bounded by the rib cage and vertebral column posteriorly to the area contained within the ventral body muscles (the abdominals) and the pelvic girdle. In mammals, a sheet of muscle, the diaphragm, breaks the ventral body cavity anteriorly into the *thoracic cavity*, which contains the heart and lungs, and posteriorly into the *abdominopelvic cavity*, which contains many organs, including the stomach, intestines, liver, kidneys, and urinary bladder (figure 43.2*a*).

Recall from the discussion of the animal body plan in chapter 32 that a coelom is a fluid-filled body cavity completely formed within the embryonic mesoderm layer of some animals

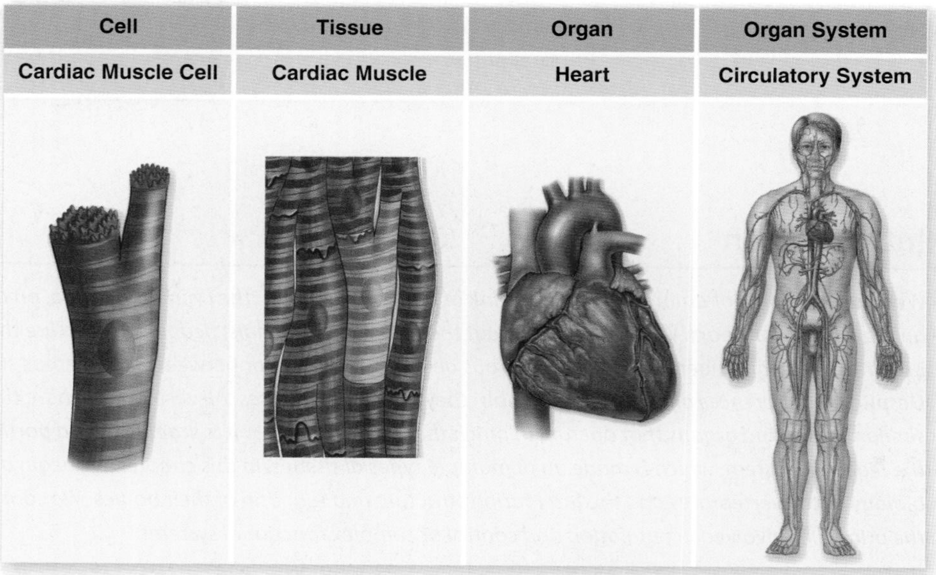

Cell	Tissue	Organ	Organ System
Cardiac Muscle Cell	Cardiac Muscle	Heart	Circulatory System

Figure 43.1 Levels of organization within the body. Similar cell types operate together and form tissues. Tissues functioning together form organs such as the heart, which is composed primarily of cardiac muscle with a lining of epithelial tissue. An organ system consists of several organs working together to carry out a function for the body. An example of an organ system is the circulatory system, which consists of the heart, blood vessels, and blood.

(vertebrates included). The coelom is present in vertebrates, but compared to invertebrates it is constricted, folded, and subdivided. The mesodermal layer that lines the coelom extends from the body wall to envelop and suspend several organs within the ventral body cavity (figure 43.2b). In the abdominopelvic cavity, the coelomic space is the *peritoneal cavity.*

In the thoracic cavity, the heart and lungs invade and greatly constrict the coelomic space. The thin space within mesodermal layers around the heart is the **pericardial cavity,** and the two thin spaces around the lungs are the **pleural cavities** (figure 43.2b).

Learning Outcomes Review 43.1

The body's cells are organized into tissues, which in turn are organized into organs and organ systems. The main types of tissues in vertebrates are epithelial, connective, muscle, and nerve tissue. The bodies of humans and other mammals contain dorsal and ventral cavities. The ventral cavity is divided by the diaphragm into thoracic and abdominopelvic cavities. The adult coelom subdivides into the peritoneal, pericardial, and pleural cavities.

■ **Can an organ be made of more than one tissue?**

43.2 Epithelial Tissue

Learning Outcomes

1. Describe the structure and function of an epithelium.
2. Identify the cell types found in an epithelial membrane.
3. Explain the structure and function of different epithelia.

An epithelial membrane, or **epithelium** (plural, *epithelia*), covers every surface of the vertebrate body. Epithelial membranes can come from any of the three germ layers. For example, the epidermis, derived from ectoderm, constitutes the outer portion of the skin. An epithelium derived from endoderm lines the inner surface of the digestive tract, and the inner surfaces of blood vessels derive from mesoderm. Some epithelia change in the course of embryonic development into glands, which are specialized for secretion.

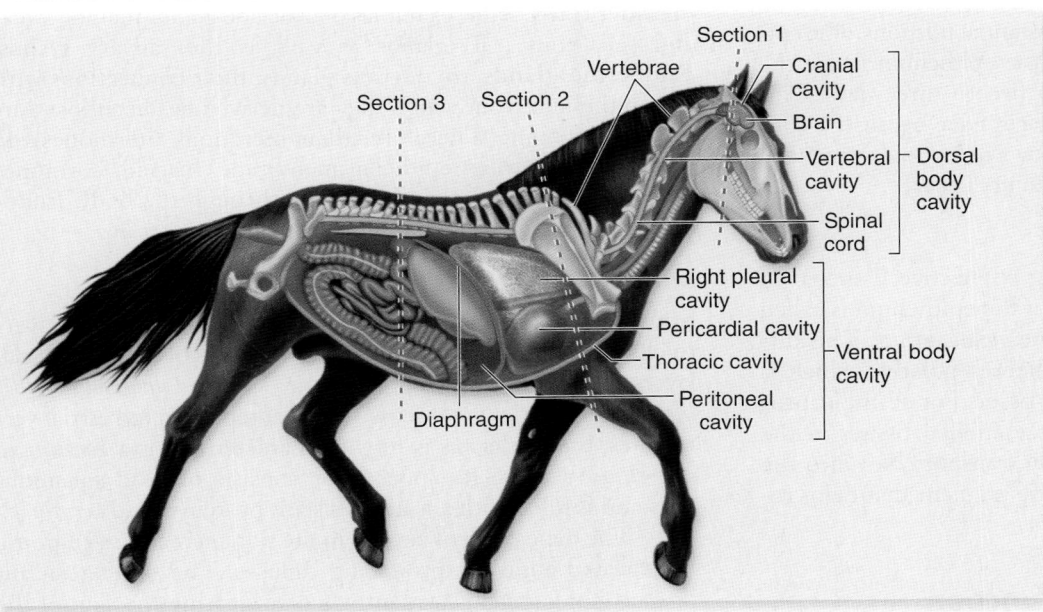

Figure 43.2 Architecture of the vertebrate body. *a.* All vertebrates have dorsal and ventral body cavities. The dorsal cavity divides into the cranial (contains the brain) and vertebral (contains the spinal cord) cavities. In mammals, a muscular diaphragm divides the ventral cavity into the thoracic and abdominopelvic cavities. *b.* Cross sections through three body regions show the relationships between body cavities, major organs, and coeloms (pericardial, pleural, and peritoneal cavities).

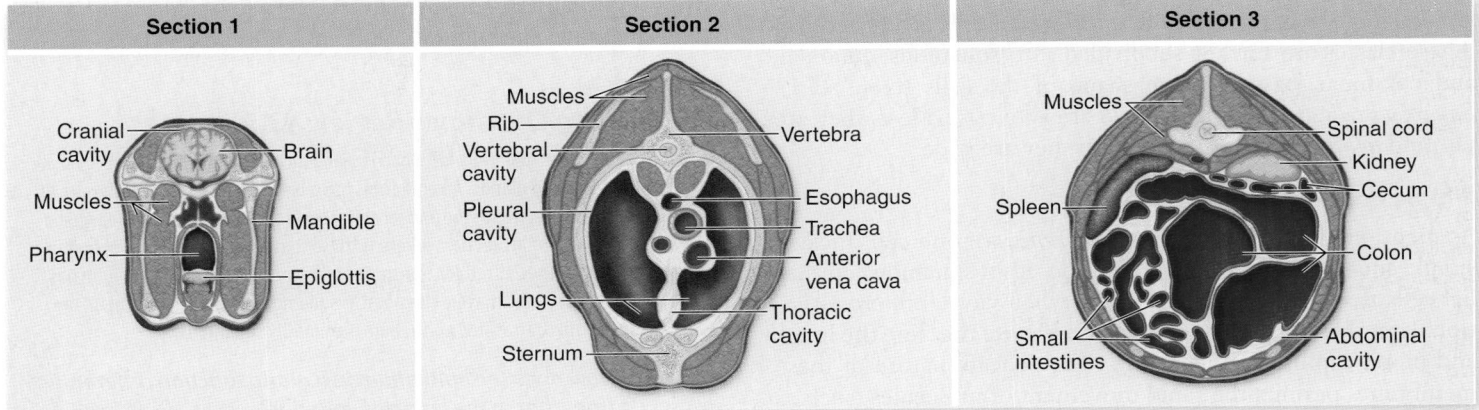

Epithelium forms a barrier

Because epithelial membranes cover all body surfaces, a substance must pass through an epithelium in order to enter or leave the body. Epithelial membranes thus provide a barrier that can impede the passage of some substances while facilitating the passage of others. For land-dwelling vertebrates, the relative impermeability of the surface epithelium (the epidermis) to water offers essential protection from dehydration and from airborne pathogens. The epithelial lining of the digestive tract, in contrast, must allow selective entry of the products of digestion while providing a barrier to toxic substances. The epithelium of the lungs must allow for the rapid diffusion of gases into and out of the blood.

A characteristic of all epithelia is that the cells are tightly bound together, with very little space between them. Nutrients and oxygen must diffuse to the epithelial cells from blood vessels supplying underlying connective tissues. This places a limit on the thickness of epithelial membranes; most are only one or a few cell layers thick.

Epithelial regeneration

Epithelium possesses remarkable regenerative powers, constantly replacing its cells throughout the life of the animal. For example, the liver, a gland formed from epithelial tissue, can readily regenerate, even after surgical removal of substantial portions. The epidermis renews every two weeks, and the epithelium inside the stomach is completely replaced every two to three days. This ability to regenerate is useful in a surface tissue because it constantly renews the surface and also allows quick replacement of the protective layer should damage or injury occur.

Structure of epithelial tissues

Epithelial tissues attach to underlying connective tissues by a fibrous membrane. The secured side of the epithelium is called the *basal surface*, and the free side is the *apical surface*. This difference gives epithelial tissues an inherent polarity, which is often important in the function of the tissue. For example, proteins stud the basal surfaces of some epithelial tissues in the kidney tubules; these proteins actively transport Na^+ into the intercellular spaces, creating an osmotic gradient that helps return water to the blood (see chapter 51).

Epithelial types reflect their function

The two general classes of epithelial membranes are termed *simple* (single layer of cells) and *stratified* (multiple layers of cells). These classes are further subdivided into squamous, cuboidal, and columnar, based on the shape of the cells (table 43.1). *Squamous cells* are flat, *cuboidal cells* are about as wide as they are tall, and *columnar cells* are taller than they are wide.

Simple epithelium

As mentioned, *simple epithelial membranes* are one cell thick. A simple squamous epithelium is composed of squamous epithelial cells that have a flattened shape when viewed in cross section. Examples of such membranes are those that line the lungs and blood capillaries, where the thin, delicate nature of these membranes permits the rapid movement of molecules (such as the diffusion of gases).

A simple cuboidal epithelium lines kidney tubules and several glands. In the case of glands, these cells are specialized for secretion.

A simple columnar epithelium lines the airways of the respiratory tract and the inside of most of the gastrointestinal tract, among other locations. Interspersed among the columnar epithelial cells of mucous membranes are numerous *goblet cells*, which are specialized to secrete mucus. The columnar epithelial cells of the respiratory airways contain cilia on their apical surface (the surface facing the lumen, or cavity), which move mucus and dust particles toward the throat. In the small intestine, the apical surface of the columnar epithelial cells forms fingerlike projections called *microvilli*, which increase the surface area for the absorption of food.

The expanded size of both cuboidal and columnar cells accommodates the added intracellular machinery needed for production of glandular secretions, active absorption of materials, or both. The glands of vertebrates form from invaginated epithelia. In **exocrine glands,** the connection between the gland and the epithelial membrane remains as a duct. The duct channels the product of the gland to the surface of the epithelial membrane, and thus to the external environment (or to an interior compartment that opens to the exterior, such as the digestive tract). A few examples of exocrine glands include sweat and sebaceous (oil) glands as well as the salivary glands. **Endocrine glands** are ductless glands; their connections with the epithelium from which they are derived has been lost during development. Therefore, their secretions (hormones) do not channel onto an epithelial membrane. Instead, hormones enter blood capillaries and circulate through the body. Endocrine glands are covered in more detail in chapter 46.

Stratified epithelium

Stratified epithelial membranes are two to several cell layers thick and are named according to the features of their apical cell layers. For example, the epidermis is a *stratified squamous epithelium*; its properties are discussed in chapter 52. In terrestrial vertebrates, the epidermis is further characterized as a *keratinized epithelium* because its upper layer consists of dead squamous cells and is filled with a water-resistant protein called *keratin*.

The deposition of keratin in the skin increases in response to repeated abrasion, producing calluses. The water-resistant property of keratin is evident when comparing the skin of the face to the red portion of the lips, which can easily become dried and chapped. Lips are covered by a nonkeratinized, stratified squamous epithelium.

Learning Outcomes Review 43.2

Epithelial tissues generally form barriers and include membranes that cover all body surfaces and glands. An epidermis has a basal surface that attaches to an underlying connective tissue and an apical surface that is free. Some epithelia are specialized for protection, whereas those that cover the surfaces of hollow organs may be specialized for transport and secretion. Simple epithelium has a single cell layer and may be classified as squamous, cuboidal, columnar, or pseudostratified; stratified epithelium is primarily squamous.

■ *How does the epithelium in a gland function differently from that in the lining of your gut?*

TABLE 43.1　**Epithelial Tissue**

SIMPLE EPITHELIUM

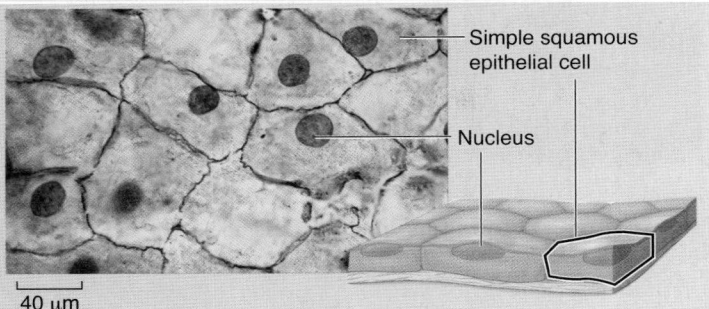

Simple squamous epithelial cell

Nucleus

40 μm

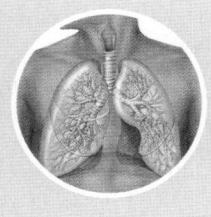

Squamous
Typical Location
Lining of lungs, capillary walls, and blood vessels
Function
Cells form thin layer across which diffusion can readily occur
Characteristic Cell Types
Epithelial cells

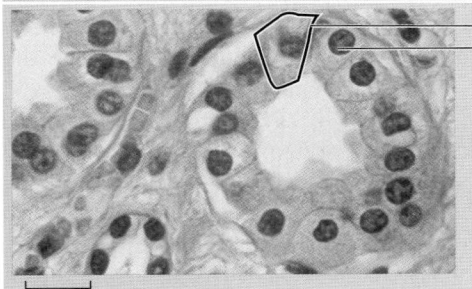

Cuboidal epithelial cell
Nucleus

50 μm

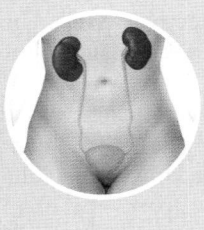

Cuboidal
Typical Location
Lining of some glands and kidney tubules; covering of ovaries
Function
Cells rich in specific transport channels; functions in secretion and absorption
Characteristic Cell Types
Gland cells

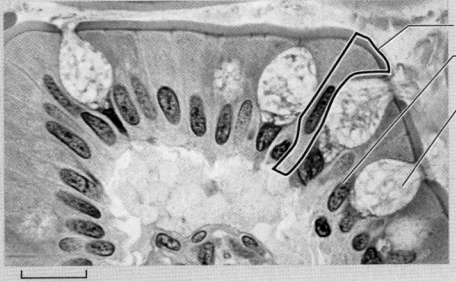

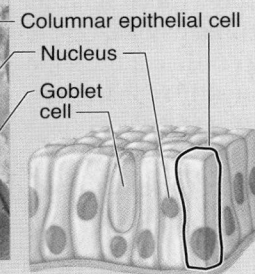

Columnar epithelial cell
Nucleus
Goblet cell

40 μm

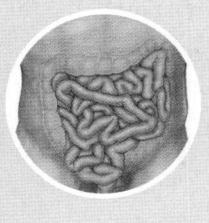

Columnar
Typical Location
Surface lining of stomach, intestines, and parts of respiratory tract
Function
Thicker cell layer; provides protection and functions in secretion and absorption
Characteristic Cell Types
Epithelial cells

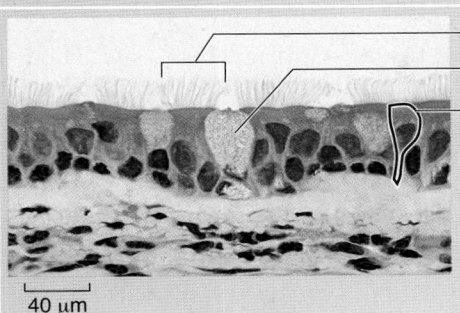

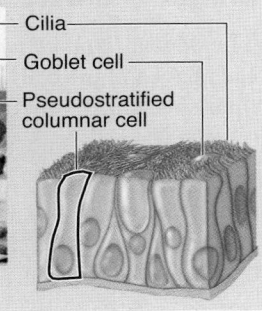

Cilia
Goblet cell
Pseudostratified columnar cell

40 μm

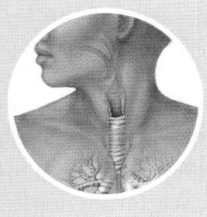

Pseudostratified Columnar
Typical Location
Lining of parts of the respiratory tract
Function
Secretes mucus; dense with cilia that aid in movement of mucus; provides protection
Characteristic Cell Types
Gland cells; ciliated epithelial cells

STRATIFIED EPITHELIUM

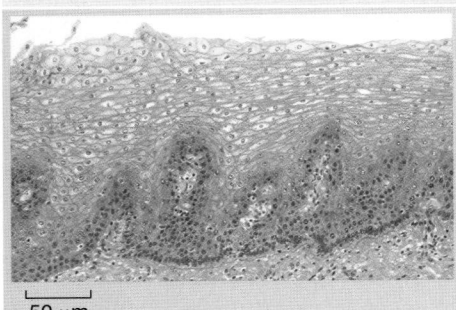

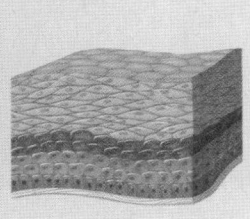

50 μm

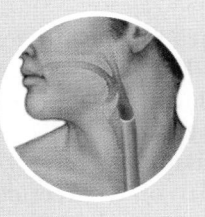

Squamous
Typical Location
Outer layer of skin; lining of mouth
Function
Tough layer of cells; provides protection
Characteristic Cell Types
Epithelial cells

Connective tissues derive from embryonic mesoderm and occur in many different forms (table 43.2). We divide these various forms into two major classes: *connective tissue proper*, which further divides into loose and dense connective tissues, and **special connective tissues,** which include cartilage, bone, and blood.

At first glance, it may seem odd that such diverse tissues are in the same category. Yet all connective tissues share a common structural feature: They all have abundant extracellular material because their cells are spaced widely apart. This extracellular material is called the **matrix** of the tissue. In bone, the matrix contains crystals that make the bones hard; in blood, the matrix is plasma, the fluid portion of the blood. The matrix itself consists of protein fibers and **ground substance,** the fluid material between cells and fibers containing a diverse array of proteins and polysaccharides.

Connective tissue proper may be either loose or dense

During the development of both loose and dense connective tissues, cells called fibroblasts produce and secrete the extracellular matrix. Loose connective tissue contains other cells as well, including mast cells and macrophages—cells of the immune system.

Loose connective tissue

Loose connective tissue consists of cells scattered within a matrix that contains a large amount of ground substance. This gelatinous material is strengthened by a loose scattering of protein fibers such as collagen, which supports the tissue by forming a meshwork (figure 43.3), elastin, which makes the tissue elastic, and reticulin, which helps support the network of collagen. The flavored gelatin of certain desserts consists primarily of extracellular material extracted from the loose connective tissues of animals.

Adipose cells, more commonly termed fat cells, are important for nutrient storage, and they also occur in loose connective tissue. In certain areas of the body, including under the skin, in bone marrow, and around the kidneys, these cells can develop in large groups, forming **adipose tissue** (figure 43.4).

Each adipose cell contains a droplet of triglycerides within a storage vesicle. When needed for energy, the adipose cell hydrolyzes its stored triglyceride and secretes fatty acids into the blood for oxidation by the cells of the muscles, liver, and other organs. Adipose cells cannot divide; the number of adipose cells in an adult is generally fixed. When a person gains

Figure 43.3 Collagen fibers. These fibers, shown under an electron microscope, are composed of many individual collagen strands and can be very strong under tension.

weight, the cells become larger, and when weight is lost, the cells shrink.

Dense connective tissue

Dense connective tissue, with less ground substance, contains tightly packed collagen fibers, making it stronger than loose connective tissue. It consists of two types: regular and irregular. The collagen fibers of *dense regular connective tissue* line up in parallel, like the strands of a rope. This is the structure of tendons, which bind muscle to bone, and ligaments, which bind bone to bone.

In contrast, the collagen fibers of *dense irregular connective tissue* have many different orientations. This type of connective tissue produces the tough coverings that package organs, such as the capsules of the kidneys and adrenal glands. It also covers muscle, nerves, and bones.

Special connective tissues have unique characteristics

The special connective tissues—cartilage, bone, and blood—each have unique cells and matrices that allow them to perform their specialized functions.

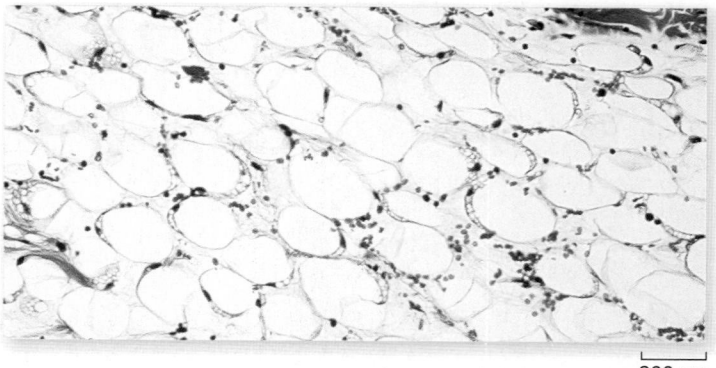

Figure 43.4 Adipose tissue. Fat is stored in globules of adipose tissue, a type of loose connective tissue. As a person gains or loses weight, the size of the fat globules increases or decreases. A person cannot decrease the number of fat cells by losing weight.

TABLE 43.2   Connective Tissue

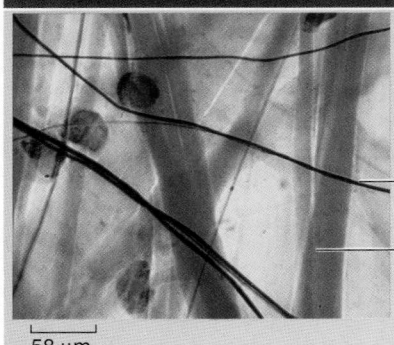

Elastin

Collagen

58 μm

Loose Connective Tissue
Typical Location
Beneath skin; between organs
Function
Provides support, insulation, food storage, and nourishment for epithelium
Characteristic Cell Types
Fibroblasts, macrophages, mast cells, fat cells

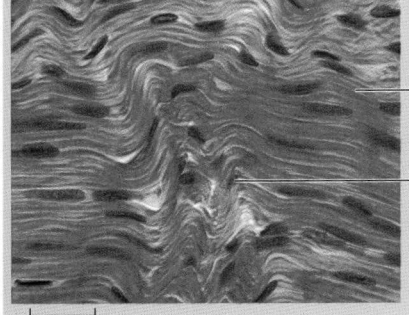
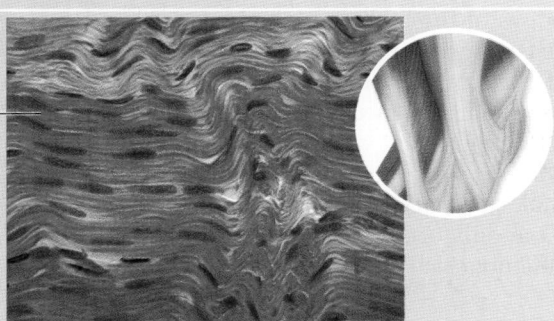

Collagen fibers

Nuclei of fibroblasts

0.16 μm

Dense Connective Tissue
Typical Location
Tendons; sheath around muscles; kidney; liver; dermis of skin
Function
Provides flexible, strong connections
Characteristic Cell Types
Fibroblasts

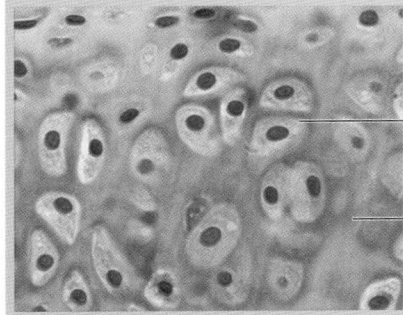
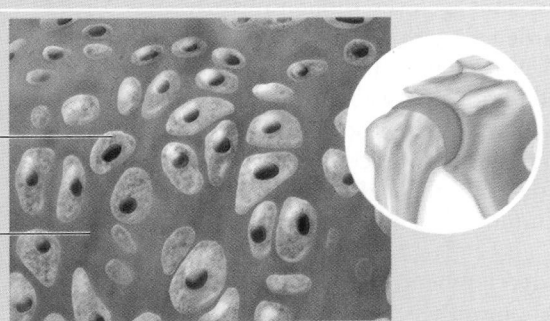

Chondrocyte

Ground substance

100 μm

Cartilage
Typical Location
Spinal disks; knees and other joints; ear; nose; tracheal rings
Function
Provides flexible support, shock absorption, and reduction of friction on load-bearing surfaces
Characteristic Cell Types
Chondrocytes

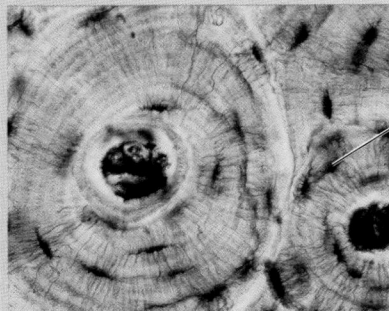
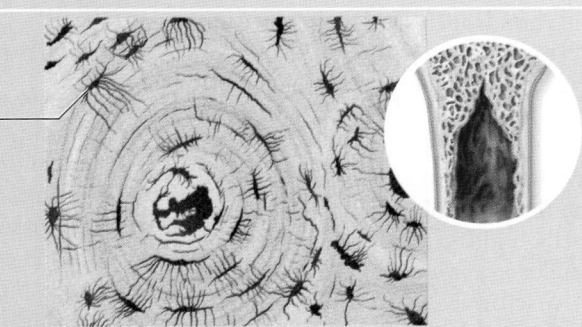

Osteocyte

100 μm

Bone
Typical Location
Most of skeleton
Function
Protects internal organs; provides rigid support for muscle attachment
Characteristic Cell Types
Osteocytes

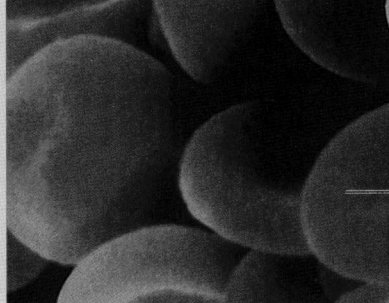
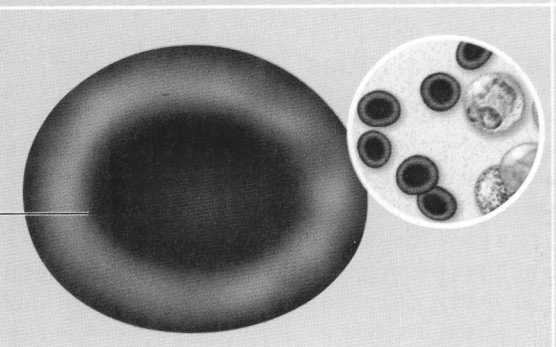

Red blood cell

5.8 μm

Blood
Typical Location
Circulatory system
Function
Functions as highway of immune system; carries nutrients and waste; and is the primary means of communication between organs
Characteristic Cell Types
Erythrocytes, leukocytes

Cartilage

Cartilage (see table 43.2) is a specialized connective tissue in which the ground substance forms from a characteristic type of glycoprotein, called *chondroitin*, and collagen fibers laid down along lines of stress in long, parallel arrays. The result is a firm and flexible tissue that does not stretch, is far tougher than loose or dense connective tissue, and has great tensile strength.

Cartilage makes up the entire skeletal system of the modern agnathans and cartilaginous fishes (see chapter 35). In most adult vertebrates, however, cartilage is restricted to the joint surfaces of bones that form freely movable joints and certain other locations. In humans, for example, the tip of the nose, the outer ear, the intervertebral disks of the backbone, the larynx, and a few other structures are composed of cartilage.

Chondrocytes, the cells of cartilage, live within spaces called **lacunae** within the cartilage ground substance. These cells remain alive even though there are no blood vessels within the cartilage matrix; they receive oxygen and nutrients by diffusion through the cartilage ground substance from surrounding blood vessels. This diffusion can only occur because the cartilage matrix is well hydrated and not calcified, as is bone.

Bone

Bone cells, or **osteocytes,** remain alive even though the extracellular matrix becomes hardened with crystals of calcium phosphate. Blood vessels travel through central canals into the bone, providing nutrients and removing wastes. Osteocytes extend cytoplasmic processes toward neighboring osteocytes through tiny canals, or *canaliculi*. Osteocytes communicate with the blood vessels in the central canal through this cytoplasmic network. Bone is described in more detail in chapter 47 along with muscle.

In the course of fetal development, the bones of vertebrate fins, arms, and legs, among other appendages, are first "modeled" in cartilage. The cartilage matrix then calcifies at particular locations, so that the chondrocytes are no longer able to obtain oxygen and nutrients by diffusion through the matrix. Living bone replaces the dying and degenerating cartilage.

Blood

We classify *blood* as a connective tissue because it contains abundant extracellular material, the fluid plasma. The cells of blood are *erythrocytes*, or red blood cells, and *leukocytes*, or white blood cells. Blood also contains platelets, or *thrombocytes*, which are fragments of a type of bone marrow cell. We discuss blood more fully in chapter 50.

All connective tissues have similarities

Although the descriptions of the types of connective tissue suggest numerous different functions for these tissues, they have some similarities. As mentioned, connective tissues originate as embryonic mesoderm, and they all contain abundant extracellular material called matrix; however, the extracellular matrix material is different in different types of connective tissue. Embedded within the extracellular matrix of each tissue type are varieties of cells, each with specialized functions.

43.4 Muscle Tissue

Muscles are the motors of the vertebrate body. The characteristic that makes muscle cells unique is the relative abundance and organization of actin and myosin filaments within them. Although these filaments form a fine network in all eukaryotic cells, where they contribute to movement of materials within the cell, they are far more abundant and organized in muscle cells, which are specialized for contraction.

Vertebrates possess three kinds of muscle: *smooth, skeletal,* and *cardiac* (table 43.3). Skeletal and cardiac muscles are also known as *striated muscles* because their cells appear to have transverse stripes when viewed in longitudinal section under the microscope. The contraction of each skeletal muscle is under voluntary control, whereas the contraction of cardiac and smooth muscles is generally involuntary.

Smooth muscle is found in most organs

Smooth muscle was the earliest form of muscle to evolve, and it is found throughout most of the animal kingdom. In vertebrates, smooth muscle occurs in the organs of the internal environment, or *viscera*, and is also called *visceral muscle*. Smooth muscle tissue is arranged into sheets of long, spindle-shaped cells, each cell containing a single nucleus. In some tissues, the cells contract only when a nerve stimulates them—and then all of the cells in the sheet contract as a unit.

In vertebrates, muscles of this type line the walls of many blood vessels and make up the iris of the eye, which contracts in bright light. In other smooth muscle tissues, such as those in the wall of the digestive tract, the muscle cells themselves may spontaneously initiate electrical impulses, leading to a slow, steady contraction of the tissue. Here nerves regulate, rather than cause, the activity.

Skeletal muscle moves the body

Skeletal muscles are usually attached to bones by tendons, so that their contraction causes the bones to move at their joints. A skeletal muscle is made up of numerous, very long muscle

| TABLE 43.3 | Muscle Tissue |

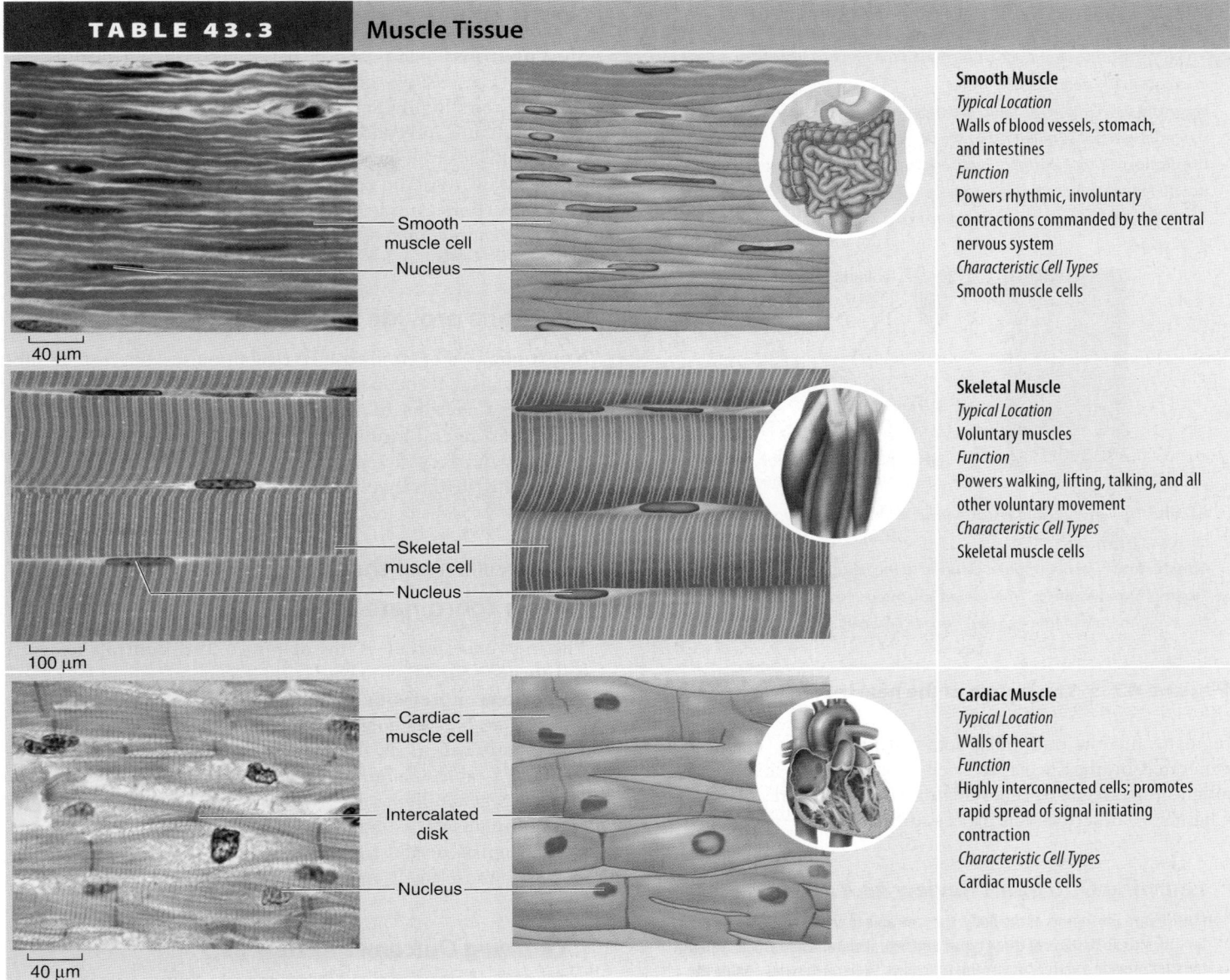

Smooth Muscle
Typical Location
Walls of blood vessels, stomach, and intestines
Function
Powers rhythmic, involuntary contractions commanded by the central nervous system
Characteristic Cell Types
Smooth muscle cells

Skeletal Muscle
Typical Location
Voluntary muscles
Function
Powers walking, lifting, talking, and all other voluntary movement
Characteristic Cell Types
Skeletal muscle cells

Cardiac Muscle
Typical Location
Walls of heart
Function
Highly interconnected cells; promotes rapid spread of signal initiating contraction
Characteristic Cell Types
Cardiac muscle cells

(Labels in figure: Smooth muscle cell; Nucleus; 40 µm; Skeletal muscle cell; Nucleus; 100 µm; Cardiac muscle cell; Intercalated disk; Nucleus; 40 µm)

cells called **muscle fibers,** which have multiple nuclei. The fibers lie parallel to each other within the muscle and are connected to the tendons on the ends of the muscle. Each skeletal muscle fiber is stimulated to contract by a motor neuron.

The nervous system controls the overall strength of a skeletal muscle contraction by controlling the number of motor neurons that fire, and therefore the number of muscle fibers stimulated to contract. Each muscle fiber contracts by means of substructures called **myofibrils** containing highly ordered arrays of actin and myosin myofilaments. These filaments give the muscle fiber its striated appearance.

Skeletal muscle fibers are produced during development by the fusion of several cells, end to end. This embryological development explains why a mature muscle fiber contains many nuclei. The structure and function of skeletal muscle is explained in more detail in chapter 47.

The heart is composed of cardiac muscle

The hearts of vertebrates are made up of striated muscle cells arranged very differently from the fibers of skeletal muscle. Instead of having very long, multinucleate cells running the length of the muscle, **cardiac muscle** consists of smaller, interconnected cells, each with a single nucleus. The interconnections between adjacent cells appear under the microscope as dark lines called **intercalated disks.** In reality, these lines are regions where gap junctions link adjacent cells. As noted in chapter 4, gap junctions have openings that permit the movement of small substances and ions from one cell to another. These interconnections enable the cardiac muscle cells to form a single functioning unit.

Certain specialized cardiac muscle cells can generate electrical impulses spontaneously, but the nervous system usually

Question: *Is the heartbeat a function of the nervous system, or does it originate in the heart itself?*

Hypothesis: *Cells in the heart are capable of generating an action potential without stimulation by the nervous system.*

Prediction: *If the heartbeat is produced by cells in the heart, then an isolated heart should continue to beat.*

Test: *Remove a frog's heart and keep in a bath of nutrient solution and oxygen.*

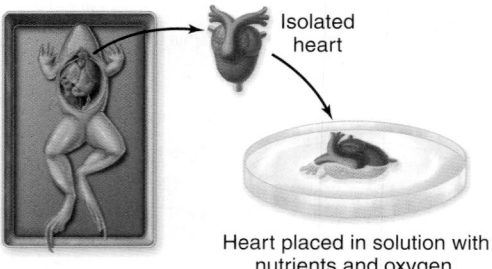

Isolated heart

Heart placed in solution with nutrients and oxygen.

Result: *The heart continues to contract with no connection to the nervous system.*

Conclusion: *The heartbeat is intrinsic to the heart.*

Further Experiments: *How would you integrate the conclusions from this experiment with the one described in figure 44.12?*

Figure 43.5 The source of the heartbeat.

regulates the rate of impulse activity (figure 43.5). The impulses generated by the specialized cell groups spread across the gap junctions from cell to cell, synchronizing the heart's contraction. Chapter 50 describes this process more fully.

Learning Outcomes Review 43.4

Muscles are the motors of the body; they are able to contract to change their length. Muscle tissue is of three types: smooth, skeletal, and cardiac. Smooth muscles provide a variety of visceral functions. Skeletal muscles enable the vertebrate body to move. Cardiac muscle forms a muscular pump, the heart.

■ *Why is it important that cardiac muscle cells have gap junctions?*

43.5 Nerve Tissue

Learning Outcomes

1. *Describe the basic structure of neurons.*
2. *Distinguish between neurons and their supporting cells.*
3. *Identify the two divisions of the nervous system.*

The fourth major class of vertebrate tissue is nerve tissue (table 43.4). Its cells include neurons and their supporting cells, called neuroglia. Neurons are specialized to produce and conduct electrochemical events, or impulses.

Neurons sometimes extend long distances

Most **neurons** consist of three parts: a cell body, dendrites, and an axon. The *cell body* of a neuron contains the nucleus. *Dendrites* are thin, highly branched extensions that receive incoming stimulation and conduct electrical impulses to the cell body. The *axon* is a single extension of cytoplasm that conducts impulses away from the cell body. Axons and dendrites can be quite long. For example, the cell bodies of neurons that control the muscles in your feet lie in the spinal cord, and their axons may extend over a meter to your feet.

Neuroglia provide support for neurons

Neuroglia do not conduct electrical impulses, but instead support and insulate neurons and eliminate foreign materials in and around neurons. In many neurons, neuroglia cells associate with the axons and form an insulating covering, a *myelin sheath*, produced by successive wrapping of the membrane around the axon. Gaps in the myelin sheath, known as *nodes of Ranvier*, serve as sites for accelerating an impulse (see chapter 44).

Two divisions of the nervous system coordinate activity

The nervous system is divided into the **central nervous system (CNS)**, which includes the brain and spinal cord, and the **peripheral nervous system (PNS)**, which includes *nerves* and *ganglia*. Nerves consist of axons in the PNS that are bundled together in much the same way as wires are bundled together in a cable. Ganglia are collections of neuron cell bodies. The CNS generally has the role of integration and interpretation of input, such as input from the senses; the PNS communicates signals to and from the CNS to the rest of the body, such as to muscle cells or endocrine glands.

Learning Outcomes Review 43.5

Nerve tissue is composed of neurons and neuroglia. Neurons are specialized to receive and conduct electrical signals; they generally have a cell body with a nucleus, dendrites that receive incoming signals, and axons that conduct impulses away from the cell body. Neuroglia have support functions, including providing insulation to axons. The central nervous system (CNS) and peripheral nervous system (PNS) both contain neurons and neuroglia.

■ *In chapter 4 you read that the surface-area-to-volume ratio limits cell size. How do neurons reach up to a meter in length in spite of this?*

43.6 Overview of Vertebrate Organ Systems

Learning Outcomes

1. *Identify the different organ systems in vertebrates.*
2. *Explain the functional organization of these systems.*

TABLE 43.4 Nerve Tissue

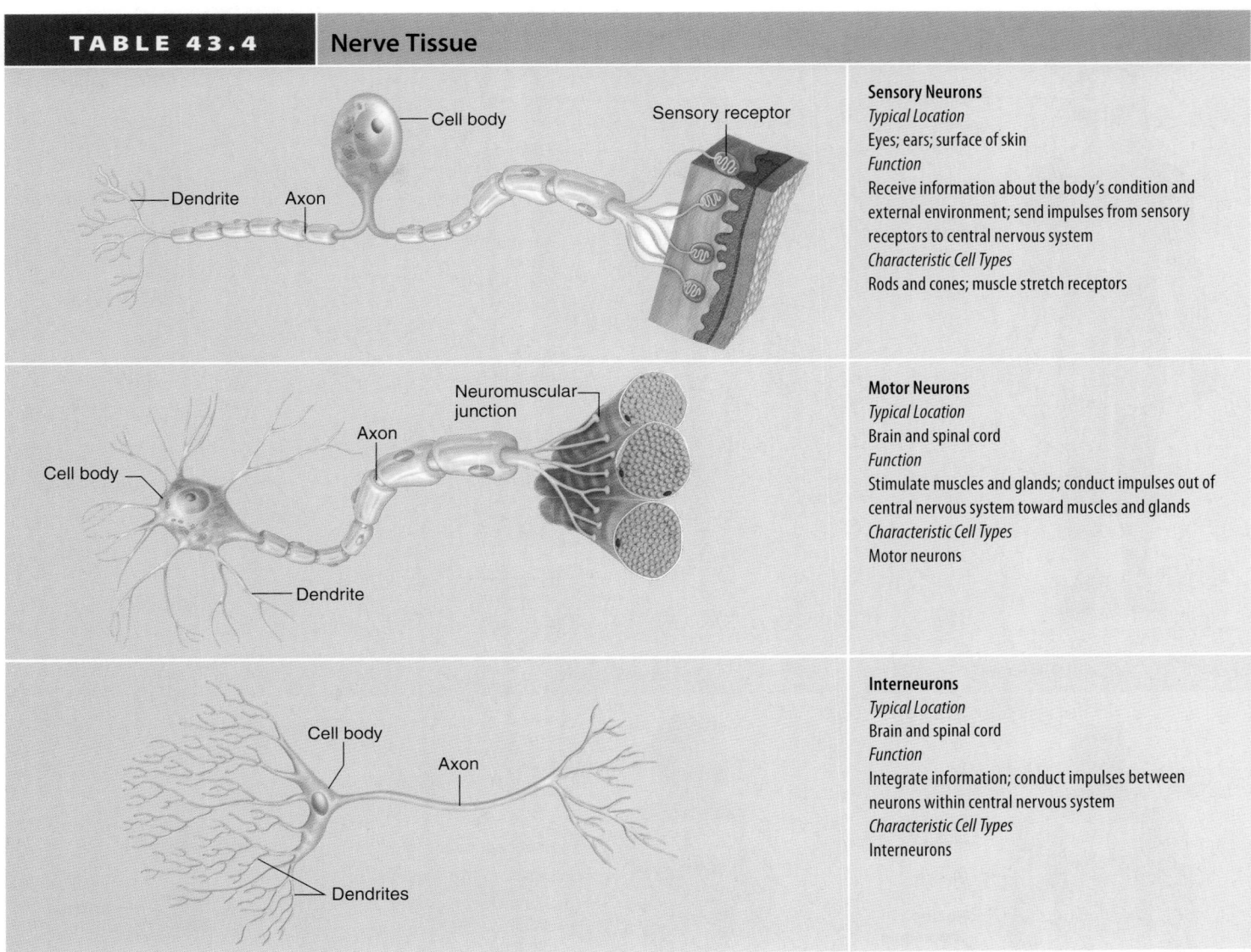

Sensory Neurons
Typical Location
Eyes; ears; surface of skin
Function
Receive information about the body's condition and external environment; send impulses from sensory receptors to central nervous system
Characteristic Cell Types
Rods and cones; muscle stretch receptors

Motor Neurons
Typical Location
Brain and spinal cord
Function
Stimulate muscles and glands; conduct impulses out of central nervous system toward muscles and glands
Characteristic Cell Types
Motor neurons

Interneurons
Typical Location
Brain and spinal cord
Function
Integrate information; conduct impulses between neurons within central nervous system
Characteristic Cell Types
Interneurons

In the chapters that follow, we look closely at the major organ systems of vertebrates (figure 43.6). In each chapter, you will be able to see the intimate relationship of structure and function. We approach the organ systems by placing them in the following functional groupings:

- Communication and integration
- Support and movement
- Regulation and maintenance
- Defense
- Reproduction and development

Communication and integration sense and respond to the environment

Two organ systems detect external and internal stimuli and co-ordinate the body's responses. The **nervous system,** which consists of the brain, spinal cord, nerves, and sensory organs, detects internal sensory feedback and external stimuli such as light, sound, and touch. This information is collected and inte-grated, and then the appropriate response is made.

The **sensory systems** are a subset of the nervous system we consider in a separate chapter. These include the organs and tissues that sense external stimuli, such as vision, hearing, smell, and so on.

Working in parallel with the nervous system, the **endocrine system** issues chemical signals that regulate and fine-tune the myriad chemical processes taking place in all other organ systems.

Skeletal support and movement are vital to all animals

The **musculoskeletal system** consists of two interrelated or-gan systems. Muscles are most obviously responsible for move-ment, but without something to pull on, a muscle is useless. The skeletal system is the rigid framework against which most muscles pull. Vertebrates have internal skeletons, but many other animals exhibit external skeletons (such as insects) or hy-drostatic skeletons (earthworms). Together, these two organ systems enable animals to exhibit a wide array of finely con-trolled movements.

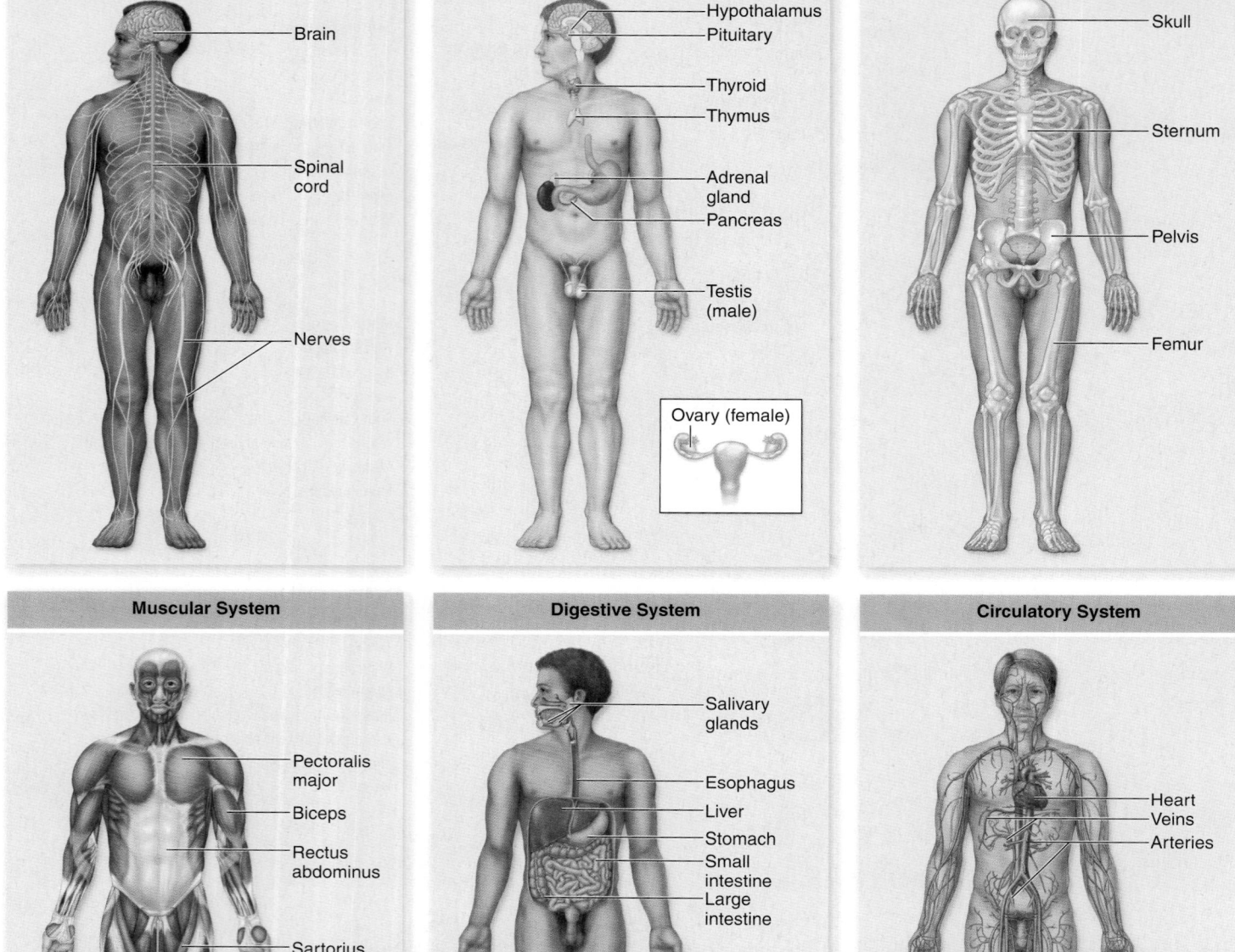

Figure 43.6 Vertebrate organ systems. Shown are the 11 principal organ systems of the human body, including both male and female reproductive systems.

Regulation and maintenance of the body's chemistry ensures continued life

The organ systems grouped under regulation and maintenance participate in nutrient acquisition, waste disposal, material distribution, and maintenance of the internal environment. The chapter on the **digestive system** describes how we eat, absorb nutrients, and eliminate solid wastes. The heart and vessels of the **circulatory system** pump and distribute blood, carrying nutrients and other substances throughout the body. The

Respiratory System

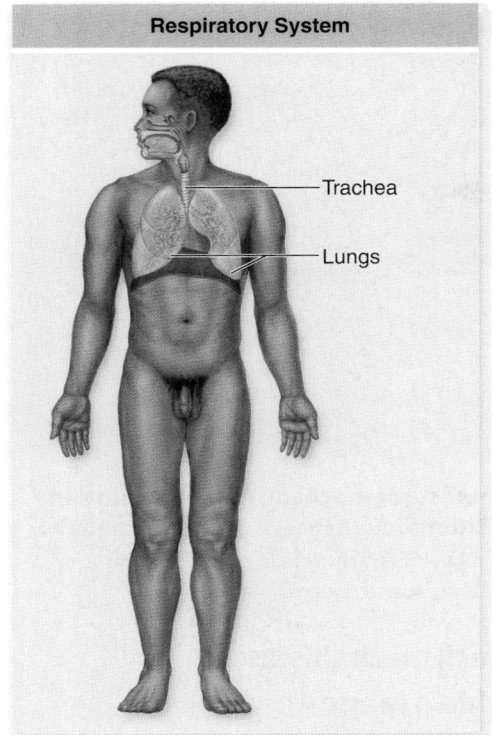

- Trachea
- Lungs

Urinary System

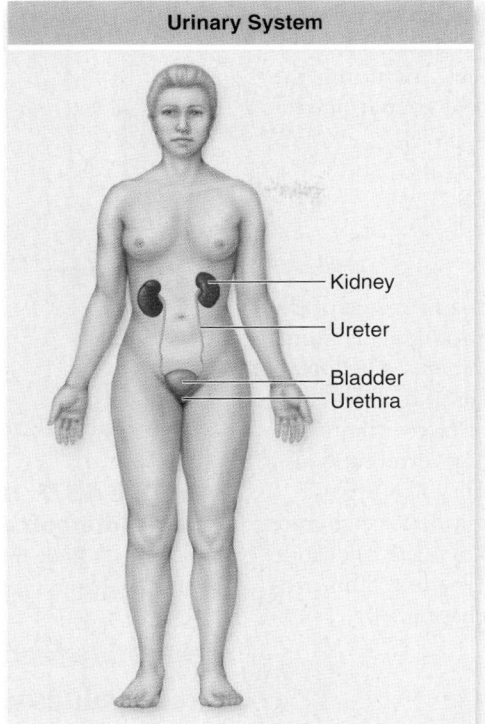

- Kidney
- Ureter
- Bladder
- Urethra

Integumentary System

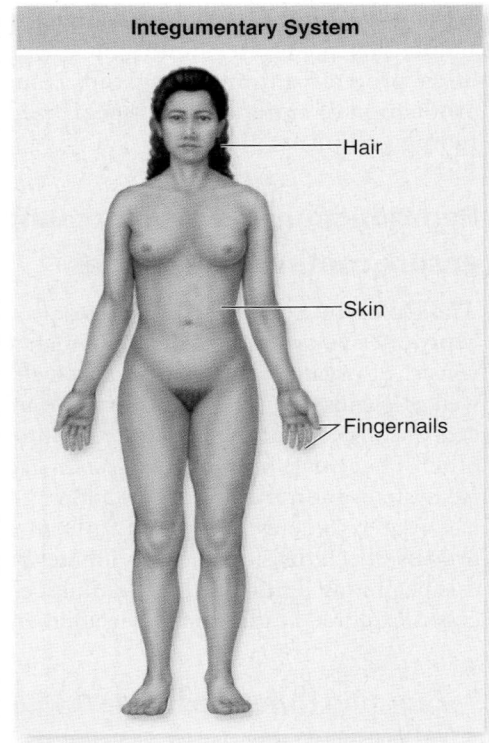

- Hair
- Skin
- Fingernails

Lymphatic/Immune System

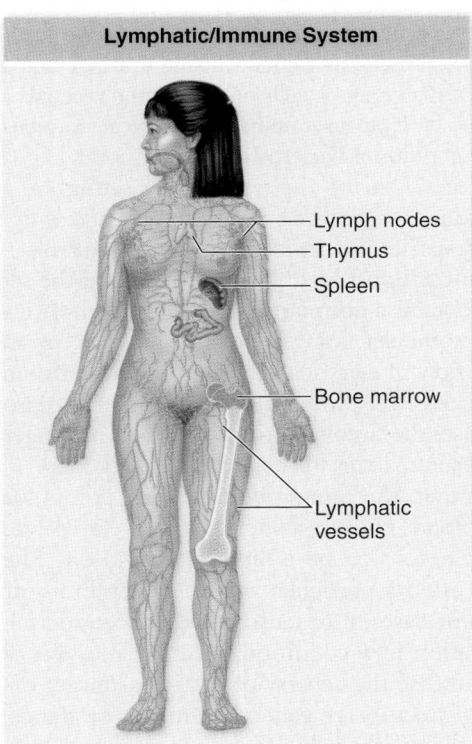

- Lymph nodes
- Thymus
- Spleen
- Bone marrow
- Lymphatic vessels

Reproductive System (male)

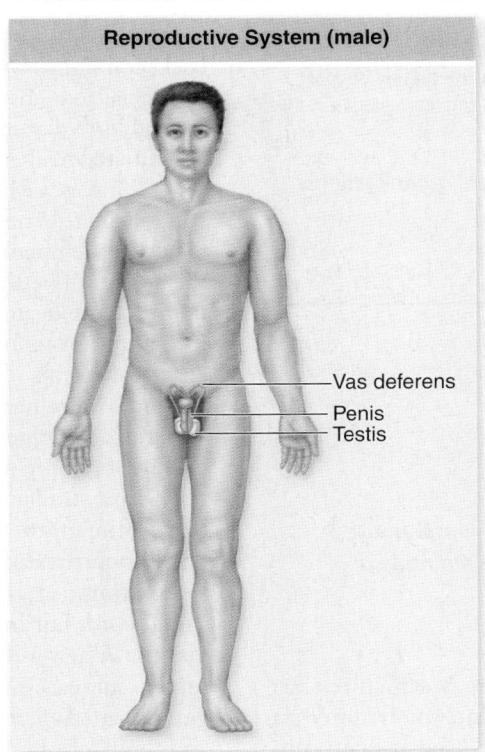

- Vas deferens
- Penis
- Testis

Reproductive System (female)

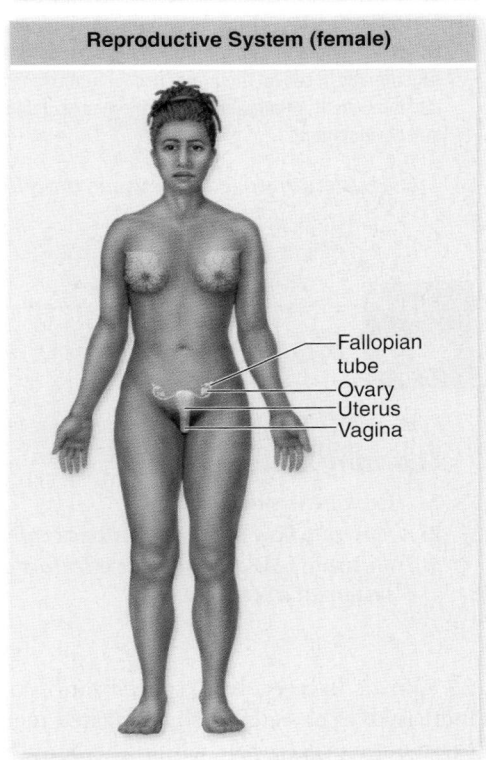

- Fallopian tube
- Ovary
- Uterus
- Vagina

body acquires oxygen and expels carbon dioxide via the **respiratory system.**

Finally, vertebrates tightly regulate the concentration of their body fluids. We explore these processes in the chapter on osmoregulation, which is largely carried out by the **urinary system.**

The body can defend itself from attackers and invaders

Every animal faces assault by bacteria, viruses, fungi, protists, and even other animals. The body's first line of defense is the **integumentary system**—intact skin. Disease-causing agents that penetrate the first defense encounter a host of other protective **immune system** responses, including the production of antibodies and specialized cells that attack invading organisms.

Reproduction and development ensure continuity of species

The biological continuity of vertebrates is the province of the **reproductive system.** Male and female reproductive systems consist of organs where male and female gametes develop, as well as glands and tubes that nurture gametes and allow gametes of complementary sexes to come into contact with one another. The female reproductive system in many vertebrates also has systems for nurturing the developing embryo and fetus.

After gametes have fused to form a *zygote*, an elaborate process of cell division and development takes place to change this beginning diploid cell into a multicellular adult. This process is explored in the animal development chapter.

Learning Outcomes Review 43.6

Vertebrate organ systems include the nervous, endocrine, skeletal, muscular, digestive, circulatory, respiratory, urinary, integumentary, lymphatic/immune, and reproductive systems. These may be grouped functionally based on their roles in communication and integration, support and movement, regulation and maintenance, defense, and reproduction and development.

■ *Is there any overlap between the different organ systems?*

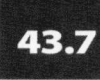

43.7 Homeostasis

Learning Outcomes

1. *Explain homeostasis.*
2. *Illustrate how negative feedback can limit a response.*
3. *Illustrate how antagonistic effectors can maintain a system at a set point.*

As animals have evolved, specialization of body structures has increased. Each cell is a sophisticated machine, finely tuned to carry out a precise role within the body. Such specialization of cell function is possible only when extracellular conditions stay within narrow limits. Temperature, pH, the concentrations of glucose and oxygen, and many other factors must remain relatively constant for cells to function efficiently and interact properly with one another. The dynamic constancy of the internal environment is called *homeostasis*. The term *dynamic* is used because conditions are never constant, but fluctuate continuously within narrow limits. Homeostasis is essential for life, and most of the regulatory mechanisms of the vertebrate body are involved with maintaining homeostasis (figure 43.7).

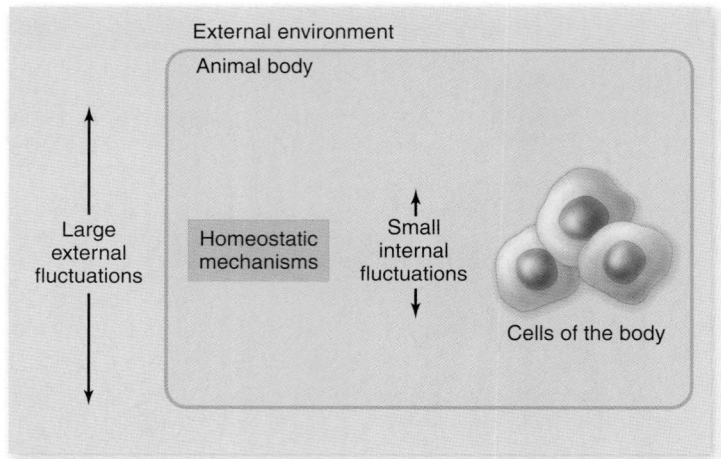

Figure 43.7 Homeostatic mechanisms help maintain stable internal conditions. Even though conditions outside of an animal's body may vary widely, the inside stays relatively constant due to many finely tuned control systems.

Negative feedback mechanisms keep values within a range

To maintain internal constancy, the vertebrate body uses a type of control system known as a **negative feedback.** In negative feedback, conditions within the body as well as outside it are detected by specialized sensors, which may be cells or membrane receptors. If conditions deviate too far from a set point, biochemical reactions are initiated to change conditions back toward the set point.

This *set point* is analogous to the temperature setting on a space heater. When room temperature drops, the change is detected by a temperature-sensing device inside the heater controls—the **sensor.** The thermostat on which you have indicated the set point for the heater contains a **comparator;** when the sensor information drops below the set point, the comparator closes an electrical circuit. The flow of electricity through the heater then produces more heat. Conversely, when the room temperature increases, the change causes the circuit to open, and heat is no longer produced. Figure 43.8 summarizes the negative feedback loop.

In a similar manner, the human body has set points for body temperature, blood glucose concentration, electrolyte (ion) concentration, the tension on a tendon, and so on. The integrating center is often a particular region of the brain or spinal cord, but in some cases, it can also be cells of endocrine glands. When a deviation in a condition occurs, a message is sent to increase or decrease the activity of particular target organs, termed *effectors*. Effectors are generally muscles or glands, and their actions can change the value of the condition in question back toward the set point value.

Mammals and birds are *endothermic*; they can maintain relatively constant body temperatures independent of the environmental temperature. In humans, when the blood temperature exceeds 37°C (98.6°F), neurons in a part of the brain called the **hypothalamus** detect the temperature change. Acting through the control of motor neurons, the hypothalamus responds by promoting the dissipation of heat through sweating, dilation of blood vessels in the skin, and other mechanisms. These responses tend to counteract the rise in body temperature.

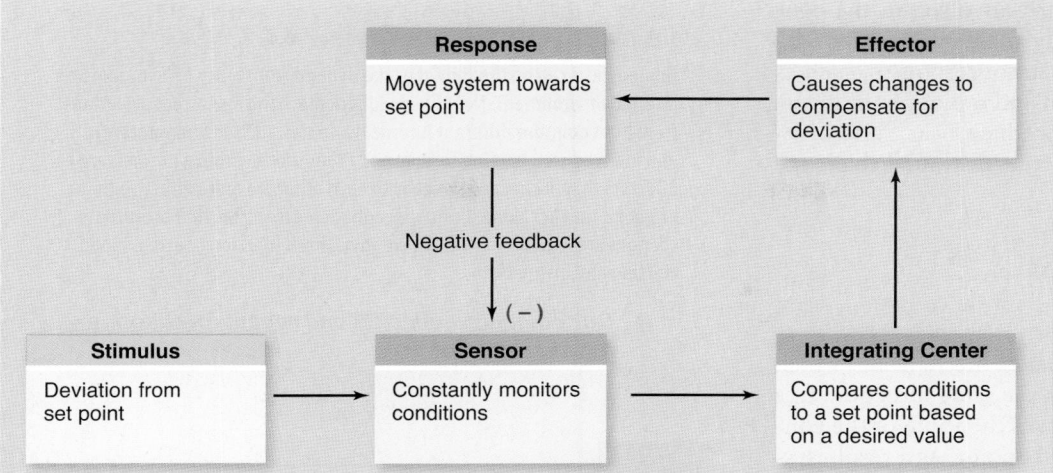

Figure 43.8 Generalized diagram of a negative feedback loop. Negative feedback loops maintain a state of homeostasis, or dynamic constancy of the internal environment. Changing conditions are detected by sensors, which feed information to an integrating center that compares conditions to a set point. Deviations from the set point lead to a response to bring internal conditions back to the set point. Negative feedback to the sensor terminates the response.

Antagonistic effectors act in opposite directions

The negative feedback mechanisms that maintain homeostasis often oppose each other to produce a finer degree of control. Most factors in the internal environment are controlled by several effectors, which often have antagonistic (opposing) actions. Control by antagonistic effectors is sometimes described as "push–pull," in which the increasing activity of one effector is accompanied by decreasing activity of an antagonistic effector. This affords a finer degree of control than could be achieved by simply switching one effector on and off.

To return to our earlier example, room temperature can be maintained by just turning the heater on and off, or turning an air conditioner on and off. A much more stable temperature is possible, however, if a thermostat controls both the air conditioner and heater. Then the heater turns on when the air conditioner shuts off, and vice versa (figure 43.9a).

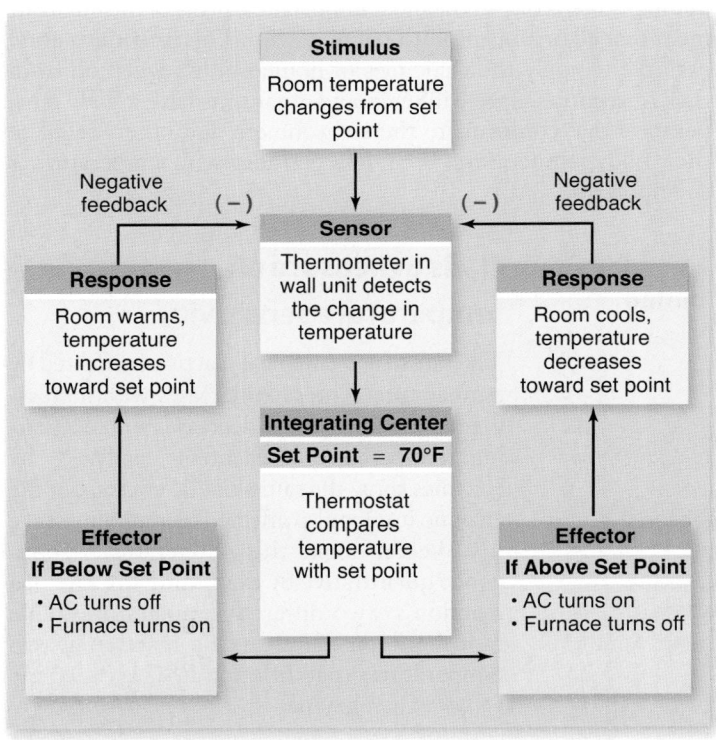

a.

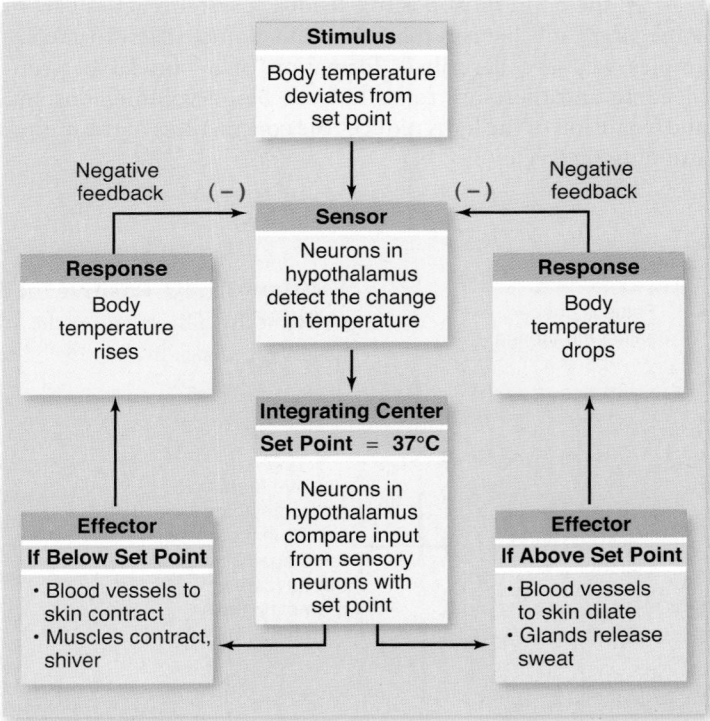

b.

Figure 43.9 Room and body temperature are maintained by negative feedback and antagonistic effectors. *a.* If a thermostat senses a low temperature (as compared with a set point), the furnace turns on and the air conditioner turns off. If the temperature is too high, the air conditioner turns on and the furnace turns off. *b.* The hypothalamus of the brain detects an increase or decrease in body temperature. The comparator (also in the hypothalamus) then processes the information and activates effectors, such as surface blood vessels, sweat glands, and skeletal muscles. Negative feedback results in a reduction in the difference of the body's temperature compared with the set point. Consequently, the stimulation of the effectors by the comparator is also reduced.

Antagonistic effectors are similarly involved in the control of body temperature. When body temperature falls, the hypothalamus coordinates a different set of responses, such as constriction of blood vessels in the skin and initiation of shivering, muscle contractions that help produce heat. These responses raise body temperature and correct the initial challenge to homeostasis (figure 43.9b).

Positive feedback mechanisms enhance a change

In a few cases, the body uses *positive feedback* mechanisms, which push or accentuate a change further in the same direction. In a positive feedback loop, the effector drives the value of the controlled variable even farther from the set point. As a result, systems in which there is positive feedback are highly unstable, analogous to a spark that ignites an explosion. They do not help to maintain homeostasis.

Nevertheless, such systems are important components of some physiological mechanisms. For example, positive feedback occurs in blood clotting, in which one clotting factor activates another in a cascade that leads quickly to the formation of a clot. Positive feedback also plays a role in the contractions of the uterus during childbirth (figure 43.10). In this case, stretching of the uterus by the fetus stimulates contraction, and contraction causes further stretching; the cycle continues until the uterus expels the fetus.

In the body, most positive feedback systems act as part of some larger mechanism that maintains homeostasis. In the examples we have described, formation of a blood clot stops bleeding and therefore tends to keep blood volume constant, and expulsion of the fetus reduces the contractions of the uterus, stopping the cycle.

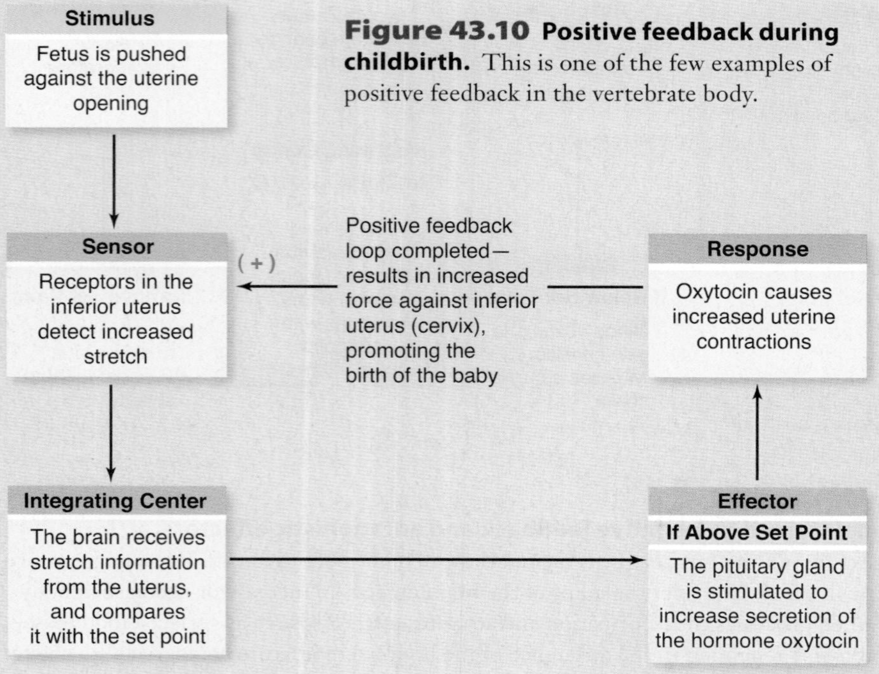

Learning Outcomes Review 43.7

Homeostasis can be thought of as the dynamic constancy of an organism's internal environment. Negative feedback mechanisms correct deviations from a set point for different internal variables, such as temperature, pH, and many others, helping to keep body conditions within a normal range. Effectors that act antagonistically to each other are more effective than effectors that act alone. Positive feedback mechanisms that accentuate changes are less common and have specialized functions, such as blood clotting and giving birth.

■ *Do antagonistic effectors and negative feedback function together?*

43.8 Regulating Body Temperature

Learning Outcomes

1. **Explain Q_{10} and its significance.**
2. **Define how organisms can be categorized with respect to temperature regulation.**
3. **Describe mechanisms for temperature homeostasis.**

Temperature is one of the most important aspects of the environment that all organisms must contend with. This provides a good example to apply the principles of homeostatic regulation from the last section. As we will see, some organisms have a body temperature that conforms to the environment and others regulate their body temperature. First, let's consider why temperature is so important.

Q_{10} is a measure of temperature sensitivity

The rate of any chemical reaction is affected by temperature: The rate increases with increasing temperature, and it decreases with decreasing temperature. Reactions catalyzed by enzymes show the same kinetic effects, but the enzyme itself is also affected by temperature.

We can make this temperature dependence quantitative by examining the rate of a reaction at two different temperatures. The ratio between the rates of a reaction at two temperatures that differ by 10°C is called the Q_{10} for the enzyme:

$$Q_{10} = R_{T+10}/R_T$$

For most enzymes the Q_{10} value is around 2, which means for every 10°C increase in temperature, the rate of the reaction doubles. Obviously, this cannot continue forever since at high temperatures the enzyme's structure is affected and it can no longer be active.

Figure 43.10 Positive feedback during childbirth. This is one of the few examples of positive feedback in the vertebrate body.

Stimulus
Fetus is pushed against the uterine opening

Sensor
Receptors in the inferior uterus detect increased stretch

Integrating Center
The brain receives stretch information from the uterus, and compares it with the set point

(+) Positive feedback loop completed—results in increased force against inferior uterus (cervix), promoting the birth of the baby

Effector
If Above Set Point
The pituitary gland is stimulated to increase secretion of the hormone oxytocin

Response
Oxytocin causes increased uterine contractions

The Q_{10} concept can also be applied to overall metabolism. The equation remains the same, but instead of the rate of a single reaction, the overall metabolic rate is used. When this has been measured, most organisms have a Q_{10} for metabolic rate around 2 to 3. This observation implies that the effect of temperature is mainly on the enzymes that make up metabolism.

In rare cases—for example, in some intertidal invertebrates—the Q_{10} is close to 1. Notice that this value means no change in metabolic rate with temperature. In the case of these intertidal invertebrates, they are exposed to large temperature fluctuations as they are alternately flooded with relatively cold water and exposed to direct sunlight and much higher air temperatures. These organisms have adapted to deal with these large temperature swings, probably through the evolution of different enzymes in a single metabolic pathway that have large differences in optimal temperature. This allows one enzyme to "make up" for others with decreased activity at a particular temperature.

Temperature is determined by internal and external factors

Body temperature appears simple, yet a large number of variables influence it. These variables include both internal and external factors, as well as behavior. As you may recall from chapter 6, the second law of thermodynamics indicates that no energy transaction is 100% efficient. Thus the reactions that make up metabolism are constantly producing heat as a result of this inefficiency. This heat must either be dissipated or can be used to raise body temperature.

Overall metabolic rate and body temperature are interrelated. Lower body temperatures do not allow high metabolic rates because of the temperature dependence of enzymes discussed earlier. Conversely, high metabolic rates may cause unacceptable heating of the body, requiring cooling.

Organisms therefore must deal with external and internal factors that relate body heat, metabolism, and the environment. The simplest model for temperature, more accurately body heat, is:

body heat = heat produced + (heat gained – heat lost)

we can simplify this further to:

body heat = heat produced + heat transferred

Notice that the heat transferred can be either positive or negative, that is, it can be used for both heating and cooling.

We recognize four mechanisms of heat transfer that are relevant to biological systems: radiation, conduction, convection, and evaporation (figure 43.11).

- **Radiation.** The transfer of heat by electromagnetic radiation, such as from the Sun, does not require direct contact. Heat is transferred from hotter bodies to colder bodies by radiation.

Figure 43.11 Methods of heat transfer. Heat can be gained or lost by conduction, convection, and radiation. Heat can also be lost by evaporation of water on the surface of an animal.

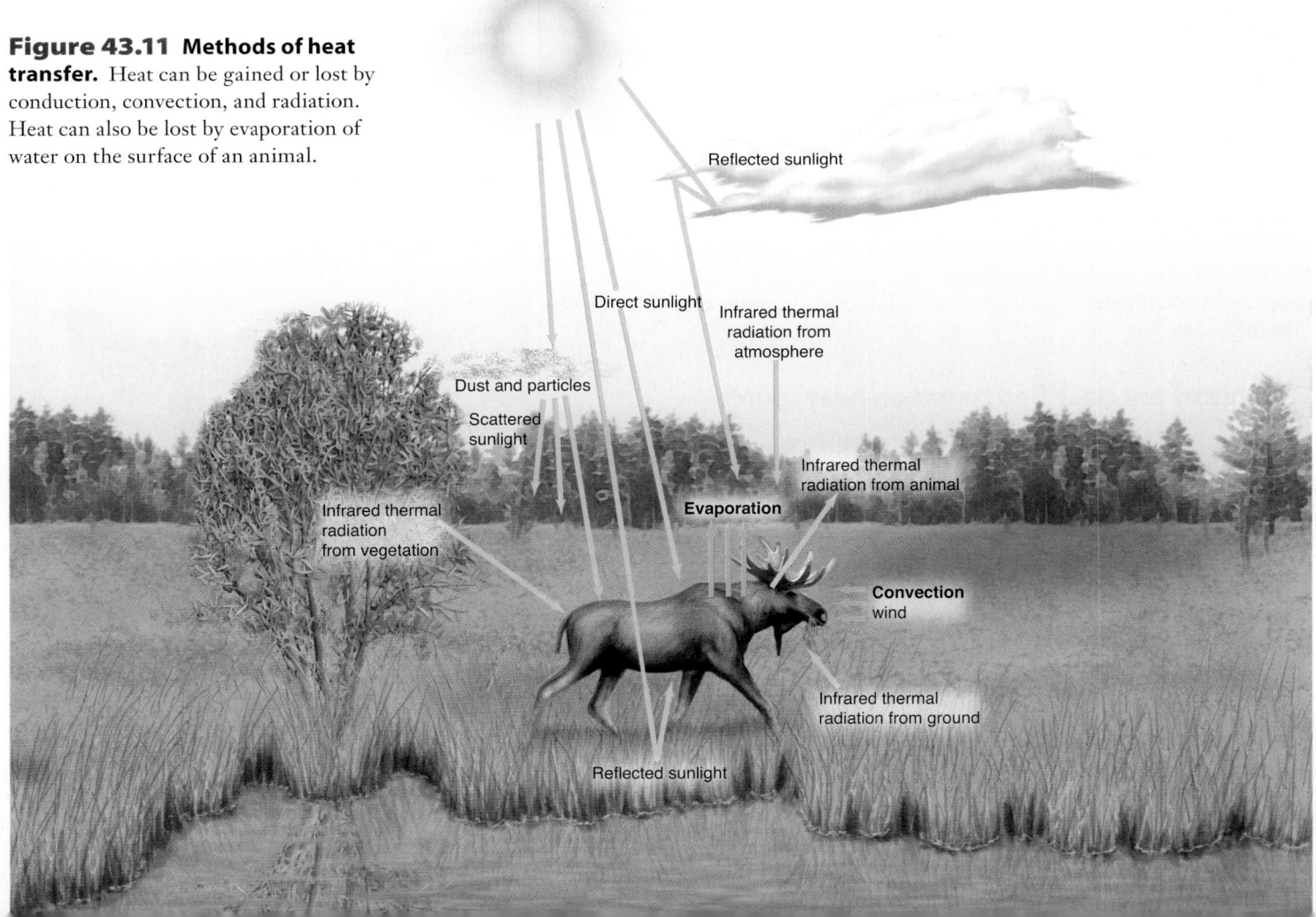

Reflected sunlight

Direct sunlight

Infrared thermal radiation from atmosphere

Dust and particles

Scattered sunlight

Infrared thermal radiation from vegetation

Evaporation

Infrared thermal radiation from animal

Convection wind

Infrared thermal radiation from ground

Reflected sunlight

- **Conduction.** The direct transfer of heat between two objects is called conduction. It is literally a direct transfer of kinetic energy between the molecules of the two objects in contact. Energy is transferred from hotter objects to colder ones.
- **Convection.** Convection is the transfer of heat brought about by the movement of a gas or liquid. This movement may be externally caused (wind) or may be due to density differences related to heating and cooling—for example, heated air is less dense and rises; the same is true for water.
- **Evaporation.** All substances have a heat of vaporization, that is, the amount of energy needed to change them from a liquid to a gas phase. Water, as you saw in chapter 2, has a high heat of vaporization, and many animals use this attribute of water as a source of cooling.

Other factors

The overall rate of heat transfer by the methods just listed depends on a number of factors that influence these physical processes. These factors include surface area, temperature difference, and specific heat conduction. Taking these in order, the larger the surface area relative to overall mass, the greater the conduction of heat. Thus, small organisms have a relatively larger surface area for their mass, and they gain or lose heat more readily to the surroundings. This can be affected to a small extent by changing posture, and by extending or pulling in the limbs.

Temperature difference is also important; the greater the difference between ambient temperature and body temperature, the greater the heat transfer. The closer an animal's temperature is to the ambient temperature, the less heat is gained or lost.

Finally, an animal with high heat conductance tends to have a body temperature close to the ambient temperature. For animals that regulate temperature, surrounding the body with a substance with lower heat conductance has an advantage: It acts as insulation. Insulating substances includes such features as feathers, fur, and blubber. For animals that regulate body temperature through behavior, a high heat conductance can maximize heat transfer.

Organisms are classified based on heat source

For many years, physiologists classified animals according to whether they maintained a constant body temperature, or their body temperature fluctuated with environment. Animals that regulated their body temperature about a set point were called *homeotherms*, and those that allow their body temperature to conform to the environment were called *poikilotherms*.

Because homeotherms tended to maintain their body temperature above the ambient temperature, they were also colloquially called "warm-blooded"; poikilotherms were termed "cold-blooded." The problem with this terminology is that a poikilotherm in an environment with a stable temperature (for example, many deep-sea fish species) has a more constant body temperature than some homeotherms.

These limitations to the dichotomy based on temperature regulation led to another view based on how body heat is generated. Animals that use metabolism to generate body heat and maintain their temperatures above the ambient temperature are called *endotherms*. Animals with a relatively low metabolic rate that do not use metabolism to produce heat and have a body temperature that conforms to the ambient temperature are called *ectotherms*. Endotherms tend to have a lower thermal conductivity due to insulating mechanisms, and ectotherms tend to have high thermal conductivity and lack insulation.

These two terms represent ideal end points of a spectrum of physiology and adaptations. Many animals fall in between these extremes and can be considered *heterotherms*. It is a matter of judgment how a particular animal is classified if it exhibits characteristics of each group.

Ectotherms regulate temperature using behavior

Despite having low metabolic rates, ectotherms can regulate their temperature using behavior. Most invertebrates use behavior to adjust their temperature. Many butterflies, for example, must reach a certain body temperature before they can fly. In the cool of the morning, they orient their bodies so as to maximize their absorption of sunlight. Moths and many other insects use a shivering reflex to warm their thoracic flight muscles so that they may take flight (figure 43.12).

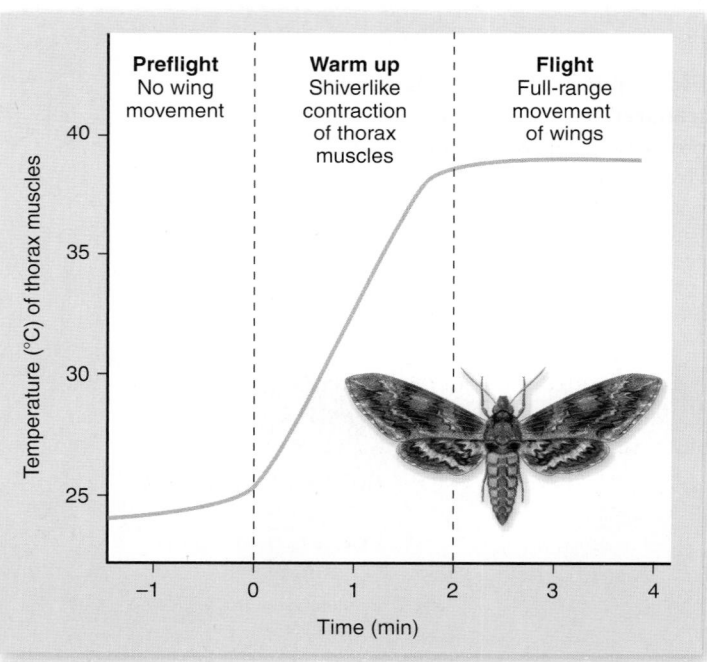

Figure 43.12 Thermoregulation in insects. Some insects, such as the sphinx moth, contract their thoracic muscles to warm up for flight.

Inquiry question

? Why does muscle temperature stop warming after 2 min?

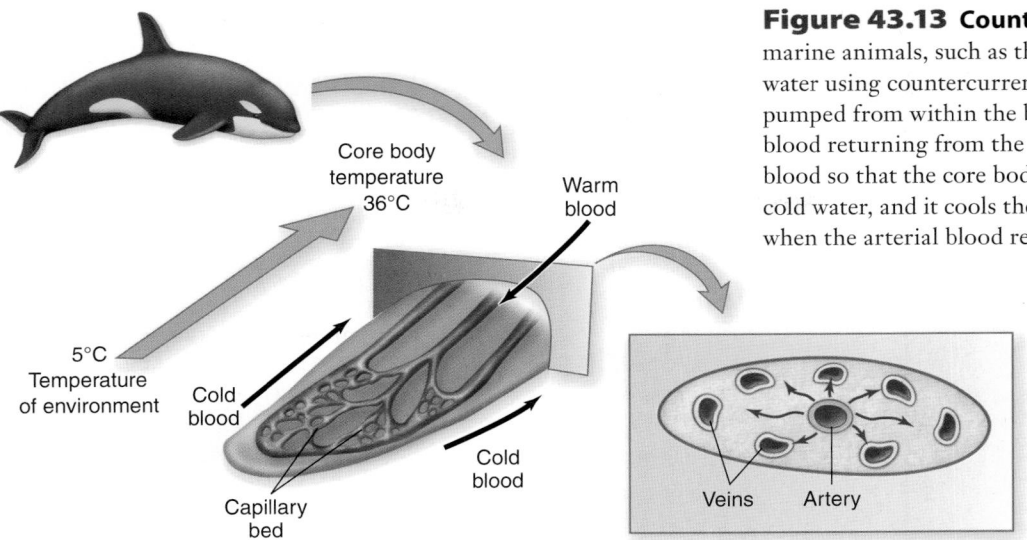

Figure 43.13 Countercurrent heat exchange. Many marine animals, such as this killer whale, limit heat loss in cold water using countercurrent heat exchange. The warm blood pumped from within the body in arteries loses heat to the cooler blood returning from the skin in veins. This warms the venous blood so that the core body temperature can remain constant in cold water, and it cools the arterial blood so that less heat is lost when the arterial blood reaches the tip of the extremity.

Vertebrates other than mammals and birds are also ectothermic, and their body temperatures are more or less dependent on the environmental temperature. This does not mean that these animals cannot maintain high and relatively constant body temperatures, but they must use behavior to do this. Many ectothermic vertebrates are able to maintain temperature homeostasis, that is, are homeothermic ectotherms.

For example, certain large fish, including tuna, swordfish, and some sharks, can maintain parts of their body at a significantly higher temperature than that of the water. They do so using *countercurrent heat exchange.* This circulatory adaptation allows the cooler blood in the veins to be warmed through radiation of heat from the warmer blood in the arteries located close to the veins. The arteries carry warmer blood from the center of the body (figure 43.13).

Reptiles attempt to maintain a constant body temperature through behavioral means—by placing themselves in varying locations of sunlight and shade. That's why you frequently see lizards basking in the sun. Some reptiles can maximize the effect of behavioral regulation by also controlling blood flow. The marine iguana can increase and decrease its heart rate and control the extent of dilation or contraction of blood vessels to regulate the amount of blood available for heat transfer by conduction. Increased heart rate and vasodilation allows them to maximize heating when on land, whereas decreased heart rate and vasoconstriction minimize cooling when diving for food.

In general, ectotherms have low metabolic rates, which has the advantage of correspondingly low intake of energy (food). It is estimated that a lizard (ectotherm) needs only 10% of the energy intake of a mouse (endotherm) of comparable size. The tradeoff is that ectotherms are not capable of sustained high-energy activity.

Endotherms create internal metabolic heat for conservation or dissipation

For endotherms, the generation of internal heat via high metabolic rate can be used to warm the organism if it is cold, but also represents a source of heat that must be dissipated at higher temperatures.

The simplest response that affects heat transfer is to control the amount of blood flow to the surface of the animal. Dilating blood vessels increases the amount of blood flowing to the surface, which in turn increases thermal heat exchange and dissipation of heat. In contrast, constriction of blood vessels decreases the amount of blood flowing to the surface and decreases thermal heat exchange, limiting the amount of heat lost due to conduction.

When ambient temperatures rise, many endotherms take advantage of evaporative cooling in the form of sweating or panting. Sweating is found in some mammals, including humans, and involves the active extrusion of water from sweat glands onto the surface of the body. As the water evaporates, it cools the skin, and this cooling can be transferred internally by capillaries near the surface of the skin. Panting is a similar adaptation used by some mammals and birds that takes advantage of respiratory surfaces for evaporative cooling. For evaporative cooling to be effective, the animal must be able to tolerate the loss of water.

The advantage of endothermy is that it allows sustained high-energy activity. The tradeoff for endotherms is that the high metabolic rate has a corresponding cost in requiring relatively constant and high rates of energy intake (food).

Body size and insulation

Size is one important characteristic affecting animal physiology. Changes in body mass have a large effect on metabolic rate. Smaller animals consume much more energy per unit body mass than larger animals. This relationship is summarized in the "mouse to elephant" curve that shows the nonproportionality of metabolic rate versus size of mammals (figure 43.14).

For small animals with a high metabolic rate, surface area is also large relative to their volume. In a cold environment, this can be disastrous as they cannot produce enough internal heat to balance conductive loss through their large surface area.

chapter **43** *The Animal Body and Principles of Regulation*

Figure 43.14 Relationship between body mass and metabolic rate in mammals. Smaller animals have a much higher metabolic rate per unit body mass relative to larger animals. In the figure, mass-specific metabolic rate (expressed as O_2 consumption per unit mass) is plotted against body mass. Note that the body mass axis is a logarithmic scale.

Inquiry question

? What does this graph predict about the different challenges faced by smaller versus larger mammals in hot and cold environments?

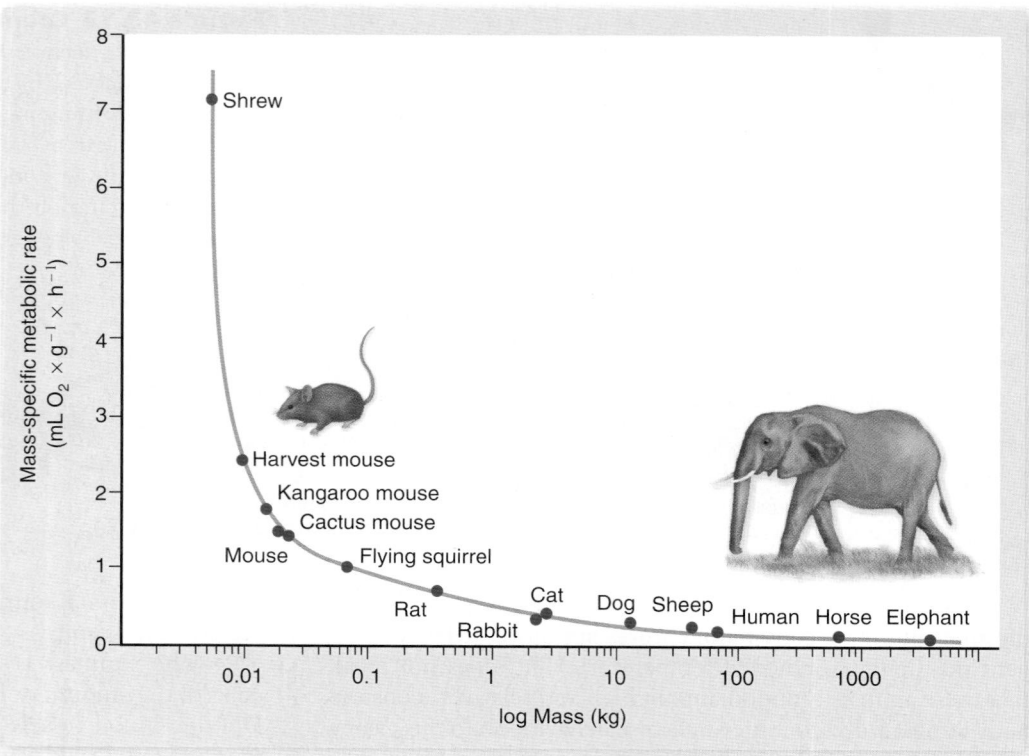

Thus, small endotherms in cold environments require significant insulation to maintain their body temperature. The amount of insulation can also vary seasonally and geographically with thicker coats in the north and in winter.

Conversely, large animals in hot environments have the opposite problem: Although their metabolic rate is relatively low, they still produce a large amount of heat with much less relative surface area to dissipate this heat by conduction. Thus large endotherms in hot environments usually have little insulation and will use behavior to lose heat, such as elephants flapping their ears to increase convective heat loss.

Thermogenesis

When temperatures fall below a critical lower threshold, normal endothermic responses are not sufficient to warm an animal. In this case, the animal resorts to **thermogenesis,** or the use of normal energy metabolism to produce heat. Thermogenesis takes two forms: shivering and nonshivering thermogenesis.

In nonshivering thermogenesis, fat metabolism is altered to produce heat instead of ATP. Nonshivering thermogenesis takes place throughout the body, but in some mammals, special stores of fat called brown fat are utilized specifically for this purpose. This brown fat is stored in small deposits in the neck and between the shoulders. This fat is highly vascularized, allowing efficient transfer of heat away from the site of production.

Shivering thermogenesis uses muscles to generate heat without producing useful work. It occurs in some insects, such as the earlier example of a butterfly warming its flight muscles, and in endothermic vertebrates. Shivering involves the use of

antagonistic muscles to produce little net generation of movement, but hydrolysis of ATP, generating heat.

Mammalian thermoregulation is controlled by the hypothalamus

Mammals that maintain a relatively constant core temperature need an overall control system (summarized in figure 43.15). The system functions much like the heating/cooling system in your house that has a thermostat connected to a furnace to produce heat and an air conditioner to remove heat. Such a system maintains the temperature of your house about a set point by alternately heating or cooling as necessary.

When the temperature of your blood exceeds 37°C (98.6°F), neurons in the hypothalamus detect the temperature change (see chapters 44 and 45). This leads to stimulation of the *heat-losing center* in the hypothalamus. Nerves from this area cause a dilation of peripheral blood vessels, bringing more blood to the surface to dissipate heat. Other nerves stimulate the production of sweat, leading to evaporative cooling. Production of hormones that stimulate metabolism is also inhibited.

When your temperature falls below 37°C, an antagonistic set of effects are produced by the hypothalamus. This is under control of the *heat-promoting center*, which has nerves that constrict blood vessels to reduce heat transfer, and inhibit sweating to prevent evaporative cooling. The adrenal medulla is stimulated to produce epinephrine, and the anterior pituitary to produce TSH, both of which stimulate metabolism. In the case of TSH, this is indirect as it stimulates the thyroid to produce thyroxin, which stimulates metabolism (see chapter 46). A

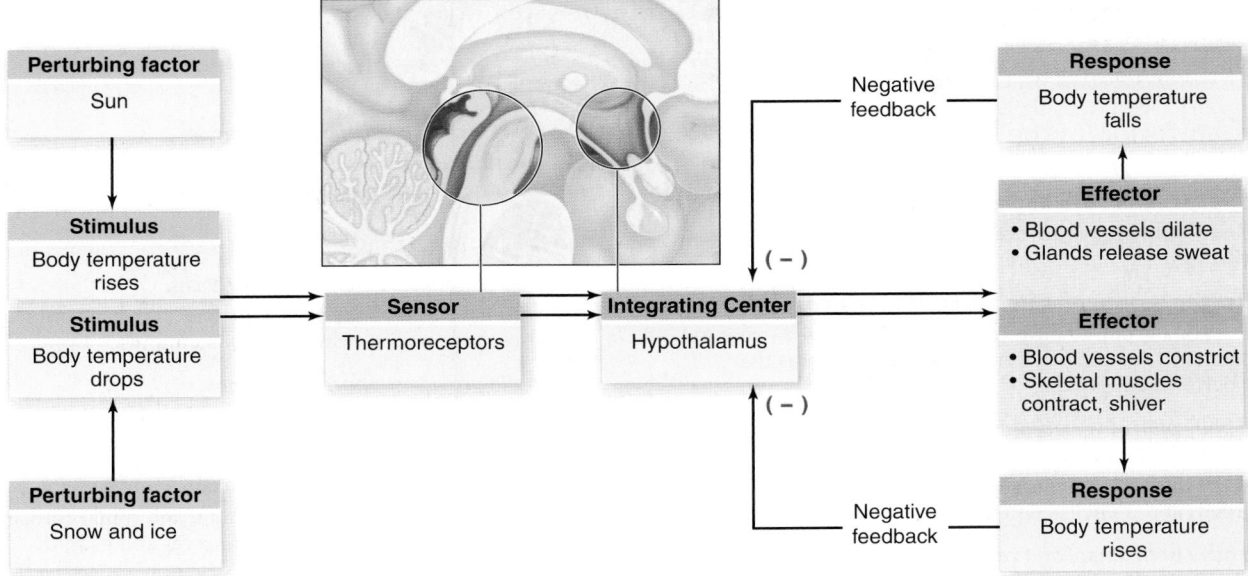

Figure 43.15 The control of body temperature by the hypothalamus. Central thermoreceptors in the brain and interior of the abdomen sense changes in core temperature. These thermoreceptors synapse with neurons on the hypothalamus, which acts as an integrating center. The hypothalamus then controls effectors such as blood vessels and sweat glands via sympathetic nerves. The hypothalamus also causes the release of hormones that stimulate the thyroid to produce thyroxin, which modulates metabolism.

combination of epinephrine and autonomic nerve stimulation of fat tissue can induce thermogenesis to produce more internal heat. Again, as temperature rises, negative feedback to the hypothalamus reduces the heat-producing response.

Fever

Substances that cause a rise in temperature are called **pyrogens,** and they produce the state we call **fever.** Fever is a result of resetting the body's normal set point to a higher temperature. A number of gram-negative bacteria have components in their cell walls called endotoxins that act as pyrogens. Substances produced by circulating white blood cells act as pyrogens as well. Pyrogens act on the hypothalamus to increase the set point.

The adaptive value of fever seems to be that increased temperature can inhibit the growth of bacteria. Evidence for this comes from the observation that some ectotherms respond to pyrogens as well. When desert iguanas were injected with pyrogen-producing bacteria, they spent more time in the sun, producing an elevated temperature: They induced fever behaviorally!

These observations have led to a reevaluation of fever as a state that should be treated medically. Fever is a normal response to infection, and treatment to reduce fever may be working against this natural defense system. Extremely high fevers, however, can be dangerous, inducing symptoms ranging from seizures to delirium.

Torpor

Endotherms can also reduce both metabolic rate and body temperature to produce a state of dormancy called *torpor*. Torpor allows an animal to reduce the need for food intake by reducing metabolism. Some birds, such as the hummingbird, allow their body temperature to drop as much as 25°C at night.

This strategy is found in smaller endotherms; larger mammals have too large a mass to allow rapid cooling.

Hibernation is an extreme state in which deep torpor lasts for several weeks or even several months. In this case, the animal's temperature may drop as much as 20°C below its normal set point for an extended period of time. The animals that practice hibernation seem to be in the midrange of size; smaller endotherms quickly consume more energy than they can easily store, even by reducing their metabolic rate.

Very large mammals do not appear to hibernate. It was long thought that bears hibernate, but in reality their temperature is reduced only a few degrees. They instead undergo a prolonged winter sleep. With their large thermal mass and low rate of heat loss, they do not seem to require the additional energy savings of hibernation.

Learning Outcomes Review 43.8

The Q_{10} value of an enzyme indicates how its activity changes with a 10°C rise in temperature. The Q_{10} can also be applied to an organism's overall metabolism. Body heat is equal to heat produced plus heat transferred. Heat is transferred by conduction, convection, radiation, and evaporation. Organisms that generate heat and can maintain a temperature above ambient levels are called endotherms. Organisms that conform to their surroundings are called ectotherms. Both types can regulate temperature, but ectotherms mainly do so with behavior. Mammals maintain a consistent body temperature through regulation of metabolic rate by the hypothalamus. Two negative feedback loops act to raise or lower temperature as needed.

■ *Why are the terms "cold-blooded" and "warm-blooded" outmoded and inaccurate?*

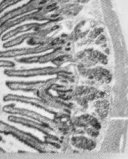

43.1 Organization of the Vertebrate Body
(see figure 43.1)

Tissues are groups of cells of a single type and function.
Adult vertebrate primary tissues are epithelial, connective, muscle, and nerve tissues.

Organs and organ systems provide specialized function.
Organs consist of a group of different tissues that form a structural and functional unit. An organ system is a group of organs that collectively perform a function.

The general body plan of vertebrates is a tube within a tube, with internal support (see figure 43.2).
The tube of the digestive tract is surrounded by the skeleton and accessory organs and is enclosed in the integument.

Vertebrates have both dorsal and ventral body cavities.
The dorsal body cavity lies within the skull and vertebrae. The ventral body cavity, bounded by the rib cage and abdominal muscles, comprises the thoracic cavity and the abdominopelvic cavity.

The coelomic space of the abdominopelvic cavity is the peritoneal cavity; that surrounding the heart is the pericardial cavity; and those around the lungs are the pleural cavities.

43.2 Epithelial Tissue

Epithelium forms a barrier.
Epithelial cells are tightly bound together, forming a selective barrier. Epithelial cells are replaced constantly and can regenerate in wound healing. Epithelium has a basal surface attached to underlying connective tissues, and a free apical surface.

Epithelial types reflect their function.
Epithelium is divided into two general classes: simple (one cell layer) and stratified (multiple cells thick). These are further divided into squamous, cuboidal, and columnar based on the shape of cells (see table 43.1). Vertebrate glands form from invaginated epithelia.

43.3 Connective Tissue

Connective tissue proper may be either loose or dense.
Connective tissues contain various cells in an extracellular matrix of proteins and ground substance. Connective tissue proper is divided into loose connective tissue and dense connective tissue.

Special connective tissues have unique characteristics.
Special connective tissues, such as cartilage, rigid bone, and blood, have unique cells and matrices (see table 43.2). Cartilage is formed by chondrocytes and bone by osteocytes.

All connective tissues have similarities.
All connective tissues originate from mesoderm and contain a variety of cells within an extracellular matrix.

43.4 Muscle Tissue (see table 43.3)

Smooth muscle is found in most organs.
Involuntary smooth muscle occurs in the viscera and is composed of long, spindle-shaped cells with a single nucleus.

Skeletal muscle moves the body.
Voluntary skeletal or striated muscle is usually attached by tendons to bones, and the cells (fibers) have multiple nuclei and contain contractile myofibrils.

The heart is composed of cardiac muscle.
Cardiac muscle consists of striated muscle cells connected to each other by gap junctions that allow coordination.

43.5 Nerve Tissue (see table 43.4)

Neurons sometimes extend long distances.
Neurons have a cell body with a nucleus; dendrites, which receive impulses; and an axon, which transmits impulses away.

Neuroglia provide support for neurons.
Neuroglia help regulate the neuronal environment. Some types form the myelin sheaths that surround some axons.

Two divisions of the nervous system coordinate activity.
The central nervous system is the brain and spinal cord, and the peripheral nervous system contains nerves and ganglia.

43.6 Overview of Vertebrate Organ Systems
(see figure 43.6)

Communication and integration sense and respond to the environment.
The three organ systems involved in communication and integration are the nervous, sensory, and endocrine systems.

Skeletal support and movement are vital to all animals.
The musculoskeletal system consists of muscles and the skeleton they act upon.

Regulation and maintenance of the body's chemistry ensures continued life.
The digestive, circulatory, respiratory, and urinary systems accomplish ingestion of nutrients and elimination of wastes.

The body can defend itself from attackers and invaders.
The integumentary system forms a barrier against attack; the immune system mounts a counterattack to foreign pathogens.

Reproduction and development ensure continuity of species.
All vertebrate species are capable of sexual reproduction.

43.7 Homeostasis

Homeostasis refers to the dynamic constancy of the internal environment and is essential for life.

Negative feedback mechanisms keep values within a range.
Negative feedback loops include a sensor, an integration center, and effectors that respond to deviations from a set point.

Antagonistic effectors act in opposite directions.
Negative feedback mechanisms often occur in antagonistic pairs that push and pull against each other.

Positive feedback mechanisms enhance a change.
In a positive feedback loop changes in one direction bring about further changes in the same direction.

43.8 Regulating Body Temperature

Q_{10} is a measure of temperature sensitivity.
Q_{10} is the ratio of reaction rates at two temperatures 10°C apart. For chemical reactions Q_{10} is about 2. Most organisms have a Q_{10} around 2 to 3, indicating temperature affects mainly enzymatic reactions.

Temperature is determined by internal and external factors.

Internal factors include metabolic rate; external factors affect heat transfer. Heat is transferred through radiation, conduction, convection, and evaporation (see figure 43.11).

Organisms are classified based on heat source.

Endotherms have high metabolic rates and generate heat internally. Ectotherms have low metabolic rates and conform to ambient temperature.

Ectotherms regulate temperature using behavior.

Ectotherms move around in an environment to alter their temperature (see figures 43.12 and 43.13).

Endotherms create internal metabolic heat for conservation or dissipation.

Endotherms regulate temperature by changes in metabolic rate, blood flow, and sweating or panting. Thermogenesis occurs when temperature falls below a critical level.

Mammalian thermoregulation is controlled by the hypothalamus (see figure 43.15).

The hypothalamus acts through a heat-losing and heat-promoting center to keep the blood temperature near a set point. Fever is an increase in body temperature; torpor is a lowered metabolic state associated with dormancy.

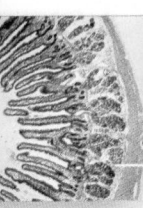

Review Questions

UNDERSTAND

1. Which of the following cavities would contain your stomach?
   a. Peritoneal
   b. Pericardial
   c. Pleural
   d. Thoracic

2. Epithelial tissues do all of the following except
   a. form barriers or boundaries.
   b. absorb nutrients in the digestive tract.
   c. transmit information in the central nervous system.
   d. allow exchange of gases in the lung.

3. Ectotherms
   a. cannot regulate their body temperatures.
   b. regulate their internal temperature using metabolic energy.
   c. can regulate temperature using behavior.
   d. regulate temperature by dissipating but not generating heat.

4. Connective tissues include a diverse group of cells, yet they all share
   a. cuboidal shape.
   b. the ability to produce hormones.
   c. the ability to contract.
   d. the presence of an extracellular matrix.

5. Skeletal muscle cells differ from the "typical" mammalian cell in that they
   a. contain multiple nuclei.
   b. have mitochondria.
   c. have no plasma membrane.
   d. are not derived from embryonic tissue.

6. Examples of smooth muscle sites include
   a. the lining of blood vessels.
   b. the iris of the eye.
   c. the wall of the digestive tract.
   d. all of these.

7. The function of neuroglia is to
   a. carry messages from the PNS to the CNS.
   b. support and protect neurons.
   c. stimulate muscle contraction.
   d. store memories.

8. Skeletal muscle cells are
   a. large multinucleate cells that arise by growth.
   b. large multinucleate cells that arise by fusion of smaller cells.
   c. small cells connected by many gap junctions.
   d. large cells with a single nucleus.

APPLY

1. Connective tissues, although quite diverse in structure and location, do share a common theme; the connection between other types of tissues. Although all of the following seem to fit that criterion, one of the tissues listed is not a type of connective tissue. Which one?
   a. Blood
   b. Muscle
   c. Adipose
   d. Cartilage

2. What do all the organs of the body have in common?
   a. Each contains the same kinds of cells.
   b. Each is composed of several different kinds of tissue.
   c. Each is derived from ectoderm.
   d. Each can be considered part of the circulatory system.

3. Rheumatoid arthritis is an autoimmune disease that attacks the linings of joints within the body. The cells that line these joints, and whose destruction causes the symptoms of arthritis, are known as
   a. osteocytes.
   b. erythrocytes.
   c. chondrocytes.
   d. thrombocytes.

4. Suppose that an alien virus arrives on Earth. This virus causes damage to the nervous system by attacking the structures of neurons. Which of the following structures would be immune from attack?
   a. Axon
   b. Dendrite
   c. Neuroglia
   d. All of these would be attacked by the virus.

5. Homeostasis
   a. is a dynamic process.
   b. describes the maintenance of the internal environment of the body.
   c. is essential to life.
   d. is all of these.

6. Which of the following scenarios correctly describes positive feedback?

    a. If the temperature increases in your room, your furnace increases its output of warm air.

    b. If you drink too much water, you produce more urine.

    c. If the price of gasoline increases, drivers decrease the length of their trips.

    d. If you feel cold, you start to shiver.

7. The three types of muscle all share

    a. a structure that includes striations.

    b. a membrane that is electrically excitable.

    c. the ability to contract.

    d. the characteristic of self-excitation.

SYNTHESIZE

1. Suppose that you discover a new disease that affects nutrient absorption in the gut as well as causes problems with the skin. Is it possible that one disease could involve the same tissues? How could this occur?

2. Which organ systems are involved in regulation and maintenance? Why do you think they are linked in this way?

3. We have all experienced hunger pangs. Is hunger a positive or negative feedback stimulus? Describe the steps involved in the response to this stimulus.

4. Why is homeostasis described as a dynamic process? How does negative feedback function in this process? How can antagonistic effectors result in a constant level, and how does this relate to the idea of a dynamic process?

ONLINE RESOURCE

www.ravenbiology.com

Understand, Apply, and Synthesize—enhance your study with animations that bring concepts to life and practice tests to assess your understanding. Your instructor may also recommend the interactive eBook, individualized learning tools, and more.

Chapter 44

The Nervous System

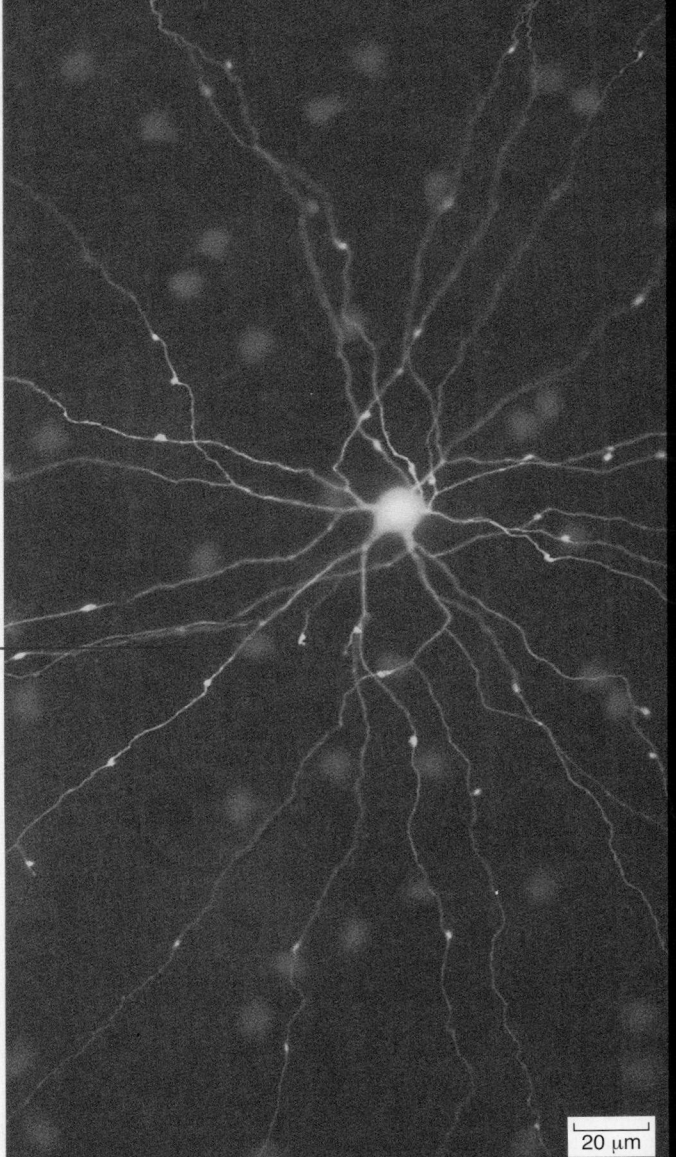

20 μm

Chapter Outline

44.1   Nervous System Organization

44.2   The Mechanism of Nerve Impulse Transmission

44.3   Synapses: Where Neurons Communicate with Other Cells

44.4   The Central Nervous System: Brain and Spinal Cord

44.5   The Peripheral Nervous System: Sensory and Motor Neurons

Introduction

All animals except sponges use a network of nerve cells to gather information about the body's condition and the external environment, to process and integrate that information, and to issue commands to the body's muscles and glands. As we saw in chapter 43, homeostasis of the animal's body is accomplished by negative feedback loops that maintain conditions within narrow limits. Negative feedback implies not only detection of appropriate stimuli but also communication of information to begin a response. The nervous system, composed of neurons, such as the one pictured here, is a fast communication system and a part of many feedback systems in the body.

An animal must be able to respond to environmental stimuli. A fly escapes a flyswatter; the antennae of a crayfish detect food and the crayfish moves toward it. To accomplish these actions, animals must have *sensory receptors* that can detect the stimulus and *motor effectors* that can respond to it. In most invertebrate phyla and in all vertebrate classes, sensory receptors and motor effectors are linked by way of the nervous system.

The central nervous system is the "command center"

As described in chapter 43, the nervous system consists of neurons and supporting cells. Figure 44.1 shows the three types of neurons. In vertebrates, **sensory neurons** (or afferent neurons) carry impulses from sensory receptors to the *central nervous system (CNS)*, which is composed of the brain and spinal cord. **Motor neurons** (or efferent neurons) carry impulses from the CNS to effectors—muscles and glands. A third type of neuron is present in the nervous systems of most invertebrates and all vertebrates: **interneurons** (or association neurons). Interneurons are located in the brain and spinal cord of vertebrates, where they help provide more complex reflexes and higher associative functions, including learning and memory.

The peripheral nervous system collects information and carries out responses

Together, sensory and motor neurons constitute the *peripheral nervous system (PNS)* in vertebrates. Motor neurons that stimulate skeletal muscles to contract make up the **somatic nervous system;** those that regulate the activity of the smooth muscles, cardiac muscle, and glands compose the **autonomic nervous system.**

The autonomic nervous system is further broken down into the *sympathetic* and *parasympathetic* divisions. These divisions counterbalance each other in the regulation of many organ systems. Figure 44.2 illustrates the relationships among the different parts of the vertebrate nervous system.

Figure 44.1 Three types of neurons. The brain and spinal cord form the central nervous system (CNS) of vertebrates, and sensory and motor neurons form the peripheral nervous system (PNS). Sensory neurons of the peripheral nervous system carry information about the environment to the CNS. Interneurons in the CNS provide links between sensory and motor neurons. Motor neurons of the PNS system carry impulses or "commands" to muscles and glands (effectors).

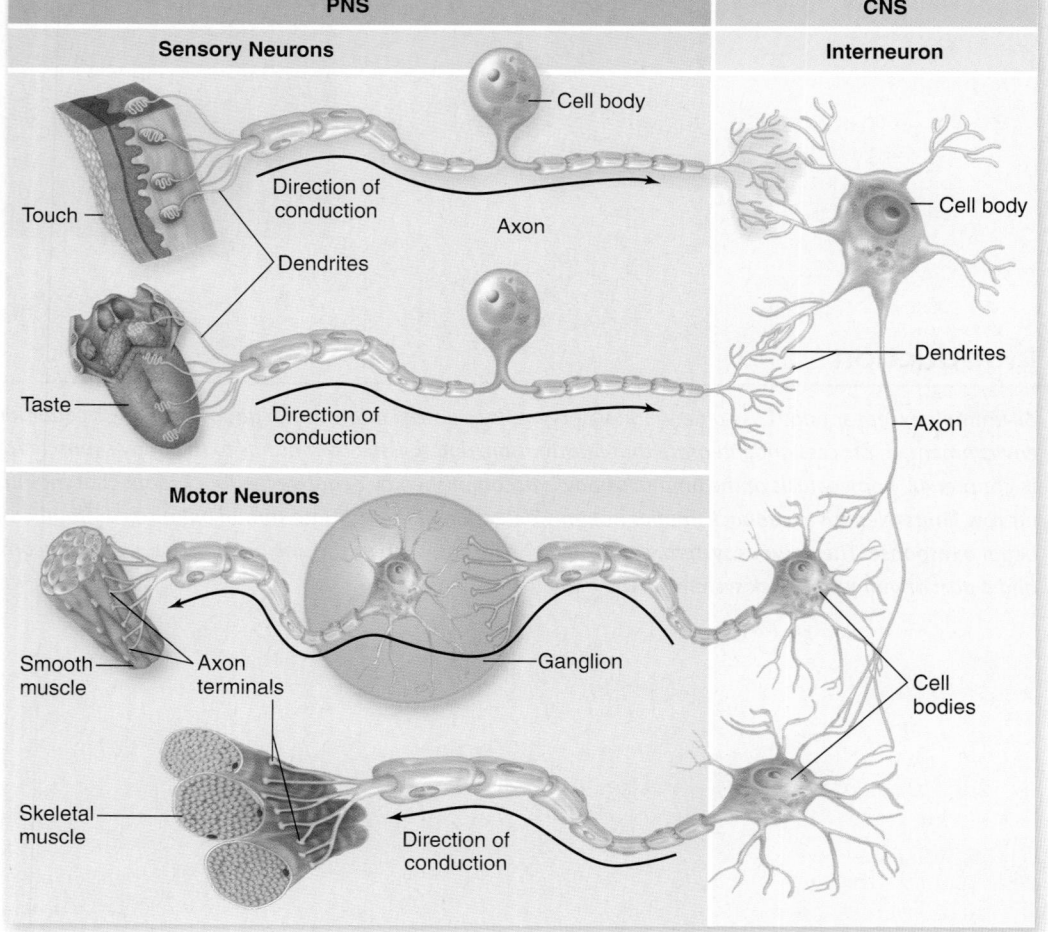

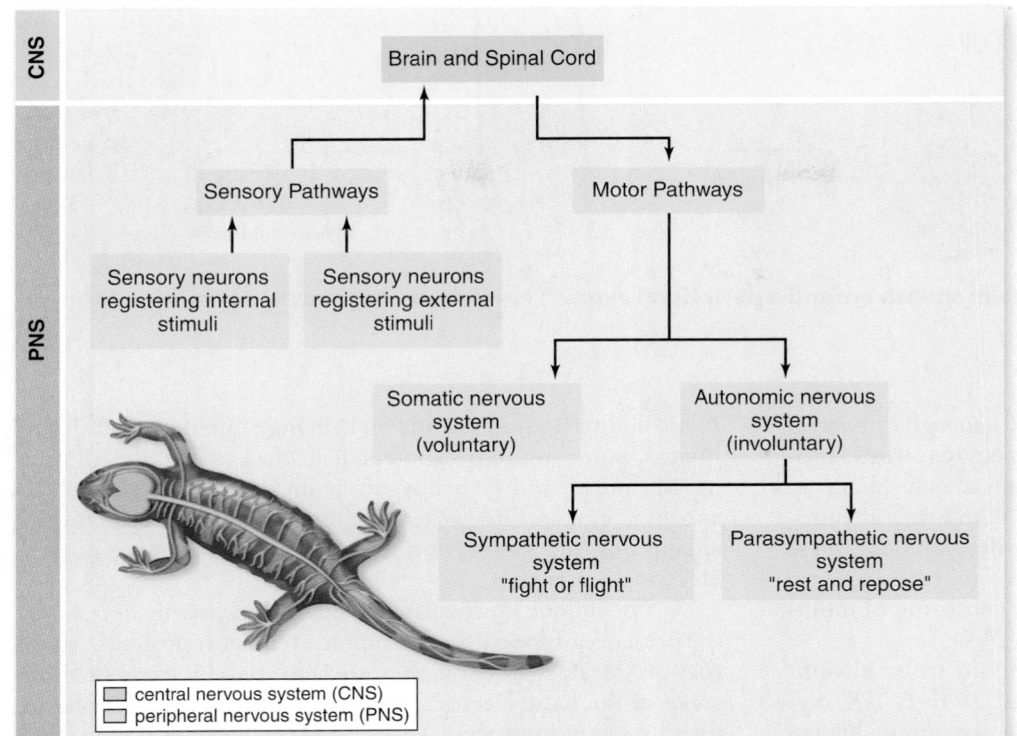

Figure 44.2 Divisions of the vertebrate nervous system. The major divisions are the central and peripheral nervous systems. The brain and spinal cord make up the central nervous system (CNS). The peripheral nervous system (PNS) includes everything outside the CNS and is divided into sensory and motor pathways. Sensory pathways can detect either external or internal stimuli. Motor pathways are divided into the somatic nervous system that activates voluntary muscles and the autonomic nervous system that activate involuntary muscles. The sympathetic and parasympathetic nervous systems are subsets of the autonomic nervous system that trigger opposing actions.

The structure of neurons supports their function

Despite their varied appearances, most neurons have the same functional architecture (figure 44.3). The **cell body** is an enlarged region containing the nucleus. Extending from the cell body are one or more cytoplasmic extensions called **dendrites.** Motor and association neurons possess a profusion of highly branched dendrites, enabling those cells to receive information from many different sources simultaneously. Some neurons have extensions from the dendrites called *dendritic spines* that increase the surface area available to receive stimuli.

The surface of the cell body integrates the information arriving at its dendrites. If the resulting membrane excitation is sufficient, it triggers the conduction of impulses away from the cell body along an **axon.** Each neuron has a single axon leaving its cell body, although an axon may also branch to stimulate a number of cells. An axon can be quite long: The axons controlling the muscles in a person's feet can be more than a meter long, and the axons that extend from the skull to the pelvis in a giraffe are about 3 m long.

Supporting cells include Schwann cells and oligodendrocytes

Neurons are supported both structurally and functionally by supporting cells, which are collectively called neuroglia. These cells are one-tenth as big and 10 times more numerous than neurons, and they serve a variety of functions, including supplying the neurons with nutrients, removing wastes from neurons, guiding axon migration, and providing immune functions.

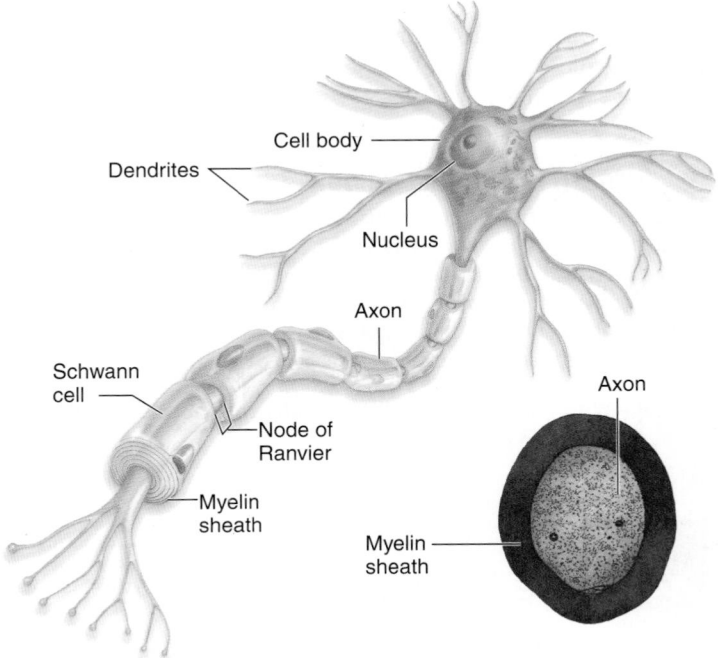

Figure 44.3 Structure of a typical vertebrate neuron. Extending from the cell body are many dendrites, which receive information and carry it to the cell body. A single axon transmits impulses away from the cell body. Many axons are encased by a myelin sheath, with multiple membrane layers that insulate the axon. Small gaps, called nodes of Ranvier, interrupt the sheath at regular intervals. Schwann cells form myelin sheaths in the PNS (as shown for this motor neuron); extensions of oligodendrocytes form myelin sheaths in the CNS.

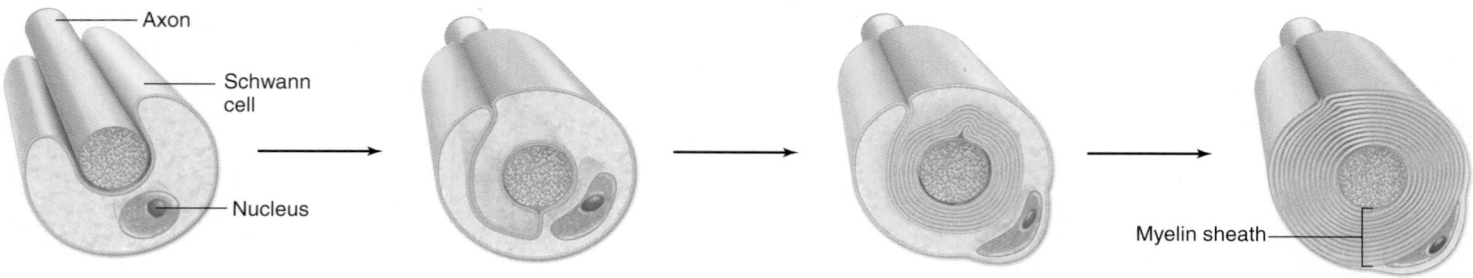

Figure 44.4 The formation of the myelin sheath around a peripheral axon. The myelin sheath forms by successive wrappings of Schwann cell membranes around the axon.

Two of the most important kinds of neuroglia in vertebrates are **Schwann cells** and **oligodendrocytes,** which produce **myelin sheaths** that surround the axons of many neurons. Schwann cells produce myelin in the PNS, and oligodendrocytes produce myelin in the CNS. During development, these cells wrap themselves around each axon several times to form the myelin sheath—an insulating covering consisting of multiple layers of compacted membrane (figure 44.4).

Axons that have myelin sheaths are said to be myelinated, and those that don't are unmyelinated. In the CNS, myelinated axons form the *white matter*, and the unmyelinated dendrites and cell bodies form the *gray matter*. In the PNS, myelinated axons are bundled together, much like wires in a cable, to form nerves.

Small gaps, known as **nodes of Ranvier** (see figure 44.3), interrupt the myelin sheath at intervals of 1 to 2 μm. We discuss the role of the myelin sheath in impulse conduction in the next section.

Learning Outcomes Review 44.1

The vertebrate nervous system consists of the central nervous system (CNS) and peripheral nervous system (PNS). The PNS comprises the somatic nervous system and autonomic nervous system; the latter has sympathetic and parasympathetic divisions. A neuron consists of a cell body, dendrites that receive information, and a single axon that sends signals. Neurons carry out nervous system functions; they are supported by a variety of neuroglia.

■ *Which division of the PNS is under conscious control?*

44.2 The Mechanism of Nerve Impulse Transmission

Learning Outcomes

1. *Identify the ions involved in nerve impulse transmission and their relative concentrations inside and outside the neuron.*
2. *Describe the production of the resting potential.*
3. *Explain how the action of voltage-gated channels produces an action potential.*

Neuronal function depends on a changeable permeability to ions. Upon stimulation, electrical changes in the plasma membrane spread or propagate from one part of the cell to another. The architecture of the neuron provides the mechanisms for the generation and spread of these membrane electrical potentials.

The unique mechanisms of neurons primarily depend on the presence of specialized membrane transport proteins, where they are located, and how they are activated. First, we examine some of the basic electrical properties common to the plasma membranes of most animal cells, and then we look at how these properties operate in neurons.

An electrical difference exists across the plasma membrane

You first learned about membrane potential in chapter 5, where transport of ions across the cell membrane was discussed. Membrane potential is similar to the electrical potential difference that exists between the two poles of a flashlight or automobile battery. One pole is positive, and the other is negative. Similarly, a potential difference exists across every cell's plasma membrane. The side of the membrane exposed to the cytoplasm is the negative pole, and the side exposed to the extracellular fluid is the positive pole.

When a neuron is not being stimulated, it maintains a **resting potential.** A cell is very small, and so its membrane potential is very small. The resting membrane potential of many vertebrate neurons ranges from –40 to –90 millivolts (mV), or 0.04 to 0.09 volts (V). For the examples and figures in this chapter, we use an average resting membrane potential value of –70 mV. The minus sign indicates that the inside of the cell is negative with respect to the outside.

Contributors to membrane potential

The inside of the cell is more negatively charged in relation to the outside because of two factors:

1. The sodium–potassium pump, described in chapter 5, brings two potassium ions (K^+) into the cell for every three sodium ions (Na^+) it pumps out (figure 44.5). This helps establish and maintain concentration differences that result in high K^+ and low Na^+ concentrations inside the cell, and high Na^+ and low K^+ concentrations outside the cell.

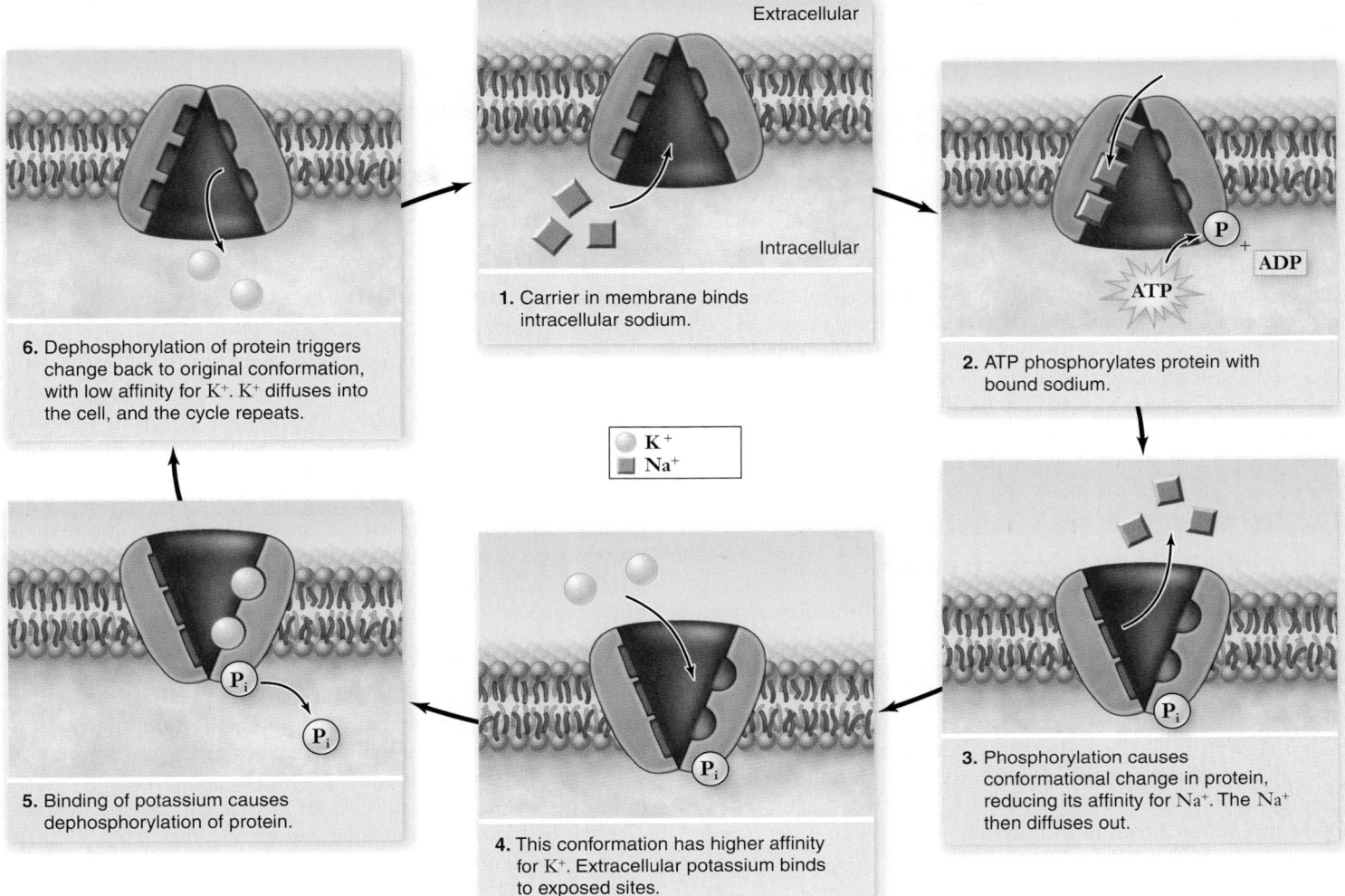

Figure 44.5 **The sodium–potassium pump.** This pump transports three Na⁺ to the outside of the cell and simultaneously transports two K⁺ to the inside of the cell. This is an active transport carrier requiring the (phosphorylating) energy of ATP.

The figure contains the following labeled steps:

1. Carrier in membrane binds intracellular sodium.

2. ATP phosphorylates protein with bound sodium.

3. Phosphorylation causes conformational change in protein, reducing its affinity for Na⁺. The Na⁺ then diffuses out.

4. This conformation has higher affinity for K⁺. Extracellular potassium binds to exposed sites.

5. Binding of potassium causes dephosphorylation of protein.

6. Dephosphorylation of protein triggers change back to original conformation, with low affinity for K⁺. K⁺ diffuses into the cell, and the cycle repeats.

Legend: ○ K⁺ ▪ Na⁺

Extracellular / Intracellular

---

2. **Ion channels** in the cell membrane are more numerous for K⁺ than for Na⁺ making the membrane more permeable for K⁺. Ion channels are membrane proteins that form pores through the membrane, allowing diffusion of specific ions across the membrane. Because there are more ion channels for K⁺, the membrane is more permeable to K⁺ and it will diffuse out of the cell.

Two major forces act on ions in establishing the resting membrane potential: (1) The electrical potential produced by unequal distribution of charges across the membrane, and (2) the chemical force produced by unequal concentrations of ions across the membrane.

The resting potential: Balance between two forces

The resting potential arises due to the action of the sodium–potassium pump and the differential permeability of the membrane to Na⁺ and K⁺ due to ion channels. The pump moves three Na⁺ outside for every two K⁺ inside, which creates a small imbalance in cations outside the cell. This has only a minor effect; however, the concentration gradients created by the pump are

significant. The concentration of K⁺ is much higher inside the cell than outside, leading to diffusion of K⁺ through open K⁺ channels. Since the membrane is not permeable to the negative ions that could counterbalance this (mainly organic phosphates, amino acids, and proteins) it leads to a buildup of positive charge outside the membrane and negative charge inside the membrane. This electrical potential then is an attractive force pulling K⁺ ions back inside the cell. The balance between the diffusional force and the electrical force leads to the **equilibrium potential** (table 44.1). By relating the work done by each type of force, we can derive a quantitative expression for this equilibrium potential called the Nernst equation. This assumes the action of a single ion, and for a positive ion with charge equal to +1, the Nernst equation is:

$$E_K = 58 \text{ mV} \log([K^+]_{out}/[K^+]m_{in})$$

The calculated equilibrium potential for K⁺ is –90 mV (see table 44.1), close to the measured value of –70 mV. The calculated value for Na⁺ is +60 mV, clearly not at all close to the measured value, but the leakage of a small amount of Na⁺ back into the cell is responsible for lowering the equilibrium potential of K⁺ to the –70 mV value observed. The resting membrane potential of a neuron

TABLE 44.1

	The Ionic Composition of Cytoplasm and Extracellular Fluid (ECF)			
Ion	Concentration in ECF (mM)	Concentration in Cytoplasm (mM)	Ratio (ECF:cytoplasm)	Equilibrium Potential (mV)
Na^+	150	15	10:1	+60
K^+	5	150	1:30	−90
Cl^-	110	7	15:1	−70

can be measured and viewed or graphed using a voltmeter and a pair of electrodes, one outside and one inside the cell (figure 44.6).

The uniqueness of neurons compared with other cells is not the production and maintenance of the resting membrane potential, but rather the sudden temporary disruptions to the resting membrane potential that occur in response to stimuli. Two types of changes can be observed: *graded potentials* and *action potentials*.

Graded potentials are small changes that can reinforce or negate each other

Graded potentials, small transient changes in membrane potential, are caused by the activation of a class of channel proteins called **gated ion channels.** Introduced in chapter 9, gated channels behave like a door that can open or close, unlike ion leakage channels that are always open. The structure of gated ion channels is such that they have alternative conformations that can be open, allowing the passage of ions, or closed, not allowing the passage of ions. Each gated channel is selective, that is, when open they allow diffusion of only one type of ion. Most gated channels are closed in the normal resting cell.

Chemically gated channels

In most neurons, gated ion channels in dendrites respond to the binding of signaling molecules (figure 44.7; see also figure 9.4a). These are referred to as *chemically gated*, or *ligand-gated, channels. Ligands* are chemical groups that attach to larger molecules to regulate or contribute to their function. When ligands temporarily bind to membrane receptor proteins or channels, they cause the shape of the protein to change, thus opening the ion channel. Hormones and neurotransmitters act as ligands, inducing opening of ligand-gated channels, and causing changes in plasma membrane permeability that lead to changes in membrane voltage.

Depolarization and hyperpolarization

Permeability changes are measurable as depolarizations or hyperpolarizations of the membrane potential. A **depolarization** makes the membrane potential less negative (more positive), whereas a **hyperpolarization** makes the membrane potential more negative. For example, a change in potential from −70 mV to −65 mV is a depolarization; a change from −70 mV to −75 mV is a hyperpolarization.

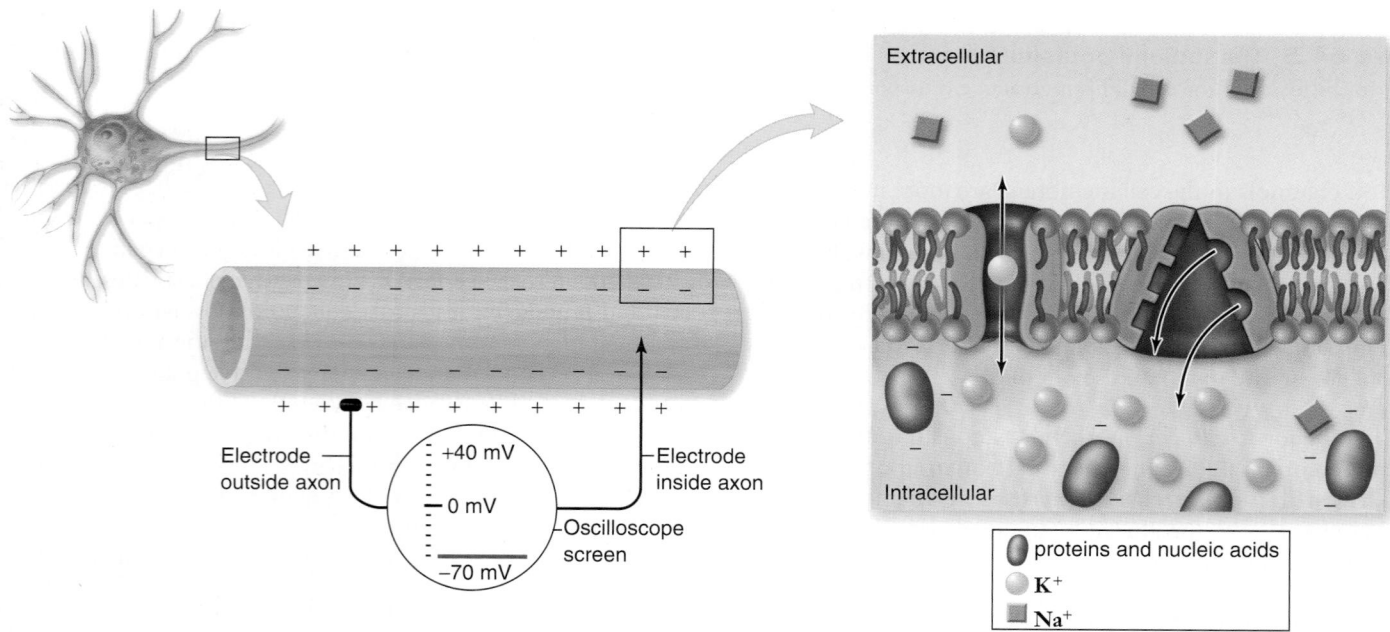

Figure 44.6 Establishment of the resting membrane potential. A voltmeter placed with one electrode inside an axon and the other outside the membrane. The electric potential inside is −70 mV relative to the outside of the membrane. K^+ diffuses out of the cell through ion channels because its concentration is higher inside than outside. Negatively charged proteins and nucleic acids inside the cell cannot leave the cell and attract cations from outside the cell, such as K^+. This balance of electrical and diffusional forces produces the resting potential. The sodium–potassium pump maintains cell equilibrium by counteracting the effects of Na^+ leakage into the cell and contributes to the resting potential by moving 3 Na^+ outside for every 2 K^+ moved inside.

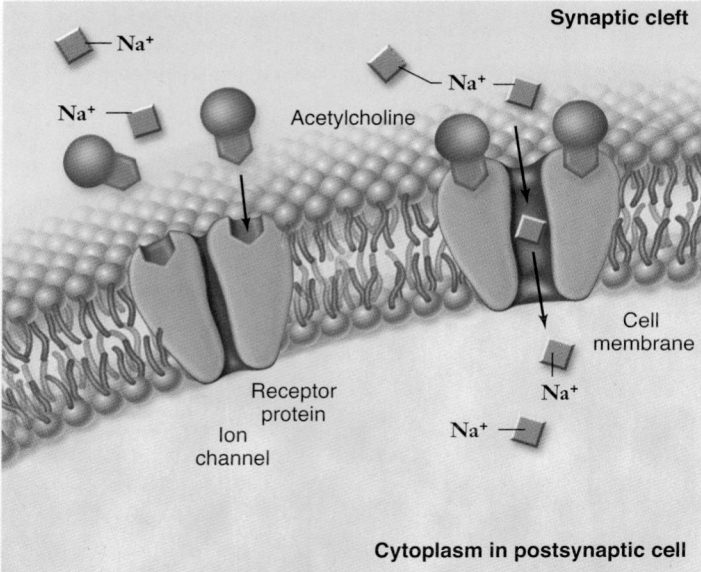

Figure 44.7 A chemically gated ion channel. The acetylcholine (ACh) receptor is a chemically gated channel that can bind the neurotransmitter ACh. Binding of ACh causes the channel to open allowing Na⁺ ions to flow into the cell by diffusion.

These small changes in membrane potential result in *graded potentials* because their size depends on either the strength of the stimulus or the amount of ligand available to bind with their receptors. These potentials diminish in amplitude as they spread from their point of origin. Depolarizing or hyperpolarizing potentials can add together to amplify or reduce their effects, just as two waves can combine to make a bigger one when they meet in synchronization or can cancel each other out when a trough meets with a crest. The ability of graded potentials to combine is called **summation** (figure 44.8). We will return to this topic in the next section after we discuss the nature of action potentials.

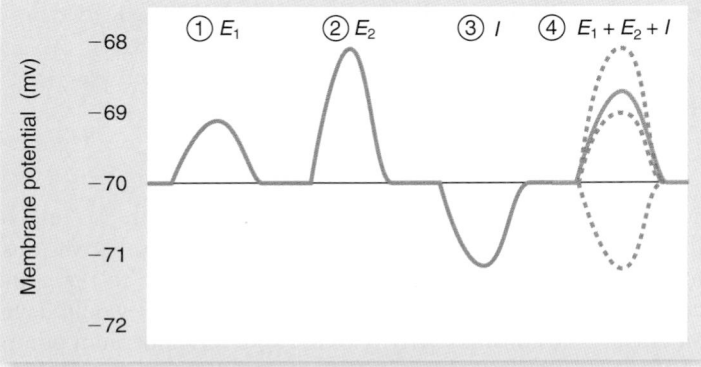

Figure 44.8 Graded potentials. Graded potentials are the summation of subthreshold potentials produced by the opening of different chemically gated channels. (1) A weak excitatory stimulus, E_1, elicits a smaller depolarization than (2) a stronger stimulus, E_2. (3) An inhibitory stimulus, I, produces a hyperpolarization. (4) If all three stimuli occur very close together, the resulting polarity change will be the sum of the three individual changes.

Action potentials result when depolarization reaches a threshold

When a particular level of depolarization is reached (about −55 mV in some mammalian axons), a nerve impulse, or action potential, is produced in the region where the axon arises from the cell body. The level of depolarization needed to produce an action potential is called the **threshold potential.** Depolarizations bring a neuron closer to the threshold, and hyperpolarizations move the neuron further from the threshold.

The action potential is caused by another class of ion channels: **voltage-gated ion channels.** These channels open and close in response to changes in membrane potential; the flow of ions controlled by these channels creates the action potential. Voltage-gated channels are found in neurons and in muscle cells. Two different channels are used to create an action potential in neurons: **voltage-gated Na⁺ channels** and **voltage-gated K⁺ channels.**

Sodium and potassium voltage-gated channels

The behavior of the voltage-gated Na⁺ channel is more complex than that of the K⁺ channel, so we will consider it first. The channel has two gates: an activation gate and an inactivation gate. In its resting state the activation gate is closed and the inactivation gate is open. When the threshold voltage is reached, the activation gate opens rapidly, leading to an influx of Na⁺ ions due to both concentration and voltage gradients. After a short period the inactivation gate closes, stopping the influx of Na⁺ ions and leaving the channel in a temporarily inactivated state. The channel is returned to its resting state by the activation gate closing and the inactivation gate opening. The result of this is a transient influx of Na⁺ that depolarizes the membrane in response to a threshold voltage.

The K⁺ channel has a single activation gate that is closed in the resting state. In response to a threshold voltage, it opens slowly. With the high concentration of K⁺ inside the cell, and the membrane now far from the equilibrium potential, an efflux of K⁺ begins. The positive charge now leaving the cell counteracts the effect of the Na⁺ channel and repolarizes the membrane.

Tracing an action potential's changes

Let us now put all of this together and see how the changing flux of ions leads to an action potential. The action potential has three phases: a *rising phase*, a *falling phase*, and an *undershoot phase* (figure 44.9). When a threshold potential is reached, the rapid opening of the Na⁺ channel causes an influx of Na⁺ that shifts the membrane potential toward the equilibrium potential for Na (+60 mV). This appears as the rising phase on an oscilloscope. The membrane potential never quite reaches +60 mV because the inactivation gate of the Na⁺ channel closes, terminating the rising phase. At the same time, the opening of the K⁺ channel leads to K⁺ diffusing out of the cell, repolarizing the membrane in the falling phase. The K⁺ channels remain open longer than necessary to restore the resting potential, resulting in a slight undershoot. This entire sequence of events for a single action potential takes about a millisecond.

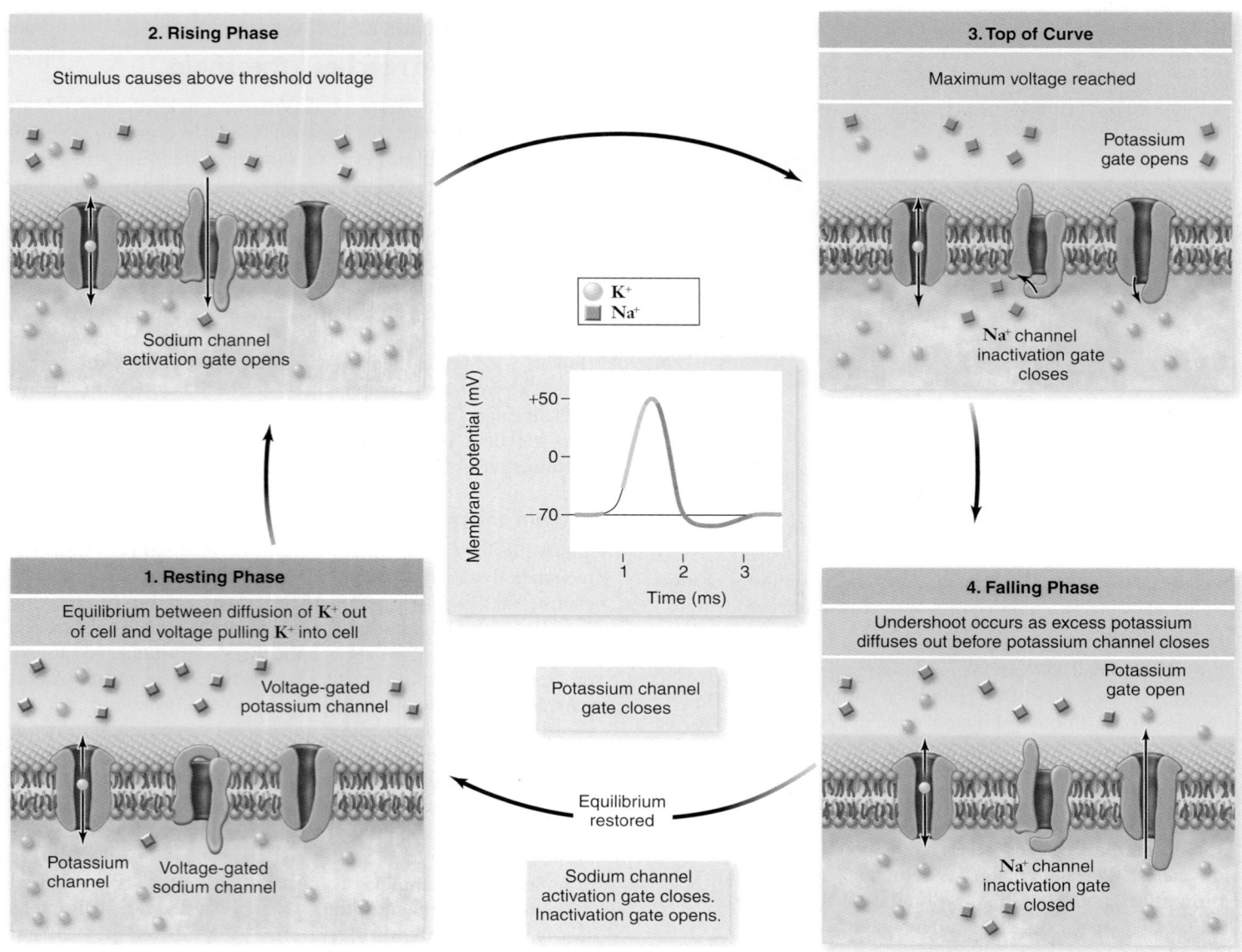

Figure 44.9 The action potential. (1) At resting membrane potential, voltage-gated ion channels are closed, but there is some diffusion of K⁺. In response to a stimulus, the cell begins to depolarize, and once the threshold level is reached, an action potential is produced. (2) Rapid depolarization occurs (the rising portion of the spike) because voltage-gated sodium channel activation gates open, allowing Na⁺ to diffuse into the axon. (3) At the top of the spike, Na⁺ channel inactivation gates close, and voltage-gated potassium channels that were previously closed begin to open. (4) With the K⁺ channels open, repolarization occurs because of the diffusion of K⁺ out of the axon. An undershoot occurs before the membrane returns to its original resting potential.

The nature of action potentials

Action potentials are separate, all-or-none events. An action potential occurs if the threshold voltage is reached, but not while the membrane remains below threshold. Action potentials do not add together or interfere with one another, as graded potentials can. After Na⁺ channels "fire" they remain in an inactivated state until the inactivation gate reopens, preventing any summing of effects. This is called the absolute refractory period when the membrane cannot be stimulated. There is also a relative refractory period during which stimulation produces action potentials of reduced amplitude.

The production of an action potential results entirely from the passive diffusion of ions. However, at the end of each action potential, the cytoplasm contains a little more Na⁺ and a little less K⁺ than it did at rest. Although the number of ions moved by a single action potential is tiny relative to the concentration gradients of Na⁺ and K⁺, eventually this would have an effect. The constant activity of the sodium–potassium pump compensates for these changes. Thus, although active transport is not required to produce action potentials, it is needed to maintain the ion gradients.

Action potentials are propagated along axons

The movement of an action potential through an axon is not generated by ions flowing from the base of the axon to the end.

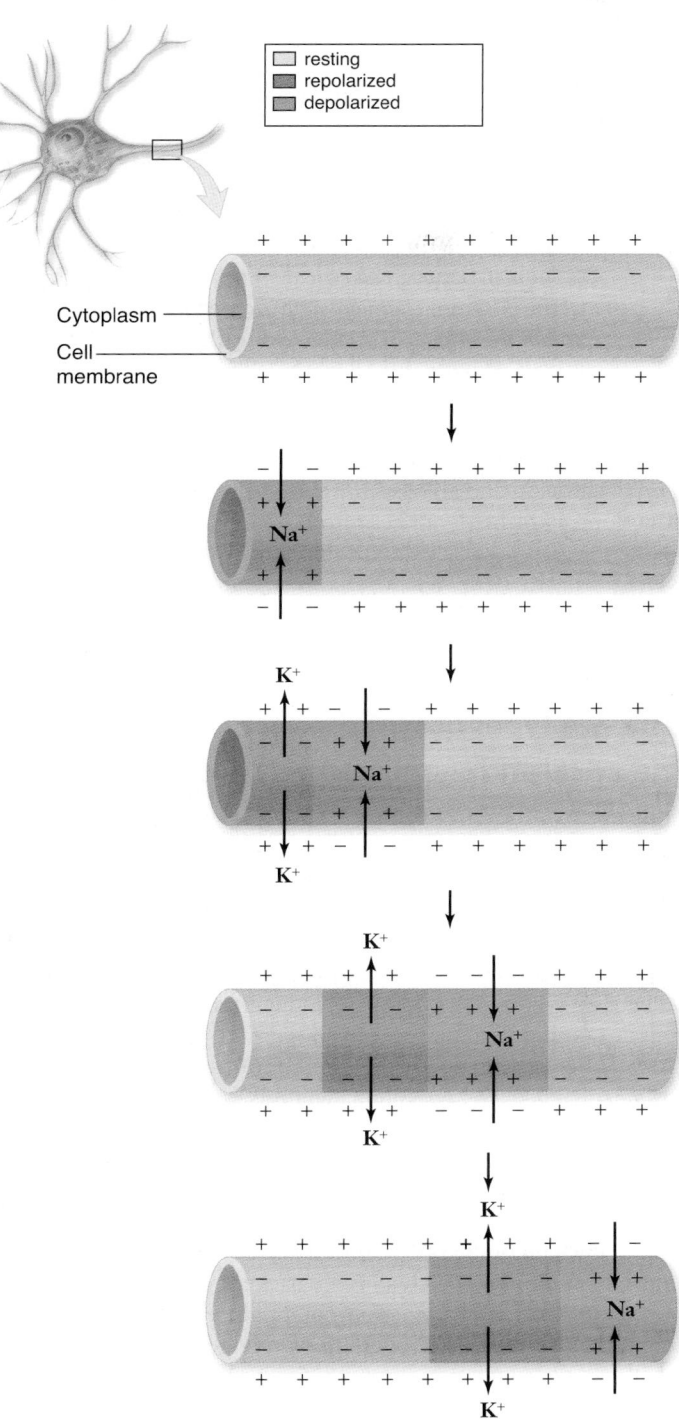

Figure 44.10 Propagation of an action potential in an unmyelinated axon. When one region produces an action potential and undergoes a reversal of polarity, it serves as a depolarization stimulus for the next region of the axon. In this way, action potentials regenerate along each small region of the unmyelinated axon membrane.

Instead an action potential originates at the base of the axon, and is then recreated in adjacent stretches of membrane along the axon.

Each action potential, during its rising phase, reflects a reversal in membrane polarity. The positive charges due to

influx of Na⁺ can depolarize the adjacent region of membrane to threshold, so that the next region produces its own action potential (figure 44.10). Meanwhile, the previous region of membrane repolarizes back to the resting membrane potential. The signal does not back up because the Na⁺ channels that have just "fired" are still in an inactivated state and are refractory (resistant) to stimulation.

The propagation of an action potential is similar to people in a stadium performing the "wave": Individuals stay in place as they stand up (depolarize), raise their hands (peak of the action potential), and sit down again (repolarize). The wave travels around the stadium, but the people stay in place.

There are two ways to increase the velocity of nerve impulses

Action potentials are conducted without decreasing in amplitude, so the last action potential at the end of an axon is just as large as the first action potential. Animals have evolved two ways to increase the velocity of nerve impulses. The velocity of conduction is greater if the diameter of the axon is large or if the axon is myelinated (table 44.2).

Increasing the diameter of an axon increases the velocity of nerve impulses due to the electrical property of resistance. Electrical resistance is inversely proportional to cross-sectional area, which is a function of diameter, so larger diameter axons have less resistance to current flow. The positive charges carried by Na⁺ flows farther in a larger diameter axon, leading to a higher than threshold voltage farther from the origin of Na⁺ influx.

Larger diameter axons are found primarily in invertebrates. For example, in the squid, the escape response is controlled by a so-called giant axon. This large axon conducts nerve impulses faster than other smaller squid axons, allowing a rapid escape response. The squid giant axon was used by Alan Lloyd Hodgkin and Andrew Huxley in their pioneering studies of nerve transmission.

Myelinated axons conduct impulses more rapidly than unmyelinated axons because the action potentials in myelinated

TABLE 44.2	Conduction Velocities of Some Axons		
	Axon Diameter (μm)	Myelin	Conduction Velocity (m/s)
Squid giant axon	500	No	25
Large motor axon to human leg muscle	20	Yes	120
Axon from human skin pressure receptor	10	Yes	50
Axon from human skin temperature receptor	5	Yes	20
Motor axon to human internal organ	1	No	2

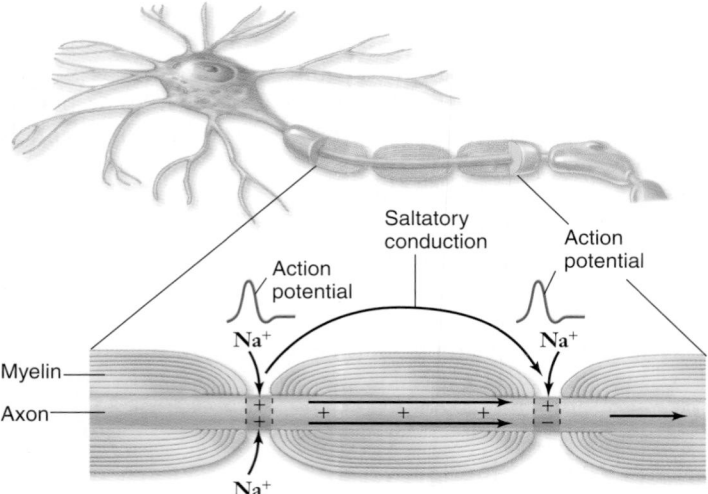

Figure 44.11 Saltatory conduction in a myelinated axon. Action potentials are only produced at the nodes of Ranvier in a myelinated axon. One node depolarizes the next node so that the action potentials can skip between nodes. As a result, saltatory ("jumping") conduction in a myelinated axon is more rapid than conduction in an unmyelinated axon.

axons are only produced at the nodes of Ranvier. One action potential still serves as the depolarization stimulus for the next, but the depolarization at one node spreads quickly beneath the insulating myelin to trigger opening of voltage-gated channels at the next node. The impulses therefore seem to jump from node to node (figure 44.11) in a process called **saltatory conduction** (Latin *saltare*, "to jump").

To see how saltatory conduction speeds impulse transmission, let's return for a moment to the stadium wave analogy to describe propagation of an action potential. The wave moves across the seats of a crowded stadium as fans seeing the people in the adjacent section stand up are triggered to stand up in turn. Because the wave skips sections of empty bleachers, it actually progresses around the stadium even faster with more empty sections. The wave doesn't have to "wait" for the missing people to stand, so it simply moves to the next populated section—just as the action potential jumps the nonconducting regions of myelin between exposed nodes.

Learning Outcomes Review 44.2

Neurons maintain high K+ levels inside the cell, and high Na+ levels outside the cell. Diffusion of K+ to the outside leads to a resting potential of about −70 mV. Opening of ligand-gated channels can depolarize or hyperpolarize the membrane, causing a graded potential. Action potentials are triggered when membrane potential exceeds a threshold value. Voltage-gated Na+ channels open, and depolarization occurs; subsequent opening of K+ channels leads to repolarization.

■ *How can only positive ions result in depolarization and repolarization of the membrane during an action potential?*

44.3 Synapses: Where Neurons Communicate with Other Cells

Learning Outcomes

1. *Distinguish between electrical and chemical synapses.*
2. *List the different chemical neurotransmitters.*
3. *Explain the effects of addictive drugs on the nervous system.*

An action potential passing down an axon eventually reaches the end of the axon and all of its branches. These branches may form junctions with the dendrites of other neurons, with muscle cells, or with gland cells. Such intercellular junctions are called **synapses.** The neuron whose axon transmits action potentials to the synapse is termed the *presynaptic cell*, and the cell receiving the signal on the other side of the synapse is the *postsynaptic cell*.

The two types of synapses are electrical and chemical

The nervous systems of animals have two basic types of synapses: electrical and chemical. **Electrical synapses** involve direct cytoplasmic connections formed by gap junctions between the pre- and postsynaptic neurons (see chapter 4; figure 4.27). Membrane potential changes, including action potentials, pass directly and rapidly from one cell to the other through the gap junctions. Electrical synapses are common in invertebrate nervous systems, but are rare in vertebrates.

The vast majority of vertebrate synapses are *chemical synapses* (figure 44.12). When synapses are viewed under a light microscope, the presynaptic and postsynaptic cells appear to touch, but when viewed with an electron microscope most have a **synaptic cleft,** a narrow space that separates these two cells (figure 44.13).

The end of the presynaptic axon is swollen and contains numerous **synaptic vesicles,** each packed with chemicals called *neurotransmitters*. When action potentials arrive at the end of the axon, they stimulate the opening of voltage-gated calcium (Ca^{2+}) channels, causing a rapid inward diffusion of Ca^{2+}. This influx of Ca^{2+} triggers a complex series of events that leads to the fusion of synaptic vesicles with the plasma membrane and the release of neurotransmitter by exocytosis (see chapter 5; figure 44.14).

The higher the frequency of action potentials in the presynaptic axon, the greater the number of vesicles that release their contents of neurotransmitters. The neurotransmitters diffuse to the other side of the cleft and bind to chemical- or ligand-gated receptor proteins in the membrane of the postsynaptic cell. The action of these receptors produces graded potentials in the postsynaptic membrane.

Neurotransmitters are chemical signals in an otherwise electrical system, requiring tight control over the duration of their action. Neurotransmitters must be rapidly removed from the synaptic cleft to allow new signals to be transmitted. This is accomplished by a variety of mechanisms, including enzymatic

Question: *Is communication between neurons, and between neurons and muscle, chemical or electrical?*

Hypothesis: *Signaling between a neuron and heart muscle is chemical.*

Prediction: *Application of chemical solutes from one heart will affect the activity of another heart.*

Test: *Two frog hearts are placed in saline, one with vagus nerve attached, the other without. The vagus heart is stimulated, then fluid from around the vagus nerve is removed and applied to the other heart.*

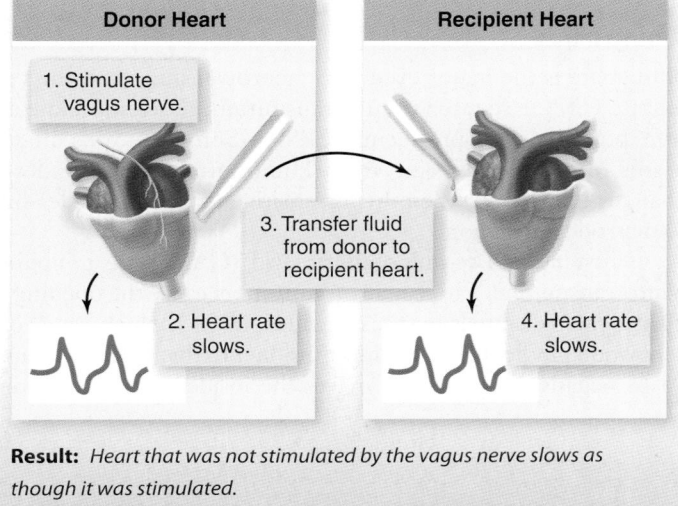

Donor Heart

1. Stimulate vagus nerve.
2. Heart rate slows.

3. Transfer fluid from donor to recipient heart.

Recipient Heart

4. Heart rate slows.

Result: *Heart that was not stimulated by the vagus nerve slows as though it was stimulated.*

Conclusion: *The nerve released a chemical signal that slowed heart rate.*

Further Experiments: *How does this conclusion extend the experiment described in Fig 43.5?*

Figure 44.12 Synaptic signaling.

digestion in the synaptic cleft, reuptake of neurotransmitter molecules by the neuron, and uptake by glial cells.

Several different types of neurotransmitters have been identified, and they act in different ways. We next consider the action of a few of the important neurotransmitter chemicals.

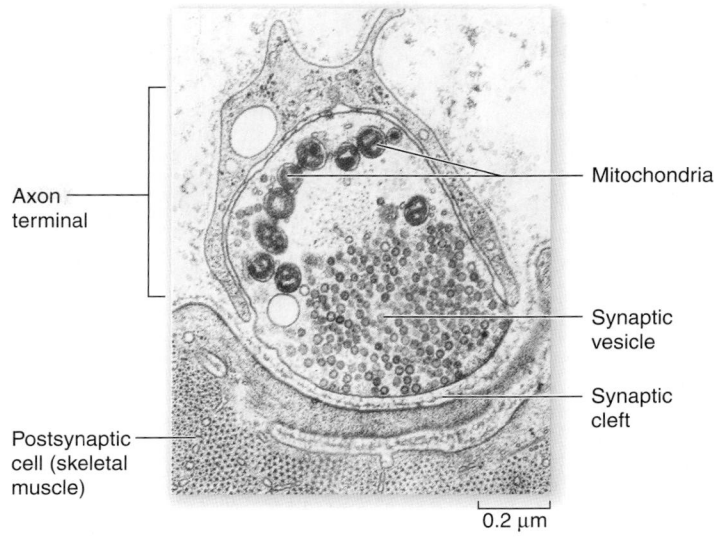

Axon terminal

Mitochondria

Synaptic vesicle

Synaptic cleft

Postsynaptic cell (skeletal muscle)

0.2 μm

Figure 44.13 A synaptic cleft. An electron micrograph showing a neuromuscular synapse. Synaptic vesicles have been colored green.

Many different chemical compounds serve as neurotransmitters

No single chemical characteristic defines a neurotransmitter, although we can group certain types according to chemical similarities. Some, such as acetylcholine, have wide use in the nervous system, particularly where nerves connect with muscles. Other neurotransmitters are found only in very specific types of junctions, such as in the CNS.

Acetylcholine

Acetylcholine (ACh) is the neurotransmitter that crosses the synapse between a motor neuron and a muscle fiber. This synapse is called a **neuromuscular junction** (figures 44.14, 44.15).

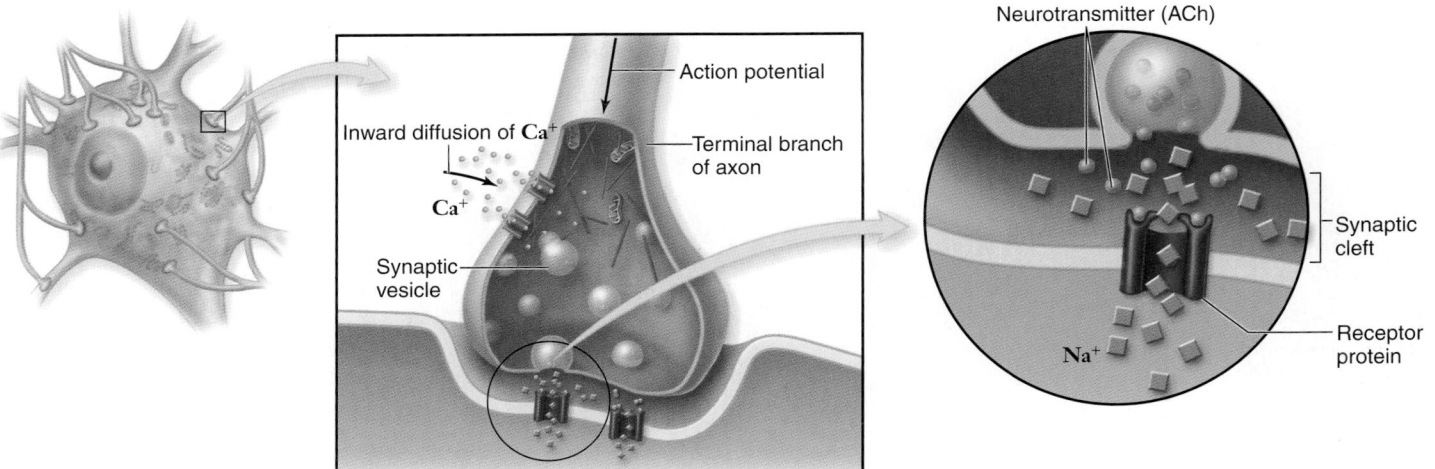

Action potential

Inward diffusion of Ca^+

Ca^+

Terminal branch of axon

Synaptic vesicle

Neurotransmitter (ACh)

Synaptic cleft

Receptor protein

Na^+

Figure 44.14 The release of neurotransmitter. Action potentials arriving at the end of an axon trigger inward diffusion of Ca^{2+}, which causes synaptic vesicles to fuse with the plasma membrane and release their neurotransmitters (acetylcholine [ACh] in this case). Neurotransmitter molecules diffuse across the synaptic gap and bind to ligand-gated receptors in the postsynaptic membrane.

Figure 44.15 Neuromuscular junctions. A light micrograph shows axons branching to make contact with several individual muscle fibers.

15.4 μm

Acetylcholine binds to its receptor proteins in the post-synaptic membrane and causes ligand-gated ion channels within these proteins to open (see figure 44.7). As a result, that site on the postsynaptic membrane produces a depolarization (figure 44.16*a*) called an *excitatory postsynaptic potential (EPSP)*. The EPSP, if large enough, can open the voltage-gated channels for Na⁺ and K⁺ that are responsible for action potentials. Because the postsynaptic cell in this case is a skeletal muscle fiber, the action potentials it produces stimulate muscle contraction through mechanisms discussed in chapter 47.

For the muscle to relax, ACh must be eliminated from the synaptic cleft. *Acetylcholinesterase (AChE)*, an enzyme in the postsynaptic membrane, eliminates ACh. This enzyme, one of the fastest known, cleaves ACh into inactive fragments. Nerve gas and the agricultural insecticide parathion are potent inhibitors of AChE; in humans, they can produce severe spastic paralysis and even death if paralysis affects the respiratory muscles. Although ACh acts as a neurotransmitter between motor neurons and skeletal muscle cells, many neurons also use ACh as a neurotransmitter at their synapses with the dendrites or cell bodies of other neurons.

Amino acids

Glutamate is the major excitatory neurotransmitter in the vertebrate CNS. Excitatory neurotransmitters act to stimulate action potentials by producing EPSPs. Some neurons in the brains of people suffering from Huntington disease undergo changes that render them hypersensitive to glutamate, leading to neurodegeneration.

Glycine and γ-aminobutyric acid (GABA) are inhibitory neurotransmitters. These neurotransmitters cause the opening of ligand-gated channels for the chloride ion (Cl⁻), which has a concentration gradient favoring its diffusion into the neuron. Because Cl⁻ is negatively charged, it makes the inside of the membrane

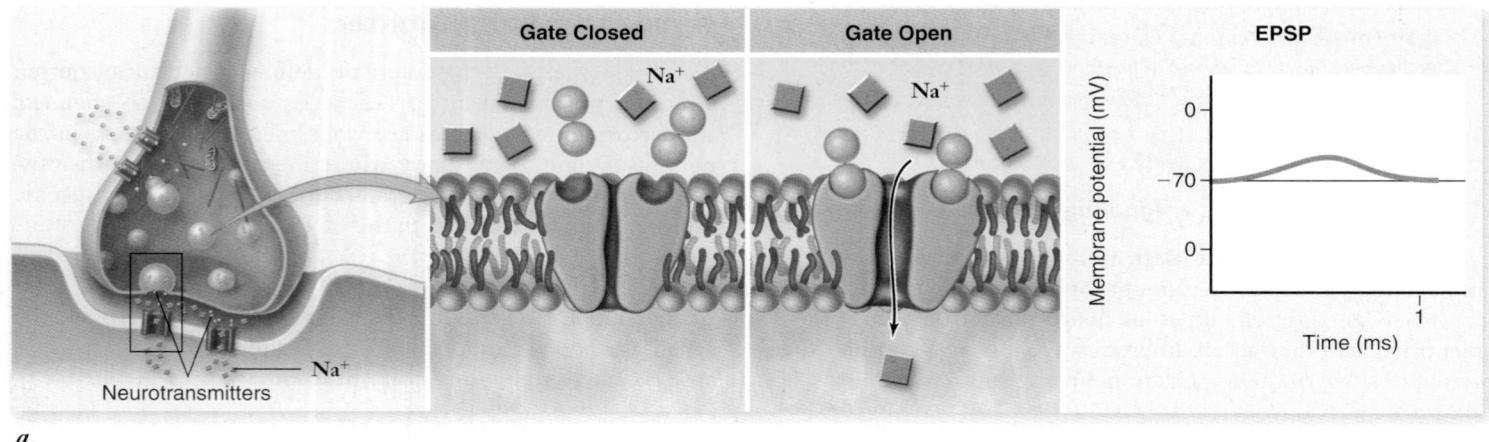

a.

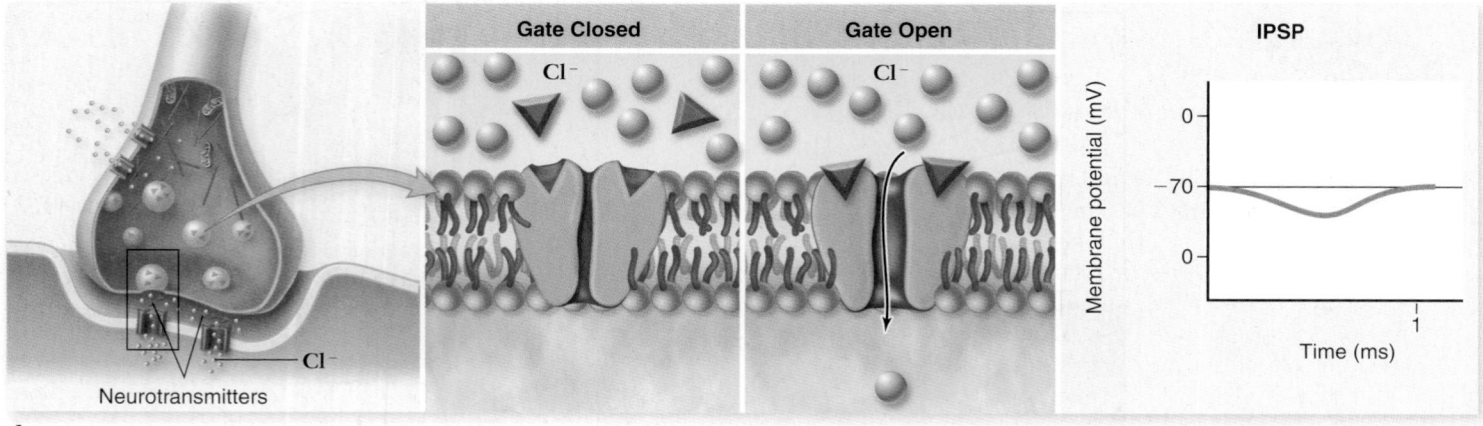

b.

Figure 44.16 Different neurotransmitters can have different effects. *a.* An excitatory neurotransmitter promotes a depolarization, or excitatory postsynaptic potential (EPSP). *b.* An inhibitory neurotransmitter promotes a hyperpolarization, or inhibitory postsynaptic potential (IPSP).

even more negative than it is at rest—for example, from –70 mV to –85 mV (see figure 44.16*b*). This hyperpolarization is called an *inhibitory postsynaptic potential (IPSP)*, and it is very important for neural control of body movements and other brain functions. The drug diazepam (Valium) causes its sedative and other effects by enhancing the binding of GABA to its receptors, thereby increasing the effectiveness of GABA at the synapse.

Biogenic amines

The **biogenic amines** include the hormone epinephrine (adrenaline), together with the neurotransmitters dopamine, norepinephrine, and serotonin. Epinephrine, norepinephrine, and dopamine are derived from the amino acid tyrosine and are included in the subcategory of *catecholamines*. Serotonin is a biogenic amine derived from a different amino acid, tryptophan.

Epinephrine is released into the blood as a hormonal secretion, while **norepinephrine** is released at synapses of neurons in the sympathetic nervous system (discussed in detail later on). The effects of these neurotransmitters on target receptors are responsible for the "fight or flight" response—faster and stronger heartbeat, increased blood glucose concentration, and diversion of blood flow into the muscles and heart.

Dopamine is a very important neurotransmitter used in some areas of the brain controlling body movements and other functions. Degeneration of particular dopamine-releasing neurons produces the resting muscle tremors of Parkinson disease, and people with this condition are treated with L-dopa (an acronym for L–3,4–dihydroxyphenylalanine), a precursor from which dopamine can be produced. Additionally, studies suggest that excessive activity of dopamine-releasing neurons in other areas of the brain is associated with schizophrenia. As a result, drugs that block the production of dopamine, such as the dopamine antagonist chlorpromazine (Thorazine), sometimes help patients with schizophrenia.

Serotonin is a neurotransmitter involved in the regulation of sleep, and it is also implicated in various emotional states. Insufficient activity of neurons that release serotonin may be one cause of clinical depression. Antidepressant drugs, such as fluoxetine (Prozac), block the elimination of serotonin from the synaptic cleft; these drugs are termed *selective serotonin reuptake inhibitors*, or SSRIs.

Other neurotransmitters

Axons also release various polypeptides, called **neuropeptides,** at synapses. These neuropeptides may have a typical neurotransmitter function, or they may have more subtle, long-term action on the postsynaptic neurons. In the latter case, they are often called **neuromodulators.** A given axon generally releases only one kind of neurotransmitter, but many can release both a neurotransmitter and a neuromodulator.

Substance P is an important neuropeptide released at synapses in the CNS by sensory neurons activated by painful stimuli. The perception of pain, however, can vary depending on circumstances. An injured football player may not feel the full extent of his trauma, for example, until he is out of the game.

The intensity with which pain is perceived partly depends on the effects of neuropeptides called *enkephalins* and *endorphins*. **Enkephalins,** released by axons descending from the brain into the spinal cord, inhibit the passage of pain informa-tion back up to the brain. **Endorphins,** released by neurons in the brain stem, also block the perception of pain. Opium and its derivatives, morphine and heroin, have an analgesic (pain-reducing) effect because they are similar enough in chemical structure to bind to the receptors normally used by enkephalins and endorphins. For this reason, the enkephalins and the endorphins are referred to as *endogenous opiates*.

Nitric oxide (NO) is the first gas known to act as a regulatory molecule in the body. Because NO is a gas, it diffuses through membranes, so it cannot be stored in vesicles. It is produced as needed from the amino acid arginine. Nitric oxide diffuses out of the presynaptic axon and into neighboring cells by simply passing through the lipid portions of the plasma membranes.

In the PNS, nitric oxide is released by some neurons that innervate the gastrointestinal tract, penis, respiratory passages, and cerebral blood vessels. These autonomic neurons cause smooth-muscle relaxation in their target organs. This relaxation can produce the engorgement of the spongy tissue of the penis with blood, causing an erection. The drug sildenafil (Viagra) increases the release of NO in the penis, thus enabling and prolonging an erection. The brain releases nitric oxide as a neurotransmitter, where it appears to participate in the processes of learning and memory.

A postsynaptic neuron must integrate input from many synapses

Different types of input from a number of presynaptic neurons influence the activity of a postsynaptic neuron in the brain and spinal cord of vertebrates. For example, a single motor neuron in the spinal cord can have in excess of 50,000 synapses from presynaptic axons.

Each postsynaptic neuron may receive both excitatory and inhibitory synapses (figure 44.17). The EPSPs (depolarizations)

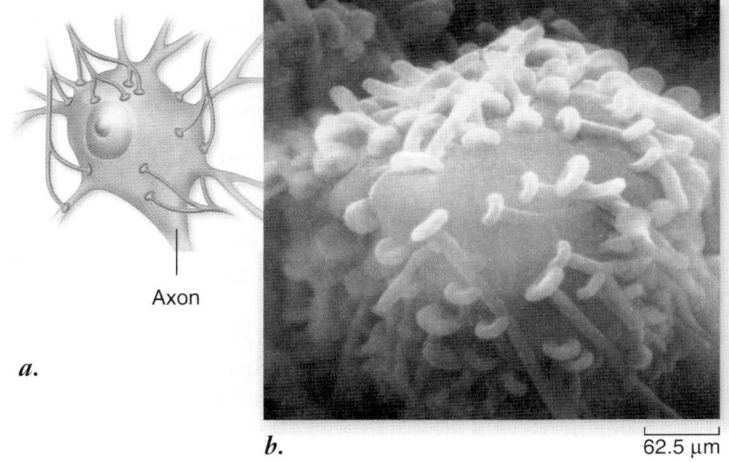

Axon

a.

b.   62.5 μm

Figure 44.17 Integration of EPSPs and IPSPs takes place on the neuronal cell body. *a.* The synapses made by some axons are excitatory *(green);* the synapses made by other axons are inhibitory *(red).* The summed influence of all of these inputs determines whether the axonal membrane of the postsynaptic cell will be sufficiently depolarized to produce an action potential. *b.* Micrograph of a neuronal cell body with numerous synapses.

and IPSPs (hyperpolarizations) from these synapses interact with each other when they reach the cell body of the neuron. Small EPSPs add together to bring the membrane potential closer to the threshold, and IPSPs subtract from the depolarizing effect of the EPSPs, deterring the membrane potential from reaching threshold. This process is called *synaptic integration.*

Because of the all-or-none characteristic of an action potential, a postsynaptic neuron is like a switch that is either turned on or remains off. Information may be encoded in the pattern of firing over time, but each neuron can only fire or not fire when it receives a signal.

The events that determine whether a neuron fires may be extremely complex and involve many presynaptic neurons. There are two ways the membrane can reach the threshold voltage: by many different dendrites producing EPSPs that sum to the threshold voltage, or by one dendrite producing repeated EPSPs that sum to the threshold voltage. We call the first **spatial summation** and the second **temporal summation.**

In spatial summation, graded potentials due to dendrites from different presynaptic neurons that occur at the same time add together to produce an above-threshold voltage. All of this input does not need to be in the form of EPSPs, just so the potential produced by summing all of the EPSPs and IPSPs is greater than the threshold voltage. When the membrane at the base of the axon is depolarized above the threshold, it produces an action potential and a nerve impulse is sent down the axon.

In temporal summation, a single dendrite can produce sufficient depolarization to produce an action potential if it produces EPSPs that are close enough in time to sum to a depolarization that is greater than threshold. A typical EPSP can last for 15 ms, so for temporal summation to occur, the next impulse must arrive in less time. If enough EPSPs are produced to raise the membrane at the base of the axon above threshold, then an impulse will be sent.

The distinction between these two methods of summation is like filling a hole in the ground with soil: you can have many shovels that add soil to the hole until it is filled, or a single shovel that adds soil at a faster rate to fill the hole. When the hole is filled, the axon will fire.

Neurotransmitters play a role in drug addiction

When certain cells of the nervous system are exposed to a constant stimulus that produces a chemically mediated signal for a prolonged period, the cells may lose their ability to respond to that stimulus, a process called **habituation.** You are familiar with this loss of sensitivity—when you sit in a chair, for example, your awareness of the chair diminishes after a certain length of time.

Some nerve cells are particularly prone to this loss of sensitivity. If receptor proteins within synapses are exposed to high levels of neurotransmitter molecules for prolonged periods, the postsynaptic cell often responds by decreasing the number of receptor proteins in its membrane. This feedback is a normal function in all neurons, one of several mechanisms that have evolved to make the cell more efficient. In this case, the cell adjusts the number of receptors downward because plenty of stimulating neurotransmitter is available. In the case of artificial neurotrans-

mitter effects produced by drugs, long-term drug use means that more of the drug is needed to obtain the same effect.

Cocaine

The drug cocaine causes abnormally large amounts of neurotransmitter to remain in the synapses for long periods. Cocaine affects neurons in the brain's "pleasure pathways" (the *limbic system,* described later). These cells use the neurotransmitter dopamine. Cocaine binds tightly to the transporter proteins on presynaptic membranes that normally remove dopamine from the synaptic cleft. Eventually the dopamine stays in the cleft, firing the receptors repeatedly. New signals add more and more dopamine, firing the pleasure pathway more and more often (figure 44.18).

Nicotine

Nicotine has been found to have no affinity for proteins on the presynaptic membrane, as cocaine does; instead, it binds directly to a specific receptor on postsynaptic neurons of the brain. Because nicotine does not normally occur in the brain, why should it have a receptor there?

Researchers have found that "nicotine receptors" are a class of receptors that normally bind the neurotransmitter acetylcholine. Nicotine evolved in tobacco plants as a secondary compound—it affects the CNS of herbivorous insects, and therefore helps to protect the plant. It is an "accident of nature" that nicotine is also able to bind to some human ACh receptors.

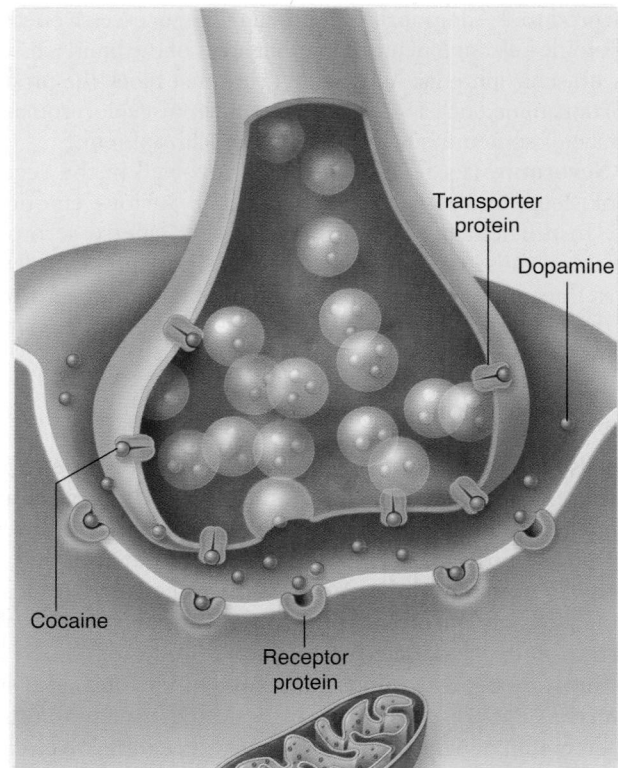

Figure 44.18 **How cocaine alters events at the synapse.** When cocaine binds to the dopamine transporters, it prevents reuptake of dopamine so the neurotransmitter survives longer in the synapse and continues to stimulate the postsynaptic cell. Cocaine thus acts to intensify pleasurable sensations.

When neurobiologists compare the nerve cells in the brains of smokers with those of nonsmokers, they find changes in both the number of nicotine receptors and the levels of RNA used to make the receptors. The brain adjusts to prolonged, chronic exposure to nicotine by "turning down the volume" in two ways: (1) by making fewer receptor proteins to which nicotine can bind; and (2) by altering the pattern of activation of the nicotine receptors—that is, their sensitivity to stimulation by neurotransmitters.

Having summarized the physiology and chemistry of neurons and synapses, we turn now to the structure of the vertebrate nervous system, beginning with the CNS and then the PNS.

Learning Outcomes Review 44.3

Electrical synapses involve direct cytoplasmic connections between two neurons; chemical synapses involve chemicals that cross the synaptic cleft, which separates neurons. Neurotransmitters include acetylcholine, epinephrine, glycine, GABA, biogenic amines, substance P, and nitric oxide. Many addictive drugs bind to sites that normally bind neurotransmitters or to membrane transport proteins in synapses.

■ **Why is tobacco use such a difficult habit to overcome?**

44.4 The Central Nervous System: Brain and Spinal Cord

Learning Outcomes

1. **Describe the organization of the brain in vertebrates.**
2. **Describe characteristics of the human cerebrum.**
3. **Explain how a simple reflex works.**

The complex nervous system of vertebrate animals has a long evolutionary history. In this section we describe the structures making up the CNS, namely the brain and the spinal cord. First, it is helpful to review the origin and development of the vertebrate nervous system.

As animals became more complex, so did their nervous systems

Among the noncoelomate invertebrates (see chapter 33), sponges are the only major phylum that lack nerves. The simplest nervous systems occur among cnidarians (figure 44.19),

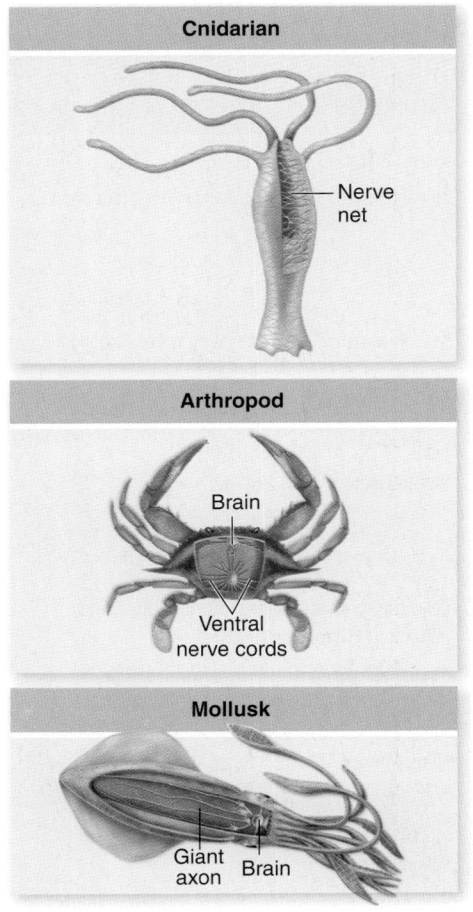
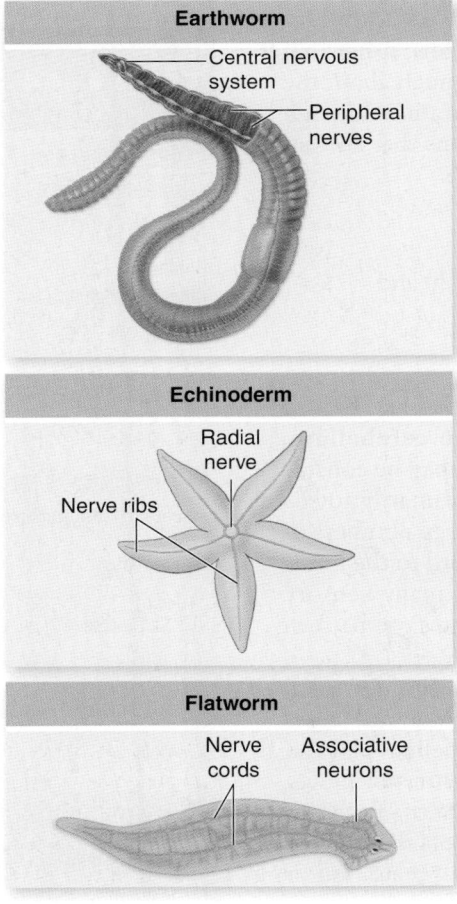
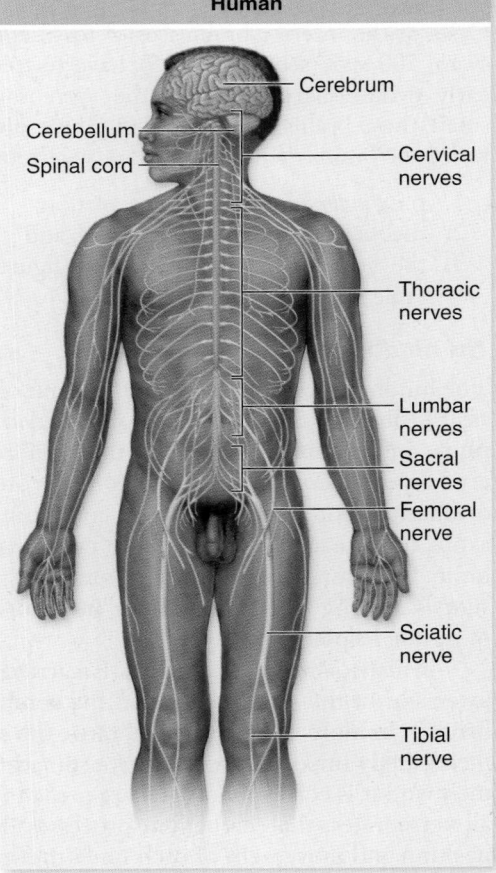

Figure 44.19 Diversity of nervous systems. Nervous systems in animals range from simple nerve nets to paired nerve cords with primitive brains to elaborate brains and sensory systems. Bilateral symmetry is correlated with the concentration of nervous tissue and sensory structures in the front end of the nerve cord. This evolutionary process is referred to as cephalization.

in which all neurons are similar and linked to one another in a web, or **nerve net.** There is no associative activity, no control of complex actions, and little coordination.

The simplest animals with associative activity in the nervous system are the free-living flatworms, phylum Platyhelminthes. Running down the bodies of these flatworms are two nerve cords, from which peripheral nerves extend outward to the muscles of the body. The two nerve cords converge at the front end of the body, forming an enlarged mass of nervous tissue that also contains interneurons with synapses connecting neurons to one another. This primitive "brain" is a rudimentary central nervous system and permits a far more complex control of muscular responses than is possible in cnidarians.

All of the subsequent evolutionary changes in nervous systems can be viewed as a series of elaborations on the characteristics already present in flatworms. For example, among coelomate invertebrates (see chapter 34), earthworms exhibit a central nervous system that is connected to all other parts of the body by peripheral nerves. And in arthropods, the central coordination of complex responses is increasingly localized in the front end of the nerve cord. As this region evolved, it came to contain a progressively larger number of interneurons and to develop tracts, which are major information highways within the brain.

Vertebrate brains have three basic divisions

Casts of the interior braincases of fossil agnathans, fishes that swam 500 MYA (see chapter 35), have revealed much about the early evolutionary stages of the vertebrate brain. Although small, these brains already had the three divisions that characterize the brains of all contemporary vertebrates:

1. the *hindbrain*, or rhombencephalon;
2. the *midbrain*, or mesencephalon; and
3. the *forebrain*, or prosencephalon (figure 44.20 and table 44.3).

The hindbrain in fishes

The hindbrain was the major component of these early brains, as it still is in fishes today. Composed of the **cerebellum, pons,** and **medulla oblongata,** the hindbrain may be considered an extension of the spinal cord devoted primarily to coordinating motor reflexes. Tracts containing large numbers of axons run like cables up and down the spinal cord to the hindbrain. The hindbrain, in turn, integrates the many sensory signals coming from the muscles and coordinates the pattern of motor responses.

Much of this coordination is carried on within a small extension of the hindbrain called the cerebellum ("little cerebrum"). In more advanced vertebrates, the cerebellum plays an increasingly important role as a coordinating center for movement and it is correspondingly larger than it is in the fishes. In all vertebrates, the cerebellum processes data on the current position and movement of each limb, the state of relaxation or contraction of the muscles involved, and the general position of the body and its relation to the outside world.

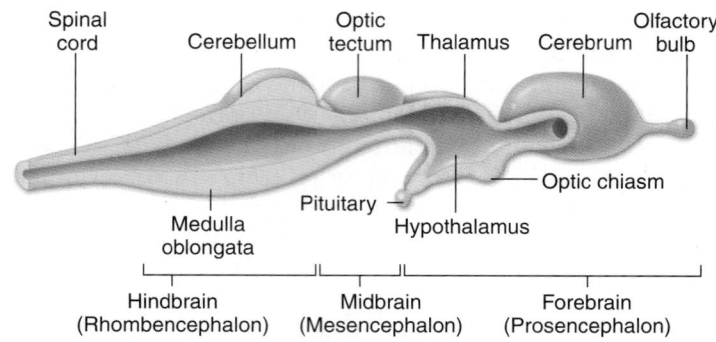

Figure 44.20 The basic organization of the vertebrate brain can be seen in the brains of primitive fishes. The brain is divided into three regions that are found in differing proportions in all vertebrates: the hindbrain, which is the largest portion of the brain in fishes; the midbrain, which in fishes is devoted primarily to processing visual information; and the forebrain, which is concerned mainly with olfaction (the sense of smell) in fishes. In terrestrial vertebrates, the forebrain plays a far more dominant role in neural processing than it does in fishes.

TABLE 44.3	Subdivisions of the Central Nervous System
Major Subdivision	**Function**
SPINAL CORD	Spinal reflexes; relays sensory and motor information
BRAIN	
Hindbrain (Rhombencephalon)	
Medulla oblongata	Sensory nuclei; reticular-activating system; autonomic functions
Pons	Reticular-activating system; autonomic functions
Cerebellum	Coordination of movements; balance
Midbrain (Mesencephalon)	Reflexes involving eyes and ears
Forebrain (Prosencephalon)	
Diencephalon	
Thalamus	Relay station for ascending sensory and descending motor tracts; autonomic functions
Hypothalamus	Autonomic functions; neuroendocrine control
Telencephalon (cerebrum)	
Basal ganglia	Motor control
Corpus callosum	Connects and relays information between the two hemispheres
Hippocampus (limbic system)	Memory; emotion
Cerebral cortex	Higher cognitive functions; integrates and interprets sensory information; organizes motor output

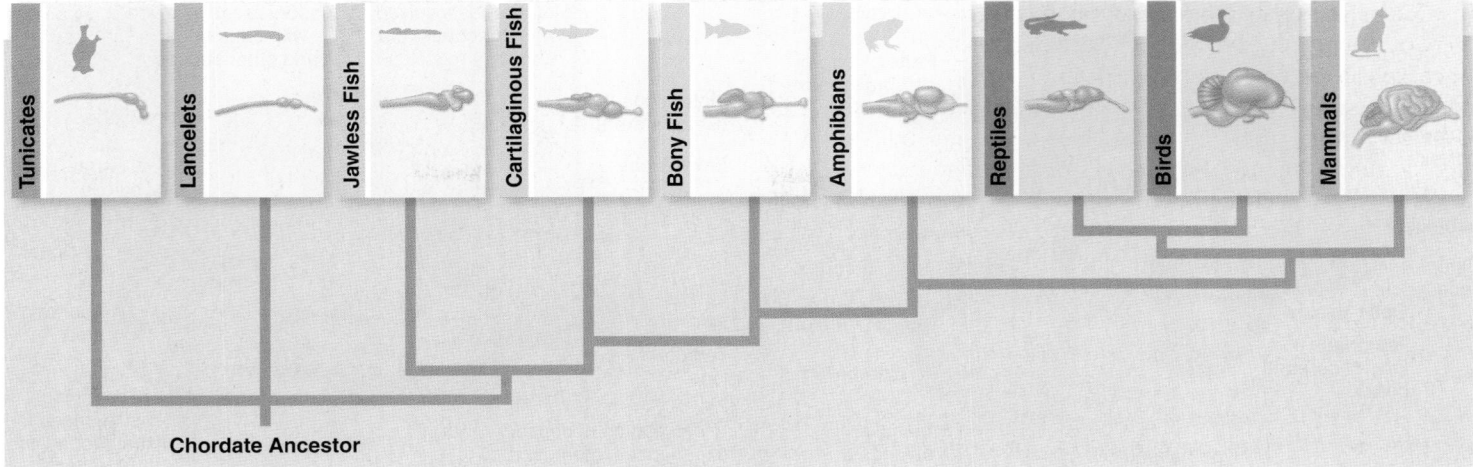

Figure 44.21 Evolution of the vertebrate brain. The relative sizes of different brain regions have changed as vertebrates have evolved. In sharks and other fishes, the hindbrain is predominant, and the rest of the brain serves primarily to process sensory information. In amphibians and reptiles, the forebrain is far larger, and it contains a larger cerebrum devoted to associative activity. In birds, which evolved from reptiles, the cerebrum is even more pronounced. In mammals, the cerebrum covers the optic tectum and is the largest portion of the brain. The dominance of the cerebrum is greatest in humans, in whom it envelops much of the rest of the brain.

The midbrain and forebrain of fishes

In fishes, the remainder of the brain is devoted to the reception and processing of sensory information. The midbrain is composed primarily of the *optic tectum*, which receives and processes visual information, whereas the forebrain is devoted to the processing of olfactory (smell) information.

The brains of fishes continue growing throughout their lives. This continued growth is in marked contrast to the brains of other classes of vertebrates, which generally complete their development by infancy. The human brain continues to develop through early childhood, but few new neurons are produced once development has ceased. One exception is the hippocampus, which has control over which experiences are filed away into long-term memory and which are forgotten. The extent of neurogenesis (production of new neurons) in adult brains is controversial, and one area of active current research.

The dominant forebrain in more recent vertebrates

Starting with the amphibians and continuing more prominently in the reptiles, processing of sensory information is increasingly centered in the forebrain. This pattern was the dominant evolutionary trend in the further development of the vertebrate brain (figure 44.21).

The forebrain in reptiles, amphibians, birds, and mammals is composed of two elements that have distinct functions. The *diencephalon* consists of the thalamus and hypothalamus. The **thalamus** is an integration and relay center between incoming sensory information and the cerebrum. The hypothalamus participates in basic drives and emotions and controls the secretions of the pituitary gland. The **telencephalon,** or "end brain," is located at the front of the forebrain and is devoted largely to associative activity. In mammals, the telencephalon is called the cerebrum. The telencephalon also includes structures we discuss later on when describing the human brain.

The expansion of the cerebrum

In examining the relationship between brain mass and body mass among the vertebrates, a remarkable difference is observed between fishes and reptiles on the one hand, and birds and mammals on the other. Mammals have brains that are particularly large relative to their body mass. This is especially true of porpoises and humans.

The increase in brain size in mammals largely reflects the great enlargement of the cerebrum, the dominant part of the mammalian brain. The **cerebrum** is the center for correlation, association, and learning in the mammalian brain. It receives sensory data from the thalamus and issues motor commands to the spinal cord via descending tracts of axons.

In vertebrates, the central nervous system is composed of the brain and the spinal cord (see table 44.3). These two structures are responsible for most of the information processing within the nervous system and they consist primarily of interneurons and neuroglia. Ascending tracts carry sensory information to the brain. Descending tracts carry impulses from the brain to the motor neurons and interneurons in the spinal cord that control the muscles of the body.

The human forebrain exhibits exceptional information-processing ability

The human cerebrum is so large that it appears to envelop the rest of the brain. It is split into right and left **cerebral hemispheres,** which are connected by a tract called the **corpus**

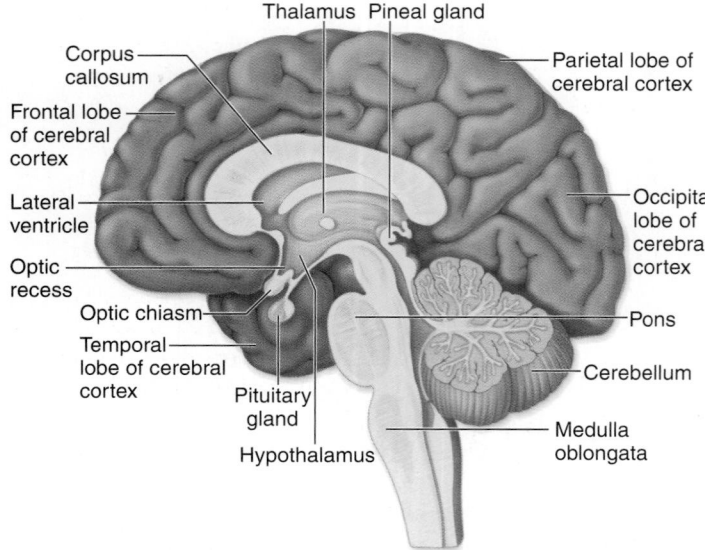

Figure 44.22 A section through the human brain. In this sagittal section showing one cerebral hemisphere, the corpus callosum, a fiber tract connecting the two cerebral hemispheres, can be clearly seen.

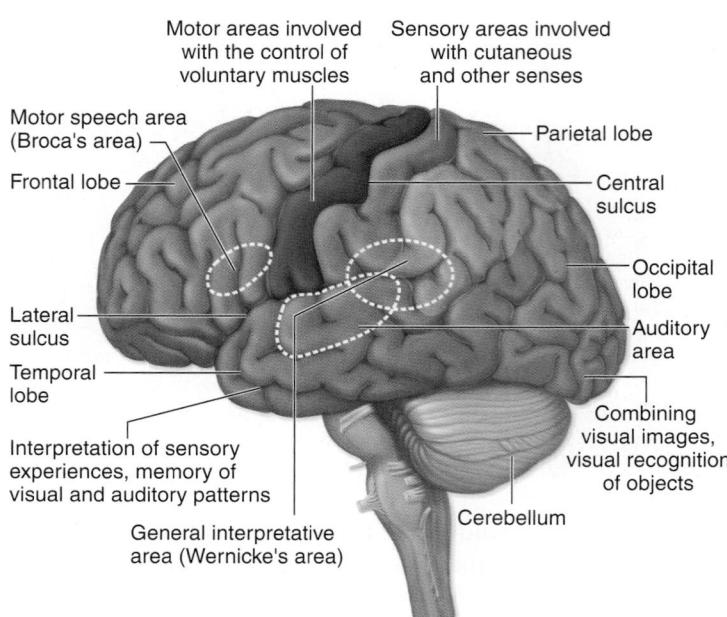

Figure 44.23 The cerebrum. This diagram shows the lobes of the cerebrum and indicates some of the known regions of specialization.

callosum (figure 44.22). The hemispheres are further divided into the *frontal, parietal, temporal,* and *occipital lobes.*

Each hemisphere primarily receives sensory input from the opposite, or contralateral, side of the body and exerts motor control primarily over that side. Therefore, a touch on the right hand is relayed primarily to the left hemisphere, which may then initiate movement of the right hand in response to the touch. Damage to one hemisphere due to a stroke often results in a loss of sensation and paralysis on the contralateral side of the body.

The cerebral cortex

Much of the neural activity of the cerebrum occurs within a layer of gray matter only a few millimeters thick on its outer surface. This layer, called the **cerebral cortex,** is densely packed with nerve cells. In humans, it contains over 10 billion nerve cells, amounting to roughly 10% of all the neurons in the brain. The surface of the cerebral cortex is highly convoluted; this is particularly true in the human brain, where the convolutions increase the surface area of the cortex threefold.

The activities of the cerebral cortex fall into one of three general categories: motor, sensory, and associative. Each of its regions correlates with a specific function (figure 44.23). The **primary motor cortex** lies along the *gyrus* (convolution) on the posterior border of the frontal lobe, just in front of the central *sulcus* (crease). Each point on the surface of the motor cortex is associated with the movement of a different part of the body (figure 44.24, right).

Just behind the central sulcus, on the anterior edge of the parietal lobe, lies the **primary somatosensory cortex.** Each point in this area receives input from sensory neurons serving skin and muscle senses in a particular part of the body (figure 44.24, left). Large areas of the primary motor cortex and primary somatosensory cortex are devoted to the fingers,

lips, and tongue because of the need for manual dexterity and speech. The auditory cortex lies within the temporal lobe, and different regions of this cortex deal with different sound frequencies. The visual cortex lies on the occipital lobe, with different sites processing information from different positions on the retina, equivalent to particular points in the visual fields of the eyes.

The portion of the cerebral cortex that is not occupied by these motor and sensory cortices is referred to as the **association cortex.** The site of higher mental activities, the association cortex reaches its greatest extent in primates, especially humans, where it makes up 95% of the surface of the cerebral cortex.

Basal ganglia

Buried deep within the white matter of the cerebrum are several collections of cell bodies and dendrites that produce islands of gray matter. These aggregates of neuron cell bodies, which are collectively termed the *basal ganglia,* receive sensory information from ascending nerve tracts and motor commands from the cerebral cortex and cerebellum.

Outputs from the basal ganglia are sent down the spinal cord, where they participate in the control of body movements. Damage to specific regions of the basal ganglia can produce the resting tremor of muscles that is characteristic of Parkinson disease.

Thalamus and hypothalamus

The thalamus is a primary site of sensory integration in the brain. Visual, auditory, and somatosensory information is sent to the thalamus, where the sensory tracts synapse with association neurons. The sensory information is then relayed via the thalamus to the occipital, temporal, and parietal lobes of the cerebral cortex, respectively. The transfer of each of these types

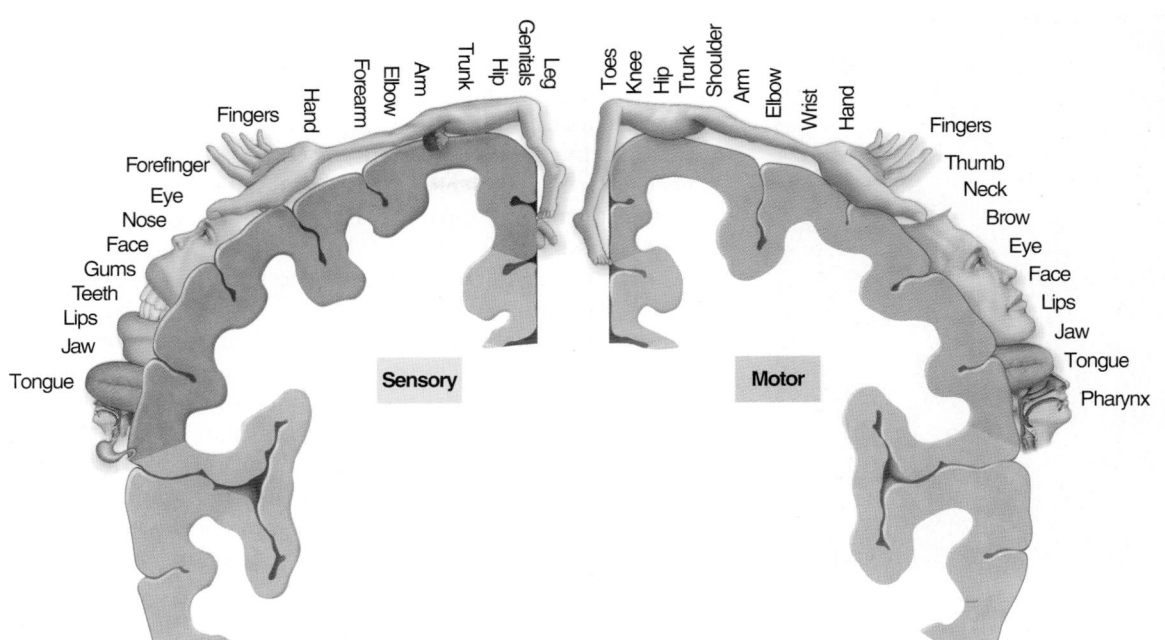

Figure 44.24 The primary somatosensory cortex (left) and the primary motor cortex (right). Each of these regions of the cerebral cortex is associated with a different region of the body, as indicated in this stylized map. The areas of the body are drawn in relative proportion to the amount of cortex dedicated to their sensation or control. For example, the hands have large areas of sensory and motor control, and the pharynx has a considerable area of motor control but little area devoted to the sensations of the pharynx.

of sensory information is handled by specific aggregations of neuron cell bodies within the thalamus.

The hypothalamus integrates the visceral activities. It helps regulate body temperature, hunger and satiety, thirst, and—along with the limbic system—various emotional states. The hypothalamus also controls the pituitary gland, which in turn regulates many of the other endocrine glands of the body. By means of its interconnections with the cerebral cortex and with control centers in the *brainstem* (a term used to refer collectively to the midbrain, pons, and medulla oblongata), the hypothalamus helps coordinate the neural and hormonal responses to many internal stimuli and emotions.

The *hippocampus* and **amygdala,** along with the hypothalamus, are the major components of the **limbic system**—an evolutionarily ancient group of linked structures deep within the cerebrum that are responsible for emotional responses, as described earlier. The hippocampus is also believed to be important in the formation and recall of memories.

Complex functions of the human brain may be controlled in specific areas

Although studying brain function is difficult, it has long fascinated researchers. The distinction between sleep and waking, the use and acquisition of language, spatial recognition, and memory are all areas of active research. Although far from understood, one generalization that emerged was the regionalization of function.

Sleep and arousal

The brainstem contains a diffuse collection of neurons referred to as the *reticular formation*. One part of this formation, the *reticular-activating system*, controls consciousness and alertness. All of the sensory pathways feed into this system, which moni-

tors the information coming into the brain and identifies important stimuli. When the reticular-activating system has been stimulated to arousal, it increases the level of activity in many parts of the brain. Neural pathways from the reticular formation to the cortex and other brain regions are depressed by anesthetics and barbiturates.

The reticular-activating system controls both sleep and the waking state. It is easier to sleep in a dark room than in a lighted one because there are fewer visual stimuli to stimulate the reticular-activating system. In addition, activity in this system is reduced by serotonin, a neurotransmitter discussed earlier. Serotonin causes the level of brain activity to fall, bringing on sleep.

Brain state can be monitored by means of an electroencephalogram (EEG), a recording of electrical activity. Awake but relaxed individuals with eyes closed exhibit a brain pattern of large, slow waves termed *alpha waves*. In an alert individual with eyes open, the waves are more rapid (*beta waves*) and more desynchronized as sensory input is being received. *Theta waves* and *delta waves* are very slow waves seen during sleep. When an individual is in REM sleep—characterized by rapid eye movements with the eyes closed—the EEG is more like that of an awake, relaxed individual.

Language

Although the two cerebral hemispheres seem structurally similar, they are responsible for different activities. The most thoroughly investigated example of this lateralization of function is language.

The left hemisphere is the "dominant" hemisphere for language in 90% of right-handed people and nearly two-thirds of left-handed people. (By *dominant*, we mean it is the hemisphere in which most neural processing related to language is performed.) Different brain regions control language in the

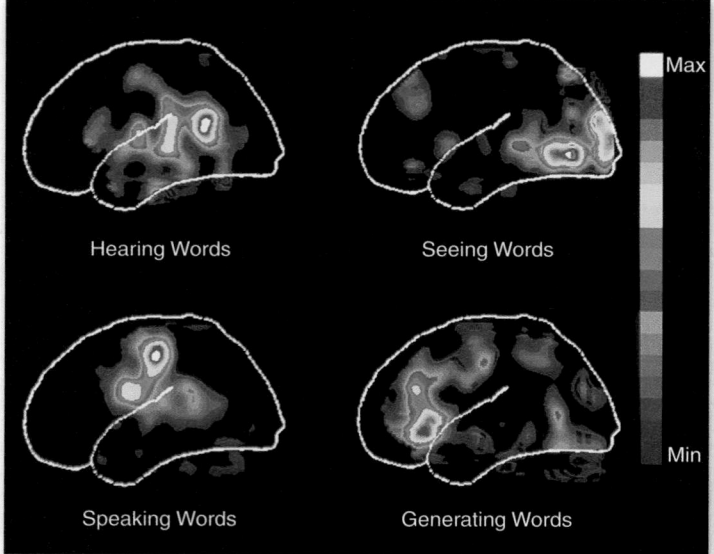

Figure 44.25 **Different brain regions control various language activities.** This illustration shows how the brain reacts in human subjects asked to listen to a spoken word, to read that same word silently, to repeat the word out loud, and then to speak a word related to the first. Regions of white, red, and yellow show the greatest activity. Compare this with figure 44.24 to see how regions of the brain are mapped.

dominant hemisphere (figure 44.25). Wernicke's area, located in the parietal lobe between the primary auditory and visual areas, is important for language comprehension and the formulation of thoughts into speech (see figure 44.23). Broca's area, found near the part of the motor cortex controlling the face, is responsible for the generation of motor output needed for language communication.

Damage to these brain areas can cause language disorders known as *aphasias*. For example, if Wernicke's area is damaged, the person's speech is rapid and fluid but lacks meaning; words are tossed together as in a "word salad."

Spatial recognition

Whereas the dominant hemisphere for language is adept at sequential reasoning, like that needed to formulate a sentence, the nondominant hemisphere (the right hemisphere in most people) is adept at spatial reasoning, the type of reasoning needed to assemble a puzzle or draw a picture. It is also the hemisphere primarily involved in musical ability—a person with damage to Broca's speech area in the left hemisphere may not be able to speak but may retain the ability to sing.

Damage to the nondominant hemisphere may lead to an inability to appreciate spatial relationships and may impair musical activities such as singing. Even more specifically, damage to the inferior temporal cortex in that hemisphere eliminates the capacity to recall faces, a condition known as prosopagnosia. Reading, writing, and oral comprehension remain normal, and patients with this disability can still recognize acquaintances by their voices. The nondominant hemisphere is also important for the consolidation of memories of nonverbal experiences.

Memory and learning

One of the great mysteries of the brain is the basis of memory and learning. Memory appears dispersed across the brain. Specific cortical sites cannot be identified for particular memories because relatively extensive cortical damage does not selectively remove memories. Although memory is impaired if portions of the brain, particularly the temporal lobes, are removed, it is not lost entirely. Many memories persist in spite of the damage, and the ability to access them is gradually recovered with time.

Fundamental differences appear to exist between short-term and long-term memory. Short-term memory is transient, lasting only a few moments. Such memories can readily be erased by the application of an electrical shock, leaving previously stored long-term memories intact. This result suggests that short-term memories are stored in the form of a transient neural excitation. Long-term memory, in contrast, appears to involve structural changes in certain neural connections within the brain.

Two parts of the temporal lobes, the hippocampus and the amygdala, are involved in both short-term memory and its consolidation into long-term memory. Damage to these structures impairs the ability to process recent events into long-term memories.

Synaptic plasticity

Part of the basis of learning and memory are changes to the function of a synapse over time. Two examples of this synaptic plasticity are long-term potentiation (LTP), and long-term depression (LTD). The mechanism of LTP is complex and not completely understood. One well-studied form involves synapses that release the neurotransmitter glutamate, and have *N*-methyl-D-aspartic acid (NMDA) type of receptors. When either the same synapse is stimulated repeatedly, or neighboring synapses are stimulated, the postsynaptic membrane becomes significantly depolarized. This releases a block of the NMDA receptor by Mg^{2+} such that glutamate binding causes an influx of Ca^{2+} that stimulates a signal transduction pathway involving calcium/calmodulin-dependent protein kinase II. This pathway leads to the insertion of another receptor type, the α-amino-3-hydroxyl-5-methyl-4-isoxazole-propionate (AMPA) receptor, into the postsynaptic membrane, making the synapse more sensitive to future stimulation (figure 44.26).

If the stimulation of an NMDA receptor is less, and the postsynaptic membrane is less depolarized, LTD can result. In this case, a different Ca^{2+}-dependent signaling pathway results in the loss of AMPA receptors from the membrane. Taken together, these two mechanisms can make a synapse more or less sensitive to future stimulation.

Alzheimer disease: Degeneration of brain neurons

In the past, little was known about *Alzheimer disease*, a condition in which the memory and thought processes of the brain become dysfunctional. Scientists disagree about the biological nature of the disease and its cause. Two hypotheses have been proposed: One suggests that nerve cells in the brain are killed from the outside in, and the other that the cells are killed from the inside out.

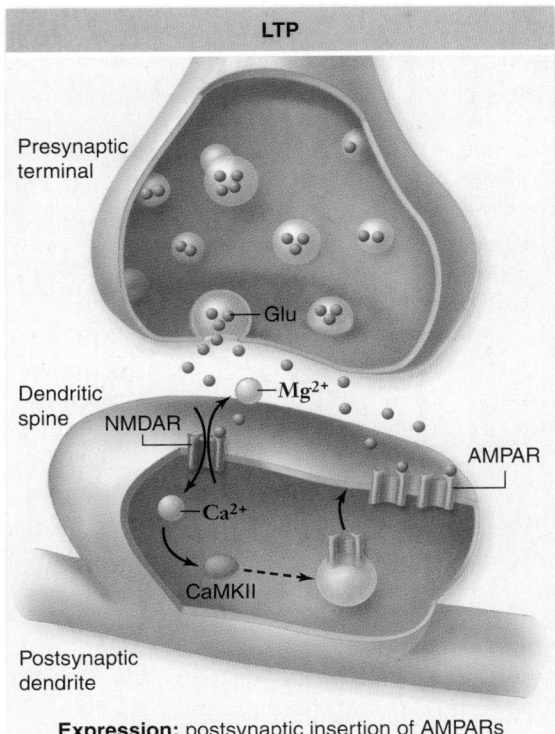

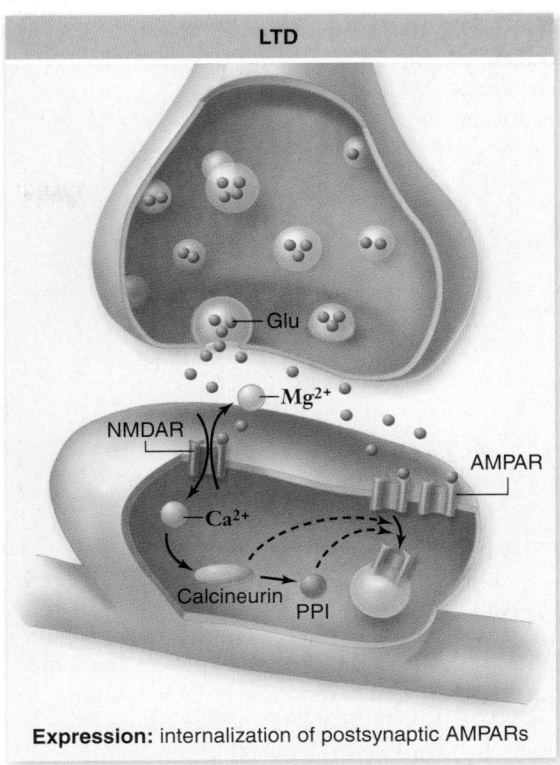

Figure 44.26 LTP and LTD modulate synaptic function. *a.* When a the postsynaptic membrane is significantly depolarized, when GABA binds to the *N*-methyl-D-aspartic acid receptor (NMDAR), the influx of Ca^{2+} leads to the insertion of α-amino-3-hydroxyl-5-methyl-4-isoxazole-propionate receptors (AMPAR). This potentiates the synapse for future stimulation. *b.* When the postsynaptic membrane does not have as large a depolarization, or there is less GABA, then GABA binding to NMDA receptor triggers a different pathway that results in removal of AMPA receptors. This depresses the synapse for future stimulation. CaMKII, calmodulin-dependent protein kinase 2.

In the first hypothesis, external proteins called β-amyloid exist in an abnormal form, which then forms aggregates, or plaques. The plaques begin to fill in the brain and then damage and kill nerve cells. However, these amyloid plaques have been found in autopsies of people who did not exhibit Alzheimer disease.

The second hypothesis maintains that the nerve cells are killed by an abnormal form of an internal protein called tau (τ), which normally functions to maintain protein transport microtubules. Abnormal forms of τ-protein assemble into helical segments that form tangles, which interfere with the normal functioning of the nerve cells. At this point, the association of tangles with actual neuronal death is stronger.

The spinal cord conveys messages and controls some responses directly

The spinal cord is a cable of neurons extending from the brain down through the backbone (figure 44.27). It is enclosed and protected by the vertebral column and layers of membranes called *meninges*, which also cover the brain. Inside the spinal cord are two zones.

The inner zone is gray matter and primarily consists of the cell bodies of interneurons, motor neurons, and neuroglia. The outer zone is white matter and contains cables of sensory axons in the dorsal columns and motor axons in the

ventral columns. These nerve tracts may also contain the dendrites of other nerve cells. Messages from the body and the brain run up and down the spinal cord, the body's "information highway."

In addition to relaying messages, the spinal cord also functions in **reflexes,** the sudden, involuntary movement of muscles. A reflex produces a rapid motor response to a stimulus because the sensory neuron passes its information to a motor

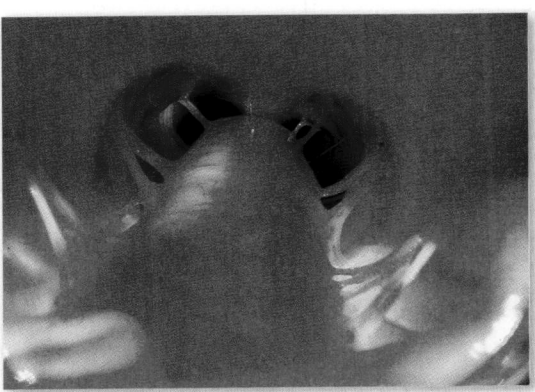

Figure 44.27 A view down the human spinal cord. Pairs of spinal nerves can be seen extending from the spinal cord. Along these nerves, as well as the cranial nerves that arise from the brain, the central nervous system communicates with the rest of the body.

Figure 44.28
The knee-jerk reflex.
This is the simplest reflex, involving only sensory and motor neurons.

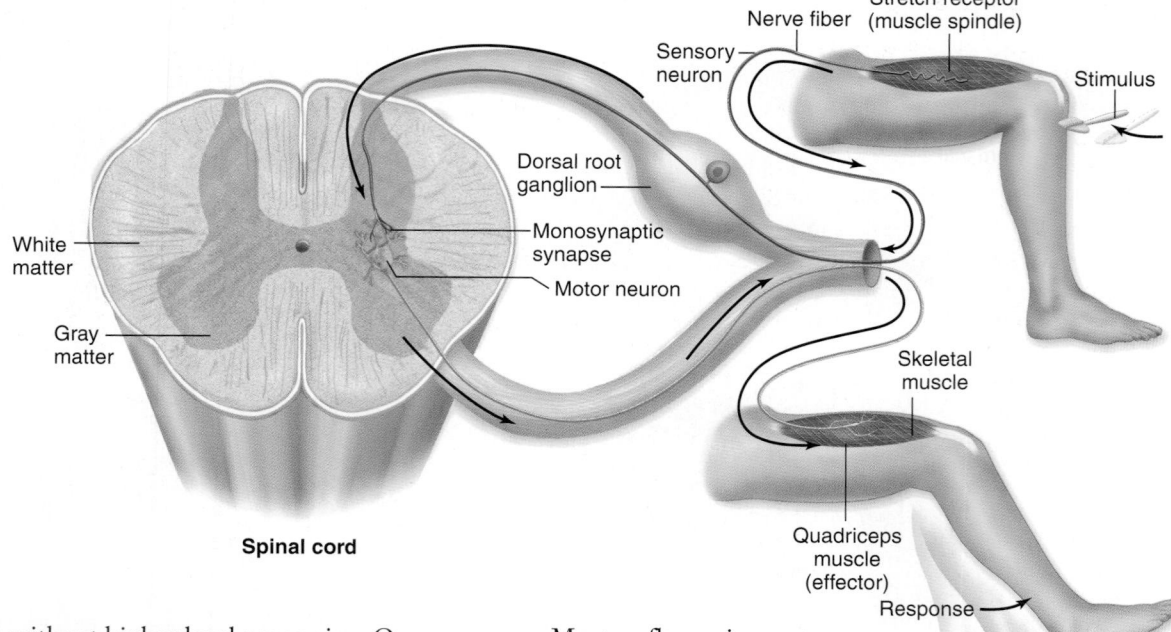

Spinal cord

neuron in the spinal cord, without higher level processing. One of the most frequently used reflexes in your body is blinking, a reflex that protects your eyes. If an object such as an insect or a cloud of dust approaches your eye, the eyelid blinks before you realize what has happened. The reflex occurs before the cerebrum is aware the eye is in danger.

Because they pass information along only a few neurons, reflexes are very fast. A few reflexes, such as the knee-jerk reflex (figure 44.28), are monosynaptic reflex arcs. In these, the sensory nerve cell makes synaptic contact directly with a motor neuron in the spinal cord whose axon travels directly back to the muscle.

Most reflexes in vertebrates, however, involve a single connecting interneuron between the sensory neuron and the motor neuron (figure 44.29). The withdrawal of a hand from a hot stove or the blinking of an eye in response to a puff of air involves a relay of information from a sensory neuron through one or more interneurons to a motor neuron. The motor neuron then stimulates the appropriate muscle to contract. Notice that the sensory neuron may also connect to other interneurons to send signals to the brain. Although you jerked your hand away from the stove, you will still feel pain.

Figure 44.29
A cutaneous spinal reflex. This reflex is more complex than a knee-jerk reflex because it requires interneurons as well as sensory and motor neurons. Interneurons connect a sensory neuron with a motor neuron to cause muscle contraction as shown. Other interneurons inhibit motor neurons, allowing antagonistic muscles to relax.

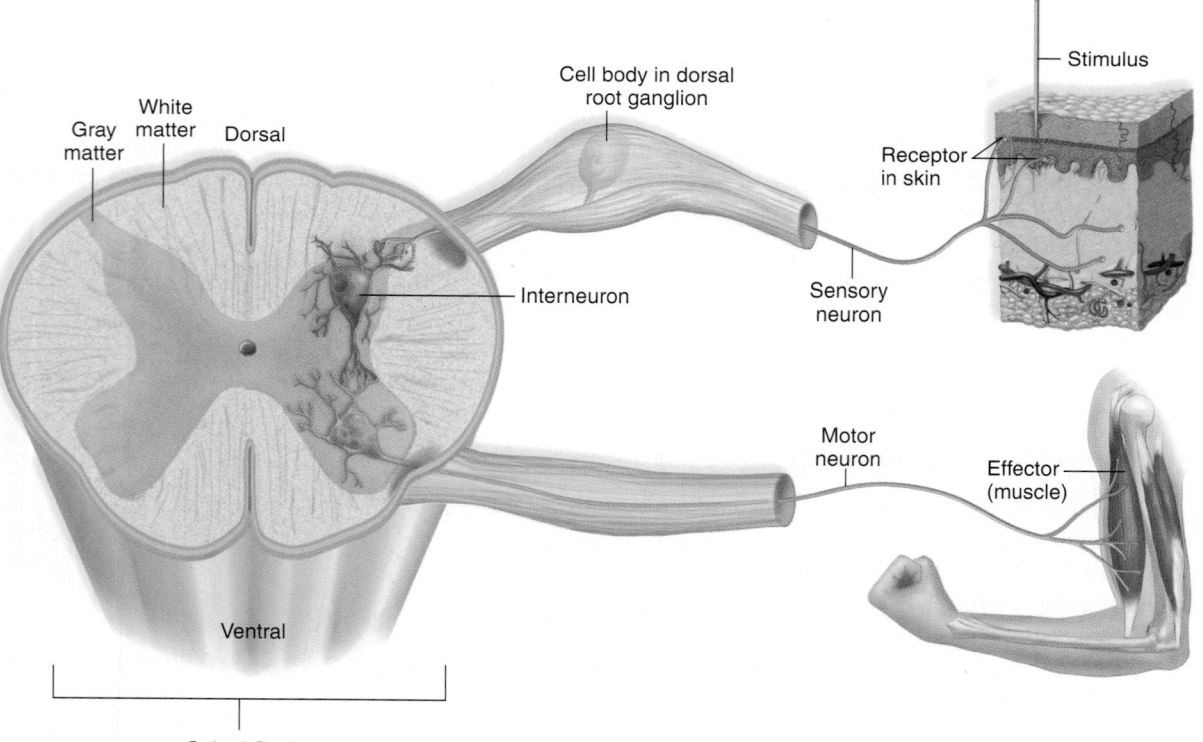

Spinal Cord

Spinal cord regeneration

In the past, scientists tried to repair severed spinal cords by installing nerves from another part of the body to bridge the gap and act as guides for the spinal cord to regenerate. But most of these experiments failed. Although axons may regenerate through the implanted nerves, they cannot penetrate the spinal cord tissue once they leave the implant. Also, a factor that inhibits nerve growth is present in the spinal cord.

After discovering that fibroblast growth factor stimulates nerve growth, neurobiologists working with rats tried "gluing" the nerves on, from the implant to the spinal cord, with fibrin that had been mixed with the fibroblast growth factor. Three months later, rats with the nerve bridges began to show movement in their lower bodies. Dye tests indicated that the spinal cord nerves had regrown from both sides of the gap.

Many scientists are encouraged by the potential to use a similar treatment in human medicine. But most spinal cord injuries in humans do not involve a completely severed spinal cord; often, nerves are crushed, which results in different tissue damage. Also, even though the rats with nerve bridges did regain some ability to move, tests indicated that they were barely able to walk or stand.

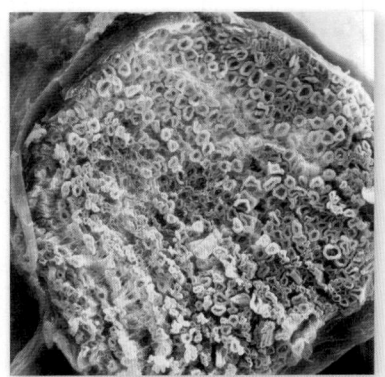

Figure 44.30 Nerves in the peripheral nervous system. Photomicrograph showing a cross section of a bullfrog nerve. The nerve is a bundle of axons bound together by connective tissue. Many myelinated axons are visible, each looking somewhat like a doughnut.

6.25 μm

Learning Outcomes Review 44.4

The vertebrate brain has three primary regions: the hindbrain, midbrain, and forebrain. The cerebrum, part of the forebrain, is composed of two cerebral hemispheres in which gray matter of the cerebral cortex overlays white matter and islands of gray matter (nuclei) called the basal ganglia. The spinal cord relays messages to and from the brain; a reflex occurs when the spinal cord processes sensory information directly and initiates a motor response.

■ *What is the advantage of having reflexes?*

44.5 The Peripheral Nervous System: Sensory and Motor Neurons

Learning Outcomes

1. Describe the organization of the peripheral nervous system.
2. Explain the actions of sensory and somatic neurons.
3. Distinguish between the somatic and autonomic nervous systems.
4. Describe differences between the sympathetic and parasympathetic divisions of the autonomic nervous system.

The PNS consists of nerves, the cablelike collections of axons (figure 44.30), and **ganglia** (singular, *ganglion*), aggregations of neuron cell bodies located outside the CNS. To review, the function of the PNS is to receive information from the environment, convey it to the CNS, and to carry responses to effectors such as muscle cells.

The PNS has somatic and autonomic systems

At the spinal cord, a spinal nerve separates into sensory and motor components. The axons of sensory neurons enter the dorsal surface of the spinal cord and form the **dorsal root** of the spinal nerve, whereas motor axons leave from the ventral surface of the spinal cord and form the **ventral root** of the spinal nerve. The cell bodies of sensory neurons are grouped together outside each level of the spinal cord in the **dorsal root ganglia.** The cell bodies of somatic motor neurons, on the other hand, are located within the spinal cord and so are not located in ganglia.

As mentioned earlier, somatic motor neurons stimulate skeletal muscles to contract, and autonomic motor neurons innervate involuntary effectors—smooth muscles, cardiac muscle, and glands. A comparison of the somatic and autonomic nervous systems is provided in table 44.4; we discuss each system in turn.

TABLE 44.4	Comparison of the Somatic and Autonomic Nervous Systems	
Characteristic	**Somatic**	**Autonomic**
Effectors	Skeletal muscle	Cardiac muscle

		Smooth muscle
		  Gastrointestinal tract
		  Blood vessels
		  Airways

		Exocrine glands
Effect on motor nerves	Excitation	Excitation or inhibition
Innervation of effector cells	Always single	Typically dual
Number of sequential neurons in path to effector	One	Two
Neurotransmitter	Acetylcholine	Acetylcholine, norepinephrine

The somatic nervous system controls movements

Somatic motor neurons stimulate the skeletal muscles of the body to contract in response to conscious commands and as part of reflexes that do not require conscious control. Voluntary control of skeletal muscles is achieved by activation of tracts of axons that descend from the cerebrum to the appropriate level of the spinal cord. Some of these descending axons stimulate spinal cord motor neurons directly, and others activate interneurons that in turn stimulate the spinal motor neurons.

When a particular muscle is stimulated to contract, however, its antagonist must be inhibited. In order to flex the arm, for example, the flexor muscles must be stimulated while the antagonistic extensor muscle is inhibited (see chapter 47). Descending motor axons produce this necessary inhibition by causing hyperpolarizations (IPSPs) of the spinal motor neurons that innervate the antagonistic muscles.

The autonomic nervous system controls involuntary functions through two divisions

The autonomic nervous system is composed of the *sympathetic* and *parasympathetic* divisions plus the medulla oblongata of the hindbrain, which coordinates this system. Although they differ, the sympathetic and parasympathetic divisions share several features. In both, the efferent motor pathway involves two neurons: The first has its cell body in the CNS and sends an axon to an autonomic ganglion; it is called *preganglionic neuron*. These neurons release acetylcholine at their synapses.

The second neuron has its cell body in the autonomic ganglion and sends its axon to synapse with a smooth muscle, cardiac muscle, or gland cell (figure 44.31). This second neuron is termed the *postganglionic neuron*. Those in the parasympathetic division release ACh, and those in the sympathetic division release norepinephrine.

The sympathetic division

In the sympathetic division, the preganglionic neurons originate in the thoracic and lumbar regions of the spinal cord (figure 44.32, left). Most of the axons from these neurons synapse in two parallel chains of ganglia immediately outside the spinal cord. These structures are usually called the *sympathetic chain* of ganglia. The sympathetic chain contains the cell bodies of postganglionic neurons, and it is the axons from these neurons that innervate the different visceral organs.

There are some exceptions to this general pattern, however. The axons of some preganglionic sympathetic neurons pass through the sympathetic chain without synapsing and, instead, terminate within the medulla of the adrenal gland (see chapter 46). In response to action potentials, the adrenal medulla cells secrete the hormone epinephrine (adrenaline). At the same time, norepinephrine is released at the synapses of the postganglionic neurons. As described earlier, both of these neurotransmitters prepare the body for action by heightening metabolism and blood flow.

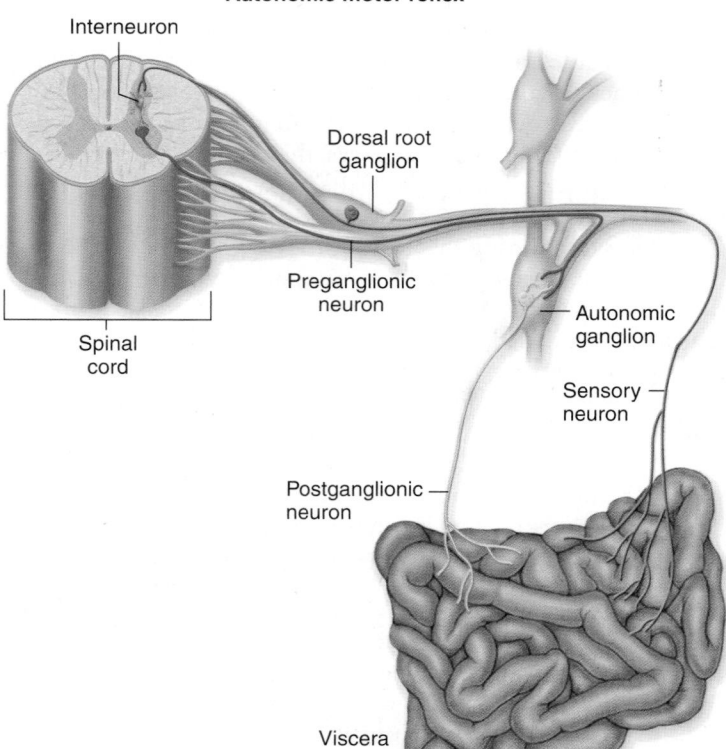

Autonomic motor reflex

Figure 44.31 An autonomic neural path. There are two motor neurons in the efferent pathway. The first, or preganglionic neuron, exits the CNS and synapses at an autonomic ganglion. The second, or postganglionic neuron, exits the ganglion and regulates the visceral effectors (smooth muscle, cardiac muscle, or glands).

The parasympathetic division

The actions of the sympathetic division are antagonized by the parasympathetic division. Preganglionic parasympathetic neurons originate in the brain and sacral regions of the spinal cord (see figure 44.32, right). Because of this origin, there cannot be a chain of parasympathetic ganglia analogous to the sympathetic chain. Instead, the preganglionic axons, many of which travel in the vagus (tenth cranial) nerve, terminate in ganglia located near or even within the internal organs. The postganglionic neurons then regulate the internal organs by releasing ACh at their synapses. Parasympathetic nerve effects include a slowing of the heart, increased secretions and activities of digestive organs, and so on. Table 44.5 compares the actions of the sympathetic and parasympathetic divisions.

G proteins mediate cell responses to autonomic signals

You might wonder how release of ACh can slow the heart rate—an inhibitory effect—when it has excitatory effects elsewhere.

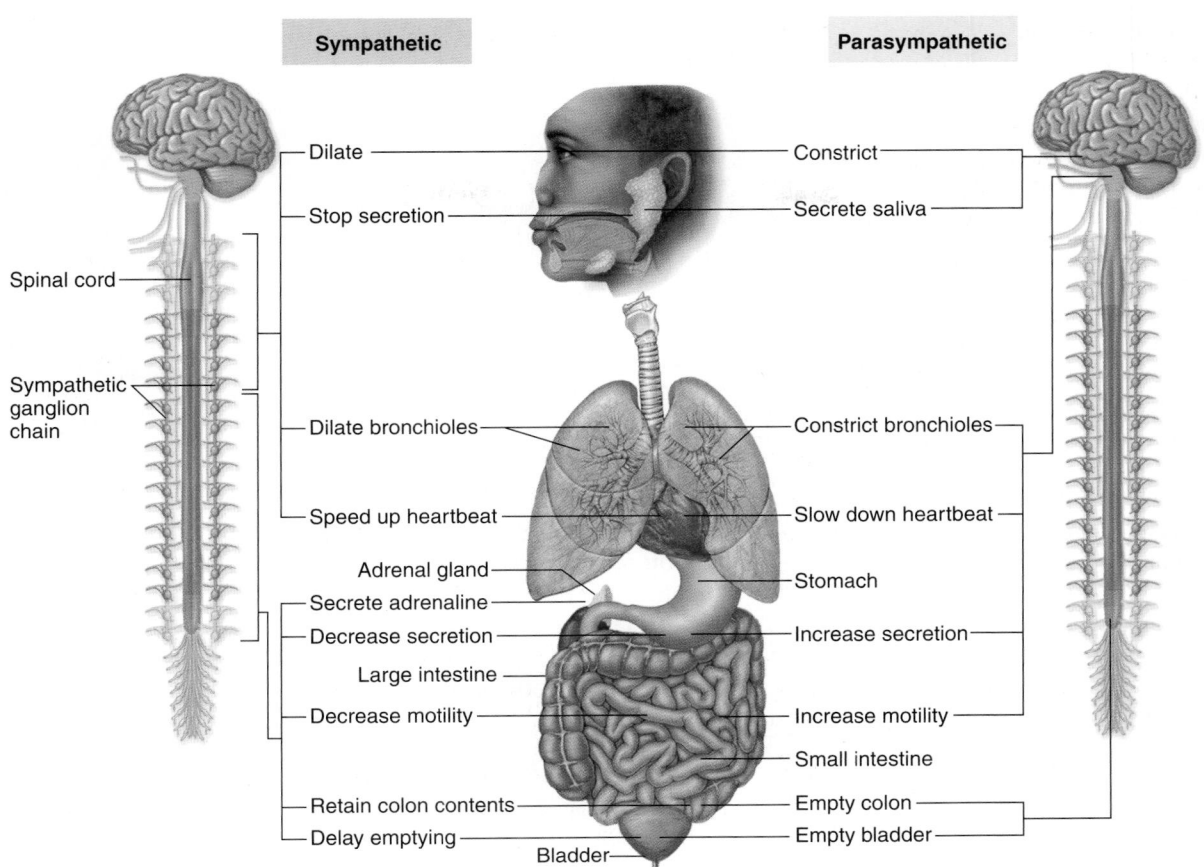

Sympathetic   **Parasympathetic**

Dilate ———————————— Constrict

Stop secretion ——————— Secrete saliva

Spinal cord

Sympathetic ganglion chain

Dilate bronchioles ——————— Constrict bronchioles

Speed up heartbeat ——————— Slow down heartbeat

Adrenal gland

Secrete adrenaline ——————— Stomach

Decrease secretion ——————— Increase secretion

Large intestine

Decrease motility ——————— Increase motility

Small intestine

Retain colon contents ——————— Empty colon

Delay emptying ——————— Empty bladder

Bladder

**Figure 44.32
The sympathetic and parasympathetic divisions of the autonomic nervous system.** The preganglionic neurons of the sympathetic division exit the thoracic and lumbar regions of the spinal cord, and those of the parasympathetic division exit the brain and sacral region of the spinal cord. The ganglia of the sympathetic division are located near the spinal cord; and those of the parasympathetic division are located near the organs they innervate. Most of the internal organs are innervated by both divisions.

TABLE 44.5	Autonomic Innervation of Target Tissues	
Target Tissue	**Sympathetic Stimulation**	**Parasympathetic Stimulation**
Pupil of eye	Dilation	Constriction
Glands		
Salivary	Vasoconstriction; slight secretion	Vasodilation; copious secretion
Gastric	Inhibition of secretion	Stimulation of gastric activity
Liver	Stimulation of glucose secretion	Inhibition of glucose secretion
Sweat	Sweating	None
Gastrointestinal tract		
Sphincters	Increased tone	Decreased tone
Wall	Decreased tone	Increased motility
Gallbladder	Relaxation	Contraction
Urinary bladder		
Muscle	Relaxation	Contraction
Sphincter	Contraction	Relaxation
Heart muscle	Increased rate and strength	Decreased rate
Lungs	Dilation of bronchioles	Constriction of bronchioles
Blood vessels		
In muscles	Dilation	None
In skin	Constriction	None
In viscera	Constriction	Dilation

Figure 44.33 The parasympathetic effects of ACh require the action of G proteins. The binding of ACh to its receptor causes dissociation of a G protein complex, releasing some components of this complex to move within the membrane and bind to other proteins that form ion channels. Shown here are the effects of ACh on the heart, where the G protein components cause the opening of K+ channels. This leads to outward diffusion of potassium and hyperpolarization, slowing the heart rate.

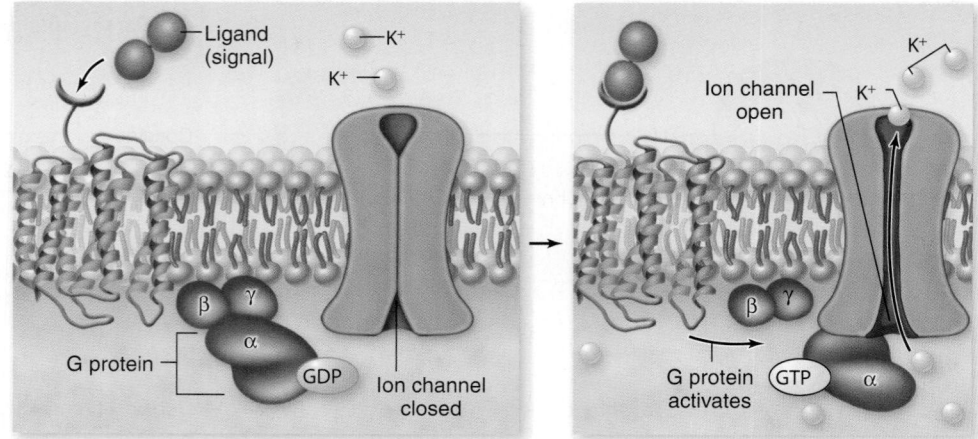

The answer is simple, the cells involved in each case have different receptors for ACh that produce different effects. In the neuromuscular junction, the receptor for ACh is a ligand-gated Na^+ channel that when open allows an influx of Na^+ that depolarizes the membrane. In the case of the heart, the inhibitory effect on the pacemaker cells is produced because binding of ACh to a different receptor leads to K^+ channels opening, resulting in the outward diffusion of K^+, hyperpolarizing the membrane. The ACh receptor in the heart is a member of the class of receptors called G protein–coupled receptors.

In chapter 9, you learned that G protein–coupled receptors consist of a membrane receptor and effector protein that are coupled by the action of a G protein. The receptor is activated by binding to its ligand, in this case ACh, and the receptor activates a G protein that in turn activates an effector protein, in this case a K^+ channel (figure 44.33).

This kind of system can also lead to excitation in other organs if the G protein acts on different effector proteins. For example, the parasympathetic nerves that innervate the stomach can cause increased gastric secretions and contractions.

The sympathetic nerve effects also are mediated by the action of G protein–coupled receptors. Stimulation by norepinephrine from sympathetic nerve endings and epinephrine from the adrenal medulla requires G proteins to activate the target cells. We describe these interactions in more detail, together with hormone action, in chapter 46.

Learning Outcomes Review 44.5

The PNS comprises the somatic (voluntary) and autonomic (involuntary) nervous systems. A spinal nerve contains sensory neurons, which carry information from sense organs to the CNS, and motor neurons, which carry directives from the CNS to targets such as muscle cells. The sympathetic division of the autonomic nervous system activates the body for fight-or-flight responses; the parasympathetic division generally promotes relaxation and digestion.

■ *Why would having the sympathetic and parasympathetic divisions be more advantageous than having a single system?*

Chapter Review

44.1 Nervous System Organization

The three types of neurons in vertebrates are sensory neurons, motor neurons, and interneurons (see figure 44.1).

The central nervous system is the "command center."
The CNS consists of the brain and the spinal cord, where sensory input is integrated and responses originate.

The peripheral nervous system collects information and carries out responses.
The PNS comprises sensory neurons that carry impulses to the CNS and motor neurons that carry impulses from the CNS to effectors.

The somatic nervous system primarily acts on skeletal muscles; the autonomic nervous system is involuntary and consists of the antagonistic sympathetic and parasympathetic divisions.

The structure of neurons supports their function.
Neurons have a cell body, dendrites that receive information, and a long axon that conducts impulses away from the cell.

Supporting cells include Schwann cells and oligodendrocytes.
Neuroglia are supporting cells of the nervous system. Schwann cells (PNS) and oligodendrocytes (CNS) produce myelin sheaths that surround and insulate axons (see figure 44.3).

44.2 The Mechanism of Nerve Impulse Transmission

An electrical difference exists across the plasma membrane.
The sodium–potassium pump moves Na^+ outside the cell and K^+ into the cell. Leakage of K^+ also moves positive charge outside the cell. The membrane resting potential is typically –70 mV.

Graded potentials are small changes that can reinforce or negate each other.

Ligand-gated ion channels are responsible for graded potentials. Graded potentials can combine in an additive way (summation).

Action potentials result when depolarization reaches a threshold.

Action potentials are all-or-nothing events resulting from the rapid and sequential opening of votage-gated ion channels (see figure 44.9).

Action potentials are propagated along axons.

Influx of Na^+ during an action potential causes the adjacent region to depolarize, producing its own action potential (see figure 44.10).

There are two ways to increase the velocity of nerve impulses.

The speed of nerve impulses increases as the diameter of the axon increases. Saltatory conduction, in which impulses jump from node to node, also increases speed (see figure 44.11).

44.3 Synapses: Where Neurons Communicate with Other Cells

An action potential terminates at the end of the axon at the synapse—a gap between the axon and another cell.

The two types of synapses are electrical and chemical.

Electrical synapses consist of gap junctions; chemical synapses release neurotransmitters to cross the synapse (see figure 44.14).

Many different chemical compounds serve as neurotransmitters.

Neurotransmitter molecules include acetylcholine, amino acids, biogenic amines, neuropeptides, and a gas—nitric oxide.

A postsynaptic neuron must integrate input from many synapses.

Excitatory postsynaptic potentials (EPSPs) depolarize the membrane; inhibitory postsynaptic potentials (IPSPs) hyperpolarize it. The additive effect may or may not produce an action potential.

Neurotransmitters play a role in drug addiction.

Addictive drugs often act by mimicking a neurotransmitter or by interfering with neurotransmitter reuptake.

44.4 The Central Nervous System: Brain and Spinal Cord

As animals became more complex, so did their nervous systems.

The nervous system has evolved from a nerve net composed of linked nerves, to nerve cords with association nerves, and to the development of coordination centers (see figure 44.19).

Vertebrate brains have three basic divisions.

The vertebrate brain is divided into hindbrain, midbrain, and forebrain (see figure 44.20). The forebrain is divided further into the diencephalon and telencephalon. The telencephalon, called the cerebrum in mammals, is the center for association and learning.

The human forebrain exhibits exceptional information-processing ability.

The cerebrum is divided into right and left hemispheres (see figure 44.22), which are subdivided into frontal, parietal, temporal, and occipital lobes (see figure 44.23). The cerebrum contains the primary motor and somatosensory cortexes as well as the basal ganglia.

The limbic system consists of the hypothalamus, hippocampus, and amygdala, and it is responsible for emotional states.

Complex functions of the human brain may be controlled in specific areas.

The reticular activating system in the brainstem controls consciousness and alertness. Short-term memory may be stored as transient neural excitation; long-term memory involves changes in neural connections.

The spinal cord conveys messages and controls some responses directly.

Reflexes are the sudden, involuntary movement of muscles in response to a stimulus (see figures 44.28 and 44.29).

44.5 The Peripheral Nervous System: Sensory and Motor Neurons

The PNS has somatic and autonomic systems.

Sensory axons (inbound) form the dorsal root of the spinal nerve. The cell bodies are in the dorsal root ganglia.

Motor axons (outbound) form the ventral root of the spinal nerve. Cell bodies are located in the spinal cord.

The somatic nervous system controls movements.

Somatic motor neurons stimulate skeletal muscles in response to conscious commands and involuntary reflexes.

The autonomic nervous system controls involuntary functions through two divisions.

Sympathetic neurons originate in the thoracic and lumbar regions of the spinal cord and synapse at an autonomic ganglion outside the spinal cord (see figure 44.31). Parasympathetic neurons originate in the brain and in sacral regions of the spinal cord and terminate in ganglia near or within internal organs (see figure 44.32 and table 44.5).

G proteins mediate cell responses to autonomic signals.

The binding of ACh activates a G protein that in turn activates a K^+ channel, allowing outflow of K^+ and hyperpolarization of the membrane and slowing heart rate.

Review Questions

UNDERSTAND

1. Which of the following best describes the electrical state of a neuron at rest?
   a. The inside of a neuron is more negatively charged than the outside.
   b. The outside of a neuron is more negatively charged than the inside.
   c. The inside and the outside of a neuron have the same electrical charge.
   d. Potassium ions leak into a neuron at rest.

2. The _____ cannot be controlled by conscious thought.
   a. motor neurons   c. autonomic nervous system
   b. somatic nervous system d. skeletal muscles

3. A fight-or-flight response in the body is controlled by the

   a. sympathetic division of the nervous system.
   b. parasympathetic division of the nervous system.
   c. release of acetylcholine from postganglionic neurons.
   d. somatic nervous system.

4. Inhibitory neurotransmitters

   a. hyperpolarize postsynaptic membranes.
   b. hyperpolarize presynaptic membranes.
   c. depolarize postsynaptic membranes.
   d. depolarize presynaptic membranes.

5. White matter is____, and gray matter is____.

   a. comprised of axons; comprised of cell bodies and dendrites
   b. myelinated; unmyelinated
   c. found in the CNS; also found in the CNS
   d. all of these are correct

6. During an action potential

   a. the rising phase is due to an influx of Na^+.
   b. the falling phase is due to an influx of K^+.
   c. the falling phase is due to an efflux of K^+.
   d. both a and c occur.

7. A functional reflex requires

   a. only a sensory neuron and a motor neuron.
   b. a sensory neuron, the thalamus, and a motor neuron.
   c. the cerebral cortex and a motor neuron.
   d. only the cerebral cortex and the thalamus.

APPLY

1. Imagine that you are doing an experiment on the movement of ions across neural membranes. Which of the following plays a role in determining the equilibrium concentration of ions across these membranes?

   a. Ion concentration gradients
   b. Ion pH gradients
   c. Ion electrical gradients
   d. Both a and c

2. The Na^+/K^+ ATPase pump is

   a. not required for action potential firing.
   b. important for long-term maintenance of resting potential.
   c. important only at the synapse.
   d. used to stimulate graded potentials.

3. Botox, a derivative of the botulinum toxin that causes food poisoning, inhibits the release of acetylcholine at the neuromuscular junction. How could this strange-sounding treatment produce desired cosmetic effects?

   a. By inhibiting the parasympathetic branch of the autonomic nervous system
   b. By inhibiting the sympathetic branch of the autonomic nervous system
   c. By causing paralysis of facial muscles, which decreases wrinkles in the face
   d. By causing facial muscles to contract, whereby the skin is stretched tighter, thereby reducing wrinkles

4. The following is a list of the components of a chemical synapse. A mutation in the structure of which of these would affect only the reception of the message, not its release or the response?

   a. Membrane proteins in the postsynaptic cell
   b. Proteins in the presynaptic cell
   c. Cytoplasmic proteins in the postsynaptic cell
   d. Both a and b

5. Suppose that you stick your finger with a sharp pin. The area affected is very small and only one pain receptor fires. However, it fires repeatedly at a rapid rate (it hurts!). This is an example of

   a. temporal summation.   c. habituation.
   b. spatial summation.   d. repolarization.

6. As you sit quietly reading this sentence, the part of the nervous system that is most active is the

   a. somatic nervous system.
   b. sympathetic nervous system.
   c. parasympathetic nervous system.
   d. none of these choices is correct.

7. G protein–coupled receptors are involved in the nervous system by

   a. controlling the release of neurotransmitters.
   b. controlling the opening and closing of Na+ channels during an action potential.
   c. controlling the opening and closing of K+ channels during an action potential.
   d. acting as receptors for neurotransmitters on postsynaptic cells.

SYNTHESIZE

1. Tetraethylammonium (TEA) is a drug that blocks voltage-gated K^+ channels. What effect would TEA have on the action potentials produced by a neuron? If TEA could be applied selectively to a presynaptic neuron that releases an excitatory neurotransmitter, how would it alter the synaptic effect of that neurotransmitter on the postsynaptic cell?

2. Describe the status of the Na^+ and K^+ channels at each of the following stages: rising, falling, and undershoot.

3. Describe the steps required to produce an excitatory postsynaptic potential (EPSP). How would these differ at an inhibitory synapse?

4. Your friend Karen loves caffeine. However, lately she has been complaining that she needs to drink more caffeinated beverages in order to get the same effect she used to. Excellent student of biology that you are, you tell her that this is to be expected. Why?

ONLINE RESOURCE

www.ravenbiology.com

Understand, Apply, and Synthesize—enhance your study with animations that bring concepts to life and practice tests to assess your understanding. Your instructor may also recommend the interactive eBook, individualized learning tools, and more.

Chapter 45

Sensory Systems

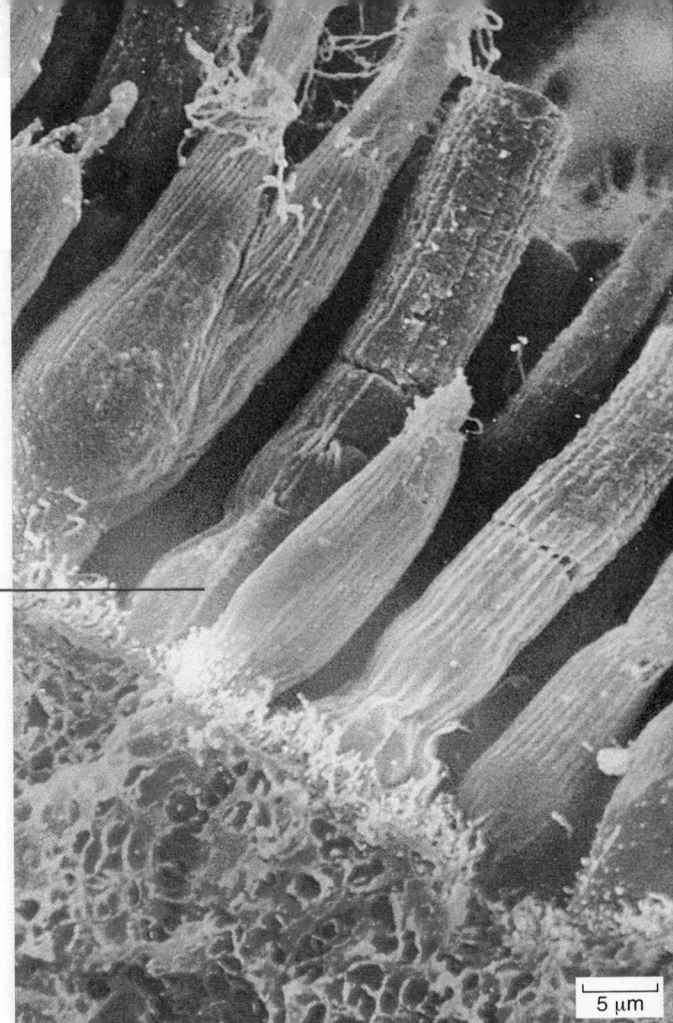

5 μm

Chapter Outline

45.1 Overview of Sensory Receptors

45.2 Mechanoreceptors: Touch and Pressure

45.3 Hearing, Vibration, and Detection of Body Position

45.4 Chemoreceptors: Taste, Smell, and pH

45.5 Vision

45.6 The Diversity of Sensory Experiences

Introduction

All input from sensory neurons to the central nervous system (CNS) arrives in the same form, as electrical signals. Sensory neurons receive input from a variety of different kinds of sense receptor cells, such as the rod and cone cells found in the vertebrate eye shown in the micrograph. Different sensory neurons lead to different brain regions and so are associated with the different senses. The intensity of the sensation depends on the frequency of action potentials conducted by the sensory neuron. The brain distinguishes a sunset, a symphony, and searing pain only in terms of the identity of the sensory neuron carrying the action potentials and the frequency of these impulses. Thus, if the auditory nerve is artificially stimulated, the brain perceives the stimulation as sound. But if the optic nerve is artificially stimulated in exactly the same manner and degree, the brain perceives a flash of light.

In this chapter, we examine sensory systems, primarily in vertebrates. We also compare some of these systems with their counterparts in invertebrates.

45.1 *Overview of Sensory Receptors*

When we think of sensory receptors, the senses of vision, hearing, taste, smell, and touch come to mind—the senses that provide information about our environment. Certainly this external information is crucial to the survival and success of animals, but sensory receptors also provide information about internal states, such as stretching of muscles, position of the body, and blood pressure. In this section, we take a general look at types of receptors and how they work.

Sensory receptors detect both external and internal stimuli

Exteroceptors are receptors that sense stimuli that arise in the external environment. Almost all of a vertebrate's exterior senses evolved in water before the invasion of land. Consequently, many senses of terrestrial vertebrates emphasize stimuli that travel well in water, using receptors that have been retained in the transition from sea to land. Mammalian hearing, for example, converts an airborne stimulus into a waterborne one, using receptors similar to those that originally evolved in the water.

A few vertebrate sensory systems that function well in the water, such as the electrical organs of fish, cannot function in the air and are not found among terrestrial vertebrates. In contrast, some land-dwellers have sensory systems that could not function in water, such as infrared heat detectors.

Interoceptors sense stimuli that arise from within the body. These internal receptors detect stimuli related to muscle length and tension, limb position, pain, blood chemistry, blood volume and pressure, and body temperature. Many of these receptors are simpler than those that monitor the external environment and are believed to bear a closer resemblance to primitive sensory receptors. In the rest of this chapter, we consider the different types of exteroceptors and interoceptors according to the kind of stimulus each is specialized to detect.

Receptors can be grouped into three categories

Sensory receptors differ with respect to the nature of the environmental stimulus that best activates their sensory dendrites. Broadly speaking, we can recognize three classes of receptors:

1. **Mechanoreceptors** are stimulated by mechanical forces such as pressure. These include receptors for touch, hearing, and balance.

2. **Chemoreceptors** detect chemicals or chemical changes. The senses of smell and taste rely on chemoreceptors.
3. **Electromagnetic receptors** react to heat and light energy. The photoreceptors of the eyes that detect light are an example, as are the thermal receptors found in some reptiles.

The simplest sensory receptors are free nerve endings that respond to bending or stretching of the sensory neuron's membrane to changes in temperature or to chemicals such as oxygen in the extracellular fluid. Other sensory receptors are more complex, involving the association of the sensory neurons with specialized epithelial cells.

Sensory information is conveyed in a four-step process

Sensory information picked up by sensory neurons is conveyed to the CNS, where the impulses are perceived in a four-step process (figure 45.1):

1. *Stimulation.* A physical stimulus impinges on a sensory neuron or an associated, but separate, sensory receptor.
2. *Transduction.* The stimulus energy is transformed into graded potentials in the dendrites of the sensory neuron.
3. *Transmission.* Action potentials develop in the axon of the sensory neuron and are conducted to the CNS along an afferent nerve pathway.
4. *Interpretation.* The brain creates a sensory perception from the electrochemical events produced by afferent stimulation. We actually perceive the five senses with our brains, not with our sense organs.

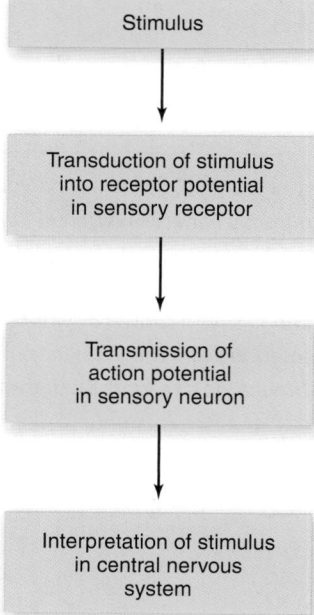

Figure 45.1 The path of sensory information. Sensory stimuli are transduced into receptor potentials, which can trigger sensory neuron action potentials that are conducted to the brain for interpretation.

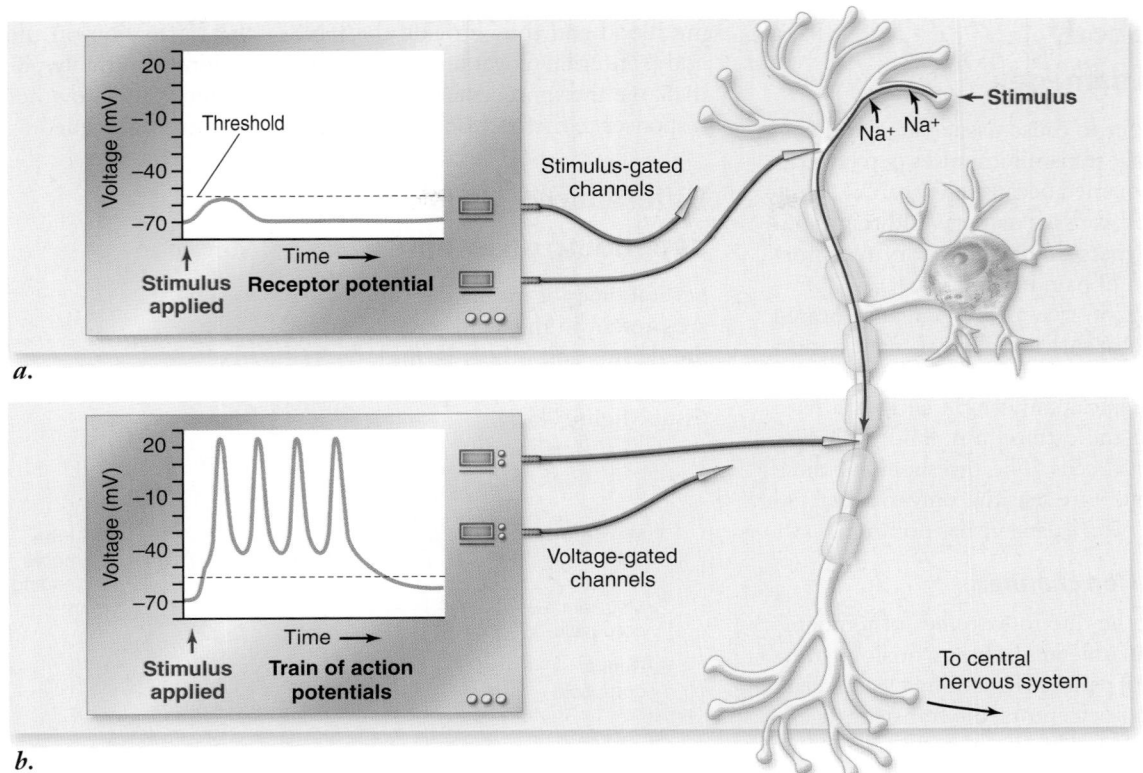

Figure 45.2 Events in sensory transduction.
a. Depolarization of a free nerve ending leads to a receptor potential that spreads by local current flow to the axon. *b.* Action potentials are produced in the axon in response to a sufficiently large receptor potential.

Sensory transduction involves gated ion channels

Sensory cells respond to stimuli because they possess **stimulus-gated ion channels** in their membranes. The sensory stimulus causes these ion channels to open or close, depending on the sensory system involved. In most cases, the sensory stimulus produces a depolarization of the receptor cell, analogous to the excitatory postsynaptic potential (EPSP, described in chapter 44) produced in a postsynaptic cell in response to a neurotransmitter. A depolarization that occurs in a sensory receptor on stimulation is referred to as a *receptor potential* (figure 45.2*a*).

Like an EPSP, a receptor potential is a graded potential: The larger the sensory stimulus, the greater the degree of depolarization. Receptor potentials also decrease in size with distance from their source. This prevents small, irrelevant stimuli from reaching the cell body of the sensory neuron. If the receptor potential or the summation of receptor potentials is great enough to generate a threshold level of depolarization, an action potential is produced that propagates along the sensory axon into the CNS (figure 45.2*b*).

The greater the sensory stimulus, the greater the depolarization of the receptor potential and the higher the frequency of action potentials. (Remember that frequency of action potentials, not their summation, is responsible for conveying the intensity of the stimulus.)

Generally, a logarithmic relationship exists between stimulus intensity and action potential frequency—for example, a particular sensory stimulus that is 10 times greater than another sensory stimulus produces action potentials at twice the frequency of the other stimulus. This relationship allows the CNS to interpret the strength of a sensory stimulus based on the frequency of incoming signals.

Learning Outcomes Review 45.1

Sensory receptors include mechanoreceptors, chemoreceptors, and electromagnetic energy-detecting receptors. The four steps by which information is conveyed to the CNS are stimulation, transduction, transmission, and interpretation in the CNS. Gated ion channels open or close in response to stimuli, altering membrane potential; if this change exceeds a threshold, an action potential is generated.

■ *Why is the relationship between intensity of stimulus and frequency of action potentials said to be logarithmic?*

45.2 Mechanoreceptors: Touch and Pressure

Learning Outcomes

1. *Explain how mechanoreceptors detect touch.*
2. *Distinguish between nociceptors, thermoreceptors, proprioceptors, and baroreceptors.*

Although the receptors of the skin, called the cutaneous receptors, are classified as interoceptors, they in fact respond to stimuli at the border between the external and internal environments. These receptors serve as good examples of the specialization of receptor structure and function, responding to pain, heat, cold, touch, and pressure.

Pain receptors alert the body to damage or potential damage

A stimulus that causes or is about to cause tissue damage is perceived as pain. The receptors that transmit impulses perceived as pain are called **nociceptors,** so named because they can be sensitive to noxious substances as well as tissue damage. Although specific nociceptors exist, many hyperstimulated sensory receptors can also produce the perception of pain in the brain.

Most nociceptors consist of free nerve endings located throughout the body, especially near surfaces where damage is most likely to occur. Different nociceptors may respond to extremes in temperature, very intense mechanical stimulation such as a hard impact, or specific chemicals in the extracellular fluid, including some that are released by injured cells. The thresholds of these sensory cells vary; some nociceptors are sensitive only to actual tissue damage, but others respond before damage has occurred.

Transient receptor potential ion channels

One kind of tissue damage can be due to extremes of temperature, and in this case the molecular details of how a noxious stimulus can result in the sensation of pain are becoming clear. A class of ion channel protein found in nociceptors, the transient receptor potential (TRP) ion channel, can be stimulated by temperature to produce an inward flow of cations, primarily Na^+ and Ca^{2+}. This depolarizing current causes the sensory neuron to fire, leading to the release of glutamate and an EPSP in neurons in the spinal cord, ultimately producing the pain response.

TRP channels that respond to both hot and cold have been found. Differences have also been found in the sensitivity of TRP channels to the degree of temperature change, with some responding only to temperature changes that damage tissues and others that respond to milder changes. Thus, we can respond to the feelings of hot and cold as well as feel pain associated with extremes of hot and cold.

The first such TRP channel identified responds to the chemical capsaicin, found in chili peppers, as well as to heat. This explains the sensation of heat we feel when we eat chili peppers, as well as the associated pain! A cold-responsive TRP receptor also responds to the chemical menthol, explaining how this substance is perceived as "cold." Chemical stimulation of TRP channels can reduce the body's pain response by desensitizing the sensory neuron. This analgesic response is why menthol is found in cough drops.

Thermoreceptors detect changes in heat energy

The skin contains two populations of **thermoreceptors,** which are naked dendritic endings of sensory neurons that are sensitive to changes in temperature. (Nociceptors are similar in that they consist of free nerve endings.) These thermoreceptors contain TRP ion channels that are responsive to hot and cold.

Cold receptors are stimulated by a fall in temperature and are inhibited by warming, whereas warm receptors are stimulated by a rise in temperature and inhibited by cooling. Cold receptors are located immediately below the epidermis; they are three to four times more numerous than are warm receptors. Warm receptors are typically located slightly deeper, in the dermis.

Thermoreceptors are also found within the hypothalamus of the brain, where they monitor the temperature of the circulating blood and thus provide the CNS with information on the body's internal (core) temperature. Information from the hypothalamic thermoreceptors alter metabolism and stimulate other responses to increase or decrease core temperature as needed.

Different receptors detect touch, depending on intensity

Several types of mechanoreceptors are present in the skin, some in the dermis and others in the underlying subcutaneous tissue (figure 45.3).

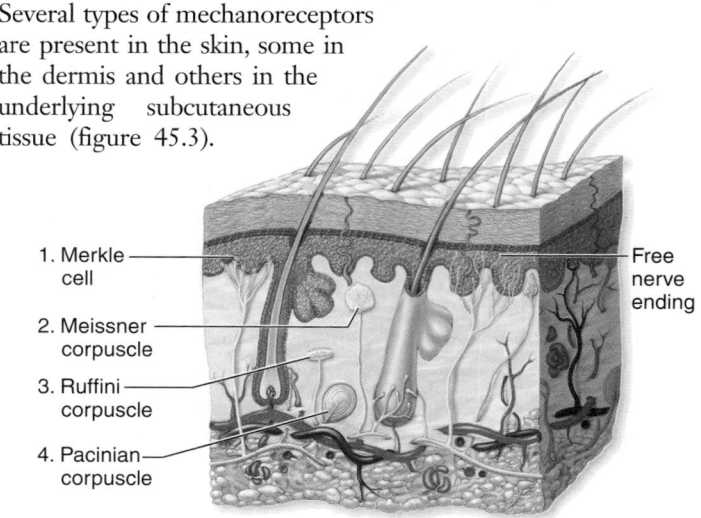

1. Merkle cell
2. Meissner corpuscle
3. Ruffini corpuscle
4. Pacinian corpuscle
Free nerve ending

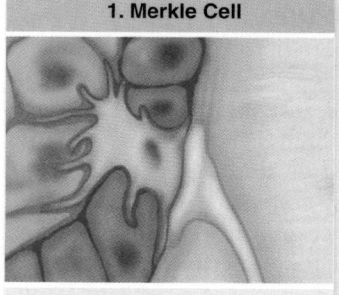

1. Merkle Cell

Tonic receptors located near the surface of the skin that are sensitive to touch pressure and duration.

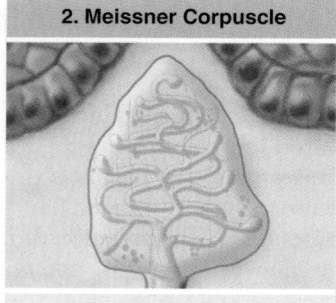

2. Meissner Corpuscle

Phasic receptors sensitive to fine touch, concentrated in hairless skin.

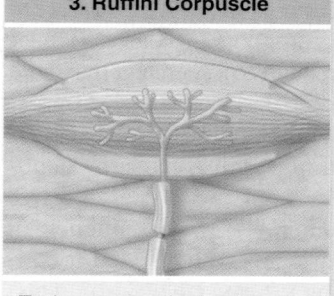

3. Ruffini Corpuscle

Tonic receptors located near the surface of the skin that are sensitive to touch pressure and duration.

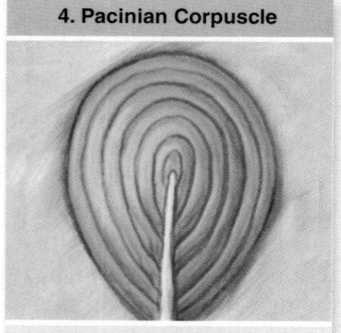

4. Pacinian Corpuscle

Pressure-sensitive phasic receptors deep below the skin in the subcutaneous tissue.

Figure 45.3 Sensory receptors in human skin.
Cutaneous receptors may be free nerve endings or sensory dendrites in association with other supporting structures.

These receptors contain sensory cells with ion channels that open in response to mechanical distortion of the membrane. They detect various forms of physical contact, known as the sense of touch.

Morphologically specialized receptors that respond to fine touch are most concentrated on areas such as the fingertips and face. They are used to localize cutaneous stimuli very precisely. These receptors can be either phasic (intermittently activated) or tonic (continuously activated). The phasic receptors include hair follicle receptors and Meissner corpuscles, which are present on surfaces that do not contain hair, such as the fingers, palms, and nipples.

The tonic receptors consist of Ruffini corpuscles in the dermis and touch dome endings (Merkel's disks) located near the surface of the skin. These receptors monitor the duration of a touch and the extent to which it is applied.

Deep below the skin in the subcutaneous tissue lie phasic, pressure-sensitive receptors called Pacinian corpuscles. Each of these receptors consists of the end of an afferent axon surrounded by a capsule of alternating layers of connective tissue cells and extracellular fluid. When sustained pressure is applied to the corpuscle, the elastic capsule absorbs much of the pressure, and the axon ceases to produce impulses. Pacinian corpuscles thus monitor only the onset and removal of pressure, as may occur repeatedly when something that vibrates is placed against the skin.

Muscle length and tension are monitored by proprioceptors

Buried within the skeletal muscles of all vertebrates except the bony fishes are **muscle spindles,** sensory stretch receptors that lie in parallel with the rest of the fibers in the muscle (figure 45.4). Each spindle consists of several thin muscle fibers wrapped together and innervated by a sensory neuron, which becomes activated when the muscle, and therefore the spindle, is stretched.

Muscle spindles, together with other receptors in tendons and joints, are known as **proprioceptors.** These sensory receptors provide information about the relative position or movement of the animal's body parts. The sensory neurons conduct action potentials into the spinal cord, where they synapse with somatic motor neurons that innervate the muscle. This pathway constitutes the muscle stretch reflex, including the knee-jerk reflex mentioned in chapter 44. When the muscle is briefly stretched by tapping the patellar ligament with a rubber mallet, the muscle spindle apparatus is also stretched. The spindle apparatus is embedded within the muscle, and, like the muscle fibers outside the spindle, is stretched along with the muscle. The result is the action potential that activates the somatic motor neurons and causes the leg to jerk.

When a muscle contracts, it exerts tension on the tendons attached to it. The **Golgi tendon organs,** another type of proprioceptor, monitor this tension. If it becomes too high, they elicit a reflex that inhibits the motor neurons innervating the muscle. This reflex helps ensure that muscles do not contract so strongly that they damage the tendons to which they are attached.

Baroreceptors detect blood pressure

Blood pressure is monitored at two main sites in the body. One is the carotid sinus, an enlargement of the left and right internal

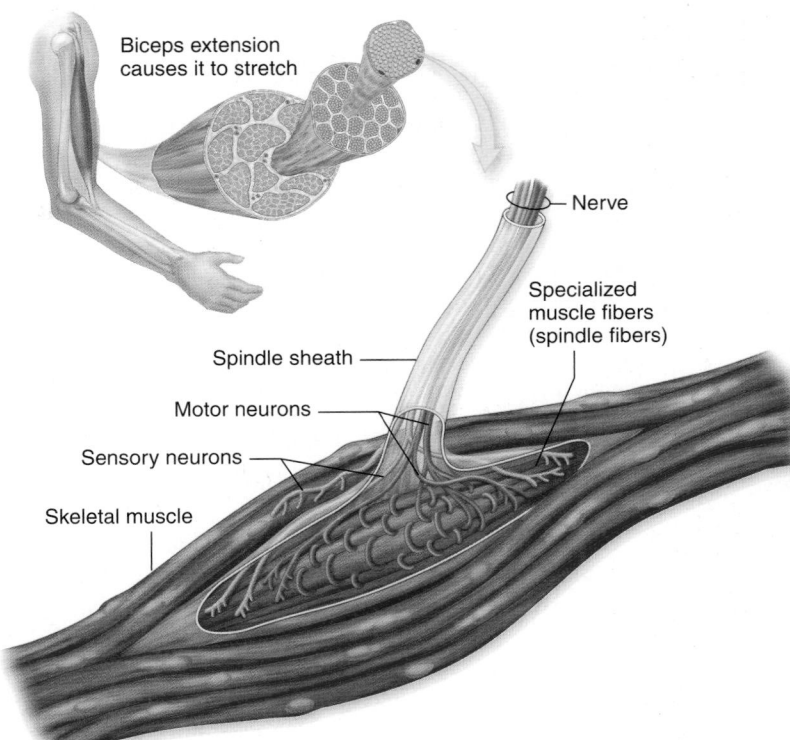

Figure 45.4 How a muscle spindle works. A muscle spindle is a stretch receptor embedded within skeletal muscle. Stretching of the muscle elongates the spindle fibers and stimulates the sensory dendritic endings wrapped around them. This causes the sensory neurons to send impulses to the CNS, where they synapse with interneurons and, in some cases, motor neurons.

carotid arteries that supply blood to the brain. The other is the aortic arch, the portion of the aorta very close to its emergence from the heart. The walls of the blood vessels at both sites contain a highly branched network of afferent neurons called baroreceptors, which detect tension or stretch in the walls.

When the blood pressure decreases, the frequency of impulses produced by the baroreceptors decreases. The CNS responds to this reduced input by stimulating the sympathetic division of the autonomic nervous system, causing an increase in heart rate and vasoconstriction. Both effects help raise the blood pressure, thus maintaining homeostasis. A rise in blood pressure increases baroreceptor impulses, which conversely reduces sympathetic activity and stimulates the parasympathetic division, slowing the heart and lowering the blood pressure.

Learning Outcomes Review 45.2

Mechanical distortion of the plasma membrane of mechanoreceptors produces nerve impulses. Nociceptors detect damage or potential damage to tissues and cause pain; thermoreceptors sense changes in heat energy; proprioceptors monitor muscle length; and baroreceptors monitor blood pressure within arteries.

■ *Why is it important to detect stretching of muscles?*

Learning Outcomes

1. Explain how sound waves in the environment lead to production of action potentials in the inner ear.
2. Describe how hearing differs between aquatic and terrestrial animals.
3. Describe how body position and movement are detected by hearing-associated structures.

Hearing, the detection of sound waves, actually works better in water than in air because water transmits pressure waves more efficiently. Despite this limitation, hearing is widely used by terrestrial vertebrates to monitor their environments, communicate with other members of their species, and detect possible sources of danger.

Sound is a result of vibration, or waves, traveling through a medium, such as water or air. Detection of sound waves is possible through the action of specialized mechanoreceptors that first evolved in aquatic organisms. The cells that are involved in the detection of sound are also evolutionarily related to the gravity-sensing systems discussed in the end of this section.

The lateral line system in fish detects low-frequency vibrations

In addition to hearing, the lateral line system in fish provides a sense of "distant touch," enabling them to sense objects that reflect pressure waves and low-frequency vibrations. This enables a fish to detect prey, for example, and to swim in synchrony with the rest of its school. It also enables a blind cave fish to sense its environment by monitoring changes in the patterns of water flow past the lateral line receptors.

The lateral line system is found in amphibian larvae, but is lost at metamorphosis and is not present in any terrestrial

vertebrate. The sense provided by the lateral line system supplements the fish's sense of hearing, which is performed by the sensory structures in their ears.

The lateral line system consists of hair cells within a longitudinal canal in the fish's skin that extends along each side of the body and within several canals in the head (figure 45.5a). The hair cells' surface processes project into a gelatinous membrane called a cupula. The hair cells are innervated by sensory neurons that transmit impulses to the brain.

Hair cells have several hairlike processes, called stereocilia, and one longer process called a **kinocilium** (figure 45.5b). The stereocilia are actually microvilli containing actin fibers, and the kinocilium is a true cilium that contains microtubules. Vibrations carried through the fish's environment produce movements of the cupula, which cause the processes to bend. When the stereocilia bend in the direction of the kinocilium, the associated sensory neurons are stimulated and generate a receptor potential. As a result, the frequency of action potentials produced by the sensory neuron is increased. In contrast, if the stereocilia are bent in the opposite direction, then the activity of the sensory neuron is inhibited.

Ear structure is specialized to detect vibration

The structure of the ear allows pressure waves to be transduced into nerve impulses based on mechanosensory cells like those in the lateral line system. We will first consider the structure of the ear in fish, which is related to the lateral line system that senses pressure waves in water. Then we will consider how the structure of the ear of terrestrial vertebrates allows the sensing of pressure waves in air.

Hearing structures in fish

Sound waves travel through the body of a fish as easily as through the surrounding water because the fish's body is composed primarily of water. For sound to be detected, therefore, an object of different density is needed. In many fish, this function is served by the **otoliths**, literally "ear rocks," composed of calcium carbonate crystals. Otoliths are contained in the otolith organs of the membranous **labyrinth**, a system of fluid-filled chambers and tubes also present in other vertebrates. When

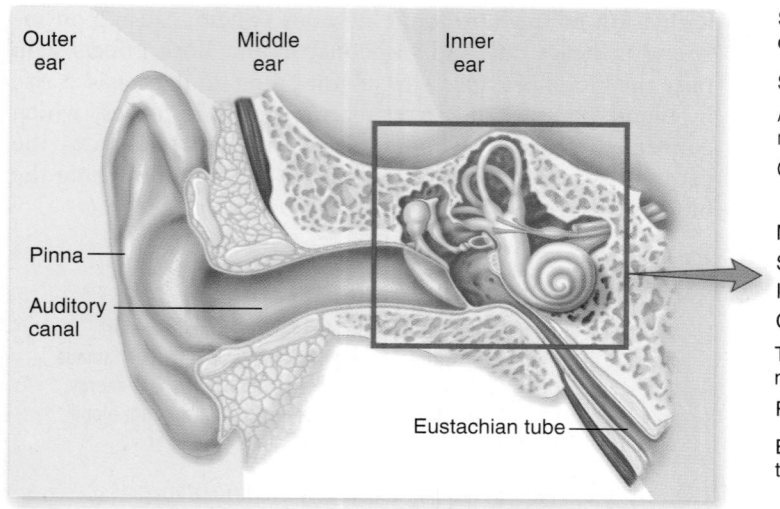

Outer ear · Middle ear · Inner ear

Pinna

Auditory canal

Eustachian tube

a.

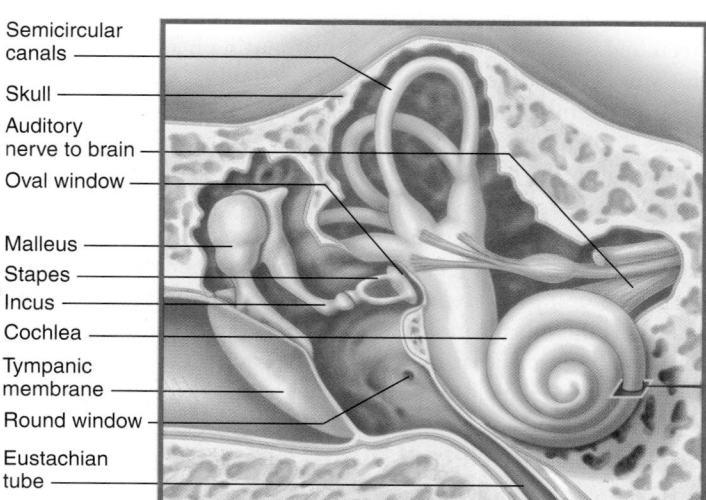

Semicircular canals

Skull

Auditory nerve to brain

Oval window

Malleus

Stapes

Incus

Cochlea

Tympanic membrane

Round window

Eustachian tube

b.

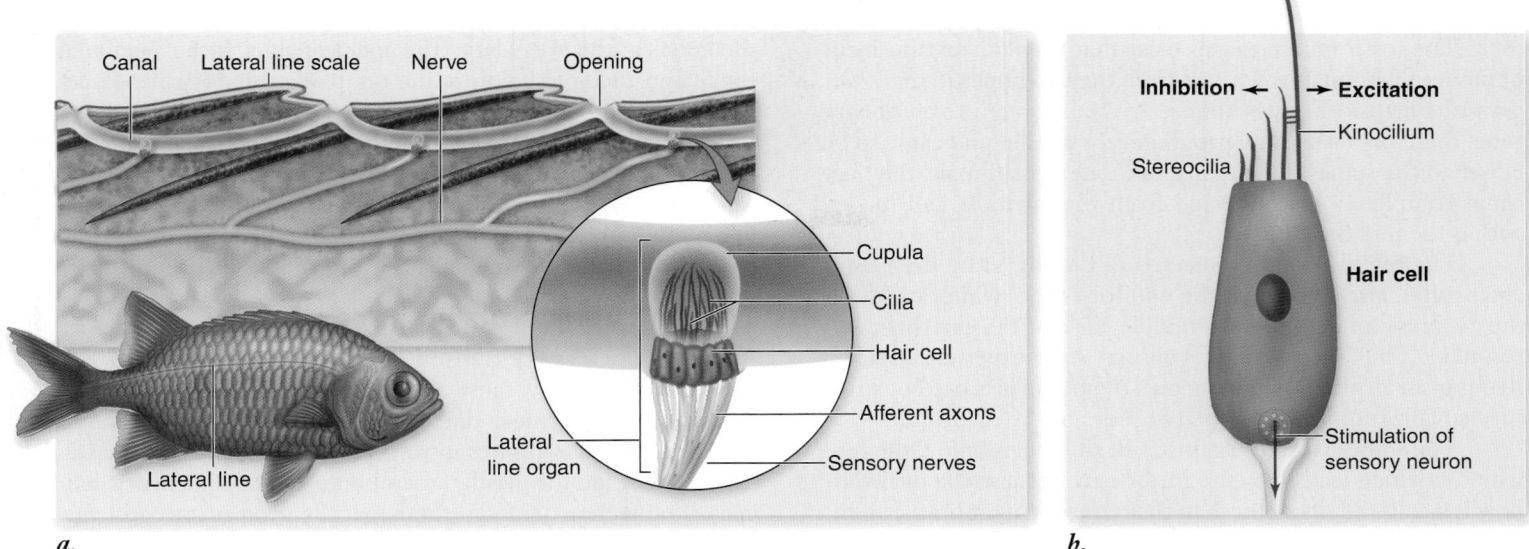

a.

b.

Figure 45.5 The lateral line system. *a.* This system consists of canals running the length of the fish's body beneath the surface of the skin. Within these canals are sensory structures containing hair cells with cilia that project into a gelatinous cupula. Pressure waves traveling through the water in the canals deflect the cilia and depolarize the sensory neurons associated with the hair cells. *b.* Hair cells are mechanoreceptors with hairlike cilia that project into a gelatinous membrane. The hair cells of the lateral line system (and the membranous labyrinth of the vertebrate inner ear) have a number of smaller cilia called stereocilia and one larger kinocilium. When the cilia bend in the direction of the kinocilium, the hair cell releases a chemical transmitter that depolarizes the associated sensory neuron. Bending of the cilia in the opposite direction has an inhibitory effect.

Inquiry question

? How would the lateral line system of a shark detect an injured and thrashing fish?

otoliths in fish vibrate against hair cells in the otolith organ, action potentials are produced. Hair cells are so-called because of the stereocilia that project from their surface.

Hearing structures of terrestrial vertebrates

In the ears of terrestrial vertebrates, vibrations in air may be channeled through an ear canal to the eardrum, or tympanic membrane. These structures are part of the **outer ear.** Vibrations of the tympanic membrane cause movement of one or more small bones that are located in a bony cavity known as the **middle ear.**

Amphibians and reptiles have a single middle ear bone, the **stapes** (stirrup), but mammals have two others: the **malleus** (hammer) and **incus** (anvil) (figure 45.6*a, b*). Where did these two additional bones come from?

Figure 45.6 Structure and function of the human ear. The structure of the human ear is shown in successive enlargements illustrating functional parts (*a* to *d*). Sound waves passing through the ear canal produce vibrations of the tympanic membrane, which causes movement of the middle-ear ossicles (the malleus, incus, and stapes) against an inner membrane (the oval window). This vibration creates pressure waves in the fluid in the vestibular and tympanic canals of the cochlea. These pressure waves cause cilia in hair cells to bend, producing signals from sensory neurons.

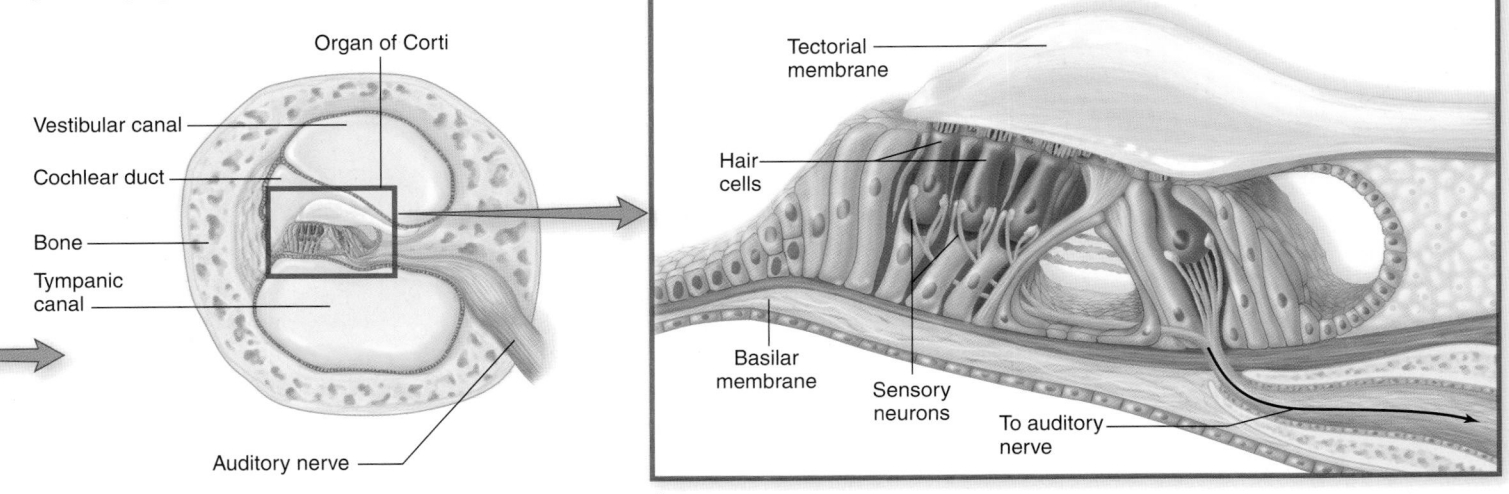

c.

d.

The fossil record makes clear that the malleus and incus of modern mammals is derived from the two bones in the lower jaws of synapsid reptiles (figure 45.7). Through evolutionary time, these bones became progressively smaller and came to lie closer to the stapes. Eventually, in modern mammals, they became completely disconnected from the jawbone and moved within the middle ear itself.

The middle ear is connected to the throat by the Eustachian tube, also known as the auditory tube, which equalizes the air pressure between the middle ear and the external environment. The "ear popping" you may have experienced when flying in an airplane or driving on a mountain is caused by pressure equalization between the two sides of the eardrum.

The stapes vibrates against a flexible membrane, the oval window, which leads into the **inner ear.** Because the oval window is smaller in diameter than the tympanic membrane, vibrations against it produce more force per unit area, transmitted into the inner ear. The inner ear consists of the **cochlea,** a bony structure containing part of the membranous labyrinth called the cochlear duct. The cochlear duct is located in the center of the cochlea; the area above the cochlear duct is the vestibular canal, and the area below is the tympanic canal (figure 45.6c). All three chambers are filled with fluid. The oval window opens to the upper vestibular canal, so that when the stapes causes it to vibrate, it produces pressure waves of fluid. These pressure waves travel down to the tympanic canal, pushing another flexible membrane, the round window, that transmits the pressure back into the middle ear cavity.

Transduction occurs in the cochlea

As pressure waves are transmitted through the cochlea to the round window, they cause the cochlear duct to vibrate. The bottom of the cochlear duct, called the basilar membrane, is quite flexible and vibrates in response to these pressure waves. The surface of the basilar membrane contains sensory hair cells. The stereocilia from the hair cells project into an overhanging gelatinous membrane, the tectorial membrane. This sensory apparatus, consisting of the basilar membrane, hair cells with associated sensory neurons, and tectorial membrane, is known as the organ of Corti (figure 45.6d).

Figure 45.7 Evolution of the mammalian inner ear. Two of the bones in the inner ear of modern mammals, the stapes and malleus, are derived from the quadrate and articular bones, respectively, of their reptilian ancestors. The transition from an early ancestor of mammals, a synapsid, through several transition forms, to a modern dog is illustrated. Note how the bones become smaller and change position, ultimately disappearing from the lower jaw entirely in modern mammals (represented by the dog) and becoming parts of the inner ear. During embryology in modern mammals, these bones develop in association with the lower jaw bone before moving inward to the inner ear, providing further evidence of their evolutionary origin.

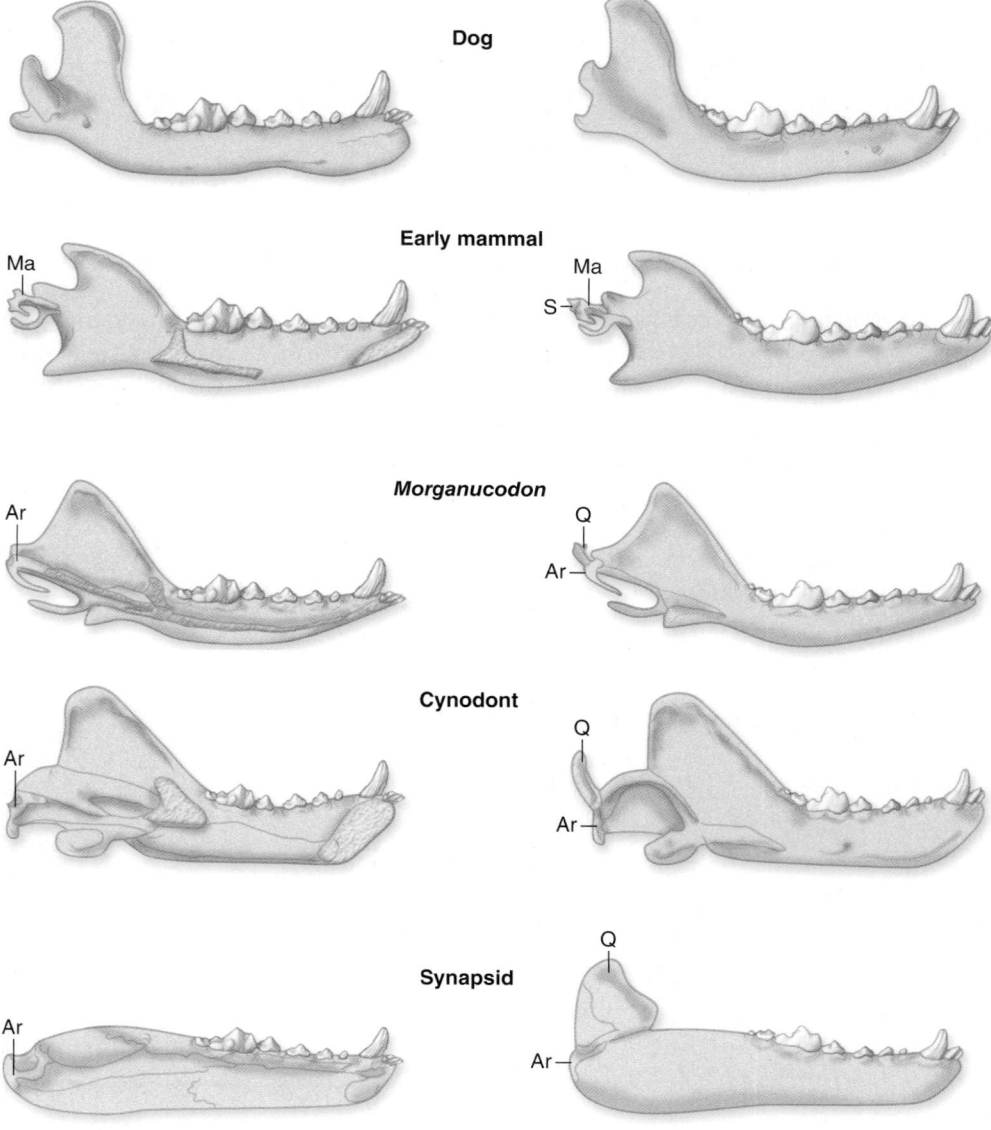

As the basilar membrane vibrates, the cilia of the hair cells bend in response to the movement of the basilar membrane relative to the tectorial membrane. The bending of these stereocilia in one direction depolarizes the hair cells. Bending in the opposite direction repolarizes or even hyperpolarizes the membrane. The hair cells, in turn, stimulate the production of action potentials in sensory neurons that project to the brain, where they are interpreted as sound.

Frequency localization in the cochlea

The basilar membrane of the cochlea consists of elastic fibers of varying length and stiffness, like the strings of a musical instrument, embedded in a gelatinous material. At the base of the cochlea (near the oval window), the fibers of the basilar membrane are short and stiff. At the far end of the cochlea (the apex), the fibers are 5 times longer and 100 times more flexible. Therefore, the resonant frequency of the basilar membrane is higher at the base than at the apex; the base responds to higher pitches, the apex to lower pitches.

When a wave of sound energy enters the cochlea from the oval window, it initiates an up-and-down motion that travels the length of the basilar membrane. However, this wave imparts most of its energy to that part of the basilar membrane with a resonant frequency near the frequency of the sound wave, resulting in a maximum deflection of the basilar membrane at that point (figure 45.8). As a result, the hair cell depolarization is greatest in that region, and the afferent axons from that region are stimulated more than those

of other regions. When these action potentials arrive in the brain, they are interpreted as representing a sound of a particular frequency, or pitch.

The range of terrestrial vertebrate hearing

The flexibility of the basilar membrane limits the frequency range of human hearing to between approximately 20 and 20,000 cycles per second (hertz, Hz) in children. Our ability to hear high-pitched sounds decays progressively throughout middle age. Other vertebrates can detect sounds at frequencies lower than 20 Hz and much higher than 20,000 Hz. Dogs, for example, can detect sounds at 40,000 Hz, enabling them to hear high-pitched dog whistles that seem silent to a human listener.

Hair cells are also innervated by efferent axons from the brain, and impulses in those axons can make hair cells less sensitive. This central control of receptor sensitivity can increase an individual's ability to concentrate on a particular auditory signal (for example, a single voice) in the midst of background noise, which is effectively "tuned out" by the efferent axons.

Some vertebrates have the ability to navigate by sound

Because terrestrial vertebrates have two ears located on opposite sides of the head, the information provided by hearing can be used to determine the direction of a sound source with some precision. Sound sources vary in strength, however, and sounds are weakened and reflected to varying degrees by the presence

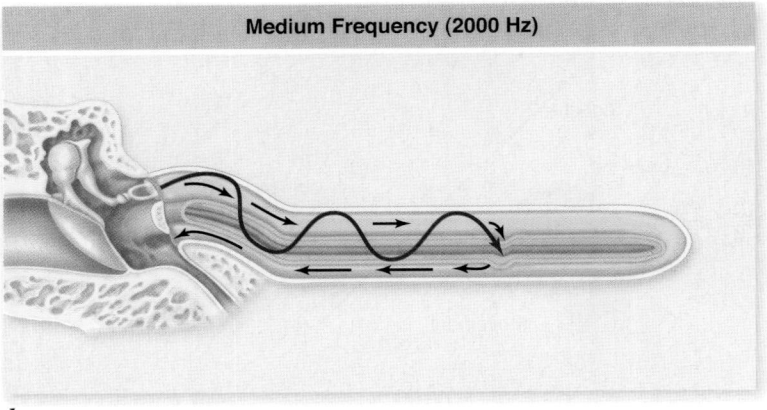

Figure 45.8 Frequency localization in the cochlea. The cochlea is shown unwound, so that the length of the basilar membrane can be seen. The fibers within the basilar membrane vibrate in response to different frequencies of sound, related to the pitch of the sound. Thus, regions of the basilar membrane show maximum vibrations in response to different sound frequencies. *a.* Notice that high-frequency (pitch) sounds vibrate the basilar membrane more toward the base whereas medium frequencies (*b*) and low frequencies (*c*) cause vibrations more toward the apex.

a.

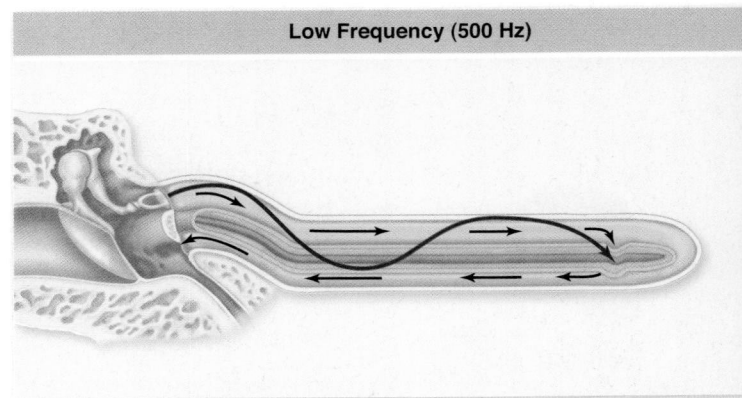

b.

c.

of objects in the environment. For these reasons, auditory sensors do not provide a reliable measure of distance.

A few groups of mammals that live and obtain their food in dark environments have circumvented the limitations of darkness. A bat flying in a completely dark room easily avoids objects placed in its path—even a wire less than a millimeter in diameter. Shrews use a similar form of "lightless vision" beneath the ground, as do whales and dolphins beneath the sea. All of these mammals are able to perceive presence and distance of objects by sound.

These mammals emit sounds and then determine the time it takes these sounds to reach an object and return to the animal. This process is called **echolocation.** A bat, for example, produces clicks that last 2 to 3 ms and are repeated several hundred times per second. By calculating the time each click takes to hit an object and return, bats can calculate the location, direction of movement, and speed of objects in their environment. The human inventions sonar and radar are based on the same principles of echolocation.

The three-dimensional imaging achieved with such an auditory sonar system is quite sophisticated. Bats can track and intercept rapidly maneuvering aerial prey and can distinguish one type of insect from another.

Body position and movement are detected by systems associated with hearing systems

The evolutionary strategy of using internal calcium carbonate crystals as a way to detect vibration has also allowed the development of sensory organs that detect body position in space and movements such as acceleration.

Most invertebrates can orient themselves with respect to gravity due to a sensory structure called a **statocyst.** Statocysts generally consist of ciliated hair cells with the cilia embedded in a gelatinous membrane containing crystals of calcium carbonate. These stones, or statoliths, increase the mass of the gelatinous membrane so that it can bend the cilia when the animal's position changes. If the animal tilts to the right, for example, the statolith membrane bends the cilia on the right side and activates associated sensory neurons.

A similar structure is found in the membranous labyrinth of the inner ear of vertebrates. This labyrinth is surrounded by bone and perilymph, which is similar in ionic content to interstitial fluid. Inside, the chambers and tubes are filled with endolymph fluid, which is similar in ionic content to intracellular fluid. Though intricate, the entire structure is very small; in a human, it is about the size of a pea.

Structure of the labyrinth and semicircular canals

The receptors for gravity in most vertebrates consist of two chambers of the membranous labyrinth called the **utricle** and **saccule** (figure 45.9). Within these structures are hair cells with stereocilia and a kinocilium, similar to those in the lateral line system of fish. The hairlike processes are embedded within a gelatinous membrane, the otolith membrane, containing calcium carbonate crystals. Because the otolith organ is oriented differently in the utricle and saccule, the utricle is more sensitive to

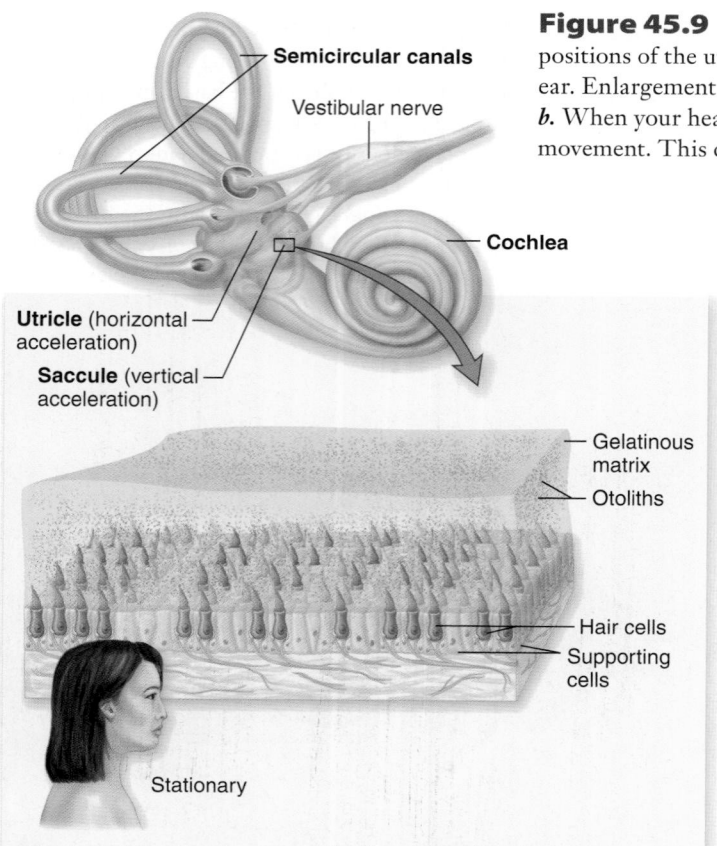

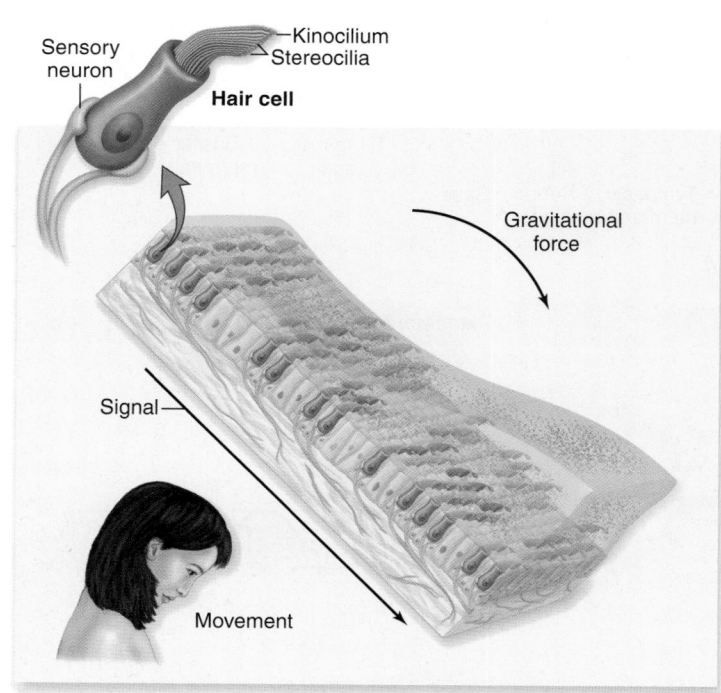

Figure 45.9 **Structure and function of the utricle and saccule.** *a.* The relative positions of the utricle and saccule within the membranous labyrinth of the human inner ear. Enlargement shows the gelatinous matrix containing otoliths covering hair cells. *b.* When your head bends forward, gravity distorts the matrix in the direction of movement. This causes the stereocilia in hair cells to bend, stimulating sensory neurons.

horizontal acceleration (as in a moving car) and the saccule to vertical acceleration (as in an elevator). In both cases, the acceleration causes the stereocilia to bend, and consequently produces action potentials in an associated sensory neuron.

The membranous labyrinth of the utricle and saccule is continuous with three **semicircular canals,** oriented in different planes so that angular acceleration in any direction can be detected (figure 45.10). At the ends of the canals are swollen chambers called ampullae, into which protrude the cilia of another group of hair cells. The tips of the cilia are embedded within a sail-like wedge of gelatinous material called a cupula (similar to the cupula of the fish lateral line system) that protrudes into the endolymph fluid of each semicircular canal.

Action of the vestibular apparatus

When the head rotates, the fluid inside the semicircular canals pushes against the cupula and causes the cilia to bend. This bending either depolarizes or hyperpolarizes the hair cells, depending on the direction in which the cilia are bent. This is similar to the way the lateral line system works in a fish: If the stereocilia are bent in the direction of the kinocilium, a receptor potential is produced, which stimulates the production of action potentials in associated sensory neurons.

The saccule, utricle, and semicircular canals are collectively referred to as the **vestibular apparatus.** The saccule and utricle provide a sense of linear acceleration, and the semicircular canals provide a sense of angular acceleration. The brain uses information that comes from the vestibular apparatus about the body's position to maintain balance and equilibrium.

Learning Outcomes Review 45.3

Sound waves cause middle-ear ossicles to vibrate; fluid in the inner ear is vibrated in turn, bending hair cells and causing action potentials. In terrestrial animals, sound waves in air must transition to the fluid in the inner ear. Hair cells in the vestibular apparatus of terrestrial vertebrates provide a sense of acceleration and balance.

- **Why is a lateral line system not useful to adult amphibians?**

45.4 Chemoreceptors: Taste, Smell, and pH

Learning Outcomes

1. **List the five taste categories.**
2. **Describe how taste buds and olfactory neurons function.**

Some sensory cells, called chemoreceptors, contain membrane proteins that can bind to particular chemicals or ligands in the extracellular fluid. In response to this chemical interaction, the membrane of the sensory neuron becomes depolarized and produces action potentials. Chemoreceptors are used in the senses of taste and smell and are also important in monitoring the chemical composition of the blood and cerebrospinal fluid.

Figure 45.10 The structure of the semicircular canals. The position of the semicircular canals in relation to the rest of the inner ear. *a.* Enlargement of a section of one ampulla, showing how hair cell cilia insert into the cupula. *b.* Angular acceleration in the plane of one of the semicircular canals causes bending of the cupula, thereby stimulating the hair cells. Each inner ear contains three semicircular canals, one for each potential axis of rotation.

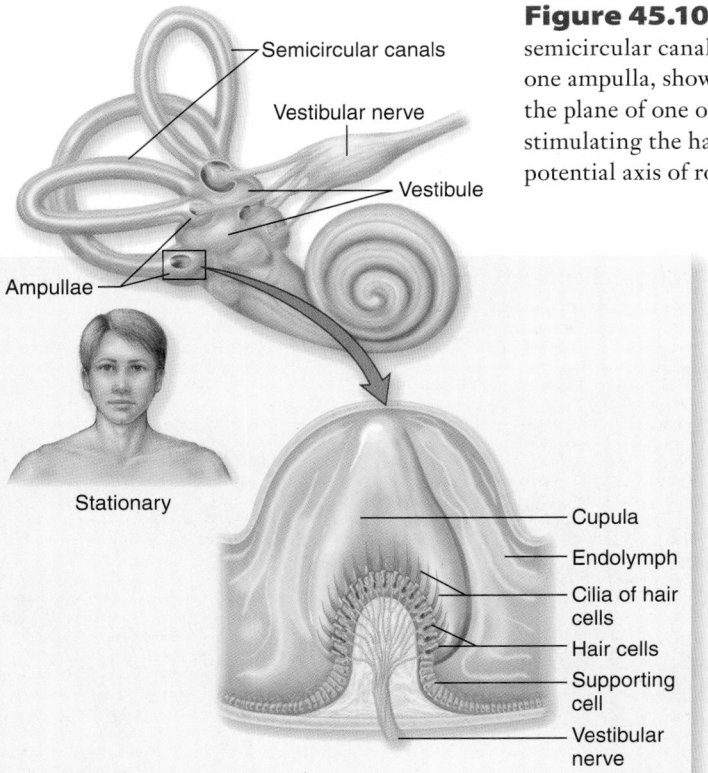

Semicircular canals
Vestibular nerve
Vestibule
Ampullae
Stationary
Cupula
Endolymph
Cilia of hair cells
Hair cells
Supporting cell
Vestibular nerve

a.

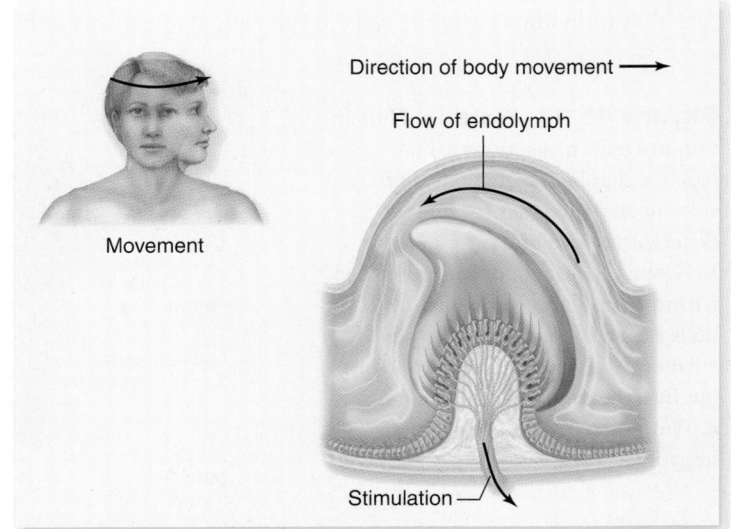

Direction of body movement →
Flow of endolymph
Movement
Stimulation

b.

Taste detects and analyzes potential food

The perception of taste (gustation), like the perception of color, is a combination of physical and psychological factors. This is commonly broken down into five categories: sweet, sour, salty, bitter, and umami (perception of glutamate and other amino acids that give a hearty taste to many protein-rich foods such as meat, cheese, and broths). Taste buds—collections of chemosensitive epithelial cells associated with afferent neurons—mediate the sense of taste in vertebrates. In a fish, the taste buds are scattered over the surface of the body. These are the most sensitive vertebrate chemoreceptors known. They are particularly sensitive to amino acids; a catfish, for example, can distinguish between two different amino acids at a concentration of less than 100 parts per billion (1 g in 10,000 L of water)! The ability to taste the surrounding water is very important to bottom-feeding fish, enabling them to sense the presence of food in an often murky environment.

The taste buds of all terrestrial vertebrates occur in the epithelium of the tongue and oral cavity, within raised areas called papillae (figure 45.11). Taste buds are onion-shaped structures of between 50 and 100 taste cells; each cell has fingerlike projections called microvilli that poke through the top of the taste bud, called the taste pore (figure 45.11c). Chemicals from food dissolve in saliva and contact the taste cells through the taste pore.

Within a taste bud, the chemicals that produce salty and sour tastes act directly through ion channels. The prototypical salty taste is due to Na^+ ions, which diffuse through Na^+ channels into cells in receptor cells in the taste bud. This Na^+ influx depolarizes the membrane, causing the receptor cell to release neurotransmitter and activate a sensory neuron that sends an impulse to the brain. The cells that detect sour taste act in a similar fashion except that the ion detected is H^+. Sour tastes are associated with increased concentration of protons that can also depolarize the membrane when they diffuse through ion channels.

The mechanism of detection of sweet, bitter, and umami are indirect. In this case substances that fall into these categories can bind to G protein–coupled receptors (see chapter 9) specific for each category. The nature and distribution of these receptors is an area of active investigation, but recent data indicate that individual receptor cells in the taste bud express only

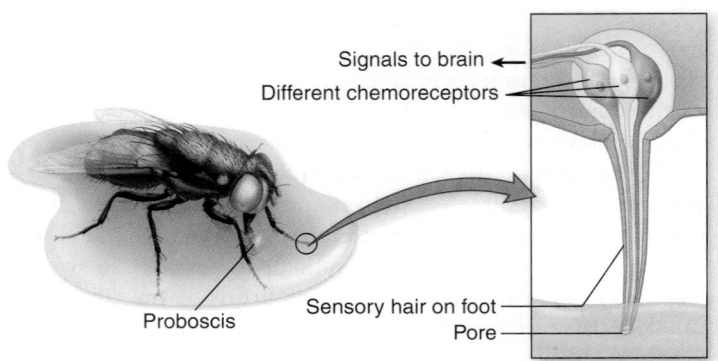

Figure 45.12 Many insects taste with their feet. In the blowfly shown here, chemoreceptors extend into the sensory hairs on the foot. Different chemoreceptors detect different types of food molecules. When the fly steps in a food substance, it can taste the different food molecules and extend its proboscis for feeding.

one type of receptor. This leads to cells that have receptors for sweet, for bitter or for umami tastes. Activation of any of these G protein–coupled receptors then stimulates a single signaling pathway that leads the release of neurotransmitter from receptor cells to activate a sensory neuron and send an impulse to the brain. There they interact with other sensory neurons carrying information related to smell, described next. In this model, the different tastes are encoded to the brain based on which receptor cells are activated.

Like vertebrates, many arthropods also have taste chemoreceptors. For example, flies, because of their mode of searching for food, have taste receptors in sensory hairs located on their feet. The sensory hairs contain a variety of chemoreceptors that are able to detect sugars, salts, and other tastes by the integration of stimuli from these chemoreceptors (figure 45.12). If they step on potential food, their proboscis (the tubular feeding apparatus) extends to feed.

Smell can identify a vast number of complex molecules

In terrestrial vertebrates, the sense of smell (olfaction) involves chemoreceptors located in the upper portion of the

Figure 45.11 Taste. *a.* Human tongues have projections called papillae that bear taste buds. Different sorts of taste buds are located on different regions of the tongue. *b.* Groups of taste buds are embedded within a papilla. *c.* Individual taste buds are bulb-shaped collections of chemosensitive receptors that open out into the mouth through a pore. *d.* Photomicrograph of taste buds in papillae.

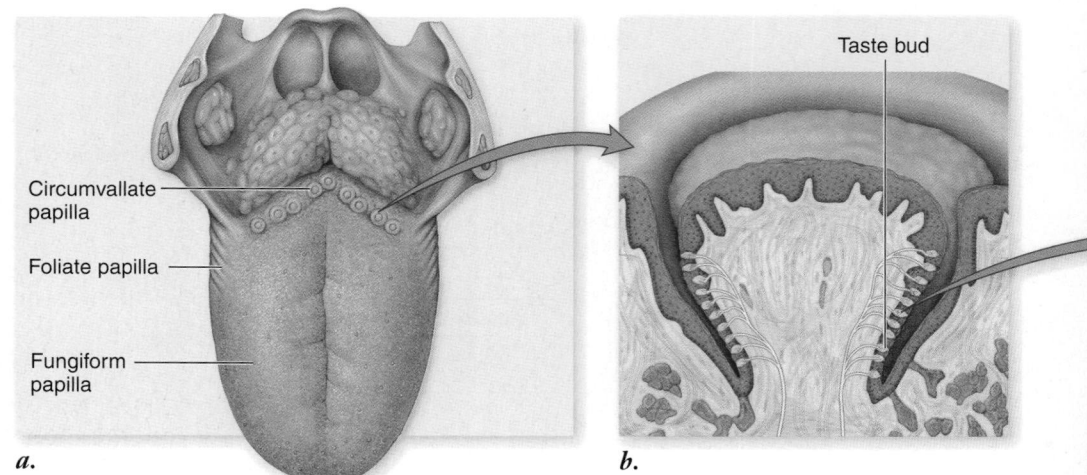

nasal passages (figure 45.13). These receptors, whose dendrites end in tassels of cilia, project into the nasal mucosa, and their axons project directly into the cerebral cortex. A terrestrial vertebrate uses its sense of smell in much the same way that a fish uses its sense of taste—to sample the chemical environment around it.

Because terrestrial vertebrates are surrounded by air, their sense of smell has become specialized to detect airborne particles—but these particles must first dissolve in extracellular fluid before they can activate the olfactory receptors. The sense of smell can be extremely acute in many mammals, so much so that a single odorant molecule may be all that is needed to excite a given receptor.

Although humans can detect only five modalities of taste, they can discern thousands of different smells. New research suggests that as many as a thousand different genes may code for different receptor proteins for smell. The particular set of olfactory neurons that respond to a given odor might serve as a "fingerprint" the brain can use to identify the odor.

Internal chemoreceptors detect pH and other characteristics

Sensory receptors within the body detect a variety of chemical characteristics of the blood or fluids derived from the blood, including cerebrospinal fluid. Included among these receptors are the **peripheral chemoreceptors** of the aortic and carotid bodies, which are sensitive primarily to plasma pH, and the **central chemoreceptors** in the medulla oblongata of the brain, which are sensitive to the pH of cerebrospinal fluid. When the breathing rate is too low, the concentration of plasma CO_2 increases, producing more carbonic acid and causing a fall in the blood pH. The carbon dioxide can also enter the cerebrospinal fluid and lower the pH, thereby stimulating the central chemoreceptors. This stimulation indirectly affects the respiratory control center of the brainstem, which increases the breathing rate. The aortic bodies can also respond to a lowering of blood oxygen concentrations, but this effect is normally not significant unless a person goes to a high altitude where the partial pressure of oxygen is lower.

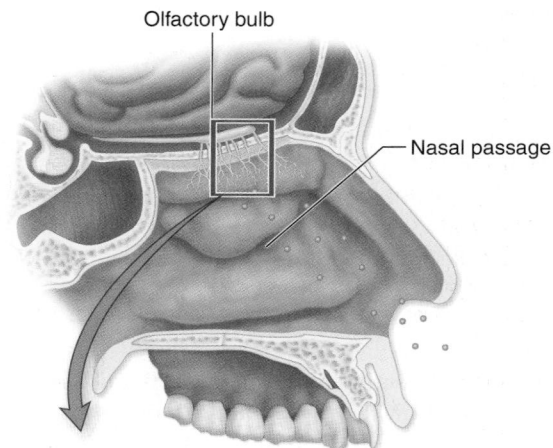

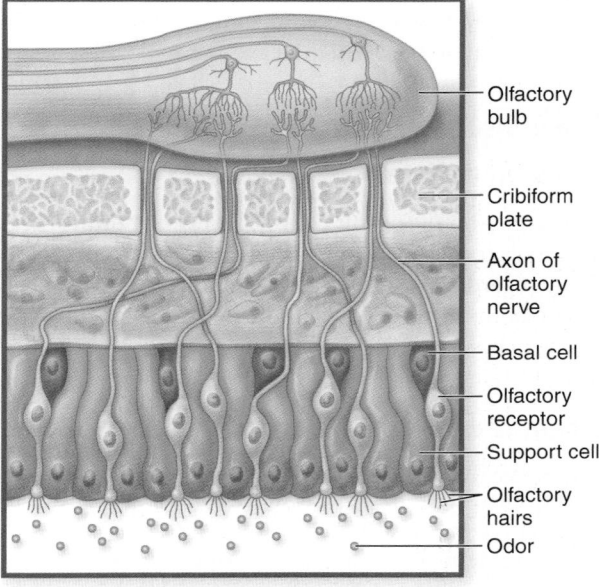

Figure 45.13 Smell. Humans detect smells by means of olfactory neurons (receptor cells) located in the lining of the nasal passages. The axons of these neurons transmit impulses directly to the brain via the olfactory nerve. Basal cells regenerate new olfactory neurons to replace dead or damaged cells. Olfactory neurons typically live about a month.

Inquiry question

? In what ways do the senses of taste and smell share similarities? How are they different?

Learning Outcomes Review 45.4

The five tastes humans perceive are sweet, sour, salty, bitter, and umami (amino acids). Taste and smell chemoreceptors detect chemicals from outside the body; olfactory receptors can identify thousands of different odors. Internal chemoreceptors monitor acid–base balance within the body and help regulate breathing.

■ *What are the advantages of insects' having taste receptors on their feet?*

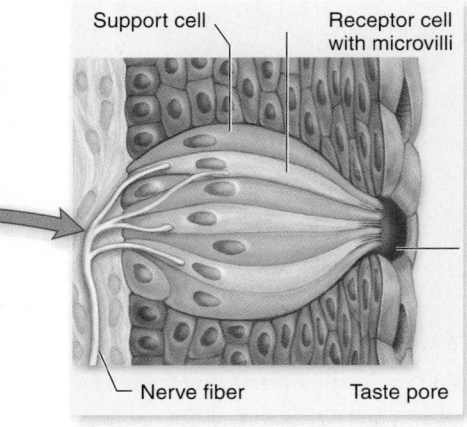

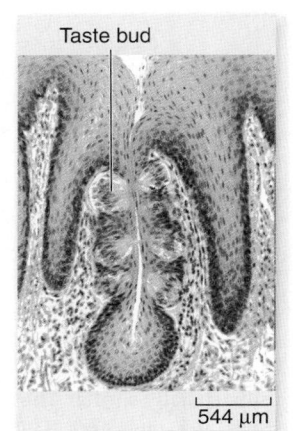

c.

d.

45.5 Vision

Learning Outcomes

1. Compare invertebrate and vertebrate eyes.
2. Explain how a vertebrate eye focuses an image.
3. Describe how photoreceptors function.

The ability to perceive objects at a distance is important to most animals. Predators locate their prey, and prey avoid their predators, based on the three long-distance senses of hearing, smell, and vision. Of these, vision can act most distantly; with the naked eye, humans can see stars thousands of light years away—and a single photon is sufficient to stimulate a cell of the retina to send an action potential.

Vision senses light and light changes at a distance

Vision begins with the capture of light energy by **photoreceptors.** Because light travels in a straight line and arrives virtually instantaneously regardless of distance, visual information can be used to determine both the direction and the distance of an object. Other stimuli, which spread out as they travel and move more slowly, provide much less precise information.

Invertebrate eyes

Many invertebrates have simple visual systems with photoreceptors clustered in an eyespot. Simple eyespots can be made sensitive to the direction of a light source by the addition of a pigment layer that shades one side of the eye. Flatworms have a screening pigmented layer on the inner and

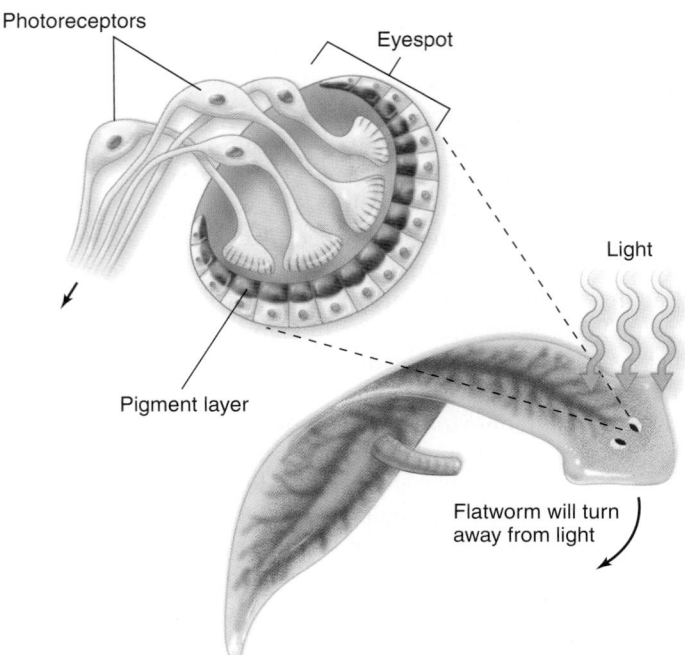

Figure 45.14 Simple eyespots in the flatworm. Eyespots can detect the direction of light because a pigmented layer on one side of the eyespot screens out light coming from the back of the animal. Light is thus detected more readily coming from the front of the animal; flatworms respond by turning away from the light.

back sides of both eyespots, allowing stimulation of the photoreceptor cells only by light from the front of the animal (figure 45.14). The flatworm will turn and swim in the direction in which the photoreceptor cells are the least stimulated. Although an eyespot can perceive the direction of light, it cannot be used to construct a visual image.

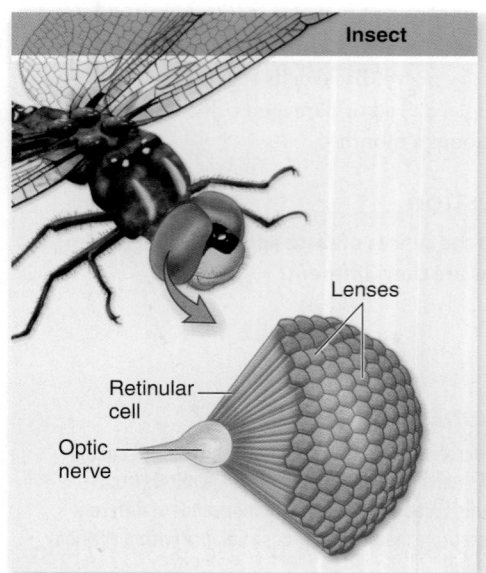

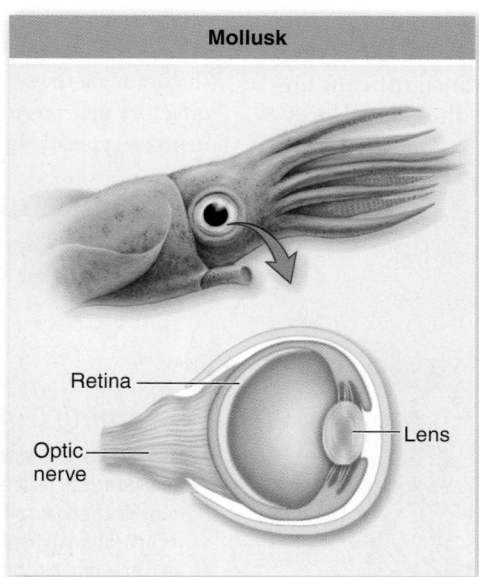

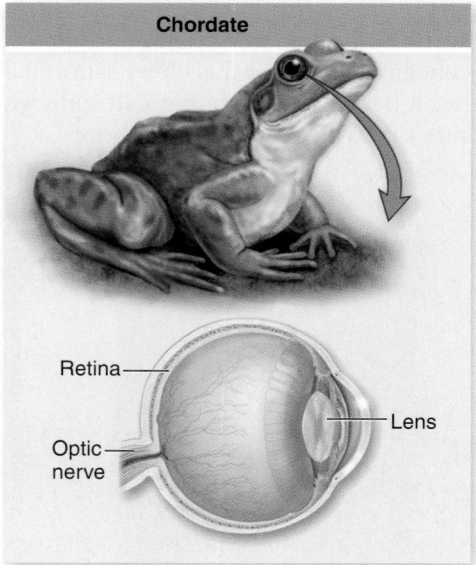

Figure 45.15 Eyes in three phyla of animals. Although they are superficially similar, these eyes differ greatly in structure from one another (see also figure 21.16 for a detailed comparison of mollusk and chordate eye structure). Each has evolved separately and, despite the apparent structural complexity, has done so from simpler structures.

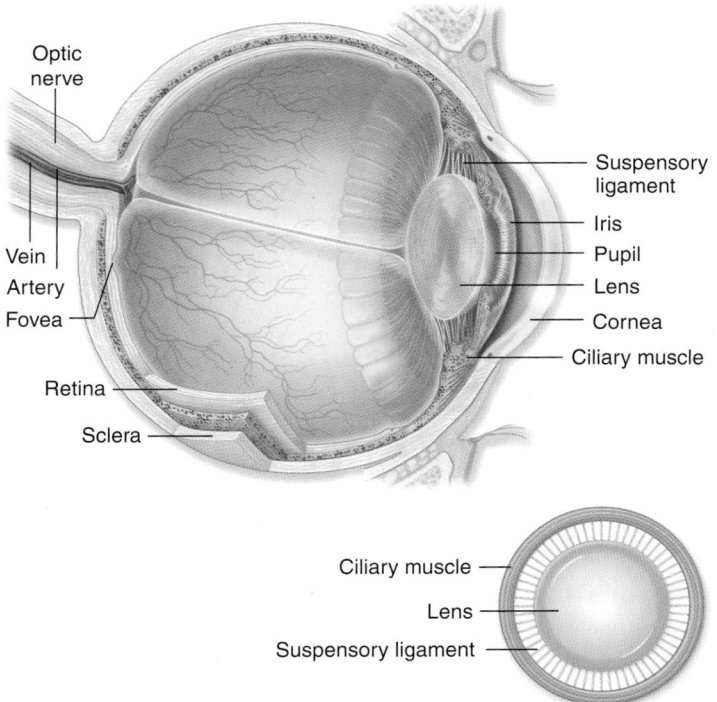

Figure 45.16 Structure of the human eye. The transparent cornea and lens focus light onto the retina at the back of the eye, which contains the photoreceptors (rods and cones). The center of each eye's visual field is focused on the fovea. Focusing is accomplished by contraction and relaxation of the ciliary muscle, which adjusts the curvature of the lens.

Inquiry question

? How does the human eye differ from the eye of a mollusk, and how do these differences create a blind spot?

The members of four phyla—annelids, mollusks, arthropods, and chordates—have evolved well-developed, image-forming eyes. True image-forming eyes in these phyla, although strikingly similar in structure, are believed to have evolved independently, an example of convergent evolution (figure 45.15). Interestingly, the photoreceptors in all of these image-forming eyes use the same light-capturing molecule, suggesting that not many alternative molecules are able to play this role.

Structure of the vertebrate eye

The human eye is typical of the vertebrate eye (figure 45.16). The "white of the eye" is the **sclera,** formed of tough connective tissue. Light enters the eye through a transparent **cornea,** which begins to focus the light. Focusing occurs because light is refracted (bent) when it travels into a medium of different density. The colored portion of the eye is the **iris;** contraction of the iris muscles in bright light decreases the size of its opening, the pupil. Light passes through the pupil to the **lens,** a transparent structure that completes the focusing of the light onto the retina at the back of the eye. The lens is attached by the suspensory ligament to the ciliary muscles.

The shape of the lens is influenced by the amount of tension in the suspensory ligament, which surrounds the lens and attaches it to the circular ciliary muscle. When the ciliary muscle contracts, it puts slack in the suspensory ligament, and the lens becomes more rounded and bends light more strongly. This rounding is required for close vision. In distance vision, the ciliary muscles relax, moving away from the lens and tightening the suspensory ligament. The lens thus becomes more flattened and bends light less, keeping the image focused on the retina. People who are nearsighted or farsighted do not properly focus the image on the retina (figure 45.17). Interestingly,

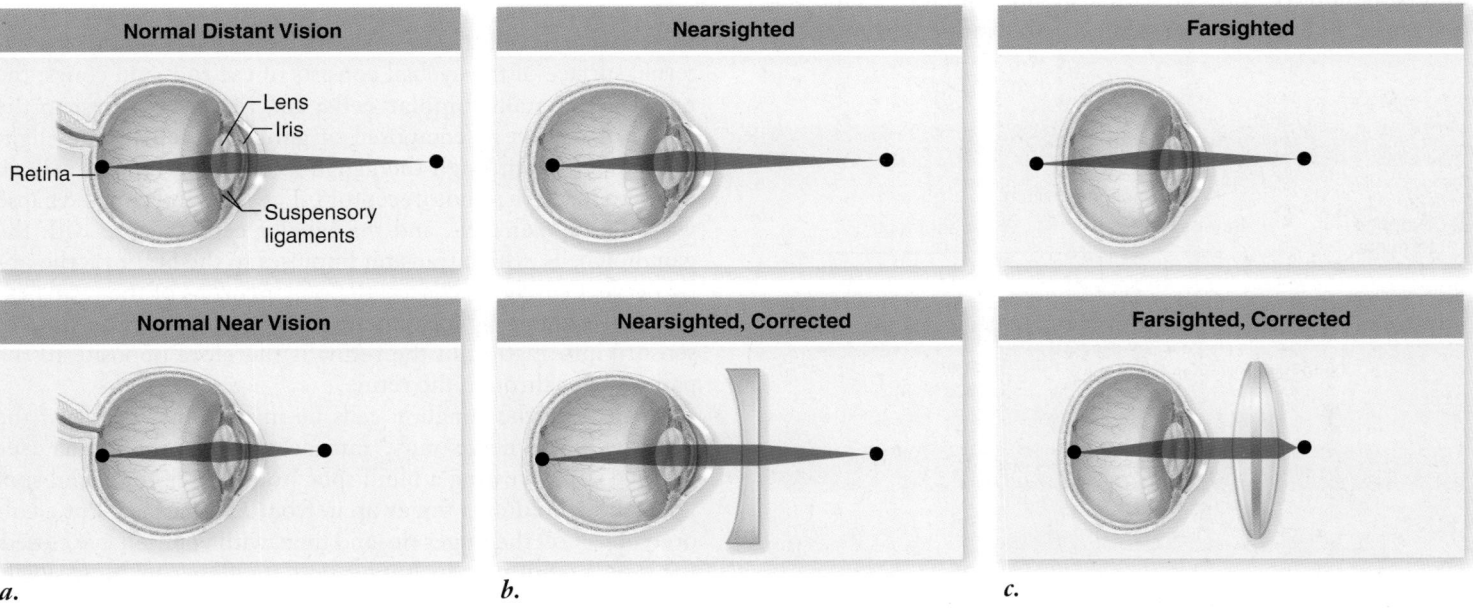

Figure 45.17 Focusing the human eye. *a.* In people with normal vision, the image remains focused on the retina in both near and far vision because of changes produced in the curvature of the lens. When a person with normal vision stands 20 feet or more from an object, the lens is in its least convex form, and the image is focused on the retina. *b.* In nearsighted people, the image comes to a focus in front of the retina, and the image thus appears blurred. *c.* In farsighted people, the focus of the image would be behind the retina because the distance from the lens to the retina is too short. Corrective lenses adjust the angle of the light as it enters the eye, focusing it on the retina.

the lens of an amphibian or a fish does not change shape; these animals instead focus images by moving their lens in and out, just as you would do to focus a camera.

Vertebrate photoreceptors are rod cells and cone cells

The vertebrate retina contains two kinds of photoreceptor cells, called rods and cones (figure 45.18). **Rods,** which get their name from the shape of their outer segment, are responsible for black-and-white vision when the illumination is dim. In contrast, **cones** are responsible for high visual acuity (sharpness) and color vision; cones have a cone-shaped outer segment. Humans have about 100 million rods and 3 million cones in each retina. Most of the cones are located in the central region of the retina known as the **fovea,** where the eye forms its sharpest image. Rods are almost completely absent from the fovea.

Structure of rods and cones

Rods and cones have the same basic cellular structure. An inner segment rich in mitochondria contains numerous vesicles filled with neurotransmitter molecules. It is connected by a narrow stalk to the outer segment, which is packed with hundreds of flattened disks stacked on top of one another. The light-capturing molecules, or photopigments, are located on the membranes of these disks (see figure 45.18).

In rods, the photopigment is called **rhodopsin.** It consists of the protein opsin bound to a molecule of *cis*-retinal, which is produced from vitamin A. Vitamin A is derived from carotene, a photosynthetic pigment in plants.

The photopigments of cones, called **photopsins,** are structurally very similar to rhodopsin. Humans have three kinds of cones, each of which possesses a photopsin consisting of *cis*-retinal bound to a protein with a slightly different amino acid sequence. These differences shift the absorption maximum, the

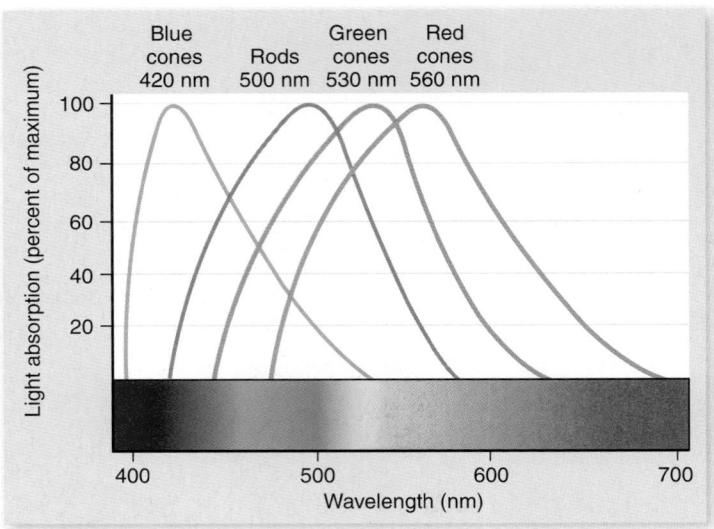

Figure 45.19 Color vision. The absorption maximum of *cis*-retinal in the rhodopsin of rods is 500 nm. However, the "blue cones" have their maximum light absorption at 420 nm; the "green cones" at 530 nm; and the "red cones" at 560 nm. The brain perceives all other colors from the combined activities of these three cones' systems.

region of the electromagnetic spectrum that is best absorbed by the pigment (figure 45.19). The absorption maximum of the *cis*-retinal in rhodopsin is 500 nanometers (nm); in contrast, the absorption maxima of the three kinds of cone photopsins are 420 nm (blue-absorbing), 530 nm (green-absorbing), and 560 nm (red-absorbing). These differences in the light-absorbing properties of the photopsins are responsible for the different color sensitivities of the three kinds of cones, which are often referred to as simply blue, green, and red cones.

The **retina,** the inside surface of the eye, is made up of three layers of cells (figure 45.20): The layer closest to the external surface of the eyeball consists of the rods and cones; the next layer contains **bipolar cells;** and the layer closest to the cavity of the eye is composed of **ganglion cells.** Thus, light must first pass through the ganglion cells and bipolar cells in order to reach the photoreceptors. The rods and cones synapse with the bipolar cells, and the bipolar cells synapse with the ganglion cells, which transmit impulses to the brain via the optic nerve. Ganglion cells are the only neurons of the retina capable of sending action potentials to the brain. The flow of sensory information in the retina is therefore opposite to the path of light through the retina.

Because the ganglion cells lie in the inner cavity of the eye, the optic nerve must intrude through the retina (see figure 45.16), creating a blind spot. You can see this blind spot yourself by holding a finger up in front of your face. Put a colored object on the finger tip, and then, with your left eye closed, focus on a point next to, but beyond, the fingertip. Now slowly move your finger to the right while keeping your eye focused on the distant point. At some point, you'll notice that you can no longer see the colored spot on your finger. The structure of the eye of mollusks avoids this problem by having the sensory neurons attach behind, rather than in front of, the retina (see figure 45.15).

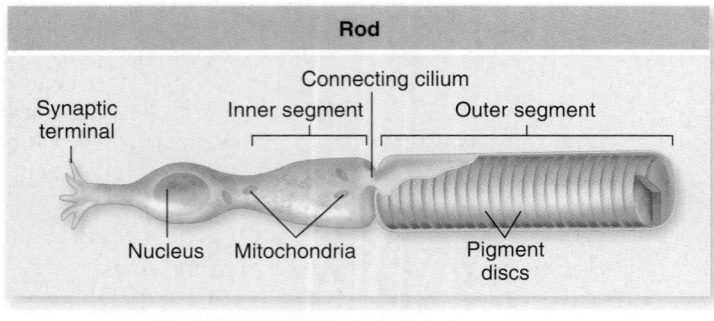

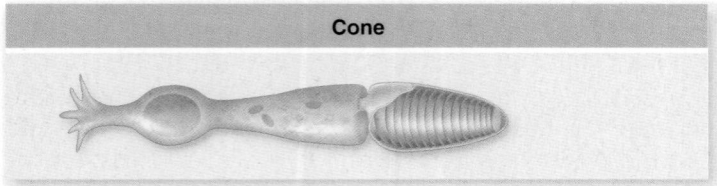

Figure 45.18 Rods and cones. The pigment-containing outer segment in each of these cells is separated from the rest of the cell by a partition through which there is only a narrow passage, the connecting cilium.

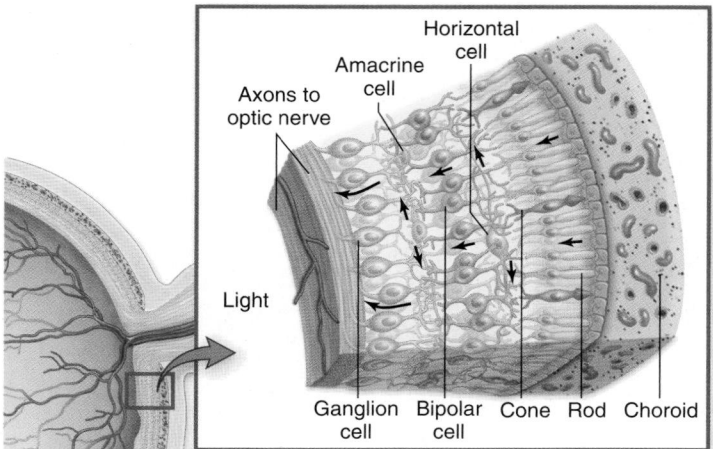

Figure 45.20 Structure of the retina. Note that the rods and cones are at the rear of the retina, not the front. Light passes through four other types of cells (ganglion, amacrine, bipolar, and horizontal) in the retina before it reaches the rods and cones. Once the photoreceptors are activated, they stimulate bipolar cells, which in turn stimulate ganglion cells. The flow of sensory information in the retina is thus opposite to the direction of light.

The retina contains two additional types of neurons called horizontal cells and amacrine cells. Stimulation of horizontal cells by photoreceptors at the center of a spot of light on the retina can inhibit the response of photoreceptors peripheral to the center. This lateral inhibition enhances contrast and sharpens the image.

Most vertebrates, particularly those that are diurnal (active during the day), have color vision, as do many insects and some other invertebrates. Indeed, honeybees—as well as some birds, lizards, and other vertebrates (figure 45.21)—can see light in the near-ultraviolet range, which is invisible to the human eye. Color vision requires the presence of more than one photopigment in different receptor cells, but not all animals with color vision have the three-cone system characteristic of humans and other primates. Fish, turtles, and birds, for example, have four or five kinds of cones; the "extra" cones enable these animals to see near-ultraviolet light and to distinguish shades of colors that we cannot detect. On the other hand, many mammals, for example, squirrels and dogs, have only two types of cones and thus have more limited ability to distinguish different colors.

Sensory transduction in photoreceptors

The transduction of light energy into nerve impulses follows a sequence that is the opposite of the usual way that sensory stimuli are detected. In the dark, the photoreceptor cells release an inhibitory neurotransmitter that hyperpolarizes the bipolar neurons. This prevents the bipolar neurons from releasing excitatory neurotransmitter to the ganglion cells that signal to the brain. In the presence of light, the photoreceptor cells stop releasing their inhibitory neurotransmitter, in effect, stimulating bipolar cells. The bipolar cells in turn stimulate the ganglion cells, which transmit action potentials to the brain.

The production of inhibitory neurotransmitter by photoreceptor cells is due to the presence of ligand-gated Na$^+$ chan-

SCIENTIFIC THINKING

Hypothesis: *Birds can see light in the ultraviolet range.*

Prediction: *Birds will respond to individuals differently depending on how much ultraviolet is detected in their feathers.*

Test: *Zebra finch feathers reflect a moderate amount of ultraviolet light. Female zebra finches were exposed to different males, some of which were behind a filter that screened out UV light, whereas others were behind a control filter that let the UV pass through.*

Result and Conclusion: *Females preferred to spend time near the UV-positive males. Not only can female zebra finches see light in the UV range, but they prefer males with UV in the feathers.*

Further Experiments: *What are two hypotheses about why females prefer UV-positive males? How would you test these hypotheses?*

Figure 45.21 Ultraviolet vision in birds. Humans cannot distinguish colors in the near ultraviolet range, whereas many animals can. This photograph was taken with a special film that shows ultraviolet patterns on a zebra finch (*Taeniopygia guttata*) that are not detectable by humans.

nels. In the dark, many of these channels are open, allowing an influx of Na$^+$. This flow of Na$^+$ in the absence of light, called the dark current, depolarizes the membrane of photoreceptor cells. In this state, the cells produce inhibitory neurotransmitter that hyperpolarizes the membrane of bipolar cells. In the light, the Na$^+$ channels in the photoreceptor cell rapidly close, reducing the dark current and causing the photoreceptor to hyperpolarize. In this state, they no longer produce inhibitory neurotransmitter. In the absence of inhibition, the membrane of the bipolar cells is depolarized, causing them to release excitatory neurotransmitter to the ganglion cells.

The control of the dark current depends on the ligand for the Na$^+$ channels in the photoreceptor cells: the nucleotide cyclic guanosine monophosphate (cGMP). In the dark, the level of cGMP is high, and the channels are open. The system is made sensitive to light by the nature and structure of the photopigments. Photopigments in the eye are actually G protein–coupled receptor proteins that are activated by absorbing light. When a photopigment absorbs light, *cis*-retinal isomerizes and dissociates from the receptor protein, opsin, in what is known as the bleaching reaction. As a result of this dissociation, the opsin receptor protein changes shape, activating its associated G protein. The activated G protein then activates its effector protein, the enzyme phosphodiesterase, which cleaves cGMP to GMP. The loss of cGMP causes the cGMP-gated Na$^+$

Figure 45.22 **Signal transduction in the vertebrate eye.** In the absence of light, cGMP keeps Na⁺ channels open causing a Na⁺ influx that leads to the release of inhibitory neurotransmitter. Light is absorbed by the retinal in rhodopsin, changing its structure. This causes rhodopsin to associate with a G protein. The activated G protein stimulates phosphodiesterase, which converts cGMP to GMP. Loss of cGMP closes Na⁺ channels and prevents release of inhibitory neurotransmitter, which causes bipolar cells to stimulate ganglion cells.

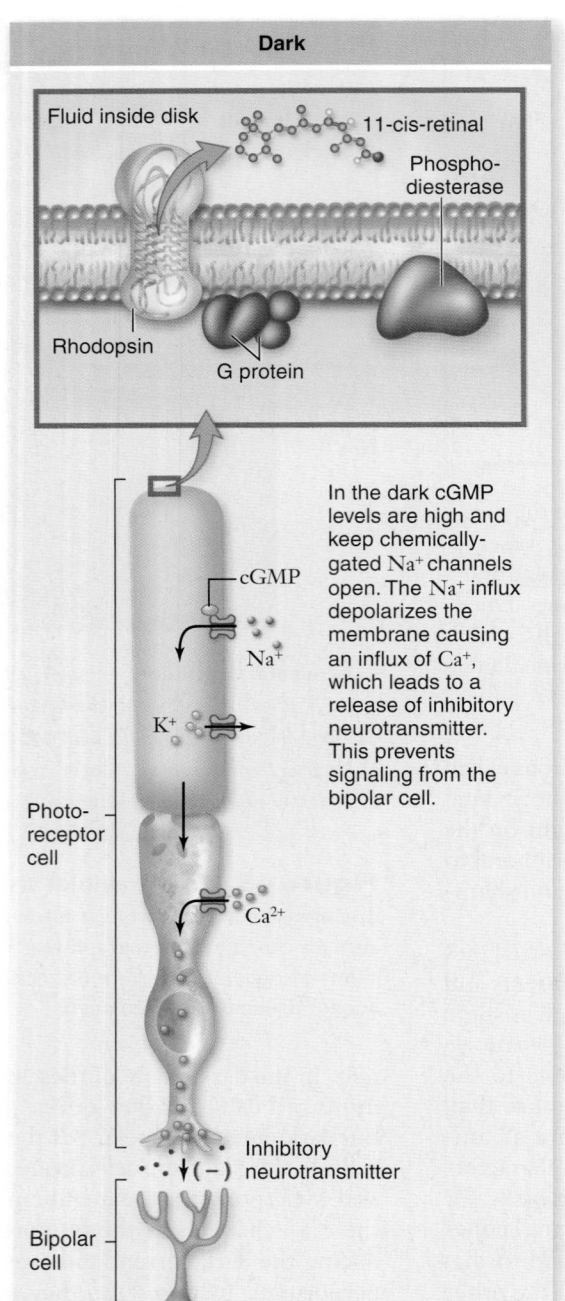

In the dark cGMP levels are high and keep chemically-gated Na⁺ channels open. The Na⁺ influx depolarizes the membrane causing an influx of Ca⁺, which leads to a release of inhibitory neurotransmitter. This prevents signaling from the bipolar cell.

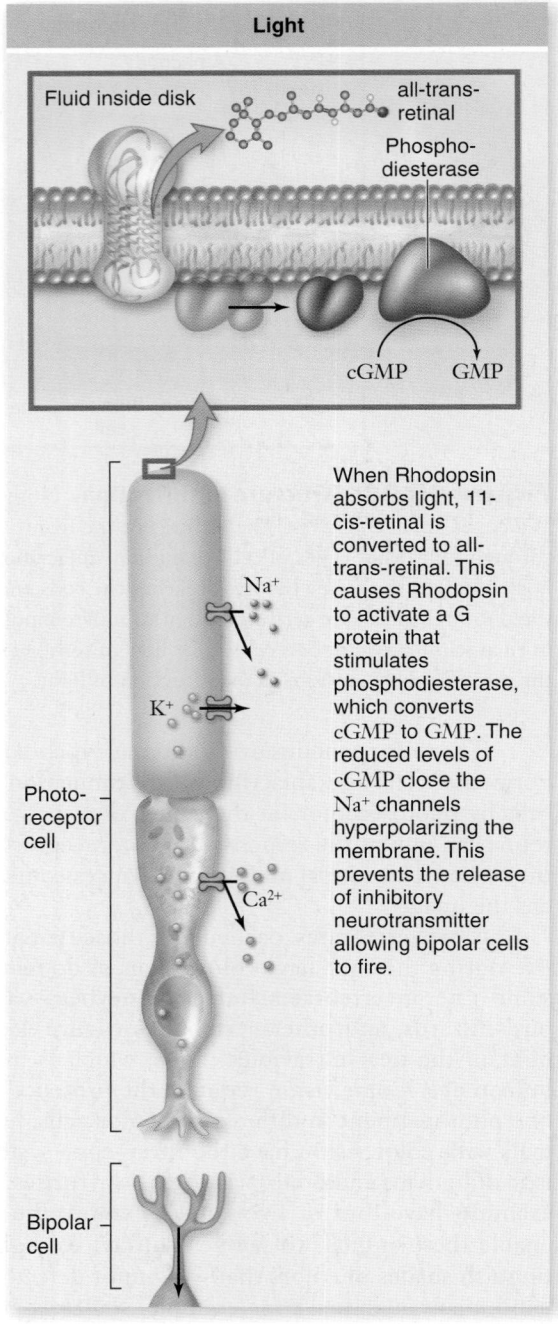

When Rhodopsin absorbs light, 11-cis-retinal is converted to all-trans-retinal. This causes Rhodopsin to activate a G protein that stimulates phosphodiesterase, which converts cGMP to GMP. The reduced levels of cGMP close the Na⁺ channels hyperpolarizing the membrane. This prevents the release of inhibitory neurotransmitter allowing bipolar cells to fire.

channels to close, reducing the dark current (figure 45.22). Each opsin is associated with over 100 regulatory G proteins, which, when activated, release subunits that activate hundreds of molecules of the phosphodiesterase enzyme. Each enzyme molecule can convert thousands of cGMP to GMP, closing the Na⁺ channels at a rate of about 1000 per second and inhibiting the dark current.

The absorption of a single photon of light can block the entry of more than a million Na⁺, without changing K⁺ permeability—the photoreceptor becomes hyperpolarized and releases less inhibitory neurotransmitter. Freed from inhibition, the bipolar cells activate the ganglion cells, which send impulses to the brain (figure 45.23).

Visual processing takes place in the cerebral cortex

Action potentials propagated along the axons of ganglion cells are relayed through structures called the **lateral geniculate nuclei** of the thalamus and projected to the occipital lobe of the cerebral cortex (see figure 45.23). There the brain interprets this information as light in a specific region of the eye's receptive field. The pattern of activity among the ganglion cells across the retina encodes a point-to-point map of the receptive field, allowing the retina and brain to image objects in visual space.

The frequency of impulses in each ganglion cell provides information about the light intensity at each point. At the same time,

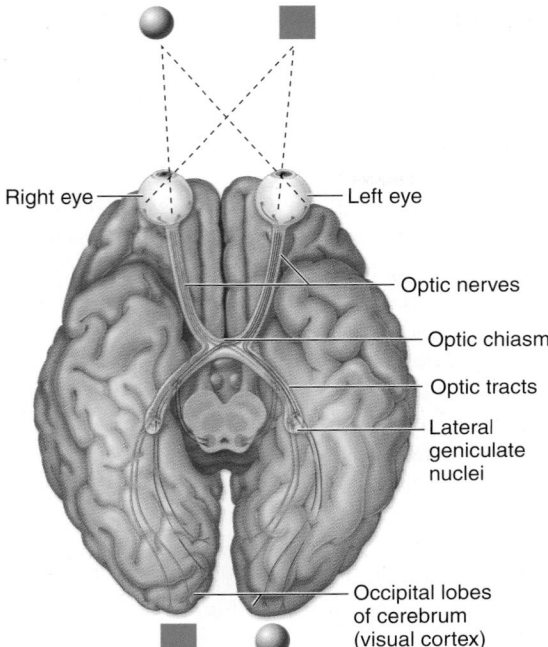

Figure 45.23 The pathway of visual information. Action potentials in the optic nerves are relayed from the retina to the lateral geniculate nuclei, and from there to the visual cortex of the occipital lobes. Note that half the optic nerves (the medial fibers arising from the inner portion of the retinas) cross to the other side at the optic chiasm, so that each hemisphere of the cerebrum receives input from both eyes.

the relative activity of ganglion cells connected (through bipolar cells) with the three types of cones provides color information.

Visual acuity

The relationship between receptors, bipolar cells, and ganglion cells varies in different parts of the retina. In the fovea, each cone makes a one-to-one connection with a bipolar cell, and each bipolar cell synapses with one ganglion cell. This point-to-point relationship is responsible for the high acuity of foveal vision.

Outside the fovea, many rods can converge on a single bipolar cell, and many bipolar cells can converge on a single ganglion cell. This convergence permits the summation of neural activity, making the area of the retina outside the fovea more sensitive to dim light than the fovea, but at the expense of acuity and color vision. This is why dim objects, such as faint stars at night, are best seen when you don't look directly at them. It has been said that we use the periphery of the eye as a detector, and the fovea as an inspector.

Color blindness can result from an inherited lack of one or more types of cones. People with normal color vision are trichromats; that is they have all three cones. Those with only two types of cones are dichromats. For example, people with red-green color blindness may lack red cones and have difficulty distinguishing red from green. Color blindness resulting from absence of one type of cone is a sex-linked recessive trait (see chapter 13), and therefore it is most often exhibited in

males. Red-green color blindness can also result from a shift in the sensitivity curve of the absorption spectrum for one type of cone, resulting in the different cone types being stimulated by the same electromagnetic wavelengths and causing the individual to be unable to distinguish between red and green.

Binocular vision

Primates (including humans) and most predators have two eyes, one located on each side of the face. When both eyes are trained on the same object, the image that each eye sees is slightly different because the views have a slightly different angle. This slight displacement of the images (an effect called parallax) permits **binocular vision,** the ability to perceive three-dimensional images and to sense depth. Having eyes facing forward maximizes the field of overlap in which this stereoscopic vision occurs.

In contrast, prey animals generally have eyes located to the sides of the head, preventing binocular vision but enlarging the overall receptive field. It seems that natural selection has favored the detection of potential predators over depth perception in many prey species. The eyes of the American woodcock (*Scolopax minor*), for example, are located at exactly opposite sides of the bird's skull so that it has a 360° field of view without turning its head.

Most birds have laterally placed eyes and, as an adaptation, have two foveas in each retina. One fovea provides sharp frontal vision, like the single fovea in the retina of mammals, and the other fovea provides sharper lateral vision.

Learning Outcomes Review 45.5

Many invertebrate groups have eyespots that detect light without forming images. Annelids, mollusks, arthropods, and chordates have independently evolved image-forming eyes. The vertebrate eye admits light through a pupil and then focuses it with an adjustable lens onto the retina, which contains photoreceptors. Photoreceptor rods and cones contain the photopigment *cis*-retinal, which indirectly activates bipolar neurons and then ganglion cells. The latter then transmit action potentials that ultimately reach the occipital lobe of the brain.

■ *Can an individual with red-green color blindness learn to distinguish these two colors? Why or why not?*

45.6 *The Diversity of Sensory Experiences*

Learning Outcomes

1. *List examples of uncommon special senses.*
2. *Explain how ampullae of Lorenzini work.*

Vision is the primary sense used by all vertebrates that live in a light-filled environment, but visible light is by no means the only part of the electromagnetic spectrum that vertebrates use to sense their environment.

Some snakes have receptors capable of sensing infrared radiation

Electromagnetic radiation with wavelengths longer than those of visible light is too low in energy to be detected by photoreceptors. Radiation from this infrared portion of the spectrum is what we normally think of as radiant heat.

Heat is an extremely poor environmental stimulus in water because water readily absorbs heat. Air, in contrast, has a low thermal capacity, so heat in air is a potentially useful stimulus. The only vertebrates known to have the ability to sense infrared radiation, however, are several types of snakes.

One type, the pit vipers, possess a pair of heat-detecting **pit organs** located on either side of the head between the eye and the nostril (figure 45.24). Each pit organ is composed of two chambers separated by a membrane. The infrared radiation falls on the membrane and warms it. Thermal receptors on the membrane are stimulated. The nature of these receptors is not known; they probably consist of temperature-sensitive neurons innervating the two chambers.

The paired pit organs appear to provide stereoscopic information, in much the same way that two eyes do. In fact, the nerves from the pits are connected to the optic tectum, the same part of the brain that controls vision; recent research suggests that information from the pits and from the eyes are overlain on each other, allowing snakes to combine visual and infrared thermal data. In fact, the pits are designed like a pinhole camera, and to some extent can focus a thermal image!

As a result, these exteroceptors are extraordinarily sensitive. Blind pit vipers can strike as accurately as a normal snake, and snakes deprived of their senses of sight and smell can accurately strike a target only 0.2° warmer than the background. Many pit vipers hunt endothermic prey at night, so the value of these capabilities is obvious.

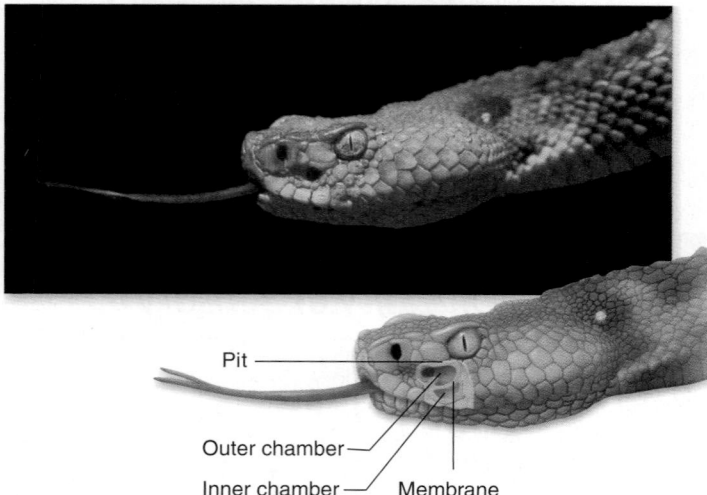

Figure 45.24 "Seeing" heat. The depression between the nostril and the eye of this rattlesnake opens into the pit organ. In the cutaway portion of the diagram, you can see that the organ is composed of two chambers separated by a membrane. Snakes known as pit vipers have the ability to sense infrared radiation (heat).

Some vertebrates can sense electrical currents

Although air does not readily conduct an electrical current, water is a good conductor. All aquatic animals generate electrical currents from contractions of their muscles. A number of different groups of fishes can detect these electrical currents. The so-called electrical fish even have the ability to produce electrical discharges from specialized electrical organs. Electrical fish use these weak discharges to locate their prey and mates and to construct a three-dimensional image of their environment, even in murky water.

The elasmobranchs (sharks, rays, and skates) have electroreceptors called the **ampullae of Lorenzini.** The receptor cells are located in sacs that open through jelly-filled canals to pores on the body surface. The jelly is a very good conductor, so a negative charge in the opening of the canal can depolarize the receptor at the base, causing the release of neurotransmitter and increased activity of sensory neurons. This allows sharks, for example, to detect the electrical fields generated by the muscle contractions of their prey. Although the ampullae of Lorenzini were lost in the evolution of teleost fish (most of the bony fish), electroreception reappeared in some groups of teleost fish that developed analogous sensory structures. Electroreceptors evolved yet another time, independently, in the duck-billed platypus, an egg-laying mammal. The receptors in its bill can detect the electrical currents created by the contracting muscles of shrimp and fish, enabling the mammal to detect its prey at night and in muddy water.

Some organisms detect magnetic fields

Eels, sharks, bees, and many birds appear to navigate along the magnetic field lines of the Earth. Even some bacteria use such forces to orient themselves.

Birds kept in dark cages, with no visual cues to guide them, peck and attempt to move in the direction in which they would normally migrate at the appropriate time of the year. They do not do so, however, if the cage is shielded from magnetic fields by steel. In addition, if the magnetic field of a blind cage is deflected 120° clockwise by an artificial magnet, a bird that normally orients to the north will orient toward the east-southeast. The nature of magnetic receptors in these vertebrates is the subject of much speculation, but the mechanism remains very poorly understood.

Learning Outcomes Review 45.6

Pit vipers can detect infrared radiation (heat). Many aquatic vertebrates can locate prey and perceive environmental contours by means of electroreceptors. The ampullae of Lorenzini, electroreceptors found in sharks and their relatives, contain a highly conductive jelly that triggers sensory neurons. Magnetic receptors may aid in bird migration.

■ *Would a heat-sensing organ be useful for hunting ectothermic prey?*

Chapter Review

45.1 Overview of Sensory Receptors

Sensory receptors detect both external and internal stimuli.
Exteroreceptors sense stimuli from the external environment, whereas interoreceptors sense stimuli from the internal environment.

Receptors can be grouped into three categories.
Receptors differ with respect to the environmental stimulus to which they respond: mechanoreceptors, chemoreceptors, and energy-detecting receptors.

Sensory information is conveyed in a four-step process.
Once detected, sensory information is conveyed in four steps: stimulation, transduction, transmission, and interpretation.

Sensory transduction involves gated ion channels.
Sensory transduction produces a graded receptor potential. A single potential or a sum of potentials may exceed a threshold to produce an action potential (see figure 45.2). A logarithmic relationship exists between stimulus intensity and action potential frequency.

45.2 Mechanoreceptors: Touch and Pressure

Pain receptors alert the body to damage or potential damage.
Nociceptors are free nerve endings located in the skin that respond to damaging stimuli, which is perceived as pain. Extreme temperatures can affect transient receptor potential (TRP) ion channels and cause depolarization by inflow of Na^+ and Ca^{2+}.

Thermoreceptors detect changes in heat energy.
Thermoreceptors are naked dendritic endings of sensory neurons that also contain TRP ion channels and respond to cold or heat.

Different receptors detect touch, depending on intensity.
Various receptors in the skin respond to mechanical distortion of the membrane to convey touch (see figure 45.3).

Muscle length and tension are monitored by proprioceptors.
Proprioceptors provide information about the relative position or movement of body parts and the degree of muscle stretching.

Baroreceptors detect blood pressure.

45.3 Hearing, Vibration, and Detection of Body Position
Hearing, the detection of sound or pressure waves, works best in water and provides directional information.

The lateral line system in fish detects low-frequency vibrations (see figure 45.5).

Ear structure is specialized to detect vibration.
The outer ear of terrestrial vertebrates channels sound to the eardrum (tympanic membrane) (see figure 45.6). Vibrations are transferred through middle ear bones to the oval window and into the cochlea, where the organ of Corti transduces them.

Transduction occurs in the cochlea.
The basilar membrane of the cochlea consists of fibers that respond to different frequencies of sound (see figure 45.8).

Some vertebrates have the ability to navigate by sound.
Echolocation allows bats, whales, and other species to navigate by sound.

Body position and movement are detected by systems associated with hearing systems.
Body position is detected by statocysts, ciliated hair cells embedded in a gelatinous matrix containing statoliths (see figure 45.9). Body movement is detected by hair cells located in the saccule and utricle (see figure 45.10).

45.4 Chemoreceptors: Taste, Smell, and pH

Taste detects and analyzes potential food.
Taste buds are collections of chemosensitive epithelial cells located on papillae (see figure 45.11). Tastes are broken down into five categories: sweet, sour, salty, bitter, and umami.

Smell can identify a vast number of complex molecules.
Smell, or olfaction, involves chemoreceptors located in the upper portion of the nasal passages (see figure 45.13). Their axons connect directly to the cerebral cortex.

Internal chemoreceptors detect pH and other characteristics.
Internal chemoreceptors of the aorta detect changes in blood pH, and central chemoreceptors in the medulla oblongata are sensitive to the pH of the cerebrospinal fluid.

45.5 Vision

Vision senses light and light changes at a distance.
Four phyla—annelids, mollusks, arthropods, and chordates—have independently evolved image-forming eyes (see figure 45.15).

In the vertebrate eye, light enters through the pupil, with intensity controlled by the iris. The lens, controlled by the ciliary muscle, focuses the light on the retina (see figure 45.16).

Vertebrate photoreceptors are rod cells and cone cells.
Rods detect black and white; cones are necessary for visual acuity and color vision (see figure 45.18).

In the retina, photoreceptors synapse with bipolar cells, which in turn synapse with ganglion cells; the ganglion cells send action potentials to the brain (see figure 45.20).

Visual processing takes place in the cerebral cortex (see figure 45.23).
In the fovea, a region of the retina responsible for high acuity, each cone cell is connected to a single bipolar cell/ganglion cell, unlike in areas outside the fovea.

Primates and most predators have binocular vision—images from each eye overlap to produce a three-dimensional image.

45.6 The Diversity of Sensory Experiences

Some snakes have receptors capable of sensing infrared radiation.
The pit organ of pit vipers detects heat.

Some vertebrates can sense electrical currents.
Electroreceptors in elasmobranchs and the duck-billed platypuses can detect electrical currents.

Some organisms detect magnetic fields.
Many organisms appear to navigate along magnetic field lines, but the mechanisms remains poorly understood.

UNDERSTAND

1. Which of these is not a method by which sensory receptors receive information about the internal or external environment?

    a. Changes in pressure
    b. Light or heat changes
    c. Changes in molecular concentration
    d. All of these are used by sensory receptors.

2. Which of the following correctly lists the steps of perception?

    a. Interpretation, stimulation, transduction, transmission
    b. Stimulation, transduction, transmission, interpretation
    c. Interpretation, transduction, stimulation, transmission
    d. Transduction, interpretation, stimulation, transmission

3. All sensory receptors are able to initiate nerve impulses by opening or closing

    a. voltage-gated ion channels.
    b. exteroceptors.
    c. interoceptors.
    d. stimulus-gated ion channels.

4. In the fairy tale, Sleeping Beauty fell asleep after pricking her finger. What kind of receptor responds to that kind of painful stimulus?

    a. Mechanoreceptor   c. Thermoreceptor
    b. Nociceptor   d. Touch receptor

5. The ear detects sound by the movement of

    a. the basilar membrane.
    b. the tectorial membrane.
    c. the Eustachian tube.
    d. fluid in the semicircular canals.

6. Hair cells in the vestibular apparatus of terrestrial vertebrates

    a. measure temperature changes within the body.
    b. sense sound in very low range of hearing.
    c. provide a sense of acceleration and balance.
    d. measure changes in blood pressure.

7. _____ is the photopigment contained within both rods and cones of the eye.

    a. Carotene   c. Photochrome
    b. Cis-retinal   d. Chlorophyll

8. Which of the following is not a method used by vertebrates to gather information about their environment?

    a. Infrared radiation
    b. Magnetic fields
    c. Electrical currents
    d. All of these are methods used for sensory reception.

9. The lobe of the brain that recognizes and interprets visual information is the

    a. occipital lobe.   c. parietal lobe.
    b. frontal lobe.   d. temporal lobe.

APPLY

1. What do the sensory systems of annelids, mollusks, arthropods, and chordates have in common?

    a. They all use the same stimuli for taste.
    b. They all use neurons to detect vibration.
    c. They all have image-forming eyes that evolved independently.
    d. They all use chemoreceptors in their skin to detect food.

2. Animals can more easily tell the direction of a visual signal than an auditory signal because

    a. light travels in straight lines.
    b. the wind provides too much background noise.
    c. sound travels faster underwater.
    d. eyes are more sensitive than ears.

3. The difference in the structure of the vertebrate and mollusk eyes

    a. results because mollusks live in water, causing images to be upside down.
    b. indicates that vertebrates have better vision than mollusks.
    c. reveals a disadvantage of vertebrate eye structure.
    d. makes color vision more efficient in vertebrates.

4. The ability of some insects, birds, and lizards to see ultraviolet light is

    a. a result of a common diet eaten by those species.
    b. an example of convergent evolution in cone cell sensitivity.
    c. the ancestral state inherited from flatworms.
    d. an adaptation for nocturnal activity.

SYNTHESIZE

1. When blood pH falls too low, a potentially fatal condition known as acidosis results. Among the variety of responses to this condition, the body changes the breathing rate. How does the body sense this change? How does the breathing rate change? How does this increase pH?

2. The function of the vertebrate eye is unusual compared with other processes found within the body. For example, the direction in which sensory information flows is actually opposite to path that light takes through the retina. Explain the sequence of events involved in the movement of light and information through the structures of the eye, and explain why they move in opposite directions. Consider, also, how this sequence of events compares to the functioning of the mollusk eye.

3. How would the otolith organs of an astronaut respond to zero gravity? Would the astronaut still have a subjective impression of motion? Would the semicircular canals detect angular acceleration equally well at zero gravity?

ONLINE RESOURCE

www.ravenbiology.com

Understand, Apply, and Synthesize—enhance your study with animations that bring concepts to life and practice tests to assess your understanding. Your instructor may also recommend the interactive eBook, individualized learning tools, and more.

Chapter **46**

The Endocrine System

Chapter Outline

46.1 Regulation of Body Processes by Chemical Messengers

46.2 Actions of Lipophilic Versus Hydrophilic Hormones

46.3 The Pituitary and Hypothalamus: The Body's Control Centers

46.4 The Major Peripheral Endocrine Glands

46.5 Other Hormones and Their Effects

Introduction

Diabetes is a disease in which well-fed people appear to starve to death. The disease was known to Roman and Greek physicians, who described a "melting away of flesh" coupled with excessive urine production "like the opening of aqueducts." Until 1922, the diagnosis of diabetes in children was effectively a death sentence. In that year, Frederick Banting and Charles Best extracted the molecule insulin from the pancreas. Injections of insulin into the bloodstream dramatically reversed the symptoms of the disease. This served as an impressive confirmation of a new concept: that certain internal organs produced powerful regulatory chemicals that were distributed via the blood.

We now know that the tissues and organs of the vertebrate body cooperate to maintain homeostasis through the actions of many regulatory mechanisms. Two systems, however, are devoted exclusively to the regulation of the body organs: the nervous system and the endocrine system. Both release regulatory molecules that control the body organs by binding to receptor proteins on or in the cells of those organs. In this chapter, we examine the regulatory molecules of the endocrine system, the cells and glands that produce them, and how they function to regulate the body's activities.

Regulation of Body Processes by Chemical Messengers

There are four mechanisms of cell communication: direct contact, synaptic signaling, endocrine signaling, and paracrine signaling. Here we are concerned with signaling methods of communication; we begin with the three signaling mechanisms.

As discussed in chapter 44, the axons of neurons secrete chemical messengers called neurotransmitters into the synaptic cleft. These chemicals diffuse only a short distance to the postsynaptic membrane, where they bind to their receptor proteins and stimulate the postsynaptic cell. Synaptic transmission generally affects only the postsynaptic cell that receives the neurotransmitter.

A *hormone*, in contrast, is a regulatory chemical that is secreted into extracellular fluid and carried by the blood and can therefore act at a distance from its source. Organs that are specialized to secrete hormones are called *endocrine glands*, but some organs, such as the liver and the kidney, can produce hormones in addition to performing other functions. The organs and tissues that produce hormones are collectively called the **endocrine system.**

The blood carries hormones to every cell in the body, but only target cells with the appropriate receptor for a given hormone can respond to it. Hormone receptor proteins function in a similar manner to neurotransmitter receptors. The receptor proteins specifically bind the hormone and activate signal transduction pathways that produce a response to the hormone. The highly specific interaction between hormones and their receptors enable hormones to be active at remarkably small concentrations. It is not unusual to find hormones circulating in the blood at concentrations of 10^{-8} to 10^{-10} M. In addition to the chemical messengers released as neurotransmitters and as hormones, other molecules are released and act within an organ on nearby cells as local regulators. These chemicals are termed **paracrine regulators.** They act in a way similar to endocrine hormones, but they do not travel through the blood to reach their target. This allows cells of an organ to regulate one another.

Cells can also release signaling molecules that affect their own behavior, or autocrine signaling. This is common in the immune system, and is also seen in cancer cells that may release growth factors that stimulate their own growth.

Chemical communication is not limited to cells within an organism. *Pheromones* are chemicals released into the environment to communicate among individuals of a single species. These aid in communication between animals

and may alter the behavior or physiology of the receiver, but are not involved in the normal metabolic regulation of an animal.

Figure 46.1 compares the different types of chemical messengers used for internal regulation.

Some molecules act as both circulating hormones and neurotransmitters

Blood delivery of hormones enables endocrine glands to coordinate the activity of large numbers of target cells distributed throughout the body, but that may not be the only role for these molecules. A molecule produced by an endocrine gland and used as a hormone may also be produced and used as a neurotransmitter by neurons. The hormone norepinephrine, for example, is secreted into the blood by the adrenal glands, but it is also released as a neurotransmitter by sympathetic nerve endings. Norepinephrine acts as a hormone to coordinate the activity of the heart, liver, and blood vessels during response to stress.

Neurons can also secrete a class of hormones called **neurohormones** that are carried by blood. The neurohormone antidiuretic hormone, for example, is secreted by neurons in the brain. Some specialized regions of the brain contain not only neurotransmitting neurons, but also clusters of neurons

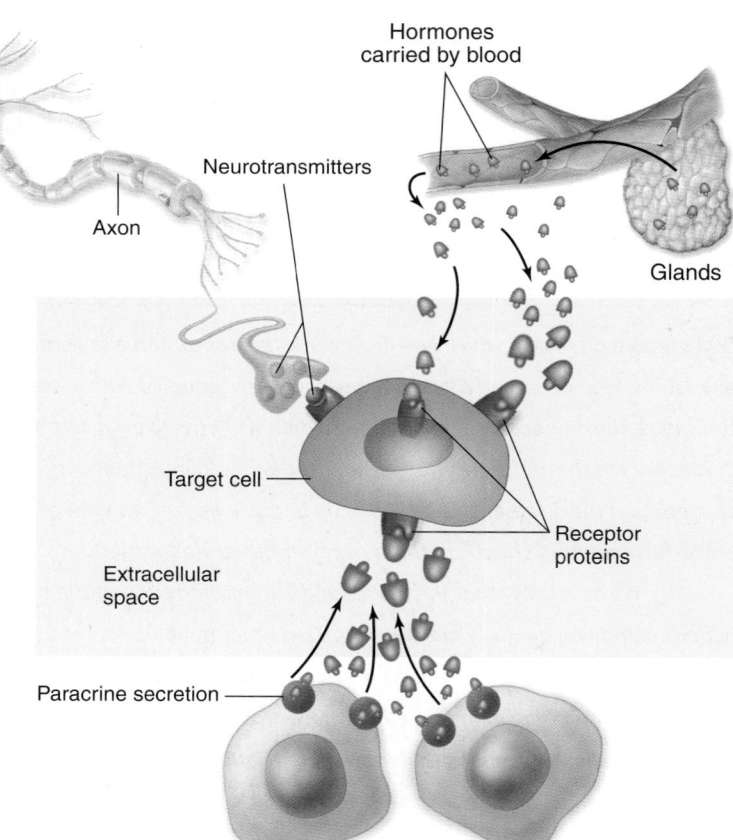

Figure 46.1 Different types of chemical messengers. The functions of organs are influenced by neural, paracrine, and endocrine regulators. Each type of chemical regulator binds to specific receptor proteins on the surface or within the cells of target organs.

producing neurohormones. In this way, neurons can deliver chemical messages beyond the nervous system itself.

The secretory activity of many endocrine glands is controlled by the nervous system. As you will see, the hypothalamus controls the hormonal secretions of the anterior-pituitary gland, and produces the hormones of the posterior pituitary.

The secretion of a number of hormones, however, can be independent of neural control. For example, the release of insulin by the pancreas and aldosterone by the adrenal cortex is stimulated by increases in the blood concentrations of glucose and potassium (K^+), respectively.

Endocrine glands produce three chemical classes of hormones

The endocrine system (figure 46.2) includes all of the organs that secrete hormones—the thyroid gland, pituitary gland, adrenal glands, and so on (table 46.1). Cells in these organs secrete hormones into extracellular fluid, where it diffuses into surrounding blood capillaries. For this reason, hormones are referred to as endocrine secretions. In contrast, cells of some glands excrete their products into a duct to outside the body, or into the gut. For example, the pancreas excretes hydrolytic enzymes into the lumen of the small intestine. These glands are termed exocrine glands,.

Molecules that function as hormones must exhibit two basic characteristics. First, they must be sufficiently complex to convey regulatory information to their targets. Simple molecules such as carbon dioxide, or ions such as Ca^{2+}, do not function as hormones. Second, hormones must be adequately stable to resist destruction prior to reaching their target cells. Three primary chemical categories of molecules meet these requirements.

1. **Peptides and proteins** are composed of chains of amino acids. Some important examples of peptide hormones include antidiuretic hormone (9 amino acids), insulin (51 amino acids), and growth hormone (191 amino acids). These hormones are encoded in DNA and produced by the same cellular machinery responsible for transcription and translation of other peptide molecules. The most complex are glycoproteins composed of two peptide chains with attached carbohydrates. Examples include thyroid-stimulating hormone and luteinizing hormone.
2. **Amino acid derivatives** are hormones manufactured by enzymatic modification of specific amino acids; this group comprises the biogenic amines discussed in chapter 44. They include hormones secreted by the adrenal medulla (the inner portion of the adrenal gland), thyroid, and pineal glands. Those secreted by the adrenal medulla are derived from tyrosine. Known as **catecholamines,** they include epinephrine (adrenaline) and norepinephrine (noradrenaline). Other hormones derived from tyrosine are the **thyroid hormones,** secreted by the thyroid gland. The pineal gland secretes a different amine hormone, **melatonin,** derived from tryptophan.
3. **Steroids** are lipids manufactured by enzymatic modifications of cholesterol. They include the hormones testosterone, estradiol, progesterone, aldosterone, and cortisol. Steroid hormones can be subdivided into sex steroids, secreted by the testes, ovaries, placenta, and adrenal cortex, and corticosteroids (mineralocoricoids and cortisol), secreted only by the adrenal cortex.

Hormones can be categorized as lipophilic or hydrophilic

The manner in which hormones are transported and interact with their targets differs depending on their chemical nature. Hormones may be categorized as lipophilic (nonpolar), which are fat-soluble, or hydrophilic (polar), which are water-soluble. The lipophilic hormones include the steroid hormones and thyroid hormones. Most other hormones are hydrophilic.

This distinction is important in understanding how these hormones regulate their target cells. Hydrophilic hormones are freely soluble in blood, but cannot pass through the membrane of

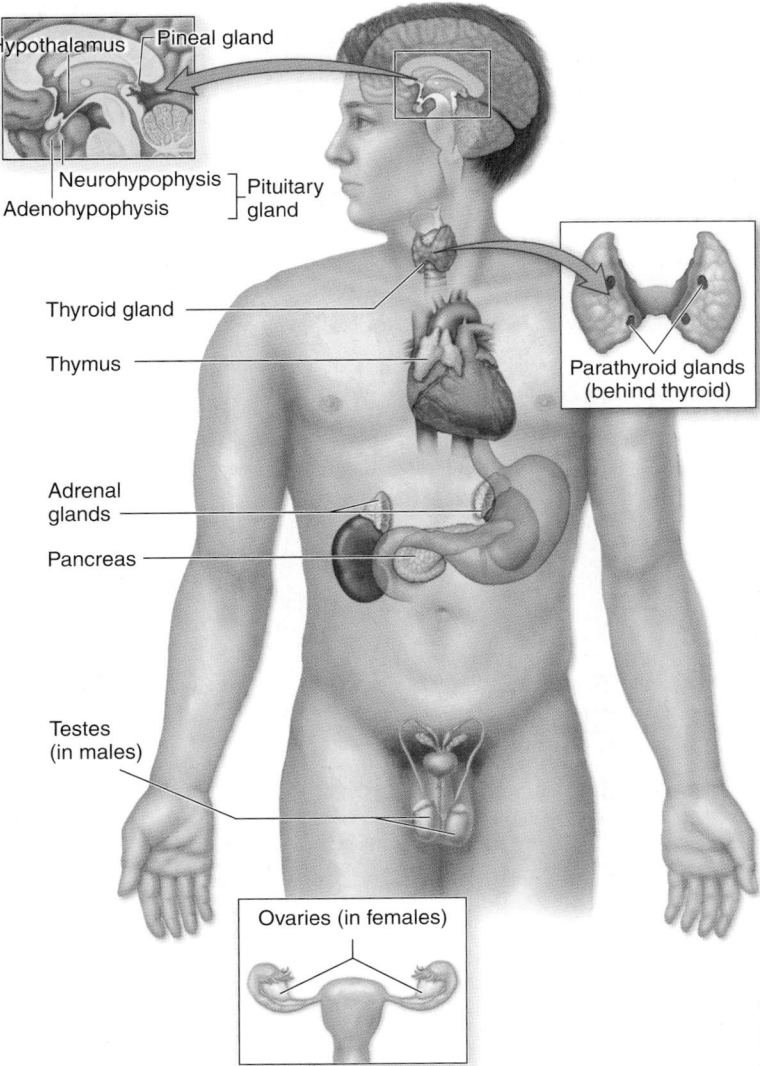

Figure 46.2 The human endocrine system. The major endocrine glands are shown, but many other organs secrete hormones in addition to their primary functions.

Hypothalamus
Pineal gland
Neurohypophysis
Adenohypophysis
Pituitary gland
Thyroid gland
Thymus
Parathyroid glands (behind thyroid)
Adrenal glands
Pancreas
Testes (in males)
Ovaries (in females)

TABLE 46.1

Principal Mammalian Endocrine Glands and Their Hormones*

Endocrine Gland and Hormone	Target Tissue	Principal Actions	Chemical Nature
Hypothalamus			
Releasing hormones	Adenohypophysis	Activate release of adenohypophyseal hormones	Peptides
Inhibiting hormones	Adenohypophysis	Inhibit release of adenohypophyseal hormones	Peptides (except prolactin-inhibiting factor, which is dopamine)
Neurohypophysis (Posterior-pituitary gland)			
Antidiuretic hormone (ADH)	Kidneys	Conserves water by stimulating its reabsorption from urine	Peptide (9 amino acids)
Oxytocin (OT)	Uterus	Stimulates contraction	Peptide (9 amino acids)
	Mammary glands	Stimulates milk ejection	
Adenohypophysis (Anterior-pituitary gland)			
Adrenocorticotropic hormone (ACTH)	Adrenal cortex	Stimulates secretion of adrenal cortical hormones such as cortisol	Peptide (39 amino acids)
Melanocyte-stimulating hormone (MSH)	Skin	Stimulates color change in reptiles and amphibians; various functions in mammals	Peptide (two forms; 13 and 22 amino acids)
Growth hormone (GH)	Many organs	Stimulates growth by promoting bone growth, protein synthesis, and fat breakdown	Protein
Prolactin (PRL)	Mammary glands	Stimulates milk production	Protein
Thyroid-stimulating hormone (TSH)	Thyroid gland	Stimulates thyroxine secretion	Glycoprotein
Luteinizing hormone (LH)	Gonads	Stimulates ovulation and corpus luteum formation in females; stimulates secretion of testosterone in males	Glycoprotein
Follicle-stimulating hormone (FSH)	Gonads	Stimulates spermatogenesis in males; stimulates development of ovarian follicles in females	Glycoprotein
Thyroid Gland			
Thyroid hormones (thyroxine and triiodothyronine)	Most cells	Stimulates metabolic rate; essential to normal growth and development	Amino acid derivative (iodinated)
Calcitonin	Bone	Inhibits loss of calcium from bone	Peptide (32 amino acids)

*These are hormones released from endocrine glands. Hormones are released from organs that have additional, nonendocrine functions, such as the liver, kidney, and intestine.

TABLE 46.1

Principal Mammalian Endocrine Glands and Their Hormones, *continued*

Endocrine Gland and Hormone	Target Tissue		Principal Actions	Chemical Nature
Parathyroid Glands				
Parathyroid hormone (PTH)	Bone, kidneys, digestive tract		Raises blood calcium level by stimulating bone breakdown; stimulates calcium reabsorption in kidneys; activates vitamin D	Peptide (34 amino acids)
Adrenal Medulla				
Epinephrine (adrenaline) and norepinephrine (noradrenaline)	Smooth muscle, cardiac muscle, blood vessels		Initiates stress responses; raises heart rate, blood pressure, metabolic rate; dilates blood vessels; mobilizes fat; raises blood glucose level	Amino acid derivatives
Adrenal Cortex				
Glucocorticoids (e.g., cortisol)	Many organs		Adaptation to long-term stress; raises blood glucose level; mobilizes fat	Steroid
Mineralocorticoids (e.g., aldosterone)	Kidney tubules		Maintains proper balance of Na^+ and K^+ in blood	Steroid
Pancreas				
Insulin	Liver, skeletal muscles, adipose tissue		Lowers blood glucose level; stimulates glycogen, fat, protein synthesis	Peptide (51 amino acids)
Glucagon	Liver, adipose tissue		Raises blood glucose level; stimulates breakdown of glycogen in liver	Peptide (29 amino acids)
Ovary				
Estradiol	General		Stimulates development of female secondary sex characteristics.	Steroid
	Female reproductive structures		Stimulates growth of sex organs at puberty and monthly preparation of uterus for pregnancy	
Progesterone	Uterus		Completes preparation for pregnancy	Steroid
	Mammary glands		Stimulates development	
Testis				
Testosterone	Many organs		Stimulates development of secondary sex characteristics in males and growth spurt at puberty	Steroid
	Male reproductive structures		Stimulates development of sex organs; stimulates spermatogenesis	
Pineal Gland				
Melatonin	Gonads, brain, pigment cells		Regulates biological rhythms	Amino acid derivative

Figure 46.3 The life of hormones.

Endocrine glands produce both hydrophilic and lipophilic hormones, which are transported to targets through the blood. Lipophilic hormones bind to transport proteins that make them soluble in blood. Target cells have membrane receptors for hydrophilic hormones, and intracellular receptors for lipophilic hormones. Hormones are eventually destroyed by their target cells or cleared from the blood by the liver or the kidney.

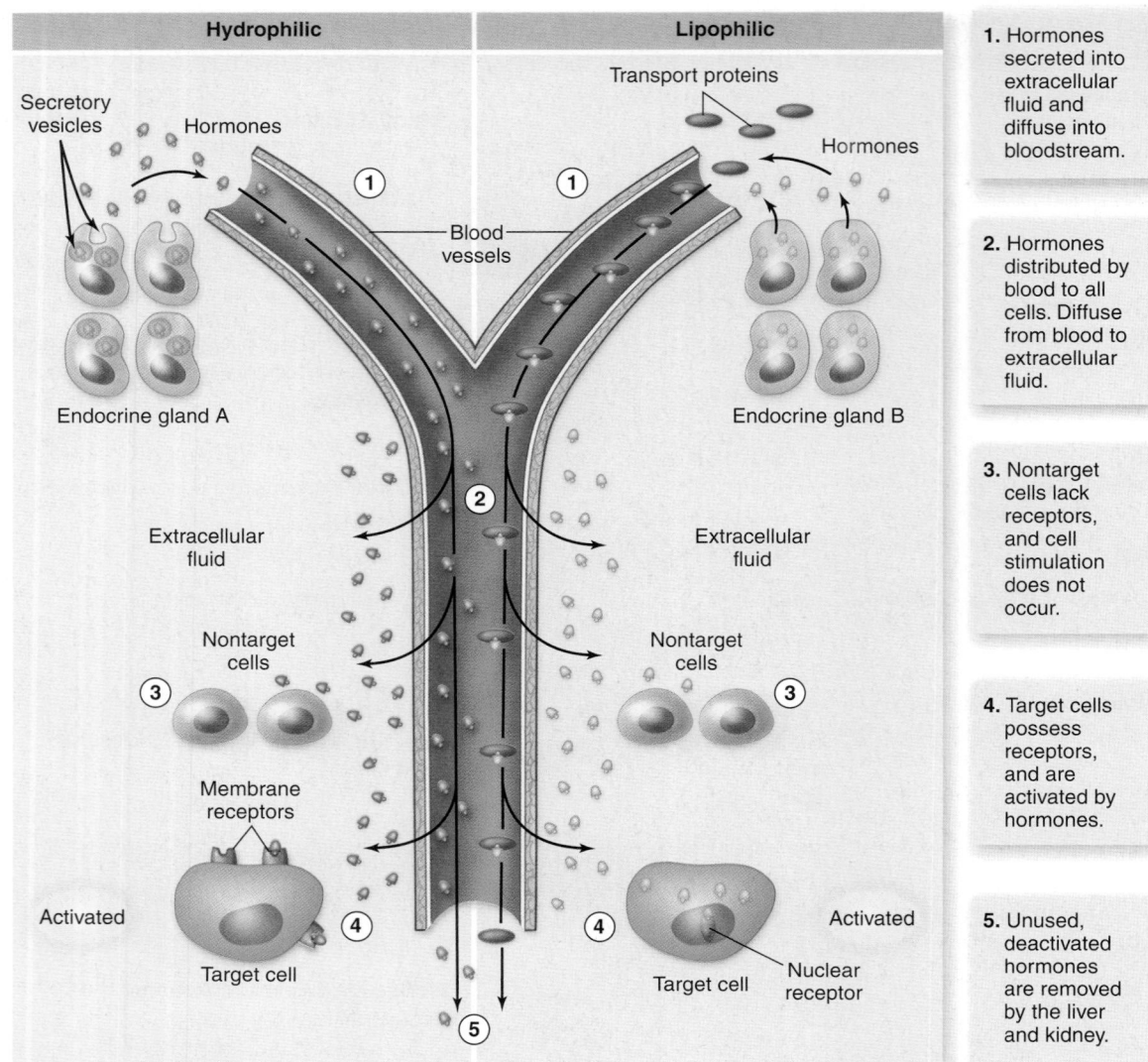

1. Hormones secreted into extracellular fluid and diffuse into bloodstream.

2. Hormones distributed by blood to all cells. Diffuse from blood to extracellular fluid.

3. Nontarget cells lack receptors, and cell stimulation does not occur.

4. Target cells possess receptors, and are activated by hormones.

5. Unused, deactivated hormones are removed by the liver and kidney.

target cells. They must therefore activate their receptors from outside the cell membrane. In contrast, lipophilic hormones travel in the blood attached to transport proteins (figure 46.3). Their lipid solubility enables them to cross cell membranes and bind to intracellular receptors.

Both types of hormones are eventually destroyed or otherwise deactivated after their use, eventually being excreted in bile or urine. However, hydrophilic hormones are deactivated more rapidly than lipophilic hormones. Hydrophilic hormones tend to act over relatively brief periods of time (minutes to hours), whereas lipophilic hormones generally are active over prolonged periods, such as days to weeks.

Paracrine regulators exert powerful effects within tissues

Paracrine regulation occurs in most organs and among the cells of the immune system. **Growth factors,** proteins that promote growth and cell division in specific organs, are among the most important paracrine regulators. Growth factors play a critical role in regulating mitosis throughout life (see chapter 10). For example, *epidermal growth factor* activates mitosis of skin and development of

connective tissue cells, whereas *nerve growth factor* stimulates the growth and survival of neurons. *Insulin-like growth factor* stimulates cell division in developing bone as well as protein synthesis in many other tissues. **Cytokines** (described in chapter 52) are growth factors specialized to control cell division and differentiation in the immune system, whereas **neurotropins** are growth factors that regulate the nervous system.

The importance of growth factor function is underscored by the observation that damage to the genes coding for growth factors or their receptors can lead to the unregulated cell division and development of tumors.

Paracrine regulation of blood vessels

The gas nitric oxide (NO), which can function as a neurotransmitter (see chapter 44), is also produced by the endothelium of blood vessels. In this context, it is a paracrine regulator because it diffuses to the smooth muscle layer of the blood vessel and promotes vasodilation. One of its major roles involves the control of blood pressure by dilating arteries. The endothelium of blood vessels is a rich source of paracrine regulators, including *endothelin*, which stimulates vasoconstriction, and *bradykinin*, which promotes vasodilation. Paracrine regulation supplements the regulation of blood vessels by autonomic nerves, enabling vessels to respond to local conditions, such as increased pressure or reduced oxygen.

Prostaglandins

A particularly diverse group of paracrine regulators are the **prostaglandins.** A prostaglandin is a 20-carbon-long fatty acid that contains a five-membered carbon ring. This molecule is derived from the precursor molecule *arachidonic acid*, released from phospholipids in the cell membrane under hormonal or other stimulation. Prostaglandins are produced in almost every organ and participate in a variety of regulatory functions. Some prostaglandins are active in promoting smooth muscle contraction. Through this action, they regulate reproductive functions such as gamete transport, labor, and possibly ovulation. Excessive prostaglandin production may be involved in premature labor, endometriosis, or dysmenorrhea (painful menstrual cramps). They also participate in lung and kidney regulation through effects on smooth muscle.

In fish, prostaglandins have been found to function as both a hormone and a paracrine regulator. Prostaglandins produced in the fish's ovary during ovulation can travel to the brain to synchronize associated spawning behavior.

Prostaglandins are produced at locations of tissue damage, where they promote many aspects of inflammation, including swelling, pain, and fever. This effect of prostaglandins has been well studied. Drugs that inhibit prostaglandin synthesis, such as aspirin, help alleviate these symptoms.

Aspirin is the most widely used of the *nonsteroidal anti-inflammatory drugs (NSAIDs)*, a class of drugs that also includes indomethacin and ibuprofen. These drugs act to inhibit two related enzymes: cyclooxygenase-1 and 2 (COX-1 and COX-2). The anti-inflammatory effects are due to the inhibition of COX-2, which is necessary for the production of prostaglandins from arachidonic acid. This reduces inflammation and associated pain from the action of prostaglandins. Unfortunately, the inhibition of COX-1 produces unwanted side effects, including gastric bleeding and prolonged clotting time.

More recently developed pain relievers, called *COX-2 inhibitors*, selectively inhibit COX-2 but not COX-1. COX-2 inhibitors may be of potentially great benefit to arthritis sufferers and others who must use pain relievers regularly, but concerns have been raised that they may also affect other aspects of prostaglandin function in the cardiovascular system. Some COX-2 inhibitors were removed from the market when a greater risk of heart attack and stroke was detected. Some have remained in use, however, and others may be reintroduced upon FDA approval. Aside from the possibly lessened gastrointestinal side effects, COX-2 inhibitors are not more effective for pain than the older NSAIDs.

Learning Outcomes Review 46.1

Hormones coordinate the activity of specific target cells. The three chemical classes of endocrine hormones are peptides and proteins, amino acid derivatives, and steroids. Lipophilic hormones such as steroids can cross membranes, but need carriers in the blood; hydrophilic hormones move readily in the blood, but cannot cross membranes. Paracrine regulators act within the organ in which they are produced.

■ *How do hormones and neurotransmitters differ?*

46.2 Actions of Lipophilic Versus Hydrophilic Hormones

Learning Outcomes

1. *Explain how steroid hormone receptors activate transcription.*
2. *Explain how the signal carried by peptide hormones crosses the membrane.*
3. *Describe the different types of membrane receptors.*

As mentioned previously, hormones can be divided into the lipophilic (lipid-soluble) and the hydrophilic (water-soluble). The receptors and actions of these two broad categories have notable differences, which we explore in this section.

Lipophilic hormones activate intracellular receptors

The lipophilic hormones include all of the steroid hormones and thyroid hormones (figure 46.4) as well as other lipophilic regulatory molecules including the retinoids, or vitamin A.

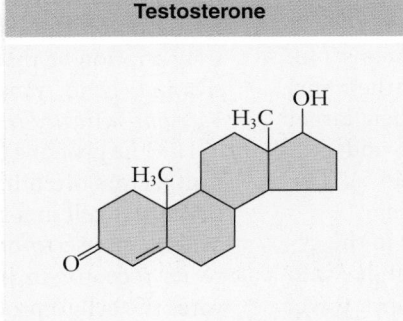

Cortisol (Hydrocortisone)	Testosterone	Thyroxine

Figure 46.4 Chemical structures of lipophilic hormones. Steroid hormones are derived from cholesterol. The two steroid hormones shown, cortisol and testosterone, differ slightly in chemical structure yet have widely different effects on the body. The thyroid hormone, thyroxine, is formed by coupling iodine to the amino acid tyrosine.

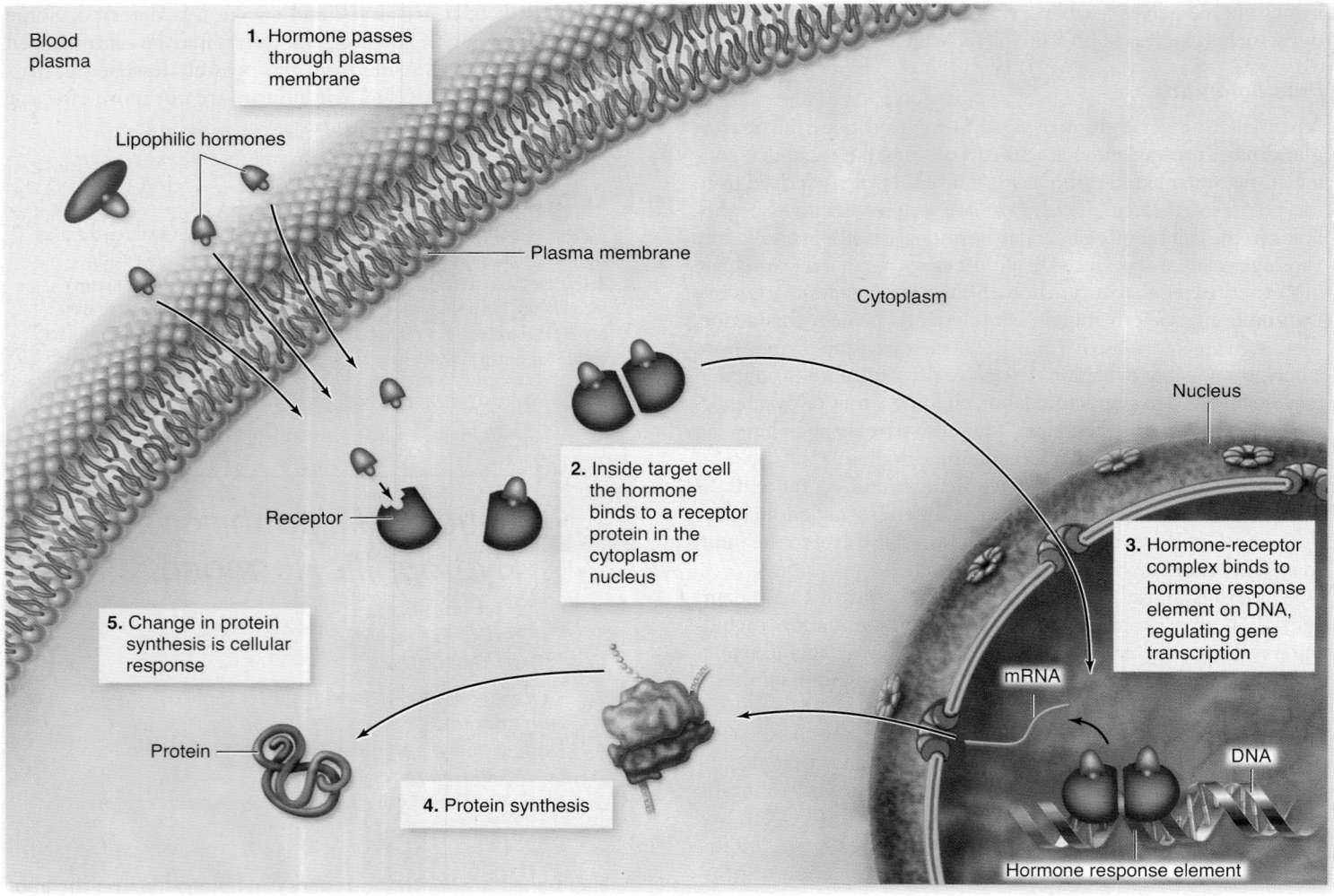

Figure 46.5 The mechanism of lipophilic hormone action. Lipophilic hormones diffuse through the plasma membrane of cells and bind to intracellular receptor proteins. The hormone-receptor complex then binds to specific regions of the DNA (hormone response elements), regulating the production of messenger RNA (mRNA). Most receptors for these hormones reside in the nucleus; if the hormone is one that binds to a receptor in the cytoplasm, the hormone-receptor complex moves together into the nucleus.

Lipophilic hormones can enter cells because the lipid portion of the plasma membrane does not present a barrier. Once inside the cell the lipophilic regulatory molecules all have a similar mechanism of action.

Transport and receptor binding

These hormones circulate bound to transport proteins (see figure 46.3), which make them soluble and prolong their survival in the blood. When the hormones arrive at their target cells, they dissociate from their transport proteins and pass through the plasma membrane of the cell (figure 46.5). The hormone then binds to an intracellular receptor protein.

Some steroid hormones bind to their receptors in the cytoplasm, and then move as a hormone-receptor complex into the nucleus. Other steroids and the thyroid hormones travel directly into the nucleus before encountering their receptor proteins. Whether the hormone finds its receptor in the nucleus or translocates with its receptor into the nucleus from the cytoplasm, the rest of the story is similar.

Activation of transcription in the nucleus

The hormone receptor, activated by binding to the hormone, is now also able to bind to specific regions of the DNA. These DNA regions, located in the promoters of specific genes, are known as **hormone response elements.** The binding of the hormone-receptor complex has a direct effect on the level of transcription at that site by activating, or in some cases deactivating, gene transcription. Receptors therefore function as *hormone-activated transcription factors* (see chapters 9 and 16).

The proteins that result from activation of these transcription factors often have activity that changes the metabolism of the target cell in a specific fashion; this change constitutes the cell's response to hormone stimulation. When estrogen binds to its receptor in liver cells of chickens, for example, it activates the cell to produce the protein vitellogenin, which is then transported to the ovary to form the yolk of eggs. In contrast, when thyroid hormone binds to its receptor in the anterior pituitary of humans, it inhibits the expression of the gene for thyrotropin, a mechanism of negative feedback (described later).

Because this activation and transcription process requires alterations in gene expression, it often takes several hours before the response to lipophilic hormone stimulation is apparent in target cells.

Hydrophilic hormones activate receptors on target cell membranes

Hormones that are too large or too polar to cross the plasma membranes of their target cells include all of the peptide, protein, and glycoprotein hormones, as well as the catecholamine hormones. These hormones bind to receptor proteins located on the outer surface of the plasma membrane. This binding must then activate the hormone response inside the cell, initiating the process of signal transduction. The cellular response is most often achieved through receptor-dependent activation of the powerful intracellular enzymes called *protein kinases*. As described in chapter 9, protein kinases are critical regulatory enzymes that activate or deactivate intracellular proteins by phosphorylation. By regulating protein kinases, hydrophilic hormone receptors exert a powerful influence over the broad range of intracellular functions.

Receptor kinases

For some hormones, such as insulin, the receptor itself is a kinase (figure 46.6), and it can directly phosphorylate intracellular proteins that alter cellular activity. In the case of insulin, this action results in the placement in the plasma membrane of glucose transport proteins that enable glucose to enter cells. Other peptide hormones, such as growth hormone, work through similar mechanisms, although the receptor itself is not a kinase. Instead, the hormone-bound receptor recruits and activates intracellular kinases, which then initiate the cellular response.

Second-messenger systems

Many hydrophilic hormones, such as epinephrine, work through second-messenger systems. A number of different molecules in the cell can serve as second messengers, as you saw in chapter 9. The interaction between the hormone and its receptor activates mechanisms in the plasma membrane that increase the concentration of the second messengers within the target cell cytoplasm.

In the early 1960s, Earl Sutherland showed that activation of the epinephrine receptor on liver cells increases intracellular cyclic adenosine monophosphate, or cyclic AMP (cAMP), which then serves as an intracellular second messenger. The

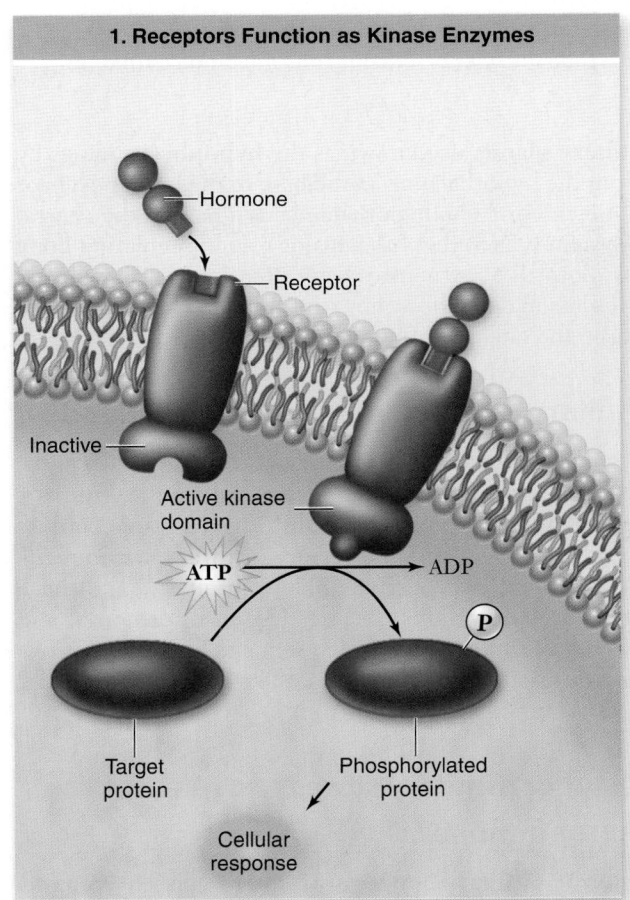

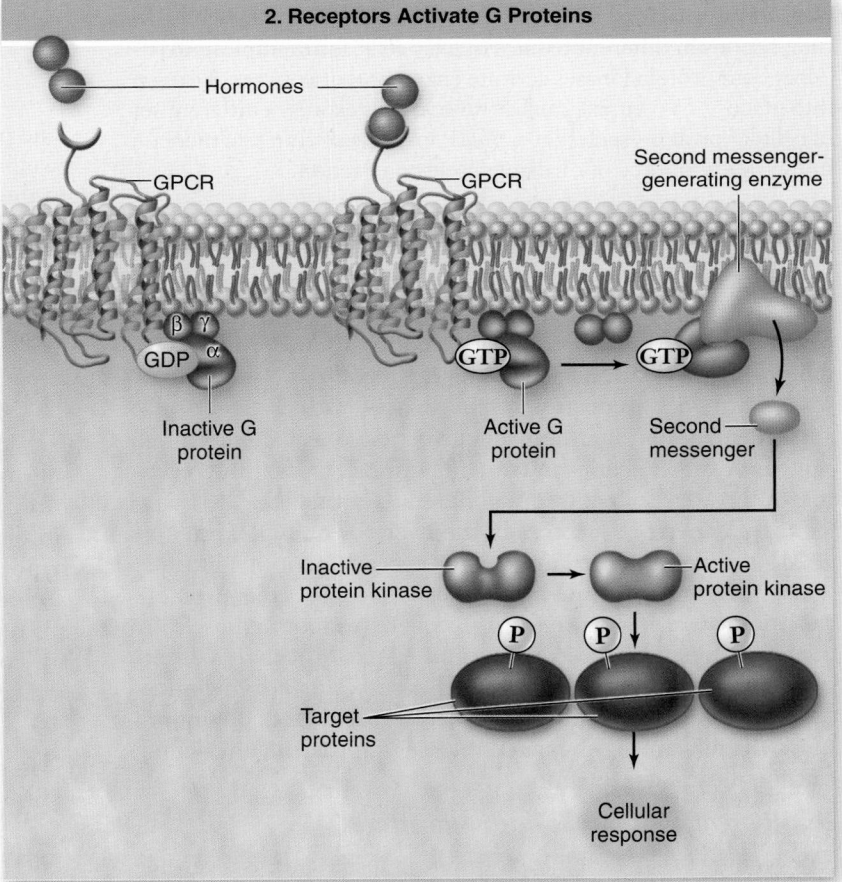

Figure 46.6 The action of hydrophilic hormones. Hydrophilic hormones cannot enter cells and must therefore work extracellularly via activation of transmembrane receptor proteins. (1) These receptors can function as kinase enzymes, activating phosphorylation of other proteins inside cells. (2) Alternatively, acting through intermediary G proteins, the hormone-bound receptor activates production of a second messenger. The second messenger activates protein kinases that phosphorylate and thereby activate other proteins. GPCR, G protein–coupled receptor.

cAMP second-messenger system was the first such system to be described. Since that time, another hormonally regulated second-messenger system has been described that generates two lipid messengers: **inositol triphosphate (IP_3)** and diacyl glycerol (DAG). These systems were described in chapter 9.

The action of G proteins

Receptors that activate second messengers do not manufacture the second messenger themselves. Rather, they are linked to a second-messenger-generating enzyme via membrane proteins called *G proteins* [that is, they are G protein–coupled receptors (GPCR); see chapter 9]. The binding of the hormone to its receptor causes the G protein to shuttle within the plasma membrane from the receptor to the second-messenger-generating enzyme (see figure 46.6). When the G protein activates the enzyme, the result is an increase in second-messenger molecules inside the cell.

In the case of epinephrine, the G protein activates an enzyme called *adenylyl cyclase*, which catalyzes the formation of the second messenger cAMP from ATP. The second messenger formed at the inner surface of the plasma membrane then diffuses within the cytoplasm, where it binds to and activates protein kinases.

The identities of the proteins that are subsequently phosphorylated by the protein kinases vary from one cell type to the next and include enzymes, membrane transport proteins, and transcription factors. This diversity provides hormones with distinct actions in different tissues. In liver cells, for example, cAMP-dependent protein kinases activate enzymes that convert glycogen into glucose. In contrast, cardiac muscle cells express a different set of cellular proteins such that a cAMP increase activates an increase in the rate and force of cardiac muscle contraction.

Activation versus inhibition

The cellular response to a hormone depends on the type of G protein activated by the hormone's receptor. Some receptors are linked to G proteins that activate second-messenger-producing enzymes, whereas other receptors are linked to G proteins that inhibit their second-messenger-generating enzyme. As a result, some hormones stimulate protein kinases in their target cells, and others inhibit their targets. Furthermore, a single hormone can have distinct actions in two different cell types if the receptors in those cells are linked to different G proteins.

Epinephrine receptors in the liver, for example, produce cAMP through the enzyme adenylyl cyclase, mentioned earlier. The cAMP they generate activates protein kinases that promote the production of glucose from glycogen. In smooth muscle, by contrast, epinephrine receptors can be linked through a different stimulatory G protein to the IP_3-generating enzyme phospholipase C. As a result, epinephrine stimulation of smooth muscle results in IP_3-regulated release of intracellular calcium, causing muscle contraction.

Duration of hydrophilic hormone effects

The binding of a hydrophilic hormone to its receptor is reversible and usually very brief; hormones soon dissociate from receptors or are rapidly deactivated by their target cells after binding. Additionally, target cells contain specific enzymes that rapidly deactivate second messengers and protein kinases. As a result, hydrophilic hormones are capable of stimulating immediate responses within cells, but often have a brief duration of action (minutes to hours).

46.3 *The Pituitary and Hypothalamus: The Body's Control Centers*

The **pituitary gland,** also known as the **hypophysis,** hangs by a stalk from the hypothalamus at the base of the brain posterior to the optic chiasm. The hypothalamus is a part of the central nervous system (CNS) that has a major role in regulating body processes. Both these structures were described in chapter 44; here we discuss in detail how they work together to bring about homeostasis and changes in body processes.

The pituitary is a compound endocrine gland

A microscopic view reveals that the gland consists of two parts, one of which appears glandular and is called the **anterior pituitary,** or **adenohypophysis.** The other portion appears fibrous and is called the **posterior pituitary,** or **neurohypophysis.** These two portions of the pituitary gland have different embryonic origins, secrete different hormones, and are regulated by different control systems. These two regions are conserved in all vertebrate animals, suggesting an ancient and important function of each.

The posterior pituitary stores and releases two neurohormones

The posterior pituitary appears fibrous because it contains axons that originate in cell bodies within the hypothalamus and that extend along the stalk of the pituitary as a tract of fibers. This anatomical relationship results from the way the posterior pituitary is formed in embryonic development. As the floor of the third ventricle of the brain forms the hypothalamus, part of this neural tissue grows downward to produce the posterior pituitary. The hypothalamus and posterior pituitary thus remain directly interconnected by a tract of axons.

Antidiuretic hormone

The endocrine role of the posterior pituitary first became evident in 1912, when a remarkable medical case was reported: A man who had been shot in the head developed the need to urinate every 30 minutes or so, 24 hours a day. The bullet had lodged in his posterior pituitary. Subsequent research demonstrated that removal of this portion of the pituitary produces the same symptoms.

In the early 1950s investigators isolated a peptide from the posterior pituitary, **antidiuretic hormone (ADH).** ADH stimulates water reabsorption by the kidneys (figure 46.7), and in doing so inhibits diuresis (urine production). When ADH is missing, as it was in the shooting victim, the kidneys do not reabsorb as much water, and excessive quantities of urine are produced. This is why the consumption of alcohol, which inhibits ADH secretion, leads to frequent urination. The role of ADH in kidney function is covered in chapter 51.

Oxytocin

The posterior pituitary also secretes **oxytocin,** a second peptide neurohormone that, like ADH, is composed of nine amino acids. In mammals, oxytocin stimulates the milk ejection reflex. During suckling, sensory receptors in the nipples send impulses to the hypothalamus, which triggers the release of oxytocin.

Oxytocin is also needed to stimulate uterine contractions in women during childbirth.

Oxytocin secretion continues after childbirth in a woman who is breast-feeding; as a result, the uterus of a nursing mother contracts and returns to its normal size after pregnancy more quickly than the uterus of a mother who does not breast-feed.

A related posterior pituitary neurohormone, *arginine vasotocin*, exerts similar effects in nonmammalian species. For example, in chickens and sea turtles, arginine vasotocin activates oviduct contraction during egg laying.

More recently, oxytocin has been identified as an important regulator of reproductive behavior. In both men and women, it is thought to be involved in promoting pair bonding (leading to its being called the "cuddle hormone") as well as regulating sexual responses, including arousal and orgasm. For these effects, it most likely functions in a paracrine fashion inside the CNS, much like a neurotransmitter.

Hypothalamic production of the neurohormones

ADH and oxytocin are actually produced by neuron cell bodies located in the hypothalamus. These two neurohormones are transported along the axon tract that runs from the hypothalamus to the posterior pituitary, where they are stored. In response to the appropriate stimulation—increased blood plasma osmolality in the case of ADH, the suckling of a baby in the case of oxytocin—the neurohormones are released by the posterior pituitary into the blood.

Because this reflex control involves both the nervous and the endocrine systems, ADH and oxytocin are said to be secreted by a **neuroendocrine reflex.**

The anterior pituitary produces seven hormones

The anterior pituitary, unlike the posterior pituitary, does not develop from growth of the brain; instead, it develops from a pouch of epithelial tissue that pinches off from the roof of the embryo's mouth. In spite of its proximity to the brain, it is not part of the nervous system.

Because it forms from epithelial tissue, the anterior pituitary is an independent endocrine gland. It produces at least seven essential hormones, many of which stimulate growth of their target organs, as well as production and secretion of other hormones from additional endocrine glands. Therefore, several hormones of the anterior pituitary are collectively termed *tropic hormones*, or *tropins*. Tropic hormones act on other endocrine glands to stimulate secretion of hormones produced by the target gland.

The hormones produced and secreted by different cell types in the anterior pituitary can be categorized into three structurally similar families: the *peptide hormones*, the *protein hormones*, and the *glycoprotein hormones*.

Peptide hormones

The **peptide hormones** of the anterior pituitary are cleaved from a single precursor protein, and therefore they share some common sequence. They are fewer than 40 amino acids in size.

1. **Adrenocorticotropic hormone (ACTH,** or *corticotropin*) stimulates the adrenal cortex to produce corticosteroid hormones, including cortisol (in humans)

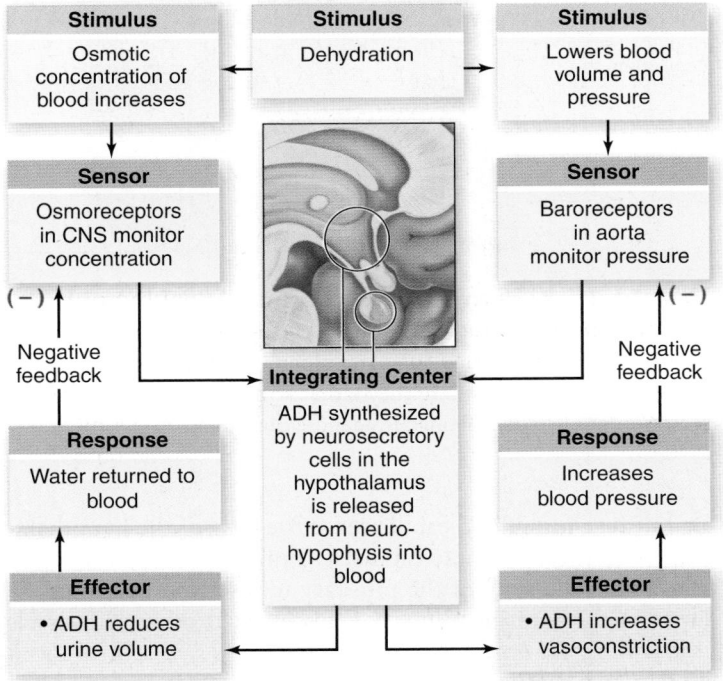

Figure 46.7 The effects of antidiuretic hormone (ADH). Dehydration increases the osmotic concentration of the blood and lowers blood pressure, stimulating the neurohypophysis to secrete ADH. ADH increases reabsorption of water by the kidneys and causes vasoconstriction, increasing blood pressure. Decreased blood osmolarity and increased blood pressure complete negative feedback loops to maintain homeostasis.

and corticosterone (in many other vertebrates). These hormones regulate glucose homeostasis and are important in the response to stress.

2. **Melanocyte-stimulating hormone (MSH)** stimulates the synthesis and dispersion of melanin pigment, which darkens the epidermis of some fish, amphibians, and reptiles, and can control hair pigment color in mammals.

Protein hormones

The **protein hormones** each comprise a single chain of approximately 200 amino acids, and they share significant structural similarities.

1. **Growth hormone (GH,** or *somatotropin*) stimulates the growth of muscle, bone (indirectly), and other tissues, and it is also essential for proper metabolic regulation.

2. **Prolactin (PRL)** is best known for stimulating the mammary glands to produce milk in mammals; however, it has diverse effects on many other targets, including regulation of ion and water transport across epithelia, stimulation of a variety of organs that nourish young, and activation of parental behaviors.

Glycoprotein hormones

The largest and most complex hormones known, the *glycoprotein hormones* are dimers, containing alpha (α) and beta (β) subunits, each around 100 amino acids in size, with covalently linked sugar residues. The α subunit is common to all three hormones. The β subunit differs, endowing each hormone with a different target specificity.

1. **Thyroid-stimulating hormone (TSH,** or *thyrotropin*) stimulates the thyroid gland to produce the hormone thyroxine, which in turn regulates development and metabolism by acting on nuclear receptors.

2. **Luteinizing hormone (LH)** stimulates the production of estrogen and progesterone by the ovaries and is needed for ovulation in female reproductive cycles (see chapter 53). In males, it stimulates the testes to produce testosterone, which is needed for sperm production and for the development of male secondary sexual characteristics.

3. **Follicle-stimulating hormone (FSH)** is required for the development of ovarian follicles in females. In males, it is required for the development of sperm. FSH stimulates the conversion of testosterone into estrogen in females, and into dihydroxytestosterone in males. FSH and LH are collectively referred to as *gonadotropins*.

Hypothalamic neurohormones regulate the anterior pituitary

The anterior pituitary, unlike the posterior pituitary, is not derived from the brain and does not receive an axon tract from the hypothalamus. Nevertheless, the hypothalamus controls the production and secretion of its hormones. This control is itself exerted hormonally rather than by means of nerve axons.

Neurons in the hypothalamus secrete two types of neurohormones, **releasing hormones** and **inhibiting hormones,**

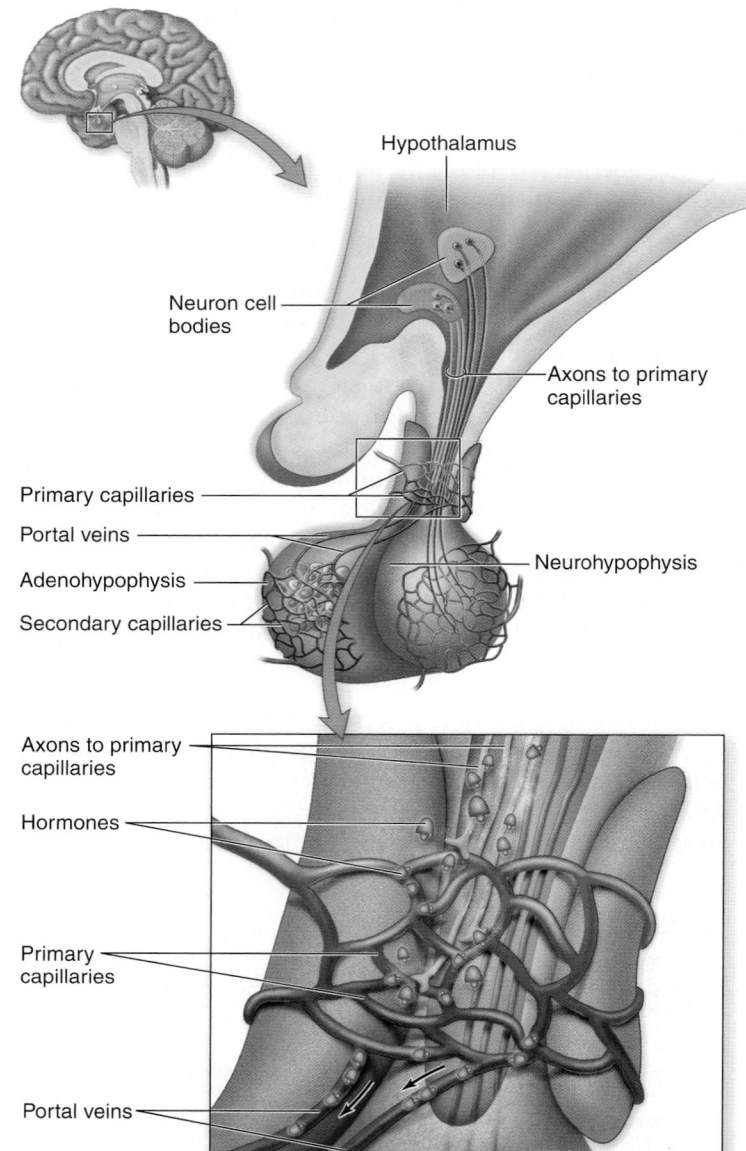

Figure 46.8 Hormonal control of the adenohypophysis by the hypothalamus. Neurons in the hypothalamus secrete hormones that are carried by portal blood vessels directly to the adenohypophysis, where they either stimulate or inhibit the secretion of hormones from the adenohypophysis.

that diffuse into blood capillaries at the base of the hypothalamus (figure 46.8). These capillaries drain into small veins that run within the stalk of the pituitary to a second bed of capillaries in the anterior pituitary. This unusual system of vessels is known as the *hypothalamohypophyseal portal system*. In a portal system, two capillary beds are linked by veins. In this case, the hormone enters the first capillary bed, and the vein delivers this to the second capillary bed where the hormone exits and enters the anterior pituitary.

Releasers

Each neurohormone released by the hypothalamus into the portal system regulates the secretion of a specific hormone in the anterior pituitary. Releasing hormones are peptide neurohormones that stimulate release of other hormones; specifically, *thyrotropin-releasing hormone* (TRH) stimulates the release of TSH; *corticotropin-releasing hormone* (CRH) stimulates the release of ACTH; and *gonadotropin-releasing hormone* (GnRH) stimulates the release of FSH and LH. A releasing hormone for growth hormone, called *growth hormone-releasing hormone* (GHRH), has also been discovered, and TRH, oxytocin and vasoactive intestinal peptide all appear to act as releasing hormones for prolactin.

Inhibitors

The hypothalamus also secretes neurohormones that inhibit the release of certain anterior-pituitary hormones. To date, three such neurohormones have been discovered: *Somatostatin*, or *growth hormone-inhibiting hormone* (GHIH), which inhibits the secretion of GH; *prolactin-inhibiting factor* (PIF), which inhibits the secretion of prolactin and has been found to be the neurotransmitter dopamine; and *MSH-inhibiting hormone* (MIH), which inhibits the secretion of MSH.

Feedback from peripheral endocrine glands regulates anterior-pituitary hormones

Because hypothalamic hormones control the secretions of the anterior pituitary, and because the hormones of the anterior pituitary in turn control the secretions of other endocrine glands, it may seem that the hypothalamus is in charge of hormonal secretion for the whole body. This however, ignores a crucial aspect of endocrine control: The hypothalamus and the anterior pituitary are themselves partially controlled by the very hormones whose secretion they stimulate. In most cases, this control is inhibitory (figure 46.9). This type of control system is called *negative feedback*, and it acts to maintain relatively constant levels of the target cell hormone.

An example of negative feedback: Thyroid gland control

To illustrate how important the negative feedback mechanism is, let's consider the hormonal control of the thyroid gland. The hypothalamus secretes TRH into the hypothalamohypophyseal portal system, which stimulates the anterior pituitary to secrete TSH. TSH in turn causes the thyroid gland to release **thyroxine.** Thyroxine and other thyroid hormones affect metabolic rate, as described in the following section.

Among thyroxine's many target organs are the hypothalamus and the anterior pituitary themselves. Thyroxine acts on these organs to inhibit their secretion of TRH and TSH, respectively. This negative feedback inhibition is essential for homeostasis because it keeps the thyroxine levels fairly constant.

The hormone thyroxine contains the element iodine; without iodine, the thyroid gland cannot produce thyroxine. Individuals living in iodine-poor areas (such as central prairies distant from seacoasts and the fish that are the natural source of iodine) lack sufficient iodine to manufacture thyroxine, so the hypothalamus and anterior pituitary receive far less negative feedback inhibition than is normal. This reduced inhibition results in elevated secretion of TRH and TSH.

High levels of TSH stimulate the thyroid gland, whose cells enlarge in a futile attempt to manufacture more thyroxine. Because they cannot without iodine, the thyroid gland keeps getting bigger and bigger—a condition known as a goiter (figure 46.10). Goiter size can be reduced by providing iodine in the diet. In most countries, goiter is prevented through the addition of iodine to table salt.

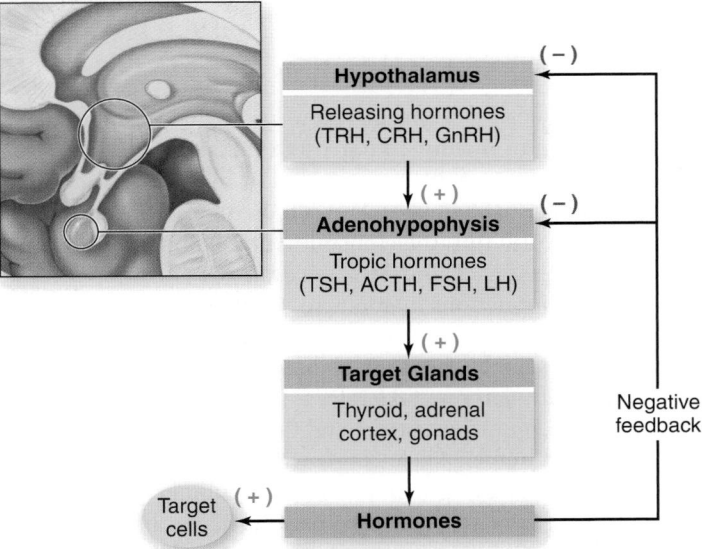

Figure 46.9 Negative feedback inhibition. The hormones secreted by some endocrine glands feed back to inhibit the secretion of hypothalamic releasing hormones and adenohypophysis tropic hormones. ACTH, adrenocorticotropic hormone; CRH, corticotropin-releasing hormone; FSH, follicle-stimulating hormone; GnRH, gonadotropin-releasing hormone; LH, luteinizing hormone; TRH, thyroid-releasing hormone; TSH, thyroid-stimulating hormone

Figure 46.10 A woman with a goiter. This condition is caused by a lack of iodine in the diet. As a result, thyroxine secretion is low, so there is less negative feedback inhibition of TSH. The elevated TSH secretion, in turn, stimulates the thyroid to enlarge in an effort to produce additional thyroxine.

An example of positive feedback: Ovulation

Positive feedback in the control of the hypothalamus and anterior pituitary by the target glands is uncommon because positive feedback causes deviations from homeostasis. Positive feedback accentuates change, driving the change in the same direction. One example is the control of **ovulation,** the explosive release of a mature egg (an oocyte) from the ovary.

As the oocyte grows, follicle cells surrounding it produce increasing levels of the steroid hormone estrogen, resulting in a progressive rise in estrogen in the blood. Peak estrogen levels signal the hypothalamus that the oocyte is ready to be ovulated. Estrogen then exerts positive feedback on the hypothalamus and pituitary, resulting in a surge of LH from the anterior pituitary. This LH surge causes the follicle cells to rupture and release the oocyte to the oviduct, where it can potentially be fertilized. The positive feedback cycle is then terminated because the tissue remaining of the ovarian follicle forms the corpus luteum, which secretes progesterone and estrogen that feed back to inhibit secretion of FSH and LH. This process is discussed in more detail in chapter 53.

Hormones of the anterior pituitary work directly and indirectly

Early in the 20th century, experimental techniques were developed for surgical removal of the pituitary gland (a procedure called *hypophysectomy*). Hypophysectomized animals exhibited a number of deficits, including reduced growth and development, diminished metabolism, and failure of reproduction. These powerful and diverse effects earned the pituitary a reputation as the "master gland." Indeed, many of these are *direct effects*, resulting from anterior-pituitary hormones activating receptors in nonendocrine targets, such as liver, muscle, and bone. The tropic hormones produced by the anterior pituitary have *indirect effects*, however, through their ability to activate other endocrine glands, such as the thyroid, adrenal glands, and gonads. Of the seven anterior-pituitary hormones, growth hormone, prolactin, and MSH work primarily through direct effects, whereas the tropic hormones ACTH, TSH, LH, and FSH have endocrine glands as their exclusive targets.

Effects of growth hormone

The importance of the anterior pituitary is illustrated by a condition known as *gigantism,* characterized by excessive growth of the entire body or any of its parts. The tallest human being ever recorded, Robert Wadlow, had gigantism (figure 46.11). Born in 1928, he stood 8 feet 11 inches tall, weighed 485 pounds, and was still growing before he died from an infection at the age of 22.

We now know that gigantism is caused by the excessive secretion of GH in a growing child. By contrast, a deficiency in GH secretion during childhood results in **pituitary dwarfism**—a failure to achieve normal stature.

GH stimulates protein synthesis and growth of muscles and connective tissues; it also indirectly promotes the elongation of bones by stimulating cell division in the cartilaginous epiphyseal growth plates of bones (see chapter 47). Researchers found that this stimulation does not occur in the absence of blood plasma, suggesting that GH must work in concert with another hormone

Figure 46.11 The Alton giant. This photograph of Robert Wadlow of Alton, Illinois, taken on his 21st birthday, shows him at home with his father and mother and four siblings. Born normal size, he developed a growth-hormone-secreting pituitary tumor as a young child and never stopped growing during his 22 years of life, reaching a height of 8 ft 11 in.

to exert its effects on bone. We now know that GH stimulates the production of **insulin-like growth factors,** which liver and bone produce in response to stimulation by GH. The insulin-like growth factors then stimulate cell division in the epiphyseal growth plates, and thus the elongation of the bones.

Although GH exhibits its most dramatic effects on juvenile growth, it also functions in adults to regulate protein, lipid, and carbohydrate metabolism. Recently a peptide hormone named **ghrelin,** produced by the stomach between meals, was identified as a potent stimulator of GH release, establishing an important linkage between nutrient intake and GH production.

Because human skeletal growth plates transform from cartilage into bone at puberty, GH can no longer cause an increase in height in adults. Excessive GH secretion in an adult results in a form of gigantism called **acromegaly,** characterized by bone and soft tissue deformities such as a protruding jaw, elongated fingers, and thickening of skin and facial features. Our knowledge of the regulation of GH has led to the development of drugs that can control its secretion, for example through activation of somatostatin, or by mimicking ghrelin. As a result, gigantism is much less common today.

Animals that have been genetically engineered to express additional copies of the GH gene grow to larger than normal size (see figure 17.16), making agricultural applications of GH manipulation an active area of investigation. Among other actions, GH has been found to increase milk yield in cows, promote weight gain in pigs, and increase the length of fish. The growth-promoting actions of GH thus appear to have been conserved throughout the vertebrates.

Other hormones of the anterior pituitary

Like growth hormone, prolactin acts on organs that are not endocrine glands. In contrast to GH, however, the actions of prolactin appear to be very diverse. In addition to stimulating production of milk in mammals, prolactin has been implicated in the regulation of tissues important in birds for the nourishment and incubation of young, such as the crop (which produces "crop milk," a nutritional fluid fed to chicks by regurgitation) and the brood patch (a vascular area on the abdomen of birds used to warm eggs).

In amphibians, prolactin promotes transformation of salamanders from terrestrial forms to aquatic breeding adults. Associated with these reproductive actions is an ability of prolactin to activate associated behaviors, such as parental care in mammals, broodiness in birds, and "water drive" in amphibians.

Prolactin also has varied effects on electrolyte balance through actions on the kidneys of mammals, the gills of fish, and the salt glands of marine birds. This variation suggests that although prolactin may have an ancient function in the regulation of salt and water movement across membranes, its actions have diversified with the appearance of new vertebrate species. The field of comparative endocrinology studies questions about hormone action across diverse species, with the objective of understanding the mechanisms of hormone evolution.

Unlike growth hormone and prolactin, the other adenohypophyseal hormones act on relatively few targets. TSH stimulates the thyroid gland, and ACTH stimulates the adrenal cortex. The gonadotropins, FSH and LH, act on the gonads. Although both FSH and LH act on the gonads, they each target different cells in the gonads of both females and males (see chapter 53). These hormones all share the common characteristic of activating target endocrine glands.

The final pituitary hormone, MSH regulates the activity of cells called melanophores, which contain the black pigment **melanin.** In response to MSH, melanin is dispersed throughout these cells, darkening the skin of reptiles, amphibians, or fish. In mammals, which lack melanophores but have similar cells called melanocytes, MSH can darken hair by increasing melanin deposition in the developing hair shaft.

Learning Outcomes Review 46.3

The posterior pituitary develops from neural tissue; the anterior pituitary develops from epithelial tissue. Axons from the hypothalamus extend into the posterior pituitary and produce neurohormones; these neurons also secrete factors that release or inhibit hormones of the anterior pituitary. Releasers stimulate secretion of hormones; TRH causes TSH release. Inhibitors suppress secretion; GHIH inhibits GH release.

■ *Could someone with a pituitary tumor causing gigantism be treated with GHIH? What outcome would you predict?*

46.4 The Major Peripheral Endocrine Glands

Learning Outcomes

1. *Identify the major peripheral endocrine glands.*
2. *Describe the components of Ca^{2+} homeostasis.*
3. *Explain the action of pancreatic hormones on blood glucose.*

Although the pituitary produces an impressive array of hormones, many endocrine glands are found in other locations. Some of these may be controlled by tropic hormones of the pituitary, but others, such as the adrenal medulla and the pancreas, are independent of pituitary control. Several endocrine glands develop from derivatives of the primitive pharynx, which is the most anterior segment of the digestive tract (see chapter 48). These glands, which include the *thyroid* and *parathyroid* glands, produce hormones that regulate processes associated with nutrient uptake, such as carbohydrate, lipid, protein, and mineral metabolism.

The thyroid gland regulates basal metabolism and development

The thyroid gland varies in shape in different vertebrate species, but is always found in the neck area, anterior to the heart. In humans it is shaped like a bow tie and lies just below the Adam's apple in the front of the neck.

The thyroid gland secretes three hormones: primarily thyroxine, smaller amounts of triiodothyronine (collectively referred to as thyroid hormones), and calcitonin. As described earlier, thyroid hormones are unique in being the only molecules in the body containing iodine (thyroxine contains four iodine atoms, triiodothyronine contains three).

Thyroid-related disorders

Thyroid hormones work by binding to nuclear receptors located in most cells in the body, influencing the production and activity of a large number of cellular proteins. The importance of thyroid hormones first became apparent from studies of human thyroid disorders. Adults with hypothyroidism have low metabolism due to underproduction of thyroxine, including a reduced ability to utilize carbohydrates and fats. As a result, they are often fatigued, overweight, and feel cold. Hypothyroidism is particularly concerning in infants and children, where it impairs growth, brain development, and reproductive maturity. Fortunately, because thyroid hormones are small, simple molecules, people with hypothyroidism can take thyroxine orally as a pill.

People with hyperthyroidism, by contrast, often exhibit opposite symptoms: weight loss, nervousness, high metabolism, and overheating because of overproduction of thyroxine. Drugs are available that block thyroid hormone synthesis in the thyroid gland, but in some cases portions of the thyroid gland must be removed surgically or by radiation treatment.

Actions of thyroid hormones

Thyroid hormones regulate enzymes controlling carbohydrate and lipid metabolism in most cells, promoting the appropriate use of these fuels for maintaining the body's basal metabolic rate. Thyroid hormones often function cooperatively, or *synergistically*, with other hormones, promoting the activity of growth hormone, epinephrine, and reproductive steroids. Through these actions, thyroid hormones function to ensure that adequate cellular energy is available to support metabolically demanding activities.

In humans, which exhibit a relatively high metabolic rate at all times, thyroid hormones are maintained in the blood at constantly elevated levels. In contrast, in reptiles, amphibians, and fish, which undergo seasonal cycles of activity, thyroid hormone levels in the blood increase during periods of metabolic activation (such as growth, reproductive development, migration, or breeding) and diminish during periods of inactivity in cold months.

Some of the most dramatic effects of thyroid hormones are observed in their regulation of growth and development. In developing humans, for example, thyroid hormones promote growth of neurons and stimulate maturation of the CNS. Children born with hypothyroidism are stunted in their growth and suffer severe mental retardation, a condition called *cretinism*. Early detection through measurement of thyroid hormone levels allows this condition to be treated with thyroid hormone administration.

The most impressive demonstration of the importance of thyroid hormones in development is displayed in amphibians. Thyroid hormones direct the metamorphosis of tadpoles into frogs, a process that requires the transformation of an aquatic, herbivorous larva into a terrestrial, carnivorous juvenile (figure 46.12). If the thyroid gland is removed from a tadpole, it will not change into a frog. Conversely, if an immature tadpole is fed pieces of a thyroid gland, it will undergo premature metamorphosis and become a miniature frog. This illustrates the powerful actions thyroid hormones can elicit by regulating the expression of multiple genes.

Calcium homeostasis is regulated by several hormones

Calcium is a vital component of the vertebrate body both because of its being a structural component of bones and because of its role in ion-mediated processes such as muscle contraction. The thyroid and parathyroid glands act with vitamin D to regulate calcium homeostasis.

Calcitonin secretion by the thyroid

In addition to the thyroid hormones, the thyroid gland also secretes **calcitonin,** a peptide hormone that plays a role in maintaining proper levels of calcium (Ca^{2+}) in the blood. When the blood Ca^{2+} concentration rises too high, calcitonin stimulates the uptake of calcium into bones, thus lowering its

Figure 46.12 Thyroxine triggers metamorphosis in amphibians. In tadpoles at the premetamorphic stage, the hypothalamus stimulates the adenohypophysis to secrete TSH (thyroid-stimulating hormone). TSH then stimulates the thyroid gland to secrete thyroxine. Thyroxine binds to its receptor and initiates the changes in gene expression necessary for metamorphosis. As metamorphosis proceeds, thyroxine reaches its maximal level, after which the forelimbs begin to form and the tail is reabsorbed.

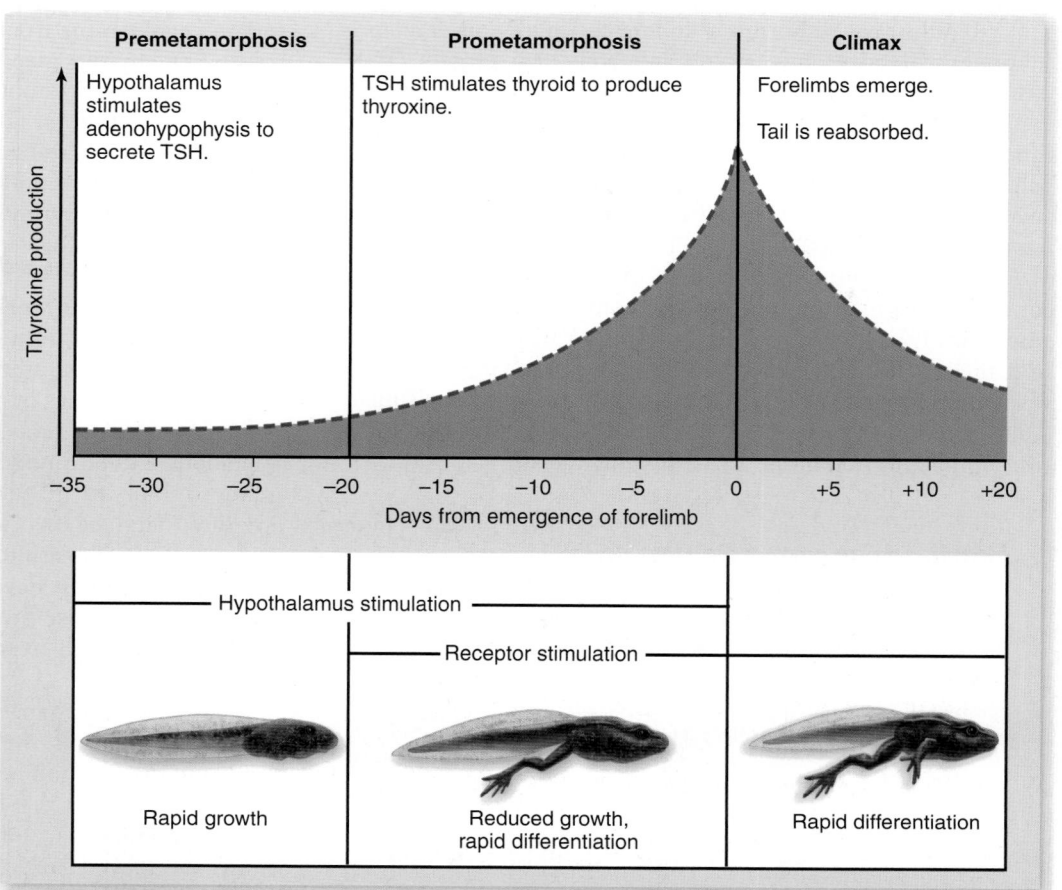

level in the blood. Although calcitonin may be important in the physiology of some vertebrates, it appears less important in the day-to-day regulation of Ca²⁺ levels in adult humans. It may, however, play an important role in bone remodeling in rapidly growing children.

Parathyroid hormone (PTH)

The parathyroid glands are four small glands attached to the thyroid. Because of their size, researchers ignored them until well into the 20th century. The first suggestion that these organs have an endocrine function came from experiments on dogs: If their parathyroid glands were removed, the Ca²⁺ concentration in the dogs' blood plummeted to less than half the normal value. The Ca²⁺ concentration returned to normal when an extract of parathyroid gland was administered. However, if too much of the extract was administered, the dogs' Ca²⁺ levels rose far above normal as the calcium phosphate crystals in their bones were dissolved. It was clear that the parathyroid glands produce a hormone that stimulates the release of calcium from bone.

The hormone produced by the parathyroid glands is a peptide called **parathyroid hormone (PTH)**. PTH is synthesized and released in response to falling levels of Ca²⁺ in the blood. This decline cannot be allowed to continue uncorrected because a significant fall in the blood Ca²⁺ level can cause severe muscle spasms. A normal blood Ca²⁺ level is important for the functioning of muscles, including the heart, and for proper functioning of the nervous and endocrine systems.

PTH stimulates the osteoclasts (bone cells) in bone to dissolve the calcium phosphate crystals of the bone matrix and release Ca²⁺ into the blood (figure 46.13). PTH also stimulates the kidneys to reabsorb Ca²⁺ from the urine and leads to the activation of vitamin D, needed for the absorption of calcium from food in the intestine.

Vitamin D

Vitamin D is produced in the skin from a cholesterol derivative in response to ultraviolet light. It is called an essential vitamin because in temperate regions of the world a dietary source is needed to supplement the amount produced by the skin. (In the tropics, people generally receive enough exposure to sunlight to produce adequate vitamin D.) Diffusing into the blood from the skin, vitamin D is actually an inactive form of a hormone. In order to become activated, the molecule must gain two hydroxyl groups (—OH); one of these is added by an enzyme in the liver, the other by an enzyme in the kidneys.

The enzyme needed for this final step is stimulated by PTH, thereby producing the active form of vitamin D known as 1,25-dihydroxyvitamin D. This hormone stimulates the intestinal absorption of Ca²⁺ and thereby helps raise blood Ca²⁺ levels so that bone can become properly mineralized. A diet deficient in vitamin D thus leads to poor bone formation, a condition called rickets.

To ensure adequate amounts of this essential hormone, vitamin D is now added to commercially produced milk in the United States and some other countries. This is certainly a preferable alternative to the prior method of vitamin D administration, the dreaded dose of cod liver oil.

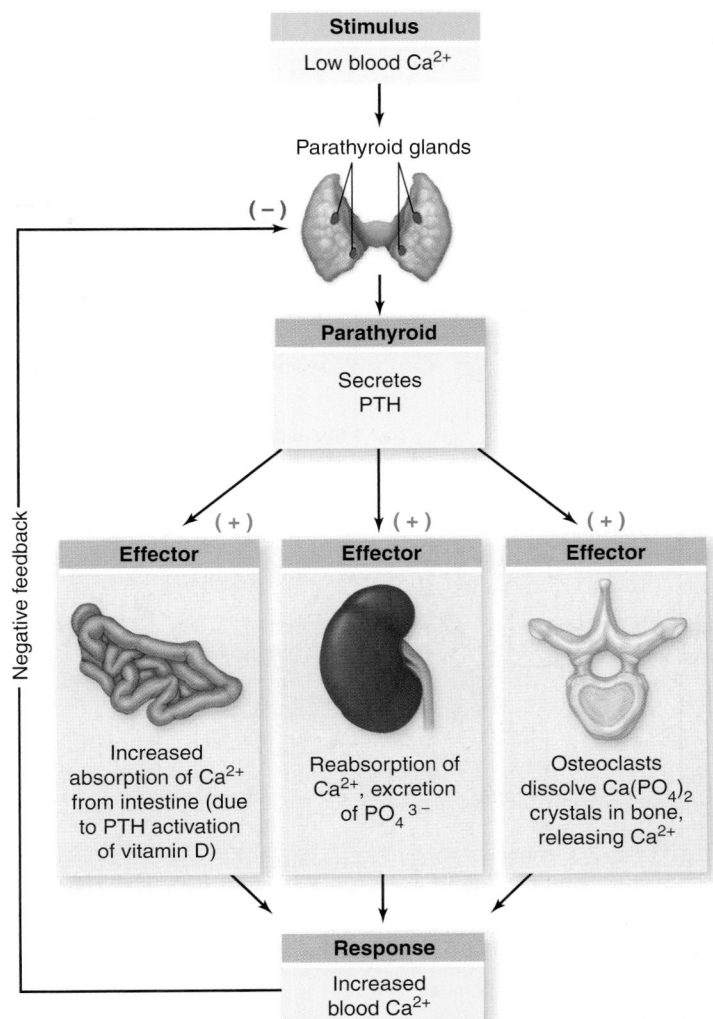

Figure 46.13 Regulation of blood Ca²⁺ levels by parathyroid hormone (PTH). When blood Ca²⁺ levels are low, PTH is released by the parathyroid glands. PTH directly stimulates the dissolution of bone and the reabsorption of Ca²⁺ by the kidneys. PTH indirectly promotes the intestinal absorption of Ca²⁺ by stimulating the production of the active form of vitamin D.

The adrenal gland releases both catecholamine and steroid hormones

The **adrenal glands** are located just above each kidney (figure 46.14). Each gland is composed of an inner portion, the *adrenal medulla*, and an outer layer, the *adrenal cortex*.

The adrenal medulla

The adrenal medulla receives neural input from axons of the sympathetic division of the autonomic nervous system, and it secretes the catecholamines epinephrine and norepinephrine in response to stimulation by these axons. The actions of these hormones trigger "alarm" responses similar to those elicited by the sympathetic division, helping to prepare the body for extreme efforts. Among the effects of these hormones are an increased heart rate, increased blood pressure, dilation of the bronchioles, elevation in blood glucose, reduced blood flow to the skin and digestive organs, and

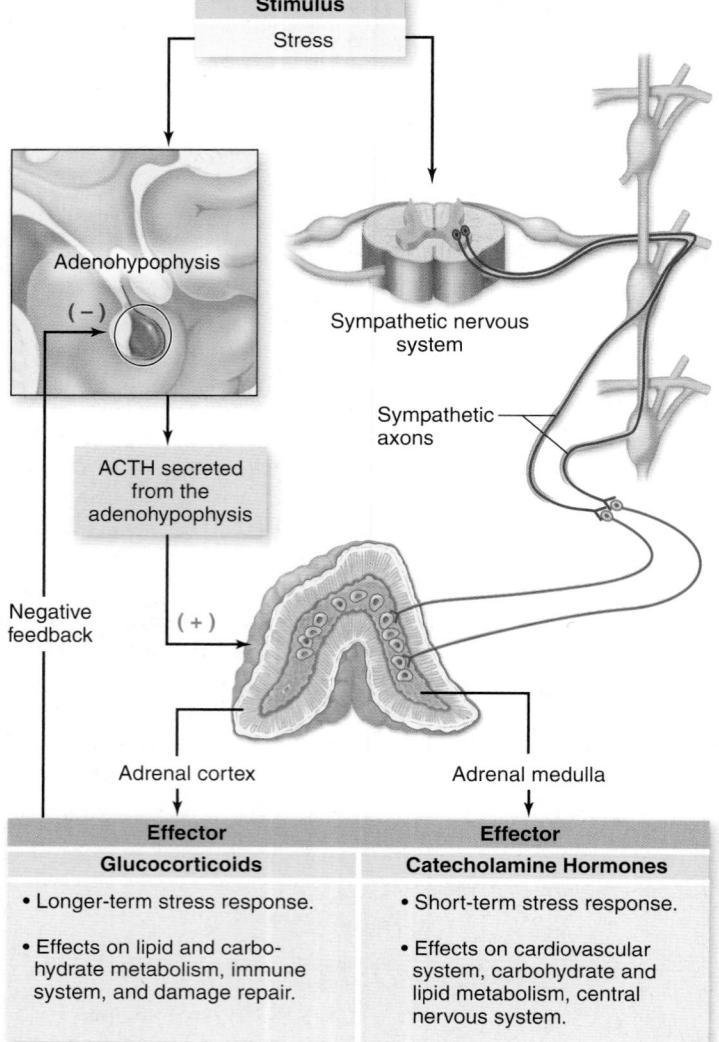

Figure 46.14 The adrenal glands. The adrenal medulla produces the catecholamines epinephrine and norepinephrine, which initiate a response to acute stress. The adrenal cortex produces steroid hormones, including the glucocorticoid cortisol. In response to stress, cortisol secretion increases glucose production and stimulates the immune response.

increased blood flow to the heart and muscles. The actions of epinephrine, released as a hormone, supplement those of neurotransmitters released by the sympathetic nervous system.

The adrenal cortex

The hormones from the adrenal cortex are all steroids and are referred to collectively as *corticosteroids*. *Cortisol* (also called hydrocortisone) and related steroids secreted by the adrenal cortex act on various cells in the body to maintain glucose homeostasis. In mammals, these hormones are referred to as glucocorticoids, and their secretion is primarily regulated by ACTH from the anterior pituitary.

The glucocorticoids stimulate the breakdown of muscle protein into amino acids, which are carried by the blood to the liver. They also stimulate the liver to produce the enzymes needed for gluconeogenesis, which can convert amino acids

into glucose. Glucose synthesis from protein is particularly important during very long periods of fasting or exercise, when blood glucose levels might otherwise become dangerously low.

Whereas glucocorticoids are important in the daily regulation of glucose and protein, they, like the adrenal medulla hormones, are also secreted in large amounts in response to stress. It has been suggested that during stress they activate the production of glucose at the expense of protein and fat synthesis.

In addition to regulating glucose metabolism, the glucocorticoids modulate some aspects of the immune response. The physiological significance of this action is still unclear, and it may be apparent only when glucocorticoids are maintained at elevated levels for long periods of time (such as long-term stress). Glucocorticoids are used to suppress the immune system in persons with immune disorders (such as rheumatoid arthritis) and to prevent the immune system from rejecting organ and tissue transplants. Derivatives of cortisol, such as prednisone, have widespread medical use as anti-inflammatory agents.

Aldosterone, the other major corticosteroid, is classified as a mineralocorticoid because it helps regulate mineral balance. The secretion of aldosterone from the adrenal cortex is activated by angiotensin II, a product of the renin–angiotensin system described in chapter 51, as well as high blood K^+. Angiotensin II activates aldosterone secretion when blood pressure falls.

A primary action of aldosterone is to stimulate the kidneys to reabsorb Na^+ from the urine. (Blood levels of Na^+ decrease if Na^+ is not reabsorbed from the urine.) Sodium is the major extracellular solute; it is needed for the maintenance of normal blood volume and pressure, as well as for the generation of action potentials in neurons and muscles. Without aldosterone, the kidneys would lose excessive amounts of blood Na^+ in the urine.

Aldosterone-stimulated reabsorption of Na^+ also results in kidney excretion of K^+ in the urine. Aldosterone thus prevents K^+ from accumulating in the blood, which would lead to malfunctions in electrical signaling in nerves and muscles. Because of these essential functions performed by aldosterone, removal of the adrenal glands, or diseases that prevent aldosterone secretion, are invariably fatal without hormone therapy.

Pancreatic hormones are primary regulators of carbohydrate metabolism

The pancreas is located adjacent to the stomach and is connected to the duodenum of the small intestine by the pancreatic duct. It secretes bicarbonate ions and a variety of digestive enzymes into the small intestine through this duct (see chapter 48), and for a long time the pancreas was thought to be solely an exocrine gland.

Insulin

In 1869, however, a German medical student named Paul Langerhans described some unusual clusters of cells scattered throughout the pancreas; these clusters came to be called *islets of Langerhans*. They are now more commonly called pancreatic islets. Laboratory workers later observed that the surgical removal of the pancreas caused glucose to appear in the urine, the hallmark of the disease diabetes mellitus. This led to the discovery that the pancreas, specifically the islets of Langerhans, produced a hormone that prevents this disease.

That hormone is **insulin,** secreted by the beta (β) cells of the islets. Insulin was not isolated until 1922 when Banting and Best succeeded where many others had not. On January 11, 1922, they injected an extract purified from beef pancreas into a 13-year-old diabetic boy, whose weight had fallen to 65 pounds and who was not expected to survive. With that single injection, the glucose level in the boy's blood fell 25%. A more potent extract soon brought the level down to near normal. The doctors had achieved the first instance of successful insulin therapy.

Glucagon

The islets of Langerhans produce another hormone; the alpha (α) cells of the islets secrete **glucagon,** which acts antagonistically to insulin (figure 46.15). When a person eats carbohydrates, the blood glucose concentration rises. Blood glucose directly activates the secretion of insulin by the β cells and inhibits the secretion of glucagon by the α cells. Insulin promotes the cellular uptake of glucose into the liver, muscle, and fat cells. It also activates the storage of glucose as glycogen in liver and muscle or as fat in fat cells. Between meals, when the concentration of blood glucose falls, insulin secretion decreases, and glucagon secretion increases. Glucagon promotes the hydrolysis of stored glycogen in the liver and fat in

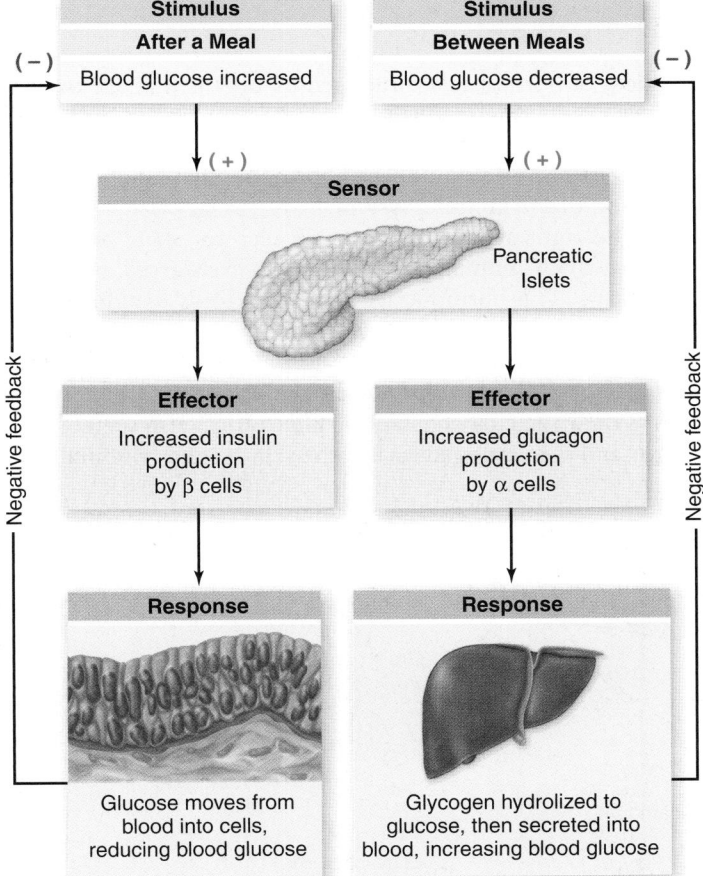

Figure 46.15 The antagonistic actions of insulin and glucagon on blood glucose. Insulin stimulates the cellular uptake of blood glucose into skeletal muscles, adipose cells, and the liver after a meal. Glucagon stimulates the hydrolysis of liver glycogen between meals, so that the liver can secrete glucose into the blood. These antagonistic effects help to maintain homeostasis of the blood glucose concentration.

adipose tissue. As a result, glucose and fatty acids are released into the blood and can be taken up by cells and used for energy.

Treatment of diabetes

Although many hormones favor the movement of glucose into cells, insulin is the only hormone that promotes movement of glucose from blood into cells. For this reason, disruptions in insulin signaling can have serious consequences. People with *type I*, or insulin-dependent, diabetes mellitus, lack the insulin-secreting β cells and consequently produce no insulin. Treatment for these patients consists of insulin injections. (Because insulin is a peptide hormone, it would be digested if taken orally and must instead be injected subcutaneously.)

In the past, only insulin extracted from the pancreas of pigs or cattle was available, but today people with insulin-dependent diabetes can inject themselves with human insulin produced by genetically engineered bacteria. Active research on the possibility of transplanting islets of Langerhans holds much promise of a lasting treatment for these patients.

Most diabetic patients, however, have *type II*, or noninsulin-dependent, diabetes mellitus. They generally have normal or even above-normal levels of insulin in their blood, but their cells have a reduced sensitivity to insulin. These people may not require insulin injections and can often control their diabetes through diet and exercise. It is estimated that over 90% of the cases of diabetes in North America are type II. Worldwide at least 171 million suffer from diabetes, and it is expected that this number will grow. Type II diabetes is especially common in developed countries, and it has been suggested that there is a linkage between type II diabetes and obesity.

Learning Outcomes Review 46.4

The major peripheral endocrine glands are the thyroid and parathyroid glands, the adrenal glands, and the pancreas. Calcium homeostasis results from the action of calcitonin, parathyroid hormone, and vitamin D. The adrenal glands produce stress hormones. Insulin and glucagon, antagonists from the pancreas, help maintain blood glucose at a normal level.

■ *Why does your body need two hormones to maintain blood sugar at a constant level?*

46.5 Other Hormones and Their Effects

Learning Outcomes

1. Characterize the role of sex steroids in development.
2. List nonendrocrine sources of hormones.
3. Identify the insect hormones involved in molting and metamorphosis.

A variety of vertebrate and invertebrate processes are regulated by hormones and other chemical messengers, and in this section we review the most important ones.

Sex steroids regulate reproductive development

The ovaries and testes in vertebrates are important endocrine glands, producing the sex steroid hormones, including estrogens, progesterone, and testosterone (to be described in detail in chapter 53). Estrogen and progesterone are the primary "female" sex steroids, and testosterone and its immediate derivatives are the primary "male" sex steroids, or androgens. Both types of hormone can be found in both sexes, however.

During embryonic development, testosterone production in the male embryo is critical for the development of male sex organs. In mammals, sex steroids are responsible for the development of secondary sexual characteristics at puberty. These characteristics include breasts in females, body hair, and increased muscle mass in males. Because of this latter effect, some athletes have misused androgens to increase muscle mass. Use of steroids for this purpose has been condemned by virtually all major sports organizations, and it can cause liver disorders as well as a number of other serious side effects.

In females, sex steroids are especially important in maintaining the sexual cycle. Estrogen and progesterone produced in the ovaries are critical regulators of the menstrual and ovarian cycles. During pregnancy, estrogen production in the placenta maintains the uterine lining, which protects and nourishes the developing embryo.

Melatonin is crucial to circadian cycles

Another major endocrine gland is the pineal gland, located in the roof of the third ventricle of the brain in most vertebrates (see figure 44.22). It is about the size of a pea and is shaped like a pinecone, which gives it its name.

The pineal gland evolved from a medial light-sensitive eye (sometimes called a "third eye," although it could not form images) at the top of the skull in primitive vertebrates. This pineal eye is still present in primitive fish (cyclostomes) and some modern reptiles. In other vertebrates, however, the pineal gland is buried deep in the brain, and it functions as an endocrine gland by secreting the hormone melatonin.

Melatonin was named for its ability to cause blanching of the skin of lower vertebrates by reducing the dispersal of melanin granules. We now know, however, that it serves as an important timing signal delivered through the blood. Melatonin levels in the blood increase in darkness and fall during the daytime.

The secretion of melatonin is regulated by activity of the *suprachiasmatic nucleus* (*SCN*) of the hypothalamus. The SCN is known to function as the major biological clock in vertebrates, entraining (synchronizing) various body processes to a circadian rhythm—one that repeats every 24 hr. Through regulation by the SCN, the secretion of melatonin by the pineal gland is activated in the dark.

This daily cycling of melatonin release regulates sleep/wake and temperature cycles. Disruptions of these cycles, as occurs with jet lag or night shift work, can sometimes be minimized by melatonin administration. Melatonin also helps regulate reproductive cycles in some vertebrate species that have distinct breeding seasons.

Some hormones are not produced by endocrine glands

A variety of hormones are secreted by organs that are not exclusively endocrine glands. The thymus is the site of T cell production in many vertebrates and T cell maturation in mammals. It also secretes a number of hormones that function in the regulation of the immune system.

The right atrium of the heart secretes *atrial natriuretic hormone*, which stimulates the kidneys to excrete salt and water in the urine. This hormone acts antagonistically to aldosterone, which promotes salt and water retention.

The kidneys secrete *erythropoietin*, a hormone that stimulates the bone marrow to produce red blood cells. Other organs, such as the liver, stomach, and small intestine, also secrete hormones, and as mentioned earlier, the skin secretes vitamin D.

Figure 46.16 Hormonal control of metamorphosis in the silkworm moth, *Bombyx mori*. Molting hormone, ecdysone, controls when molting occurs. Brain hormone stimulates the prothoracic gland to produce ecdysone. Juvenile hormone determines the result of a particular molt. Juvenile hormone is produced by bodies near the brain called the corpora allata. High levels of juvenile hormone inhibit the formation of the pupa. Low levels of juvenile hormone are necessary for the pupal molt and metamorphosis.

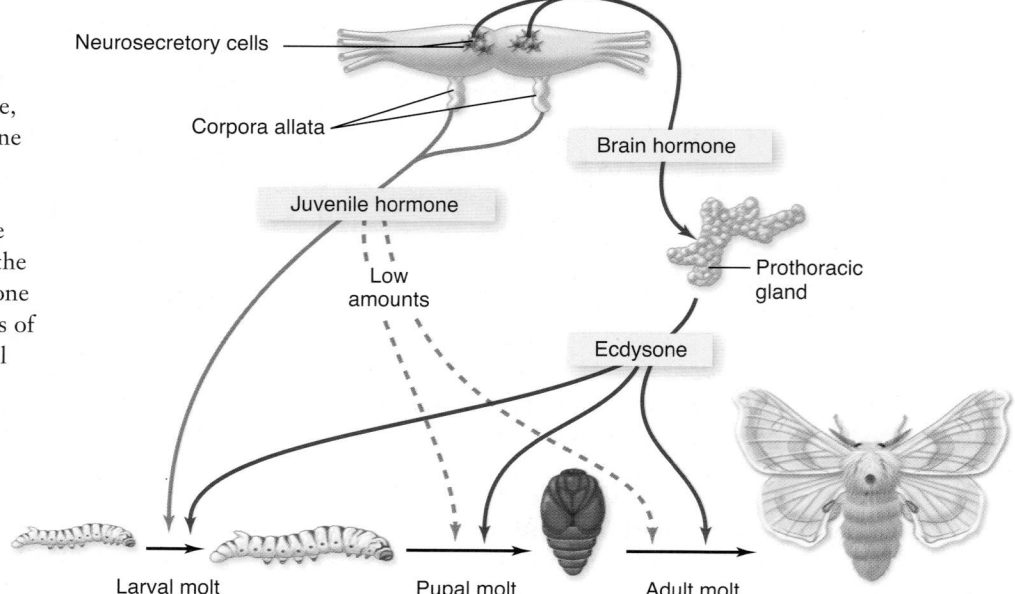

Neurosecretory cells

Corpora allata

Juvenile hormone

Low amounts

Brain hormone

Prothoracic gland

Ecdysone

Larval molt   Pupal molt   Adult molt

Insect hormones control molting and metamorphosis

Most invertebrate groups produce hormones as well; these control reproduction, growth, and color change. A dramatic action of hormones in insects is similar to the role of thyroid hormones in amphibian metamorphosis.

As insects grow during postembryonic development, their hardened exoskeletons do not expand. To overcome this problem, insects undergo a series of molts wherein they shed their old exoskeleton (figure 46.16) and secrete a new, larger one. In some insects, a juvenile insect, or larva, undergoes a radical transformation to the adult form during a single molt. This process is called metamorphosis.

Hormonal secretions influence both molting and metamorphosis in insects. Prior to molting, neurosecretory cells on the surface of the brain secrete a small peptide, **prothoracicotropic hormone (PTTH),** which in turn stimulates a gland in the thorax called the prothoracic gland to produce **molting hormone,** or **ecdysone** (see figure 46.16). High levels of ecdysone bring about the biochemical and behavioral changes that cause molting to occur.

Another pair of endocrine glands near the brain, called the *corpora allata*, produce a hormone called **juvenile hormone.** High levels of juvenile hormone prevent the transformation to the adult and result in a larval-to-larval molt. If the level of juvenile hormone is low, however, the molt will result in metamorphosis (figure 46.17).

Cancer cells may alter hormone production or have altered hormonal responses

Hormones and paracrine secretions actively regulate growth and cell division. Normally, hormone production is kept under precise control, but malfunctions in signaling systems can sometimes occur. Unregulated hormone stimulation can then lead to serious physical consequences.

Tumors that develop in endocrine glands, such as the anterior pituitary or the thyroid, can produce excessive amounts of hormones, causing conditions such as gigantism or hyperthyroidism. Spontaneous mutations can damage receptors or intracellular signaling proteins, with the result that target cell responses are activated even in the absence of hormone stimulation. Mutations in growth factor receptors, for example, can activate excessive cell division, resulting in tumor formation. Some tumors that develop in steroid-responsive tissues, such as the breast and prostate, remain sensitive to hormone stimulation. Blocking steroid hormone production can therefore diminish tumor growth.

The important effects of hormones on development and differentiation are illustrated by the case of diethystilbestrol (DES). DES is a synthetic estrogen that was given to pregnant women from 1940 to 1970 to prevent miscarriage. It was subsequently discovered that daughters who had been exposed to DES as fetuses had an elevated probability of developing a rare form of cervical cancer later in life. Developmental alterations elicited by hormone treatment may thus take many years to become apparent.

Hypothesis: *Juvenile hormone blocks or inhibits the stimulation of gene expression by ecdysone.*

Prediction: *Treatment of isolated imaginal discs with ecdysone plus increasing amounts of JH should show a decrease in ecdysone stimulated transcription.*

Test: *Discs dissected from late third instar* Drosophila *larvae are incubated in the presence of ecdysone, with and without JH. Incorporation of ^{3}H-UTP into RNA was used as a measure of gene expression.*

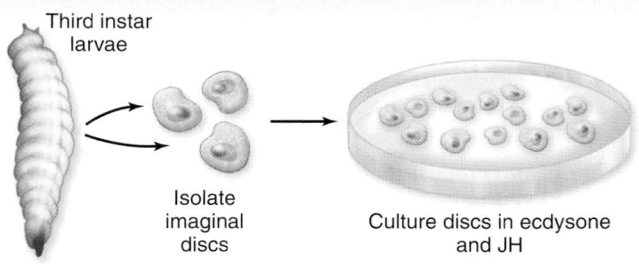

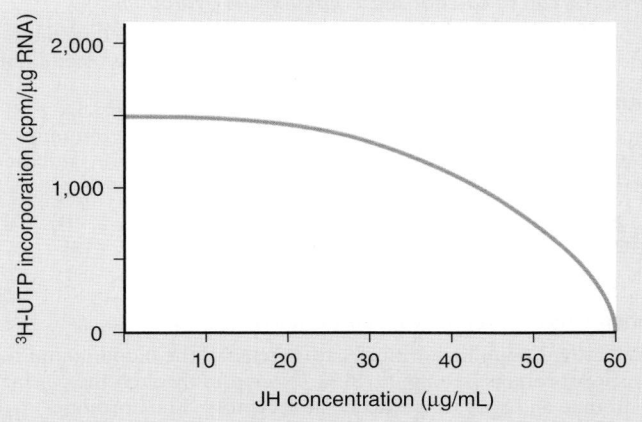

Result: *The graph shows a relatively high incorporation of ^{3}H-UTP in the presence of ecdysone alone. The addition of JH causes dose-dependent reduction of RNA synthesis.*

Conclusion: *JH inhibits the ecdysone-stimulated synthesis of RNA in imaginal discs.*

Further Experiments: *How else can this system with isolated imaginal discs be used to analyze metamorphosis?*

Figure 46.17 **Effect of ecdysone and juvenile hormone on RNA synthesis in isolated *Drosophila* imaginal discs.**

Learning Outcomes Review 46.5

Testosterone causes an embryo to develop as a male; testosterone and estrogen produced at puberty are responsible for secondary sex characteristics. The female menstrual cycle is regulated by sex hormone balance. The thymus, the right atrium of the heart, and the kidneys secrete hormones although it is not their main function. In insects, molting hormone elicits molting, and low levels of juvenile hormone cause metamorphosis.

■ *Atrial natriuretic hormone reduces blood volume; would this affect blood pressure?*

46.1 Regulation of Body Processes by Chemical Messengers

Hormones are signaling molecules carried by the blood and may have distant targets. Paracrine regulators act locally, and pheromones released into the environment communicate between individuals of the same species.

Some molecules act as both circulating hormones and neurotransmitters.

Norepinephrine is a neurotransmitter in the sympathetic nervous system and also is a hormone that is released into the blood by the adrenal glands.

Endocrine glands produce three chemical classes of hormones.

The three classes of endocrine hormones are peptides and proteins, such as TSH; amino acid derivatives, such as thyroxine; and steroids, such as estrogen and testosterone (see table 46.1).

Hormones can be categorized as lipophilic or hydrophilic.

Lipophilic hormones are fat-soluble and can cross the cell membrane; hydrophilic hormones are water-soluble and cannot cross membranes.

Paracrine regulators exert powerful effects within tissues.

Paracrine regulation occurs in most organs and among immune-system cells. Prostaglandins are involved in inflammation, and they are the target of NSAIDs.

46.2 Actions of Lipophilic Versus Hydrophilic Hormones

Lipophilic hormones activate intracellular receptors.

Circulating lipophilic hormones are carried in the blood bound to transport proteins (see figure 46.3). They pass through the plasma membrane and activate intracellular receptors. The hormone-receptor complex can bind to specific gene promoter regions termed hormone response elements to activate transcription.

Hydrophilic hormones activate receptors on target cell membranes.

Hydrophilic hormones bind to a membrane receptor to initiate a signal transduction pathway (see figure 46.6). Many receptors are kinases that phosphorylate proteins directly. Others are G protein–coupled receptors that activate a second-messenger system. Hydrophilic hormones tend to be short-lived, but lipophilic hormones tend to have effects of longer duration.

46.3 The Pituitary and Hypothalamus: The Body's Control Centers

The pituitary is a compound endocrine gland.

The anterior pituitary (adenohypophysis) is composed of glandular tissue derived from epithelial tissue; the posterior pituitary (neurohypophysis) is fibrous and is derived from neural tissue.

The posterior pituitary stores and releases two neurohormones.

The posterior pituitary contains axons from the hypothalamus that release neurohormones. One of these is ADH, involved in water reabsorption; the other is oxytocin.

The anterior pituitary produces seven hormones.

The hormones produced by the anterior pituitary include peptide, protein and glycoprotein hormones. These hormones tend to stimulate growth, and many are tropic hormones that stimulate other endocrine glands (see table 46.1).

Hypothalamic neurohormones regulate the anterior pituitary.

Releasing and inhibiting hormones produced in the hypothalamus pass to the anterior pituitary through a portal system and regulate the anterior pituitary's hormone production (see figure 46.8).

Feedback from peripheral endocrine glands regulates anterior-pituitary hormones.

The activity of the anterior pituitary is also regulated by negative feedback; for example, thyroxine, produced by the thyroid in response to TSH, inhibits further secretion of TSH (see figure 46.9).

Hormones of the anterior pituitary work directly and indirectly.

Three of the seven hormones, GH, prolactin, and MSH, work directly on nonendocrine tissues; the other four, ACTH, TSH, LH, and FSH, are tropic hormones that have endocrine glands as their targets. Defects in GH production can lead to either pituitary dwarfism (low), or gigantism (high).

46.4 The Major Peripheral Endocrine Glands

Some endocrine glands are controlled by tropic hormones of the pituitary, others are independent of pituitary control.

The thyroid gland regulates basal metabolism and development.

The thyroid hormones thyroxine and triiodothyronine regulate basal metabolism in vertebrates and trigger metamorphosis in amphibians (see figure 46.12).

Calcium homeostasis is regulated by several hormones.

Blood calcium is regulated by calcitonin, which lowers blood calcium levels, and parathyroid hormone, which raises blood calcium levels (see figure 46.13).

The adrenal gland releases both catecholamine and steroid hormones.

Catecholamines, epinephrine and norepinephrine, trigger "alarm" responses (see figure 46.14). Corticosteroids maintain glucose homeostasis and modulate some aspects of the immune response.

Pancreatic hormones are primary regulators of carbohydrate metabolism.

Blood glucose is controlled by antagonistic hormones. The pancreas secretes insulin, which reduces blood glucose, and glucagon, which raises blood glucose (see figure 46.15). Type I diabetes arises from loss of insulin-producing cells, and type II is a result of insulin insensitivity.

46.5 Other Hormones and Their Effects

Sex steroids regulate reproductive development.

Sex steroids regulate sexual development and reproduction. The ovaries primarily produce estrogen and progesterone, which are responsible for the menstrual cycle. The testes produce testosterone.

Melatonin is crucial to circadian cycles.

The pineal gland produces melatonin, which can control the dispersion of pigment granules and the daily wake–sleep cycles.

Some hormones are not produced by endocrine glands.

The thymus secretes hormones that regulate the immune system. The right atrium of the heart secretes atrial natriuretic hormone, which acts antagonistically to aldosterone. The skin manufactures and secretes vitamin D.

Insect hormones control molting and metamorphosis.

In insects the hormone ecdysone stimulates molting, and juvenile hormone levels control the nature of the molt. Metamorphosis requires high ecdysone and low juvenile hormone.

Cancer cells may alter hormone production or have altered hormonal responses.

Cancer developing from cells targeted by hormones, such as in the breast and prostate, may still be stimulated by those hormones.

Review Questions

UNDERSTAND

1. Which of the following best describes hormones?
   a. Hormones are relatively unstable and work only in the area adjacent to the gland that produced them.
   b. Hormones are long-lasting chemicals released from glands.
   c. All hormones are lipid-soluble.
   d. Hormones are chemical messengers that are released into the environment.

2. Steroid hormones
   a. can diffuse through the membrane without a carrier.
   b. have a direct effect on gene expression.
   c. bind to membrane receptors.
   d. both a and b

3. Second messengers are activated in response to
   a. steroid hormones.   c. hydrophilic hormones.
   b. thyroxine.   d. all of these.

4. Which of the following is true about lipophilic hormones?
   a. They are freely soluble in the blood.
   b. They require a transport protein in the bloodstream.
   c. They cannot enter their target cells.
   d. They are rapidly deactivated after binding to their receptors.

5. An organ is classified as part of the endocrine system if it
   a. produces cholesterol.
   b. is capable of converting amino acids into hormones.
   c. has intracellular receptors for hormones.
   d. secretes hormones into the circulatory system.

6. Hormones released from the pituitary gland have two different sources. Those that are produced by the neurons of the hypothalamus are released through the _____, and those produced within the pituitary are released through the _____.
   a. thalamus; hippocampus
   b. neurohypophysis; adenohypophysis
   c. right pituitary; left pituitary
   d. cortex; medulla

7. Which of the following conditions is unrelated to the production of growth hormone?
   a. Control of blood calcium
   b. Pituitary dwarfism
   c. Increased milk production in cows
   d. Acromegaly

APPLY

1. You think one of your teammates is using anabolic steroids to build muscle. You know that continued use of steroids can cause profound changes in cell function. This is due in part to the fact that these hormones act
   a. to regulate gene expression.
   b. by activating second messengers.
   c. as protein kinases.
   d. via G protein–coupled receptors.

2. Your Uncle Sal likes to party. When he goes out drinking, he complains that he needs to urinate more often. You explain to him that this is because alcohol suppresses the release of the hormone
   a. thyroxine, which increases water reabsorption from the kidney.
   b. thyroxine, which decreases water reabsorption from the kidney.
   c. ADH, which decreases water reabsorption from the kidney.
   d. ADH, which increases water reabsorption from the kidney.

3. Your new research project is to design a pesticide that will disrupt the endocrine systems of arthropods without harming humans and other mammals. Which of the following substances should be the target of your investigations?
   a. Insulin   c. Juvenile hormone
   b. ADH   d. Cortisol

4. Coat color in mammals is controlled by a hormone receptor called the melanocortin receptor. When this receptor is bound by the hormone MSH, pigment cells produce dark eumelanin. When the receptor is bound by an MSH antagonist that prevents MSH binding, pigment cells make yellow/red pheomelanin. In the Irish Setter, the overall red coat color could be due to a mutation in the
   a. receptor that prevents the antagonist from binding.
   b. receptor that prevents MSH from binding.
   c. MSH protein such that it binds the receptor more efficiently.
   d. antagonist such that it no longer binds to the receptor.

5. Tumors that affect the pituitary can lead to decreases in some, but not all, hormones released by the pituitary. A patient with such a tumor exhibits fatigue, weight loss, and low blood sugar. This is probably due to lack of production of
   a. GH, which leads to loss of muscle mass.
   b. ACTH, which leads to loss of production of glucocorticoids.

c. TSH, which leads to loss of production of thyroxin.

d. ADH, which leads to excess urine production.

6. You experience a longer period than normal between meals. Your body's response to this will be to produce

    a. insulin to raise your blood sugar.

    b. glucagon to raise your blood sugar.

    c. insulin to lower your blood sugar.

    d. glucagon to lower your blood sugar.

7. Mild vitamin D deficiency can lead to osteoporosis, or reduced bone mineral density. This is thought to be due to an association with increased levels of

    a. calcitonin, which leads to an increase in serum Ca^{2+} and bone loss.

    b. PTH, which leads to an increase in serum Ca^{2+} and bone loss.

    c. ADH, which reduces blood pressure and leads to bone loss.

    d. insulin, which leads to a decrease in blood glucose and bone loss.

SYNTHESIZE

1. How can blocking hormone production decrease cancerous tumor growth?

2. Suppose that two different organs, such as the liver and heart, are sensitive to a particular hormone (such as epinephrine). The cells in both organs have identical receptors for the hormone, and hormone-receptor binding produces the same intracellular second messenger in both organs. However, the hormone produces different effects in the two organs. Explain how this can happen.

3. Many physiological parameters, such as blood Ca^{2+} concentration and blood glucose levels, are controlled by two hormones that have opposite effects. What is the advantage of achieving regulation in this manner instead of by using a single hormone that changes the parameters in one direction only?

ONLINE RESOURCE

www.ravenbiology.com

Understand, Apply, and Synthesize—enhance your study with animations that bring concepts to life and practice tests to assess your understanding. Your instructor may also recommend the interactive eBook, individualized learning tools, and more.

Chapter 47

The Musculoskeletal System

Chapter Outline

47.1   Types of Skeletal Systems

47.2   A Closer Look at Bone

47.3   Joints and Skeletal Movement

47.4   Muscle Contraction

47.5   Modes of Animal Locomotion

Introduction

The ability to move is so much a part of our daily lives that we tend to take it for granted. It is made possible by the combination of a semirigid skeletal system, joints that act as hinges, and a muscular system that can pull on this skeleton. Animal locomotion can be thought of as muscular action that produces a change in body shape, which places a force on the outside environment. When a race horse runs down the track, its legs move forward and backward. As its feet contact the ground, the force they exert move its body forward at a considerable speed. In a similar way, when a bird takes off into flight, its wings exert force on the air; a swimming fish's movements push against the water. In this chapter, we will examine the nature of the muscular and skeletal systems that allow animal movement.

Muscles have to pull against something to produce the changes that cause movement. This necessary form of supporting structure is called a skeletal system. Zoologists commonly recognize three types of skeletal systems in animals: **hydrostatic skeletons**, **exoskeletons**, and **endoskeletons**.

Hydrostatic skeletons use water pressure inside a body wall

Hydrostatic skeletons are found primarily in soft-bodied terrestrial invertebrates, such as earthworms and slugs, and soft-bodied aquatic invertebrates, such as jellyfish, and squids.

Musculoskeletal action in earthworms

In these animals a fluid-filled central cavity is encompassed by two sets of muscles in the body wall: circular muscles that are repeated in segments and run the length of the body, and longitudinal muscles that oppose the action of the circular muscles.

Muscles act on the fluid in the body's central space, which represents the hydrostatic skeleton. As locomotion begins (figure 47.1) the anterior circular muscles contract, pressing on the inner fluid, and forcing the front of the body to become thin as the body wall in this region extends forward.

On the underside of a worm's body are short, bristle-like structures called chaetae. When circular muscles act, the chaetae of that region are pulled up close to the body and lose contact with the ground. Circular-muscle activity is passed backward, segment by segment, to create a backward wave of contraction.

As this wave continues, the anterior circular muscles now relax, and the longitudinal muscles take over, thickening the front end of the worm and allowing the chaetae to protrude and regain contact with the ground. The chaetae now prevent that body section from slipping backward. This locomotion process proceeds as waves of circular muscle contraction are followed by waves of longitudinal muscle effects.

Exoskeletons consist of a rigid outer covering

Exoskeletons are a rigid, hard case that surrounds the body. Arthropods, such as crustaceans and insects, have exoskeletons made of the polysaccharide *chitin* (figure 47.2a). As you learned in earlier chapters, chitin is found in the cell walls of fungi and some protists as well as in the exoskeletons of arthropods.

A chitinous exoskeleton resists bending and thus acts as the skeletal framework of the body; it also protects the internal organs and provides attachment sites for the muscles, which lie inside the exoskeletal casing. But in order to grow, the animal must periodically molt, shedding the exoskeleton (see chapter 34). The animal is vulnerable to predation until the new (slightly larger) exoskeleton forms. Molting crabs and lobsters often hide until the process is completed.

Exoskeletons have other limitations. The chitinous framework is not as strong as a bony, internal one. This fact by itself would set a limit for insect size, but there is a more important factor: Insects breathe through openings in their body that lead into tiny tubes, and as insect size increases beyond a certain limit, the ratio between the inside surface area of the tubes and the volume of the body overwhelms this sort of respiratory system. Finally, when muscles are confined within an

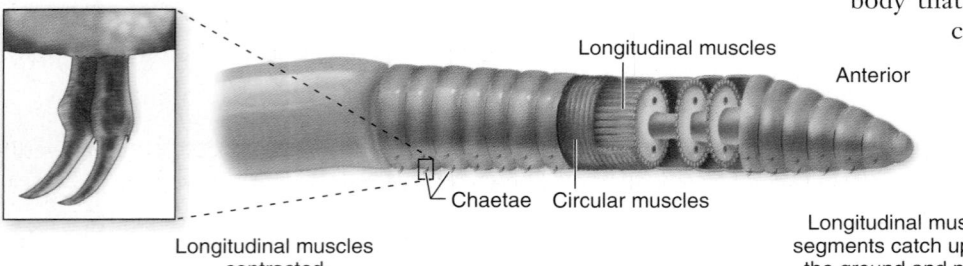

Longitudinal muscles
Anterior
Chaetae   Circular muscles

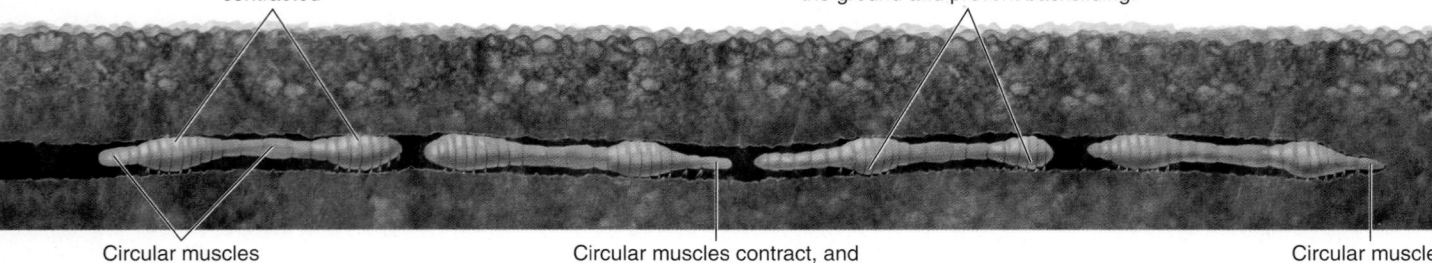

Longitudinal muscles contracted

Longitudinal muscles contract, and segments catch up. Chaetae attach to the ground and prevent backsliding.

Circular muscles contracted

Circular muscles contract, and anterior end moves forward. Chaetae lose attachment to ground.

Circular muscles contract, and anterior end moves forward.

Figure 47.1 Locomotion in earthworms. The hydrostatic skeleton of the earthworm uses muscles to move fluid within the segmented body cavity, changing the shape of the animal. When circular muscles contract the pressure in the fluid rises. At the same time the longitudinal muscles relax, and the body becomes longer and thinner. When the longitudinal muscles contract and the circular muscles relax, the chaetae of the worm's lower surface extend to prevent backsliding. A wave of circular followed by longitudinal muscle contractions down the body produces forward movement.

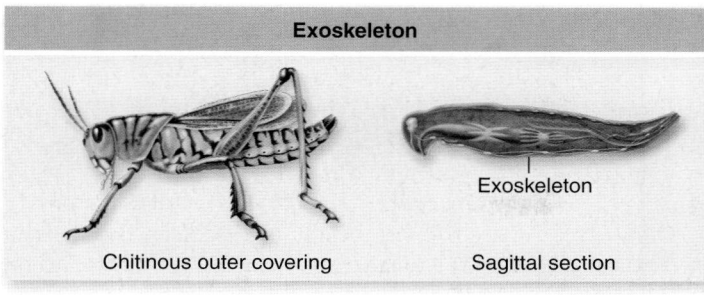

Exoskeleton

Chitinous outer covering

Exoskeleton

Sagittal section

a.

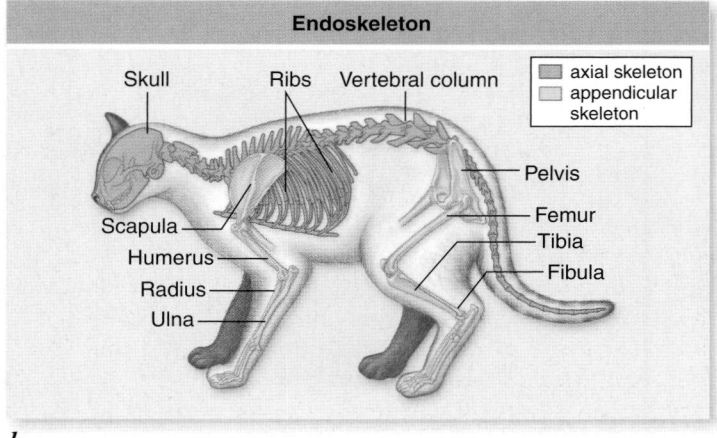

Endoskeleton

Skull · Ribs · Vertebral column

☐ axial skeleton
☐ appendicular skeleton

Pelvis
Femur
Tibia
Fibula

Scapula
Humerus
Radius
Ulna

b.

Figure 47.2 Exoskeleton and endoskeleton.
a. The hard, tough outer covering of an arthropod, such as this grasshopper, is its exoskeleton and is composed of chitin.
b. Vertebrates, such as this cat, have endoskeletons formed of bone and cartilage. Some of the major bony features are labeled.

exoskeleton, they cannot enlarge in size and power with increased use, as they can in animals with endoskeletons.

Endoskeletons are composed of hard, internal structures

Endoskeletons, found in vertebrates and echinoderms, are rigid internal skeletons that form the body's framework and offer surfaces for muscle attachment. Echinoderms, such as sea urchins and sand dollars, have skeletons made of calcite, a crystalline form of calcium carbonate. This calcium compound is different from that in bone, which is based on calcium phosphate.

Vertebrate skeletal tissues

The vertebrate endoskeleton (figure 47.2b) includes fibrous dense connective tissue along with the more rigid special connective tissues, cartilage or bone (see chapter 43). Cartilage is strong and slightly flexible, a characteristic important in such functions as padding the ends of bones where they come together in a joint. Although some large, active animals such as sharks have totally cartilaginous skeletons, bone is the main component in vertebrate skeletons. Bone is much stronger than cartilage and much less flexible.

Unlike chitin, both cartilage and bone are living tissues. Bone, particularly, can have high metabolic activity,

especially if bone cells are present throughout the matrix, a common condition. Bone, and to some extent cartilage, can change and remodel itself in response to injury or to physical stresses.

47.2 A Closer Look at Bone

Bone is a hard but resilient tissue that is unique to vertebrate animals. This connective tissue first appeared over 520 MYA and is now found in all vertebrates except cartilaginous fishes (see chapter 35).

Bones can be classified by two modes of development

Bone tissue itself can be of several types classified in a few different ways. The most common system is based on the way in which bone develops.

Intramembranous development

In intramembranous development, bones form within a layer of connective tissue. Many of the flat bones that make up the exterior of the skull and jaw are intramembranous.

Typically, the site of the intramembranous bone-to-be begins in a designated region in the dermis of the skin. During embryonic development, the dermis is formed largely of **mesenchyme**—a loose tissue consisting of undifferentiated mesenchyme cells and other cells that have arisen from them—along with collagen fibers. Some of the undifferentiated mesenchyme cells differentiate to become specialized cells called **osteoblasts** (figure 47.3). These osteoblasts arrange themselves along the collagenous fibers and begin to secrete the enzyme alkaline phosphatase, which causes calcium phosphate salts to form in a crystalline configuration called *hydroxyapatite*. The crystals merge along the fibers to encase them.

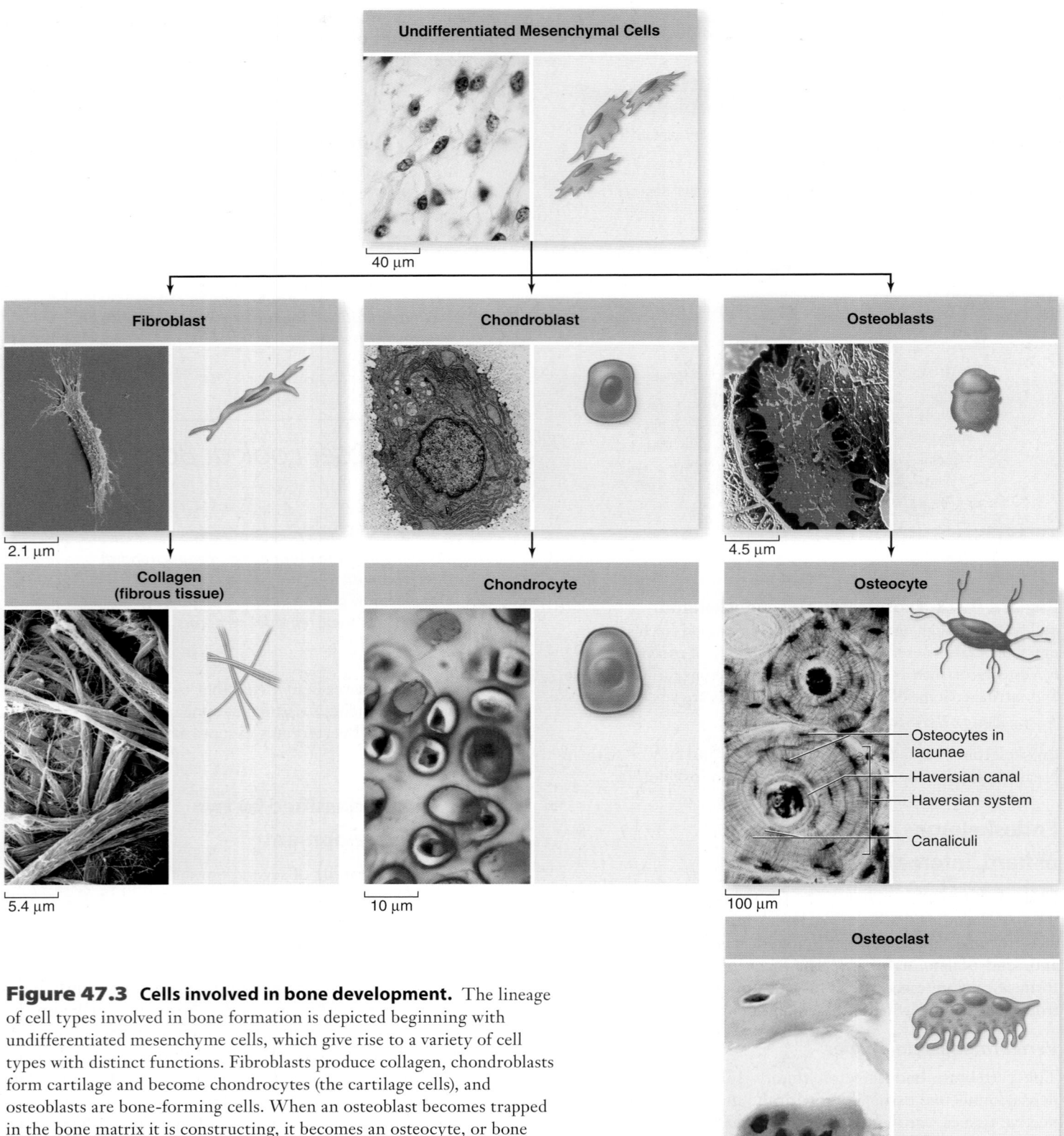

Figure 47.3 Cells involved in bone development. The lineage of cell types involved in bone formation is depicted beginning with undifferentiated mesenchyme cells, which give rise to a variety of cell types with distinct functions. Fibroblasts produce collagen, chondroblasts form cartilage and become chondrocytes (the cartilage cells), and osteoblasts are bone-forming cells. When an osteoblast becomes trapped in the bone matrix it is constructing, it becomes an osteocyte, or bone cell. The osteocyte is shown with a section of bone with Haversian systems and osteocytes between their lamellae. Osteocytes reside in spaces called lacunae. Small canals (canaliculi) radiate out from the central lacunar space, which contains the arms of the osteocyte. Osteoclasts, bone-removing cells, are not derived from mesenchyme cells but are formed by fusion of monocytes, a type of white blood cell.

The crystals give the bone its hardness, but without the resilience afforded by collagen's stretching ability, bone would be rigid but dangerously brittle. Typical bones have roughly equal volumes of collagen and hydroxyapatite, but hydroxyapatite contributes about 65% to the bone's weight.

As the osteoblasts continue to make bone crystals, some become trapped in the bone matrix and undergo dramatic changes in shape and function, now becoming cells called osteocytes (see figure 47.3). They lie in tight spaces within the bone matrix called lacunae. Little canals extending from the lacunae, called **canaliculi,** permit contact of the starburst-like extensions of each osteocyte with those of its neighbors (see figure 47.3). In this way, many cells within bones can participate in intercellular communication.

As an intramembranous bone grows, it requires alterations of shape. Imagine that you were modeling with clay, and you wanted to take a tiny clay bowl and make it larger. Simply putting more clay on the outside would not work; you would need to remove clay from the inside to increase the bowl's capacity as well. As bone grows, it must also undergo a remodeling process, with matrix being added in some regions and removed in others. This is where osteoclasts come in. These unusual cells are formed from the fusion of monocytes, a type of white blood cell, to form large multinucleate cells. Their function is to break down the bone matrix.

Endochondral development

Bones that form through endochondral development are typically those that are deeper in the body and form its architectural framework. Examples include vertebrae, ribs, bones of the shoulder and pelvis, long bones of the limbs, and the most internal of the skull bones. Endochondral bones begin as tiny, cartilaginous models that have the rough shape of the bones that eventually will be formed. Bone development of this kind consists of adding bone to the outside of the cartilaginous model, while replacing the interior cartilage with bone.

Bone added to the outside of the model is produced in the fibrous sheath that envelopes the cartilage. This sheath is tough and made of collagen fibers, but it also contains undifferentiated mesenchyme cells. Osteoblasts arise and sort themselves out along the fibers in the deepest part of the sheath. Bone is then formed between the sheath and the cartilaginous matrix. This process is somewhat similar to what occurs in the dermis in the production of intramembranous bone.

As the outer bone is formed, the interior cartilage begins to calcify. The calcium source for this process seems to be the cartilage cells themselves. As calcification continues, the inner cartilaginous tissue breaks down into pieces of debris. Blood vessels from the sheath, now called the periosteum, force their way through the outer bony jacket, thus entering the interior of the cartilaginous model, and cart off the debris. Again, trapped osteoblasts transform into osteocytes, and osteoclasts for bone remodeling arise from cell fusions in the same manner as occurs in intramembranous bone. Growth in bone thickness occurs by adding additional bone layers just beneath the periosteum.

Endochondral bones increase in length in a different way, unlike growth in intramembranous development. As an example, consider a long bone such as a mammalian humerus (in humans, the upper arm bone). Like many limb bones, it is formed of a slender shaft with widened ends, called **epiphyses** (figure 47.4).

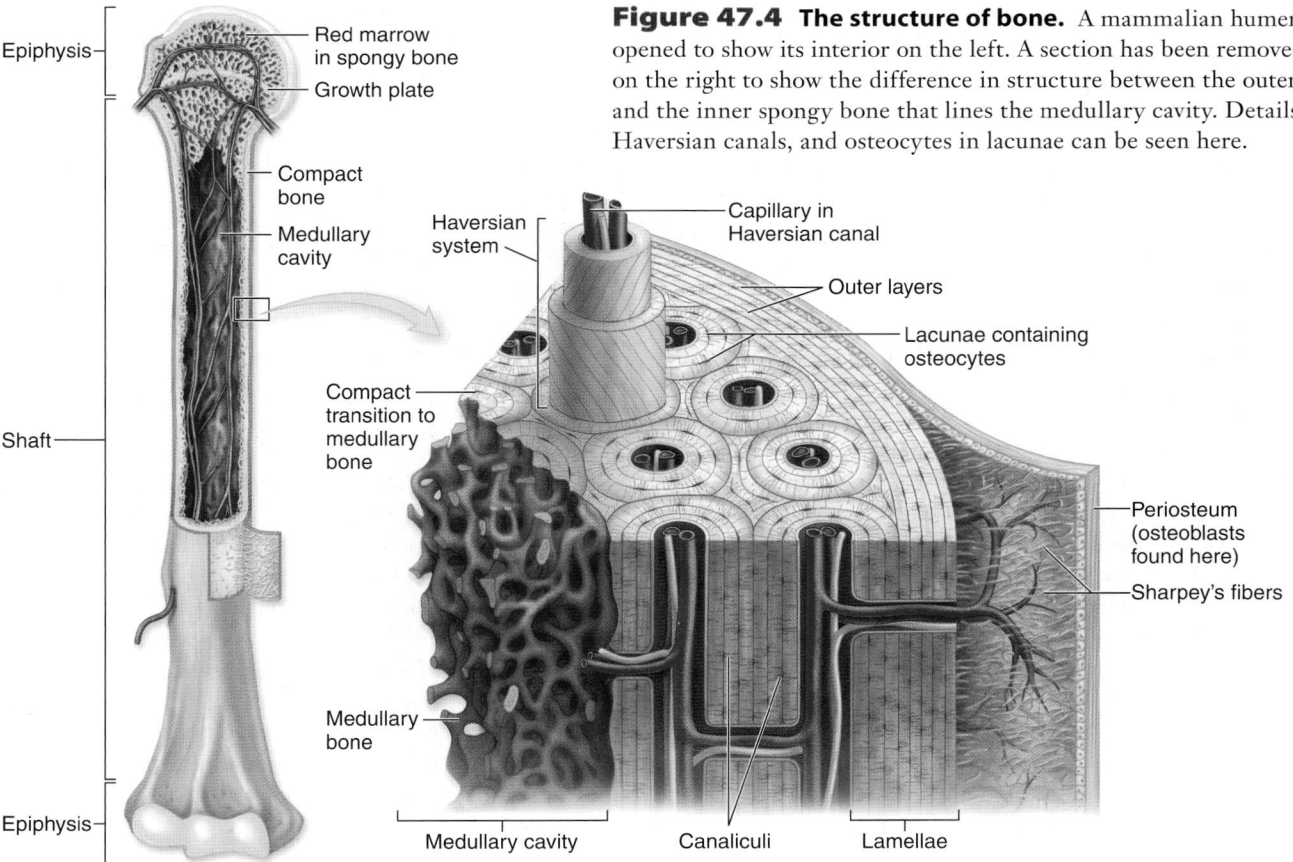

Figure 47.4 The structure of bone. A mammalian humerus is partly opened to show its interior on the left. A section has been removed and magnified on the right to show the difference in structure between the outer compact bone and the inner spongy bone that lines the medullary cavity. Details of basic layers, Haversian canals, and osteocytes in lacunae can be seen here.

Within the epiphyses are the *epiphyseal growth plates* that separate the epiphyses from the shaft itself. As long as the bone is growing in length, these growth plates are composed of cartilage (see figure 47.4). The actual events taking place in the plates are not simple, but they can be simply summarized.

1. During growth of a long bone, the cartilage of the growth plates is actively growing in the lengthwise direction to thicken the plate.
2. This growth pushes the epiphysis farther away from the slender shaft portion, which effectively increases the length of the bone.
3. At the same time, from the shaft's side, a process of cartilage calcification encroaches on the cartilaginous growth plate, so that the bony portion of the shaft elongates.

As long as the rate of new cartilage thickening stays ahead of the creeping calcification, the bone continues to grow in length. Eventually the cartilaginous expansion slows and is overtaken by the calcification, which obliterates this region of growth.

Growth in length usually ceases in humans by late adolescence. Although growth of the bone length is curtailed at this time, growth in width is not. The diameter of the shaft can be enhanced by bone addition just beneath the periosteum throughout an individual's life.

Bone structure may include blood vessels and nerves

Developing bone often has an internal blood supply, which is especially evident in endochondral bones. The internal blood routes, however, do not necessarily remain after the bones have completed development. In most mammals the endochondral bones retain internal blood vessels and are called **vascular bones.** Vascular bone is also found in many reptiles and a few amphibians. *Cellular bones* contain osteocytes, and many such bones are also vascular. This bone remains metabolically active (see figure 47.4).

In fishes and birds, bones are **avascular.** Typically avascular bone does not contain osteocytes and is termed *acellular bone.* This type of bone is fairly inert except for its surface, where the periosteum with its mesenchyme cells is capable of repairing the bone.

Many bones, particularly the endochondral long bones, contain a central cavity termed the *medullary cavity.* In many vertebrates, the medullary cavity houses the bone marrow, important in the manufacture of red and white blood cells. In such cases this cavity is termed the **marrow cavity.** Not all medullary cavities contain marrow, however. Light-boned birds, for example, have huge interior cavities, but they are empty of marrow. Birds depend on stem cells in other body locations to produce red blood cells.

Bone lining the medullary cavities differs from the smooth, dense bone found closer to the outer surface. Based on density and texture, bone falls into three categories: the outer dense **compact bone,** the **medullary bone** that lines the internal cavity, and **spongy bone** that has a honeycomb structure and typically forms the epiphyses inside a thick shell of compact bone. Both compact and spongy bone contribute to a bone's strength. Medullary cavities are lined with thin tissues called the **endosteum,** which contains no

collagenous fibers but does possess other constituents including mesenchyme cells.

Vascular bone usually has a special internal organization called the **Haversian system.** Beneath the outer basic layers, endochondral bone is constructed of concentric layers called *Haversian lamellae.* These concentric tubes are laid down around narrow channels called *Haversian canals* that run parallel to the length of the bone. Haversian canals may contain nerve fibers but always contain blood vessels that keep the osteocytes alive even though they are entombed in the bony matrix.

The small vessels within the canals include both arterioles and venules or capillaries, and they connect to larger vessels that extend internally from both the periosteum and endosteum and that run in canals perpendicular to the Haversian canals.

Bone remodeling allows bone to respond to use or disuse

It is easy to think of bones as being inert, especially since we rarely encounter them except as the skeletons of dead animals. But just as muscles, skin, and other body tissues may change depending on the stresses of the environment, bone also is a dynamic tissue that can change with demands made on it.

Mechanical stresses such as compression at joints, the forces of muscles on certain portions and features of a bone, and similar effects may all be remodeling factors that not only shape the bone during its embryonic development, but after birth as well. Depending on the directions and magnitudes of forces impinging on a bone, it may thicken; the size and shape of surface features to which muscles, tendons, or ligaments attach may change in size and shape; even the direction of the tiny bony struts that make up spongy bone may be altered.

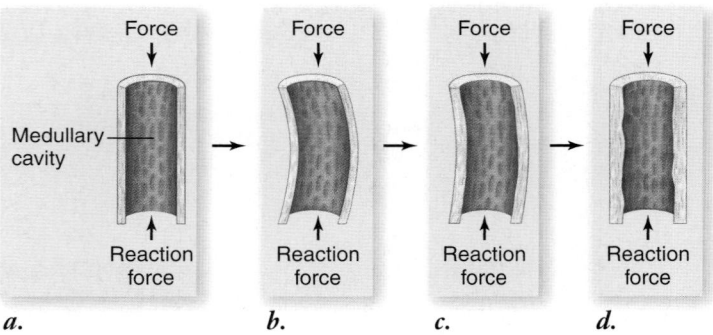

Figure 47.5 Model of stress and remodeling in a long bone. This figure shows a diagrammatic section of a long bone, such as a leg bone. The section is placed under a load or force, which causes a reaction force from the ground the leg is standing upon. *a.* Under a mild compressive load the bone does not bend. *b.* If the load is large enough, and the bone is not sufficiently thick, the bone will bend (the bending shown is exaggerated for clarity). *c.* Osteoblasts are signaled by the stresses in the bending section to produce additional bone. As the bone becomes thicker, the degree of bending is reduced. *d.* When sufficient bone is added to prevent significant bending, the production of new osteoblasts stops and no more bone is added.

Exercise and frequent use of muscles for a particular task change more than just the muscles; blood vessels and fibrous connective tissue increase, and the skeletal frame becomes more robust through bone thickening and enhancement.

The phenomenon of remodeling is known for all bones, but it is easiest to demonstrate in a long bone. Small forces may not have much of an effect on the bone, but larger ones—if frequent enough—can initiate remodeling (figure 47.5). In the example shown, larger compressive forces may tend to bend a bone, even if the bend is imperceptible to the eye. This bending stress promotes bone formation that thickens the bone. As the bone becomes thicker the amount of bending is reduced (figure 47.5c). Further bone addition produces sufficient bone thickness to entirely prevent significant bending (figure 47.5d). Once this point has been attained, the bone addition stops. This is another example of a negative-feedback system.

The effect of remodeling can be seen by examining bone thickness in rodents forced to exercise. The continual stresses placed on the limb bones cause additional bone to be deposited, leading to thicker and stronger bone (figure 47.6).

This phenomenon also has important medical implications. Osteoporosis, which is characterized by a loss of bone mineral density, is a debilitating and potentially life-threatening ailment that afflicts more than 25 million people in the United States, affecting primarily postmenopausal women, but also those suffering from malnutrition and a number of diseases. One treatment is a regimen of weight-lifting to stimulate bone deposition and thus counter the effects of osteoporosis.

SCIENTIFIC THINKING

Hypothesis: *Bone remodeling strengthens bones in response to external pressures.*

Prediction: *Bones that are used in more strenuous activities will deposit more bone and become stronger.*

Test: *Provide laboratory mice with an exercise wheel and make sure they run for several hours a day; keep a control group without a wheel.*

Mouse with exercise wheel   Mouse without exercise wheel

Result: *After 10 weeks, the running mice developed thicker limb bones.*

Further Experiments: *Modern microelectronics allow the development of stress sensors small enough to implant on the limb bone of a mouse. With such sensors, experiments can quantify how much stress different activities place on a bone and can more accurately investigate the relationship between the direction and magnitude of forces placed on a bone and the extent to which the bone remodels.*

Figure 47.6 **The effect of exercise on bone remodeling.**

Intramembranous bone forms within a layer of connective tissue; endochondral bone originates with a cartilaginous model that is then replaced with bone tissue. Epiphyses are cartilaginous growth plates of endochondral bones. As the epiphyseal cartilage becomes calcified, bone growth ceases. Bone remodeling occurs in response to repeated stresses on bones from weight or muscle use, allowing bones to adapt.

■ *Why is vitamin D especially important for children and the elderly?*

47.3 *Joints and Skeletal Movement*

Learning Outcomes

1. *Define the different types of joints.*
2. *Explain how muscles produce movement at joints.*
3. *Describe how antagonistic muscles work at a joint.*

Movements of the endoskeleton are powered by the skeletal musculature. The skeletal movements that respond to muscle action occur at **joints,** or articulations, where one bone meets another.

Moveable joints have different ranges of motion, depending on type

Each movable joint within the skeleton has a characteristic range of motion. Four basic joint movement patterns can be distinguished: *ball-and-socket, hinge, gliding,* and *combination.*

Ball-and-socket joints are like those of the hip, where the upper leg bone forms a ball fitting into a socket in the pelvis. This type of joint can perform universal movement in all directions, plus twisting of the ball (figure 47.7a).

The simplest type of joint is the **hinge joint,** such as the knee, where movement of the lower leg is restricted to rotate forward or backward, but not side to side (figure 47.7b).

Gliding joints can be found in the skulls of a number of nonmammalian vertebrates, but are also present between the lateral vertebral projections in many of them and in mammals as well (figure 47.7c). The vertebral projections are paired and extend from the front and back of each vertebra. The projections in front are a little lower, and each can slip along the undersurface of the posterior projection from the vertebra just ahead of it. This sliding joint gives stability to the vertebral column while allowing some flexibility of movement between vertebrae.

Combination joints are, as you might suppose, those that have movement characteristics of two or more joint types. The typical mammalian jaw joint is a good example.

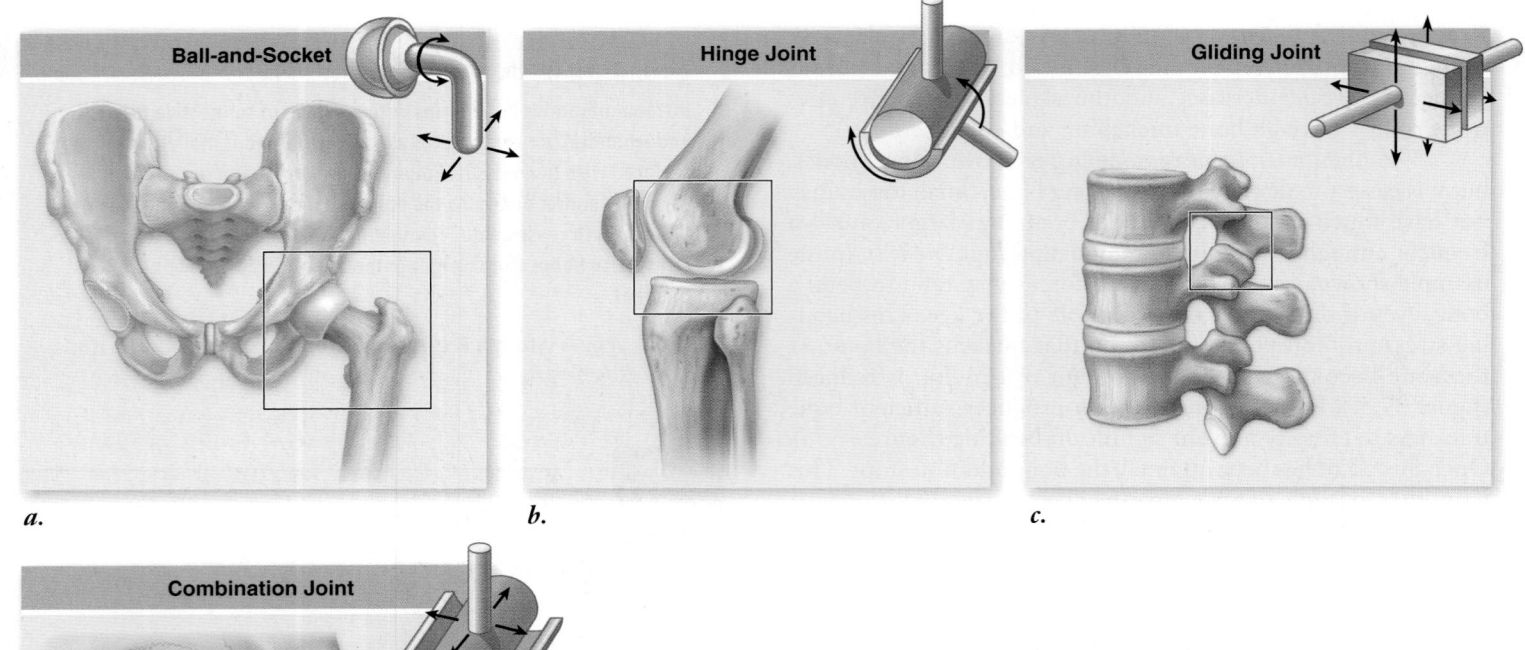

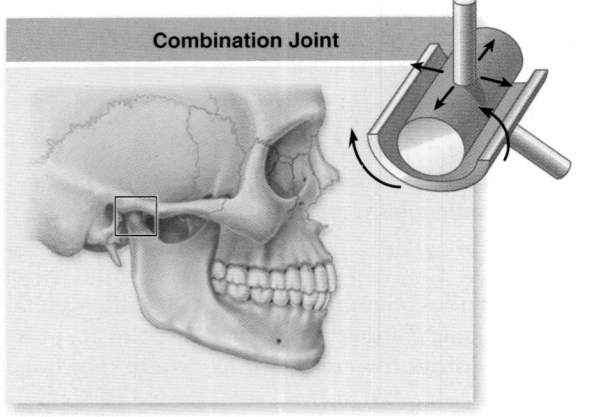

Figure 47.7 **Patterns of joint movement.** *a.* Ball-and-socket joints, such as the hip joint, permit movement and twisting of the leg within the hip socket. *b.* A hinge joint, as the term implies, allows movement in only one plane. *c.* Gliding joints are well represented by the lateral vertebral joints (not the central ones) that permit sliding of one surface on another. *d.* Combination joints have features of more than one type of joint, such as the mammalian jaw joint that allows both rotation and side-to-side sliding.

Most mammals chew food into small pieces. To chew food well, the lower jaw needs to move from side to side to get the best contact between upper and lower teeth. The lower jaw can also slip forward and backward to some extent. At the same time, the jaw joint must be shaped to allow the hinge-like opening and closing of the mouth. The mammalian joint conformation thus combines features from hinge and gliding joints (figure 47.7*d*).

Skeletal muscles pull on bones to produce movement at joints

Skeletal muscles produce movement of the skeleton when they contract. Usually, the two ends of a skeletal muscle are attached to different bones, although some may be attached to other structures, such as skin. There are two means of bone attachment: Muscle fibers may connect directly to the periosteum, the bone's fibrous covering, or sheets of muscle may be connected to bone by a dense connective tissue strap or cord, called a *tendon* that attaches to the periosteum (figure 47.8).

One attachment of the muscle, the origin, remains relatively stationary during a contraction. The other end, the insertion, is attached to a bone that moves when the muscle

contracts. For example, contraction of the quadriceps muscles of the leg causes the lower leg to rotate forward relative to the upper leg section.

Typically, muscles are arranged so that any movement produced by one muscle can be reversed by another. The leg flexor muscles, called hamstrings (see figure 47.8), draw the lower leg back and upward, bending the knee. Its movement is countered by the quadriceps muscles. The important concept is that two muscles or muscle groups can be mutually antagonistic, with the action of one countered by the action of the other.

Learning Outcomes Review 47.3

Types of joints include ball-and-socket, hinge, gliding, and combination joints. Muscles, positioned across joints, cause movement of bones relative to each other by contracting and exerting pulling force. Antagonistic muscles oppose each other, a key feature since muscles can only contract and cannot push.

■ *In what ways does a bony endoskeleton overcome the limitations of an exoskeleton for terrestrial life forms?*

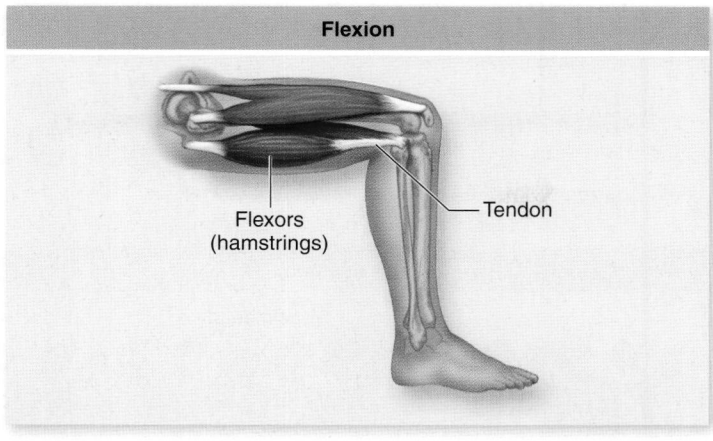

Flexion

Flexors (hamstrings)

Tendon

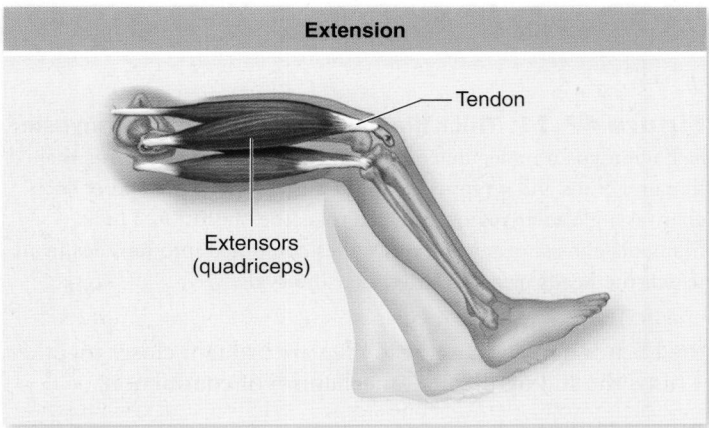

Extension

Tendon

Extensors (quadriceps)

Figure 47.8 Flexor and extensor muscles of the leg.
Antagonistic muscles act in opposite ways. In humans, the hamstrings, a group of three muscles, cause the lower leg to move backward relative to the upper leg, whereas the quadriceps, a group of four muscles, pull the lower leg forward.

Inquiry question

? Would the antagonistic muscles work in the same way in the legs of an animal with an exoskeleton, such as the grasshopper in figure 47.2?

47.4 Muscle Contraction

Learning Outcomes

1. *Explain the sliding filament mechanism of muscle contraction.*
2. *Describe the role of calcium in muscle contraction.*
3. *Differentiate between slow-twitch and fast-twitch muscle fibers.*

This section concentrates on the skeletal muscle of vertebrates. Vertebrate muscle has enjoyed the most attention and is thus the best understood of animal muscular func-tion. Each skeletal muscle contains numerous muscle fibers, as described in chapter 43. Each muscle fiber encloses a bundle of 4 to 20 elongated structures called **myofibrils.** Each myofibril, in turn, is composed of thick and thin **myofilaments** (figure 47.9).

Under a microscope, the myofibrils have alternating dark and light bands, which give skeletal muscle fiber its striped appearance. The thick myofilaments are stacked together to produce the dark bands, called *A bands;* the thin filaments alone are found in the light bands, or *I bands.*

Each I band in a myofibril is divided in half by a disk of protein called a *Z line* because of its appearance in electron micrographs. The thin filaments are anchored to these disks. In an electron micrograph of a myofibril (figure 47.10), the structure of the myofibril can be seen to repeat from Z line to Z line. This repeating structure, called a **sarcomere,** is the smallest subunit of muscle contraction.

Muscle fibers contract as overlapping filaments slide together

The thin filaments overlap with thick filaments on each side of an A band, but in a resting muscle, they do not project all the way to the center of the A band. As a result, the center of an A band (called an *H band*) is lighter than the areas on each side, which have interdigitating thick and thin filaments. This appearance of the sarcomeres changes when the muscle contracts.

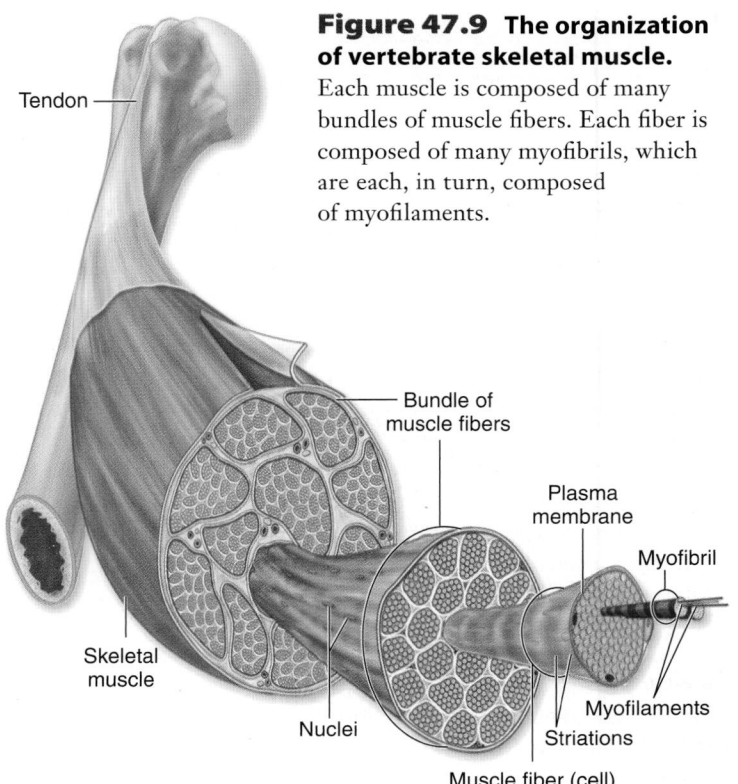

Figure 47.9 The organization of vertebrate skeletal muscle.
Each muscle is composed of many bundles of muscle fibers. Each fiber is composed of many myofibrils, which are each, in turn, composed of myofilaments.

Tendon

Bundle of muscle fibers

Plasma membrane

Myofibril

Skeletal muscle

Nuclei

Myofilaments

Striations

Muscle fiber (cell)

Relaxed Muscle

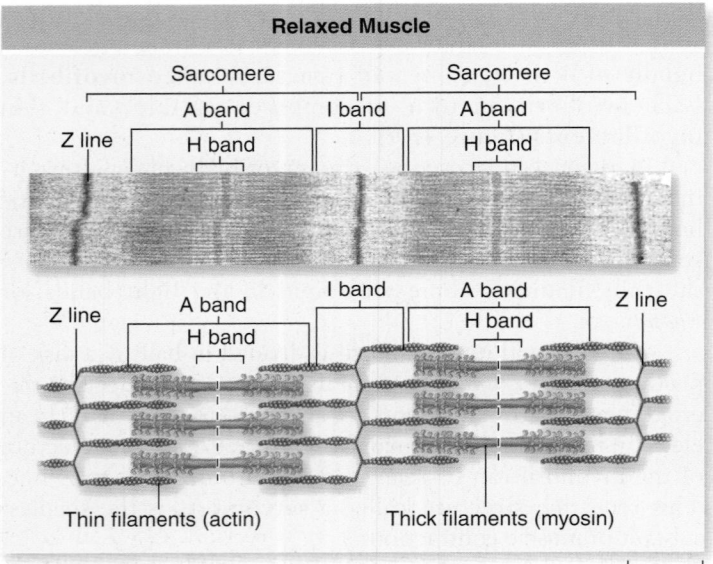

0.49 µm

Contracted Muscle

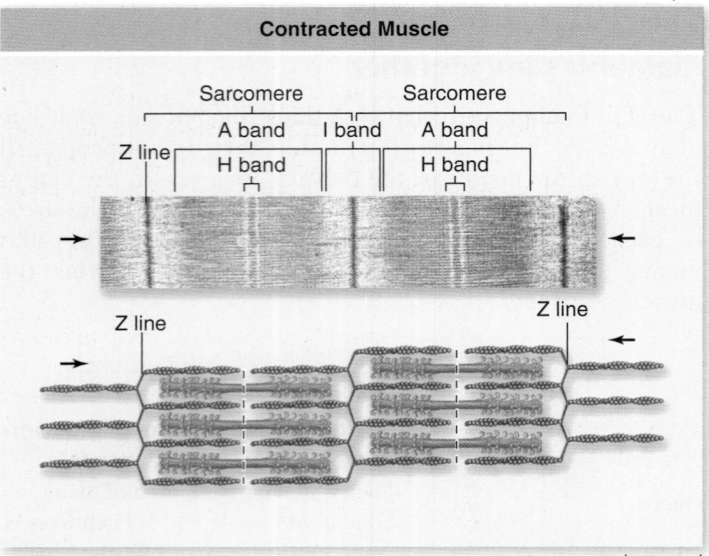

0.45 µm

Figure 47.10 **The structure of sarcomeres in relaxed and contracted muscles.** Two sarcomeres are shown in micrographs and as drawings of thick and thin filaments. The Z lines form the borders of each sarcomere and the A bands represent thick filaments. The thin filaments are within the I bands and extend into the A bands interdigitated with thick filaments. The H band is the lighter-appearing central region of the A band containing only thick filaments. The muscle on the top is shown relaxed. In the contracted muscle in the bottom, the Z lines have moved closer together, with the I bands and H bands becoming shorter. The A band does not change in size as it contains the thick filaments, which do not change in length.

A muscle contracts and shortens because its myofibrils contract and shorten. When this occurs, the myofilaments do *not* shorten; instead, the thick and thin myofilaments slide relative to each other (see figure 47.10). The thin filaments slide deeper into the A bands, making the H bands narrower until, at maximal shortening, they disappear entirely. This also makes

Myosin Molecule

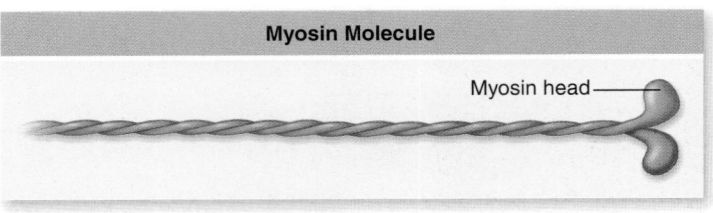

a.

Thick Filament

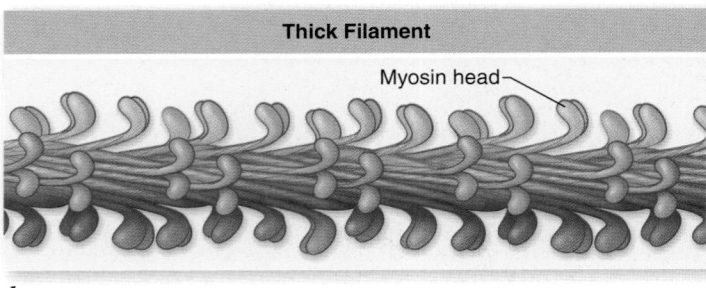

b.

Figure 47.11 **Thick filaments are composed of myosin.** *a.* Each myosin molecule consists of two polypeptide chains shaped like golf clubs and wrapped around each other; at the end of each chain is a globular region referred to as the "head." *b.* Thick filaments consist of myosin molecules combined into bundles from which the heads protrude at regular intervals.

the I bands narrower, as the Z lines are brought closer together. This is the sliding filament mechanism of contraction.

The sliding filament mechanism

Electron micrographs reveal cross-bridges that extend from the thick to the thin filaments, suggesting a mechanism that might cause the filaments to slide. To understand how this is accomplished requires examining the thick and thin filaments at a molecular level. Biochemical studies show that each thick filament is composed of many subunits of the protein myosin packed together. The myosin protein consists of two subunits, each shaped like a golf club with a head region that protrudes from a long filament, with the filaments twisted together. Thick filaments are composed of many copies of myosin arranged with heads protruding from along the length of the fiber (figure 47.11). The myosin heads form the cross-bridges seen in electron micrographs.

Each thin filament consists primarily of many globular actin proteins arranged into two fibers twisted into a double helix (figure 47.12). If we were able to see a sarcomere at the molecular level, it would have the structure depicted in figure 47.13.

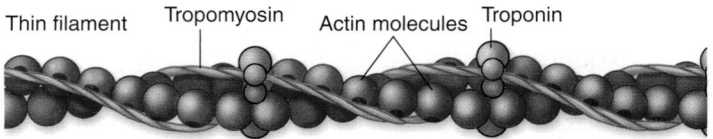

Figure 47.12 **Thin filaments are composed of globular actin proteins.** Two rows of actin proteins are twisted together in a helix to produce the thin filaments. Other proteins, tropomyosin and troponin, associate with the strands of actin and are involved in muscle contraction. These other proteins are discussed later in the chapter.

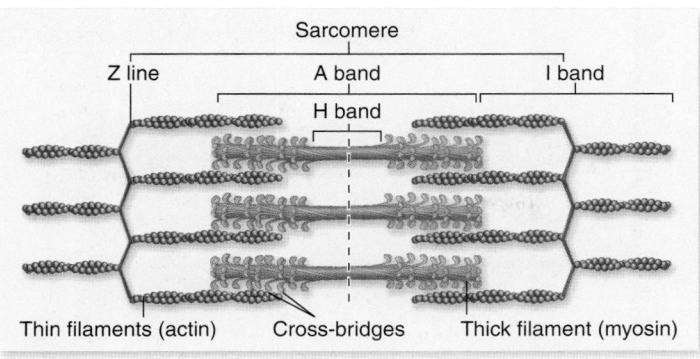

a.

b.

Figure 47.13 The interaction of thick and thin filaments in striated muscle sarcomeres. *a.* The heads on the two ends of the thick filaments are oriented in opposite directions so that the cross-bridges pull the thin filaments and the Z lines on each side of the sarcomere toward the center. *b.* This sliding of the filaments produces muscle contraction.

Myosin is a member of the class of protein called *motor proteins* that are able to convert the chemical energy in ATP into mechanical energy (see chapter 4). This occurs by a series of events called the cross-bridge cycle (figure 47.14). When the myosin heads hydrolyze ATP into ADP and P_i, the conformation of myosin is changed, activating it for the later power stroke. The ADP and P_i both remain attached to the myosin head, keeping it in this activated conformation. The analogy to a mousetrap, set and ready to spring, is often made to describe this action. In this set position, the myosin head can bind to actin, forming cross-bridges. When a myosin head binds to actin, it releases the P_i and undergoes another conformational change, pulling the thin filament toward the center of the sarcomere in the *power stroke*, at which point it loses the ADP (see figures 47.13*b*, 47.14). At the end of the power stroke, the myosin head binds to a new molecule of ATP, which displaces it from actin. This cross-bridge cycle repeats as long as the muscle is stimulated to contract. This sequence of events can be thought of like pulling a rope hand-over-hand. The myosin heads are the hands and the actin fibers the rope.

In death, the cell can no longer produce ATP, and therefore the cross-bridges cannot be broken—causing the muscle stiffness of death called *rigor mortis*. A living cell, however, always has enough ATP to allow the myosin heads to detach from actin. How, then, is the cross-bridge cycle arrested so that the muscle can relax? We discuss the regulation of contraction and relaxation next.

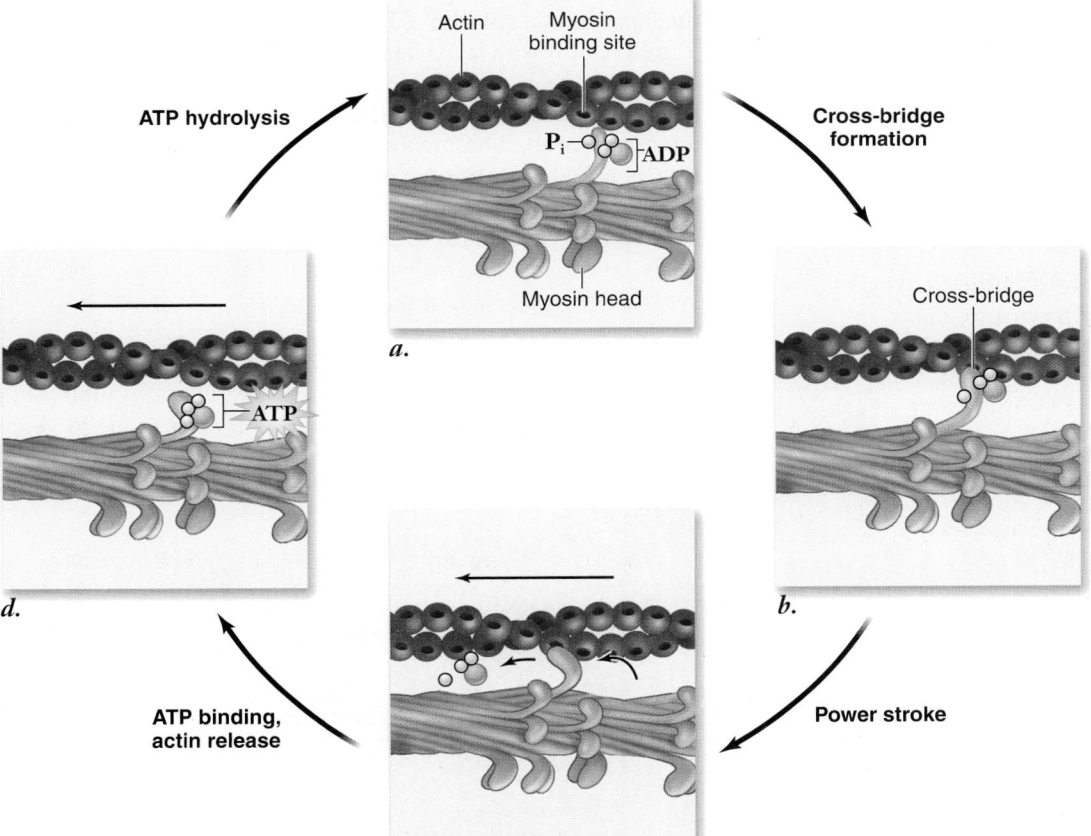

a.

b.

c.

d.

Figure 47.14 The cross-bridge cycle in muscle contraction. *a.* Hydrolysis of ATP by myosin causes a conformational change that moves the head into an energized state. The ADP and P_i remain bound to the myosin head, which can bind to actin. *b.* Myosin binds to actin forming a cross-bridge. *c.* During the power stroke, myosin returns to its original conformation, releasing ADP and P_i. *d.* ATP binds to the myosin head breaking the cross-bridge. ATP hydrolysis returns the myosin head to its energized conformation, allowing the cycle to begin again.

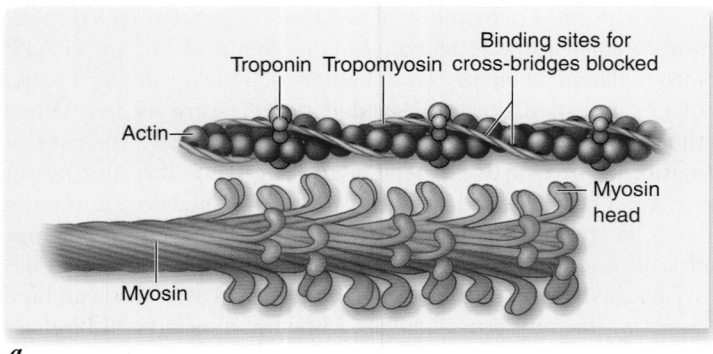

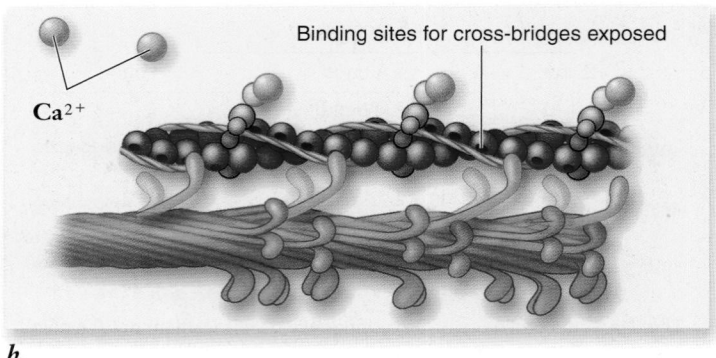

Figure 47.15 How calcium controls striated muscle contraction. *a.* When the muscle is at rest, a long filament of the protein tropomyosin blocks the myosin-binding sites on the actin molecule. Because myosin is unable to form cross-bridges with actin at these sites, muscle contraction cannot occur. *b.* When Ca^{2+} binds to another protein, troponin, the Ca^{2+}–troponin complex displaces tropomyosin and exposes the myosin-binding sites on actin, permitting cross-bridges to form and contraction to occur.

Contraction depends on calcium ion release following a nerve impulse

When a muscle is relaxed, its myosin heads are in the activated conformation bound to ADP and P_i, but they are unable to bind to actin. In the relaxed state, the attachment sites for the myosin heads on the actin are physically blocked by another protein, known as **tropomyosin,** in the thin filaments. Cross-bridges therefore cannot form and the filaments cannot slide.

For contraction to occur, the tropomyosin must be moved out of the way so that the myosin heads can bind to the uncovered actin-binding sites. This requires the action of **troponin,** a regulatory protein complex that holds tropomyosin and actin together. The regulatory interactions between troponin and tropomyosin are controlled by the calcium ion (Ca^{2+}) concentration of the muscle fiber cytoplasm.

When the Ca^{2+} concentration of the cytoplasm is low, tropomyosin inhibits cross-bridge formation (figure 47.15*a*). When the Ca^{2+} concentration is raised, Ca^{2+} binds to tro-

ponin, altering its conformation and shifting the troponin–tropomyosin complex. This shift in conformation exposes the myosin-binding sites on the actin. Cross-bridges can thus form, undergo power strokes, and produce muscle contraction (figure 47.15*b*).

Muscles need a reliable supply of Ca^{2+}. Muscle fibers store Ca^{2+} in a modified endoplasmic reticulum called a **sarcoplasmic reticulum (SR)** (figure 47.16). When a muscle fiber is stimulated to contract, the membrane of the muscle fiber becomes depolarized. This is transmitted deep into the muscle fiber by invaginations of the cell membrane called the **transverse tubules (T tubules).** Depolarization of the T tubules causes Ca^{2+} channels in the SR to open, releasing Ca^{2+} into the cytosol. Ca^{2+} then diffuses into the myofibrils, where it binds to troponin, altering its conformation and allowing contraction. The involvement of Ca^{2+} in muscle contraction is called **excitation–contraction coupling** because it is the release of Ca^{2+} that links the excitation of the muscle fiber by the motor neuron to the contraction of the muscle.

Figure 47.16 Relationship between the myofibrils, transverse tubules, and sarcoplasmic reticulum. Neurotransmitter released at a neuromuscular junction binds chemically gated Na^+ channels, causing the muscle cell membrane to depolarize. This depolarization is conducted along the muscle cell membrane and down the transverse tubules to stimulate the release of Ca^{2+} from the sarcoplasmic reticulum. Ca^{2+} diffuses through the cytoplasm to myofibrils, causing contraction.

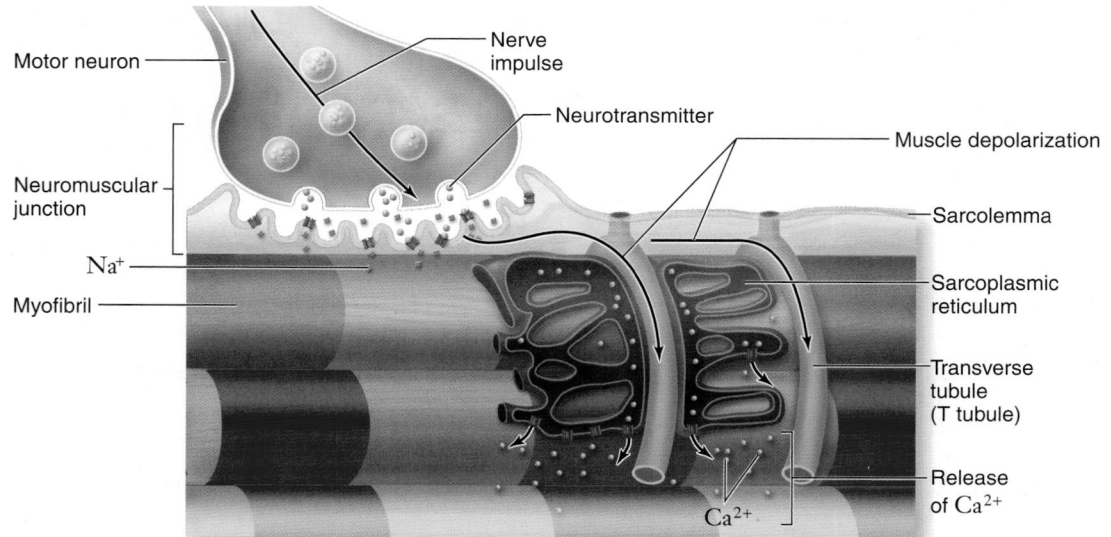

Nerve impulses from motor neurons

Muscles are stimulated to contract by motor neurons. The motor neurons that stimulate skeletal muscles are called *somatic motor neurons*. The axon of a somatic motor neuron extends from the neuron cell body and branches to make synapses with a number of muscle fibers. These synapses between neurons and muscle cells are called *neuromuscular junctions* (see figure 47.16). One axon can stimulate many muscle fibers, and in some animals, a muscle fiber may be innervated by more than one motor neuron. However, in humans, each muscle fiber has only a single synapse with a branch of one axon.

When a somatic motor neuron delivers electrochemical impulses, it stimulates contraction of the muscle fibers it innervates (makes synapses with) through the following events:

1. The motor neuron, at the neuromuscular junction, releases the neurotransmitter acetylcholine (ACh). ACh binds to receptors in the muscle cell membrane to open Na^+ channels. The influx of Na^+ ions depolarizes the muscle cell membrane.
2. The impulses spread along the membrane of the muscle fiber and are carried into the muscle fibers through the T tubules.
3. The T tubules conduct the impulses toward the sarcoplasmic reticulum, opening Ca^{2+} channels and releasing Ca^{2+}. The Ca^{2+} binds to troponin, exposing the myosin-binding sites on the actin myofilaments and stimulating muscle contraction.

When impulses from the motor neuron cease, it stops releasing ACh, in turn stopping the production of impulses in the muscle fiber. Another membrane protein in the SR then uses energy from ATP hydrolysis to pump Ca^{2+} back into the SR by active transport. Troponin is no longer bound to Ca^{2+}, so tropomyosin returns to its inhibitory position, allowing the muscle to relax.

Motor units and recruitment

A single muscle fiber can produce variable tension depending on the frequency of stimulation. The response of an entire muscle depends on the number of individual fibers involved and their degree of tension. The set of muscle fibers innervated by all the axonal branches of a motor neuron, plus the motor neuron itself, is defined as a **motor unit** (figure 47.17).

Every time the motor neuron produces impulses, all muscle fibers in that motor unit contract together. The division of the muscle into motor units allows the muscle's strength of contraction to be finely graded, a requirement for coordinated movements. Muscles that require a finer degree of control, such as those that move the eyes, have smaller motor units (fewer muscle fibers per neuron). Muscles that require less precise control but must exert more force, such as the large muscles of the legs, have more fibers per motor neuron.

Most muscles contain motor units in a variety of sizes, and these can be selectively activated by the nervous system. The weakest contractions of a muscle involve activation of a few small motor units. If a slightly stronger contraction is necessary, additional small motor units are also activated. The initial increments of increased force are therefore relatively small. As ever greater forces are required, more units and larger units are brought into action, and the force increments become larger.

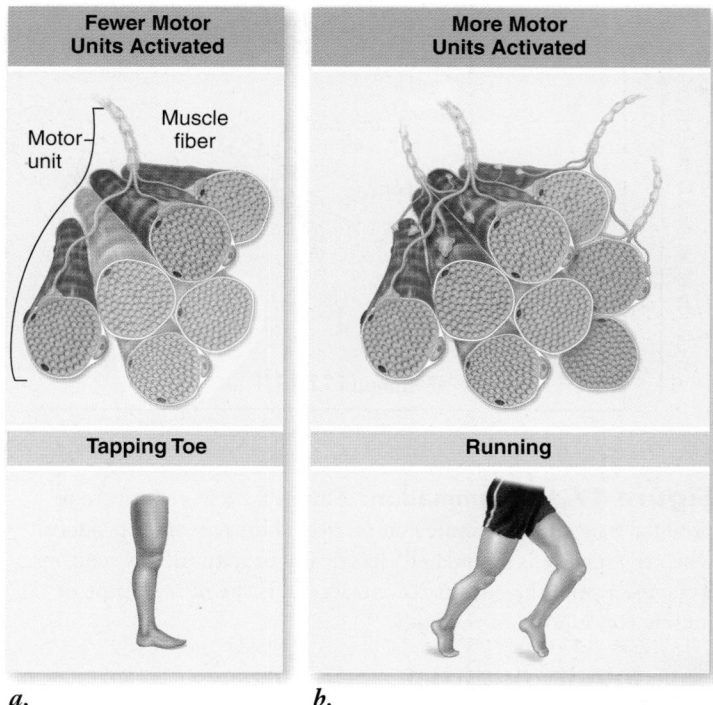

Figure 47.17 The number and size of motor units.
A motor unit consists of a motor neuron and all of the muscle fibers it innervates. *a.* Precise muscle contractions require smaller motor units. *b.* Large muscle movements require larger motor units. The more motor units activated, the stronger the contraction.

This cumulative increase of numbers and sizes of motor units to produce a stronger contraction is termed **recruitment.**

The two main types of muscle fibers are slow-twitch and fast-twitch

An isolated skeletal muscle can be studied by stimulating it artificially with electric shocks. A muscle stimulated with a single electric shock quickly contracts and relaxes in a response called a twitch. Increasing the stimulus voltage increases the strength of the twitch up to a maximum. If a second electric shock is delivered immediately after the first, it produces a second twitch that may partially "ride piggyback" on the first. This cumulative response is called summation (figure 47.18).

An increasing frequency of electric shocks shortens the relaxation time between successive twitches as the strength of contraction increases. Finally, at a particular frequency of stimulation, no visible relaxation occurs between successive twitches. Contraction is smooth and sustained, as it is during normal muscle contraction in the body. This sustained contraction is called **tetanus.** (The disease known as tetanus gets its name because the muscles of its victims go into an agonizing state of contraction.)

Skeletal muscle fibers can be divided on the basis of their contraction speed into *slow-twitch*, or *type I*, *fibers* and *fast-twitch*, or *type II*, *fibers*. The muscles that move the eyes, for example, have a high proportion of fast-twitch fibers and reach maximum tension in about 7.3 milliseconds (msec); the soleus muscle in the leg, by contrast, has a high proportion

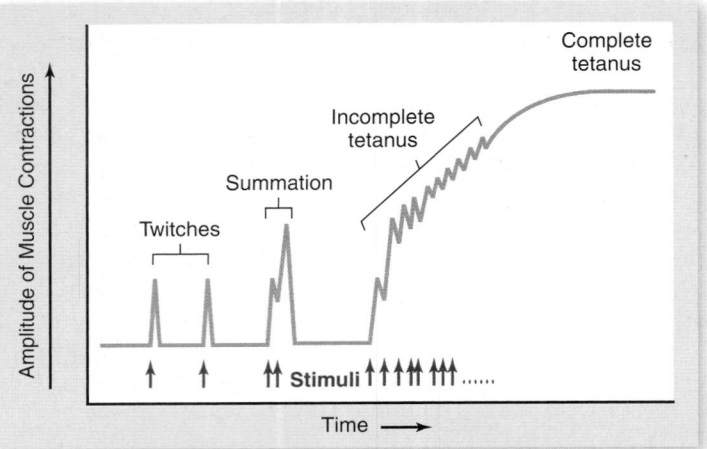

Figure 47.18 Summation. Muscle twitches summate to produce a sustained, tetanic contraction. This pattern is produced when the muscle is stimulated electrically or naturally by neurons. Tetanus, a smooth, sustained contraction, is the normal type of muscle contraction in the body.

Inquiry question

? What determines the maximum amplitude of a summated muscle contraction?

of slow-twitch fibers and requires about 100 msec to reach maximum tension (figure 47.19).

Slow-twitch fibers

Slow-twitch fibers have a rich capillary supply, numerous mitochondria and aerobic respiratory enzymes, and a high concentration of **myoglobin** pigment. Myoglobin is a red pigment similar to the hemoglobin in red blood cells, but its higher affinity for oxygen improves the delivery of oxygen to the slow-

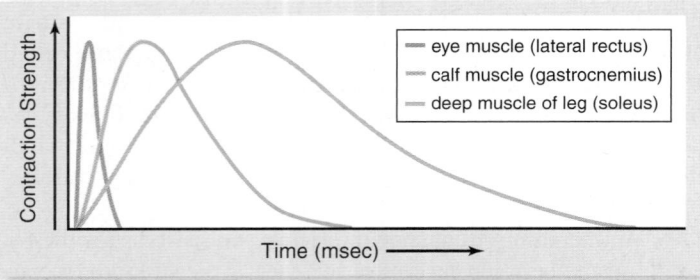

eye muscle (lateral rectus)
calf muscle (gastrocnemius)
deep muscle of leg (soleus)

Figure 47.19 Skeletal muscles have different proportions of fast-twitch and slow-twitch fibers.
The muscles that move the eye contain mostly fast-twitch fibers, whereas the deep muscle of the leg (the soleus) contains mostly slow-twitch fibers. The calf muscle (gastrocnemius) is intermediate in its composition.

Inquiry question

? How would you determine if the calf muscle contains a mix of fast-twitch and slow-twitch fibers, or instead is composed of an intermediate form of fiber?

twitch fibers. Because of their high myoglobin content, slow-twitch fibers are also called *red fibers*. These fibers can sustain action for a long period of time without fatigue.

Fast-twitch fibers

The thicker **fast-twitch fibers** have fewer capillaries and mitochondria than slow-twitch fibers and not as much myoglobin; hence, these fibers are also called *white fibers*. Fast-twitch fibers can respire anaerobically by using a large store of glycogen and high concentrations of glycolytic enzymes. The "dark meat" and "white meat" found in chicken and turkey consists of muscles with primarily red and white fibers, respectively. Fast-twitch fibers are adapted for the rapid generation of power and can grow thicker and stronger in response to weight training; however, they lack the endurance characteristics of slow-twitch fibers.

In addition to the type I and type II fibers, human muscles have an intermediate form of fibers that are fast-twitch, but they also have a high oxidative capacity and so are more resistant to fatigue. Endurance training increases the proportion of these fibers in muscles.

In general, human sprinters tend to have more fast-twitch fibers, whereas long-distance runners have more slow-twitch fibers. These differences are paralleled in the animal world. Comparisons of closely related species that differ in their lifestyles show that species that rely on short, high-speed movements to capture prey or evade predators tend to have more fast-twitch fibers, whereas closely related species that move more slowly, but for longer periods of time, have more slow-twitch fibers.

Muscle metabolism changes with the demands made on it

Skeletal muscles at rest obtain most of their energy from the aerobic respiration of fatty acids (see chapter 7). During use of the muscle, such as during exercise, muscle stores of glycogen and glucose delivered by the blood are also used as energy sources. The energy obtained by cellular respiration is used to make ATP, which is needed for the movement of the cross-bridges during muscle contraction and the pumping of Ca^{2+} back into the sarcoplasmic reticulum during muscle relaxation.

Skeletal muscles respire anaerobically for the first 45 to 90 sec of moderate-to-heavy exercise because the cardiopulmonary system requires this amount of time to increase the oxygen supply to the muscles. If exercise is not overly strenuous, aerobic respiration then contributes the major portion of the skeletal muscle energy requirements following the first 2 min of exercise. However, more vigorous exercise may require more ATP than can be provided by aerobic respiration, in which case anaerobic respiration continues to provide ATP as well.

Whether exercise is light, moderate, or intense for a particular individual depends on that person's maximal capacity for aerobic exercise. The maximum rate of oxygen consumption in the body is called the *aerobic capacity*. In general, individuals in better condition have greater aerobic capacity and thus can sustain higher levels of aerobic exercise for longer periods without having to also use anaerobic respiration.

Physical training increases aerobic capacity and muscle strength

Muscle fatigue refers to the use-dependent decrease in the ability of a muscle to generate force. Fatigue is highly variable and can arise from a number of causes. The intensity of contraction as well as duration of contraction are involved. In addition, fatigue is affected by cellular metabolism: aerobic or anaerobic. In the case of short-duration maximal exertion, fatigue was long thought to be caused by a buildup of lactic acid (from anaerobic metabolism). More recent data also implicate a buildup in inorganic phosphate (P_i) from the breakdown of creatine phosphate, which also occurs during anaerobic metabolism. In longer term, lower intensity exertion, fatigue appears to result from depletion of glycogen.

Because the depletion of muscle glycogen places a limit on exercise, any adaptation that spares muscle glycogen will improve physical endurance. Trained athletes have an increased proportion of energy derived from the aerobic respiration of fatty acids, resulting in a slower depletion of their muscle glycogen reserve. Athletes also have greater muscle vascularization, which facilitates both oxygen delivery and lactic acid removal. Because the aerobic capacity of endurance-trained athletes is higher than that of untrained people, athletes can perform for longer and put forth more effort before muscle fatigue occurs.

Endurance training does not increase muscle size. Muscle enlargement is produced only by frequent periods of high-intensity exercise in which muscles work against high resistance, as in weight lifting. Resistance training increases the thickness of type II (fast-twitch) muscle fibers, causing skeletal muscles to grow by hypertrophy (increased cell size) rather than by cell division and an increased number of cells.

Learning Outcomes Review 47.4

Sliding of myofilaments within muscle myofibrils is responsible for contraction; it involves the motor protein myosin, which forms cross-bridges on actin fibers. The process of shortening is controlled by Ca^{2+} ions released from the sarcoplasmic reticulum. The Ca^{2+} binds to troponin, making myosin-binding sites in actin available. Slow-twitch fibers can sustain activity for a longer period of time; fast-twitch fibers use glycogen for rapid generation of power.

■ *What advantages do increased myoglobin and mitochondria confer on slow-twitch fibers?*

47.5 Modes of Animal Locomotion

Learning Outcomes

1. *Describe how friction and gravity affect locomotion.*
2. *Discuss how lift is created by wings.*
3. *Explain how evolution has shaped structures used for locomotion.*

Animals are unique among multicellular organisms in their ability to move actively from one place to another. Locomotion requires both a propulsive mechanism and a control mechanism. There are a wide variety of propulsive mechanisms, most involving contracting muscles to generate the necessary force. Ultimately, it is the nervous system that activates and coordinates the muscles used in locomotion. In large animals, active locomotion is almost always produced by appendages that oscillate—*appendicular locomotion*—or by bodies that undulate, pulse, or undergo peristaltic waves—*axial locomotion*.

Although animal locomotion occurs in many different forms, the general principles remain much the same in all groups. The physical constraints to movement—gravity and friction—are the same in every environment, differing only in degree.

Swimmers must contend with friction when moving through water

For swimming animals, the buoyancy of water reduces the effect of gravity. As a result, the primary force retarding forward movement is frictional drag, so body shape is important in reducing the force needed to push through the water.

Some marine invertebrates move about using hydraulic propulsion. For example, scallops clap the two sides of their shells together forcefully, and squids and octopuses squirt water like a marine jet, as described in chapter 34.

In contrast, many invertebrates and all aquatic vertebrates swim. Swimming involves pushing against the water with some part of the body. At one extreme, eels and sea snakes swim by sinuous undulations of the entire body (figure 47.20a). The undulating body waves of eel-like swimming are created by waves of muscle contraction alternating between the left and right axial musculature. As each body segment in turn pushes against the water, the moving wave forces the eel forward.

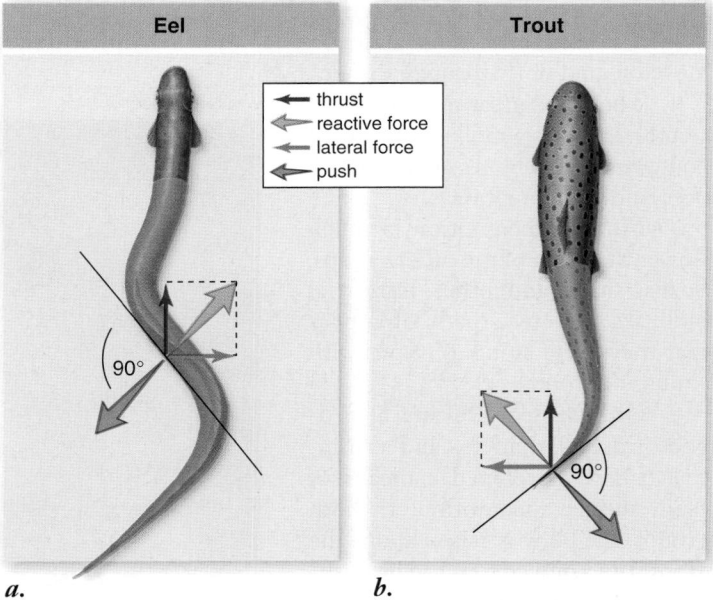

a. *b.*

Figure 47.20 Movements of swimming fishes. *a.* An eel pushes against the water with its whole body, whereas (*b*) a trout pushes only with its posterior half.

Other types of fish use similar mechanics as the eel but generate most of their propulsion from the posterior part of the body using the caudal (rear) fin (figure 47.20*b*). This also allows considerable specialization in the front end of the body without sacrificing propulsive force. Reptiles, such as alligators, swim in the same manner using undulations of the tail.

Whales and other marine mammals such as sea lions have evolutionarily returned to an aquatic lifestyle (see figure 21.12) and have convergently evolved a similar form of locomotion. Like fish, marine mammals also swim using undulating body waves. However, unlike any of the fishes, the waves pass from top to bottom and not from side to side. This difference illustrates how past evolutionary history can shape subsequent evolutionary change. The mammalian vertebral column is structured differently from that of fish in a way that stiffens the spine and allows little side-to-side flexibility. For this reason, when the ancestor of whales reentered aquatic habitats, they evolved adaptations for swimming that used dorsoventral (top-to-bottom) flexing.

Many terrestrial tetrapod vertebrates are able to swim, usually through movement of their limbs. Most birds that swim, such as ducks and geese, propel themselves through the water by pushing against it with their hind legs, which typically have webbed feet. Frogs and most aquatic mammals also swim with their hind legs and have webbed feet. Tetrapod vertebrates that swim with their forelegs usually have these limbs modified as flippers and "fly" through the water using motions very similar to those used by aerial fliers; examples include sea turtles, penguins, and fur seals.

Terrestrial locomotion must deal primarily with gravity

Air is a much less dense medium than water, and thus the frictional forces countering movement on land are much less than those in water. Instead, countering the force of gravity is the biggest challenge for nonaquatic organisms, which either must move on land or fly through the air.

The three great groups of terrestrial animals—mollusks, arthropods, and vertebrates—each move over land in different ways.

Mollusk locomotion is much slower than that of the other groups. Snails, slugs, and other terrestrial mollusks secrete a path of mucus that they glide along, pushing with a muscular foot.

Only vertebrates and arthropods (insects, spiders, and crustaceans) have developed a means of rapid surface locomotion. In both groups, the body is raised above the ground and moved forward by pushing against the ground with a series of jointed appendages, the legs.

Although animals may walk on only two legs or more than 100, the same general principles guide terrestrial locomotion. Because legs must provide support as well as propulsion, it is important that the sequence of their movements not shove the body's center of gravity outside the legs' zone of support, unless the duration of such imbalance is short. Otherwise, the animal will fall. The need to maintain stability determines the sequence of leg movements, which are similar in vertebrates and arthropods.

The apparent differences in the walking gaits of these two groups reflect the differences in leg number. Vertebrates walk on two or four legs; all arthropods have six or more limbs. Although the many legs of arthropods increase stability during locomotion, they also appear to reduce the maximum speed that can be attained.

The basic walking pattern of quadrupeds, from salamanders to most mammals, is left hind leg, right foreleg, right hind leg, left foreleg. The highest running speeds of quadruped mammals, such as the gallop of a horse, may involve the animal being supported by only one leg, or even none at all. This is because mammals have evolved changes in the structure of both their axial and appendicular skeleton that permit running by a series of leaps.

Vertebrates such as kangaroos, rabbits, and frogs are effective leapers (figure 47.21). However, insects are the true Olympians of the leaping world. Many insects, such as grasshoppers, have enormous leg muscles, and some small insects can jump to heights more than 100 times the length of their body!

Flying uses air for support

The evolution of flight is a classic example of convergent evolution, having occurred independently four times, once in insects and three times among vertebrates (figure 47.22*a*). All three vertebrate fliers modified the forelimb into a wing structure, but they did so in different ways, illustrating how natural selection can sometimes build similar structures through different evolutionary pathways (figure 47.22*b*). In both birds and pterosaurs (an extinct group of reptiles that flourished alongside

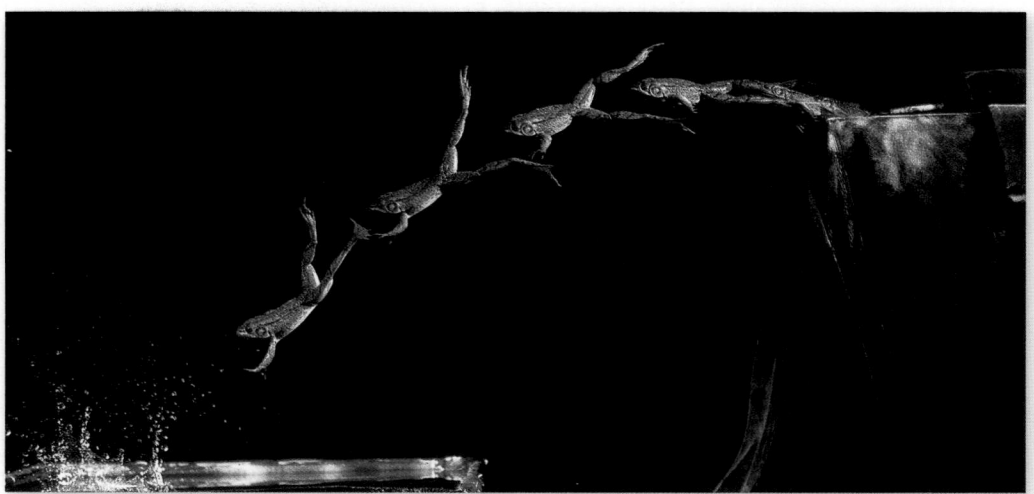

Figure 47.21 Animals that hop or leap use their rear legs to propel themselves through the air. The powerful leg muscles of this frog allow it to explode from a crouched position to a takeoff in about 100 msec.

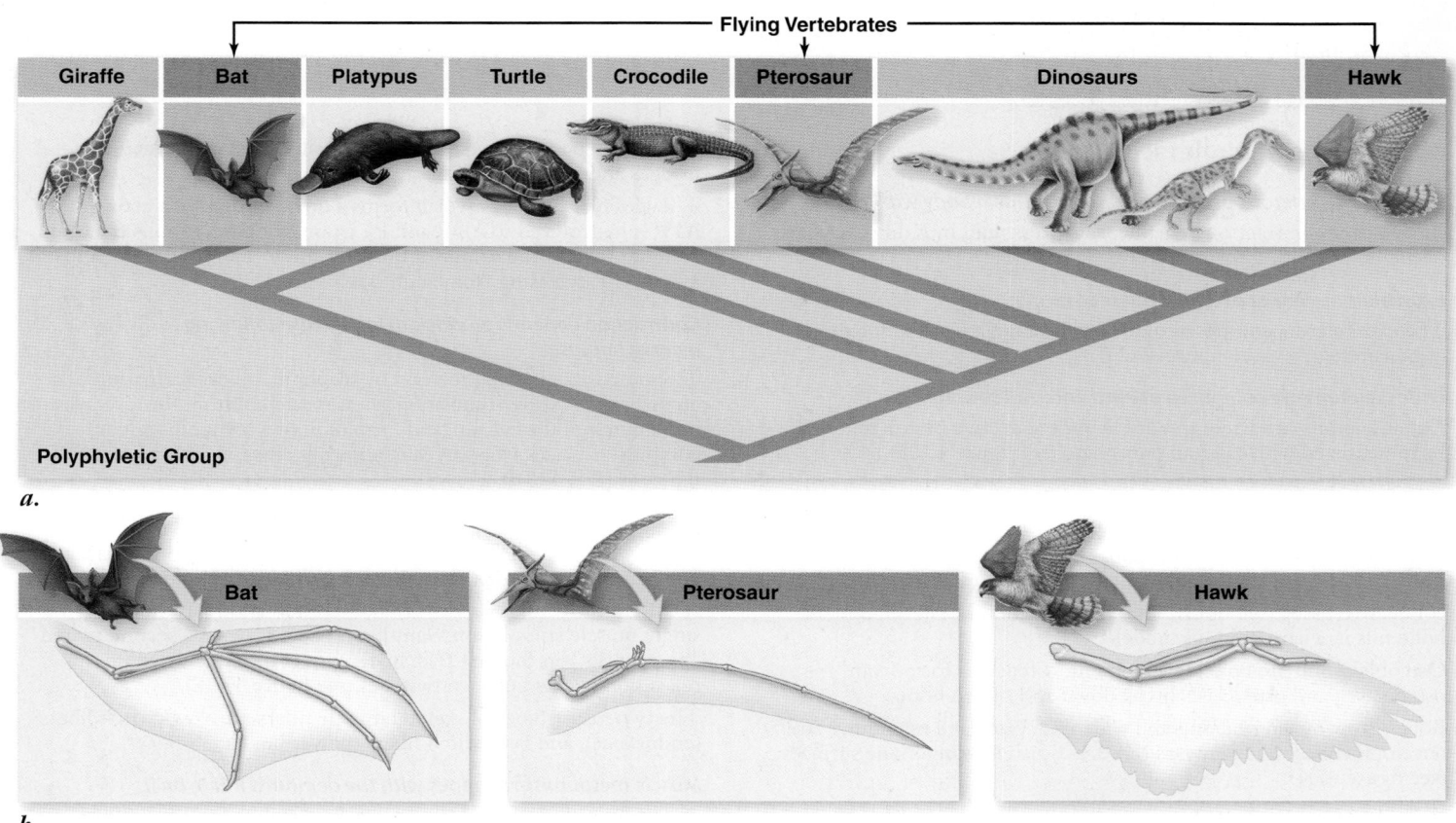

Figure 47.22 Convergent evolution of wings in vertebrates. Wings evolved independently in birds, bats and pterosaurs, in each case by elongation of different elements of the forelimb.

the dinosaurs), the wing is built on a single support, but in birds it is elongation of the radius, ulna, and wrist bones, whereas in pterosaurs it is an elongation of the fourth finger bone. By contrast, in bats the wing is supported by multiple bones, each of which is an elongated finger bone. A second difference is that the wings of pterosaurs and bats are composed of a membrane formed from skin, whereas birds use feathers, which are modified from reptile scales.

In all groups, active flying takes place in much the same way. Propulsion is achieved by pushing down against the air with wings. This alone provides enough lift to keep insects in the air. Vertebrates, being larger, need greater lift, obtaining it with wings whose upper surface is more convex (in cross section) than the lower. Because air travels farther over the top surface, it moves faster. A fluid, like air, decreases its internal pressure the faster it moves. Thus, there is a lower pressure on top of the wing and higher pressure on the bottom of the wing. This is the same principle used by airplane wings.

In birds and most insects, the raising and lowering of the wings is achieved by the alternate contraction of extensor muscles (elevators) and flexor muscles (depressors). Four insect orders (including those containing flies, mosquitoes, wasps, bees, and beetles) beat their wings at frequencies ranging from 100 to more than 1000 times per second, faster than nerves can carry successive impulses!

In these insects, the flight muscles are not attached to the wings at all, but rather to the stiff wall of the thorax, which is distorted in and out by their contraction. The reason these muscles can contract so fast is that the contraction of one muscle set stretches the other set, triggering its contraction in turn without waiting for the arrival of a nerve impulse.

In addition to active flight, many species have evolved adaptations—primarily flaps of skin that increase surface area and thus slow down the rate of descent—to enhance their ability to glide long distances. Gliders have done this in many ways, including flaps of skin along the body in flying squirrels, snakes, and lizards; webbing between the toes in frogs; and the evolution in some lizards of ribs that extend beyond the body wall and that are connected by skin that can be spread out to form a large gliding surface.

Learning Outcomes Review 47.5

Locomotion involves friction and pressure created by body parts, often appendages, against water, air, or ground. Walking, running, and flying require supporting the body against gravity's pull. Flight is achieved when a pressure difference between air flowing over the top and bottom of a wing creates lift. Solutions to locomotion have evolved convergently many times, in both homologous and nonhomologous structures.

■ *In what ways would locomotion by a series of leaps be more advantageous than by alternation of legs?*

47.1 Types of Skeletal Systems

Hydrostatic skeletons use water pressure inside a body wall.
By muscular contractions, earthworms press fluid into different parts of the body, causing them to move (see figure 47.1).

Exoskeletons consist of a rigid outer covering.
The exoskeleton, composed of hard chitin, must be shed for the organism to grow (see figure 47.2a).

Endoskeletons are composed of hard, internal structures.
Endoskeletons of vertebrates are living connective tissues that may be mineralized with calcium phosphate (see figure 47.2b).

47.2 A Closer Look at Bone

Bones can be classified by two modes of development.
In intramembranous development, bone forms within a layer of connective tissue (see figure 47.3). In endochondral development, bone fills in a cartilaginous model.

Osteoblasts initiate bone development; osteocytes form from osteoblasts; and osteoclasts break down and resorb bone.

Bones grow by lengthening and widening. Cartilage remaining after development of the epiphyses serves as a pad between bone surfaces (see figure 47.4).

Bone structure may include blood vessels and nerves.
In birds and fishes, bone is avascular and basically acellular. In other vertebrates, bone contains bone cells, blood capillaries, and nerves collected in Haversian systems.

Bone remodeling allows bone to respond to use or disuse.
Bone structure may thicken or thin depending on use and on forces impinging on the bone (see figure 47.5).

47.3 Joints and Skeletal Movement

Moveable joints have different ranges of motion, depending on type.
Ball-and-socket joints can perform movement in all directions; hinge joints have restricted movement; gliding joints slide, providing stability and flexibility; and combination joints allow rotation and sliding (see figure 47.7).

Skeletal muscles pull on bones to produce movement at joints.
Muscles attach to the periosteum directly or through a tendon. Skeletal muscles occur in antagonistic pairs that oppose each other's movement (see figure 47.8).

47.4 Muscle Contraction

Muscle fibers contract as overlapping filaments slide together.
The different myofibril bands seen microscopically result from the degree of overlap of actin and myosin filaments (see figure 47.10). Muscle contraction occurs when actin and myosin filaments form cross-bridges and slide relative to each other.

The globular head of myosin forms a cross-bridge with actin when ATP is hydrolyzed to ADP and P_i. Upon bridging, it pulls the thin filament toward the center of the sarcomere. The head then binds to a new ATP, releasing from actin (see figure 47.14).

Contraction depends on calcium ion release following a nerve impulse.
Tropomyosin, attached to actin by troponin, blocks formation of a cross-bridge. Nerve stimulation releases calcium from the sarcoplasmic reticulum into the cytosol, and formation of a troponin–calcium complex displaces tropomyosin, allowing cross-bridges to form (see figures 47.15, 47.16).

Motor units are composed of a single motor neuron and all the muscle fibers innervated by its branches (see figure 47.17).

The two main types of muscle fibers are slow-twitch and fast-twitch.
A twitch is the interval between contraction and relaxation of a single muscle stimulation. Summation occurs when a second twitch "piggybacks" on the first twitch. Tetanus is the state when no relaxation occurs between twitches (see figure 47.18).

The two major types of skeletal muscle fibers are slow-twitch fibers (endurance), and fast-twitch fibers (power bursts).

Muscle metabolism changes with the demands made on it.
At rest skeletal muscles obtain energy by metabolism of fatty acids. When active, energy comes from glucose and glycogen.

Muscle fatigue is a use-dependent decrease in the ability of the muscle to generate force.

Endurance training does not increase muscle size; high-intensity exercise with resistance increases the size of the muscle (hypertrophy).

47.5 Modes of Animal Locomotion

Swimmers must contend with friction when moving through water.
Among vertebrates, aquatic locomotion occurs by pushing some or all of the body against the water. Many vertebrates undulate the body or tail for propulsion, but others use their limbs (see figure 47.20).

Terrestrial locomotion must deal primarily with gravity.
Most terrestrial animals move by lifting their bodies off the ground and pushing against the ground with appendages. Terrestrial animals that walk or run use fundamentally the same mechanisms during locomotion.

Flying uses air for support.
Propulsion is accomplished as wings push down against the air. Lift in larger organisms is created by a pressure difference as air flows above and below a convex wing.

In both flying and gliding, convergent evolution has produced the same outcome through different evolutionary pathways.

UNDERSTAND

1. Exoskeletons and endoskeletons differ in that
   a. an exoskeleton is rigid, and an endoskeleton is flexible.
   b. endoskeletons are found only in vertebrates.
   c. exoskeletons are composed of calcium, and endoskeletons are built from chitin.
   d. exoskeletons are external to the soft tissues, and endoskeletons are internal.

2. Worms use a hydrostatic skeleton to generate movement. How do they do this?
   a. Their bones are filled with water, which provides the weight of the skeleton.
   b. The change in body structure is caused by contraction of muscles compressing the watery body fluid.
   c. The muscles contain water vacuoles, which, when filled, provide a rigid internal structure.
   d. The term *hydrostatic* simply refers to moist environment. They generate movement just as arthropods do.

3. You take X-rays of two individuals. Ray has been a weight lifter and body builder for 30 years; Ben has led a mostly sedentary life. What differences would you expect in their X-rays?
   a. No difference, they would both have thicker bones than a younger person due to natural thickening with age.
   b. No difference, lifestyle does not affect bone density.
   c. Ray would have thicker bones due to reshaping as a result of physical stress.
   d. Ben would have thicker bones because bone accumulates like fat tissue from a sedentary lifestyle.

4. Which of the following statements best describes the sliding filament mechanism of muscle contraction?
   a. Actin and myosin filaments do not shorten, but rather, slide past each other.
   b. Actin and myosin filaments shorten and slide past each other.
   c. As they slide past each other, actin filaments shorten, but myosin filaments do not shorten.
   d. As they slide past each other, myosin filaments shorten, but actin filaments do not shorten.

5. Motor neurons stimulate muscle contraction via the release of
   a. Ca^{2+}.
   b. ATP.
   c. acetylcholine.
   d. hormones.

6. Which of the following statements about muscle metabolism is false?
   a. Skeletal muscles at rest obtain most of their energy from muscle glycogen and blood glucose.
   b. ATP can be quickly obtained by combining ADP with phosphate derived from creatine phosphate.
   c. Exercise intensity is related to the maximum rate of oxygen consumption.
   d. ATP is required for the pumping of the Ca^{2+} back into the sarcoplasmic reticulum.

7. If you wanted to study the use of ATP during a single contraction cycle within a muscle cell, which of the following processes would you use?
   a. Summation
   b. Twitch
   c. Treppe
   d. Tetanus

8. Place the following events in the correct order.
   1. Sarcoplasmic reticulum releases Ca^{2+}.
   2. Myosin binds to actin.
   3. Action potential arrives from neuron.
   4. Ca^{2+} binds to troponin.

   a. 1, 2, 3, 4
   b. 3, 1, 2, 4
   c. 2, 4, 3, 1
   d. 3, 1, 4, 2

APPLY

1. Bone develops by one of two mechanisms depending on the underlying scaffold. Which pairing correctly describes these mechanisms?
   a. Intramembranous and extramembranous
   b. Endochondral and exochondral
   c. Extramembranous and exochondral
   d. Endochondral and intramembranous

2. You have identified a calcium storage disease in rats. How would this inability to store Ca^{2+} affect muscle contraction?
   a. Ca^{2+} would be unable to bind to tropomyosin, which enables troponin to move and reveal binding sites for cross-bridges.
   b. Ca^{2+} would be unable to bind to troponin, which enables tropomyosin to move and reveal binding sites for cross-bridges.
   c. Ca^{2+} would be unable to bind to tropomyosin, which enables troponin to release ATP.
   d. Ca^{2+} would be unable to bind to troponin, which enables tropomyosin to release ATP.

3. How do the muscles move your hand through space?
   a. By contraction
   b. By attaching to two bones across a joint
   c. By lengthening
   d. Both a and b are correct

4. How can osteocytes remain alive within bone?
   a. Bones are composed of only dead or dormant cells.
   b. Haversian canals are bone structures that contain blood vessels that provide materials for the osteocytes.
   c. Osteocytes have membrane extensions that protrude from bone and allow them to exchange materials with the surrounding fluids.
   d. Bones are hollow in the middle and the low pressure there draws fluid from the blood that nourishes the osteocytes.

5. Swimming underwater using forelimbs for propulsion is similar to flying through the air because
   a. birds are the only class of vertebrates that have species that do both.
   b. both involve coordinating movements of the forelimbs and hindlimbs.
   c. both must counter strong forces caused by friction.
   d. both involve generating lift by pushing down on the air or water to counter gravity.

6. If a drug inhibits the release of ACh, what will happen?
   a. Somatic motor neurons will fail to activate.
   b. Somatic motor neuron impulses will not lead to muscle fiber contraction.
   c. Myosin molecules will fail to release ADP.
   d. An influx of sodium ions will lead to muscle cell membrane depolarization.

SYNTHESIZE

1. You are designing a space-exploration vehicle to use on a planet with a gravity greater than Earth. Given a choice between a hydrostatic or an exoskeleton, which would you choose? Why?

2. You start running as fast as you can. Then, you settle into a jog that you can easily maintain. How do energy sources utilized by your skeletal muscles change during the switch? Why?

3. The nerve gas methylphosphonofluoridic acid (sarin) inhibits the enzyme acetylcholinesterase, required to break down acetylcholine. Based on this information, what are the likely effects of this nerve gas on muscle function?

4. If natural selection favors the evolution of wings in different types of vertebrates, why didn't it produce structures that were built in the same way?

ONLINE RESOURCE

www.ravenbiology.com

Understand, Apply, and Synthesize—enhance your study with animations that bring concepts to life and practice tests to assess your understanding. Your instructor may also recommend the interactive eBook, individualized learning tools, and more.

Chapter 48

The Digestive System

Chapter Outline

48.1 Types of Digestive Systems

48.2 The Mouth and Teeth: Food Capture and Bulk Processing

48.3 The Esophagus and the Stomach: The Beginning of Digestion

48.4 The Intestines: Breakdown, Absorption, and Elimination

48.5 Variations in Vertebrate Digestive Systems

48.6 Neural and Hormonal Regulation of the Digestive Tract

48.7 Accessory Organ Function

48.8 Food Energy, Energy Expenditure, and Essential Nutrients

Introduction

Plants and other photosynthetic organisms can produce the organic molecules they need from inorganic components. Therefore, they are autotrophs, or self-sustaining. Animals, such as the chipmunk shown, are heterotrophs: They must consume organic molecules present in other organisms. The molecules heterotrophs eat must be digested into smaller molecules in order to be absorbed into the animal's body. Once these products of digestion enter the body, the animal can use them for energy in cellular respiration or for the construction of the larger molecules that make up its tissues. The process of animal digestion is the focus of this chapter.

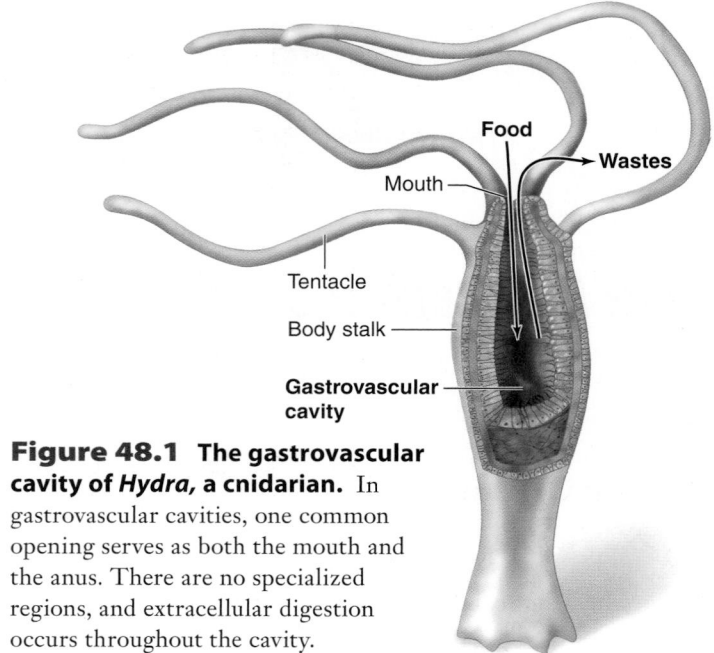

Heterotrophs are divided into three groups on the basis of their food sources. Animals that eat plants exclusively are classified as **herbivores;** common examples include algae-eating snails, sapsucking insects, and vertebrates such as cattle, horses, rabbits, and sparrows. Animals that eat other animals, such as crabs, squid, many insects, cats, eagles, trout, and frogs, are **carnivores.** Animals that eat both plants and other animals are **omnivores.** Humans are omnivores, as are pigs, bears, and crows.

Figure 48.1 **The gastrovascular cavity of *Hydra,* a cnidarian.** In gastrovascular cavities, one common opening serves as both the mouth and the anus. There are no specialized regions, and extracellular digestion occurs throughout the cavity.

Invertebrate digestive systems are bags or tubes

Single-celled organisms as well as sponges digest their food intracellularly. Other multicellular animals digest their food extracellularly, within a digestive cavity. In this case, the digestive enzymes are released into a cavity that is continuous with the animal's external environment. In cnidarians and in flatworms such as planarians, the digestive cavity has only one opening that serves as both mouth and anus (see chapter 33). There is no specialization within this type of digestive system, called a *gastrovascular cavity,* because every cell is exposed to all stages of food digestion (figure 48.1).

Specialization occurs when the digestive tract, or alimentary canal, has a separate mouth and anus, so that transport of food is one-way. The most primitive digestive tract is seen in nematodes (phylum Nematoda), where it is simply a tubular *gut* lined by an epithelial membrane. Earthworms (phylum Annelida) have a digestive tract specialized in different regions for the ingestion, storage, fragmentation, digestion, and absorption of food. All more complex animal groups, including all vertebrates, show similar specializations (figure 48.2).

The ingested food may be stored in a specialized region of the digestive tract or it may first be subjected to physical frag-

mentation. This fragmentation may occur through the chewing action of teeth (in the mouth of many vertebrates) or the grinding action of pebbles (in the gizzard of earthworms and birds). Chemical digestion then occurs, breaking down the larger food molecules of polysaccharides and disaccharides, fats, and proteins into their smallest subunits.

Chemical digestion involves hydrolysis reactions that liberate the subunit molecules—primarily monosaccharides, amino acids, and fatty acids—from the food. These products of chemical digestion pass through the epithelial lining of the gut into the blood, in a process known as *absorption.* Any molecules in the food that are not absorbed cannot be used by the animal. These waste products are excreted, or defecated, from the anus.

Vertebrate digestive systems include highly specialized structures molded by diet

In humans and other vertebrates, the digestive system consists of a tubular gastrointestinal tract and accessory digestive organs (figure 48.3).

Nematode	Earthworm	Salamander
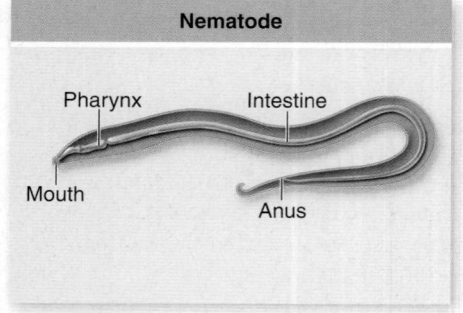	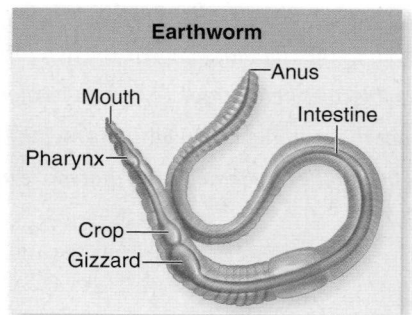	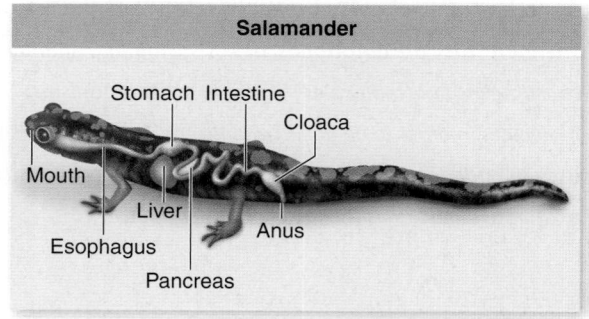

Figure 48.2 **The one-way digestive tract of nematodes, earthworms, and vertebrates.** One-way movement through the digestive tract allows different regions of the digestive system to become specialized for different functions.

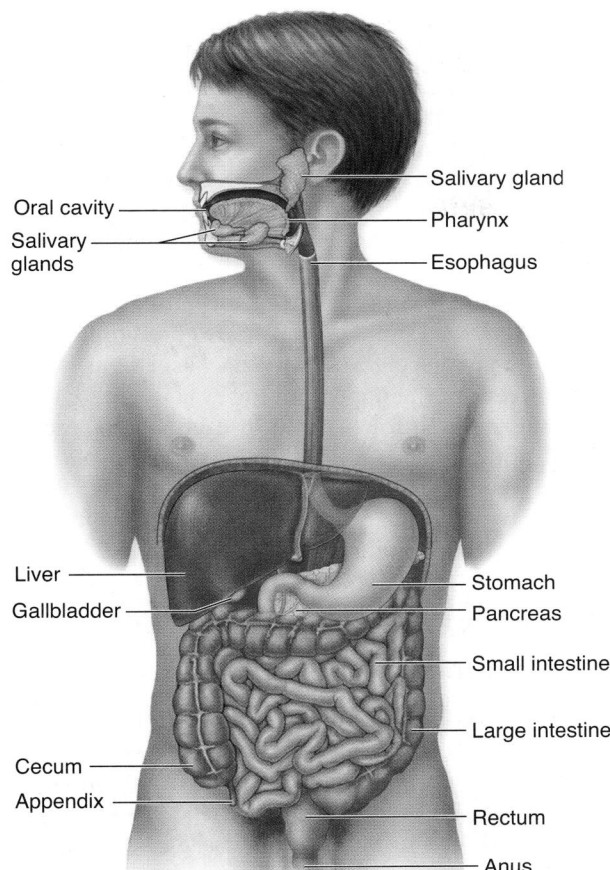

Figure 48.3 **The human digestive system.** The human digestive system consists of the oral cavity, esophagus, stomach, small intestine, large intestine, rectum, and anus; and is aided by accessory organs.

Overview of the digestive tract

The initial components of the gastrointestinal tract are the mouth and the pharynx, which is the common passage of the oral and nasal cavities. The pharynx leads to the esophagus, a muscular tube that delivers food to the stomach, where some preliminary digestion occurs.

From the stomach, food passes to the small intestine, where a battery of digestive enzymes continues the digestive process. The products of digestion, together with minerals and water, are absorbed across the wall of the small intestine into the bloodstream. What remains is emptied into the large intestine, where some of the remaining water and minerals are absorbed.

In most vertebrates other than mammals, the waste products emerge from the large intestine into a cavity called the cloaca (see figure 48.2), which also receives the products of the urinary and reproductive systems. In mammals, the urogenital products are separated from the fecal material in the large intestine; the fecal material enters the rectum and is expelled through the anus.

The accessory digestive organs include the liver, which produces *bile* (a green solution that emulsifies fat), the gallbladder, which stores and concentrates the bile, and the pancreas. The pancreas produces *pancreatic juice*, which contains digestive enzymes and bicarbonate buffer. Both bile and pancreatic juice

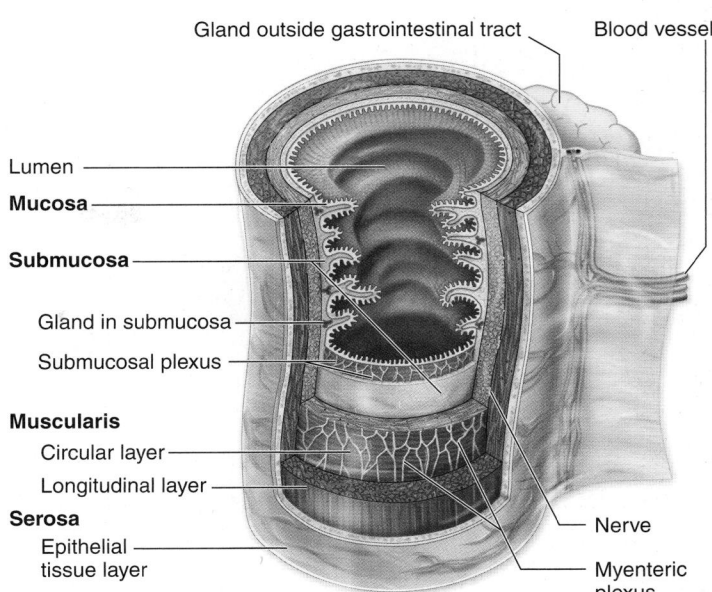

Figure 48.4 **The layers of the gastrointestinal tract.** The mucosa contains an epithelial lining; the submucosa is composed of connective tissue; and the muscularis consists of smooth muscles. Glands secrete substances via ducts into specific regions of the tract.

are secreted into the first region of the small intestine, the duodenum, where they aid digestion.

Tissues of the digestive tract

The tubular gastrointestinal tract of a vertebrate has a characteristic layered structure (figure 48.4). The innermost layer is the **mucosa,** an epithelium that lines the interior, or lumen, of the tract. The next major tissue layer, made of connective tissue, is called the **submucosa.**

Just outside the submucosa is the **muscularis,** which consists of a double layer of smooth muscles. The muscles in the inner layer have a circular orientation and serve to constrict the gut, whereas those in the outer layer are arranged longitudinally and work to shorten it. Another epithelial tissue layer, the **serosa,** covers the external surface of the tract. Nerve networks, intertwined in *plexuses* between muscle layers, are located in the submucosa and help regulate the gastrointestinal activities.

In the rest of this chapter, we focus on the details of the vertebrate digestive system's structure and function. We close the chapter with discussion of nutrients that are essential to vertebrates.

Learning Outcomes Review 48.1

Incomplete digestive tracts have only one opening; complete digestive tracts are flow-through, with a mouth and an anus. The digestive system of vertebrates includes mouth and pharynx, esophagus, stomach, small and large intestines, cloaca or rectum, anus, and accessory organs. The layers of tissue that compose the tubular tract are the mucosa, the submucosa, the muscularis, and the serosa.

■ *What might be the advantages of a one-way digestive system?*

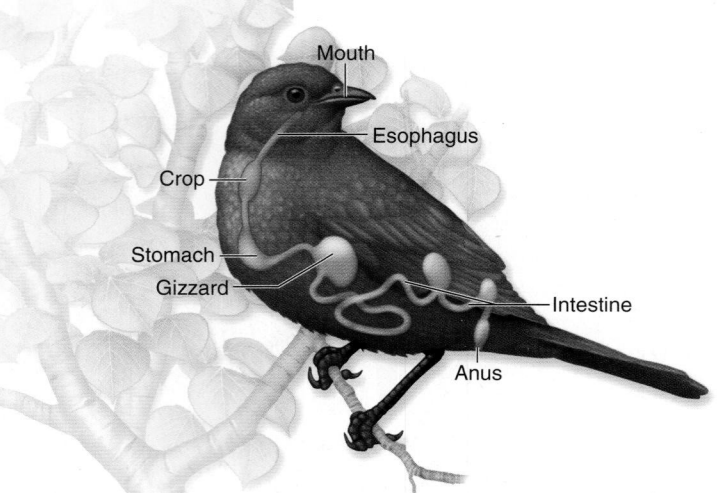

Figure 48.5 The digestive tract of birds. Birds lack teeth but have a muscular chamber called the gizzard that works to break down food. Birds swallow gritty objects or pebbles that lodge in the gizzard and pulverize food before it passes into the intestine. Food is stored in the crop.

48.2 *The Mouth and Teeth: Food Capture and Bulk Processing*

Learning Outcomes

1. *Identify adaptive variation in vertebrate tooth shape.*
2. *Understand the role of the mouth in the digestive process.*

Specializations of the digestive systems in different kinds of vertebrates reflect the way these animals live. Birds, which lack teeth, break up food in their two-chambered stomachs (figure 48.5). In one of these chambers, called the *gizzard*, small pebbles ingested by the bird are churned together with the food by muscular action. This churning grinds up the seeds and other hard plant material into smaller chunks that can be digested more easily.

Vertebrate teeth are adapted to different types of food items

Many vertebrates have teeth (figure 48.6), used for chewing, or *mastication*, that break up food into small particles and mix it with fluid secretions. Carnivorous mammals have pointed teeth that lack flat grinding surfaces. Such teeth are adapted for cutting and shearing. Carnivores often tear off pieces of their prey but have little need to chew them, because digestive enzymes can act directly on animal cells. By contrast, grass-eating herbivores must pulverize the cellulose cell walls of plant tissue before the bacteria in their rumens or cecae can digest them. These animals have large, flat teeth with complex ridges well suited to grinding.

Human teeth are specialized for eating both plant and animal food. Viewed simply, humans are carnivores in the front of the mouth and herbivores in the back (see figure 48.6). The four front teeth in the upper and lower jaws are sharp, chisel-shaped incisors used for biting. On each side of the incisors are sharp, pointed teeth called cuspids (sometimes referred to as "canine" teeth), which are used for tearing food. Behind the canines are two premolars and three molars, all with flattened, ridged surfaces for grinding and crushing food.

The mouth is a chamber for ingestion and initial processing

Inside the mouth, the tongue mixes food with a mucous solution, saliva. In humans, three pairs of salivary glands secrete saliva into the mouth through ducts in the mouth's mucosal lining. Saliva moistens and lubricates the food so that it is easier to swallow and does not abrade the tissue of the esophagus as it passes through.

Saliva also contains the hydrolytic enzyme salivary amylase, which initiates the breakdown of the polysaccharide starch into the disaccharide maltose. This digestion is usually minimal in humans, however, because most people don't chew their food very long.

Stimulation of salivation

The secretions of the salivary glands are controlled by the nervous system, which in humans maintains a constant flow of about half a milliliter per minute when the mouth is empty of food. This continuous secretion keeps the mouth moist.

The presence of food in the mouth triggers an increased rate of secretion. Taste buds as well as olfactory (smell) neurons send impulses to the brain, which responds by stimulating the salivary glands (see chapter 46). The most potent stimuli are acidic solutions; lemon juice, for example, can increase the rate of salivation eightfold. The sight, sound, or smell of food can stimulate salivation markedly in many

Figure 48.6 Patterns of dentition depend on diet. Different vertebrates (herbivore, carnivore, or omnivore) have evolved specific variations from a generalized pattern of dentition depending on their diets.

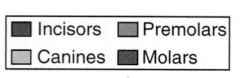

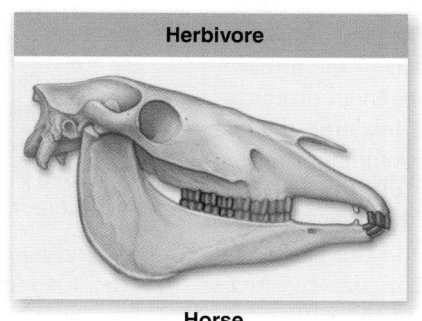
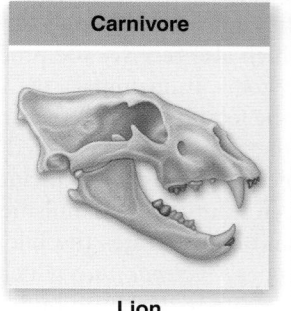
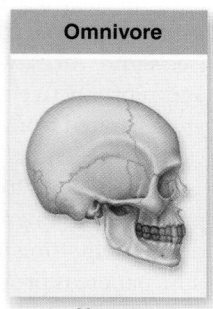

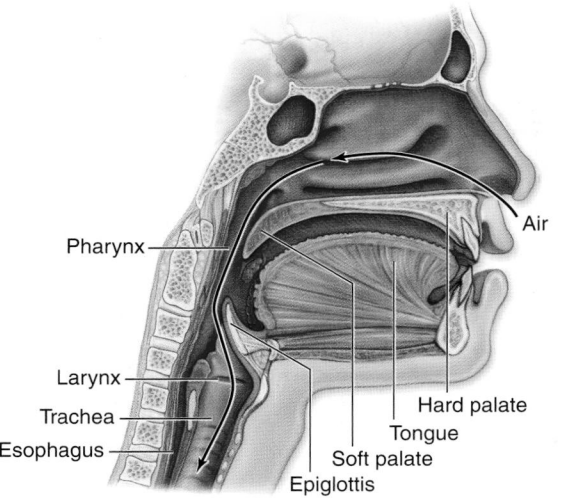

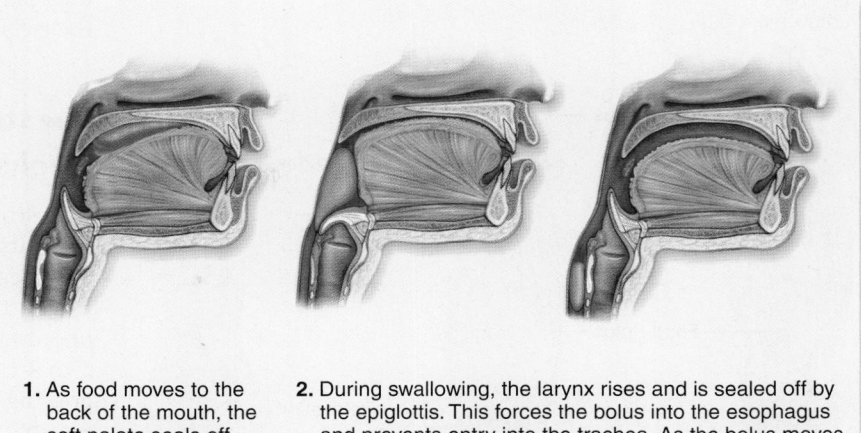

1. As food moves to the back of the mouth, the soft palate seals off the nasal cavity.

2. During swallowing, the larynx rises and is sealed off by the epiglottis. This forces the bolus into the esophagus and prevents entry into the trachea. As the bolus moves into the esophagus the larynx relaxes.

Figure 48.7 The mechanics of swallowing. Cross section through head and throat showing relevant structures (left). During swallowing (right) the tongue pushes the palate upward, and the soft palate seals off the nasal cavity. Elevation of the larynx causes the epiglottis to seal off the trachea, thus preventing food from entering the airway.

Inquiry question

? **What goes wrong to cause someone to choke?**

animals; in humans, thinking or talking about food can also have this effect.

Swallowing

Swallowing is initiated by voluntary action, then is continued under involuntary control. When food is ready to be swallowed, the tongue moves it to the back of the mouth. In mammals, the process of swallowing begins when the soft palate elevates, pushing against the back wall of the pharynx (figure 48.7). Elevation of the soft palate seals off the nasal cavity and prevents food from entering it. Pressure against the pharynx triggers an automatic, involuntary response, the swallowing reflex. Because it is a reflex, swallowing cannot be stopped once it is initiated.

Neurons within the walls of the pharynx send impulses to the swallowing center in the brain. In response, electrical impulses in motor neurons stimulate muscles to contract and raise the **larynx** (voice box). This pushes the glottis, the opening from the larynx into the trachea (windpipe), against a flap of tissue called the **epiglottis.** These actions keep food out of the respiratory tract, directing it instead into the esophagus.

Learning Outcomes Review 48.2

In vertebrates with teeth, tooth shape exhibits adaptations to diet: herbivores have large, flat teeth for grinding, whereas carnivores have pointed teeth for tearing. The mouth serves as an initial processing center, tasting ingested food, breaking it down, and beginning digestion with saliva secretion prior to swallowing.

■ *Which parts of the food ingestion process are voluntary and which are involuntary?*

48.3 The Esophagus and the Stomach: The Early Stages of Digestion

Learning Outcomes

1. *Describe how food moves through the esophagus.*
2. *Explain what digestive processes take place in the stomach.*

Swallowed food enters a muscular tube called the esophagus, which connects the pharynx to the stomach. The esophagus actively moves a processed lump of food, called a **bolus,** through the action of muscles. Food from a meal is stored in the stomach where it undergoes early stages of digestion.

Muscular contractions of the esophagus move food to the stomach

In adult humans, the esophagus is about 25 cm long; the upper third is enveloped in skeletal muscle for voluntary control of swallowing, whereas the lower two-thirds is surrounded by involuntary smooth muscle. The swallowing center stimulates successive one-directional waves of contraction in these muscles that move food along the esophagus to the stomach. These rhythmic waves of muscular contraction are called

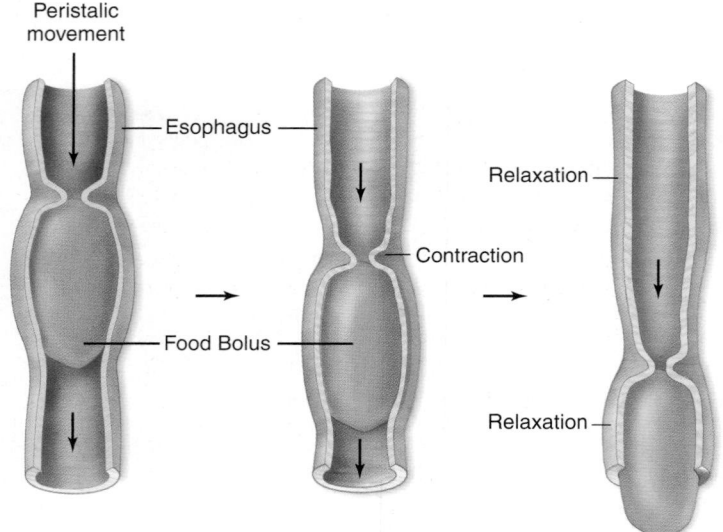

Figure 48.8 The esophagus and peristalsis. After food has entered the esophagus, rhythmic waves of muscular contraction, called peristalsis, move the food down to the stomach.

peristalsis (figure 48.8); they enable humans and other vertebrates to swallow even if they are upside down.

In many vertebrates, the movement of food from the esophagus into the stomach is controlled by a ring of circular smooth muscle, or a *sphincter*, that opens in response to the pressure exerted by the food. Contraction of this sphincter prevents food in the stomach from moving back into the esophagus. Rodents and horses have a true sphincter at this site, and as a result

they cannot regurgitate; humans lack a true sphincter. Normally, the esophagus is closed off except during swallowing.

The stomach is a "holding station" involved in acidic breakdown of food

The **stomach** (figure 48.9) is a saclike portion of the digestive tract. Its inner surface is highly convoluted, enabling it to fold up when empty and open out like an expanding balloon as it fills with food. For example, the human stomach has a volume of only about 50 mL when empty, but, it may expand to contain 2 to 4 L of food when full. Carnivores that engage in sporadic gorging as an important survival strategy possess stomachs that are able to distend even more.

Secretory systems

The stomach contains a third layer of smooth muscle for churning food and mixing it with **gastric juice,** an acidic secretion of the tubular gastric glands of the mucosa (see figure 48.9). These exocrine glands contain three kinds of secretory cells: *mucus-secreting cells*, *parietal cells*, which secrete hydrochloric acid (HCl), and *chief cells*, which secrete **pepsinogen,** the inactive form of the protease (protein-digesting enzyme) **pepsin.**

Pepsinogen has 44 additional amino acids that block its active site. HCl causes pepsinogen to unfold, exposing the active site, which then acts to remove the 44 amino acids. This yields the active protease, pepsin. This process of secreting an inactive form that is then converted into an active enzyme outside the cell prevents the chief cells from digesting themselves. In the stomach, mucus produced by mucus-secreting cells serves

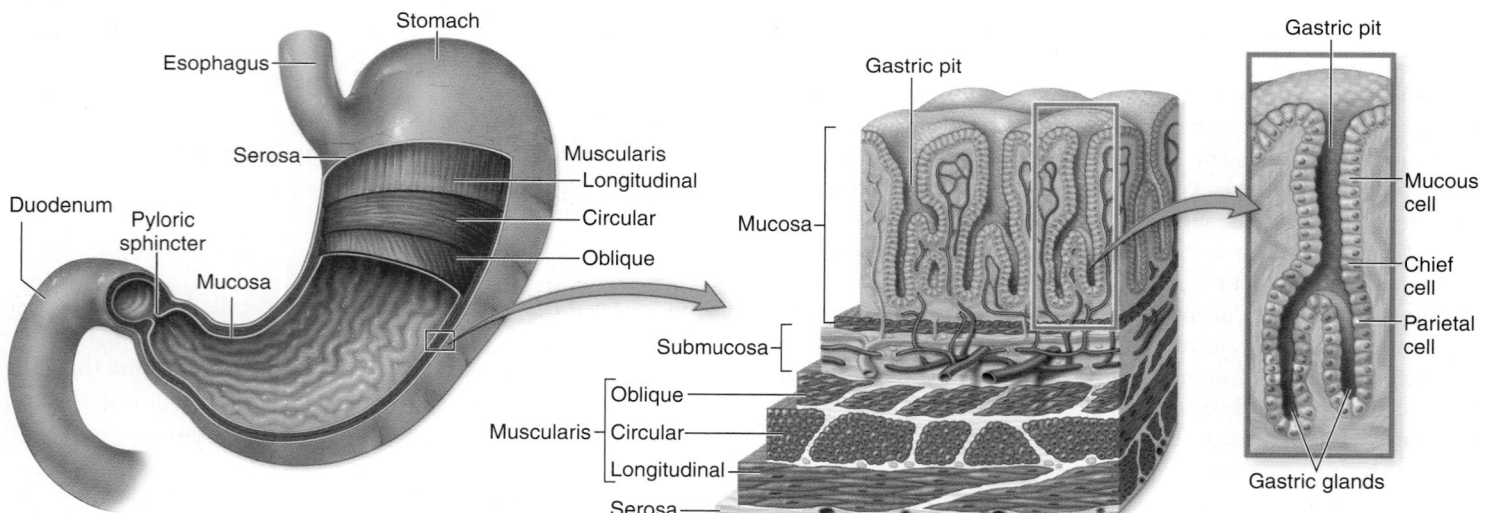

Figure 48.9 The stomach and duodenum. Food enters the stomach from the esophagus. A ring of smooth muscle called the pyloric sphincter controls the entrance to the duodenum, the upper part of the small intestine. The epithelial walls of the stomach are dotted with deep infoldings called gastric pits that contain gastric glands. The gastric glands consist of mucous cells, chief cells that secrete pepsinogen, and parietal cells that secrete HCl. Gastric pits are the openings of the gastric glands.

Inquiry question

? How does the digestive system keep from being digested by the gastric secretions it produces?

the same purpose, covering the interior walls and preventing them from being digested.

In addition to producing HCl, the parietal cells of the stomach also secrete **intrinsic factor,** a polypeptide needed for the intestinal absorption of vitamin B_{12}. Because this vitamin is required for the production of red blood cells, people who lack sufficient intrinsic factor develop a type of anemia (low red blood cell count) called *pernicious anemia.*

Action of acid

The human stomach produces about 2 L of HCl and other gastric secretions every day, creating a very acidic solution. The concentration of HCl in this solution is about 10 milli-molar (mM), equal to a pH of 2. Thus, gastric juice is about 250,000 times more acidic than blood, whose normal pH is 7.4.

The low pH in the stomach helps denature food proteins, making them easier to digest, and keeps pepsin maximally active. Active pepsin hydrolyzes food proteins into shorter chains of polypeptides that are not fully digested until the mixture enters the small intestine. The mixture of partially digested food and gastric juice is called **chyme.** In adult humans, only proteins are partially digested in the stomach—no significant digestion of carbohydrates or fats occurs there.

The acidic solution within the stomach also kills most of the bacteria that are ingested with the food. The few bacteria that survive the stomach and enter the intestine intact are able to grow and multiply there, particularly in the large intestine. In fact, vertebrates harbor thriving colonies of bacteria within their intestines, and bacteria are a major component of feces. As we discuss later, bacteria that live within the digestive tracts of ruminants play a key role in the ability of these mammals to digest cellulose.

Ulcers

Overproduction of gastric acid can occasionally eat a hole through the wall of the stomach or the duodenum, causing a peptic ulcer. Although we once blamed consumption of spicy food, the most common cause of peptic ulcers is now thought to be infection with the bacterium *Heliobacter pylori.*

H. pylori can grow on the lining of the human stomach, surviving the acid pH by secreting substances that buffer the pH of its immediate surroundings. Although infection with *H. pylori* is common in the United States (about 20% of people younger than 40 and 50% older than 60), most people are asymptomatic. However, in some cases, infection by *H. pylori* can reduce or weaken the mucosal layer in the stomach or duodenum, allowing acidic secretions to attack the underlying epithelium. Antibiotic treatment of the infection can reduce symptoms and often even cure the ulcer.

Leaving the stomach

Chyme leaves the stomach through the *pyloric sphincter* (see figure 48.9) to enter the small intestine. This is where all terminal digestion of carbohydrates, lipids, and proteins occurs and where the products of digestion—amino acids, glucose, and so on—are absorbed into the blood. Only some of the water in

chyme and a few substances, such as aspirin and alcohol, are absorbed through the wall of the stomach.

Learning Outcomes Review 48.3

Peristaltic waves of contraction and relaxation of smooth muscle propel food along the esophagus to the stomach. Gastric juice contains strong hydrochloric acid and the enzyme pepsin, a protease that begins the breakdown of proteins into shorter polypeptides. The acidic chyme is then transferred through the pyloric sphincter into the small intestine.

■ *Suppose you ate a chicken sandwich (chicken breast on bread with mayonnaise). Which of these foods would begin its breakdown in the stomach?*

48.4 *The Intestines: Breakdown, Absorption, and Elimination*

Learning Outcomes

1. *Compare the structures of the small and large intestines.*
2. *Name the accessory organs and describe their roles.*
3. *Explain how absorbed nutrients move into the blood or lymph capillaries.*

The capacity of the small intestine is limited, and its digestive processes take time. Consequently, efficient digestion requires that only relatively small amounts of chyme be introduced from the stomach into the small intestine at any one time. Coordination between gastric and intestinal activities is regulated by neural and hormonal signals, which we will describe in section 48.6.

The structure of the small intestine is specialized for digestion and nutrient uptake

The small intestine is approximately 4.5 m long in a living person, but 6 m long at autopsy when all the muscles have relaxed. The first 25 cm is the **duodenum;** the remainder of the small intestine is divided into the **jejunum** and the **ileum.**

The duodenum receives acidic chyme from the stomach, digestive enzymes and bicarbonate from the pancreas, and bile from the liver and gallbladder. Enzymes in the pancreatic juice digest larger food molecules into smaller fragments. This digestion occurs primarily in the duodenum and jejunum.

The epithelial wall of the small intestine is covered with tiny, fingerlike projections called **villi** (singular, *villus;* figure 48.10). In turn, each epithelial cell lining the villi is covered on its apical surface (the side facing the lumen) by many foldings of the plasma membrane that form cytoplasmic extensions called **microvilli.** These are quite tiny and can be seen clearly only with an electron microscope. Under a light micrograph, the microvilli resemble the

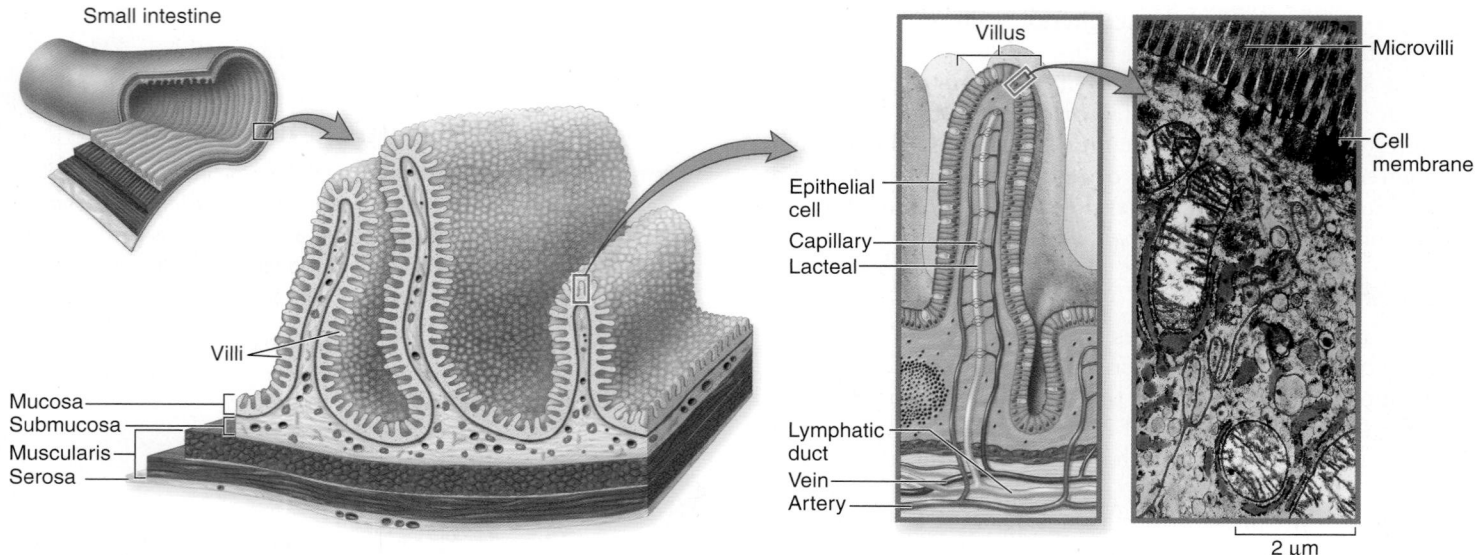

Figure 48.10 The small intestine. Successive enlargements show folded epithelium studded with villi that increase the surface area. The micrograph shows an epithelial cell with numerous microvilli.

bristles of a brush, and for that reason the epithelial wall of the small intestine is also called a *brush border*.

The villi and microvilli greatly increase the surface area of the small intestine; in humans, this surface area is 300 m²—about 3200 square feet, larger than a tennis court! It is over this vast surface that the products of digestion are absorbed.

The microvilli also participate in digestion because a number of digestive enzymes are embedded within the epithelial cells' plasma membranes, with their active sites exposed to the chyme. These brush border enzymes include those that hydrolyze the disaccharides lactose and sucrose, among others. Many adult humans lose the ability to produce the brush border enzyme lactase and therefore cannot digest lactose (milk sugar), a rather common condition called *lactose intolerance*. The brush border enzymes complete the digestive process that started with the action of salivary amylase in the mouth.

Accessory organs secrete enzymes into the small intestine

The main organs that aid digestion are the pancreas, liver, and gallbladder. They empty their secretions, primarily enzymes, through ducts directly into the small intestine.

Secretions of the pancreas

The pancreas (figure 48.11), a large gland situated near the junction of the stomach and the small intestine, secretes pancreatic fluid into the duodenum through the *pancreatic duct*; thus, the pancreas functions as an exocrine gland. This fluid contains a host of enzymes, including **trypsin** and **chymotrypsin,** which digest proteins; **pancreatic amylase,** which digests starch; and **lipase,** which digests fat. Like pepsin in the stomach, these enzymes are released into the duodenum primarily as inactive enzymes and are then activated by trypsin, which is first activated by a brush border enzyme of the intestine.

Pancreatic enzymes digest proteins into smaller polypeptides, polysaccharides into shorter chains of sugars, and fats

into free fatty acids and monoglycerides. Digestion of proteins and carbohydrates is then completed by the brush border enzymes. Pancreatic fluid also contains bicarbonate, which neutralizes the HCl from the stomach and gives the chyme in the duodenum a slightly alkaline pH. The digestive enzymes and

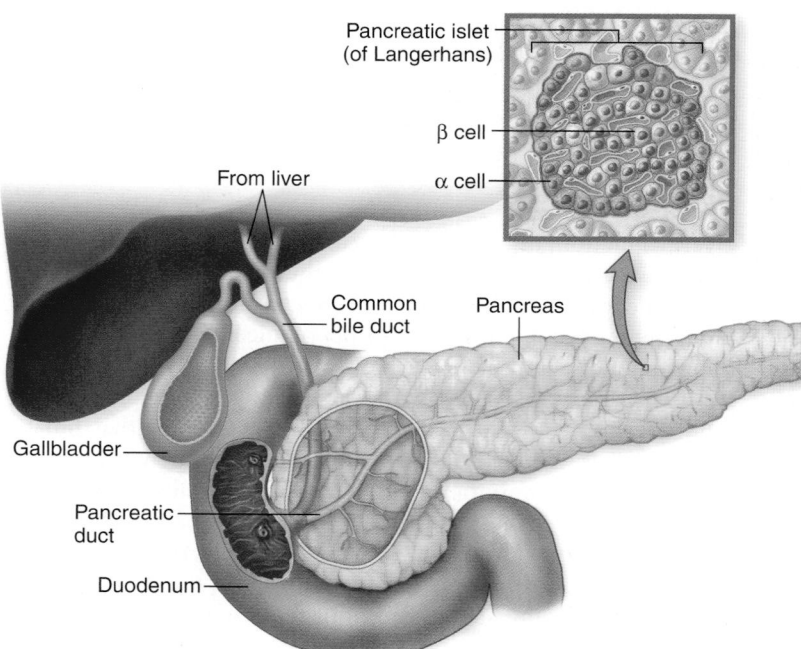

Figure 48.11 The pancreas. The pancreatic and bile ducts empty into the duodenum. The pancreas secretes pancreatic juice into the pancreatic duct. The pancreatic islets of Langerhans secrete hormones into the blood; α cells secrete glucagon, and β cells secrete insulin. The liver secretes bile, which consists of bile pigments (waste products from the liver) and bile salts. Bile salts play a role in the digestion of fats. Bile is concentrated and stored in the gallbladder until it is needed in the duodenum on the arrival of fatty food.

bicarbonate are produced by clusters of secretory cells known as **acini.**

In addition to its exocrine role in digestion, the pancreas also functions as an endocrine gland, secreting several hormones into the blood that control the blood levels of glucose and other nutrients. These hormones are produced in the **islets of Langerhans,** clusters of endocrine cells scattered throughout the pancreas. The two most important pancreatic hormones, insulin and glucagon, were described in chapter 46; their actions are also discussed later on.

Liver and gallbladder

The **liver** is the largest internal organ of the body (see figure 48.3). In an adult human, the liver weighs about 1.5 kg and is the size of a football. The main exocrine secretion of the liver is bile, a fluid mixture consisting of *bile pigments* and *bile salts* that is delivered into the duodenum during the digestion of a meal.

The bile pigments do not participate in digestion; they are waste products resulting from the liver's destruction of old red blood cells and are ultimately eliminated with the feces. If the excretion of bile pigments by the liver is blocked, the pigments can accumulate in the blood and cause a yellow staining of the tissues known as *jaundice.*

In contrast, the bile salts play a very important role in preparing fats for subsequent enzymatic digestion. Because fats are insoluble in water, they enter the intestine as drops within the watery chyme. The bile salts, which are partly lipid-soluble and partly water-soluble, work like detergents, dispersing the large drops of fat into a fine suspension of smaller droplets. This emulsification action produces a greater surface area of fat for the action of lipase enzymes, and thus allows the digestion of fat to proceed more rapidly.

After bile is produced in the liver, it is stored and concentrated in the gallbladder. The arrival of fatty food in the duodenum triggers a neural and endocrine reflex that stimulates the gallbladder to contract, causing bile to be transported through the common bile duct and injected into the duodenum (these reflexes are the topic of a later section). Gallstones are hardened precipitates of cholesterol that form in some individuals. If these stones block the bile duct, contraction of the gallbladder causes intense pain, often felt in the back. In severe cases of blockage, surgical removal of the gallbladder may be performed.

Absorbed nutrients move into blood or lymph capillaries

After their enzymatic breakdown, proteins and carbohydrates are absorbed as amino acids and monosaccharides, respectively. They are transported across the brush border into the epithelial cells that line the intestine by a combination of active transport and facilitated diffusion (figure 48.12a). Glucose is transported by coupled transport with Na^+ ions (also called secondary active transport). Fructose, found in most fruit, is transported by facilitated diffusion. Most amino acids are transported by active transport using a variety of different transporters. Some of these carrier proteins use cotransport with Na^+ ions; others transport only amino acids. Once they have entered epithelial cells across the apical membrane, these monosaccharides and amino acids move through the cytoplasm and are transported across the basolateral membrane and into the blood capillaries within the villi.

The blood carries these products of digestion from the intestine to the liver via the hepatic portal vein. A portal vein connects two beds of capillaries instead of returning to the heart. In

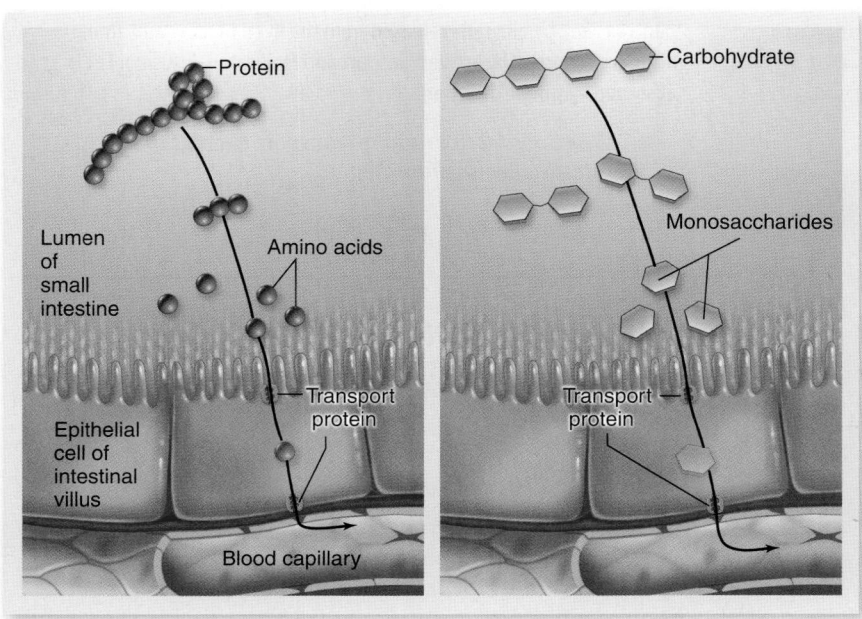
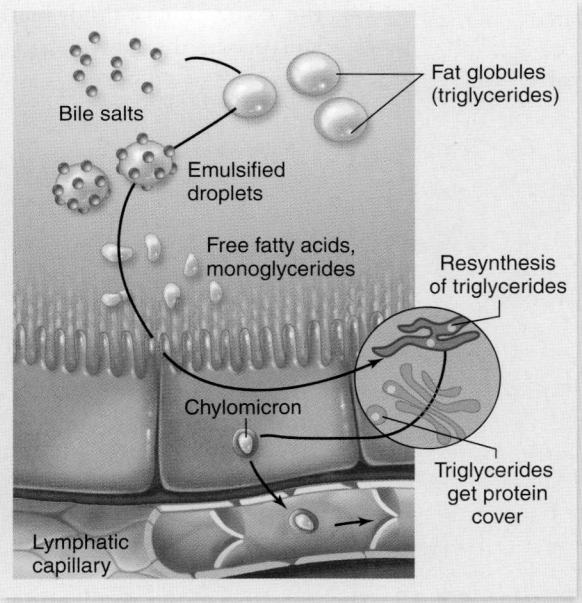

a.

b.

Figure 48.12 **Absorption of the products of digestion.** *a.* Monosaccharides and amino acids are transported into blood capillaries. *b.* Fatty acids and monoglycerides within the intestinal lumen are absorbed and converted within the intestinal epithelial cells into triglycerides. These are then coated with proteins to form structures called chylomicrons, which enter lymphatic capillaries.

this case, the intestine is connected to the liver by the hepatic portal vein, thus the liver receives blood-borne molecules from the intestine. Because of the hepatic portal vein, the liver is the first organ to receive most of the products of digestion, except for fat.

The products of fat digestion are absorbed by a different mechanism (figure 48.12*b*). Fats (triglycerides) are hydrolyzed into fatty acids and monoglycerides by digestion. These fatty acids and monoglycerides are nonpolar and can thus enter epithelial cells by simple diffusion. Once inside the intestinal epithelial cells they are reassembled into triglycerides. The triglycerides then combine with proteins to form small particles called **chylomicrons,** which are too bulky to enter blood capillaries in the intestine. Instead of entering the hepatic portal circulation, the chylomicrons are absorbed into lymphatic capillaries (see chapter 50), which empty their contents into the blood in veins near the neck. Chylomicrons can make the blood plasma appear cloudy if a sample of blood is drawn after a fatty meal.

The amount of fluid passing through the small intestine in a day is startlingly large: approximately 9 L. However, almost all of this fluid is absorbed into the body rather than eliminated in the feces: About 8.5 L is absorbed in the small intestine and an additional 350 mL in the large intestine. Only about 50 g of solid and 100 mL of liquid leaves the body as feces. The normal fluid absorption efficiency of the human digestive tract approaches 99%, which is very high indeed.

The large intestine eliminates waste material

The large intestine, or **colon,** is much shorter than the small intestine, occupying approximately the last meter of the digestive tract; it is called "large" because of its larger diameter, not its length. The small intestine empties directly into the large intestine at a junction where two vestigial structures, the **cecum** and the **appendix,** remain (figure 48.13). No digestion takes place within the large intestine, and only about 4% of the absorption of fluids by the intestine occurs there.

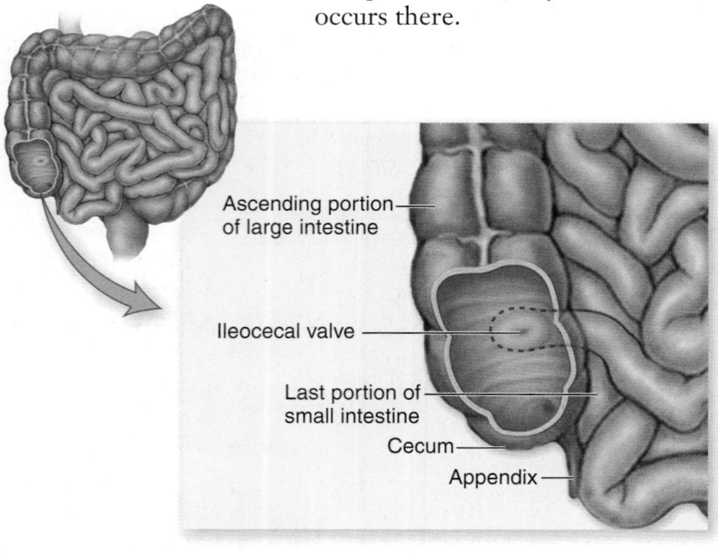

Figure 48.13 The junction of the small and large intestines in humans. The large intestine, or colon, starts with the cecum, which is relatively small in humans compared with that in other mammals. A vestigial structure called the appendix extends from the cecum.

The large intestine is not as convoluted as the small intestine, and its inner surface has no villi. Consequently, the large intestine has less than 1/30 the absorptive surface area of the small intestine. The function of the large intestine is to absorb water, remaining electrolytes, and products of bacterial metabolism (including vitamin K). The large intestine prepares waste material to be expelled from the body.

Many bacteria live and reproduce within the large intestine, and the excess bacteria are incorporated into the refuse material, called *feces*. Bacterial fermentation produces gas within the colon at a rate of about 500 mL per day. This rate increases greatly after the consumption of beans or other types of vegetables because the passage of undigested plant material (fiber) into the large intestine provides substrates for bacterial fermentation.

The human colon has evolved to process food with a relatively high fiber content. Diets that are low in fiber, which are common in the United States and other developed countries, result in a slower passage of food through the colon. Low dietary fiber content is thought to be associated with the level of colon cancer in the United States, which is among the highest in the world.

Compacted feces, driven by peristaltic contractions of the large intestine, pass from the large intestine into a short tube called the rectum. From the rectum, the feces exit the body through the anus. Two sphincters control passage through the anus. The first is composed of smooth muscle and opens involuntarily in response to pressure inside the rectum. The second, composed of striated muscle, can be controlled voluntarily by the brain, thus permitting a conscious decision to delay defecation.

Learning Outcomes Review 48.4

The small intestine is where most digestion takes place; its inner surface is covered with villi that increase its absorptive surface area. The large intestine absorbs water, electrolytes, and bacterial metabolites. Digestion is accomplished by a combination of enzymes from the pancreas and by bile salts released from the liver. Glucose and amino acids are absorbed by active transport and facilitated diffusion. Fat is absorbed by simple diffusion.

■ *Why does fat not require transport to cross the intestinal epithelium?*

48.5 *Variations in Vertebrate Digestive Systems*

Learning Outcomes

1. *Explain how vertebrates digest cellulose.*
2. *Describe how rumination works.*
3. *Discuss convergent evolution at the molecular level in herbivores.*

Animals lack the enzymes necessary to digest cellulose, but the digestive tracts of some animals contain bacteria and

Nonruminant Herbivore

Simple stomach, large cecum

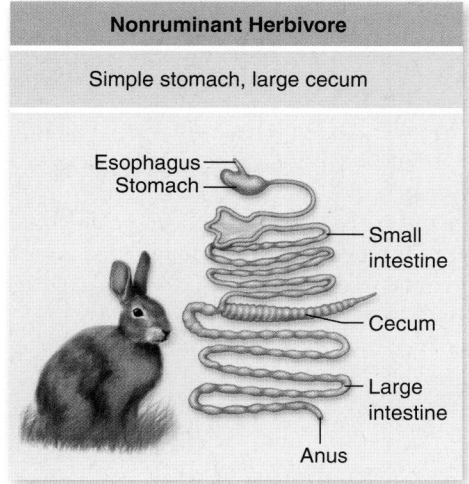

Ruminant Herbivore

Four-chambered stomach with large rumen; long small and large intestine

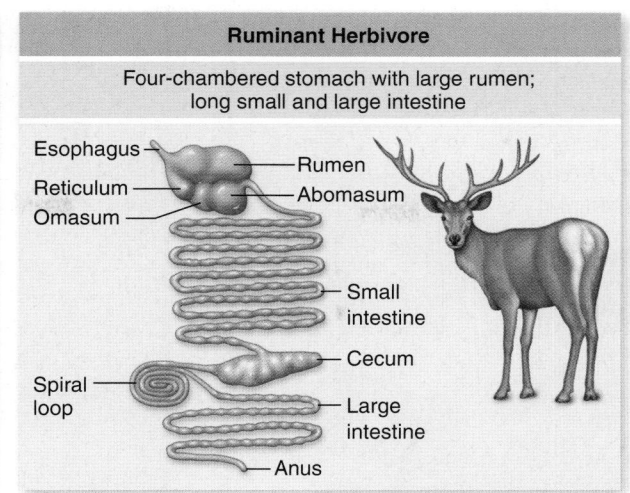

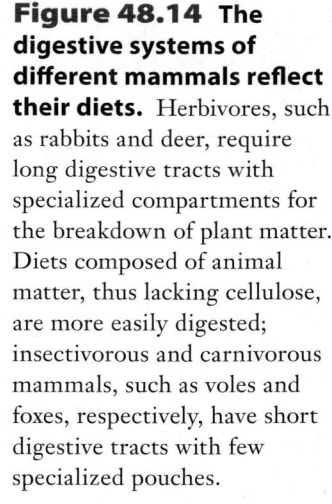

Figure 48.14 The digestive systems of different mammals reflect their diets. Herbivores, such as rabbits and deer, require long digestive tracts with specialized compartments for the breakdown of plant matter. Diets composed of animal matter, thus lacking cellulose, are more easily digested; insectivorous and carnivorous mammals, such as voles and foxes, respectively, have short digestive tracts with few specialized pouches.

Insectivore

Short intestine, no cecum

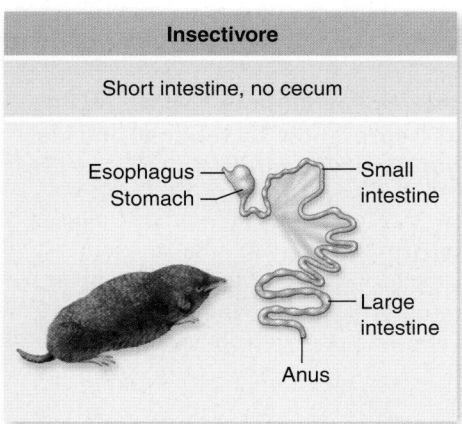

Carnivore

Short intestine and colon, small cecum

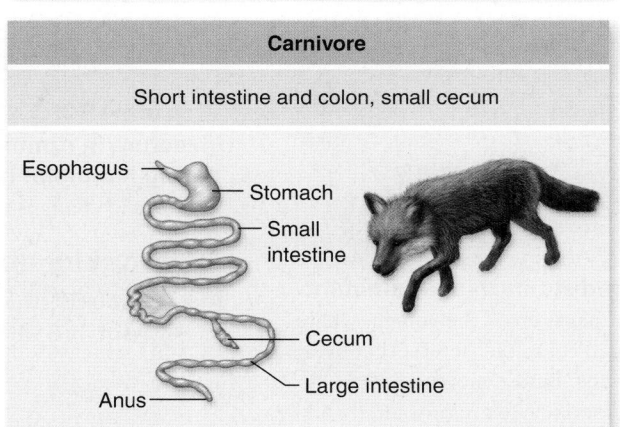

protists that convert cellulose into substances the host can absorb. Although digestion by gastrointestinal microorganisms plays a relatively small role in human nutrition, it is an essential element in the nutrition of many other kinds of animals, including insects such as termites and cockroaches, and a few groups of herbivorous mammals. The relationships between these microorganisms and their animal hosts are mutually beneficial and provide an excellent example of symbiosis (see chapter 57).

Plant cellulose is particularly resistant to digestion. As a result, herbivores tend to have much longer digestive tracts than carnivores, allowing greater time for digestion to occur (figure 48.14). In addition, many herbivores have modified their digestive tracts to enhance digestion of plant material.

Ruminants rechew regurgitated food

Ruminants have a four-chambered stomach (figure 48.15). The first three portions include the reticulum, the rumen, and the omasum. These are followed by the true stomach, the abomasum.

The rumen, which may hold up to 50 gallons, serves as a fermentation vat where bacteria and protists convert cellulose and other molecules into a variety of simpler compounds. The location of the rumen at the front of the four chambers allows the animal to regurgitate and rechew the contents of the rumen, an activity called *rumination*, or "chewing the cud." This

breaks tougher fiber in the diet into smaller particles, increasing the surface area for microbial attachment.

After chewing, the cud is swallowed for further microbial digestion in the rumen, then passes to the omasum, and then to the abomasum, where it is finally mixed with gastric juice. This process leads to far more efficient digestion of cellulose in ruminants than in mammalian herbivores such as horses, that lack a rumen.

Foregut fermentation has evolved convergently many times

Although the four-chambered stomach has only evolved once, many other types of herbivores—including hippopotamuses, langur monkeys, sloths, kangaroos, and hoatzins (a type of bird)—have evolved large stomachs to enhance microbial fermentation. In many cases, these species have evolved a variety of other anatomical structures that serve to slow down the passage of food through the stomach, leading to increased time for fermentation.

A remarkable case of convergent evolution at the molecular level is exhibited by ruminants and the langur monkey, which subsists primarily on leaves. In most mammals, lysozymes are enzymes found in saliva and tears, which attack invading bacteria. However, in ruminants and langurs, lysozymes have been modified to take on a new role, digesting bacteria in the stomach. In both cases, five identical amino acid changes have

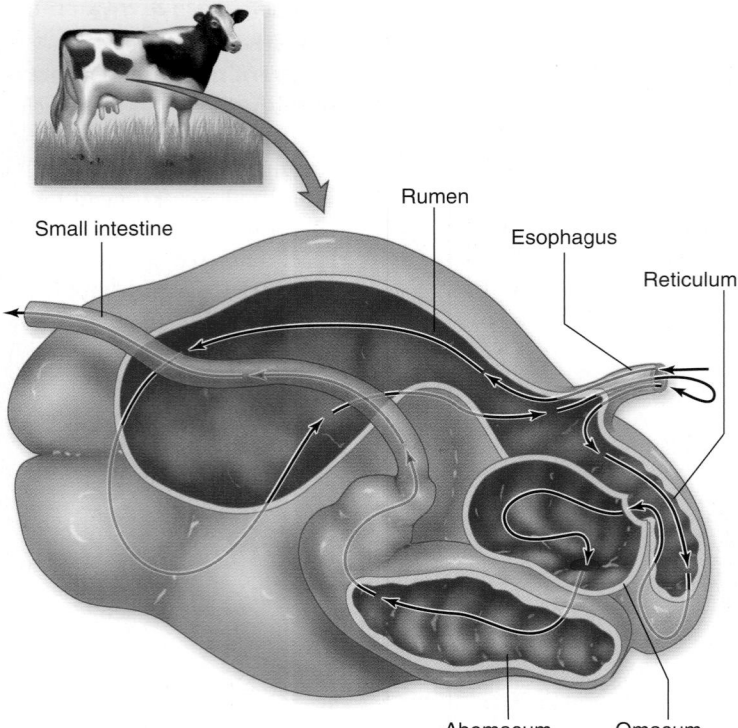

Figure 48.15 Four-chambered stomach of a ruminant.
Grass and other plants eaten by ruminants enter the rumen, where they are partially digested. The rumen contains bacteria that break down cellulose from the plant cell walls. Before moving into a second chamber, the reticulum, the food may be regurgitated and rechewed. The food is then transferred to the rear two chambers: the omasum and abomasum. Only the abomasum secretes gastric juice as in the human stomach.

evolved (figure 48.16); the result is that the lysozyme molecules of ruminants and langurs are more similar to each other than they are to lysozymes in more closely related species. In contrast to many cases of convergent evolution, this example illustrates that convergent evolution has occurred in distantly related species by the exact same evolutionary changes.

Other herbivores have alternative strategies for digestion

In some animals, such as rodents, horses, deer, and lagomorphs (rabbits and hares), the digestion of cellulose by microorganisms takes place in the cecum, which is greatly enlarged (see figure 48.14). Because the cecum is located beyond the stomach, regurgitation of its contents is impossible.

Rodents and lagomorphs have evolved another way to capture nutrients from cellulose that achieves a degree of efficiency similar to ruminant digestion. They do this by eating their feces, a practice known as coprophagy—thus passing the food through their digestive tract a second time. The second passage allows the animal to absorb the nutrients produced by the microorganisms in its cecum. Coprophagic animals cannot remain healthy if they are prevented from eating their feces.

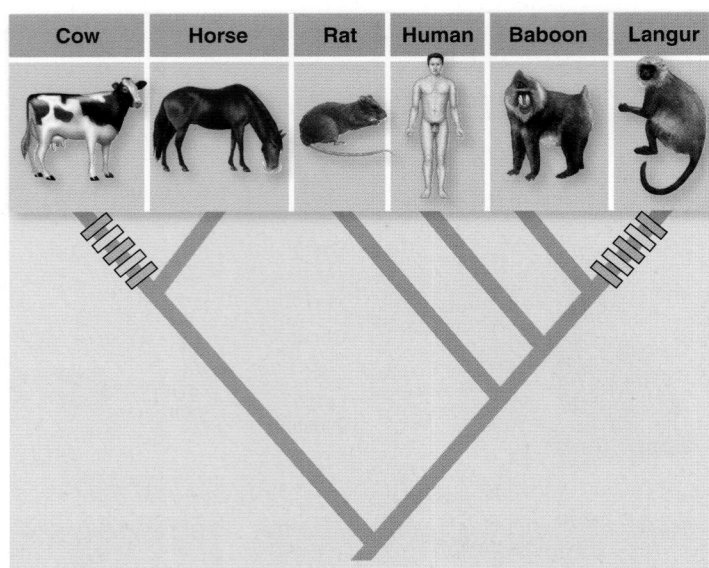

Figure 48.16 Convergent evolution of lysozyme structure in ruminants (represented by the cow) and leaf-eating hanuman langur (Presbytis entellus). The same five amino acid changes evolved independently in both groups.

Inquiry question
? If you constructed a phylogeny using molecular data from lysozyme, what would it look like?

Animals with diets that don't include cellulose, such as insectivores or carnivores, don't have a cecum, or if they do, it is greatly reduced.

Vitamin K
Another example of the way intestinal microorganisms function in the metabolism of their animal hosts is provided by the synthesis of vitamin K. All mammals rely on intestinal bacteria to synthesize this vitamin, which is necessary for the clotting of blood. Birds, which lack these bacteria, must consume the required quantities of vitamin K in their food.

In humans, prolonged treatment with antibiotics greatly reduces the populations of bacteria in the intestine; under such circumstances, it may be necessary to provide supplementary vitamin K. Restoring the normal flora of the digestive tract with beneficial bacteria may also help replace vitamin K.

Learning Outcomes Review 48.5
The digestive tracts of many herbivores harbor colonies of cellulose-digesting microorganisms. Complex fermentation chambers have also evolved in the digestive tract. In rumination, partially digested food is regurgitated from the rumen for additional processing by the mouth. In distantly related herbivorous species, similar digestive enzymes have evolved by identical but independent changes.

■ Would you expect identical mutations to be successful in different species? Why or why not?

48.6 Neural and Hormonal Regulation of the Digestive Tract

Learning Outcomes

1. Explain how the nervous system stimulates the digestive process.
2. Identify the major enterogastrones.

The activities of the gastrointestinal tract are coordinated by the nervous system and the endocrine system. The nervous system, for example, stimulates salivary and gastric secretions in response to the sight, smell, and consumption of food. When food arrives in the stomach, proteins in the food stimulate the secretion of a stomach hormone called **gastrin,** which in turn stimulates the secretion of pepsinogen and HCl from the gastric glands (figure 48.17). The secreted HCl then lowers the pH of the gastric juice, which acts to inhibit further secretion of gastrin in a negative feedback loop. In this way, the secretion of gastric acid is kept under tight control.

The passage of chyme from the stomach into the duodenum of the small intestine inhibits the contractions of the stomach, so that no additional chyme can enter the duodenum until the previous amount can be processed. This stomach or gastric inhibition is mediated by a neural reflex and by duodenal hormones secreted into the blood. These hormones are collectively known as the **enterogastrones.**

The major enterogastrones include **cholecystokinin (CCK), secretin,** and **gastric inhibitory peptide (GIP).** Chyme with high fat content is the strongest stimulus for CCK and GIP secretions, whereas increasing chyme acidity primarily influences the release of secretin. All three of these enterogastrones inhibit gastric motility (churning action) and gastric juice secretions; the result is that fatty meals remain in the stomach longer than nonfatty meals, allowing more time for digestion of complex fat molecules.

In addition to gastric inhibition, CCK and secretin have other important regulatory functions in digestion. CCK also stimulates increased pancreatic secretions of digestive enzymes and gallbladder contractions. Gallbladder contractions inject more bile into the duodenum, which enhances the emulsification and efficient digestion of fats. The other major function of secretin is to stimulate the pancreas to release more bicarbonate, which neutralizes the acidity of the chyme. Secretin has the distinction of being the first hormone ever discovered. Table 48.1 summarizes the actions of the digestive hormones and enzymes.

Learning Outcomes Review 48.6

Sensory input such as sight, smell, and taste stimulate salivary and gastric activity, as does the arrival of food in the stomach. The major enterogastrones are cholecystokinin (CCK), secretin, and gastric inhibitory peptide (GIP); these regulate passage of chyme into the duodenum and also release of pancreatic enzymes and bile.

■ *Would you expect anosmia, an inability to perceive scents, to affect digestion?*

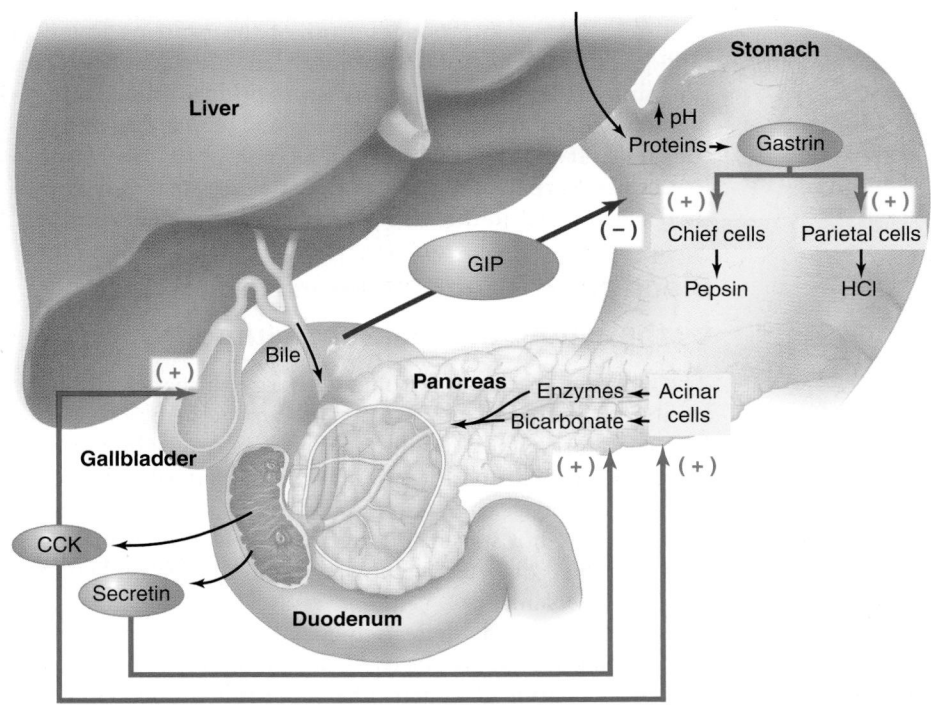

Figure 48.17 Hormonal control of the gastrointestinal tract. Gastrin, secreted by the mucosa of the stomach, stimulates the secretion of HCl and pepsinogen (which is converted into pepsin). The duodenum secretes three hormones: cholecystokinin (CCK), which stimulates contraction of the gallbladder and secretion of pancreatic enzymes; secretin, which stimulates secretion of pancreatic bicarbonate; and gastric inhibitory peptide (GIP), which inhibits stomach emptying.

TABLE 48.1 Hormones and Enzymes of Digestion

HORMONES

Hormone	Class	Source	Stimulus	Action	Note
Gastrin	Polypeptide	Pyloric portion of stomach	Entry of food into stomach	Stimulates secretion of HCl and pepsinogen by stomach	Acts on same organ that secretes it
Cholecystokinin (CCK)	Polypeptide	Duodenum	Fatty chyme in duodenum	Stimulates gallbladder contraction and secretion of digestive enzymes by pancreas	Structurally similar to gastrin
Gastric inhibitory peptide (GIP)	Polypeptide	Duodenum	Fatty chyme in duodenum	Inhibits stomach emptying	Also stimulates insulin secretion
Secretin	Polypeptide	Duodenum	Acidic chyme in duodenum	Stimulates secretion of bicarbonate by pancreas	The first hormone to be discovered (1902)

ENZYMES

Location	Enzymes	Substrates	Digestion Products
Salivary glands	Amylase	Starch, glycogen	Disaccharides
Stomach	Pepsin	Proteins	Short peptides
Pancreas	Lipase	Triglycerides	Fatty acids, monoglycerides
	Trypsin, chymotrypsin	Proteins	Peptides
	DNase	DNA	Nucleotides
	RNase	RNA	Nucleotides
Small intestine (brush border)	Peptidases	Short peptides	Amino acids
	Nucleases	DNA, RNA	Sugars, nucleic acid bases
	Lactase, maltase, sucrase	Disaccharides	Monosaccharides

48.7 Accessory Organ Function

Learning Outcomes

1. Describe the liver's role in maintaining homeostasis.
2. Explain how the pancreas acts to control blood glucose concentration.

The liver and pancreas both have critical roles beyond the production of digestive enzymes. The liver is a key organ in the breakdown of toxins, and the pancreas secretes hormones that regulate the blood glucose level, in part through actions on liver cells.

The liver modifies chemicals to maintain homeostasis

Because the hepatic portal vein carries blood from the stomach and intestine directly to the liver, the liver is in a position to chemically modify the substances absorbed in the gastrointestinal tract before they reach the rest of the body. For example, ingested alcohol and other drugs are taken into liver cells and metabolized; this is one reason that the liver is often damaged as a result of alcohol and drug abuse.

The liver also removes toxins, pesticides, carcinogens, and other poisons, converting them into less toxic forms. For example, the liver's converts the toxic ammonia produced by intestinal bacteria into urea, a compound that can be contained safely and carried by the blood at higher concentrations.

Similarly, the liver regulates the levels of many compounds produced within the body. Steroid hormones, for instance, are converted into less active and more water-soluble forms by the liver. These molecules are then included in the bile and eliminated from the body in the feces or are carried by the blood to the kidneys and excreted in the urine.

The liver also produces most of the proteins found in blood plasma. The total concentration of plasma proteins is significant because it must be kept within certain limits to maintain osmotic balance between blood and interstitial (tissue) fluid. If the concentration of plasma proteins drops too low, as can happen as a result of liver disease such as cirrhosis, fluid accumulates in the tissues, a condition called *edema*.

Blood glucose concentration is maintained by the actions of insulin and glucagon

The neurons in the brain obtain energy primarily from the aerobic respiration of glucose obtained from the blood plasma. It is therefore vitally important that the blood glucose concentration not fall too low, as might happen during fasting or prolonged exercise. It is also important that the blood glucose concentration not stay at too high a level, as it does in people with untreated diabetes mellitus, because too high a level can lead to tissue damage.

After a carbohydrate-rich meal, the liver and skeletal muscles remove excess glucose from the blood and store it as the polysaccharide glycogen. This process is stimulated by the

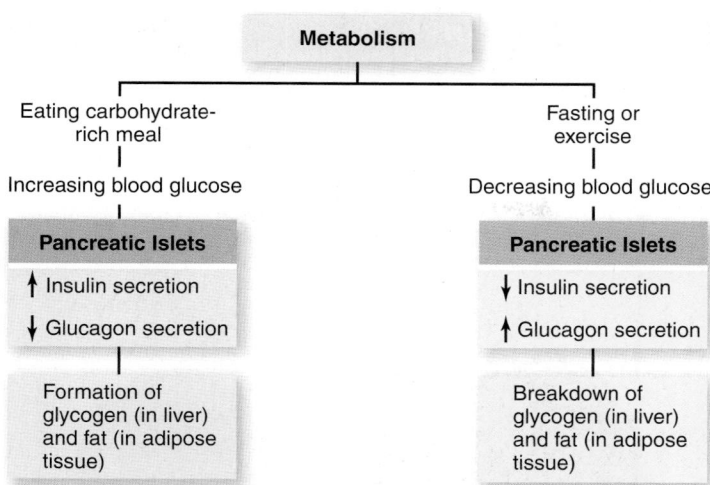

Figure 48.18 The actions of insulin and glucagon.
After a meal, an increased secretion of insulin by the β cells of the pancreatic islets promotes the deposition of glycogen and fat. During fasting or exercising, increased glucagon secretion by the α cells of the pancreatic islets and decreased insulin secretion promote the breakdown (through hydrolysis reactions) of glycogen and fat.

hormone insulin, secreted by the β (beta) cells in the pancreatic islets of Langerhans (figure 48.18).

When blood glucose levels decrease, as they do between meals, during periods of fasting, and during exercise, the liver secretes glucose into the blood. This glucose is obtained in part from the breakdown of liver glycogen to glucose-6-phosphate, a process called **glycogenolysis.** The phosphate group is then removed, and free glucose is secreted into the blood. Skeletal muscles lack the enzyme needed to remove the phosphate group, and so, even though they have glycogen stores, they cannot secrete glucose into the blood. However, muscle cells can use this glucose directly for energy metabolism because glucose-6-phosphate is actually the product of the first reaction in glycolysis. The breakdown of liver glycogen is stimulated by another hormone, glucagon, which is secreted by the α (alpha) cells of the islets of Langerhans in the pancreas (see figure 48.18).

If fasting or exercise continues, the liver begins to convert other molecules, such as amino acids and lactic acid, into glucose. This process is called **gluconeogenesis** ("new formation of glucose"). The amino acids used for gluconeogenesis are obtained from muscle protein, which explains the severe muscle wasting that occurs during prolonged fasting.

Learning Outcomes Review 48.7

The liver is responsible for neutralizing potentially harmful toxins and also for modification of steroid hormones. The liver also produces vital plasma proteins. Pancreatic hormones and the liver regulate blood glucose concentrations. Insulin stimulates the formation of glycogen and fat in the liver. Glucagon stimulates the breakdown of glycogen in the liver, which releases glucose into the blood.

■ *What is one important advantage of the hepatic portal system?*

48.8 Food Energy, Energy Expenditure, and Essential Nutrients

Learning Outcomes

1. *Explain the basal metabolic rate and the effect of exercise.*
2. *List hormones involved in regulating appetite and body weight.*
3. *Name the essential nutrients.*

The ingestion of food serves two primary functions: It provides a source of energy and it provides raw materials the animal is unable to manufacture for itself.

Even an animal completely at rest requires energy to support its metabolism; the minimum rate of energy consumption under defined resting conditions is called the **basal metabolic rate (BMR).** The BMR is relatively constant for a given individual, depending primarily on the person's age, sex, and body size.

Exertion increases metabolic rate

Physical exertion raises the metabolic rate above the basal levels, so the amount of energy the body consumes per day is determined not only by the BMR but also by the level of physical activity. If food energy taken in is greater than the energy consumed per day, the excess energy will be stored in glycogen and fat (figure 48.18). Because glycogen reserves are limited, however, continued ingestion of excess food energy results primarily in the accumulation of fat.

The intake of food energy is measured in **kilocalories** (1 kilocalorie = 1000 calories; nutritionists use Calorie with a capital C instead of kilocalorie). The measurement of kilocalories in food is determined by the amount of heat generated when the food is "burned," either literally, in a testing device called a calorimeter, or in the body, when the food is digested and later oxidized during cellular respiration. Caloric intake can be altered by the choice of foods, and the amount of energy expended can be changed by the choice of lifestyle.

The daily energy expenditures (metabolic rates) of humans vary between 1300 and 5000 kilocalories per day, depending on the person's BMR and level of physical activity. When the total kilocalories ingested exceeds the metabolic rate for a sustained period, a person accumulates an amount of fat that is deleterious to health, a condition called obesity. In the United States, about 34% of all adults between 40 and 59 are classified as obese. If 20- to 40-year-olds are added to this group, the percentage of obese individuals drops some but is still fully 30%.

Food intake is under neuroendocrine control

For many years the neuronal and hormonal basis of appetite was a mystery. Experiments with fasting and overfeeding in rats showed an increase in food intake when fasting ends. This increase restores lost body weight to baseline values and food intake then drops. These experiments indicated the existence of control mechanisms to link food intake to energy balance. The presence of a hormonal *satiety factor* produced by adipose tissue was hypothesized to explain these observations. It has also been shown that regions of the hypothalamus are involved in feeding behavior. Other studies in rodent models had identified a number of genes that can lead to obesity. As modern molecular genetics has allowed the cloning of many of these genes, the outlines of a model to link dietary intake to energy balance have emerged. This model involves afferent signaling from adipose tissue and feeding behavior into the central nervous system (CNS), and efferent signaling outward from the CNS tied to energy expenditure, storage, reproduction and feeding behavior. We will discuss the relevant hormones first, then show how they fit into an overall control circuit.

Leptin

One of the rodent models for obesity, the obese mouse, is caused by a mutation in a single gene named *ob* (for obese). Animals homozygous for the recessive mutant allele become obese compared with wild-type mice (figure 48.19). When the gene responsible for this dramatic phenotype was isolated, it proved to encode a peptide hormone named leptin, leading to the hypothesis that the lack of leptin production in mutant individuals is responsible for obesity. Sure enough, when *ob/ob* animals are injected with leptin, they stop overeating and lose weight (see figure 48.19). These experiments identified leptin as the main satiety factor, and the key to the control of appetite. The gene for the leptin receptor *(db)* has also been isolated and it is expressed in brain neurons in the hypothalamus involved in energy intake.

Leptin is now thought to be the main signaling molecule in the afferent portion of the control circuit for energy sensing, food intake, and energy expenditure. Leptin is produced by adipose tissue in response to feeding, and leptin levels correlate with feeding behavior and amount of body fat. Dietary restriction reduces leptin levels, signaling the brain that food intake is necessary, whereas refeeding after fasting leads to rapid increase in leptin levels and a loss of appetite. The efferent part of this control circuit is complex and includes control of energy expenditure, energy storage, and feeding behavior by the CNS. Reproduction is even affected by this system as reproduction is inhibited under starvation conditions.

The leptin gene has also been isolated in humans and leptin appears to function in humans much as it does in mice. However, recent studies in humans show that the activity of the *ob* gene and the blood concentrations of leptin are actually higher in obese than in lean people, and that the leptin produced by obese people appears to be normal. It has been suggested that, in contrast with the mutant mice, most cases of human obesity may result from a reduced sensitivity to the actions of leptin in the brain, rather than from reduced leptin production by adipose cells. Research on leptin in humans is ongoing and is of great interest to both academic scientists and to the pharmaceutical industry.

Insulin

Although the extreme obesity associated with the loss-of-function mutations in the *ob* gene indicate that other hormonal signals cannot substitute for leptin signaling, other hormones are also in-

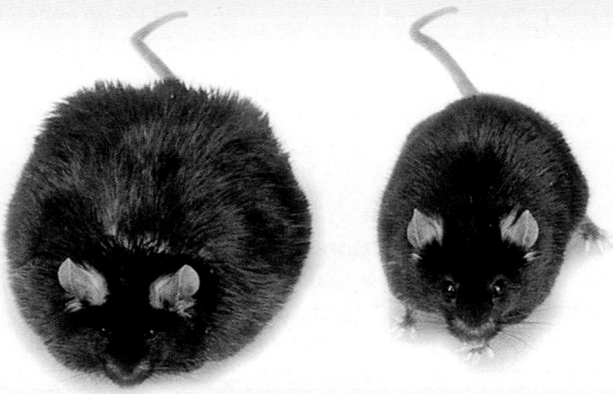
Figure 48.19 Effects of the hormone leptin.

volved. Insulin has been implicated in signaling satiety as well, and insulin levels also fall with fasting and rise with obesity. As insulin's primary role is homeostasis of blood glucose, as described earlier, its role in the control circuit of energy balance is complex.

Gut hormones (enterogastrones)

The gut produces a number of hormones that control the physiology of digestion described earlier. Several of these have also been implicated in the regulation of food intake. They are produced directly in response to feeding, necessary for their role in digestion.

The hormones GIP and CCK have receptors in the hypothalamus and seem to send the same kind of inhibitory signals to the brain as leptin and insulin. The levels of these gut hormones also vary with feeding behavior in a pattern similar to leptin and insulin.

The gut hormone ghrelin has the opposite effect of these appetite-suppressing hormones. Ghrelin also has receptors in the hypothalamus, but ghrelin appears to stimulate food intake. This role is supported by studies in rats showing that chronic administration of ghrelin leads to obesity. Ghrelin levels appear to rise before feeding and may be involved in initiating feeding behavior. One of the treatments for severe obesity, gastric bypass surgery, leads to reduced levels of ghrelin. It has been suggested that this is one of the reasons for the suppression of appetite seen after this surgery.

Neuropeptides

The efferent control over feeding and energy balance is less clear than the afferent control detailed earlier. The central regulator is the hypothalamus and two brain neuropeptides have been implicated: neuropeptide Y (NPY) and alpha-melanocyte-stimulating hormone (α-MSH). These peptides are antagonistic, with NPY inducing feeding activity and α-MSH suppressing it.

Evidence for this comes from experiments that show that production and release of α-MSH is stimulated by leptin and that administration of α-MSH suppresses feeding. Loss of function for the α-MSH receptor also leads to obesity. In contrast, the expression of NPY is negatively regulated by leptin and administration of NPY stimulates feeding behavior.

Model for energy balance

The current model for energy balance and feeding behavior is summarized in figure 48.20. The role of both leptin and insulin is long-term regulation of the afferent portion of this signaling network. Leptin and insulin are produced by adipose tissue and the pancreas, respectively, in response to the effects of feeding behavior, not as a direct response to feeding itself. This leads to circulating levels of leptin that correlate with the amount of adipose tissue. The extreme example of this is the very high level of leptin seen in obese individuals. High levels of leptin and insulin then act on the hypothalamus to increase levels of α-MSH and reduce levels of NPY. This causes a reduction in appetite and increased energy expenditure and al-lows reproduction and growth. Low levels of these hormones act on the hypothalamus to reduce α-MSH levels and increase NPY levels. This leads to increased appetite and decreased energy expenditure. If very low levels of leptin persist, this can inhibit reproduction and growth.

The gut hormones CCK and GIP are produced in response to feeding and represent short-term regulators of the afferent portion of the energy balance control circuit. Their action is the same as that of leptin and insulin. The gut hormone ghrelin is also a short-term regulator that stimulates feeding.

Essential nutrients are those that the body cannot manufacture

Over the course of evolution, many animals have lost the ability to synthesize certain substances that nevertheless continue to play critical roles in their metabolism. Substances that an animal cannot manufacture for itself but that are necessary for its health and must be obtained in the diet are referred to as essential nutrients.

Included among the essential nutrients are **vitamins,** certain organic substances required in trace amounts. For example, humans, apes, monkeys, and guinea pigs have lost the ability to synthesize ascorbic acid (vitamin C). If vitamin C is

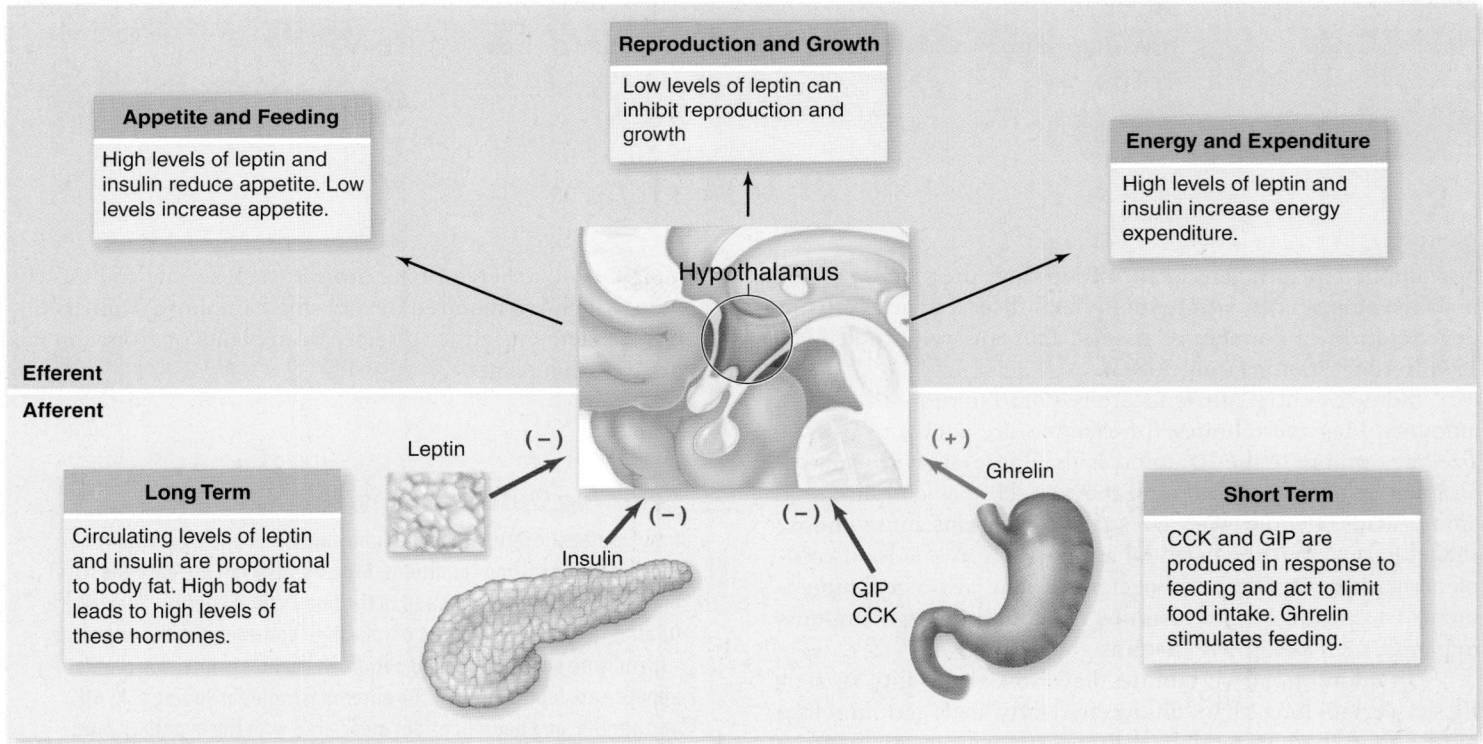

Figure 48.20 Hormonal control of feeding behavior. The control of feeding behavior is under both long-term control related to the amount of adipose tissue, and short-term control related to the act of feeding. This control is mediated by the CNS. The major brain region involved is the hypothalamus.

Inquiry question

? Suppose the GIP and CCK sensors in the hypothalamus didn't work. How would this affect levels of leptin production?

TABLE 48.2 Major Vitamins Required by Humans

Vitamin	Function	Source	Deficiency Symptoms
Vitamin A (retinol)	Used in making visual pigments, maintaining epithelial tissues	Green vegetables, milk products, liver	Night blindness, flaky skin
B-complex vitamins			
B$_1$	Coenzyme in CO_2 removal during cellular respiration	Meat, grains, legumes	Beriberi, weakening of heart, edema
B$_2$ (riboflavin)	Part of coenzymes FAD and FMN, which play metabolic roles	Many different kinds of foods	Inflammation and breakdown of skin, eye irritation
B$_3$ (niacin)	Part of coenzymes NAD$^+$ and NADP$^+$	Liver, lean meats, grains	Pellagra, inflammation of nerves, mental disorders
B$_5$ (pantothenic acid)	Part of coenzyme-A, a key connection between carbohydrate and fat metabolism	Many different kinds of foods	Rare: fatigue, loss of coordination
B$_6$ (pyridoxine)	Coenzyme in many phases of amino acid metabolism	Cereals, vegetables, meats	Anemia, convulsions, irritability
B$_{12}$ (cyanocobalamin)	Coenzyme in the production of nucleic acids	Red meats, dairy products	Pernicious anemia
Biotin	Coenzyme in fat synthesis and amino acid metabolism	Meat, vegetables	Rare: depression, nausea
Folic acid	Coenzyme in amino acid and nucleic acid metabolism	Green vegetables	Anemia, diarrhea
Vitamin C	Important in forming collagen, cementum of bone, teeth, connective tissue of blood vessels; may help maintain resistance to infection	Fruit, green leafy vegetables	Scurvy, breakdown of skin, blood vessels
Vitamin D (calciferol)	Increases absorption of calcium and promotes bone formation	Dairy products, cod liver oil	Rickets, bone deformities
Vitamin E (tocopherol)	Protects fatty acids and cell membranes from oxidation	Margarine, seeds, green leafy vegetables	Rare
Vitamin K	Essential to blood clotting	Green leafy vegetables	Severe bleeding

not supplied in sufficient quantities in their diets, these mammals develop scurvy, a potentially fatal disease that results in degeneration of connective tissues. Humans require at least 13 different vitamins (table 48.2).

Some essential nutrients are required in more than trace amounts. Many vertebrates, for example, are unable to synthesize one or more of the 20 amino acids. These *essential amino acids* must be obtained from food they eat. Humans require nine amino acids. People who are strict vegetarians must choose their foods so that the essential amino acids in one food complement those in another. Vegetarians may also need supplements to provide certain vitamins not found in large amounts in plants, such as some B vitamins.

In addition, all vertebrates have lost the ability to synthesize certain long-chain unsaturated fatty acids and therefore must obtain them in food. In contrast, some essential nutrients that vertebrates can synthesize cannot be manufactured by the members of other animal groups. For example, vertebrates can synthesize cholesterol, a key component of steroid hormones, but some carnivorous insects cannot.

Food also supplies essential minerals such as calcium, magnesium, phosphorus, and other inorganic substances, including a wide variety of *trace elements* such as zinc and molybdenum, which are required in very small amounts. Animals obtain trace elements either directly from plants or from animals that have eaten plants.

Learning Outcomes Review 48.8

Basal metabolic rate is the minimum amount of energy consumption under defined resting conditions. Exercise does not increase the basal metabolic rate, but it does add to the body's total energy expenditure. Obesity results if the amount of ingested food energy exceeds energy expenditure over a prolonged period. Hormones involved in regulating appetite are leptin; insulin; the enterogastrones including CCK, GIP, and ghrelin; and neuropeptides associated with the hypothalamus. The essential nutrients for humans are 13 vitamins, essential minerals, and essential amino acids and fatty acids that the body cannot synthesize.

■ *What might explain obesity in a person with normal leptin levels?*

48.1 Types of Digestive Systems

Invertebrate digestive systems are bags or tubes.

In cnidarians and flatworms, the incomplete digestive system is a gastrovascular cavity with only one opening (see figure 48.1). In contrast, a complete digestive system, with a one-way tube from mouth to anus, allows specialization of digestive organs.

Vertebrate digestive systems include highly specialized structures molded by diet.

The gastrointestinal tract includes the mouth and pharynx, esophagus, stomach, small and large intestines, cloaca or rectum, and anus (see figure 48.3). The four tissue layers of the tract are the mucosa, submucosa, muscularis, and serosa (see figure 48.4).

48.2 The Mouth and Teeth: Food Capture and Bulk Processing

Vertebrate teeth are adapted to different types of food items.

Birds lack teeth but have a gizzard where small pebbles grind food. The teeth of mammals are adapted to reflect their feeding habits (see figure 48.6).

The mouth is a chamber for ingestion and initial processing.

Salivary glands secrete saliva containing amylase that moistens food and begins digestion as the food is chewed. Swallowing, once begun, is involuntary (see figure 48.7).

48.3 The Esophagus and the Stomach: The Early Stages of Digestion

Muscular contractions of the esophagus move food to the stomach.

Rhythmic muscular contractions and relaxation, called peristalsis, propel a bolus of food to the stomach.

The stomach is a "holding station" involved in acidic breakdown of food.

In the stomach, hydrochloric acid breaks down food and converts pepsinogen into pepsin, an active protease. The mixture of food and gastric juice, termed chyme, moves through the pyloric sphincter to the small intestine.

48.4 The Intestines: Breakdown, Absorption, and Elimination

The structure of the small intestine is specialized for digestion and nutrient uptake.

The surface area of the small intestine is increased by fingerlike projections called villi (see figure 48.10). The duodenum receives digestive secretions from the pancreas and liver.

Accessory organs secrete enzymes into the small intestine.

Accessory organs include the salivary glands, pancreas, liver, and gallbladder (see figure 48.11). The pancreas secretes digestive enzymes and bicarbonate. The liver secretes bile, which is stored in the gallbladder. Bile disperses fats into small droplets.

Absorbed nutrients move into blood or lymph capillaries.

Amino acids and monosaccharides move into epithelial cells by active transport and facilitated diffusion (see figure 48.12) and then pass into the bloodstream. Fatty acids and monoglycerides simply diffuse into epithelial cells. They are reassembled into chylomicrons that enter the lymphatic system.

Absorbed molecules that pass into the bloodstream are transported to the liver through the hepatic portal vein.

The large intestine eliminates waste material.

The large intestine absorbs water and concentrates waste material, which is stored in the rectum until it can be eliminated.

48.5 Variations in Vertebrate Digestive Systems

Ruminants rechew regurgitated food.

The four-chambered stomach of ruminants consists of the rumen, reticulum, omasum, and abomasum. Food initially processed in the rumen is regurgitated for further chewing.

Foregut fermentation has evolved convergently many times.

Enlarged foreguts have evolved in many species to provide a chamber for microbial fermentation. In some unrelated herbivores, identical changes in lysozyme have evolved.

Other herbivores have alternative strategies for digestion.

In some herbivores, digestion of cellulose by microorganisms takes place in the cecum, located beyond the stomach.

48.6 Neural and Hormonal Regulation of the Digestive Tract

The activities of the gastrointestinal tract are coordinated by the nervous and endocrine systems.

Duodenal hormones regulate passage of chyme into the duodenum. High fat content in the chyme stimulates the release of CCK and GIP; low chyme pH stimulates the release of secretin. In turn, CCK stimulates release of pancreatic enzymes and bile. Secretin stimulates release of bicarbonate.

48.7 Accessory Organ Function

The liver modifies chemicals to maintain homeostasis.

The liver is involved in detoxification, regulation of steroid hormone levels, and production of proteins found in the blood plasma.

Blood glucose concentration is maintained by the actions of insulin and glucagon.

Insulin lowers blood glucose and increases glycogen storage; glucagon increases blood glucose and utilization of glycogen.

48.8 Food Energy, Energy Expenditure, and Essential Nutrients

Exertion increases metabolic rate.

The basal metabolic rate is the minimum rate of energy consumption under resting conditions. Activity leads to an increase in the metabolic rate.

Food intake is under neuroendocrine control.

Food intake is regulated by the hormones leptin and insulin, by enterogastrones, and by neuropeptides (see figure 48.20).

Essential nutrients are those that the body cannot manufacture.

Essential nutrients are those that cannot be synthesized by animals. For humans, they are 13 vitamins (see table 48.2), the essential amino acids, essential minerals, and certain fatty acids.

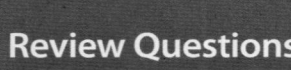

Review Questions

UNDERSTAND

1. How is the digestion of fats different from that of proteins and carbohydrates?
   a. Fat digestion occurs in the small intestine, and the digestion of proteins and carbohydrates occurs in the stomach.
   b. Fats are absorbed into cells as fatty acids and monoglycerides but are then modified for absorption; amino acids and glucose are not modified further.
   c. Fats enter the hepatic portal circulation, but digested proteins and carbohydrates enter the lymphatic system.
   d. Digested fats are absorbed in the large intestine, and digested proteins and carbohydrates are absorbed in the small intestine.

2. Although the stomach is normally thought of as the major player in the digestive process, the bulk of chemical digestion actually occurs in the
   a. mouth.   c. duodenum.
   b. appendix.   d. large intestine.

3. After being absorbed through the intestinal mucosa, glucose and amino acids are
   a. absorbed directly into the systemic circulation.
   b. used to build glycogen and peptides before being released to the body cells.
   c. transported directly to the liver by the hepatic portal vein.
   d. further digested by bile before release into the circulation.

4. Which of these pairings is incorrect?
   a. Fat transport/lymphatic system
   b. Glucose transport/lymphatic system
   c. Amino acid transport/circulatory system
   d. All of these pairings are correct.

5. Intestinal microorganisms aid digestion and absorption by
   a. digesting cellulose.   c. synthesizing vitamin K.
   b. producing glucose.   d. both a and c.

6. The _____ and _____ play important roles in the digestive process by producing chemicals that are required to digest proteins, lipids, and carbohydrates.
   a. liver; pancreas   c. kidneys; appendix
   b. liver; gallbladder   d. pancreas; gallbladder

7. Which of the following represents the action of insulin?
   a. Increases blood glucose levels by the hydrolysis of glycogen
   b. Increases blood glucose levels by stimulating glucagon production
   c. Decreases blood glucose levels by forming glycogen
   d. Increases blood glucose levels by promoting cellular uptake of glucose

APPLY

1. The small intestine is specialized for absorption because it
   a. is the last section of the digestive tract and retains food the longest.
   b. has saclike extensions along its length that collect food.
   c. has no outlet so food remains within it for longer periods of time.
   d. has an extremely large surface area that allows extended exposure to food.

2. The primary function of the large intestine is to concentrate wastes into solid form (feces) for release from the body. How does it accomplish this?
   a. By adding additional cells from the mucosal layer
   b. By absorbing water
   c. By releasing salt
   d. All of these are methods used by the large intestine.

3. Inactive forms of some molecules are secreted
   a. because they take less material and energy.
   b. because they must combine with water to be activated.
   c. so their activity can be regulated.
   d. to prevent them from clogging the gland from which they are secreted.

4. Obese humans probably have high levels of leptin because
   a. leptin stimulates eating.
   b. something is wrong with the leptin receptors in their brain, leading to increased leptin production to make up for the apparent shortage.
   c. weight gain leads to the production of leptin.
   d. leptin responds to mechanical stimulation in the adrenal cortex.

SYNTHESIZE

1. Many birds possess crops, although few mammals do. Suggest a reason for this difference between birds and mammals.

2. Suppose that you wanted to develop a new treatment for obesity based on the hormone leptin. What structures in the body produce leptin? What does it do? Should your treatment cause an increase in blood levels of leptin or a decrease? Could this treatment affect any other systems in the body?

3. How could a drop in plasma proteins and a decrease in bile production be related to alcohol and drug abuse?

4. Unlike many cases of convergence (see section 47.5), ruminants and langur monkeys have modified the enzyme lysozyme in the same way to achieve the same end result. Why might this case be different?

5. Birds do not have teeth. Do you think they have adaptations to processing different types of food, comparable to the diversity seen in mammals? If so, what might these adaptive differences be?

ONLINE RESOURCE

www.ravenbiology.com

Understand, Apply, and Synthesize—enhance your study with animations that bring concepts to life and practice tests to assess your understanding. Your instructor may also recommend the interactive eBook, individualized learning tools, and more.

Chapter **49**

The Respiratory System

Chapter Outline

49.1 Gas Exchange Across Respiratory Surfaces

49.2 Gills, Cutaneous Respiration, and Tracheal Systems

49.3 Lungs

49.4 Structures and Mechanisms of Ventilation in Mammals

49.5 Transport of Gases in Body Fluids

Introduction

Every cell in the animal body must exchange materials with its surrounding environment. In single-celled organisms, this exchange occurs directly across the cell membrane to and from the external environment. In multicellular organisms, however, most cells are not in contact with the external environment and must rely on specialized systems for transport and exchange. Although these systems aid in bulk transport, the properties of transport across the plasma membrane do not change. Many structural adaptations throughout the animal kingdom increase surface areas where transport occurs, so that the needs of every cell are met. The interface between air from the environment and blood in the mammalian lungs provides an excellent example of the efficiency associated with increased surface area. In the time it takes you to breathe in, trillions of oxygen molecules have been transported across 80 m^2 of alveolar membrane into blood capillaries. In this and the next chapter, we describe respiration and circulation, the two systems that directly support the other organ systems and tissues of the body.

Gas Exchange Across Respiratory Surfaces

Learning Outcomes

1. *Describe gas exchange across membranes.*
2. *Explain Fick's Law of Diffusion.*
3. *Compare evolutionary strategies for maximizing gas diffusion.*

One of the major physiological challenges facing all multicellular animals is obtaining sufficient oxygen and disposing of excess carbon dioxide (figure 49.1). Oxygen is used in mitochondria for cellular respiration—a process that also produces CO_2 as waste (see chapter 7). Respiration at the body system level involves a host of processes not found at the cellular level, ranging from the mechanics of breathing to the exchange of oxygen and carbon dioxide in respiratory organs.

Invertebrates display a wide variety of respiratory organs, including the epithelium, tracheae, and gills. Some vertebrates, such as fish and larval amphibians, also use gills; adult amphibians use their skin or other epithelia either as a supplemental or primary external respiratory organ.

Many adult amphibians, reptiles, birds, and mammals have lungs to perform external respiration. In both aquatic and terrestrial animals, these highly vascularized respiratory organs are the site at which oxygen diffuses into the blood, and carbon dioxide diffuses out. In the body tissues, the direction of gas diffusion is the reverse of that in the respiratory organs.

The mechanics, structure, and evolution of respiratory systems, along with the principles of gas diffusion between the blood and tissues, are the subjects of this chapter.

Gas exchange involves diffusion across membranes

Because plasma membranes must be surrounded by water to be stable, the external environment in gas exchange is always aqueous. This is true even in terrestrial vertebrates; in these cases, oxygen from air dissolves in a thin layer of fluid that covers the respiratory surfaces.

In vertebrates, the gases diffuse into the aqueous layer covering the epithelial cells that line the respiratory organs. The diffusion process is passive, driven only by the difference in O_2 and CO_2 concentrations on the two sides of the membranes and their relative solubilities in the plasma membrane. For dissolved gases, concentration is usually expressed as pressure; we explain this more fully a little later.

In general, the rate of diffusion between two regions is governed by a relationship known as **Fick's Law of Diffusion.** Fick's Law states that for a dissolved gas, the rate of diffusion (R) is directly proportional to the pressure difference (Δp) between the two sides of the membrane and the area (A) over which the diffusion occurs. Furthermore, R is inversely proportional to the distance (d) across which the diffusion must occur. A molecule-specific diffusion constant, D, accounts for the size of molecule, membrane permeability, and temperature. Shown as a formula, Fick's Law is stated as:

$$R = \frac{DA\,\Delta p}{d}$$

Major evolutionary changes in the mechanism of respiration have occurred to optimize the rate of diffusion (see figure 49.1). R can be optimized by changes that (1) increase the surface area, A; (2) decrease the distance, d; or (3) increase the concentration difference, as indicated by Δp. The evolution of respiratory systems has involved changes in all of these factors.

Inquiry question

? **What part of the vertebrate cardiovascular system maximizes surface area?**

Evolutionary strategies have maximized gas diffusion

The levels of oxygen needed for cellular respiration cannot be obtained by diffusion alone over distances greater than about 0.5 mm. This restriction severely limits the size and structure of organisms that obtain oxygen entirely by diffusion from the environment. Bacteria, archaea, and protists are small enough that such diffusion can be adequate, even in some colonial forms (figure 49.2a), but most multicellular animals require structural adaptations to enhance gas exchange.

Figure 49.1 Elephant seals are respiratory champions. Diving to great depths, elephant seals can hold their breath for over 2 hr, descend and ascend rapidly in the water, and endure repeated dives without suffering any apparent respiratory distress.

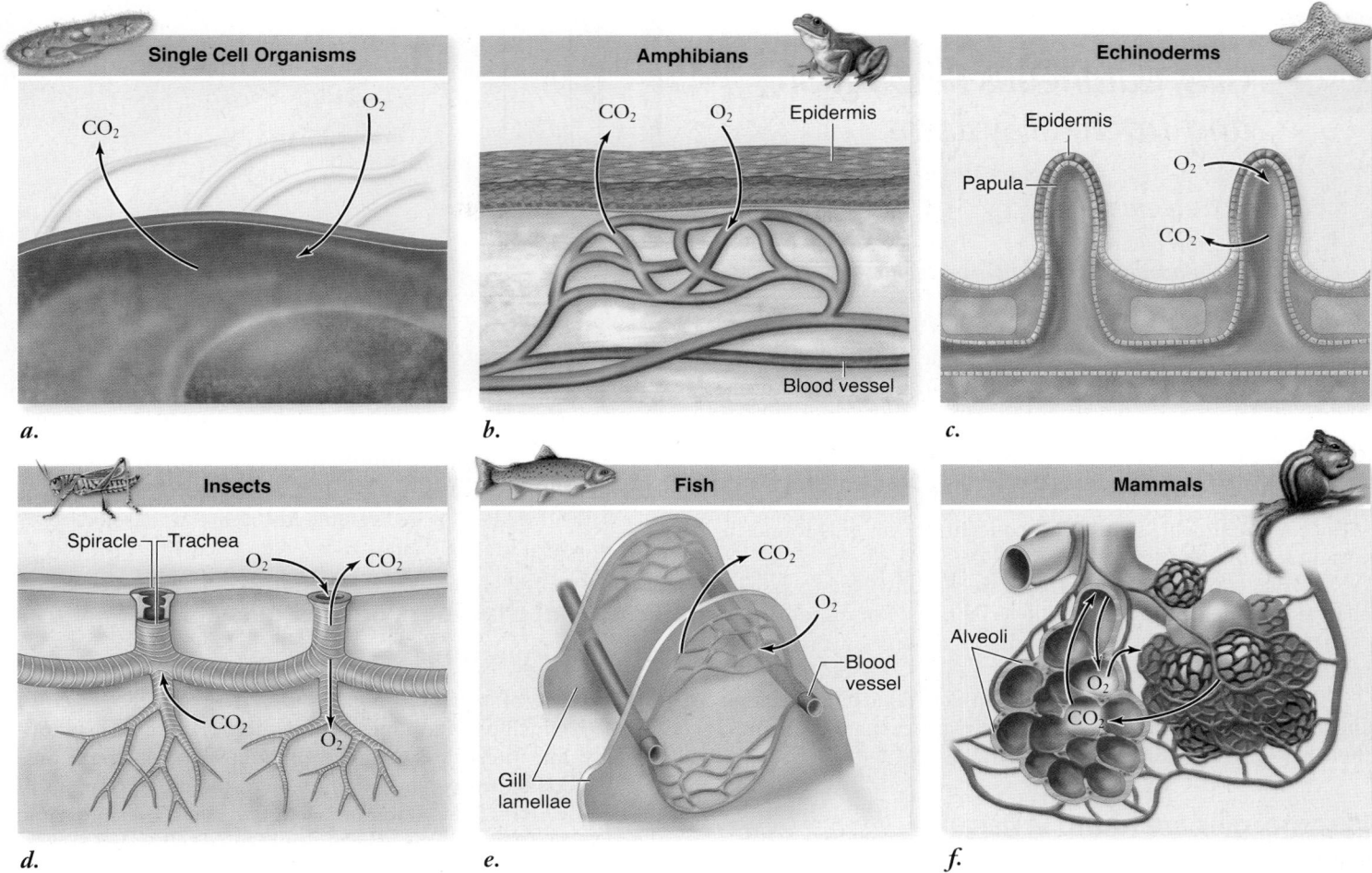

Figure 49.2 Different gas exchange systems in animals. *a.* Gases diffuse directly into single-celled organisms. *b.* Most amphibians and many other animals respire across their skin. Amphibians also exchange gases via lungs. *c.* Echinoderms have protruding papulae, which provide an increased respiratory surface area. *d.* Insects respire through an extensive tracheal system. *e.* The gills of fishes provide a very large respiratory surface area and countercurrent exchange. *f.* The alveoli in mammalian lungs provide a large respiratory surface area but do not permit countercurrent exchange. Inhaled fresh air contains some CO_2, but levels are higher in the lungs, so more CO_2 is exhaled than inhaled; similarly, O_2 levels are higher in fresh air, leading to an influx of O_2.

Increasing oxygen concentration difference

Most phyla of invertebrates lack specialized respiratory organs, but they have developed means of improving diffusion. Many organisms create a water current that continuously replaces the water over the respiratory surfaces; often, beating cilia produce this current. Because of this continuous replenishment of water, the external oxygen concentration does not decrease along the diffusion pathway. Although some of the oxygen molecules that pass into the organism have been removed from the surrounding water, new water continuously replaces the oxygen-depleted water. This maximizes the concentration difference—the Δp of the Fick equation.

Increasing area and decreasing distance

Other invertebrates (mollusks, arthropods, echinoderms) and vertebrates possess respiratory organs—such as gills, tracheae, and lungs—that increase the surface area available for diffu-

sion (see figure 49.2). These adaptations also bring the external environment (either water or air) close to the internal fluid, which is usually circulated throughout the body—such as blood or hemolymph. The respiratory organs thus increase the rate of diffusion by maximizing surface area *(A)* and decreasing the distance *(d)* the diffusing gases must travel.

Learning Outcomes Review 49.1

Gases must be dissolved to diffuse across living membranes. Direction of diffusion is driven by a concentration difference (gradient) between the two sides. Fick's Law states that the rate of diffusion is increased by a greater pressure difference and membrane area, and decreased by greater distance. Evolutionary strategies have therefore aimed to increase gradient and area and to lessen the distance gases must travel.

■ *Which factor is affected by continuously beating cilia?*

Gills, Cutaneous Respiration, and Tracheal Systems

Gills are specialized extensions of tissue that project into water. Gills can be simple, as in the papulae of echinoderms (figure 49.2c), or complex, as in the highly convoluted gills of fish (figure 49.2e). The great increase in diffusion surface area that gills provide enables aquatic organisms to extract far more oxygen from water than would be possible from their body surface alone. In this section we concentrate on gills found in vertebrate animals.

Other moist external surfaces are also involved in gas exchange in some vertebrates and invertebrates. For example, gas exchange across the skin is a common strategy in many amphibian groups.

Terrestrial arthropods such as insects take an alternative approach; their tracheal systems allow gas exchange through their hard exoskeletons (figure 49.2d).

External gills are found in fish and amphibian larvae

External gills are not enclosed within body structures. Examples of vertebrates with external gills are the larvae of many fish and amphibians, as well as amphibians such as the axolotl, which retains larval features throughout life (figure 49.3).

One of the disadvantages of external gills is that they must constantly be moved to ensure contact with fresh water having high oxygen content. The highly branched gills, however, offer significant resistance to movement, making this form of respiration ineffective except in smaller animals. Another disadvantage is that external gills, with their thin epithelium for gas exchange, are easily damaged.

Figure 49.3 Some amphibians have external gills. External gills are used by aquatic amphibians, both larvae and some species that live their entire lives in water such as this axolotl, to extract oxygen from the water.

Branchial chambers protect gills of some invertebrates

Other types of aquatic animals evolved specialized *branchial chambers*, which provide a means of pumping water past stationary gills. The internal *mantle cavity* of mollusks opens to the outside and contains the gills. Contraction of the muscular walls of the mantle cavity draws water in through the inhalant siphon and then expels it through the exhalant siphon (see chapter 34).

In crustaceans, the branchial chamber lies between the bulk of the body and the hard exoskeleton of the animal. This chamber contains gills and opens to the surface beneath a limb. Movement of the limb draws water through the branchial chamber, thus creating currents over the gills.

Gills of bony fishes are covered by the operculum

The gills of bony fishes are located between the oral cavity, sometimes called the buccal (mouth) cavity, and the *opercular cavities* where the gills are housed (figure 49.4). The two sets

Figure 49.4 How most bony fishes respire. The gills are suspended between the buccal (mouth) cavity and the opercular cavity. Respiration occurs in two stages. The oral valve in the mouth is opened and the jaw is depressed, drawing water into the buccal cavity while the opercular cavity is closed. The oral valve is closed and the operculum is opened, drawing water through the gills to the outside.

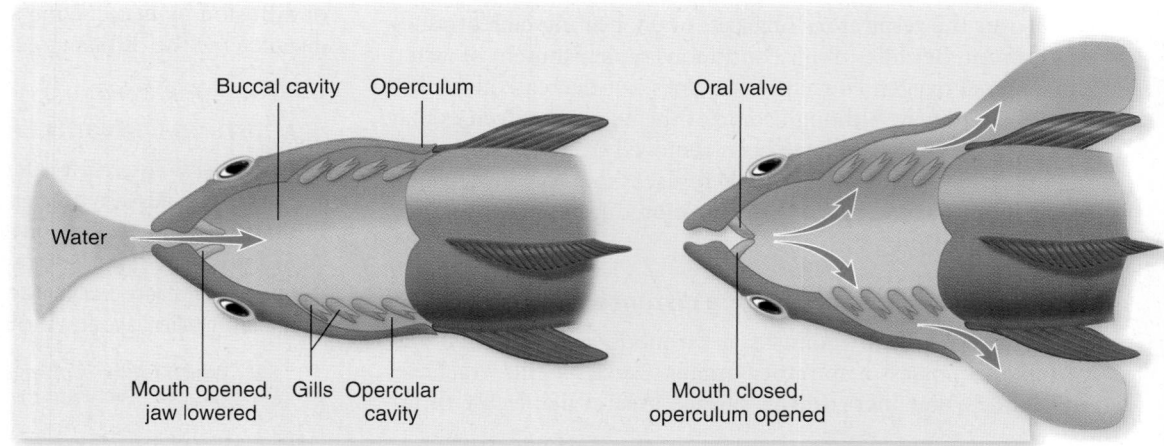

of cavities function as pumps that expand alternately to move water into the mouth, through the gills, and out of the fish through the open operculum, or gill cover.

Some bony fishes that swim continuously, such as tuna, have practically immobile opercula. These fishes swim with their mouths partly open, constantly forcing water over the gills in what is known as *ram ventilation*. Most bony fishes, however, have flexible gill covers. For example, the remora, a fish that rides "piggyback" on sharks, uses ram ventilation while the shark is swimming, but employs the pumping action of its opercula when the shark stops swimming.

There are between three and seven gill arches on each side of the fish's head. Each gill arch is composed of two rows of *gill filaments*, and each gill filament contains thin membranous plates, or *lamellae*, that project out into the flow of water (figure 49.5). Water flows past the lamellae in one direction only.

Within each lamella, blood flows opposite to the direction of water movement. This arrangement is called **countercurrent flow,** and it acts to maximize the oxygenation of the blood by maintaining a positive oxygen gradient along the entire pathway for diffusion, increasing Δp in Fick's Law of Diffusion. The advantages of a countercurrent flow system are illustrated in figure 49.6a. Countercurrent flow ensures that an oxygen concentration gradient remains between blood and water throughout the length of the gill lamellae. This permits oxygen to continue to diffuse all along the lamellae, so that the blood leaving the gills has nearly as high an oxygen concentration as the water entering the gills.

If blood and water flowed in the same direction, the flow would be *concurrent* (figure 49.6b). In this case, the concentration difference across the gill lamellae would fall rapidly as the water lost oxygen to the blood, and net diffusion of oxygen

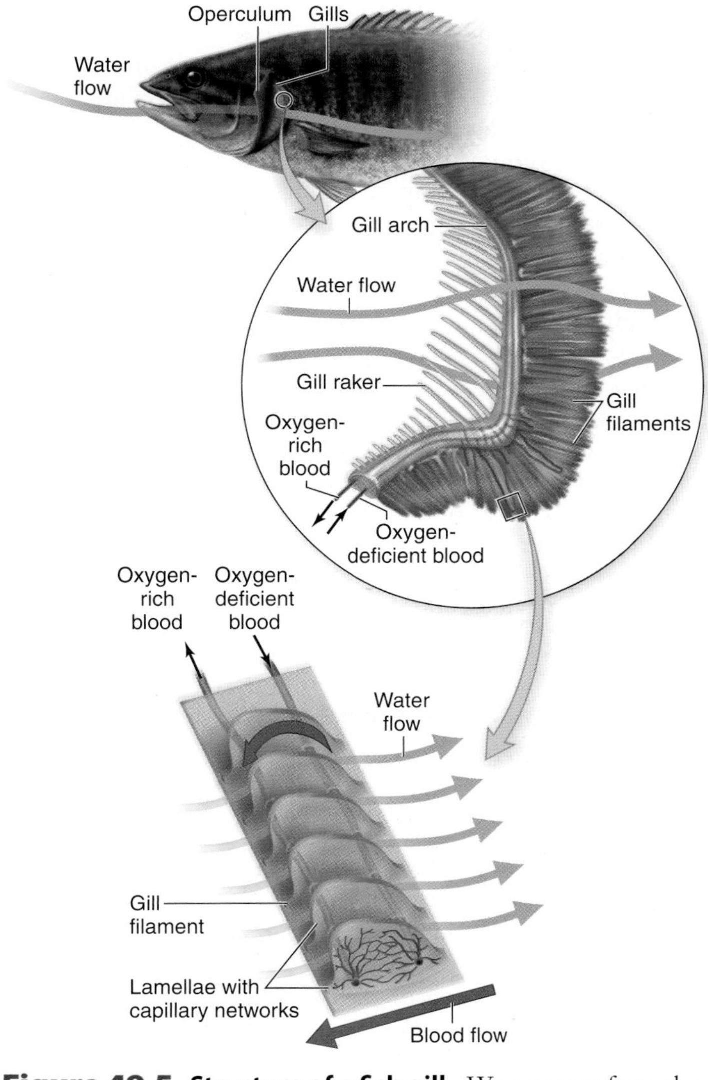

Figure 49.5 Structure of a fish gill. Water passes from the gill arch over the filaments (from left to right in the diagram). Water always passes the lamellae in a direction opposite to the direction of blood flow through the lamellae. The success of the gill's operation critically depends on this countercurrent flow of water and blood.

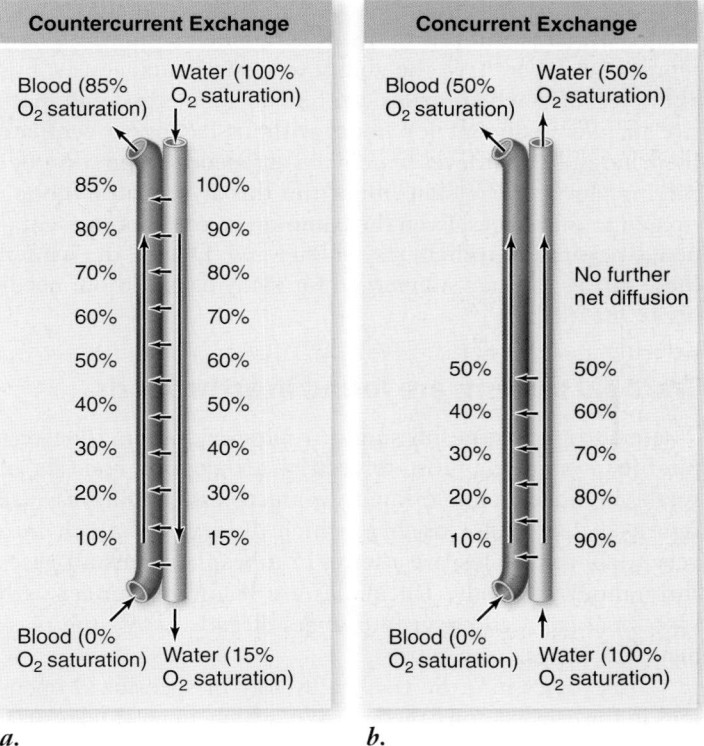

a.   *b.*

Figure 49.6 Countercurrent exchange. This process allows for the most efficient blood oxygenation. When blood and water flow in opposite directions (*a*), the initial oxygen (O_2) concentration difference between water and blood is small, but is sufficient for O_2 to diffuse from water to blood. As more O_2 diffuses into the blood, raising the blood's O_2 concentration, the blood encounters water with ever higher O_2 concentrations. At every point, the O_2 concentration is higher in the water, so that diffusion continues. In this example, blood attains an O_2 concentration of 85%. When blood and water flow in the same direction (*b*), O_2 can diffuse from the water into the blood rapidly at first, but the diffusion rate slows as more O_2 diffuses from the water into the blood, until finally the concentrations of O_2 in water and blood are equal. In this example, blood's O_2 concentration cannot exceed 50%.

would cease when the level of oxygen became the same in the water and in the blood.

Because of the countercurrent exchange of gases, fish gills are the most efficient of all respiratory organs.

Cutaneous respiration requires constant moisture

Oxygen and carbon dioxide can diffuse across cutaneous (skin) surfaces in some vertebrates (see figure 49.2b). Most commonly, these vertebrates are aquatic, such as amphibians and some turtles, and they have highly vascularized areas of thin epidermis. The process of exchanging oxygen and carbon dioxide across the skin is called **cutaneous respiration.** In amphibians, cutaneous respiration supplements—and sometimes replaces—the action of lungs. Although not common, some terrestrial amphibians, such as plethodontid salamanders, rely on cutaneous respiration exclusively.

Terrestrial reptiles have dry, tough, scaly skins that not only prevent desiccation, but also prohibit cutaneous respiration, which is utilized by many amphibians. Some aquatic reptiles, however, have the ability to respire cutaneously. For example, soft-shelled turtles can remain submerged and inactive in river sediment for hours without having to ventilate their lungs. At that level of activity, cutaneous respiration occurring through the skin lining the throat provides enough oxygen to the tissues. Even the common pond slider uses cutaneous respiration to help stay submerged. During the winter, these turtles can stay submerged for many days without needing to breathe air.

Tracheal systems are found in arthropods

The arthropods have no single respiratory organ. The respiratory system of most terrestrial arthropods consists of small, branched cuticle-lined air ducts called *tracheae* (see figure 49.2d). These trachea, which ultimately branch into very small tracheoles, are a series of tubes that transmit gases throughout the body. Tracheoles are in direct contact with individual cells, and oxygen diffuses directly across the plasma membranes.

Air passes into the trachea by way of specialized openings in the exoskeleton called *spiracles*, which, in most terrestrial arthropods, can be opened and closed by valves. The ability to prevent water loss by closing the spiracles was a key adaptation that facilitated the invasion of land by arthropods.

Learning Outcomes Review 49.2

Gills are highly subdivided structures providing a large surface area for exchange. In countercurrent flow, blood in the gills flows opposite to the direction of water to maintain a gradient difference and maximize gas exchange. Some amphibians rely on cutaneous respiration. Highly subdivided tracheal systems have evolved in arthropods, and these have been modified with valves as an adaptation to terrestrial life.

- *What are the anatomical requirements for a countercurrent flow system?*

49.3 Lungs

Learning Outcomes

1. *Explain why lungs work better than gills in air.*
2. *Compare the breathing mechanisms of amphibians and reptiles.*
3. *Describe the breathing cycle of birds.*

Despite the high efficiency of gills as respiratory organs in aquatic environments, gills were replaced in terrestrial animals for two principal reasons:

1. **Air is less supportive than water.** The fine membranous lamellae of gills lack inherent structural strength and rely on water for their support. A fish out of water, although awash in oxygen, soon suffocates because its gills collapse into a mass of tissue. Unlike gills, internal air passages such as trachaea and lungs can remain open because the body itself provides the necessary structural support.
2. **Water evaporates.** Air is rarely saturated with water vapor, except immediately after a rainstorm. Consequently, terrestrial organisms constantly lose water to the atmosphere. Gills would provide an enormous surface area for water loss.

The lung minimizes evaporation by moving air through a branched tubular passage. The tracheal system of arthropods also uses internal tubes to minimize evaporation.

The air drawn into the respiratory passages becomes saturated with water vapor before reaching the inner regions of the lung. In these areas, a thin, wet membrane permits gas exchange. Unlike the one-way flow of water that is so effective in the respiratory function of gills, gases move in and out of lungs by way of the same airway passages, a two-way flow system. Birds have an exceptional respiratory system, as described later on.

Breathing of air takes advantage of partial pressures of gases

Dry air contains 78.09% nitrogen, 20.95% oxygen, 0.93% argon and other inert gases, and 0.03% carbon dioxide. Convection currents cause the atmosphere to maintain a constant composition to altitudes of at least 100 km, although the *amount* (number of molecules) of air that is present decreases as altitude increases.

Because of the force of gravity, air exerts a pressure downward on objects below it. An apparatus that measures air pressure is called a *barometer*, and 760 mm Hg is the barometric pressure of the air at sea level. A pressure of 760 mm Hg is also defined as one atmosphere (1.0 atm) of pressure.

Each type of gas contributes to the total atmospheric pressure according to its fraction of the total molecules present. The pressure contributed by a gas is called its **partial pressure,** and it is indicated by P_{N_2}, P_{O_2}, P_{CO_2}, and so on. At sea level, the partial pressures of N_2, O_2, and CO_2 are as follows:

$$P_{N_2} = 760 \times 79.02\% = 600.6 \text{ mm Hg}$$

$$P_{O_2} = 760 \times 20.95\% = 159.2 \text{ mm Hg}$$

$$P_{CO_2} = 760 \times 0.03\% = 0.2 \text{ mm Hg}$$

Humans do not survive for long at altitudes above 6000 m. Although the air at these altitudes still contains 20.95% oxygen, the atmospheric pressure is only about 380 mm Hg, so the P_{O_2} is only 80 mm Hg ($380 \times 20.95\%$), half the amount of oxygen available at sea level.

In the following sections, we describe respiration in vertebrates with lungs, beginning with reptiles and amphibians. We then summarize mammalian lungs and the highly adapted and specialized lungs of birds.

Amphibians and reptiles breathe in different ways

The lungs of amphibians are formed as saclike outpouchings of the gut (figure 49.7). Although the internal surface area of these sacs is increased by folds, much less surface area is available for gas exchange in amphibian lungs than in the lungs of other terrestrial vertebrates. Each amphibian lung is connected to the rear of the oral cavity, or pharynx, and the opening to each lung is controlled by a valve, the glottis.

Amphibians do not breathe the same way as other terrestrial vertebrates. Amphibians force air into their lungs; they fill their oral cavity with air (figure 49.7a), close their mouth and nostrils, and then elevate the floor of their oral cavity. This pushes air into their lungs in the same way that a pressurized tank of air is used to fill balloons (figure 49.7b). This is called **positive pressure breathing;** in humans, it would be analogous to forcing air into a person's lungs by performing mouth-to-mouth resuscitation.

Most reptiles breathe in a different way, by expanding their rib cages by muscular contraction. This action creates a lower pressure inside the lungs compared with the atmosphere, and the greater atmospheric pressure moves air into the lungs. This type of ventilation is termed **negative pressure breathing** because of the air being "pulled in" by the animal, like sucking water through a straw, rather than being "pushed in."

Mammalian lungs have greatly increased surface area

Endothermic animals, such as birds and mammals, have consistently higher metabolic rates and thus require more oxygen (see chapter 7). Both these vertebrate groups exhibit more complex and efficient respiratory systems than ectothermic animals. The evolution of more efficient respiratory systems accommodates the increased demands on cellular respiration of endothermy.

The lungs of mammals are packed with millions of **alveoli,** tiny sacs clustered like grapes (figure 49.8). This provides each lung with an enormous surface area for gas exchange. Each alveolus is composed of an epithelium only one cell thick,

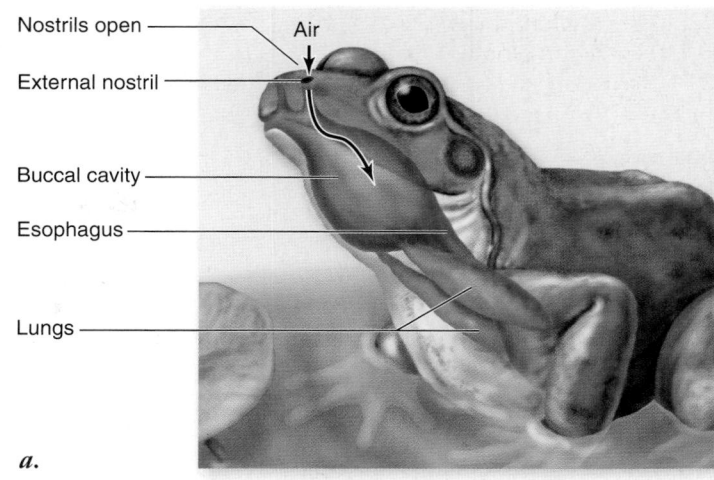

a.

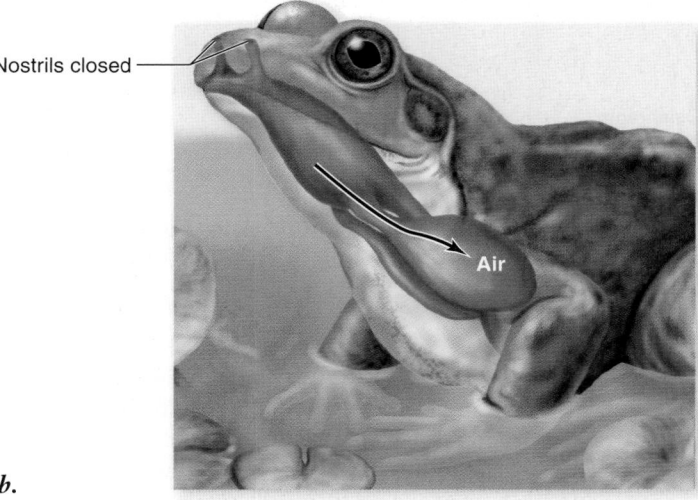

b.

Figure 49.7 Amphibian lungs. Each lung of this frog is an outpouching of the gut and is filled with air by the creation of a positive pressure in the buccal cavity. *a.* The buccal cavity is expanded and air flows through the open nostrils. *b.* The nostrils are closed and the buccal cavity is compressed, thus creating the positive pressure that fills the lungs. The amphibian lung lacks the structures present in the lungs of other terrestrial vertebrates that provide an enormous surface area for gas exchange, and so are not as efficient as the lungs of other vertebrates.

and is surrounded by blood capillaries with walls that are also only one cell layer thick. Thus, the distance *d* across which gas must diffuse is very small—only 0.5 to 1.5 μm.

Inhaled air is taken in through the mouth and nose past the pharynx to the larynx (voice box), where it passes through an opening in the vocal cords, the *glottis*, into a tube supported by C-shaped rings of cartilage, the trachea (windpipe). The term *trachea* is used both for the vertebrate windpipe and the respiratory tubes of arthropods, although the structures are obviously not homologous. The mammalian trachea bifurcates into right and left bronchi (singular, *bronchus*), which enter each lung and further subdivide into bronchioles that deliver the air into the alveoli.

The alveoli are surrounded by an extensive capillary network. All gas exchange between the air and blood takes place

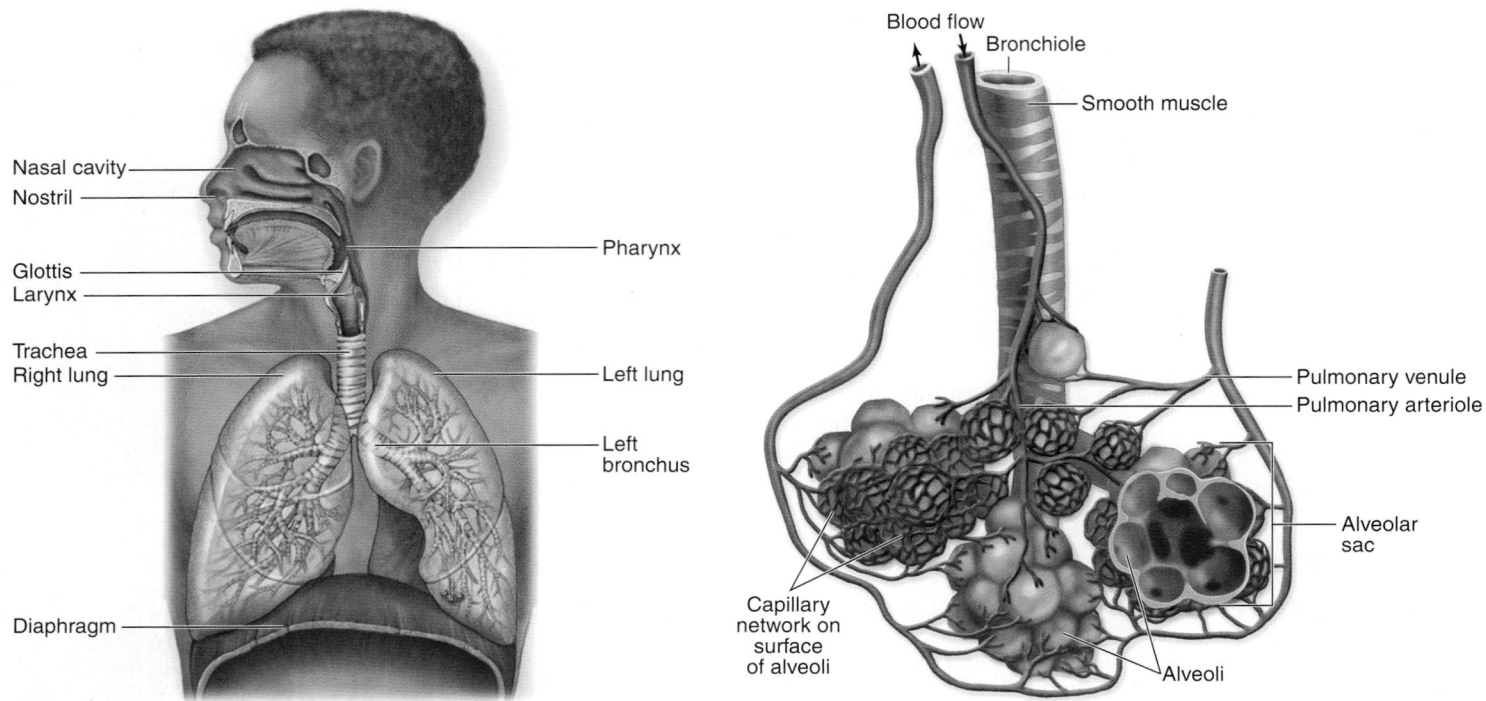

Figure 49.8 The human respiratory system and the structure of the mammalian lung. The lungs of mammals have an enormous surface area because of the millions of alveoli that cluster at the ends of the bronchioles. This provides for efficient gas exchange with the blood.

across the walls of the alveoli. The branching of bronchioles and the vast number of alveoli combine to increase the respiratory surface area far above that of amphibians or reptiles. In humans, each lung has about 300 million alveoli, and the total surface area available for diffusion can be as much as 80 m², or about 42 times the surface area of the body. Details of gas exchange at the alveolar interface with blood capillaries is described in sections that follow.

The respiratory system of birds is a highly efficient flow-through system

The avian respiratory system is a unique structure that affords birds the most efficient respiration of all terrestrial vertebrates. Unlike the mammalian lung, which ends in blind alveoli, the bird lung channels air through tiny air vessels called parabronchi, where gas exchange occurs. Air flows through the parabronchi in one direction only. This flow is similar to the unidirectional flow of water through a fish gill.

In other terrestrial vertebrates, inhaled fresh air is mixed with "old," oxygen-depleted air left from the previous breathing cycle. The lungs of amphibians, reptiles, and mammals are never completely empty of the gases within them. In birds, only fresh air enters the parabronchi of the lung, and the "old" air exits the lung by a different route. The unidirectional flow of air is achieved through the action of anterior and posterior air sacs unique to birds (figure 49.9a). When these sacs are expanded during inhalation, they take in air, and when they are compressed during exhalation, they push air into and through the lungs.

Respiration in birds occurs in two cycles (figure 49.9b). Each cycle has an inhalation and exhalation phase—but the air inhaled in one cycle is not exhaled until the second cycle.

Upon inhalation, both anterior and posterior air sacs expand. The inhaled air, however, only enters the posterior air sacs; the anterior air sacs fill with air pulled from the lungs. Upon exhalation, the air forced out of the anterior air sacs is released outside the body, but the air forced out of the posterior air sacs now enters the lungs. This process is repeated in the second cycle.

The unidirectional flow of air also permits further respiratory efficiency: The flow of blood through the avian lung runs at a 90° angle to the air flow. This crosscurrent flow is not as efficient as the 180° countercurrent flow in fishes' gills, but it has a greater capacity to extract oxygen from the air than does a mammalian lung.

Because of these respiratory adaptations, a sparrow can be active at an altitude of 6000 m, whereas a mouse, which has a similar body mass and metabolic rate, would die from lack of oxygen in a fairly short time.

Learning Outcomes Review 49.3

Lungs provide a large surface area for gas exchange while minimizing evaporation; unlike gills, they contain structural support that prevents their collapse. Amphibians push air into their lungs; most reptiles and all birds and mammals pull air into their lungs by expanding the thoracic cavity. The respiratory system of birds has efficient, one-way air flow and crosscurrent blood flow through the lungs.

■ *What selection pressure would bring about the evolution of birds' highly efficient lungs?*

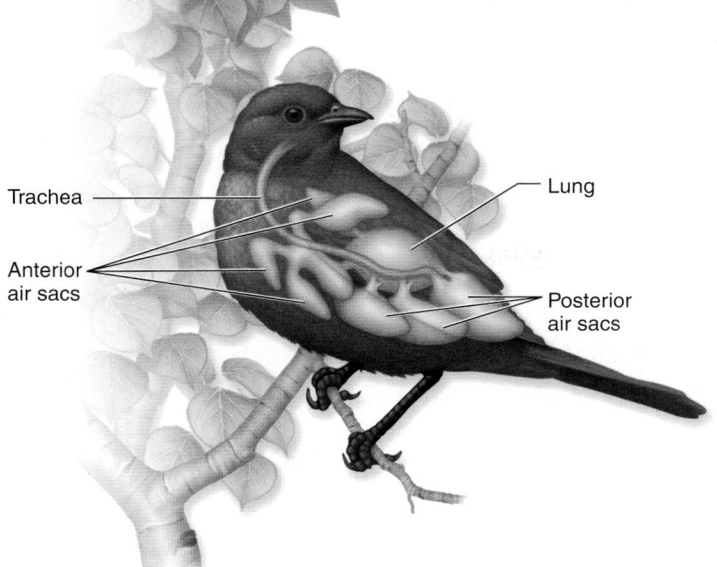

Trachea

Anterior
air sacs

Lung

Posterior
air sacs

a.

Cycle 1	
Inhalation	**Exhalation**

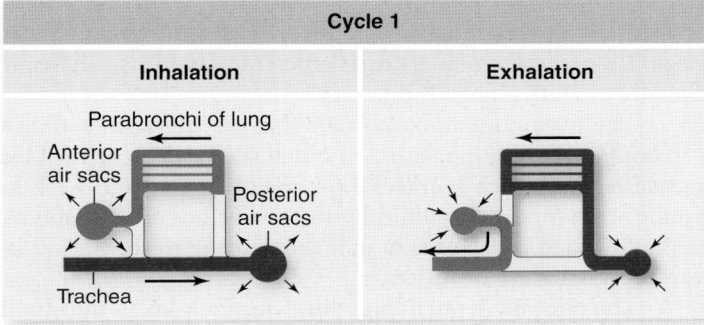

Parabronchi of lung
Anterior air sacs
Posterior air sacs
Trachea

Cycle 2	
Inhalation	**Exhalation**

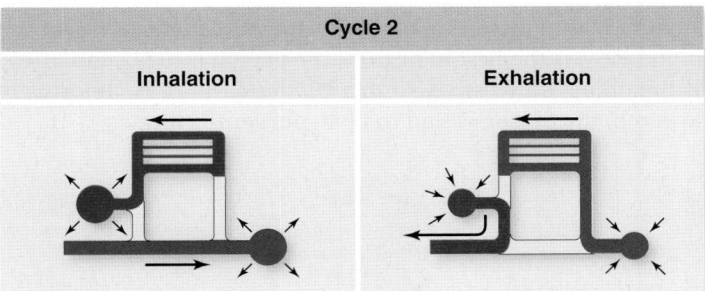

b.

Figure 49.9 How a bird breathes. *a.* Birds have a system of air sacs, divided into an anterior group and posterior group, that extend between the internal organs and into the bones. *b.* Breathing occurs in two cycles. Cycle 1: Inhaled air (shown in red) is drawn from the trachea into the posterior air sacs (shown expanding as it fills with air) and then is exhaled into the lungs (posterior air sacs deflate). Cycle 2: Air is drawn from the lungs into the anterior air sacs, which expand, and then is exhaled from these air sacs through the trachea. Passage of air through the lungs is always in the same direction, from posterior to anterior (right to left in this diagram). These cycles are always going on simultaneously; during inhalation, fresh air enters the posterior air sacs at the same time that air from the previous breath that was in the lungs moves into the anterior air sacs. In exhalation, the newer air moves from the posterior air sacs to the lung at the same time that air in the anterior air sacs is exhaled from the body. At the same time, another breath of inhaled air (purple) is moving through cycle 1.

49.4 Structures and Mechanisms of Ventilation in Mammals

Learning Outcomes

1. **Explain what is meant by anatomical dead space.**
2. **Describe how the nervous system regulates breathing.**
3. **List and characterize the major respiratory diseases.**

About 30 billion capillaries can be found in each lung, roughly 100 capillaries per alveolus. Thus, an alveolus can be visualized as a microscopic air bubble whose entire surface is bathed by blood. Gas exchange occurs very rapidly at this interface.

Blood returning from the systemic circulation, depleted in oxygen, has a partial oxygen pressure (P_{O_2}) of about 40 mm Hg. By contrast, the P_{O_2} in the alveoli is about 105 mm Hg. The difference in pressures, namely the Δp of Fick's Law, is 65 mm Hg, leading to oxygen moving into the blood. The blood leaving the lungs, as a result of this gas exchange, normally contains a P_{O_2} of about 100 mm Hg. As you can see, the lungs do a very effective, but not perfect, job of oxygenating the blood. These changes in the P_{O_2} of the blood, as well as the changes in plasma carbon dioxide (indicated as the P_{CO_2}), are shown in figure 49.10.

Lung structure and function supports the respiratory cycle

In humans and other mammals, the outside of each lung is covered by a thin membrane called the **visceral pleural membrane.** A second membrane, the **parietal pleural membrane,** lines the inner wall of the thoracic cavity. The space between these two membrane sheets, the **pleural cavity,** is normally very small and filled with fluid. This fluid causes the two membranes to adhere, effectively coupling the lungs to the thoracic cavity. The pleural membranes package each lung separately—if one lung collapses due to a perforation of the membranes, the other lung can still function.

During inhalation, the thoracic volume is increased through contraction of two sets of muscles: the *external intercostal muscles* and the *diaphragm.* Contraction of the external intercostal muscles between the ribs raises the ribs and expands the rib cage. Contraction of the **diaphragm,** a convex sheet of striated muscle separating the thoracic cavity from the abdominal cavity, causes the diaphragm to lower and assume a more flattened shape. This expands the volume of the thorax and lungs, bringing about negative pressure ventilation, while it increases the pressure on the abdominal organs (figure 49.11*a*).

The thorax and lungs have a degree of elasticity; expansion during inhalation places these structures under elastic tension. The relaxation of the external intercostal muscles and diaphragm produces unforced exhalation because the elastic tension is released, allowing the thorax and lungs to recoil. You can produce a greater exhalation force by actively contracting your abdominal muscles—such as when blowing up a balloon (figure 49.11*b*).

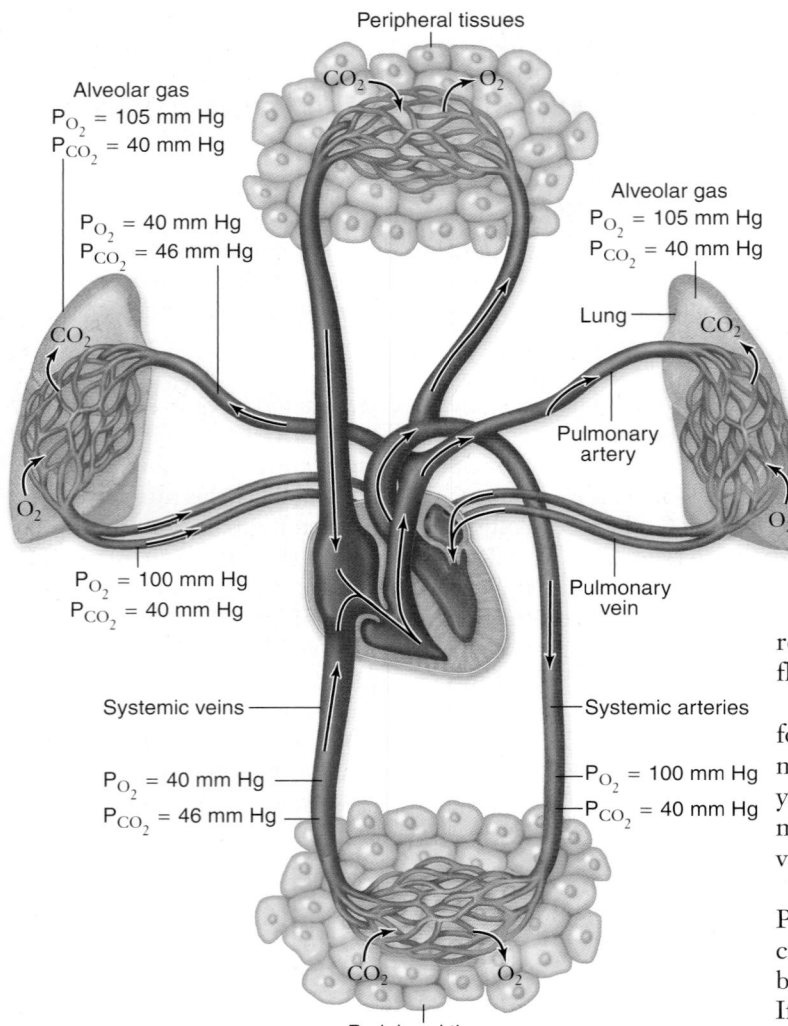

Peripheral tissues

Alveolar gas
P_{O_2} = 105 mm Hg
P_{CO_2} = 40 mm Hg

P_{O_2} = 40 mm Hg
P_{CO_2} = 46 mm Hg

CO_2

O_2

P_{O_2} = 100 mm Hg
P_{CO_2} = 40 mm Hg

Systemic veins

P_{O_2} = 40 mm Hg
P_{CO_2} = 46 mm Hg

Alveolar gas
P_{O_2} = 105 mm Hg
P_{CO_2} = 40 mm Hg

Lung

CO_2

Pulmonary artery

O_2

Pulmonary vein

Systemic arteries

P_{O_2} = 100 mm Hg
P_{CO_2} = 40 mm Hg

CO_2 O_2

Peripheral tissues

Figure 49.10 Gas exchange in the blood capillaries of the lungs and systemic circulation. As a result of gas exchange in the lungs, the systemic arteries carry oxygenated blood with a relatively low carbon dioxide (CO_2) concentration. After the oxygen (O_2) is unloaded to the tissues, the blood in the systemic veins has a lowered O_2 content and an increased CO_2 concentration.

Ventilation efficiency depends on lung capacity and breathing rate

A variety of terms are used to describe the volume changes of the lung during breathing. In a person at rest, each breath moves a tidal volume of about 500 mL of air into and out of the lungs. About 150 mL of the tidal volume is contained in the tubular passages (trachea, bronchi, and bronchioles), where no gas exchange occurs—termed the *anatomical dead space*. The gases in this space mix with fresh air during inhalation. This mixing is one reason that respiration in mammals is not as efficient as in birds, where air flow through the lungs is one-way.

The maximum amount of air that can be expired after a forceful, maximum inhalation is called the vital capacity. This measurement, which averages 4.6 L in young men and 3.1 L in young women, can be clinically important because an abnormally low vital capacity may indicate damage to the alveoli in various pulmonary disorders.

The rate and depth of breathing normally keeps the blood P_{O_2} and P_{CO_2} within a normal range. If breathing is insufficient to maintain normal blood gas measurements (a rise in the blood P_{CO_2} is the best indicator), the person is hypoventilating. If breathing is excessive, so that the blood P_{CO_2} is abnormally lowered, the person is said to be **hyperventilating.**

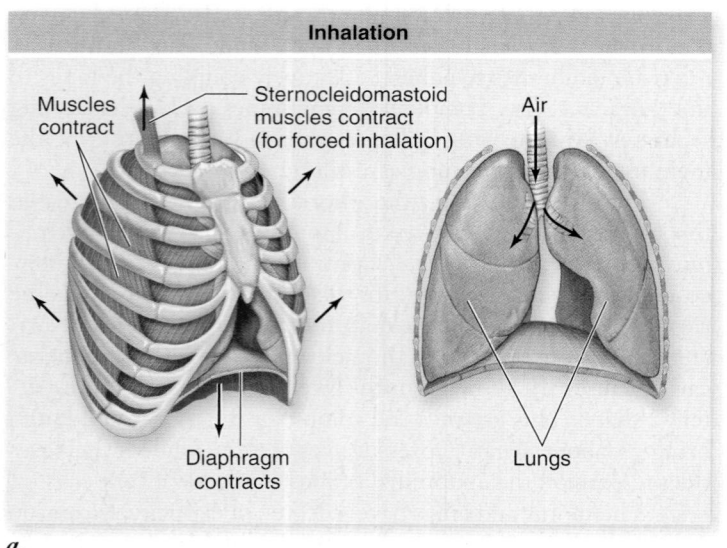

Inhalation

Muscles contract

Sternocleidomastoid muscles contract (for forced inhalation)

Air

Diaphragm contracts

Lungs

a.

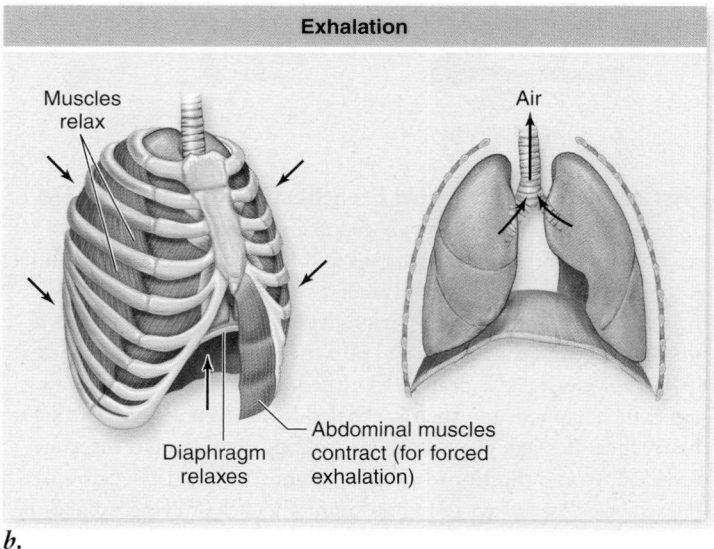

Exhalation

Muscles relax

Air

Diaphragm relaxes

Abdominal muscles contract (for forced exhalation)

b.

Figure 49.11 How a human breathes. *a.* Inhalation. The diaphragm contracts and the walls of the chest cavity expand, increasing the volume of the chest cavity and lungs. As a result of the larger volume, air is drawn into the lungs. *b.* Exhalation. The diaphragm and chest walls return to their normal positions as a result of elastic recoil, reducing the volume of the chest cavity and forcing air out of the lungs through the trachea. Note that inhalation can be forced by contracting accessory respiratory muscles (such as the sternocleidomastoid), and exhalation can be forced by contracting abdominal muscles.

The increased breathing that occurs during moderate exertion is not necessarily hyperventilation because the faster and more forceful breathing is matched to the higher metabolic rate, and blood gas measurements remain normal. Next, we describe how breathing is regulated to keep pace with metabolism.

Ventilation is under nervous system control

Each breath is initiated by neurons in a *respiratory control center* located in the medulla oblongata. These neurons stimulate the diaphragm and external intercostal muscles to contract, causing inhalation. When these neurons stop producing impulses, the inspiratory muscles relax and exhalation occurs. Although the muscles of breathing are skeletal muscles, they are usually controlled automatically. This control can be voluntarily overridden, however, as in hypoventilation (breath holding) or hyperventilation.

Neurons of the medulla oblongata must be responsive to changes in blood P_{O_2} and P_{CO_2} in order to maintain homeostasis. You can demonstrate this mechanism by simply holding your breath. Your blood carbon dioxide level immediately rises, and your blood oxygen level falls. After a short time, the urge to breathe induced by the changes in blood gases becomes overpowering. The rise in blood carbon dioxide, as indicated by a rise in P_{CO_2}, is the primary initiator, rather than the fall in oxygen levels.

A rise in P_{CO_2} causes an increased production of carbonic acid (H_2CO_3), which lowers the blood pH. A fall in blood pH stimulates chemosensitive neurons in the **aortic** and **carotid bodies,** in the aorta and the carotid artery (figure 49.12*b*). These

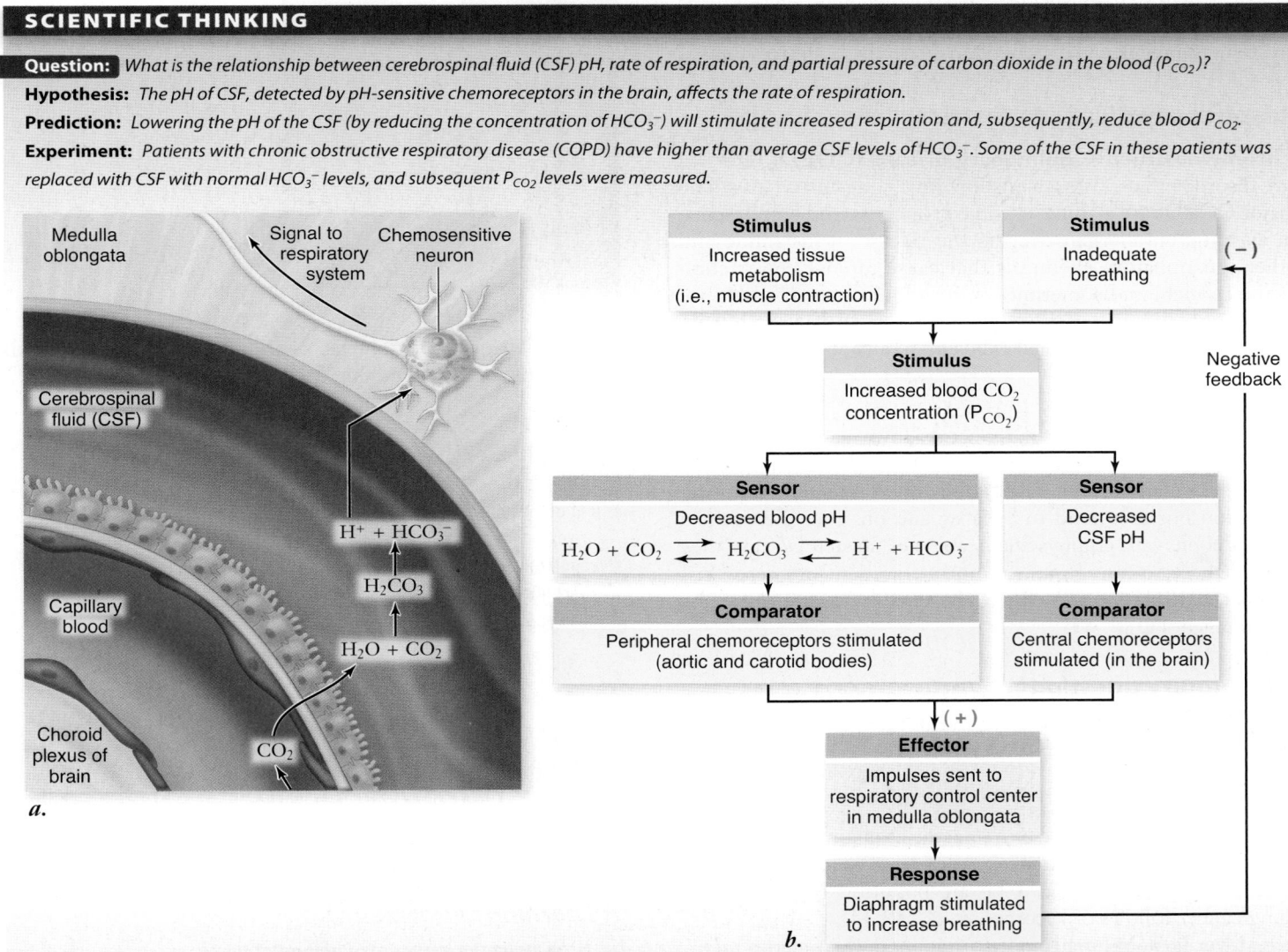

SCIENTIFIC THINKING

Question: *What is the relationship between cerebrospinal fluid (CSF) pH, rate of respiration, and partial pressure of carbon dioxide in the blood (P_{CO_2})?*

Hypothesis: *The pH of CSF, detected by pH-sensitive chemoreceptors in the brain, affects the rate of respiration.*

Prediction: *Lowering the pH of the CSF (by reducing the concentration of HCO_3^-) will stimulate increased respiration and, subsequently, reduce blood P_{CO_2}.*

Experiment: *Patients with chronic obstructive respiratory disease (COPD) have higher than average CSF levels of HCO_3^-. Some of the CSF in these patients was replaced with CSF with normal HCO_3^- levels, and subsequent P_{CO_2} levels were measured.*

Result: *The reduced HCO_3^- levels (and corresponding drop in CSF pH) resulted in increased respiration, which subsequently resulted in lower arterial P_{CO_2}.*

Conclusion: *The drop in pH (caused by the change in HCO_3^- levels) is detected by H^+ ion chemoreceptors in the brain. The brain sends impulses to the respiratory control center in the medulla oblongata, which directs an increase in breathing. Likewise, when the concentration of CO_2 in the blood rises as a result of inadequate breathing or increased tissue metabolism, the pH of the blood and the CSF decreases, stimulating the central chemoreceptors in the brain and the peripheral chemoreceptors in the aortic and carotid bodies. The receptors signal the brain stem control center, increasing ventilation and reducing the P_{CO_2} to normal levels.*

Figure 49.12 **Regulation of breathing by pH-sensitive chemoreceptors.**

peripheral receptors send impulses to the respiratory control center, which then stimulates increased breathing. The brain also contains central chemoreceptors that are stimulated by a drop in the pH of cerebrospinal fluid (CSF) (figure 49.12*a*).

A person cannot voluntarily hyperventilate for too long. The decrease in plasma P_{CO_2} and increase in pH of plasma and CSF caused by hyperventilation suppress the reflex drive to breathe. Deliberate hyperventilation allows people to hold their breath longer—not because it increases oxygen in the blood, but because the carbon dioxide level is lowered and takes longer to build back up, postponing the need to breathe.

In people with normal lungs, P_{O_2} becomes a significant stimulus for increased breathing rates only at high altitudes, where the P_{O_2} of the atmosphere is low. The symptoms of low oxygen at high altitude are known as mountain sickness, which may include feelings of weakness, headache, nausea, vomiting, and reduced mental function. All of these symptoms are related to the low P_{O_2}, and breathing supplemental oxygen often may remove all symptoms.

Respiratory diseases restrict gas exchange

Chronic obstructive pulmonary disease (COPD) refers to any disorder that obstructs airflow on a long-term basis. The major COPDs are asthma, chronic bronchitis, and emphysema. In **asthma,** an allergen triggers the release of histamine and other inflammatory chemicals that cause intense constriction of the bronchi and sometimes suffocation. Other COPDs are commonly caused by cigarette smoking but can also result from air pollution or occupational exposure to airborne irritants.

Emphysema

In **emphysema,** alveolar walls break down and the lung exhibits larger but fewer alveoli. The lungs also become fibrotic and less elastic. The air passages open adequately during inhalation but they tend to collapse and obstruct the outflow of air. People with emphysema become exhausted because they expend three to four times the normal amount of energy just to breathe. Eighty to 90% of emphysema deaths are caused by cigarette smoking.

 Inquiry question

How does emphysema affect the diffusion of gases in and out of the lung, based on Fick's Law?

Lung cancer

Lung cancer accounts for more deaths than any other form of cancer. The most important cause of lung cancer is cigarette smoking, distantly followed by air pollution (figure 49.13). Lung cancer follows or accompanies COPD.

Over 90% of lung tumors originate in the mucous membranes of the large bronchi. As a tumor invades the bronchial wall and grows around it, it compresses the airway and may cause collapse of more distal parts of the lung. Growth of a tumor often produces coughing, but coughing is such an everyday occurrence for smokers, it seldom causes alarm. Often, the first sign of serious trouble is the coughing up of blood.

Lung cancer metastasizes (spreads) so rapidly that it has usually invaded other organs by the time it is diagnosed. The

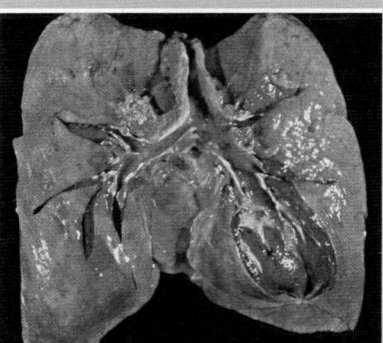
Healthy Lungs

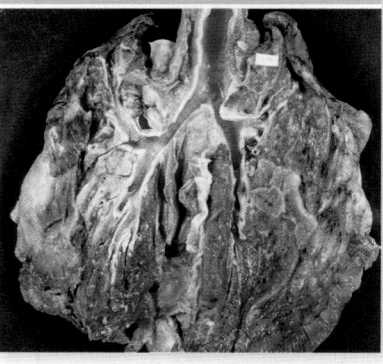
Cancerous Lungs

Figure 49.13
Comparison of healthy lung (*a*) and a lung with cancer (*b*).

chance of recovery from metastasized lung cancer is poor, with only 3% of patients surviving for 5 years after diagnosis.

Learning Outcomes Review 49.4

In humans, each breath moves a tidal volume of about 500 mL in and out of the lungs; 150 mL remains in the tubular passages where no gases are exchanged (anatomical dead space). Depth and rate of ventilation is regulated primarily by neurons in the medulla oblongata that detect CO_2 concentration. Diseases such as COPD limit gas exchange by obstructing airflow. Lung cancer, associated with tobacco use, has a low survival rate.

■ *How do mammals breathe differently from birds?*

49.5 Transport of Gases in Body Fluids

Learning Outcomes

1. *Depict the structure of hemoglobin.*
2. *Describe how hemoglobin's oxygen affinity changes depending on environmental conditions.*
3. *Explain how carbon dioxide is transported by the blood.*

The amount of oxygen that can be dissolved in the blood plasma depends directly on the P_{O_2} of the air in the alveoli, as explained earlier. When mammalian lungs are functioning normally, the blood plasma leaving the lungs has almost as much dissolved oxygen as is theoretically possible, given the P_{O_2} of the air. Because of oxygen's low solubility, however, blood plasma can contain a maximum of only about 3 mL of O_2 per liter. But whole blood normally carries almost 200 mL of O_2 per liter. Most of the oxygen in the blood is bound to molecules of hemoglobin inside red blood cells.

Respiratory pigments bind oxygen for transport

Hemoglobin is a protein composed of four polypeptide chains and four organic compounds called *heme groups*. At the center of each heme group is an atom of iron, which can bind to a molecule of oxygen (figure 49.14). Thus, each hemoglobin molecule can carry up to four molecules of oxygen.

Hemoglobin loads up with oxygen in the alveolar capillaries of the pulmonary circulation, forming oxyhemoglobin. This molecule has a bright red color. As blood passes through capillaries in the systemic circulation, some of the oxyhemoglobin releases oxygen, becoming **deoxyhemoglobin**. Deoxyhemoglobin has a darker red color; but it imparts a bluish tinge to tissues. Illustrations of the cardiovascular system show vessels carrying oxygenated blood with a red color and vessels that carry oxygen-depleted blood with a blue color.

Hemoglobin is an ancient protein; it is not only the oxygen-carrying molecule in all vertebrates, but is also used as an oxygen carrier by many invertebrates, including annelids, mollusks, echinoderms, flatworms, and even some protists. Many other invertebrates, however, employ different oxygen carriers, such as **hemocyanin**. In hemocyanin, the oxygen-binding atom is copper instead of iron. Hemocyanin is not found associated with blood cells, but is instead one of the free proteins in the circulating fluid (hemolymph) of arthropods and some mollusks.

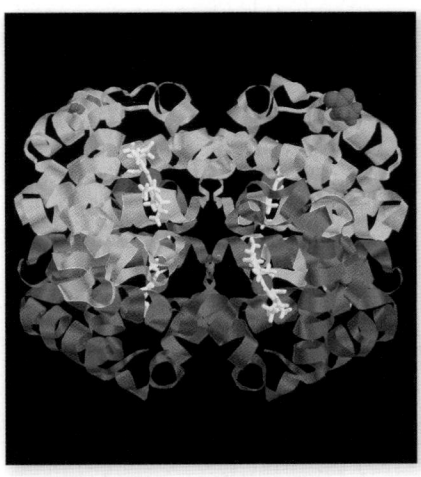

**Figure 49.14
The structure of the adult hemoglobin protein.** Hemoglobin consists of four polypeptide chains: two α chains and two β chains. Each chain is associated with a heme group (in white), and each heme group has a central iron atom (red ball), which can bind to a molecule of O_2.

Inquiry question

? If oxygen-depleted vessels have a bluish color, does this mean that all veins in the body have a bluish color? Why or why not?

Hemoglobin and myoglobin provide an oxygen reserve

At a blood P_{O_2} of 100 mm Hg, the level found in blood leaving the alveoli, approximately 97% of the hemoglobin within red blood cells is in the form of oxyhemoglobin—indicated as a percent oxyhemoglobin saturation of 97%.

In a person at rest, blood that returns to the heart in the systemic veins has a P_{O_2} that is decreased to about 40 mm Hg. At this lower P_{O_2}, the percent saturation of hemoglobin is only 75%. In a person at rest, therefore, 22% (97% minus 75%) of the oxyhemoglobin has released its oxygen to the tissues. Put another way, roughly one-fifth of the oxygen is unloaded in the tissues, leaving four-fifths of the oxygen in the blood as a reserve. A graphic representation of these changes is called an oxyhemoglobin dissociation curve (figure 49.15).

This large reserve of oxygen serves an important function. It enables the blood to supply the body's oxygen needs during exertion as well as at rest. During exercise, for example, the muscles' accelerated metabolism uses more oxygen and decreases the venous blood P_{O_2}. The P_{O_2} of the venous blood

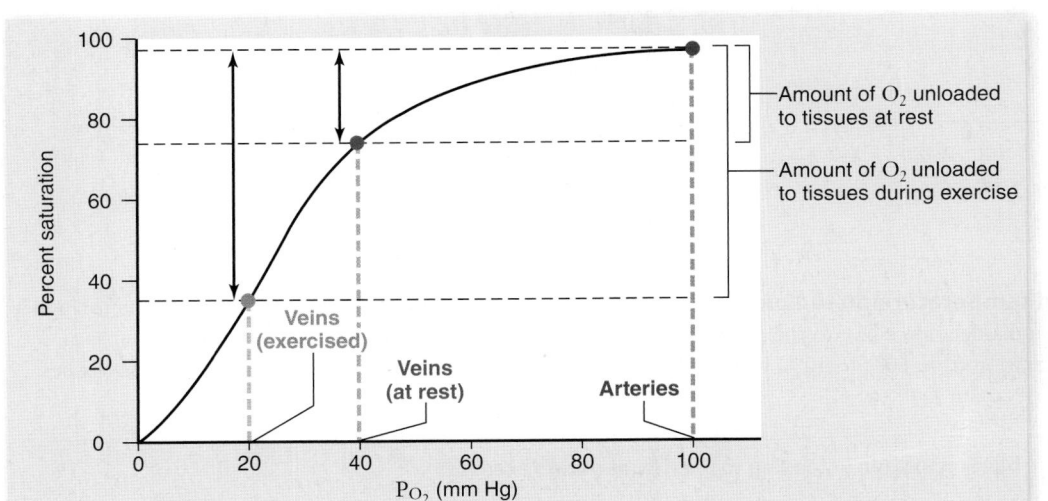

Figure 49.15 The oxyhemoglobin dissociation curve. Hemoglobin combines with O_2 in the lungs, and this oxygenated blood is carried by arteries to the body cells. After O_2 is removed from the blood to support cellular respiration, the blood entering the veins contains less O_2.

Inquiry question

? How would you determine how much oxygen was unloaded to the tissues?

chapter **49** *The Respiratory System*

could drop to 20 mm Hg; in this case, the percent saturation of hemoglobin would be only 35% (see figure 49.15). Because arterial blood would still contain 97% oxyhemoglobin, the amount of oxygen unloaded would now be 62% (97% minus 35%), instead of the 22% at rest.

In addition to this function, the oxygen reserve also ensures that the blood contains enough oxygen to maintain life for 4 to 5 min if breathing is interrupted or if the heart stops pumping.

A second oxygen reserve is available in myoglobin, an oxygen-binding molecule found in muscle cells. Myoglobin is composed of a single polypeptide chain with an iron atom that can bind to an O_2 molecule. Myoglobin has a higher affinity for oxygen than hemoglobin, which means that when oxygen levels fall in muscle cells, myoglobin will contain oxygen after the hemoglobin supplies have been exhausted. Deep sea-diving mammals, such as the elephant seal in figure 49.1, are able to stay under water for long periods in part because of the high levels of oxygen stored in the myoglobin in their muscles.

Inquiry question

? Based on the preceding information, would an otherwise healthy person benefit significantly from breathing 100% oxygen following a bout of intense exercise such as a 400-m sprint?

Hemoglobin's affinity for oxygen is affected by pH and temperature

Oxygen transport in the blood is affected by other conditions including temperature and pH. The CO_2 produced by metabolizing tissues combines with H_2O to form carbonic acid (H_2CO_3). H_2CO_3 dissociates into bicarbonate (HCO_3^-) and H^+, thereby lowering blood pH. This reaction occurs primarily inside red blood cells, where the lowered pH reduces hemoglobin's affinity for oxygen, causing it to release oxygen more readily.

The effect of pH on hemoglobin's affinity for oxygen, known as the **Bohr effect** or **Bohr shift,** is the result of H^+ binding to hemoglobin. It is shown graphically by a shift of the oxyhemoglobin dissociation curve to the right (figure 49.16a).

Increasing temperature has a similar effect on hemoglobin's affinity for oxygen (figure 49.16b). Because skeletal muscles produce carbon dioxide more rapidly during exercise, and because active muscles produce heat, the blood unloads a higher percentage of the oxygen it carries during exercise.

Carbon dioxide is primarily transported as bicarbonate ion

About 8% of the CO_2 in blood is simply dissolved in plasma; another 20% is bound to hemoglobin. Because CO_2 binds to the protein portion of hemoglobin, and not to the iron atoms of the heme groups, it does not compete with oxygen; however, it does cause hemoglobin's shape to change, lowering its affinity for oxygen.

The remaining 72% of the CO_2 diffuses into the red blood cells, where the enzyme carbonic anhydrase catalyzes the combining of CO_2 with water to form H_2CO_3. H_2CO_3 dissociates into HCO_3^- and H^+ ions. The H^+ binds to deoxyhemoglobin, and the HCO_3^- moves out of the erythrocyte into the plasma via a transporter that exchanges one Cl^- for a HCO_3^- (this is called the "chloride shift").

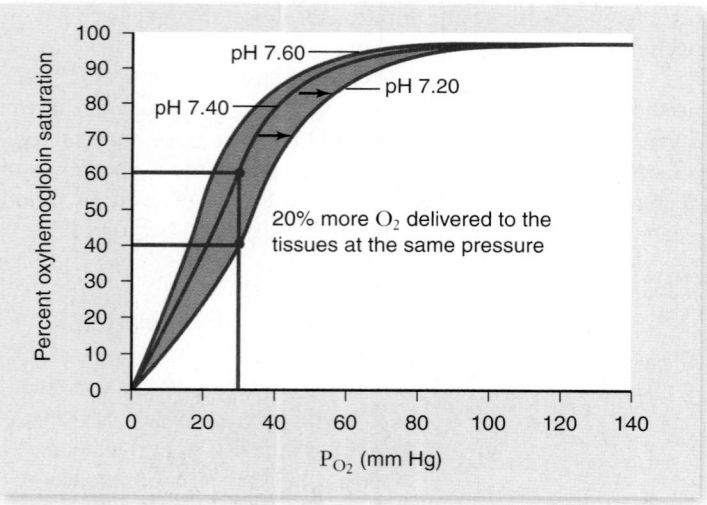

a. pH shift

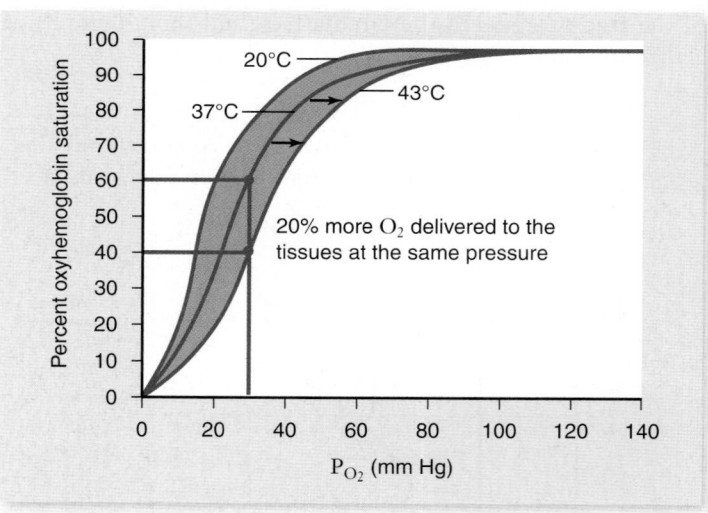

b. Temperature shift

Figure 49.16 **The effect of pH and temperature on the oxyhemoglobin dissociation curve.** *a.* Lower blood pH and (*b*) higher blood temperatures shift the oxyhemoglobin dissociation curve to the right, facilitating O_2 unloading. In this example, this can be seen as a lowering of the oxyhemoglobin percent saturation from 60% to 40%, indicating that the difference of 20% more O_2 is unloaded to the tissues.

Inquiry question

? What effect does high blood pressure have on oxygen unloading to the tissues during exercise?

This reaction removes large amounts of CO_2 from the plasma, maintaining a diffusion gradient that allows additional CO_2 to move into the plasma from the surrounding tissues (figure 49.17a). The formation of H_2CO_3 is also important in maintaining the acid–base balance of the blood; HCO_3^- serves as the major buffer of the blood plasma.

In the lungs, the lower P_{CO_2} of the gas mixture inside the alveoli causes the carbonic anhydrase reaction to proceed in the reverse direction, converting H_2CO_3 into H_2O and CO_2 (figure 49.17b). The CO_2 diffuses out of the red blood cells and into the alveoli, so that it can leave the body in the next exhalation.

Other dissolved gases are also transported by hemoglobin, most notably nitric oxide (NO), which plays an important role in vessel dilation. Carbon monoxide (CO) binds more strongly to hemoglobin than does oxygen, which is why carbon monoxide poi- soning can be deadly. Victims of carbon monoxide poisoning often have bright red skin due to hemoglobin's binding with CO.

Learning Outcomes Review 49.5

Hemoglobin consists of four polypeptide chains, each associated with an iron-containing heme group that can bind O_2. Hemoglobin's affinity for oxygen is affected by pH and temperature; more O_2 is released into tissues at lower pH and at higher temperature. Carbon dioxide is transported in the blood in three ways: dissolved in the plasma, bound to hemoglobin, and as bicarbonate in the plasma following a reaction with carbonic anhydrase in the red blood cells.

■ **What are the differences in the way that oxygen and carbon dioxide are transported in blood?**

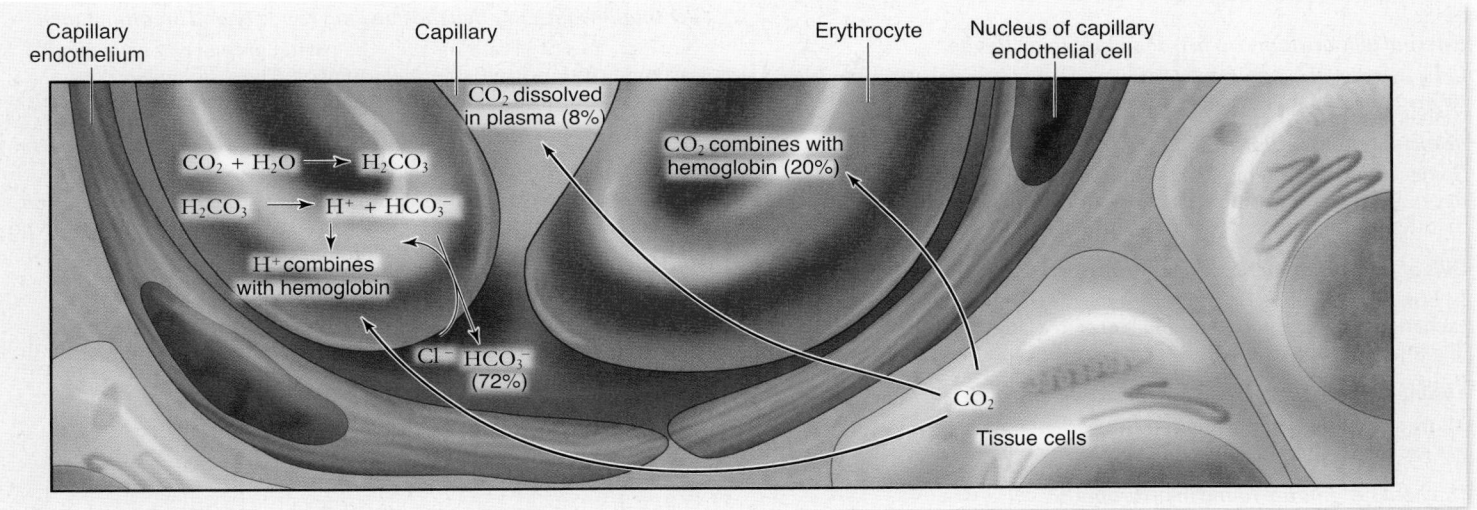

a.

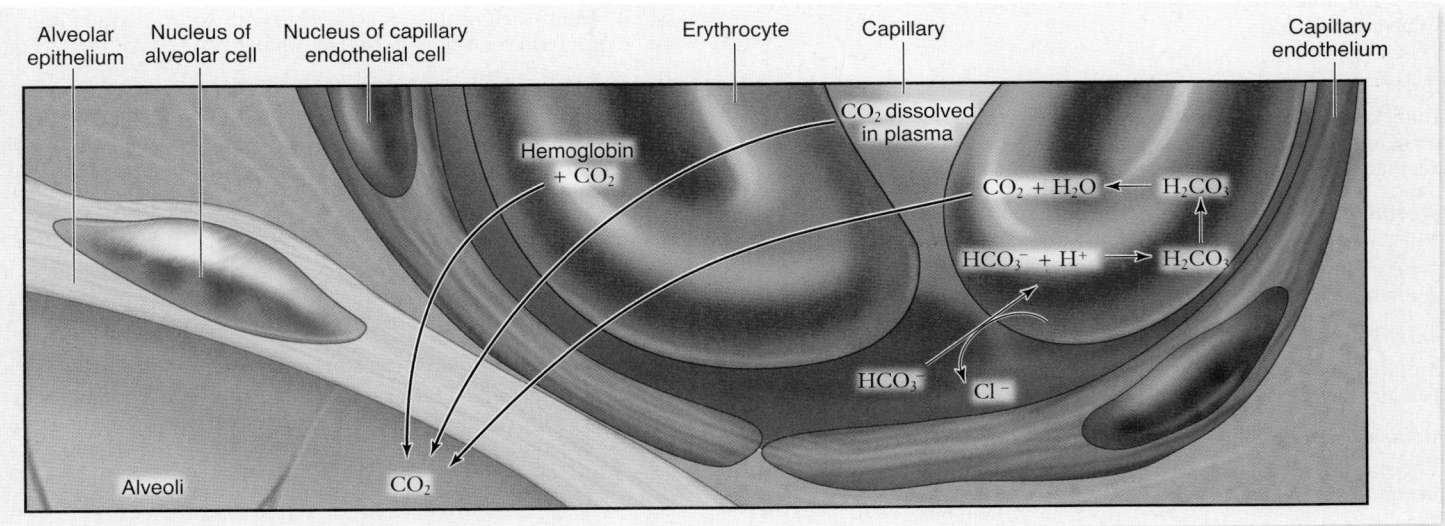

b.

Figure 49.17 The transport of carbon dioxide by the blood. a. Passage into bloodstream. CO_2 is transported in three ways: dissolved in plasma, bound to the protein portion of hemoglobin, and as bicarbonate (HCO_3^-), which forms in red blood cells. The reaction of CO_2 with H_2O to form H_2CO_3 (carbonic acid) is catalyzed by the enzyme carbonic anhydrase in red blood cells. **b.** Removal from bloodstream. When the blood passes through the pulmonary capillaries, these reactions are reversed so that CO_2 gas is formed, which is exhaled.

49.1 Gas Exchange Across Respiratory Surfaces

Gas exchange involves diffusion across membranes.

Diffusion is a passive process; the rate of diffusion (*R*) increases with a higher concentration gradient and greater surface area, but decreases with distance (Fick's Law).

Evolutionary strategies have maximized gas diffusion.

Most invertebrate phyla lack specialized respiratory organs, but have evolved ways to increase oxygen concentration differences. Most other animals possess respiratory organs.

49.2 Gills, Cutaneous Respiration, and Tracheal Systems

External gills are found in fish and amphibian larvae.

Gills increase the respiratory surface area for gas exchange; however, they require an aqueous environment.

Branchial chambers protect gills of some invertebrates.

Some aquatic invertebrates have branchial chambers in which oxygenated water is pumped past stationary gills. Mollusks possess a mantle in which water is drawn in and expelled.

Gills of bony fishes are covered by the operculum.

In bony fishes, diffusion of gases is maximized by countercurrent exchange, in which blood in gills flows in a direction opposite the flow of water over the gills (see figures 49.4 and 49.5).

Cutaneous respiration requires constant moisture.

Many amphibians and a few reptiles use cutaneous respiration for gas exchange.

Tracheal systems are found in arthropods.

Tracheae and tracheoles are a series of small tubes, connected with the outside environment by spiracles, that carry air directly to the cells. The ability to open and close the spiracles allowed arthropods to invade the land.

49.3 Lungs

Lungs minimize evaporation and contain supporting tissues to prevent collapse of exchange membranes, and thus have become well adapted to terrestrial living (see figure 49.8).

Breathing of air takes advantage of partial pressures of gases.

The partial pressure of gases refers to the proportion of atmospheric pressure attributed to each gas. It is responsible for the pressure gradient that brings about gas exchange.

Amphibians and reptiles breathe in different ways.

Amphibians force air into their lungs by positive pressure; reptiles pull air in using negative pressure (see figure 49.7).

Mammalian lungs have greatly increased surface area.

The surface area of mammalian lungs is enormous due to numerous alveoli, encased by an extensive capillary network (see figure 49.8).

The respiratory system of birds is a highly efficient flow-through system.

The respiratory system of birds involves one-way direction of air flow. Air moves through the respiratory system in a two-cycle process so that fresh and used air never mix (see figure 49.9).

49.4 Structures and Mechanisms of Ventilation in Mammals

Lung structure and function supports the respiratory cycle.

Gas exchange is driven by differences in partial pressures. Lungs are filled by contraction of the diaphragm and external intercostal muscles, creating negative pressure (see figure 49.11).

Ventilation efficiency depends on lung capacity and breathing rate.

Normal rates of breathing keep the partial pressure of oxygen and carbon dioxide within a limited range of values. Hypoventilation occurs when carbon dioxide levels are too high, and hyperventilation when they are too low.

Ventilation is under nervous system control.

Each breath is initiated by neurons in the respiratory control center, primarily those that detect CO_2 levels. Humans can voluntarily hypo- or hyperventilate, but only for a limited time.

Respiratory diseases restrict gas exchange.

Emphysema occurs when alveolar walls break down, which makes breathing very energetically expensive. Lung cancer is highly deadly and caused primarily by smoking.

49.5 Transport of Gases in Body Fluids

Respiratory pigments bind oxygen for transport.

Hemoglobin increases the ability of the blood to transport oxygen beyond what can dissolve in plasma (see figure 49.15).

Hemoglobin consists of four polypeptide chains, two α chains and two β chains; each of these is associated with an iron-containing heme group that can bind to O_2 (see figure 49.14).

Hemoglobin and myoglobin provide an oxygen reserve.

Most oxygen carried by hemoglobin remains in the blood and is available when needed. In addition, myoglobin molecules in muscle cells retain oxygen at lower partial pressures than hemoglobin and thus serve as an additional oxygen reserve.

Hemoglobin's affinity for oxygen is affected by pH and temperature.

The affinity of hemoglobin for oxygen decreases as pH decreases and as temperature increases (see figure 49.16). Therefore at lower pH and higher temperature, more oxygen is released.

Carbon dioxide is primarily transported as bicarbonate ion.

Most carbon dioxide diffuses into red blood cells and combines with water to form bicarbonate atoms in a reaction catalyzed by the enzyme carbonic anhydrase.

UNDERSTAND

1. If you hold your breath for a long time, body CO_2 levels are likely to ____, and the pH of body fluids is likely to ____.

   a. increase; increase   c. increase; decrease
   b. decrease; increase   d. decrease; decrease

2. Increased efficiency of gas exchange in vertebrates has been brought about by all of the following mechanisms except

   a. cutaneous respiration.
   b. unidirectional air flow.
   c. crosscurrent blood flow.
   d. cartilaginous rings in the trachea.

3. Which of the following is the primary method by which carbon dioxide is transported to the lungs?

   a. Dissolved in plasma   c. As carbon monoxide
   b. Bound to hemoglobin   d. As bicarbonate

4. Gills are found in

   a. fish.   c. aquatic invertebrates.
   b. amphibians.   d. all of these.

5. Fick's Law of Diffusion states the rate of diffusion is directly proportional to

   a. the area differences between the cross section of the blood vessel and the tissue.
   b. the pressure differences between the two sides of the membrane and area over which the diffusion occurs.
   c. the pressure differences between the inside of the organism and the outside.
   d. the temperature of the gas molecule.

6. Cutaneous respiration requires

   a. moist and highly vascularized skin.
   b. the absence of gills and lungs.
   c. an environment rich in oxygen.
   d. low temperatures.

7. Hyperventilation occurs

   a. as a result of breathing rapidly.
   b. when oxygen levels become low.
   c. when tidal volumes are unusually low.
   d. when the partial pressure of carbon dioxide is low.

8. Most carbon dioxide is

   a. dissolved in the plasma.
   b. bound to hemoglobin.
   c. combined with water in red blood cells to form carbonic acid.
   d. stored in the lungs prior to exhalation.

APPLY

1. When you take a deep breath, your stomach moves out because

   a. swallowing air increases the volume of the thoracic cavity.
   b. your stomach shouldn't move out when you take a deep breath because you want the volume of your chest cavity to increase, not your abdominal cavity.
   c. contracting your abdominal muscles pushes your stomach out, generating negative pressure in your lungs.
   d. when your diaphragm contracts, it moves down, pressing your abdominal cavity out.

2. Marine mammals are able to hold their breath for extended periods underwater because

   a. unlike humans, they don't hypoventilate.
   b. partial pressure of carbon dioxide does not increase underwater.
   c. myoglobin in muscle tissue provides an oxygen reserve.
   d. the brains of marine mammals do not have receptors that respond to impulses initiated in the aortic and carotid bodies.

3. Countercurrent flow systems do not occur in lungs because they

   a. require oxygen suspended in flowing water.
   b. are limited to fish.
   c. only work in moving organisms.
   d. cannot operate in the presence of carbon dioxide.

4. Respiratory organs of invertebrates and vertebrates are similar in that

   a. they use negative pressure breathing.
   b. they take advantage of countercurrent flow systems.
   c. they increase the surface area available for diffusion.
   d. the air flows through the organ in one direction.

5. Mountain climbers may have difficulty at high elevations because

   a. the partial pressure of oxygen is lower at higher elevations.
   b. more CO_2 occurs at higher altitudes.
   c. the concentration of all elements of the air is lower at higher elevations.
   d. cooler temperatures restrict the metabolic activity of oxygen at high elevations.

6. During exercise more oxygen is delivered to the muscles because

   a. active muscles produce more CO_2, lowering the pH of the blood.
   b. active muscles produce heat.
   c. both a and b
   d. neither a nor b

SYNTHESIZE

1. Compare the operation and efficiency of fish gills with amphibian, bird, and mammal lungs.

2. What happens when, during exercise, the oxygen needs of the peripheral tissues increase greatly?

3. Explain how bacteria, archaea, protists, and many phyla of invertebrates can survive without respiratory organs.

ONLINE RESOURCE

www.ravenbiology.com

Understand, Apply, and Synthesize—enhance your study with animations that bring concepts to life and practice tests to assess your understanding. Your instructor may also recommend the interactive eBook, individualized learning tools, and more.

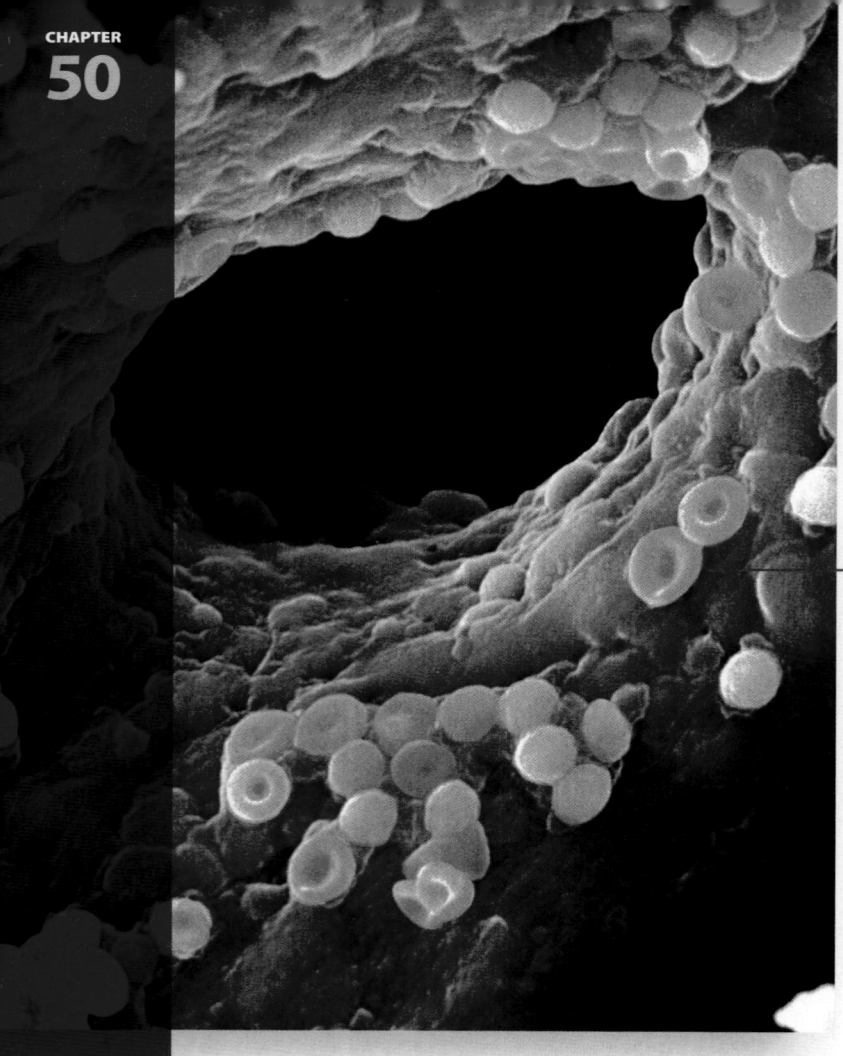

Chapter *50*

The Circulatory System

Chapter Outline

50.1 The Components of Blood

50.2 Invertebrate Circulatory Systems

50.3 Vertebrate Circulatory Systems

50.4 The Four-Chambered Heart and the Blood Vessels

50.5 Characteristics of Blood Vessels

50.6 Regulation of Blood Flow and Blood Pressure

Introduction

In multicellular organisms, oxygen obtained by the respiratory system and nutrients processed by the digestive system must be transported to cells throughout the body. Conversely, carbon dioxide and other waste products produced within the cells must be returned to the respiratory, digestive, and urinary systems for elimination from the body. These tasks are the responsibility of the circulatory system. All multicellular organisms have a heart that pumps fluids through the body. Many invertebrates have an open system in which fluids move through the body cavity. Vertebrates also have a system like this that moves lymph through the body; however, the primary circulatory fluid is blood, which means through a closed system of blood vessels.

50.1 *The Components of Blood*

Learning Outcomes

1. *Describe the functions of circulating blood.*
2. *Distinguish between the types of formed elements.*
3. *Delineate the process of blood clotting.*

Blood is a connective tissue composed of a fluid matrix, called **plasma,** and several different kinds of cells and other **formed elements** that circulate within that fluid (figure 50.1). Blood

platelets, although included in figure 50.1, are not complete cells; rather, they are fragments of cells that are produced in the bone marrow. (We describe the action of platelets in blood clotting later in this section.)

Circulating blood has many functions:

1. **Transportation.** All of the substances essential for cellular metabolism are transported by blood. Red blood cells transport oxygen attached to hemoglobin; nutrient molecules are carried in the plasma, sometimes bound to carriers; and metabolic wastes are eliminated as blood passes through the liver and kidneys.
2. **Regulation.** The cardiovascular system transports regulatory hormones from the endocrine glands and also

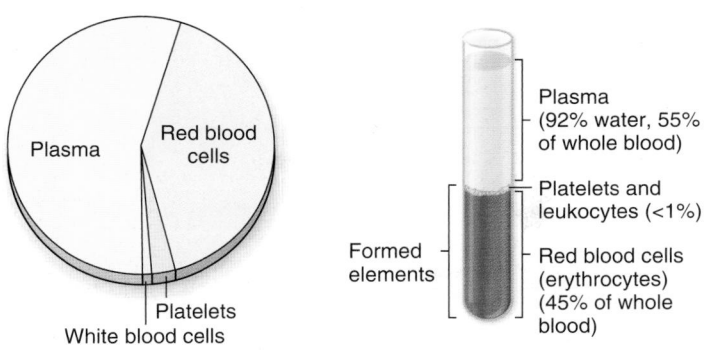

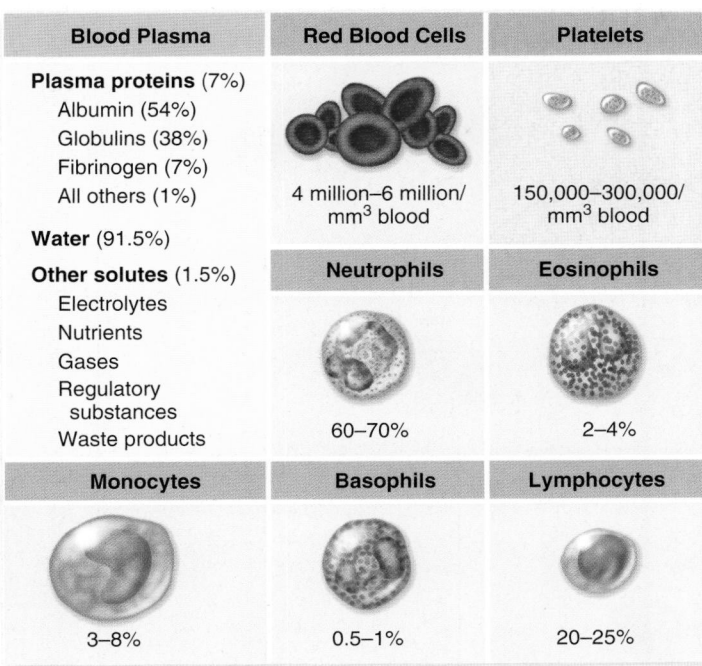

Blood Plasma	Red Blood Cells	Platelets
Plasma proteins (7%) Albumin (54%) Globulins (38%) Fibrinogen (7%) All others (1%) **Water** (91.5%) **Other solutes** (1.5%) Electrolytes Nutrients Gases Regulatory substances Waste products	4 million–6 million/ mm³ blood	150,000–300,000/ mm³ blood

Neutrophils	Eosinophils
60–70%	2–4%

Monocytes	Basophils	Lymphocytes
3–8%	0.5–1%	20–25%

Figure 50.1 Composition of blood.

participates in temperature regulation. Contraction and dilation of blood vessels near the surface of the body, beneath the epidermis, helps to conserve or to dissipate heat as needed.

3. **Protection.** The circulatory system protects against injury and foreign microbes or toxins introduced into the body. Blood clotting helps to prevent blood loss when vessels are damaged. White blood cells, or leukocytes, help to disarm or disable invaders such as viruses and bacteria (see chapter 52).

Blood plasma is a fluid matrix

Blood plasma is the matrix in which blood cells and platelets are suspended. Interstitial (extracellular) fluids originate from the fluid present in plasma.

Although plasma is 92% water, it also contains the following solutes:

1. **Nutrients, wastes, and hormones.** Dissolved within the plasma are all of the nutrients resulting from digestive breakdown that can be used by cells, including glucose, amino acids, and vitamins. Also dissolved in the plasma are wastes such as nitrogen compounds and CO_2 produced by metabolizing cells. Endocrine hormones released from glands are also carried through the blood to their target cells.

2. **Ions.** Blood plasma is a dilute salt solution. The predominant plasma ions are Na^+, Cl^-, and bicarbonate ions (HCO_3^-). In addition, plasma contains trace amounts of other ions such as Ca^{2+}, Mg^{2+}, Cu^{2+}, K^+, and Zn^{2+}.

3. **Proteins.** As mentioned earlier, the liver produces most of the plasma proteins, including **albumin,** which constitutes most of the plasma protein; the alpha (α) and beta (β) **globulins,** which serve as carriers of lipids and steroid hormones; and **fibrinogen,** which is required for blood clotting. Blood plasma with the fibrinogen removed is called **serum.**

Formed elements include circulating cells and platelets

The formed elements of blood cells and cell fragments include red blood cells, white blood cells, and platelets. Each element has a specific function in maintaining the body's health and homeostasis.

Erythrocytes

Each microliter of blood contains about 5 million **red blood cells,** or **erythrocytes.** The fraction of the total blood volume that is occupied by erythrocytes is called the blood's *hematocrit;* in humans, the hematocrit is typically around 45%.

Each erythrocyte resembles a doughnut-shaped disk with a central depression that does not go all the way through. Mature mammalian erythrocytes lack nuclei. The erythrocytes of vertebrates contain hemoglobin, a pigment that binds and transports oxygen. (Hemoglobin was described more fully in the previous chapter when we discussed respiration.) In vertebrates, hemoglobin is found only in erythrocytes. In invertebrates, the oxygen-binding pigment (not always hemoglobin) is also present in plasma.

Leukocytes

Less than 1% of the cells in human blood are **white blood cells,** or **leukocytes;** there are only 1 or 2 leukocytes for every 1000 erythrocytes. Leukocytes are larger than erythrocytes and have nuclei. Furthermore, leukocytes are not confined to the blood as erythrocytes are, but can migrate out of capillaries through the intercellular spaces into the surrounding interstitial (tissue) fluid.

Leukocytes come in several varieties, each of which plays a specific role in defending against invading microorganisms and other foreign substances, as described in chapter 52. **Granular leukocytes** include neutrophils, eosinophils, and basophils, which are named according to the staining properties of granules in their cytoplasm. **Nongranular leukocytes** include monocytes and lymphocytes. In humans, neutrophils are the most numerous of the leukocytes, followed in order by lymphocytes, monocytes, eosinophils, and basophils.

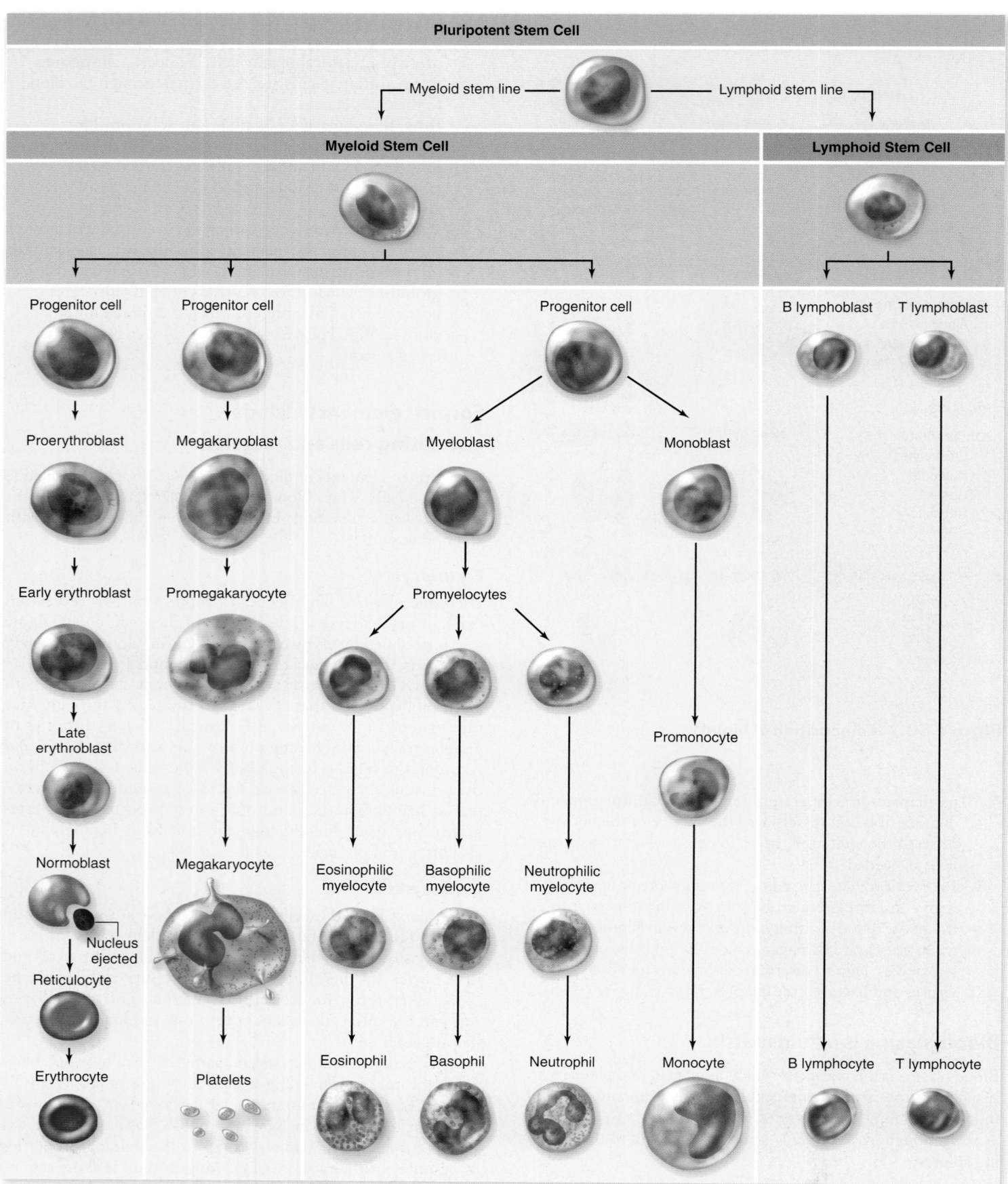

Figure 50.2 Stem cells and the production of formed elements.

Platelets

Platelets are cell fragments that pinch off from larger cells in the bone marrow. They are approximately 3 μm in diameter, and following an injury to a blood vessel, the liver releases *prothrombin* into the blood. In the presence of this clotting factor, fibrinogen is converted into insoluble threads of **fibrin.** Fibrin then aggregates to form the clot.

Formed elements arise from stem cells

The formed elements of blood each have a finite life span and therefore must be constantly replaced. Many of the old cell fragments are digested by phagocytic cells of the spleen; however, many products from the old cells, such as iron and amino acids, are incorporated into new formed elements. The creation of new formed elements begins in the bone marrow (see chapter 47).

All of the formed elements develop from **pluripotent stem cells** (see chapter 19). The production of blood cells occurs in the bone marrow and is called **hematopoiesis.** This process generates two types of stem cells with a more restricted fate: a lymphoid stem cell that gives rise to lymphocytes and a myeloid stem cell that gives rise to the rest of the blood cells (figure 50.2).

When the oxygen available in the blood decreases, the kidney converts a plasma protein into the hormone **erythropoietin.** Erythropoietin then stimulates the production of erythrocytes from the myeloid stem cells through a process called **erythropoiesis.**

In mammals, maturing erythrocytes lose their nuclei prior to release into circulation. In contrast, the mature erythrocytes of all other vertebrates remain nucleated. *Megakaryocytes* are examples of committed cells formed in bone marrow from stem cells. Pieces of cytoplasm are pinched off the megakaryocytes to form the platelets.

Blood clotting is an example of an enzyme cascade

When a blood vessel is broken or cut, smooth muscle in the vessel walls contracts, causing the vessel to constrict. Platelets then accumulate at the injured site and form a plug by sticking to one another and to the surrounding tissues (figure 50.3). A cascade of enzymatic reactions is triggered by the platelets, plasma factors, and molecules released from the damaged tissue.

One of the results of this cascade is that fibrinogen, normally dissolved in the plasma, comes out of solution in a reaction that forms fibrin. The platelet plug is then reinforced by fibrin threads, which contract to form a tighter mass. The tightening plug of platelets, fibrin, and often trapped erythrocytes constitutes a blood clot.

Once the tissue damage is healed, the careful process of dissolving the blot clot begins. This process is significant because if a clot breaks loose and travels in the circulatory system, it may end up blocking a blood vessel in the brain, causing a stroke, or in the heart, causing a heart attack.

> **Learning Outcomes Review 50.1**
>
> The circulatory system functions in transport of materials, regulation of temperature and body processes, and protection of the body. Formed elements in blood include red blood cells, white blood cells, and platelets. Blood clotting involves a cascade of enzymatic reactions triggered by platelets and plasma factors to produce insoluble fibrin from fibrinogen.
>
> ■ *How does a blood clot form?*

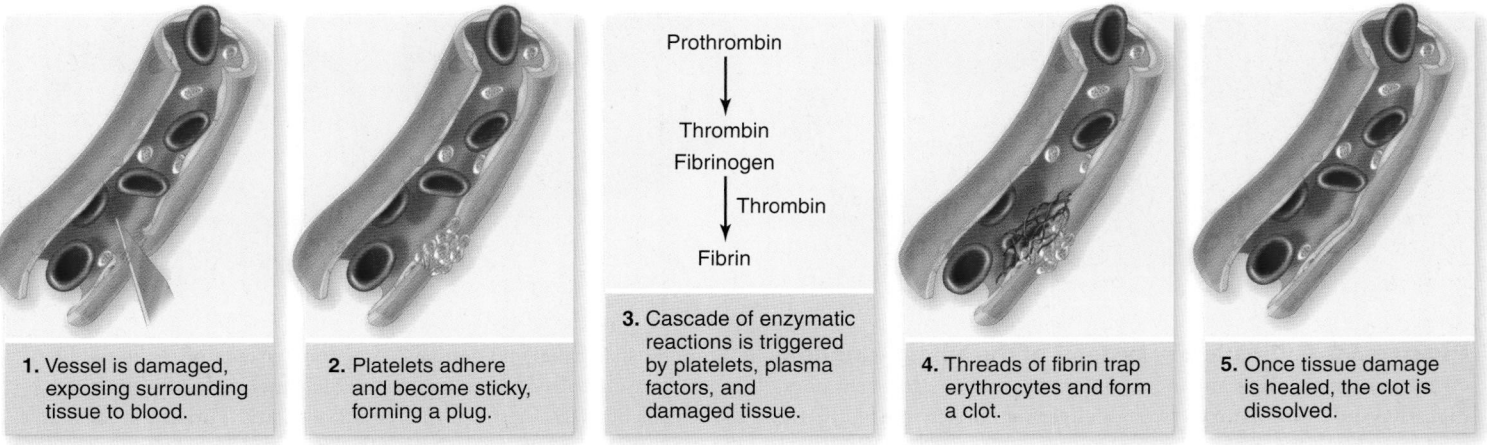

1. Vessel is damaged, exposing surrounding tissue to blood.

2. Platelets adhere and become sticky, forming a plug.

Prothrombin
↓
Thrombin
Fibrinogen
↓ Thrombin
Fibrin

3. Cascade of enzymatic reactions is triggered by platelets, plasma factors, and damaged tissue.

4. Threads of fibrin trap erythrocytes and form a clot.

5. Once tissue damage is healed, the clot is dissolved.

Figure 50.3 Blood clotting. Fibrin is formed from a soluble protein, fibrinogen, in the plasma. This reaction is catalyzed by the enzyme thrombin, which is formed from an inactive enzyme called prothrombin. The activation of thrombin is the last step in a cascade of enzymatic reactions that produces a blood clot when a blood vessel is damaged.

50.2 Invertebrate Circulatory Systems

Learning Outcomes

1. *Distinguish between open and closed circulatory systems.*
2. *Define hemolymph.*

The nature of the circulatory system in multicellular invertebrates is directly related to the size, complexity, and lifestyle of the organism in question. Sponges and most cnidarians utilize water from the environment as a circulatory fluid. Sponges pass water through a series of channels in their bodies, and *Hydra* and other cnidarians circulate water through a **gastrovascular cavity** (figure 50.4*a*). Because the body wall in *Hydra* species is only two cell layers thick, each cell layer is in direct contact with either the external environment or the gastrovascular cavity.

Pseudocoelomate invertebrates (roundworms, rotifers) use the fluids of the body cavity for circulation. Most of these invertebrates are quite small or are long and thin, and therefore adequate circulation is accomplished by movements of the body against the body fluids, which are in direct contact with the internal tissues and organs. Larger animals, however, have tissues that are several cell layers thick, so that many cells are

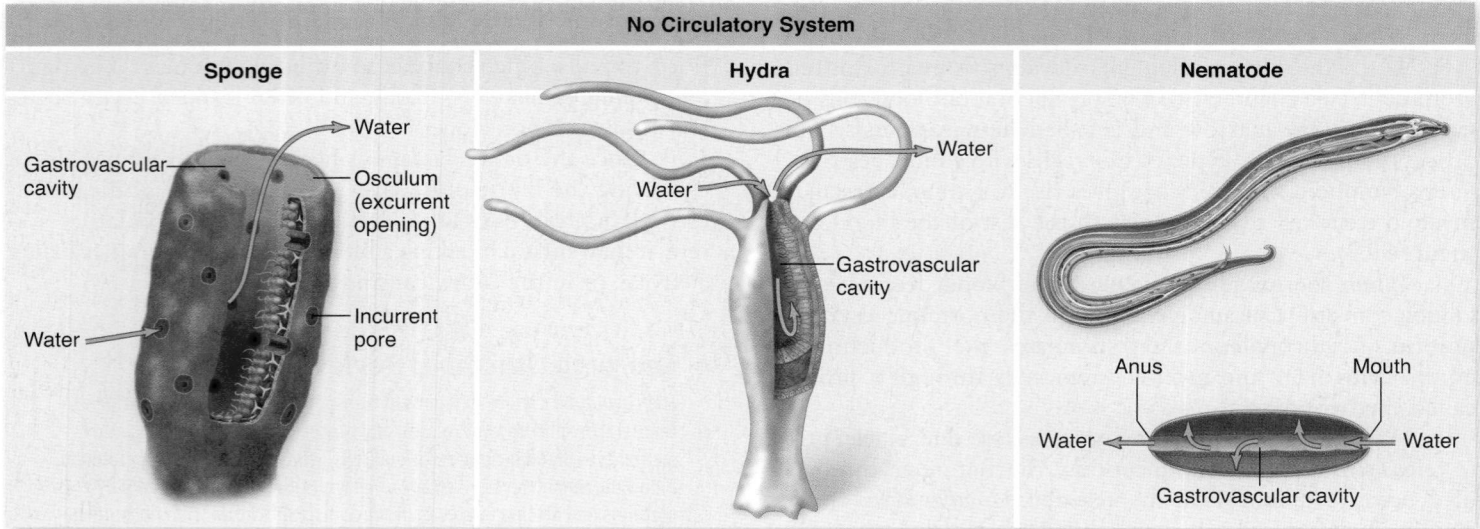

a.

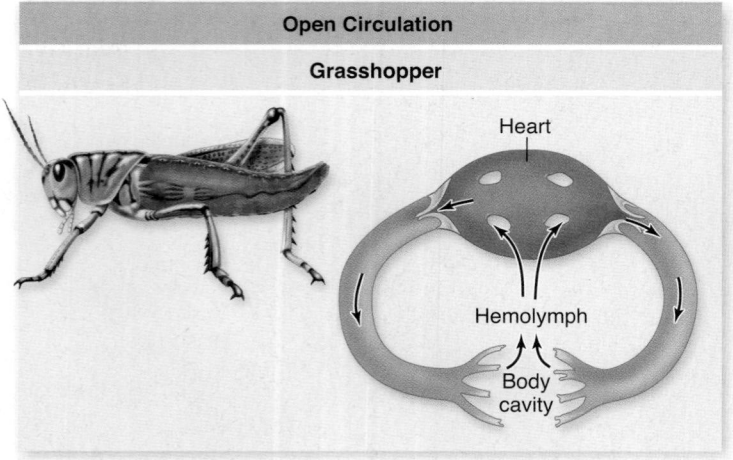

b.

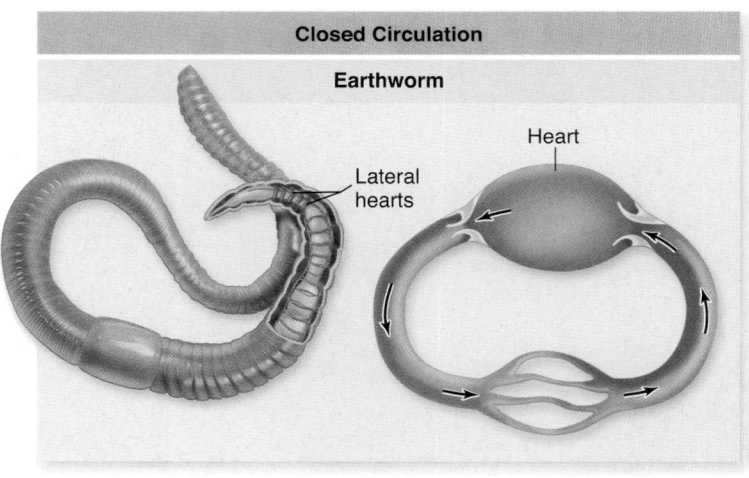

c.

Figure 50.4 Circulatory systems of the animal kingdom. *a.* Sponges (left panel) do not have a separate circulatory system. They circulate water using many incurrent pores and one excurrent pore. The gastrovascular cavity of a hydra (middle panel) serves as both a digestive and a circulatory system, delivering nutrients directly to the tissue cells by diffusion from the digestive cavity. The nematode (right panel) is thin enough that the digestive tract can also be used as a circulatory system. Larger animals require a separate circulatory system to carry nutrients to and wastes away from tissues. *b.* In the open circulation of an insect, hemolymph is pumped from a tubular heart into cavities in the insect's body; the hemolymph then returns to the blood vessels so that it can be recirculated. *c.* In the closed circulation of the earthworm, blood pumped from the hearts remains within a system of vessels that returns it to the hearts. All vertebrates also have closed circulatory systems.

too far away from the body surface or digestive cavity to directly exchange materials with the environment. Instead, oxygen and nutrients are transported from the environment and digestive cavity to the body cells by an internal fluid within a circulatory system.

Open circulatory systems move fluids in a one-way path

The two main types of circulatory systems are *open* and *closed.* In an open circulatory system, such as that found in most mollusks and in arthropods (figure 50.4*b*), there is no distinction between the circulating fluid and the extracellular fluid of the body tissues. This fluid is thus called **hemolymph.**

In insects, a muscular tube, or **heart,** pumps hemolymph through a network of channels and cavities in the body. The fluid then drains back into the central cavity.

Closed circulatory systems move fluids in a loop

In a closed circulatory system, the circulating fluid, blood, is always enclosed within blood vessels that transport it away from and back to the heart (figure 50.4*c*). Some invertebrates, such as cephalopod mollusks and annelids (see chapter 34), and all vertebrates have a closed circulatory system.

In annelids such as earthworms, a dorsal vessel contracts rhythmically to function as a pump. Blood is pushed through five small connecting arteries, which also function as pumps, to a ventral vessel, which transports the blood posteriorly until it eventually reenters the dorsal vessel. Smaller vessels branch from each artery to supply the tissues of the earthworm with oxygen and nutrients and to remove waste products.

Learning Outcomes Review 50.2

In invertebrates, open circulatory systems pump hemolymph into tissues, from which it then drains into a central cavity. Closed circulatory systems move fluid in a loop to and from a muscular pumping region such as a heart. Hemolymph (invertebrates) is identical to the extracellular fluid in the tissues.

■ *In the open circulatory system of insects, how does hemolymph get back to the heart?*

50.3 Vertebrate Circulatory Systems

Learning Outcomes

1. *Trace the evolution of the chambered heart from lancelets to birds and mammals.*
2. *Delineate the flow of blood through the circulatory system in birds and mammals.*

The evolution of large and complex hearts and closed circulatory systems put a premium on efficient circulation. In response, vertebrates have evolved a remarkable set of adaptations inextricably linking circulation and respiration, which has facilitated diversification throughout aquatic and terrestrial habitats and permitted the evolution of large body size.

In fishes, more efficient circulation developed concurrently with gills

Chordates ancestral to the vertebrates are thought to have had simple tubular hearts, similar to those now seen in lancelets (see chapter 35). The heart was little more than a specialized zone of the ventral artery that was more heavily muscled than the rest of the arteries; it contracted in simple peristaltic waves.

The development of gills by fishes required a more efficient pump, and in fishes we see the evolution of a true chamber-pump heart. The fish heart is, in essence, a tube with four structures arrayed one after the other to form two pumping chambers (figure 50.5). The first two structures—the **sinus venosus** and **atrium**—form the first chamber; the second two, the **ventricle** and **conus arteriosus,** form the second chamber. The sinus venosus is the first to contract, followed by the atrium, the ventricle, and finally the conus arteriosus.

Despite shifts in the relative positions of these structures, this heartbeat sequence is maintained in all vertebrates. In fish, the electrical impulse that produces the contraction is initiated in the sinus venosus; in other vertebrates, the electrical impulse is initiated by a structure homologous to the sinus venosus— the **sinoatrial (SA) node.**

After blood leaves the conus arteriosus, it moves through the gills, becoming oxygenated. Blood leaving the gills then flows through a network of arteries to the rest of the body, finally returning to the sinus venosus. This simple loop has one serious limitation: in passing through the capillaries in the gills, blood pressure drops significantly. This slows circulation from the gills to the rest of the body and can limit oxygen delivery to tissues.

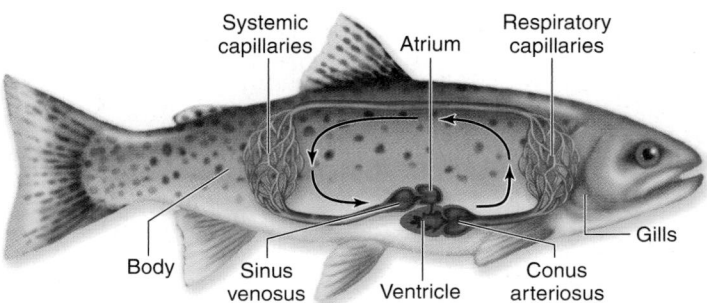

Figure 50.5 The heart and circulation of a fish. Diagram of a fish heart, showing the structures in series with each other (sinus venosus; atrium; ventricles; conus arteriosus) that form two pumping chambers. Blood is pumped by the ventricle through the gills and then to the body. Blood rich in oxygen (oxygenated) is shown in red; blood low in oxygen (deoxygenated) is shown in blue.

In amphibians and most reptiles, lungs required a separate circulation

The advent of lungs in amphibians (see chapter 49) involved a major change in the pattern of circulation, a second pumping circuit. After blood is pumped by the heart through the *pulmonary arteries* to the lungs, it does not go directly to the tissues of the body. Instead, it is returned via the *pulmonary veins* to the heart. Blood leaves the heart a second time to be circulated through other tissues. This system is termed **double circulation:** One system, the **pulmonary circulation,** moves blood between heart and lungs, and another, the **systemic circulation,** moves blood between the heart and the rest of the body.

Amphibian circulation

Optimally, oxygenated blood from lungs would go directly to tissues, rather than being mixed in the heart with deoxygenated blood returning from the body. The amphibian heart has two structural features that significantly reduce this mixing (figure 50.6). First, the atrium is divided into two chambers: The right atrium receives deoxygenated blood from the systemic circulation, and the left atrium receives oxygenated blood from the lungs. These two types of blood, therefore, do not mix in the atria.

Because an amphibian heart has a single ventricle, the separation of the pulmonary and systemic circulations is incomplete. The extent of mixing when the contents of each atrium enter the ventricle is reduced by internal channels created by recesses in the ventricular wall. The conus arteriosus is partially separated by a dividing wall, which directs deoxygenated blood into the pulmonary arteries and oxygenated blood into the *aorta*, the major artery of the systemic circulation.

Amphibians living in water can obtain additional oxygen by diffusion through their skin. Thus, amphibians have a *pulmocutaneous circuit* that sends blood to both the lungs and the skin. Cutaneous respiration is also seen in many aquatic reptiles such as turtles.

Reptilian circulation

Among reptiles, additional modifications have further reduced the mixing of blood in the heart. In addition to having two separate atria, reptiles have a septum that partially subdivides the ventricle. This separation is complete in one order of reptiles, the crocodilians, which have two separate ventricles divided by a complete septum (see the following section). Another change in the circulation of reptiles is that the conus arteriosus has become incorporated into the trunks of the large arteries leaving the heart.

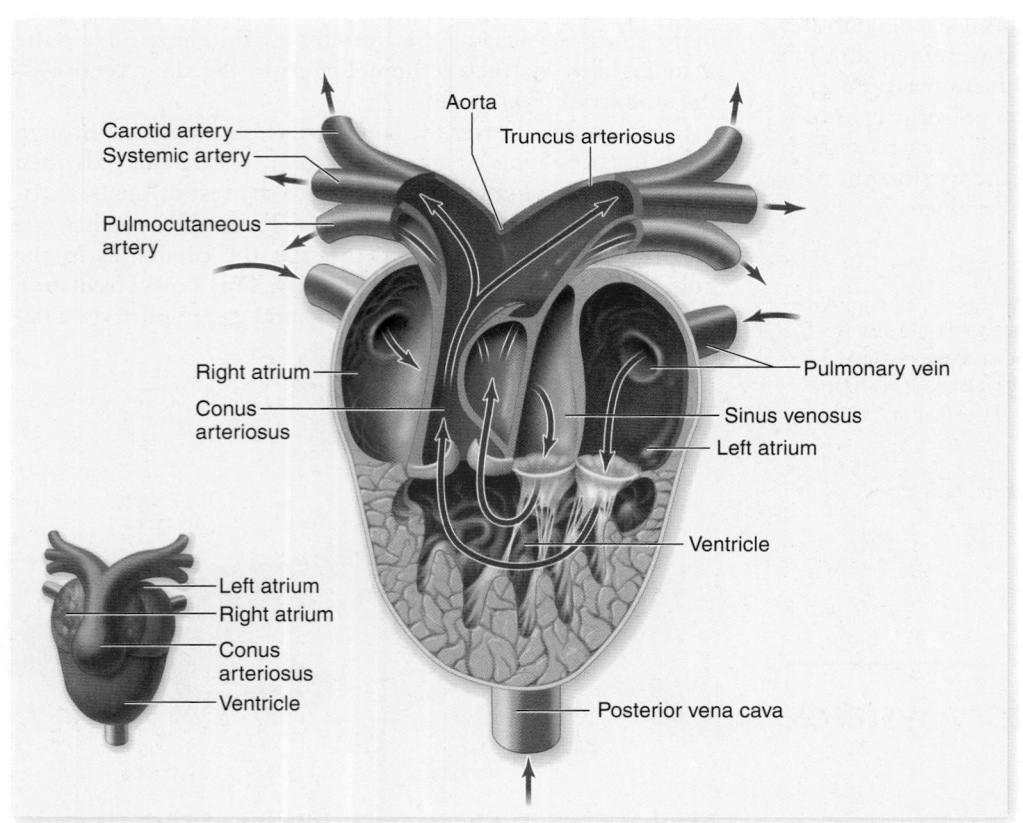

a.

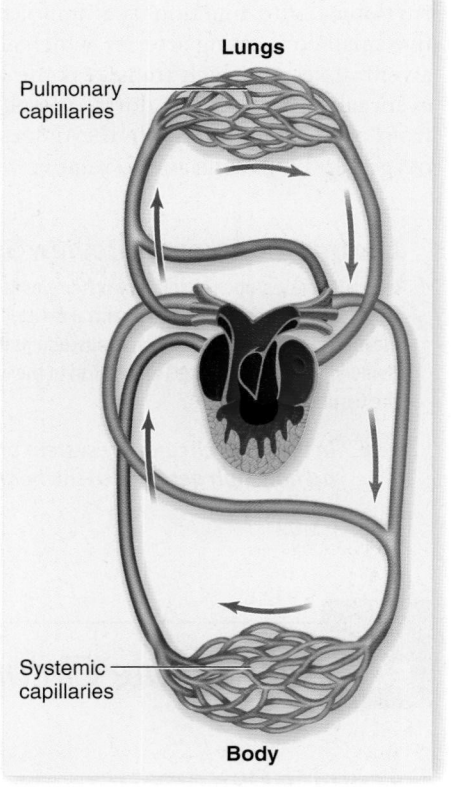

b.

Figure 50.6 The heart and circulation of an amphibian. *a.* The frog has a three-chambered heart with two atria but only one ventricle, which pumps blood both to the lungs and to the body. *b.* Despite the potential for mixing, the oxygenated and deoxygenated bloods (red and blue lines, respectively) mix little as they are pumped to the body and lungs. Oxygenation of blood also occurs by gas exchange through the skin.

Mammals, birds, and crocodilians have two completely separated circulatory systems

Mammals, birds, and crocodilians have a four-chambered heart with two separate atria and two separate ventricles (figure 50.7). The hearts of birds and crocodiles exhibit some differences, but overall are quite similar, which is not surprising given their close evolutionary relationship (figure 50.8). However, the extreme similarity of the hearts of birds and mammals—so alike that a single illustration can suffice for both (see figure 50.7)—is a remarkable case of convergent evolution (see figure 50.8).

In a four-chambered heart, the right atrium receives deoxygenated blood from the body and delivers it to the right ventricle, which pumps the blood to the lungs. The left atrium receives oxygenated blood from the lungs and delivers it to the left ventricle, which pumps the oxygenated blood to the rest of the body (see figure 50.7).

The heart in these vertebrates is a two-cycle pump. Both atria fill with blood and simultaneously contract, emptying their blood into the ventricles. Both ventricles also contract at the same time, pushing blood simultaneously into the pulmonary and systemic circulations.

The increased efficiency of the double circulatory system in mammals and birds is thought to have been important in the evolution of endothermy. More efficient circulation is neces-sary to support the high metabolic rate required for maintenance of internal body temperature about a set point.

Throughout the evolutionary history of the vertebrate heart, the sinus venosus has served as a pacemaker, the site where the impulses that initiate the heartbeat originate. Although the sinus venosus constitutes a major chamber in the fish heart, it is reduced in size in amphibians and is further reduced in reptiles. In mammals and birds, the sinus venosus is no longer present as a separate chamber, although some of its tissue remains in the wall of the right atrium. This tissue, the sinoatrial (SA) node, is still the site where each heartbeat originates as detailed later in the chapter.

Learning Outcomes Review 50.3

The chordate heart has evolved from a muscular region of a vessel, to the two-chambered heart of fish, the three-chambered heart of amphibians and most reptiles, and the four-chambered heart of crocodilians, birds, and mammals. Deoxygenated blood travels in the pulmonary circuit from the right atrium into the right ventricle and then to the lungs; it returns to the left atrium. Oxygenated blood travels in the systemic circuit from the left atrium into the left ventricle and then to the body; it returns to the right atrium.

■ **What is the physiological advantage of having separated ventricles?**

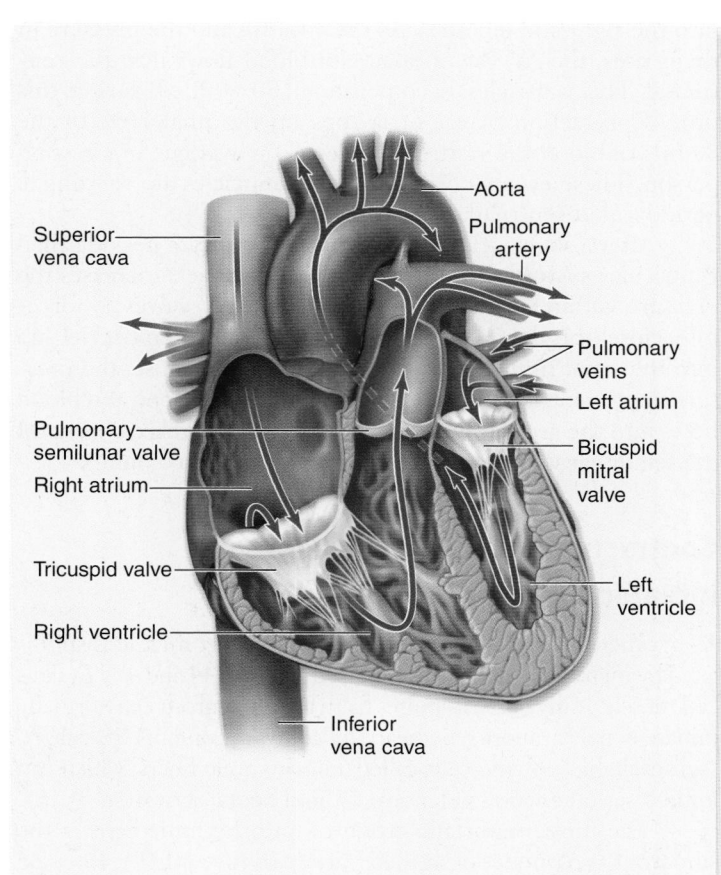

a.

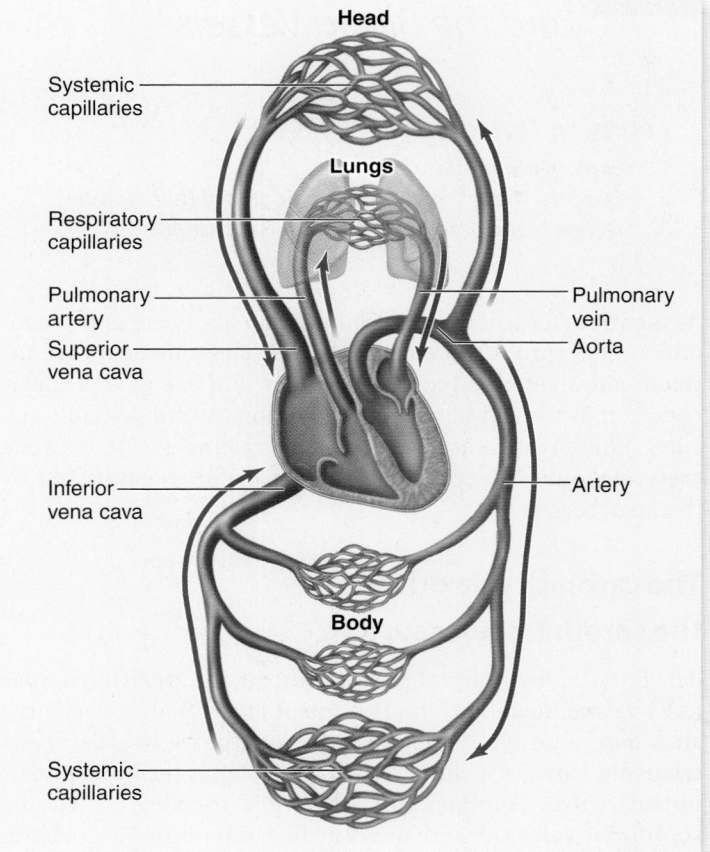

b.

Figure 50.7 The heart and circulation of mammals and birds. *a.* The path of blood through the four-chambered heart. *b.* The right side of the heart receives deoxygenated blood and pumps it to the lungs; the left side of the heart receives oxygenated blood and pumps it to the body. In this way, the pulmonary and systemic circulations are kept completely separate.

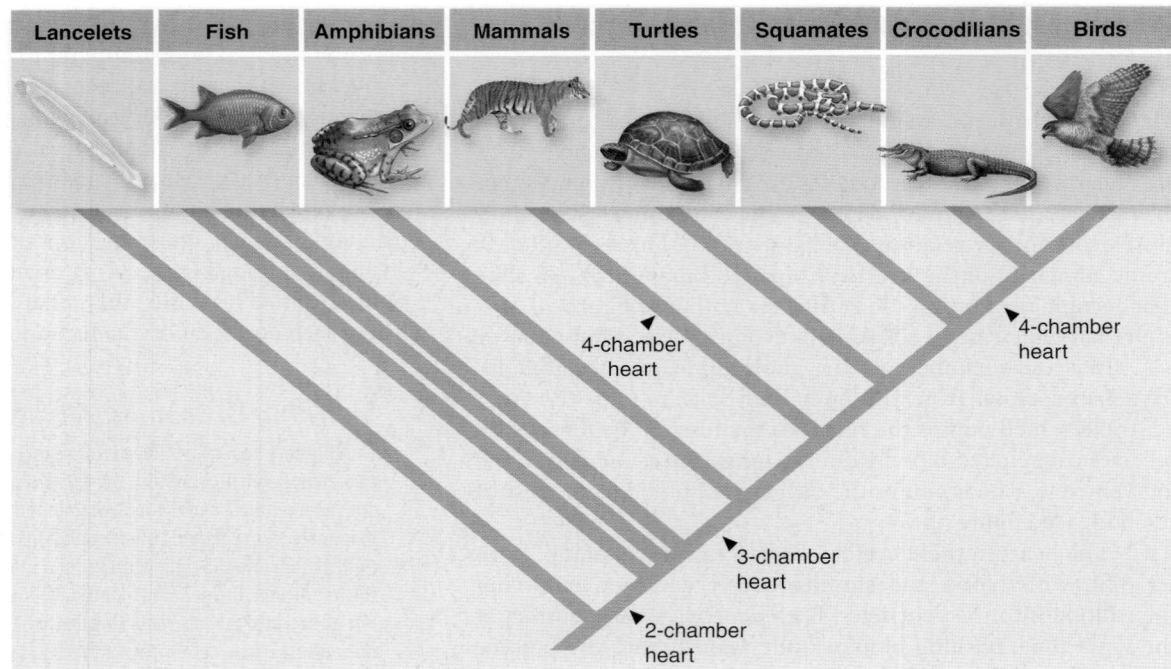

Figure 50.8
Evolution of the heart in vertebrates. Despite their similarity, the four-chambered hearts of mammals and birds evolved convergently.

Labels in figure: Lancelets | Fish | Amphibians | Mammals | Turtles | Squamates | Crocodilians | Birds

4-chamber heart
4-chamber heart
3-chamber heart
2-chamber heart

The Four-Chambered Heart and the Blood Vessels

Learning Outcomes

1. Explain the cardiac cycle.
2. Describe the role of autorhythmic cells of the SA node.
3. Define blood pressure and how it is measured

As mentioned earlier, the heart of mammals, birds, and crocodilians goes through two contraction cycles, one of atrial contraction to send blood to the ventricles, and one of ventricular contraction to send blood to the pulmonary and systemic circuits. These two contractions plus the resting period between these make up the complete **cardiac cycle** encompassed by the heartbeat.

The cardiac cycle drives the cardiovascular system

The heart has two pairs of valves. One pair, the **atrioventricular (AV) valves,** maintains unidirectional blood flow between the atria and ventricles. The AV valve on the right side is the **tricuspid valve,** and the AV valve on the left is the **bicuspid,** or **mitral, valve.** Another pair of valves, together called the **semilunar valves,** ensure one-way flow out of the ventricles to the arterial systems. The **pulmonary valve** is located at the exit of the right ventricle, and the **aortic valve** is located at the exit of the left ventricle. These valves open and close as the heart goes through its cycle. The closing of these valves produces the "lub-dub" sounds heard with a stethoscope.

The cardiac cycle is portrayed in figure 50.9. It begins as blood returns to the resting heart through veins that empty into the right and left atria. As the atria fill and the pressure in them rises, the AV valves open and blood flows into the ventricles. The ventricles become about 80% filled during this time. Contraction of the atria tops up the final 20% of the 80 mL of blood the ventricles receive, on average, in a resting person. These events occur while the ventricles are relaxing, a period called ventricular **diastole.**

After a slight delay, the ventricles contract, a period called ventricular **systole.** Contraction of each ventricle increases the pressure within each chamber, causing the AV valves to forcefully close (the "lub" sound), preventing blood from backing up into the atria. Immediately after the AV valves close, the pressure in the ventricles forces the semilunar valves open and blood flows into the arterial systems. As the ventricles relax, closing of the semilunar valves prevents backflow (the "dub" sound).

Contraction of heart muscle is initiated by autorhythmic cells

As in other types of muscle, contraction of heart muscle is stimulated by membrane depolarization (see chapters 44 and 47). In skeletal muscles, only nerve impulses from motor neurons can normally initiate depolarization. The heart, by contrast, contains specialized "self-excitable" muscle cells called autorhythmic fibers, which can initiate periodic action potentials without neural activation.

The most important group of autorhythmic cells is the sinoatrial (SA) node, described earlier (figure 50.10). Located in the wall of the right atrium, the SA node acts as a pacemaker for the rest of the heart by producing spontaneous action potentials at a faster rate than other autorhythmic cells. These spontaneous action potentials are due to a constant leakage of Na^+ ions into the cell that depolarize the membrane. When the

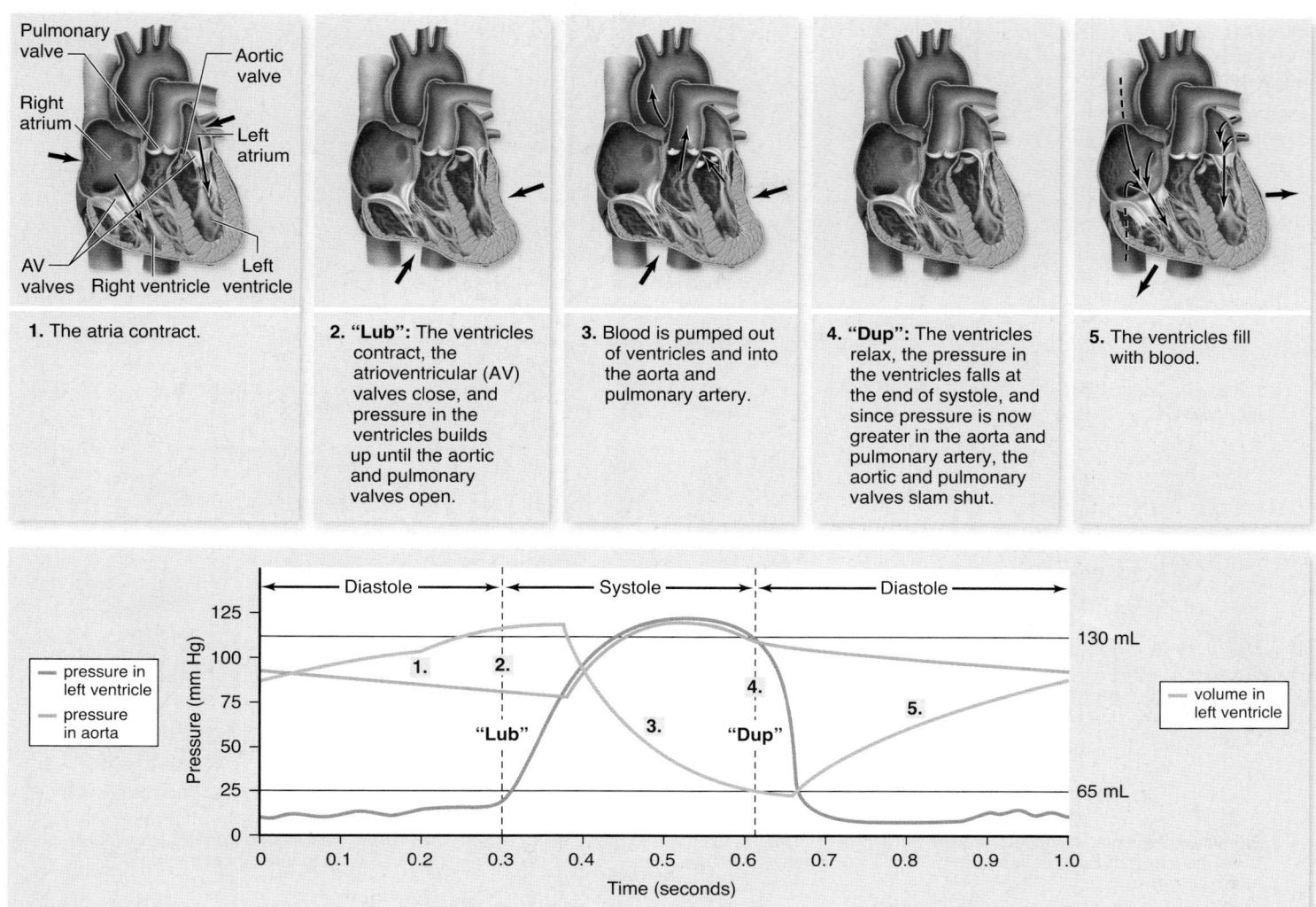

Figure 50.9 The cardiac cycle. *a.* Contraction and relaxation of the atria and ventricles moves blood through the heart. *b.* Blood pressure and volume changes through the cardiac cycle, shown here for the left ventricle.

threshold is reached, an action potential occurs. At the end of the action potential, the membrane is again below threshold and the process begins again. The cells of the SA node generate an action potential every 0.6 sec, equivalent to about 100 a minute. As we will see later in the chapter, the autonomic nervous system can modulate this rate.

Each depolarization initiated by this pacemaker is transmitted through two pathways: one to the cardiac muscle fibers of the left atrium, and the other to the right atrium and the atrioventricular (AV) node. Once initiated, depolarizations spread quickly from one muscle fiber to another in a wave that envelops the right and left atria nearly simultaneously. The rapid spread of depolarization is made possible because special conducting fibers are present and because the cardiac muscle cells are coupled by groups of gap junctions located within *intercalated disks* (see chapter 44).

A sheet of connective tissue separating the atria from the ventricles blocks the spread of excitation through muscle fibers from one chamber to the other. The AV node provides the only pathway for conduction of the depolarization from the atria to the ventricles. The fibers of the AV node slow down the conduction of the depolarizing signals, delaying the contraction of

the ventricle by about 0.1 sec. This delay permits the atria to finish contracting and emptying their blood into the ventricles before the ventricles contract.

From the AV node, the wave of depolarization is conducted rapidly over both ventricles by a network of fibers called the atrioventricular bundle, or bundle of His. These fibers relay the depolarization to Purkinje fibers, which directly stimulate the myocardial cells of the left and right ventricles, causing their almost simultaneous contraction.

The stimulation of myocardial cells produces an action potential that leads to contraction. Contraction is controlled by Ca^{2+} and the troponin/tropomyosin system similar to skeletal muscle (see chapter 47), but the shape of the action potential is different. The initial rising phase due to an influx of Na^+ from voltage-gated Na^+ channels is followed by a plateau phase that leads to more sustained contraction. The plateau phase is due to the opening of voltage-gated Ca^{2+} channels. The resulting influx of Ca^{2+} keeps the membrane depolarized when the Na^+ channels inactivate. This, in turn, leads to more voltage-gated Ca^{2+} channels in the sarcoplasmic reticulum opening. The additional Ca^{2+} in the cytoplasm produces a more sustained contraction. The Ca^{2+} is

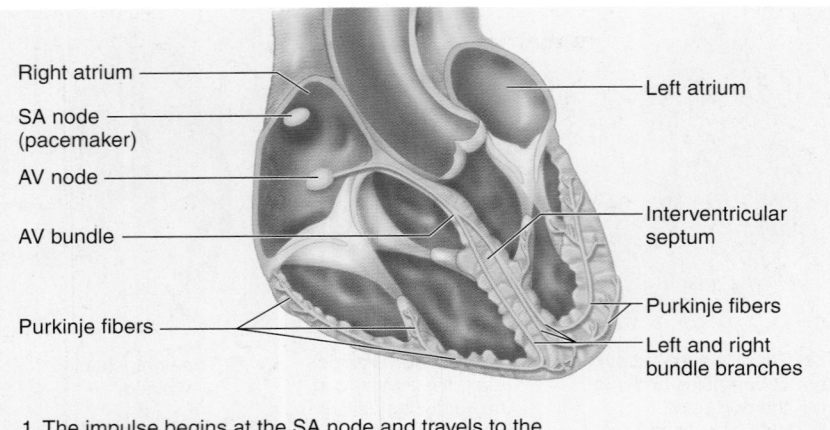

Right atrium
SA node (pacemaker)
AV node
AV bundle
Purkinje fibers
Left atrium
Interventricular septum
Purkinje fibers
Left and right bundle branches

1. The impulse begins at the SA node and travels to the AV node.

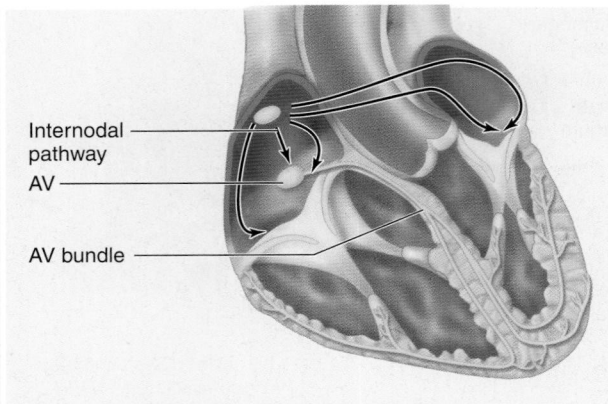

Internodal pathway
AV
AV bundle

2. The impulse is delayed at the AV node. It then travels to the AV bundle.

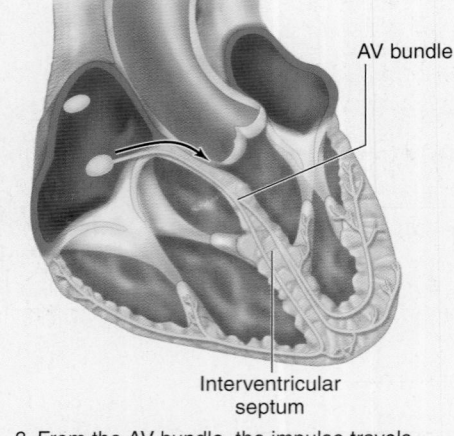

AV bundle
Interventricular septum

3. From the AV bundle, the impulse travels down the interventricular septum.

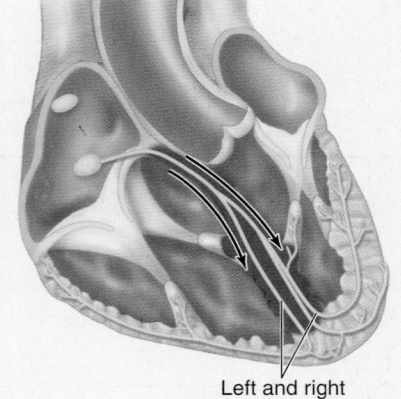

Left and right bundle branches

4. The impulse spreads to branches from the interventricular septum.

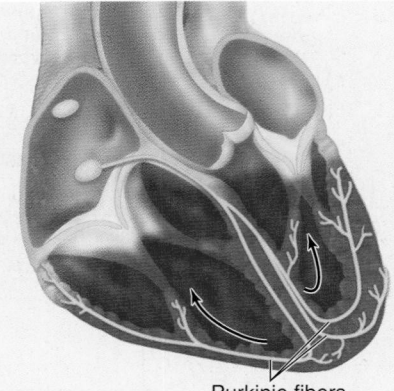

Purkinje fibers

5. Finally reaching the Purkinje fibers, the impulse is distributed throughout the ventricles.

Figure 50.10 The path of electrical excitation in the heart. The events occurring during contraction of the heart are correlated with the measurement of electrical activity by an electrocardiogram (ECG also called EKG). The depolarization/contraction of the atrium is shown in green above and corresponds to the P wave of the ECG (also in green). The depolarization/contraction of the ventricle is shown in red above and corresponds to the QRS wave of the ECG (also in red). The T wave on the ECG corresponds to the repolarization of the ventricles. The atrial repolarization is masked by the QRS wave.

removed from the cytoplasm by a pump in the sarcoplasmic reticulum similar to skeletal muscle, and an additional carrier in the plasma membrane pumps Ca^{2+} into the interstitial space.

The electrical activity of the heart can be recorded from the surface of the body with electrodes placed on the limbs and chest. The recording, called an electrocardiogram (ECG or EKG), shows how the cells of the heart depolarize and repolarize during the cardiac cycle (see figure 50.10). Depolarization causes contraction of the heart, and repolarization causes relaxation.

The first peak in the recording, P, is produced by the depolarization of the atria, and is associated with atrial systole.

The second, larger peak, QRS, is produced by ventricular depolarization; during this time, the ventricles contract (ventricular systole). The last peak, T, is produced by ventricular repolarization; at this time, the ventricles begin diastole.

Arteries and veins branch to and from all parts of the body

The right and left **pulmonary arteries** deliver oxygen-depleted blood from the right ventricle to the right and left lungs. As previously mentioned, the **pulmonary veins** return oxygenated blood from the lungs to the left atrium of the heart.

The **aorta** and all its branches are systemic arteries, carrying oxygen-rich blood from the left ventricle to all parts of the body. The **coronary arteries** are the first branches off the aorta; these supply oxygenated blood to the heart muscle itself (see figure 50.7b). Other systemic arteries branch from the aorta as it makes an arch above the heart and as it descends and traverses the thoracic and abdominal cavities.

The blood from the body's organs, now lower in oxygen, returns to the heart in the systemic veins. These eventually empty into two major veins: the **superior vena cava,** which drains the upper body, and the **inferior vena cava,** which drains the lower body. These veins empty into the right atrium, completing the systemic circulation.

The flow of blood through the arteries, capillaries, and veins is driven by the pressure generated by ventricular contraction. The ventricles must contract forcefully enough to move the blood through the entire circulatory system.

Arterial blood pressure can be measured

As the ventricles contract, great pressure is generated within them and transferred through the arteries once the aortic valve opens. The pulse that you can detect in your wrist or neck results from changes in pressure as elastic arteries expand and contract with the periodic blood flow. Doctors use blood pressure as an general indicator of cardiovascular health because a variety of conditions can cause increases or decreases in pressure.

A *sphygmomanometer* measures the blood pressure in the brachial artery found on the inside part of the arm, above the elbow (figure 50.11). A cuff wrapped around the upper part of the arm is tightened enough to stop the flow of blood to the lower part of the arm. As the cuff is slowly loosened, eventually the blood pressure produced by the heart is greater than the constricting pressure of cuff and blood begins pulsating through the artery, producing a sound that can be detected using a stethoscope. The point at which this pulsing sound begins marks the peak pressure, or **systolic pressure,** at which ventricles are contracting. As the cuff is loosened further, the point is reached where the pressure of the cuff is lower than the blood pressure throughout the cardiac cycle, at which time the blood vessel is no longer distorted and the pulsing sound stops. This point marks the minimum pressure between heartbeats or **diastolic pressure,** at which the ventricles are relaxed.

The blood pressure is written as a ratio of systolic over diastolic pressure, and for a healthy person in his or her twenties, a typical blood pressure is 120/75 (measured in millimeters

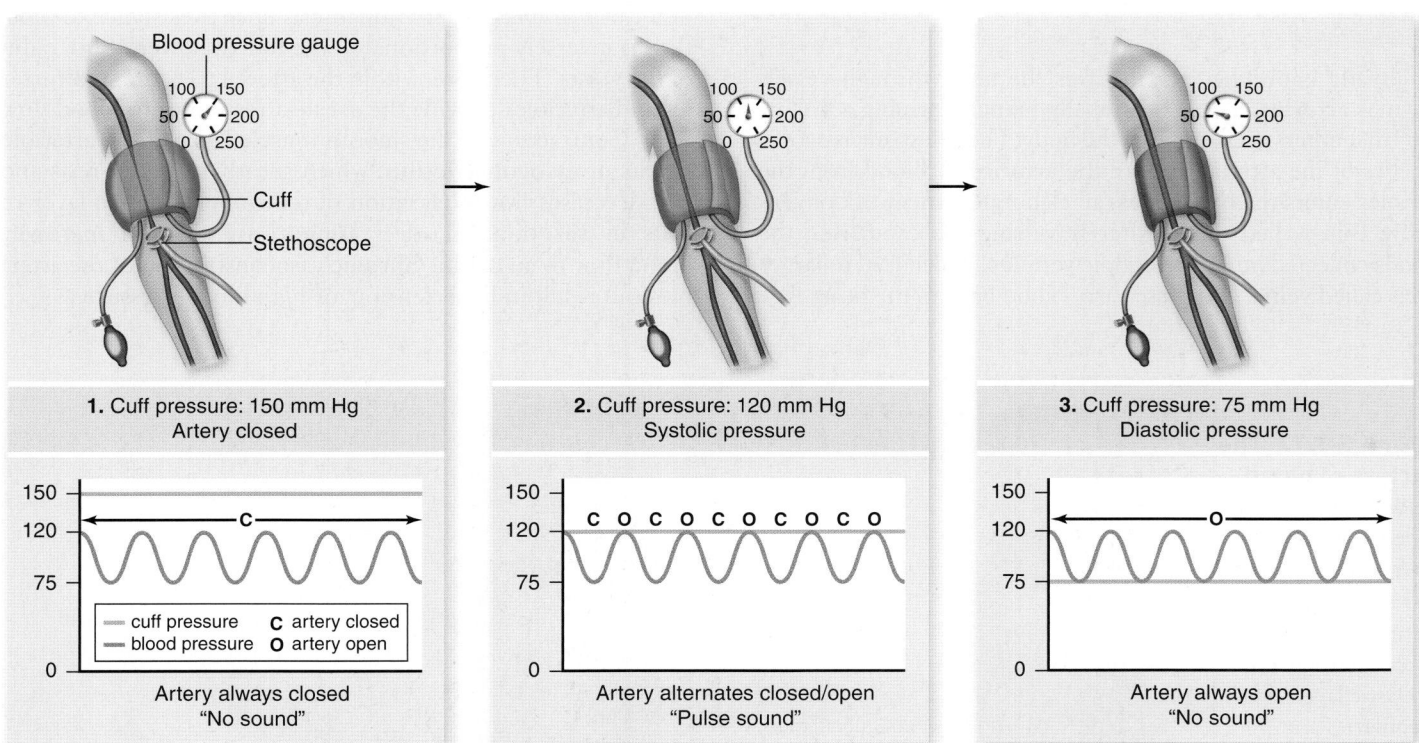

Figure 50.11 Measurement of blood pressure. The blood pressure cuff is tightened to stop the blood flow through the brachial artery. As the cuff is loosened, the maximal (systolic) pressure becomes greater than the cuff pressure and blood can momentarily pass through, producing a pulse that can be heard with a stethoscope. The pressure at this point is recorded as the systolic pressure. As the cuff pressure continues to drop, blood pressure is greater than cuff pressure for larger portions of the cardiac cycle. Eventually, even the minimum pressure during the cycle is greater than the cuff pressure, at which time the blood vessel is no longer distorted and silent laminar flow returns, replacing the pulsing sound. The diastolic pressure is recorded as the pressure at which a sound is no longer heard.

of mercury, or mm Hg). The medical condition called **hypertension** (high blood pressure) is defined as either a systolic pressure greater than 150 mm Hg or a diastolic pressure greater than 90 mm Hg.

Learning Outcomes Review 50.4

The cardiac cycle consists of systole and diastole; the ventricles contract at systole and relax at diastole. The SA node in the right atrium initiates waves of depolarization that stimulate first the atria and then travel to the AV node, which stimulates the ventricles. Blood pressure is expressed as the ratio of systolic pressure over diastolic pressure and is measured with a device called a sphygmomanometer.

- ■ *What would happen without a delay between auricular and ventricular contraction?*

50.5 *Characteristics of Blood Vessels*

Learning Outcomes

1. *Describe the four tissue layers in blood vessels.*
2. *Explain the distinctions among arteries, capillaries, and veins.*
3. *Describe how the lympathic system operates.*

You already know that blood leaves the heart through vessels known as **arteries.** These continually branch, forming a hollow "tree" that enters each organ of the body. The finest, microscopic branches of the arterial tree are the **arterioles.** Blood from the arterioles enters the **capillaries,** an elaborate latticework of very narrow, thin-walled tubes. After traversing the capillaries, the blood is collected into microscopic **venules,** which lead to larger vessels called **veins,** and these carry blood back to the heart.

Larger vessels are composed of four tissue layers

Arteries, arterioles, veins, and venules all have the same basic structure (figure 50.12). The innermost layer is an epithelial sheet called the *endothelium.* Covering the endothelium is a thin layer of elastic fibers, a smooth muscle layer, and a connective tissue layer. The walls of these vessels, therefore, are thick enough to significantly reduce exchange of materials between the blood and the tissues outside the vessels.

The walls of capillaries, in contrast, are composed only of endothelium, so molecules and ions can leave the blood plasma by diffusion, by filtration through pores between the cells of the capillary walls, and by transport through the endothelial cells. Therefore, exchange of gases and metabolites between the blood and the interstitial fluids and cells of the body takes place through the capillaries.

Arteries and arterioles have evolved to withstand pressure

The larger arteries contain more elastic fibers in their walls than other blood vessels, allowing them to recoil each time they receive a volume of blood pumped by the heart. Smaller arteries and arterioles are less elastic, but their relatively thick smooth muscle layer enables them to resist bursting.

The narrower the vessel, the greater the frictional resistance to flow. In fact, a vessel that is half the diameter of another has *16 times* the frictional resistance. Resistance to blood flow is inversely proportional to the fourth power of the radius of the vessel. Therefore, within the arterial tree, the small arteries and arterioles provide the greatest resistance to blood flow.

Contraction of the smooth muscle layer of the arterioles results in **vasoconstriction,** which greatly increases resistance and decreases flow. Relaxation of the smooth muscle layer results in **vasodilation,** decreasing resistance and increasing blood flow to an organ. Chronic vasoconstriction of the arterioles can result in hypertension, or high blood pressure.

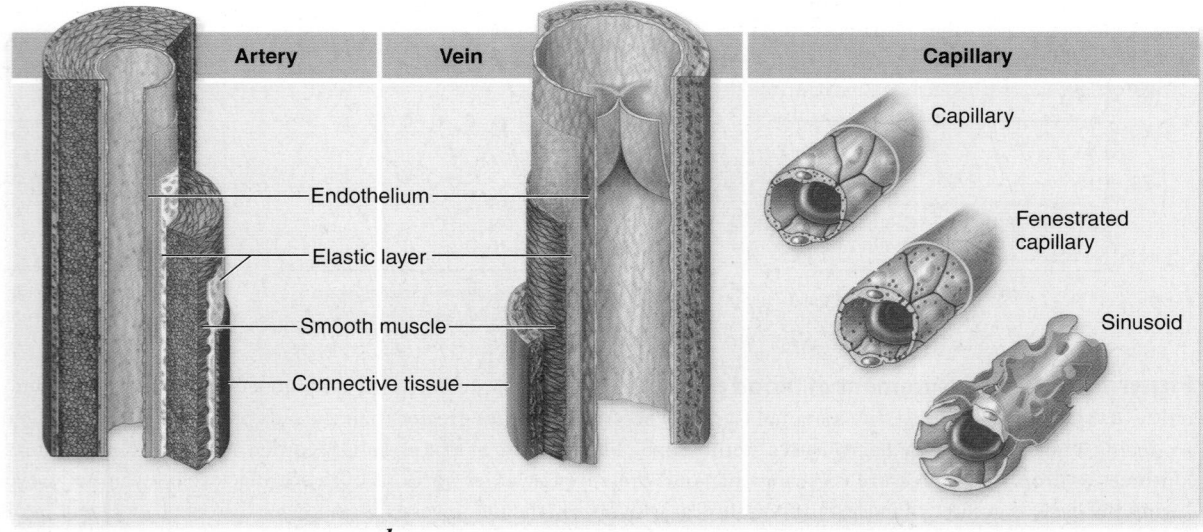

Figure 50.12 The structure of blood vessels. Arteries *(a)* and veins *(b)* have the same tissue layers, but the smooth muscle layer in arteries is much thicker and there are two elastic layers. *c.* Capillaries are composed of only a single layer of endothelial cells. (Not to scale.)

Artery   Vein   Capillary

Endothelium
Elastic layer
Smooth muscle
Connective tissue

Capillary
Fenestrated capillary
Sinusoid

a.   *b.*   *c.*

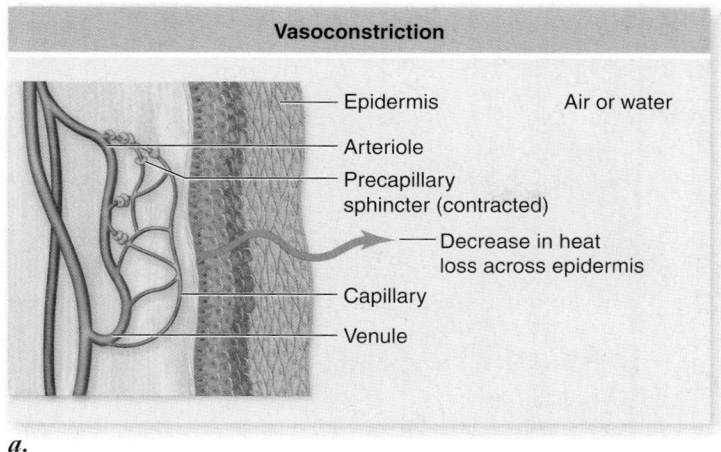

Vasoconstriction

Epidermis   Air or water

Arteriole

Precapillary sphincter (contracted)

Decrease in heat loss across epidermis

Capillary

Venule

a.

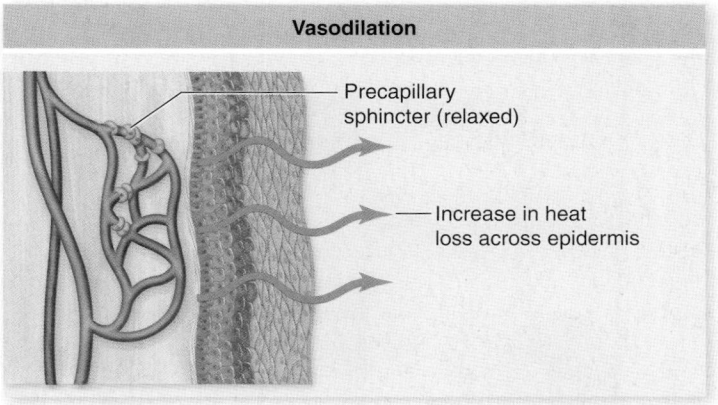

Vasodilation

Precapillary sphincter (relaxed)

Increase in heat loss across epidermis

b.

Figure 50.13 Regulation of heat exchange. The amount of heat gained or lost at the body's surface can be regulated by controlling the flow of blood to the surface. *a.* Constriction of surface blood vessels limits flow and heat loss when the animal is warmer than the surrounding air; when the animal is cooler than the surrounding air (not shown here), constriction minimizes heat gain; *(b)* dilation of these vessels increases flow and heat exchange.

Vasoconstriction and vasodilation are important means of regulating body heat in both ectotherms and endotherms (figure 50.13). By increasing blood flow to the skin, an animal can increase the rate of heat exchange, which is beneficial for gaining or losing heat. Conversely, shunting blood away from the skin is effective when an animal needs to minimize heat exchange, as might happen in cold weather.

Capillaries form a vast network for exchange of materials

The huge number and extensive branching of the capillaries ensure that every cell in the body is within 100 micrometers (µm) of a capillary. On the average, capillaries are about 1 mm long and 8 µm in diameter, this diameter is only slightly larger than a red blood cell (5 to 7 µm in diameter). Despite the close fit, normal red blood cells are flexible enough to squeeze through capillaries without difficulty.

The rate of blood flow through vessels is governed by hydrodynamics. The smaller the cross-sectional area of a vessel, the faster fluid moves through it. Given this, flow in the capillaries would be expected to be the fastest in the system. This would not be ideal for diffusion, and is actually not the case. Although each capillary is very narrow, so many of them exist that the capillaries have the greatest *total* cross-sectional area of any other type of vessel. Consequently, blood moving through capillaries goes more slowly and has more time to exchange materials with the surrounding extracellular fluid. By the time the blood reaches the end of a capillary, it has released some of its oxygen and nutrients and picked up carbon dioxide and other waste products. Blood loses pressure and velocity as it moves through the arterioles and capillaries, but as cross-sectional area decreases in the venous side, velocity increases.

Venules and veins have less muscle in their walls

Venules and veins have the same tissue layers as arteries, but they have a thinner layer of smooth muscle. Less muscle is needed because the pressure in the veins is only about one-tenth that in the arteries. Most of the blood in the cardiovascular system is contained within veins, which can expand to hold additional amounts of blood. You can see the expanded veins in your feet when you stand for a long time.

The venous pressure alone is not sufficient to return blood to the heart from the feet and legs, but several other sources of pressure provide help. Most significantly, skeletal muscles surrounding the veins can contract to move blood by squeezing the veins, a mechanism called the **venous pump**. Blood moves in one direction through the veins back to the heart with the help of **venous valves** (figure 50.14). When a

Figure 50.14 One-way flow of blood through veins. Venous valves ensure that blood moves through the veins in only one direction, back to the heart.

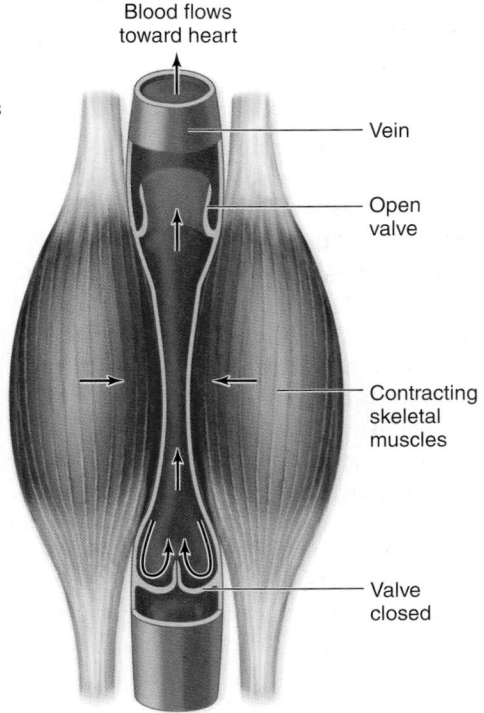

Blood flows toward heart

Vein

Open valve

Contracting skeletal muscles

Valve closed

person's veins expand too much with blood, the venous valves may no longer work and the blood may pool in the veins. Veins in this condition are known as varicose veins.

The lymphatic system handles fluids that leave the cardiovascular system

The cardiovascular system is considered a closed system because all its vessels are connected with one another—none are simply open-ended. But a significant amount of water and solutes in the blood plasma filter through the walls of the capillaries to form the interstitial (tissue) fluid. Most of the fluid leaves the capillaries near their arteriolar ends, where the blood pressure is higher; it is returned to the capillaries near their venular ends (figure 50.15).

Fluid returns by osmosis (see chapter 5). Most of the plasma proteins cannot escape through the capillary pores because of their large size, and so the concentration of proteins in the plasma is greater than the protein concentration in the interstitial fluid. The difference in protein concentration produces an osmotic pressure gradient that causes water to move into the capillaries from the interstitial space.

High capillary blood pressure can cause too much interstitial fluid to accumulate. In pregnant women, for example, the enlarged uterus, carrying the fetus, compresses veins in the abdominal cavity, thereby adding to the capillary blood pressure in the woman's lower limbs. The increased interstitial fluid can cause swelling of the tissues, or **edema,** of the feet.

Edema may also result if the plasma protein concentration is too low. Fluids do not return to the capillaries, but remain as interstitial fluid. Low protein concentration in the plasma may be caused either by liver disease, because the liver produces most of the plasma proteins, or by insufficient dietary protein such as occurs in starvation.

Even under normal conditions, the amount of fluid filtered out of the capillaries is greater than the amount that returns to the capillaries by osmosis. The remainder does eventually return to the cardiovascular system by way of an open circulatory system called the **lymphatic system.**

The lymphatic system consists of lymphatic capillaries, lymphatic vessels, lymph nodes, and lymphatic organs, including the spleen and thymus. Excess fluid in the tissues drains into blind-ended lymph capillaries with highly permeable walls. This fluid, now called **lymph,** passes into progressively larger lymphatic vessels, which resemble veins and have one-way valves (similar to figure 50.14). The lymph eventually enters two major lymphatic vessels, which drain into the left and right subclavian veins located under the collarbones.

Movement of lymph in mammals results as skeletal muscles squeeze against the lymphatic vessels, a mechanism similar to the venous pump that moves blood through veins. In some cases, the lymphatic vessels also contract rhythmically. In many fishes, all amphibians and reptiles, bird embryos, and some adult birds, movement of lymph is propelled by **lymph hearts**.

As the lymph moves through lymph nodes and lymphatic organs, it is modified by phagocytic cells (see chapter 4) that line the channels of those organs. In addition, the lymph nodes

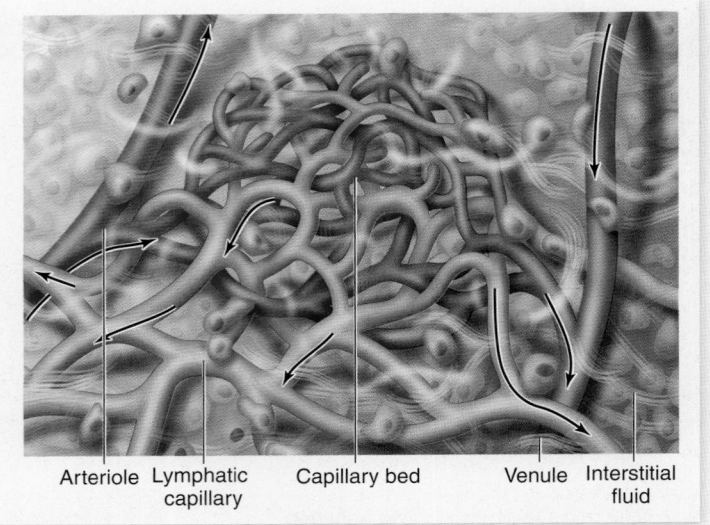

Arteriole Lymphatic capillary Capillary bed Venule Interstitial fluid

a.

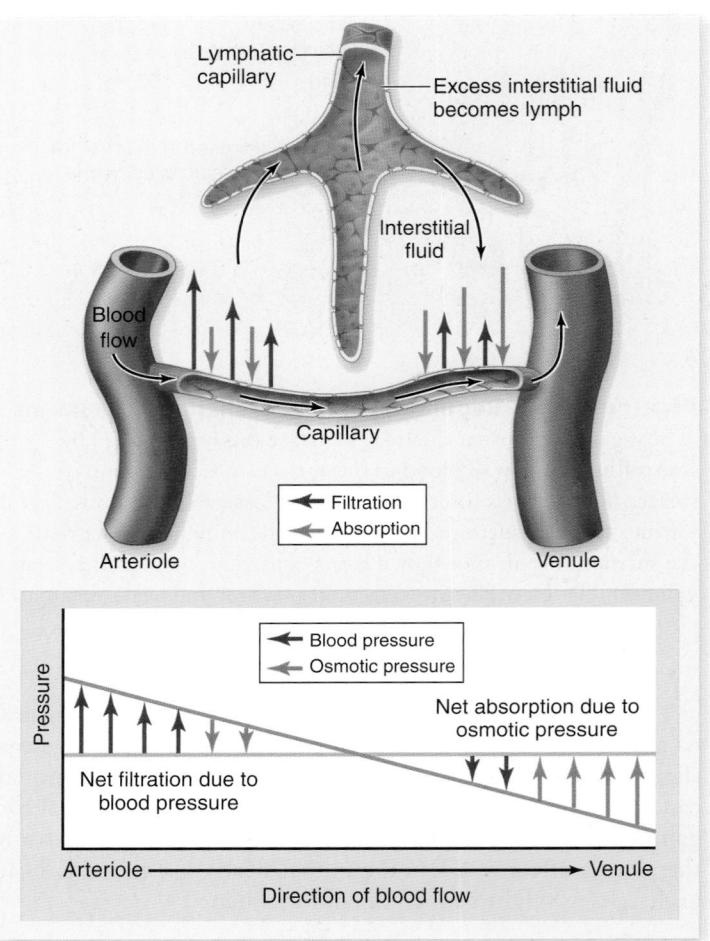

b.

Figure 50.15 Relationship between blood, lymph, and interstitial fluid. *a.* Vessels of the circulatory and lymphatic systems with arrows indicating the direction of flow of fluid in the vessels. *b.* Plasma fluid, minus proteins, is filtered out of capillaries, forming interstitial fluid that bathes tissues. Much of this fluid is returned to the capillaries by osmosis due to the higher protein concentration in plasma. Excess interstitial fluid drains into open-ended lymphatic capillaries, which ultimately return the fluid to the cardiovascular system.

and lymphatic organs contain *germinal centers*, where the activation and proliferation of lymphocytes occurs.

Cardiovascular diseases affect the delivery system

Cardiovascular diseases are the leading cause of death in the United States; more than 80 million people have some form of cardiovascular disease. Many disease conditions result from problems in arteries, such as blockage or rupture.

Atherosclerosis, or hardening of the arteries, is an accumulation within the arteries of fatty materials, abnormal amounts of smooth muscle, deposits of cholesterol or fibrin, or various kinds of cellular debris. These accumulations cause an increase in vascular resistance, which impedes blood flow (figure 50.16). The lumen (interior) of the artery may be further narrowed by a clot that forms as a result of the atherosclerosis. In the severest cases, the artery becomes completely blocked.

The accumulation of cholesterol in vessels is affected by a number of factors including total serum cholesterol and the levels of different cholesterol carrier proteins. Because cholesterol is not very water-soluble, it is carried in blood in the form of lipoprotein complexes. Two main forms are observed that differ in density: low-density lipoproteins (LDL) and high-density lipoproteins (HDL)—often called "bad cholesterol" and "good cholesterol," respectively. The reason for this is that HDLs tend to take cholesterol out of circulation, transporting it to the liver for elimination, and LDL is the carrier that brings cholesterol to all cells in the body. The problem arises when cells have enough cholesterol. This causes a reduction in the amount of LDL receptors, leading to high levels of circulating LDLs, which can end up being deposited in blood vessels.

Atherosclerosis is promoted by genetic factors, smoking, hypertension (high blood pressure), and the effects of cholesterol just discussed. Stopping smoking is the single most effective action a smoker can take to reduce the risk of atherosclerosis.

Arteriosclerosis occurs when calcium is deposited in arterial walls. It tends to occur when atherosclerosis is severe. Not only do such arteries have restricted blood flow, but they also lack the ability to expand as normal arteries do. This decrease in flexibility forces the heart to work harder because blood pressure increases to maintain flow.

Heart attacks (myocardial infarctions) are the main cause of cardiovascular deaths in the United States, accounting for about one-fifth of all deaths. Heart attacks result from an insufficient supply of blood to one or more parts of the heart muscle, which causes myocardial cells in those parts to die. Heart attacks may be caused by a blood clot forming somewhere in the coronary arteries and may also result if an artery is blocked by atherosclerosis. Recovery from a heart attack is possible if the portion of the heart that was damaged is small enough that the heart can still contract as a functional unit.

Angina pectoris, which literally means "chest pain," occurs for reasons similar to those that cause heart attacks, but it is not as severe. The pain may occur in the heart and often also in the left arm and shoulder. Angina pectoris is a warning sign that the blood supply to the heart is inadequate but is still sufficient to avoid myocardial cell death.

Strokes are caused by an interference with the blood supply to the brain. They may occur when a blood vessel bursts in the brain (hemorrhagic stroke), when blood flow in a cerebral artery is blocked by a blood clot or by atherosclerosis (ischemic stroke). The effects of a stroke depend on the severity of the damage and where in the brain the stroke occurs.

Learning Outcomes Review 50.5

The four layers of blood vessels are (1) endothelium, (2) an elastic layer, (3) smooth muscle, and (4) connective tissue. In contrast, capillaries have only endothelium. Arteries have more muscle in their walls than do veins to help withstand greater pressure; large arteries also have more elastic fibers for recoil. Excess interstitial fluid, called lymph, is returned to the cardiovascular system via the lymphatic system, a one-way system.

■ *What is the connection between the lymphatic and circulatory systems?*

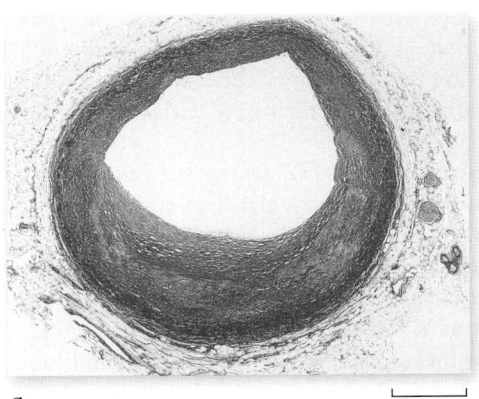 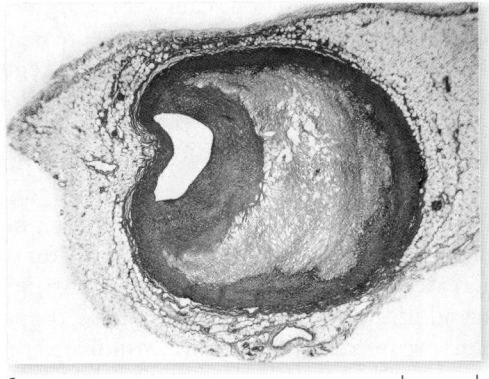 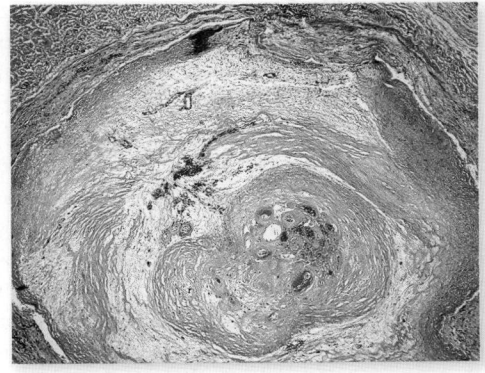

a. 2000 μm   *b.* 2500 μm   *c.* 1000 μm

Figure 50.16 Atherosclerosis. *a.* The coronary artery shows only minor blockage. *b.* The artery exhibits severe atherosclerosis—much of the passage is blocked by buildup on the interior walls of the artery. *c.* The coronary artery is essentially completely blocked.

Regulation of Blood Flow and Blood Pressure

Learning Outcomes

1. Describe how exertion affects cardiac output.
2. Explain how hormones regulate blood volume.

Although the autonomic nervous system does not initiate the heartbeat, it does modulate its rhythm and force of contraction. In addition, several mechanisms regulate characteristics of the cardiovascular system, including cardiac output, blood pressure, and blood volume.

The nervous system may speed up or slow down heart rate

Heart rate is under the control of the autonomic nervous system. The cardiac center of the medulla oblongata (a part of the hindbrain; see chapter 44) consists of two neuronal centers that modulate heart rate. The **cardioacceleratory center** sends signals by way of the sympathetic cardiac accelerator nerves to the SA node, AV node, and myocardium. These nerves secrete norepinephrine, which increases the heart rate. Sympathetic nervous system stimulation can also increase contractility of the heart muscle itself, thus ejecting more blood per contraction (stroke volume).

The **cardioinhibitory center** sends signals via the parasympathetic fibers in the vagus nerve to the SA and AV nodes. The vagus nerve secretes acetylcholine, which inhibits the development of action potentials and so slows the heart down.

Cardiac output increases with exertion

Cardiac output is the volume of blood pumped by each ventricle per minute. It is calculated by multiplying the heart rate by the *stroke volume*, which is the volume of blood ejected by each ventricle per beat. For example, if the heart rate is 72 beats per minute and the stroke volume is 70 mL, the cardiac output is 5 L/min, which is about average in a resting human.

Cardiac output increases during exertion because of an increase in both heart rate and stroke volume. When exertion begins, such as running, the heart rate increases up to about 100 beats per minute to provide more oxygen to cells in the body. As movement becomes more intense, skeletal muscles squeeze on veins more vigorously, returning blood to the heart more rapidly. In addition, the ventricles contract more strongly, so they empty more completely with each beat.

During exercise, the cardiac output increases to a maximum of about 25 L/min in an average young adult. Although the cardiac output has increased fivefold, not all organs receive five times the blood flow; some receive more, others less. Arterioles in some organs, such as in the digestive system, constrict, while the arterioles in the working muscles and heart dilate.

The baroreceptor reflex maintains homeostasis in blood pressure

The arterial blood pressure (BP) depends on two factors: the cardiac output (CO) and the resistance (R) to blood flow in the vascular system. This relationship can be expressed as:

$$BP = CO \times R$$

An increased blood pressure, therefore, could be produced by an increase in either heart rate or blood volume (because both increase the cardiac output), or by vasoconstriction, which increases the resistance to blood flow. Conversely, blood pressure falls if the heart rate slows or if the blood volume is reduced—for example, by dehydration or excessive bleeding (hemorrhage).

Changes in arterial blood pressure are detected by **baroreceptors** located in the arch of the aorta and in the carotid arteries (see chapter 46). These sensors are stretch receptors sensitive to expansion and contraction of arteries. When the baroreceptors detect a fall in blood pressure, the number of impulses to the cardiac center is decreased, resulting in increased sympathetic stimulation and decreased parasympathetic stimulation of the heart and other targets. This increases heart rate and stroke volume to amplify cardiac output. This also causes vasoconstriction of blood vessels in the skin and viscera, raising resistance. These combine to increase blood pressure, closing the feedback loop in this direction (figure 50.17, top).

When baroreceptors detect a rise in blood pressure, the number of impulses to the cardiac center is increased. This has the opposite effect of decreasing sympathetic stimulation and increasing parasympathetic simulation of the heart. This lowers heart rate and stroke volume to reduce cardiac output. The cardiac center also sends signals causing vasodilation of blood vessels in the skin and viscera, lowering resistance. These combine to decrease blood pressure closing the feedback loop in this direction. Thus, the baroreceptor reflex forms a negative feedback loop responding to changes in blood pressure (figure 50.17, bottom).

Blood volume is regulated by hormones

Blood pressure depends in part on the total blood volume because this can affect the cardiac output. A decrease in blood volume decreases blood pressure, if all else remains equal. Blood volume regulation involves the effects of four hormones: (1) antidiuretic hormone, (2) aldosterone, (3) atrial natriuretic hormone, and (4) nitric oxide.

Antidiuretic hormone (ADH), also called **vasopressin,** is secreted by the posterior-pituitary gland in response to an increase in the osmolarity of the blood plasma (see chapter 46). Dehydration, for example, causes the blood volume to decrease. Osmoreceptors in the hypothalamus promote thirst and stimulate ADH secretion from the posterior pituitary gland. ADH, in turn, stimulates the kidneys to retain more water in the blood, excreting less in the urine. A dehydrated person thus drinks more and urinates less, helping to raise the blood volume and restore homeostasis.

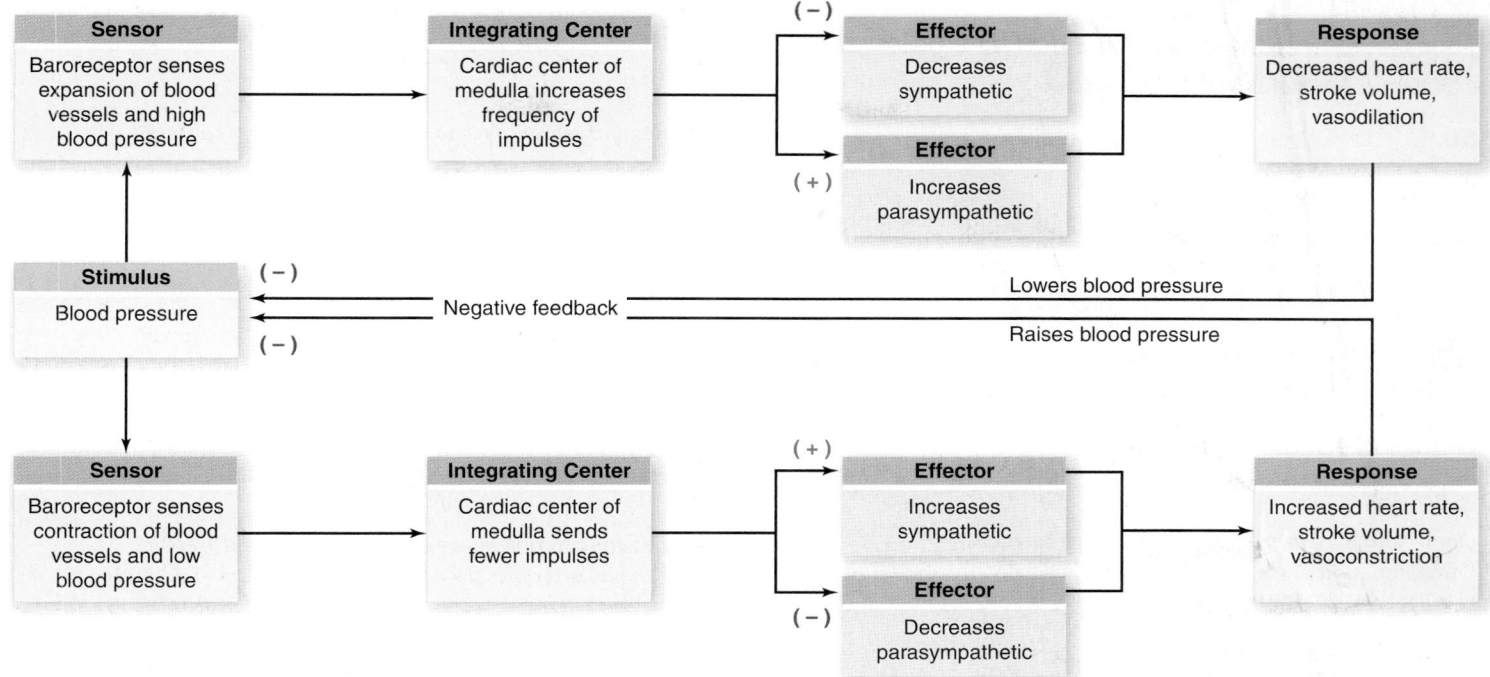

Figure 50.17 Baroreceptor negative feedback loops control blood pressure. Baroreceptors form the afferent portion of a feedback loop controlling blood pressure. The frequency of nerve impulses from these stretch receptors correlates with blood pressure. This information is processed in the cardiac center of the medulla. The efferent portion of the loop involves sympathetic and parasympathetic nerves that innervate the heart. This control can raise or lower heart rate and stroke volume to raise and lower blood pressure in response to baroreceptors signaling.

Whenever the kidneys experience a decreased blood flow, a group of kidney cells initiate the release of an enzyme known as renin into the blood. Renin activates a blood protein, angiotensin, which stimulates vasoconstriction throughout the body while stimulating the adrenal cortex to secrete **aldosterone.** This steroid hormone acts on the kidneys to promote the retention of Na^+ and water in the blood (see chapter 46).

When excess Na^+ is present, less aldosterone is secreted by the adrenals, so that less Na^+ is retained by the kidneys. Na^+ excretion in the urine is promoted by another hormone, **atrial natriuretic hormone.** This hormone is secreted by the right atrium of the heart in response to stretching caused by an increased blood volume. The action of atrial natriuretic hormone completes a negative feedback loop, lowering the blood volume and pressure.

Nitric oxide (NO) is a gas produced by endothelial cells of blood vessels. As described in chapter 46, it is one of a number of paracrine regulators of blood vessels. In solution, NO passes outward through the cell layers of the vessel, causing the smooth muscles that encase it to relax and the blood vessels to dilate (become wider). For over a century, heart patients have been prescribed nitroglycerin to relieve chest pain, but only now has it become clear that nitroglycerin acts by releasing nitric oxide.

Learning Outcomes Review 50.6

Cardiac output is the heart rate times the heart's stroke volume. As exertion increases, cardiac output increases to meet the body's demands. Blood pressure depends on cardiac output and the resistance to blood flow due to constriction of the arteries. The blood volume is regulated by antidiuretic hormone, aldosterone, and atrial natriuretic hormone; nitric oxide causes vasodilation that lessens resistance.

■ *What are the connections between regulation of heart rate and breathing rate?*

50.1 The Components of Blood

Blood plasma is a fluid matrix.
Plasma is 92% water plus nutrients, hormones, ions, plasma proteins, and wastes (see figure 50.1).

Formed elements include circulating cells and platelets.
Blood cells include erythrocytes (red cells), leukocytes (white cells), and platelets. Erythrocytes contain hemoglobin for oxygen transport, and leukocytes are part of the immune system. Platelets help initiate blood clotting (see figure 50.3).

Formed elements arise from stem cells.
Blood cells are derived from pluripotent stem cells in bone marrow by hematopoiesis (see figure 50.2).

Blood clotting is an example of an enzyme cascade.
Upon initiation of clotting, fibrinogen, normally dissolved in the plasma, is turned into fibrin, an insoluble protein, via an enzyme cascade. As a wound heals, the clot must be dissolved.

50.2 Invertebrate Circulatory Systems

Open circulatory systems move fluids in a one-way path.
Sponges pass water through channels, and cnidarians circulate water through a gastrovascular cavity. Small animals can use body cavity fluids for circulation.

Closed circulatory systems move fluids in a loop.
Closed systems have a distinct circulatory fluid, such as blood, enclosed in vessels and transported in a loop.

50.3 Vertebrate Circulatory Systems

In fishes, more efficient circulation developed concurrently with gills.
Fishes have a linear heart with two pumping chambers to increase efficiency of blood flow through the gills; from the gills, the blood moves into the rest of the body (see figure 50.5).

In amphibians and most reptiles, lungs required a separate circulation.
Pulmonary circulation pumps blood to the lungs, and systemic circulation pumps blood to the body.

Amphibian hearts have two atria that separate blood flow to the lungs and body, and a single ventricle (figure 50.6). The heart of most reptiles has a septum that partially divides the ventricle, reducing mixing of blood from the atria.

Mammals, birds, and crocodilians have two completely separated circulatory systems.
The four-chambered heart has two ventricles (see figure 50.7). The extreme similarity between the heart of mammals and birds is an example of convergent evolution.

50.4 The Four-Chambered Heart and the Blood Vessels

The cardiac cycle drives the cardiovascular system.
The unidirectional flow of blood through the heart is maintained by two atrioventricular valves (see figure 50.9). During diastole ventricles relax and atria contract; during systole ventricles contract.

Contraction of heart muscle is initiated by autorhythmic cells.
Contraction is initiated by the SA node, a natural pacemaker, and impulses then travel to the AV node (see figure 50.10).

Arteries and veins branch to and from all parts of the body.
Arteries and arterioles carry oxygenated blood to the body; veins and venules return deoxygenated blood to the heart (see figure 50.7).

Arterial blood pressure can be measured.
A sphygmomanometer measures the peak (systolic) and minimum (diastolic) blood pressure. Blood pressure is expressed as the ratio of systolic to diastolic.

50.5 Characteristics of Blood Vessels

Larger vessels are composed of four tissue layers.
Arteries and veins consist of endothelium, elastic fibers, smooth muscle, and connective tissues (see figure 50.12). Capillaries have only one layer of endothelium.

Arteries and arterioles have evolved to withstand pressure.
Arteries and arterioles have thicker muscular layer and more elastic fibers to control blood flow and to recoil with changes in blood pressure.

Capillaries form a vast network for exchange of materials.
Capillaries are the region of the circulatory system where exchange takes place with the body's tissues (see figure 50.13).

Venules and veins have less muscle in their walls.
The return of blood to the heart through veins is facilitated by skeletal muscle contractions and one-way valves (see figure 50.14).

The lymphatic system handles fluids that leave the cardiovascular system.
Fluid from plasma filters out of capillaries, then returns via the separate, one-way lymphatic system (see figure 50.15). The lymphatic system connects with the blood circulation at the subclavian veins.

Cardiovascular diseases affect the delivery system.
Atherosclerosis is an accumulation of fatty materials in arteries; it is one cause of a heart attack, which results from an insufficient supply of blood to heart muscle. Strokes are caused by blockage of the blood supply to the brain.

50.6 Regulation of Blood Flow and Blood Pressure

The nervous system may speed up or slow down heart rate.
Norepinephrine from sympathetic neurons increases heart rate; acetylcholine from parasympathetic neurons decreases the rate.

Cardiac output increases with exertion.
Both heart rate and stroke volume increase with exertion.

The baroreceptor reflex maintains homeostasis in blood pressure.
Arterial blood pressure is monitored by baroreceptors in the aortic arch and carotid arteries, which relay impulses to the cardiac center (see figure 50.17).

Blood volume is regulated by hormones.
Blood volume regulation and arterial resistance involves the effects of four hormones: (1) antidiuretic hormone, (2) aldosterone, (3) atrial natriuretic hormone, and (4) nitric oxide.

Review Questions

UNDERSTAND

1. An ECG measures
   a. changes in electrical potential during the cardiac cycle.
   b. Ca^{2+} concentration of the ventricles in diastole.
   c. the force of contraction of the atria during systole.
   d. the volume of blood being pumped during the contraction cycle.

2. Systole is vitally important to heart function and begins in the heart with the
   a. activation of the AV node.
   b. activation of the SA node.
   c. opening of the voltage-gated potassium gates.
   d. opening of the semilunar valves.

3. Which of the following is the correct sequence of events in the circulation of blood?
   a. Heart $\longrightarrow$ arteries $\longrightarrow$ arterioles $\longrightarrow$ capillaries $\longrightarrow$ venules $\longrightarrow$ lymph $\longrightarrow$ heart
   b. Heart $\longrightarrow$ arteries $\longrightarrow$ arterioles $\longrightarrow$ capillaries $\longrightarrow$ veins $\longrightarrow$ venules $\longrightarrow$ heart
   c. Heart $\longrightarrow$ arteries $\longrightarrow$ arterioles $\longrightarrow$ capillaries $\longrightarrow$ venules $\longrightarrow$ veins $\longrightarrow$ heart
   d. Heart $\longrightarrow$ arterioles $\longrightarrow$ arteries $\longrightarrow$ capillaries $\longrightarrow$ venules $\longrightarrow$ veins $\longrightarrow$ heart

4. Which of the following statements is not true?
   a. Only arteries carry oxygenated blood.
   b. Both arteries and veins have a layer of smooth muscle.
   c. Both arteries and veins branch out into capillary beds.
   d. Precapillary sphincters regulate blood flow through capillaries.

5. The lymphatic system is like the circulatory system in that they both
   a. have nodes that filter out pathogens.
   b. have a network of arteries.
   c. have capillaries.
   d. are closed systems.

6. Which pairing of structure and function is incorrect?
   a. Erythrocytes: oxygen transport
   b. Platelets: blood clotting
   c. Plasma: waste transport
   d. All of these are correct.

7. When a sphygmomanometer is used,
   a. blood pulses through the vein when systolic pressure is greater than the pressure caused by the cuff.
   b. pulsing ceases when blood pressure falls below the systolic pressure.
   c. blood does not move through the vein when cuff pressure is greater than maximal blood pressure.
   d. cuff pressure stops decreasing when it equals systolic pressure.

APPLY

1. In vertebrate hearts, atria contract from the top, and ventricles contract from the bottom. How is this accomplished?
   a. Depolarization from the SA node proceeds across the atria from the top; depolarization from the AV node is carried to the bottom of the ventricles before it emanates over ventricular tissue.
   b. The depolarization from the SA node is initiated from motor neurons coming down from our brain; depolarization from the AV node is initiated from motor neurons coming up from our spinal cord.
   c. Gravity carries the depolarization from the SA node down from the top of the heart; contraction of the diaphragm forces depolarization from the AV node from the bottom up.
   d. This statement is false; both contract from the bottom.

2. A molecule of CO_2 that is generated in the cardiac muscle of the left ventricle would *not* pass through which of the following structures before leaving the body?
   a. Right atrium   c. Right ventricle
   b. Left atrium   d. Left ventricle

3. Blood clots are made of
   a. fibrin.   c. prothrombin.
   b. fibrinogen.   d. all of these.

4. The difference between the amphibian and mammal hearts is that
   a. in the amphibian heart, oxygenated and deoxygenated blood mix completely in the single ventricle.
   b. in the amphibian heart, there are two SA nodes so that contractions occur simultaneously throughout the heart.
   c. in the ventricle in the amphibian heart, internal channels reduce mixing of blood.
   d. in the amphibian heart, only the left aorta pumps oxygen obtained by diffusion through the skin.

5. Contraction of the smooth muscle layers of the arterioles
   a. increases the frictional resistance to blood flow.
   b. may be a way of increasing heat exchange through the skin.
   c. can increase blood flow to an organ.
   d. includes all of the above.

SYNTHESIZE

1. Humans have a number of mechanisms that help to maintain blood pressure, particularly when it falls too low. Explain how the kidney and the endocrine systems help to maintain blood pressure.

2. What is the difference among blood, lymph, and hemolymph?

3. Is the evolution of the four-chambered heart related to the evolution of endothermy?

4. What do you think are the clinical symptoms indicating that a person requires the surgical implantation of a mechanical pacemaker?

ONLINE RESOURCE

www.ravenbiology.com

Understand, Apply, and Synthesize—enhance your study with animations that bring concepts to life and practice tests to assess your understanding. Your instructor may also recommend the interactive eBook, individualized learning tools, and more.

Chapter **51**

Osmotic Regulation and the Urinary System

Chapter Outline

51.1   Osmolarity and Osmotic Balance

51.2   Osmoregulatory Organs

51.3   Evolution of the Vertebrate Kidney

51.4   Nitrogenous Wastes: Ammonia, Urea, and Uric Acid

51.5   The Mammalian Kidney

51.6   Hormonal Control of Osmoregulatory Functions

Introduction

The majority of your body weight is actually water, but you exist in a very dehydrating environment. The kangaroo rat pictured lives in a desert environment that is even more dehydrating and yet is so parsimonious with water that it never needs to drink; it generates sufficient water as a by-product of oxidizing its food. Fish can exist in both freshwater and marine environments, facing the challenge of either gaining or losing water, respectively. Life in these different environments is possible because elaborate mechanisms enable organisms to control the osmotic strength of their blood and extracellular fluids. The regulation of internal fluid and its composition is an example of homeostasis—the ability of living organisms to maintain internal conditions within an optimal range. In this chapter, we describe the osmoregulatory systems of a number of animals, including the mammalian urinary system. These organ systems maintain the water and ionic balance of fluids in the body.

51.1 Osmolarity and Osmotic Balance

Learning Outcomes

1. *Explain the importance of osmotic balance.*
2. *Describe how organisms are classified based on their method of osmotic regulation.*

Water in a multicellular animal's body is distributed between the intracellular and extracellular compartments (figure 51.1). To maintain osmotic balance, the extracellular compartment of an animal's body (including its blood plasma) must be able to take water from the environment and to excrete excess water into the environment. Inorganic ions must also be exchanged between the extracellular body fluids and the external environment to maintain homeostasis. Exchanges of water and electrolytes between the body and the external environment occur across specialized epithelial cells and, in most vertebrates, through a filtration process in the kidneys.

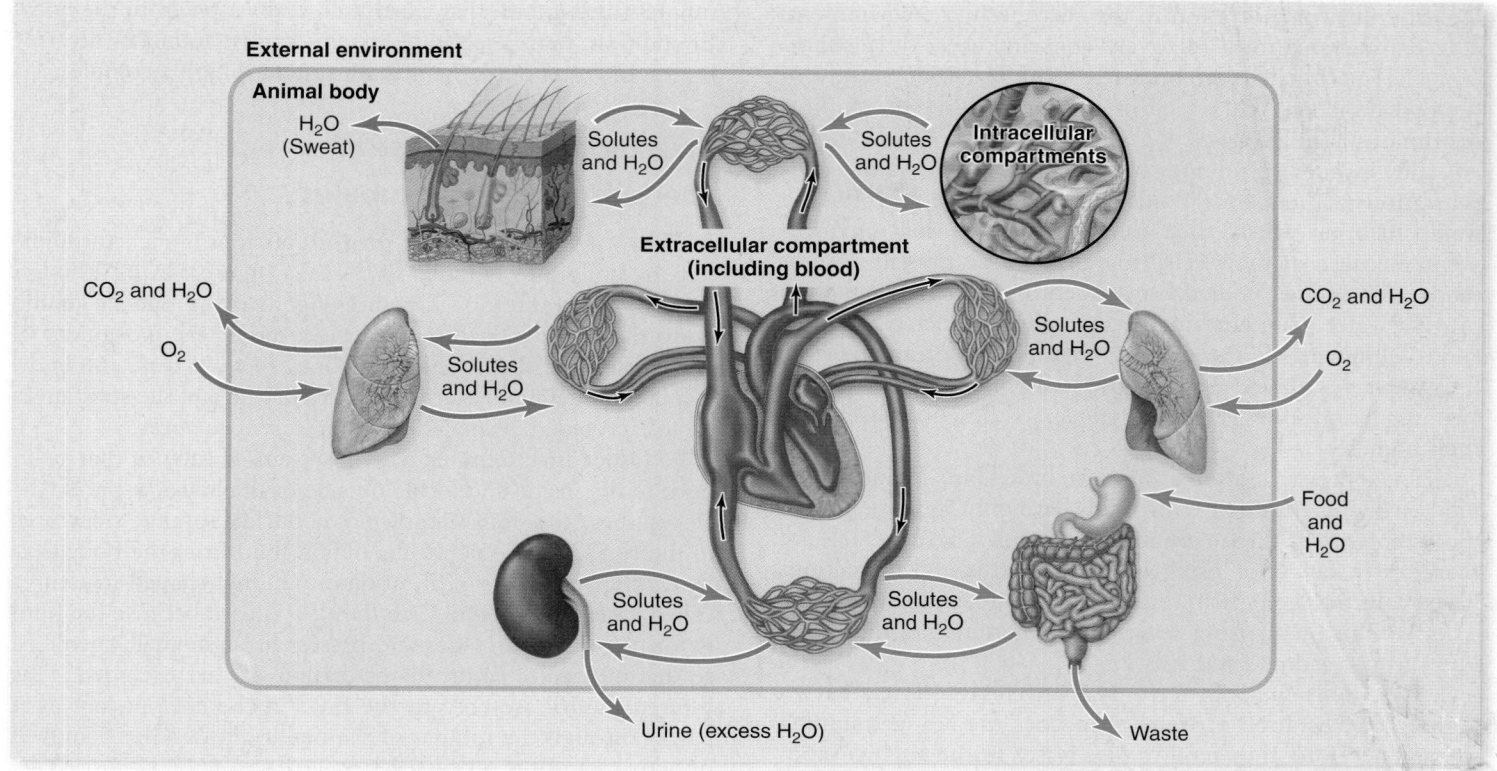

External environment

Animal body

H_2O (Sweat)

Solutes and H_2O

Solutes and H_2O

Intracellular compartments

CO_2 and H_2O

O_2

Solutes and H_2O

Extracellular compartment (including blood)

Solutes and H_2O

CO_2 and H_2O

O_2

Food and H_2O

Solutes and H_2O

Solutes and H_2O

Solutes and H_2O

Urine (excess H_2O)

Waste

Figure 51.1 **The interaction between intracellular and extracellular compartments of the body and the external environment.** Water can be taken in from the environment or lost to the environment. Exchanges of water and solutes between the extracellular fluids of the body and the environment occur across transport epithelia, and water and solutes can be filtered out of the blood by the kidneys. Overall, the amount of water and solutes that enters and leaves the body must be balanced in order to maintain homeostasis.

Most vertebrates maintain homeostasis for both the total solute concentration of their extracellular fluids and the concentration of specific inorganic ions. Sodium (Na^+) is the major cation in extracellular fluids, and chloride (Cl^-) is the major anion. The divalent cations, calcium (Ca^{2+}) and magnesium (Mg^{2+}), the monovalent cation K^+, as well as other ions, also have important functions and are maintained at constant levels.

Osmotic pressure is a measure of concentration difference

You learned in chapter 5 that osmosis is the diffusion of water across a semipermeable membrane. Osmosis always occurs from a more dilute solution (with a lower solute concentration) to a less dilute solution (with a higher solute concentration). The osmotic pressure of a solution is a measure of its tendency to take in water by osmosis. This is the amount of pressure needed to balance the pressure created by the movement of water.

A solution with a higher concentration of solute exerts more osmotic pressure. This is measured as the **osmolarity** of a solution, the number of osmotically active moles of solute per liter of solution. Notice that osmolarity can differ from molar concentration if a substance dissociates in solution into more than one osmotically active particle. For example, a 1 molar (M) solution of sucrose is also 1 osmolar (Osm), but a 1 M solution of NaCl is 2 Osm as it dissociates into two osmotically active ions.

The **tonicity** of a solution is a measure of the ability of the solution to change the volume of a cell by osmosis. An animal cell placed in a *hypertonic* solution loses water to the surrounding solution and shrinks. In contrast, an animal cell placed in a *hypotonic* solution gains water and expands. A cell in an *isotonic* solution shows no net water movement. In medical care, isotonic solutions such as normal saline and 5% dextrose are used to bathe exposed tissues and are given as intravenous fluids.

Osmoconformers live in marine environments

The osmolarity of body fluids in most marine invertebrates is the same as that of seawater (although the concentrations of particular solutes, such as Mg^{2+}, are not equal). Because the extracellular fluids are isotonic to seawater, no osmotic gradient exists, and there is no tendency for water to leave or enter the body. Such organisms are termed **osmoconformers**—they are in osmotic equilibrium with their environment.

Among the vertebrates, only the primitive hagfish are strict osmoconformers. The sharks and their relatives in the class Chondrichthyes (cartilaginous fish) are also isotonic to seawater, even though their blood level of NaCl is lower than that of seawater; the difference in total osmolarity is made up by retaining urea, as described later on.

Osmoregulators control their osmolarity internally

All other vertebrates are **osmoregulators**—that is, animals that maintain a relatively constant blood osmolarity despite the different concentration in the surrounding environment. The maintenance of a relatively constant body fluid osmolarity has permitted vertebrates to exploit a wide variety of ecological niches. Achieving this constancy, however, requires continuous regulation.

Freshwater vertebrates have a much higher solute concentration in their body fluids than that of the surrounding water. In other words, they are hypertonic to their environment. Because of their cells' higher osmotic pressure, water tends to enter their bodies. Consequently, they have adapted to prevent water from entering their bodies as much as possible and to eliminate the excess water that does enter. In addition, freshwater vertebrates tend to lose inorganic ions to their environment and so must actively transport these ions back into their bodies.

In contrast, most marine vertebrates are hypotonic to their environment; their body fluids have only about one-third the osmolarity of the surrounding seawater. These animals are therefore in danger of losing water by osmosis, and adaptations have evolved to help them retain water to prevent dehydration. They do this by drinking seawater and eliminating the excess ions through kidneys and gills.

The body fluids of terrestrial vertebrates clearly have a higher concentration of water than does the air surrounding them. Therefore, they tend to lose water to the air by evaporation from the skin and lungs. All reptiles, birds, and mammals, as well as amphibians during the time when they live on land, face this problem. Urinary/osmoregulatory systems have evolved in these vertebrates that help them retain water.

Learning Outcomes Review 51.1

Osmotic balance must be maintained so that tissues can carry out metabolic functions. Physiological mechanisms help most vertebrates keep blood osmolarity and ion concentrations relatively constant. Marine invertebrates are osmoconformers; their body fluids are isotonic to their environment. Most vertebrates are osmoregulators; their body fluids are either hypertonic or hypotonic compared to their environment.

■ *During osmosis, does water move toward regions of higher or lower osmolarity?*

51.2 Osmoregulatory Organs

Learning Outcomes

1. Describe invertebrate osmoregulatory organs.
2. Define reabsorption and secretion.

A variety of mechanisms have evolved in animals to cope with problems of water balance. In many animals, the removal of water or salts from the body is coupled with the removal of metabolic wastes through the excretory system. Single-celled protists employ contractile vacuoles for this purpose, as do sponges. Other multicellular animals have a system of excretory

tubules (little tubes) that expel fluid and wastes from the body. In addition, more elaborate systems can be found in invertebrates. In vertebrates, the urinary system is highly complex.

Invertebrates make use of specialized cells and tubules

In flatworms, tubules called **protonephridia** branch throughout the body into bulblike flame cells (figure 51.2). Although these simple excretory structures open to the outside of the body, they do not open to the inside; rather, the movement of cilia within the flame cells must draw in fluid from the body. Water and metabolites are then reabsorbed, and the substances to be excreted are expelled through excretory pores.

Other invertebrates have a system of tubules that open both to the inside and to the outside of the body. In the earthworm, these tubules are known as nephridia (orange structures in figure 51.3). The nephridia obtain fluid from the body cavity through a process of filtration into funnel-shaped structures called *nephrostomes*. The term *filtration* is used because the fluid is formed under pressure and passes through small openings, so that molecules larger than a certain size are excluded. This filtered fluid is isotonic to the fluid in the coelom, but as it passes through the tubules of the nephridia, NaCl is removed by active transport processes.

The general term for transport out of the tubule and into the surrounding body fluids is **reabsorption.** Because salt is

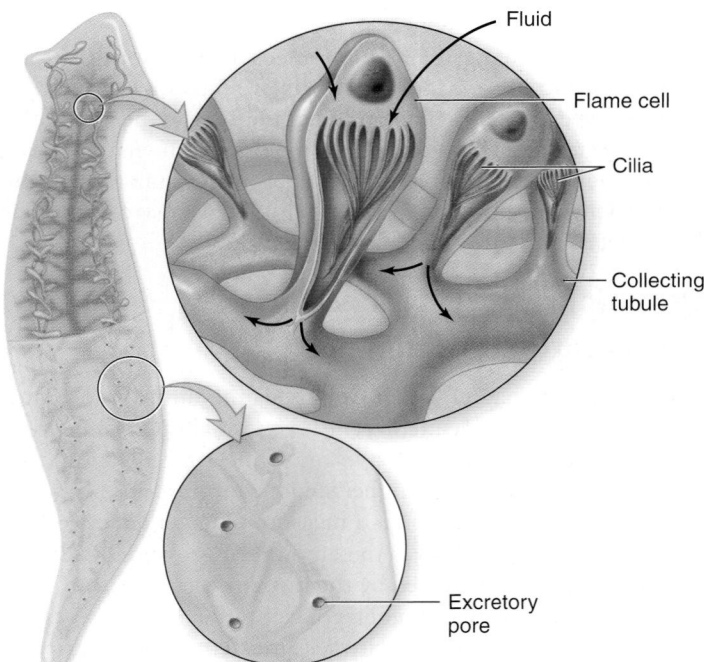

Figure 51.2 The protonephridia of flatworms. A branching system of tubules, bulblike flame cells, and excretory pores make up the protonephridia of flatworms. Cilia inside the flame cells draw in fluids from the body by their beating action. Substances are then expelled through pores that open to the outside of the body.

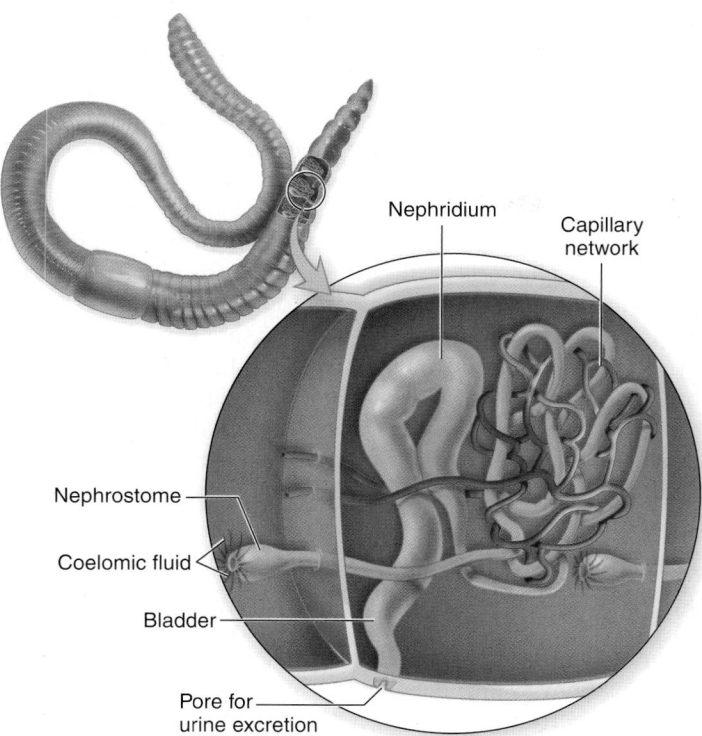

Figure 51.3 **The nephridia of annelids.** Most invertebrates, such as the annelid shown here, have nephridia (*orange*). These consist of tubules that receive a filtrate of coelomic fluid, which enters the funnel-like nephrostomes. Salt can be reabsorbed from these tubules, and the fluid that remains, urine, is released from pores into the external environment.

reabsorbed from the filtrate, the urine excreted is more dilute than the body fluids—that is, the urine is hypotonic. The kidneys of mollusks and the excretory organs of crustaceans (called *antennal glands*) also produce urine by filtration and reclaim certain ions by reabsorption.

Insects have a unique osmoregulatory system

The excretory organs in insects are the Malpighian tubules (figure 51.4), extensions of the digestive tract that branch off anterior to the hindgut. Urine is not formed by filtration in these tubules because there is no pressure difference between the blood in the body cavity and the tubule. Instead, waste molecules and potassium (K^+) ions are secreted into the tubules by active transport.

Secretion is the opposite of reabsorption—ions or molecules are transported from the body fluid into the tubule. The secretion of K^+ creates an osmotic gradient that causes water to enter the tubules by osmosis from the body's open circulatory system. Most of the water and K^+ is then reabsorbed into the circulatory system through the epithelium of the hindgut, leaving only small molecules and waste products to be excreted from the rectum along with feces. Malpighian tubules thus provide a very efficient means of water conservation.

The vertebrate kidney filters and then reabsorbs

The **kidneys** of vertebrates, unlike the Malpighian tubules of insects, create a tubular fluid by filtering the blood under pressure. In addition to waste products and water, the filtrate contains many small molecules, including glucose, amino acids, and vitamins, that are of value to the animal. These molecules and most of the water are reabsorbed from the tubules into the blood, while wastes remain in the filtrate. Additional wastes may be secreted by the tubules and added to the filtrate, and the final waste product, urine, is eliminated from the body.

It may seem odd that the vertebrate kidney should filter out almost everything from blood plasma (except proteins, which are too large to be filtered) and then spend energy to take back or reabsorb what the body needs. But selective reabsorption provides great flexibility. Various vertebrate groups have evolved the ability to reabsorb molecules that are especially valuable in particular habitats. This flexibility is a key factor underlying the successful colonization of many diverse environments by the vertebrates. In the rest of this chapter, we focus on the vertebrate kidney and its elimination of waste materials, notably nitrogen compounds.

Learning Outcomes Review 51.2

Many invertebrates filter fluid into a system of tubules and then reabsorb ions and water, leaving waste products for excretion. Insects create an excretory fluid by secreting K^+ and waste products into tubules, which draw water osmotically. The vertebrate kidney produces a filtrate that enters tubules and is modified to become urine.

■ *How are the function of Malpighian tubules and kidneys similar?*

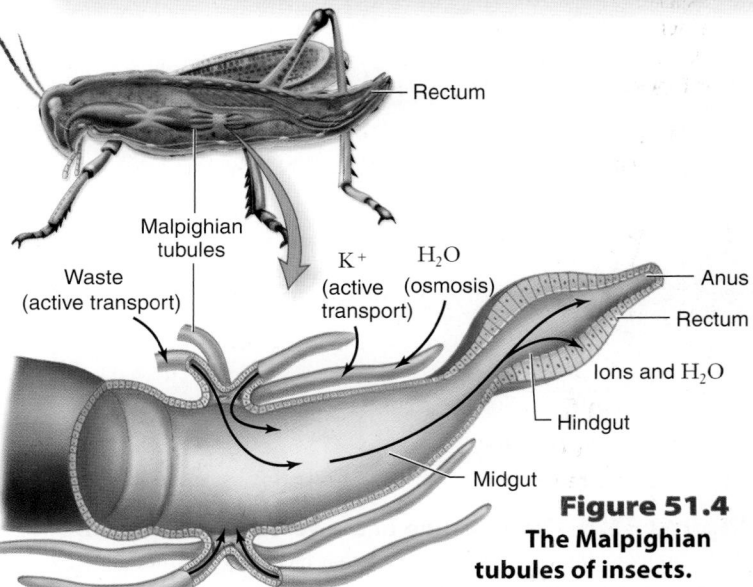

Figure 51.4 **The Malpighian tubules of insects.** The Malpighian tubules of insects are extensions of the digestive tract that collect water and wastes from the body's circulatory system. K^+ is secreted into these tubules, drawing water with it osmotically. Much of this water (*arrows*) is reabsorbed across the wall of the hindgut.

51.3 Evolution of the Vertebrate Kidney

Learning Outcomes

1. Contrast osmotic adaptations of freshwater fish with those of marine fish.
2. Explain the significance of the loop of Henle in mammalian and avian kidneys.

The kidney is a complex organ made up of thousands of repeating units called **nephrons,** each with the structure of a loop that penetrates deep into the medulla of the kidney (shown schematically in figure 51.5). Blood pressure forces the fluid in blood out of a ball of capillaries called the *glomerulus* into *Bowman's capsule,* the beginning of the tubule system. This process filters the blood forming the tubular filtrate that can then be modified by the rest of the nephron. The glomerulus retains blood cells, proteins, and other useful large molecules in the blood, but it allows the water, and the small molecules and wastes dissolved in it, to pass through and into the tubule system of the nephron. As the filtered fluid passes through the nephron tube, useful nutrients and ions are reabsorbed from it by both active and passive transport mechanisms, leaving the water and metabolic wastes behind in a fluid urine. (The details of this process are described in a later section.)

Although the same basic design has been retained in all vertebrate kidneys, a few modifications have occurred. Because the original glomerular filtrate is isotonic to blood, all vertebrates can produce a urine that is isotonic to blood by reabsorbing ions and water in equal proportions. Or, they can produce a urine that is hypotonic to blood—more dilute than the blood—by reabsorbing relatively less water. Only birds and mammals can reabsorb enough water from their glomerular filtrate to produce a urine that is hypertonic to blood—more concentrated than the blood—by reabsorbing relatively more water.

Freshwater fishes must retain electrolytes and keep water out

Kidneys are thought to have evolved among the freshwater teleosts, or bony fishes. Because the body fluids of a freshwater fish are hypertonic with respect to the surrounding water, these animals face two serious problems: (1) Water tends to enter the body from the environment; and (2) solutes tend to leave the body and enter the environment.

Freshwater fish address the first problem by *not* drinking water and by excreting a large volume of dilute urine, which is hypotonic to their body fluids. They address the second problem by reabsorbing ions across the nephron tubules, from the glomerular filtrate back into the blood. In addition, they actively transport ions across their gill surfaces from the surrounding water into the blood (figure 51.6, left).

Marine bony fishes must excrete electrolytes and keep water in

Although most groups of animals seem to have evolved first in the sea, marine bony fish (teleosts) probably evolved from freshwater ancestors. They faced significant new problems in making the transition to the sea because their body fluids were, and are, hypotonic to seawater. Consequently, water tends to leave their bodies by osmosis across their gills, and they also lose water in their urine. To compensate for this continuous water loss, marine fish drink large amounts of seawater (figure 51.6, right).

Many of the divalent cations (principally, Ca^{2+} and Mg^{2+}) in the seawater that a marine fish drinks remain in the digestive tract and are eliminated through the anus. Some, however, are absorbed into the blood, as are the monovalent ions K^+, Na^+, and Cl^-. Most of the monovalent ions are actively transported out of the blood across the gill surfaces, whereas the divalent ions that enter the blood are secreted into the nephron tubules and excreted in the urine. In these two ways, marine bony fish eliminate the ions they get from the seawater they drink. The urine they excrete is isotonic to their body fluids. It is more concentrated than the urine of freshwater fish, but not as concentrated as that of birds and mammals.

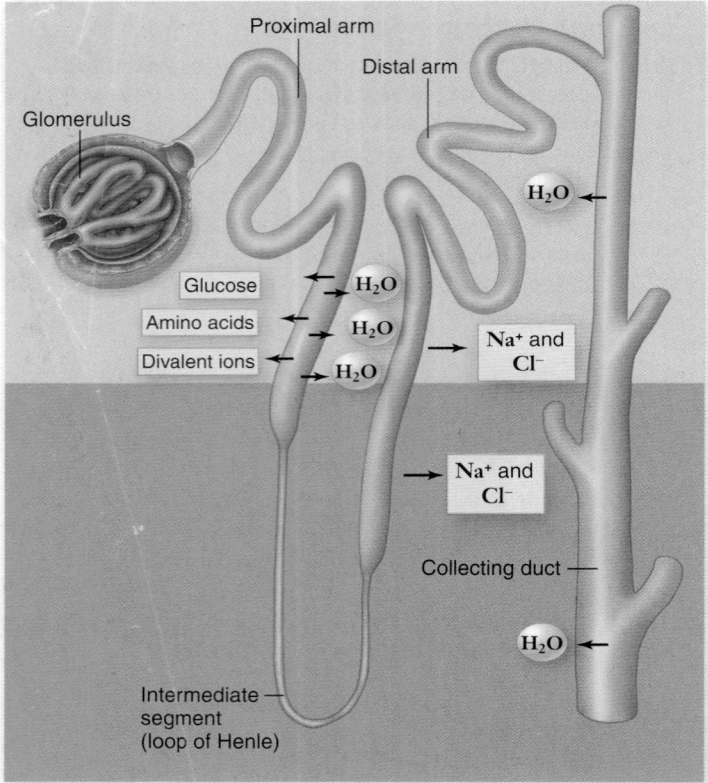

Figure 51.5 Organization of the vertebrate nephron. The nephron tubule is a basic design that has been retained in the kidneys of vertebrates. Sugars, amino acids, water, important monovalent ions, and divalent ions are reabsorbed in the proximal arm; water and monovalent ions such as Na^+ and Cl^- are reabsorbed in the loop of Henle; varying amounts of water and monovalent ions (Na^+ and Cl^-) can be reabsorbed in the distal arm and the collecting duct, depending on hormonal influences.

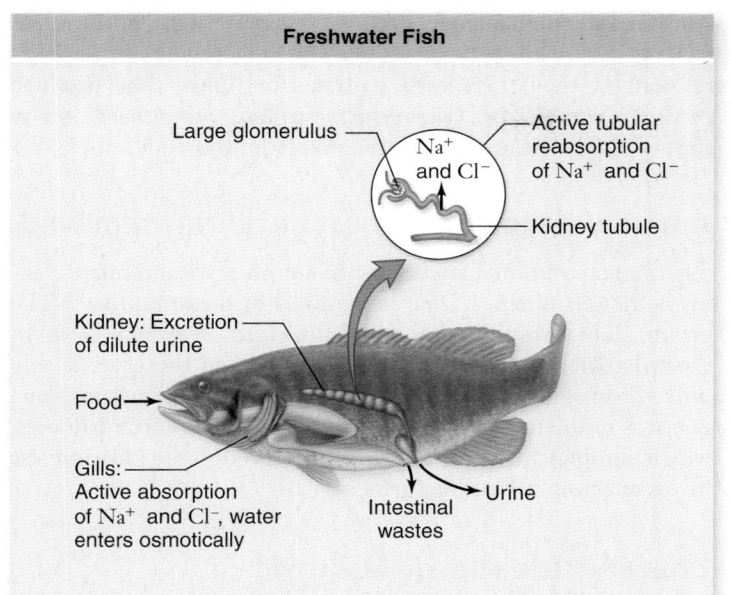

Freshwater Fish

Large glomerulus

Na⁺ and Cl⁻

Active tubular reabsorption of Na⁺ and Cl⁻

Kidney tubule

Kidney: Excretion of dilute urine

Food

Gills: Active absorption of Na⁺ and Cl⁻, water enters osmotically

Intestinal wastes

Urine

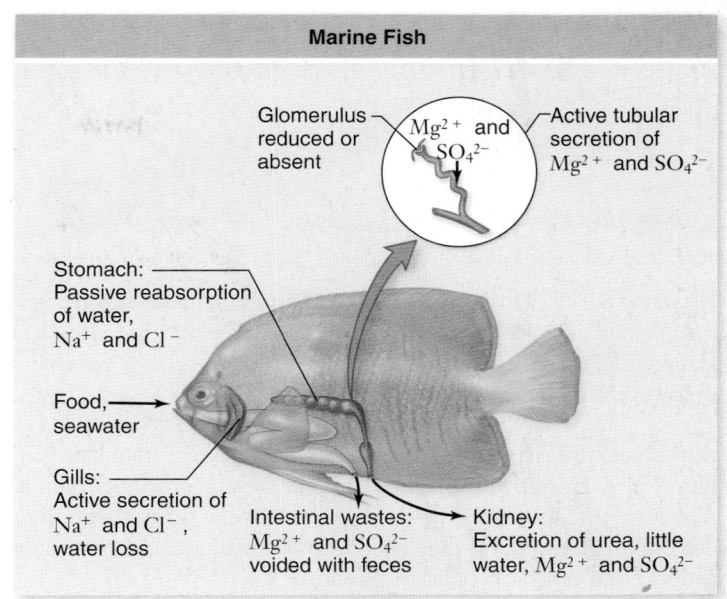

Marine Fish

Glomerulus reduced or absent

Mg^{2+} and SO_4^{2-}

Active tubular secretion of Mg^{2+} and SO_4^{2-}

Stomach: Passive reabsorption of water, Na⁺ and Cl⁻

Food, seawater

Gills: Active secretion of Na⁺ and Cl⁻, water loss

Intestinal wastes: Mg^{2+} and SO_4^{2-} voided with feces

Kidney: Excretion of urea, little water, Mg^{2+} and SO_4^{2-}

Figure 51.6 **Freshwater and marine teleosts face different osmotic problems.** Whereas the freshwater teleost is hypertonic to its environment, the marine teleost is hypotonic to seawater. To compensate for its tendency to take in water and lose ions, a freshwater fish excretes dilute urine, avoids drinking water, and reabsorbs ions across the nephron tubules. To compensate for its osmotic loss of water, the marine teleost drinks seawater and eliminates the excess ions through active transport across epithelia in the gills and kidneys.

Cartilaginous fishes pump out electrolytes and retain urea

The elasmobranchs, including sharks and rays, are by far the most common subclass in the class Chondrichthyes (cartilaginous fish). Elasmobranchs have solved the osmotic problem posed by their seawater environment in a different way. Instead of having body fluids that are hypotonic to seawater, so that they have to continuously drink seawater and actively pump out ions, the elasmobranchs reabsorb urea from the nephron tubules and maintain a blood urea concentration that is 100 times higher than that of mammals.

The added urea makes elasmobranchs' blood approximately isotonic to the surrounding sea. Because no net water movement occurs between isotonic solutions, water loss is therefore prevented. As a result, these fishes do not need to drink seawater for osmotic balance, and their kidneys and gills do not have to remove large amounts of ions from their bodies. The enzymes and tissues of the cartilaginous fish have evolved to tolerate the high urea concentrations.

Amphibians and reptiles have osmotic adaptations to their environments

The first terrestrial vertebrates were the amphibians, and the amphibian kidney is identical to that of freshwater fish. This is not surprising because amphibians spend a significant portion of their time in fresh water, and when on land, they generally stay in wet places. Amphibians produce a very dilute urine and compensate for their loss of Na⁺ by actively transporting Na⁺ across their skin from the surrounding water.

Reptiles, on the other hand, live in diverse habitats. Those living mainly in fresh water occupy a habitat similar to that of the freshwater fish and amphibians, and thus have similar kidneys. Marine reptiles, including some crocodilians, sea turtles, sea snakes, and one lizard, possess kidneys similar to those of their freshwater relatives, but they face opposite problems—they tend to lose water and take in salts. Like marine bony fish, they drink seawater and excrete an isotonic urine. Marine reptiles eliminate excess salt through salt glands located near the nose or the eye.

The kidneys of terrestrial reptiles also reabsorb much of the salt and water in their nephron tubules, helping somewhat to conserve blood volume in dry environments. Like fish and amphibians, they cannot produce urine that is more concentrated than the blood plasma; however, they don't really excrete urine, but instead empty it into a cloaca (the common exit of the digestive and urinary tracts), where additional water can be reabsorbed and the wastes excreted with the feces.

Mammals and birds are able to excrete concentrated urine and retain water

Mammals and birds are the only vertebrates able to produce urine with a higher osmotic concentration than their body fluids. These vertebrates are therefore able to excrete their waste products in a small volume of water, so that more water can be retained in the body.

Human kidneys can produce urine that is as much as 4.2 times as concentrated as blood plasma, but the kidneys of some other mammals are even more efficient at conserving water. For example, camels, gerbils, and pocket mice of the genus *Perognathus*

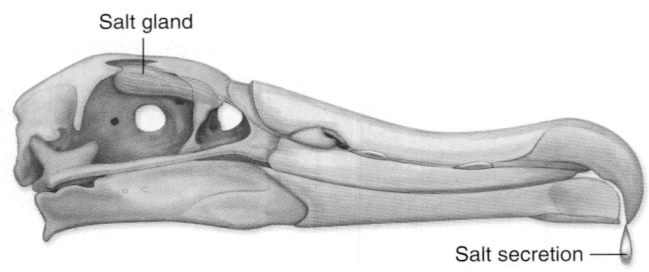

Salt gland

Salt secretion

Figure 51.7 How marine birds cope with excess salt.
Marine birds drink seawater and then excrete the salt through salt glands. The extremely salty fluid excreted by these glands can then dribble down the beak.

can excrete urine that is 8, 14, and 22 times as concentrated as their blood plasma, respectively. The kidneys of kangaroo rats (genus *Dipodomys*) are so efficient that they never have to drink water; they can obtain all the water they need from their food and from water produced in aerobic cellular respiration.

The production of hypertonic urine is accomplished by the *loop of Henle* portion of the nephron (see figures 51.5 and 51.11), found only in mammals and birds. The degree of concentration depends on the length of the loop; most mammals have some nephrons with short loops and other nephrons with much longer loops. Birds, however, have relatively few or no nephrons with long loops, so they cannot produce urine that is as concentrated as that of mammals. At most, they can only reabsorb enough water to produce a urine that is about twice the concentration of their blood. Marine birds solve the problem of water loss by drinking salt water and then excreting the excess salt from salt glands near the eyes (figure 51.7).

The moderately hypertonic urine of a bird is delivered to its cloaca, along with the fecal material from its digestive tract. If needed, additional water can be absorbed across the wall of the cloaca to produce a semisolid white paste or pellet, which is excreted.

Learning Outcomes Review 51.3

The kidneys of freshwater fishes must excrete copious amounts of very dilute urine. Marine bony fishes drink seawater and excrete an isotonic urine; cartilaginous fishes retain urea, which prevents water loss. In mammals and birds, the loop of Henle allows reabsorption of water from the urine, making it hypertonic to their body fluids.

■ *Mammals and birds have nephrons with a loop of Henle, but reptiles do not. What are the possible evolutionary explanations for this?*

51.4 Nitrogenous Wastes: Ammonia, Urea, and Uric Acid

Learning Outcome

1. Describe the different kinds of nitrogenous waste and their relative toxicity.

Amino acids and nucleic acids are nitrogen-containing molecules. When animals catabolize these molecules for energy or convert them into carbohydrates or lipids, they produce nitrogen-containing by-products called *nitrogenous wastes* (figure 51.8) that must be eliminated from the body.

Ammonia is toxic and must be quickly removed

The first step in the metabolism of amino acids and nucleic acids is the deamination, that is, removal of the amino ($-NH_2$) group, and its combination with H^+ to form *ammonia* (NH_3) in the liver. Ammonia is quite toxic to cells and therefore is safe only in very dilute concentrations. The excretion of ammonia is not a problem for the bony fishes and amphibian tadpoles, which eliminate most of it by diffusion through the gills and less by excretion in very dilute urine.

Urea and uric acid are less toxic but have different solubilities

In elasmobranchs, adult amphibians, and mammals, the nitrogenous wastes are eliminated in the far less toxic form of **urea.** Urea is water-soluble and so can be excreted in large amounts in the urine. It is carried in the bloodstream from its place of synthesis in the liver to the kidneys where it is excreted.

Reptiles, birds, and insects excrete nitrogenous wastes in the form of **uric acid,** which is only slightly soluble in water. As a result of its low solubility, uric acid precipitates and thus can be excreted using very little water. Uric acid forms the pasty white material in bird droppings called *guano*. It costs the animal energy to synthesize uric acid, but this is offset by the conservation of water.

The ability to synthesize uric acid in these groups of animals is also important because their eggs are encased within shells, and nitrogenous wastes build up as the embryo grows within the egg. The formation of uric acid, although a lengthy process that requires considerable energy, produces a compound that crystallizes and precipitates. As a solid precipitate, uric acid is unable to affect the embryo's development even though it is still inside the egg.

Mammals also produce some uric acid, but it is a waste product of the degradation of purine nucleotides, not of amino acids. Most mammals have an enzyme called *uricase*, which converts uric acid into a more soluble derivative, **allantoin.** Only humans, apes, and the Dalmatian dog lack this enzyme, and they must excrete the uric acid. In humans, excessive accumulation of uric acid in the joints produces a condition known as *gout*.

Learning Outcome Review 51.4

Metabolic breakdown of amino acids and nucleic acids produces ammonia as a by-product. Bony fishes and gilled amphibians excrete ammonia; other vertebrates convert nitrogenous wastes into urea (reptiles and birds) and uric acid (mammals and adult amphibians), which are less toxic. Most mammals produce a small amount of uric acid that is broken down by uricase except in humans, apes, and the Dalmatian dog.

■ *Why is nitrogenous waste problematic?*

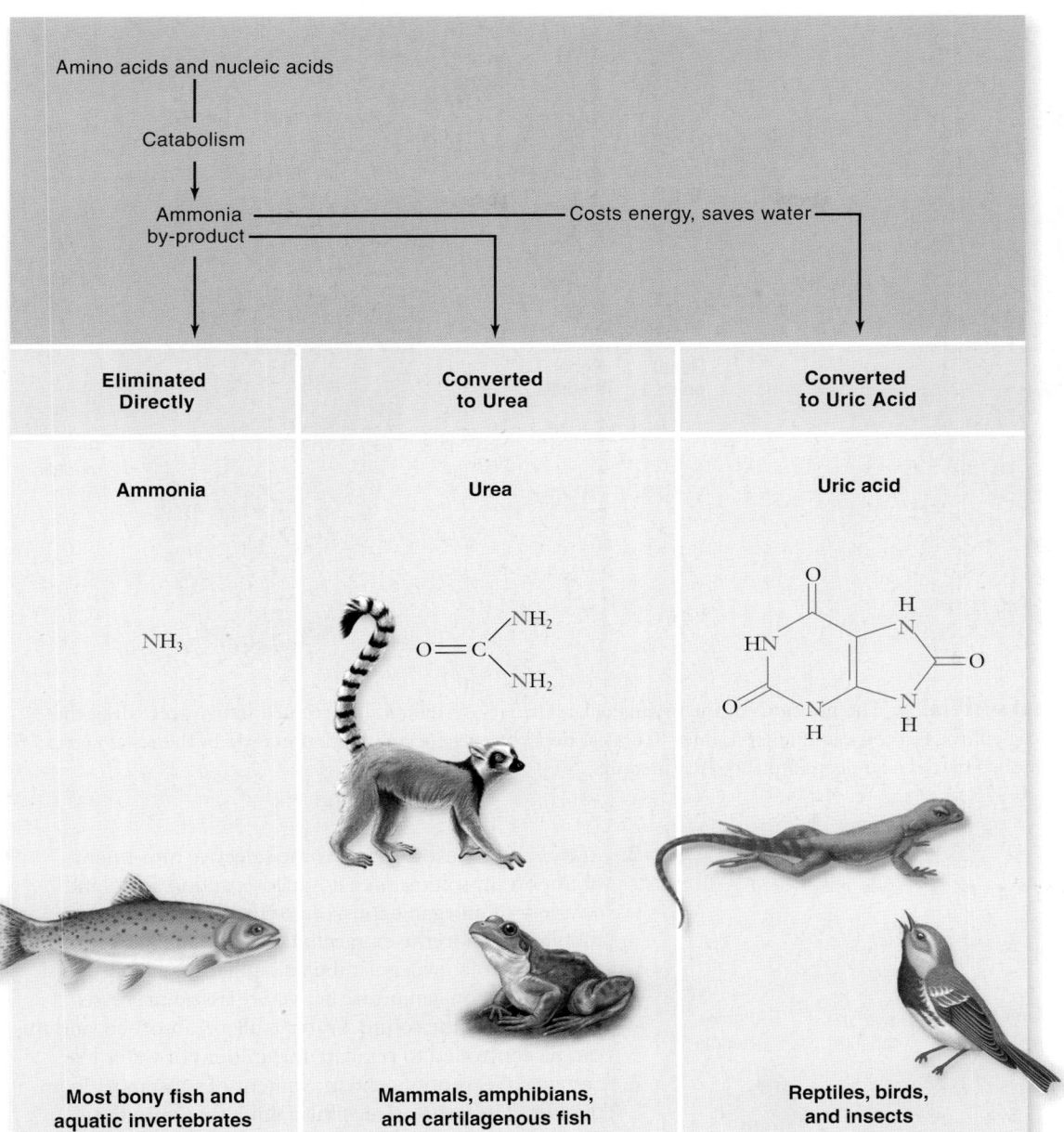

Figure 51.8
Nitrogenous wastes.
When amino acids and nucleic acids are metabolized, the immediate by-product is ammonia, which is quite toxic but can be eliminated through the gills of teleost fish. Mammals convert ammonia into urea, which is less toxic. Birds and terrestrial reptiles convert it instead into uric acid, which is insoluble in water. Production of uric acid is the most energetically expensive of the three but also saves the most water.

Within the figure:

Amino acids and nucleic acids

Catabolism

Ammonia by-product — Costs energy, saves water —

Eliminated Directly	Converted to Urea	Converted to Uric Acid
Ammonia	Urea	Uric acid
NH₃	O=C(NH₂)(NH₂)	
Most bony fish and aquatic invertebrates	Mammals, amphibians, and cartilagenous fish	Reptiles, birds, and insects

51.5 The Mammalian Kidney

Learning Outcomes

1. *Describe the actions of filtration, reabsorption, and secretion.*
2. *Name the primary components of the kidney.*
3. *Describe the main parts of a neprhon.*

In humans, the kidneys are fist-sized organs located in the lower back. Each kidney receives blood from a renal artery, and from this blood, urine is produced. Urine drains from each kidney through a **ureter,** which carries the urine to a **urinary bladder.**

From the bladder, urine is passed out of the body through the **urethra** (figure 51.9).

Within the kidney, the mouth of the ureter flares open to form a funnel-like structure, the *renal pelvis.* The renal pelvis, in turn, has cup-shaped extensions that receive urine from the renal tissue. The renal tissue is divided into an outer **renal cortex** and an inner **renal medulla.**

The kidney has three basic functions summarized in figure 51.10:

1. *Filtration:* Fluid in the blood is filtered into the tubule system, leaving cells and large protein in the blood and a filtrate composed of water and all of the blood solutes. This filtrate is modified by the rest of the kidney to produce urine for excretion.

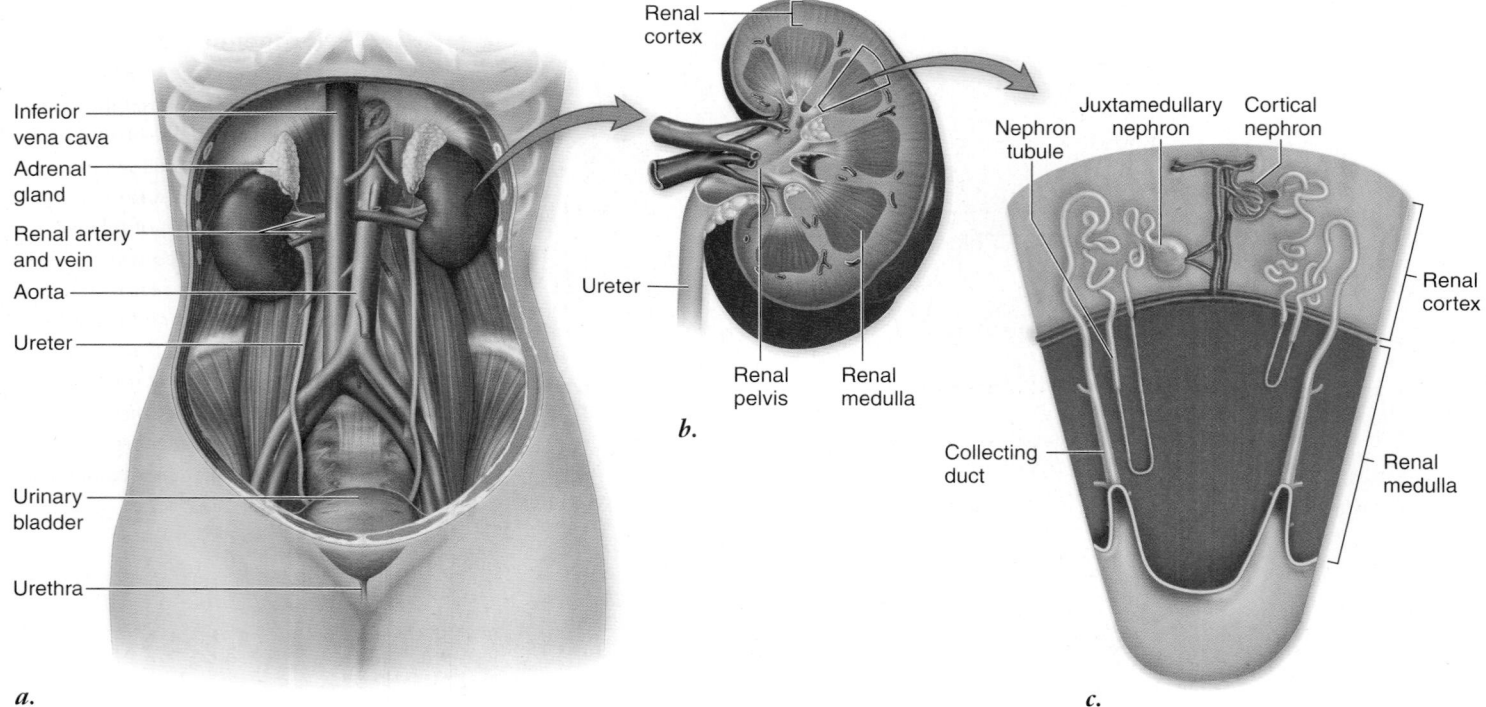

Figure 51.9 The human renal system. *a.* The positions of the organs of the urinary system. *b.* A sectioned kidney, revealing the internal structure. *c.* The position of nephrons in the mammalian kidney. Cortical nephrons are located predominantly in the renal cortex; juxtamedullary nephrons have long loops that extend deep into the renal medulla.

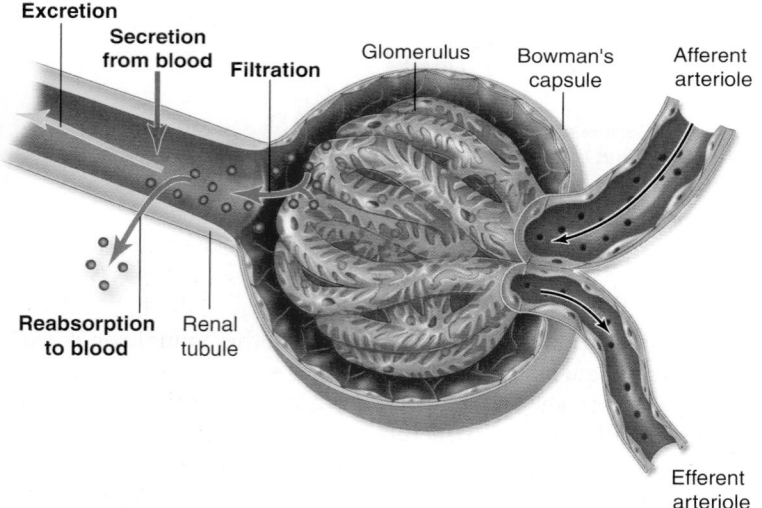

Figure 51.10 Four functions of the kidney. Molecules enter the urine by filtration out of the glomerulus and by secretion into the tubules from surrounding peritubular capillaries. Molecules that entered the filtrate can be returned to the blood by reabsorption from the tubules into surrounding peritubular capillaries. The fluid exiting the kidney is eliminated from the body by excretion through the tubule to a ureter and then to the bladder.

2. *Reabsorption:* Reabsorption is the selective movement of important solutes such as glucose, amino acids, and a variety of inorganic ions, out of the filtrate in the tubule system to the extracellular fluid, then back into the bloodstream via peritubular capillaries. The process of reabsorption can utilize active or passive processes depending on the solute. Water is also reabsorbed, and this can be controlled to regulate the amount of water loss.
3. *Secretion:* Secretion is the movement of substances from the blood into the extracellular fluid, then into the filtrate in the tubule system. Unlike reabsorption, which preserves substances in the body, this adds to what will be expelled from the body and can be used to remove toxic substances.

The nephron is the filtering unit of the kidney

On a microscopic level, each kidney contains about a million functioning *nephrons.* Mammalian kidneys contain a mixture of **juxtamedullary nephrons,** which have long loops that dip deeply into the medulla, and **cortical nephrons** with shorter loops. The significance of the length of the loops will be explained a little later.

The production of filtrate

Each nephron consists of a long tubule and associated small blood vessels (figure 51.11). First, blood is carried by an *afferent arteriole* to a tuft of capillaries in the renal cortex—the **glomerulus.** Here the blood is filtered as the blood pressure forces fluid through the porous capillary walls. Blood cells

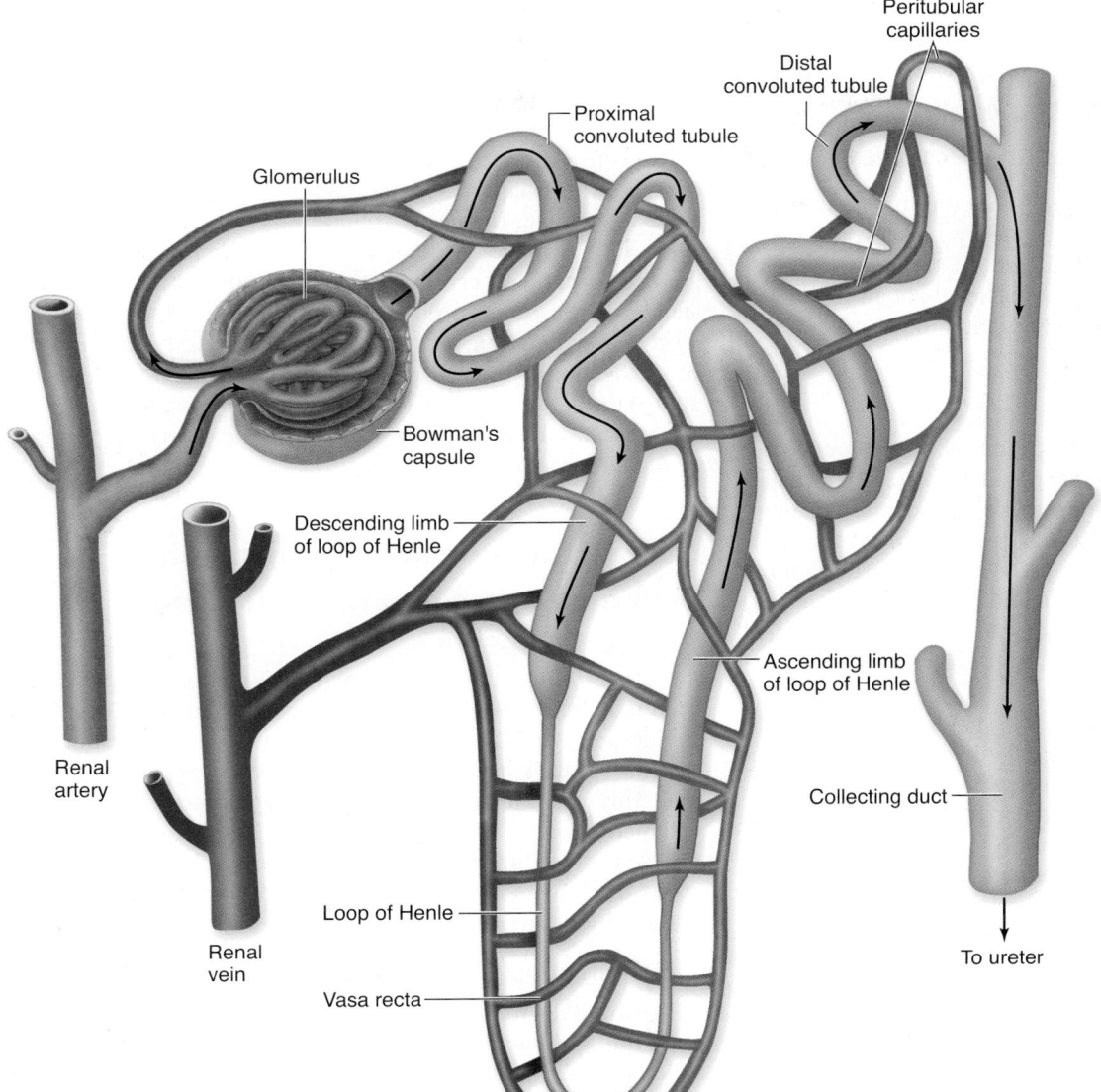

Figure 51.11
A nephron in a mammalian kidney.
The nephron tubule is surrounded by peritubular capillaries in the cortex, and their vasa recta extensions surround the loop of Henle in the medulla. This capillary bed carries away molecules and ions that are reabsorbed from the filtrate.

Peritubular capillaries

Distal convoluted tubule

Proximal convoluted tubule

Glomerulus

Bowman's capsule

Descending limb of loop of Henle

Ascending limb of loop of Henle

Renal artery

Renal vein

Loop of Henle

Vasa recta

Collecting duct

To ureter

and plasma proteins are too large to enter this glomerular filtrate, but large amounts of the plasma, consisting of water and dissolved molecules, leave the vascular system at this step. The filtrate immediately enters the first region of the nephron tubules. This region, **Bowman's capsule,** envelops the glomerulus much as a large, soft balloon surrounds your hand if you press your fist into it. The capsule has slit openings so that the glomerular filtrate can enter the system of nephron tubules.

Blood components that were not filtered out of the glomerulus drain into an *efferent arteriole,* which then empties into a second bed of capillaries called **peritubular capillaries** that surround the tubules. This is only one of several locations in the body where two capillary beds occur in series. In juxtamedullary nephrons, efferent arteriole and peritubular capillaries also feed the **vasa recta** capillaries that surround the loop of Henle. As described later, the peritubular capillaries are needed for the processes of reabsorption and secretion.

After the filtrate enters Bowman's capsule, it goes into a portion of the nephron called the **proximal convoluted tubule,** located in the cortex. In a cortical nephron, the fluid then flows through the **loop of Henle** that dips only minimally into the medulla before ascending back into the cortex. In juxtamedullary nephrons, the loop of Henle extends much deeper into the medulla before ascending back up into the cortex. More water can be reabsorbed from juxtamedullary nephrons than from cortical nephrons. The fluid then moves deeper into the medulla and back up again into the cortex in a loop of Henle. As mentioned earlier, only the kidneys of mammals and birds have loops of Henle, and this is why only birds and mammals have the ability to concentrate their urine.

Collection of urine

After leaving the loop, the fluid is delivered to a **distal convoluted tubule** in the cortex that next drains into a **collecting duct.** The collecting duct again descends into the medulla, where it merges with other collecting ducts to empty its contents, now called urine, into the renal pelvis.

Water, some nutrients, and some ions are reabsorbed; other molecules are secreted

Most of the water and dissolved solutes that enter the glomerular filtrate must be returned to the blood by reabsorption, or the animal would literally urinate to death. In a human, for example, approximately 2000 L of blood passes through the kidneys each day, and 180 L of water leaves the blood and enters the glomerular filtrate.

Water

Because humans have a total blood volume of only about 5 L and produce only 1 to 2 L of urine per day, it is obvious that each liter of blood is filtered many times per day, and most of the filtered water is reabsorbed. Water is reabsorbed from the filtrate by the proximal convoluted tubule, as it passes through the descending loop of Henle and the collecting duct. The selective reabsorption in the collecting duct is driven by an osmotic gradient produced by the loop of Henle, as is described shortly.

Glucose and other nutrients

The reabsorption of glucose, amino acids, and many other molecules needed by the body is driven by active transport and secondary active transport (cotransport) carriers. As in all carrier-mediated transport, a maximum rate of transport is reached whenever the carriers are saturated (see chapter 5).

In the case of the renal glucose carriers in the proximal convoluted tubule, saturation occurs when the concentration of glucose in the blood (and thus in the glomerular filtrate) is about 180 mg/100 mL of blood. If a person has a blood glucose concentration in excess of this amount, as happens in untreated diabetes mellitus, the glucose remaining in the filtrate is expelled in the urine. Indeed, the presence of glucose in the urine is diagnostic of diabetes mellitus.

Secretion of wastes

The secretion of foreign molecules and particular waste products of the body involves the transport of these molecules across the membranes of the blood capillaries and kidney tubules into the filtrate. This process is similar to reabsorption, but it proceeds in the opposite direction.

Some secreted molecules are eliminated in the urine so rapidly that they may be cleared from the blood in a single pass through the kidneys. This rapid elimination explains why penicillin, which is secreted by the nephrons, must be administered in very high doses and several times per day.

Excretion of toxins and excess ions maintains homeostasis

A major function of the kidney is the elimination of a variety of potentially harmful substances that animals eat and drink. In addition, urine contains nitrogenous wastes, described earlier, that are products of the catabolism of amino acids and nucleic acids. Urine may also contain excess K^+, H^+, and other ions that are removed from the blood.

Urine's generally high H^+ concentration (pH 5 to 7) helps maintain the acid–base balance of the blood within a narrow range (pH 7.35 to 7.45). Moreover, the excretion of water in urine contributes to the maintenance of blood volume and pressure (see chapter 50); the larger the volume of urine excreted, the lower the blood volume.

The purpose of kidney function is therefore homeostasis; the kidneys are critically involved in maintaining the constancy of the internal environment. When disease interferes with kidney function, it causes a rise in the blood concentration of nitrogenous waste products, disturbances in electrolyte and acid–base balance, and a failure in blood pressure regulation. Such potentially fatal changes highlight the central importance of the kidneys in normal body physiology.

Each part of the mammalian nephron performs a specific transport function

As previously described, approximately 180 L of isotonic glomerular filtrate enters the Bowman's capsules of human kidneys each day. After passing through the remainder of the nephron tubules, this volume of fluid would be lost as urine if it were not reabsorbed back into the blood. It is clearly impossible to produce this much urine, yet water is only able to pass through a cell membrane by osmosis, and osmosis is not possible between two isotonic solutions. Therefore, some mechanism is needed to create an osmotic gradient between the glomerular filtrate and the blood, to allow reabsorption of water.

Proximal convoluted tubule

Virtually all the nutrient molecules in the filtrate are reabsorbed back into the systemic blood by the proximal convoluted tubule. In addition, approximately two-thirds of the NaCl and water filtered into Bowman's capsule is immediately reabsorbed across the walls of the proximal convoluted tubule.

This reabsorption is driven by the active transport of Na^+ out of the filtrate and into surrounding peritubular capillaries. Cl^- follows Na^+ passively because of electrical attraction, and water follows them both because of osmosis. Because NaCl and water are removed from the filtrate in proportionate amounts, the filtrate that remains in the tubule is still isotonic to the blood plasma.

Although only one-third of the initial volume of filtrate remains in the nephron tubule after the initial reabsorption of NaCl and water, it still represents a large volume (60 L out of the original 180 L of filtrate). Obviously, no animal can afford to excrete that much urine, so most of this water must also be reabsorbed. It is reabsorbed primarily across the wall of the collecting duct.

Loop of Henle

The function of the loop of Henle is to create a gradient of increasing osmolarity from the cortex to the medulla. This allows water to be reabsorbed by osmosis in the collecting duct as it runs down into the medulla past the loop of Henle. The descending and ascending limbs of the loop of Henle differ structurally and in their permeability to ions and water. This produces a gradient of increasing osmolarity from cortex to medulla (figure 51.12). The structure of the loop also forms another example of a countercurrent system, this time acting to increase the osmolarity of interstitial fluid. To understand the functioning of the loop of Henle, it is easiest to start in the ascending limb:

1. The entire ascending limb is impermeable to water. The thick portion of the ascending limb actively transports Na^+ out of the tubule, with Cl^- passively following. The thin ascending limb is permeable to both Na^+ and Cl^-, which move out by diffusion.

2. The descending limb is thin and permeable to water but not to NaCl. Because of the Na^+ and Cl^- lost by the ascending limb, the osmolarity of the interstitial fluid is higher than in the descending limb, and water moves out of the descending limb by osmosis. This also increases the osmolarity of the fluid in the tubule such that as it turns at the bottom, it will lose NaCl by diffusion in the thin ascending loop as described earlier.

3. The loss of water from the descending limb multiplies the concentration that can be achieved at each level of the loop through the active extrusion of Na^+ (with Cl^- following passively) by the ascending limb. The longer the loop of Henle, the longer the region of interaction between the descending and ascending limbs, and the greater the total concentration that can be achieved. In a human kidney, the concentration of filtrate entering the loop is 300 milliosmolar (mOsm), and this concentration is multiplied to more than 1200 mOsm at the bottom of the longest loops of Henle in the renal medulla.

4. The NaCl pumped out of the ascending limb of the loop is reabsorbed from the surrounding interstitial fluid into the loops of the *vasa recta*, so that NaCl can diffuse from the blood leaving the medulla to the blood entering the medulla. Thus, the vasa recta also functions in a countercurrent exchange, similar to that described for the countercurrent flow of blood in the fins of large aquatic vertebrates for heat exchange (see chapter 43), and of water and blood through gills to enhance oxygen exchange (see chapter 49). In the case of the vasa recta, this exchange prevents the flow of blood through the capillaries from destroying the osmotic gradient established by the loop of Henle. Thus, blood can be supplied to this region of the kidney without affecting the ability of the collecting duct to selectively reabsorb water.

Because fluid flows in opposite directions in the two limbs of the loop, the action of the loop of Henle in creating a hypertonic renal medulla is known as the countercurrent multiplier system. The osmotic gradient that is established is greater than what would be produced by just active transport of salts out of the tubule system.

The high solute concentration of the renal medulla is primarily the result of NaCl accumulation by the countercurrent multiplier system, but urea also contributes to the total osmolarity of the medulla. The descending limb of the loop of Henle and the collecting duct are both permeable to urea, which leaves these regions of the nephron by diffusion.

Distal convoluted tubule and collecting duct

Because NaCl was pumped out of the ascending limb, the filtrate that arrives at the distal convoluted tubule and enters the collecting duct in the renal cortex is hypotonic (with a concentration of only 100 mOsm). The collecting duct carrying this dilute fluid now plunges into the medulla. As a result of the hypertonic interstitial fluid of the renal medulla, a strong osmotic gradient pulls water out of the collecting duct and into the surrounding blood vessels.

The osmotic gradient is normally constant, but the permeability of the distal convoluted tubule and the collecting duct to water is adjusted by a hormone, *antidiuretic hormone* (ADH), mentioned in chapters 46 and 50. When an animal needs to conserve water, the posterior pituitary gland secretes more ADH, and this hormone increases the number of water channels in the plasma membranes of the collecting duct cells. This increases the permeability of the collecting ducts to water so that more water is reabsorbed and less is excreted in the urine. The animal thus excretes a hypertonic urine.

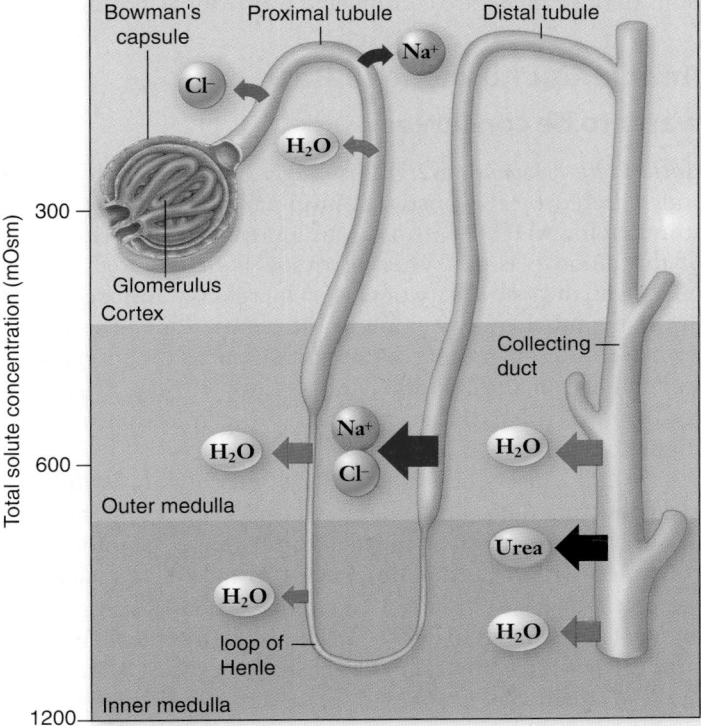

Figure 51.12 The reabsorption of salt and water in the mammalian kidney. Active transport of Na^+ out of the proximal tubules is followed by the passive movement of Cl^- and water. Active extrusion of NaCl from the ascending limb of the loop of Henle creates the osmotic gradient required for the reabsorption of water from the descending limb of the loop of Henle and the collecting duct. The two limbs of the loop form a countercurrent multiplier system that increases the osmotic gradient. The changes in osmolarity from the cortex to the medulla are indicated to the left of the figure.

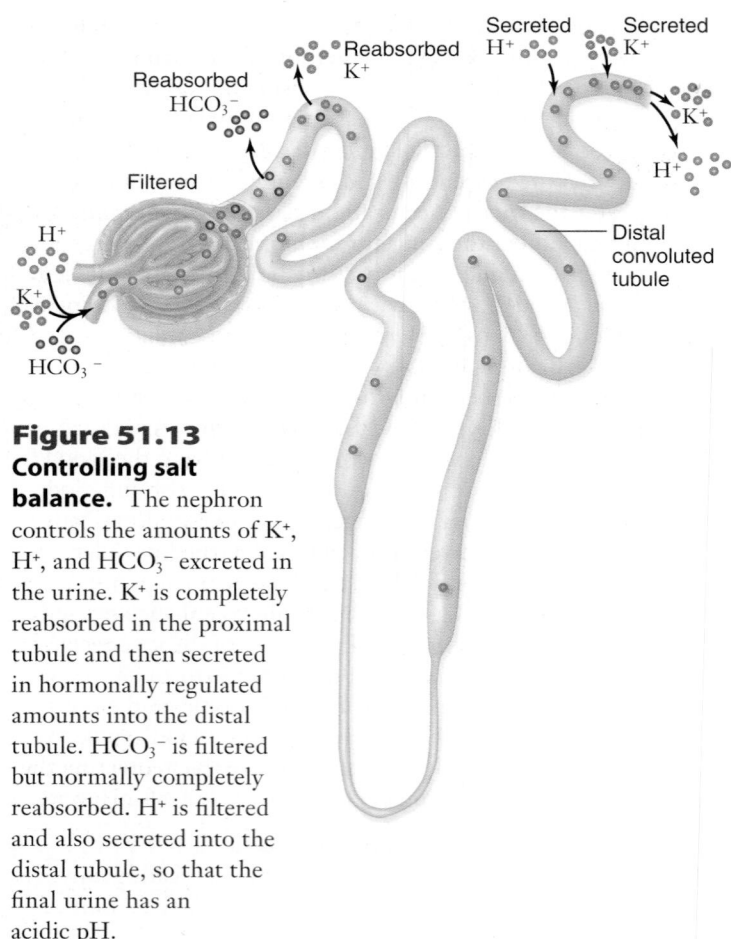

Figure 51.13
Controlling salt balance. The nephron controls the amounts of K⁺, H⁺, and HCO₃⁻ excreted in the urine. K⁺ is completely reabsorbed in the proximal tubule and then secreted in hormonally regulated amounts into the distal tubule. HCO₃⁻ is filtered but normally completely reabsorbed. H⁺ is filtered and also secreted into the distal tubule, so that the final urine has an acidic pH.

In addition to regulating water balance, the kidneys regulate the balance of electrolytes in the blood by reabsorption and secretion. For example, the kidneys reabsorb K⁺ in the proximal tubule and then secrete an amount of K⁺ needed to maintain homeostasis into the distal convoluted tubule (figure 51.13). The kidneys also maintain acid–base balance by excreting H⁺ into the urine and reabsorbing HCO₃⁻.

The reabsorption of NaCl in the distal convoluted tubule and collecting duct depends on the needs of the body and is under the control of the hormone *aldosterone*. Both ADH and aldosterone influence the distal convoluted tubule and collecting duct, although aldosterone is more significant in terms of NaCl. We present more about hormonal control of excretion in the next section.

Learning Outcomes Review 51.5

Fluid and certain solutes move out of the blood and into the tubular systems of the kidneys through filtration (passive) and secretion (transported); important solutes and water are returned to the blood through reabsorption. The mammalian kidney is divided into a cortex and a medulla and contains about a million nephrons. The parts of a nephron include the glomerulus and Bowman's capsule, proximal convoluted tubule, loop of Henle, distal convoluted tubule, and collecting duct.

■ *The compound mannitol is filtered but cannot be reabsorbed. How would this affect the volume of urine produced?*

Learning Outcomes

1. **Explain the actions of ADH, aldosterone, and ANH.**
2. **Describe the relationship between control of blood osmolarity and blood pressure.**

In mammals and birds, the amount of water excreted in the urine, and thus the concentration of the urine, varies according to the changing needs of the body. Acting through the mechanisms described next, the kidneys excrete a hypertonic urine when the body needs to conserve water. If an animal drinks excess water, the kidneys excrete a hypotonic urine.

As a result, the volume of blood, the blood pressure, and the osmolarity of blood plasma are maintained relatively constant by the kidneys, no matter how much water you drink. The kidneys also regulate the plasma K⁺ and Na⁺ concentrations and blood pH within very narrow limits. These homeostatic functions of the kidneys are coordinated primarily by hormones.

Antidiuretic hormone causes water to be conserved

Antidiuretic hormone (ADH) is produced by the hypothalamus and secreted by the posterior-pituitary gland. The primary stimulus for ADH secretion is an increase in the osmolarity of the blood plasma. When a person is dehydrated or eats salty food, the osmolarity of plasma increases. Osmoreceptors in the hypothalamus respond to the elevated blood osmolarity by sending increasing action potentials to the integration center (also in the hypothalamus). This, in turn, triggers a sensation of thirst and an increase in the secretion of ADH (figure 51.14).

ADH causes the walls of the distal convoluted tubules and collecting ducts in the kidney to become more permeable to water. Water channels called aquaporins (see chapter 5) are contained within the membranes of intracellular vesicles in the epithelium of the distal convoluted tubules and collecting ducts; ADH stimulates the fusion of the vesicle membrane with the plasma membrane, similar to the process of exocytosis. The aquaporins are now in place and allow water to flow out of the tubules and ducts in response to the hypertonic condition of the renal medulla. This water is reabsorbed into the bloodstream.

When secretion of ADH is reduced, the plasma membrane pinches in to form new vesicles that contain aquaporins. This removes the aquaporins from the plasma membrane of the distal convoluted tubule and collecting duct, making them less permeable to water. Thus more water is excreted in urine.

Under conditions of maximal ADH secretion, a person excretes only 600 mL of highly concentrated urine per day. A person who lacks ADH due to pituitary damage has the disorder known as *diabetes insipidus* and constantly excretes a large volume

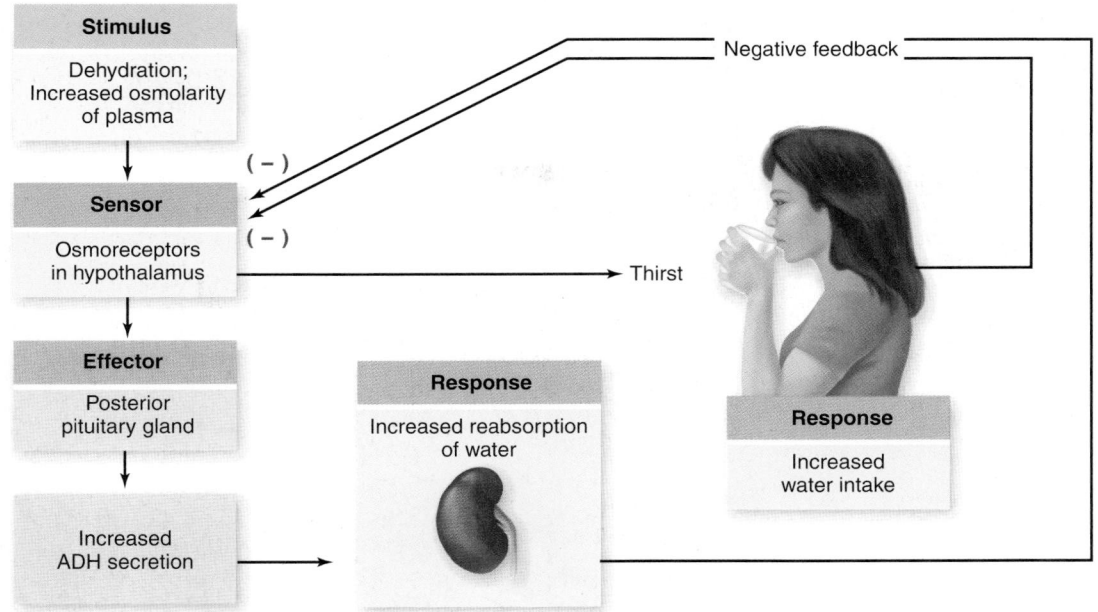

Figure 51.14 Antidiuretic hormone stimulates the reabsorption of water by the kidneys. This action completes a negative feedback loop and helps to maintain homeostasis of blood volume and osmolarity.

of dilute urine. Such a person is in danger of becoming severely dehydrated and succumbing to dangerously low blood pressure.

Homeostasis via ADH action is also affected by the common drugs ethanol and caffeine, both of which inhibit secretion of ADH. This is the basis for the dehydration that is the after effect of drinking too much alcohol.

Aldosterone and atrial natriuretic hormone control sodium ion concentration

Sodium ions are the major solute in the blood plasma. When the blood concentration of Na^+ falls, therefore, the blood osmolarity also falls. This drop in osmolarity inhibits ADH secretion, causing more water to remain in the collecting duct for excretion in the urine. As a result, the blood volume and blood pressure decrease.

A decrease in extracellular Na^+ also causes more water to be drawn into cells by osmosis, partially offsetting the drop in plasma osmolarity, but further decreasing blood volume and blood pressure. If Na^+ deprivation is severe, the blood volume may fall so low that blood pressure is insufficient to sustain life. For this reason, salt is necessary for life. Many animals have a "salt hunger" and actively seek salt, such as when deer gather at "salt licks."

A drop in blood Na^+ concentration is normally compensated for by the kidneys under the influence of the hormone *aldosterone*, which is secreted by the adrenal cortex. Aldosterone stimulates the distal convoluted tubules and collecting ducts to reabsorb Na^+, decreasing the excretion of Na^+ in the urine. Indeed, under conditions of maximal aldosterone secretion, Na^+ may be completely absent from the urine. The reabsorption of Na^+ is followed by reabsorption of Cl^- and water, so aldosterone has the net effect of promoting the retention of both salt

and water. It thereby helps to maintain blood volume, osmolarity, and pressure.

The secretion of aldosterone in response to a decreased blood level of Na^+ is indirect. Because a fall in blood Na^+ is accompanied by decreased blood volume, the flow of blood past a group of cells called the juxtaglomerular apparatus is reduced. The juxtaglomerular apparatus is located in the region of the kidney between the distal convoluted tubule and the afferent arteriole (figure 51.15).

When blood flow is reduced, the juxtaglomerular apparatus responds by secreting the enzyme *renin* into the blood (figure 51.16). Renin catalyzes the production of the polypeptide angiotensin I from the protein angiotensinogen. Angiotensin I is then converted by another enzyme into angiotensin II, which stimulates blood vessels to constrict and the adrenal cortex to secrete aldosterone. Thus, homeostasis of blood volume and pressure can be maintained by the activation of this renin–angiotensin–aldosterone system. In addition to stimulating Na^+ reabsorption, aldosterone also promotes the secretion of K^+ into the distal convoluted tubules and collecting ducts. Consequently, aldosterone lowers the blood K^+ concentration, helping to maintain constant blood K^+ levels in the face of changing amounts of K^+ in the diet. People who lack the ability to produce aldosterone will die if untreated because of the excessive loss of salt and water in the urine and the buildup of K^+ in the blood.

The action of aldosterone in promoting salt and water retention is opposed by another hormone, *atrial natriuretic hormone (ANH)*, mentioned in chapter 50. This hormone is secreted by the right atrium of the heart in response to an increased blood volume, which stretches the atrium. Under these conditions, aldosterone secretion from the adrenal cortex decreases, and ANH secretion increases, thus promoting the excretion of salt and water in the urine and lowering the blood volume.

Learning Outcomes Review 51.6

ADH stimulates the insertion of water channels into the cells of the distal convoluted tubule and collecting duct, making them more permeable to water and increasing its reabsorption. Aldosterone promotes reabsorption of Na^+, Cl^-, and water across the distal convoluted tubule and collecting duct, as well as the secretion of K^+ into the tubules. ANH decreases Na^+ and Cl^- reabsorption. When blood osmolarity increases, more water is retained by the release of ADH, and blood pressure increases; if blood osmolarity falls, ADH release is inhibited, less water is retained, and blood pressure drops.

■ *What would be the effect of a compound that blocks aquaporin water channels?*

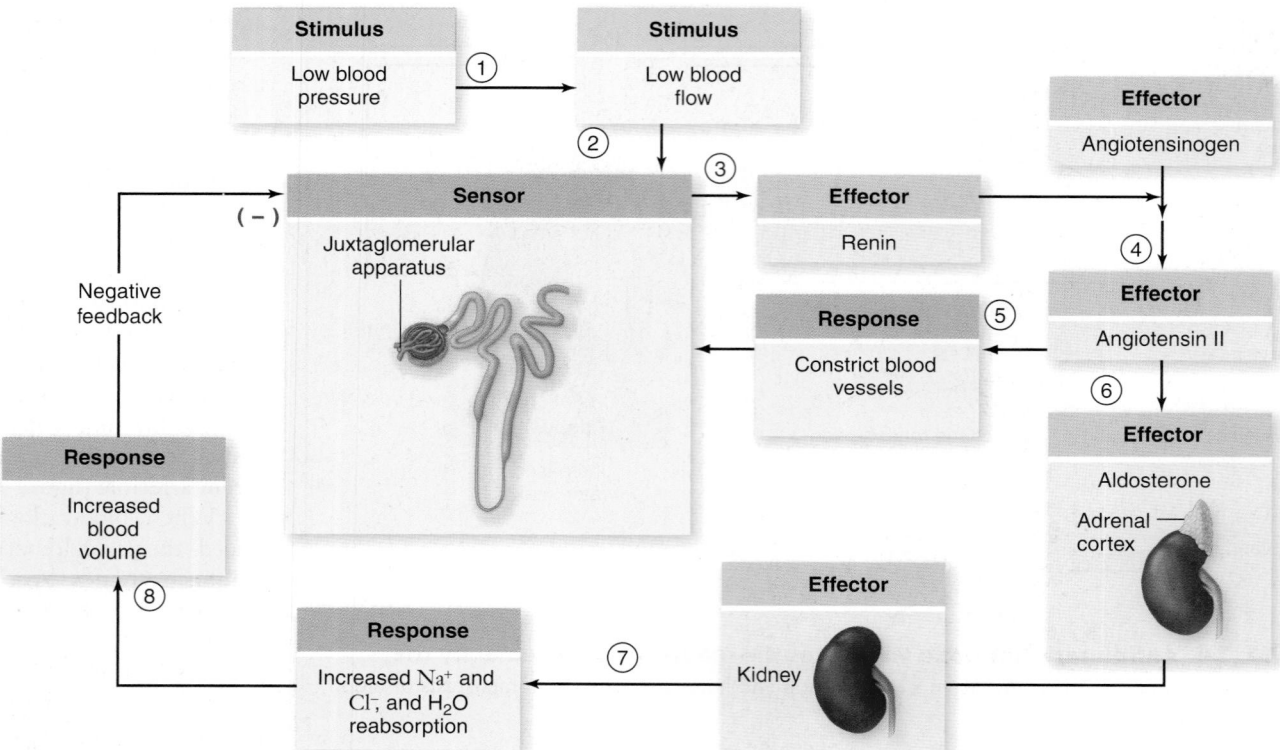

Figure 51.15 A lowering of blood volume activates the renin–angiotensin–aldosterone system. (1) Low blood volume and a decrease in blood Na$^+$ levels reduce blood pressure. (2) Reduced blood flow past the juxtaglomerular apparatus triggers (3) the release of renin into the blood, which catalyzes the production of angiotensin I from angiotensinogen. (4) Angiotensin I converts into a more active form, angiotensin II. (5) Angiotensin II stimulates blood vessel constriction and (6) the release of aldosterone from the adrenal cortex. (7) Aldosterone stimulates the reabsorption of Na$^+$ in the distal convoluted tubules. Increased Na$^+$ reabsorption is followed by the reabsorption of Cl$^-$ and water. (8) This increases blood volume. An increase in blood volume may also trigger the release of an atrial natriuretic hormone, which inhibits the release of aldosterone. These two systems work together to maintain homeostasis.

Figure 51.16 Reduced blood flow to the kidney can cause hypertension.

SCIENTIFIC THINKING

Question: *What is the relationship between atherosclerosis and elevated blood pressure?*

Hypothesis: *Atherosclerotic plaques in the renal artery will reduce blood flow to the kidney and consequently filtration pressure. The system will respond by raising blood pressure.*

Prediction: *If blood flow to the renal artery is reduced, this will mimic the effect of plaque deposition and should result in increased blood pressure.*

Test: *Clamp a renal artery to restrict blood flow, and measure blood pressure before, while clamped, and with clamp removed.*

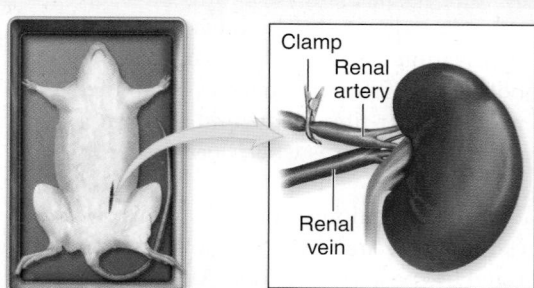

Result: *Clamping the renal artery results in increased blood pressure. This increase is relieved by removing the clamp.*

Conclusion: *Restricting blood flow to the kidney causes a homeostatic response to increase blood pressure.*

Further Experiments: *If this increase in blood pressure involved the renin–angiotensis system, what changes would you expect in the level and function of these proteins?*

51.1 Osmolarity and Osmotic Balance

Osmotic pressure is a measure of concentration difference.

Osmotic pressure is a solution's propensity to take in water by osmosis. Osmolarity is defined as moles of solute per liter of solution. Cells in a hypertonic solution lose water, and cells in a hypotonic solution gain water. In an isotonic solution, cells are at equilibrium.

Osmoconformers live in marine environments.

Osmoconformers are in osmotic equilibrium with their environment. Most marine invertebrates are osmoconformers.

Osmoregulators control their osmolarity internally.

Tissues of freshwater vertebrates are hypertonic to their environment, and those of marine vertebrates are hypotonic; both must maintain their osmolarity. Terrestrial vertebrates are all osmoregulators and have adaptations to retain water.

51.2 Osmoregulatory Organs

Invertebrates make use of specialized cells and tubules.

Flatworms use tubular protonephridia connected to flame cells that draw fluid from the body (see figure 51.2). Other invertebrates have nephridia open to both the inside and outside of the body for filtering and reabsorption (see figure 51.3).

Insects have a unique osmoregulatory system.

Insects have Malpighian tubules through which uric acid and wastes are secreted into the excretory organ, and water and salts are reabsorbed before excretion (see figure 51.4).

The vertebrate kidney filters then reabsorbs.

Kidneys of vertebrates produce urine by filtration, secretion, and selective reabsorption of water and important solutes.

51.3 Evolution of the Vertebrate Kidney

The kidney is made up of a cortex, a medulla, and thousands of units called nephrons that regulate body fluids (see figure 51.5).

Freshwater fishes must retain electrolytes and keep water out.

Freshwater fishes maintain hypertonicity by excreting large quantities dilute, hypotonic urine and reabsorbing ions (see figure 51.6).

Marine bony fishes must excrete electrolytes and keep water in.

Saltwater fish maintain hypotonicity by drinking large amounts of seawater and excreting or actively transporting ions out through the gills. Their urine is isotonic to the blood.

Cartilaginous fishes pump out electrolytes and retain urea.

Cartilaginous fishes are isotonic to their environment because they retain urea, and actively pump out electrolytes. They also produce isotonic urine.

Amphibians and reptiles have osmotic adaptations to their environments.

Freshwater amphibians and reptiles act like freshwater fishes, and the kidneys of marine reptiles function like marine bony fishes. Terrestrial reptiles can't produce hypertonic urine.

Mammals and birds are able to excrete concentrated urine and retain water.

Mammals and birds can excrete hypertonic urine and retain water. The degree of concentration of urine depends on the length of the loop of Henle.

51.4 Nitrogenous Wastes: Ammonia, Urea, and Uric Acid

Ammonia is toxic and must be quickly removed.

When animals catabolize amino acids and nucleic acids they produce toxic nitrogenous wastes (see figure 51.8).

In fishes and gilled amphibians, abundant water is used to flush ammonia quickly from the body, or it is eliminated through gills.

Urea and uric acid are less toxic but have different solubilities.

Mammals convert ammonia to urea, which is less toxic. Urea requires less water, but requires energy to manufacture. Birds and terrestrial reptiles convert ammonia to uric acid. Uric acid is the least toxic and requires the least water to eliminate, but is the most energetically expensive.

51.5 The Mammalian Kidney (see figure 51.10)

The nephron is the filtering unit of the kidney.

Blood is filtered through the capillaries of the glomerulus driven by blood pressure. The filtrate passes through the Bowman's capsule, proximal convoluted tubule, loop of Henle, distal convoluted tubule, and collecting duct (see figure 51.11). Blood passes from the afferent arteriole to the glomerulus, the efferent arteriole, the peritubular capillaries, and the vasa recta.

Water, some nutrients, and some ions are reabsorbed; other molecules are secreted.

Glucose, amino acids, and many other molecules are reabsorbed by active transport. Water is reabsorbed osmotically in the proximal convoluted tubule and the collecting duct. Foreign molecules and some wastes are secreted from the blood capillaries and into the tubules by active transport.

Excretion of toxins and excess ions maintains homeostasis.

The kidney eliminates many potentially harmful substances including nitrogenous wastes, excess ions, and toxins. The kidneys therefore are critical to homeostasis.

Each part of the mammalian nephron performs a specific transport function.

Reabsorption of nutrients and NaCl occurs in the proximal tubule. The loop of Henle creates a gradient of increasing osmolarity from the cortex to the medulla. The gradient allows selective reabsorption of water from the collecting duct. A longer loop of Henle produces more concentrated urine (see figure 51.12).

51.6 Hormonal Control of Osmoregulatory Functions

Antidiuretic hormone causes water to be conserved.

ADH, produced by the hypothalamus, increases the permeability of the collecting duct (see figure 51.14), allowing greater reabsorption of water.

Aldosterone and atrial natriuretic hormone control sodium ion concentration.

Low Na^+ levels inhibit ADH secretion, and aldosterone stimulates Na^+ uptake by the distal convoluted tubule. ANH antagonizes the action of aldosterone.

UNDERSTAND

1. Which of the following is *not* an ion homeostatically maintained in vertebrates?
   a. Cl⁻
   b. Na⁺
   c. Ca⁺⁺
   d. Fl⁻

2. Suppose that your research mentor has decided to do a project on the filtering capabilities of Malpighian tubules. Which of the following creatures will you be spending your summer studying?
   a. Ants
   b. Birds
   c. Mammals
   d. Earthworms

3. A shark's blood is isotonic to the surrounding seawater because of the reabsorption of _____ in its blood.
   a. ammonia
   b. uric acid
   c. urea
   d. NaCl

4. An important function of the excretory system is to eliminate excess nitrogen produced by metabolic processes. Which of the following organisms is most efficient at packaging nitrogen for excretion?
   a. Frog
   b. Freshwater fish
   c. Iguana
   d. Camel

5. Which of the following is a function of the kidneys?
   a. The kidneys remove harmful substances from the body.
   b. The kidneys recapture water for use by the body.
   c. The kidneys regulate the levels of salt in the blood.
   d. All of these are functions of the kidneys.

6. Humans excrete their excess nitrogenous wastes as
   a. uric acid crystals.
   b. compounds containing protein.
   c. ammonia.
   d. urea.

7. An osmoregulator would maintain its internal fluids at a concentration that is _____ relative to its surroundings.
   a. isotonic
   b. hypertonic
   c. hypotonic
   d. hypertonic, hypotonic, or isotonic

APPLY

1. In comparing invertebrate and vertebrate excretory systems, you conclude that
   a. both filter body fluids and then reabsorb water and solutes.
   b. both use a tubule system to process the filtrate.
   c. both reabsorb ions and water to control osmotic balance.
   d. only vertebrates filter fluids and reabsorb water and ions.

2. A viral infection that specifically interferes with the reabsorption of ions from the glomerular filtrate would attack cells located in the
   a. Bowman's capsule.
   b. glomerulus.
   c. renal tubules.
   d. collecting duct.

3. Diuretics are drugs that can be used to treat high blood pressure by increasing urinary output. Possible mechanisms of action in the kidney include
   a. increasing ADH secretion.
   b. inhibition of NaCl reabsorption from the loop of Henle or the proximal tubule.
   c. increasing permeability of the collecting duct.
   d. increasing NaCl reabsorption in the proximal tubule.

4. Caffeine inhibits the secretion of ADH. Prior to an exam, you have a large coffee. During the exam, you can expect
   a. greater water reabsorption from the collecting duct.
   b. less water reabsorption from the collecting duct.
   c. an increase in reabsorption of glucose from the proximal convoluted tubule.
   d. a decrease in reabsorption of glucose from the proximal convoluted tubule.

5. You and your study partner want to draw the pathway that controls the reabsorption of sodium ion when blood pressure falls. Which of the following is the correct sequence of events?
   1. Aldosterone is released.
   2. Kidney tubules reabsorb Na⁺.
   3. Renin is released.
   4. Juxtaglomerular apparatus recognizes a drop in blood pressure.
   5. Angiotensin II is produced.
   a. 1, 3, 5, 2, 4
   b. 4, 2, 3, 1, 5
   c. 4, 3, 5, 1, 2
   d. 2, 4, 3, 1, 5

6. You are studying renal function in different species of mammals that are found in very different environments. You look at species from a desert environment and compare them with ones from a tropical environment. The desert species would be expected to have
   a. shorter loops of Henle than the tropical species.
   b. longer loops of Henle than the tropical species.
   c. shorter proximal convoluted tubule than the tropical species.
   d. longer distal convoluted tubules than the tropical species.

SYNTHESIZE

1. Indicate the areas of the nephron that the following hormones target, and describe when and how the hormones elicit their actions.
   a. Antidiuretic hormone
   b. Aldosterone
   c. Atrial natriuretic hormone

2. John's doctor is concerned that John's kidneys may not be functioning properly due to a circulatory condition. The doctor wants to determine if the blood volume flowing through the kidneys (called renal blood flow rate) is within normal range. Calculate what would be a "normal" renal blood flow rate based on the following information:

   John weighs 90 kg. Assume a normal total blood volume is 80 mL/kg of body weight, and a normal heart pumps the total blood volume through the heart once per minute (cardiac output). Also assume that the normal renal blood flow rate is 21% of cardiac output.

ONLINE RESOURCE

www.ravenbiology.com

Understand, Apply, and Synthesize—enhance your study with animations that bring concepts to life and practice tests to assess your understanding. Your instructor may also recommend the interactive eBook, individualized learning tools, and more.

Chapter 52

The Immune System

Chapter Outline

52.1 Innate Immunity

52.2 Adaptive Immunity

52.3 Cell-Mediated Immunity

52.4 Humoral Immunity and Antibody Production

52.5 Autoimmunity and Hypersensitivity

52.6 Antibodies in Medical Treatment and Diagnosis

52.7 Pathogens That Evade the Immune System

Introduction

When you consider how animals defend themselves, it is natural to think of turtles and armadillos with their obvious external armor. However, armor offers little protection against the greatest dangers vertebrates face—microorganisms and viruses. We live in a world awash with organisms too tiny to see with the naked eye, and no vertebrate could long withstand their onslaught unprotected. We survive because we have evolved a variety of very effective defenses. However, our defenses are far from perfect. Some 40 million people died from influenza in 1918–1919, and more than a million people will die of malaria this year. Attempts to improve our defenses against infectious diseases are being actively researched.

52.1 Innate Immunity

Learning Outcomes

1. *Distinguish between innate and adaptive immunity.*
2. *Give examples of pathogen-associated molecular patterns.*
3. *Describe the inflammatory response.*

For many years, the response of vertebrates to microbial invasion was divided into specific and nonspecific forms of defense. It has now become clear that this is not only an oversimplifica-tion, it is not a productive way to view the body's defenses. We now view the response as much more integrated and consisting of two parts: innate and adaptive immunity.

The innate system involves the *recognition* of molecules that are conserved in particular pathogens, such as lipopolysac-charide in gram-negative bacteria. The molecules that bind to these conserved proteins do not result from genomic rearrange-ments and are limited in number, but do involve recognition of invading pathogens. The characteristic of this system is a rapid response that brings cells to the site of infection and uses soluble antimicrobial proteins to fight the pathogen.

Innate immunity is evolutionarily ancient, with some of the proteins involved recently being identified in cnidarians. Parts of the complement system (described later) have also been identified in horseshoe crabs, indicating that this system is also more ancient than previously thought. This also implies that the lack of complement in other protostomes is probably due to loss. Together, this implies that the ancestor to all bilaterians had some form of innate immunity.

Adaptive immunity is characterized by the genetic rearrangements that generate a diverse set of molecules that can recognize virtually any invading pathogen. This is the basis for a slower, but highly specific response to invading pathogens, and for the more rapid response to a second attack that is the basis for vaccines. In this chapter, we will discuss innate and adaptive immunity and how they are interrelated. We will begin with a brief description of the barrier that a pathogen must cross to gain access to the interior of the body.

The skin is a barrier to infection

The skin is the largest organ of the body, accounting for 15% of an adult human's total weight. The integument not only defends the body by providing a nearly impenetrable barrier, but also reinforces this defense with chemical weapons on the surface. Oil and sweat glands give the skin's surface a pH of 3 to 5, which is acidic enough to inhibit the growth of many pathogenic microorganisms. Sweat also contains the enzyme lysozyme, which digests bacterial cell walls. Epithelial cells also produce a variety of small antimicrobial peptides.

The skin is also home to many normal flora, nonpathogenic bacteria or fungi that are well adapted to the skin conditions in different regions of the body. Pathogenic bacteria that might attempt to colonize the skin generally are unable to compete with the normal flora. The epidermis of skin is approximately 10 to 30 cells thick, about as thick as this page. The outer layer contains cells that are continuously abraded, injured, and worn by friction and stress during the body's many activities. Cells are shed continuously and are replaced by new cells produced in the innermost layer of the epidermis.

Mucosal epithelial surfaces also prevent entry of pathogens

In addition to the skin, three other potential routes of entry by microorganisms and viruses must be guarded: the digestive tract, the respiratory tract, and the urogenital tract. Recall that each of these tracts opens to the external environment. Each of these tracts is lined by epithelial cells, which are continuously replaced, as are those of the skin.

A layer of mucus, secreted by specialized cells scattered between the epithelial cells, covers all these epithelial surfaces. Pathogens are frequently trapped within this mucus layer and are eliminated by mechanisms specific to the particular tract.

Microbes are present in food, but many are killed by saliva (which contains lysozyme), by the very acidic environment of the stomach, and by digestive enzymes in the intestine. Additionally, the gastrointestinal tract is home to a vast array of nonpathogenic normal flora, whose presence inhibits the growth of pathogenic competitors. These nonpathogenic organisms not only outcompete pathogens, but they also may secrete substances that kill harmful agents.

Microorganisms present in inhaled air are trapped by the mucus within the smaller bronchi and bronchioles before they can reach the warm, moist lungs, which would provide ideal breeding grounds for them. The epithelial cells lining these passages have cilia that continually sweep the mucus toward the glottis. There the mucus can be swallowed, carrying potential invaders out of the lungs and into the digestive tract. One of the pitfalls of smoking is that nicotine paralyzes the cilia of the respiratory system so that this natural cleaning of the air passages does not take place.

Vaginal secretions are sticky and acidic, and they also promote the growth of normal flora; all of these characteristics help prevent foreign invasion. In both males and females, acidic urine continually washes potential pathogens from the urinary tract. In addition to these physical and chemical barriers to pathogen invasion, the body also uses defense mechanisms such as vomiting, diarrhea, coughing, and sneezing to expel potential pathogens.

Innate immunity recognizes molecular patterns

Innate immunity is a response to invading pathogens that involves both soluble factors and a variety of different types of blood cells. The innate response to invading pathogens is based on the recognition of molecules that are characteristic of the pathogen. Collectively we call these pathogen-associated molecular patterns (PAMPs), or microbe-associated molecular patterns (MAMPs). Examples include the lipopolysaccharide (LPS) found in gram-negative bacterial cell walls; peptidoglycan, which is found in all bacterial cell walls; and viral DNA and RNA. These PAMPs are recognized by **pattern recognition receptors** (**PRRs**) that can be either soluble or on the surface of blood cells.

Toll-like Receptors

The best studied PRR is the Toll receptor in *Drosophila* and the Toll-like receptors (TLR) found in many species. In *Drosophila*, Toll was originally discovered as a part of the dorsal–ventral patterning pathway. Later, the same membrane receptor was found to mediate a response to fungal infection.

In vertebrates 11 TLRs have been found in humans and 13 in mouse. These bind to a variety of specific targets important to pathogen survival, which therefore do not vary greatly. These include gram-negative LPS, bacterial lipoproteins, bacterial peptidoglycan fragments, yeast cell wall components, unmethylated CpG motifs in bacterial DNA, and viral RNA. This represents a wide range of possible invading pathogens that vertebrates have been host to over a long period of evolutionary time.

The structure of TLRs that allows recognition of these PAMPs are repeated leucine-rich regions that fold to form binding pockets. These pockets can bind to a variety of shapes. As these recognize structures that are critical to the pathogen, a single TLR can recognize a range of pathogens that share a feature such as LPS or peptidoglycan.

Activation of TLRs leads to signal transduction pathways that result in the expression of genes encoding products that enhance the response of both innate and adaptive immune responses. Activation of TLRs can lead to induction of the transcription factor NF-κβ, which turns on the inflammatory response described later on; to the production of antimicrobial peptides; and to the production of cytokines that attract phagocytic cells as well as B and T cells.

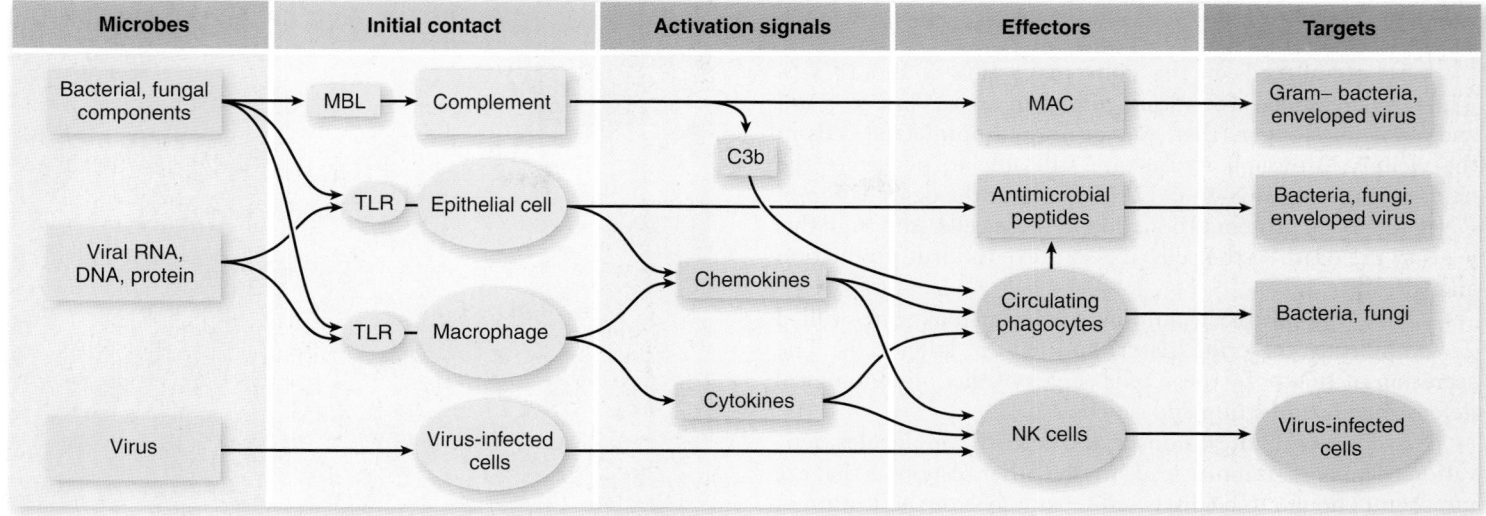

| Microbes | Initial contact | Activation signals | Effectors | Targets |

Figure 52.1 Overview of innate immunity. Pathogens have critical molecules that adhere to either membrane-bound (TLR), or soluble receptors (MBL). This results in the production of cytokines and chemokines that attract phagocytes, of antimicrobial peptides, the membrane attack complex (MAC) of the complement cascade, and the activation of natural killer cells (NK cells).

Cytoplasmic receptors

Two newly characterized kinds of receptors are not membrane proteins, rather they are found in the cytoplasm. These are the nucleotide oligerization domain (NOD)-like receptors (NLRs) and Rig helicase-like receptors (RLRs). These internal receptors can recognize PAMPs in the cytoplasm of cells after phagocytosis. The RLRs also help in responding to viral RNA.

Soluble receptors

In addition to the surface receptors described earlier, some circulating molecules can respond to molecules derived from pathogens. These include some of the lectin family, such as the mannose-binding lectin (MBL) protein. This protein is found in serum and can bind to mannose-containing carbohydrates on microbial surfaces. MBL is important in activating the complement system described later.

Innate immunity leads to diverse responses to a pathogen

Binding of a pathogen-associated molecule to any of the innate immune-type receptors activates signal transduction pathways that lead to a rapid response. This includes the production of secreted signaling molecules, release of antimicrobial peptides, and activation of complement. An overview of all of these activities is shown in figure 52.1.

The secretion of antimicrobial peptides normally found in the integument can be increased when TLRs on the surface of epithelial cells and phagocytic cells bind components of invading pathogens. In humans, the major categories of antimicrobial peptides are called defensins and cathelicidin. Defensins are small peptides with 6 disulfide-linked cyteines that expose positively charged amino acids on the surface. The defensins bind to the outer membranes of bacterial species, which tend to be negatively charged. This can both disrupt the outer membrane and enhance phagocytosis. Defensins have also been shown to

work against enveloped viruses (figure 52.2). The antimicrobial enzyme lysozyme can also be induced by TLR activation.

Another class of proteins induced by innate defenses that play a key role in body defense are interferons. Interferons are important secreted signaling molecules with diverse functions.

Hypothesis: *Defensin peptides have activity against viruses.*

Prediction: *Viruses incubated with the human neutraphil defensin one (HNP-1) in vitro will have reduced infectivity.*

Test: *Direct test by incubating different viruses with HNP-1, then using standard infectivity assay expressed as plaque-forming units (PFU)/mL.*

Virus	Mean $\log_{10}$ Reduction in PFU/mL		
	25 µg/mL	50 µg/mL	100 µg/mL
HSV-1	2	2.9	3
HSV-2	0.8	1.2	2
Vesicular stomatitus virus	0.4	0.7	0.9
Influenza virus	0.4	0.5	0.7
Cytomegalovirus	-0.02	0.09	0.3

Result: *HNP-1 has activity against a variety of viruses as shown in the table.*

Conclusion: *HNP-1 has activity against different enveloped viruses, although this activity is not equally effective against the different viruses.*

Further Experiments: *How could you determine the mechanisms of action?*

Figure 52.2 Activity of defensin against different viruses.

The three major categories of interferons are alpha, beta, and gamma (IFN-α, IFN-β, IFN-γ).

Almost all cells in the body make IFN-α and IFN-β. These polypeptides are synthesized when a virus infects a cell and act as messengers that protect normal uninfected cells in the vicinity. Although viruses are still able to penetrate the neighboring cells, IFN-α and IFN-β induce the degradation of RNA and block protein production in these cells. Although this leads to the death of the cells, it also prevents virus production and spread.

IFN-γ is produced only by particular leukocytes called T lymphocytes (described later) and natural killer cells. The secretion of IFN-γ by these cells is part of the immunological defense against infection and cancer.

In addition to these nonspecific defensive molecules, activation of innate immunity leads to two other responses that are important enough to be discussed separately later: activation of the inflammatory response, and activation of the complement pathway. Signaling from both TLR and internal receptors can lead to the secretion of a variety of cytokines, or regulatory signaling molecules. These attract other nonspecific phagocytic cells, cause inflammation, and even signal to the adaptive immune system.

Phagocytic cells are associated with innate immunity

Among the most important innate defenses are some types of *leukocytes*, or white blood cells, that circulate through the body and nonspecifically attack pathogens within tissues (see chapter 50 for an overview of blood and blood cells). Three basic kinds of defending leukocytes have been identified, and each kills invading microorganisms differently.

Macrophages

Macrophages ("big eaters") are large, irregularly shaped cells that kill microorganisms by ingesting them through phagocytosis (figure 52.3). Once within the macrophage, the membrane-bound phagosome fuses with a lysosome. Fusion activates lysosomal enzymes that kill and digest the microorganism. Additionally, large quantities of oxygen-containing free radicals are frequently produced within the phagosome; these free radicals are very reactive and degrade the pathogen.

In addition to bacteria, macrophages also engulf viruses, cellular debris, and dust particles in the lungs. Macrophages roam continuously in the extracellular fluid that bathes tissues. In response to an infection, monocytes, which are undifferentiated macrophages found in the blood, squeeze through the endothelial cells of capillaries to enter the connective tissues. There, at the site of the infection, the monocytes mature into active, phagocytic macrophages.

Neutrophils

Neutrophils are the most abundant circulating leukocytes, accounting for 50 to 70% of the peripheral blood leukocytes. They are the first type of cell to appear at the site of tissue damage or infection. Like macrophages, they squeeze between capillary endothelial cells to enter infected tissues, where they

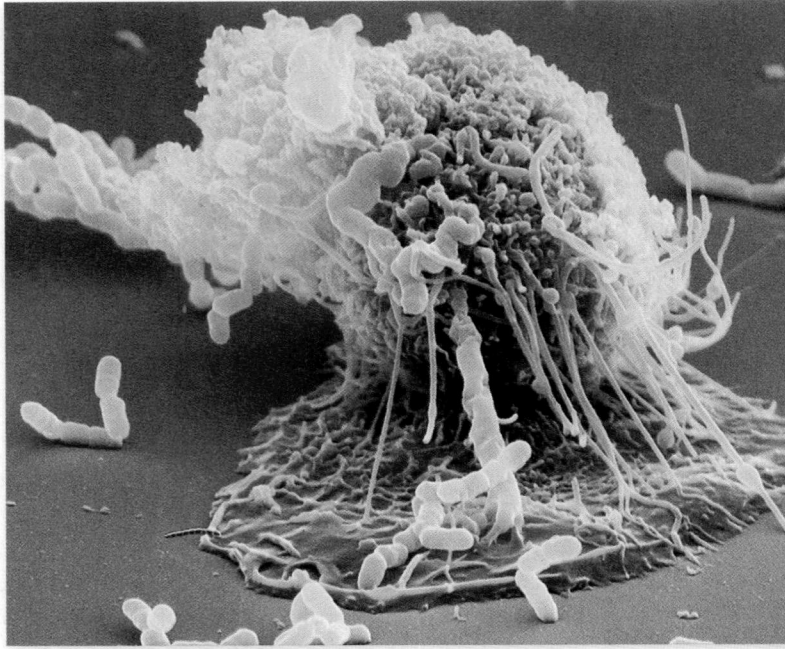

Figure 52.3 A macrophage in action. In this scanning electron micrograph, a macrophage is "fishing" with long, sticky cytoplasmic extensions. Bacterial cells that come in contact with the extensions are drawn toward the macrophage and engulfed.

ingest a variety of pathogens by phagocytosis. Their mechanism of pathogen destruction is similar to that of macrophages except that they produce an even greater range of reactive oxygen radicals. Neutrophils also produce defensin peptides.

Natural killer cells

Natural killer (NK) cells do not attack invading microbes directly. Instead, they kill cells of the body that have been infected with viruses. They kill not by phagocytosis, but rather by inducing apoptosis (programmed cell death) of the target cell (see chapter 19). Proteins called *perforins*, released from the NK cells, insert into the membrane of the target cell, polymerizing into a pore. Other NK-produced proteins, *granzymes*, then enter the pores created by the perforin molecules and activate proteins known as *caspases*, found within the target cells, which in turn induce apoptosis (figure 52.4). Macrophages ingest the resulting membrane-bounded vesicular cell debris.

NK cells also attack tumor cells, often before the tumor cells have had a chance to divide sufficiently to be detectable as a tumor. The vigilant surveillance by NK cells is one of the body's most potent defenses against cancer. Thus, these cells are often said to play a role in **immune surveillance.**

The inflammatory response is a nonspecific response to infection or tissue injury

The inflammatory response involves several systems of the body, and it may be either localized or systemic. An acute response is one that generally starts rapidly but lasts for only a relatively short while.

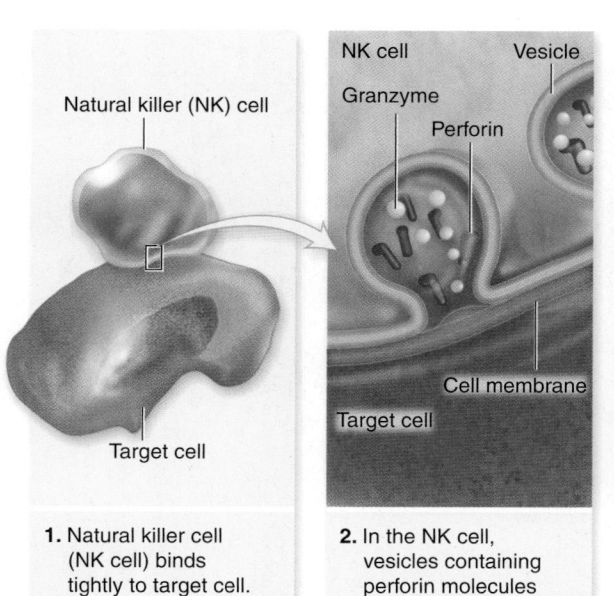
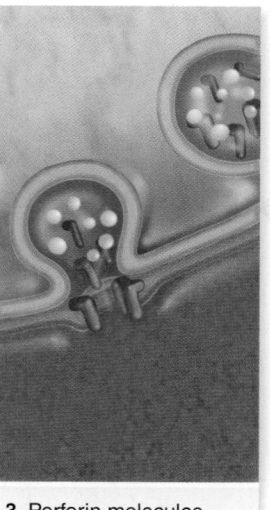
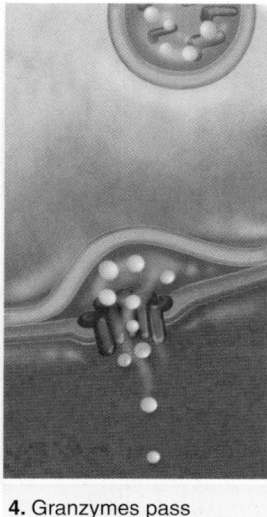
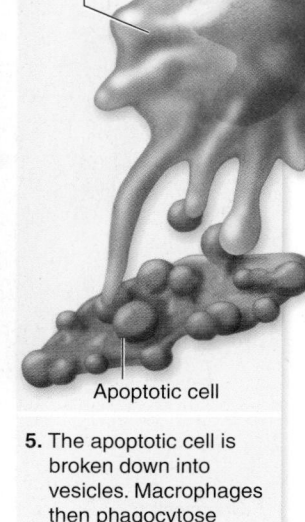

1. Natural killer cell (NK cell) binds tightly to target cell.

2. In the NK cell, vesicles containing perforin molecules and granzymes release their contents by exocytosis.

3. Perforin molecules polymerize in the plasma membrane of the target cell, forming pores.

4. Granzymes pass through the pores and activate caspase enzymes that induce apoptosis in the target cell.

5. The apoptotic cell is broken down into vesicles. Macrophages then phagocytose these vesicles.

Figure 52.4 How natural killer cells eliminate target cells. Natural killer cells kill virally infected cells by programmed cell death, or apoptosis. This is accomplished by secreting proteins that form pores in the cell to be killed, along with proteins that diffuse through these pores and induce apoptosis.

Inquiry question

? What would happen if an NK cell killed a virally infected target cell by simply causing the cell to burst, releasing all the cell contents into the tissues?

Certain infected or injured cells release chemical alarm signals—most notably histamine, along with prostaglandins and bradykinin (see chapter 46). These chemicals promote the dilation of local blood vessels, which increases the flow of blood to the site and causes the area to become red and warm, two of the hallmark signs of inflammation. These chemicals also increase the permeability of capillaries in the area, producing the third hallmark sign of inflammation, the edema (tissue swelling) often associated with infection. Swelling puts pressure on nerve endings in the region, and this, in combination with the release of other mediators, leads to pain and potential loss of function, the final two hallmark signs of inflammation.

Increased capillary permeability initially promotes the migration of phagocytic neutrophils from the blood to the extracellular fluid bathing the tissues, where the neutrophils can ingest and degrade pathogens; the pus associated with some infections is a mixture of dead or dying pathogens, tissue cells, and neutrophils. The neutrophils also secrete signaling molecules that attract monocytes several hours later; as the monocytes differentiate into macrophages, they too engulf pathogens and the remains of the dead cells (figure 52.5).

The inflammatory response is accompanied by an *acute-phase response*. One manifestation of this response is an elevation of body temperature, or fever (see chapter 43). When a macrophage with a TLR on its surface binds to a PAMP, the cytokine called **interleukin-1 (IL-1)** is released and is carried by the blood to the brain. IL-1 causes neurons in the

hypothalamus to raise the body's temperature several degrees above the normal value of 37°C (98.6°F). This increase in body temperature promotes the activity of phagocytic cells and impedes the growth of some microorganisms.

Fever contributes to the body's defense by stimulating phagocytosis and causing the liver and spleen to store iron. This storage reduces blood levels of iron, which bacteria need in large amounts to grow. Very high fevers are hazardous, however, because excessive heat may denature critical enzymes. In general, temperatures greater than 39.4°C (103°F) are considered dangerous for humans, and those greater than 40.6°C (105°F) are often fatal.

A group of proteins collectively referred to as *acute-phase proteins* are also released from cells of the liver during an inflammatory response, sometimes at levels 1000-fold above the normal serum concentration. These proteins bind to a variety of microorganisms and promote their ingestion by phagocytic cells—the neutrophils and macrophages.

Complement can form a membrane attack complex

The cellular defenses of vertebrates are enhanced by a very effective chemical defense called the **complement system**—a group of approximately 30 different proteins that circulate freely in the blood plasma. Usually they occur in an inactive form, which can enter the tissues during an inflammatory

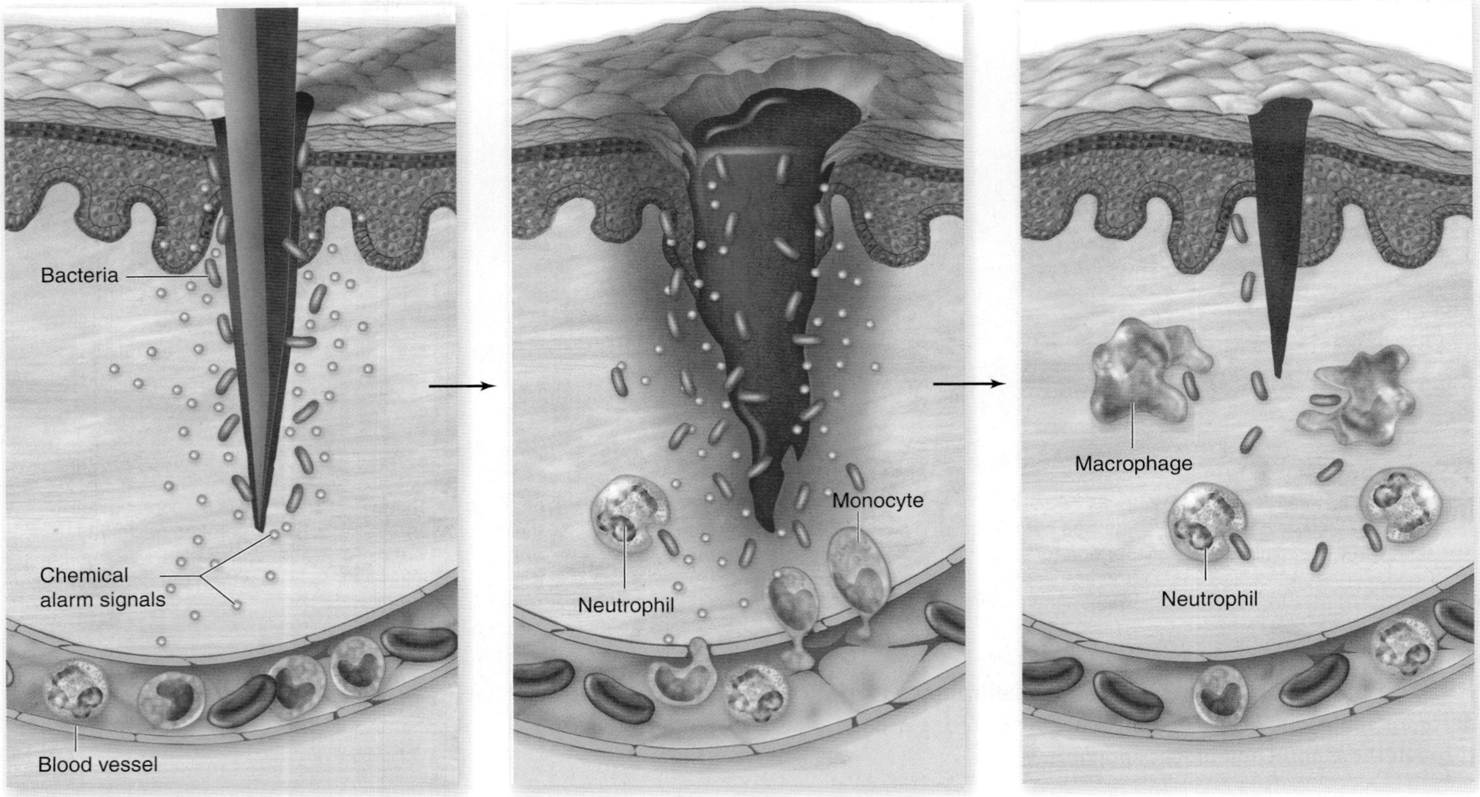

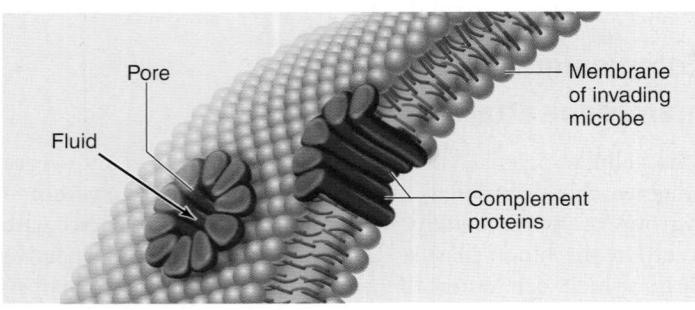

Figure 52.5 The events in local inflammation. When invading pathogens have penetrated an epithelial surface, chemical alarm signals, such as histamine and prostaglandins, released from damaged cells, cause nearby blood vessels to dilate and increase in permeability. Increased blood flow causes swelling and promotes the accumulation of phagocytic cells, specifically neutrophils followed by macrophages, which attack and engulf invading the pathogens.

response. Complement can be activated by mannose-binding lectin protein (MBL), one of the soluble sensors of innate immunity, or can be activated by a complex series of reactions involving charged species on the surface of pathogens.

When the complement system is activated, complement proteins aggregate to form a **membrane attack complex (MAC)** that inserts itself into the pathogen's plasma membrane (or the lipid membrane around an enveloped virus), forming a pore. Extracellular fluid enters the pathogen through this pore, causing the pathogen to swell and burst. Activation of the complement proteins is also triggered in a specific fashion when antibodies (which are secreted by B lymphocytes) are bound to invading pathogens, as we describe in a later section.

Other complement proteins, particularly one known as *C3b*, may coat the surface of invading pathogens. Phagocytic neutrophils and macrophages, which have receptors for C3b, may thus be "directed" to bind to the pathogens, promoting their phagocytosis and destruction. This is a particularly efficient way of eliminating those pathogens that do not have an outer lipid membrane into which a MAC may insert itself. Some complement proteins stimulate the release of histamine and other mediators by cells known as mast cells and basophils, promoting the dilation and increased permeability of capillaries; other complement proteins attract more phagocytes, especially neutrophils, to the area of infection through the more-permeable blood vessels.

Learning Outcomes Review 52.1

Innate immunity is ancient and recognizes molecular patterns; adaptive immunity involves genetic rearrangements to attack specific pathogens. The molecular patterns that innate immunity recognizes include bacterial lipopolysaccharide and peptidoglycan, as well as viral RNA and DNA. The inflammatory response begins with histamine release and involves a variety of molecules and signals that attract neutrophils, increase permeability, activate the complement system, and trigger fever.

■ *Is innate immunity nonspecific?*

52.2 Adaptive Immunity

Learning Outcomes

1. Define the characteristics of adaptive immunity.
2. Describe how lymphocytes acquire receptors.
3. Distinguish between humoral and cellular forms of immunity.

Few of us pass through childhood without contracting a variety of infectious illnesses. Prior to the advent of an effective vaccine in about 1991, most children contracted chicken pox before reaching their teens. Chicken pox and some other such diseases were considered diseases of childhood because most people, once recovered, never experienced them again. They developed immunity to the chicken pox-causing *varicella-zoster* virus and maintained this immunity as long as their immune systems remained intact. Similarly, immunization today with a nonpathogenic form of *varicella* virus can also confer protection. This immunity is produced by adaptive immune defense mechanisms, also called acquired immunity.

Immunity had long been observed, but the mechanisms have only recently been understood

Societies have known for over 2000 years that an individual who experiences an infectious disease is often protected against a subsequent occurrence of the same disease. The scientific study of immunity, however, did not begin until 1796, when an English country doctor, Edward Jenner, carried out an experiment to protect people again smallpox.

Jenner and the smallpox virus

Smallpox, caused by the *variola* virus, was a common and deadly disease in the 1700s and earlier centuries. As with chicken pox, those who survived smallpox rarely caught the disease again, and people had been known to deliberately infect themselves through inoculation hoping to survive a mild case and become immune. Jenner observed, however, that milkmaids who had caught a much milder form of "the pox" called cowpox (presumably from cows) rarely experienced smallpox.

Jenner set out to test the idea that cowpox could confer protection against smallpox. He inoculated a healthy child with fluid from a cowpox vesicle and later deliberately infected him with fluid from a smallpox vesicle; as he had predicted, the child did not become ill. (Jenner's experiment would be considered unethical today.) Subsequently, many people were protected from smallpox by immunization with fluid from cowpox vesicles, a much less risky proposition (figure 52.6).

We now know that smallpox and cowpox are caused by two different viruses that have similar surfaces. Jenner's patients who were injected with the cowpox virus mounted a defense that was also effective against a later infection of the smallpox virus.

Jenner's procedure of injecting a harmless agent to confer resistance to a dangerous one is called *vaccination*. Modern attempts to develop resistance to malaria, herpes, and other diseases often involve delivering antigens via a harmless *vaccinia* virus related to the cowpox virus (see chapter 17).

Pasteur and avian cholera

Many years passed before anyone learned how exposure to an infectious agent could confer resistance to a disease. A key step toward answering this question was taken more than a half-century later by the famous French scientist Louis Pasteur. Pasteur was studying avian cholera, a form that infects birds. He isolated a culture of bacteria from diseased chickens that would produce the disease if injected into healthy birds.

It is reported that before departing on a two-week vacation, he accidentally left his bacterial culture out on a shelf. When he returned, he injected this old culture into healthy birds and found that it had apparently been weakened; the injected birds became only slightly ill and then recovered. Surprisingly, however, those birds did not get sick when subsequently infected with fresh cholera bacteria that did produce the disease in control chickens. Clearly, something about the bacteria could elicit immunity, as long as the bacteria did not kill the animals first. We now know that molecules protruding from the surfaces of the bacteria evoked active immunity in the chickens.

Antigens stimulate specific immune responses

An **antigen** is a molecule that provokes a specific immune response. The most effective antigens are large, complex molecules such as proteins. The greater their "foreignness," or put another way, their phylogenetic distance from the host, the greater will be the immune response they elicit.

Antigens may be components of a microorganism or a virus, but they may also be proteins or glycoproteins on the surface of transfused red blood cells or on transplanted tissue.

Figure 52.6
The birth of immunology.
This painting shows Edward Jenner inoculating patients with cowpox in the 1790s and thus protecting them from smallpox.

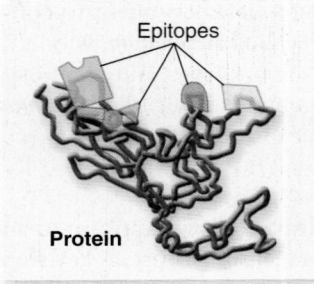

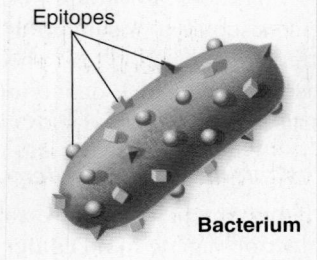

a.   *b.*

Figure 52.7 Many different epitopes are exhibited by any one antigen. *a.* A single protein, with associated carbohydrate, may have many different antigenic determinants called epitopes, each of which can stimulate a distinct immune response. *b.* A pathogen such as a bacterium has many proteins on its surface, and there are likely to be multiple copies of each. Note that the protein and bacterium are not drawn to scale with respect to each other.

They may also be components of foods or pollens. A large antigen is likely to have many different parts, known as *antigenic determinants*, or *epitopes* (figure 52.7), each of which can stimulate a distinct immune response.

Hematopoiesis gives rise to the cells of the immune system

All the cells that are found in the blood are derived from the division and differentiation of hematopoietic stem cells, a process called hematopoiesis (see chapter 50). Embryologically, these stem cells are initially found in the yolk sac, then migrate to the fetal liver and spleen and finally to the bone marrow. Stem cells give rise to lymphoid progenitors and myeloid progenitors. A lymphoid progenitor, in turn, gives rise to both the B and T lymphocytes as well as to natural killer cells. A myeloid progenitor gives rise to all the other cells of the immune system as well as to erythrocytes and platelets (see figure 50.2).

Although the lymphocytes are responsible for adaptive immunity, all the other leukocytes illustrated in figure 50.2 play supporting roles in this specific response or are part of innate immunity. **Monocytes** give rise to the macrophages, and these along with the **neutrophils** are phagocytic cells. **Eosinophils** are important in the elimination of helminths (flatworms; see chapter 33), either via secretion of digestive enzymes through perforin pores inserted in the plasma membrane of the helminths or occasionally by phagocytosis. They also play a role in exacerbating chronic inflammatory diseases such as asthma or inflammatory bowel disease.

Basophils and **mast cells** are not phagocytic but rather secrete inflammatory mediators such as histamine and prostaglandin in response to the binding of complement proteins during the elimination of pathogens. These cells, and mast cells in particular, are also activated during an allergic response, and the inflammatory mediators they release cause the symptoms of allergy.

Dendritic cells are important in the activation of T cells, as will be described further. Dendritic cells also form a link

TABLE 52.1	Cells of the Immune System
Cell Type	**Function**
Helper T cell	Specifically recognizes foreign peptides on antigen-presenting cells, inducing the release of cytokines that activate B cells or macrophages
Cytotoxic T cell	Specifically recognizes and kills "altered-self" cells: virally infected, or tumor cells
B cell	Binds specific soluble antigens with its membrane-bound antibody; serves as an antigen-presenting cell to T_H cells; on activation differentiates into plasma and memory B cells
Plasma cell	Derived from activated B cell; is a biochemical factory devoted to the secretion of antibodies directed against specific antigens
Natural killer cell	Rapidly recognizes and kills virally infected or tumor cells
Monocyte	Precursor of macrophage; located in blood
Macrophage	Phagocytic tissue cell that is a component of the body's first cellular line of defense; also serves as an antigen-presenting cell to T_H cells
Neutrophil	A phagocytic cell that is a component of the body's first cellular line of defense; found in the blood in large numbers until attracted to tissues during inflammation
Eosinophil	Important to the elimination of parasites and involved in chronic inflammatory diseases
Basophil	Circulating cell that releases mediators such as histamine that promote inflammation
Mast cell	Located primarily under mucosal surfaces and releases mediators such as histamine that promote inflammation; triggered both during inflammatory and allergic responses
Dendritic cell	Important antigen-presenting cell to naive T_H cells; also helps in the activation of naive T_C cells

between innate and adaptive immunity. Dendritic cells have a variety of TLRs that recognize pathogens and stimulate secretion of cytokines and the inflammatory response. Thus they can present antigens and recognize pathogen patterns via innate receptors as well. The roles of these cells are summarized in table 52.1.

Lymphocytes carry out the adaptive immune responses

The adaptive immune system is characterized by

1. Specificity of recognition of antigen
2. Wide diversity of antigens can be specifically recognized
3. Memory, whereby the immune system responds more quickly and more intensely to an antigen it encountered previously than to one it is meeting for the first time
4. Ability to distinguish self-antigens from nonself

The cells in the blood involved in the adaptive immune response are leukocytes derived from a stem cell line called lymphoid progenitor cells (see figure 50.2). These **lymphocytes** have receptor proteins on their surfaces that recognize specific epitopes on an antigen and direct an immune response against either the antigen in solution or on the cell surface (figure 52.8). This response is also affected by signals derived from the innate system described earlier. The innate system dominates early in infection by a new pathogen, and the adaptive response dominates in later stages of infection.

Lymphocytes and antigen recognition

Although all the receptor proteins on any one lymphocyte have the same epitope specificity, it is rare that any two lymphocytes

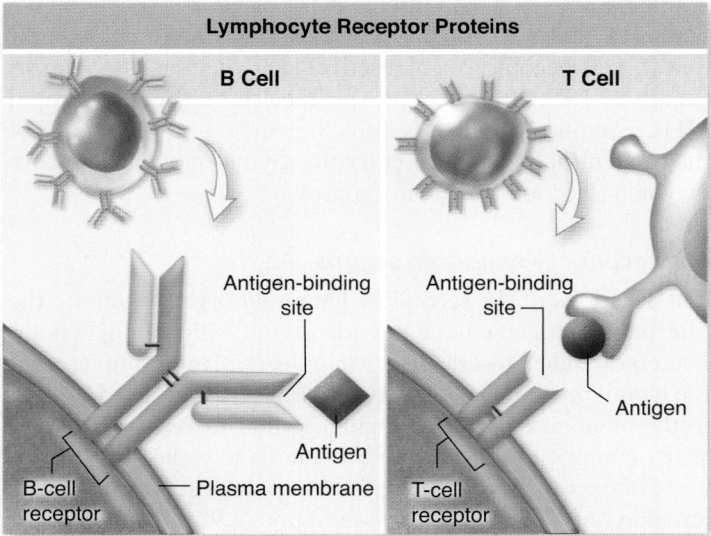

Lymphocyte Receptor Proteins

B Cell | T Cell

Antigen-binding site | Antigen-binding site

Antigen

B-cell receptor | Plasma membrane | T-cell receptor

Antigen

Figure 52.8 **B- and T-cell receptors bind antigens.** B-cell receptors are immunoglobulin (Ig) molecules with a characteristic Y-shaped structure. Every B cell has a single kind of Ig on its surface that binds to a single antigenic determinant. T-cell receptors are simpler than Ig molecules, but also bind to specific antigenic determinants. T cells only bind to antigens bound to another cell.

have identical specificities. This feature produces the diversity of immune responses that ensures that at least some epitopes of any antigen that might be encountered are recognized.

A lymphocyte that has never before encountered antigen is referred to as a *naive lymphocyte*. When a naive lymphocyte binds to a foreign antigen, the lymphocyte is activated, causing it to divide producing a clone of cells with identical antigen specificity, a process called **clonal selection.** Some of these cells respond immediately to the antigen, and others become memory cells, which can remain in our bodies for years and perhaps for the remainder of our lives. Memory cells are easily and rapidly activated on subsequent encounters with the same antigen.

B cells

Lymphocytes called **B lymphocytes,** or **B cells,** respond to antigens by secreting proteins called **antibodies,** or **immunoglobulins (Ig).** Antigen recognition occurs when an antigen binds to immunoglobulins on the B cell's membrane. Binding to antigen, in conjunction with other signals to be described later, initiates a signaling pathway that leads to the production of plasma cell's that secrete antibodies specific for the epitope recognized by the antibody in the B-cell membrane. This B-cell–mediated response producing secreted antibodies is called **humoral immunity.**

T cells

Other lymphocytes, called **T lymphocytes,** or **T cells,** do not secrete antibodies but instead regulate the immune responses of other cells or directly attack the cells that carry the specific antigens. These cells participate in the other arm of adaptive immunity called **cell-mediated immunity.** Both cell-mediated and humoral immunity processes are described in detail in later sections.

Inquiry question

 Jenner used cowpox virus to elicit an immune response against smallpox. What does this tell us about the antigenic properties of the two viruses?

Adaptive immunity can be active or passive

Immunity can be acquired in different ways. First, an individual can gain immunity when infected by a pathogen and perhaps developing the disease it causes. Alternatively, an individual can be immunized with portions of a pathogen or with a less virulent form of the pathogen. Both of these situations result in *active immunity*, associated with the activation of specific lymphocytes and the generation of memory cells by the individual. Second, an individual can gain immunity by obtaining antibodies from another individual. This happened to you before you were born, as some antibodies made by your mother were transferred to your body across the placenta. Immunity gained in this way is called *passive immunity*, and it does not result in the generation of memory cells. The immunity is only effective as long as the antibodies remain in your body. Like any other proteins, they will degrade in time.

The immune system is supported by two classes of organs

The organs of the immune system consist of the **primary lymphoid organs**—the bone marrow and the thymus—as well as the **secondary lymphoid organs**—the lymph nodes, spleen, and mucosa-associated lymphoid tissue, or MALT (figure 52.9).

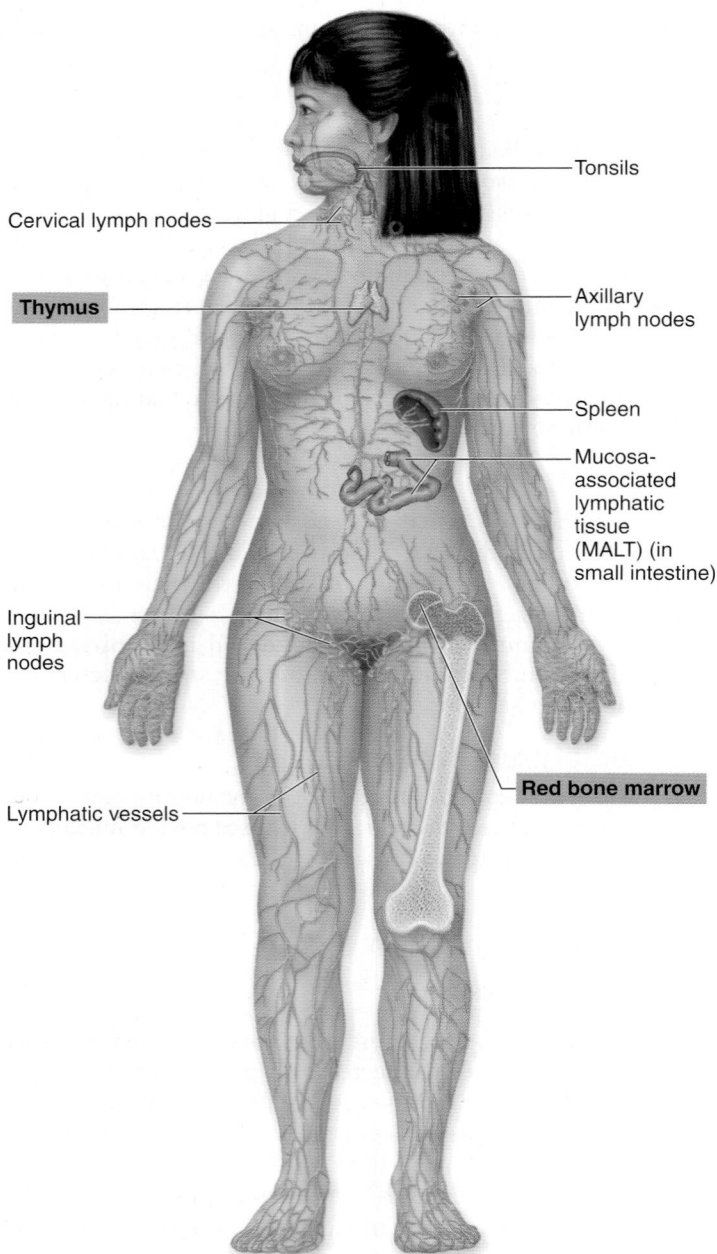

Figure 52.9 Organs of the specific immune system.
There are two types of immune system organs: primary lymphoid organs (red boxes), in which B and T lymphocytes mature and acquire their specific receptors, and secondary lymphoid organs (labeled in black) in which antigen is collected and through which the mature naive lymphocytes circulate in order to meet and be stimulated by antigen.

The primary lymphoid organs

The **bone marrow** is not only the source of stem cells, it is where B cells mature. After hematopoiesis gives rise to the most immature B cells, progenitor B cells, these cells complete their maturation in the bone marrow. It is here that DNA rearrangements of the immunoglobulin genes, to be discussed later, dictate the specificity of each B cell. Every B cell has about 10^5 Ig molecules on its surface, all with identical specificity of epitope binding and all different from cell to cell.

Any lymphocytes that are likely to bind to self-antigens undergo apoptosis (figure 52.10a). The remainder are released to circulate in the blood and lymph and pass through the secondary lymphoid organs, where they may encounter antigen.

After their origin in the bone marrow, progenitor T cells migrate to the **thymus**, a primary lymphoid organ located just above the heart. The thymus is very large in infants; it starts to shrink in the teenage years, which it continues to do throughout life.

The antigen receptor on T cells is designated the **T-cell receptor,** or **TCR.** The TCR is produced by gene rearrangements as T cells mature in the thymus, similar to those that occur for Ig genes of progenitor B cells. Thus, T cells may express about 10^5 identical TCRs per T cell, all likely to be different from one T cell to the next.

B cells recognize an epitope of an intact antigen that may or may not be a protein. In contrast, T cells recognize only a peptide fragment of a protein antigen, and this peptide fragment must be bound to one of a series of self-proteins that are present on the surface of almost all of the body's cells. These proteins are encoded by genes in the **major histocompatibility complex,** or **MHC.** The MHC is discussed in detail in subsequent sections.

During selection in the thymus, T cells are exposed to many thymic cells, all expressing self-MHC proteins with bound self-peptides on their surfaces. If a T cell's TCRs bind too strongly to these self-MHC protein complexes, that T cell becomes "self-reactive" and undergoes apoptosis (figure 52.10b). Conversely, if the T cell's TCR does not bind MHC complexes at all, it is also eliminated. Only about 5% of the progenitor T cells that enter the thymus pass this rigorous two-step selection and avoid apoptosis.

The secondary lymphoid organs

The locations of the secondary lymphoid organs promote the filtering of antigens that enter any part of an individual's body. Bacteria attached to a thorn stuck in the skin, for example, enter the lymph that bathes the tissues. Lymph is eventually returned to the blood circulation through a series of vessels referred to as the lymphatics (see chapter 50). On its way, the lymph is filtered in the thousands of lymph nodes, which are located at the junction of lymphatic vessels (see figure 52.9).

The many mature but naive B and T lymphocytes that have entered a lymph node on exiting the primary lymphoid organs, or the memory cells that are located here, become activated on meeting with antigen. Antibodies secreted on activation of B cells in the lymph nodes, as well as the clonal progeny of the activated B and T cells, then leave the lymph node and enter the blood circulation when the lymph is returned to blood vessels near the heart.

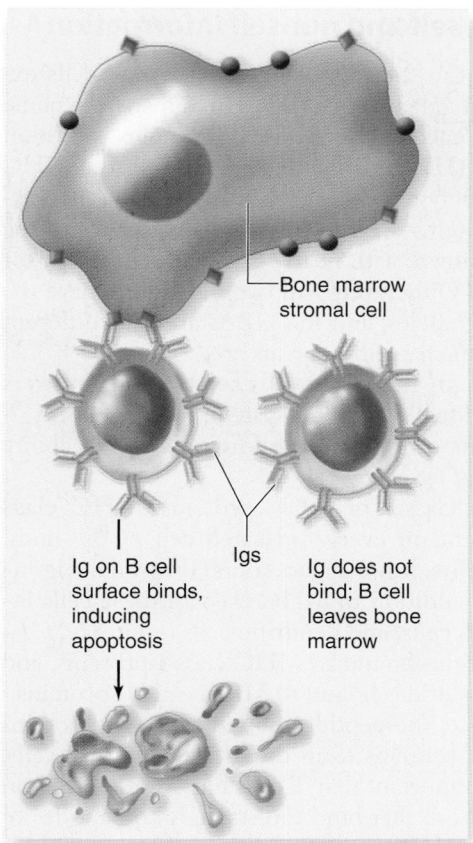

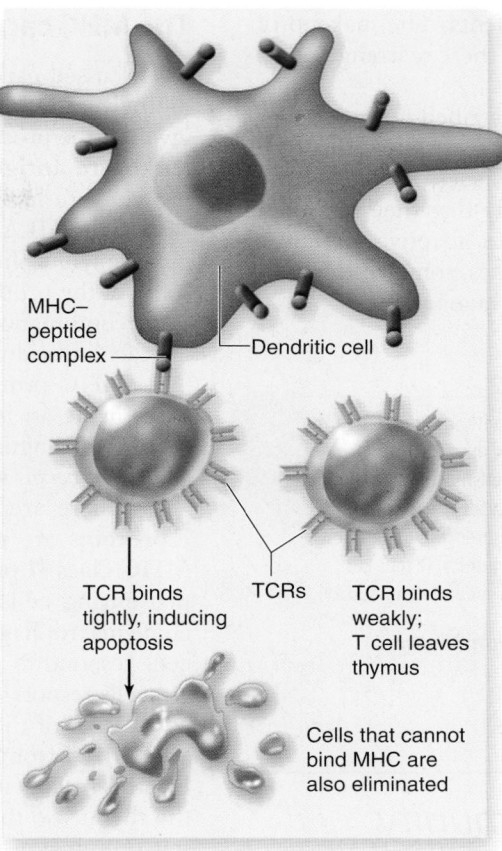

Figure 52.10 **Selection against self-reactive lymphocytes in primary lymphoid organs.** After B and T lymphocytes acquire their specific receptors, self-reactive cells are eliminated by apoptosis. *a.* If Igs on the surface of a maturing B cell bind to an epitope on a bone marrow stromal cell, that cell will undergo apoptosis. The small percentage (10%) of B cells whose Igs do not recognize stromal cell epitopes will be released from the bone marrow. *b.* If TCRs on a maturing T cell bind too tightly to self-MHC/self-peptide complexes on dendritic cells in the thymus, that T cell will undergo apoptosis. Cells that don't bind MHC complexes at all are also eliminated. The very small percentage (2–5%) of maturing T cells that bind MHC peptide complexes with intermediate affinity are released from the thymus. These cells bind self-MHC/foreign peptide complexes with high affinity.

Lymphocytes responding to antigens in a lymph node may pass out of capillaries supplying blood to the lymph node and enter the node's tissues. This is the cause of the "swollen glands" that sometimes accompany infection. The local lymph nodes enlarge due to the vast influx of lymphocytes.

Some antigens are found primarily in the blood, or in the blood as well as in the tissues. One example is the bacterium *Neisseria meningitidis*, a cause of a potentially fatal meningitis (infection of the meninges, layers of membranes covering the brain). Immune responses to such antigens occur in the spleen.

The splenic artery carries blood to the spleen where it then subdivides into arterioles. Antigens released into the ground tissue of the spleen are recognized by B and T cells present in the white pulp, regions of the spleen immediately surrounding the arterioles. Lymphocytes in the white pulp may be activated, as in the lymph node. Antibodies along with some of the activated lymphocytes exit via the splenic vein.

The final important secondary lymphoid organ is the **mucosa-associated lymphoid tissue (MALT),** which includes the tonsils, the appendix, and a large number of follicles located in the connective tissue under mucosal surfaces. These follicles are composed of lymphocytes, primarily B cells but also some T cells, and some macrophages. Any antigens that pass through the mucosa immediately encounter lymphocytes in these follicles and their entry further into the body may be stopped at this point.

If invading organisms manage to escape or evade innate defenses of mucosal surfaces as well as the specific responses of the lymphocytes in the MALT, then they still face a further chance of being stopped by responses in the other secondary lymphoid organs.

Two forms of adaptive immunity have evolved

Adaptive immunity, involving the ability to distinguish between self and nonself, was long thought to have evolved once in vertebrates. The type of adaptive immunity described in this chapter first arose in the cartilaginous fish that evolved some 450 MYA (see chapter 35).

Sharks and rays possess a thymus and a spleen, as well as a rather diffuse MALT. These animals mount cell-mediated responses with T cells bearing TCRs, and humoral responses with B cells that secrete Ig. Bone marrow in which hematopoiesis occurs appeared first in amphibians, although its exact role appears to vary in different species. Lymph nodes appeared first in birds, and their immune system differs little from that of mammals.

Recently, a second form of adaptive immunity has been described in jawless fish. This system does not involve B and T cells with their characteristic receptors. Instead, lymphocytes have receptor proteins composed of variable repeats rich in the amino acid leucine. These proteins appear to function much like Ig, but with a completely different protein architecture. The number of different receptor proteins produced by this system appears similar to the number of potential Ig. The generation of diversity in the two systems appears to have some similarity as the different lymphocyte receptors in jawless fish are also assembled by DNA rearrangements. The makeup of the genes involved and the mechanism of these rearrangements is currently unknown.

It is unclear whether this newly described form of adaptive immunity was present in the ancestor to all chordates, or if it evolved in the lineage that gave rise to jawless fish. Given the differences in the two systems, it is likely that they represent independent events. If this other form of adaptive immunity was present in the ancestor to all chordates, some vestige may remain in modern vertebrates, including humans.

Learning Outcomes Review 52.2

Adaptive immunity is able to recognize individual pathogens and mount a specific response. Lymphocytes, produced in bone marrow, must acquire their specific receptors and undergo selection for self-reactivity in primary lymphoid organs. These mature but naive lymphocytes circulate to secondary lymphoid organs, where they may encounter foreign antigens. B cells produce circulating antibodies (humoral immunity); T cells kill pathogens or help other cells respond to them (cell-mediated immunity).

- **What type of adult stem cells are found in the immune system?**

52.3 Cell-Mediated Immunity

Learning Outcomes

1. **Describe the function of cytotoxic T cells.**
2. **Explain the role of helper T cells.**

T cells may be characterized as either **cytotoxic T cells (T$_C$)** or *helper T cells (T$_H$)*. These cells can also be identified based on cell surface markers. T$_C$ cells have CD8 protein on their cell surface, making them CD8$^+$ cells. T$_H$ cells have CD4 protein on their cell surface, making them CD4$^+$ cells.

To be activated, both of these T cell types must recognize peptide fragments bound to MHC proteins, but the two cell types may be distinguished by (1) recognition of different classes of MHC proteins, which have distinct cell distributions, and (2) differing roles of the T cells after they are activated.

The MHC carries self and nonself information

As discussed earlier, the surfaces of most vertebrate cells exhibit glycoproteins encoded by the MHC. In humans, the name given to the proteins encoded by the MHC complex is **human leukocyte antigens (HLAs).** The genes encoding the MHC proteins are highly polymorphic (have many alleles). For example, the HLA proteins are specified by genes that are the most polymorphic known, with nearly 500 alleles detected for some of the proteins. Only rarely will two individuals have the same combination of alleles, and the HLAs are thus different for each individual, much as fingerprints are.

MHC proteins on the tissue cells serve as self markers that enable an individual's immune system, specifically its T cells, to distinguish its own cells from foreign cells, an ability called *self versus nonself recognition.*

There are two classes of MHC proteins. **MHC class I proteins** are present on every nucleated cell of the body. **MHC class II proteins,** however, are found only on **antigen-presenting cells** (in addition to MHC class I); these cells include macrophages, B cells, and dendritic cells (table 52.2). T$_C$ cells respond to peptides bound to MHC class I proteins, and T$_H$ cells respond to peptides bound to MHC class II proteins.

Most of the time, the peptides bound to MHC proteins are derived from self-proteins from the individual's own cells. For this reason, it is important that T cells undergo selection in the thymus so that those that bind too strongly to peptides of self-proteins on self-MHC are eliminated. In this way, T cells normally are activated only outside the primary lymphoid organs in which they mature, when they encounter peptides of foreign proteins on self-MHC—for example, in the case of viral infection or cancer.

Cytotoxic T cells eliminate virally infected cells and tumor cells

Activated cytotoxic T cells recognize "altered-self" cells, particularly those that are virally infected or tumor cells. The TCRs of cytotoxic T lymphocytes recognize peptides of endogenous antigens bound to MHC class I proteins. Peptides of endogenous antigens are generated in a cell's cytosol and then are pumped by special transport proteins into the rough endoplasmic reticulum where they become bound to MHC class I proteins. These proteins continue on their way through the endomembrane system to the cell surface.

TABLE 52.2	Lymphocyte Recognition of Antigen			
	Recognize epitopes of soluble or particulate antigen	Recognize peptides bound to self-MHC proteins	Class of MHC proteins recognized	Cell types on which recognized MHC is expressed
B cells	Yes	No	None	NA
T$_H$ (CD4$^+$) cells	No	Yes	Class II	Antigen-presenting cells: dendritic cells, B cells, and macrophages
T$_C$ (CD8$^+$) cells	No	Yes	Class I	All nucleated cells

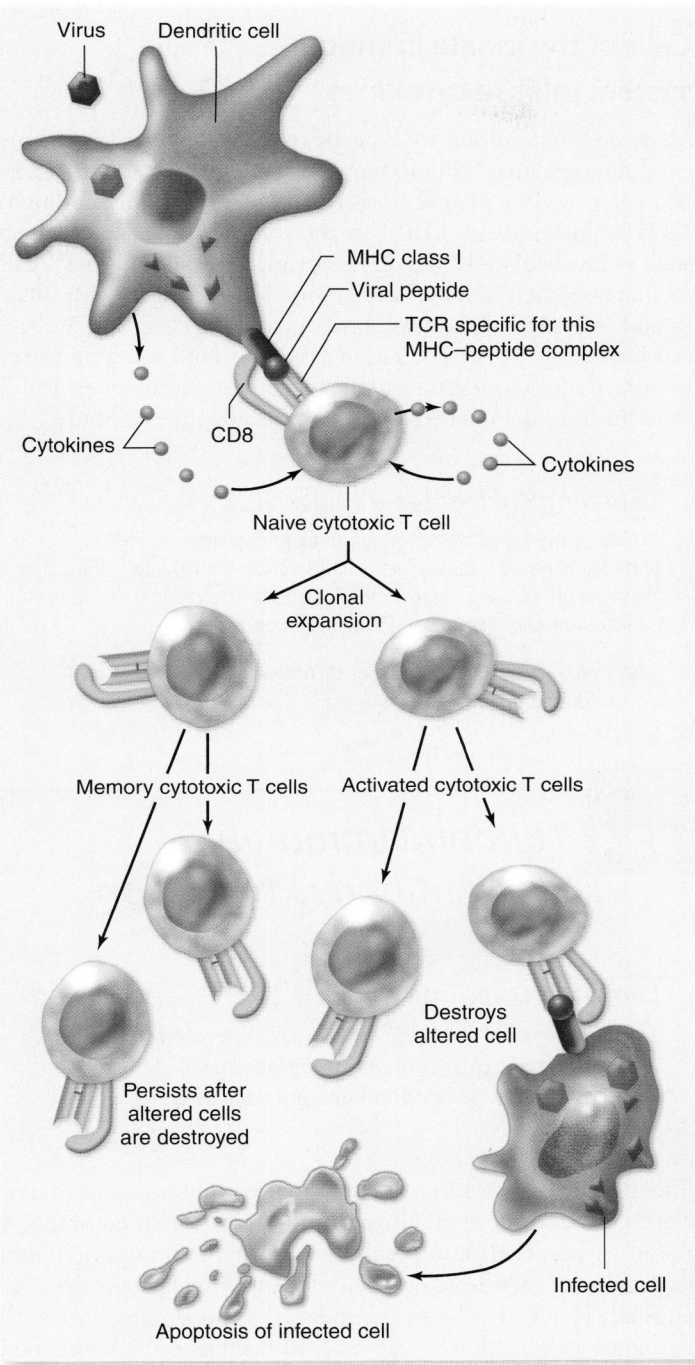

Figure 52.11 Cytotoxic T cells induce apoptosis of "altered-self" cells. Naive cytotoxic T cells are initially activated on TCR recognition of foreign peptide displayed on self-MHC class I proteins on dendritic cells in a secondary lymphoid organ. Activation results in clonal expansion and differentiation into memory cells and activated cells. Activated progeny of the T_C cell can induce apoptosis of any cell in the periphery (outside the secondary lymphoid organ) that displays the same self-MHC class I–peptide combination on its surface. This will most likely be a virally infected cell or a tumor cell.

An endogenous antigen may be a self-protein, or it may be a viral protein produced within a virally infected cell or an unusual protein produced by a cancerous cell. T_C cells respond only to the peptides of these unusual proteins bound to self-MHC class I. T-cell activation occurs in a secondary lymphoid organ, as described earlier. In a lymph node, for example, T cells encounter antigen-presenting cells. Dendritic cells in particular often present antigens that activate T_C cells.

Because not all viruses can infect dendritic cells, the dendritic cells must ingest viruses or tumor cells and then, through a mechanism referred to as cross-presentation, place the viral or tumor peptides on MHC class I proteins. Binding of the T_C cell through its TCR and its CD8 site to the dendritic cell induces clonal expansion of the T_C cell, generating many activated T_C cells as well as memory T_C cells (figure 52.11). The activated T_C cells then circulate around the body where they bind to "target" host cells that express the same combination of foreign peptide on self-MHC class I (figure 52.12).

Apoptosis of the target cell is induced in a very similar fashion to that used by NK cells; a T_C cell secretes perforin monomers that create pores in the target's membrane; granzymes enter and activate caspases, which in turn cause apoptosis of the target.

Helper T cells secrete proteins that direct immune responses

Activated helper T cells, T_H cells, secrete low-molecular-weight proteins known as **cytokines.** A vast array of cytokines is known, many but not all of which are secreted by T_H cells. These cytokines bind to specific receptors on the membranes of many other cells, particularly but not exclusively those of the immune system. On binding, they initiate signaling cascades in these cells that promote their activation or differentiation.

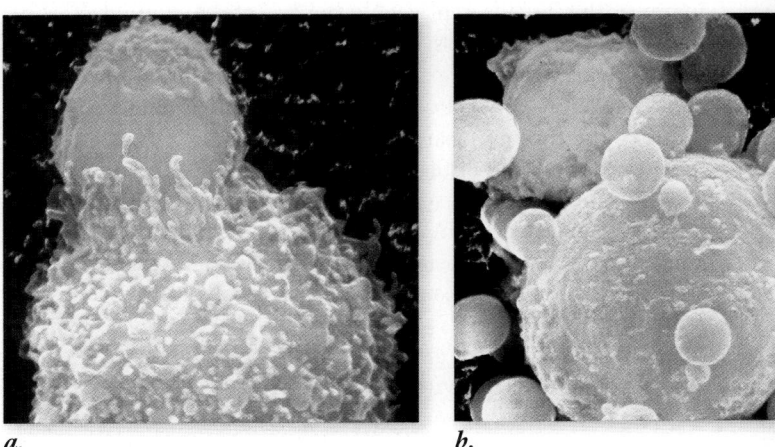

a.   *b.*

Figure 52.12 Cytotoxic T cells destroy tumor cells.
a. The cytotoxic T cell (orange) comes into contact with a tumor cell (purple). *b.* The T cell recognizes that the tumor cell is "altered-self" and induces the apoptosis of the tumor cell.

Because cytokines are quite potent, they are generally secreted at very low concentrations so that, with a few exceptions, they bind only to nearby cells. IL-1 is an exception in that it travels to the hypothalamus to induce the fever response. Different subsets of T_H cells secrete cytokines specific for different cell receptors, so it is largely the T_H cells and the cytokines they secrete that determine whether an immune response will be humoral or cell-mediated in nature.

T_H cells respond to exogenous antigen that has been brought into an antigen-presenting cell. Macrophages or dendritic cells acquire these antigens by phagocytosis or endocytosis, and B cells gain them through receptor-mediated endocytosis. Once inside these cells, the antigen is gradually degraded in increasingly acidic endosomes or lysosomes. Peptides of the antigen join with MHC class II proteins in certain of these endosomes, and the MHC class II–peptide complexes are then transported to and displayed on the cell surface of the antigen-presenting cell. T_H cells encounter these cells within the secondary lymphoid organs and bind to the complexes. The CD4 protein of the T_H cells additionally bind to conserved regions of MHC class II.

A naive T_H cell expresses a protein called CD28 that must bind to a protein called B7 if that T cell is to be activated. B7 is found only on antigen-presenting cells and is at highest levels on dendritic cells. This requirement ensures that T_H cells are activated only when needed; this careful regulation is necessary due to the potency of the cytokines these cells release.

As with T_C cells, an activated T_H cell gives rise to a clone of T_H cells including both effector T_H cells and memory T_H cells, with identical TCR specificity. Most of the effector cells will leave the lymphoid organ and circulate around the body.

T cells are the primary cells that mediate transplant rejection

When T cells encounter the nonself MHC–peptide complexes present on transplanted tissue, such as a kidney, the TCRs on many of the T cells can weakly bind to these complexes. This is simply a case of cross-reactivity: The structure of a nonself MHC–peptide complex sufficiently resembles that of the self-MHC–foreign-peptide complex. The result is that the T cell binds to the foreign tissue cell.

Although the interactions between TCRs and nonself MHC–peptide complexes are relatively weak, many interactions occur between any one T cell and any one transplanted cell because a high density of MHC proteins is present on the surface of all cells. This activates the T cells and initiates the attack on the foreign tissues.

Because of the genetic basis of MHC proteins, the more closely two individuals are related, the less their MHC proteins vary, and thus the more likely they will be to tolerate each other's tissues. As a result, relatives are often sought as donors for patients in need of an organ transplant, and HLA typing is done to find matching alleles.

A variety of drugs are used to suppress immune system rejection of a transplant; most individuals with a non-MHC-matched transplant continue to take some of these drugs for the remainder of their lives. One very effective drug is cyclosporin, which blocks the activation of lymphocytes.

Cells of the innate immune system release cytokines

Many cells in addition to T_H cells release cytokines, always in a carefully regulated fashion. For example, macrophages that have been activated by phagocytosis of antigen, or by the binding of PAMP molecules to TLRs on their surface, release cytokines such as interleukin-12 (IL-12) that can, in turn, bind to T_H cells to increase their level of activation. Macrophages with TLRs bound to PAMP also release other cytokines, such as tumor necrosis factor-α (TNF-α). These cytokines bind to blood vessels to induce a local or even systemic increase in vascular permeability. This links the innate response to the adaptive response.

Learning Outcomes Review 52.3

T cells respond to peptides of foreign antigens displayed on self-MHC proteins. Activated T_C cells induce apoptosis of altered self cells—those that are virally infected or are tumor cells. T_H cells secrete cytokines that promote either cell-mediated or humoral immune responses.

■ **How are T-cell receptors different from Toll-like receptors?**

52.4 Humoral Immunity and Antibody Production

Learning Outcomes

1. **Explain how antibody diversity is generated.**
2. **List the five classes of immunoglobulins.**
3. **Explain how vaccination prevents disease.**

The B-cell receptors for antigen are the immunoglobulin molecules present as integral proteins in the plasma membrane. As noted earlier, each B cell exhibits about 10^5 immunoglobulin molecules of identical specificity for a particular epitope of an antigen. Naive B cells in secondary lymph organs encounter antigens. When immunoglobulin molecules on a B cell bind to a specific epitope on an antigen, and the B cell receives additional required signals, particularly cytokines secreted by T_H cells, then that B cell becomes activated, proliferating into plasma cells and memory cells (figure 52.13).

Each plasma B cell is a miniature factory producing soluble antibodies of the same specificity as the membrane-bound antibodies of the parent B cell. These antibodies enter the lymph and blood circulation as well as the extracellular fluid, and they bind to the appropriate epitopes of antigen encountered anywhere in the body. Any one antigen may present a variety of epitopes, so that different B cells might recognize different epitopes of a single antigen.

Once immunoglobulins coat an antigen, many other cells and processes may be activated to eliminate the antigen. The immunity to avian cholera that Pasteur observed in his chickens resulted from such antibodies and from the continued presence of the progeny of the B cells that produced them.

Immunoglobulin structure reveals variable and constant regions

Each immunoglobulin molecule consists of two identical short polypeptides called *light chains* and two identical longer polypeptides called **heavy chains** (figure 52.14). The four chains in an immunoglobulin molecule are held together by disulfide bonds, forming a Y-shaped molecule (figure 52.14*a*). Each "arm" of the molecule is referred to as an Fab region, and the "stem" is the Fc region (figure 52.14*b*).

Antibody specificity: The variable region

Comparison of the amino acid sequences of many different immunoglobulin molecules has demonstrated that the specificity of immunoglobulins for antigen epitopes resides in the amino-terminal half of each Fab region. This half of the Fab has an amino acid sequence that varies from one immunoglobulin to the next and is thus designated the *variable region*. Both the light chain and the heavy chain have a variable region.

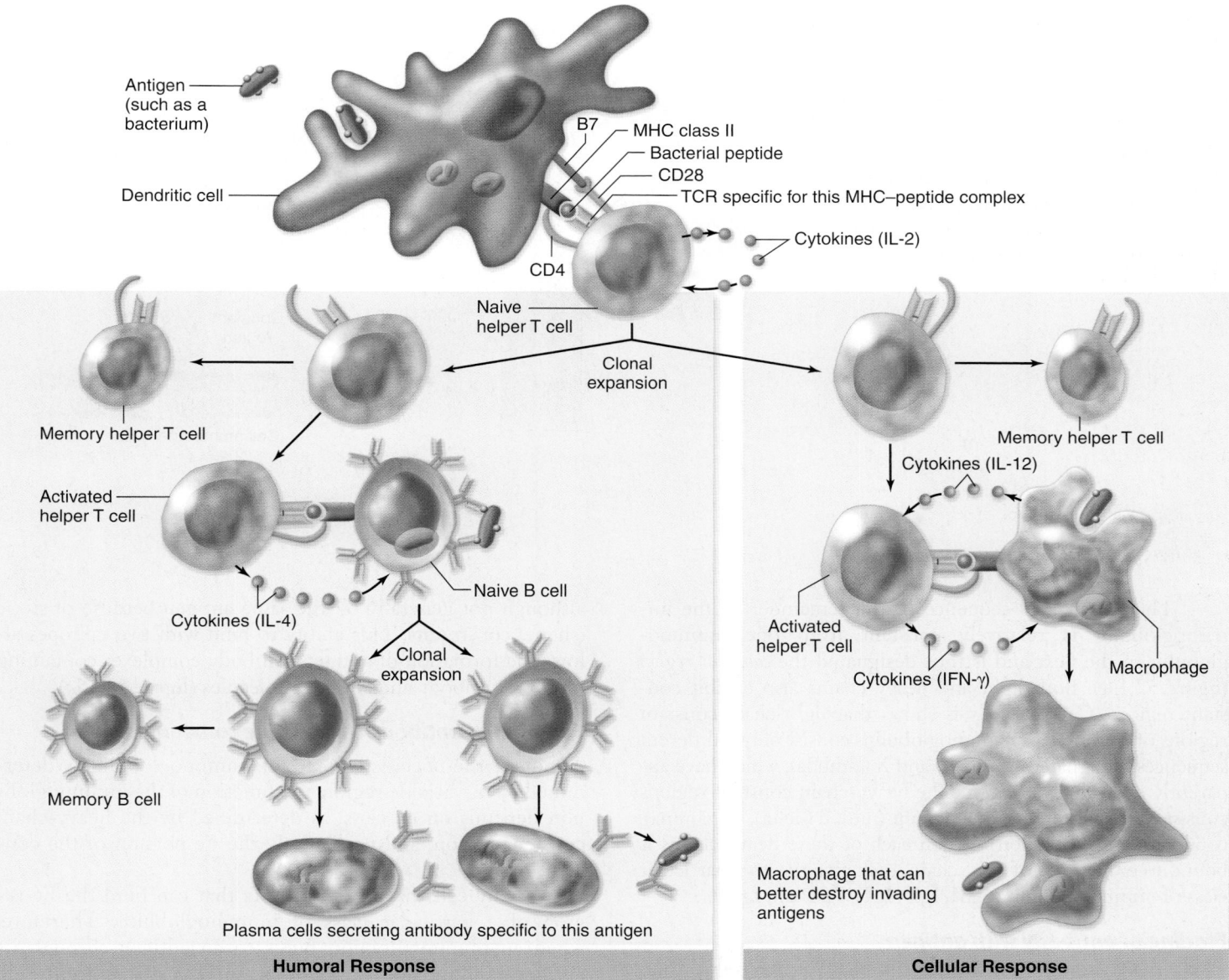

Figure 52.13 Helper T cells secrete cytokines promoting either cell-mediated or humoral immune responses. Naive helper T cells are initially activated by TCR bound to a foreign peptide displayed on self-MHC class II proteins on dendritic cells. Activation results in clonal expansion and differentiation into memory cells and activated cells. T_H cells promote the humoral response when they recognize the same antigen displayed by a B cell. Cytokines such as interleukin-4 (IL-4) released from the T_H cell then activate the B cell, producing memory cells and plasma that secrete antibodies against the antigen. T_H cells also secrete interferon-γ (IFN-γ), which stimulates cells involved in the cellular response such as the macrophage shown here. Macrophages secrete other cytokines that stimulate T_H cells.

Figure 52.14 The structure of an immunoglobulin molecule. *a.* In this model of an immunoglobulin (Ig) molecule, amino acids in the peptide chains are represented by small spheres. The molecule consists of two heavy chains *(brown)* and two light chains *(yellow)*. The four chains form a Y shape, with two identical antigen-binding sites at the arms of the Y, the Fab regions, and a stem, or Fc region. The two Fab regions are joined to the Fc region by a flexible hinge. *b.* A more schematic depiction showing heavy chains *(brown)* and light chains *(yellow)* as rods. The two identical halves of the molecule are joined by disulfide bonds *(red)* as are the heavy and light chains of each half. *c.* Ig molecule shown as a membrane protein. This depiction highlights the domain structure of heavy and light chains. Each chain contains a series of domains, each about 110 amino acids, which include an immunoglobulin fold motif. These are represented as loops with globular structure maintained by disulfide bonds *(red)*. The amino-terminal half of each Fab is a variable region *(blue)* that binds to an epitope and the remainder of the molecule is the constant region.

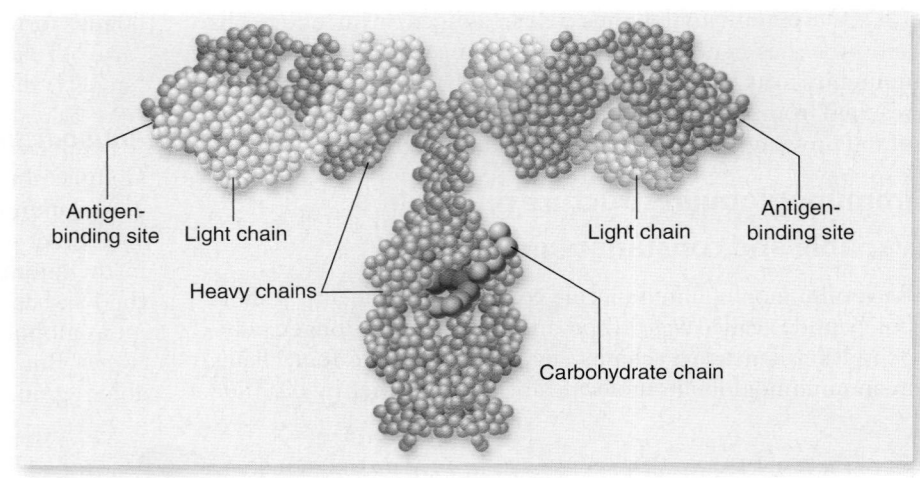

a.

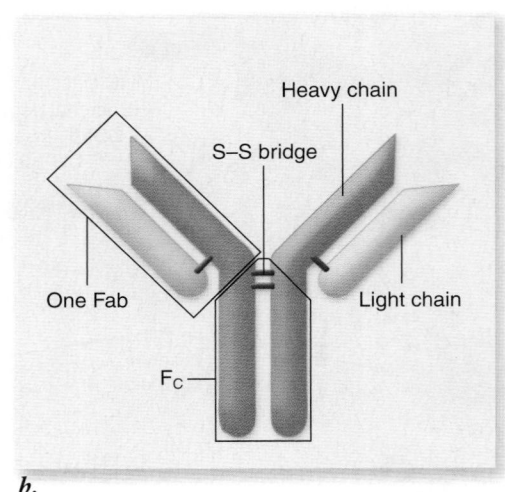

b.

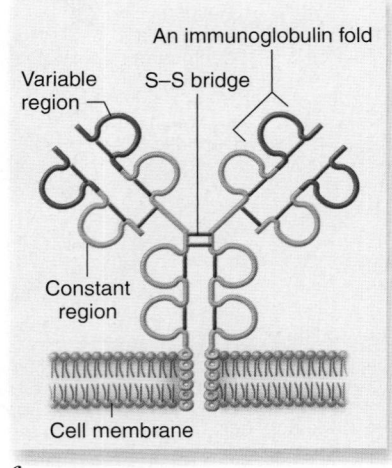

c.

The amino acid sequence of the remainder of the immunoglobulin is relatively constant from one immunoglobulin to the next and is thus designated the *constant region* (figure 52.14c). Both light and heavy chains also exhibit constant regions. Careful analysis shows that light-chain constant regions of mammalian immunoglobulins consist of two different sequences, designated κ (kappa) and λ (lambda), which have apparently equivalent function. The heavy-chain constant regions consist of five different sequences: μ (mu), δ (delta), γ (gamma), α (alpha), and ε (epsilon). When each of these heavy chains is bound to either type of light chain, they give rise to a particular class of immunoglobulin: IgM, IgD, IgG, IgA, and IgE.

Binding of antibody with antigen

The variable regions of the heavy and light chains fold together to form a sort of cleft, the *antigen-binding site* (see figure 52.14). The size and shape of the antigen-binding site, as well as which amino acids line its surface, determine the specificity of each immunoglobulin for an antigen epitope.

Because each immunoglobulin is composed of two identical halves, they can each bind with two identical epitopes, although not generally on the same antigen because of steric (shape) constraints. This ability to bind with two epitopes allows the formation of antigen–antibody complexes containing multiple antibody and antigen molecules (figure 52.15a).

Function of antibody classes: The constant region

Although the specificity of each immunoglobulin is determined by its variable region, the function of the immunoglobulin depends on its class, as determined by the heavy-chain constant region, and particularly the Fc portion of the constant region.

Many cells have Fc receptors that can bind the Fc region of a particular class of immunoglobulin. Therefore, when an immunoglobulin binds to an antigen through its antigen-binding site, another cell, such as a phagocytic cell, may be brought close to the antigen by binding to the Fc region of the immunoglobulin (figure 52.15c). This binding of antigen–antibody complex to Fc receptors can also activate these cells. In this way, specific immunoglobulins can promote the interaction of nonspecific cells with the antigen, generally resulting in the elimination of the antigen.

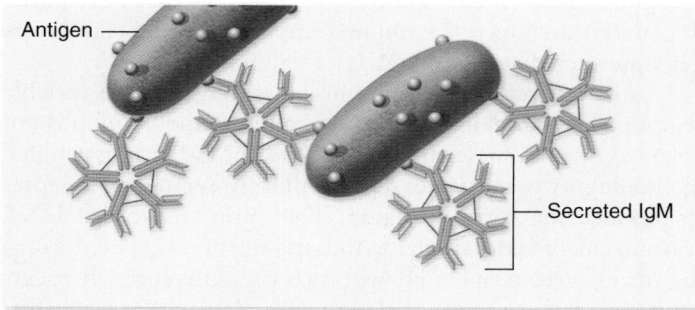

a.

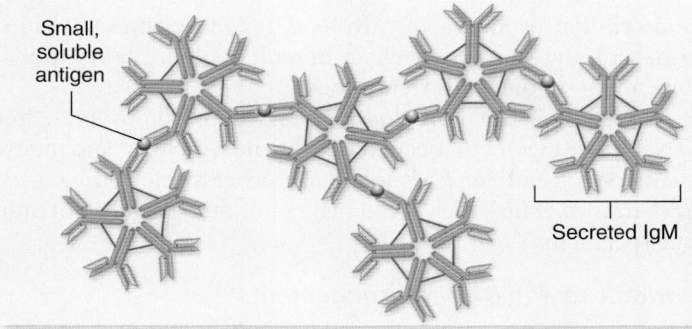

b.

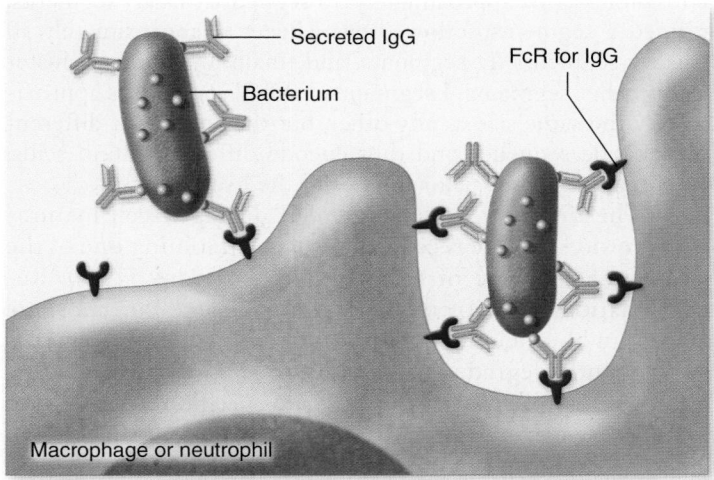

c.

Figure 52.15 **Binding of antibody to antigens can cause agglutination, precipitation, or neutralization of the antigens.** *a.* Binding of secreted IgM to larger particulate antigens leads to the clumping, or agglutination, of the antigens. *b.* Binding of secreted IgM to small soluble antigens can lead to their precipitation. Secreted IgG, due to its high concentration (75% of plasma Ig), can also agglutinate and precipitate antigens. IgG does not precipitate as efficiently as IgM because of the pentameric nature of secreted IgM. *c.* Secreted IgG can coat or neutralize an antigen by blocking its ability to bind to a host. Macrophages and neutrophils that have Fc receptors for IgG can thus attach to an antigen–antibody complex, which they will then phagocytose and destroy.

The five classes of immunoglobulins have different functions

The five classes of antibodies are based on the sequence and structure of the constant regions of their heavy chains. These five classes have different functions in the protection of an individual. Characteristics of the different classes are summarized in table 52.3 and are described in the following sections.

Keep in mind that antibodies don't kill invading pathogens directly; rather, they cause destruction of pathogens by targeting them for attack by other, nonspecific cells or by activating the complement system.

IgM is a receptor on the surface of all mature, naive B cells and is the first type of antibody to be secreted during an immune response. Although IgM in the membrane of a B cell is monomeric in form, it is secreted as a pentamer (five units) of about 900,000 kDa. Its large size restricts it to the circulation, but its pentameric form means that it very efficiently promotes agglutination of larger antigens (figure 52.15*a*) and precipitation

TABLE 52.3	Five Classes of Immunoglobulins	
Class		**Function**
IgM	Pentamer	First antibody secreted during the primary immune response; promotes agglutination and precipitation reactions and activates complement
IgD	Monomer	Present only on surfaces of B cells; serves as antigen receptor
IgG	Monomer	Major antibody secreted during the secondary response; neutralizes antigens and promotes their phagocytosis and activates complement
IgA	Dimer	Most abundant form of antibody in body secretions; high density of IgA-secreting plasma cells in the MALT
IgE	Monomer	Fc binds to mast cells and basophils; allergen binding to V regions promotes the release of mediators, which triggers allergic reactions

of soluble antigens (figure 52.15b). IgM bound to an antigen also activates a complement protein cascade, triggered by the binding of certain complement proteins to the exposed Fc ends.

IgD is also present, along with IgM, on mature naive B cells. The B cells can be activated by cross-linking of two IgD molecules, although under normal circumstances this class of immunoglobulin is not secreted by the cells. On B-cell activation, IgD is no longer displayed on the cell surface. Other roles for IgD remain elusive.

IgG is the major form of antibody in the blood plasma and in most tissues, making up about 75% of plasma antibodies. It is the most common form of antibody produced in a secondary immune response (any response triggered on a subsequent exposure to an antigen). IgG can bind to an antigen in such quantity that the antigen—a virus, bacterium, or bacterially derived toxin—is said to be neutralized, meaning that it can no longer bind to the host. Macrophages and neutrophils have Fc receptors that bind to IgGs bound to antigens, and in this way IgG binding or coating of antigens facilitates their elimination by phagocytosis (figure 52.15c). IgG is also important in providing passive immunity to a fetus; it readily crosses the placenta from the mother. Finally, IgG can also activate complement, although not as efficiently as IgM, leading to pathogen elimination.

IgA is the major form of antibody in external secretions, such as saliva, tears, and the mucus that coats the gastrointestinal tract, bronchi, and genitourinary tract. IgA plays a major role in protection of these surfaces; it is usually secreted as a dimer. The many plasma cells present in the MALT, under the mucosal surfaces, secrete IgA that crosses the epithelial cells to the lumen of these tracts; here it can bind and neutralize antigens. Additionally, any pathogen that passes through a mucosal surface becomes bound to IgA because it is secreted by cells in follicles under that surface. The bound IgA crosses the epithelial cells into the lumen, taking the pathogen with it. The pathogen can then be eliminated by innate defenses. IgA also provides passive immunity to a nursing infant since it is present in mother's milk.

IgE is present at very low concentration in the plasma. On secretion, most becomes bound to mast cells and basophils that recognize the Fc portion of IgE. As described later, binding of certain normally harmless antigens to IgE molecules bound to mast cells and basophils produces the symptoms of allergy, such as the runny nose and itchy eyes of hay fever. IgE is also often secreted in response to an infection by helminth worms. In this instance, secreted IgE binds to epitopes on the worms and is then recognized by Fc receptors on eosinophils. The eosinophils generally kill the worms by secreting digestive enzymes through perforin pores into the worms.

Immunoglobulin diversity is generated through DNA rearrangement

The vertebrate immune system is capable of recognizing as foreign virtually any nonself molecule presented to it. It is estimated that human or mouse B cells can generate antibodies with over 10^{10} different antigen-binding sites. Although an individual probably does not have antibodies specific to all epitopes of an antigen, it is fairly certain that antibodies will recognize some of the epitopes, which is all that is required to generate an effective immune response. How do vertebrates generate such diversity of antigen recognition?

The answer lies in the unusual genetics of the variable region. This region in each chain of an immunoglobulin is not encoded by one single stretch of DNA but rather is assembled by joining two or three separate DNA segments together to produce the variable region. This process is called DNA rearrangement and is similar to the crossing over that occurs during meiosis (see chapter 11) with two key differences: It occurs between loci on the same chromosome and it is site-specific.

DNA rearrangement occurs as a progenitor B cell matures in the bone marrow. After DNA rearrangement, RNA transcription produces an mRNA that can be translated into either a heavy- or a light-chain immunoglobulin polypeptide, depending on the locus transcribed.

Cells contain homologous pairs of chromosomes, but DNA rearrangement occurs for the heavy-chain and light-chain loci on only one homologue, a process referred to as *allelic exclusion*. Thus, each B cell makes immunoglobulins of only one specificity.

Variable region DNA rearrangements

Sequencing of human immunoglobulin heavy-chain gene loci from several different individuals shows that the locus contains a cluster of approximately 50 sequential DNA segments, termed V segments, followed by a cluster of approximately 30 smaller segments, D segments, and finally by another cluster of 6 smaller segments, J segments. Each V segment is approximately the same size as any other, but they are all of different nucleo-tide sequence and thus encode different amino acids; the situation is similar for the D and the J segments.

The first DNA rearrangement during B-cell maturation is a site-specific recombination event joining one of the D segments to one of the J segments (figure 52.16). Recombination between two sites on the same chromosome results in the deletion of the intervening DNA, which is subsequently degraded.

This is followed by another site-specific recombination joining a V segment to the rearranged DJ, with the deletion of all the intervening DNA. Which V, which D, and which J are chosen by any cell appears to be completely random.

Because of the many combinations of V, D, and J that can be formed, one can calculate the generation of about 9000 different heavy-chain variable-region sequences. A similar situation occurs for light-chain variable region formation, except that each light-chain variable region is encoded by only a V segment and a J segment.

Other processes contribute even further to the diversity of variable region sequence. As the DNA segments are joined to each other, a few nucleotides may be added to or deleted from the ends of each segment, and this is generally followed by somewhat imprecise joining of the segments to each other, resulting in a shift of the reading frame. B cells may end up expressing any heavy-chain variable region with any light-chain variable region during its maturation. Lastly, these genes show an elevated mutation rate, termed somatic hyper-mutation. Taking all these processes into account has allowed the estimate of more than 10^{10} possible variable regions.

Transcription and translation

After the DNA rearrangements that encode the variable region are complete, pre-mRNA transcripts are formed with 5′ ends that begin at the rearranged variable region-encoding segments and continue through constant region exons. More specifically, heavy-chain-encoding pre-mRNA transcripts start at the rearranged VDJ and continue through exons encoding μ and δ constant regions (see figure 52.16).

Alternative splicing of these RNA transcripts removes any extra J segments that remain 3′ to the rearranged VDJ, as well as either δ or μ sequences, resulting in transcripts that all encode the same variable region but either μ or δ constant region exons, respectively. Translation results in a μ or δ heavy-chain polypeptide, which associates with a light-chain polypeptide in the rough endoplasmic reticulum. Thus, the mature naive B cell expresses both IgM and IgD on its surface, both having the same antigen-binding specificity (see figure 52.16).

T-cell receptors

At this point, we must briefly return to T-cell receptors and examine their similarity to the immunoglobulins of B cells. The structure of a TCR is essentially like a single Fab region of an immunoglobulin molecule (figure 52.17).

The TCR is a dimeric (two-chain) protein, with about 95% of TCRs composed of an α chain and a β chain. The amino terminal halves of the two polypeptides are the variable domains that bind to self-MHC plus peptide, and the membrane-proximal halves are the constant domains of each polypeptide. The TCR variable-region gene loci also contain multiple DNA segments—V, D, and J, or only V and J—that

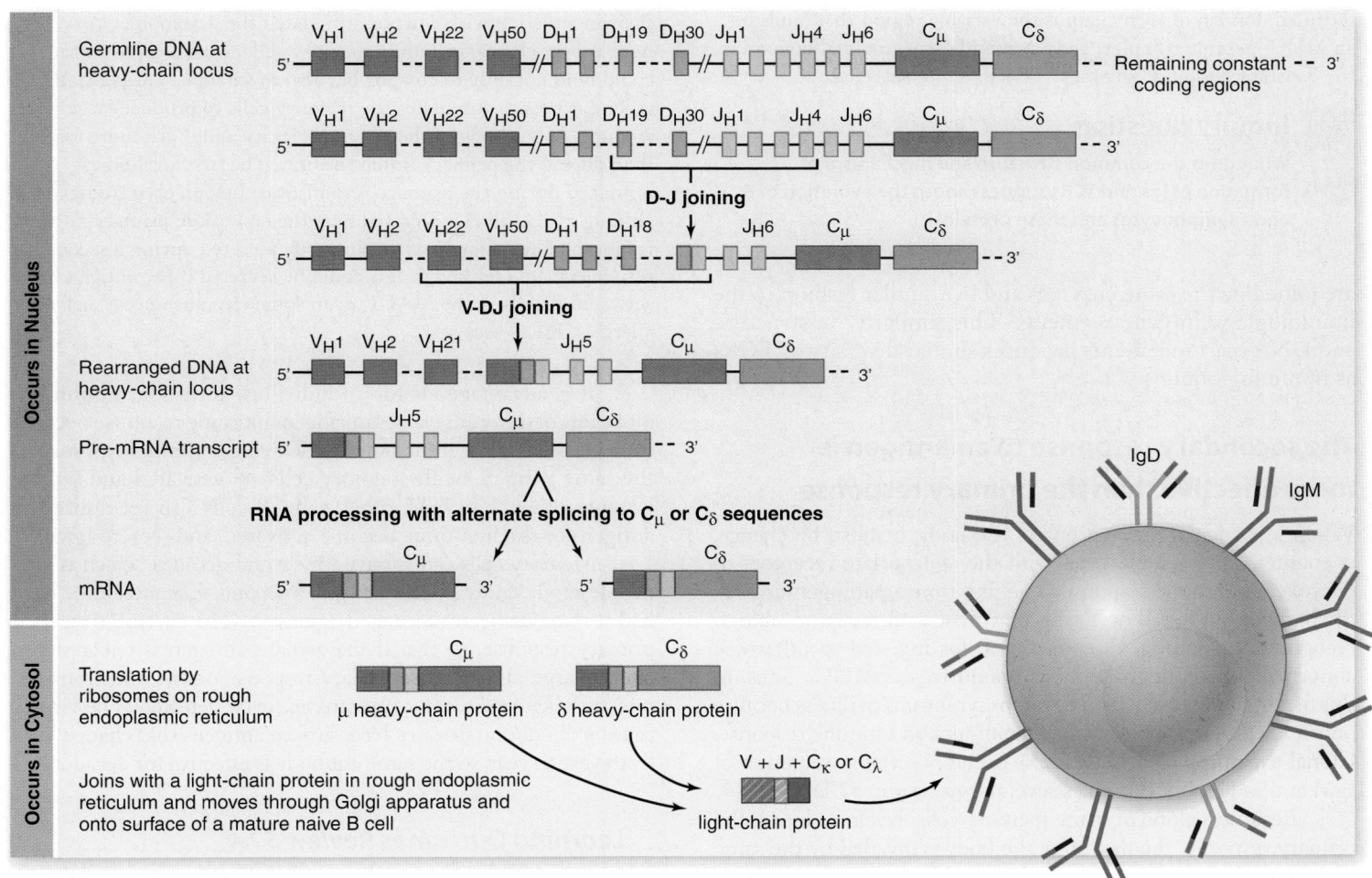

Figure 52.16 **Immunoglobulin diversity is generated by rearrangement of segments of DNA.** An immunoglobulin (Ig) protein is encoded by different segments of DNA: a V (variable), a D (diversity), and a J (joining) segment, plus a constant region. These are joined by a precise sequence of DNA rearrangements during maturation in the bone marrow. This first joins a D to a J segment, then this combined DJ joins to a V segment. Other cells will select other V, D, and J segments, contributing to Ig diversity. Transcription starts at the rearranged VDJ and continues through constant-region exons. PreRNA splicing joins the variable region to either a μ or a δ constant region. These transcripts are translated by ribosomes on the RER to produce heavy-chain polypeptides that join with light chains (encoded by a V, a J, and a C). These proteins are transported to the cell surface, resulting in a mature naive B cell that expresses both IgM (μ constant region) and IgD (δ constant region), with the same variable region and thus the same antigen specificity.

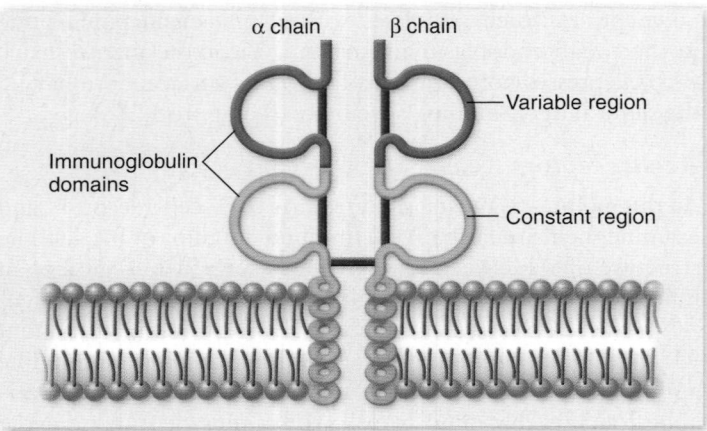

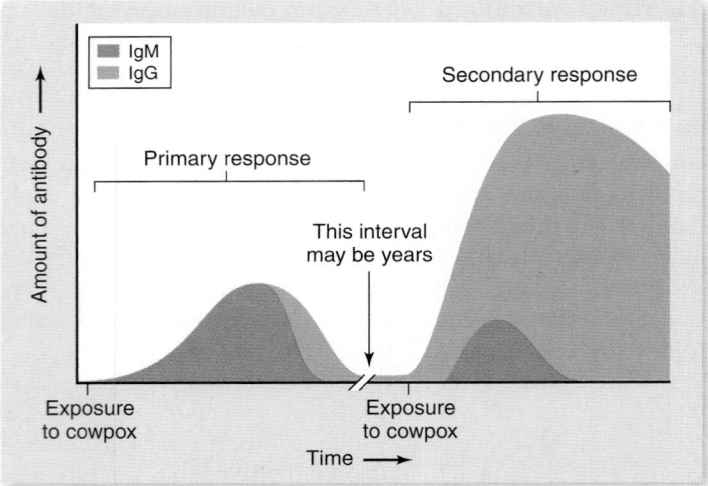

Figure 52.17 The structure of a TCR is similar to an immunoglobulin Fab. TCRs are composed of two chains—generally α and β—joined by a disulfide bond (red). Each also includes two immunoglobulin domains as in an Ig Fab. The amino-terminal domain of each chain is the variable region that binds to an MHC–peptide complex, and the membrane-proximal domain is the constant region. Unlike Igs, TCRs are not secreted.

Inquiry question

? What does the common structure and mechanism of formation of Igs and TCRs suggest about the evolution of B and T lymphocytes and these proteins?

are joined by the same enzymes and in a similar fashion to the immunoglobulin gene segments. This similarity in structure and DNA rearrangements produces similar diversity of TCRs as immunoglobulins.

The secondary response to an antigen is more effective than the primary response

When a particular antigen enters the body, it must, by chance, encounter naive lymphocytes with the appropriate receptors to provoke an immune response. The first time a pathogen invades the body only a few B or T cells may exist with receptors able to recognize the pathogen's epitopes or, for infected or otherwise abnormal cells, foreign peptides bound to self-MHC. Thus, in this first encounter, a person develops symptoms of illness because only a few cells are present that can mount an immune response. Clonal expansion of T and B cells occurs, as well as secretion of IgM antibodies, but this takes several days (figure 52.18).

Because a clone of many memory cells develops during the primary response, the next time the body is invaded by the same pathogen, the immune system is ready. Memory cells are more rapidly activated than are naive lymphocytes, so a secondary immune response both initiates and peaks much more rapidly than a primary response. Further clonal expansion takes place, along with the secretion of large amounts of antibodies that are generally of the IgG class, although IgA and IgE are also possible (see figure 52.18). The class of immunoglobulin produced is dictated by the identity of the cytokines, derived from activated T_H memory cells, that bind to the B cells during their secondary response.

Figure 52.18 The development of active immunity. Immunity to smallpox in Jenner's patients occurred because their inoculation with cowpox stimulated the development of lymphocyte clones, including memory cells, with receptors that could bind not only to cowpox but also to smallpox antigens. A second exposure stimulates the memory cells to produce large amounts of antibody of the same specificity and much more rapidly than during the primary immunization. The first antibodies produced during the primary response are IgM in class (red), although IgG (blue) is secreted near the end of the primary response. The majority of the antibody secreted during a secondary response is IgG, although IgA could be secreted if the antigen has activated B cells in the MALT, or in some circumstances, such as allergies, IgE is secreted.

It is advantageous for an individual to produce immuno-globulins of different classes during an immune response because each class has a different function. During a second exposure to the same antigen, while memory cells are activated and secrete isotypes other than IgM, other naive B cells also recognize the antigen for the first time, become activated, and secrete IgM.

Memory cells can survive for several decades, which is why people rarely contract chicken pox a second time after they have had it once or been vaccinated against it. The vaccine triggers a primary response, so that if the actual pathogen is encountered later, a large and rapid secondary response occurs and stops the infection before disease symptoms are even detected. The viruses causing childhood diseases have surface antigens that change little from year to year, so the same antibody is effective for decades.

Learning Outcomes Review 52.4

Antibodies have variable regions by which they recognize and bind to an antigen. Variable regions are encoded by joining distinct DNA segments, providing recognition diversity. Each antibody also has one of five kinds of constant region that determines its function; these five classes are IgA, IgD, IgE, IgG, and IgM. Vaccination artificially presents an antigen to elicit the primary response; when encountered later, a pathogen with this antigen is eliminated quickly by the secondary response.

■ **How do Ig receptors differ from TLR innate receptors?**

Autoimmunity and Hypersensitivity

Learning Outcomes

1. Define autoimmune diseases.
2. Explain the cellular basis of the allergic reaction.

Sometimes the immune system is the cause of disease rather than the cure. Inappropriate responses to self-antigens may occur, as well as inappropriate or greatly heightened responses to foreign antigens, which, in turn, causes tissue damage.

A mature animal's immune system normally does not respond to that animal's own tissue. This acceptance of self cells is known as **immunological tolerance.** The immune system of a fetus undergoes the process of tolerance to lose the ability to respond to self-molecules as its development proceeds.

We now know that not all self-reactive T and B lymphocytes undergo apoptosis during selection in primary lymphoid organs. Normal healthy individuals are known to possess mature, potentially self-reactive lymphocytes. The activity of these cells, however, is regulated or suppressed so that they do not respond to the self-antigens they encounter. When this regulation or suppression breaks down, then humoral or cell-mediated responses can occur against self-antigens, causing serious and sometimes fatal disease.

Additionally, an immune response against a foreign antigen may be a greater one than is actually required to eliminate the antigen, or the response may be seemingly inappropriate to the antigen. Thus, instead of eliminating the antigen with only a localized inflammatory response, extensive tissue damage and occasionally death occurs.

Autoimmune diseases result from immune system attack on the body's own tissues

Autoimmune diseases are produced by the failure of immunological tolerance. Autoreactive T cells become activated, and autoreactive B cells produce autoantibodies, causing inflammation and organ damage. More than 40 known or suspected autoimmune diseases exist, affecting 5 to 7% of the population. For reasons that are not understood, two-thirds of the people with autoimmune diseases are women.

Autoimmune diseases can result from a variety of mechanisms. For example, the self-antigen may normally be hidden from the immune system; if later it is exposed, the immune system may treat it as foreign. This happens, for example, when a protein normally trapped in the thyroid follicles triggers autoimmune destruction of the thyroid (Hashimoto thyroiditis). It also occurs in sympathetic ophthalmia in which antigens are released from the eye.

Because the immune attack triggers inflammation, and inflammation causes tissue and organ damage, the immune system must be suppressed to alleviate the symptoms of autoimmune diseases. Immune suppression is generally accomplished by administering corticosteroids and nonsteroidal anti-inflammatory drugs, including aspirin.

Allergies are caused by IgE secretion in response to antigens

The most common form of allergy is known as immediate hypersensitivity. It is the result of excessive IgE production in response to antigens, generally referred to as allergens in this context. Allergens that provoke immediate hypersensitivity include various foods, the venom in insect stings, molds, animal danders, and pollen grains. The most common allergy of this type is seasonal hay fever, which may be provoked by the pollen from ragweed (*Ambrosia* spp.) or other plants. Allergies have earned the designation "immediate" because a response to an allergen occurs within seconds or minutes.

The first time or even the first few times that one encounters an allergen, the allergen binds to and activates B cells, which start to secrete allergen-specific immunoglobulins. Activated T_H cells release cytokines such as IL-4, which bind to the B cells and dictate that the antibodies secreted should be IgE. The B cells rapidly switch from the more common IgG secretion to IgE secretion.

Unlike IgG, IgE rapidly binds to mast cells and basophils. When the individual is again exposed to the same allergen, the allergen now specifically binds to the exposed variable regions of identical IgE molecules attached to mast cells and basophils. This binding triggers these cells to secrete histamine, prostaglandins, and other chemical mediators, which produce the symptoms of allergy (figure 52.19).

In *systemic anaphylaxis*, the allergic reaction is severe and potentially life-threatening because of the rapid inflammatory response and release of chemical mediators. The individual experiences a tremendous drop in blood pressure; swelling of the epiglottis can block the trachea, and bronchial constriction can prevent the exit of air from the lungs. This combination of effects is referred to as *anaphylactic shock*. Death can result within 20 to 30 min without prompt medical treatment.

Fortunately, most people with allergies only experience *local anaphylaxis*, such as the itchy welts from hives, or the respiratory constriction of mild asthma. Diarrhea from response to food allergens is another form of local anaphylaxis.

Allergies have traditionally been treated with antihistamines that prevent histamine released by mast cells from binding to its receptor. More recently, a variety of drugs have been developed that block the activation of mast cells and basophils, so that they do not release their mediators. Hyposensitization treatment is another alternative; it consists of the injection, over several months, of an increasing concentration of the allergens to which one is allergic. In some individuals, particularly those with allergic rhinitis (runny nose and eyes) or asthma, this treatment seems to cause a preferential secretion of IgG rather than IgE, and allergy symptoms diminish over time.

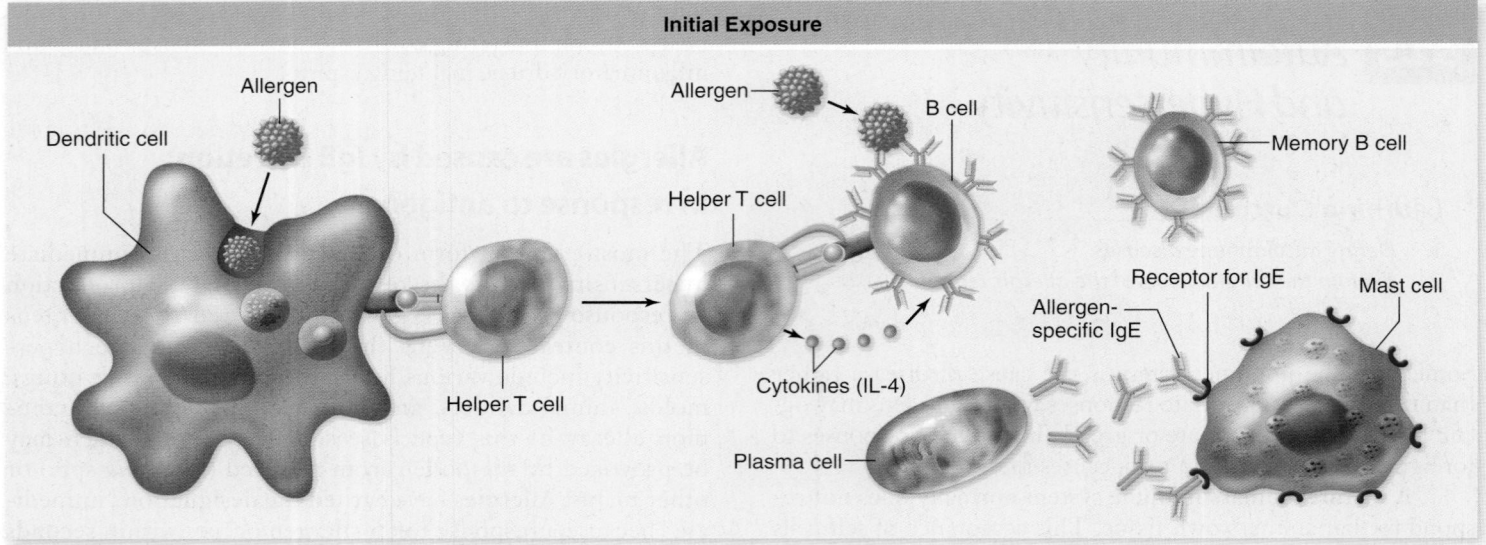

Initial Exposure

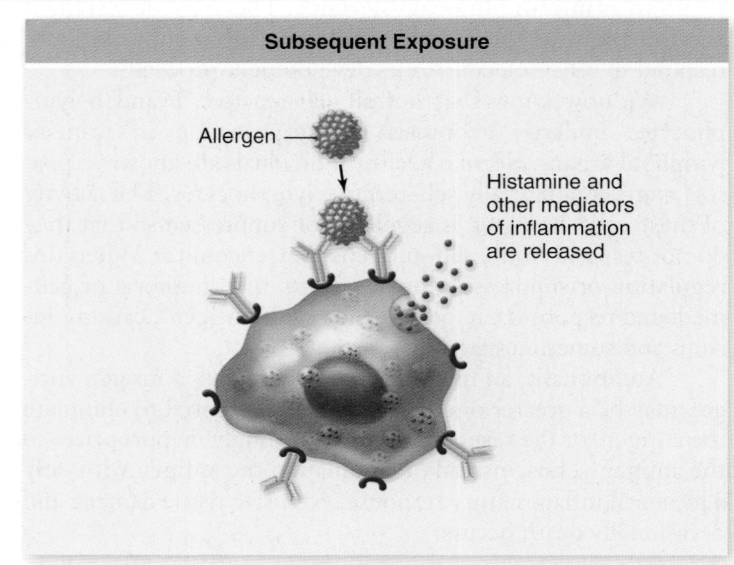

Subsequent Exposure

Figure 52.19 An allergic response. On initial exposure to an allergen, B cells are activated to secrete antibodies of the IgE class. These antibodies are in very low levels in the plasma but rapidly bind to Fc receptors on mast cells or basophils. On subsequent exposure to allergen, the allergen cross-links variable regions of two neighboring IgEs with the same epitope specificity on mast cells and basophils. This induces the cells to release histamine and other mediators of inflammation that will cause the symptoms of allergy.

Delayed-type hypersensitivity is mediated by T$_H$ cells and macrophages

Delayed-type hypersensitivity, which is mediated by T$_H$ cells and macrophages, produces symptoms within about 48 hr after a second exposure to an antigen. (A first exposure causes a much slower primary response, such as described earlier, frequently without the manifestation of any symptoms.) A form of delayed-type hypersensitivity is contact dermatitis, caused by such varied materials as poison ivy, nickel in jewelry, and some cosmetics. After contact with poison ivy, oils that enter the skin complex with skin proteins, causing the proteins to appear foreign. A delayed-type hypersensitivity response requires that antigen entering the body travel to a secondary lymphoid organ, generally lymph nodes, where T$_H$ cells can be activated. These activated T$_H$ cells then recirculate around the body, and on encountering macrophages that have

ingested the antigen, they release cytokines that activate the macrophages. This induces the macrophages to release other cytokines, and in the case of poison ivy, itchy welts on the skin erupt. The time required for the activation of T$_H$ cells and then of macrophages is the reason for the "delayed" response to the antigens.

Learning Outcomes Review 52.5

Autoimmunity, allergies (immediate hypersensitivity), and delayed hypersensitivity are all examples of inappropriate or heightened immune responses. Autoimmunity results from a loss of self-tolerance. Allergies are associated with a rapid response from mast cells when an allergen binds to IgE on these cells' membrane. Delayed hypersensitivity to pathogens or irritants such as poison ivy is mediated by T$_H$ cells and macrophages.

■ *How are allergies different from autoimmune diseases?*

52.6 Antibodies in Medical Treatment and Diagnosis

Learning Outcomes

1. Explain antigen–antibody reactions in the ABO blood group system.
2. Define monoclonal antibodies.
3. Describe the use of monoclonal antibodies in diagnosis.

The vertebrate immune system can have a range of effects on medical treatment of disease. As two examples, we discuss blood type and its effect on transfusion, as well as the use of monoclonal antibodies for diagnosis and treatment.

Blood type indicates the antigens present on an individual's red blood cells

A person's blood type is determined by certain antigens found on the red blood cell surface. These antigens are clinically important because they must be matched between donor and recipient during a blood transfusion.

ABO groups

In chapter 12, you learned about the genetic basis of the human *ABO blood groups*. The protein–sugar complex on the surface of the red blood cells acts as an antigen, and these antigens differ with regard to the sugar present (or absent, in the case of type O). The immune system is tolerant to its own red blood cell antigens but makes antibodies that bind to those that differ, causing agglutination (clumping) and lysis of foreign red blood cells. Apparently, IgM antibodies made in response to carbohydrates on bacteria that are part of our normal flora also recognize the monosaccharide differences on red blood cells. Such antibodies are not made against carbohydrate patterns that are also present on our own cells.

Rh factor

Another important blood-borne antigen is the Rh antigen or *Rh factor*. This protein is either present (Rh positive) or absent (Rh negative) on the surface of red blood cells. An Rh-negative person who receives an Rh-positive blood transfusion produces antibodies to the foreign Rh protein on the transfused cells.

An additional complication occurs when Rh-negative mothers carry Rh-positive fetuses, which may result in the infant exhibiting a condition called hemolytic disease of newborns (HDN). A first child is usually not harmed; however, at the time of the first birth, the Rh-negative mother's immune system may be exposed to fetal blood. As a result, the woman may become sensitized and produce antibodies and memory B cells against the Rh antigen. If any exposure to fetal blood occurs during a subsequent pregnancy, IgG antibodies, secreted on activation of these memory cells, can cross the placenta and cause destruction of the red blood cells of the fetus.

Blood typing is done by taking advantage of the circulating IgM antibodies, which are produced against foreign blood antigens but not against self. If type A blood is mixed with serum from a person with type B or type O blood, the anti-A antibodies in the serum cause the type A red blood cells to agglutinate. This does not happen if type A blood is mixed with serum from another type A individual or from a type AB individual.

Similarly, if serum from an Rh-negative individual is added to red blood cells, agglutination of the red blood cells indicates that they came from an Rh-positive individual. This individual's blood would not be an appropriate match for transfusion.

Typing of blood prior to transfusions prevents destruction of mismatched cells by a transfusion recipient, as described next. Over 20 blood groups, including the ABO and Rh groups, have been identified; most variants of these other blood groups are rare, but individuals at risk for mismatch may need to "stockpile" their own blood before elective surgery—a practice termed *autologous blood donation*.

Transfusion reactions result from mismatched blood transfusions

Prior to the advent of blood typing in the early 20th century, transfusion of blood was a last resort because of the danger of death from transfusion reaction. An immediate transfusion reaction occurs when an individual receives blood that is not correctly ABO matched. Typically, within 5 to 8 hr of the start of the transfusion, tremendous intravascular hemolysis (rupture) of the transfused red blood cells is detected. This rupture is a result of IgM binding to foreign antigens and activating the complement system. The result is the formation of MACs in the red blood cell membranes and rapid osmotic lysis of the cells.

The hemoglobin released from the red blood cells is converted to a molecule called *bilirubin*, which is particularly toxic to cells and can cause severe organ damage, especially to the kidneys. The major treatment in such situations is to stop the transfusion immediately and to administer large amounts of intravenous fluids to "wash" the bilirubin from the body.

Monoclonal antibodies are a valuable tool for diagnosis and treatment

Antibodies to a known antigen may be obtained by chemically purifying an antigen and then injecting it into a laboratory animal (vertebrate). Periodic bleeding of the animal after a few immunizations allows the isolation of serum antibodies against the antigen. But because an antigen typically has many different epitopes, the antibodies obtained by this method are *polyclonal*, that is, they are secreted by B-cell clones with many different specificities. Their polyclonal nature decreases their sensitivity to any one particular epitope, and it may result in some degree of cross-reactivity with closely related epitopes of different antigens.

Monoclonal antibodies, by contrast, exhibit specificity for one epitope only. In the preparation of monoclonal antibodies, an animal, generally a mouse, is immunized several times with an antigen and is subsequently killed. B lymphocytes, many of

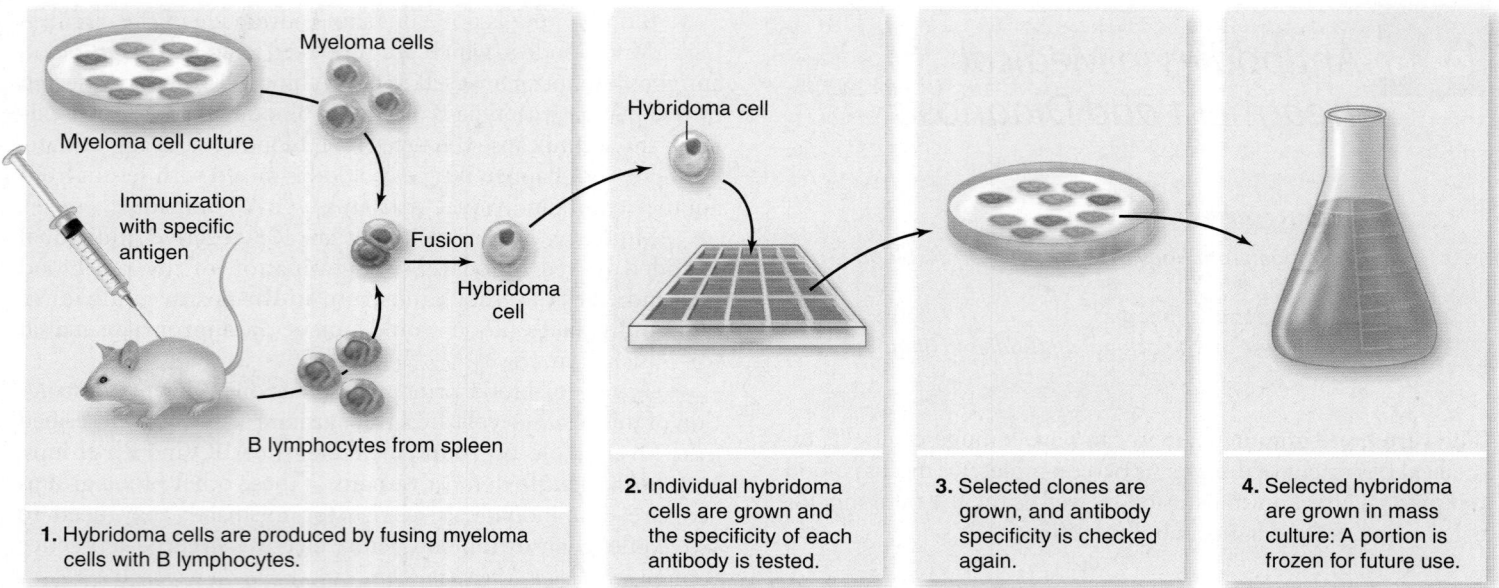

Figure 52.20 The production of monoclonal antibodies. These antibodies are of a single specificity and are produced by "hybridoma" cells. These result from the fusion of B cells, specific for a particular antigenic determinant, with myeloma cells, a B-cell tumor that no longer secretes Ig but provides immortality to the fusion. After hybridoma production, the antibody produced by each hybridoma is tested to see whether it produces specific antibodies against the desired antigen. Selected hybridomas are grown in mass culture for antibody production and are frozen for future use.

which should now be specific for epitopes of the antigen, are collected from the animal's spleen. These B cells would soon die in culture, but utilizing a technique first described in 1975, they are fused with cancerous multiple myeloma cells. These myeloma cells have all the characteristics of plasma cells, except for the secretion of immunoglobulins—but more importantly, they are immortal, meaning they will divide indefinitely. The outcome of a B-cell/myeloma cell fusion is a *hybridoma cell*, that can divide indefinitely and that continues to secrete a large quantity of identical, monoclonal antibodies of the specificity produced by a single B cell (figure 52.20).

Monoclonal antibodies and diagnostic testing

The availability of large quantities of pure monoclonal antibodies has allowed the development of much more sensitive clinical laboratory tests. Some pregnancy tests, for example, use a monoclonal antibody produced against the hormone human chorionic gonadotrophin (hCG, secreted early in pregnancy). The test uses hCG-coated latex particles that are exposed to a urine sample and anti-hCG antibody. If the urine contains hCG, it will block binding of the antibody to the hCG-coated particles and prevent their agglutination, indicating pregnancy based on the presence of hCG (figure 52.21).

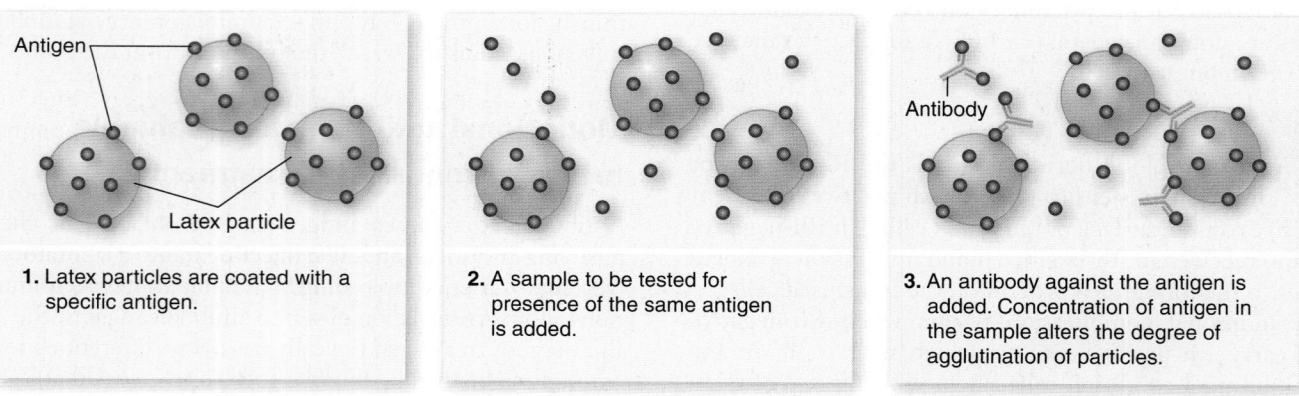

Figure 52.21 Using monoclonal antibodies to detect an antigen. Many clinical tests, such as pregnancy testing, use monoclonal antibodies. A specific antigen is attached to latex beads that are mixed with the test sample and a monoclonal antibody specific for the antigen. If no antigen is present in the sample, the antibody will cause agglutination of the beads. If the sample contains the antigen, it will bind to the antibodies and prevent agglutination of the beads by the antibody.

Inquiry question

? How would a high level of HCG present in a urine sample be indicated in this agglutination test?

Acquired immunodeficiency syndrome (AIDS) is characterized in part by destruction of T_H cells. The progression of this disease can be monitored by examining the reactivity of a patient's leukocytes with a monoclonal antibody against CD4, a marker of T_H cells, to track a decrease in the number of these cells.

Learning Outcomes Review 52.6

Blood group antibodies in plasma made blood transfusion risky and often fatal in the past. Type O RBCs have no surface antigen, but serum from a type O person has both anti-A and anti-B antibodies; someone with type A produces anti-B, and someone with B produces anti-A. Type AB serum lacks A or B antibodies, but RBCs have both surface antigens. Monoclonal antibodies are specific for only a single epitope (antigenic determinant). Hybridoma technology has allowed production of monoclonal antibodies for use in diagnostic tests and elimination of tumors.

- **Why do diagnostic kits use monoclonal rather than polyclonal antibodies?**

52.7 Pathogens That Evade the Immune System

Learning Outcomes

1. **Explain how pathogens can change antigenic specificity.**
2. **Describe how the immune system has affected the evolution of pathogens.**

For any pathogen to establish itself in a host and to cause a productive infection in which the pathogen successfully reproduces, the pathogen must evade both the nonspecific and specific immune systems. In response to the selective pressure caused by the development of previous immunity against specific epitopes on the pathogen, many pathogens can alter the structure of their surface antigens so that they are no longer recognized. This is a form of natural selection that allows pathogens with altered surface antigens to survive and continue to cause infection. Other pathogens have simply evolved ways to evade destruction. Infection by still other pathogens can actually cause the death of cells of the immune system.

Many pathogens change surface antigens to avoid immune system detection

Influenza virus is perhaps the most universally known example of an organism or virus altering its surface antigens and thus avoiding immune system recognition and destruction. Because of this tendency of the virus to change, yearly immunizations against influenza virus are recommended.

The two viral proteins expressed on the influenza virus' envelope, as well as on the surface of cells infected by influenza virus, are hemaglutinin (HA) and neuraminidase (NA). Because this virus has an RNA genome, it is replicated by a viral RNA polymerase that lacks proofreading ability. As a result, mutations are likely to accumulate over time, including point mutations to the HA and NA genes. This is referred to as **antigen drift.**

Even more dramatically but less frequently, the HA and NA proteins may also undergo **antigen shift,** referring to the sudden appearance of a new subtype of influenza virus in which the expressed HA or NA proteins (or both) are completely different. Such a change makes the population particularly susceptible to infection. Immunization with a new vaccine created every year using the most common strains of the virus attempts to establish immunity in the population prior to infection by the strains circulating.

Antigen shifting and the resulting lack of immunity is the reason for the recent interest in "bird flu." The subtype of influenza that causes bird flu is characterized as H5N1, a primarily avian form of influenza to which people have no immunity. There is no evidence as of this writing, however, that the H5N1 virus can infect people except through contact with infected birds. This strain has been a source of concern due to the high mortality rates seen in human infections. Even more recently, a flu strain with the subtype H1N1 has jumped from pigs to humans and is proving to be very infectious. Current evidence is that the mortality rate is not higher than most strains of influenza, but the World Health Organization has now declared that this particular strain has reached pandemic levels in the population (see chapter 27).

Many other pathogens can alter or shift their surface antigens in order to avoid immune system destruction. As another example, every year, more than 1 million people, the vast majority of whom are African children under the age of 5, die from malaria. This disease, as described in chapter 29, is caused by the protozoan parasite *Plasmodium* and contracted when humans are bitten by an infected *Anopheles* mosquito. These protozoans have several life-cycle stages and are hidden from the immune system alternately within host hepatocytes or red blood cells. In addition, they can alter some of the proteins expressed during certain life cycle stages. Continued use of certain anti-*Plasmodium* drugs has also selected for the emergence of multi-drug-resistant organisms. Work is ongoing to develop a vaccine that would induce effective immunity to specific life cycle stages and that would thus promote immune system elimination of the *Plasmodium.*

Inquiry question

 Why were we able to eliminate smallpox virus using a vaccine but cannot eliminate influenza?

Many mechanisms have evolved in bacteria to evade immune system attack

Salmonella typhimurium, a common cause of food poisoning, can alternate between expression of two different flagellar proteins, so that antibodies made to one protein do not recognize the other protein and therefore cannot be used to promote phagocytosis of the bacteria.

Mycobacterium tuberculosis bacteria, once phagocytosed into macrophages, inhibit fusion of the phagosome with lysosomes. These organisms can then multiply quite successfully within the macrophages.

Other bacteria that invade mucosal surfaces, such as *Neisseria meningitidis* or *Neisseria gonorrhoeae*, secrete proteases that degrade the IgA antibodies that protect the mucosal surface. External capsules on many particularly pathogenic strains of bacteria block binding of the phagocytosis-inducing complement protein C3b, slowing the phagocytosis response. Because bacteria utilizing any of these mechanisms are better able to survive, the immune response acts as selective pressure favoring the evolution of such mechanisms.

HIV infection kills T_H cells and causes immunosuppression

One mechanism for defeating vertebrate defenses is to attack the adaptive immune system itself. CD4+ T_H cells play a central role in the activity of the immune system: The cytokines they secrete directly or indirectly affect the activity of all other cells of the immune system.

HIV, human immunodeficiency virus, mounts a direct attack on T_H cells (see chapter 27). It binds to the CD4 proteins present on these cells and utilizes these proteins to promote endocytosis into the cells. (The virus infects monocytes as well because they too express CD4.) HIV-infected cells die only after releasing replicated viruses that infect other CD4+ cells (figure 52.22). Over time, the number of T_H cells in an infected individual decreases.

An individual is considered to have AIDS when his or her T_H cell levels have dropped dramatically, leading to an increase in infections due to opportunistic organisms as well as other diseases.

The progression of HIV infection

The immune system initially controls an HIV infection by the production of antibodies to the virus and by the elimination of virally infected cells by cytotoxic T cells. For a time, the level of HIV in the serum does not increase beyond a steady state, and the number of T_H cells does not significantly decrease.

As the virus reproduces in the T_H cells, it rapidly kills some of them, but many others continue to divide on antigen stimulation. Eventually, however, HIV kills T_H cells more rapidly than they can proliferate. HIV-encoded proteins also cause a decrease in the expression of MHC class I on the infected cells, so that these cells are less likely to be recognized and killed by T_C cells.

Finally, because HIV is a retrovirus (see chapter 27), it can integrate itself into the genome of infected cells and hide in a "latent" form. When any of these cells divides, the HIV genome is present in the progeny cells and thus these progeny can start to produce HIV at any point in time.

The combined effect of these responses to HIV infection is to ravage the human immune system. With little defense against infection, any of a variety of otherwise commonplace infections may prove fatal. Death by cancer also becomes far more likely. In fact, AIDS was first recognized as a disease when a cluster of previously healthy young men all died of *Pneumocystis jiroveci*–induced pneumonia, a disease that gener-

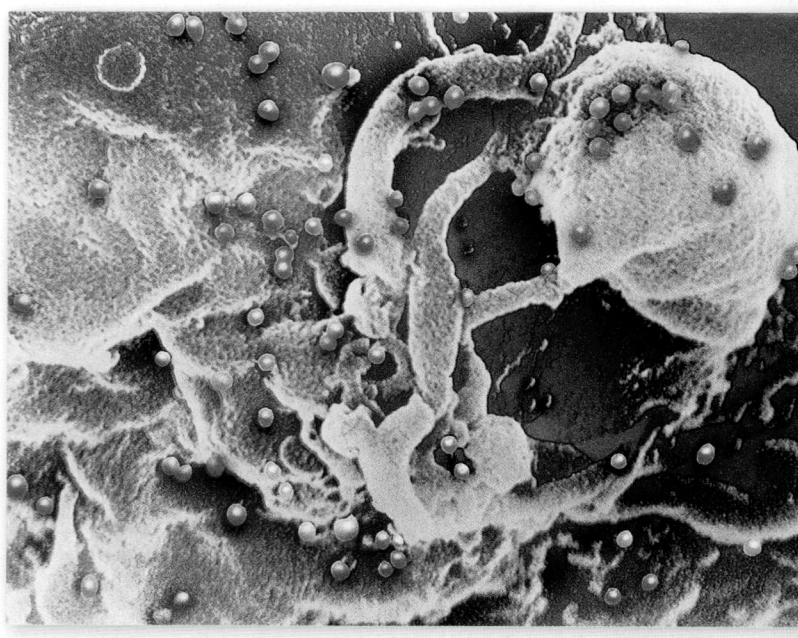

Figure 52.22 HIV, the virus that causes AIDS. Viruses released from infected CD4+ T_H cells soon spread to neighboring T_H cells, infecting them in turn. The individual viruses, colored red in this scanning electron micrograph, are extremely small; over 200 million would fit on the period at the end of this sentence.

ally affects the immunosuppressed, or of Kaposi's sarcoma, a rare form of cancer.

The human effect of HIV

Although HIV became a human disease only recently, AIDS is already clearly one of the most serious diseases in human history. The WHO estimates that for the year 2007 between 30 and 36 million people are living with AIDS, with the greatest number in sub-Saharan Africa (about 22 million), followed by south and southeast Asia (4.2 million). For 2007, the WHO estimates there were 2.5 million people newly infected, and an estimated 2.1 million deaths worldwide.

The fatality rate of untreated AIDS is close to 100%. No patient exhibiting the symptoms of AIDS has been known to survive more than a few years without treatment. The disease is not highly contagious, however; it is transmitted from one individual to another through the transfer of internal body fluids, typically semen and blood.

Learning Outcomes Review 52.7

Pathogens such as influenza virus frequently alter epitopes on their surfaces and thus evade specific immune-system recognition. Other pathogens, such as HIV, infect and destroy T_H cells, simply disabling the immune system. The diseases associated with AIDS often result from destruction of the immune system.

■ *Polio is a viral disease against which vaccines have been very successful. How would you say this virus differs from influenza virus?*

Chapter Review

52.1 Innate Immunity

The skin is a barrier to infection.
In addition to being a physical barrier, skin has a low surface pH, lysozyme secreted in sweat, and a population of nonpathogenic organisms, all of which deter pathogens.

Mucosal epithelial surfaces also prevent entry of pathogens.
The epithelia of the digestive, respiratory, and urogenital tracts produce mucus to trap microorganisms.

Innate immunity recognizes molecular patterns.
Toll-like receptors have leucine-rich regions that recognize molecules such as LPS and peptidoglycan.

Innate immunity leads to diverse responses to a pathogen.
Binding of pathogen-associated molecular patterns (PAMPs) leads to production of antimicrobial peptides and cytokines, and activation of complement, among other actions.

Phagocytic cells are associated with innate immunity.
Macrophages and neutrophils are associated with phagocytosis (see figure 52.4). Natural killer (NK) cells induce apoptosis.

The inflammatory response is a nonspecific response to infection or tissue injury.
Histamines increase blood flow and permeability of capillaries (see figure 52.5). Acute-phase fever promotes phagocytic activity and impedes growth of microbes.

Complement can form a membrane attack complex.
Complement forms pores in invading cells, coats pathogens with C3b proteins, and targets cells for destruction.

52.2 Adaptive Immunity

Immunity had long been observed, but the mechanisms have only recently been understood.
Jenner's and Pasteur's work on cowpox and avian cholera indicated that prior exposure to a disease prevented subsequent infections

Antigens stimulate specific immune responses.
Surface receptors on lymphocytes recognize antigens and direct a specific immune response (see figure 52.8).

Hematopoiesis gives rise to the cells of the immune system (see table 52.1).

Lymphocytes carry out the adaptive immune responses.
A naive lymphocyte binds to a foreign antigen and divides, producing a clone of activated cells and memory cells.

Humoral immunity is the production of Ig by B cells. Cell-mediated immunity involves T cells that regulate the immune responses of other cells or directly attack cells.

Adaptive immunity can be active or passive.

The immune system is supported by two classes of organs.
Immune system organs include the primary lymphoid organs and secondary lymphoid organs (see figure 52.9).

Two forms of adaptive immunity have evolved.
An immune system based on proteins with variable repeats has been found in jawless fishes, in contrast to the immunoglobulin system of other vertebrates.

52.3 Cell-Mediated Immunity

The MHC carries self and nonself information.
Most cells exhibit glycoproteins encoded by the MHC. In humans these proteins are called human leukocyte antigens (HLAs). MHC class I proteins, found on every nucleated cell, present antigen brought into the cell by phagocytosis; MHC class II proteins are found only on antigen-presenting cells.

Cytotoxic T cells eliminate virally infected cells and tumor cells.
T_C cells recognize virally infected cells and tumor cells. They destroy cells in a fashion similar to NK cells (see figure 52.11).

Helper T cells secrete proteins that direct immune responses.
T_H cells secrete cytokines in response to foreign antigens and promote both cell-mediated and humoral immune responses. Activated T_C and T_H produce both effector and memory cells.

T cells are the primary cells that mediate transplant rejection.

Cells of the innate immune system release cytokines.
Macrophages release interleukin-12 and tumor necrosis factor-α.

52.4 Humoral Immunity and Antibody Production

Immunoglobulin structure reveals variable and constant regions.
B cells are activated by membrane Ig molecules binding to a specific epitope on an antigen. Activated B cells produce antibody secreting plasma cells and memory cells.

Immunoglobulins consists of two light chain and two longer heavy-chain polypeptides, with the binding site in the Fab region (see figure 52.14). Antibodies can agglutinate, precipitate, or neutralize antigens (see figure 52.15).

The five classes of immunoglobulins have different functions (see table 52.3).

Immunoglobulin diversity is generated through DNA rearrangement.
Ig diversity is generated by DNA rearrangements (see figure 52.16). T cell receptors (TCRs) are similar to a single Fab region of an Ig. Their diversity also results from DNA rearrangements .

The secondary response to an antigen is more effective than the primary response.
On second exposure to a pathogen, a rapid secondary immune response is launched due to memory cells (see figure 52.18).

52.5 Autoimmunity and Hypersensitivity

Autoimmune diseases result from immune system attack on the body's own tissues.
The acceptance of self-cells is called immunological tolerance. Autoimmunity is a failure of immunological tolerance.

Allergies are caused by IgE secretion in response to antigens.
Immediate hypersensitivity is caused by allergens' binding to IgE, triggering the release of histamine (see figure 51.19). Anaphylaxis is a severe reaction with rapid inflammation and release of chemical mediators.

Delayed-type hypersensitivity is mediated by T_H cells and macrophages.
Symptoms appear about 48 hr after second exposure.

52.6 Antibodies in Medical Treatment and Diagnosis

Blood type indicates the antigens present on an individual's red blood cells.

The ABO blood group antigens, Rh factor antigens, and many others constitute the blood type.

HLA antigens can be used to match tissues between donors and recipients in transplants.

Transfusion reactions result from mismatched blood transfusions.

Before blood type was understood, many died from mismatched blood transfusions.

Monoclonal antibodies are a valuable tool for diagnosis and treatment.

Monoclonal antibodies are specific to a single epitope and can be used in testing and manufacture of immunotoxins.

52.7 Pathogens That Evade the Immune System

Many pathogens change surface antigens to avoid immune system detection.

Antigen drift and antigen shift, such as exhibited in influenza viruses, allow alteration of surface antigens to avoid immune detection.

Many mechanisms have evolved in bacteria to evade immune system attack.

Some bacteria have evolved mechanisms to inhibit normal immune system processes, such as slowing phagocytosis.

HIV infection kills T_H cells and causes immunosuppression.

Destruction of T_H cells lowers the body's ability to fend off infections, leading to the characteristic illnesses of AIDS.

Review Questions

UNDERSTAND

1. Cells that target and kill body cells infected by viruses are
   a. macrophages.
   b. natural killer cells.
   c. monocytes.
   d. neutrophils.

2. Structures on invading cells recognized by the adaptive immune system are known as
   a. antigens.
   b. interleukins.
   c. antibodies.
   d. lymphocytes.

3. Which one of the following acts as the "alarm signal" to activate the body's adaptive immune system by stimulating helper T cells?
   a. B cells
   b. Interleukin-1
   c. Complement
   d. Histamines

4. Cytotoxic T cells are called into action by the
   a. presence of histamine.
   b. presence of interleukin-1.
   c. presence of interleukin-2.
   d. interferon.

5. Receptors that trigger innate immune responses
   a. are antibodies recognizing specific antigens.
   b. are T-cell receptors recognizing specific antigens.
   c. recognize pathogen-associated molecular patterns.
   d. are not specific at all.

6. Diseases in which the person's immune system no longer recognizes its own MHC proteins are called
   a. allergies.
   b. autoimmune diseases.
   c. immediate hypersensitivity.
   d. delayed hypersensitivity.

7. Suppose that a new disease is discovered that suppresses the immune system. Which of the following would indicate that the disease specifically affects the B cells rather than the helper or cytotoxic T cells?
   a. A decrease in the production of interleukin-2
   b. A decrease in interferon production
   c. A decrease in the number of plasma cells
   d. A decrease in the production of interleukin-1

APPLY

1. You start a new job in a research lab. The lab protocols state that you should check your hands for any breaks in the skin before handling infectious agents. This is because the epidermis fights microbial infections by
   a. making the surface of the skin acidic.
   b. excreting lysozyme to attack bacteria.
   c. producing mucus to trap microorganisms.
   d. all of these.

2. In comparing T-cell receptors and immunoglobulins
   a. the proteins have unrelated structures, but diversity is generated by a similar mechanism.
   b. the proteins have related structures, but diversity is generated by different mechanisms.
   c. the proteins have related structures, and diversity is generated by a similar mechanism.
   d. the proteins have unrelated structures, and diversity is generated by different mechanisms.

3. If you have type AB blood, which of the following results would be expected?
   a. Your blood agglutinates with anti-A antibodies only.
   b. Your blood agglutinates with anti-B antibodies only.

    c.   Your blood agglutinates with both anti-A and anti-B antibodies.

    d.   Your blood would not agglutinate with either anti-A or anti-B antibodies.

4. Suppose that you get a paper cut while studying. Arrange the following into the correct order in time.

    a.   Injured epidermal cells release histamine.
    b.   Bacteria enter the cut.
    c.   Helper T cells are activated.
    d.   Macrophages engulf bacteria.

5. If you wanted to cure allergies by bioengineering an antibody that would bind and disable the antibody responsible for allergic reactions, which of the following would you target?

    a.   IgG   c.   IgE
    b.   IgA   d.   IgD

6. Why do we need to be repeatedly vaccinated for influenza viruses?

    a.   Because they attack only the helper T cells, thereby suppressing the immune system
    b.   Because they alter their surface proteins and thus avoid immune recognition
    c.   Because they don't actually generate an immune response, the "flu" is actually an inflammatory response
    d.   Because they are too small to serve as good antigens

7. If you wanted to design an artificial cell that could safely carry drugs inside the body, which of the following molecules would you need to mimic to deter the immune system?

    a.   MHC-1   c.   Antigen
    b.   Interleukin-1   d.   Complement

SYNTHESIZE

1. Suppose you take a job in the marketing department of a cosmetics company. Always seeking a competitive advantage, the vice president of marketing has decided to advertise the new skin lotion as having immune-enhancing effects. The lotion is produced from secretions of a plant that releases extremely watery, alkaline fluid. Explain how you will market this product as an immune-enhancer.

2. Your new kitten scratches your roommate. Her skin is reddened and feels warm and sore to the touch; she thinks she has contracted some kind of fatal infection. In order to deflect her anger (she is definitely not a cat person!), you try telling her about the activities of the innate defense system. Explain what is actually happening to her skin.

3. Some people claim that they never catch colds. How could you show that this is due to a difference in receptors on their respective cell surfaces?

4. Toll-like receptors have been found in a wide variety of organisms, including both protostomes and deuterostomes, and now in cnidarians. In addition, parts of the signaling system have been found in a wide variety of organisms as have parts of the complement system. What does this say about the evolution of innate immunity?

ONLINE RESOURCE

www.ravenbiology.com

Understand, Apply, and Synthesize—enhance your study with animations that bring concepts to life and practice tests to assess your understanding. Your instructor may also recommend the interactive eBook, individualized learning tools, and more.

Chapter 53

The Reproductive System

Chapter Outline

53.1 Animal Reproductive Strategies

53.2 Vertebrate Fertilization and Development

53.3 Structure and Function of the Human Male Reproductive System

53.4 Structure and Function of the Human Female Reproductive System

53.5 Contraception and Infertility Treatments

Introduction

Bird song in the spring, insects chirping outside the window, frogs croaking in swamps, and wolves howling in a frozen northern forest are all sounds of evolution's essential act, reproduction. These distinctive noises, as well as the bright coloration of some animals, function to attract mates. Few subjects pervade our everyday thinking more than sex, and few urges are more insistent. This chapter deals with sex and reproduction among the vertebrates, including humans.

53.1 Animal Reproductive Strategies

Learning Outcomes

1. **Distinguish between sexual and asexual methods of reproduction.**
2. **Describe the different types of hermaphroditism.**
3. **Explain factors that influence sex determination.**

Most animals, including humans, reproduce sexually. As described in chapter 11, sexual reproduction requires a spe-cialized form of cell division, meiosis, to produce haploid gametes, each of which has a single complete set of chromosomes. These gametes, including sperm and eggs (or *ova*; singular *ovum*), are united by fertilization to restore the diploid complement of chromosomes. The diploid fertil-ized egg, or zygote, develops by mitotic division into a new multicellular organism.

Bacteria, archaea, protists, and multicellular animals in-cluding cnidarians and tunicates, as well as many other types of animals, reproduce asexually. In asexual reproduction, ge-netically identical cells are produced from a single parent cell through mitosis. In single-celled organisms, an individ-ual organism divides, a process called fission, and then each part becomes a separate but identical organism. Cnidarians commonly reproduce by budding, whereby a part of the parent's body becomes separated from the rest and differentiates into a new individual (figure 53.1). The new individual may become an independent animal or may remain attached to the parent, forming a colony.

Some species have developed novel reproductive methods

Another form of asexual reproduction, **parthenogenesis,** is common in many species of arthropods. In parthenogenesis, females produce offspring from unfertilized eggs. Some species are exclusively parthenogenic (and all female), whereas others switch between sexual reproduction and parthenogenesis, producing progeny that are both diploid and haploid, respectively. In honeybees, for example, a queen bee mates only once and stores the sperm. She then can control the release of the sperm. If no sperm are released, the eggs develop parthenogenetically into haploid drones, which are males. If sperm are allowed to fertilize the eggs, the fertilized eggs develop into diploid worker bees, which are female. However, when fertilized eggs are exposed to the appropriate hormone, they will develop into queens.

In 1958, the Russian biologist Ilya Darevsky reported one of the first cases of unusual modes of reproduction among vertebrates. He observed that some populations of small lizards of the genus *Lacerta* were exclusively female, and he suggested that these lizards could lay eggs that were viable even if they were not fertilized. In other words, they were capable of asexual reproduction in the absence of sperm, a type of parthenogenesis. Further work has shown that parthenogenesis has evolved a number of times in lizards, as well as in fish and salamanders.

Another variation in reproductive strategies is hermaphroditism, in which one individual has both testes and ovaries, and so can produce both sperm and eggs. A tape-

Figure 53.2 Hermaphroditism and protogyny. The bluehead wrasse, *Thalassoma bifasciatium*, is protogynous—females sometimes turn into males. Here, a large male, which had been a female before changing sex, is seen among females, which are typically much smaller.

Inquiry question

? Why might it be adaptive for an individual to be female at small size and become male when very large? Under what circumstances might the opposite condition, protandry, evolve?

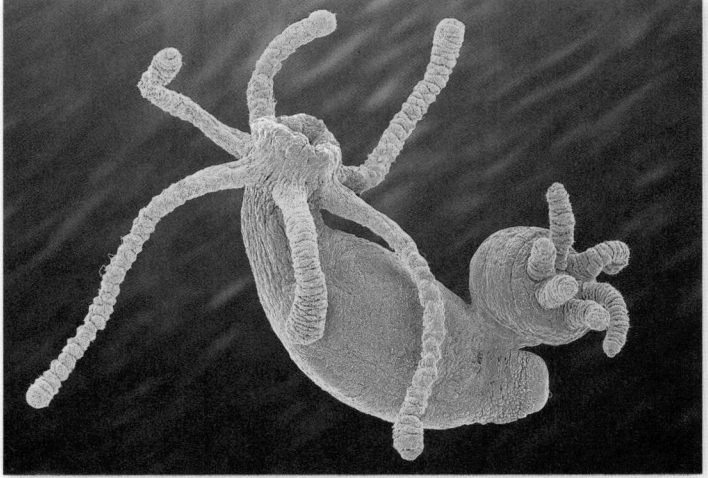

Figure 53.1 Cnidarian budding. This cnidarian reproduces asexually by budding. The new individual can be seen in the lower right of the micrograph.

worm is hermaphroditic and can fertilize itself, a useful strategy because it is unlikely to encounter another tapeworm. Most hermaphroditic animals, however, require another individual in order to reproduce. Two earthworms, for example, are required for reproduction—each functions as both male and female during copulation, and each leaves the encounter with fertilized eggs.

Numerous fish genera include species whose individuals can change their sex, a process called *sequential hermaphroditism.* Among coral reef fish, for example, both protogyny ("first female," a change from female to male) and protandry ("first male," a change from male to female) occur. In fish that practice protogyny (figure 53.2), the sex change appears to be under social control. These fish commonly live in large groups, or schools, where successful reproduction is typically limited to one or a few large, dominant males. If those males are removed, the largest female rapidly changes sex and becomes a dominant male.

Sex can be determined genetically or by environmental conditions

An individual's sex is determined during development as an embryo, but the way in which it occurs varies among species.

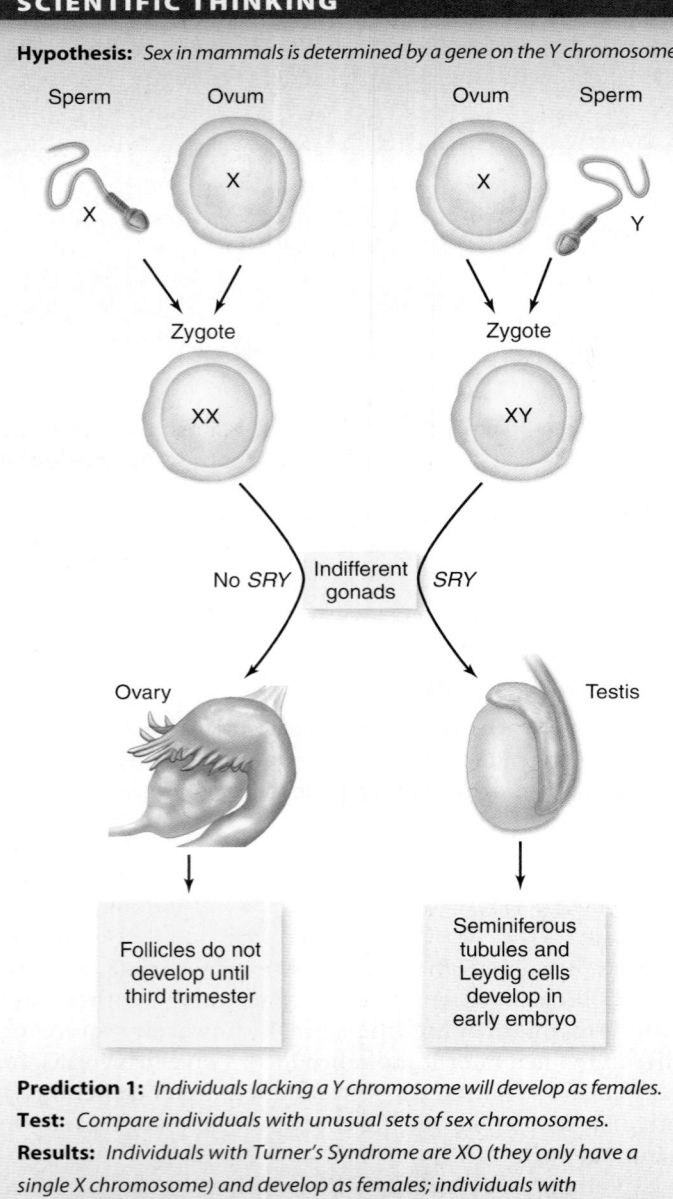

Hypothesis: *Sex in mammals is determined by a gene on the Y chromosome.*

Sperm   Ovum   Ovum   Sperm

X   X   X   Y

Zygote   Zygote

XX   XY

No *SRY*   Indifferent gonads   *SRY*

Ovary   Testis

Follicles do not develop until third trimester

Seminiferous tubules and Leydig cells develop in early embryo

Prediction 1: *Individuals lacking a Y chromosome will develop as females.*

Test: *Compare individuals with unusual sets of sex chromosomes.*

Results: *Individuals with Turner's Syndrome are XO (they only have a single X chromosome) and develop as females; individuals with Klinefelter's Syndrome are XXY and develop as males.*

Prediction 2: *The SRY gene on the Y chromosome is responsible for the development of male sexual characteristics.*

Test: *Breed transgenic mice that are XY but have a mutation of the SRY gene.*

Results: *These mice develop as females.*

Figure 53.3 Sex determination in mammals. The sex-determining region of the mammalian Y chromosome is designated *SRY*. Testes are formed when the Y chromosome and *SRY* are present; ovaries are formed when they are absent.

Temperature-sensitive sex determination

In many fish and reptiles, an individual's sex is determined by the temperature it experiences during development. In some species, cold temperatures produce males and warm temperatures produce females, but in others, the opposite occurs. In still others, males are produced at both high and low temperatures, and females at temperatures in-between.

Phylogenetic analyses indicate that temperature-sensitive sex determination has evolved many times from ancestors in which sex was genetically determined. The molecular mechanisms that determine sex in this species are now being discovered, but why this trait has evolved so often is not well understood. One possibility is that sometimes it may be advantageous for a female to be able to determine the sex of her offspring by laying eggs in appropriate locations. Currently, the jury is still out on this hypothesis.

Genetic sex determination

In all birds and mammals and many other vertebrates, the sex is determined by an individual's genes. In mammals and some other animals, individuals with an X and a Y chromosome are males, whereas individuals with two X chromosomes are females. However, in other animals, such as birds, it is females that are the heterozygous sex.

Sexual differentiation in humans

The reproductive systems of human males and females appear similar for the first 40 days after conception. During this time, the cells that will give rise to ova or sperm migrate from the yolk sac to the embryonic gonads, which have the potential to become either ovaries in females or testes in males (figure 53.3). For this reason, the embryonic gonads are said to be "indifferent."

If the embryo is a male, a gene on the Y chromosome converts the indifferent gonads into testes. In females, which lack a Y chromosome, this gene and the protein it encodes are absent, and the gonads become ovaries. An important gene involved in sex determination is known as *SRY* (for "sex-determining region of the Y chromosome").

Once testes have formed in the embryo, the testes secrete testosterone and other hormones that promote the development of the male external genitalia and accessory reproductive organs.

If the embryo lacks the *SRY* gene, the embryo develops female external genitalia and accessory organs. In other words, all mammalian embryos will develop into females unless a functional *SRY* gene is present.

Learning Outcomes Review 53.1

Sexual reproduction involves fusion of gametes derived from different individuals of a species. Asexual reproduction in some species may be accomplished by fission, budding, or parthenogenesis. In hermaphroditic species, an individual may have both testes and ovaries; in sequential hermaphroditism, an individual may change from one sex to the other. Sex can be determined either by genes or by environmental conditions such as temperature experienced while an embryo.

■ *Why might natural selection favor genetic sex determination?*

53.2 Vertebrate Fertilization and Development

Learning Outcomes

1. **Distinguish among viviparity, oviparity, and ovoviviparity.**
2. **Describe the advantages of internal fertilization.**

Vertebrate sexual reproduction evolved in the ocean before vertebrates colonized the land. The females of most species of marine bony fish produce eggs in batches and release them into the water. The males generally release their sperm into the water containing the eggs, where the union of the free gametes occurs. This process is known as external fertilization.

Although seawater is not a hostile environment for gametes, it does cause the gametes to disperse rapidly, so their release by females and males must be almost simultaneous. Thus, most marine fish restrict the release of their eggs and sperm to a few brief and well-defined periods. Some reproduce just once a year, but others do so more frequently. The ocean has few seasonal clues that organisms can use as signals for synchronizing reproduction, but one all-pervasive signal is the cycle of the Moon. Once each month, the Moon approaches closer to the Earth than usual, and when it does, its increased gravitational attraction causes somewhat higher tides. Many marine organisms sense the tidal changes and link the production and release of their gametes to the lunar cycle.

Once vertebrates began living on land, they encountered a new danger—desiccation, a problem that can be especially severe for the small and vulnerable gametes. On land, the gametes could not simply be released near each other because they would soon dry up and perish. Consequently, intense selective pressure resulted in the evolution of internal fertilization in terrestrial vertebrates (as well as some groups of fish)—that is, the introduction of male gametes directly into the female reproductive tract. By this means, fertilization still occurs in a nondesiccating environment, even when the adult animals are fully terrestrial.

Internal fertilization has led to three strategies for development of offspring

The vertebrates that practice internal fertilization exhibit three strategies for embryonic and fetal development, namely *oviparity*, *ovoviviparity*, and *viviparity*.

1. **Oviparity** is found in some bony fish, most reptiles, some cartilaginous fish, some amphibians, a few mammals, and all birds. The eggs, after being fertilized internally, are deposited outside the mother's body to complete their development.
2. **Ovoviviparity** is found in some bony fish (including mollies, guppies, and mosquito fish), some cartilaginous fish, and many reptiles. The fertilized eggs are retained within the mother to complete their development, but

Figure 53.4 Viviparous fish carry live, mobile young within their bodies. The young complete their development within the body of the mother and are then released as small but competent adults. Here, a lemon shark has just given birth to a young shark, which is still attached by the umbilical cord.

the embryos still obtain all of their nourishment from the egg yolk. The young are fully developed when they are hatched and released from the mother.
3. **Viviparity** is found in most cartilaginous fish, some amphibians, a few reptiles, and almost all mammals (figure 53.4). The young develop within the mother and obtain nourishment directly from their mother's blood, rather than from the egg yolk. A placenta, the structure through which blood and gas exchange occurs, has not evolved only in mammals (see next chapter), but also several times in fishes and lizards.

Evolution of reproductive systems

Live birth—either viviparity or ovoviviparity—has evolved many times in vertebrates: once in mammals, but many times independently in fishes, amphibians, and reptiles (figure 53.5). The evolution of live birth appears to be a one-way evolutionary street: once it evolves, it is almost never lost. Live birth requires internal fertilization so that the eggs can develop within the body of the female; internal fertilization has evolved only once in amniotes (the clade composed of reptiles, birds, and mammals), but multiple times within fishes and amphibians.

Internal fertilization requires some means of transferring the sperm from the male to the female. Salamanders evolved one way: males deposit their sperm on top of a mass of eggs and then the female positions her cloaca above them and then lowers her body, picking up the fertilized eggs. All other vertebrates have taken a different approach, evolving an intromittent organ that the male uses to transfer the sperm directly into the female's body. The variety of structures that has evolved to accomplish this includes a modified pelvic fin in cartilaginous fishes; a modification of the cloaca (the common opening through which waste and reproductive products exit the body) in some frogs, caecilians, and birds; penises derived from different embryological structures in turtles, crocodiles, and mammals; and a pair of hemipenises—one on

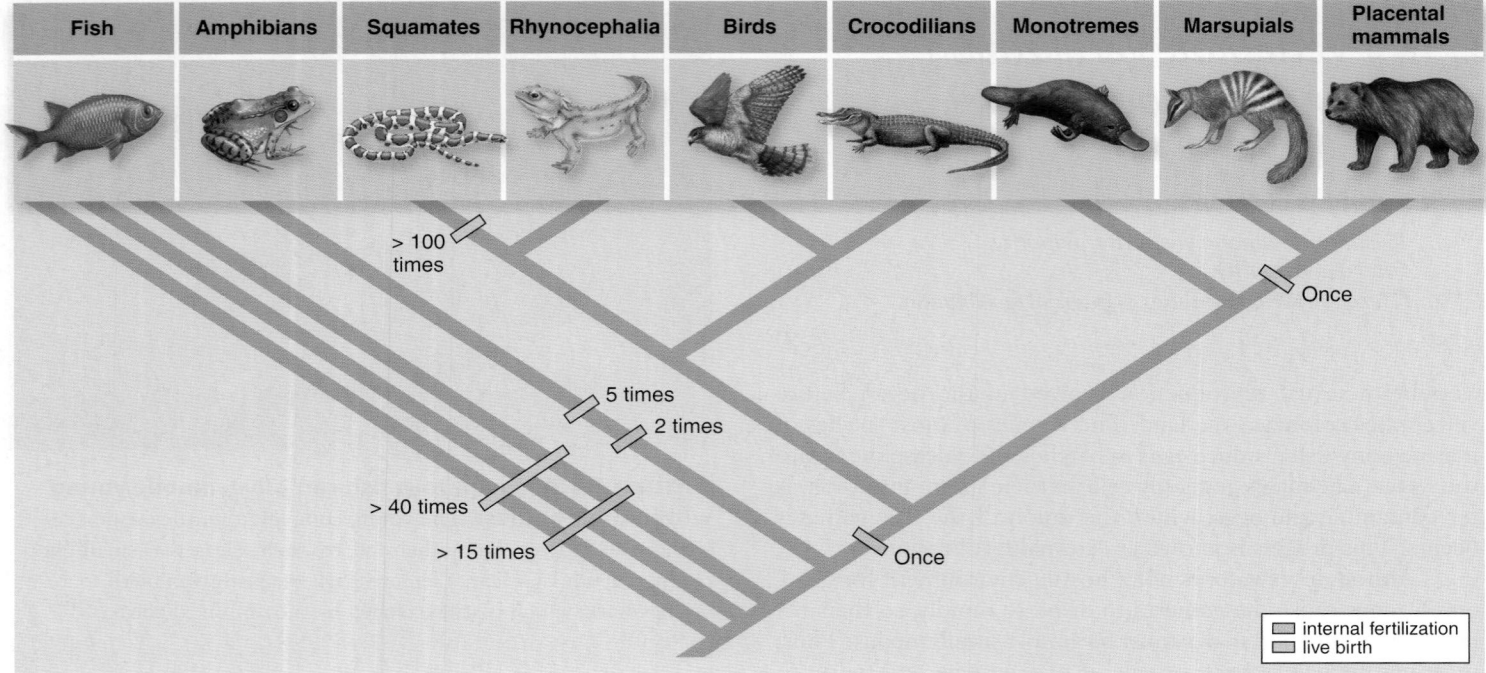

Figure 53.5 **Evolution of internal fertilization and live birth in vertebrates.** Although live birth has evolved many times in fishes and squamate reptiles, most species in both groups lay eggs. Evolutionary reversal from live birth to egg-laying has occurred very rarely, if at all. Estimates of the number of origins in fishes and squamates is based on detailed phylogenetic analyses within each group; uncertainty in numbers is a result of incomplete information in some groups.

Inquiry question

? Why do you think that egg-laying rarely evolves from live-bearing?

each side—in snakes and lizards. Moreover, intromittent organs have been lost entirely in birds and rhynchocephalians; to achieve internal fertilization, males and females of these species simply align their cloacae and pass the sperm from male to female.

Most fishes and amphibians have external fertilization

Most fishes and amphibians, unlike other vertebrates, reproduce by means of external fertilization, although internal fertilization has arisen many times.

Fishes

Fertilization in most species of bony fish (teleosts) is external, and the eggs contain only enough yolk to sustain the developing embryo for a short time. After the initial supply of yolk has been exhausted, the young fish must seek its food from the waters around it. Development is speedy, and the young that survive mature rapidly. Although thousands or even millions of eggs are fertilized in a single mating, many of the resulting individuals succumb to microbial infection or predation, and few grow to maturity.

In marked contrast to the bony fish, fertilization in most cartilaginous fish is internal. Development of the young is generally viviparous, and the female usually gives birth to few, well-developed offspring.

Amphibians

The life cycle of amphibians is still tied to the water. Fertilization is external in most amphibians. Gametes from both males and females are released through the cloaca. Among the frogs and toads, the male grasps the female and discharges fluid containing the sperm onto the eggs as the female releases them into the water (figure 53.6).

Although the eggs of most amphibians develop in the water, there are some interesting exceptions (figure 53.7). In some frogs, for example, the eggs develop in the back of the parents; in others, males carry around the tadpoles in their vocal sacs, and the young frogs leave through their parents' mouths.

Reptiles and birds have internal fertilization

All birds and about 80% of reptile species are oviparous. After the eggs are fertilized internally, they are deposited outside the mother's body to complete their development.

Figure 53.6 The eggs of frogs are fertilized externally.
When frogs mate, the clasp of the male induces the female to release a large mass of mature eggs, over which the male discharges his sperm.

Reptiles

Most oviparous reptiles lay eggs and then abandon them. These eggs are surrounded by a leathery shell that is deposited as the egg passes through the oviduct, the part of the female reproductive tract leading from the ovary. Other species of reptiles are ovoviviparous, forming eggs that develop into embryos within the body of the mother, and some species are viviparous.

Birds

All birds practice internal fertilization, though most male birds lack a penis (some, including swans, geese, and ostriches, have modified the wall of the cloaca wall to serve as an intromittent organ).

Figure 53.8 Crested penguins incubating their egg.
This nesting pair is changing the parental guard in a stylized ritual.

As the egg passes along the oviduct, glands secrete albumin proteins (the egg white) and the hard, calcareous shell that distinguishes bird eggs from reptilian eggs. Although modern reptiles are ectotherms, birds are endotherms (see chapter 43); therefore, most birds incubate their eggs after laying them to keep them warm (figure 53.8). The young that hatch from the eggs of most bird species are unable to survive unaided because their development is still incomplete. These young birds are fed and nurtured by their parents, and they grow to maturity gradually.

The shelled eggs of reptiles and birds constitute one of the most important adaptations of these vertebrates to life on land. As described in chapter 35, these eggs are known as *amniotic eggs* because the embryo develops within a fluid-filled cavity surrounded by a membrane called the *amnion*. Other extraembryonic membranes in amniotic eggs include the *chorion*, which lines the inside of the eggshell, the *yolk sac*, and the *allantois*. Together, these extraembryonic membranes in combination with the external calcareous shell help form a desiccation-resistant egg that can be laid in dry places. In

 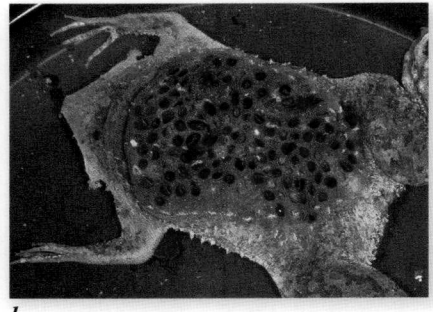  

a.   *b.*   *c.*   *d.*

Figure 53.7 Different ways young develop in frogs. *a.* In poison arrow frogs (family Dendrobatidae), the male carries the tadpoles on his back. *b.* In the female Surinam toad *(Pipa pipa)*, froglets develop from eggs in special brooding pouches on the back. *c.* In the South American pygmy marsupial frog *(Flectonotus pygmaeus)*, the female carries the developing larvae in a pouch on her back. *d.* Tadpoles of the Darwin's frog *(Rhinoderma darwinii)* develop into froglets in the vocal pouch of the male and emerge from the mouth.

contrast, the eggs of fish and amphibians contain only one extraembryonic membrane, the yolk sac, and must be deposited in an aquatic habitat to keep from drying out.

The viviparous mammals, including humans, also have extraembryonic membranes, as described in the following chapter.

Mammals generally do not lay eggs, but give birth to their young

Some mammals are seasonal breeders, reproducing only once a year, while others have more frequent reproductive cycles. Among the latter, the females generally undergo the reproductive cycles, and the males are more constant in their reproductive capability.

Female reproductive cycles

Cycling in females involves the periodic release of a mature ovum from the ovary in a process known as *ovulation*. Most female mammals are "in heat," or sexually receptive to males, only around the time of ovulation. This period of sexual receptivity is called **estrus,** and the reproductive cycle is therefore called an estrous cycle. Reproductive cycles continue in females until they become pregnant.

In the estrous cycle of most mammals, changes in the secretion by the anterior pituitary gland of follicle-stimulating hormone (FSH) and luteinizing hormone (LH) cause changes in egg cell development and hormone secretion in the ovaries (see chapter 46). Humans and apes have menstrual cycles that are similar to the estrous cycles of other mammals in their pattern of hormone secretion and ovulation. Unlike mammals with estrous cycles, however, human and ape females bleed when they shed the inner lining of their uterus, a process called **menstruation,** and they may engage in copulation at any time during the cycle.

Rabbits and cats differ from most other mammals in that they are induced ovulators. Instead of ovulating in a cyclic fashion regardless of sexual activity, the females ovulate only after copulation, as a result of a reflex stimulation of LH secretion.

Monotremes, marsupials, and placental mammals

The most primitive mammals, the **monotremes** (consisting solely of the duck-billed platypus and the echidna), are oviparous, like the reptiles from which they evolved. They incubate their eggs in a nest (figure 53.9a) or specialized pouch, and the young hatchlings obtain milk from their mother's mammary glands by licking her skin (because monotremes lack nipples).

All other mammals are viviparous and are divided into two subcategories based on how they nourish their young. The **marsupials,** a group that includes opossums and kangaroos, give birth to small, fetuslike offspring that are incompletely developed. The young complete their development in a pouch of their mother's skin, where they can obtain nourishment from nipples of the mammary glands (figure 53.9b).

The placental mammals (figure 53.9c) retain their young for a much longer period of development within the mother's uterus. The fetuses are nourished by a structure known as the placenta, which is derived from both an extraembryonic membrane (the chorion) and the mother's uterine lining. Because the fetal and maternal blood vessels are in very close proximity in the placenta, the fetus can obtain nutrients by diffusion from the mother's blood. The functioning of the placenta is discussed in more detail in chapter 54.

Learning Outcomes Review 53.2

Oviparous species lay eggs; the amniotic eggs of reptiles and birds protect the embryo from dessication. Females of ovoviviparous species retain fertilized eggs inside their bodies and release fully developed young when eggs hatch. Most mammals are viviparous, giving birth to young that have been nourished by the mother's body. Internal fertilization allows embryos to develop inside the female's body, leading to greater reproductive success.

■ *Under what circumstances would an estrous cycle be advantageous?*

Figure 53.9 Reproduction in mammals. *a.* Monotremes lay eggs in a nest, such as the duck-billed platypus (*Ornithorhynchus anatinus*) shown here with newly hatched offspring. *b.* Marsupials, such as this red kangaroo (*Macropus rufus*), give birth to small offspring that complete their development in a pouch. *c.* In placental mammals, such as this spotted deer doe (*Axis axis*) nursing her fawn, the young remain inside the mother's uterus for a longer period of time and are born relatively more developed.

a.

b.

c.

53.3 Structure and Function of the Human Male Reproductive System

Learning Outcomes

1. Describe the sequence of events in spermatogenesis.
2. Describe semen and explain how it is released during mating.
3. Explain how hormones regulate male reproductive function.

The structures of the human male reproductive system, typical of male mammals, are illustrated in figure 53.10. When testes form in the human embryo, they develop seminiferous tubules, the sites of sperm production, beginning around 43 to 50 days after conception. At about 9 to 10 weeks, the Leydig cells, located in the interstitial tissue between the seminiferous tubules, begin to secrete testosterone (the major male sex hormone, or androgen). Testosterone secretion during embryonic development converts indifferent structures into the male external genitalia, the *penis* and the *scrotum*, the latter being a sac that contains the testes. In the absence of testosterone, these structures develop into the female external genitalia. Testosterone is also responsible at puberty for male secondary sex characteristics, such as development of the beard, a deeper voice, and body hair.

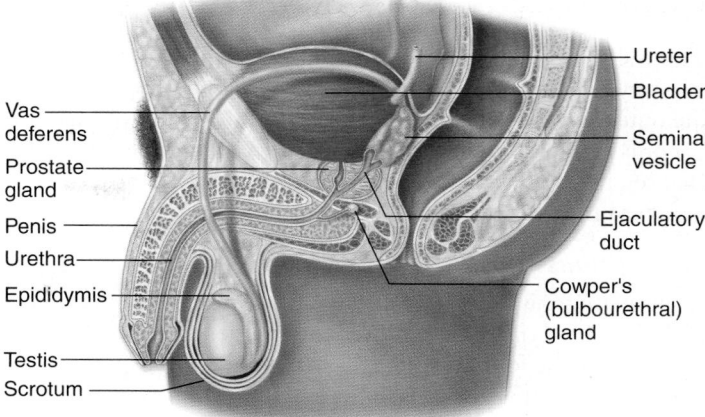

Figure 53.10 Organization of the human male reproductive system. The penis and scrotum are the external genitalia, the testes are the gonads, and the other organs are accessory sex organs, aiding the production and ejaculation of semen.

In an adult, each testis is composed primarily of the highly convoluted seminiferous tubules (figure 53.11, left). Although the testes are actually formed within the abdominal cavity, shortly before birth they descend through an opening called the inguinal canal into the scrotum, which suspends them outside the abdominal cavity. The scrotum maintains the testes at around 34°C, slightly lower than the core body temperature (37°C). This lower temperature is required for normal sperm development in humans.

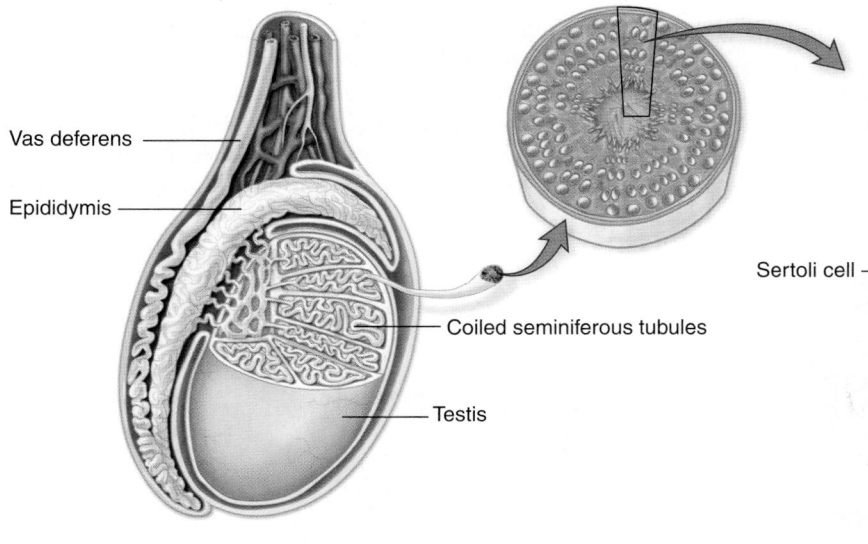

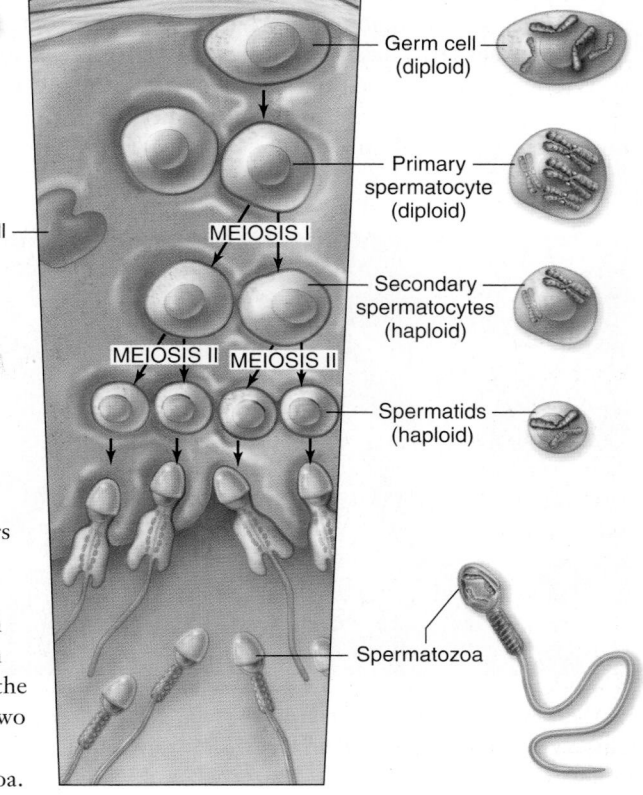

Figure 53.11 The testis and spermatogenesis. Spermatogenesis occurs in the seminiferous tubules, shown on the left. Enlargements show the radial arrangement of meiotic cells within the tubule, then the process of meiosis and differentiation to produce spermatozoa. Sertoli cells are nongerminal cells within the walls of the seminiferous tubules that assist spermatogenesis. Events begin on the outside of the tubule progressing inward to release mature spermatozoa into the tubule. The first meiotic division separates homologous chromosomes, forming two haploid secondary spermatocytes. The second meiotic division separates sister chromatids to form four haploid spermatids, which are converted into spermatozoa.

Sperm cells are produced by the millions

The wall of the seminiferous tubule consists of spermatogonia, or *germ cells*, and supporting Sertoli cells. The germ cells near the outer surface of the seminiferous tubule are diploid and are the only cells that will undergo meiosis to produce gametes (see chapter 11). The developing gamete cells, located closer to the lumen of the tubule, are haploid.

Cell divisions leading to sperm

A spermatogonium cell divides by mitosis to produce two diploid cells. One of these two cells then undergoes meiotic division to produce four haploid cells that will become sperm while the other remains as a spermatogonium. In that way, the male never runs out of spermatogonia to produce sperm. Adult males produce an average of 100 to 200 million sperm each day and can continue to do so throughout most of the rest of their lives.

The diploid daughter cell that begins meiosis is called a primary spermatocyte. In humans it has 23 pairs of chromosomes (46 chromosomes total), and each chromosome is duplicated, with two chromatids. The first meiotic division separates the homologous chromosome pairs, producing two haploid secondary spermatocytes. However, each chromosome still consists of two duplicate chromatids.

Each of these cells then undergoes the second meiotic division to separate the chromatids and produce two haploid cells, the **spermatids.** Therefore, a total of four haploid spermatids are produced from each primary spermatocyte (see figure 53.11, right). All of these cells constitute the germinal epithelium of the seminiferous tubules because they "germinate" the gametes.

Supporting tissues

In addition to the germinal epithelium, the walls of the seminiferous tubules contain nongerminal cells such as the Sertoli cells mentioned earlier. These cells nurse the developing sperm and secrete products required for spermatogenesis. They also help convert the spermatids into **spermatozoa (sperm)** by engulfing their extra cytoplasm.

Sperm structure

Spermatozoa are relatively simple cells, consisting of a head, body, and flagellum (tail) (figure 53.12). The head encloses a compact nucleus and is capped by a vesicle called an acrosome, which is derived from the Golgi complex. The acrosome contains enzymes that aid in the penetration of the protective layers surrounding the egg. The body and tail provide a propulsive mechanism: Within the tail is a flagellum, and inside the body are a centriole, which acts as a basal body for the flagellum, and mitochondria, which generate the energy needed for flagellar movement.

Male accessory sex organs aid in sperm delivery

After the sperm are produced within the seminiferous tubules, they are delivered into a long, coiled tube called the **epididymis**. The sperm are not motile when they arrive in the epididymis, and they must remain there for at least 18 hours before their motility develops. From the epididymis, the sperm enter another long tube, the **vas deferens,** which passes into the abdominal cavity via the inguinal canal.

Semen production

Semen is a complex mixture of fluids and sperm. The vas deferens from each testis joins with one of the ducts from a pair of glands called the seminal vesicles (see figure 53.10), which produce a fructose-rich fluid constituting about 60% of semen volume. From this point, the vas deferens continues as the ejaculatory duct and enters the prostate gland at the base of the urinary bladder.

In humans, the **prostate gland** is about the size of a golf ball and is spongy in texture. It contributes up to 30% of the bulk of the semen. Within the prostate gland, the ejaculatory duct merges with the urethra from the urinary bladder. The urethra carries the semen out of the body through the tip of the penis. A pair of pea-sized bulbourethral glands add secretions to make up the last 10% of semen, also secreting a fluid that lines the urethra and lubricates the tip of the penis prior to coitus (sexual intercourse).

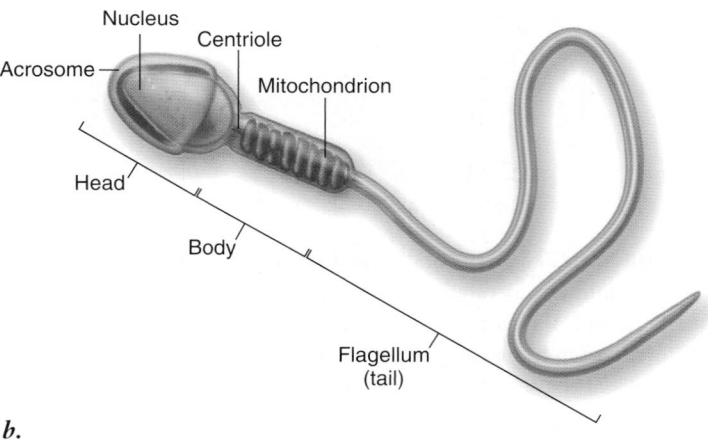

a.

b.

Figure 53.12 Human sperm. *a.* A scanning electron micrograph with sperm digitally colored yellow. *b.* A diagram of the main components of a sperm cell.

Structure of the penis and erection

In addition to the urethra, the penis has two columns of erectile tissue, the corpora cavernosa, along its dorsal side and one column, the corpus spongiosum, along the ventral side (figure 53.13). Penile erection is produced by neurons in the parasympathetic division of the autonomic nervous system, which release nitric oxide (NO), causing arterioles in the penis to dilate. The erectile tissue becomes turgid as it engorges with blood. This increased pressure in the erectile tissue compresses the veins, so blood flows into the penis but cannot flow out.

Most mammals have a bone in the penis, called a *"baculum,"* that contributes to its stiffness during erection, but humans do not.

Ejaculation

The result of erection and continued sexual stimulation is ejaculation, the ejection from the penis of about 2 to 5 mL of semen containing an average of 300 million sperm. Successful fertilization requires such a high sperm count because the odds against any one sperm cell completing the journey to the egg and fertilizing it are extraordinarily high, and the acrosomes of many sperm need to interact with the egg before a single sperm can penetrate the egg (fertilization is described in chapter 54). Males with fewer than 20 million sperm per milliliter are generally considered sterile. Despite their large numbers, sperm constitute only about 1% of the volume of the semen ejaculated.

Hormones regulate male reproductive function

As you saw in chapter 46, the anterior pituitary gland secretes two gonadotropic hormones: follicle-stimulating hormone (FSH) and luteinizing hormone (LH). Although these hormones are named for their actions in the female, they are also involved in regulating male reproductive function (table 53.1). In males, FSH stimulates the Sertoli cells to facilitate sperm development, and LH stimulates the Leydig cells to secrete testosterone.

The principle of negative feedback inhibition applies to the control of FSH and LH secretion (figure 53.14). The hypo-

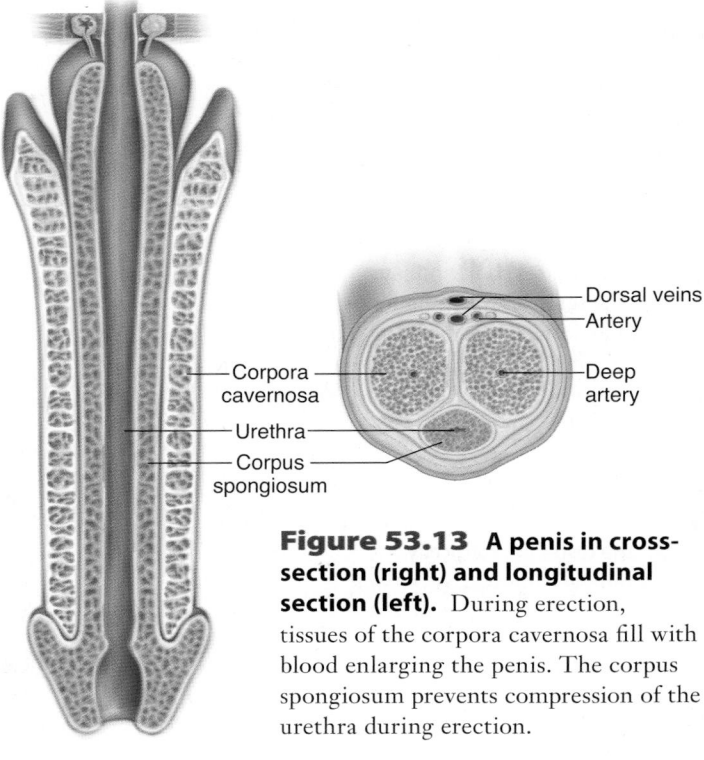

Figure 53.13 A penis in cross-section (right) and longitudinal section (left). During erection, tissues of the corpora cavernosa fill with blood enlarging the penis. The corpus spongiosum prevents compression of the urethra during erection.

thalamic hormone gonadotropin-releasing hormone (GnRH) stimulates the anterior pituitary gland to secrete both FSH and LH. FSH causes the Sertoli cells to release a peptide hormone called inhibin, which specifically inhibits FSH secretion. Similarly, LH stimulates testosterone secretion, and testosterone feeds back to inhibit the release of LH, both directly at the anterior pituitary gland and indirectly by reducing GnRH release from the hypothalamus.

The importance of negative feedback inhibition can be demonstrated by removing the testes; in the absence of testosterone and inhibin, the secretion of FSH and LH from the anterior pituitary is greatly increased.

TABLE 53.1	Mammalian Reproductive Hormones
MALE	
Follicle-stimulating hormone (FSH)	Stimulates spermatogenesis via Sertoli cells
Luteinizing hormone (LH)	Stimulates secretion of testosterone by Leydig cells
Testosterone	Stimulates development and maintenance of male secondary sexual characteristics, accessory sex organs, and spermatogenesis
FEMALE	
Follicle-stimulating hormone (FSH)	Stimulates growth of ovarian follicles and secretion of estradiol
Luteinizing hormone (LH)	Stimulates ovulation, conversion of ovarian follicles into corpus luteum, and secretion of estradiol and progesterone by corpus luteum
Estradiol (estrogen)	Stimulates development and maintenance of female secondary sexual characteristics; prompts monthly preparation of uterus for pregnancy
Progesterone	Completes preparation of uterus for pregnancy; helps maintain female secondary sexual characteristics
Oxytocin	Stimulates contraction of uterus and milk-ejection reflex
Prolactin	Stimulates milk production

Figure 53.14 Hormonal interactions between the testes and anterior pituitary.

The hypothalamus secretes GnRH, which stimulates the anterior pituitary to produce LH and FSH. LH stimulates the Leydig cells to secrete testosterone, which is involved in development and maintenance of secondary sexual characteristics, and stimulates spermatogenesis. FSH stimulates the Sertoli cells of the seminiferous tubules, which facilitate spermatogenesis. FSH also stimulates Sertoli cells to secrete inhibin. Testosterone and inhibin exert negative feedback inhibition on the secretion of LH and FSH, respectively.

Inquiry question

? Why do you think the brain is affected when the testes are surgically removed (termed *castration*)?

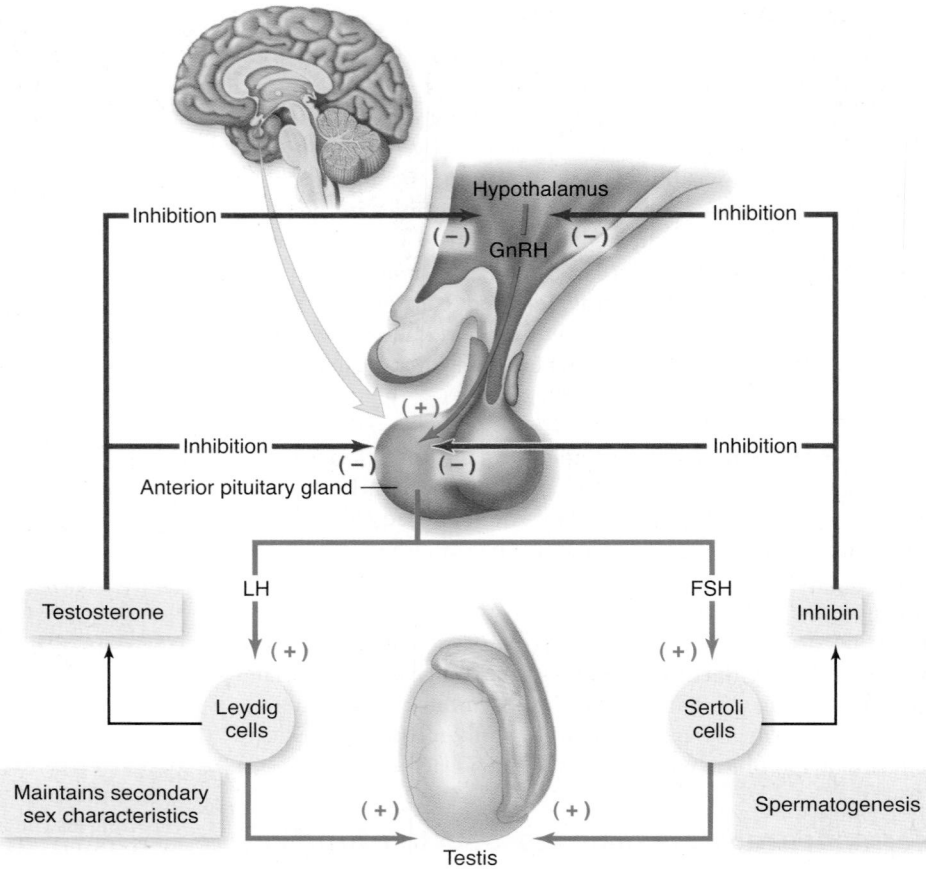

Learning Outcomes Review 53.3

Each of the spermatogonia lining the seminiferous tubules of the testes undergoes mitosis; one of the two daughter cells then undergoes meiosis to produce four haploid sperm cells. Semen consists of sperm from the testes and fluid from the seminal vesicles and prostate gland. Sexual stimulation causes erection of the penis, and continued stimulation leads to ejaculation of semen. Production of sperm and secretion of testosterone from the testes are controlled by FSH and LH from the anterior pituitary.

 Would natural selection favor those males that produce more sperm? Explain your answer.

53.4 Structure and Function of the Human Female Reproductive System

Learning Outcomes

1. Describe the sequence of events in production of an oocyte.
2. Explain ovulation and the female reproductive cycle.
3. Explain how hormones regulate female reproductive function.

The structures of the reproductive system in a human female are shown in figure 53.15. In contrast to the testes, the ovaries develop much more slowly. In the absence of testosterone, the female embryo develops a **clitoris** and labia majora from the same embryonic structures that produce a penis and a scrotum in males. Thus, the clitoris and penis, and the labia majora and scrotum, are said to be homologous structures.

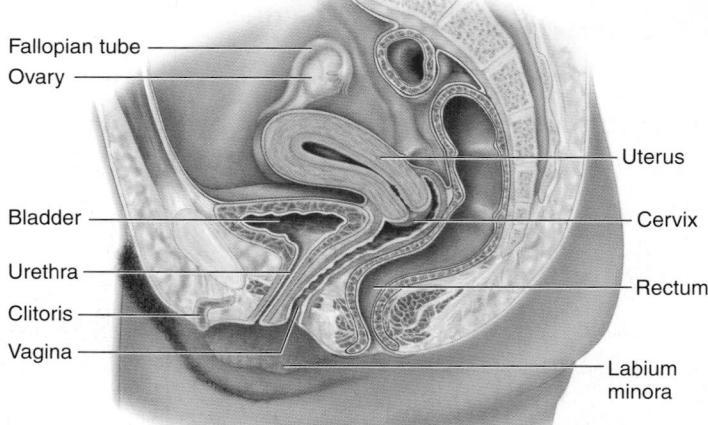

Figure 53.15 Organization of the human female reproductive system. The ovaries are the gonads, the Fallopian tubes receive the ovulated ova, and the uterus is the womb, the site of development of an embryo if the egg cell becomes fertilized.

The clitoris, like the penis, contains corpora cavernosa and is therefore erectile.

The ovaries contain microscopic structures called ovarian follicles, which each contain a potential egg cell called a primary oocyte and smaller **granulosa cells.**

At puberty, the granulosa cells begin to secrete the major female sex hormone, estradiol (also called estrogen), triggering *menarche*, the onset of menstrual cycling. Estradiol also stimulates the formation of the female secondary sexual characteristics, including breast development and the production of pubic hair. In addition, estradiol and another steroid hormone, progesterone, help maintain the female accessory sex organs: the fallopian tubes, uterus, and vagina.

Usually only one egg is produced per menstrual cycle

At birth, a female's ovaries contain about 1 million follicles, each containing a **primary oocyte** that has begun meiosis but is arrested in prophase of the first meiotic division. Some of these primary oocyte-containing follicles are stimulated to develop during each cycle. The human menstrual cycle lasts approximately one month (28 days on the average) and can be divided in terms of ovarian activity into a follicular phase and luteal phase, with the two phases separated by the event of ovulation (figure 53.16).

Follicular phase

During each *follicular phase*, several follicles in the ovaries are stimulated to grow under FSH stimulation, but only one achieves full maturity as a **tertiary,** or **Graafian, follicle** by ovulation. This follicle forms a thin-walled blister on the surface of the ovary. The uterus is lined with a simple columnar epithelial membrane called the endometrium, and during the follicular phase estradiol causes growth of the endometrium. This phase is therefore also known as the **proliferative phase** of the endometrium (see figure 53.16).

The primary oocyte within the Graafian follicle completes the first meiotic division during the follicular phase. Instead of forming two equally large daughter cells,

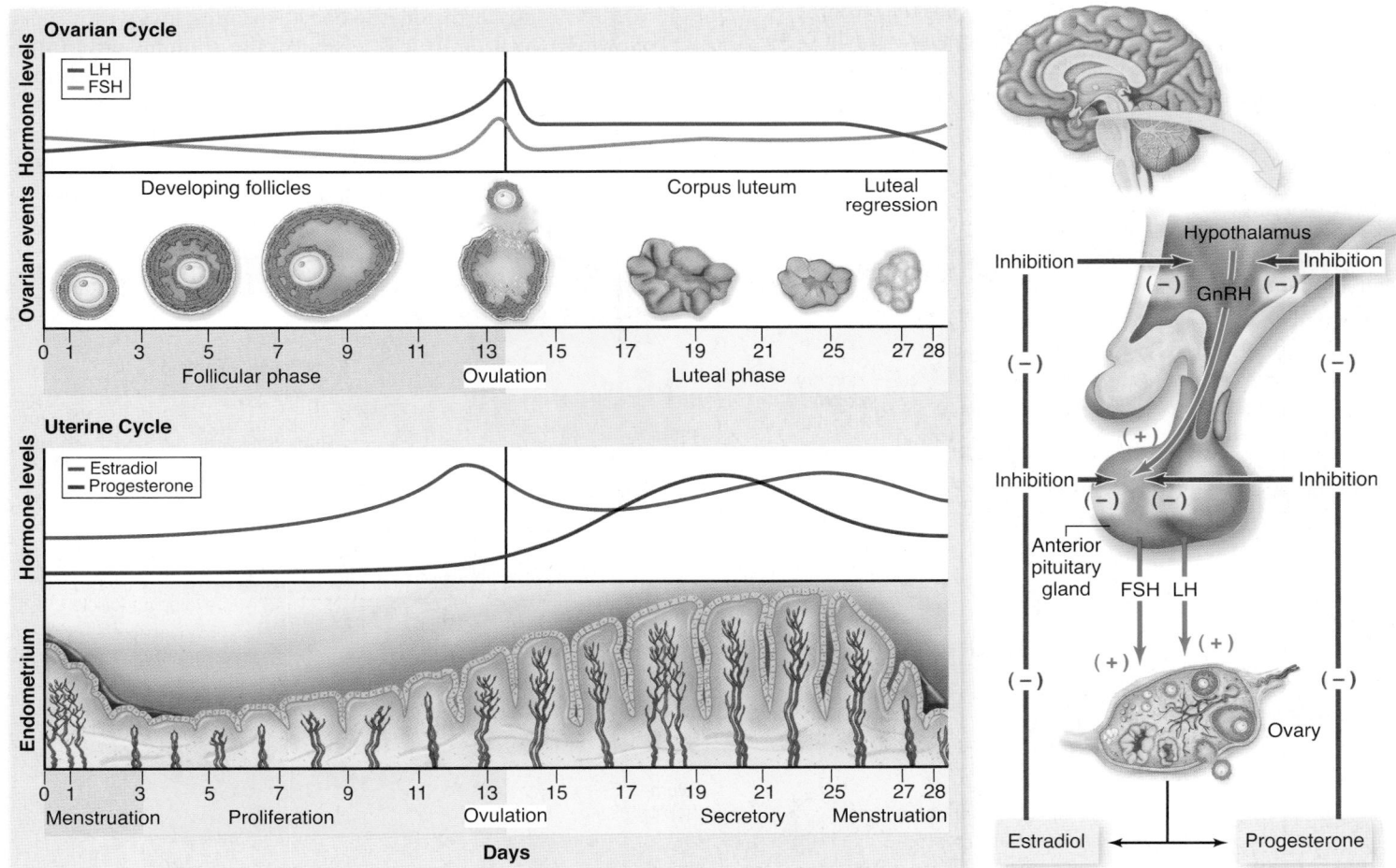

Figure 53.16 The human menstrual cycle. Left: Hormone levels during the cycle are correlated with ovulation and the growth of the endometrial lining of the uterus. Growth and thickening of the endometrium is stimulated by estradiol during the proliferative phase. Estradiol and progesterone maintain and regulate the endometrium during the secretory phase. Decline in the levels of these two hormones triggers menstruation. Right: Production of estradiol and progesterone by the anterior pituitary is controlled by negative feedback.

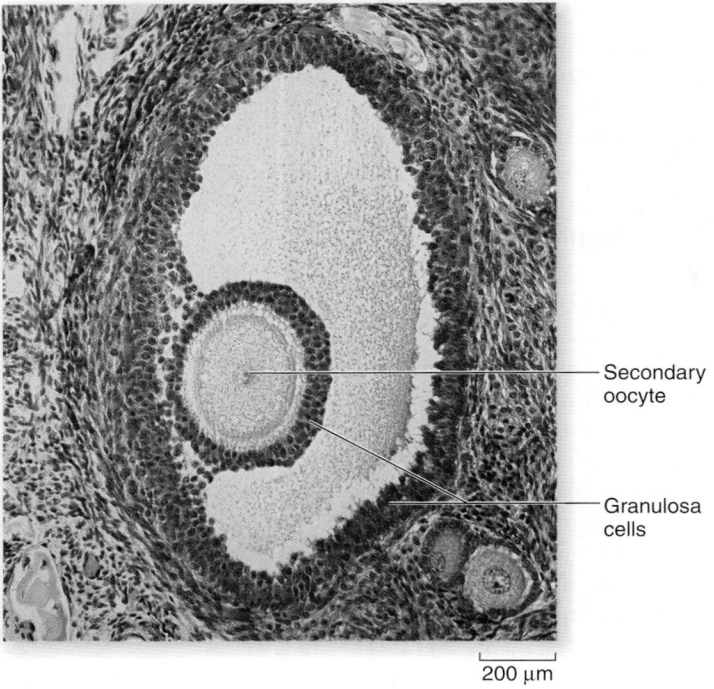

Figure 53.17 A mature Graafian follicle in a cat ovary.
Note the ring of granulosa cells that surrounds the secondary oocyte. This ring will remain around the egg cell when it is ovulated, and sperm must tunnel through the ring in order to reach the plasma membrane of the secondary oocyte.

however, it produces one large daughter cell, the secondary oocyte (figure 53.17), and one tiny daughter cell, called a **polar body.** Thus, the secondary oocyte acquires almost all of the cytoplasm from the primary oocyte (unequal cytokinesis), increasing its chances of sustaining the early embryo should the oocyte be fertilized. The polar body, on the other hand, disintegrates.

The secondary oocyte then begins the second meiotic division, but its progress is arrested at metaphase II. It is in this form that the potential egg cell is discharged from the ovary at ovulation, and it does not complete the second meiotic division unless it becomes fertilized in the Fallopian tube.

Ovulation

The increasing level of estradiol in the blood during the follicular phase stimulates the anterior pituitary gland to secrete LH about midcycle. This sudden secretion of LH causes the fully developed Graafian follicle to burst in the process of ovulation, releasing its secondary oocyte.

The released oocyte enters the abdominal cavity near the fimbriae, the feathery projections surrounding the opening to the Fallopian tube. The ciliated epithelial cells lining the Fallopian tube draw in the oocyte and propel it through the Fallopian tube toward the uterus.

If it is not fertilized, the oocyte disintegrates within a day following ovulation. If it is fertilized, the stimulus of fertilization allows it to complete the second meiotic division, forming a fully mature ovum and a second polar body (figure 53.18). Fusion of the nuclei from the ovum and the sperm produces a diploid zygote. Fertilization normally occurs in the upper one-third of the Fallopian tube, and in humans the zygote takes

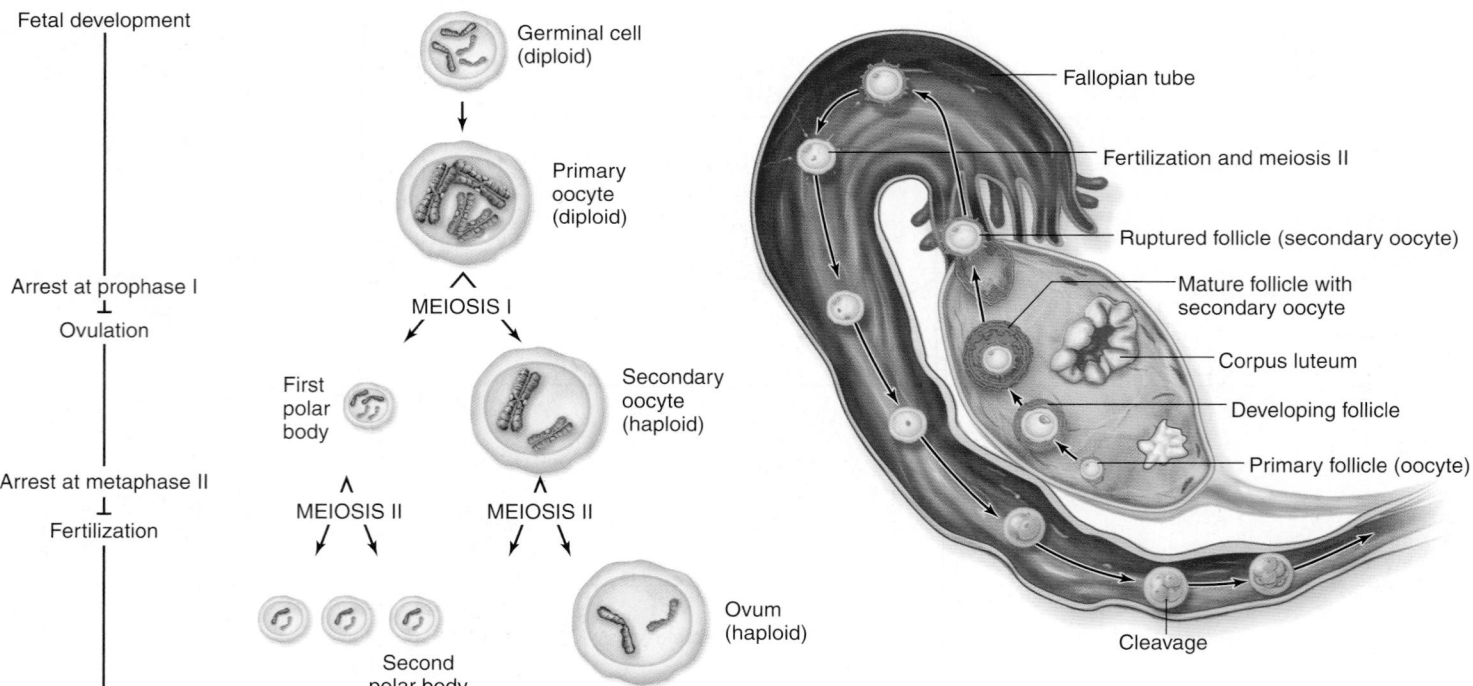

Figure 53.18 The meiotic events of oogenesis in humans. A primary oocyte is diploid. At the completion of the first meiotic division, one division product is eliminated as a polar body, and the other, the secondary oocyte, is released during ovulation. The secondary oocyte does not complete the second meiotic division until after fertilization; that division yields a second polar body and a single haploid egg, or ovum. Fusion of the haploid egg nucleus with a haploid sperm nucleus produces a diploid zygote.

approximately 3 days to reach the uterus and then another 2 to 3 days to implant in the endometrium (figure 53.19).

Luteal phase

After ovulation, LH stimulation completes the development of the Graafian follicle into a structure called the **corpus luteum.** For this reason, the second half of the menstrual cycle is referred to as the **luteal phase.** The corpus luteum secretes both estradiol and another steroid hormone, progesterone. The high blood levels of estradiol and progesterone during the luteal phase now exert negative feedback inhibition of FSH and LH secretion by the anterior pituitary gland (see figure 53.16). This inhibition during the luteal phase is in contrast to the stimulation exerted by estradiol on LH secretion at midcycle, which caused ovulation. The inhibitory effect of estradiol and progesterone after ovulation acts as a natural contraceptive mechanism, preventing both the development of additional follicles and continued ovulation.

During the luteal phase of the cycle, the combination of estradiol and progesterone cause the endometrium to become more vascular, glandular, and enriched with glycogen deposits. Because of the endometrium's glandular appearance and function, this portion of the cycle is known as the **secretory phase** of the endometrium. These changes prepare the uterine lining for embryo implantation.

In the absence of fertilization, the corpus luteum degenerates due to the decreasing levels of LH and FSH near the end of the luteal phase. Estradiol and progesterone, which the corpus luteum produces, inhibit the secretion of LH, the hormone needed for its survival. The disappearance of the corpus luteum results in an abrupt decline in the blood concentration of estradiol and progesterone at the end of the luteal phase, causing the built-up endometrium to be sloughed off with accompanying bleeding. This is menstruation; the portion of the cycle in which it occurs is known as the *menstrual phase* of the endometrium.

If the ovulated oocyte is fertilized, however, the tiny embryo prevents regression of the corpus luteum and subsequent menstruation by secreting *human chorionic gonadotropin (hCG),* an LH-like hormone produced by the chorionic membrane of the embryo. By maintaining the corpus luteum, hCG keeps the levels of estradiol and progesterone high and thereby prevents menstruation, which would terminate the pregnancy. Because hCG comes from the embryonic chorion and not from the mother, it is the hormone tested for in all pregnancy tests.

Mammals with estrous cycles

Menstruation is absent in mammals with an estrous cycle. Although such mammals do cyclically shed cells from the endometrium, they don't bleed in the process. The estrous cycle is divided into four phases: proestrus, estrus, metestrus, and diestrus, which correspond to the proliferative, midcycle, secretory, and menstrual phases of the endometrium in the menstrual cycle.

Female accessory sex organs receive sperm and provide nourishment and protection to the embryo

The Fallopian tubes (also called uterine tubes or oviducts) transport ova from the ovaries to the uterus. In humans, the

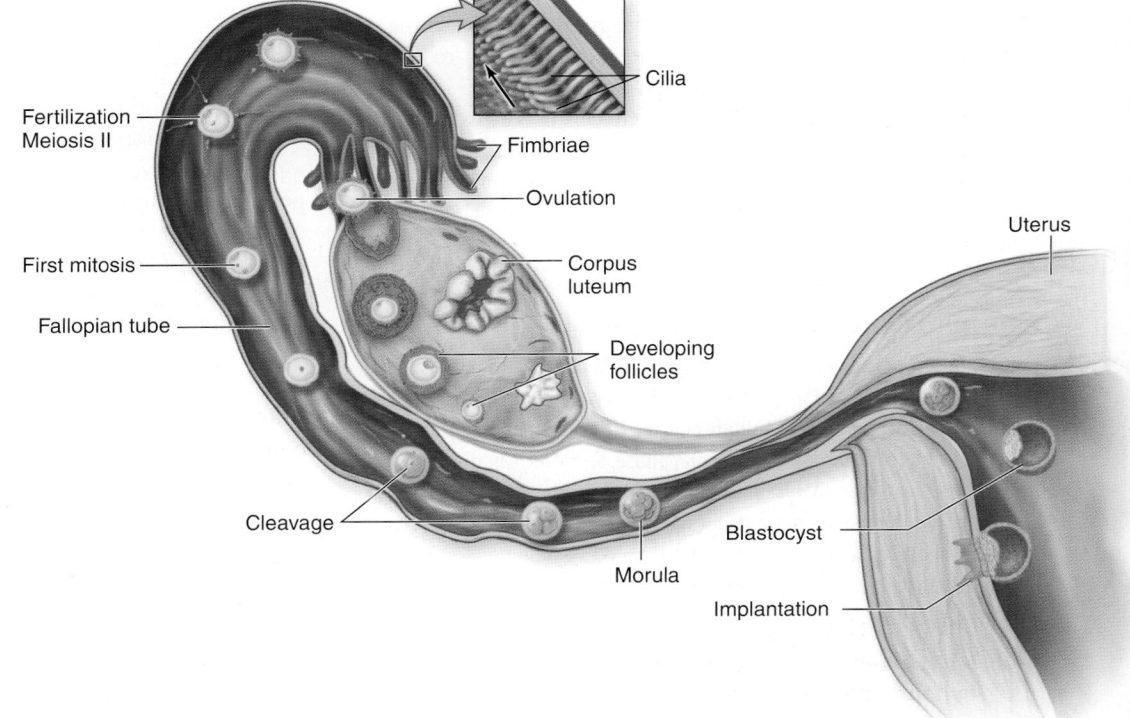

Figure 53.19 The journey of an egg. Produced within a follicle and released at ovulation, the secondary oocyte is swept into a Fallopian tube and carried along by waves of ciliary motion in the tube walls. Sperm journeying upward from the vagina penetrate the secondary oocyte, meiosis is completed and fertilization of the resulting ovum occurs within the Fallopian tube. The resulting zygote undergoes several mitotic divisions while still in the tube. By the time it enters the uterus, it is a hollow sphere of cells called a blastocyst. The blastocyst implants within the wall of the uterus, where it continues its development. (The egg and its subsequent stages have been enlarged for clarification.)

Fertilization
Meiosis II

First mitosis

Fallopian tube

Cleavage

Cilia

Fimbriae

Ovulation

Corpus luteum

Developing follicles

Morula

Blastocyst

Implantation

Uterus

Figure 53.20
A comparison of mammalian uteruses.
a. Humans and other primates; *(b)* cats, dogs, and cows; and *(c)* marsupials.

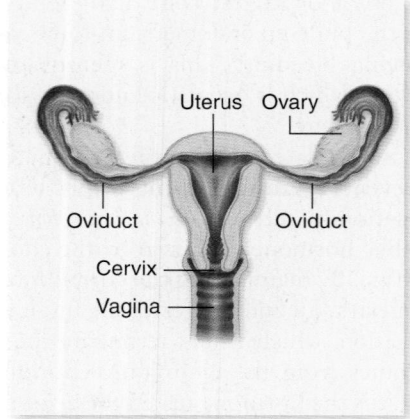

a.

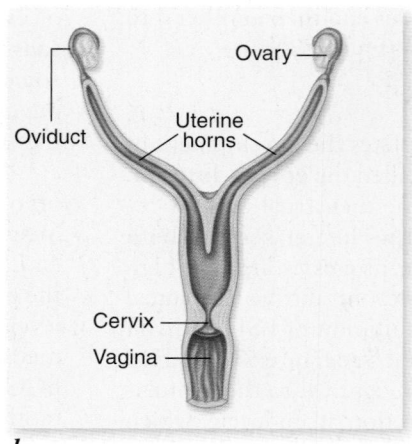

b.

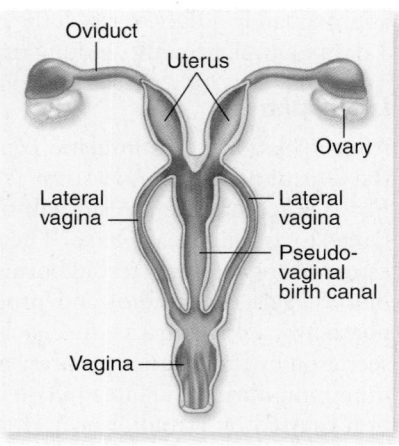

c.

uterus is a muscular, pear-shaped organ that narrows to form a neck, the cervix, which leads to the vagina (figure 53.20*a*).

The entrance to the vagina is initially covered by a membrane called the *hymen*. This will eventually be disrupted by vigorous activity or actual sexual intercourse. In the latter case, this can make the first experience painful when the hymen is ruptured.

During sexual arousal, the labia minora, clitoris, and vagina all become engorged with blood, much like the male erectile tissues. The clitoris has many sensory nerve endings and is one of the most sensitive and responsive areas for female arousal. During sexual arousal, glands located near the vaginal opening called Bartholin's glands, secrete a lubricating fluid that facilitates penetration by the penis. Ejaculation by the male introduces sperm cells that must then make the long swim out of the vagina and up the Fallopian tubes to encounter a secondary oocyte for fertilization to occur.

Mammals other than primates have more complex female reproductive tracts, in which part of the uterus divides to form uterine "horns," each of which leads to an oviduct (figure 53.20*b*, *c*). Cats, dogs, and cows, for example, have one cervix but two uterine horns separated by a septum, or wall. Marsupials, such as opossums, carry the split even further, with two unconnected uterine horns, two cervices, and two vaginas. A male marsupial has a forked penis that can enter both vaginas simultaneously.

Learning Outcomes Review 53.4

Primary oocytes reside in follicles in the ovaries. At puberty, some oocytes are triggered by FSH to develop with every menstrual cycle. Unequal cytokinesis produces a single egg and three polar bodies from each primary oocyte. During the follicular phase, one follicle matures; ovulation is the release of this follicle's secondary oocyte triggered by LH. This oocyte completes division only if fertilization occurs. During the luteal phase, development of additional oocytes is inhibited. If fertilization does not occur, the endometrium is sloughed off as menstrual bleeding.

■ *Would more than one offspring per pregnancy be favored by natural selection? Under what conditions?*

53.5 Contraception and Infertility Treatments

Learning Outcomes

1. Compare the different types of birth control.
2. Describe causes of infertility.

In most vertebrates, copulation is associated solely with reproduction. Reflexive behavior that is deeply ingrained in the female limits sexual receptivity to those periods of the sexual cycle when she is fertile. In humans and a few species of apes, the female can be sexually receptive throughout her reproductive cycle, and this extended receptivity to sexual intercourse serves a second important function—it reinforces pair-bonding, the emotional relationship between two individuals.

Sexual intercourse may be a necessary and important part of humans' emotional lives—and yet not all couples desire to initiate a pregnancy every time they engage in sex. Throughout history, people and cultures have attempted to control reproduction while still being able to engage in sexual intercourse. The prevention of pregnancy or giving birth is known as birth control. Physiologically, pregnancy begins not at fertilization but approximately a week later with successful implantation. Methods of birth control that act prior to implantation are usually termed contraception.

In contrast, some couples desire to have children, but find for a variety of reasons that pregnancy is not occurring—a condition termed infertility. Technologies have also been developed to assist these couples in having children.

Contraception is aimed at preventing fertilization or implantation

A variety of approaches, differing in effectiveness and in their acceptability to different couples, religions, and cultures, are commonly taken to prevent pregnancy (figure 53.21 and table 53.2).

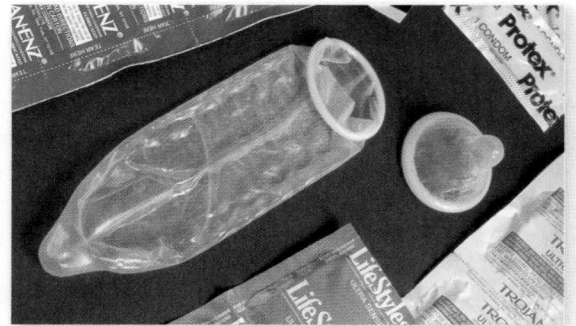

a.

b.

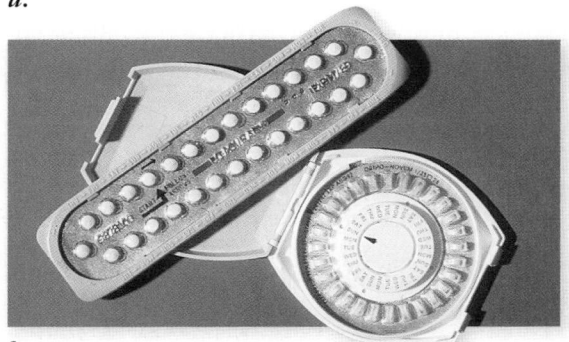

c.

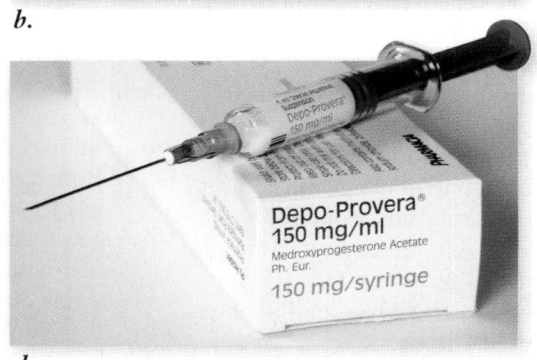

d.

Figure 53.21 Four common methods of birth control. *a.* Condom; *(b)* diaphragm and spermicidal jelly; *(c)* oral contraceptives; *(d)* medroxyprogesterone acetate (Depo-Provera).

TABLE 53.2	Methods of Birth Control				
Device	Action	Failure Rate*	Advantages	Disadvantages
Oral contraceptive	Hormones (progesterone analogue alone or in combination with other hormones) primarily prevent ovulation	1–5, depending on type	Convenient; highly effective; provides significant noncontraceptive health benefits such as protection against ovarian and endometrial cancers	Must be taken regularly; possible minor side effects, which new formulations have reduced; not for women with cardiovascular risks (mostly smokers over age 35)
Condom	Thin sheath for penis collects semen; "female condoms" sheath vaginal walls	3–15	Easy to use, effective, inexpensive, protects against some sexually transmitted diseases	Requires male cooperation, may diminish spontaneity, may deteriorate on the shelf
Diaphragm	Soft rubber cup covers entrance to uterus; prevents sperm from reaching egg, holds spermicide	4–25	No dangerous side effects; reliable if used properly; provides some protection against sexually transmitted diseases and cervical cancer	Requires careful fitting, some inconvenience associated with insertion and removal; may be dislodged during intercourse
Intrauterine device (IUD)	Small plastic or metal device placed in the uterus, prevents implantation; some contain copper, others release hormones	1–5	Convenient, highly effective; infrequent replacement	Can cause excess menstrual bleeding and pain; risk of perforation, infection, expulsion, pelvic inflammatory disease, and infertility; not recommended for those who eventually intend to conceive or are not monogamous; dangerous in pregnancy
Cervical cap	Miniature diaphragm covers cervix closely, prevents sperm from reaching egg, holds spermicide	Probably similar to that of diaphragm	No dangerous side effects; fairly effective; can remain in place longer than diaphragm	Problems with fitting and insertion; comes in limited number of sizes
Foams, creams, jellies, vaginal suppositories	Chemical spermicides inserted in vagina before intercourse prevent sperm from entering uterus	10–25	Can be used by anyone who is not allergic; protect against some sexually transmitted diseases; no known side effects	Relatively unreliable; sometimes messy; must be used 5–10 minutes before each act of intercourse
Implant (levonorgestrel; Norplant)	Capsules surgically implanted under skin slowly release hormone that blocks ovulation	0.03	Very safe, convenient, and effective; very long-lasting (5 years); may have nonreproductive health benefits like those of oral contraceptives	Irregular or absent periods; minor surgical procedure needed for insertion and removal; some scarring may occur
Injectable contraceptive (medroxyprogesterone; Depo-Provera)	Injection every 3 months of a hormone that is slowly released and prevents ovulation	1	Convenient and highly effective; no serious side effects other than occasional heavy menstrual bleeding	Animal studies suggest it may cause cancer, though new studies in humans are mostly encouraging; occasional heavy menstrual bleeding

*Failure rate is expressed as pregnancies per 100 actual users per year.

Source: Data from American College of Obstetricians and Gynecologists: Contraception, Patient Education Pamphlet No. AP005. ACOG, Washington, D.C., 1990.

Abstinence

The most reliable way to avoid pregnancy is to not have sexual intercourse at all, which is called *abstinence*. Of all the methods of contraception, this is the most certain. It is also the most limiting and the most difficult method to sustain. The drive to engage in sexual intercourse is compelling, and many unwanted pregnancies result when a couple who desire each other and are attempting to adhere to abstinence fail in the attempt.

Sperm blockage

If sperm cannot reach the uterus, fertilization cannot occur. One way to prevent the delivery of sperm is to encase the penis within a thin sheath, or condom. Some males do not favor the use of condoms, which tend to decrease males' sensory pleasure during intercourse. In principle, this method is easy to apply and foolproof, but in practice it has a failure rate of 3 to 15% per year because of incorrect or inconsistent use or condom failure. Nevertheless, condom use is the most commonly employed form of contraception in the United States. Condoms are also widely used to prevent the transmission of AIDS and other sexually transmitted diseases (STDs). Over a billion condoms are sold in the United States each year.

A second way to prevent the entry of sperm into the uterus is to place a cover over the cervix. The cover may be a relatively tight-fitting cervical cap, which is worn for days at a time, or a rubber dome called a diaphragm, which is inserted before intercourse. Because the dimensions of individual cervices vary, a cervical cap or diaphragm must be initially fitted by a physician. Pregnancy rates average 4 to 25% per year for women using diaphragms. Failure rates for cervical caps are somewhat lower.

Sperm destruction

A third general approach to pregnancy prevention is to eliminate the sperm after ejaculation. This can be achieved in principle by washing out the vagina immediately after intercourse, before the sperm have a chance to enter the uterus. Such a procedure is called a douche. The douche method is difficult to apply well, because it involves a rapid dash to the bathroom immediately after ejaculation and a very thorough washing. Douching can, in fact, increase the possibility of conception by forcing sperm farther up into the vagina and uterus, thereby accounting for its high failure rate (40%).

Alternatively, sperm delivered to the vagina can be destroyed there with spermicidal agents, jellies, or foams. These treatments generally require application immediately before intercourse. Their failure rates vary from 10 to 25%. The use of a spermicide with a condom or diaphragm increases the effectiveness over each method used independently.

Prevention of ovulation

Since about 1960, a widespread form of contraception in the United States has been the daily ingestion of birth control pills, or oral contraceptives, by women. These pills contain analogues of progesterone, sometimes in combination with estrogens. As described earlier, progesterone and estradiol act by negative feedback to inhibit the secretion of FSH and LH during the luteal phase of the ovarian cycle, thereby preventing follicle development and ovulation. They also cause a buildup of the endometrium. The hormones in birth control pills have the same effects. Because the pills block ovulation, no ovum is available to be fertilized.

A woman generally takes the hormone-containing pills for 3 weeks; during the fourth week, she takes pills without hormones, allowing the levels of those hormones in her blood to fall, which causes menstruation.

Oral contraceptives provide a very effective means of birth control, with a failure rate of only 1 to 5% per year. In a variation of the oral contraceptive, hormone-containing capsules are implanted beneath the skin. These implanted capsules have failure rates below 1%.

A small number of women using birth control pills or implants experience undesirable side effects, such as blood clotting and nausea. These side effects have been reduced in newer generations of birth control pills, which contain less estrogen and different analogues of progesterone. Moreover, these new oral contraceptives provide a number of benefits, including reduced risks of endometrial and ovarian cancer, cardiovascular disease, and osteoporosis (for older women). However, they may increase the risk of developing breast cancer and cervical cancer.

The risks involved with birth control pills increase in women who smoke and increase greatly in women over 35 who smoke. The current consensus is that, for many women, the health benefits of oral contraceptives outweigh their risks, although a physician must help each woman determine the relative risks and benefits.

Prevention of embryo implantation

The insertion of an intrauterine device (IUD), such as a coil or other irregularly shaped object, is an effective means of contraception because the irritation it produces prevents the implantation of an embryo. IUDs have a failure rate of only 1 to 5%. Their high degree of effectiveness probably reflects their convenience; once they are inserted, they can be forgotten. The great disadvantage of this method is that almost a third of the women who attempt to use IUDs experience cramps, pain, and sometimes bleeding and therefore must discontinue using them. There is also a risk of uterine infection with insertion of the IUD.

Another method of preventing embryo implantation is the "morning-after pill," or Plan B, which contains 50 times the dose of estrogen present in birth control pills. The pill works by temporarily stopping ovum development, by preventing fertilization, or by stopping the implantation of a fertilized ovum. Its failure rate is 1 to 10% per use.

Many women are uneasy about taking such high hormone doses because side effects can be severe. This pill is not designed as a regular method of pregnancy prevention, but rather as a method of emergency contraception.

Sterilization

Sterilization is usually accomplished by the surgical removal of portions of the tubes that transport the gametes from the gonads (figure 53.22). It is an almost 100% effective means of contraception. Sterilization may be performed on either males or females, preventing sperm from entering the semen in males and preventing an ovulated oocyte from reaching the uterus in females.

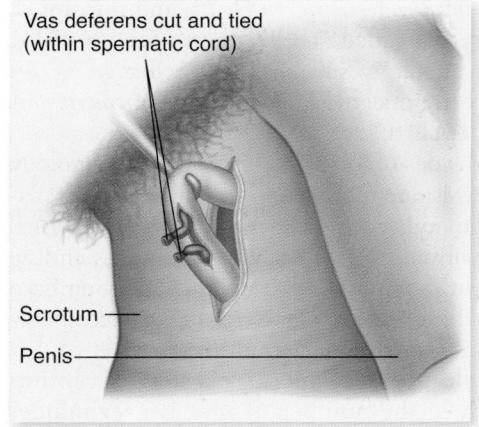

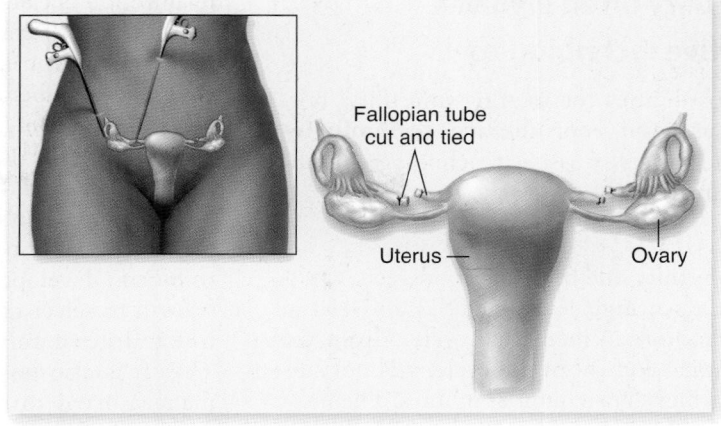

Figure 53.22
Birth control through sterilization.
a. Vasectomy; *(b)* tubal ligation.

Vas deferens cut and tied (within spermatic cord)

Scrotum

Penis

a.

Fallopian tube cut and tied

Uterus

Ovary

b.

In males, sterilization involves a vasectomy, the removal and tying off of a portion of the vas deferens from each testis. In females, the comparable operation, called tubal ligation, involves the removal of a section of each Fallopian tube and tying off the tube. In very rare cases, it is possible for the tubes to grow back together, restoring fertility. This is more common in vasectomy but does occur in both at a very low level. This accounts for the less than 100% effectiveness statistically. Both methods can also be reversed surgically, though for vasectomy the surgery is both expensive and frequently unsuccessful.

Infertility occurs in both males and females

Infertility is defined as the inability to conceive after 12 months of contraception-free sexual intercourse. In about 40% of cases, the failure to conceive is due to problems on the male side with about 45% due to problems on the female side, leaving another 15% unexplained (idiopathic infertility). Given these background statistics, it is clear that we still have a lot to learn about human fertility, despite a significant amount of study.

Female infertility

Infertility in females can occur due to a failure at any stage from the production of an oocyte, to the implantation of the zygote. The most common problems arise from failure to ovulate, and from some kind of mechanical blockage preventing either fertilization or implantation.

The leading cause of infertility worldwide is pelvic inflammatory disease (PID). This can be caused by infection with a number of different bacteria that all lead to blockage of the Fallopian tubes. This blockage then causes problems in sperm passage, and of transfer of fertilized eggs to the uterus.

Endometriosis, the presence of ectopic endometrial tissue, can lead to infertility by a mechanism similar to PID. The body responds to the ectopic tissue by trying to wall it off with scar tissue. The buildup of scar tissue can then prevent the transfer of eggs to the uterus.

Another common cause of infertility in females is age, or premature ovarian failure (POF). Fertility declines significantly in females with age, and the incidence of some genetic abnor-malities caused by nondisjunction of chromosomes increases (see chapter 13). If a women younger than 40 has a diminished supply of eggs, this is considered diagnostic of POF.

Disruption of the normal hormonal control of ovulation discussed earlier is also a common cause of infertility in females. Decreased levels of GnRH will disrupt ovulation, a condition referred to as hypogonadotropic hypogonadism. This can arise from damage to the hypothalamus or pituitary, or by any disorder that affects normal levels of hypothalamic hormones. For example, diabetes, thyroid disease, and excessive adrenal androgen production all affect hormonal feedback to the hypothalamus and can disrupt its normal function, leading to decreased levels of GnRH and infertility. Excessive exercise and anorexia can also lead to reduced GnRH levels and produce infertility.

Hormonal imbalances can occur during the luteal phase as well. Inadequate levels of progesterone during the luteal phase reduce the thickening of the uterine wall. If the uterine wall is inadequately prepared, implantation may not occur or can lead to an increased likelihood of spontaneous abortion.

Male infertility

Infertility in males can be due to a reduced number, viability, or motility of sperm in the ejaculate. These can be due to a variety of factors from infection to hormonal imbalances. Analysis on the male side is easier since sperm collection is noninvasive. Sperm can be easily analyzed for number, viability, morphology, and motility.

Infertility can arise from autoimmunity to sperm, leading to sperm loss, as well as due to abnormalities of all of the glands that contribute to the production of semen. Damage to the vas deferens or to the seminiferous tubules can also result in infertility. Anything that disrupts the maturation process of sperm can result in possible infertility.

After all possible causes have been ruled out, up to 5% of infertile men suffer from idiopathic, or unexplained, infertility. This may be due to genetic causes as the numbers seem to be similar worldwide despite different environments. It has been estimated in studies of *Drosophila* that up to 1500 recessive genes contribute to male fertility. Work is ongoing to examine the human genome for evidence of similar genes.

Treatment of infertility often involves assisted reproductive technologies

There are two basic possibilities for treating infertility: hormonal treatment and **assisted reproductive technologies (ART).** The number and variety of assisted technologies available today is large and growing.

Hormone treatment

In the case of female infertility due to ovulatory defects, treatment is designed to produce high levels of FSH and LH at a single point during the normal menstrual cycle. Given the complexity of the hormonal control of the cycle, it is not surprising that this can be achieved in a number of ways. The most common drug currently used is clomiphine (Clomid), which is a competitive inhibitor of the estrogen receptor. This interferes with the negative feedback loop controlling estradiol production by the ovaries and consequently increases FSH and LH levels. If this is not successful, gonadatropins can be injected to stimulate ovulation.

Assistive reproductive technology

The simplest method to assist reproduction is to use artificial insemination, a process by which sperm are introduced into the female reproductive tract artificially. This is widely used in reproduction of domestic animals and is also used in humans. This has also been extended in cases of infertility in which both sperm and egg are introduced artificially by a technique called *gametic intrafallopian transfer*, or *GIFT*.

The birth of the first "test tube baby" in 1978 was heralded as the beginning of a new age of reproductive technology. Even the early pioneers may not have envisioned how far this technology would proceed. The basic technique of external fertilization is called *in vitro fertilization* (*IVF*), and transfer of the developing embryo is called simply *embryo transfer* (*ET*). When the sperm are unable to successfully fertilize an egg in vitro, they can be directly injected into an egg by *intracytoplasmic sperm injection* (*ICSI*).

One of the downsides of much of this assisted technology is multiple births. This is due to the common practice of transferring more than one embryo to ensure that at least one implants and develops normally. With advances in understanding of human development, it is possible to monitor early embryo growth to select the "best" embryos for transfer and to therefore transfer fewer embryos to reduce multiple births.

It is also possible to freeze sperm, eggs, and even human embryos to reduce the number of invasive techniques such as harvesting oocytes. Live births have been achieved using all combinations of frozen eggs, sperm, and embryos. This allows the transfer of a single embryo while freezing others produced by in vitro fertilization. If the first embryo transferred does not implant, then the others can be thawed and transferred later.

Learning Outcomes Review 53.5

Pregnancy can be prevented by a variety of contraception methods, including abstinence, barrier contraceptives, hormonal inhibition, and sterilization surgery. Some methods are more susceptible to human error than others and thus have a lower success rate. Infertility can be treated by hormonal manipulation to induce ovulation or by the use of assisted reproductive technologies. These assisted technologies include in vitro fertilization and intracytoplasmic sperm injection.

- *Why isn't there a male birth control pill?*

Chapter Review

53.1 Animal Reproductive Strategies

Some species have developed novel reproductive methods.
Sexual reproduction involves production by meiosis of haploid gametes (eggs and sperm). These join at fertilization to produce a diploid zygote.

Asexual reproduction produces offspring with the same genes as the parent organism.

In budding, a part of an individual becomes separated and develops into a new, identical individual. In parthenogenesis, females produce offspring from unfertilized eggs. In hermaphroditism, an individual has both testes and ovaries (simultaneous) or may change sex (sequential).

Sex can be determined genetically or by environmental conditions.
In some animals, the temperature an individual experiences as an embryo determines its sex. In mammals, sex is genetically determined by the presence of a Y chromosome (see figure 53.3).

53.2 Vertebrate Fertilization and Development

Internal fertilization has led to three strategies for development of offspring.
Vertebrates with internal fertilization exhibit three strategies for development: oviparity, ovoviviparity, and viviparity. Both internal fertilization and live birth have evolved many times.

Most fishes and amphibians have external fertilization.
Most fish and amphibians release eggs and sperm into the water, where the gametes unite by chance. Few fertilized eggs grow to maturity.

Reptiles and birds have internal fertilization.
The embryos of reptiles and birds develop in a fluid-filled cavity surrounded by the amnion and extraembryonic membranes and a shell to help prevent desiccation.

Mammals generally do not lay eggs, but give birth to their young.
Mammals are also amniotic, but most species are viviparous. Most mammals have an estrus cycle, but primates have a menstrual cycle.

53.3 Structure and Function of the Human Male Reproductive System

Sperm cells are produced by the millions.
Haploid sperm are produced by meiosis of spermatogonia with the aid of Sertoli cells (see figure 53.11). Each spermatogonium produces four sperm cells. A sperm cell has three parts: a head with an acrosome, a body containing mitochondria, and a flagellar tail.

Male accessory sex organs aid in sperm delivery.
Semen is a complex mixture of sperm and fluids from the seminal vesicles, prostate gland, and bulbourethral glands.

The urethra of the penis transports both sperm and urine and contains two columns of erectile tissue, blood vessels, and nerves (see figure 53.13). Ejaculation is the ejection of semen from the penis by smooth muscle contraction.

Hormones regulate male reproductive function.
Male reproductive function is controlled by the hormones FSH and LH and negative feedback loops (see figure 53.14, table 53.1).

53.4 Structure and Function of the Human Female Reproductive System

Usually only one egg is produced per menstrual cycle.
The female clitoris and labial lips have the same embryonic origin as the penis and scrotum. They develop in the absence of testosterone.

In adult females, FSH stimulates follicular development, which in turn produces estrogen. LH stimulates ovulation and corpus luteum development, which produces progesterone and more estrogen. Estrogen and progesterone are necessary to develop and maintain the uterine lining (see figure 53.16).

The ovarian cycle has three phases: follicular phase, ovulation, and luteal phase. The uterine cycle has three stages that mirror the ovarian cycle: menstruation, proliferation, and secretion.

At birth, all primary oocytes are arrested in the first meiotic division. Each oocyte is capable of producing one ovum and three polar bodies. Each month, one oocyte completes meiosis I. This secondary oocyte begins the second meiotic division and arrests until the egg is fertilized (see figure 53.18).

A fertilized egg, or zygote, develops into a blastocyst and implants in the wall of the uterus. Here it produces hCG, which maintains the corpus luteum and prevents menstruation.

If fertilization and implantation do not occur, the production of hormones declines, causing the built-up endometrium in the uterus to be sloughed off during menstruation.

Female accessory organs receive sperm and provide nourishment and protection to the embryo.
The Fallopian tubes transport ova from the ovaries to the uterus. The vagina receives sperm, which enters the uterus via the cervix (see figure 53.20). Other female organs are involved in sexual response.

53.5 Contraception and Infertility Treatments

Contraception is aimed at preventing fertilization or implantation.
Pregnancy can be avoided by abstinence, by blocking sperm from reaching the ovum, by destroying sperm after ejaculation, by preventing ovulation or embryo implantation, or by sterilization. Some methods are more successful in practice than others.

Infertility occurs in both males and females.
Female infertility ranges from failure of oocyte production to failure of zygote implantation. Male infertility is usually due to reduction in sperm number, viability, or motility; hormonal imbalance; or damage to the sperm delivery system.

Treatment of infertility often involves assisted reproductive technologies.
Hormonal treatment may be used to correct ovulatory defects or sperm production defects. Assistive reproduction technologies involve artificial insemination, in vitro fertilization and embryo transfer, or intracytoplasmic sperm injection.

Review Questions

UNDERSTAND

1. You have discovered a new organism living in tide pools at your favorite beach. Every so often, one of the creature's appendages will break off and gradually grow into a whole new organism, identical to the first. This is an example of
   a. sexual reproduction. c. budding.
   b. fission. d. parthenogenesis.

2. If you decided that the organism you discovered in question 1 used parthenogenesis, what would you also know about this species?
   a. It is asexual.
   b. All the individuals are female.
   c. Each individual develops from an unfertilized egg.
   d. All of these would be true.

3. Which of the following terms describes your first stage as a diploid organism?
   a. Sperm c. Gamete
   b. Egg d. Zygote

4. Which of the following structures is the site of spermatogenesis?
   a. Prostate c. Urethra
   b. Bulbourethral gland d. Seminiferous tubule

5. FSH and LH are produced by the
   a. ovaries. c. anterior pituitary.
   b. testes. d. adrenal glands.

6. Gametogenesis requires the conclusion of meiosis II. When does this occur in females?
   a. During fetal development
   b. At the onset of puberty
   c. After fertilization
   d. After implantation

7. Mutations that affect proteins in the acrosome would impede which of the following functions?
   a. Fertilization c. Meiosis
   b. Locomotion d. Semen production

8. In humans, fertilization occurs in the____, and implantation of the zygote occurs in the____.
   a. seminiferous tubules; uterus
   b. vagina; oviduct
   c. oviduct; uterus
   d. urethra; uterus

9. The testicles of male mammals are suspended in the scrotum because
   a. the optimum temperature for sperm production is less than the normal core body temperature of the organism.
   b. the optimum temperature for sperm production is higher than the normal core body temperature of the organism.
   c. there is not enough room in the pelvic area for the testicles to be housed internally.
   d. it is easier for the body to expel sperm during ejaculation.

APPLY

1. The major difference between an estrous cycle and a menstrual cycle is that
   a. sexual receptivity occurs only around ovulation in the estrous cycle, but it can occur during any time of the menstrual cycle.
   b. estrous cycles occur in reptiles, but menstrual cycles occur in mammals.
   c. estrous cycles are determined by FSH, but menstrual cycles are determined by LH.
   d. estrous cycles occur monthly, but menstrual cycles occur sporadically.

2. Which of the following is a major difference between spermatogenesis and oogenesis?
   a. Spermatogenesis involves meiosis, and oogenesis involves mitosis.
   b. Spermatogenesis is continuous, but oogenesis is variable.
   c. Spermatogenesis produces fewer gametes per precursor cell than oogenesis.
   d. All of these are significant differences between oogenesis and spermatogenesis.

3. In species with environmental sex determination
   a. sex is determined during development as an embryo.
   b. environmental conditions determine the sex of an individual.
   c. hermaphroditism always occurs.
   d. a and b are correct.

4. Internal and external fertilization differ in that all species that
   a. produce an amniotic egg have internal fertilization.
   b. do not produce an amniotic egg have external fertilization.
   c. produce live young have a penis or other intromittent organ.
   d. lay eggs are external fertilizers.

SYNTHESIZE

1. Suppose that the *SRY* gene mutated such that a male embryo could not produce functional protein. What kinds of changes would you expect to see in the embryo?

2. Why do you think that amphibians and many fish have external fertilization, whereas lizards, birds, and mammals rely on internal fertilization?

3. How are the functions of FSH and LH similar in male and female mammals? How do they differ?

4. You are interested in developing a contraceptive that blocks hCG receptors. Will it work? Why or why not?

5. Why are all parthenogenic parents female?

ONLINE RESOURCE

www.ravenbiology.com

Understand, Apply, and Synthesize—enhance your study with animations that bring concepts to life and practice tests to assess your understanding. Your instructor may also recommend the interactive eBook, individualized learning tools, and more.

Chapter 54

Animal Development

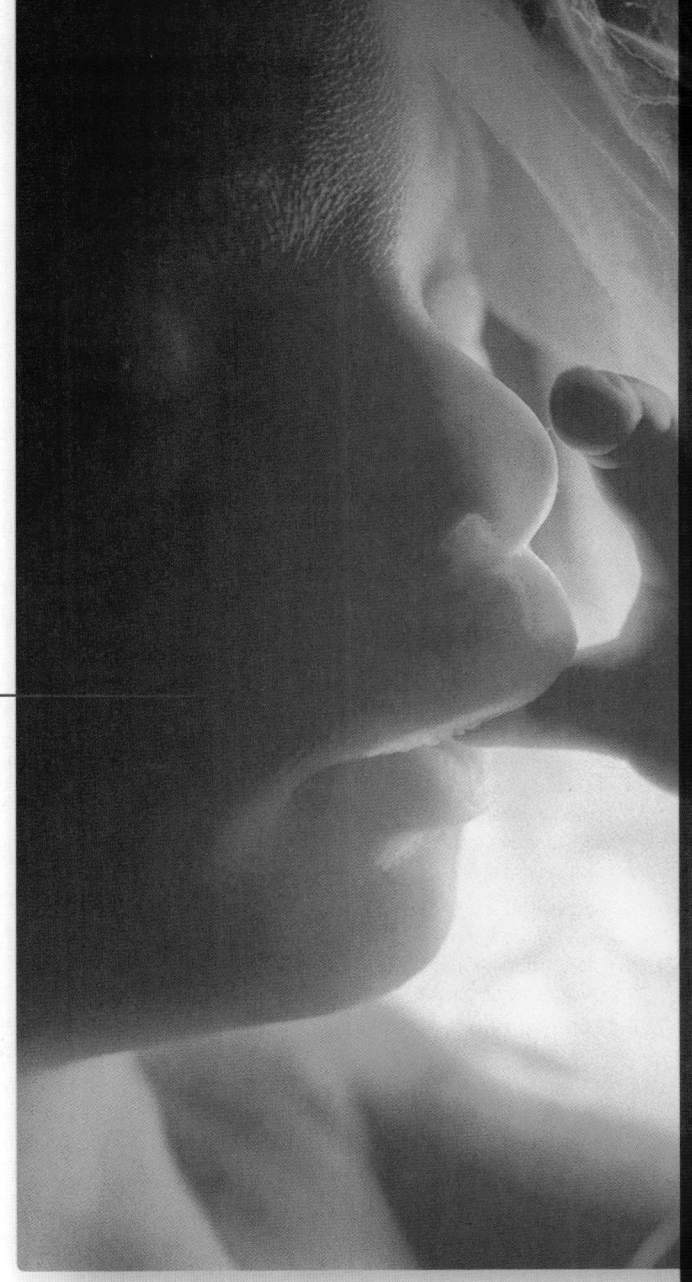

Chapter Outline

54.1   Fertilization

54.2   Cleavage and the Blastula Stage

54.3   Gastrulation

54.4   Organogenesis

54.5   Vertebrate Axis Formation

54.6   Human Development

Introduction

Sexual reproduction in all but a few animals unites two haploid gametes to form a single diploid cell called a zygote. *The zygote develops by a process of cell division and differentiation into a complex multicellular organism, composed of many different tissues and organs, as the picture illustrates. At the same time, a group of cells that constitute the* germ line *are set aside to enable the developing organism to engage in sexual reproduction as an adult. In this chapter, we focus on the stages that all coelomate animals pass through during embryogenesis: fertilization, cleavage, gastrulation, and organogenesis (table 54.1). Development is a dynamic process, and so the boundaries between these stages are somewhat artificial. Although differences can be found in the details, developmental genes and cellular pathways have been greatly conserved, and they create similar structures in different organisms.*

TABLE 54.1	Stages of Animal Development (Using a Mammal as an Example)	
Fertilization	The haploid male and female gametes fuse to form a diploid zygote.	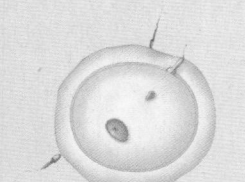
Cleavage	The zygote rapidly divides into many cells, with no overall increase in size. In many animals, these divisions affect future development because different cells receive different portions of the egg cytoplasm and, hence, different cytoplasmic determinants. Cleavage ends with formation of a blastula (called a blastocyst in mammals), which varies in structure among animal embryos.	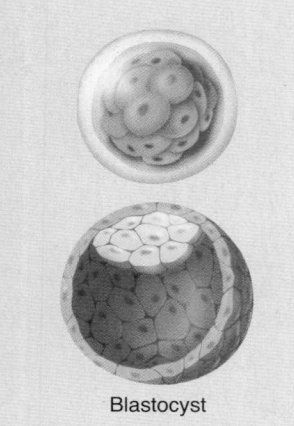 Blastocyst
Gastrulation	The cells of the embryo move, forming the three primary germ layers: ectoderm, mesoderm, and endoderm.	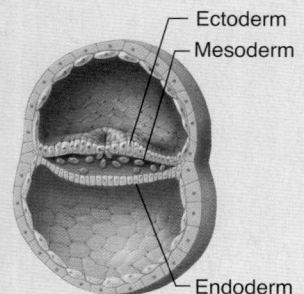 Ectoderm Mesoderm Endoderm
Organogenesis	Cells from the three primary germ layers interact in various ways to produce the organs of the body. In chordates, organogenesis begins with formation of the notochord and the hollow dorsal nerve cord in the process of neurulation.	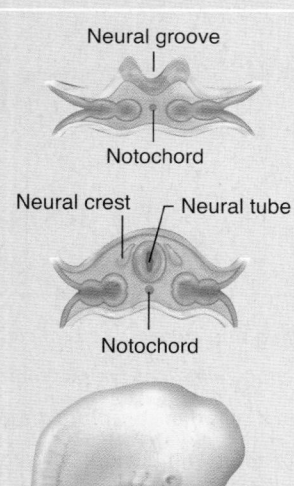 Neural groove Notochord Neural crest Neural tube Notochord

54.1 *Fertilization*

Learning Outcomes

1. *Describe the events necessary for fertilization to occur.*
2. *List different ways that polyspermy is blocked.*

In all sexually reproducing animals, the first step in development is the union of male and female gametes, a process called *fertilization.* As you learned in the preceding chapter, fertilization is typically external in aquatic animals. In contrast, internal fertilization is used by most terrestrial animals to provide a nondessicating environment for the gametes.

One physical challenge of sexual reproduction is for gametes to get together. Many elaborate strategies have evolved to enhance the likelihood of such encounters. For example, most marine invertebrates release hundreds of millions of eggs and sperm into the surrounding sea water on spawning; others use lunar cycles to time gamete release. Elaborate courtship behaviors are typical of many animals that utilize internal fertilization (see chapter 53). Fertilization itself consists of three events: sperm penetration and membrane fusion, egg activation, and fusion of nuclei.

A sperm must penetrate to the plasma membrane of the egg for membrane fusion to occur

Embryonic development begins with the fusion of the sperm and egg plasma membranes. But the unfertilized egg presents a challenge to this process, since it is enveloped by one or more protective coats. These protective coats include the *chorion* of insect eggs, the *jelly layer* and *vitelline envelope* of sea urchin and frog eggs, and the *zona pellucida* of mammalian eggs. Mammalian oocytes are also surrounded by a layer of supporting granulosa cells (figure 54.1). Thus, the first challenge of fertilization is that sperm have to penetrate these external layers to reach the plasma membrane of the egg.

A saclike organelle named the **acrosome** is positioned between the plasma membrane and the nucleus of the sperm head. The acrosome contains digestive enzymes, which are released by the process of exocytosis when a sperm reaches the outer layers of the egg. These enzymes create a hole in the protective layers, enabling the sperm to tunnel its way through to the egg's plasma membrane.

In sea urchin sperm, actin monomers assemble into cytoskeletal filaments just under the plasma membrane to create a long narrow offshoot—the *acrosomal process.* The acrosomal process extends through the vitelline envelope to the egg's plasma membrane, and the sperm nucleus then passes through the acrosomal process to enter the egg.

In mice, an acrosomal process is not formed, and the entire sperm head burrows through the zona pellucida to the egg. Membrane fusion of the sperm and egg then allows the sperm nucleus to pass directly into the egg cytoplasm. In many species, egg cytoplasm bulges out at membrane fusion to engulf the head of the sperm (figure 54.2).

Sperm
Jelly layer
Plasma membrane
Vitelline envelope
Nucleus of egg
Cytoplasm
Cortical granules
a.
Sperm
Granulosa cell
Zona pellucida
Plasma membrane
First polar body
Cortical granules
Cytoplasm
b.
Oocyte
Granulosa cell
c.
1.2 μm
d.
3.3 μm

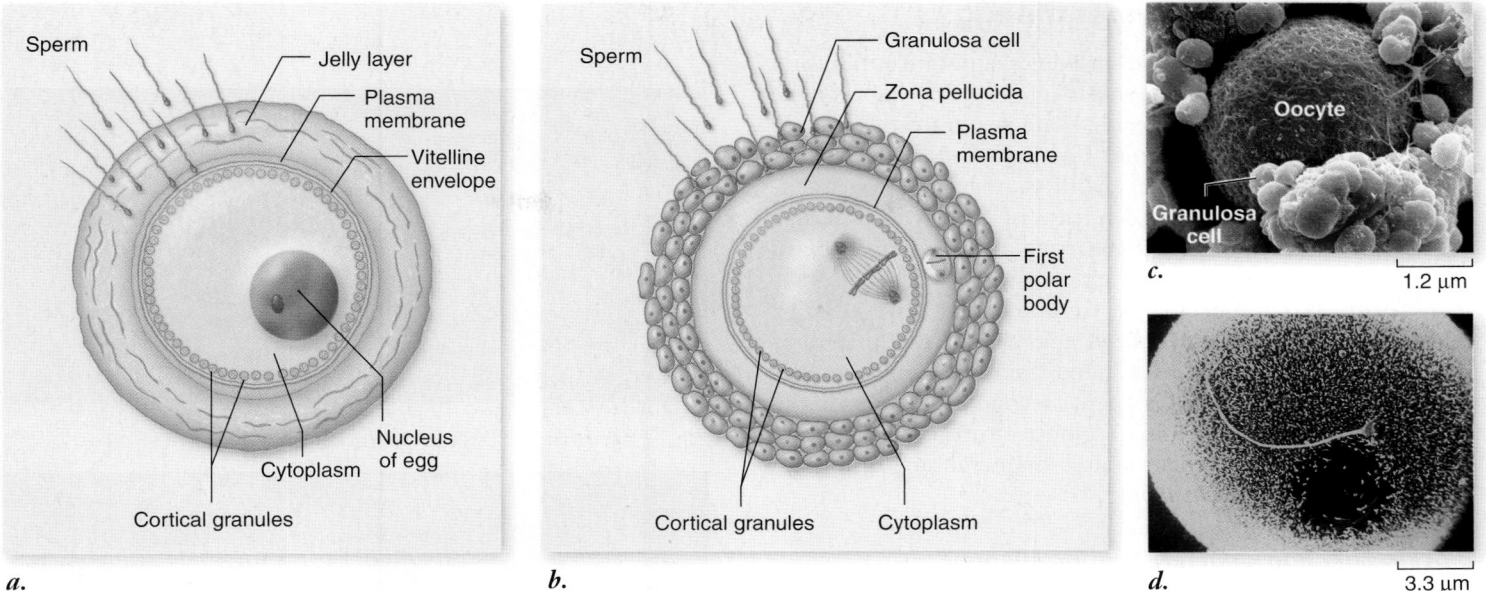

Figure 54.1 Animal reproductive cells. *a.* The structure of a sea urchin egg at fertilization. This diagram also shows the relative sizes of the sperm and egg. *b.* A mammalian sperm must penetrate a layer of granulosa cells and then a glycoprotein layer called the zona pellucida before it reaches the oocyte membrane. The scanning electron micrographs show *(c)* a human oocyte surrounded by numerous granulosa cells and *(d)* a human sperm on an egg.

1. Sperm penetrates between granulosa cells.
2. Some of the zona pellucida is degraded by acrosomal enzymes.
3. Sperm and egg plasma membranes fuse.
4. The sperm nucleus dissociates and enters cytoplasm.
6. Additional sperm can no longer penetrate the zona pellucida.
5. Cortical granules release enzymes that harden zona pellucida and strip it of sperm receptors. Hyalin attracts water by osmosis.
7. Sperm and egg pronuclei are enclosed in a nuclear envelope.
Cortical granules
Zona pellucida
Plasma membrane
Granulosa cells

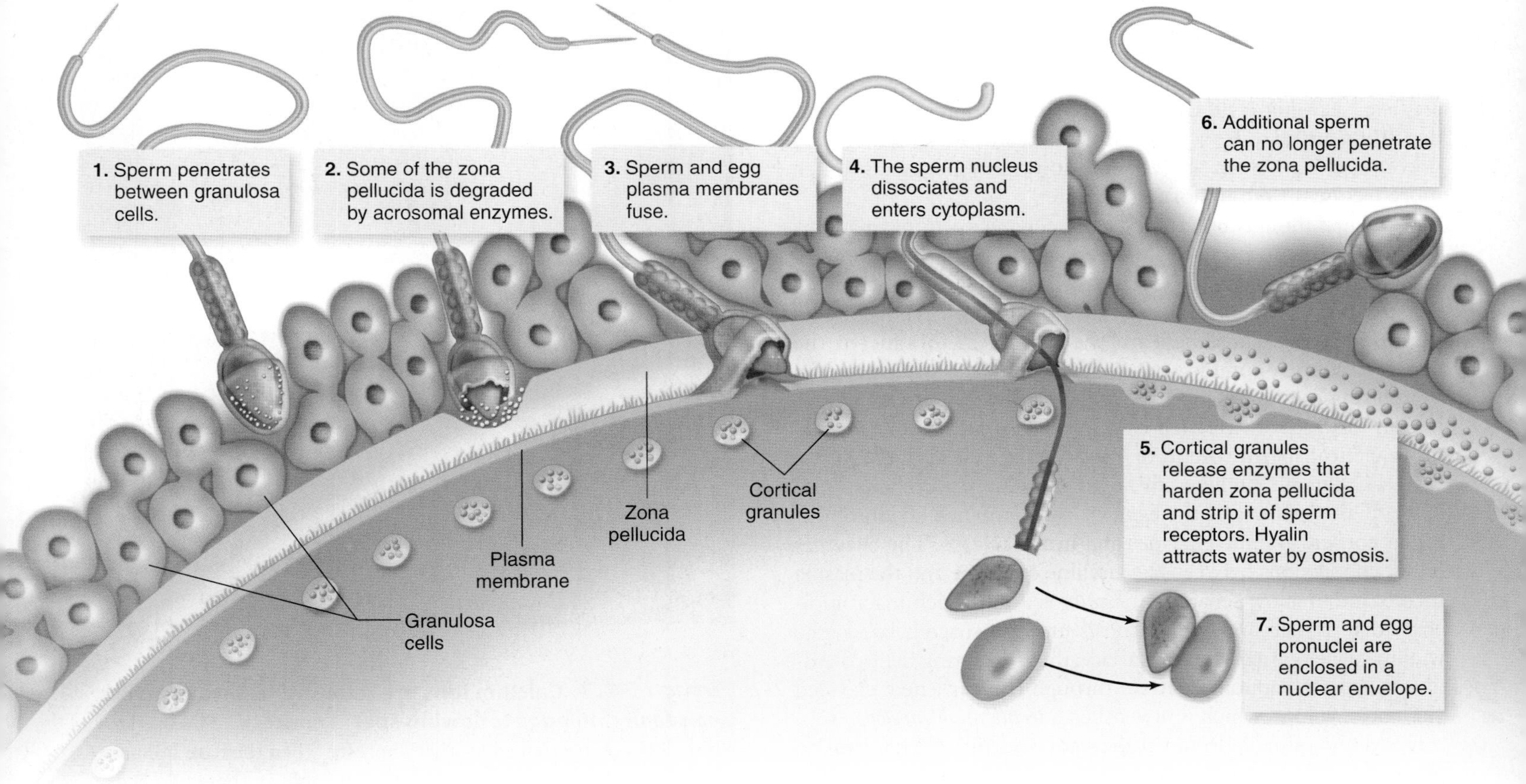

Figure 54.2 Sperm penetration and fusion. The sperm must penetrate the outer layers around the egg before fusion of sperm and egg plasma membranes can occur. Fusion activates the egg and leads to a series of events that prevent polyspermy.

Membrane fusion activates the egg

After ovulation, the egg remains in a quiescent state until fusion of the sperm and egg membranes triggers reactivation of the egg's metabolism. In most species, there is a dramatic increase in the levels of free intracellular Ca^{2+} ions in the egg shortly after the sperm makes contact with the egg's plasma membrane. This increase is due to release of Ca^{2+} from internal, membrane-bounded organelles, starting at the point of sperm entry and traversing across the egg.

Scientists have been able to watch this wave of Ca^{2+} release by preloading unfertilized eggs with a dye that fluoresces when bound to free Ca^{2+}, and then fertilizing the eggs (figure 54.3). The released Ca^{2+} act as second messengers in the cytoplasm of the egg, to initiate a host of changes in protein activity. These many events initiated by membrane fusion are collectively called *egg activation*.

Blocking of additional fertilization events

Because large numbers of sperm are released during spawning or ejaculation, many more than one sperm is likely to reach, and try to fertilize, a single egg. Multiple fertilization would result in a zygote that has three or more sets of chromosomes, a condition known as *polyploidy*. Polyploidy is incompatible with animal development, although it is frequently found in plants. As a result, an early response to sperm fusion in many animal eggs is to prevent fusion of additional sperm—in other words, to initiate a block to *polyspermy*.

In sea urchins, membrane contact by the first sperm results in a rapid, transient change in membrane potential of the egg, which prevents other sperm from fusing to the egg's plasma membrane. The importance of this event was shown by experiments where sea urchin eggs are fertilized in low-sodium, artificial seawater. The change in membrane potential is mostly due to an influx of Na^+, so fertilization in low-sodium water prevents this. Under these conditions polyspermy is much more frequent than in normal seawater.

Many animals use additional mechanisms to permanently alter the composition of the exterior egg coats, preventing any further sperm from penetrating through these layers. In sea urchins and mammals, specialized vesicles called **cortical granules,** located just beneath the plasma membrane of the egg, release their contents by exocytosis into the space between the plasma membrane and the vitelline envelope or zona pellucida, respectively. In each case, cortical granule enzymes remove critical sperm receptors from the outer coat of the egg.

Finally, the vitelline envelopes in many sea urchin species "lift off" the surfaces of the eggs via the combined action of different cortical granule enzymes and hyalin release. The enzymes digest connections between the vitelline envelope and the plasma membrane to allow separation. *Hyalin* is a sugar-rich macromolecule that attracts water by osmosis into the space between the vitelline envelope and the egg surface, thus separating the two. Additional sperm cannot penetrate through the hardened, elevated vitelline envelope, which is now called a *fertilization envelope*.

Many animals do not utilize any specific mechanisms to prevent multiple sperm from entering an egg. In these species, all but one of the sperm nuclei is degraded or subsequently extruded from the egg to prevent polyploidy.

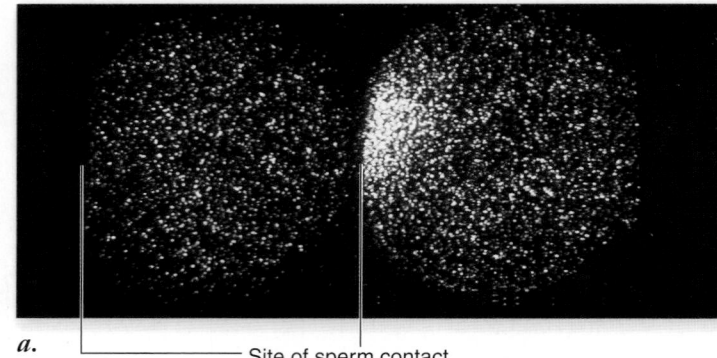

a. ————— Site of sperm contact

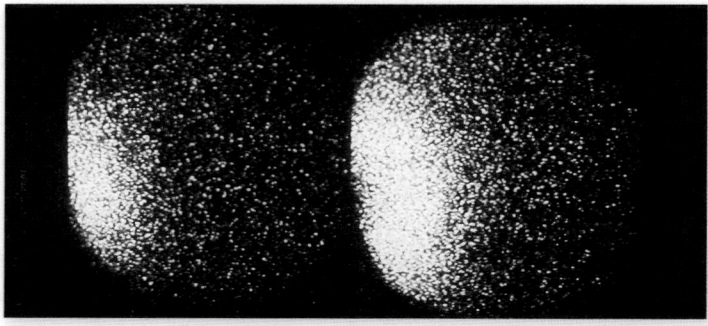

b.

c.

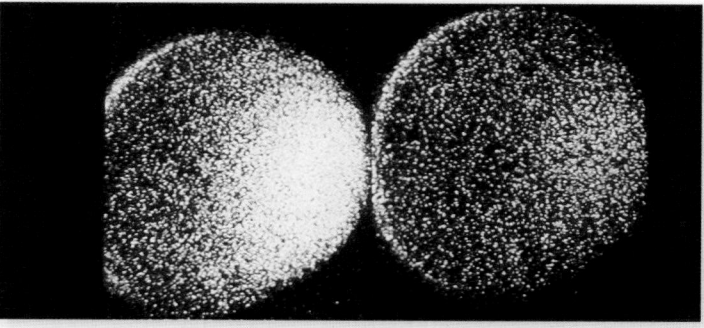

d.

Figure 54.3 Calcium ions are released in a wave across two sea urchin eggs following sperm contact. The bright white dots are dye molecules that fluoresce when they are bound to Ca^{2+}. The Ca^{2+} wave moves from left to right in these two eggs *(a–d)*. The egg on the right was fertilized a few seconds before the egg on the left. The wave takes about 30 sec to cross the entire egg.

Sperm
Jelly layer
Plasma membrane
Vitelline envelope
Nucleus of egg
Cytoplasm
Cortical granules
a.
Sperm
Granulosa cell
Zona pellucida
Plasma membrane
First polar body
Cortical granules
Cytoplasm
b.
Oocyte
Granulosa cell
c.
1.2 μm
d.
3.3 μm

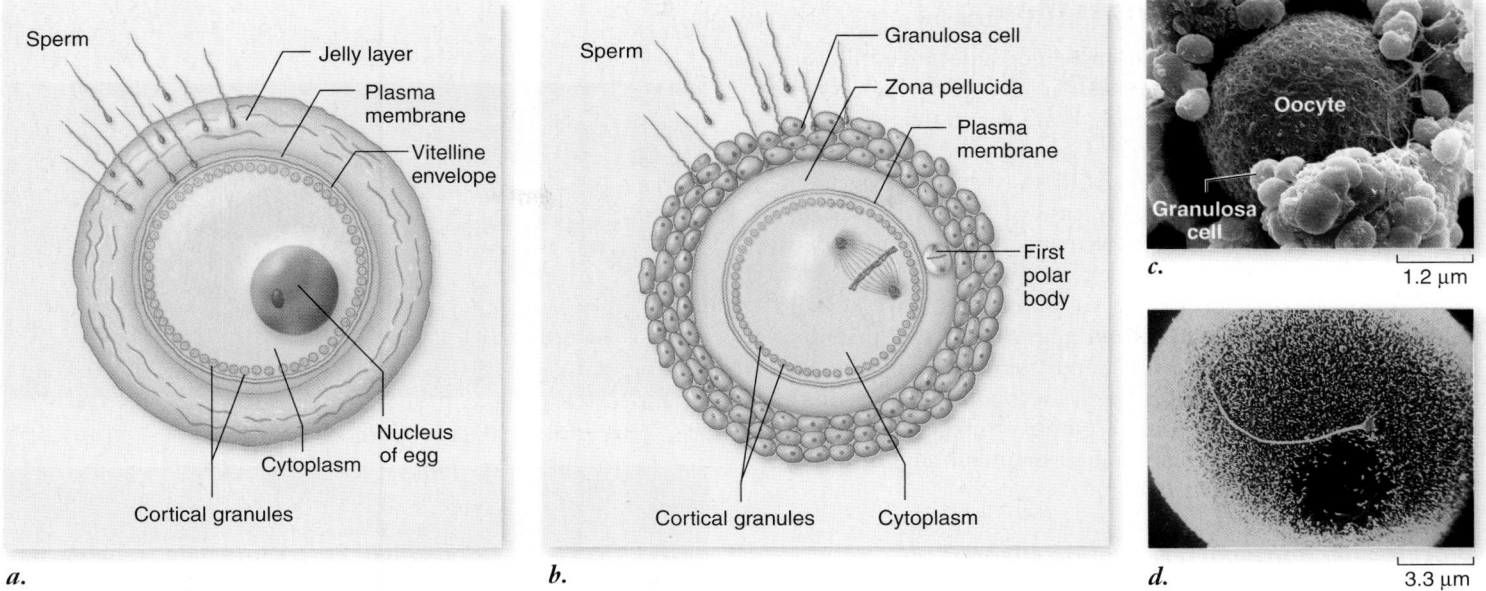

Figure 54.1 Animal reproductive cells. *a.* The structure of a sea urchin egg at fertilization. This diagram also shows the relative sizes of the sperm and egg. *b.* A mammalian sperm must penetrate a layer of granulosa cells and then a glycoprotein layer called the zona pellucida before it reaches the oocyte membrane. The scanning electron micrographs show *(c)* a human oocyte surrounded by numerous granulosa cells and *(d)* a human sperm on an egg.

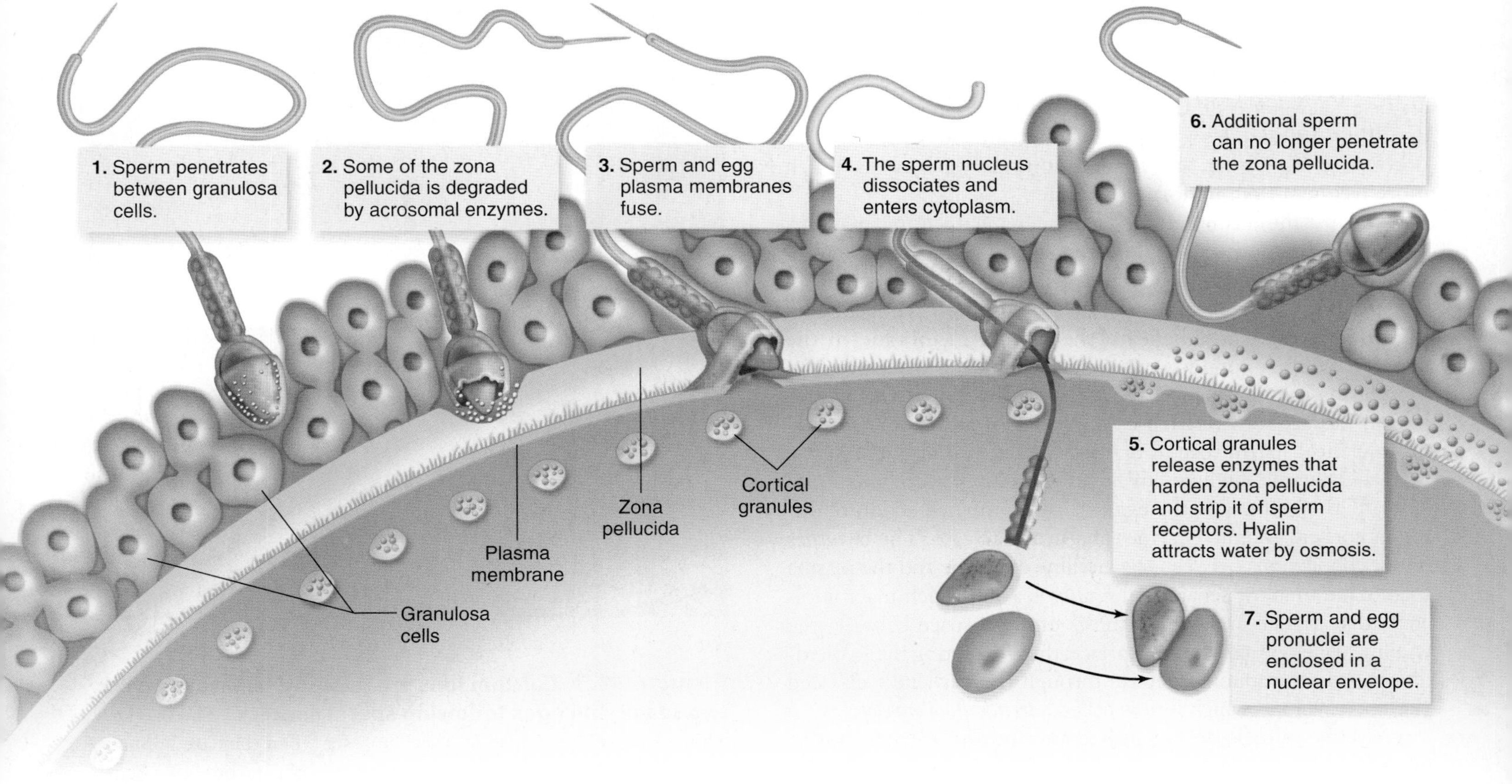

1. Sperm penetrates between granulosa cells.
2. Some of the zona pellucida is degraded by acrosomal enzymes.
3. Sperm and egg plasma membranes fuse.
4. The sperm nucleus dissociates and enters cytoplasm.
6. Additional sperm can no longer penetrate the zona pellucida.
5. Cortical granules release enzymes that harden zona pellucida and strip it of sperm receptors. Hyalin attracts water by osmosis.
Zona pellucida
Cortical granules
Plasma membrane
Granulosa cells
7. Sperm and egg pronuclei are enclosed in a nuclear envelope.

Figure 54.2 Sperm penetration and fusion. The sperm must penetrate the outer layers around the egg before fusion of sperm and egg plasma membranes can occur. Fusion activates the egg and leads to a series of events that prevent polyspermy.

Membrane fusion activates the egg

After ovulation, the egg remains in a quiescent state until fusion of the sperm and egg membranes triggers reactivation of the egg's metabolism. In most species, there is a dramatic increase in the levels of free intracellular Ca^{2+} ions in the egg shortly after the sperm makes contact with the egg's plasma membrane. This increase is due to release of Ca^{2+} from internal, membrane-bounded organelles, starting at the point of sperm entry and traversing across the egg.

Scientists have been able to watch this wave of Ca^{2+} release by preloading unfertilized eggs with a dye that fluoresces when bound to free Ca^{2+}, and then fertilizing the eggs (figure 54.3). The released Ca^{2+} act as second messengers in the cytoplasm of the egg, to initiate a host of changes in protein activity. These many events initiated by membrane fusion are collectively called *egg activation*.

Blocking of additional fertilization events

Because large numbers of sperm are released during spawning or ejaculation, many more than one sperm is likely to reach, and try to fertilize, a single egg. Multiple fertilization would result in a zygote that has three or more sets of chromosomes, a condition known as *polyploidy*. Polyploidy is incompatible with animal development, although it is frequently found in plants. As a result, an early response to sperm fusion in many animal eggs is to prevent fusion of additional sperm—in other words, to initiate a block to *polyspermy*.

In sea urchins, membrane contact by the first sperm results in a rapid, transient change in membrane potential of the egg, which prevents other sperm from fusing to the egg's plasma membrane. The importance of this event was shown by experiments where sea urchin eggs are fertilized in low-sodium, artificial seawater. The change in membrane potential is mostly due to an influx of Na^+, so fertilization in low-sodium water prevents this. Under these conditions polyspermy is much more frequent than in normal seawater.

Many animals use additional mechanisms to permanently alter the composition of the exterior egg coats, preventing any further sperm from penetrating through these layers. In sea urchins and mammals, specialized vesicles called **cortical granules,** located just beneath the plasma membrane of the egg, release their contents by exocytosis into the space between the plasma membrane and the vitelline envelope or zona pellucida, respectively. In each case, cortical granule enzymes remove critical sperm receptors from the outer coat of the egg.

Finally, the vitelline envelopes in many sea urchin species "lift off" the surfaces of the eggs via the combined action of different cortical granule enzymes and hyalin release. The enzymes digest connections between the vitelline envelope and the plasma membrane to allow separation. *Hyalin* is a sugar-rich macromolecule that attracts water by osmosis into the space between the vitelline envelope and the egg surface, thus separating the two. Additional sperm cannot penetrate through the hardened, elevated vitelline envelope, which is now called a *fertilization envelope*.

Many animals do not utilize any specific mechanisms to prevent multiple sperm from entering an egg. In these species, all but one of the sperm nuclei is degraded or subsequently extruded from the egg to prevent polyploidy.

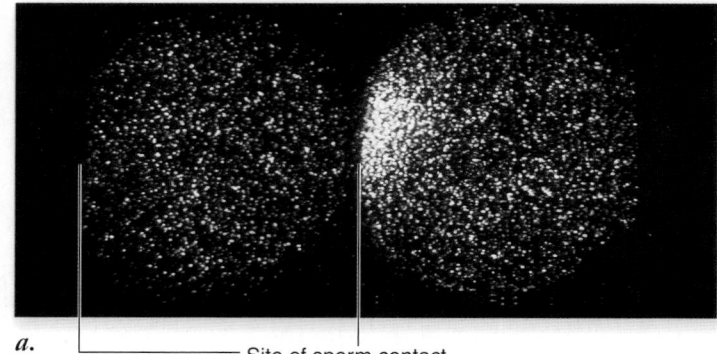

a. — Site of sperm contact

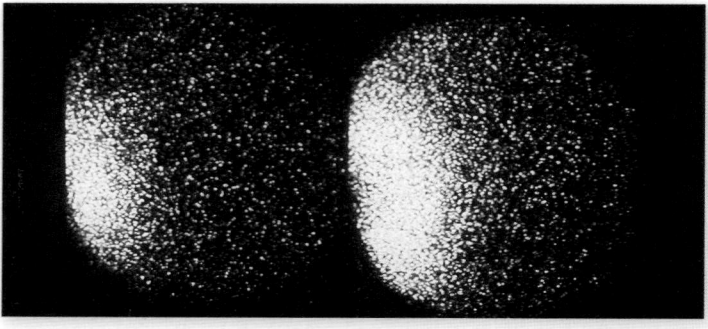

b.

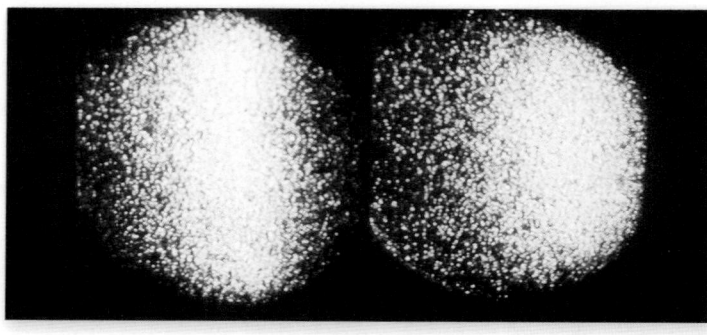

c.

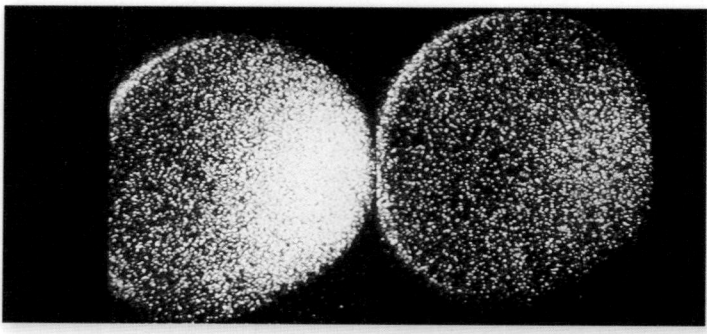

d.

Figure 54.3 **Calcium ions are released in a wave across two sea urchin eggs following sperm contact.** The bright white dots are dye molecules that fluoresce when they are bound to Ca^{2+}. The Ca^{2+} wave moves from left to right in these two eggs *(a–d)*. The egg on the right was fertilized a few seconds before the egg on the left. The wave takes about 30 sec to cross the entire egg.

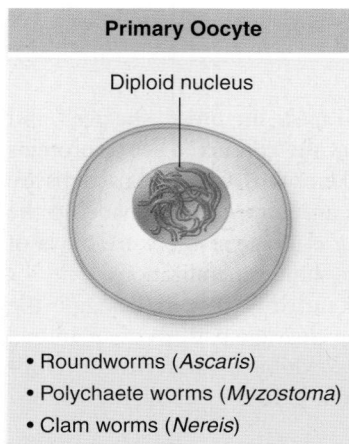

Primary Oocyte	First Metaphase of Meiosis	Second Metaphase of Meiosis	Meiosis Complete
Diploid nucleus		Polar body	Polar bodies / Female pronucleus (haploid)
• Roundworms (*Ascaris*) • Polychaete worms (*Myzostoma*) • Clam worms (*Nereis*) • Clams (*Spisula*)	• Nemertean worms (*Cerebratulus*) • Polychaete worms (*Chaetopterus*) • Mollusks (*Dentalium*) • Many insects • Sea stars	• Lancelets (*Branchiostoma*) • Amphibians • Mammals • Fish	• Cnidarians • Sea urchins

Figure 54.4 Stage of egg maturation at time of sperm binding in representative animals.

Other effects of sperm penetration

In addition to the previously mentioned surface changes, sperm penetration can have three other effects on the egg. First, in many animals, the nucleus of the unfertilized egg is not yet haploid because it had not entered or completed meiosis prior to ovulation (figure 54.4). Fusion of the sperm plasma membrane then triggers the eggs of these animals to complete meiosis. In mammals, a single large egg with a haploid nucleus and one or more small polar bodies, which contain the other nuclei, are produced (see chapter 53).

Second, sperm penetration in many animals triggers movements of the egg cytoplasm. In chapter 19, we discussed the cytoplasmic rearrangements of newly fertilized tunicate eggs, which result in the asymmetrical localization of pigment granules that determine muscle development. In amphibian embryos, the point of sperm entry is the focal point of cytoplasmic movements in the egg, and these movements ultimately establish the bilateral symmetry of the developing animal.

In some frogs, for example, sperm penetration causes an outer pigmented cap of egg cytoplasm to rotate toward the point of entry, uncovering a gray crescent of interior cytoplasm opposite the point of penetration (figure 54.5). The position of this gray crescent determines the orientation of the first cell division.

A line drawn between the point of sperm entry and the gray crescent would bisect the right and left halves of the future adult.

Third, activation is characterized by a sharp increase in protein synthesis and an increase in metabolic activity in general. Experiments demonstrate that the burst of protein synthesis in an activated egg uses mRNAs that were deposited into the cytoplasm of the egg during oogenesis.

In some animals, it is possible to artificially activate an egg without the entry of a sperm, simply by pricking the egg membrane. An egg that is activated in this way may go on to develop parthenogenetically. A few kinds of amphibians, fish, and reptiles rely entirely on parthenogenetic reproduction in nature, as we mentioned in chapter 53.

The fusion of nuclei restores the diploid state

In the third and final stage of fertilization, the haploid sperm nucleus fuses with the haploid egg nucleus to form the diploid nucleus of the zygote. The process involves migration of the two nuclei toward each other along a microtubule-based aster. A centriole that enters the egg cell with the sperm nucleus organizes the microtubule array, which is made from stored tubulin proteins in the egg's cytoplasm.

In mammals, including humans, the nuclei do not actually fuse. Instead sperm and egg nuclear membranes each break down prior to the formation of a new diploid nucleus. A new nuclear membrane forms around the two sets of chromosomes.

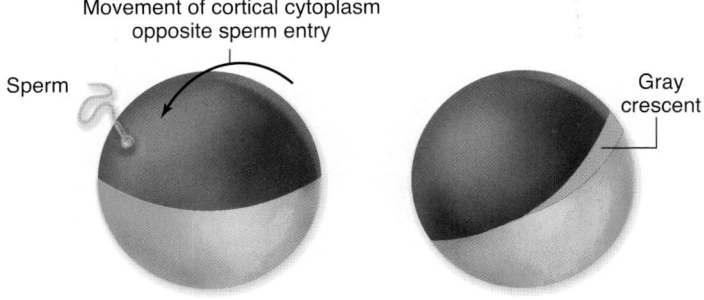

Figure 54.5 Gray crescent formation in frog eggs.
The gray crescent forms on the side of the egg opposite the point of penetration by the sperm.

> ### Learning Outcomes Review 54.1
>
> Following penetration, fusion of sperm with the egg membrane initiates a series of events including egg activation, blocks to polyspermy, and major rearrangements of cytoplasm. Polyspermy is blocked by changes in membrane polarity, release of enzymes that remove sperm receptors, and release of hyalin that lifts the vitelline envelope from the cell membrane. Egg and sperm nuclei then fuse to create a diploid zygote.
>
> ■ *What is the role of Ca²⁺ in egg activation?*

Cleavage and the Blastula Stage

Learning Outcomes

1. *Define the terms cleavage and blastula.*
2. *Describe the different patterns of cleavage.*
3. *Explain what is meant by regulative development.*

Following fertilization, the second major event in animal development is the rapid division of the zygote into a larger and larger number of smaller and smaller cells (see table 54.1). This period of division, called *cleavage*, is not accompanied by an increase in the overall size of the embryo. Each individual cell in the resulting tightly packed mass of cells is referred to as a *blastomere*. In many animals, the two ends of the egg and subsequent embryo are traditionally referred to as the **animal pole** and the **vegetal pole.** In general, the blastomeres of the animal pole go on to form the external tissues of the body, and those of the vegetal pole form the internal tissues.

The blastula is a hollow mass of cells

In many animal embryos, the outermost blastomeres in the ball of cells produced during cleavage become joined to one another by tight junctions, belts of protein that encircle a cell and weld it to its neighbors (see chapter 4). These tight junctions create a seal that isolates the interior of the cell mass from the surrounding medium.

Subsequently, cells in the interior of the mass begin to pump Na$^+$ from their cytoplasm into the spaces between cells. The resulting osmotic gradient causes water to be drawn into the center of the embryo, enlarging the intercellular spaces. Eventually, the spaces coalesce to form a single large cavity within the embryo. The resulting hollow ball of cells is called a *blastula* (or *blastocyst* in mammals), and the fluid-filled cavity within the blastula is known as the **blastocoel** (see table 54.1).

Cleavage patterns are highly diverse and distinctive

Cleavage divisions are quite rapid in most species, and chapter 19 provides an overview of the conserved set of proteins that control the cell cycle in animal embryos. Cleavage patterns are quite diverse, and there are about as many ways to divide up the cytoplasm of an animal egg during cleavage as there are phyla of animals! Nonetheless, we can make some generalizations.

First, the relative amount of nutritive yolk in the egg is the characteristic that most affects the cleavage pattern of an animal embryo (figure 54.6). Vertebrates exhibit a variety of developmental strategies involving different patterns of yolk utilization.

Cleavage in insects

Insects have yolk-rich eggs, and in chapter 19 we discussed the *syncytial blastoderm* of insects, in which multiple mitotic divisions of the nucleus occur in the absence of cytokinesis. Because there are no membranes separating the early embryonic nuclei of insects, gradients of diffusible proteins termed *morphogens* within the egg's cytoplasm can directly and differentially affect the activity of these embryonic nuclei, and thus the pattern of the early embryo. The nuclei eventually migrate to the periphery of the egg, where cell membranes form around each nucleus. The resulting *cellular blastoderm* of an insect has a single layer of cells surrounding a central mass of yolk (see figure 19.12 and table 54.2).

Cleavage of eggs with moderate or little yolk

In eggs that contain moderate to little yolk, cleavage occurs throughout the whole egg, a pattern called **holoblastic cleavage** (figure 54.7). This pattern of cleavage is characteristic of invertebrates such as mollusks, annelids, echinoderms, and tunicates, and also of amphibians and mammals (described shortly).

In sea urchins, holoblastic cleavage results in the formation of a symmetrical blastula composed of a single layer of cells of approximately equal size surrounding a spherical blastocoel. In contrast, amphibian eggs contain much more cytoplasmic yolk in the vegetal hemisphere than in the animal hemisphere. Because yolk-rich regions divide much more

Sea Urchin	Frog	Chicken
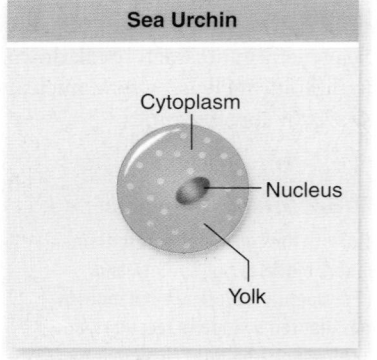	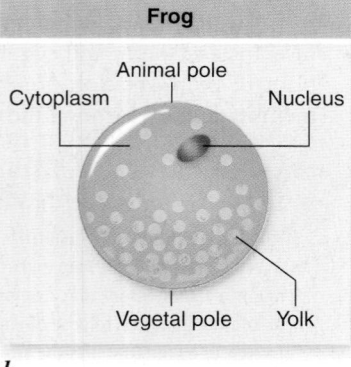	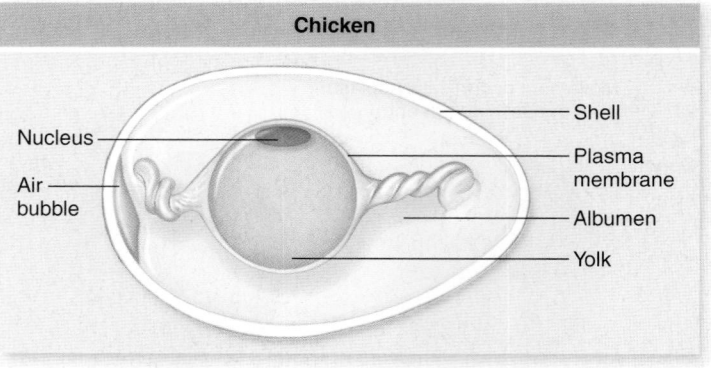

Figure 54.6 Yolk distribution in three kinds of eggs. *a.* In a sea urchin egg, the cytoplasm contains a small amount of evenly distributed yolk and a centrally located nucleus. *b.* In a frog egg, there is much more yolk, and the nucleus is displaced toward one pole. *c.* Bird eggs are complex, with the nucleus contained in a small disc of cytoplasm that sits on top of a large, central yolk mass.

TABLE 54.2	The Major Cleavage Patterns of Animal Embryos			
HOLOBLASTIC (COMPLETE) CLEAVAGE				
Isolecithal (Sparse, evenly distributed yolk)				
Radial cleavage Echinoderms				
Spiral cleavage Annelids Mollusks Flatworms				
Rotational cleavage Mammals Nematodes				
Mesolecithal (Moderate vegetal yolk disposition)				
Displaced radial cleavage Amphibians				
MEROBLASTIC (INCOMPLETE) CLEAVAGE				
Telolecithal (Dense yolk throughout most of cell)				
Discoidal cleavage Fish Reptiles Birds				
Centrolecithal (Yolk in center of egg)				
Syncytial cleavage Most insects				

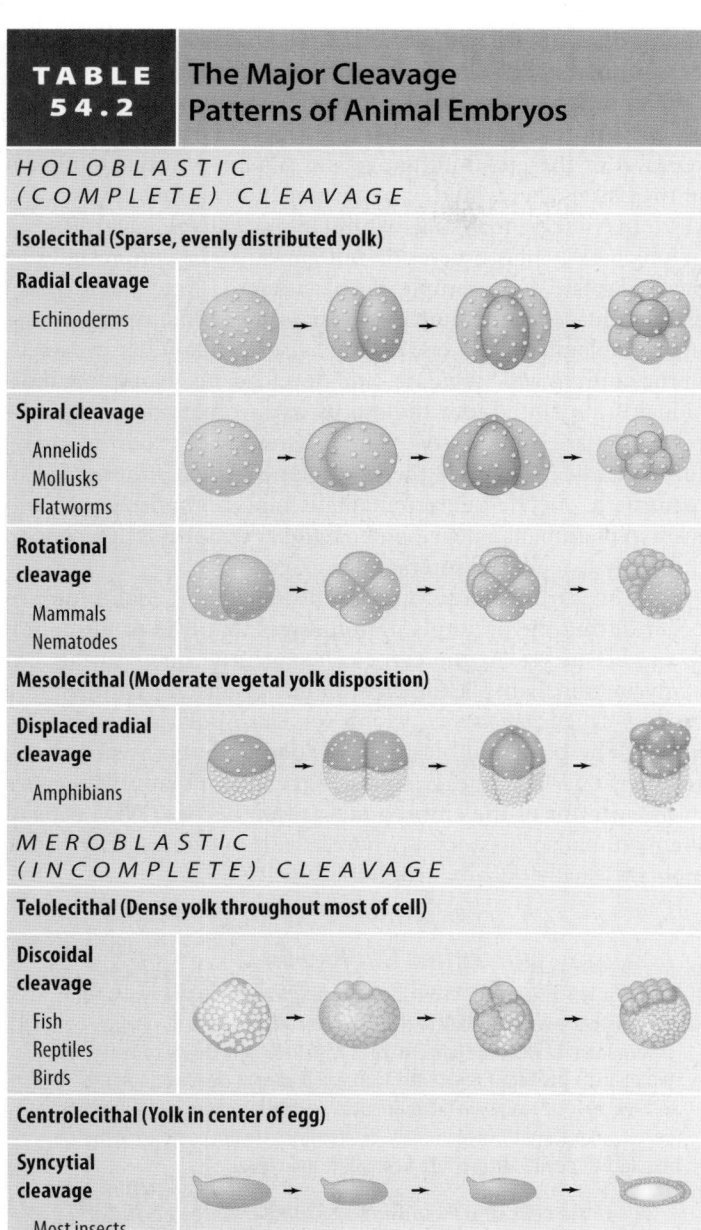

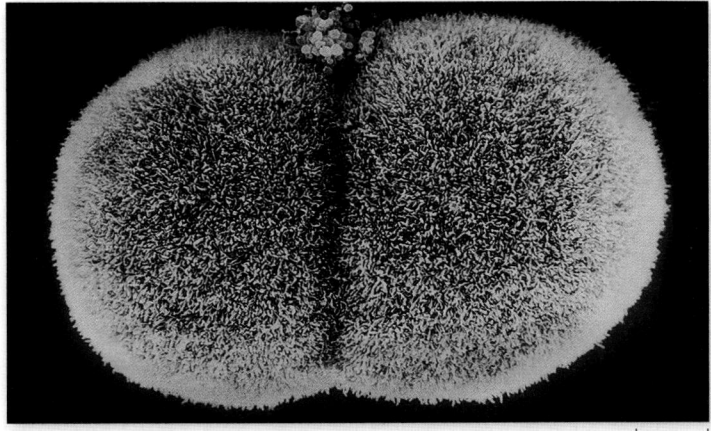

Figure 54.7 Holoblastic cleavage. In this type of cleavage, which is characteristic of eggs with relatively small amounts of yolk, cell division occurs throughout the entire egg.

3.3 μm

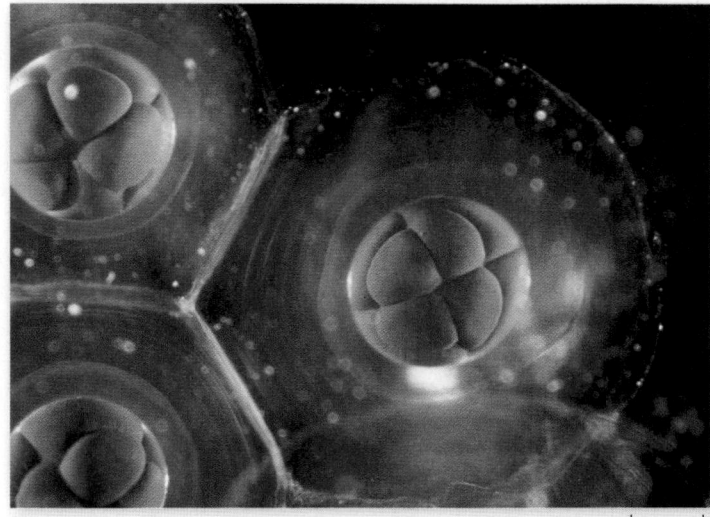

a.

333.3 μm

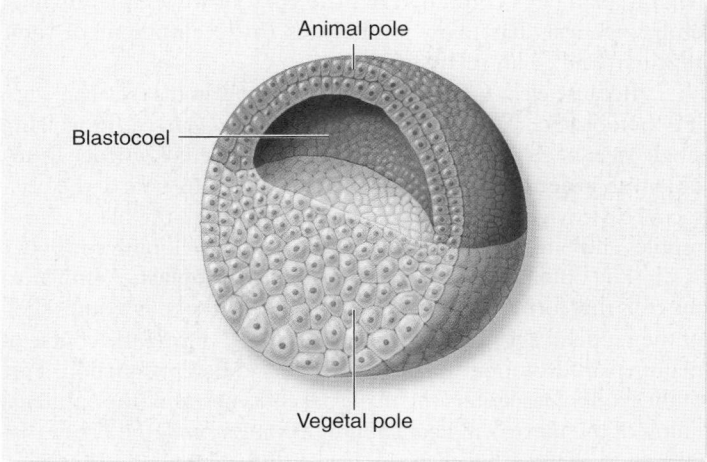

b.

Figure 54.8 Frog cleavage and blastula formation.
a. The closest cells in this photo (those near the animal pole) divide faster and are smaller than those near the vegetal pole (below cells of the animal pole). *b.* A cross-section of a frog blastula, showing an eccentric blastocoel, larger yolk-filled cells at the vegetal pole, and smaller cells with little yolk at the animal pole.

slowly than areas with little yolk, horizontal cleavage furrows are displaced toward the animal pole (figure 54.8*a*). Thus, holoblastic cleavage in frog eggs results in an asymmetrical blastula, with a displaced blastocoel. The blastula consists of large cells containing a lot of yolk at the vegetal pole, and smaller, more numerous cells containing little yolk at the animal pole (figure 54.8*b*).

Cleavage of eggs with large amounts of yolk

The eggs of reptiles, birds, and some fishes are composed almost entirely of yolk, with a small amount of clear cytoplasm concentrated at one pole called the **blastodisc**. Cleavage in these eggs is restricted to the blastodisc. The yolk is essentially an inert mass. This type of cleavage pattern is called **meroblastic**

Figure 54.9 **Meroblastic cleavage.** Only a portion of the egg actively divides to form a mass of cells in this type of cleavage, which occurs in eggs with relatively large amounts of yolk.

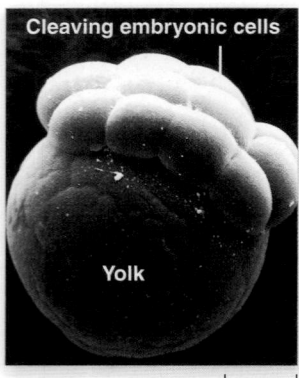

Cleaving embryonic cells

Yolk

25 μm

cleavage (figure 54.9). The resulting embryo is not spherical, but rather has the form of a thin cap perched on the yolk.

Cleavage in mammals

Mammalian eggs contain very little yolk; however, mammalian embryogenesis has many similarities to development of their reptilian and avian relatives.

Because cleavage is not impeded by yolk in mammalian eggs, it is holoblastic, forming a structure called a *blastocyst*, in which a single layer of cells surrounds a central fluid-filled blastocoel. In addition, an **inner cell mass (ICM)** is located at one pole of the blastocoel cavity (figure 54.10). The ICM is similar to the blastodisc of reptiles and birds, and it goes on to form the developing embryo.

The outer layer of cells, called the **trophoblast,** is similar to the cells that form the membranes underlying the tough outer shell of the reptilian egg. These cells have changed during the course of mammalian evolution to carry out a very different function: Part of the trophoblast enters the maternal endometrium (the epithelial lining of the uterus) and contributes to the *placenta*, the organ that permits exchanges between the fetal and maternal blood supplies. The placenta will be discussed in more detail in a later section.

The major cleavage patterns of animal embryos are summarized in table 54.2.

Blastomeres may or may not be committed to developmental paths

Viewed from the outside, cleavage-stage embryos often look like a simple ball or disc of similar cells. In many animals, this

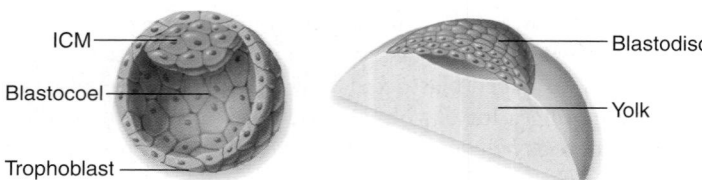

ICM

Blastocoel

Trophoblast

Blastodisc

Yolk

Figure 54.10 **The embryos of mammals and birds are more similar than they seem.** A mammalian blastula *(left)*, called a blastocyst, is composed of a sphere of cells, the trophoblast, surrounding a cavity, the blastocoel, and an inner cell mass (ICM). An avian (bird) blastula consists of a cap of cells, the blastodisc, resting atop a large yolk mass *(right)*. The blastodisc will form an upper and a lower layer with a compressed blastocoel in between.

appearance is misleading; for example, the unequal segregation of cytoplasmic determinants into specific blastomeres of tunicate embryos (described in chapter 19) commits those cells to different developmental paths. The experimental destruction or removal of these committed cells results in embryos deficient in the tissues that would have developed from those cells.

In contrast, mammals exhibit highly *regulative development*, in which early blastomeres do not appear to be committed to a particular fate. For example, if a blastomere is removed from an early eight-cell stage human embryo (as is done in the process of preimplantation genetic diagnosis), the remaining seven cells of the embryo will "regulate" and develop into a complete individual if implanted into the uterus of a woman. Similarly, embryos that are split into two (either naturally or experimentally) form identical twins. It therefore appears that inheritance of maternally encoded determinants is not an important mechanism in mammalian development, and body form is determined primarily by cell–cell interactions.

The earliest patterning events in mammalian embryos occur during the preimplantation stages that lead to formation of the blastocyst. At the eight-cell stage, the outer surfaces of many mammalian blastomeres flatten against each other in a process called *compaction*, which serves to polarize the blastomeres. The polarized blastomeres then undergo asymmetrical cell divisions. Cell lineage studies have shown that cells that are in the interior of the embryo most often become ICM cells of the mammalian blastocyst, whereas cells on the exterior of the embryo usually become trophoblast cells.

Learning Outcomes Review 54.2

Cleavage is a series of rapid cell divisions that transforms the zygote into the blastula—a hollow ball of cells. The amount of yolk is the major determinant of cleavage pattern. Eggs with little yolk cleave completely (holoblastic cleavage); eggs with a large yolk cannot cleave completely (meroblastic cleavage). In many animals, each blastomere is committed to a developmental path; in mammals, blastomeres are not committed but can regulate as needed to produce a complete individual.

■ *If the cells of a mammalian embryo were separated at the four-cell stage, would they develop normally? What about a frog embryo at the four-cell stage?*

54.3 Gastrulation

Learning Outcomes

1. *Define gastrulation.*
2. *Compare gastrulation in different animals.*
3. *Name the extraembryonic membranes in amniotes.*

In a complex series of cell shape changes and cell movements, the cells of the blastula rearrange themselves to form the basic body plan of the embryo. This process, called *gastrulation*, forms the three primary germ layers and converts the blastula

TABLE 54.3	Developmental Fates of the Primary Germ Layers in Vertebrates
Ectoderm	Epidermis of skin, nervous system, sense organs
Mesoderm	Skeleton, muscles, blood vessels, heart, blood, gonads, kidneys, dermis of skin
Endoderm	Lining of digestive and respiratory tracts, liver, pancreas, thymus, thyroid

into a bilaterally symmetrical embryo with a central progenitor gut and visible anterior–posterior and dorsal–ventral axes.

Gastrulation produces the three germ layers

Gastrulation creates the three primary *germ layers:* endoderm, ectoderm, and mesoderm. The cells in each germ layer have very different developmental fates. The cells that move into the embryo to form the tube of the primitive gut are *endoderm;* they give rise to the lining of the gut and its derivatives (pancreas, lungs, liver, etc.). The cells that remain on the exterior are *ectoderm,* and their derivatives include the epidermis on the outside of the body and the nervous system. The cells that move into the space between the endoderm and ectoderm are *mesoderm;* they eventually form the notochord, bones, blood vessels, connective tissues, muscles and internal organs such as the kidneys and gonads (table 54.3).

Cells move during gastrulation using a variety of cell shape changes. Some cells use broad, actin-filled extensions called *lamellipodia* to crawl over neighboring cells. Other cells send out narrow extensions called *filopodia,* which are used to "feel out" the surfaces of other cells or the extracellular matrix. Once a satisfactory attachment is made, the filopodia retract to pull the cell forward. Contractions of actin filament bundles are responsible for many of these cell shape changes. Cells that are

tightly attached to one another via desmosomes or adherens junctions will move as cell sheets.

In embryos with little yolk and a hollow blastula, the cell sheet at the vegetal pole of the blastula **invaginates** (dents inward) to form the primitive gut tube. In embryos with large yolky cells that are hard to move, sheets of smaller cells **involute** (roll inward) from the surface of the blastula and move over the basal surfaces of the outer cells. Other cells break away from cell sheets and migrate as individual cells during **ingression.**

Avian and mammalian gastrulation begins with **delamination,** in which one sheet of cells splits into two sheets. Each migrating cell possesses particular cell-surface glycoproteins, which adhere to specific molecules on the surfaces of other cells or in the extracellular matrix. Changes in cell adhesiveness, as described in chapter 19, are key events in gastrulation. The extracellular matrix protein fibronectin and the corresponding integrin receptors of cells are essential molecules of gastrulation in many animals.

Gastrulation patterns also vary according to the amount of yolk

Just as in cleavage patterns, yolk quantity also affects the types of cell movements that occur during gastrulation. Here, we examine gastrulation in four representative classes of embryos with differing quantities of yolk.

Gastrulation in sea urchins

Echinoderms such as sea urchins develop from relatively yolk-poor eggs and form hollow, symmetrical blastulas. Gastrulation begins when cells at the vegetal surface of the blastula change their shape to form a flattened **vegetal plate.** In an example of ingression, a subset of cells in the vegetal plate breaks away from the blastula wall and moves into the blastocoel cavity. These **primary mesenchyme cells** are future mesoderm cells, and they use *filopodia* to migrate through the blastocoel cavity (figure 54.11).

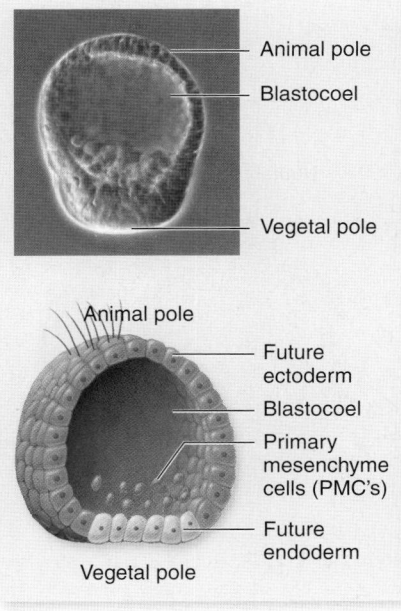

Animal pole
Blastocoel
Vegetal pole

Animal pole
Future ectoderm
Blastocoel
Primary mesenchyme cells (PMC's)
Future endoderm
Vegetal pole

a.

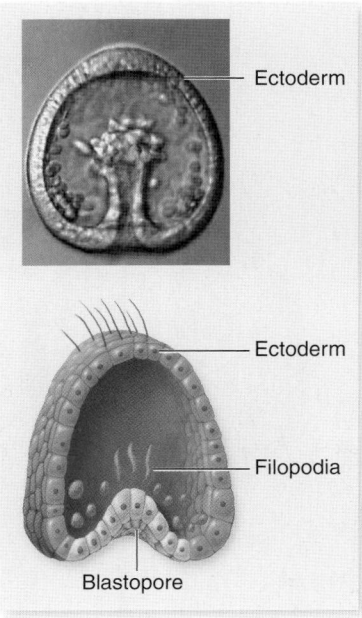

Ectoderm

Ectoderm
Filopodia
Blastopore

b.

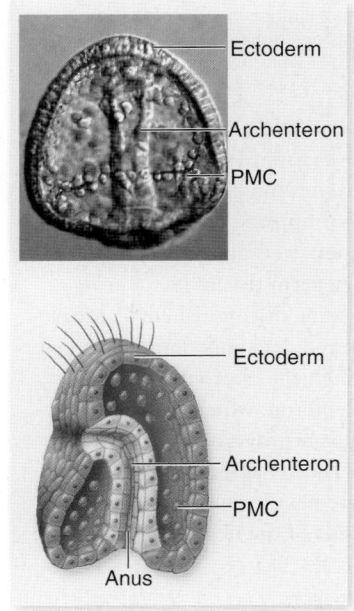

Ectoderm
Archenteron
PMC

Ectoderm
Archenteron
PMC
Anus

c.

Figure 54.11 Gastrulation in a sea urchin. *a.* Gastrulation begins with formation of the vegetal plate and ingression of primary mesenchyme cells (prospective mesoderm cells) into the blastocoel cavity. *b.* The endoderm is then formed by invagination of the remaining vegetal plate cells and extension of a cellular tube to produce the primitive gut, or archenteron. *c.* Cells that remain on the surface form the ectoderm.

Eventually, they become localized in the ventrolateral corners of the blastocoel, where they form the larval skeleton.

The remaining cells of the vegetal plate then invaginate into the blastocoel to form the endoderm layer, creating a structure that looks something like an indented tennis ball. Eventually, the inward-moving tube of cells contacts the opposite side of the gastrula and stops moving. The hollow structure resulting from the invagination is called the *archenteron*, and it is the progenitor of the digestive tube. The opening of the archenteron, the future anus, is known as the *blastopore*. A secondary opening develops at the point where the archenteron contacts the opposite side of the gastrula, forming the mouth (see figure 54.11). Animals in which the anus develops first and the mouth second are termed *deuterostomes*, as was discussed in chapter 32.

Gastrulation in frogs

The blastula of an amphibian has an asymmetrical yolk distribution, and the yolk-laden cells of the vegetal pole are less numerous but much larger than the yolk-free cells of the animal pole. Consequently, gastrulation is more complex than it is in sea urchins. In frogs, a layer of surface cells first invaginates to form a small, crescent-shaped slit, which initiates formation of the blastopore. Next, cells from the animal pole involute over the dorsal lip of the blastopore (see figure 54.12a), which forms at the same location as the gray crescent of the fertilized egg (see figure 54.5).

The involuting cell layer eventually presses against the inner surface of the opposite side of the embryo, eliminating the blastocoel and producing an archenteron with a blastopore. In this case, however, the blastopore is filled with yolk-rich cells, forming the **yolk plug** (figure 54.12b, c). The outer layer of cells resulting from these movements is the ectoderm, and the inner layer is the endoderm. Other cells that involute over the dorsal lip and ventral lip (the two lips of the blastopore that are separated by the yolk plug) migrate between the ectoderm and endoderm to form the third germ layer—the mesoderm (figure 54.12c–e).

Gastrulation in birds

At the end of cleavage in a bird or reptile, the developing embryo is a small cap of cells called the **blastoderm,** which sits on top of the large ball of yolk (figure 54.13a). As a result, gastrulation proceeds somewhat differently.

In birds, the blastoderm first separates into two layers, and a blastocoel cavity forms between them (figure 54.13b).

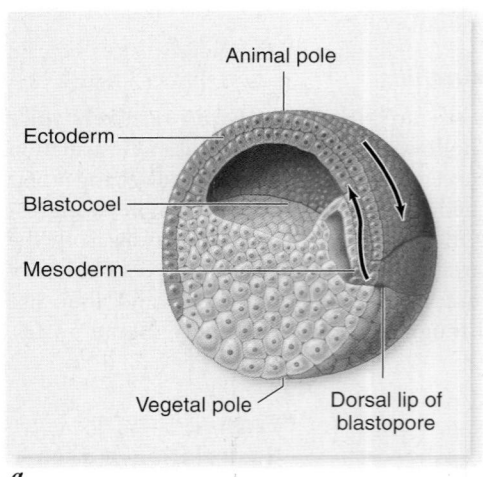

a.

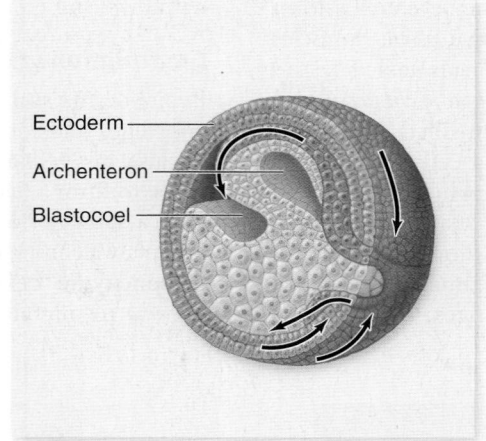

b.

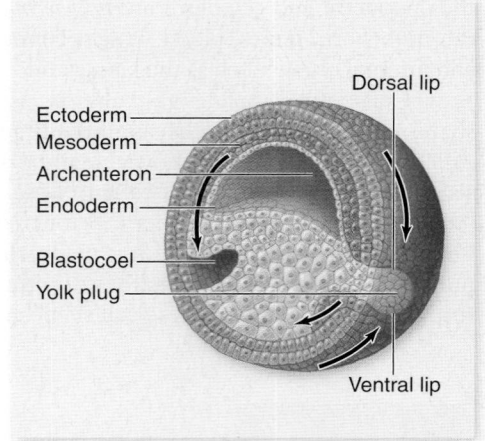

c.

Figure 54.12 Frog gastrulation. *a.* A layer of cells from the animal pole moves toward the vegetal pole, ultimately involuting through the dorsal lip of the blastopore. *b.* Cells in the dorsal lip zone then involute into the hollow interior, or blastocoel, eventually pressing against the far wall. The three primary germ tissues (ectoderm, mesoderm, and endoderm) become distinguished. Ectoderm is shown in blue, mesoderm in red, and endoderm in yellow. *c.* The movement of cells through the blastopore creates a new internal cavity, the archenteron, which displaces the blastocoel. *d.* Organogenesis begins when the neural plate forms from dorsal ectoderm to begin the process of neurulation. *e.* The neural plate next forms a neural groove and then a neural tube. The cells of the neural ectoderm are shown in purple.

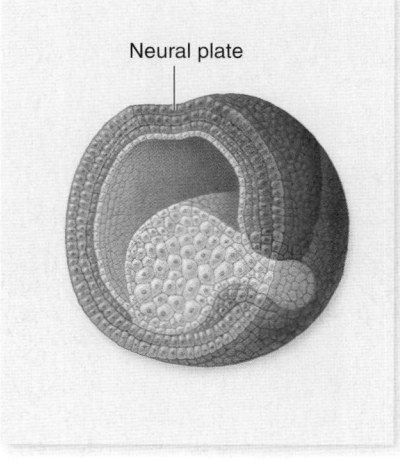

d.

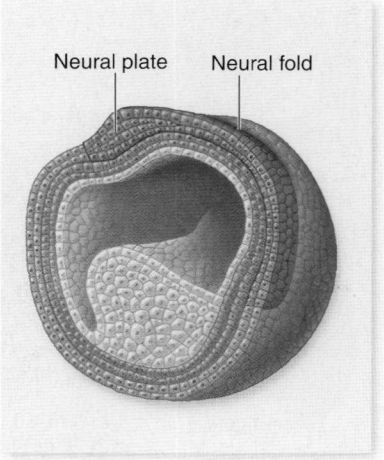

e.

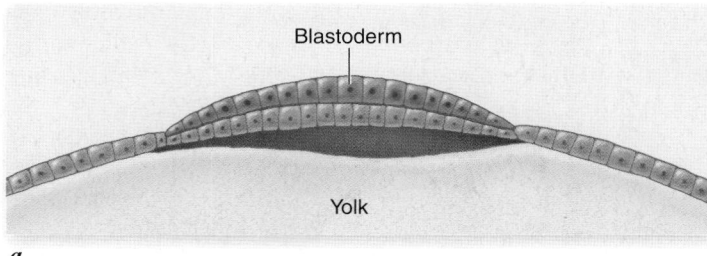

a.

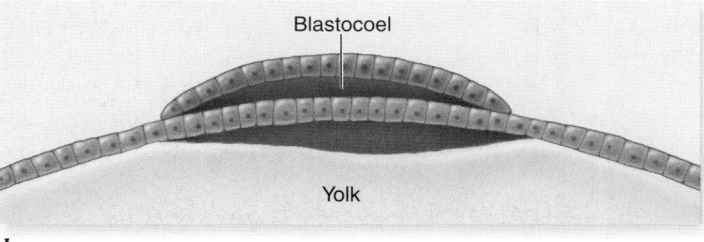

b.

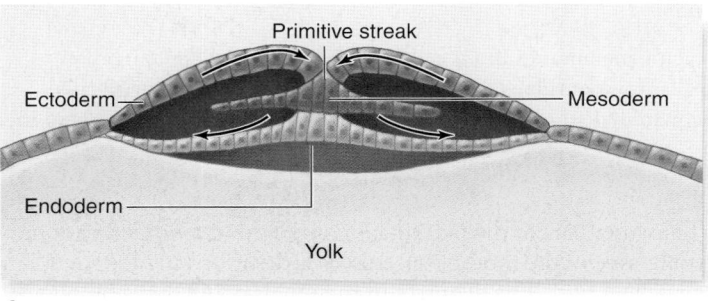

c.

Figure 54.13 Gastrulation in birds. *a.* The avian blastula is made up of a disc of cells sitting atop the large yolk mass. *b.* Gastrulation commences with the delamination of the blastoderm into two layers. All three germ layers are derived from the upper layer of the blastoderm. *c.* Cells that migrate through the primitive streak into the interior of the embryo are future endoderm or mesoderm cells. Cells that remain in the upper layer form the ectoderm.

The deep, internal layer of the bilayered blastoderm gives rise to extraembryonic tissues only (described later on), whereas all cells of the embryo proper are derived from the upper layer of cells. Thus, the upper layer of the blastoderm gives rise to all three germ layers.

Some of the surface cells begin moving to the midline, where they break away from the surface sheet of cells and ingress into the blastocoel cavity. A furrow along the longitudinal midline marks the site of this ingression (figure 54.13*c*). This furrow, analogous to an elongated blastopore, is called the **primitive streak.** Some cells migrate through the primitive streak and across the blastocoel cavity to displace cells in the lower layer. These deep-migrating cells form the endoderm. Other cells that move through the primitive streak migrate laterally into intermediate regions and form a new layer—the mesoderm. Cells that remain on the surface and do not enter the primitive streak form the ectoderm.

Gastrulation in mammals

Mammalian gastrulation proceeds much the same as it does in birds. In both types of animals, the embryo develops from a flattened collection of cells—the blastoderm in birds or the inner cell mass in mammals. Although the blastoderm of a bird is flattened because it is pressed against a mass of yolk, the inner cell mass of a mammal is flat despite the absence of a yolk mass.

In mammals, the placenta has made yolk dispensable; the embryo obtains nutrients from its mother following implantation into the uterine wall. However, the embryo still gastrulates as though it were sitting on top of a ball of yolk.

In mammals, a primitive streak forms, and cell movements through the primitive streak give rise to the three primary germ layers, much the same as in birds (figure 54.14). Similarly, mammalian embryos envelop their "missing" yolk by forming a yolk sac from extraembryonic cells that migrate away from the lower layer of the blastoderm and line the blastocoel cavity.

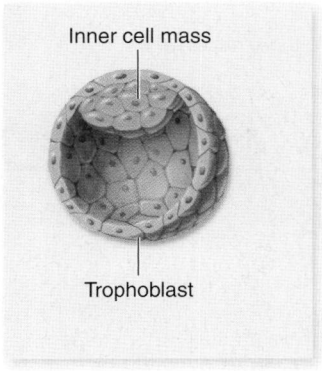

a.

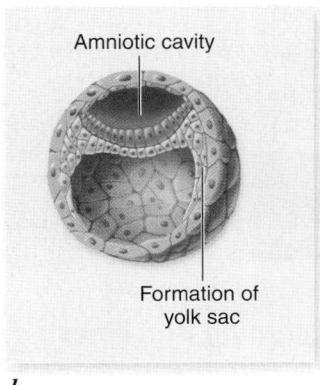

b.

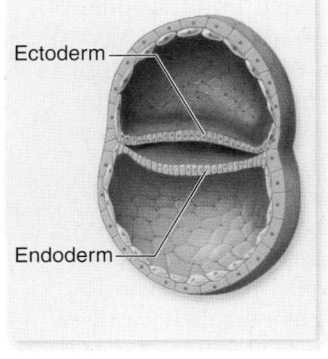

c.

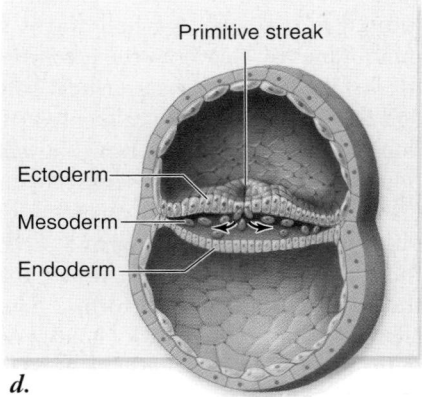

d.

Figure 54.14 Mammalian gastrulation. *a.* Cross section of the mammalian blastocyst at the end of cleavage. *b.* The amniotic cavity forms between the inner cell mass (ICM) and the pole of the embryo. Meanwhile, the ICM flattens and delaminates into two layers that will become ectoderm and endoderm. *b.* and *c.* Cells of the lower layer migrate out to line the blastocoel cavity to form the yolk sac. *d.* A primitive streak forms the ectoderm layer, and cells destined to become mesoderm migrate into the interior, similar to gastrulation in birds.

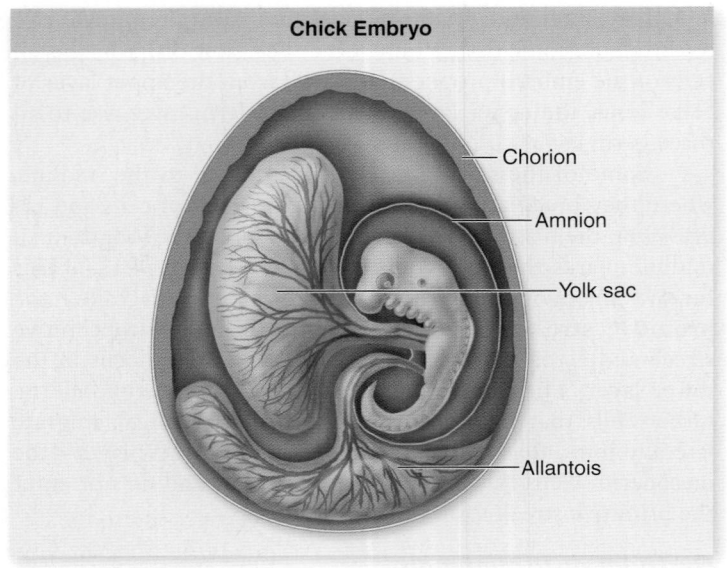

Chick Embryo

- Chorion
- Amnion
- Yolk sac
- Allantois

a.

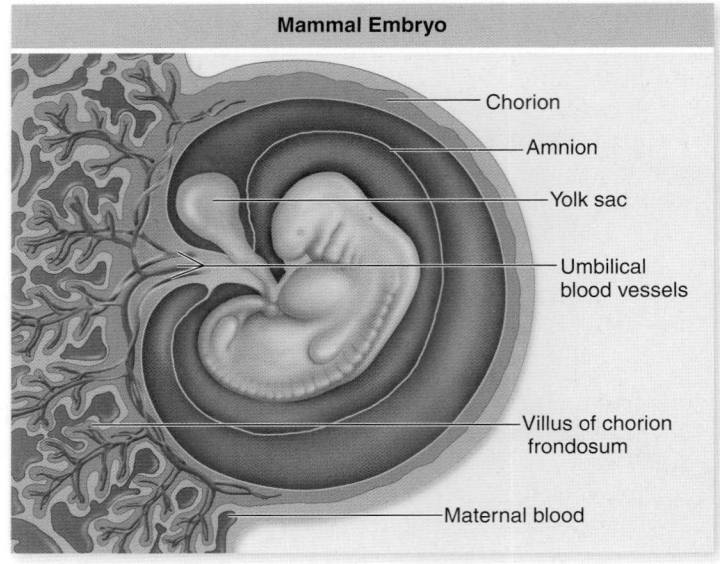

Mammal Embryo

- Chorion
- Amnion
- Yolk sac
- Umbilical blood vessels
- Villus of chorion frondosum
- Maternal blood

b.

Figure 54.15 The extraembryonic membranes. The extraembryonic membranes in *(a)* a chick embryo and *(b)* a mammalian embryo share some of the same characteristics. However, in the chick, the allantois continues to grow until it eventually unites with the chorion just under the eggshell, where it is involved in gas exchange. In the mammalian embryo, the allantois contributes blood vessels to the developing umbilical cord.

Extraembryonic membranes are an adaptation to life on dry land

As an adaptation to terrestrial life, the embryos of reptiles, birds, and mammals develop within a fluid-filled *amniotic membrane*, or *amnion* (chapter 35). The amniotic membrane and several other membranes form from embryonic cells, but they are located outside of the body of the embryo. For this reason, they are known as **extraembryonic membranes.** The extraembryonic membranes include the amnion, chorion, yolk sac, and allantois.

In birds, the amnion and chorion arise from two folds that grow to completely surround the embryo (figure 54.15a). The amnion is the inner membrane that surrounds the embryo and suspends it in *amniotic fluid*, thereby mimicking the aquatic environments of fish and amphibian embryos. The chorion is located next to the eggshell and is separated from the other membranes by a cavity—the *extraembryonic coelom.*

The *yolk sac* plays a critical role in the nutrition of bird and reptile embryos; it is also present in mammals, although it does not nourish the embryo. The *allantois* is derived as an out-pouching of the gut and serves to store the uric acid excreted in the urine of birds. During development, the allantois of a bird embryo expands to form a sac that eventually fuses with the overlying chorion, just under the eggshell. The fusion of the allantois and chorion form a functioning unit, the chorio-allantoic membrane, in which embryonic blood vessels, carried in the allantois, are brought close to the porous eggshell for gas exchange. The chorioallantoic membrane is thus the respiratory membrane of a bird embryo.

In mammals, the trophoblast cells of the blastocyst implant into the endometrial lining of the mother's uterus and become the chorionic membrane (figure 54.15b). The part of the chorion in contact with endometrial tissue contributes to the placenta.

The other part of the placenta is composed of modified endometrial tissue of the mother's uterus, as is described in more detail in a later section. The allantois in mammals contributes blood vessels to the structure that will become the umbilical cord, so that fetal blood can be delivered to the placenta for gas exchange.

Learning Outcomes Review 54.3

Gastrulation involves cell rearrangement and migration to produce ectoderm, mesoderm, and endoderm. In sea urchins, endoderm forms by invagination of the blastula; mesodermal cells form from other surface cells. In vertebrates with moderate to extensive amounts of yolk, surface cells move through a blastopore or a primitive streak, respectively. Mammalian gastrulation is similar to gastrulation in birds. Extraembryonic membranes of amniote species form from embryonic cells outside the embryo's body and include the yolk sac, amnion, chorion, and allantois.

- **What kind of cellular behaviors are necessary for gastrulation?**

54.4 *Organogenesis*

Learning Outcomes

1. *Describe examples of organogenesis.*
2. *Describe neurulation and somitogenesis.*
3. *Explain the migration and role of neural crest cells.*

Gastrulation establishes the basic body plan and creates the three primary germ layers of animal embryos. The stage is now set for *organogenesis*—the formation of the organs in their proper locations—which occurs by interactions of cells within and between the three germ layers. Thus, organogenesis follows rapidly on the heels of gastrulation, and in many animals begins before gastrulation is complete. Over the course of subsequent development, tissues develop into organs and animal embryos assume their unique body form (see table 54.1).

Changes in gene expression lead to cell determination

All of the cells in an animal's body, with the exception of a few specialized ones that have lost their nuclei, have the same complement of genetic information. Despite the fact that all of its cells are genetically identical, an adult animal contains dozens to hundreds of cell types, each expressing some unique aspect of the total genetic information for that individual. The information for other cell types is not lost, but most cells within a developing organism progressively lose the capacity to express ever-larger portions of their genomes. What factors determine which genes are to be expressed in a particular cell?

To a large degree, a cell's location in the developing embryo determines its fate. By changing a cell's location, an experimenter can often alter its developmental destiny, as mentioned in chapter 19. But this is only true up to a certain point in the cell's development. At some stage, every cell's ultimate fate becomes fixed, a process referred to as *cell determination*.

A cell's fate can be established by inheritance of cytoplasmic determinants or by interactions with neighboring cells. The process by which a cell or group of cells instructs neighboring cells to adopt a particular fate is called *induction*. If a nonporous barrier, such as a layer of cellophane, is imposed between the inducer and the target tissue, no induction takes place. In contrast, a porous filter, through which proteins can pass, does permit induction to occur.

In these experiments, researchers concluded that the inducing cells secrete a paracrine signal molecule that binds to the cells of the target tissue. Such signal molecules are capable of producing changes in the patterns of gene transcription in the target cells. You will learn more about the origin of embryonic induction a little later in this chapter.

Development of selected systems in *Drosophila* illustrates organogenesis

In chapter 19, you saw how the creation of morphogen gradients in a fruit fly embryo leads to hierarchies of gene expression that direct cell fate decisions along both the anterior–posterior and dorsal–ventral axes. These two axes form a coordinate system to specify the position of tissues and organs within the *Drosophila* embryo. In this section we look at development of three different organs: salivary glands, the heart, and the tracheae of the respiratory system.

Salivary gland development

The fruit fly larva is a mobile eating machine, and thus it has very active salivary glands. The primordia of the salivary glands develop as simple tubular invaginations of ectodermal cells on the ventral surface of the third head segment.

Salivary glands develop only from an anterior strip of cells that express the *sex combs reduced (scr)* gene. No salivary glands form in *scr*-deficient embryos, whereas experimental expansion of *scr* expression along the anterior–posterior axis results in the formation of additional salivary gland primordia along the length of the embryo.

The *scr* gene is one of the homeotic genes in the Antennapedia complex, which encode transcription factors that bind to DNA via their homeodomains to regulate gene expression (see chapter 19). One downstream target of the *scr* gene is the *fork head (fkh)* gene, which has Scr-binding sites in its enhancer. The *fkh* gene is required for secretory cell development in salivary gland rudiments, and it encodes a transcription factor that directly activates expression of salivary gland-specific genes. Thus, action of the *scr* gene activates *fkh* expression at the proper anterior location for salivary gland formation.

The inhibitory action of a dorsally expressed protein, Decapentaplegic (Dpp), determines the ventral position of the salivary glands. Activation of the Dpp-signaling pathway represses salivary gland specification in neighboring cells. This restricts development of salivary gland rudiments to their specific ventral patch of ectoderm cells (figure 54.16). In mutant embryos deficient for Dpp or any of the downstream Dpp-signaling proteins,

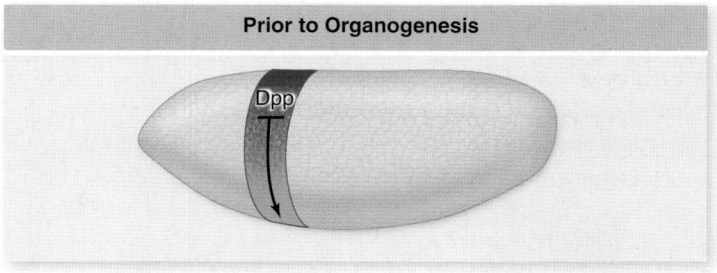

Prior to Organogenesis

Dpp

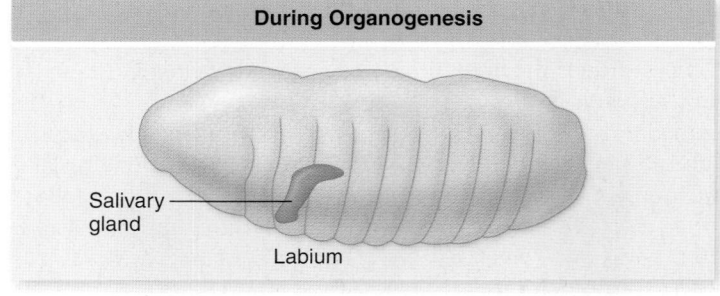

During Organogenesis

Salivary gland

Labium

b.

Figure 54.16 Salivary gland formation in *Drosophila*. Prospective salivary gland cells are determined by the intersection of the anterior–posterior and dorsal–ventral axes. *a.* Prior to organogenesis, the sex combs reduced *(scr)* gene is expressed in an anterior band of cells (shaded blue). At the same time, Decapentaplegic protein (Dpp) is released by cells on the dorsal side of the embryo, forming a gradient in the dorsal–ventral direction. Dpp specifies dorsal cell fates and inhibits formation of salivary gland rudiments. *b.* During organogenesis, the salivary glands develop in areas where Scr is expressed but Dpp is absent. Each salivary gland rudiment forms as a ventral invagination of the surface ectoderm on either side of the third head segment (the labium).

salivary gland rudiments are not restricted to this ventral patch, and they form from the entire ectoderm of the third segment.

Heart development

The heart is a mesoderm-derived structure in all animals, and it is the first organ to become functional during embryonic development. The dorsal vessel is the heart-equivalent structure in *Drosophila melanogaster*. The homeobox-containing gene *tinman* is expressed in the prospective heart mesoderm and in the developing dorsal vessel, and its activity is required for dorsal vessel development in *Drosophila* (figure 54.17).

Dorsal vessel development in *Drosophila* is also dependent on two other types of transcription factors (known as GATA and T-box factors). In an illuminating case of evolutionary conservation, scientists have discovered gene families similar to each of these three *Drosophila* genes in vertebrates. Moreover, members of these gene families play important roles in vertebrate heart specification.

This evolutionary conservation includes not just the structure of these genes, but their function as well. Research-

ers have discovered that specification of cardiac mesoderm is subject to inductive signals from adjoining germ layers in both *Drosophila* and vertebrates. In vertebrates, the heart develops in an internal location, and the inductive signals come from the underlying anterior endoderm. In *Drosophila*, the dorsal vessel forms in a more superficial location, and the signals come from the overlying ectoderm.

Despite the different sources, the signals that regulate the expression of these three key types of transcription factors are themselves conserved between *Drosophila* and vertebrates. Given the critical and conserved circulatory function of the heart, it is perhaps not surprising that similar gene families mediate the specification of heart mesoderm in both *Drosophila* and vertebrates.

Tracheae: Branching morphogenesis

As you learned in chapters 34 and 49, insects exchange gases via a branching system of finer and finer tubes called *tracheae*. The repeated branching of simple epithelial tubes that leads to formation of the tracheal system is an example of **branching morphogenesis.**

Mutations in the *branchless* gene in *Drosophila* result in embryos with greatly reduced tracheal systems. The *branchless* gene encodes a member of the large family of **fibroblast growth factors (FGF),** which bind to receptor tyrosine kinase proteins (see chapter 9) to stimulate proliferation of target cells. In another interesting case of evolutionary conservation, the mammalian FGF homologue of the *branchless* gene is required for branching morphogenesis that creates the alveolar passageways in the mammalian lung.

In both animals, loose clusters of mesenchymal cells adjacent to distal regions of the epithelial tube secrete FGF. The FGF binds to a specific FGF receptor in the membrane of the epithelial cells, stimulating them to proliferate and to grow out into a new tube bud.

In vertebrates, organogenesis begins with neurulation and somitogenesis

The process of organogenesis in vertebrates begins with the formation of two morphological features found only in chordates: the *notochord* and the hollow **dorsal nerve cord** (see chapter 35). The development of the dorsal nerve cord is called *neurulation*.

Development of the neural tube

The notochord forms from mesoderm and is first visible soon after gastrulation is complete. It is a flexible rod located along the dorsal midline in the embryos of all chordates, although its function as a supporting structure is supplanted by the subsequent development of the vertebral column in the vertebrates. After the notochord has been laid down, the region of dorsal ectodermal cells situated above the notochord begins to thicken to form the *neural plate*.

The thickening is produced by the elongation of the dorsal ectoderm cells. Those cells then assume a wedge shape because of contracting bundles of actin filaments at their apical end. This change in shape causes the neural tissue to roll up into a **neural groove** running down the long axis of the embryo. The edges of the neural groove then move toward each

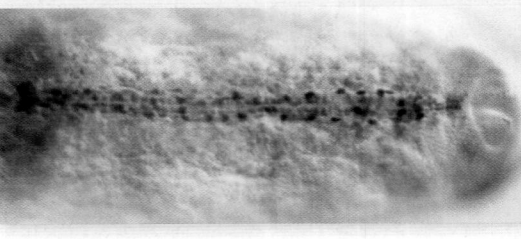

Figure 54.17 A gene necessary for heart formation in *Drosophila*.

other and fuse, creating a long hollow cylinder, the **neural tube** (figure 54.18). The neural tube eventually pinches off from the surface ectoderm to end up beneath the surface of the embryo's back. Regional changes, which are under control of the *Hox* gene complexes (see chapter 19), then occur in the neural tube as it differentiates into the spinal cord and brain.

Generation of somites

While the neural tube is forming from dorsal ectoderm, the rest of the basic architecture of the body is being rapidly established by changes in the mesoderm. The sheets of mesoderm on either side of the developing notochord separate into a series of rounded regions called **somitomeres**. The somitomeres then separate into segmented blocks called **somites** (see figure 54.18). The mesoderm in the head region does not separate into discrete somites but remains connected as somitomeres, which form the skeletal muscles of the face, jaws, and throat.

Somites form in an anterior–posterior wave with a regular periodicity that can be easily timed—for example, by using a vital dye, which marks cells without killing them, to mark each somite as it forms in a chick embryo. Cells at the presumptive boundary regions in the presomitic mesoderm instruct cells anterior to them to condense and separate into somites at specific times (for example, every 90 min in a chick embryo). This "clock" appears to be regulated by contact-mediated cell signaling between neighboring cells.

Somites themselves are transient embryonic structures, and soon after their formation, cells disperse and start differentiating along different pathways to ultimately form the skeleton, skeletal musculature, and associated connective tissues. The total number of somites formed is species-specific; for example, chickens form 50 somites, whereas some species of snakes form as many as 400 somites.

Some body organs, including the kidneys, adrenal glands, and gonads, develop within a strip of mesoderm that runs lateral to each row of somites. The remainder of the mesoderm, which is most ventrally located, moves out and around the endoderm and eventually surrounds it completely. As a result of this movement, the mesoderm becomes separated into two layers. The outer layer is associated with the inner body wall, and the inner layer is associated with the outer lining of the gut tube. Between these two layers of mesoderm is the *coelom* (see chapter 32), which becomes the body cavity of the adult. Figure 54.19 shows the major mesoderm lineages of amniote embryos.

Migratory neural crest cells differentiate into many cell types

Neurulation occurs in all chordates, and the process in the simple lancelet, a nonvertebrate chordate, is much the same as it is in a human. However, neurulation is accompanied by an additional step in vertebrates. Just before the neural groove closes

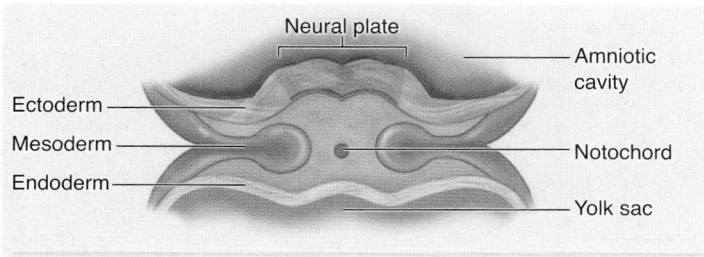

a.

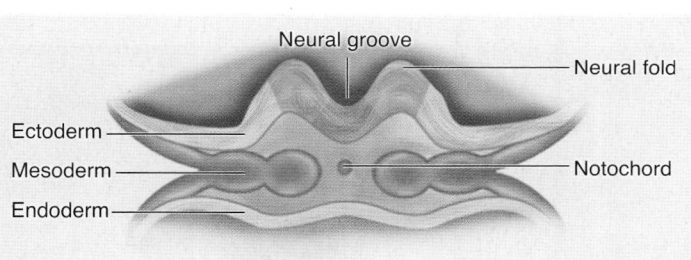

b.

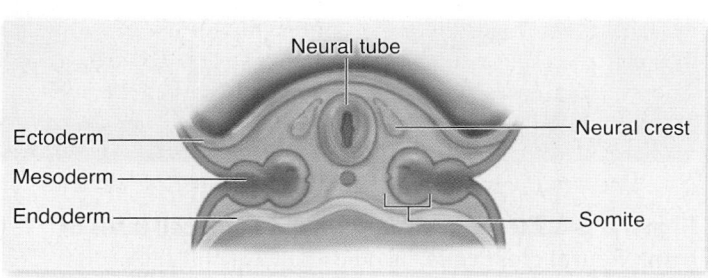

c.

Figure 54.18 Mammalian neural tube formation.
a. The neural plate forms from ectoderm above the notochord. *b.* The cells of the neural plate fold together to form the neural groove. *c.* The neural groove eventually closes to form a hollow tube called the neural tube, which will become the brain and spinal cord. As the tube closes, some of the cells from the dorsal margin of the neural tube differentiate into the neural crest, migratory cells that form a variety of structures and are characteristic of vertebrates.

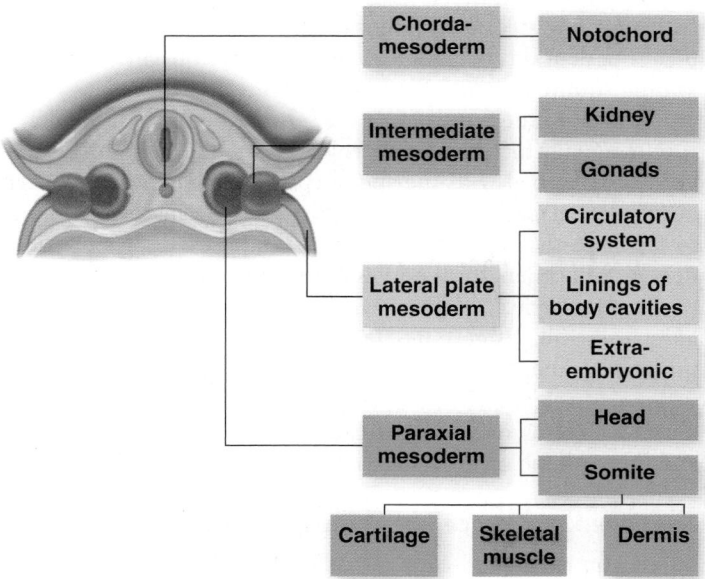

Figure 54.19 Mesoderm-derived structures of birds and mammals.

to form the neural tube, its edges pinch off, forming a small cluster of cells—the *neural crest*—between the roof of the neural tube and the surface ectoderm (figure 54.18c).

In another example of extensive cell movements during animal development, the neural crest cells then migrate away from the neural tube to colonize many different regions of the developing embryo. The appearance of the neural crest was a key event in the evolution of the vertebrates because neural crest cells, after reaching their final destinations, ultimately develop into many structures characteristic of the vertebrate body.

The differentiation of neural crest cells depends on their migration pathway and final location. Neural crest cells migrate along one of three pathways in the embryo. Cranial neural crest cells are anterior cells that migrate into the head and neck; trunk neural crest cells migrate along one of two different pathways (to be described shortly). Each population of neural crest cells develops into a variety of cell types.

Cranial neural crest cells' migration

Cranial neural crest cells contribute significantly to development of the skeletal and connective tissues of the face and skull, as well as differentiating into nerve and glial cells of the nervous system, and melanocyte pigment cells. Changes in the placement of cranial neural crest cells during development have led to the evolution of the great complexity and variety of vertebrate heads.

There are two waves of cranial neural crest cell migration. The first produces both dorsal and ventral structures, and the second produces only dorsal structures and makes much less cartilage and bone. Transplantation experiments indicate that the developmental potential of the cells in these two waves is identical. The differences in cell fate are due to the environment the migrating cells encounter and not due to prior determination of cell fate.

Trunk neural crest cells: Ventral pathway

Neural crest cells located in more posterior positions have very different developmental fates depending on their migration pathway. The first trunk neural crest cells that migrate away from the neural tube pass through the anterior half of each adjoining somite to ventral locations (figure 54.20a).

Some of these cells form the sensory neurons of the dorsal root ganglia, which send out projections to connect the periphery of the animal with the spinal cord (see chapter 44). Others become specialized as Schwann cells, which insulate nerve fibers to facilitate the rapid conduction of impulses along peripheral nerves. Still others form nerves of the autonomic ganglia, which regulate the activity of internal organs, and endocrine cells of the adrenal medulla (figure 54.20b). The chemical similarity of the hormone epinephrine and the neurotransmitter norepinephrine, which are released by sympathetic neurons of the autonomic nervous systems, may result because both adrenal medullary cells and sympathetic neurons derive from the neural crest.

Trunk neural crest cells: Lateral pathway

The second group of trunk neural crest cells migrate away from the neural tube in the space just under the surface ectoderm, to occupy this space around the entire body of the embryo. There, they will differentiate into the pigment cells of the skin

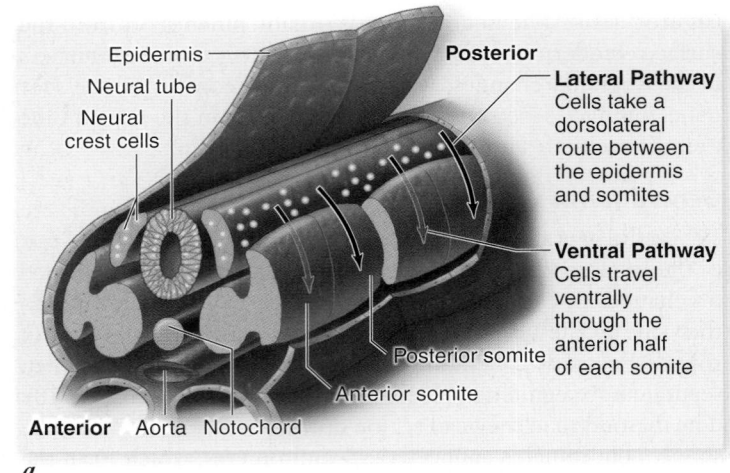

a.

b.

c.

Figure 54.20 Migration pathways and cell fates of trunk neural crest cells. *a.* The first wave of trunk neural crest cells migrates ventrally through the anterior half of each somite, whereas the second wave of cells leaves dorsally and migrates through the space between the epidermis and the somites. *b.* Ventral pathway neural crest cells differentiate into a variety of specialized cell types, but lateral pathway cells develop into the melanocytes (pigment cells) of the skin. *c.* A mutation in a gene that promotes survival of neural crest cells in all mammals leads to white spotting on the bellies and foreheads of both human babies and mice! Each individual is heterozygous for this mutation and thus has only half as much of the survival factor as unaffected individuals.

(figure 54.20a, b). Mutations in genes that affect the survival and migration of neural crest cells lead to white spotting in the skin on ventral surfaces, as well as internal problems in other neural crest-derived tissues (figure 54.20c).

Because the fate of a neural crest cell is dictated by its migration pathway, many studies have been done to identify the molecules that control the migration pathways of neural crest cells. Cell adhesion molecules on cell surfaces and in the extracellular matrix are expected to play prominent roles. For example, prospective neural crest cells down-regulate the expression of N-cadherin on their surfaces, which enables them to break away from the neural tube. Then, soon after leaving the neural tube, integrin receptors appear on the surfaces of neural crest cells, allowing them to interact with proteins in the extracellular matrix pathways along which they will migrate.

Neural crest derivatives are important in vertebrate evolution

Primitive chordates such as lancelets are filter feeders, using the rapid beating of cilia to draw water into their mouths, which then exits through slits in their pharynx. These pharyngeal slits evolved into the vertebrate gill chamber, a structure that provides a greatly improved means of gas exchange. Thus, evolution of the gill chamber was certainly a key event in the transition from filter feeding to active predation, which requires a much higher metabolic rate.

In the development of the gill chamber, some of the cranial neural crest cells form cartilaginous bars between the em-bryonic pharyngeal slits. Other cranial neural crest cells induce portions of the mesoderm to form muscles along the cartilage, and still others to form neurons that carry impulses between the central nervous system and these muscles.

Many of the unique vertebrate adaptations that contribute to their varied ecological roles involve structures that arise from neural crest cells. The vertebrates became fast-swimming predators with much higher metabolic rates. This accelerated metabolism permitted a greater level of activity than was possible among the more primitive chordates. Other evolutionary changes associated with the derivatives of the neural crest provided better detection of prey, a greatly improved ability to orient spatially during prey capture, and the means to respond quickly to sensory information. The evolution of the neural crest and of the structures derived from it were thus crucial steps in the evolution of the vertebrates (figure 54.21).

Learning Outcomes Review 54.4

Genetic control of organogenesis relies on conserved families of cell-signaling molecules and transcription factors. The control of heart development in *Drosophila* and mammals uses some of the same proteins. The process of neurulation forms the basic nervous system in vertebrates. Somitogenesis is the division of mesoderm into somites. Neural crest cells arise from the neural tube and migrate to many sites to form a variety of cell types. The evolution of the neural crest led to the appearance of many vertebrate-specific adaptations.

■ *Are neural crest cells determined prior to migration?*

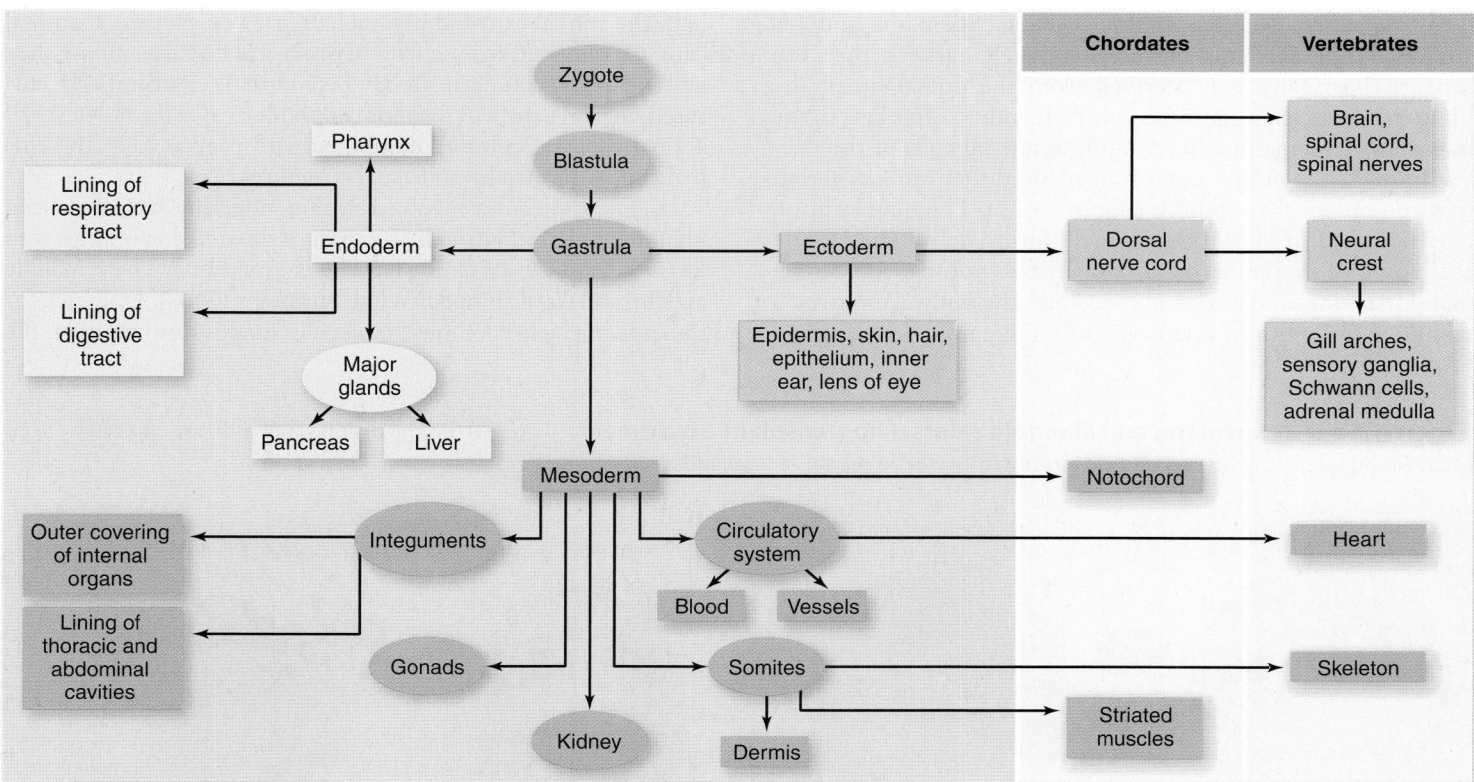

Figure 54.21 **Germ-layer derivation of the major tissue types in animals.** The three germ layers that form during gastrulation give rise to all the organs and tissues in the body, but the neural crest cells that form from ectodermal tissue give rise to structures that are prevalent in vertebrates, such as gill arches and bones of the face and skull.

Vertebrate Axis Formation

In animal development, the relative position of cells in particular germ layers determines, to a large extent, the organs that develop from them. In *Drosophila*, you have seen that formation of morphogen gradients in the syncytial blastoderm establishes the anterior–posterior and dorsal–ventral axes of the embryo. The *Hox* gene complexes in vertebrates function similarly to the homeotic genes of *Drosophila* to specify the position of organs along the anterior–posterior axis. But how is cell fate selection along the dorsal–ventral axis accomplished in vertebrate embryos? Put another way, how do cells of the dorsal ectoderm "know" they are above the mesoderm-derived notochord, and thus fated to develop into the neural tube? The solution to this puzzle is one of the outstanding accomplishments of experimental embryology.

The Spemann organizer determines dorsal–ventral axis

The renowned German biologist Hans Spemann and his student Hilde Mangold solved this puzzle early in the 20th century. Normally, cells derived from the dorsal lip of the blastopore of a gastrulating amphibian embryo give rise to the notochord. Spemann and Mangold removed cells of the dorsal lip from one embryo and transplanted them to a different location on another embryo (figure 54.22). The new location corresponded to that of the animal's future belly. They found that some of the embryos developed two notochords: a normal dorsal one, and a second one along the belly. Moreover, a complete set of dorsal axial structures (e.g., notochord, neural

tube, and somites) formed at the ventral transplantation site in most of these embryos.

By using genetically different donor and host blastulas, Spemann and Mangold were able to show that the second notochord produced by transplanting dorsal lip cells contained host cells as well as transplanted ones. The transplanted dorsal lip cells had thus acted as *organizers*, stimulating cells that would normally form skin and belly structures to develop into dorsal axial structures. The belly cells must clearly contain the genetic information for dorsal axial developmental program, but they do not express it in the normal course of their development. Signals from the transplanted dorsal lip cells, however, must have caused them to do so.

How the organizer works

An organizer is a cluster of cells that release diffusible signal molecules, which then convey positional information to other cells. As seen earlier, organizers can have a profound influence on the development of surrounding tissues. Working as signal beacons, they inform surrounding cells of their distance from the organizer. The closer a particular cell is to an organizer, the higher the concentration of the signal molecule (*morphogen*) it experiences. Organizers and the diffusible morphogens that they release are thought to be part of a widespread mechanism for determining relative position and cell fates during vertebrate development.

The action of morphogens

The action of morphogens can be studied by using isolated portions of the blastula. The blastula can be bisected into an animal half (the animal cap) and vegetal half (the vegetal cap). If animal caps are removed from a frog blastula and cultured alone, they will form only ectoderm-derived epidermal cells. Similarly, cultured vegetal caps will form only endodermal cells. However, if animal caps are cultured combined with vegetal caps, the animal caps will form mesodermal structures.

The molecules involved in this induction have not been unambiguously identified. Members of the transforming growth factor beta (TGF-β) family have been implicated. These include activin, and *Xenopus* nodal-related proteins (Xnrs). Evidence for the inducing action of these molecules ranges from indirect: the

Figure 54.22 Spemann and Mangold's dorsal lip transplant experiment. Tissue from the dorsal lip of a donor embryo induced the formation of a second axis in the future belly region of a second, recipient embryo.

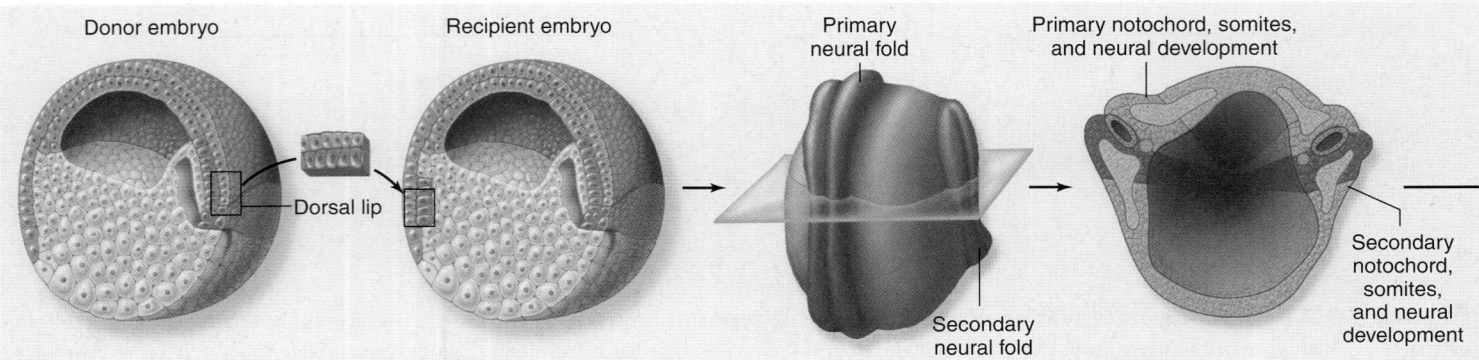

timing and pattern of expression correlates with inducing tissue, to depleting developing embryos of these proteins with specific reagents that block gene expression.

The origin of the organizer

How do cells of the frog blastopore's dorsal lip become the Spemann organizer and how do they acquire their ability to specify cell fate along the dorsal–ventral axis? In frogs, as in fruit flies, this process starts during oogenesis in the mother. At that time, maternally encoded dorsal determinants are put into the developing oocyte, one of which accumulates at the vegetal pole of the unfertilized egg. At fertilization, cytoplasmic rearrangements cause this determinant to shift to the future dorsal side of the egg.

First, a signal from the point of sperm entry initiates the assembly of a microtubule array, which enables the egg's plasma membrane and the underlying cortical cytoplasm to rotate over the surface of the deeper cytoplasm. This physical rotation shifts this maternally encoded dorsal determinant to the opposite side of the egg from the point of sperm entry (figure 54.23a, b). In some frogs, a gray crescent forms opposite the sperm entry point, as mentioned earlier, and this crescent marks the future site of the dorsal lip.

Cells that form in this area during cleavage (called the Nieuwkoop center for the scientist who did the previously mentioned animal cap studies) receive the dorsal determinants that moved during cortical rotation. The dorsal determinants cause a change in gene expression in these cells, producing a signaling molecule that induces the cells above them to develop into the dorsal lip of the blastopore (figure 54.23c).

Maternally encoded dorsal determinants activate Wnt signaling

Experiments carried out over the last 15 years suggest that the maternally encoded dorsal determinants in *Xenopus* are mRNAs for proteins that function in the intracellular **Wnt** signaling pathway. *Wnt* genes encode a large family of cell-signaling proteins that affect the development of a number of structures in both vertebrates and invertebrates. Turning on the Wnt pathway in the dorsal vegetal cells of the Nieuwkoop center leads ultimately to activation of a transcription factor, which moves into the nucleus to activate the expression of genes necessary for organizer specification.

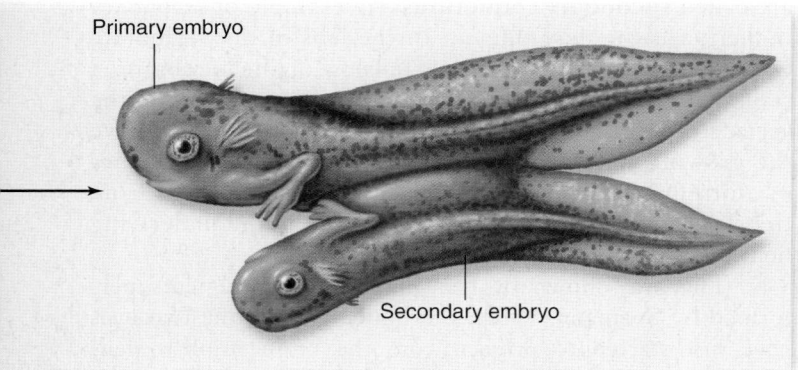

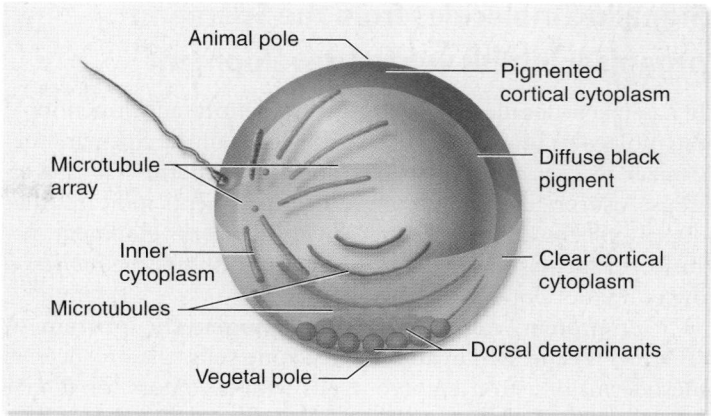

a.

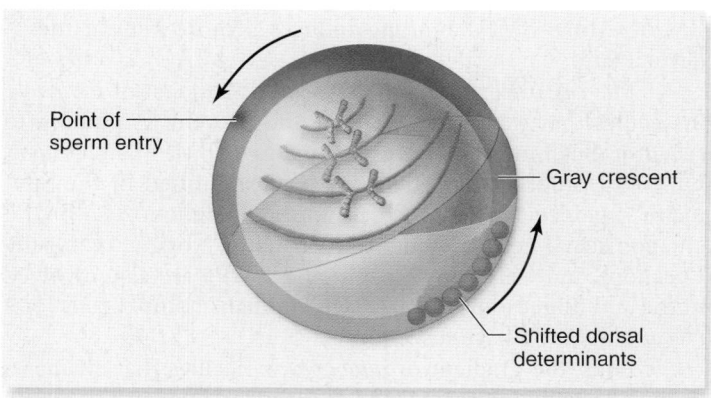

b.

c.

Figure 54.23 Creation of the Spemann organizer.
a. Dorsal determinants are localized at the vegetal pole of the unfertilized frog egg. At fertilization, a microtubule array forms at the site of sperm entry. These microtubules organize parallel microtubules to line the vegetal half of the egg between the cortex and cytoplasm. *b.* The cortical cytoplasm and dorsal determinants ride on this parallel array of microtubules, shifting to a site opposite sperm entry. *c.* Cells that inherit these shifted dorsal determinants form the Nieuwkoop center, which releases diffusible signaling molecules that specify the cells in the overlying dorsal marginal zone to become the organizer. The organizer forms at the area of the gray crescent, visible following the cytoplasmic rearrangements at fertilization.

Signaling molecules from the Spemann organizer inhibit ventral development

It has taken decades to establish the identity and function of the molecules that are synthesized by cells of the Spemann organizer to subsequently specify dorsal mesoderm cell fates in frogs. A surprising finding of recent experiments indicates that dorsal lip cells do not directly *activate* dorsal development. Instead, dorsal mesoderm development is a result of the *inhibition* of ventral development.

A protein called **bone morphogenetic protein 4 (BMP4)** is expressed in all marginal zone cells (the prospective mesoderm) of a frog embryo. Cells with receptors for BMP4 have the potential to develop into mesodermal derivatives. The specific mesodermal fate depends on how many receptors bind BMP4: More BMP4 binding induces a more ventral mesodermal fate.

The organizer functions by secreting a host of *inhibitory* molecules that can bind to BMP4 and prevent its binding to receptor. Such molecules are referred to as BMP4 antagonists. Up to 13 different proteins have been identified in the Spemann organizer, most of which appear to function as BMP4 antagonists. These include the proteins Noggin, Chordin, Dickkopf, and Cerebrus. Noggin and BMP4 are also involved in toe and finger joint formation, so humans homozygous for a *Noggin* mutation have fused joints.

Thus, the gradient of *inhibitory* molecules that emanates from the Spemann organizer leads to a declining level of BMP4 *function* in the ventral-to-dorsal direction. Cells farthest from the organizer bind the highest levels of BMP4 and differentiate into ventral mesoderm structures such as blood and connective tissues. Cells that are midway from the organizer bind intermediate amounts of BMP4, differentiate into intermediate mesoderm, and form organs such as the kidneys and gonads. BMP4 binding is completely inhibited by the high levels of antagonists in the organizer itself. Thus, these cells adopt the most dorsal of mesoderm fates and develop into somites. The influence of the organizer also extends to ectoderm as inhibition of BMP4 in ectoderm leads to formation of neural tissue instead of epidermis (figure 54.24).

Evidence indicates that organizers are present in all vertebrates

In chicks, a group of cells at the anterior limit of the primitive streak called *Hensen's node* functions similarly to the dorsal lip of the blastopore: Hensen's node induces a second axis when transplanted to another area of a chick embryo. Recent studies have shown that cells of Hensen's node act like the Spemann organizer, secreting molecules that inhibit ventral development. These molecules are the same as those found in frog embryos. Therefore, these experiments once again illustrate the evolutionary conservation of particular genes in animal development.

In addition, notochord signaling acts to pattern the neural tube. The notochord produces the signaling molecule sonic hedgehog (Shh), which is related to a signaling molecule in

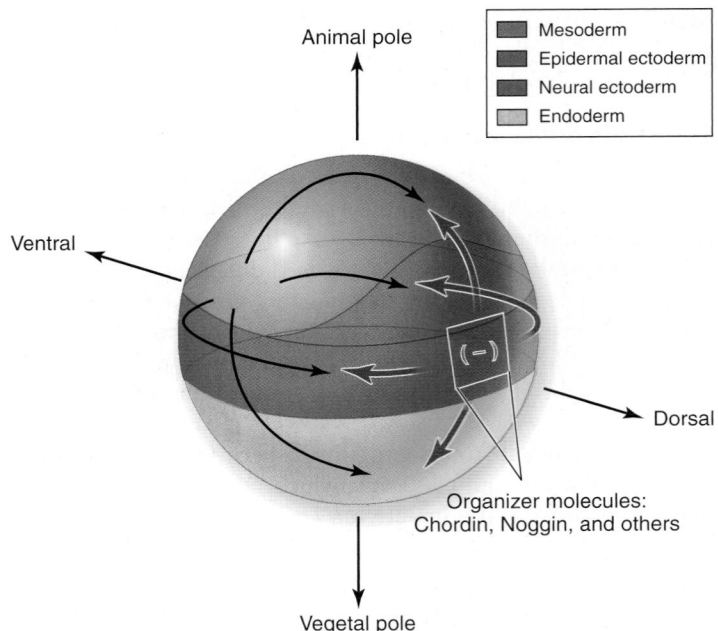

Figure 54.24 Function of the Spemann organizer.
The organizer is a hotbed of secreted molecules that bind to and antagonize the action of BMP4, a morphogen that at high levels specifies ventral mesoderm cell fates.

Drosophila called hedgehog. Signaling by Shh specifies ventral cell fate with dose-related effects similar to those described for the TGF-β family proteins discussed earlier. In this way, induction by the notochord causes somites to form vertebrae, ribs, muscle, and skin, depending on the levels of Shh cells are exposed to.

Induction can be primary or secondary

The process of induction that Spemann initially discovered appears to be a fundamental mode of development in vertebrates. Inductions between the three primary germ layers—ectoderm, mesoderm, and endoderm—are referred to as **primary inductions.** The differentiation of the central nervous system during neurulation by the interaction of dorsal ectoderm and dorsal mesoderm to form the neural tube is an example of primary induction.

Inductions between tissues that have already been specified to develop along a particular developmental pathway are called **secondary inductions.** An example of secondary induction is the development of the lens of the vertebrate eye. The eye develops as an extension of the forebrain, a stalk that grows outward until it comes into contact with the surface ectoderm (figure 54.25). At a point directly above the growing stalk, a layer of the surface ectoderm pinches off, forming a transparent lens. The formation of lens from the surface ectoderm requires induction by the underlying neural ectoderm.

This was shown by transplantation experiments performed by Spemann. When the optic stalks of the two eyes have just started to project from the brain prior to lens

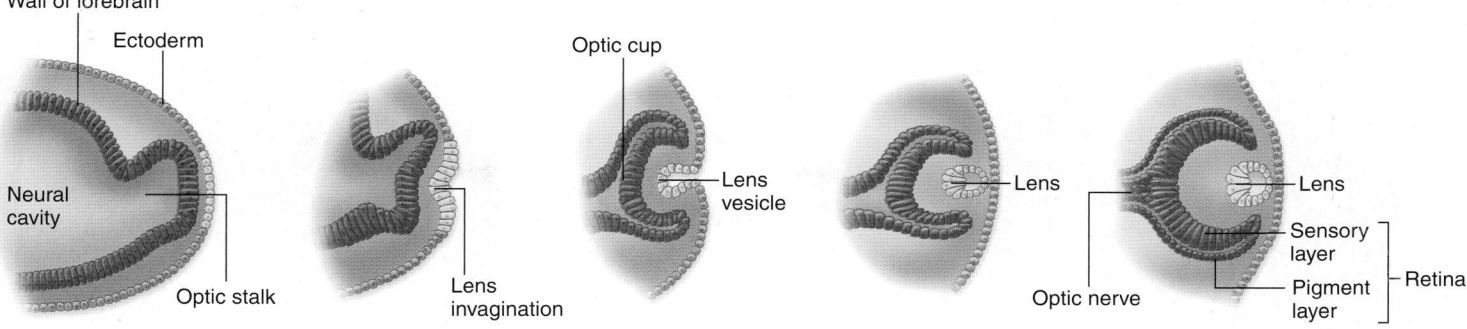

Figure 54.25 Development of the vertebrate eye by induction. An extension of the optic stalk grows until it contacts the surface ectoderm, where it induces a section of the ectoderm to pinch off and form the lens. Other structures of the eye develop from the optic stalk, with lens cells reciprocally inducing the formation of photoreceptors in the optic cup.

formation, one of the budding stalks can be removed and transplanted underneath surface ectoderm in a region that would normally develop into the epidermis of the skin (such as that of the belly). When this is done, a lens forms from belly ectoderm cells in the region above where the budding stalk was transplanted. This lens forms due to inductive signals from the underlying optic stalk.

Learning Outcomes Review 54.5

The Spemann-Mangold experiment showed that transplanted cells of the dorsal lip of the blastopore act as organizers stimulating development of a notochord. Hensen's node plays an equivalent role in vertebrates. By inhibiting BMP4, the organizer induces ectoderm to form neural tissue and mesoderm to form dorsal mesoderm. Primary inductions between germ layers lead to development of the vertebrate nervous system, whereas secondary inductions result in formation of structures such as the lens of the eye.

■ *How can the organizer function by inhibiting the action of other molecules?*

54.6 Human Development

Learning Outcomes

1. *Describe the major developmental events in first trimester.*
2. *Explain the role of the placenta.*
3. *Describe the hormonal control of the birth process.*

Human development from fertilization to birth takes an average of 266 days, or about 9 months. This time is commonly divided into three periods called *trimesters.* We describe here the development of the embryo as it takes place during these trimesters. Later, we summarize the process of birth, nursing of the infant, and postnatal development.

During the first trimester, the zygote undergoes rapid development and differentiation

About 30 hr after fertilization, the zygote undergoes its first cleavage; the second cleavage occurs about 30 hr after that. By the time the embryo reaches the uterus, 6 to 7 days after fertilization, it has differentiated into a blastocyst. As mentioned earlier, the blastocyst consists of an inner cell mass, which will become the body of the embryo, and a surrounding layer of trophoblast cells (see figure 54.10).

The trophoblast cells of the blastocyst digest their way into the endometrial lining of the uterus in the process known as **implantation.** The blastocyst begins to grow rapidly and initiates the formation of the amnion and the chorion.

Development in the first month

During the second week after fertilization, the developing chorion and the endometrial tissues of the mother engage to form the placenta (figure 54.26). Within the placenta, the mother's blood and the blood of the embryo come into close proximity but do not mix. Gases are exchanged, however, and the placenta provides nourishment for the embryo, detoxifies certain molecules that may pass into the embryonic circulation, and secretes hormones. Certain substances, such as alcohol, drugs, and antibiotics, are not stopped by the placenta and pass from the mother's bloodstream into the embryo.

One of the hormones released by the placenta is human chorionic gonadotropin (hCG), which was discussed in chapter 53. This hormone is secreted by the trophoblast cells even before they become the chorion, and it is the hormone assayed in pregnancy tests. Human chorionic gonadotropin maintains the mother's corpus luteum. The corpus luteum, in turn, continues to secrete estradiol and progesterone, thereby preventing menstruation and further ovulations.

Gastrulation also takes place in the second week after fertilization, and the three germ layers are formed. Neurulation occurs in the third week. The first somites appear, which give rise to the muscles, vertebrae, and connective tissues. By the end of the third week, over a dozen somites are evident, and the blood vessels and gut have begun to develop. At this point, the embryo is about 2 mm long.

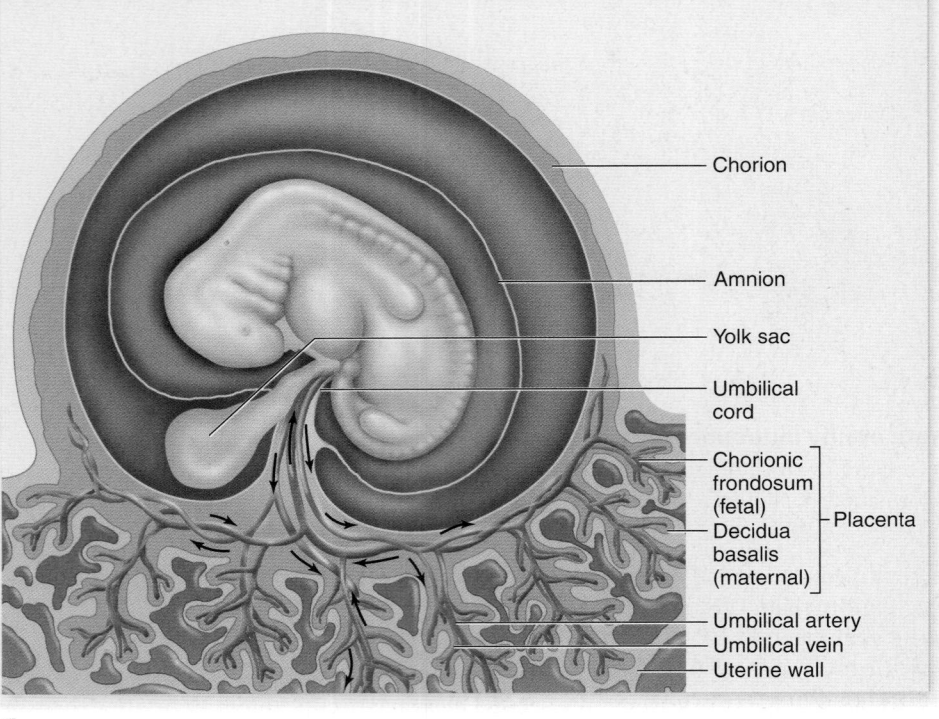

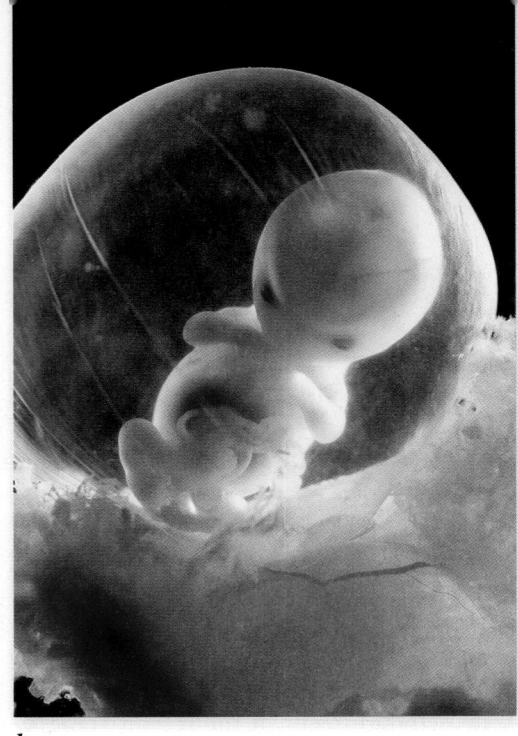

a.   *b.*

Labels in figure a:
- Chorion
- Amnion
- Yolk sac
- Umbilical cord
- Chorionic frondosum (fetal) — Placenta
- Decidua basalis (maternal) — Placenta
- Umbilical artery
- Umbilical vein
- Uterine wall

Figure 54.26 **Structure of the placenta.** *a.* The placenta contains a fetal component, the chorionic frondosum, and a maternal component, the decidua basalis. Deoxygenated fetal blood from the umbilical arteries (shown in blue) enters the placenta, where it picks up oxygen and nutrients from the mother's blood. Oxygenated fetal blood returns in the umbilical vein (shown in red) to the fetus. *b.* Note that the 7-week embryo is surrounded by a fluid-filled amniotic sac.

Organogenesis begins during the fourth week (figure 54.27*a*). The eyes form. The tubular heart develops its four chambers and starts to pulsate rhythmically, as it will for the rest of the individual's life. At 70 beats per minute, the heart is destined to beat more than 2.5 billion times during a lifetime of 70 years. Over 30 pairs of somites are visible by the end of the fourth week, and the arm and leg buds have begun to form. The embryo has increased in length to about 5 mm. Although the developmental scenario is now far advanced, many women are still unaware they are pregnant at this stage. Most spontaneous abortions (miscarriages), which frequently occur in the case of a defective embryo, occur during this period.

The second month

Organogenesis continues during the second month (figure 54.27*b*). The miniature limbs of the embryo assume their adult shapes. The arms, legs, knees, elbows, fingers, and toes can all be seen—as well as a short bony tail. The bones of the embryonic tail, an evolutionary reminder of our past, later fuse to form the coccyx.

Within the abdominal cavity, the major organs, including the liver, pancreas, and gallbladder, become evident. By the end of the second month, the embryo has grown to about 25 mm in length, weighs about 1 g, and begins to look distinctly human. The ninth week marks the transition from embryo to fetus. At this time, all of the major organs of the body have been established in their proper locations.

The third month

The nervous system develops during the third month, and the arms and legs start to move (figure 54.27*c*). The embryo begins to show facial expressions and carries out primitive reflexes such as the startle reflex and sucking.

At around 10 weeks, the secretion of hCG by the placenta declines, and the corpus luteum regresses as a result. However, menstruation does not occur because the placenta itself secretes estradiol and progesterone (figure 54.28).

The high levels of estradiol and progesterone in the blood during pregnancy continue to inhibit the release of FSH and LH, thereby preventing ovulation. They also help maintain the uterus and eventually prepare it for labor and delivery, and they stimulate the development of the mammary glands in preparation for lactation after delivery.

During the second trimester, the basic body plan develops further

Bones actively enlarge during the fourth month (figure 54.27*d*), and by the end of the month, the mother can feel the baby kicking. By the end of the fifth month, the rapid heartbeat of the fetus can be heard with a stethoscope, although it can also be detected as early as 10 weeks with a fetal monitor.

Growth begins in earnest in the sixth month; by the end of that month, the fetus weighs 600 g (1.3 lb) and is over 300 mm (1 ft) long. Most of its prebirth growth is still to come, however. The fetus cannot yet survive outside the uterus without special medical intervention.

During the third trimester, organs mature to the point at which the baby can survive outside the womb

The third trimester is predominantly a period of growth and maturation of organs. The weight of the fetus doubles several

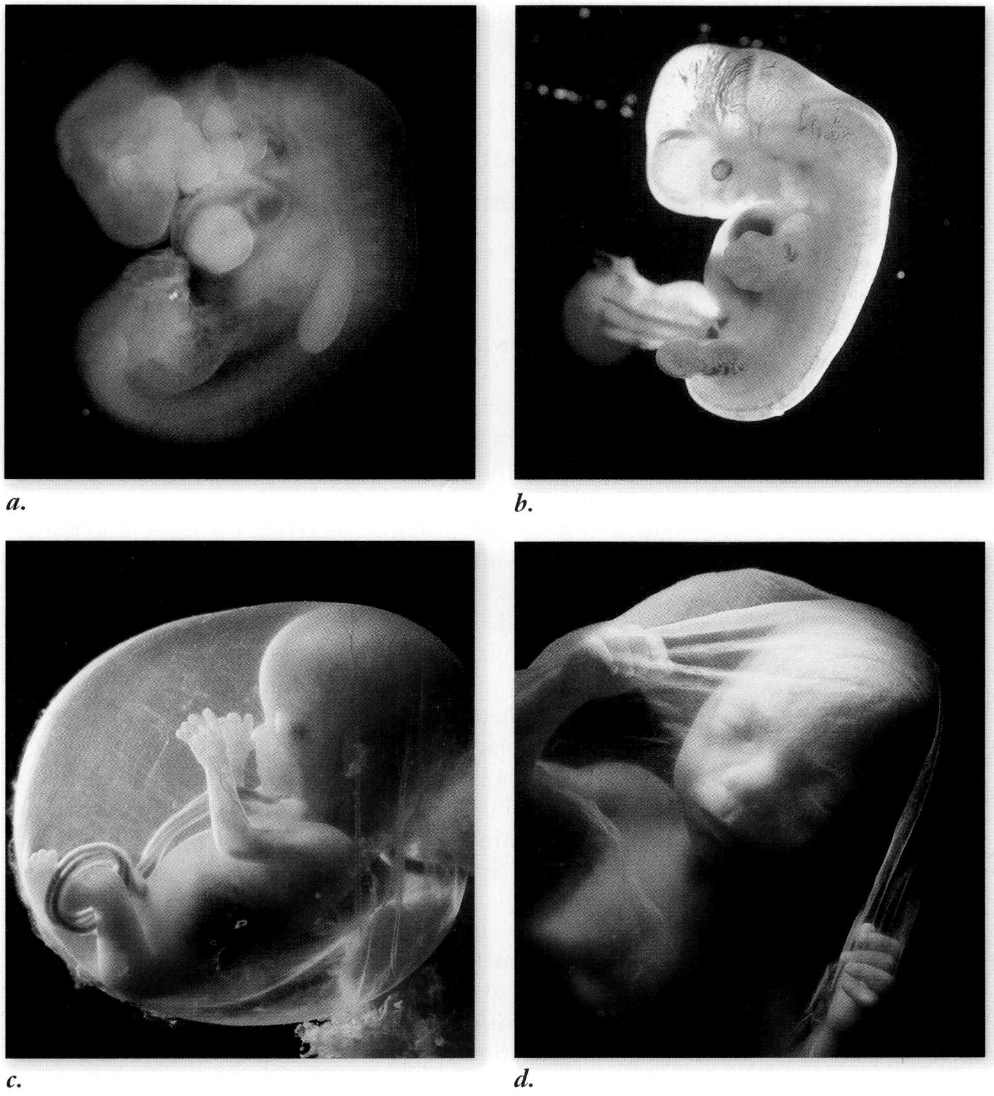

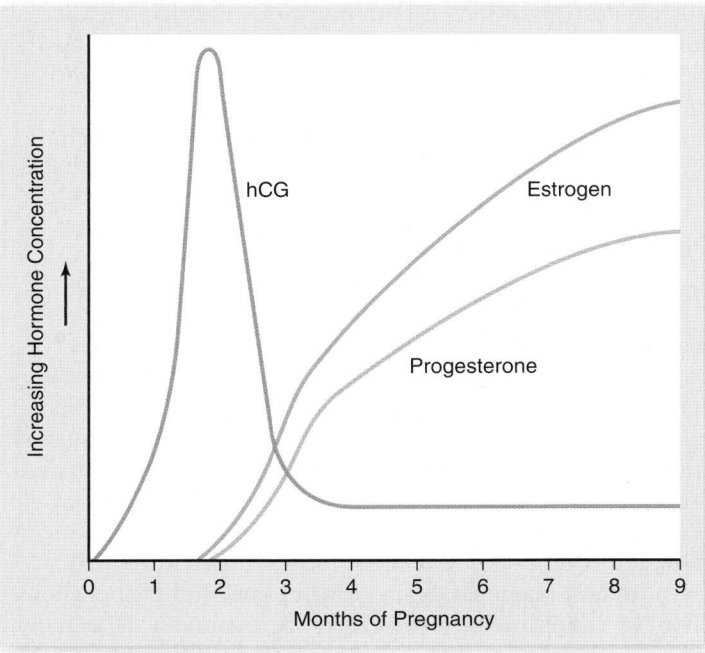

a.

b.

c.

d.

Figure 54.27 **The developing human.** (*a*) 4 weeks, (*b*) end of 5th week, (*c*) 3 months, and (*d*) 4 months.

times, but this increase in bulk is not the only kind of growth that occurs. Most of the major nerve tracts in the brain, as well as many new neurons (nerve cells), are formed during this period. Neurological growth is far from complete when birth takes place, however. If the fetus remained in the uterus until its neurological development was complete, it would grow too large for safe delivery through the pelvis. Instead, the infant

Figure 54.28 **Hormonal secretion by the placenta.** The placenta secretes human chorionic gonadotropin (hCG), which peaks in the second month and then declines. After 5 weeks, it secretes increasing amounts of estrogen and progesterone.

 Inquiry question

The high levels of estradiol and progesterone secreted by the placenta prevent ovulation and thus formation of any additional embryos during pregnancy. What would be the expected effect of these high hormone levels in the absence of pregnancy?

is born as soon as the probability of its survival is high, and its brain continues to develop and produce new neurons for months after birth.

Critical changes in hormones bring on birth

In some mammals, changing hormone levels in the developing fetus initiate the process of birth. The fetuses of these mammals have an extra layer of cells in their adrenal cortex, which secrete corticosteroids that induce the uterus of the mother to manufacture prostaglandins. Prostaglandins trigger powerful contractions of the uterine smooth muscles.

In humans, fetal secretion of cortisol increases during late pregnancy, which appears to stimulate estradiol secretion by the placenta. The mother's uterus releases prostaglandins, possibly as a result of the high levels of estradiol secreted by the placenta. Estradiol also stimulates the uterus to produce more oxytocin receptors, and as a result, the uterus becomes increasingly sensitive to oxytocin.

Prostaglandins begin the uterine contractions, but then sensory feedback from the uterus stimulates the release of oxytocin from the mother's posterior-pituitary gland. Working together, oxytocin and prostaglandins further stimulate uterine contractions, forcing the fetus downward (figure 54.29). This positive feedback mechanism accelerates during labor. Initially, only a few contractions occur each hour, but the rate eventually increases to one contraction every 2 to 3 min. Finally, strong contractions, aided by the mother's voluntary pushing, expel the fetus, which is now a newborn baby, or *neonate*.

After birth, continuing uterine contractions expel the placenta and associated membranes, collectively called the *afterbirth*. The umbilical cord is still attached to the baby, and to free the newborn, a doctor or midwife clamps and cuts the cord. Blood clotting and contraction of muscles in the cord prevent excessive bleeding.

Nursing of young is a distinguishing feature of mammals

Milk production, or *lactation*, occurs in the alveoli of mammary glands when they are stimulated by the anterior-pituitary hormone prolactin. Milk from the alveoli is secreted into a series of alveolar ducts, which are surrounded by smooth muscle and lead to the nipple.

During pregnancy, high levels of progesterone stimulate the development of the mammary alveoli, and high levels of estradiol stimulate the development of the alveolar ducts. However, estradiol blocks the actions of prolactin on the mammary glands, and it inhibits prolactin secretion by promoting the release of prolactin-inhibiting hormone from the hypothalamus. During pregnancy, therefore, the mammary glands are prepared for, but prevented from, lactating. The growth of mammary glands is also stimulated by the placental hormones human chorionic somatomammotropin, a prolactin-like hormone, and human somatotropin, a growth hormone-like hormone.

When the placenta is discharged after birth, the concentrations of estradiol and progesterone in the mother's blood decline rapidly. This decline allows the anterior-pituitary gland to secrete prolactin, which stimulates the mammary alveoli to produce milk. Sensory impulses associated with the baby's suckling trigger the posterior-pituitary gland to release oxytocin. Oxytocin stimulates contraction of the smooth muscle surrounding the alveolar ducts, thus causing milk to be ejected by the breast. This pathway is known as the *milk let-down reflex*, and it is found in other mammals as well. The secretion of oxytocin during lactation also causes some uterine contractions, as it did during labor. These contractions help restore the tone of uterine muscles in mothers who are breast-feeding.

The first milk produced after birth is a yellowish fluid called colostrum, which is both nutritious and rich in maternal antibodies. Milk synthesis begins about 3 days following the birth and is referred to as the milk "coming in." Many mothers nurse for a year or longer. When nursing stops, the accumulation of milk in the breasts signals the brain to stop secreting prolactin, and milk production ceases.

Postnatal development in humans continues for years

Growth of the infant continues rapidly after birth. Babies typically double their birth weight within 2 months. Because different organs grow at different rates and cease growing at different times, the body proportions of infants are different from those of adults. The head, for example, is disproportionately large in newborns, but after birth it grows more slowly than the rest of the body. Such a pattern of growth, in which different components grow at different rates, is referred to as **allometric growth.**

In most mammals, brain growth is mainly a fetal phenomenon. In chimpanzees, for instance, the brain and the cerebral

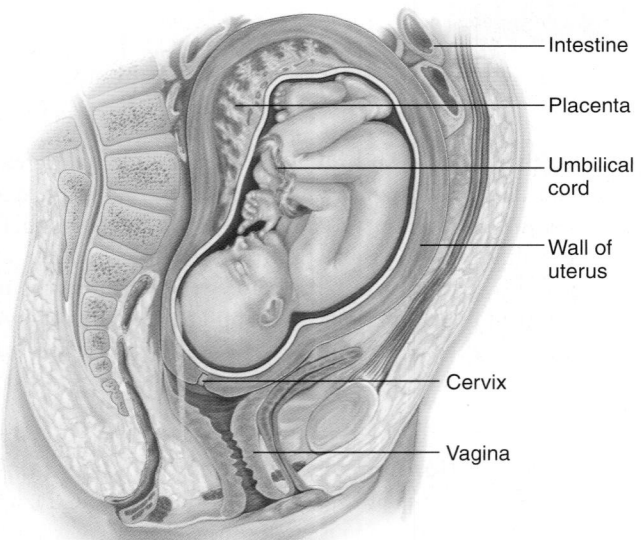

Figure 54.29 Position of the fetus just before birth.
A developing fetus causes major changes in a woman's anatomy. The stomach and intestines are pushed far up, and considerable discomfort often results from pressure on the lower back. In a normal vaginal delivery, the fetus exits through the cervix, which must dilate (expand) considerably to permit passage.

Intestine

Placenta

Umbilical cord

Wall of uterus

Cervix

Vagina

portion of the skull grow very little after birth, whereas the bones of the jaw continue to grow. As a result, the head of an adult chimpanzee looks very different from that of a fetal or infant chimpanzee. In human infants, by contrast, the brain and cerebral skull grow at the same rate as the jaw. Therefore, the jaw–skull proportions do not change after birth, and the head of a human adult looks very similar to that of a human fetus or infant.

The fact that the human brain continues to grow significantly for the first few years of postnatal life means that adequate nutrition and a safe environment are particularly crucial during this period for the full development of a person's intellectual potential.

Learning Outcomes Review 54.6

The critical stages of human development occur in the first trimester of gestation; the subsequent 6 months involve growth and maturation. Growth of the brain is not complete at birth and must be completed postnatally. Hormones in the mother's blood maintain the nutritive uterine environment for the developing fetus; changes in hormone secretion and levels stimulate birth (prostaglandins and oxytocin) and lactation (oxytocin and prolactin).

■ **Why are teratogens (agents that cause birth defects) most potent in the first trimester?**

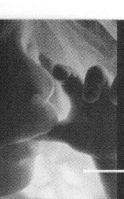

Chapter Review

54.1 Fertilization

A sperm must penetrate to the plasma membrane of the egg for membrane fusion to occur.
The sperm's acrosome releases digestive enzymes to penetrate the egg's external layers (see figure 54.1). Fusion with the egg's membrane allows the sperm nucleus to pass into the egg's cytoplasm.

Membrane fusion activates the egg.
Fusion of membranes triggers egg activation by the release of calcium (see figure 54.2). Blocks to polyspermy include changes in membrane potential and alterations to the external coat of the egg. Upon egg activation, meiosis is completed (see figures 54.4 and 54.5).

The fusion of nuclei restores the diploid state.
Fertilization is complete when the haploid sperm nucleus fuses with the haploid egg nucleus.

54.2 Cleavage and the Blastula Stage

The blastula is a hollow mass of cells.
Cleavage is a rapid series of cell divisions that produces blastomeres, which form a hollow ball of cells called a blastula.

Cleavage patterns are highly diverse and distinctive.
Cleavage patterns are primarily influenced by the amount of yolk (see table 54.2). With little or no yolk, cleavage is holoblastic (involving the whole egg); where more yolk is present, cleavage is meroblastic (involving the blastodisc only). Cleavage in mammals is holoblastic.

Blastomeres may or may not be committed to developmental paths.
In many animals, unequal segregation of cytoplasmic determinants commits each blastomere to a different path. Mammals exhibit regulative development in which the fate of early blastomeres is not predetermined.

54.3 Gastrulation

Gastrulation produces the three germ layers.
During gastrulation the three germ layers differentiate: endoderm, ectoderm, and mesoderm (see table 54.3). Cells move during gastrulation using a variety of cell shape changes.

Gastrulation patterns also vary according to the amount of yolk.
The amount of yolk also influences cell movement. In frogs, a layer of cells involutes through the dorsal lip of the blastopore. In birds, surface cells migrate through the primitive streak. Mammalian gastrulation is similar to that of birds.

Extraembryonic membranes are an adaptation to life on dry land.
The yolk sac, amnion, chorion, and allantois prevent dessication and nourish and protect the developing embryo (see figure 54.15).

54.4 Organogenesis

Changes in gene expression lead to cell determination.
A cell's location in the developing embryo often determines its fate. Differentiation can be established by inheritance of cytoplasmic determinants and by interactions with other cells (induction).

Development of selected systems in Drosophila illustrates organogenesis.
The development of salivary glands, the dorsal vessel, and tracheae all demonstrate the action of gene expression on development.

In vertebrates, organogenesis begins with neurulation and somitogenesis (see figures 55.18–55.20).
Neurulation is the formation of the neural tube from ectoderm near the notochord; somitogenesis is the establishment of mesoderm into units called somites.

Migratory neural crest cells differentiate into many cell types.
Neural crest cells migrate widely to become connective tissue, nerve and glial cells, melanocytes, sensory neurons, and other cells.

Neural crest derivatives are important in vertebrate evolution.
Many of the unique adaptations of vertebrates have arisen from neural crest cells (see figure 54.21).

54.5 Vertebrate Axis Formation

The Spemann organizer determines dorsal–ventral axis.
Organizers are a cluster of cells that produce gradients of diffusible signal molecules, conveying positional information to other cells.

Maternally encoded dorsal determinants activate Wnt signaling.

Turning on the Wnt pathway activates organizer specification.

Signaling molecules from the Spemann organizer inhibit ventral development.

Morphogens can either activate or inhibit development along a certain path. The Spemann organizer induces formation of the dorsum by inhibiting ventral development (see figure 54.24).

Evidence indicates that organizers are present in all vertebrates.

Cells at the anterior edge of the primitive streak, termed Hensen's node, function similarly to the Spemann organizer.

Induction can be primary or secondary.

Primary induction occurs between the three germ layers; secondary induction occurs between already determined tissues.

54.6 Human Development

During the first trimester, the zygote undergoes rapid development and differentiation.

Implantation of the blastocyst occurs at the end of the first week of pregnancy. During the second week, the embryonic chorion and the mother's endometrial tissues form the placenta, and gastrulation occurs. Organogenesis begins during the fourth week. The eighth week marks the transition from embryo to fetus.

During the second trimester, the basic body plan develops further.

During the third trimester, organs mature to the point at which the baby can survive outside the womb.

Critical changes in hormones bring on birth.

Birth is initiated by secretions of steroids from the fetal adrenal cortex that induce prostaglandins, which cause contractions.

Nursing of young is a distinguishing feature of mammals.

Nursing involves a neuroendocrine reflex, causing the release of oxytocin and the milk let-down response.

Postnatal development in humans continues for years.

Postnatal development continues with different organs growing at different rates—called allometric growth.

Review Questions

UNDERSTAND

1. Which of the following events occur immediately after fertilization?
   a. Egg activation
   b. Polyspermy defense
   c. Cytoplasm changes
   d. All of these occur after fertilization

2. Which of the following plays the greatest role in determining how cytoplasmic division occurs during cleavage?
   a. Number of chromosomes
   b. Amount of yolk
   c. Orientation of the vegetal pole
   d. Sex of the zygote

3. Gastrulation is a critical event during development. Why?
   a. Gastrulation converts a hollow ball of cells into a bilaterally symmetrical structure.
   b. Gastrulation causes the formation of a primitive digestive tract.
   c. Gastrulation causes the blastula to develop a dorsal–ventral axis.
   d. All of these are significant events that occur during gastrulation.

4. Gastrulation in a mammal would be most similar to gastrulation in
   a. a gecko.
   b. a tuna.
   c. an eagle.
   d. no other species; mammalian gastrulation is unique.

5. Somites
   a. begin forming at the tail end of the embryo and then move forward in a wavelike fashion.
   b. are derived from endoderm.
   c. develop into only one type of tissue per somite.
   d. may vary in number from one species to the next.

6. Of the following processes, which occurs last?
   a. Cleavage   c. Gastrulation
   b. Neurulation   d. Fertilization

APPLY

1. Your cousin just had twins. She tells you that twinning occurs when two sperm fertilize the same egg. You reply that
   a. yes, she is right, that is the most common source of twinning.
   b. no, only one sperm survives passage through the uterine cervix, so two sperm are never present at fertilization.
   c. no, cortical granules are used to prevent additional sperm penetration.
   d. no, twinning occurs when unfertilized eggs divide spontaneously and thus is parthenogenic in nature.

2. In the Spemann experiment, when the dorsal lip is transplanted, the recipient embryo then has a second source of molecules that
   a. specifies ventral fate.
   b. inhibits the molecules that specify ventral fate.
   c. specifies dorsal fate.
   d. inhibits the molecules that specify dorsal fate.

3. Suppose that a burst of electromagnetic radiation were to strike the blastomeres of only the animal pole of a frog embryo. Which of the following would be most likely to occur?

   a. A change or mutation relevant to the epidermis or skin
   b. A switching of the internal organs so that reverse orientation (left/right) occurs along the midline of the body
   c. The migration of the nervous system to form outside of the body
   d. Failure of the reproductive system to develop

4. Which of the following would qualify as a secondary induction?

   a. The formation of the lens of the eye due to induction by the neural ectoderm
   b. Differentiation during neurulation by the dorsal ectoderm and mesoderm
   c. Both of these
   d. Neither of these

5. Your Aunt Ida thinks that babies can stimulate the onset of their own labor. You tell her that

   a. among mammals the onset of labor has been most closely linked to a change in the phases of the Moon.
   b. it is the mother's circadian clock that determines the onset of labor.
   c. body weight determines the onset of labor.
   d. changes in fetal hormone levels can affect the onset of labor.

6. Drug or alcohol exposure during which of the following stages is most likely to have a profound effect on the neural development of the fetus?

   a. Preimplantation   c. Second trimester
   b. First trimester   d. Third trimester

7. Axis formation in amniotic embryos could be affected by

   a. mutations in cells in the dorsal lip of the blastopore.
   b. mutations in cells in the primitive streak.
   c. both of these.
   d. neither of these.

SYNTHESIZE

1. Suppose you discover a new species whose development mechanisms have not been documented before. How could you determine at what stage the cell fate is determined?

2. You look up from your studying to see your dog, Fifi, acting silly again. Using this as a teachable moment, compare and contrast the homeoboxes in your dog and the fruit fly she just ate.

3. Why doesn't a woman menstruate while she is pregnant?

4. Spemann and Mangold were able to demonstrate that some cells act as "organizers" during development. What types of cells did they use? How did they determine that these cells were organizers?

ONLINE RESOURCE

www.ravenbiology.com

Understand, Apply, and Synthesize—enhance your study with animations that bring concepts to life and practice tests to assess your understanding. Your instructor may also recommend the interactive eBook, individualized learning tools, and more.

Part **VIII** Ecology and Behavior

Chapter **55**

Behavioral Biology

Chapter Outline

55.1 The Natural History of Behavior

55.2 Nerve Cells, Neurotransmitters, Hormones, and Behavior

55.3 Behavioral Genetics

55.4 Learning

55.5 The Development of Behavior

55.6 Animal Cognition

55.7 Orientation and Migratory Behavior

55.8 Animal Communication

55.9 Behavioral Ecology

55.10 Reproductive Strategies and Sexual Selection

55.11 Altruism

55.12 The Evolution of Group Living and Animal Societies

Introduction

The study of behavior is at the center of many disciplines of biology. Observing behavior provides important insights into the workings of the brain and nervous system, the influences of genes and the environment, when and how animals reproduce, and how they adapt to their environment. Behavior is shaped by natural selection and is controlled by internal mechanisms involving genes, hormones, neurotransmitters, and neural circuits. In this chapter, we explore how behavioral biology integrates approaches from several branches of biological science to provide a detailed understanding of the mechanisms that underscore behavior and its evolution.

The Natural History of Behavior

Learning Outcomes

1. **Contrast the proximate and ultimate causation of behavior.**
2. **Explain instinct theory.**
3. **Describe the physiological factors that might be the basis for innate behaviors.**

Observing animal behavior and making inferences about what one sees is at once simple and profound. Behavior is what an animal does. It is the most immediate way an animal responds adaptively to its environment by tracking environmental cues and signals such as odors, sounds, or visual signals associated with food, predators, or mates. Behavior also concerns thinking and cognition, monitoring one's social environment, and making decisions as to whether or not to cooperate or act altruistically. Behavior allows animals to survive and reproduce and is thus critical to the evolutionary process. The work of behavioral biologists has provided important insights into animal behavior, including the very meaning of human behavior.

Behavior can be analyzed in terms of mechanisms (cause) and evolutionary origin (adaptive nature)

Why does an animal behave in a particular way? Consider hearing a bird sing. We could ask how it vocalizes or determine the time of the year it sings most frequently. We could also ask about the function of the song, that is, ask why it sings. Answers to questions about how birds sing consider the role of internal factors such as hormones and nerve cells and other physiological processes. Such questions concern proximate causation: the mechanisms that are the reason for behavior. To analyze the proximate cause of bird song, we could measure hormone levels or study the development of brain regions and neural circuits associated with singing. For example, a male songbird may sing during the breeding season because of an increased level of the steroid sex hormone testosterone, which binds to receptors in the brain and triggers the production of song. Additionally, neural connections between the brain and the syrinx (the bird's vocal organ) must develop to allow songs to be produced. These explanations describe the proximate cause of bird song.

Asking about the function of a behavior (once again, bird song) is to ask why it evolved. To answer this question, we would determine how it influenced survival or reproductive success. A male bird sings to defend a territory from other males and to attract a female with which to reproduce. This is the ultimate, or evolutionary, explanation for the male's vocalization. Now we can understand its ultimate causation, or adaptive value. Researchers often study behavior from both perspectives to fully appreciate its mechanisms and ecological function, and thus its role in evolution. Behavior can be analyzed at four levels: (1) physiology (how it is influenced by hormones, nerve cells, and other internal factors); (2) ontogeny (how it develops in an individual), (3) phylogeny (its origin in groups of related species), and (4) adaptive significance (its role in survival and fitness). We'll begin by tracing the history of the study of mechanisms of behavior by focusing on the work of ethologists—biologists who first began to study behavior at the turn of the 20th century.

Ethology emphasizes the study of instinct and its origins

Ethology is the study of the natural history of behavior, with an emphasis on behaviors that form an animal's instincts, or programmed behaviors. Ethologists observed that individuals of a given species behaved in stereotyped ways, showing the same pattern of behavior in response to a particular stimulus. Because their behavior seemed reflexive, they considered it to be instinctive, or *innate*. Behaviors were thought to be programmed by the nervous system, which in turn was designed by genes, and responses would occur without experience. Ethologists based their instinct model on observations and experiments of simple behaviors such as egg retrieval by geese. Geese incubate their eggs in a nest. If an egg falls out of the nest, the goose will roll the egg back into the nest with a side-to-side motion of its neck while the egg is tucked beneath its bill (figure 55.1). Even if the egg is removed during retrieval, the goose will still complete the egg-retrieval sequence, as if driven by a program activated by the initial sight of the egg outside the nest.

This example is one paradigm of instinct theory and illustrates the way ethologists conceptualized the mechanisms of behavior. Egg retrieval behavior is triggered by a *key stimulus* (sometimes called a *sign stimulus*); this is the egg out of the nest. Early ethologists thought the nervous system regulated behavior via the *innate releasing mechanism*, a neural circuit involved

Sign stimulus

Fixed action pattern

Figure 55.1 Innate egg-rolling response in geese. The series of movements used by a goose to retrieve an egg is a fixed action pattern. Once it detects the sign stimulus (in this case, an egg outside the nest), the goose goes through the entire set of movements: It will extend its neck toward the egg, get up, and roll the egg back into the nest with a side-to-side motion of its neck while the egg is tucked beneath its bill.

in the perception of the key stimulus and the triggering of a motor program, the *fixed action pattern*, in this case the act of guiding the egg back to the nest. Ethologists generalized that the key stimulus is a cue or signal in the environment that initiates neural events that cause behavior. The innate releasing mechanism involves the sensory apparatus that detects the signal and the neural circuit controlling muscles to generate the fixed action pattern.

Learning Outcomes Review 55.1

Proximate causation of behavior involves the immediate mechanisms that bring about an action; ultimate causation refers to the adaptive value of a behavior. Ethology is the study of the nature of behavior, emphasizing instinct and the regulation of behavior by internal factors such as genes, nerve cells, and hormones. Ethologists are also interested in the origins of behavior.

■ **Why is it important to understand the phylogeny (evolutionary origins) of behavior?**

55.2 Nerve Cells, Neurotransmitters, Hormones, and Behavior

Learning Outcomes

1. Relate the structure of neural circuits to their function.
2. Describe the role of hormones and neurotransmitters in behavior.

Although early ethologists had little understanding of neurobiology, they hypothesized elements of the nervous system (the innate releasing mechanism) controlled behavior. Today, neuroethologists—researchers who examine the neurobiology of behavior—can describe in detail how information in the environment is processed by sensory cells and how nerve impulses are transmitted to other neurons and muscles to form neural circuits that regulate behaviors important to survival. Behavior reflects the organization of the peripheral and central nervous system, and studying behavior can help us understand how neurons function individually and in combination with other neurons in circuits (see chapters 44 and 45).

Behaviors that must occur rapidly, like those used to capture prey or flee predators, involve neural mechanisms that enable such functions. Some moths have an earlike sensory organ equipped with sensory neurons designed to detect the ultrasonic cries of bats, the first step in evading predation. Specialized cells in the frog's retina detect moving objects like insects and release the tongue in fractions of a second once suitable prey is sighted. Likewise, the jaws of a predatory ant snap shut when prey trigger sensory hairs between the mandibles. Rapid responses to predators or prey often involve large nerve cell axons that can quickly transmit impulses to muscles. In the example of "trap jaw" ants, large axons of the mandibular motor neuron—the fastest neuron yet identified—fire nerve impulses

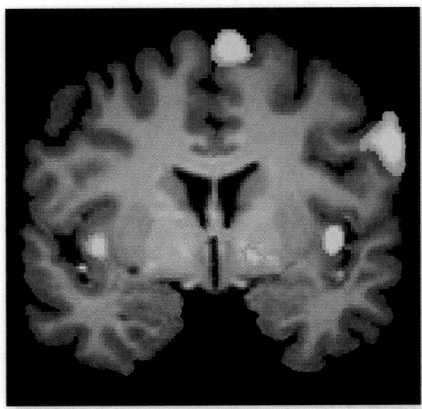

Figure 55.2 Functional Magnetic Resonance Imaging (fMRI). MRIs reveal neural activity in specific regions of the brain. In this case, activity in part of the brain called the nucleus accumbens is associated with viewing images of food.

that close the jaws in only 33 msec. Neural circuits that enable quick responses often are made up of few sensory and motor neurons, and their connecting nerve cells.

Behavioral biologists examine the relationship of hormones to behavior to understand the endocrine mechanisms that are the foundation of reproduction, parental care, aggression, and stress (see chapter 46). In this way, the effects of the steroid sex hormones estrogen and testosterone on behavior have been determined. Testosterone in the male, for example, regulates territorial behavior and courtship, whereas estrogen in the female controls her mating behavior. Glucocorticoid hormones are involved in stress.

Neuroscientists may measure levels of neurotransmitters such as serotonin and dopamine in the nervous system or blood and associate these chemicals with behavior (see chapter 44). These chemicals are released by nerve cells and can affect activity in different brain regions. Serotonin has been shown to influence aggression in an incredibly wide range of animals including lobsters, mice, and humans. Researchers may inject a neurotransmitter or pharmacologically change its level in the brain to examine how it affects behavior.

The techniques of neuroethology include identifying and mapping individual neurons, their dendrites and connections to other neurons, and how their impulses and neurochemicals regulate behavior. Today, techniques such as functional magnetic resonance imaging (fMRI) are generating exciting data on the specialized functions of different regions of the human brain. One striking example concerns how the brain responds to images of food (figure 55.2). In contrast to expectation, the brain's response does not occur in the visual cortex, the region associated with object recognition, but in a circuit in the nucleus accumbens in the forebrain, normally involved in reward and pleasure.

Learning Outcomes Review 55.2

Instinctive behaviors appear to involve programmed circuits in the nervous system that are likely to be genetically controlled. Research in neuroethology supports the instinct concept of behavior by describing the organization of neural circuits governing behavior. Chemical signals provided by hormones and by neurotransmitters such as serotonin and dopamine cause behaviors to occur.

■ **If a male songbird is injected with testosterone two weeks earlier than when these birds normally start to sing in the spring, what would you expect to happen?**

Behavioral Genetics

Learning Outcomes

1. *Discuss the types of studies that have provided evidence to link genes and behavior.*
2. *Explain how single genes can influence behavior.*
3. *Describe the role of genes in complex behaviors such as aggression, parental care, and pair bonding.*

Instinct theory assumed that genes play a role in behavior, but ethologists did not conclusively demonstrate the role genes can play. The study of genes and behavior has often been highly controversial, as ethologists and social scientists engaged in a seemingly endless debate over whether behavior is determined more by an individual's genes (nature) or by its learning and experience (nurture). One problem with this nature/nurture controversy is that the question is framed as an "either/or" proposition, which fails to consider that both instinct and experience can have significant roles, often interacting in complex ways to shape behavior.

Behavioral genetics deals with the contribution that heredity makes to behavior. It is obvious that genes, the units of heredity, are passed from one generation to the next and guide the development of the nervous system and potentially the behavioral responses it regulates. But animals may also develop in a rich social environment and have experiences that guide behavior. The importance of "nature" and "nurture" to behavior can be seen by first reviewing the history of studies in behavioral genetics and next examining the importance of experience and development. We'll then consider their interaction.

Artificial selection and hybrid studies link genes and behavior

Pioneering research indicated that behavioral differences among individuals result from genetic differences. Research on a variety of animals demonstrated that hybrids showed behaviors involved in nest building and courtship that were intermediate between those of parents. These early efforts to define the role of genes in behavior demonstrated that behavior can have a heritable component, but fell short of identifying the genes involved. With the development of molecular biology, far greater precision was added to the analysis of the genetics of behavior.

Learning itself can be influenced by genes. In one classic study, rats had to find their way through a maze of blind alleys and only one exit, where a reward of food awaited them. Some rats quickly learned to zip through the maze to the food, making few mistakes, but other rats made more errors in learning the correct path. Researchers bred rats that made few errors with one another to establish a "maze-bright" group, and error-prone rats were interbred, forming a "maze-dull" group. Offspring in each group were then tested for their maze-learning ability. The offspring of maze-bright rats learned to negotiate the maze with fewer errors than their parents, while the offspring of maze-dull parents performed more poorly. Repeating this artificial selection method for several generations led to two behaviorally distinct types of rat with very different maze-learning abilities (figure 55.3). This type of study suggests the ways in which natural selection could shape behavior over time, making genes for certain abilities more prevalent.

Inquiry question

? What would happen if, after the seventh generation, rats were randomly assigned mates regardless of their ability to learn the maze?

Some behaviors appear to be controlled by a single gene

Artificial selection and hybrid studies only suggested a role for genes in behavior. Subsequent research took advantage of advances in molecular biology and identified the genes involved. Fruit flies, *Drosophila*, have traditionally provided a useful model system in which the effect of single genes have been identified.

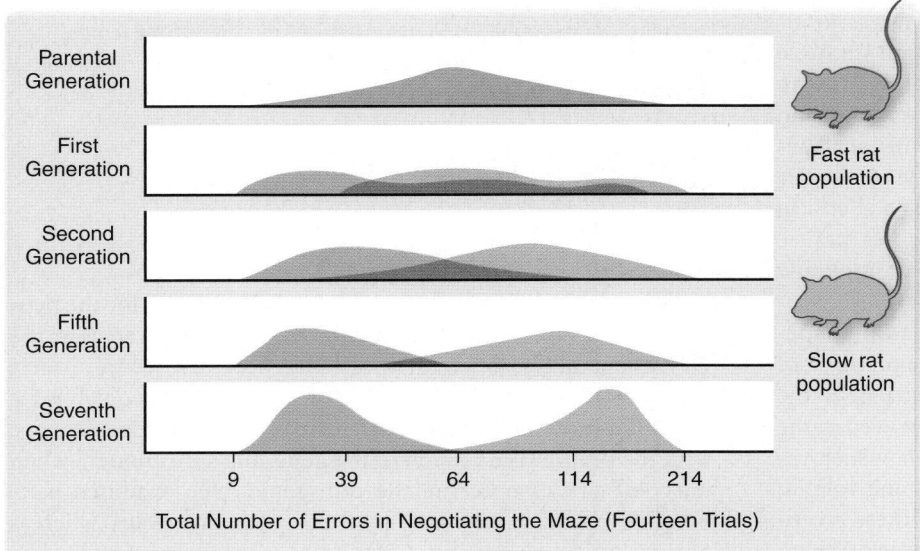

Parental Generation

First Generation

Second Generation

Fifth Generation

Seventh Generation

Total Number of Errors in Negotiating the Maze (Fourteen Trials)

9   39   64   114   214

Fast rat population

Slow rat population

Figure 55.3 The genetics of learning. Rats that made the fewest errors in the parental population were interbred to select for rats that had improved maze-learning ability (green), and rats that made the most errors were interbred to select for rats that were error prone (red).

Inquiry question

? What would happen if, after the seventh generation, rats were randomly assigned mates regardless of their ability to learn the maze?

Single genes have also been shown to influence behavior in animals ranging from mice to humans.

In fruit flies, individuals that possess alternative alleles for a particular gene differ greatly in their feeding behavior as larvae: Larvae with one allele move around a great deal as they eat, whereas individuals with the alternative allele move hardly at all. A wide variety of experimentally induced mutations at other genes affect courtship behavior in males and females. For example, *fru* is a regulatory gene whose transcription products govern the design of the courtship center of the fruit fly brain. This gene turns on other genes involved in the neural circuitry of courtship.

Single genes in mice are associated with spatial memory and parenting. For example, some mice with a particular mutation have trouble remembering recently learned information about where objects are located. This is apparently because they lack the ability to produce the enzyme α-calcium-calmodulin-dependent kinase II, which plays an important role in the functioning of the hippocampus, a part of the brain important for spatial learning.

It is particularly interesting that genes are involved in behavior as complex as maternal care: The presence or absence of *fosB* determines whether female mice nurture their young in particular ways. Females with both *fosB* alleles disabled initially investigate their newborn babies, but then ignore them, in stark contrast to the caring and protective maternal behavior displayed by normal females (figure 55.4). The cause of this inattentiveness appears to result from a chain reaction. When mothers of new babies initially inspect them, information from their auditory, olfactory, and tactile senses is transmitted to the hypothalamus, where *fosB* alleles are activated. The *fosB* alleles produce a protein, which in turn activates other enzymes and genes that affect the neural circuitry of the hypothalamus. These modifications in the brain cause the female to behave maternally. If mothers lack the *fosB* alleles, this process is stopped midway. No protein is activated, the brain's neural circuitry is not rewired, and maternal behavior does not result. The "maternal instincts" of mice can thus be defined genetically!

Another fascinating example of the genetic basis of behavior concerns prairie and montane voles, two closely related species of North American rodents that differ profoundly in their social behavior. Male and female prairie voles form monogamous pair bonds and share parental care, whereas montane voles are promiscuous (meaning they mate with multiple partners and go their separate ways). The act of mating leads to the release of the neuropeptides vasopressin and oxytocin, and the response to these peptides differs dramatically in each species. Injection of either peptide into prairie voles leads to pair bonding even without mating. Conversely, injecting a chemical that blocks the action of these neuropeptides causes prairie voles not to form pair bonds after mating. By contrast, montane voles are unaffected by either of these manipulations.

These different responses have been traced to interspecific differences in brain structure (figure 55.5). The prairie vole has many receptors for these peptides in a particular part of the brain, the nucleus accumbens, which seems to be involved in the expression of pair-bonding behavior. By contrast, few such receptors occur in the same brain region in the montane vole. In laboratory experiments with prairie voles, blocking these receptors tends to prevent pair-bonding, whereas stimulating them

fosB **Alleles Present**

a.

fosB **Alleles Inactivated**

b.

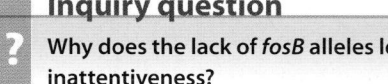

c. *d.*

Figure 55.4 Genetically caused defect in maternal care.
a. In mice, normal mothers take very good care of their offspring, retrieving them if they move away and crouching over them.
b. Mothers with the mutant *fosB* allele perform neither of these behaviors, leaving their pups exposed. *c.* Amount of time female mice were observed crouching in a nursing posture over offspring. *d.* Proportion of pups retrieved when they were experimentally moved.

Inquiry question

? Why does the lack of *fosB* alleles lead to maternal inattentiveness?

leads to pair-bonding behavior. The gene that codes for the peptide receptors has also been identified, and a difference in the DNA structure between the species has been discovered. To test the hypothesis that this genetic difference was responsible for the differences in behavior, scientists created transgenic mice with the prairie vole version of the gene, and sure enough, when injected with vasopressin, the transgenic mice exhibited pair-bonding behavior very similar to that of prairie voles, whereas normal mice showed no response (see figure 55.5). The

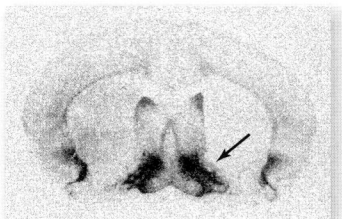
a. Prairie vole

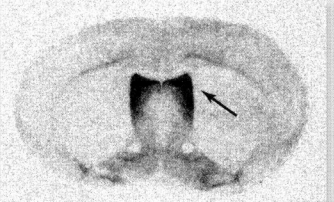
b. Montane vole

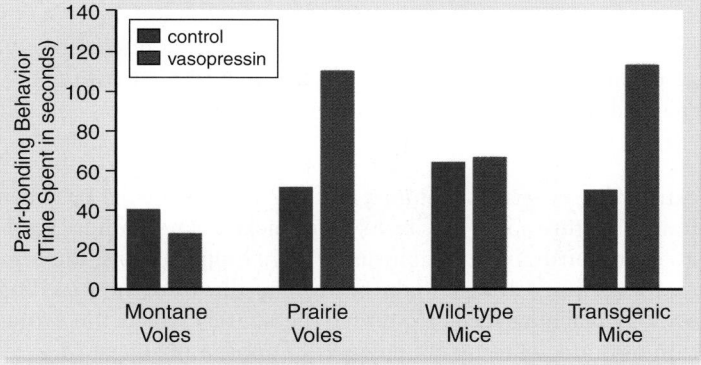
c.

Figure 55.5 Genetic basis of differences in pair-bonding behavior in two rodent species. *a.* and *b.* The prairie (*Microtus ochrogaster*) and montane (*M. montanus*) voles differ in the distribution of one type of vasopressin receptor in the brain. *c.* Transgenic mice created with the prairie-vole version of the receptor genes respond to injections of vasopressin by exhibiting heightened levels of pair-bonding behavior in 5-min trials compared with their response to a control injection. By contrast, normal wild-type mice (control) show no increase in such behaviors.

vasopressin receptor gene varies in structure among primate species that vary in degree of pair bonding. In human males, the gene has recently been found to be associated with the strength of marital bonds and satisfaction in marriage.

The production of monoamine oxidases (MAOs), enzymes that degrade neurotransmitters such as serotonin and dopamine, are controlled by single genes. Transgenic mice that lack MAOA (monoamine oxidase-A) are highly aggressive. In humans, a single point mutation results in the lack of the ability to produce MAOA, resulting in antisocial behavior and violence. MAO abnormalities are also associated with mood disorders in humans.

Learning Outcomes Review 55.3

A relationship between genes and behavior has been demonstrated in many ways, including artificial selection experiments and studies on the effects of single genes. Genes can regulate behavior by producing molecular factors that influence the function of the nervous system; mutations altering these factors have been found to affect behavior.

■ *What would you infer about the role of genes in pair-bonding in prairie voles if you learned that males sometimes seek to copulate with females other than their own mate?*

Learning Outcomes

1. **Describe the mechanisms of learning.**
2. **Define learning preparedness.**
3. **Explain how instinct influences learning preparedness.**

Instincts can guide an animal's actions, but behavior can also develop from previous experiences, a process termed learning. Traditionally, psychologists studied the mechanisms of learning using laboratory rodents, but today both proximate and ultimate causes of learning are understood by integrating learning into an ecological and evolutionary framework.

Learning mechanisms include habituation and association

Habituation is a simple form of learning defined as a decrease in response to a repeated stimulus that has no positive or negative consequences. Initially, the stimulus may evoke a strong response, but the response declines with repeated exposure. For example, young birds see many types of objects moving overhead. At first, they may respond by crouching and remaining still. But frequently seen objects, such as falling leaves or members of their own species flying overhead, have no positive or negative consequence to the nestlings. Over time, the young birds may habituate to such stimuli and stop responding. Thus, habituation can be thought of as learning not to respond to a stimulus.

One ecological context in which habituation has adaptive value is prey defense. Birds that feed on insects search for suitable prey in a visually complex environment. Insects that have camouflaged bodies appear to be twigs or leaves, which are commonly encountered as birds search for prey. Because birds see these objects very frequently, they habituate to their appearance. Insects that look like twigs or leaves are therefore protected because they do not trigger an attack, and they survive to reproduce.

More complex forms of learning concern changes in behavior through an association between two stimuli or between a stimulus and a response. In associative learning, for example, (figure 55.6) a behavior is modified, or conditioned, through the association. The two major types of associative learning—classical conditioning and operant conditioning—differ in the way the associations are established. In **classical conditioning,** the paired presentation of two different kinds of stimuli causes the animal to form an association between the stimuli. Classical conditioning is also called **Pavlovian conditioning,** after the Russian psychologist Ivan Pavlov, who first described it.

Pavlov presented meat powder, an unconditioned stimulus, to a dog and noted that the dog responded by salivating, an unconditioned response. If an unrelated stimulus, such as the ringing of a bell, was repeatedly presented at the same time as the meat powder, the dog would soon salivate in response to the sound of the bell alone. The dog had learned to associate the unrelated sound stimulus with the meat powder stimulus. Its

a.   b.   c.

Figure 55.6 Learning what is edible. Associative learning is involved in predator–prey interactions. *a.* A naive toad is offered a bumblebee as food. *b.* The toad is stung, and *(c)* subsequently avoids feeding on bumblebees or any other insects having black-and-yellow coloration. The toad has associated the appearance of the insect with pain and modifies its behavior.

response to the sound stimulus was, therefore, conditioned, and the sound of the bell is referred to as a conditioned stimulus.

In **operant conditioning,** an animal learns to associate its behavioral response with a reward or punishment. American psychologist B. F. Skinner studied operant conditioning in rats by placing them in an apparatus that came to be called a "Skinner box." As the rat explored the box, it would occasionally press a lever by accident, causing a pellet of food to appear. Soon it learned to associate pressing the lever (the behavioral response) with obtaining food (the reward). This sort of trial-and-error learning is of major importance to most vertebrates. Learning provides flexibility that allows behavior to be fine-tuned to an environment.

Instinct governs learning preparedness

Psychologists once believed that any two stimuli could be linked through learning and that animals could be conditioned to perform any learnable behavior. This view has changed. Today, researchers believe that instinct guides learning by determining what type of information can be learned. Animals may have innate predispositions toward forming certain associations. For example, if a rat is offered a food pellet at the same time it is exposed to X-rays (which later produce nausea), the rat remembers the taste of the food pellet but not its size, and in the future will avoid food with that taste, but will readily eat pellets of the same size if they have a different taste. Similarly, pigeons can learn to associate food with colors, but not with sounds. In contrast, they can associate danger with sounds, but not with colors.

These examples of learning preparedness demonstrate that what an animal can learn is biologically influenced—that is, learning is possible only within the boundaries set by evolution. Innate programs for learning have evolved because they lead to adaptive responses. In nature, food that is toxic to a rat is likely to have a particular taste; thus, it is adaptive to be able to associate a taste with a feeling of sickness that may develop hours later. The seed a pigeon eats may have a distinctive color that the pigeon can see, but it makes no sound the pigeon can hear.

An animal's ecology is key to understanding its learning capabilities. Some species of birds, such as Clark's nutcracker, feed on seeds. When seeds are abundant, these birds store them in buried caches so they will have food during the winter. Seed caches (up to 2000!) may be buried and then recovered as long as nine months later. One would expect these birds to have an extraordinary spatial memory, and this is indeed what has been found (figure 55.7). Clark's nutcracker, and other seed-hoarding birds, have an unusually large hippocampus, the center for memory storage in the brain. This illustrates how feeding ecology (caching seeds to survive the winter) affects the evolution of brain anatomy (an enlarged hippocampus).

Learning Outcomes Review 55.4

Habituation is a diminishing response to a repeated stimulus that is neither positive nor negative. Association may occur as either classical conditioning or operant conditioning. Animals can change their behavior through learning in a variety of ways. Although learning mechanisms may be similar across species, animals also differ in their learning abilities according to their ecology.

■ *In some rodents, males travel far while females remain close to the nest. Do males or females have greater spatial memory? What experiment could you conduct to test your hypothesis?*

Figure 55.7 The Clark's nutcracker has an extraordinary memory. A Clark's nutcracker (*Nucifraga columbiana*) can remember the locations of up to 2000 seed caches months after hiding them. After conducting experiments, scientists have concluded that the birds use features of the landscape and other surrounding objects as spatial references to memorize the locations of the caches.

55.5 *The Development of Behavior*

Learning Outcomes

1. *Discuss the role of the critical period in imprinting.*
2. *Explain how social contact can influence growth and development.*
3. *Explain how the study of song learning in white-crowned sparrows illustrates the interaction of instinct and learning.*

Behavioral biologists recognize that behavior has both genetic and learned components. Thus far in this chapter, we have discussed the influence of genes and learning separately. But as you will see, these factors interact during development to shape behavior.

Parent–offspring interactions influence how behavior develops

As an animal matures, it may form social attachments to other individuals or develop preferences that will influence behavior later in life. This process of behavioral development is called **imprinting.** The success of imprinting is highest during a critical period (roughly 13 to 16 hours after hatching in geese). During this time, information required for normal development must be acquired. In **filial imprinting,** social attachments form between parents and offspring. For example, young birds like ducks and geese begin to follow their mother within a few hours after hatching, and their following response results in a social bond between mother and young. The young birds' initial experience, through imprinting, can determine how social behavior develops later in life. The ethologist Konrad Lorenz showed that geese will follow the first object they see after hatching and direct their social behavior toward that object, even if it is not their mother! Lorenz raised geese from eggs, and when he offered himself as a model for imprinting, the goslings treated him as if he were their parent, following him dutifully (figure 55.8).

Interactions between parents and offspring are key to the normal development of social behavior. The psychologist Harry Harlow gave orphaned rhesus monkey infants the opportunity to form social attachments with two surrogate "mothers," one made of soft cloth covering a wire frame and the other made only of wire (figure 55.9). The infants chose to spend time with the cloth mother, even if only the wire mother provided food, indicating that texture and tactile contact, rather than provision of food, may be among the key qualities in a mother that promote infant social attachment. If infant monkeys are deprived of normal social contact, their development is abnormal. Greater degrees of deprivation lead to greater abnormalities in social behavior during childhood and adulthood. Studies of orphaned human infants similarly suggest that a constant "mother figure" is required for normal growth and psychological development.

Figure 55.8 An unlikely parent. The eager goslings follow Konrad Lorenz as if he were their mother. He is the first object they saw when they hatched, and they have used him as a model for imprinting. Lorenz won the 1973 Nobel Prize in medicine or physiology for this work.

Recent research has revealed a biological need for the stimulation that occurs during parent–offspring interactions early in life. Female rats lick their pups after birth, and this stimulation inhibits the release of a brain peptide that can block normal growth. Pups that receive normal tactile stimulation also have more brain receptors for glucocorticoid hormones, thus a greater tolerance for stress, and longer-lived brain cells. Premature human infants who are massaged gain weight rapidly. These studies indicate that the need for normal social interaction is based in the brain, and that touch and

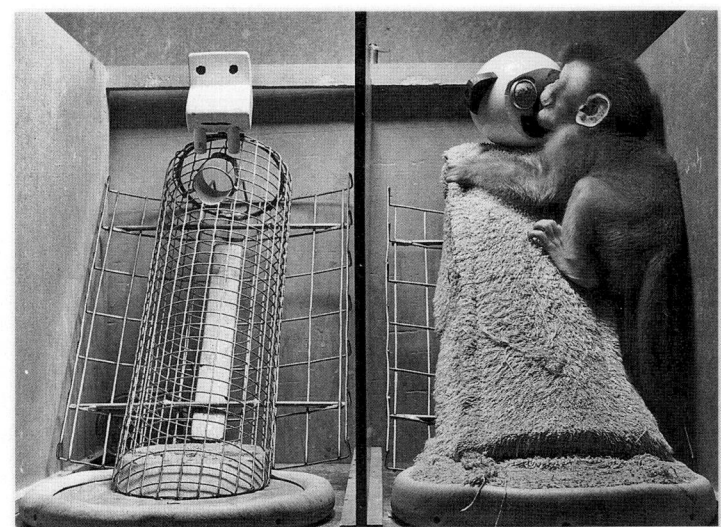

Figure 55.9 Choice trial on infant monkeys. Given a choice between a wire frame that provided food and a similar frame covered with cloth and given a monkey-like head, orphaned rhesus monkeys (*Macaca mulatta*) chose the monkeylike figure over the food.

other aspects of contact between parents and offspring are important for physical as well as behavioral development.

Instinct and learning may interact as behavior develops

We began this chapter by considering the proximate and ultimate causation of bird song. Let's continue with the classic studies by Peter Marler on song learning in white-crowned sparrows to examine how innate programs and experience each contribute to the development of behavior.

Mature male white-crowned sparrows sing a species-specific courtship song during the mating season. Through a series of elegant experiments, Peter Marler asked if the song was the result of an instinctive program, learning, or both. Marler reared male birds in soundproof incubators equipped with speakers and microphones to control what a bird heard as it matured, and then recorded the song it produced as an adult. Males that heard no song at all during development sang a poorly developed song as adults (figure 55.10), indicating that instinct alone did not guide song production. In a second study, males were played only the song of a different species, the song sparrow. These males sang a poorly structured song as well. This experiment showed that males would not imitate any song they heard to learn to sing. But birds that heard the song of their own species, or that heard the songs of both the white-crowned sparrow and the song sparrow, sang a fully developed, white-crowned sparrow song as adults.

These results suggest males have a selective **genetic template,** or innate program, that guides them to learn the appropriate song. During a critical period in development, the template will accept the white-crowned sparrow song as a model. Thus, song acquisition depends on learning, but only the song of the correct species can be learned; the genetic template limits what can be learned.

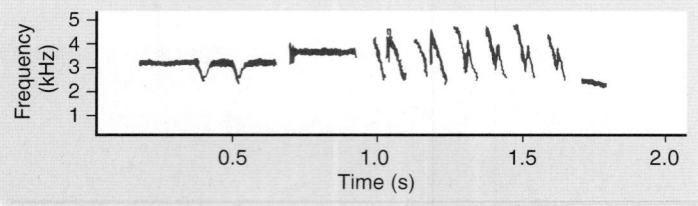

a.

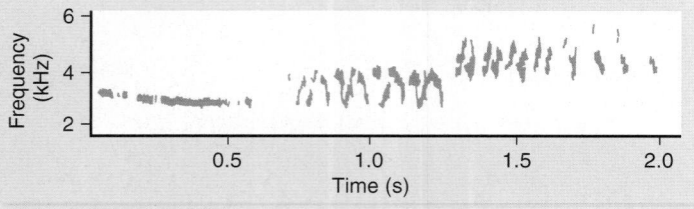

b.

Figure 55.10 Song development in birds. *a.* The sonograms of songs produced by male white-crowned sparrows (*Zonotrichia leucophrys*) that had been exposed to their own species' song during development are different from (*b*) those of male sparrows that heard no song during rearing. This difference indicates that the genetic program itself is insufficient to produce a normal song.

Figure 55.11 Brood parasite. Cuckoos lay their eggs in the nests of other species of birds. Because the young cuckoos (large bird to the right) are raised by a different species (such as this meadow pipit, smaller bird to the left), they have no opportunity to learn the cuckoo song; the cuckoo song they later sing is innate.

But learning plays a prominent role as well. If a young male becomes deaf after it hears its species' song during the critical period, it will sing a poorly developed song as an adult. Therefore, the bird must hear the correct song at the right time, and then "practice" listening to himself sing, matching what he hears to the model his genetic template has accepted.

Although this explanation of song development stood unchallenged for many years, white-crowned sparrow males can learn another species' song under certain conditions. If a live male strawberry finch is placed in a cage next to a young male sparrow, the young sparrow will learn to sing the strawberry finch's song. This finding indicates that social stimuli—in this case, being able to see, hear, and interact with another bird—is more effective than a tape-recorded song in altering the innate template that guides song development.

The males of some bird species may have no opportunity to hear the song of their own species. In such cases, it appears that the males instinctively "know" their own species' song. For example, cuckoos are **brood parasites;** females lay their eggs in the nest of another species of bird, and the young that hatch are reared by the foster parents (figure 55.11). When the cuckoos become adults, they sing the song of their own species rather than that of their foster parents. Because male brood parasites would most likely hear the song of their host species during development, it is adaptive for them to ignore such "incorrect" stimuli. They hear no adult males of their own species singing, so no correct song models are available. In these species, natural selection has produced a completely genetically guided song. Other birds can also sing a correct species-typical song, even if reared in isolation.

Inquiry question

? Imagine there is only one bird species on an island. Do you think instinct, learning, or both will guide song development?

Studies on twins reveal a role for both genes and environment in human behavior

The interaction of genes and the environment can be seen in humans by comparing the behavior of identical twins (which are genetically the same), raised in the same environment or separated at birth and raised apart in different environments. Data on human twins raised together or raised apart allows researchers to determine whether similarities in behavior result from their genetic similarity or from shared environmental experiences. Twins studies indicate many similarities in a wide range of personality traits even though twins were raised in very different environments. Other studies show that antisocial behavior in humans, for which genetic factors such as MAOA deficiencies are known in individuals in the study sample, results from a combination of genes and experience during childhood. These similarities indicate that genetics plays a role in behavior even in humans, although the relative importance of genetics versus environment is still debated.

Learning Outcomes Review 55.5

During the critical period, offspring must engage in certain social interactions for normal behavioral development. Parent–offspring contact stimulates the release of physiological factors, such as hormones and brain receptors, crucial to growth and brain development. In white-crowned sparrows, young males must hear their species' song to sing it correctly, indicating that both instinct and learning affect song development.

■ *Some researchers have tried to link IQ and genes in humans. Why would this research be seen as controversial?*

55.6 Animal Cognition

Learning Outcome

1. *Explain why behavioral biologists today are more open to considering that animals can think.*

For many decades, students of animal behavior flatly rejected the notion that nonhuman animals can think. Now serious attention is given to animal awareness. The central question of whether animals show **cognitive behavior**—that is, they process information and respond in a manner that suggests thinking—is widely supported (figure 55.12).

In a series of classic experiments conducted in the 1920s, a chimpanzee was left in a room with bananas hanging from the ceiling out of reach. Also in the room were several boxes lying on the floor. After some unsuccessful attempts to jump up and grab the bananas, the chimp stacked the boxes beneath the suspended bananas, and climbed up to claim its prize (figure 55.13). Field researchers have observed that Japanese macaques learned

a. *b.*

Figure 55.12 Animal thinking? *a.* This chimpanzee is stripping the leaves from a twig, which it will then use to probe a termite nest. This behavior strongly suggests that the chimpanzee is consciously planning ahead, with full knowledge of what it intends to do. *b.* This sea otter is using a rock as an "anvil," against which it bashes a clam to break it open. A sea otter will often keep a favorite rock for a long time, as though it has a clear idea of its future use of the rock. Behaviors such as these suggest that animals have cognitive abilities.

to wash sand off potatoes and to float grain to separate it from sand. Chimpanzees pull leaves off a tree branch and then stick the branch into the entrance of a termite nest to "fish" for food. Chimps also crack open nuts using pieces of wood in a "hammer and anvil" technique. Even more remarkable is that parents appear to teach nut cracking to their offspring!

Recent studies have found that chimpanzees and other primates show amazing behaviors that provide strong evidence of cognition. Chimpanzees will eat the leaves of medicinal plants when infected with certain parasites. Chimps also cooperate with other chimps in ways that suggest an understanding of past success. Cognitive ability is not limited to primates: Ravens and other corvid birds also show extraordinary insight and problem-solving ability (figure 55.14).

Figure 55.13 Problem solving by a chimpanzee. Unable to get the bananas by jumping, the chimpanzee devises a solution.

Figure 55.14 Problem solving by a raven.
Confronted with a problem it has never previously faced, the raven figures out how to get the meat at the end of the string by repeatedly pulling up a bit of string and stepping on it.

Learning Outcome Review 55.6

Research has provided compelling evidence that some nonhuman animals are able solve problems and use reasoning, cognitive abilities once thought uniquely human.

- ■ *How could you determine whether a chimpanzee had the ability to count objects?*

55.7 Orientation and Migratory Behavior

Learning Outcomes

1. *Define migration.*
2. *Distinguish between orientation and navigation.*
3. *Describe different systems for navigation.*

Monarch butterflies and many birds travel thousands of miles over continents to overwintering sites in the tropics. Many animals travel away from a nest and then return. To do so, they track cues in the environment, often showing exceptional skill at orientation. Animals with a homing instinct, such as pigeons, recognize complex features of the environment to return to their home. Despite decades of study, our understanding of animal orientation is far from complete.

Migration often involves populations moving large distances

Long-range, two-way movements are known as migrations. Each fall, ducks, geese, and many other birds migrate south along flyways from Canada across the United States, heading as far as South America, and then returning each spring.

Monarch butterflies also migrate each fall from central and eastern North America to their overwintering sites in several small, geographically isolated areas of coniferous forest in the mountains of central Mexico (figure 55.15). Each August, the butterflies begin a flight southward and at the end of winter, the monarchs begin the return flight to their summer breeding ranges. Two to five generations may be produced as the butterflies fly north: butterflies that migrate in the autumn to the precise locations in Mexico have never been there before!

Recent geographic range expansions by some migrating birds have revealed how migratory patterns change. When colonies of bobolinks became established in the western United States, far from their normal range in the Midwest and East, they did not migrate directly to their winter range in South America. Instead, they migrated east to their ancestral range, and then south along the original flyway (figure 55.16). Rather than changing the original migration pattern, they simply added a new segment. Scientists continue to study the western bobolinks to learn whether, in time, a more efficient migration path will evolve or

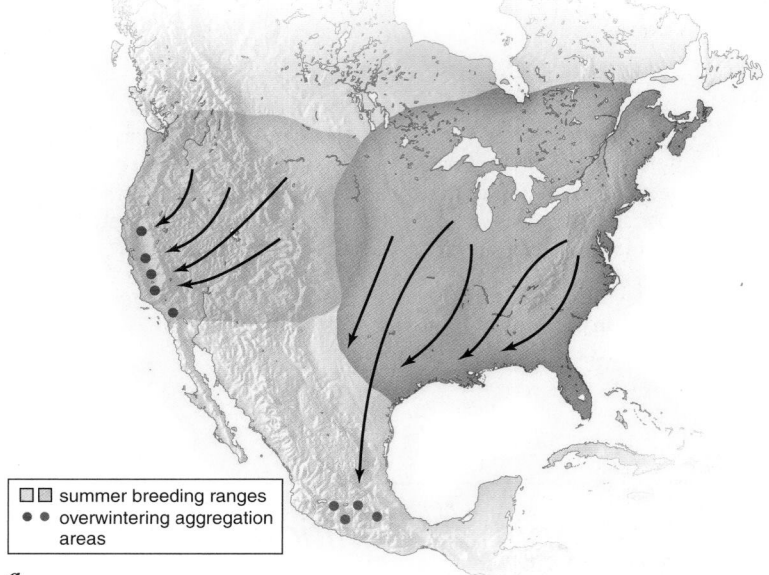

▢▢ summer breeding ranges
●● overwintering aggregation areas

a.

b.

c.

Figure 55.15 Migration of monarch butterflies (*Danaus plexippus*). *a.* Monarchs from western North America overwinter in areas of mild climate along the Pacific coast. Those from eastern North America migrate over 3000 kilometers to Mexico. *b.* Monarch butterflies arrive at the remote forests of the overwintering grounds in Mexico, where they *(c)* form aggregations on the tree trunks.

whether the birds will always follow their ancestral course. The behavior of butterflies and birds accentuate the mysteries of the mechanism employed during migration.

Migrating animals must be capable of orientation and navigation

To get from one place to another, animals must have a "map" (that is, know where to go) and a "compass" (use environmental cues to guide their journey). Orientation requires following a bearing such as a source of light, but navigation is the ability to set or adjust a bearing, and then follow it. The former is analogous to using a compass, while the latter is like using a compass in conjunction with a map. The nature of the "map" animals use is unclear.

Birds and other animals navigate by looking at the sun during the day and the stars at night. The indigo bunting is a short-distance nocturnal migrant bird. It flies during the day using the Sun as a guide, and compensates for the movement of the Sun in the sky as the day progresses. These birds use the positions of constellations around the North Star in the night sky as a compass.

Many migrating birds also have the ability to detect Earth's magnetic field and to orient themselves with respect

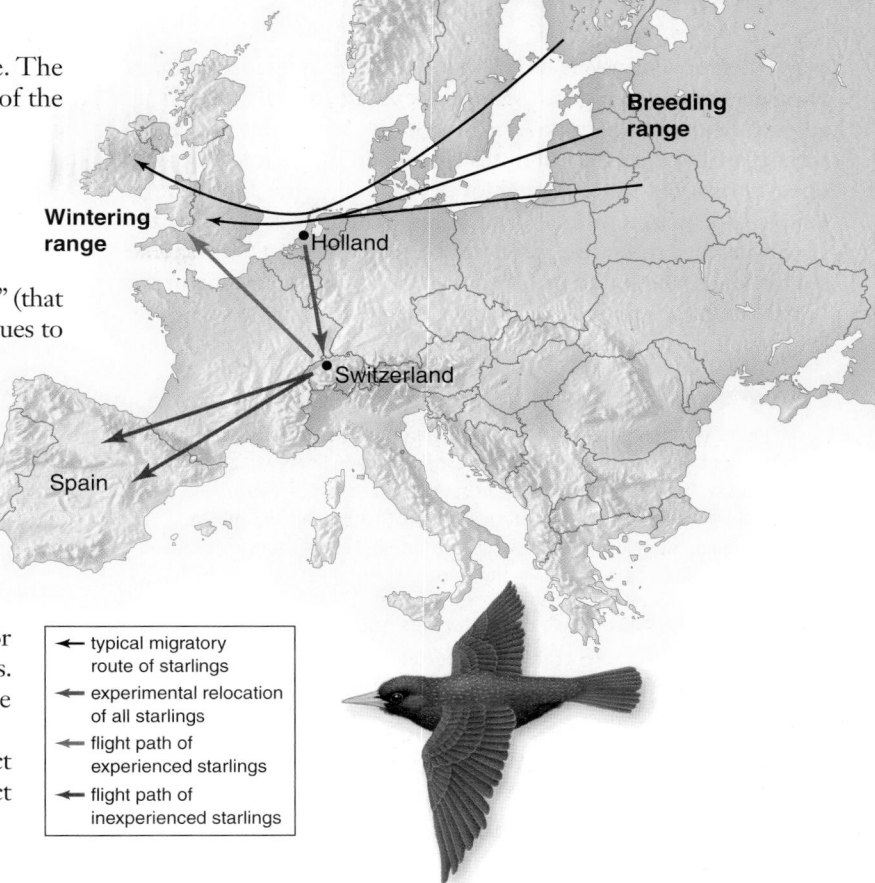

- ← typical migratory route of starlings
- ← experimental relocation of all starlings
- ← flight path of experienced starlings
- ← flight path of inexperienced starlings

Figure 55.17 Migratory behavior of starlings (Sturnus vulgaris). The navigational abilities of inexperienced birds differ from those of adults that have made the migratory journey before. Starlings were captured in Holland, halfway along their full migratory route from Baltic breeding grounds to wintering grounds in the British Isles; these birds were transported to Switzerland and released. Experienced older birds compensated for the displacement and flew toward the normal wintering grounds (blue arrow). Inexperienced young birds kept flying in the same direction, on a course that took them toward Spain (red arrows). These observations imply that inexperienced birds fly by orientation, but experienced birds learn true navigation.

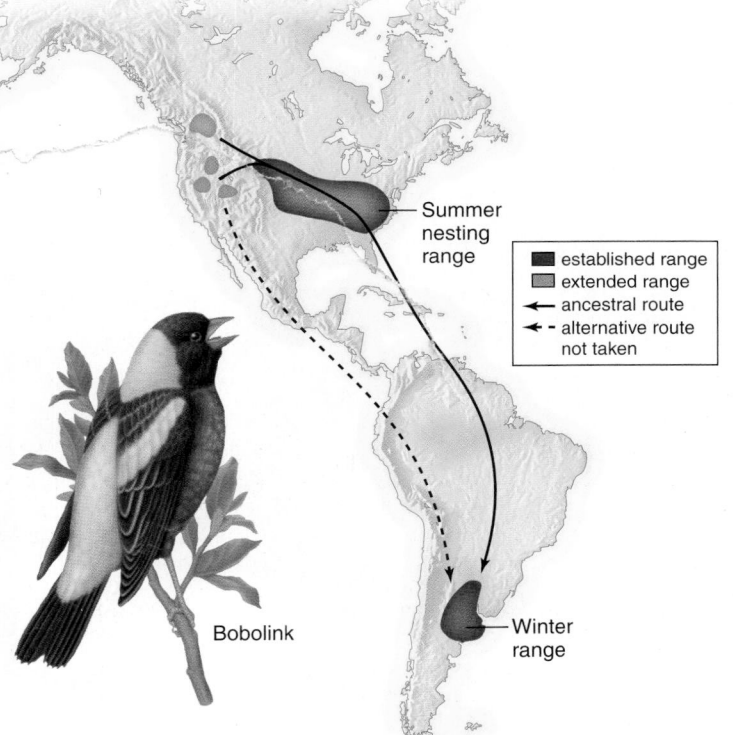

- ■ established range
- ■ extended range
- ← ancestral route
- ←- alternative route not taken

Figure 55.16 Birds on the move. The summer range of bobolinks (*Dolichonyx oryzivorus*) recently extended to the far western United States from their established range in the Midwest. When birds in these newly established populations migrate to South America in the winter, they do not fly directly to the winter range; instead, they first fly to the Midwest and then use the ancestral flyway, going much farther than if they flew directly to their winter range.

to it when cues from the Sun or stars are not available. In an indoor cage, they will attempt to move in the correct geographic direction, even though there are no visible external cues. However, the placement of a magnet near the cage can alter the direction in which the birds attempt to move. Researchers have found magnetite, a magnetized iron ore, in the eyes and upper beaks of some birds, but how these sensory organs function is not known.

The first migration of a bird appears to be innately guided by both celestial cues (the birds fly mainly at night) and Earth's magnetic field. When the two cues are experimentally manipulated to give conflicting directions, the information provided by the stars seems to override the magnetic information. Recent studies, however, indicate that celestial cues indicate the general direction for migration, whereas magnetic cues indicate the specific migratory path (perhaps a turn the bird must make midroute). Experiments on starlings indicate that inexperienced birds migrate by orientation, but older birds that have migrated previously use true navigation (figure 55.17).

We know relatively little about how other migrating animals navigate. For instance, green sea turtles migrate from Brazil halfway across the Atlantic Ocean to Ascension Island, where the females lay their eggs. How do they find this tiny island in the middle of the ocean, which they haven't seen for perhaps 30 years? How do the young that hatch on the island know how to find their way to Brazil? Newly hatched turtles use wave action as a cue to head to sea. Some sea turtles use the Earth's magnetic field to maintain position in the North Atlantic, but turtle migration is still largely a mystery.

Learning Outcomes Review 55.7

Migration is the long-distance movement of a population, often in a cyclic way. Orientation refers to following a bearing or a direction; navigation involves setting a bearing or direction based on some sort of map or memory. Many species use celestial navigation; they may also be able to detect magnetic fields when those cues are absent. The precision of animal migration remains a mystery in many species.

■ *Animals as diverse as butterflies and birds migrate over long distances. Would you expect them to use different navigation systems? Why or why not?*

55.8 Animal Communication

Learning Outcomes

1. *Explain the nature of signals used in mate attraction.*
2. *Explain the role of courtship signals in reproductive isolation.*
3. *Describe how honeybees communicate information about the location of new food sources.*

Communication is central to species recognition and reproductive isolation, and to the interactions that are essential to social behavior. Much research in behavior analyzes the nature of communication signals, determining how they are produced and received, and identifies their ecological roles and evolutionary origins. Communication involves several signal modalities, including visual, acoustic, chemical, electric, and vibrational signals.

Figure 55.18 A stimulus–response chain. Stickleback courtship involves a sequence of behaviors leading to the fertilization of eggs.

1. Female gives head-up display to male

2. Male swims zigzag to female and then leads her to nest

3. Male shows female entrance to nest

4. Female enters nest and spawns while male stimulates tail

5. Male enters nest and fertilizes eggs

Successful reproduction depends on appropriate signals and responses

During courtship, animals produce signals to communicate with potential mates and with other members of their own sex. A stimulus–response chain sometimes occurs, in which the behavior of the male in turn releases a behavior in the female, resulting in mating (figure 55.18). These signals are usually highly species-specific. Many studies on communication involve designing experiments to determine which key stimuli associated with an animal's visual appearance, sounds, or odors convey information about the nature of the signals produced by the sender. One classical study analyzed territorial defense and courtship communication in stickleback fish (figure 55.19).

Finding a mate: Communicating information about species identity

Courtship signals often restrict communication to members of the same species and in doing so serve a key function in reproductive isolation (see chapter 22). The flashes of fireflies (which are actually beetles) are species-specific signals: females recognize conspecific males by their flash pattern (figure 55.20), and

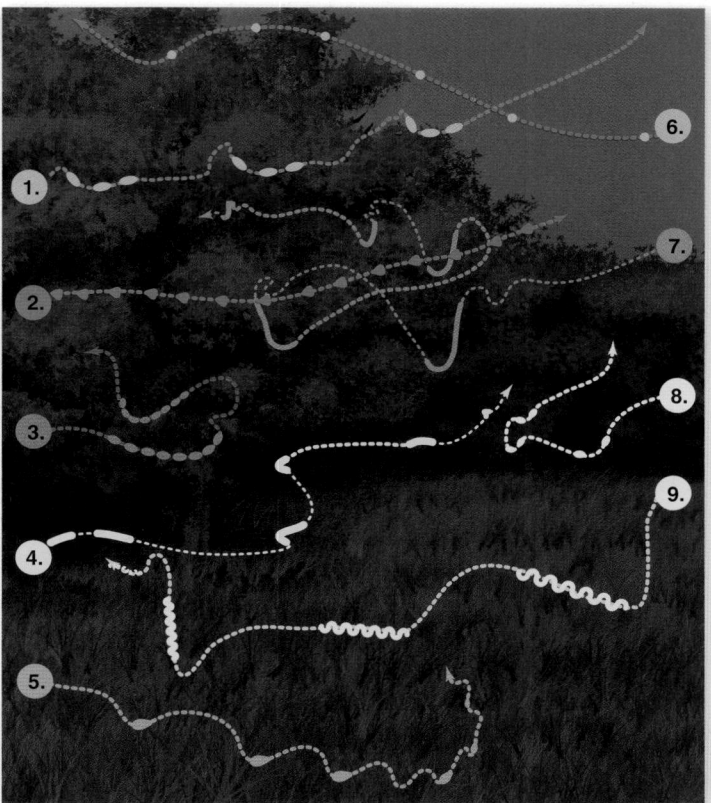

Figure 55.20 Firefly fireworks. The bioluminescent displays of these lampyrid beetles are species-specific and serve as behavioral mechanisms of reproductive isolation. Each number represents the flash pattern of a male of a different species.

SCIENTIFIC THINKING

Hypothesis: *The red underside of male stickleback is the key stimulus that releases an aggressive response by a territory-holding male.*

Prediction: *Models with red coloration will trigger an attack by a resident male.*

Test: *Construct plastic models, some of which accurately resemble a stickleback male, but lack the red underside. Construct other models that vary in their fishlike appearance, but have red-colored undersides. Expose a territorial male to the models one at a time, and record the number of attacks.*

Model with red belly

A realistic white model

White model

White model

Male stickleback

Result: *Realistic models lacking red elicit no response. Odd-shape models trigger an attack if they have red undersides, even if they poorly resemble fish.*

Conclusion: *The red underside of a male stickleback is the key stimulus that triggers aggressive behavior.*

Further Experiments: *How would you determine if the color of a male stickleback was a releaser of aggressive behavior? How would you know if sound was important? Could you determine if stimuli have additive effects? How? Why do you think the color red is important in territorial defense? Might it also be a courtship signal? What information might the color red encode for a female looking for a mate? (see also figure 55.18)*

Figure 55.19 Key stimulus in stickleback fish.

---

males recognize conspecific females by their flash response. This series of reciprocal responses provides a continuous "check" on the species identity of potential mates.

Pheromones, chemical messengers used for communication between individuals of the same species, serve as sex attractants in many animals. Female silk moths (*Bombyx mori*) produce a sex pheromone called bombykol in a gland associated with the reproductive system. The male's antennae contain numerous highly sensitive sensory receptors, and neurophysiological studies show they specifically detect bombykol. In some moth species, males can detect extremely low concentrations of sex pheromone and locate females from as far as 7 km away!

Many insects, amphibians, and birds produce species-specific acoustic signals to attract mates. Bullfrog males call by inflating and discharging air from their vocal sacs, located beneath the lower jaw. Females can distinguish a conspecific male's call from those of other frogs that may be in the same habitat and calling at the same time. As mentioned earlier, male birds sing to advertise their presence and to attract females. In many species, variations in the males' songs identify individual males in a population. In these species, the song is individually specific as well as species-specific. Vibrations, like sound signals, are a form of mechanical communication used by insects, amphibians, and other animals.

Courtship behaviors play a major role in sexual selection, which we discuss later in this chapter.

Figure 55.21 Alarm calling by a prairie dog (Cynomys ludovicianus). When a prairie dog sees a predator, it stands on its hind legs and gives an alarm call, which causes other prairie dogs to rapidly return to their burrows.

Communication enables information exchange among group members

Many insects, fish, birds, and mammals live in social groups in which information is communicated between group members. For example, some individuals in mammalian societies serve as sentinels, vigilantly on the lookout for danger. When a predator appears, they give an alarm call, and group members respond by seeking shelter (figure 55.21). Social insects such as ants and honeybees produce alarm pheromones that trigger attack behavior. Ants also deposit trail pheromones between the nest and a food source to lead other colony members to food. Honeybees have an extremely complex dance language that directs hivemates to nectar sources.

The dance language of the honeybee

The European honeybee lives in colonies of tens of thousands of individuals whose behaviors are integrated into a complex, cooperative society. Worker bees may forage miles from the hive, collecting nectar and pollen from a variety of plants and switching between plant species depending on their energetic rewards. Food sources used by bees tend to occur in patches, and each patch offers much more food than a single bee can transport to the hive. A colony is able to exploit the resources of a patch because of the behavior of scout bees, which locate patches and communicate their location to hivemates through a dance language. Over many years, Nobel laureate Karl von Frisch (who shared the 1973 prize with Tinbergen and Lorenz), together with generations of students and colleagues, was able to unravel the details of dance language communication.

When a scout bee returns after finding a distant food source, she performs a remarkable behavior pattern called a waggle dance on a vertical comb in the darkness of the hive. The path of the bee during the dance resembles a figure-eight. On the straight part of the path (indicated with dashes in figure 55.22), the bee vibrates ("waggles") her abdomen while producing bursts of sound. The bee may stop periodically to give her hivemates a sample of the nectar carried in her crop. As she dances, she is followed closely by other bees, which soon appear at the new food source to assist in collecting food.

Von Frisch and his colleagues performed experiments to show that hivemates use information in the waggle dance to locate new food sources. The scout bee indicates the direction of the food source by representing the angle between the food source, the hive, and the Sun as the deviation from vertical of the straight run of the dance performed on the hive comb. Thus if the bee danced with the straight run pointing directly up, then the food source would be in the direction of the Sun. If the food is at a 30° angle to the right of the Sun's position, then the straight run would be oriented upward at a 30° angle to the right of vertical) (figure 55.22a). The distance to the food source is indicated by the duration of the straight run. One ingenious experiment designed to show that the bees actually use the information in the dance tricked bees that were unaware of the location of food into misinterpreting the directions given by the scout bee's dance. Computer-controlled robot bees have also been used to give hivemates incorrect information, again demonstrating that bees use the directions coded in the dance!

Figure 55.22 The waggle dance of honeybees (Apis mellifera). *a.* The angle between the food source, the nest, and the Sun is represented by a dancing bee as the angle between the straight part of the dance and vertical. The food is 30° to the right of the Sun, and the straight part of the bee's dance on the hive is 30° to the right of vertical. *b.* A scout bee dances on a comb in the hive.

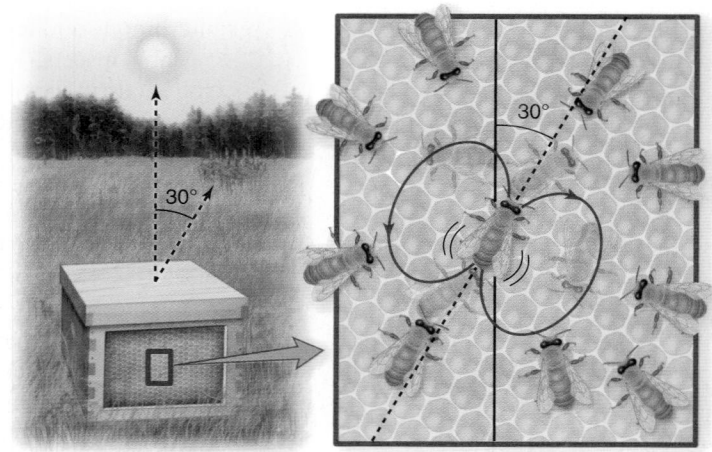

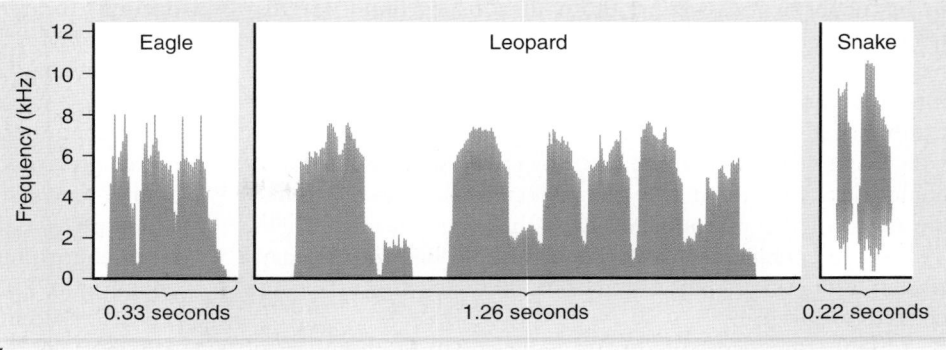

a.

b.

Figure 55.23 Primate semantics. Vervet monkeys (*Cercopithecus aethiops*) give different alarm calls (*a*) when troop members sight an eagle, leopard, or snake. *b.* Each distinctive call elicits a different and adaptive escape behavior.

Language in nonhuman primates and humans

Evolutionary biologists have sought the origins of human language in the communication systems of monkeys and apes. Some nonhuman primates have a "vocabulary" that allows individuals to signal the identity of specific predators. Different vocalizations of African vervet monkeys, for example, indicate eagles, leopards, or snakes, among other threats (figure 55.23).

The complexity of human language would at first appear to defy biological explanation, but closer examination suggests that the differences are in fact superficial—all languages share many basic similarities. All of the roughly 3000 languages draw from the same set of 40 consonant and vowel sounds (English uses two dozen of them), and humans of all cultures can acquire and learn them. Researchers believe these similarities reflect the way our brains handle abstract information. The discovery of *FoxP2*, the so-called "language gene," supports the idea that human language has a hereditary basis.

Learning Outcomes Review 55.8

Animal communication involves production and reception of signals, in the form of sounds, chemicals, or movements, that primarily have an ecological function. Courtship signals are highly species-specific and serve as a mechanism of reproductive isolation. Animals living in social groups, such as honeybees, may use complex systems of communication to exchange information about food and predators.

■ *Two species of moth use the same sex pheromone to locate mates. Explain how these species could nevertheless be reproductively isolated.*

55.9 Behavioral Ecology

Learning Outcomes

1. Describe behavioral ecology.
2. Discuss the economic analysis of behaviors.

Niko Tinbergen pioneered the study of the adaptive function of behavior. Stated simply, this is how behavior allows an animal to stay alive and keep its offspring alive. For example, Tinbergen observed that after gull nestlings hatch, the parents remove the eggshells from the nest. To understand why (ultimate causation), he painted chicken eggs to resemble gull eggs (figure 55.24), which had camouflage coloration to allow them

Figure 55.24 The adaptive value of egg coloration. Niko Tinbergen, a winner of the 1973 Nobel Prize in physiology or medicine, painted chicken eggs to resemble the mottled brown camouflage of gull eggs. The eggs were used to test the hypothesis that camouflaged eggs are more difficult for predators to find and thus increase the young's chances of survival.

to be inconspicuous against the natural background. He distributed them throughout the area in which the gulls were nesting, placing broken eggshells with their prominent white interiors next to some of the eggs. As a control, he left other camouflaged eggs alone without eggshells. He then noted which eggs were found more easily by crows. Because the crows could use the white interior of a broken eggshell as a cue, they ate more of the camouflaged eggs that were near eggshells. Tinbergen concluded that eggshell removal behavior is adaptive: it reduces predation and thus increases the offspring's chances of survival.

Tinbergen is credited with being one of the founders of **behavioral ecology,** the study of how natural selection shapes behavior. This branch of ecology examines the adaptive significance of behavior, or how behavior may increase survival and reproduction. Current research in behavioral ecology focuses on how behavior contributes to an animal's reproductive success, or fitness. As we saw in section 55.3, differences in behavior among individuals often result from genetic differences. Therefore, natural selection operating on behavior has the potential to produce evolutionary change.

Consequently, the field of behavioral ecology is concerned with two questions. First, is behavior adaptive? Although it is tempting to assume that behavior must in some way represent an adaptive response to the environment, this need not be the case. As you saw in chapter 20, traits can appear for many reasons other than natural selection, such as genetic drift, gene flow, or the correlated consequences of selection on other traits. Moreover, traits may be present in a population because they evolved as adaptations in the past, but are no longer useful. These possibilities hold true for behavioral traits as much as for any other kind of trait.

If behavior is adaptive, the next question is: How is it adaptive? Although the ultimate criterion is reproductive success, behavioral ecologists are interested in how behavior can lead to greater reproductive success. Does a behavior enhance energy intake, thus increasing the number of offspring produced? Does it increase mating success? Does it decrease the chance of predation? The job of a behavioral ecologist is to determine the effect of a behavioral trait—for example, foraging efficiency—on each of these activities and then to discover whether increases translate into increased fitness. Benefits and costs of behaviors, estimated in terms of energy or offspring, are often used to analyze the adaptive nature of behavior.

Foraging behavior can directly influence energy intake and individual fitness

A useful way to understand the approach of behavioral ecology is by focusing on foraging behavior. For many animals, food comes in a variety of sizes. Larger foods may contain more energy but may be harder to capture and less abundant. In addition, animals may forage for some types of food that are farther away than other types. For these animals foraging involves a trade-off between a food's energy content and the cost of obtaining it. The net energy (estimated in calories or joules) gained by feeding on prey of each size is simply the energy content of the prey minus the energy costs of pursuing and handling it. According to

optimal foraging theory, natural selection favors individuals whose foraging behavior is as energetically efficient as possible. In other words, animals tend to feed on prey that maximize their net energy intake per unit of foraging time.

A number of studies have demonstrated that foragers do prefer prey that maximize energy return. Shore crabs, for example, tend to feed primarily on intermediate-sized mussels, which provide the greatest energy return; larger mussels yield more energy, but also take considerably more energy to crack open (figure 55.25).

This optimal foraging approach assumes natural selection will favor behavior that maximizes energy acquisition if the increased energy reserves lead to increases in reproductive success. In both Colombian ground squirrels and captive zebra finches, a direct relationship exists between net energy intake and the number of offspring raised; similarly, the reproductive success of orb-weaving spiders is related to how much food they can capture.

Animals have other needs besides energy, however, and sometimes these needs conflict. One obvious need is the avoidance of predators: Often, the behavior that maximizes energy intake is not the one that minimizes predation risk. In this case, the behavior that maximizes fitness often may reflect a trade-off between obtaining the most energy at the least risk of being eaten. Not surprisingly, many studies have shown that a wide variety of animal species alter their foraging behavior— becoming less active, spending more time watching for predators, or staying nearer to cover—when predators are present. Compromises, in this case a trade-off between vigilance and feeding, may thus be made during foraging.

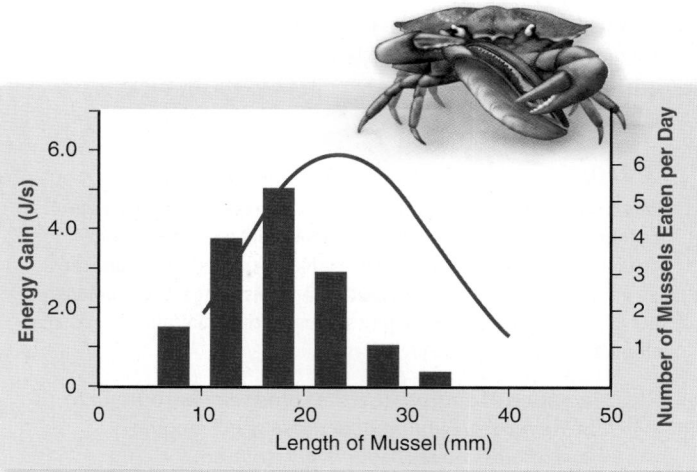

Figure 55.25 Optimal diet. The shore crab selects a diet of energetically profitable prey. The curve describes the net energy gain (equal to energy gained minus energy expended) derived from feeding on different sizes of mussels. The bar graph shows the numbers of mussels of each size in the diet. Shore crabs tend to feed on those mussels that provide the most energy.

Inquiry question

? What factors might be responsible for the slight difference in peak prey length relative to the length optimal for maximum energy gain?

Optimal foraging theory assumes that energy-maximizing behavior has evolved by natural selection. Therefore, it must have a genetic basis. For example, female zebra finches particularly successful in maximizing net energy intake tend to have similarly successful offspring. In this study, young birds were removed from their mothers before they were able to leave the nest, so this similarity indicates that foraging behavior probably has a genetic component. Studies on other animals show that age, experience, and learning are also important to the development of efficient foraging.

Territorial behavior evolves if the benefits of holding a territory exceed the costs

Animals often move over a large area, or home range, during their course of activity. In many species, the home range of several individuals overlaps in time or in space, but each individual defends a portion of its home range and uses it and its resources exclusively. This behavior is called **territoriality** (figure 55.26).

The defining characteristic of territorial behavior is defense against intrusion and resource use by other individuals. Territories are defended by displays advertising that territories are occupied, and by overt aggression. A bird sings from its perch within a territory to prevent take-over by a neighboring bird. If a potential usurper is not deterred by the song, the territory owner may attack and try to drive it away. But territorial defense has its costs. Singing is energetically expensive, and attacks can lead to injury. Using a signal (a song or visual display) to advertise occupancy can reveal a bird's position to a predator.

Why does an animal bear the costs of territorial defense? Energetic benefits of territoriality may take the form of increased food intake due to exclusive use of resources, access to mates, or access to refuges from predators. Studies of nectar-feeding birds such as hummingbirds and sunbirds provide an example (figure 55.27). A bird benefits from having the exclusive use of a patch of flowers because it can efficiently harvest the nectar the flowers produce. To maintain exclusive use, the bird

Figure 55.27 The benefit of territoriality. Sunbirds (on the left), found in Africa and ecologically similar to New World hummingbirds (on the right), protect their food source by attacking other sunbirds that approach flowers in their territory.

must actively defend the patch. The benefits of exclusive use outweigh the costs of defense only under certain conditions.

Sunbirds, for example, expend 3000 calories per hour chasing intruders from a territory. Whether the benefit of defending a territory will exceed this cost depends on the amount of nectar in the flowers and how efficiently the bird can collect it. When flowers are very scarce or nectar levels are very low, a nectar-feeding bird may not gain enough energy to balance the energy used in defense. Under these conditions, it is not energetically advantageous to be territorial. Similarly, when flowers are very abundant, a bird can efficiently meet its daily energy requirements without behaving territorially and adding the costs of defense. Again, from an energetic standpoint, defending abundant resources isn't worth the cost, either. Territoriality therefore only occurs at intermediate levels of flower availability and nectar production, when the benefits of defense outweigh the costs.

In many species, access to females is a more important determinant of territory size for males than is food availability. In some lizards, for example, males maintain enormous territories during the breeding season. These territories, which encompass the territories of several females, are much larger than would be required to supply enough food, and they are defended vigorously. In the nonbreeding season, by contrast, male territory size decreases dramatically, as does aggressive territorial behavior.

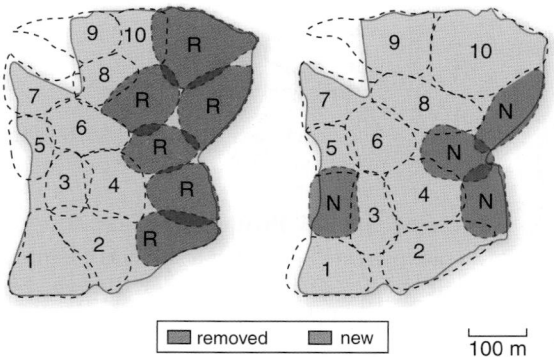

removed   new

100 m

Figure 55.26 Competition for space. Territory size in birds is adjusted according to the number of competitors. When six pairs of great tits (*Parus major*) were removed from their territories (indicated by R in the left figure), their territories were taken over by other birds in the area and by four new pairs (indicated by N in the right figure). Numbers correspond to the birds present before and after.

Learning Outcomes Review 55.9

Behavioral ecology is the study of the adaptive significance of behavior—that is, how it affects survival and reproductive success. An economic approach estimates the energy benefits and costs of a behavior and assumes that animals gain more from a behavior than they expend, obtaining a fitness advantage. Foraging behavior and defense of a territory can be analyzed in this way. Apart from energy gains, considerations such as avoiding predators are also important to fitness.

■ *The Hawaiian honeycreeper, a nectar-feeding bird, fails to defend flowers that are either infrequently encountered or very abundant. Why?*

Reproductive Strategies and Sexual Selection

Learning Outcomes

1. **Explain parental investment and the prediction it makes about mate choice.**
2. **Describe how sexual selection leads to the evolution of secondary sexual characteristics.**
3. **Explain why some species are generally monogamous and other are polygynous.**

During the breeding season, animals make several important life-history "decisions" concerning their choice of mates, how many mates to have, and how much time and energy to devote to rearing offspring. These decisions are all aspects of an animal's **reproductive strategy,** a set of behaviors that presumably have evolved to maximize reproductive success. Energetic costs of reproduction appear to have been critically important to behavioral differences between females and males. Ecological factors such as the way food resources, nest sites, and members of the opposite sex are spatially distributed in the environment, as well as disease, are important in the evolution of reproductive decisions.

The sexes often have different reproductive strategies

Males and females have the common goal of improving the quantity and quality of offspring they produce, but usually differ in the way they attempt to maximize fitness. Such a difference in reproductive behavior is clearly seen in mate choice. Darwin was the first to observe that females often do not mate with the first male they encounter, but instead seem to evaluate a male's quality and then decide whether to mate. Peahens prefer to mate with peacocks that have more eyespots on their elaborate tail feathers (figure 55.28*b, c*). Similarly, female frogs prefer to mate with males having more acoustically complex, and thus attractive, calls. This behavior, called mate choice, is well known in many invertebrate and vertebrate species.

Males are selective in choosing a mate much less frequently than females. Why should this be? Many of the differences in reproductive strategies between the sexes can be understood by comparing the parental investment made by males and females. **Parental investment** refers to the energy and time each sex makes ("invests") in producing and rearing offspring; it is, in effect, an estimate of the energy expended by males and females in each reproductive event.

Numerous studies have shown that females generally have a higher parental investment. One reason is that eggs are much larger than sperm—195,000 times larger in humans! Eggs contain proteins and lipids in the yolk and other nutrients for the developing embryo, but sperm are little more than mobile DNA packages. In some groups of animals (mammals, for example), females are responsible for gestation and lactation, costly reproductive functions only they can carry out.

The consequence of such inequalities in reproductive investment is that the sexes face very different selective pressures. Because any single reproductive event is relatively inexpensive for males, they can best increase their fitness by mating with as many females as possible. This is because

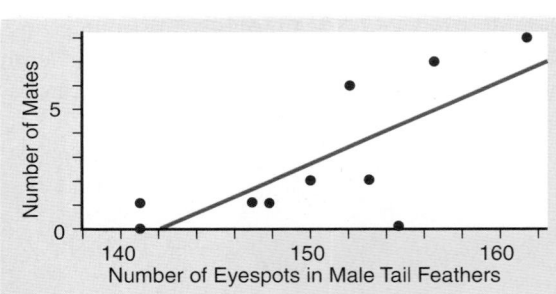

c.

Figure 55.28 Products of sexual selection.

Attracting mates with long feathers is common in bird species such as *(a)* the African paradise whydah (*Vidua paradisaea*), and *(b)* the peacock (*Pavo cristatus*) which show pronounced sexual dimorphism. *c.* Female peahens prefer to mate with males having greater numbers of eyespots in their tail feathers.

Inquiry question

? **Why do females prefer males with more spots?**

a.   *b.*

male fitness is likely limited by the amount of sperm they can produce. By contrast, each reproductive event for females is much more costly, and the number of eggs that can be produced often limits reproductive success. For this reason, a female should be choosy, trying to pick the male that can provide the greatest benefit to her offspring and thus improve her fitness.

These conclusions hold only when female reproductive investment is much greater than that of males. In species with biparental care, males may contribute equally to the cost of raising young; in this case, the degree of mate choice should be more equal between the sexes.

In some cases, male investment exceeds that of females. For example, male Mormon crickets transfer a protein-containing packet (a spermatophore) to females during mating. Almost 30% of a male's body weight is made up by the spermatophore, which provides nutrition for the female and helps her develop her eggs. As we might expect from our model of mate choice, in this case it is the females that compete with one another for access to males, which are the choosy sex. Indeed, males are quite selective, favoring heavier females. Heavier females have more eggs; thus, males that choose larger females leave more offspring (figure 55.29).

Males care for eggs and developing young in many species, including seahorses and a number of birds and insects. As with Mormon crickets, these males are often choosy, and females compete for mates.

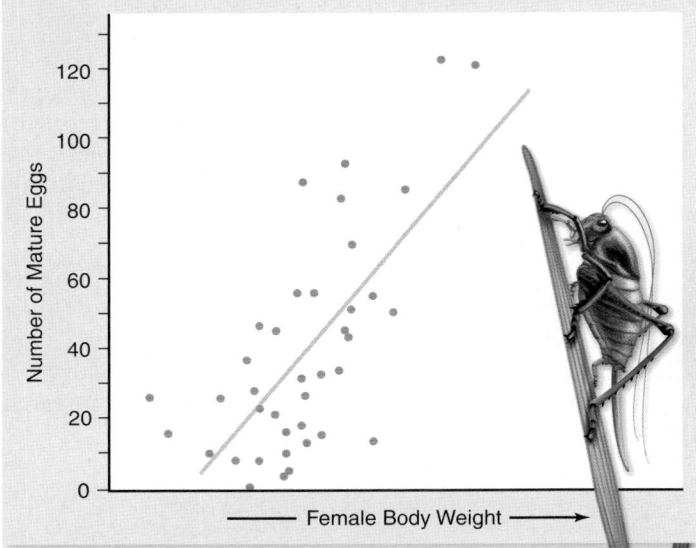

Figure 55.29 **The advantage of male mate choice.** Male Mormon crickets (*Anabrus simplex*) choose heavier females as mates, and larger females have more eggs. Thus, male mate selection increases fitness.

Inquiry question

? Is there a benefit to females for mating with large males?

Sexual selection occurs through mate competition and mate choice

As discussed in chapter 20, the reproductive success of an individual is determined by how long the individual lives, how frequently it mates, and how many offspring it produces per mating. The second of these factors, competition for mates, is termed **sexual selection.** Some people consider sexual selection to be distinctive from natural selection, but others see it as a subset of natural selection, just one of the many factors affecting an organism's fitness.

Sexual selection involves both **intrasexual selection,** or competitive interactions between members of one sex ("the power to conquer other males in battle," as Darwin put it), and **intersexual selection,** which is another name for mate choice ("the power to charm"). Sexual selection leads to the evolution of structures used in combat with other males, such as a deer's antlers and a ram's horns, as well as ornaments used to "persuade" members of the opposite sex to mate, such as long tail feathers and bright plumage (see figure 55.28a, b). These traits are called **secondary sexual characteristics.**

Selection strongly favors any trait that confers greater ability in mate competition. Larger body size is a great advantage if dominance is important, as it is in territorial species. Males may thus be considerably larger than females. Such differences between the sexes are referred to as sexual dimorphism. In other species, structures used for fighting, such as horns, antlers, and large canine teeth, have evolved to be larger in males because of the advantage they give in intrasexual competition.

Sometimes **sperm competition** occurs between the sperm of different males if females mate with multiple males. This type of competition, which occurs after mating, has selected for sperm-transfer organs designed to remove the sperm of a prior mating, large testes to produce more sperm per mating, and sperm that hook themselves together to swim more rapidly. These traits enhance the likelihood of fertilizing an egg.

Intrasexual selection

In many species, individuals of one sex—usually males—compete with one another for the opportunity to mate. Competition can occur for a territory in which females feed or bear young. Males may also directly compete for the females themselves. A few successful males may engage in an inordinate number of matings, while most males do not mate at all. For example, elephant seal males control territories on breeding beaches and a few dominant males do most of the breeding (figure 55.30). On one beach, for example, eight males impregnated 348 females, while the remaining males mated rarely, if at all.

Intersexual selection

Intersexual selection concerns the active choice of a mate. Mate choice has both direct and indirect benefits.

Direct benefits of mate choice. In some cases, the benefits of mate choice are obvious. If males help raise offspring, females benefit by choosing the male that can provide the best

Figure 55.30 Female defense polygyny in northern elephant seals (*Mirounga angustirostris*). Male elephant seals fight with one another for possession of territories. Only the largest males can hold territories, which contain many females.

care—the better the parent, the more offspring she is likely to rear. In other species, males provide no care, but maintain territories that provide food, nesting sites, and predator refuges. In red deer, males that hold territories with the highest quality grasses mate with the most females. In this case, there is a direct benefit of a female mating with such a territory owner: She feeds with little disturbance on quality food.

Indirect benefits of mate choice. In many species, however, males provide no direct benefits of any kind to females. In such cases, it is not intuitively obvious what females have to gain by being "choosy." Moreover, what could be the possible benefit of choosing a male with an extremely long tail or a complex song?

A number of theories have been proposed to explain the evolution of such preferences. One idea is that females choose the male that is the healthiest or oldest. Large males, for example, have probably been successful at living long, acquiring a lot of food, and resisting parasites and disease. In other species, features other than size may indicate a male's condition. In guppies and some birds, the brightness of a male's color reflects the quality of his diet and overall health. Females may gain two benefits from mating with the healthiest males. First, healthy males are less likely to be carrying diseases, which might be transmitted to the female during mating. Second, to the extent that the males' success in living long and prospering is the re-

sult of his genetic makeup, the female will be ensuring that her offspring receive good genes from their father.

Several experimental studies in fish and moths have examined whether female mate choice leads to greater reproductive success. In these experiments, females in one group were allowed to choose males, whereas males were randomly mated to a different group of females. Offspring of females that chose their mates were more vigorous and survived better than offspring from females given no choice, which suggests that females preferred males with a better genetic makeup.

A variant of this theory goes one step further. In some cases, females prefer mates with traits that appear to be detrimental to survival (see figure 55.28c). The long tail of the peacock is a hindrance in flying and makes males more vulnerable to predators. Why should females prefer males with such traits? The **handicap hypothesis** states that only genetically superior mates can survive with such a handicap. By choosing a male with the largest handicap, the female is ensuring that her offspring will receive these quality genes. Of course, the male offspring will also inherit the genes for the handicap. For this reason, evolutionary biologists are still debating the merit of this hypothesis.

Alternative theories about the evolution of mate choice. Some courtship displays appear to have evolved from a predisposition in the female's sensory system to respond to certain stimuli. For example, females may be better able to detect particular colors or sounds at a certain frequency, and thus be attracted to such signals. **Sensory exploitation** involves the evolution in males of a signal that "exploits" these preexisting biases. For example, if females are particularly adept at detecting red objects, then red coloration may evolve in males as part of a courtship display.

To understand the evolution of courtship calls, consider the vocalizations of the Túngara frog (figure 55.31). Unlike related species, males include a short burst of sound, termed a "chuck," at the end of their calls. Recent research suggests that not only are females of this species particularly attracted to calls of this sort, but so are females of related species, even though males of these species do not produce "chucks."

A great variety of other hypotheses have been proposed to explain the evolution of mating preferences. Many of these hypotheses may be correct in some circumstances, but none seems capable of explaining all of the variation in mating behavior in the animal world. This is an area of vibrant research, with new discoveries appearing regularly.

Figure 55.31 Male Túngara frog (*Physalaemus pustulosus*) calling. Female frogs of several species in the genus *Physalaemus* prefer males that include a "chuck" in their call. However, only males of the Túngaru frog (*a*) produce such calls (*b*); males of other species do not (*c*).

a.

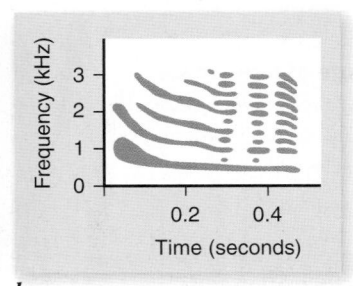

b.

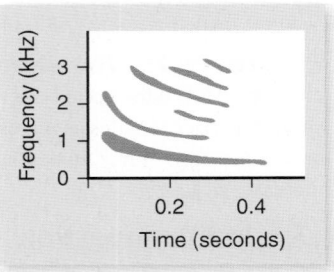

c.

Mating systems reflect the ability of parents to care for offspring and are influenced by ecology

The number of individuals with which an animal mates during the breeding season varies among species. Mating systems include monogamy (one male mates with one female), polygyny (one male mates with more than one female; see figure 55.30), and polyandry (one female mates with more than one male). Only monogamous mating includes a pair bond (like prairie voles). Like mate choice, mating systems have evolved to allow females and males to maximize fitness.

The option of having more than one mate may be constrained by the need for offspring care. If females and males are able to care for young, then the presence of both parents may be necessary for young to be reared successfully. Monogamy may thus be favored. Generally this is the case for birds, in which over 90% of all species appear to be monogamous. A male may either remain with his mate and provide care for the offspring or desert that mate to search for others; both strategies may increase his fitness. The strategy that natural selection will favor depends on the requirement for male assistance in feeding or defending the offspring. In some species (like humans!), offspring are **altricial**—they require prolonged and extensive care. In these species, the need for care by two parents reduces the tendency for the male to desert his mate and seek other matings. In species in which the young are **precocial** (requiring little parental care), males may be more likely to be polygynous because the need for their parenting is lower. In mammals, only females lactate, freeing males from feeding offspring. It follows that most mammals are polygynous.

Mating systems are strongly influenced by ecology. A male may defend a territory that holds nest sites or food sources sufficient for more than one female. If territories vary in quality or quantity of resources, a female's fitness is maximized if she mates with a male holding a high-quality territory, even if he has mated. Although a male may already have a mate, it is still more advantageous for the female to breed with a mated male holding a high-quality territory than with an unmated male holding a low-quality territory. This favors the evolution of polygyny.

Polyandry is relatively rare, but the evolution of multiple mating by females is becoming better understood. It is best known in birds like spotted sandpipers and jacanas living in highly productive environments such as marshes and wetlands. Here, females take advantage of the increased resources available to rear offspring by laying clutches of eggs with more than one male. Males provide all incubation and parenting, and females mate and leave eggs with two or more males.

Females may also mate with several males to genetically diversify their offspring, which in turn increases disease resistance. This appears to be the case in honey bees, for example, in which a queen may mate with many males.

Extra-pair copulations

The "monogamy" of many bird species has been re-evaluated as DNA fingerprinting (see chapter 15) has become commonly used to determine paternity and precisely quantify the reproductive success of individual males (figure 55.32a). In red-winged blackbirds (figure 55.32b), researchers established that

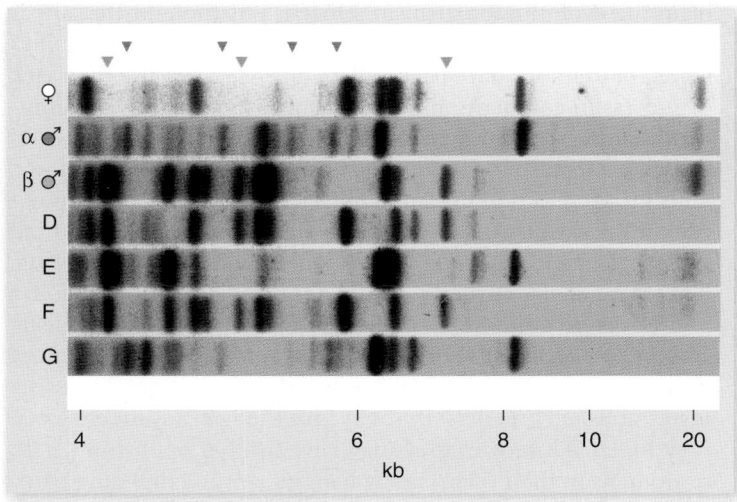

a.

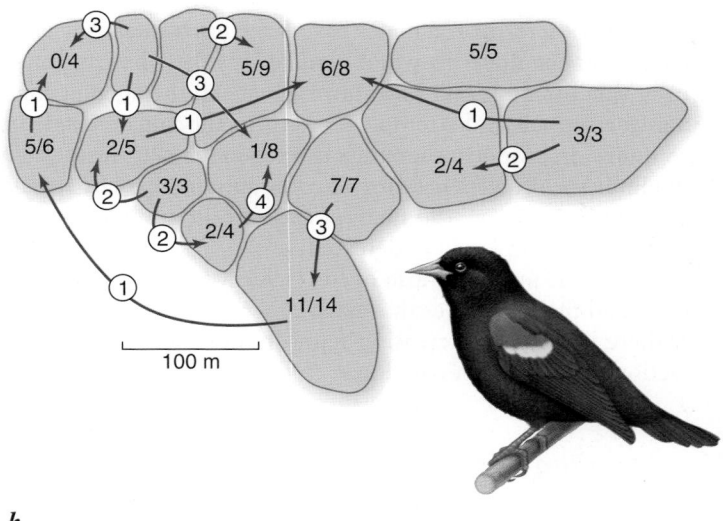

b.

Figure 55.32 The study of paternity. *a.* A DNA fingerprinting gel from the dunnock *(Prunella modularis)*. The bands represent fragments of DNA of different lengths. The four nestlings (D–G) were in the nest of the female. By comparing the bands present in the two males and the female, we can determine which male fathered which offspring. The triangles point to the bands that are diagnostic for one male and not the other. In this case, the β-male fathered three (D, E, F, but not G) of the four offspring. *b.* Results of a DNA fingerprinting study in red-winged blackbirds *(Agelaius phoeniceus)*. Fractions indicate the proportion of offspring fathered by the male in whose territory the nest occurred. Arrows indicate how many offspring were fathered by particular males outside of each territory. Nests on some territories were not sampled.

half of all nests contained at least one hatchling fertilized by a male other than the territory owner; overall, 20% of the offspring were the result of such **extra-pair copulations (EPCs).**

What is the evolutionary advantage of EPCs? For males, the answer is obvious: increased reproductive success. Females, on the other hand, may mate with genetically superior individuals even if already paired with a male, thus enhancing the genes passed on to their offspring. The female doesn't produce more offspring, but offpring of better genetic quality. In some birds and other animals, EPCs may help females increase the amount of care they get from males to raise their offspring. This is exactly what happens in a common English bird, the dunnock. Females mate not only with the territory owner, but also with subordinate males that hang around the edge of the territory. If these subordinates mate a sufficient number of times with a female, they will help raise her young, presumably because they may have fathered some of these young.

Alternative mating strategies

Natural selection has led to the evolution of many ways of increasing reproductive success. For example, in many species of fish, there are two genetic classes of males. One group is large and defends territories to obtain matings. The other group is small and adopts a completely different strategy. These males do not maintain territories, but loiter at the edge of the territories of large males. Just at the end of a male's courtship, when the female is laying her eggs and the territorial male is depositing sperm, the smaller male darts in and releases its own sperm into the water, thus fertilizing some of the eggs. If this strategy is successful, natural selection will favor the evolution of these two different male reproductive strategies.

Similar patterns are seen in other organisms. In some dung beetles, territorial males have large horns that they use to guard the chambers in which females reside, whereas genetically small males don't have horns. Instead, the smaller males dig side tunnels and attempt to intercept the female inside her chamber. In Isopods, there are three genetic size classes. The medium-sized males pass for females and enter a large male's territory in this way; the smallest class are so tiny, they are able to sneak in completely undetected.

This is just a glimpse of the rich diversity in mating systems and mating tactics that have evolved. The bottom line is: If there is a way of increasing reproductive success, natural selection will favor its evolution.

Learning Outcomes Review 55.10

The sex that invests more in reproduction (parental investment) tends to exhibit mate choice. Females or males can be selective, depending on the energy and time they devote to parental care. Sexual selection governs evolution of secondary sex characteristics in that mates are chosen on the basis of phenotype and competitive success. Reproductive success influences whether males and females mate monogamously or with multiple partners.

■ *Pipefish males incubate young in a brood pouch. Which sex would you expect to show mate choice? Why?*

55.11 Altruism

Learning Outcomes

1. *Explain altruism and its benefits.*
2. *Explain kin selection and inclusive fitness.*
3. *Discuss how haplodiploidy influences kin selection in eusocial insects.*

Understanding the evolution of altruism has been a particular challenge to evolutionary biologists, including Darwin himself. Why should an individual decrease his or her own fitness to help another? How could genes for altruism be favored by natural selection, given that the frequency of such genes should decrease in populations through time?

In fact, there can be great benefits to being an altruist, even if the altruism leads an individual to forego reproduction or even sacrifice its own life. Let's examine how this can work.

Altruism is behavior that benefits another individual at a cost to the actor. Humans sacrificing themselves in times of war or placing themselves in jeopardy to help their children are examples, but altruism also has been described in an extraordinary variety of organisms. In many bird species, for example, there are "helpers at the nest"—birds other than parents who assist in raising their young. In both mammals and birds, individuals that spy a predator may give an alarm call, alerting other members of their group to allow them to escape, even though such an act might call the predator's attention to the caller. And in social insects like ants, workers are sterile offspring that help their mother, the colony's queen, to reproduce.

A number of explanations have been put forward to explain the evolution of altruism. Once it was thought that altruism evolved for the "good of the species." Individuals that fail to mate, for example, have been called "altruists" because their lack of success in competition has been misinterpreted as a willingness to forego reproduction so that the population or species does not increase in size, exhaust its resources, and go extinct. This group selection explanation (selection acting on a population or species) is simply incorrect because individuals that fail to secure mates and not breed will not leave any offspring. Therefore, their "altruism" would not be favored by selection.

Current studies of altruism note that seemingly altruistic acts are in fact selfish. For example, helpers at the nest are often young birds that gain valuable parenting experience by assisting established breeders; this may give them an advantage when they breed. Moreover, they may have limited opportunities to reproduce on their own, and by hanging around breeding pairs, may inherit the territory when established breeders die.

Reciprocity theory explains altruism between unrelated individuals

One explanation of altruism proposes that genetically unrelated individuals may form "partnerships" in which mutual exchanges of altruistic acts occur because they benefit both participants.

Partners are willing to give aid at one time and delay "repayment" for the good deed to a time in the future when they themselves are in need. In **reciprocal altruism,** the partnerships are stable because "cheaters" (nonreciprocators) are discriminated against and do not receive future aid. According to this hypothesis, if the altruistic act is relatively inexpensive, the small benefit a cheater receives by not reciprocating is far outweighed by the potential cost of not receiving future aid. Under these conditions, cheating behavior should be eliminated by selection.

Vampire bats roost in hollow trees, caves, and mines in groups of 8 to 12 individuals (figure 55.33). Because bats have a high metabolic rate, individuals that have not fed recently may die. Bats that have found a host imbibe a great deal of blood, so giving up a small amount to keep a roostmate from starvation presents no great energy cost to the donor. Vampire bats tend to share blood with past reciprocators that are not necessarily relatives. If an individual fails to give blood to a bat from which it received blood in the past, it will be excluded from future bloodsharing. Reciprocity routinely occurs in many primates, including humans (obviously!).

Kin selection theory proposes a direct genetic advantage to altruism

The great population geneticist J. B. S. Haldane once passionately said in a pub that he would willingly lay down his life for two brothers or eight first cousins.

Evolutionarily speaking, this sacrifice makes sense, because for each allele Haldane received from his parents, his brothers each had a 50% chance of receiving the same allele (figure 55.34). Statistically, it is expected that two of his brothers would pass on as many of Haldane's particular combination

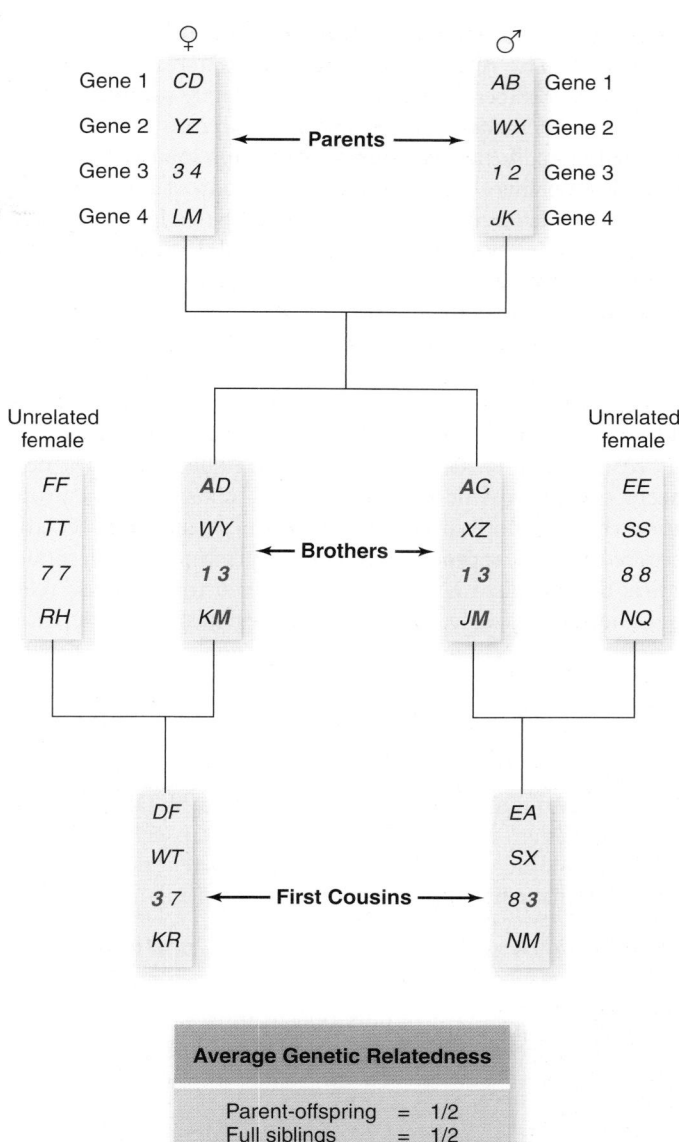

Average Genetic Relatedness	
Parent-offspring	= 1/2
Full siblings	= 1/2
Half-siblings	= 1/4
1st cousins	= 1/8

Figure 55.34 Hypothetical example of genetic relationships. On average, full siblings share half of their alleles. By contrast, cousins only share one-eighth of their alleles on average. Each letter and number represents a different allele.

of alleles to the next generation as Haldane himself would. Similarly, Haldane and a first cousin would share an eighth of their alleles (see figure 55.34). Their parents, who are siblings, would each share half their alleles, and each of their children would receive half of these, of which half on the average would be in common: $1/2 \times 1/2 \times 1/2 = 1/8$. Eight first cousins would therefore pass on as many of those alleles to the next generation as Haldane himself would.

The most compelling explanation for the kin-related origin of altruism was presented by one of the most influential evolutionary biologists of our time, William D. Hamilton, in 1964. Hamilton understood Haldane's point: Natural selection will favor any behavior, including the sacrifice of life, that increases the propagation of an individual's alleles.

Figure 55.33 Truth is stranger than fiction: Reciprocal altruism in vampire bats *(Desmodus rotundus).* Vampire bats do feed on the blood of large mammals, but they don't transform into people and sleep in coffins. Vampires live in groups and share blood meals. They remember which bats have provided them with blood in the past and are more likely to share with those bats that have shared with them previously. The bats here are feeding on cattle in Brazil.

Hamilton mathematically showed that by directing aid toward close genetic relatives, an altruist may increase the reproductive success of its relatives enough to not only compensate for the reduction in its own fitness, but even increase its fitness beyond what would be possible without assisting relatives. Because the altruist's behavior increases the propagation of alleles in relatives, it will be favored by natural selection. Selection that favors altruism directed toward relatives is called kin selection. Although the behaviors are altruistic, the genes are actually "behaving selfishly," because they encourage the organism to favor the success of copies of themselves in relatives. In other words, if an individual has a dominant allele that causes altruism, any action that increases the frequency of this allele in future generations will be favored, even if that action is detrimental to the actor.

Hamilton then defined reproductive success with a new concept—inclusive fitness. Inclusive fitness considers gene propagation through both direct (personal fitness) and indirect (the fitness of relatives) reproduction. Hamilton's kin selection model predicts that altruism is likely to be directed toward close relatives. The more closely related two individuals are, the greater the potential genetic payoff, and the greater inclusive fitness. This is described by Hamilton's rule, which states that altruistic acts are favored when $rb > c$. In this expression, b and c are the benefits and costs of the altruistic act, respectively, and r is the coefficient of relatedness, the proportion of alleles shared by two individuals through common descent. For example, an individual should be willing to have one less child ($c = 1$) if such actions allow a half-sibling, which shares one-quarter of its genes ($r = 0.25$), to have five or more additional offspring ($b = 5$).

Haplodiploidy and altruism in ants, bees, and wasps

The relationship between genetic relatedness, kin selection, and altruism can be best understood using social insects as an example. A hive of honeybees consists of a single queen, who is the sole egg-layer, and tens of thousands of her offspring, female workers with nonfunctional ovaries (figure 55.35). Honeybees are eusocial ("truly" social): their societies are defined by reproductive division of labor (only the queen reproduces), cooperative care of the brood (workers nurse, clean, and forage), and overlap of generations (the queen lives with several generations of her offspring).

Darwin was perplexed by eusociality. How could natural selection favor the evolution of sterile workers that left no offspring? It remained for Hamilton to explain the origin of eusociality in hymenopterans (bees, wasps, and ants) using his kin selection model. In these insects, males are haploid (produced from unfertilized eggs) and females are diploid. This system of sex determination and parthenogenesis, called haplodiploidy, leads to unusual genetic relatedness among colony members. If the queen is fertilized by a single male, then all female offspring will inherit exactly the same alleles from their father (because he is haploid and has only one copy of each allele). Female offspring (workers and future queens) will also share among themselves, on average, half of the alleles they get from their mother, the queen. Consequently, they will share, on average, 75% of their alleles with each sister (to verify this, rework figure 55.34, but allow the father to only have one allele for each gene).

Now recall Haldane's statement of commitment to family while you read this section. If a worker should have offspring of

Figure 55.35 Reproductive division of labor in honeybees. The queen (center) is the sole egg-layer. Her daughters are sterile workers.

her own, she would share only half of her alleles with her young (the other half would come from their father). Thus, because of this close genetic relatedness due to haplodiploidy, workers would propagate more of their own alleles by giving up their own reproduction to assist their mother in rearing their sisters, some of whom will be new queens, start new colonies, and reproduce.

In this way, the unusual haplodiploid system may have set the "genetic stage" for the evolution of eusociality. Indeed, eusociality has evolved at least 12 separate times in the Hymenoptera. One wrinkle in this theory, however, is that eusocial systems have evolved in other insects (thrips, weevils, and termites), and mammals (naked mole rats). Although thrips are also haplodiploid, termites and naked mole rats are not. Thus, although haplodiploidy may have facilitated the evolution of eusociality, other factors can influence social evolution.

Other examples of kin selection

Kin selection may explain altruism in other animals. Belding's ground squirrels give alarm calls when they spot a predator such as a coyote or a badger. Such predators may attack a calling squirrel, so giving the signal places the caller at risk. A ground squirrel colony consists of a female and her daughters, sisters, aunts, and nieces. When males mature, they disperse long distances from where they are born, so adult males in the colony are not genetically related to the females. By marking all squirrels in a colony with an individual dye pattern on their fur and by recording which individuals gave calls and the social circumstances of their calling, researchers found that females who have relatives living nearby are more likely to give alarm calls than females with no kin nearby. Males tend to call much less frequently, as would be expected because they are not related to most colony members.

Another example of kin selection is provided by the white-fronted bee-eater, a bird which lives along river banks in Africa in colonies of 100 to 200 individuals (figure 55.36). In contrast to ground squirrels, the male bee-eaters usually remain in the colony in which they were born, and the females disperse to join new colonies. Many bee-eaters do not raise their own offspring, but instead help others. Most helpers are young birds,

Figure 55.36 Kin selection in the white-fronted bee-eater (*Merops bullockoides*). Bee-eaters are small insectivorous birds that live in Africa in large colonies. Bee-eaters often help others raise their young; helpers usually choose to help close relatives.

but older birds whose nesting attempts have failed may also be helpers. The presence of a single helper, on average, doubles the number of offspring that survive. Two lines of evidence support the idea that kin selection is important in determining helping behavior in this species. First, helpers are normally males, which are usually related to other birds in the colony, and not females, which are not related. Second, when birds have the choice of helping different parents, they almost invariably choose the parents to which they are most closely related.

Learning Outcomes Review 55.11

Genetic and ecological factors have contributed to evolution of altruism, a behavior that benefits another individual at a cost to the actor. Individuals may benefit directly if cooperative acts are reciprocated among unrelated interactants. Kin selection explains how altruistic acts directed toward relatives, which share alleles, increase an individual's inclusive fitness. Haplodiploidy has resulted in eusociality among some insects by increasing genetic relatedness; it is not found in vertebrates.

■ *Imagine that you witness older group members rescuing infants in a troupe of monkeys when a predator appears. How would you test whether the altruistic act you see is reciprocity or kin selection?*

55.12 The Evolution of Group Living and Animal Societies

Learning Outcomes

1. Explain the possible advantages of group living.
2. Contrast the nature of insect and vertebrate societies.
3. Discuss social organization in African weaver birds and how it is influenced by ecology.

Organisms from cnidarians and insects to fish, whales, chimpanzees, and humans live in social groups. To encompass the wide variety of social phenomena, we can broadly define a society as a group of organisms of the same species that are organized in a cooperative manner.

Why have individuals in some species given up a solitary existence to become members of a group? One hypothesis is that individuals in groups benefit directly from social living. For example, a bird in a flock may be better protected from predators. As flock size increases, the risk of predation decreases because there are more individuals to scan the environment for predators (figure 55.37).

A member of a flock may also increase its feeding success if it can acquire information from other flock members about the location of new, rich food sources. In some predators, hunting in groups can increase success and allow the group to tackle prey too large for any one individual.

Insect societies form efficient colonies containing specialized castes

We've already discussed the origin of eusociality in the insect order Hymenoptera (ants, bees, and wasps). Additionally, all termites (order Isoptera) are also eusocial, and a few other insect and arthropod species are eusocial. Social insect colonies are composed of different *castes*, groups of individuals that differ in reproductive ability (queens vs. workers), size, and morphology and perform different tasks. Workers nurse, maintain the nest, and forage; soldiers are large and have powerful jaws specialized for defense.

The structure of an insect society is illustrated by leaf-cutters, which form colonies of as many as several million individuals. These ants cut leaves and use it to grow crops of fungi beneath the ground. Workers divide the tasks of leaf cutting, defense, mulching the fungus garden, and implanting fungal hyphae according to their body size (figure 55.38).

The structure of a vertebrate society is related to ecology

In contrast to the highly structured and integrated insect societies and their remarkable forms of altruism, vertebrate social

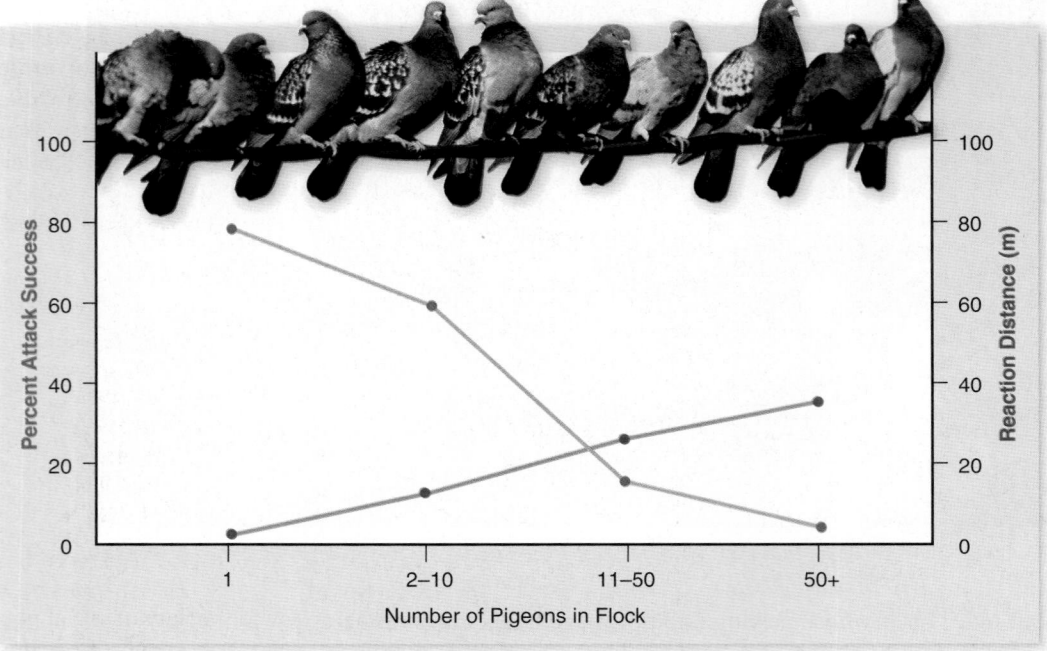

Figure 55.37 Flocking behavior decreases predation. When more pigeons are present in the flock, they can detect hawks at greater distances, thus allowing more time for the pigeons to escape. As a result, as the size of a pigeon flock increases, hawks are less successful at capturing pigeons.

Inquiry question

? How would living in a flock affect the time available for foraging by individual pigeons?

---

groups are usually less rigidly organized and less cohesive. It seems paradoxical that vertebrates, which have larger brains and are capable of more complex behaviors, are generally less altruistic than insects (the exception, of course, is humans). Reciprocity and kin-selected altruism are common in vertebrate societies, although there is often more conflict and aggression among group members. Conflicts generally center on access to food and mates and occur because a vertebrate society is a made up of individuals striving to improve their own fitness.

Social groups of vertebrates have a size, stability of members, number of breeding males and females, and type of mating system characteristic of a given species. Diet and predation are important factors in shaping social groups. For example, meerkats take turns watching for predators while other group members forage for food (figure 55.39).

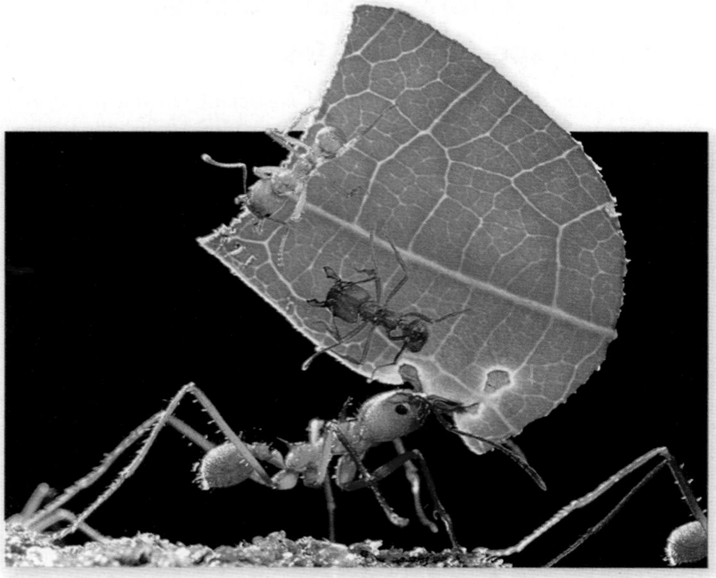

African weaver birds, which construct nests from vegetation, provide an excellent example of the relationship between ecology and social organization. Their roughly 90 species can be divided according to the type of social group they form. One group of species lives in the forest and builds camouflaged, solitary nests. Males and females are monogamous; they forage for insects to feed their young. The second group of species nests in colonies in trees on the savanna. They are polygynous and feed in flocks on seeds.

The feeding and nesting habits of these two groups of species are correlated with their mating systems. In the forest, insects are hard to find, and both parents must cooperate in feeding the young. The camouflaged nests do not call the attention of predators to their brood. On the open savanna, building a hidden nest is not an option. Rather, savanna-dwelling weaver birds protect their young from predators by nesting in trees, which are not very abundant. This shortage of safe nest sites means that birds must nest together in colonies. Because seeds occur abundantly, a female can acquire all the food needed to rear young without a male's help. The male, free from the duties of parenting, spends his time courting many females—a polygynous mating system.

One exception to the general rule that vertebrate societies are not organized like those of insects is the naked mole rat, a small, hairless rodent that lives in and near East Africa. Unlike other kinds of mole rats, which live alone or in small family groups, naked mole rats form large underground colonies with a far-ranging system of tunnels and a central nesting area. It is not unusual for a colony to contain 80 individuals.

Naked mole rats feed on bulbs, roots, and tubers, which they locate by constant tunneling. As in insect societies, there is a division of labor among the colony members, with some individuals working as tunnelers while others perform different

Figure 55.38 Castes of ants. These leaf-cutter ants are members of different castes. The large ant is a worker carrying leaves to the nest, whereas the smaller ants are protecting the worker from attack.

Figure 55.39 Foraging and predator avoidance. A meerkat sentinel on duty. Meerkats (*Suricata suricata*) are a species of highly social mongoose living in the semiarid sands of the Kalahari Desert in southern Africa. This meerkat is taking its turn to act as a lookout for predators. Under the security of its vigilance, the other group members can focus their attention on foraging.

tasks, depending on the size of their bodies. Large mole rats defend the colony and dig tunnels.

Naked mole rat colonies have a reproductive division of labor similar to the one normally associated with the eusocial insects. All of the breeding is done by a single female, or "queen," who has one or two male consorts. The workers, consisting of both sexes, keep the tunnels clear and forage for food.

Learning Outcomes Review 55.12

Advantages of group living include protection from predators and increased feeding success. Eusocial insects form complex, highly altruistic societies that increase the fitness of the colony. The members of vertebrate societies exhibit more conflict and competition, but also cooperate and behave altruistically, especially toward kin. African weaver birds have developed different types of societies depending on the ecology of their habitat, particularly the safety of nesting sites.

- **What are the benefits and costs associated with living in social groups?**
- **Why is altruism directed toward kin considered to be selfish behavior?**
- **Is a human army more like an insect society or a vertebrate society? Explain your answer.**

Chapter Review

55.1 The Natural History of Behavior

Behavior can be analyzed in terms of mechanisms (cause) and evolutionary origin (adaptive nature).
Proximate causation refers to the mechanisms of behavior. Ultimate causation examines a behavior's evolutionary significance.

Ethology emphasizes the study of instinct and its origins.
Innate, or instinctive, behavior is a response to an environmental stimulus or trigger that does not require learning (see figure 55.1).

55.2 Nerve Cells, Neurotransmitters, Hormones, and Behavior

Instinctive behaviors are accomplished by neural circuits, which develop under genetic control. Hormones and neurotransmitters can act to regulate behavior.

55.3 Behavioral Genetics

Artificial selection and hybrid studies link genes and behavior.
Breeding fast-learning and slow-learning rats among each other for several generations produced two distinct behavioral populations (see figure 55.3).

Some behaviors appear to be controlled by a single gene.

55.4 Learning

Learning mechanisms include habituation and association.
Habituation, a form of nonassociative learning, is a decrease in response to repeated nonessential stimuli. Associative learning is a change in behavior by association of two stimuli or of a behavior and a response (conditioning).

Classical (Pavlovian) conditioning occurs when two stimuli are associated with each other. Operant conditioning occurs when an animal associates a behavior with reward or punishment.

Instinct governs learning preparedness.
What an animal can learn is biologically influenced—that is, learning is possible only within the boundaries set by evolution.

55.5 The Development of Behavior

Parent–offspring interactions influence how behavior develops.
In imprinting, a young animal forms an attachment to other individuals or develops preferences that influence later behavior.

Instinct and learning may interact as behavior develops.
Animals may have an innate genetic template that guides their learning as behavior develops, such as song development in birds.

Studies on twins reveal a role for both genes and environment in human behavior.

55.6 Animal Cognition

Some animals exhibit cognitive behavior and can respond to novel situations using logic (see figures 55.12, 55.13).

55.7 Orientation and Migratory Behavior

Migration often involves populations moving large distances.

Migrating animals must be capable of orientation and navigation (see figure 55.16).
Orientation is the mechanism by which animals move by tracking environmental stimuli such as celestial clues or Earth's magnetic field. Navigation is following a route based on orientation and some sort of "map." The nature of the map in animals is not known.

55.8 Animal Communication

Successful reproduction depends on appropriate signals and responses.
Courtship signals are usually species-specific and help to ensure reproductive isolation (see figure 55.19).

Communication enables information exchange among group members (see figures 55.20, 55.21).

55.9 Behavioral Ecology

Foraging behavior can directly influence energy intake and individual fitness.
Natural selection favors optimal foraging strategies in which energy acquisition (cost) is minimized and reproductive success (benefit) is maximized.

Territorial behavior evolves if the benefits of holding a territory exceed the costs.

55.10 Reproductive Strategies and Sexual Selection

The sexes often have different reproductive strategies.
One sex may be choosier than the other, and which one often depends on the degree of parental investment.

Sexual selection occurs through mate competition and mate choice.
Intrasexual selection involves competition among members of the same sex for the chance to mate. Intersexual selection is one sex choosing a mate.
Mate choice may provide direct benefits (increased resource availability or parental care) or indirect benefits (genetic quality of the mate).

Mating systems reflect the ability of parents to care for offspring and are influenced by ecology.
Mating systems include monogamy, polygyny, and polyandry; they are influenced by ecology and constrained by needs of offspring.

55.11 Altruism

Reciprocity theory explains altruism between unrelated individuals.
Mutual exchanges benefit both participants; a participant that does not reciprocate would not receive future aid.

Kin selection theory proposes a direct genetic advantage to altruism.
Kin selection increases the reproductive success of relatives and increased frequency of alleles shared by kin, and thus increases an individual's inclusive fitness.
Ants, bees, and wasps have haplodiploid reproduction, and therefore high degree of gene sharing.

55.12 The Evolution of Group Living and Animal Societies

A social system is a group organized in a cooperative manner.

Insect societies form efficient colonies containing specialized castes (see figure 55.38).
Social insect societies are composed of different castes that are specialized to reproduce or to perform certain colony maintenance tasks.

The structure of a vertebrate society is related to ecology.
Vertebrate social systems are less rigidly organized and cohesive and are influenced by food availability and predation.

Review Questions

UNDERSTAND

1. A key stimulus, innate releasing mechanism, and fixed action pattern
    a. are mechanisms associated with behaviors that are learned.
    b. are components of behaviors that are innate.
    c. involve behaviors that cannot be explained in terms of ultimate causation.
    d. involve behaviors that are not subject to natural selection.

2. In operant conditioning
    a. an animal learns that a particular behavior leads to a reward or punishment.
    b. an animal associates an unconditioned stimulus with a conditioned response.
    c. learning is unnecessary.
    d. habituation is required for an appropriate response.

3. The study of song development in sparrows showed that
   a. the acquisition of a species-specific song is innate.
   b. there are two components to this behavior: a genetic template and learning.
   c. song acquisition is an example of associative learning.
   d. All of these are correct.

4. The difference between following a set of driving directions given to you by somebody on the street (for example ". . . take a right at the next light, go four blocks and turn left . . .") and using a map to find your destination is
   a. the difference between navigation and orientation, respectively.
   b. the difference between learning and migration, respectively.
   c. the difference between orientation and navigation, respectively.
   d. why birds are not capable of orientation.

5. In courtship communication
   a. the signal itself is always species-specific.
   b. the sign communicates species identity.
   c. it involves a stimulus–response chain.
   d. courtship signals are produced only by males.

6. Behavioral ecology assumes
   a. that all behavioral traits are innate.
   b. learning is the dominant determinant of behavior.
   c. behavioral traits are subject to natural selection.
   d. behavioral traits do not affect fitness.

7. According to optimal foraging theory
   a. individuals minimize energy intake per unit of time.
   b. energy content of a food item is the only determinant of a forager's food choice.
   c. time taken to capture a food item is the only determinant of a forager's food choice.
   d. a higher energy item might be less valuable than a lower energy item if it takes too much time to capture the larger item.

8. The elaborate tail feathers of a male peacock evolved because they
   a. improve reproductive success of males and females.
   b. improve male survival.
   c. reduce survival.
   d. None of the above.

9. From the perspective of females, extra-pair copulations (EPCs)
   a. are always disadvantageous to females.
   b. can be associated with receiving male aid.
   c. are too rare to affect female fitness.
   d. can only be of benefit if the EPC male has elaborate secondary sexual traits.

10. In the haplodiploidy system of sex determination, males are
    a. haploid.
    b. diploid.
    c. sterile.
    d. not present because bees exist as single-sex populations.

11. According to kin selection, saving the life of your _____ would do the least for increasing your inclusive fitness.
    a. mother   c. sister-in-law
    b. brother   d. niece

12. Altruism
    a. is only possible through reciprocity.
    b. is only possible through kin selection.

    c. can only be explained by group selection.
    d. will only occur when the fitness benefit of a given act is greater than the fitness cost.

APPLY

1. Refer to figure 55.25. Data on size of mussels eaten by shore crabs suggest they eat sizes smaller than expected by an optimal foraging model. Suggest a hypothesis for why and describe an experiment to test your hypothesis.

2. Refer to figure 55.26. Six pairs of birds were removed but only four pairs moved in. Where did the new pairs come from? Additionally, it appears that many of the birds that were not removed expanded their territories and that the new residents ended up with smaller territories than the pairs they replaced. Explain.

3. Refer to figure 55.28. Peahens prefer to mate with peacocks that have more eyespots in their tail feathers (that is, longer tail feathers). It has also been suggested that the longer the tail feathers, the more impaired the flight of the males. One possible hypothesis to explain such a preference by females is that the males with the longest tail feathers experience the most severe handicap, and if they can nevertheless survive, it reflects their "vigor." Suggest some studies that would allow you to test this idea. Your description should include the kinds of traits that you would measure and why.

4. An altruistic act is defined as one that benefits another individual at a cost to the actor. There are two theories to explain how such behavior evolves: reciprocity and kin selection. How would you distinguish between the two in a field study? In the context of natural selection, is an altruistic act "costly" to an individual who performs it?

SYNTHESIZE

1. Insects that sting or contain toxic chemicals often have black and yellow coloration and consequentially are not eaten by predators. How could you determine if a predator has an innate avoidance of insects that are colored this way, or if the avoidance is learned? If avoidance is learned, how would you determine the learning mechanism involved? How would you measure the adaptive significance of the black and yellow coloration to the prey insect?

2. Behavioral genetics has made great advances from detailed studies of a single animal such as the fruit fly as a model system to develop general principles of how genes regulate behavior. What are advantages and disadvantages of this "model system" approach? How would you determine how broadly applicable the results of such studies are to other animals?

3. If a female bird chooses to live in the territory of a particular male, why might she mate with a male other than the territory owner?

ONLINE RESOURCE

www.ravenbiology.com

Understand, Apply, and Synthesize—enhance your study with animations that bring concepts to life and practice tests to assess your understanding. Your instructor may also recommend the interactive eBook, individualized learning tools, and more.

Chapter 56

Ecology of Individuals and Populations

Chapter Outline

56.1   The Environmental Challenges

56.2   Populations: Groups of a Single Species
       in One Place

56.3   Population Demography and Dynamics

56.4   Life History and the Cost of Reproduction

56.5   Environmental Limits to Population Growth

56.6   Factors That Regulate Populations

56.7   Human Population Growth

Introduction

Ecology, the study of how organisms relate to one another and to their environments, is a complex and fascinating area of biology that has important implications for each of us. In our exploration of ecological principles, we first consider how organisms respond to the abiotic environment in which they exist and how these responses affect the properties of populations, emphasizing population dynamics. In chapter 57, we discuss communities of coexisting species and the interactions that occur among them. In subsequent chapters, we discuss the functioning of entire ecosystems and of the biosphere, concluding with a consideration of the problems facing our planet and our fellow species.

56.1 The Environmental Challenges

Learning Outcomes

1. *List some challenges that organisms face in their environments.*
2. *Describe ways in which individuals respond to environmental changes.*
3. *Explain how species adapt to environmental conditions.*

The nature of the physical environment in large measure determines which organisms live in a particular climate or region. Key elements of the environment include:

Temperature. Most organisms are adapted to live within a relatively narrow range of temperatures and will not thrive if temperatures are colder or warmer. The growing season of plants, for example, is importantly influenced by temperature.

Water. All organisms require water. On land, water is often scarce, so patterns of rainfall have a major influence on life.

Figure 56.1 Meeting the challenge of obtaining moisture. On the dry sand dunes of the Namib Desert in southwestern Africa, the fog-basking beetle (*Onymacris unguicularis*) collects moisture from the fog by holding its abdomen up at the crest of a dune to gather condensed water; water condenses as droplets and trickles down to the beetle's mouth.

Sunlight. Almost all ecosystems rely on energy captured by photosynthesis; the availability of sunlight influences the amount of life an ecosystem can support, particularly below the surface in marine communities.

Soil. The physical consistency, pH, and mineral composition of the soil often severely limit terrestrial plant growth, particularly the availability of nitrogen and phosphorus.

An individual encountering environmental variation may maintain a "steady-state" internal environment, a condition known as *homeostasis*. Many animals and plants actively employ physiological, morphological, or behavioral mechanisms to maintain homeostasis. The beetle in figure 56.1 is using a behavioral mechanism to cope with drastic changes in water availability. Other animals and plants are known as conformers because they conform to the environment in which they find themselves, their bodies adopting the temperature, salinity, and other physical aspects of their surroundings.

Responses to environmental variation can be seen over both the short and the long term. In the short term, spanning periods of a few minutes to an individual's lifetime, organisms have a variety of ways of coping with environmental change. Over longer periods, natural selection can operate to make a population better adapted to the environment.

Organisms are capable of responding to environmental changes that occur during their lifetime

During the course of a day, a season, or a lifetime, an individual organism must cope with a range of living conditions. They do so through the physiological, morphological, and behavioral abilities they possess. These abilities are a product of natural selection acting in a particular environmental setting over time, which explains why an individual organism that is moved to a different environment may not survive.

TABLE 56.1	Physiological Changes at High Elevation
Increased rate of breathing	
Increased erythrocyte production, raising the amount of hemoglobin in the blood	
Decreased binding capacity of hemoglobin, increasing the rate at which oxygen is unloaded in body tissues	
Increased density of mitochondria, capillaries, and muscle myoglobin	

Physiological responses

Many organisms are able to adapt to environmental change by making physiological adjustments. For example, you sweat when it is hot, increasing evaporative heat loss and thus preventing overheating. Similarly, people who visit high altitudes may initially experience altitude sickness—the symptoms of which include heart palpitations, nausea, fatigue, headache, mental impairment, and in serious cases, pulmonary edema—because of the lower atmospheric pressure and consequent lower oxygen availability in the air. After several days, however, the same people usually feel fine, because a number of physiological changes have increased the delivery of oxygen to their body tissues (table 56.1).

Some insects avoid freezing in the winter by adding glycerol "antifreeze" to their blood; others tolerate freezing by converting much of their glycogen reserves into alcohols that protect their cell membranes from freeze damage.

Morphological capabilities

Animals that maintain a constant internal temperature (endotherms) in a cold environment have adaptations that tend to minimize energy expenditure. For example, many mammals grow thicker coats during the winter, their fur acting as insulation to retain body heat. In general, the thicker the fur, the greater the insulation (figure 56.2). Thus, a wolf's fur is about three times thicker in winter than in summer and insulates more than twice as well.

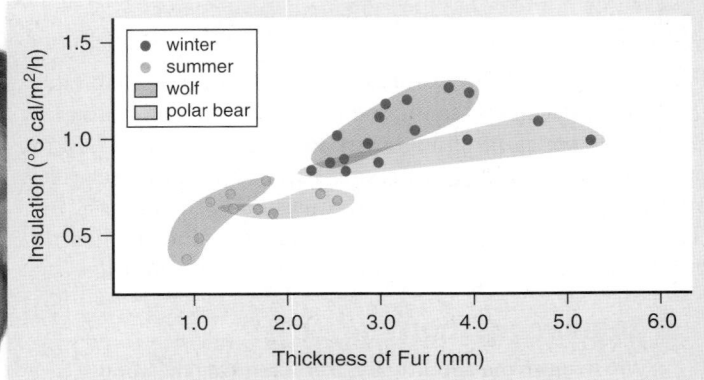

Figure 56.2 Morphological adaptation. Fur thickness in North American mammals has a major effect on the degree of insulation the fur provides.

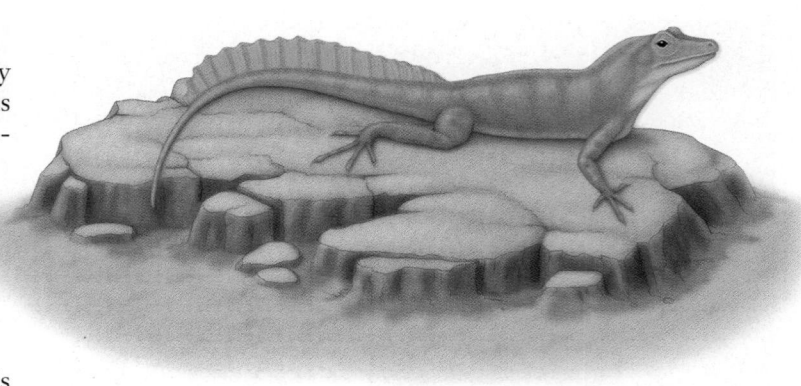

Behavioral responses

Many animals deal with variation in the environment by moving from one patch of habitat to another, avoiding areas that are unsuitable. The tropical lizard in figure 56.3 manages to maintain a fairly uniform body temperature in an open habitat by basking in patches of sunlight and then retreating to the shade when it becomes too hot. By contrast, in shaded forests, the same lizard does not have the opportunity to regulate its body temperature through behavioral means. Thus, it becomes a conformer and adopts the temperature of its surroundings.

Behavioral adaptations can be extreme. Spadefoot toads (genus *Scaphiophus*), which live in the deserts of North America, can burrow nearly a meter below the surface and remain there for as long as nine months of each year, their metabolic rates greatly reduced as they live on fat reserves. When moist, cool conditions return, the toads emerge and breed. The young toads mature rapidly and burrow underground.

Natural selection leads to evolutionary adaptation to environmental conditions

The ability of an individual to alter its physiology, morphology, or behavior is itself an evolutionary adaptation, the result of natural selection. The results of natural selection can also be detected by comparing closely related species that live in different environments. In such cases, species often have evolved striking adaptations to the particular environment in which they live.

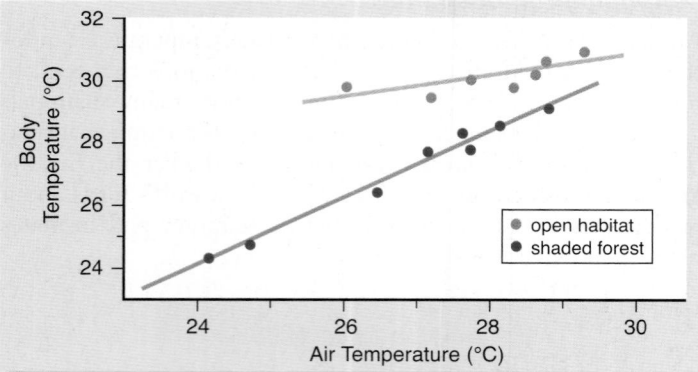

Figure 56.3 Behavioral adaptation. In open habitats, the Puerto Rican crested lizard (*Anolis cristatellus*) maintains a relatively constant temperature by seeking out and basking in patches of sunlight; as a result, it can maintain a relatively high temperature even when the air is cool. In contrast, in shaded forests, this behavior is not possible, and the lizard's body temperature conforms to that of its surroundings.

Inquiry question

? When given the opportunity, lizards regulate their body temperature to maintain a temperature optimal for physiological functioning. Would lizards in open habitats exhibit different escape behaviors from lizards in shaded forest?

For example, animals that live in different climates show many differences. Mammals from colder climates tend to have shorter ears and limbs—a phenomenon termed *Allen's rule*—which reduces the surface area across which animals lose heat. Lizards that live in different climates exhibit physiological adaptations for coping with life at different temperatures. Desert lizards are unaffected by high temperatures that would kill a lizard from northern Europe, but the northern lizards are capable of running, capturing prey, and digesting food at cooler temperatures at which desert lizards would be completely immobilized.

Many species also exhibit adaptations to living in areas where water is scarce. Everyone knows of the camel and other desert animals that can go extended periods without drinking water. Another example of desert adaptation is seen in frogs. Most frogs have moist skins through which water permeates readily. Such animals could not survive in arid climates because they would rapidly dehydrate and die. However, some frogs have solved this problem by evolving a greatly reduced rate of water loss through the skin. One species, for example, secretes a waxy substance from specialized glands that waterproofs its skin and reduces rates of water loss by 95%.

Adaptation to different environments can also be studied experimentally. For example, when strains of *E. coli* were grown at high temperatures (42°C), the speed at which the bacteria utilized resources improved through time. After 2000 generations, this ability increased 30% over what it had been when the experiment started. The means by which efficiency of resource use increased is unknown and is the focus of current research.

56.2 Populations: Groups of a Single Species in One Place

Learning Outcomes

1. Distinguish between a population and a metapopulation.
2. Understand what causes a species' geographic ranges to change through time.

Organisms live as members of populations, groups of individuals that occur together at one place and time. In the rest of this chapter, we consider the properties of populations, focusing on factors that influence whether a population grows or shrinks, and at what rate. The explosive growth of the world's human population in the last few centuries provides a focus for our inquiry.

The term *population* can be defined narrowly or broadly. This flexibility allows us to speak in similar terms of the world's human population, the population of protists in the gut of a termite, or the population of deer that inhabit a forest. Sometimes the boundaries defining a population are sharp, such as the edge of an isolated mountain lake for trout, and sometimes they are fuzzier, as when deer readily move back and forth between two forests separated by a cornfield.

Three characteristics of population ecology are particularly important: (1) population range, the area throughout which a population occurs; (2) the pattern of spacing of individuals within that range; and (3) how the population changes in size through time.

A population's geographic distribution is termed its range

No population, not even one composed of humans, occurs in all habitats throughout the world. Most species, in fact, have relatively limited geographic ranges, and the range of some species is miniscule. For example, the Devil's Hole pupfish lives in a single spring in southern Nevada (figure 56.4), and the Socorro isopod *(Thermosphaeroma thermophilus)* is known from a single spring system in New Mexico. At the other extreme, some species are widely distributed. The common dolphin *(Delphinus delphis)*, for example, is found throughout all the world's oceans.

As discussed earlier, organisms must be adapted for the environment in which they occur. Polar bears are exquisitely adapted to survive the cold of the Arctic, but you won't find them in the tropical rain forest. Certain prokaryotes can live in the near-boiling waters of Yellowstone's geysers, but they do not occur in cooler streams nearby. Each population has its own requirements—temperature, humidity, certain types of food, and a host of other factors—that determine where it can live and reproduce and where it can't. In addition, in places that are otherwise suitable, the presence of predators, competitors, or parasites may prevent a population from occupying an area, a topic we will take up in chapter 57.

Figure 56.4 **The Devil's Hole pupfish *(Cyprinodon diabolis)*.** This fish has the smallest range of any vertebrate species in the world.

Ranges undergo expansion and contraction

Population ranges are not static but change through time. These changes occur for two reasons. In some cases, the environment changes. As the glaciers retreated at the end of the last ice age, approximately 10,000 years ago, many North American plant and animal populations expanded northward. At the same time, as climates warmed, species experienced shifts in the elevation at which they could live (figure 56.5).

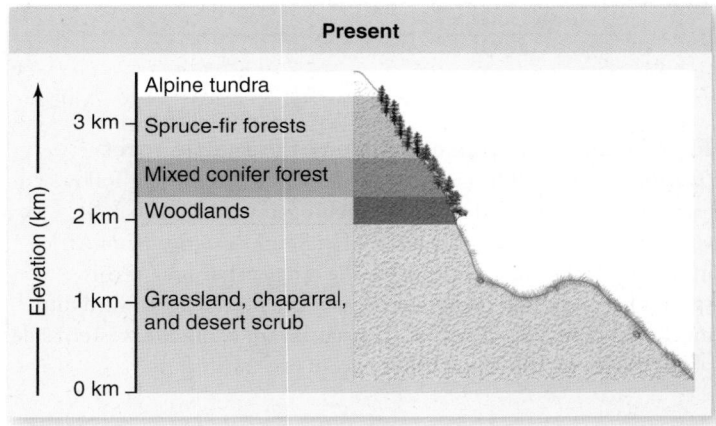

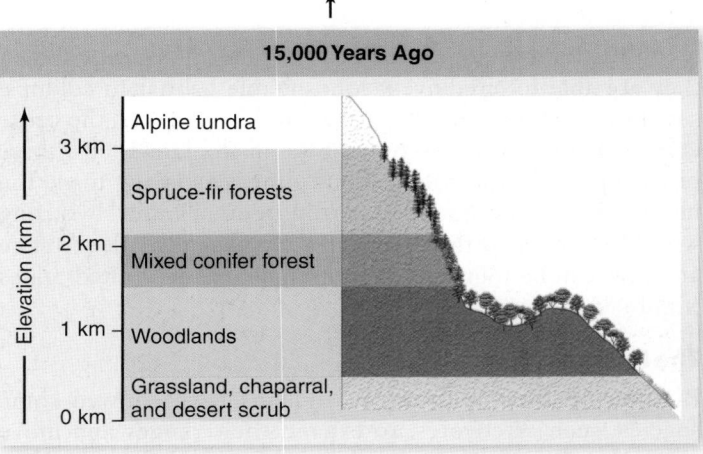

Figure 56.5 **Altitude shifts in altitudinal distributions of trees in the mountains of southwestern North America.** During the glacial period 15,000 years ago, conditions were cooler than they are now. As the climate warmed, tree species that require colder temperatures shifted their range upward in altitude so that they live in the climatic conditions to which they are adapted.

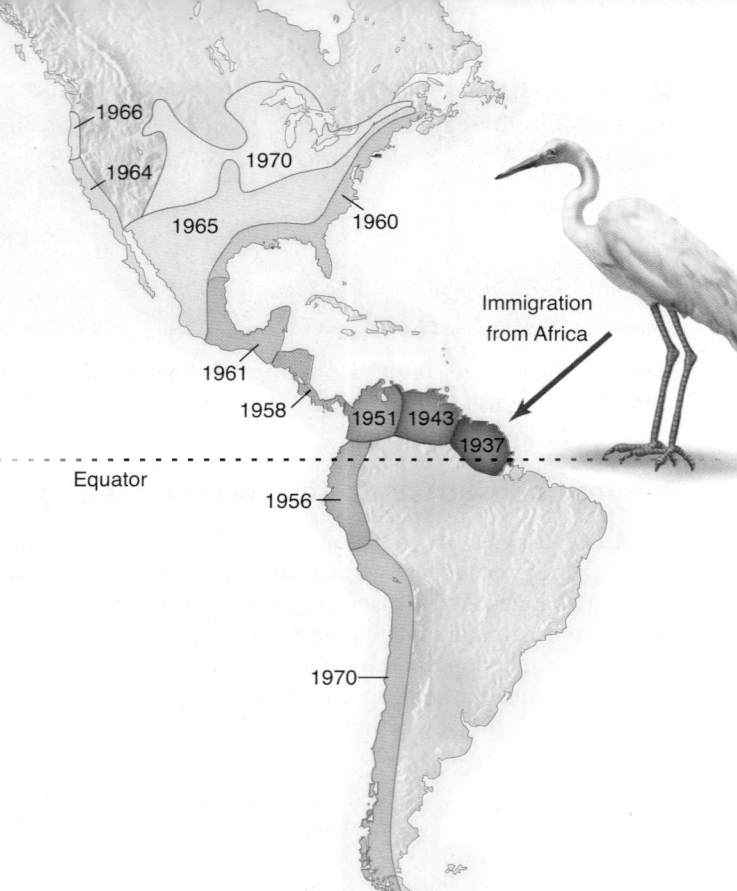

Figure 56.6 Range expansion of the cattle egret (*Bubulcus ibis*). The cattle egret—so named because it follows cattle and other hoofed animals, catching any insects or small vertebrates it disturbs—first arrived in South America from Africa in the late 1800s. Since the 1930s, the range expansion of this species has been well documented, as it has moved northward into much of North America, as well as southward along the western side of the Andes to near the southern tip of South America.

In addition, populations can expand their ranges when they are able to circumvent inhospitable habitat to colonize suitable, previously unoccupied areas. For example, the cattle egret is native to Africa. Some time in the late 1800s, these birds appeared in northern South America, having made the nearly 3500-km transatlantic crossing, perhaps aided by strong winds. Since then, they have steadily expanded their range and now can be found throughout most of the United States (figure 56.6).

The human effect

By altering the environment, humans have allowed some species, such as coyotes, to expand their ranges and move into areas they previously did not occupy. Moreover, humans have served as an agent of dispersal for many species. Some of these transplants have been widely successful, as is discussed in greater detail in chapter 60. For example, 100 starlings were introduced into New York City in 1896 in a misguided attempt to establish every species of bird mentioned by Shakespeare. Their population steadily spread so that by 1980, they occurred throughout the United States. Similar stories could be told for countless plants and animals, and the list increases every year. Unfortunately, the success of these invaders often comes at the expense of native species.

Dispersal mechanisms

Dispersal to new areas can occur in many ways. Lizards have colonized many distant islands, as one example, probably due to individuals or their eggs floating or drifting on vegetation. Bats are the only mammals on many distant islands because they can fly to them.

Seeds of plants are designed to disperse in many ways (figure 56.7). Some seeds are aerodynamically designed to be blown long distances by the wind. Others have structures that stick to the fur or feathers of animals, so that they are carried long distances before falling to the ground. Still others are enclosed in fleshy fruits. These seeds can pass through the digestive systems of mammals or birds and then germinate where they are defecated. Finally, seeds of mistletoes (*Arceuthobium*) are violently propelled from the base of the fruit in an explosive discharge. Although the probability of long-distance dispersal events leading to successful establishment of new populations is low, over millions of years, many such dispersals have occurred.

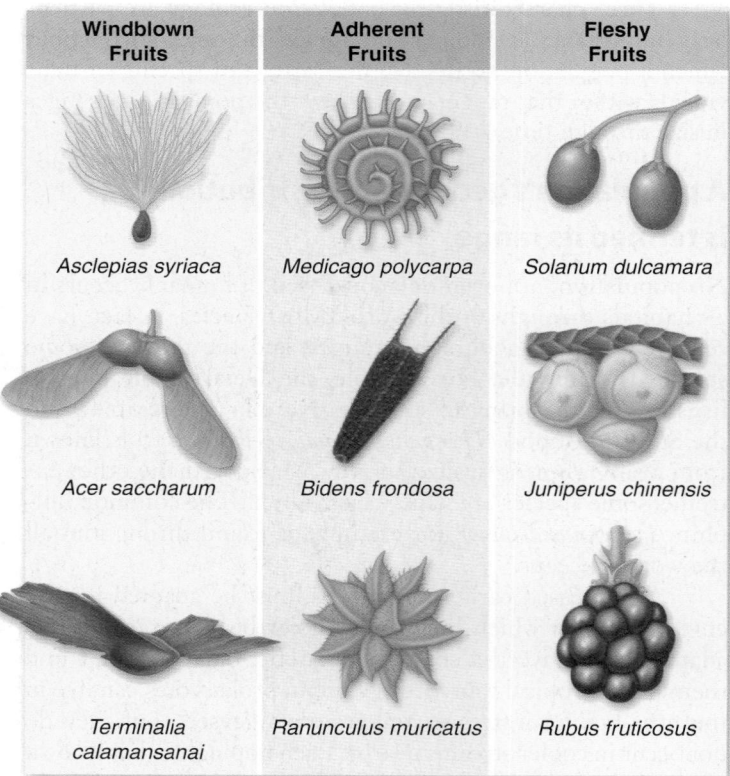

Windblown Fruits	Adherent Fruits	Fleshy Fruits
Asclepias syriaca	*Medicago polycarpa*	*Solanum dulcamara*
Acer saccharum	*Bidens frondosa*	*Juniperus chinensis*
Terminalia calamansanai	*Ranunculus muricatus*	*Rubus fruticosus*

Figure 56.7 Some of the many adaptations of seeds. Seeds have evolved a number of different means of facilitating dispersal from their maternal plant. Some seeds can be transported great distances by the wind, whereas seeds enclosed in adherent or fleshy fruits can be transported by animals.

Individuals in populations exhibit different spacing patterns

Another key characteristic of population structure is the way in which individuals of a population are distributed. They may be randomly spaced, uniformly spaced, or clumped.

Random spacing

Random spacing of individuals within populations occurs when they do not interact strongly with one another and when they are not affected by nonuniform aspects of their environment. Random distributions are not common in nature. Some species of trees, however, appear to exhibit random distributions in Panamanian rain forests.

Uniform spacing

Uniform spacing within a population may often, but not always, result from competition for resources. This spacing is accomplished, however, in many different ways

In animals, uniform spacing often results from behavioral interactions, as described in chapter 55. In many species, individuals of one or both sexes defend a territory from which other individuals are excluded. These territories provide the owner with exclusive access to resources, such as food, water, hiding refuges, or mates, and tend to space individuals evenly across the habitat. Even in nonterritorial species, individuals often maintain a defended space into which other animals are not allowed to intrude.

Among plants, uniform spacing is also a common result of competition for resources. Closely spaced individual plants compete for available sunlight, nutrients, or water. These contests can be direct, as when one plant casts a shadow over another, or indirect, as when two plants compete by extracting nutrients or water from a shared area. In addition, some plants, such as the creosote bush, produce chemicals in the surrounding soil that are toxic to other members of their species. In all of these cases, only plants that are spaced an adequate distance from each other will be able to coexist, leading to uniform spacing.

Clumped spacing

Individuals clump into groups or clusters in response to uneven distribution of resources in their immediate environments. Clumped distributions are common in nature because individual animals, plants, and microorganisms tend to occur in habitats defined by soil type, moisture, or other aspects of the environment to which they are best adapted.

Social interactions also can lead to clumped distributions. Many species live and move around in large groups, which go by a variety of names (for example, flock, herd, pride). These groupings can provide many advantages, including increased awareness of and defense against predators, decreased energy cost of moving through air and water, and access to the knowledge of all group members.

On a broader scale, populations are often most densely populated in the interior of their range and less densely distributed toward the edges. Such patterns usually result from the manner in which the environment changes in different areas.

Populations are often best adapted to the conditions in the interior of their distribution. As environmental conditions change, individuals are less well adapted, and thus densities decrease. Ultimately, the point is reached at which individuals cannot persist at all; this marks the edge of a population's range.

A metapopulation comprises distinct populations that may exchange members

Species often exist as a network of distinct populations that interact with one another by exchanging individuals. Such networks, termed **metapopulations,** usually occur in areas in which suitable habitat is patchily distributed and is separated by intervening stretches of unsuitable habitat.

Dispersal and habitat occupancy

The degree to which populations within a metapopulation interact depends on the amount of dispersal; this interaction is often not symmetrical: Populations increasing in size tend to send out many dispersers, whereas populations at low levels tend to receive more immigrants than they send off. In addition, relatively isolated populations tend to receive relatively few arrivals.

Not all suitable habitats within a metapopulation's area may be occupied at any one time. For a number of reasons, some individual populations may become extinct, perhaps as a result of an epidemic disease, a catastrophic fire, or the loss of genetic variation following a population bottleneck (see chapter 60). Dispersal from other populations, however, may eventually recolonize such areas. In some cases, the number of habitats occupied in a metapopulation may represent an equilibrium in which the rate of extinction of existing populations is balanced by the rate of colonization of empty habitats.

Source–sink metapopulations

A species may also exhibit a metapopulation structure in areas in which some habitats are suitable for long-term population maintenance, but others are not. In these situations, termed **source–sink metapopulations,** the populations in the better areas (the sources) continually send out dispersers that bolster the populations in the poorer habitats (the sinks). In the absence of such continual replenishment, sink populations would have a negative growth rate and would eventually become extinct.

Metapopulations of butterflies have been studied particularly intensively. In one study, researchers sampled populations of the Glanville fritillary butterfly at 1600 meadows in southwestern Finland (figure 56.8). On average, every year, 200 populations became extinct, but 114 empty meadows were colonized. A variety of factors seemed to increase the likelihood of a population's extinction, including small population size, isolation from sources of immigrants, low resource availability (as indicated by the number of flowers on a meadow), and lack of genetic variation within the population.

The researchers attribute the greater number of extinctions than colonizations to a string of very dry summers. Because none of the populations is large enough to survive on its own, continued survival of the species in southwestern Finland would appear to require the continued existence of a metapopulation network in which new populations are continually

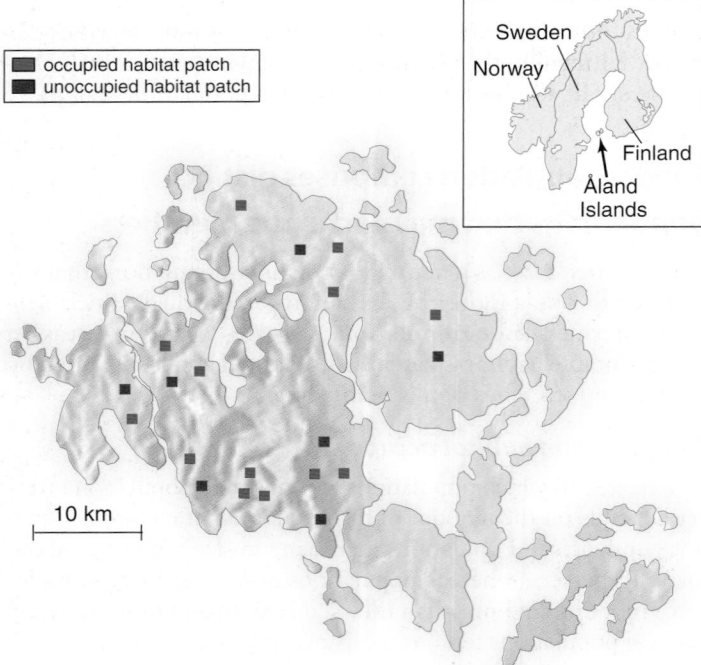

occupied habitat patch
unoccupied habitat patch

Sweden
Norway
Finland
Åland Islands

10 km

Figure 56.8 Metapopulations of butterflies.
The Glanville fritillary butterfly *(Melitaea cinxia)* occurs in metapopulations in southwestern Finland on the Åland Islands. None of the populations is large enough to survive for long on its own, but continual immigration of individuals from other populations allows some populations to survive. In addition, continual establishment of new populations tends to offset extinction of established populations, although in recent years, extinctions have outnumbered colonizations.

created and existing populations are supplemented by immigrants. Continued bad weather thus may doom the species, at least in this part of its range.

Metapopulations, where they occur, can have two important implications for the range of a species. First, through continuous colonization of empty patches, metapopulations prevent long-term extinction. If no such dispersal existed, then each population might eventually perish, leading to disappearance of the species from the entire area. Moreover, in source–sink metapopulations, the species occupies a larger area than it otherwise might, including marginal areas that could not support a population without a continual influx of immigrants. For these reasons, the study of metapopulations has become very important in conservation biology as natural habitats become increasingly fragmented.

Learning Outcomes Review 56.2

A population is a group of individuals of a single species existing together in an area. A population's range, the area it occupies, changes over time. Populations, in turn, may form a network, or metapopulation, connected by individuals that move from one group to another. Within a population, the distribution of individuals can be random, uniform, or clumped, and the distribution is determined in part by the availability of resources.

■ *How might the geographic range of a species change if populations could not exchange individuals with each other?*

56.3 Population Demography and Dynamics

Learning Outcomes

1. Define demography.
2. Describe the factors that influence a species' demography.
3. Explain the significance of survivorship curves.

The dynamics of a population—how it changes through time—are affected by many factors. One important factor is the age distribution of individuals—that is, what proportion of individuals are adults, juveniles, and young.

Demography is the quantitative study of populations. How the size of a population changes through time can be studied at two levels: as a whole or broken down into parts. At the most inclusive level, we can study the whole population to determine whether it is increasing, decreasing, or remaining constant. Put simply, populations grow if births outnumber deaths and shrink if deaths outnumber births. Understanding these trends is often easier, however, if we break the population into smaller units composed of individuals of the same age (for example, 1-year-olds) and study the factors affecting birth and death rates for each unit separately.

Sex ratio and generation time affect population growth rates

Population growth can be influenced by the population's sex ratio. The number of births in a population is usually directly related to the number of females; births may not be as closely related to the number of males in species in which a single male can mate with several females. In many species, males compete for the opportunity to mate with females, as you learned in the preceding chapter; consequently, a few males have many matings, and many males do not mate at all. In such species, the sex ratio is female-biased and does not affect population growth rates; reduction in the number of males simply changes the identities of the reproductive males without reducing the number of births. By contrast, among monogamous species, pairs may form long-lasting reproductive relationships, and a reduction in the number of males can then directly reduce the number of births.

Generation time is the average interval between the birth of an individual and the birth of its offspring. This factor can also affect population growth rates. Species differ greatly in generation time. Differences in body size can explain much of this variation—mice go through approximately 100 generations during the course of one elephant generation (figure 56.9). But small size does not always mean short generation time. Newts, for example, are smaller than mice, but have considerably longer generation times.

In general, populations with short generations can increase in size more quickly than populations with long generations. Conversely, because generation time and life span are

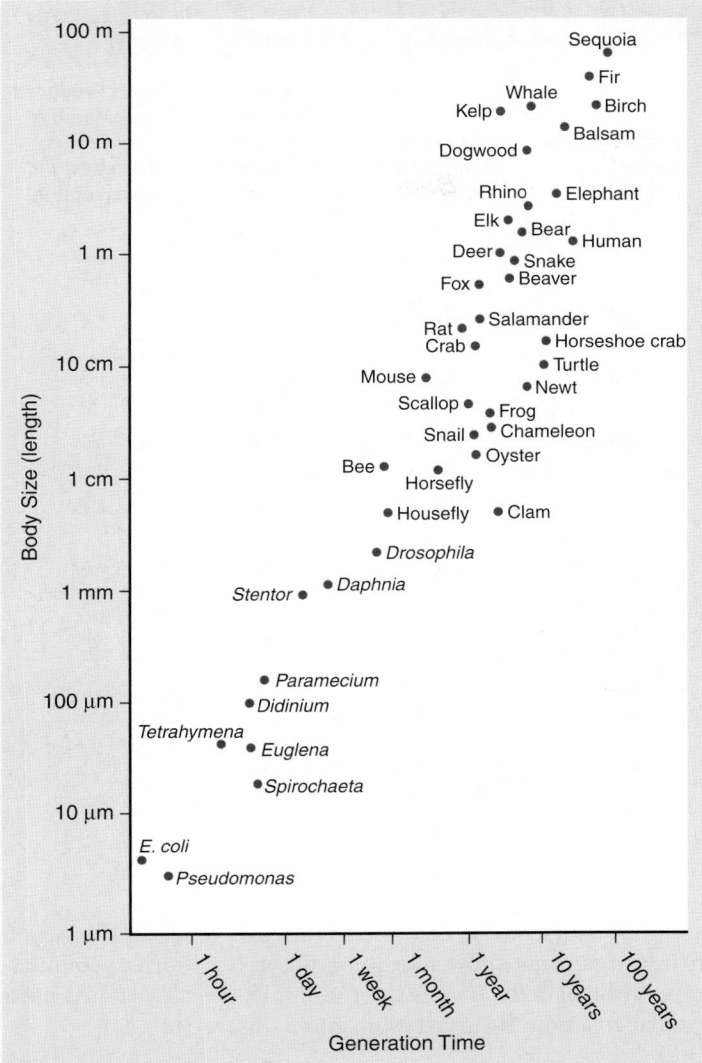

Figure 56.9 **The relationship between body size and generation time.** In general, larger organisms have longer generation times, although there are exceptions.

Inquiry question

? If resources became more abundant, would you expect smaller or larger species to increase in population size more quickly?

usually closely correlated, populations with short generation times may also diminish in size more rapidly if birth rates suddenly decrease.

Age structure is determined by the numbers of individuals in different age groups

A group of individuals of the same age is referred to as a cohort. In most species, the probability that an individual will reproduce or die varies through its life span. As a result, within a population, every cohort has a characteristic birth rate, or **fecundity,** defined as the number of offspring produced in a standard time (for example, per year), and death rate, or **mortality,** the number of individuals that die in that period.

The relative number of individuals in each cohort defines a population's **age structure.** Because different cohorts have different fecundity and death rates, age structure has a critical influence on a population's growth rate. Populations with a large proportion of young individuals, for example, tend to grow rapidly because an increasing proportion of their individuals are reproductive. Human populations in many developing countries are an example, as will be discussed later in this chapter. Conversely, if a large proportion of a population is relatively old, populations may decline. This phenomenon now characterizes Japan and some countries in Europe.

Life tables show probability of survival and reproduction through a cohort's life span

To assess how populations in nature are changing, ecologists use a **life table,** which tabulates the fate of a cohort from birth until death, showing the number of offspring produced and the number of individuals that die each year. Table 56.2 shows an example of a life table analysis from a study of the meadow grass *Poa annua*. This study follows the fate of 843 individuals through time, charting how many survive in each interval and how many offspring each survivor produces.

In table 56.2, the first column indicates the age of the cohort (that is, the number of 3-month intervals from the start of the study). The second and third columns indicate the number of survivors and the proportion of the original cohort still alive at the beginning of that interval. The fifth column presents the **mortality rate,** the proportion of individuals that started that interval alive but died by the end of it. The seventh column indicates the average number of seeds produced by each surviving individual in that interval, and the last column shows the number of seeds produced relative to the size of the original cohort.

Much can be learned by examining life tables. In the case of *P. annua*, we see that both the probability of dying and the number of offspring produced per surviving individual steadily increases with age. By adding up the numbers in the last column, we get the total number of offspring produced per individual in the initial cohort. This number is almost 2, which means that for every original member of the cohort, on average two new individuals have been produced. A figure of 1.0 would be the break-even number, the point at which the population was neither growing nor shrinking. In this case, the population appears to be growing rapidly.

In most cases, life table analysis is more complicated than this. First, except for organisms with short life spans, it is difficult to track the fate of a cohort until the death of the last individual. An alternative approach is to construct a cross-sectional study, examining the fate of cohorts of different ages in a single period. In addition, many factors—such as offspring

Age (in 3-month intervals)	Number Alive at Beginning of Time Interval	Proportion of Cohort Alive at Beginning of Time Interval (survivorship)	Deaths During Time Interval	Mortality Rate During Time Interval	Seeds Produced During Time Interval	Seeds Produced per Surviving Individual (fecundity)	Seeds Produced per Member of Cohort (fecundity × survivorship)
0	843	1.000	121	0.143	0	0.00	0.00
1	722	0.857	195	0.271	303	0.42	0.36
2	527	0.625	211	0.400	622	1.18	0.74
3	316	0.375	172	0.544	430	1.36	0.51
4	144	0.171	90	0.626	210	1.46	0.25
5	54	0.064	39	0.722	60	1.11	0.07
6	15	0.018	12	0.800	30	2.00	0.04
7	3	0.004	3	1.000	10	3.33	0.01
8	0	0.000	—		Total = 1665		Total = 1.98

TABLE 56.2 Life Table of the Meadow Grass (*Poa annua*) for a Cohort Containing 843 Seedlings

reproducing before all members of their parents' cohort have died—complicate the interpretation of whether populations are growing or shrinking.

Survivorship curves demonstrate how survival probability changes with age

The percentage of an original population that survives to a given age is called its **survivorship.** One way to express some aspects of the age distribution of populations is through a *survivorship curve.* Examples of different survivorship curves are shown in figure 56.10. Oysters produce vast numbers of offspring, only a few of which live to reproduce. However, once they become established and grow into reproductive individuals, their mortality rate is extremely low (type III survivorship curve). Note that in this type of curve, survival and mortality rates are inversely related. Thus, the rapid decrease in the proportion of oysters surviving indicates that few individuals survive, thus producing a high mortality rate. In contrast, the relatively flat line at older ages indicates high survival and low mortality.

In hydra, animals related to jellyfish, individuals are equally likely to die at any age. The result is a straight survivorship curve (type II).

Finally, mortality rates in humans, as in many other animals and in protists, rise steeply later in life (type I survivorship curve).

Of course, these descriptions are just generalizations, and many organisms show more complicated patterns. Examination of the data for *P. annua*, for example, reveals that it is most similar to a type II survivorship curve (figure 56.11).

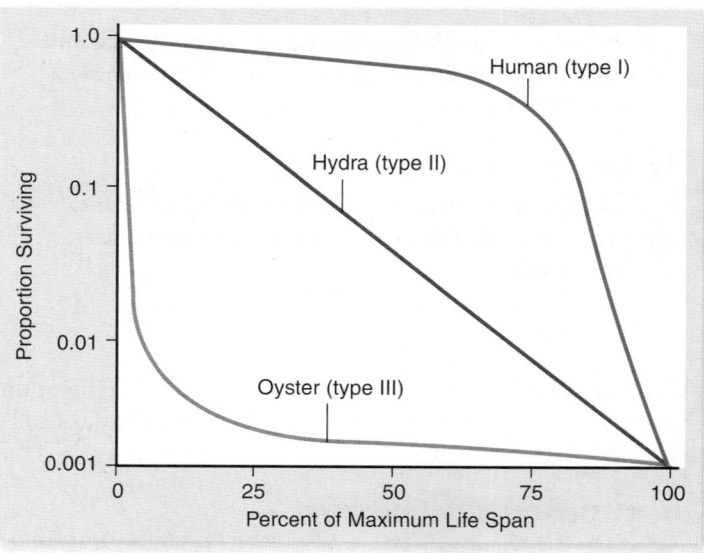

Figure 56.10 Survivorship curves. By convention, survival (the vertical axis) is plotted on a log scale. Humans have a type I life cycle, hydra (an animal related to jellyfish) type II, and oysters type III.

Figure 56.11 Survivorship curve for a cohort of the meadow grass. After several months of age, mortality increases at a constant rate through time.

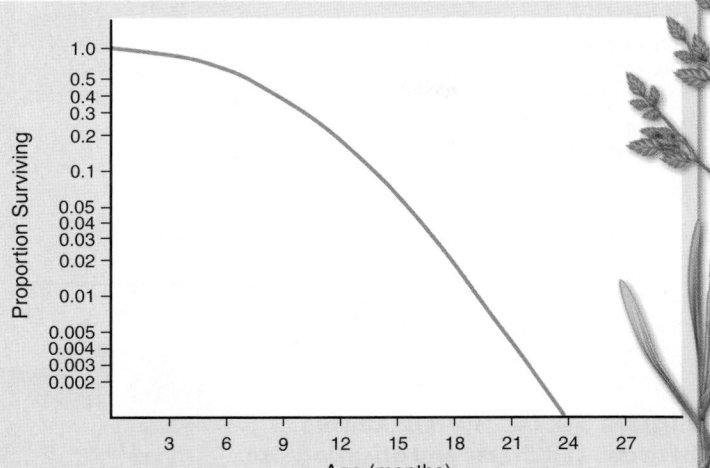

Inquiry question

? Suppose you wanted to keep meadow grass in your room as a houseplant. Suppose, too, that you wanted to buy an individual plant that was likely to live as long as possible. What age plant would you buy? How might the shape of the survivorship curve affect your answer?

Learning Outcomes Review 56.3

Demography is the quantitative study of populations. Demographic characteristics include age structure, life span, sex ratio, generation time, and birth and mortality rates. The age structure of a population and the manner in which mortality and birth rates vary among different age cohorts, determine whether a population will increase or decrease in size.

■ *Will populations with higher survivorship rates always have higher population growth rates than populations with lower survivorship rates?*

56.4 Life History and the Cost of Reproduction

Learning Outcomes

1. *Describe reproductive trade-offs in an organism's life history.*
2. *Compare the costs and benefits of allocating resources to reproduction.*

Natural selection favors traits that maximize the number of surviving offspring left in the next generation by an individual organism. Two factors affect this quantity: how long an individual lives, and how many young it produces each year.

Why doesn't every organism reproduce immediately after its own birth, produce large families of offspring, care for them intensively, and perform these functions repeatedly throughout a long life, while outcompeting others, escaping predators, and capturing food with ease? The answer is that no one organism can do all of this, simply because not enough resources are available. Consequently, organisms allocate resources either to current reproduction or to increasing their prospects of surviving and reproducing at later life stages.

The complete life cycle of an organism constitutes its life history. All life histories involve significant trade-offs. Because resources are limited, a change that increases reproduction may decrease survival and reduce future reproduction. As one example, a Douglas fir tree that produces more cones increases its current reproductive success—but it also grows more slowly. Because the number of cones produced is a function of how large a tree is, this diminished growth will decrease the number of cones it can produce in the future. Similarly, birds that have more offspring each year have a higher probability of dying during that year or of producing smaller clutches the following year (figure 56.12). Conversely, individuals that delay reproduction may grow faster and larger, enhancing future reproduction.

In one elegant experiment, researchers changed the number of eggs in the nests of a bird, the collared flycatcher (figure 56.13). Birds whose clutch size (the number of eggs produced in one breeding event) was decreased expended less energy raising their young and thus were able to lay more eggs the next year, whereas those given more eggs worked harder and consequently produced fewer eggs the following year. Ecologists refer to the reduction in future reproductive potential resulting from current reproductive efforts as the **cost of reproduction.**

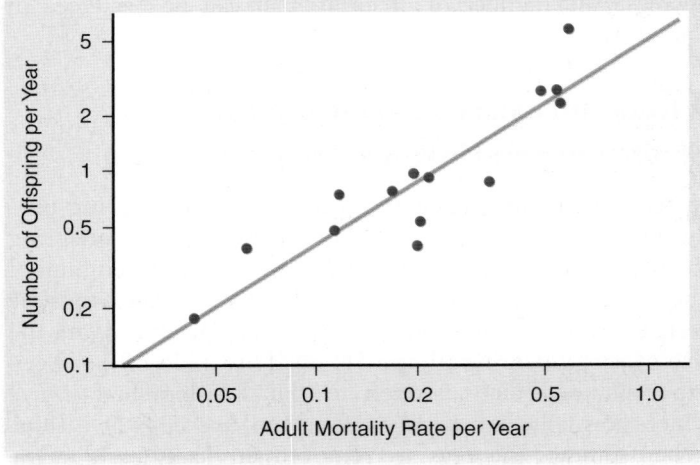

Figure 56.12 Reproduction has a price. Data from many bird species indicate that increased fecundity in birds correlates with higher mortality, ranging from the albatross (lowest) to the sparrow (highest). Birds that raise more offspring per year have a higher probability of dying during that year.

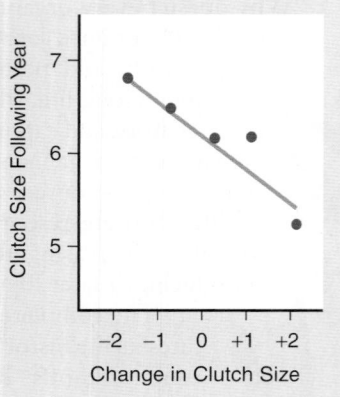

Figure 56.13 Reproductive events per lifetime. Adding eggs to nests of collared flycatchers (*Ficedula albicollis*), which increases the reproductive efforts of the female rearing the young, decreases clutch size the following year; removing eggs from the nest increases the next year's clutch size. This experiment demonstrates the trade-off between current reproductive effort and future reproductive success.

Natural selection favors the life history that maximizes lifetime reproductive success. When the cost of reproduction is low, individuals should produce as many offspring as possible because there is little cost. Low costs of reproduction may occur when resources are abundant and may also be relatively low when overall mortality rates are high. In the latter case, individuals may be unlikely to survive to the next breeding season anyway, so the incremental effect of increased reproductive efforts may have little effect on future survival.

Alternatively, when costs of reproduction are high, lifetime reproductive success may be maximized by deferring or minimizing current reproduction to enhance growth and survival rates. This situation may occur when costs of reproduction significantly affect the ability of an individual to survive or decrease the number of offspring that can be produced in the future.

A trade-off exists between number of offspring and investment per offspring

In terms of natural selection, the number of offspring produced is not as important as how many of those offspring themselves survive to reproduce. Assuming that the amount of energy to be invested in offspring is limited, a balance must be reached between the number of offspring produced and the size of each offspring (figure 56.14). This trade-off has been experimentally demonstrated in the side-blotched lizard, which normally lays between four and five eggs at a time. When some of the eggs are removed surgically early in the reproductive cycle, the female lizard produces only one to three eggs, but supplies each of these eggs with greater amounts of yolk, producing eggs and, subsequently, hatchlings that are much larger than normal (figure 56.15). Alternatively, by removing yolk from eggs, scientists have demonstrated that smaller young would be produced.

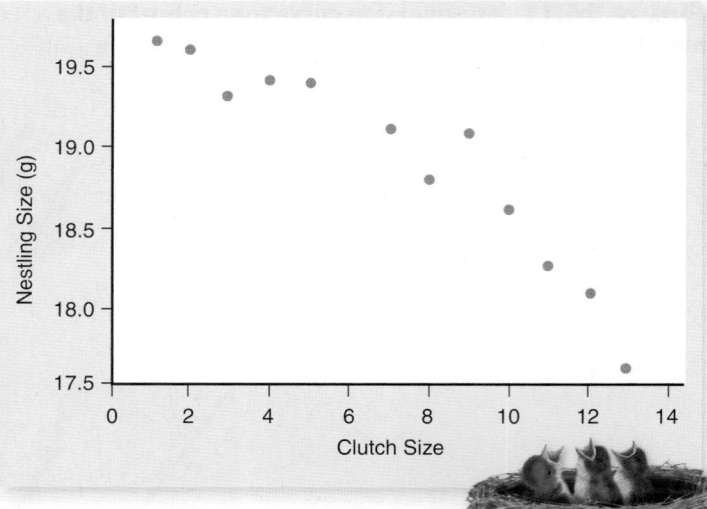

Figure 56.14 The relationship between clutch size and offspring size. In great tits (*Parus major*), the size of the nestlings is inversely related to the number of eggs laid. The more mouths they have to feed, the less the parents can provide to any one nestling.

? Inquiry question

Would natural selection favor producing many small young or a few large ones?

Figure 56.15 Variation in the size of baby side-blotched lizards (*Uta stansburiana*) produced by experimental manipulations. In clutches in which some developing eggs were surgically removed, the remaining offspring were larger (center) than lizards produced in control clutches in which all the eggs were allowed to develop (right). In experiments in which some of the yolk was removed from the eggs, smaller lizards hatched (left).

In the side-blotched lizard and many other species, the size of offspring is critical—larger offspring have a greater chance of survival. Producing many offspring with little chance of survival might not be the best strategy, but producing only a single, extraordinarily robust offspring also would not maximize the number of surviving offspring. Rather, an intermediate situation, in which several fairly large offspring are produced, should maximize the number of surviving offspring.

Reproductive events per lifetime represent an additional trade-off

The trade-off between age and fecundity plays a key role in many life histories. Annual plants and most insects focus all their reproductive resources on a single large event and then die. This life history adaptation is called **semelparity.** Organisms that produce offspring several times over many seasons exhibit a life history adaptation called **iteroparity.**

Species that reproduce yearly must avoid overtaxing themselves in any one reproductive episode so that they will be able to survive and reproduce in the future. Semelparity, or "big bang" reproduction, is usually found in short-lived species that have a low probability of staying alive between broods, such as plants growing in harsh climates. Semelparity is also favored when fecundity entails large reproductive cost, exemplified by Pacific salmon migrating upriver to their spawning grounds. In these species, rather than investing some resources in an unlikely bid to survive until the next breeding season, individuals put all their resources into one reproductive event.

Age at first reproduction correlates with life span

Among mammals and many other animals, longer-lived species put off reproduction longer than short-lived species, relative to expected life span. The advantage of delayed reproduction is that juveniles gain experience before expending the high costs of reproduction. In long-lived animals, this advantage outweighs the energy that is invested in survival and growth rather than reproduction.

In shorter-lived animals, on the other hand, time is of the essence; thus, quick reproduction is more critical than juvenile training, and reproduction tends to occur earlier.

Learning Outcomes Review 56.4

Life history adaptations involve many trade-offs between reproductive cost and investment in survival. These trade-offs take a variety of forms, from laying fewer than the maximum possible number of eggs to putting all energy into a single bout of reproduction. Natural selection favors maximizing reproductive success, but number of offspring produced must be tempered by available resources.

■ *How might the life histories of two species differ if one was subject to high levels of predation and the other had few predators?*

Learning Outcomes

1. *Explain exponential growth.*
2. *Discuss why populations cannot grow exponentially forever.*
3. *Define carrying capacity.*

Populations often remain at a relatively constant size, regardless of how many offspring are born. As you saw in chapter 1, Darwin based his theory of natural selection partly on this seeming contradiction. Natural selection occurs because of checks on reproduction, with some individuals producing fewer surviving offspring than others. To understand populations, we must consider how they grow and what factors in nature limit population growth.

The exponential growth model applies to populations with no growth limits

The rate of population increase, r, is defined as the difference between the birth rate, b, and the death rate, d, corrected for movement of individuals in or out of the population (e, rate of movement out of the area; i, rate of movement into the area). Thus,

$$r = (b - d) + (i - e)$$

Movements of individuals can have a major influence on population growth rates. For example, the increase in human population in the United States during the closing decades of the 20th century was mostly due to immigration.

The simplest model of population growth assumes that a population grows without limits at its maximal rate and also that rates of immigration and emigration are equal. This rate, called the **biotic potential,** is the rate at which a population of a given species increases when no limits are placed on its rate of growth. In mathematical terms, this is defined by the following formula:

$$\frac{dN}{dt} = r_i N$$

where N is the number of individuals in the population, dN/dt is the rate of change in its numbers over time, and r_i is the intrinsic rate of natural increase for that population—its innate capacity for growth.

The biotic potential of any population is exponential (red line in figure 56.16). Even when the *rate* of increase remains constant, the actual *number* of individuals accelerates rapidly as the size of the population grows. The result of unchecked exponential growth is a population explosion.

A single pair of houseflies, laying 120 eggs per generation, could produce more than 5 trillion descendants in a year. In 10 years, their descendants would form a swarm more than 2 m thick over the entire surface of the Earth! In practice, such patterns of unrestrained growth prevail only for short periods, usually when an organism reaches a new habitat with abundant

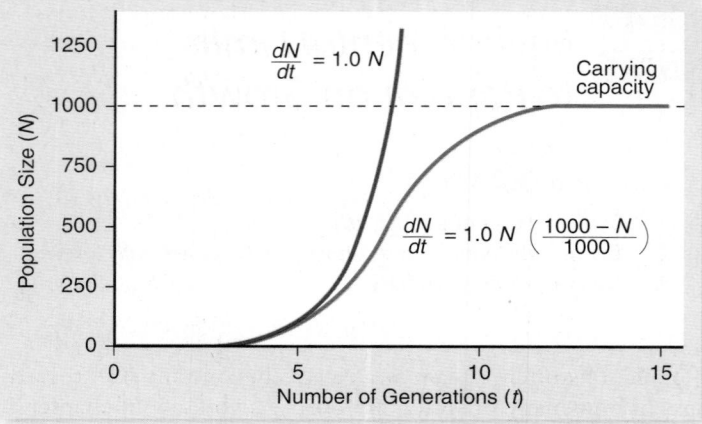

Figure 56.16 Two models of population growth. The red line illustrates the exponential growth model for a population with an *r* of 1.0. The blue line illustrates the logistic growth model in a population with *r* = 1.0 and *K* = 1000 individuals. At first, logistic growth accelerates exponentially; then, as resources become limited, the death rate increases and growth slows. Growth ceases when the death rate equals the birth rate. The carrying capacity *(K)* ultimately depends on the resources available in the environment.

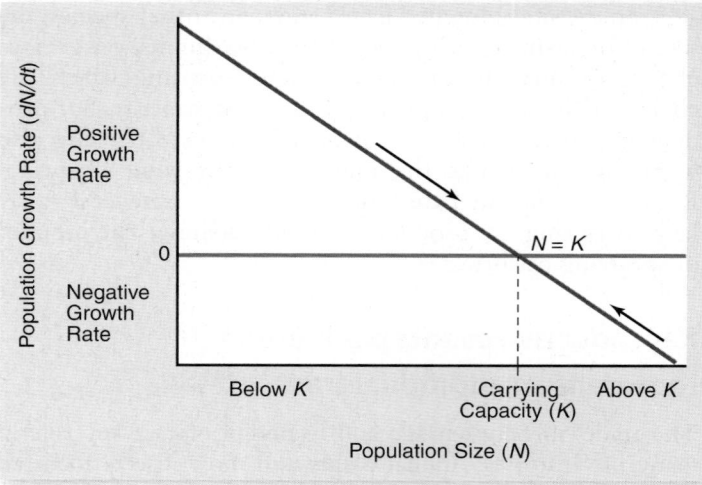

Figure 56.17 Relationship between population growth rate and population size. Populations far from the carrying capacity *(K)* have high growth rates—positive if the population is below *K*, and negative if it is above *K*. As the population approaches *K*, growth rates approach zero.

Inquiry question

? **Why does the growth rate converge on zero?**

resources. Natural examples of such short period of unrestrained growth include dandelions arriving in the fields, lawns, and meadows of North America from Europe for the first time; algae colonizing a newly formed pond; or cats introduced to an island with many birds, but previously lacking predators.

Carrying capacity

No matter how rapidly populations grow, they eventually reach a limit imposed by shortages of important environmental factors, such as space, light, water, or nutrients. A population ultimately may stabilize at a certain size, called the **carrying capacity** of the particular place where it lives. The carrying capacity, symbolized by *K*, is the maximum number of individuals that the environment can support.

The logistic growth model applies to populations that approach their carrying capacity

As a population approaches its carrying capacity, its rate of growth slows greatly, because fewer resources remain for each new individual to use. The growth curve of such a population, which is always limited by one or more factors in the environment, can be approximated by the following logistic growth equation:

$$\frac{dN}{dt} = rN\left(\frac{K-N}{K}\right)$$

In this model of population growth, the growth rate of the population *(dN/dt)* is equal to its intrinsic rate of natural increase (*r* multiplied by *N*, the number of individuals present at any one time), adjusted for the amount of resources available. The adjust-

ment is made by multiplying *rN* by the fraction of *K*, the carrying capacity, still unused [(*K* – *N*)/*K*]. As *N* increases, the fraction of resources by which *r* is multiplied becomes smaller and smaller, and the rate of increase of the population declines.

Graphically, if you plot *N* versus *t* (time), you obtain a **sigmoidal growth curve** characteristic of many biological populations. The curve is called "sigmoidal" because its shape has a double curve like the letter **S**. As the size of a population stabilizes at the carrying capacity, its rate of growth slows, eventually coming to a halt (blue line in figure 56.16).

In mathematical terms, as *N* approaches *K*, the *rate* of population growth *(dN/dt)* begins to slow, reaching 0 when *N* = *K* (figure 56.17). Conversely, if the population size exceeds the carrying capacity, then *K* – *N* will be negative, and the population will experience a negative growth rate. As the population size then declines toward the carrying capacity, the magnitude of this negative growth rate will decrease until it reaches 0 when *N* = *K*.

Notice that the population tends to move toward the carrying capacity regardless of whether it is initially above or below it. For this reason, logistic growth tends to return a population to the same size. In this sense, such populations are considered to be in equilibrium because they would be expected to be at or near the carrying capacity at most times.

In many cases, real populations display trends corresponding to a logistic growth curve. This is true not only in the laboratory, but also in natural populations (figure 56.18*a*). In some cases, however, the fit is not perfect (figure 56.18*b*), and as we shall see shortly, many populations exhibit other patterns.

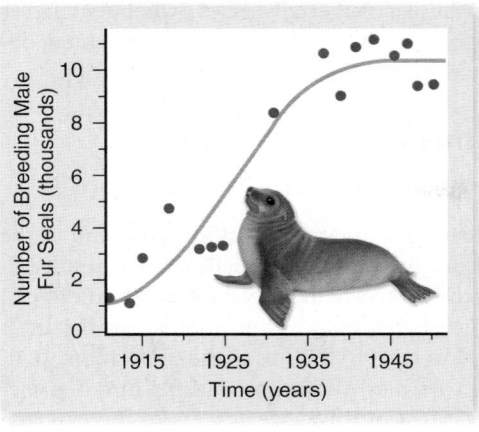

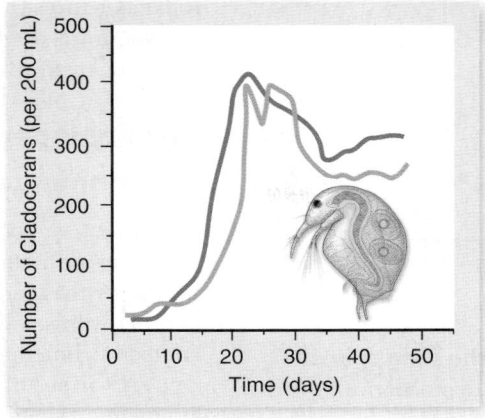

Figure 56.18 Many populations exhibit logistic growth. *a.* A fur seal (*Callorhinus ursinus*) population on St. Paul Island, Alaska. *b.* Two laboratory populations of the cladoceran *Bosmina longirostris*. Note that the populations first exceeded the carrying capacity, before decreasing to a size that was then maintained.

a.

b.

Learning Outcomes Review 56.5

Exponential growth refers to population growth in which the number of individuals accelerates even when the rate of increase remains constant; it results in a population explosion. Exponential growth is eventually limited by resource availability. The size at which a population in a particular location stabilizes is defined as the carrying capacity of that location for that species. Populations often grow to the carrying capacity of their environment.

■ *What might cause a population's carrying capacity to change, and how would the population respond?*

56.6 *Factors That Regulate Populations*

Learning Outcomes

1. *Compare density-dependent and density-independent factors.*
2. *Evaluate why the size of some populations cycle.*
3. *Consider how the life history adaptations of species may differ depending on how often populations are at their carrying capacity.*

A number of factors may affect population size through time. Some of these factors depend on population size and are therefore termed *density-dependent*. Other factors, such as natural disasters, affect populations regardless of size; these factors are termed *density-independent*. Many populations exhibit cyclic fluctuations in size that may result from complex interactions of factors.

Density-dependent effects occur when reproduction and survival are affected by population size

The reason population growth rates are affected by population size is that many important processes have **density-dependent effects.** That is, as population size increases, either reproductive rates decline or mortality rates increase, or both, a phenomenon termed *negative feedback* (figure 56.19).

Populations can be regulated in many different ways. When populations approach their carrying capacity, competition for resources can be severe, leading both to a decreased birth rate and an increased risk of death (figure 56.20). In addition, predators often focus their attention on a particularly common prey species, which also results in increasing rates of mortality as populations increase. High population densities can also lead to an accumulation of toxic wastes in the environment.

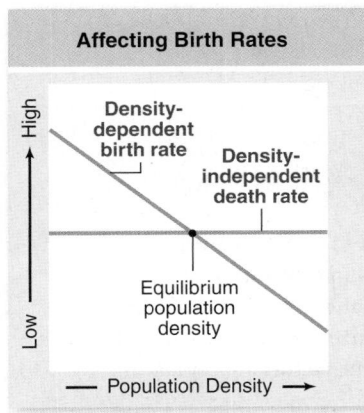

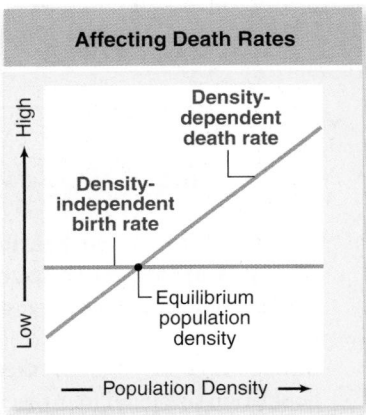

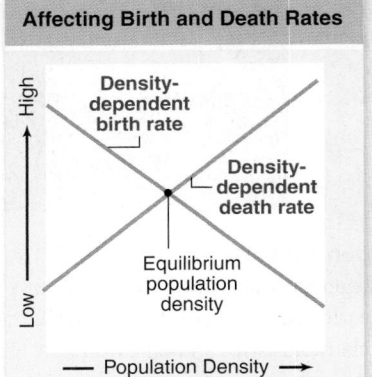

Figure 56.19 Density-dependent population regulation. Density-dependent factors can affect birth rates, death rates, or both.

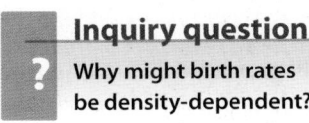

Inquiry question

? Why might birth rates be density-dependent?

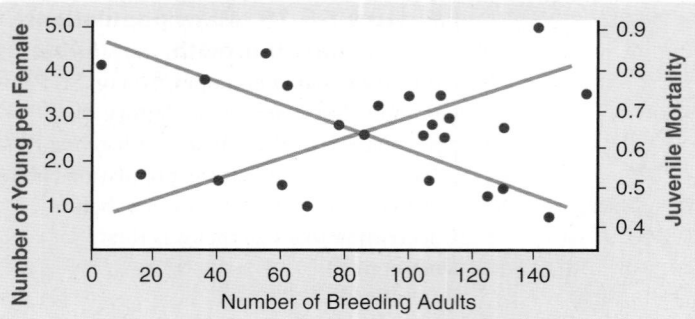

Figure 56.20 Density dependence in the song sparrow (*Melospiza melodia*) on Mandarte Island. Reproductive success decreases and mortality rates increase as population size increases.

Inquiry question

? What would happen if researchers supplemented the food available to the birds?

Behavioral changes may also affect population growth rates. Some species of rodents, for example, become antisocial, fighting more, breeding less, and generally acting stressed-out. These behavioral changes result from hormonal actions, but their ultimate cause is not yet clear; most likely, they have evolved as adaptive responses to situations in which resources are scarce. In addition, in crowded populations, the population growth rate may decrease because of an increased rate of emigration of individuals attempting to find better conditions elsewhere (figure 56.21).

However, not all density-dependent factors are negatively related to population size. In some cases, growth rates increase with population size. This phenomenon is referred to as the **Allee effect** (after Warder Allee, who first described it), and is an example of *positive feedback*. The Allee effect can take several forms. Most obviously, in populations that are too sparsely distributed, individuals may have difficulty finding mates. Moreover, some species may rely on large groups to deter predators or to provide the necessary stimulation for breeding activities. The Allee effect

Figure 56.21 Density-dependent effects. Migratory locusts (*Locusta migratoria*) are a legendary plague of large areas of Africa and Eurasia. At high population densities, the locusts have different hormonal and physical characteristics and take off as a swarm.

is a major threat for many endangered species, which may never recover from decreased population sizes caused by habitat destruction, overexploitation, or other causes (see chapter 60).

Density-independent effects include environmental disruptions and catastrophes

Growth rates in populations sometimes do not correspond to the logistic growth equation. In many cases, such patterns result because growth is under the control of **density-independent effects.** In other words, the rate of growth of a population at any instant is limited by something unrelated to the size of the population.

A variety of factors may affect populations in a density-independent manner. Most of these are aspects of the external environment, such as extremely cold winters, droughts, storms, or volcanic eruptions. Individuals often are affected by these occurrences regardless of the size of the population.

Populations in areas where such events occur relatively frequently display erratic growth patterns in which the populations increase rapidly when conditions are benign, but exhibit large reductions whenever the environment turns hostile (figure 56.22). Needless to say, such populations do not produce the sigmoidal growth curves characteristic of the logistic equation.

Population cycles may reflect complex interactions

In some populations, density-dependent effects lead not to an equilibrium population size but to cyclic patterns of increase and decrease. For example, ecologists have studied cycles in hare

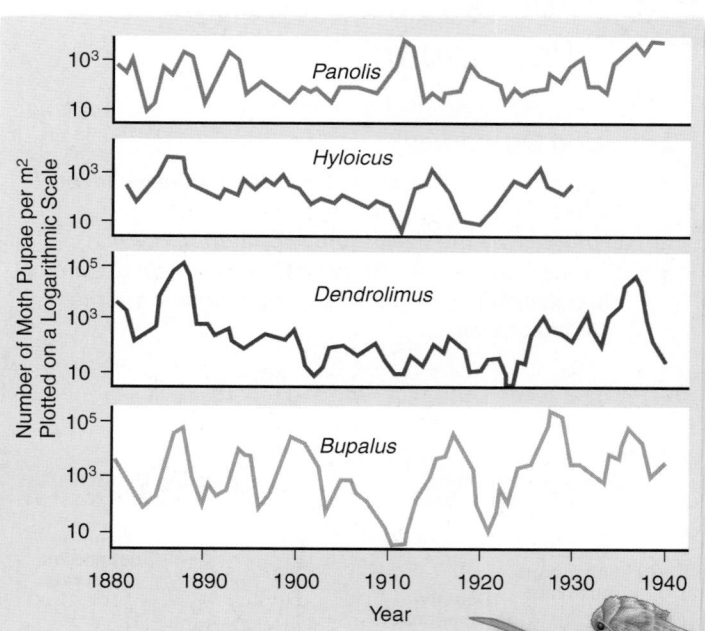

Figure 56.22 Fluctuations in the number of pupae of four moth species in Germany. The population fluctuations suggest that density-independent factors are regulating population size. The concordance in trends through time suggests that the same factors are regulating population size in all four species.

populations since the 1820s. They have found that the North American snowshoe hare *(Lepus americanus)* follows a "10-year cycle" (in reality, the cycle varies from 8 to 11 years). Hare population numbers fall 10-fold to 30-fold in a typical cycle, and 100-fold changes can occur (figure 56.23). Two factors appear to be generating the cycle: food plants and predators.

Food plants. The preferred foods of snowshoe hares are willow and birch twigs. As hare density increases, the quantity of these twigs decreases, forcing the hares to feed on high-fiber (low-quality) food. Lower birthrates, low juvenile survivorship, and low growth rates follow. The hares also spend more time searching for food, an activity that increases their exposure to predation. The result is a precipitous decline in willow and birch twig abundance, and a corresponding fall in hare abundance. It takes 2 to 3 years for the quantity of mature twigs to recover.

Predators. A key predator of the snowshoe hare is the Canada lynx. The Canada lynx shows a "10-year" cycle of abundance that seems remarkably entrained to the hare abundance cycle (see figure 55.23). As hare numbers increase, lynx numbers do too, rising in response to the increased availability of the lynx's food. When hare numbers fall, so do lynx numbers, their food supply depleted.

Which factor is responsible for the predator–prey oscillations? Do increasing numbers of hares lead to overharvesting of plants (a hare–plant cycle), or do increasing numbers of lynx lead to overharvesting of hares (a hare–lynx cycle)? Field experiments carried out by Charles Krebs and coworkers in 1992 provide an answer.

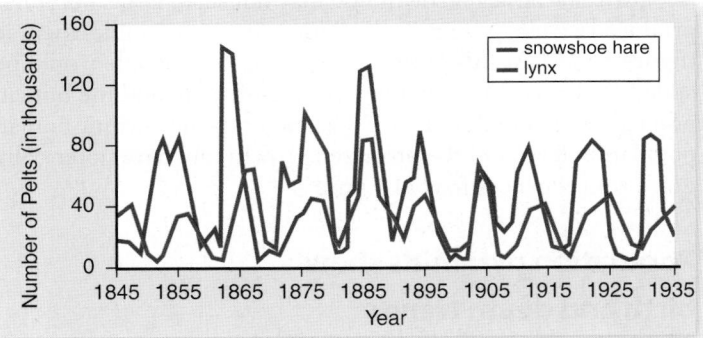

Figure 56.23 Linked population cycles of the snowshoe hare *(Lepus americanus)* and the northern lynx *(Lynx canadensis)*. These data are based on records of fur returns from trappers in the Hudson Bay region of Canada. The lynx population carefully tracks that of the snowshoe hare, but lags behind it slightly.

Inquiry question

? Suppose experimenters artificially kept the hare population at a high and constant level; what would happen to the lynx population? Conversely, if experimenters artificially kept the lynx population at a high and constant level, what would happen to the hare population?

In Canada's Yukon, Krebs set up experimental plots that contained hare populations. If food is added (no food shortage effect) and predators are excluded (no predator effect) in an experimental area, hare numbers increase 10-fold and stay there—the cycle is lost. However, the cycle is retained if either of the factors is allowed to operate alone: exclude predators but don't add food (food shortage effect alone), or add food in the presence of predators (predator effect alone). Thus, both factors can affect the cycle, which in practice seems to be generated by the interaction between the two.

Population cycles traditionally have been considered to occur rarely. However, a recent review of nearly 700 long-term (25 years or more) studies of trends within populations found that cycles were not uncommon; nearly 30% of the studies—including birds, mammals, fish, and crustaceans—provided evidence of some cyclic pattern in population size through time, although most of these cycles are nowhere near as dramatic in amplitude as the hare–lynx cycles. In some cases, such as that of the snowshoe hare and lynx, density-dependent factors may be involved, whereas in other cases, density-independent factors, such as cyclic climatic patterns, may be responsible.

Resource availability affects life history adaptations

As you have seen, some species usually maintain stable population sizes near the carrying capacity, whereas in other species population sizes fluctuate markedly and are often far below carrying capacity. The selective factors affecting such species differ markedly. Individuals in populations near their carrying capacity may face stiff competition for limited resources; by contrast, individuals in populations far below carrying capacity have access to abundant resources.

We have already described the consequences of such differences. When resources are limited, the cost of reproduction often will be very high. Consequently, selection will favor individuals that can compete effectively and utilize resources efficiently. Such adaptations often come at the cost of lowered reproductive rates. Such populations are termed **K-selected** because they are adapted to thrive when the population is near its carrying capacity *(K)*. Table 56.3 lists some of the typical features of *K*-selected populations. Examples of *K*-selected species include coconut palms, whooping cranes, whales, and humans.

By contrast, in populations far below the carrying capacity, resources may be abundant. Costs of reproduction are low, and selection favors those individuals that can produce the maximum number of offspring. Selection here favors individuals with the highest reproductive rates; such populations are termed **r-selected.** Examples of organisms displaying *r*-selected life history adaptations include dandelions, aphids, mice, and cockroaches.

Most natural populations show life history adaptations that exist along a continuum ranging from completely *r*-selected traits to completely *K*-selected traits. Although these tendencies hold true as generalities, few populations are purely *r*- or *K*-selected and show all of the traits listed in table 56.3. These attributes should be treated as generalities, with the recognition that many exceptions exist.

TABLE 56.3 — r-Selected and K-Selected Life History Adaptations

Adaptation	r-Selected Populations	K-Selected Populations
Age at first reproduction	Early	Late
Life span	Short	Long
Maturation time	Short	Long
Mortality rate	Often high	Usually low
Number of offspring produced per reproductive episode	Many	Few
Number of reproductions per lifetime	Few	Many
Parental care	None	Often extensive
Size of offspring or eggs	Small	Large

Learning Outcomes Review 56.6

Density-dependent factors such as resource availability come into play particularly when population size is larger; density-independent factors such as natural disasters operate regardless of population size. Population density may be cyclic due to complex interactions such as resource cycles and predator effects. Populations with density-dependent regulation often are near their carrying capacity; in species with populations well below carrying capacity, natural selection may favor high rates of reproduction when resources are abundant.

■ *Can a population experience both positive and negative density-dependent effects?*

56.7 Human Population Growth

Learning Outcomes

1. *Explain how the rate of human population growth has changed through time.*
2. *Describe the effects of age distribution on future growth.*
3. *Evaluate the relative importance of rapid population growth and resource consumption as threats to the biosphere and human welfare.*

Humans exhibit many K-selected life history traits, including small brood size, late reproduction, and a high degree of parental care. These life history traits evolved during the early history of hominids, when the limited resources available from the environment controlled population size. Throughout most of human history, our populations have been regulated by food availability, disease, and predators. Although unusual disturbances, including floods, plagues, and droughts, no doubt affected the pattern of human population growth, the overall size of the human population grew slowly during our early history.

Two thousand years ago, perhaps 130 million people populated the Earth. It took a thousand years for that number to double, and it was 1650 before it had doubled again, to about 500 million. In other words, for over 16 centuries, the human population was characterized by very slow growth. In this respect, human populations resembled many other species with predominantly K-selected life history adaptations.

Human populations have grown exponentially

Starting in the early 1700s, changes in technology gave humans more control over their food supply, enabled them to develop superior weapons to ward off predators, and led to the development of cures for many diseases. At the same time, improvements in shelter and storage capabilities made humans less vulnerable to climatic uncertainties. These changes allowed humans to expand the carrying capacity of the habitats in which they lived and thus to escape the confines of logistic growth and re-enter the exponential phase of the sigmoidal growth curve.

Responding to the lack of environmental constraints, the human population has grown explosively over the last 300 years. Although the birth rate has remained unchanged at about 30 per 1000 per year over this period, the death rate has fallen dramatically, from 20 per 1000 per year to its present level of 13 per 1000 per year. The difference between birth and death rates meant that the population grew as much as 2% per year, although the rate has now declined to 1.2% per year.

A 1.2% annual growth rate may not seem large, but it has produced a current human population of nearly 7 billion people (figure 56.24). At this growth rate, 78 million people would be added to the world population in the next year, and the human population would double in 58 years. Both the current human population level and the projected growth rate have potentially grave consequences for our future.

Population pyramids show birth and death trends

Although the human population as a whole continues to grow rapidly at the beginning of the 21st century, this growth is not occurring uniformly over the planet. Rather, most of the population growth is occurring in Africa, Asia, and Latin America (figure 56.25). By contrast, populations are actually decreasing in some countries in Europe.

The rate at which a population can be expected to grow in the future can be assessed graphically by means of a **population pyramid**, a bar graph displaying the numbers of people in each age category (figure 56.26). Males are conventionally shown to the left of the vertical age axis, females to the right. A human population pyramid thus displays the age composition of a population by sex. In most human population pyramids, the number of older females is disproportionately large compared with the

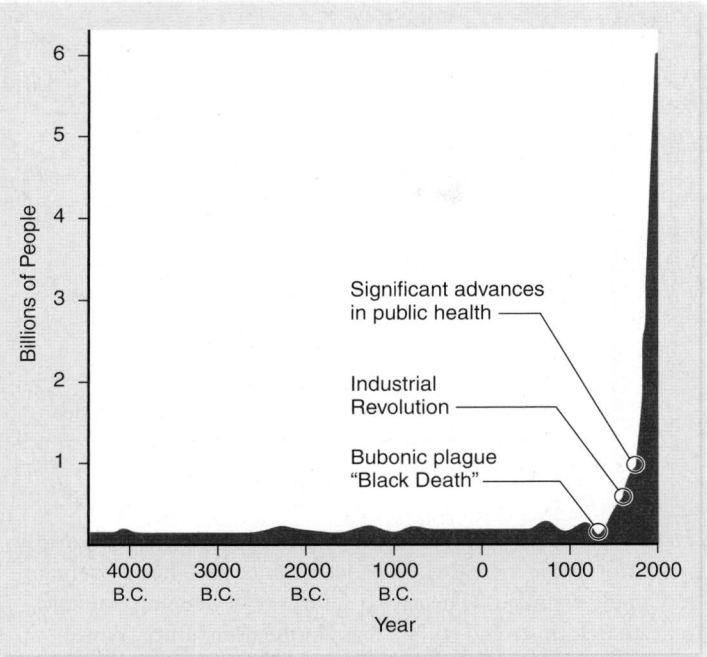

Figure 56.24 History of human population size.
Temporary increases in death rate, even a severe one such as that occurring during the Black Death of the 1300s, have little lasting effect. Explosive growth began with the Industrial Revolution in the 1800s, which produced a significant, long-term lowering of the death rate. The current world population is 6.9 billion, and at the present rate, it will double in 58 years.

Inquiry question

? Based on what we have learned about population growth, what do you predict will happen to human population size?

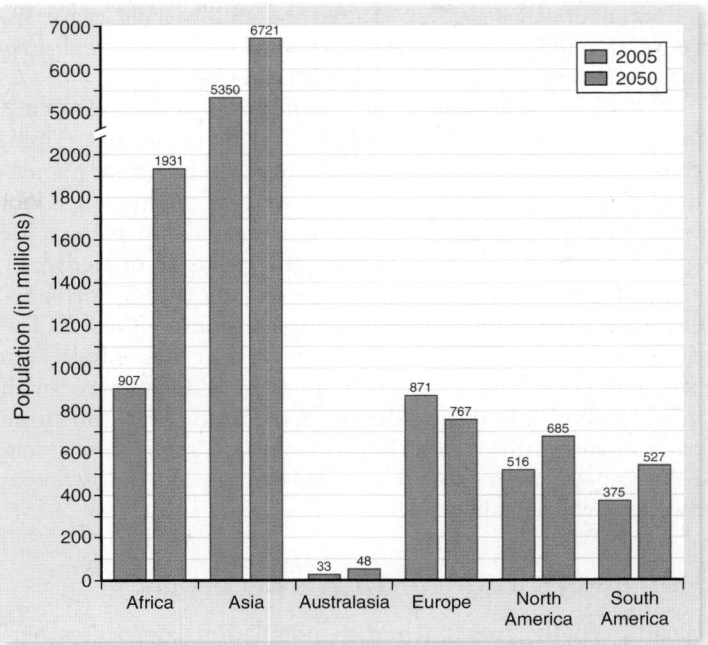

Figure 56.25 Projected population growth in 2050.
Developed countries are predicted to grow little; almost all of the population increase will occur in less-developed countries.

number of older males, because females in most regions have a longer life expectancy than males.

Viewing such a pyramid, we can predict demographic trends in births and deaths. In general, a rectangular pyramid is characteristic of countries whose populations are stable, neither growing nor shrinking. A triangular pyramid is characteristic of a country that will exhibit rapid future growth because most of

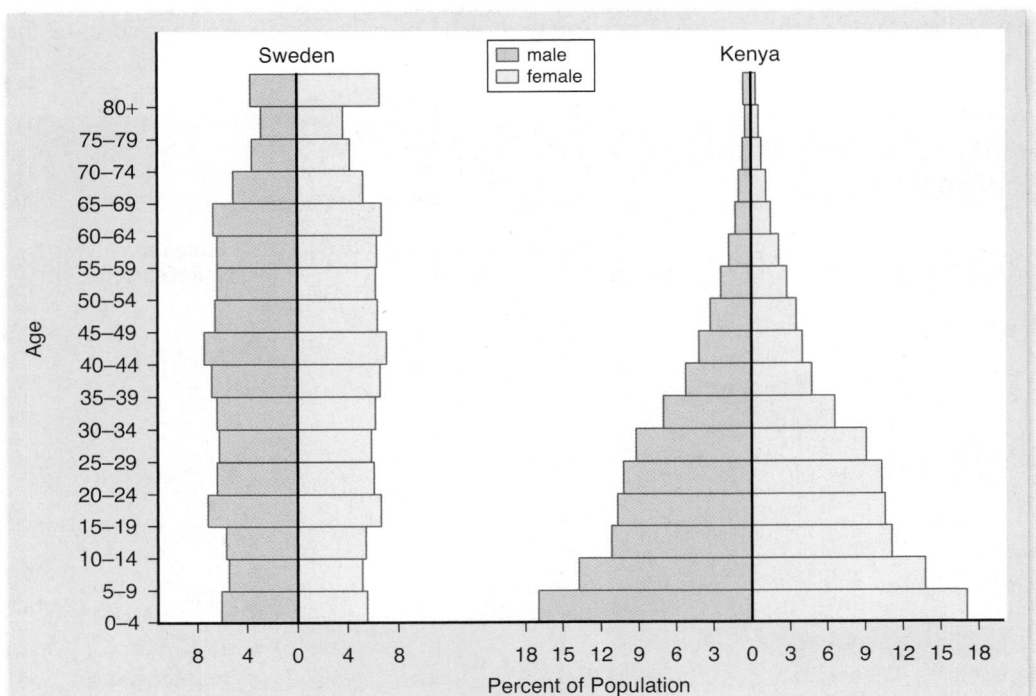

Figure 56.26 Population pyramids from 2008. Population pyramids are graphed according to a population's age distribution. Kenya's pyramid has a broad base because of the great number of individuals below childbearing age. When the young people begin to bear children, the population will experience rapid growth. The Swedish pyramid exhibits a slight bulge among middle-aged Swedes, the result of the "baby boom" that occurred in the middle of the 20th century, and many postreproductive individuals resulting from Sweden's long average life span.

Inquiry question

? What will the population distributions look like in 20 years?

its population has not yet entered the childbearing years. Inverted triangles are characteristic of populations that are shrinking, usually as a result of sharply declining birth rates.

Examples of population pyramids for Sweden and Kenya in 2008 are shown in figure 56.26. The two countries exhibit very different age distributions. The nearly rectangular population pyramid for Sweden indicates that its population is not expanding because birth rates have decreased and average life span has increased. The very triangular pyramid of Kenya, by contrast, results from relatively high birthrates and shorter average life spans, which can lead to explosive future growth. The difference is most apparent when we consider that only 16% of Sweden's population is less than 15 years old, compared with nearly half of all Kenyans. Moreover, the fertility rate (offspring per woman) in Sweden is 1.7; in Kenya, it is 4.7. As a result, Kenya's population could double in less than 35 years, whereas Sweden's will remain stable.

Humanity's future growth is uncertain

Earth's rapidly growing human population constitutes perhaps the greatest challenge to the future of the biosphere, the world's interacting community of living things. Humanity is adding 78 million people a year to its population—over a million every 5 days, 150 every minute! In more rapidly growing countries, the resulting population increase is staggering (table 56.4). India, for example, had a population of 1.05 billion in 2002; by 2050, its population likely will exceed 1.6 billion.

A key element in the world's population growth is its uneven distribution among countries. Of the billion people added to the world's population in the 1990s, 90% live in developing countries (figure 56.27). The fraction of the world's population that lives in industrialized countries is therefore diminishing. In 1950, fully one-third of the world's population lived in industrialized countries; by 1996, that proportion had fallen to one-quarter; and in 2020, the proportion will have fallen to one-sixth.

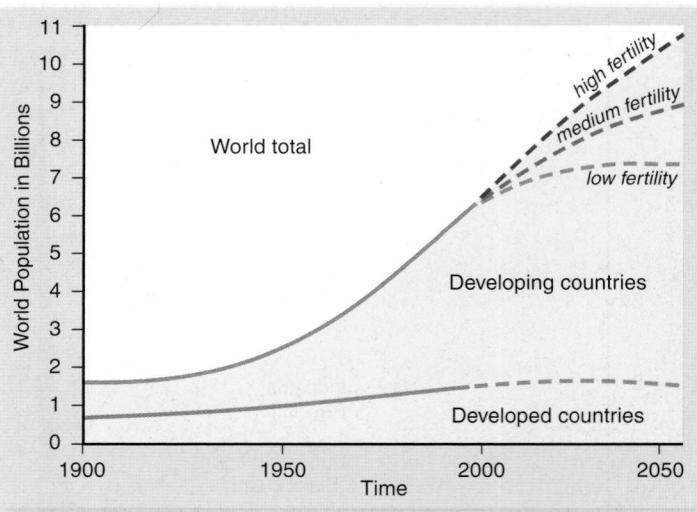

Figure 56.27 Distribution of population growth. Most of the worldwide increase in population since 1950 has occurred in developing countries. The age structures of developing countries indicate that this trend will increase in the near future. World population in 2050 likely will be between 7.3 and 10.7 billion, according to a recent United Nations study. Depending on fertility rates, the population at that time will either be increasing rapidly or slightly, or in the best case, declining slightly.

In the future, the world's population growth will be centered in the parts of the world least equipped to deal with the pressures of rapid growth.

Rapid population growth in developing countries has had the harsh consequence of increasing the gap between rich and poor. Today, the 19% of the world's population that lives in the industrialized world have a per capita income of $22,060, but 81% of the world's population lives in developing countries and has a per capita income of only $3,580. Furthermore, of the

TABLE 56.4	A Comparison of 2005 Population Data in Developed and Developing Countries		
	United States (highly developed)	**Brazil (moderately developed)**	**Ethiopia (poorly developed)**
Fertility rate	2.1	1.9	5.3
Doubling time at current rate (years)	75	65	29
Infant mortality rate (per 1000 births)	6.5	30	95
Life expectancy at birth (years)	78	72	49
Per capita GDP (U.S. $)*	$40,100	$8100	$800
Population < 15 years old (%)	21	26	44

*GDP, gross domestic product.

people in the developing world, about one-quarter of the population gets by on $1 per day. Eighty percent of all the energy used today is consumed by the industrialized world, but only 20% is used by developing countries.

No one knows whether the world can sustain today's population of 6.9 billion people, much less the far greater numbers expected in the future. As chapter 58 outlines, the world ecosystem is already under considerable stress. We cannot reasonably expect to expand its carrying capacity indefinitely, and indeed we already seem to be stretching the limits.

Despite using an estimated 45% of the total biological productivity of Earth's landmasses and more than one-half of all renewable sources of fresh water, between one-fourth and one-eighth of all people in the world are malnourished. Moreover, as anticipated by Thomas Malthus in his famous 1798 work, *Essay on the Principle of Population*, death rates are beginning to rise in some areas. In sub-Saharan Africa, for example, population projections for the year 2025 have been scaled back from 1.33 billion to 1.05 billion (21%) because of the effect of AIDS. Similar decreases are projected for Russia as a result of higher death rates due to disease.

If we are to avoid catastrophic increases in the death rate, birth rates must fall dramatically. Faced with this grim dichotomy, significant efforts are underway worldwide to lower birth rates.

The population growth rate has declined

The world population growth rate is declining, from a high of 2.0% in the period 1965–1970 to 1.2% in 2008. Nonetheless, because of the larger population, this amounts to an increase of 78 million people per year to the world population, compared with 53 million per year in the 1960s.

The United Nations attributes the growth rate decline to increased family planning efforts and the increased economic power and social status of women. The United States has led the world in funding family planning programs abroad, but some groups oppose spending money on international family planning. The opposition believes that money is better spent on improving education and the economy in other countries, leading to an increased awareness and lowered fertility rates. The U.N. certainly supports the improvement of education programs in developing countries, but interestingly, it has reported increased education levels *following* a decrease in family size as a result of family planning.

Most countries are devoting considerable attention to slowing the growth rate of their populations, and there are genuine signs of progress. For example, from 1984 to 2008, family planning programs in Kenya succeeded in reducing the fertility rate from 8.0 to 4.7 children per couple, thus lowering the population growth rate from 4.0% per year to 2.8% per year. Because of these efforts, the global population may stabilize at about 8.9 billion people by the middle of the current century. How many people the planet can support sustainably depends on the quality of life that we want to achieve; there are already more people than can be sustainably supported with current technologies.

Consumption in the developed world further depletes resources

Population size is not the only factor that determines resource use; per capita consumption is also important. In this respect, we in the industrialized world need to pay more attention to lessening the impact each of us makes because, even though the vast majority of the world's population is in developing countries, the overwhelming percentage of consumption of resources occurs in the industrialized countries. Indeed, the wealthiest 20% of the world's population accounts for 86% of the world's consumption of resources and produces 53% of the world's carbon dioxide emissions, whereas the poorest 20% of the world is responsible for only 1.3% of consumption and 3% of carbon dioxide emissions. Looked at another way, in terms of resource use, a child born today in the industrialized world will consume many more resources over the course of his or her life than a child born in the developing world.

One way of quantifying this disparity is by calculating what has been termed the **ecological footprint,** which is the amount of productive land required to support an individual at the standard of living of a particular population through the course of his or her life. This figure estimates the acreage used for the production of food (both plant and animal), forest products, and housing, as well as the area of forest required to absorb carbon dioxide produced by the combustion of fossil fuels. As figure 56.28 illustrates, the

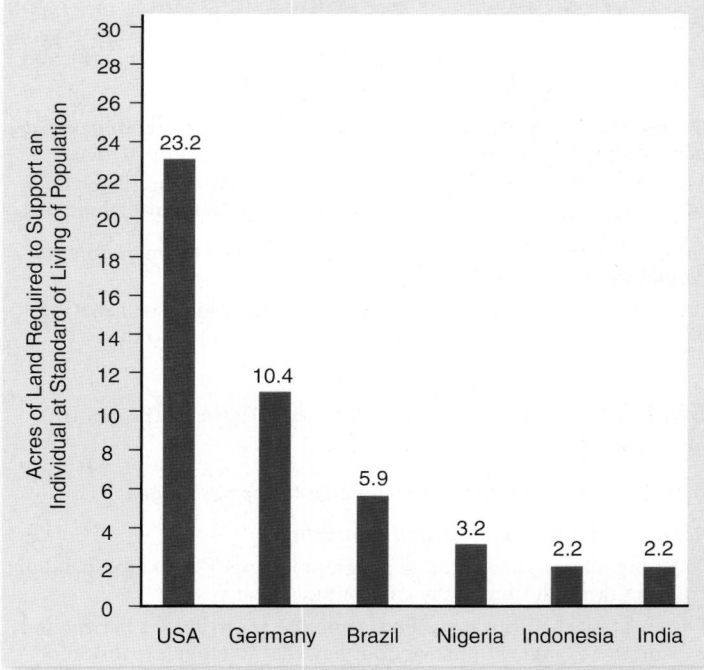

Figure 56.28 Ecological footprints of individuals in different countries. An ecological footprint calculates how much land is required to support a person through his or her life, including the acreage used for production of food, forest products, and housing, in addition to the forest required to absorb the carbon dioxide produced by the combustion of fossil fuels.

Inquiry question

? Which is a more important cause of resource depletion, overpopulation or overconsumption?

ecological footprint of an individual in the United States is more than 10 times greater than that of someone in India.

Based on these measurements, researchers have calculated that resource use by humans is now one-third greater than the amount that nature can sustainably replace. Moreover, consumption is increasing rapidly in parts of the developing world; if all humans lived at the standard of living in the industrialized world, two additional planet Earths would be needed.

Building a sustainable world is the most important task facing humanity's future. The quality of life available to our children will depend to a large extent on our success in limiting both population growth and the amount of per capita resource consumption.

Learning Outcomes Review 56.7

For most of its history, the *K*-selected human population increased gradually. In the last 400 years, with resource control, the human population has grown exponentially; at the current rate, it would double in 58 years. A population pyramid shows the number of individuals in different age categories. Pyramids with a wide base are undergoing faster growth than those that are uniform from top to bottom. Growth rates overall are declining, but consumption per capita in the developed world is still a significant drain on resources.

■ **Which is more important, reducing global population growth or reducing resource consumption levels in developed countries?**

Chapter Review

56.1 The Environmental Challenges

Key environmental factors include temperature, water, sunlight, and soil type. Individuals seek to maintain internal homeostasis.

Organisms are capable of responding to environmental changes that occur during their lifetime.

Most individuals can cope with variations in their natural habitat, such as short-term changes in temperature and water availability.

Natural selection leads to evolutionary adaptation to environmental conditions.

Over evolutionary time, physiological, morphological, or behavioral adaptations evolve that make organisms better suited to the environment in which they live.

56.2 Populations: Groups of a Single Species in One Place

A population's geographic distribution is termed its range.

Ranges undergo expansion and contraction.

Most populations have limited geographic ranges that can expand or contract through time as the environment changes.

Dispersal mechanisms may allow some species to cross a barrier and expand their range. Human actions have led to range expansion of some species, often with detrimental effects.

Individuals in populations exhibit different spacing patterns.

Within a population, individuals are distributed randomly, uniformly, or are clumped . Nonrandom distributions may reflect resource distributions or competition for resources.

A metapopulation comprises distinct populations that may exchange members.

The degree of exchange between populations in a metapopulation is highest when populations are large and more connected.

Metapopulations may act as a buffer against extinction by permitting recolonization of vacant areas or marginal areas.

56.3 Population Demography and Dynamics

Sex ratio and generation time affect population growth rates.

Abundant females, a short generation time, or both can be responsible for more rapid population growth.

Age structure is determined by the numbers of individuals in different age groups.

Every age cohort has a characteristic fecundity and death rate, and so the age structure of a population affects growth.

Life tables show probability of survival and reproduction through a cohort's life span.

Survivorship curves demonstrate how survival probability changes with age (see figures 56.11, 56.12).

In some populations, survivorship is high until old age, whereas in others, survivorship is lowest among the youngest individuals.

56.4 Life History and the Cost of Reproduction

Because resources are limited, reproduction has a cost. Resources allocated toward current reproduction cannot be used to enhance survival and future reproduction (see figure 56.13).

A trade-off exists between number of offspring and investment per offspring.

When reproductive cost is high, fitness can be maximized by deferring reproduction, or by producing a few large-sized young that have a greater chance of survival.

Reproductive events per lifetime represent an additional trade-off.

Semelparity is reproduction once in a single large event. Iteroparity is production of offspring several times over many seasons.

Age at first reproduction correlates with life span.

Longer-lived species delay first reproduction longer compared with short-lived species, in which time is of the essence.

56.5 Environmental Limits to Population Growth

The exponential growth model applies to populations with no growth limits.

The rate of population increase, *r*, is defined as the difference between birth rate, *b*, and death rate, *d*.

Exponential growth occurs when a population is not limited by resources or by other species (see figure 56.16).

The logistic model applies to populations that approach their carrying capacity.

Logistic growth is observed as a population reaches its carrying capacity. Usually, a population's growth rate slows to a plateau. In some cases the population overshoots and then drops back to the carrying capacity.

56.6 Factors That Regulate Populations

Density-dependent effects occur when reproduction and survival are affected by population size.

Density-dependent factors include increased competition and disease. To stabilize a population size, birth rates must decline, death rates must increase, or both.

Density-independent effects include environmental disruptions and catastrophes.

Density-independent factors are not related to population size and include environmental events that result in mortality.

Population cycles may reflect complex interactions.

In some cases, population size is cyclic because of the interaction of factors such as food supply and predation (see figure 56.23).

Resource availability affects life history adaptations.

Populations at carrying capacity have adaptations to compete for limited resources; populations well below carrying capacity exhibit a high reproductive rate to use abundant resources.

56.7 Human Population Growth

Human populations have grown exponentially.

Technology and other innovations have simultaneously increased the carrying capacity and decreased mortality in the past 300 years.

Population pyramids show birth and death trends.

Populations with many young individuals are likely to experience high growth rates as these individuals reach reproductive age.

Humanity's future growth is uncertain.

The human population is unevenly distributed. Rapid growth in developing countries has resulted in poverty, whereas most resources are utilized by the industrialized world.

The population growth rate has declined.

Even at lower growth rates, the number of individuals on the planet is likely to plateau at 7 to 10 billion.

Consumption in the developed world further depletes resources.

Resource consumption rates in the developed world are very high; a sustainable future requires limits both to population growth and to per capita resource consumption.

Review Questions

UNDERSTAND

1. Source–sink metapopulations are distinct from other types of metapopulations because
   a. exchange of individuals only occurs in the former.
   b. populations with negative growth rates are a part of the former.
   c. populations never go extinct in the former.
   d. all populations eventually go extinct in the former.

2. The potential for social interactions among individuals should be maximized when individuals
   a. are randomly distributed in their environment.
   b. are uniformly distributed in their environment.
   c. have a clumped distribution in their environment.
   d. None of the above

3. When ecologists talk about the cost of reproduction they mean
   a. the reduction in future reproductive output as a consequence of current reproduction.
   b. the amount of calories it takes for all the activity used in successful reproduction.
   c. the amount of calories contained in eggs or offspring.
   d. None of the above

4. A life history trade-off between clutch size and offspring size
   a. means that as clutch size increases, offspring size increases.
   b. means that as clutch size increases, offspring size decreases.
   c. means that as clutch size increases, adult size increases.
   d. means that as clutch size increases, adult size decreases.

5. The difference between exponential and logistic growth rates is
   a. exponential growth depends on birth and death rates and logistic does not.
   b. in logistic growth, emigration and immigration are unimportant.
   c. that both are affected by density, but logistic growth is slower.
   d. that only logistic growth reflects density-dependent effects on births or deaths.

6. The logistic population growth model, $dN/dt = rN[(K - N)/K]$, describes a population's growth when an upper limit to growth is assumed. As N approaches (numerically) the value of K
   a. dN/dt increases rapidly.
   b. dN/dt approaches 0.
   c. dN/dt increases slowly.
   d. the population becomes threatened by extinction.

7. Which of the following is an example of a density-dependent effect on population growth?

   a. An extremely cold winter
   b. A tornado
   c. An extremely hot summer in which cool burrow retreats are fewer than number of individuals in the population
   d. A drought

APPLY

1. If the size of a population is reduced due to a natural disaster such as a flood

   a. population growth rates may increase because the population is no longer near its carrying capacity.
   b. population growth rates may decrease because individuals have trouble finding mates.
   c. both effects a. and b. may occur and whether population rates increase or decrease cannot be predicted.
   d. All of the above

2. In populations subjected to high levels of predation

   a. individuals should invest little in reproduction so as to maximize their survival.
   b. individuals should produce few offspring and invest little in any of them.
   c. individuals should invest greatly in reproduction because their chance of surviving to another breeding season is low.
   d. individuals should stop reproducing altogether.

3. In a population in which individuals are uniformly distributed

   a. the population is probably well below its carrying capacity.
   b. natural selection should favor traits that maximize the ability to compete for resources.
   c. immigration from other populations is probably keeping the population from going extinct.
   d. None of the above

4. The elimination of predators by humans

   a. will cause its prey to experience exponential growth until new predators arrive or evolve.
   b. will lead to an increase in the carrying capacity of the environment.
   c. may increase the population size of a prey species if that prey's population was being regulated by predation from the predator.
   d. will lead to an Allee effect.

SYNTHESIZE

1. Refer to figure 56.8. What are the implications for evolutionary divergence among populations that are part of a metapopulation versus populations that are independent of other populations?

2. Refer to figure 56.13. Given a trade-off between current reproductive effort and future reproductive success (the so-called cost of reproduction), would you expect old individuals to have the same "optimal" reproductive effort as young individuals?

3. Refer to figure 56.14. Because the number of offspring that a parent can produce is often a trade-off with the size of individual offspring, many circumstances lead to an intermediate number and size of offspring being favored. If the size of an offspring was completely unrelated to the quality of that offspring (its chances of surviving until it reaches reproductive age), would you expect parents to fall on the left or right side of the *x*-axis (clutch size)? Explain.

4. Refer to figure 56.26. Would increasing the mean generation time have the same kind of effect on population growth rate as reducing the number of children that an individual female has over her lifetime? Which effect would have a bigger influence on population growth rate? Explain.

ONLINE RESOURCE

www.ravenbiology.com

Understand, Apply, and Synthesize—enhance your study with animations that bring concepts to life and practice tests to assess your understanding. Your instructor may also recommend the interactive eBook, individualized learning tools, and more.

Chapter **57**

Community Ecology

Chapter Outline

57.1 Biological Communities: Species Living Together

57.2 The Ecological Niche Concept

57.3 Predator–Prey Relationships

57.4 The Many Types of Species Interactions

57.5 Ecological Succession, Disturbance, and Species Richness

Introduction

All the organisms that live together in a place are members of a community. The myriad of species that inhabit a tropical rain forest are a community. Indeed, every inhabited place on Earth supports its own particular array of organisms. Over time, the different species that live together have made many complex adjustments to community living, evolving together and forging relationships that give the community its character and stability. Both competition and cooperation have played key roles; in this chapter, we look at these and other factors in community ecology.

Biological Communities: Species Living Together

Learning Outcomes

1. *Define community.*
2. *Describe how community composition may change across a geographic landscape.*

Almost any place on Earth is occupied by species, sometimes by many of them, as in the rain forests of the Amazon, and sometimes by only a few, as in the near-boiling waters of Yellowstone's geysers (where a number of microbial species live). The term **community** refers to the species that occur at any particular locality (figure 57.1). Communities can be characterized either by their constituent species or by their properties, such as **species richness** (the number of species present) or **primary productivity** (the amount of energy produced).

Interactions among community members govern many ecological and evolutionary processes. These interactions, such as predation and mutualism, affect the population biology of particular species—whether a population increases or decreases in abundance, for example—as well as the ways in which energy and nutrients cycle through the ecosystem. Moreover, the community context affects the patterns of natural selection faced by a species, and thus the evolutionary course it takes.

Scientists study biological communities in many ways, ranging from detailed observations to elaborate, large-scale experiments. In some cases, studies focus on the entire community, whereas in other cases only a subset of species that are likely to interact with one another are studied. Although scientists sometimes refer to such subsets as communities (for example, the "spider community"), the term **assemblage** is more appropriate to connote that the species included are only a portion of those present within the entire community.

Communities have been viewed in different ways

Two views exist on the structure and functioning of communities. The *individualistic concept* of communities holds that a community is simply an aggregation of species that happen to occur together at one place.

By contrast, the **holistic concept** of communities views communities as an integrated unit. In this sense, the community could be viewed as a superorganism whose constituent species have coevolved to the extent that they function as part of a greater whole, just as the kidneys, heart, and lungs all function together within an animal's body. In this view, then, a community would amount to more than the sum of its parts.

These two views make differing predictions about the integrity of communities across space and time. If, as the individualistic view implies, communities are nothing more than a combination of species that occur together, then moving geographically across the landscape or back through time, we would not expect to see the same community. That is, species should appear and disappear independently, as a function of each species' own unique ecological requirements. By contrast, if a community is an integrated whole, then we would make the opposite prediction: Communities should stay the same through space or time, until being replaced by completely different communities when environmental differences are sufficiently great.

Figure 57.1 An African savanna community. A community consists of all the species—plants, animals, fungi, protists, and prokaryotes—that occur at a locality, in this case Etosha National Park in Namibia.

Communities change over space and time

Most ecologists today favor the individualistic concept. For the most part, species seem to respond independently to changing environmental conditions. As a result, community composition changes gradually across landscapes as some species appear and become more abundant, while others decrease in abundance and eventually disappear.

A famous example of this pattern is the abundance of tree species in the Santa Catalina Mountains of Arizona along a geographic gradient running from very dry to very moist. Figure 57.2 shows that species can change abundance in patterns that are for the most part independent of one another. As a result, tree communities at different localities in these mountains fall on a continuum, one merging into the next, rather than representing discretely different sets of species.

Similar patterns through time are seen in paleontological studies. For example, a very good fossil record exists for the trees and small mammals that occurred in North America over the past 20,000 years. Examination of prehistoric communities shows little similarity to those that occur today. Many species that occur together today were never found together in the past. Conversely, species that used to occur in the same communities often do not overlap in their geographic ranges today. These findings suggest that as climate has changed during the waxing and waning of the Ice Ages, species have responded independently, rather than shifting their distributions together, as would be expected if the community were an integrated unit.

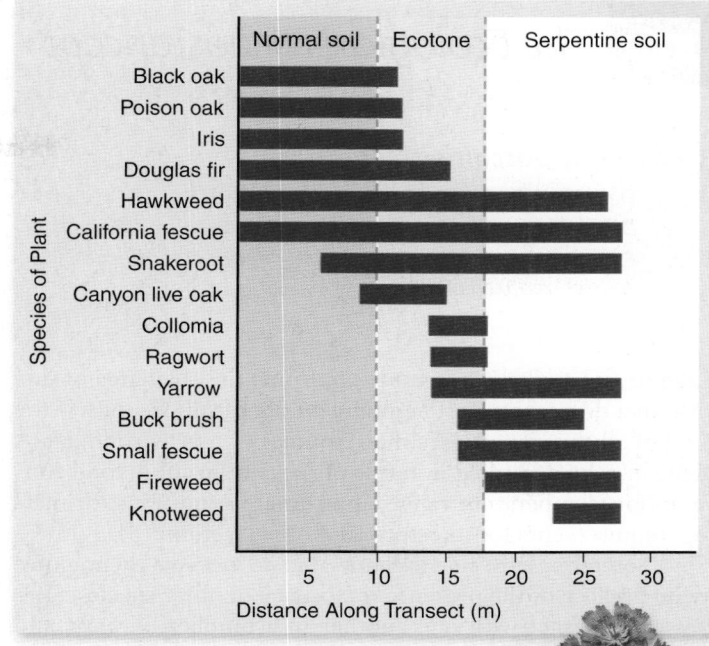

Figure 57.3 Change in community composition across an ecotone. The plant assemblages on normal and serpentine soils are greatly different, and the transition from one community to another occurs over a short distance.

Inquiry question

? Why is there a sharp transition between the two community types?

Nonetheless, in some cases the abundance of species in a community does change geographically in a synchronous pattern. Often, this occurs at **ecotones,** places where the environment changes abruptly. For example, in the western United States, certain patches of habitat have serpentine soils. This soil differs from normal soil in many ways—for example, high concentrations of nickel, chromium, and iron; low concentrations of copper and calcium. Comparison of the plant species that occur on different soils shows that distinct communities exist on each type, with an abrupt transition from one to the other over a short distance (figure 57.3). Similar transitions are seen wherever greatly different habitats come into contact, such as at the interface between terrestrial and aquatic habitats or where grassland and forest meet.

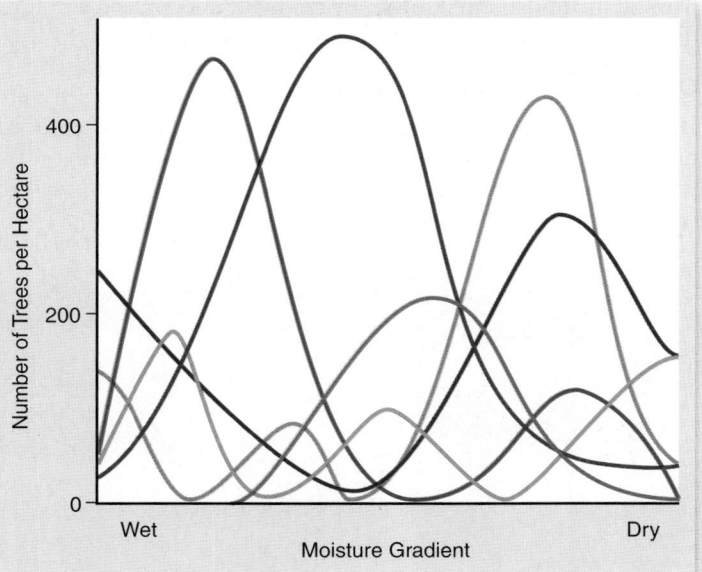

Figure 57.2 Abundance of tree species along a moisture gradient in the Santa Catalina Mountains of southeastern Arizona. Each line represents the abundance of a different tree species. The species' patterns of abundance are independent of one another. Thus, community composition changes continually along the gradient.

Inquiry question

? Why do species exhibit different patterns of response to change in moisture?

Learning Outcomes Review 57.1

A community comprises all species that occur at one site. In most cases, the abundance of community members appears to vary independently across space and through time. Community composition also changes gradually depending on environmental factors when moving from one location to another, such as from a very dry area to a very moist area.

■ *In a community, would you expect greater variation over time in abundance of animal life or plant life? Why?*

The Ecological Niche Concept

Each organism in a community confronts the challenge of survival in a different way. The **niche** an organism occupies is the total of all the ways it uses the resources of its environment. A niche may be described in terms of space utilization, food consumption, temperature range, appropriate conditions for mating, requirements for moisture, and other factors.

Sometimes species are not able to occupy their entire niche because of the presence or absence of other species. Species can interact with one another in a number of ways, and these interactions can either have positive or negative effects. One type of interaction, **interspecific competition,** occurs when two species attempt to use the same resource and there is not enough of the resource to satisfy both. Physical interactions over access to resources—such as fighting to defend a territory or displacing an individual from a particular location—are referred to as **interference competition;** consuming the same resources is called **exploitative competition.**

Fundamental niches are potential; realized niches are actual

The entire niche that a species is capable of using, based on its physiological tolerance limits and resource needs, is called the **fundamental niche.** The actual set of environmental conditions, including the presence or absence of other species, in which the species can establish a stable population is its **realized niche.** Because of interspecific interactions, the realized niche of a species may be considerably smaller than its fundamental niche.

Competition between species for niche occupancy

In a classic study, Joseph Connell of the University of California, Santa Barbara, investigated competitive interactions between two species of barnacles that grow together on rocks along the coast of Scotland. Of the two species Connell studied, *Chthamalus stellatus* lives in shallower water, where tidal action often exposes it to air, and *Semibalanus balanoides* (called *Balanus balanoides* prior to 1995) lives lower down, where it is rarely exposed to the atmosphere (figure 57.4). In these areas, space is at a premium. In the deeper zone, *S. balanoides* could always outcompete *C. stellatus* by crowding it off the rocks, undercutting it, and replacing it even where it had begun to grow, an example of interference competition.

When Connell removed *S. balanoides* from the area, however, *C. stellatus* was easily able to occupy the deeper zone, indicating that no physiological or other general obstacles prevented it from becoming established there. In contrast, *S. balanoides* could not survive in the shallow-water habitats where *C. stellatus* normally occurs; it does not have the physiological adaptations to warmer temperatures that allow *C. stellatus* to occupy this zone. Thus, the fundamental niche of *C. stellatus* includes both shallow and deeper zones, but its realized niche is much narrower because *C. stellatus* can be outcompeted by *S. balanoides* in parts of its fundamental niche. By contrast, the realized and fundamental niches of *S. balanoides* appear to be identical.

Other causes of niche restriction

Processes other than competition can also restrict the realized niche of a species. For example, the plant St. John's wort (*Hypericum perforatum*) was introduced and became widespread in

Figure 57.4
Competition among two species of barnacles. The fundamental niche of *Chthamalus stellatus* includes both deep and shallow zones, but *Semibalanus balanoides* forces *C. stellatus* out of the part of its fundamental niche that overlaps the realized niche of *Semibalanus.*

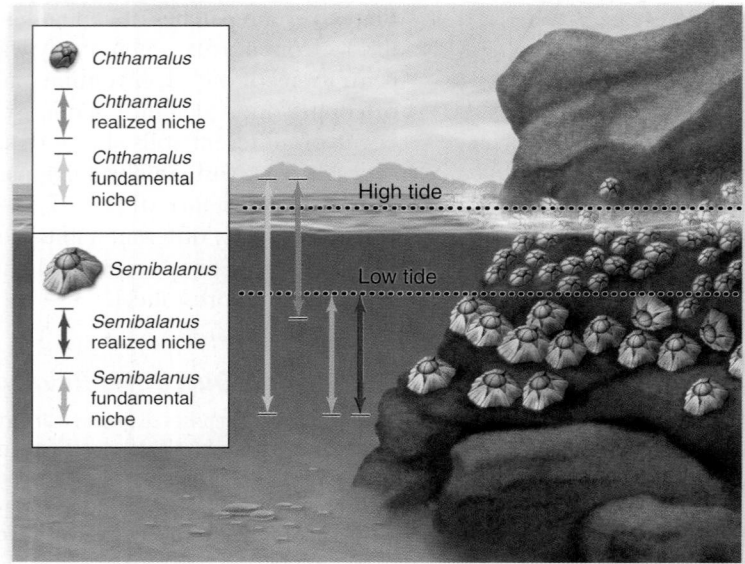

Chthamalus
Chthamalus realized niche
Chthamalus fundamental niche

High tide

Semibalanus
Semibalanus realized niche
Semibalanus fundamental niche

Low tide

S. balanoides and *C. stellatus* competing

C. stellatus fundamental and realized niches are identical when *S. balanoides* is removed.

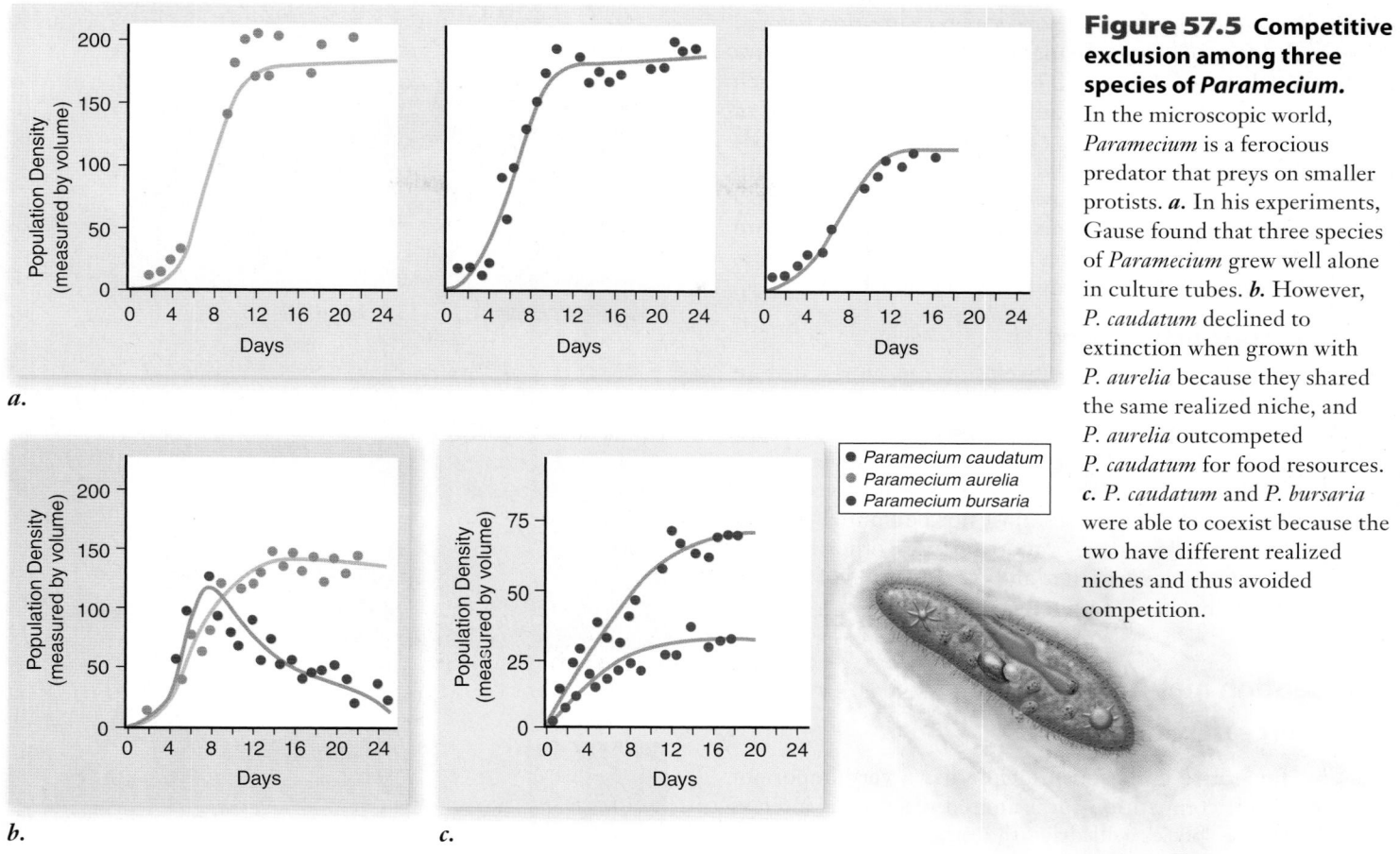

Figure 57.5 Competitive exclusion among three species of *Paramecium*. In the microscopic world, *Paramecium* is a ferocious predator that preys on smaller protists. *a.* In his experiments, Gause found that three species of *Paramecium* grew well alone in culture tubes. *b.* However, *P. caudatum* declined to extinction when grown with *P. aurelia* because they shared the same realized niche, and *P. aurelia* outcompeted *P. caudatum* for food resources. *c. P. caudatum* and *P. bursaria* were able to coexist because the two have different realized niches and thus avoided competition.

● *Paramecium caudatum*
● *Paramecium aurelia*
● *Paramecium bursaria*

open rangeland habitats in California until a specialized beetle was introduced to control it. Population size of the plant quickly decreased, and it is now only found in shady sites where the beetle cannot thrive. In this case, the presence of a predator limits the realized niche of a plant.

In some cases, the absence of another species leads to a smaller realized niche. Many North American plants depend on insects for pollination; indeed, the value of insect pollination for American agriculture has been estimated as more than $2 billion per year. However, pollinator populations are currently declining for several reasons. Conservationists are concerned that if these insects disappear from some habitats, the realized niche of many plant species will decrease or even disappear entirely. In this case, the absence—rather than the presence—of another species will be the cause of a relatively small realized niche.

Competitive exclusion can occur when species compete for limited resources

In classic experiments carried out in 1934 and 1935, Russian ecologist Georgii Gause studied competition among three species of *Paramecium*, a tiny protist. Each of the three species grew well in culture tubes by themselves, preying on bacteria and yeasts that fed on oatmeal suspended in the culture fluid (figure 57.5*a*). However, when Gause grew *P. aurelia* together

with *P. caudatum* in the same culture tube, the numbers of *P. caudatum* always declined to extinction, leaving *P. aurelia* the only survivor (figure 57.5*b*). Why did this happen? Gause found that *P. aurelia* could grow six times faster than its competitor *P. caudatum* because it was able to better utilize the limited available resources, an example of exploitative competition.

From experiments such as this, Gause formulated what is now called the principle of **competitive exclusion.** This principle states that if two species are competing for a limited resource such as food or water, the species that uses the resource more efficiently will eventually eliminate the other locally. In other words, no two species with the same niche can coexist when resources are limiting.

Niche overlap and coexistence

In a revealing experiment, Gause challenged *Paramecium caudatum*—the defeated species in his earlier experiments—with a third species, *P. bursaria*. Because he expected these two species to also compete for the limited bacterial food supply, Gause thought one would win out, as had happened in his previous experiments. But that's not what happened. Instead, both species survived in the culture tubes, dividing the food resources.

The explanation for the species' coexistence is simple. In the upper part of the culture tubes, where the oxygen concentration and bacterial density were high, *P. caudatum* dominated because it was better able to feed on bacteria. In the lower part

chapter **57** *Interspecific Interactions and the Ecology of Communities* of the tubes, however, the lower oxygen concentration favored the growth of a different potential food, yeast, and *P. bursaria* was better able to eat this food. The fundamental niche of each species was the whole culture tube, but the realized niche of each species was only a portion of the tube. Because the realized niches of the two species did not overlap too much, both species were able to survive. However, competition did have a negative effect on the participants (figure 57.5c). When grown without a competitor, both species reached densities three times greater than when they were grown with a competitor.

Competitive exclusion refined

Gause's principle of competitive exclusion can be restated as: No two species can occupy the same niche *indefinitely* when resources are limiting. Certainly species can and do coexist while competing for some of the same resources. Nevertheless, Gause's hypothesis predicts that when two species coexist on a long-term basis, either resources must not be limited or their niches will always differ in one or more features; otherwise, one species will outcompete the other, and the extinction of the second species will inevitably result.

Competition may lead to resource partitioning

Gause's competitive exclusion principle has a very important consequence: If competition for a limited resource is intense, then either one species will drive the other to extinction, or natural selection will reduce the competition between them.

When the ecologist Robert MacArthur studied five species of warblers, small insect-eating forest songbirds, he discovered that they appeared to be competing for the same resources. But when he studied them more carefully, he found that each species actually fed in a different part of spruce trees and so ate different subsets of insects. One species fed on insects near the tips of branches, a second within the dense foliage, a third on the lower branches, a fourth high on the trees, and a fifth at the very apex of the trees. Thus, each species of warbler had evolved so as to utilize a different portion of the spruce tree resource. They had *subdivided the niche* to avoid direct competition with one another. This niche subdivision is termed **resource partitioning.**

Resource partitioning is often seen in similar species that occupy the same geographic area. Such sympatric species often avoid competition by living in different portions of the habitat or by using different food or other resources (figure 57.6). This pattern of resource partitioning is thought to result from the process of natural selection causing initially similar species to diverge in resource use to reduce competitive pressures.

Whether such evolutionary divergence occurs can be investigated by comparing species whose ranges only partially overlap. Where the two species occur together, they often tend to exhibit greater differences in morphology (the form and structure of an organism) and resource use than do allopatric populations of the same species that do not occur with the other species. Called *character displacement*, the differences evident between sympatric species are thought to have been favored by

Figure 57.6 Resource partitioning among sympatric lizard species. Species of *Anolis* lizards on Caribbean islands partition their habitats in a variety of ways. *a.* Some species occupy leaves and branches in the canopy of trees, *(b)* others use twigs on the periphery, and *(c)* still others are found at the base of the trunk. In addition, *(d)* some use grassy areas in the open. When two species occupy the same part of the tree, they either utilize different-sized insects as food or partition the thermal microhabitat; for example, one might only be found in the shade, whereas the other would only bask in the sun.

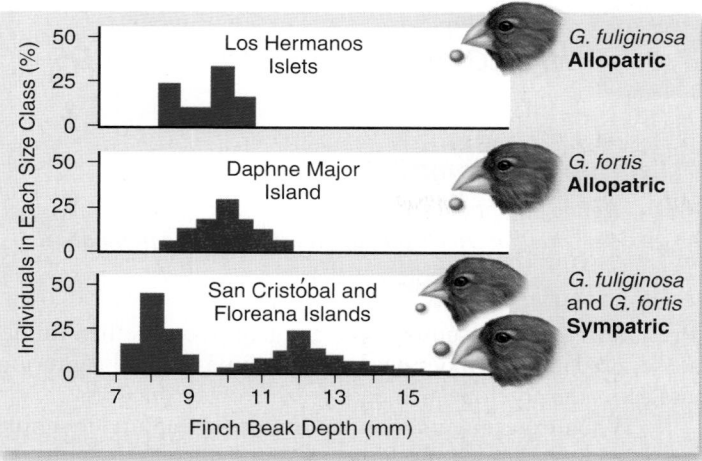

Figure 57.7 Character displacement in Darwin's finches. These two species of finches (genus *Geospiza*) have beaks of similar size when allopatric, but different size when sympatric.

natural selection as a means of partitioning resources and thus reducing competition.

As an example, the two Darwin's finches in figure 57.7 have bills of similar size where the finches are allopatric (that is, each living on an island where the other does not occur). On islands where they are sympatric (that is, occur together), the two species have evolved beaks of different sizes, one adapted to larger seeds and the other to smaller ones. Character displacement such as this may play an important role in adaptive radiation, leading new species to adapt to different parts of the environment, as discussed in chapter 22.

Detecting interspecific competition can be difficult

It is not simple to determine when two species are competing. The fact that two species use the same resources need not imply competition if that resource is not in limited supply. Even if the population sizes of two species are negatively correlated, such that where one species has a large population, the other species has a small population and vice versa, the two species may not be competing for the same limiting resource. Instead, the two species might be independently responding to the same feature of the environment—perhaps one species thrives best in warm conditions and the other where it's cool.

Experimental studies of competition

Some of the best evidence for the existence of competition comes from experimental field studies. By setting up experiments in which two species occur either alone or together, scientists can determine whether the presence of one species has a negative effect on a population of the second species.

For example, a variety of seed-eating rodents occur in North American deserts. In 1988, researchers set up a series of 50-m × 50-m enclosures to investigate the effect of kangaroo rats on smaller, seed-eating rodents. Kangaroo rats were removed from half of the enclosures, but not from the others. The walls of all of the enclosures had holes that allowed rodents to come and go, but in the plots in which the kangaroo

rats had been removed, the holes were too small to allow the kangaroo rats to reenter.

Over the course of the next 3 years, the researchers monitored the number of the smaller rodents present in the plots. As figure 57.8 illustrates, the number of other rodents was substantially higher in the absence of kangaroo rats, indicating that kangaroo rats compete with the other rodents and limit their population sizes.

A great number of similar experiments have indicated that interspecific competition occurs between many species of plants and animals. The effects of competition can be seen in aspects of population biology other than population size, such

SCIENTIFIC THINKING

Question: *Does interspecific interaction occur between rodent species?*

Hypothesis: *The larger kangaroo rat will have a negative effect on other species.*

Experiment: *Build large cages in desert areas. Remove kangaroo rats from some cages, leaving them present in others.*

Result: *In the absence of kangaroo rats, the number of other rodents increases quickly and remains higher than in the control cages throughout the course of the experiment.*

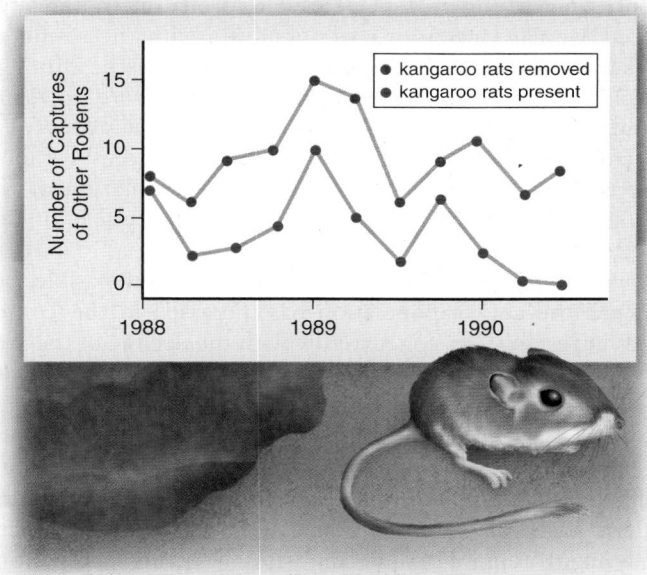

Interpretation: *Why do you think population sizes rise and fall in synchrony in the two cages?*

Figure 57.8 Detecting interspecific competition.
This experiment tested how removal of kangaroo rats affected the population size of other rodents. Immediately after kangaroo rats were removed, the number of other rodents increased relative to the enclosures that still contained kangaroo rats. Notice that population sizes (as estimated by number of captures) changed in synchrony in the two treatments, probably reflecting changes in the weather.

Inquiry question

? Why are there more individuals of other rodent species when kangaroo rats are excluded?

as behavior and individual growth rates. For example, two species of *Anolis* lizards occur on the Caribbean island of St. Maarten. When one of the species, *A. gingivinus*, is placed in 12-m × 12-m enclosures without the other species, individual lizards grow faster and perch lower than do lizards of the same species when placed in enclosures in which *A. pogus*, a species normally found near the ground, is also present.

Limitations of experimental studies

Experimental studies are a powerful means of understanding interactions between coexisting species and are now commonly conducted by ecologists. Nonetheless, they have their limitations.

First, care is necessary in interpreting the results of field experiments. Negative effects of one species on another do not automatically indicate the existence of competition. For example, many similarly sized fish have a negative effect on one another, but it results not from competition, but from the fact that adults of each species prey on juveniles of the other species.

In addition, the presence of one species may attract predators or parasites, which then also prey on the second species. In this case, even if the two species are not competing, the second species may have a lower population size in the presence of the first species due to predators or parasites. Indeed, we can't rule out this possibility with the results of the kangaroo rat exclusion study just mentioned, although the close proximity of the enclosures (they were adjacent) would suggest that the same predators and parasites were present in all of them. Thus, experimental studies are most effective when combined with detailed examination of the ecological mechanisms causing the observed effect of one species on another.

Second, experimental studies are not always feasible. For example, the coyote population has increased in the United States in recent years concurrently with the decline of the grey wolf. Is this trend an indication that the species compete? Because of the size of the animals and the large geographic areas occupied by each individual, manipulative experiments involving fenced areas with only one or both species—with each experimental treatment replicated several times for statistical analysis—are not practical. Similarly, studies of slow-growing trees might require many centuries to detect competition between adult trees. In such cases, detailed studies of the ecological requirements of each species are our best bet for understanding interspecific interactions.

Learning Outcomes Review 57.2

A niche comprises the total number of ways in which an organism utilizes resources in its environment. A fundamental niche is the entire niche possible to a species; a realized niche is the niche a species actually utilizes. If resources are limiting, two species cannot occupy the same niche indefinitely without competition driving one to local extinction. Resource partitioning allows two sympatric species to occupy a niche, reducing competition between them and also lessening the size of the realized niche.

■ *Under what circumstances can two species with identical niches coexist indefinitely?*

Learning Outcomes

1. Define predation.
2. Describe the effects predation can have on a population.

Predation is the consuming of one organism by another. In this sense, predation includes everything from a leopard capturing and eating an antelope, to a deer grazing on spring grass.

When experimental populations are set up under simple laboratory conditions, as illustrated in figure 57.9 with the predatory protist *Didinium* and its prey *Paramecium*, the predator often exterminates its prey and then becomes extinct itself, having nothing left to eat. If refuges are provided for the *Paramecium*, however, its population drops to low levels but not to extinction. Low prey population levels then provide inadequate food for the *Didinium*, causing the predator population to decrease. When this occurs, the prey population can recover.

Predation strongly influences prey populations

In nature, predators often have large effects on prey populations. As the previous example indicates, however, the interaction is a two-way street: prey can also affect the dynamics of predator populations. The outcomes of such interactions are complex and depend on a variety of factors.

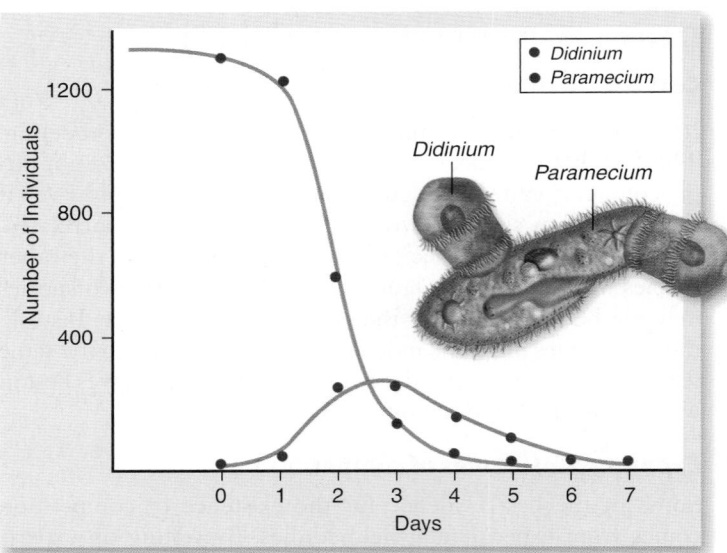

Figure 57.9 Predator–prey in the microscopic world. When the predatory *Didinium* is added to a *Paramecium* population, the numbers of *Didinium* initially rise, and the numbers of *Paramecium* steadily fall. When the *Paramecium* population is depleted, however, the *Didinium* individuals also die.

? Inquiry question

Can you think of any ways this experiment could be changed so that Paramecium might not go extinct?

Prey population explosions and crashes

Some of the most dramatic examples of the interconnection between predators and their prey involve situations in which humans have either added or eliminated predators from an area. For example, the elimination of large carnivores from much of the eastern United States has led to population explosions of white-tailed deer, which strip the habitat of all edible plant life within their reach. Similarly, when sea otters were hunted to near extinction on the western coast of the United States, populations of sea urchins, a principal prey item of the otters, exploded.

Conversely, the introduction of rats, dogs, and cats to many islands around the world has led to the decimation of native fauna. Populations of Galápagos tortoises on several islands are endangered by introduced rats, pigs, dogs, and cats, which eat the eggs and the young tortoises. Similarly, in New Zealand, several species of birds and reptiles have been eradicated by rat predation and now only occur on a few offshore islands that the rats have not reached. On Stephens Island, near New Zealand, every individual of the now-extinct Stephens Island wren was killed by a single lighthouse keeper's cat.

A classic example of the role predation can play in a community involves the introduction of prickly pear cactus to Australia in the 19th century. In the absence of predators, the cactus spread rapidly, so that by 1925 it occupied 12 million hectares of rangeland in an impenetrable morass of spines that made cattle ranching difficult. To control the cactus, a predator from its natural habitat in Argentina, the moth *Cactoblastis cactorum*, was introduced, beginning in 1926. By 1940, cactus populations had been greatly reduced and it now usually occurs in small populations.

Predation and coevolution

Predation provides strong selective pressures on prey populations. Any feature that would decrease the probability of capture should be strongly favored. In turn, the evolution of such features causes natural selection to favor counteradaptations in predator populations. The process by which these adaptations are selected in lockstep fashion in two or more interacting species is termed **coevolution**. A coevolutionary "arms race" may ensue in which predators and prey are constantly evolving better defenses and better means of circumventing these defenses. In the sections that follow, you'll learn more about these defenses and responses.

Plant adaptations defend against herbivores

Plants have evolved many mechanisms to defend themselves from herbivores. The most obvious are morphological defenses: Thorns, spines, and prickles play an important role in discouraging large plant eaters, and plant hairs, especially those that have a glandular, sticky tip, deter insect herbivores. Some plants, such as grasses, deposit silica in their leaves, both strengthening and protecting themselves. If enough silica is present, these plants are simply too tough to eat.

Chemical defenses

As significant as morphological adaptations are, the chemical defenses that occur so widely in plants are even more widespread. Plants exhibit some amazing chemical adaptations to combat herbivores. For example, recent work demonstrates that when attacked by caterpillars, wild tobacco plants emit a chemical into the air that attracts a species of bug that feeds on that caterpillar (discussed in greater detail in chapter 40).

The best known and perhaps most important of the chemical defenses of plants against herbivores are *secondary chemical compounds*. These chemicals are distinguished from primary compounds, which are the components of a major metabolic pathway, such as respiration. Many plants, and apparently many algae as well, contain structurally diverse secondary compounds that are either toxic to most herbivores or disturb their metabolism greatly, preventing, for example, the normal development of larval insects. Consequently, most herbivores tend to avoid the plants that possess these compounds.

The mustard family (Brassicaceae) produces a group of chemicals known as mustard oils. These substances give the pungent aromas and tastes to plants such as mustard, cabbage, watercress, radish, and horseradish. The flavors we enjoy indicate the presence of chemicals that are toxic to many groups of insects. Similarly, plants of the milkweed family (Asclepiadaceae) and the related dogbane family (Apocynaceae) produce a milky sap that deters herbivores from eating them. In addition, these plants usually contain cardiac glycosides, molecules that can produce drastic deleterious effects on the heart function of vertebrates.

The coevolutionary response of herbivores

Certain groups of herbivores are associated with each family or group of plants protected by a particular kind of secondary compound. These herbivores are able to feed on these plants without harm, often as their exclusive food source.

For example, cabbage butterfly caterpillars (subfamily Pierinae) feed almost exclusively on plants of the mustard and caper families, as well as on a few other small families of plants that also contain mustard oils (figure 57.10). Similarly, caterpillars of

Figure 57.10
Insect herbivores well suited to their plant hosts. *a.* The green caterpillars of the cabbage white butterfly (*Pieris rapae*) are camouflaged on the leaves of cabbage and other plants on which they feed. Although mustard oils protect these plants against most herbivores, the cabbage white butterfly caterpillars are able to break down the mustard oil compounds. *b.* An adult cabbage white butterfly.

monarch butterflies and their relatives (subfamily Danainae) feed on plants of the milkweed and dogbane families. How do these animals manage to avoid the chemical defenses of the plants, and what are the evolutionary precursors and ecological consequences of such patterns of specialization?

We can offer a potential explanation for the evolution of these particular patterns. Once the ability to manufacture mustard oils evolved in the ancestors of the caper and mustard families, the plants were protected for a time against most or all herbivores that were feeding on other plants in their area. At some point, certain groups of insects—for example, the cabbage butterflies—evolved the ability to break down mustard oils and thus feed on these plants without harming themselves. Having developed this new capability, the butterflies were able to use a new resource without competing with other herbivores for it. As we saw in chapter 22, exposure to an underutilized resource often leads to evolutionary diversification and adaptive radiation.

Animal adaptations defend against predators

Some animals that feed on plants rich in secondary compounds receive an extra benefit. For example, when the caterpillars of monarch butterflies feed on plants of the milkweed family, they do not break down the cardiac glycosides that protect these plants from herbivores. Instead, the caterpillars concentrate and store the cardiac glycosides in fat bodies; they then pass them through the chrysalis stage to the adult and even to the eggs of the next generation.

The incorporation of cardiac glycosides protects all stages of the monarch life cycle from predators. A bird that eats a monarch butterfly quickly regurgitates it (figure 57.11) and in the future avoids the conspicuous orange-and-black pattern that characterizes the adult monarch. Some bird species have

a.   *b.*

Figure 57.11 A blue jay learns not to eat monarch butterflies. *a.* This cage-reared jay had never seen a monarch butterfly before it tried eating one. *b.* The same jay regurgitated the butterfly a few minutes later. This bird will probably avoid trying to capture all orange-and-black insects in the future.

Figure 57.12 Vertebrate chemical defenses. Frogs of the family Dendrobatidae, abundant in the forests of Central and South America, are extremely poisonous to vertebrates; 80 different toxic alkaloids have been identified from different species in this genus. Dendrobatids advertise their toxicity with bright coloration. As a result of either instinct or learning, predators avoid such brightly colored species that might otherwise be suitable prey.

evolved the ability to tolerate the protective chemicals; these birds eat the monarchs.

Chemical defenses

Animals also manufacture and use a startling array of defensive substances. Bees, wasps, predatory bugs, scorpions, spiders, and many other arthropods use chemicals to defend themselves and to kill their own prey. In addition, various chemical defenses have evolved among many marine invertebrates, as well as a variety of vertebrates, including frogs, snakes, lizards, fishes, and some birds.

The poison-dart frogs of the family Dendrobatidae produce toxic alkaloids in the mucus that covers their brightly colored skin; these alkaloids are distasteful and sometimes deadly to animals that try to eat the frogs (figure 57.12). Some of these toxins are so powerful that a few micrograms will kill a person if injected into the bloodstream. More than 200 different alkaloids have been isolated from these frogs, and some are playing important roles in neuromuscular research. Similarly intensive investigations of marine animals, venomous reptiles, algae, and flowering plants are underway in search of new drugs to fight cancer and other diseases, or to use as sources of antibiotics.

Defensive coloration

Many insects that feed on milkweed plants are brightly colored; they advertise their poisonous nature using an ecological strategy known as warning coloration.

Showy coloration is characteristic of animals that use poisons and stings to repel predators; organisms that lack specific chemical defenses are seldom brightly colored. In fact, many have cryptic coloration—color that blends with the surroundings and thus hides the individual from predators (figure 57.13). Camouflaged animals usually do not live together in groups because a predator that discovers one individual gains a valuable clue to the presence of others.

Figure 57.13 Cryptic coloration and form. An inchworm caterpillar (*Nacophora quernaria*) closely resembles the twig on which it is hanging..

Mimicry allows one species to capitalize on defensive strategies of another

During the course of their evolution, many species have come to resemble distasteful ones that exhibit warning coloration. The mimic gains an advantage by looking like the distasteful model. Two types of mimicry have been identified: Batesian mimicry and Müllerian mimicry.

Batesian mimicry

Batesian mimicry is named for Henry Bates, the British naturalist who first brought this type of mimicry to general attention in 1857. In his journeys to the Amazon region of South America, Bates discovered many instances of palatable insects that resembled brightly colored, distasteful species. He reasoned that the mimics would be avoided by predators, who would be fooled by the disguise into thinking the mimic was the distasteful species.

Many of the best-known examples of Batesian mimicry occur among butterflies and moths. Predators of these insects must use visual cues to hunt for their prey; otherwise, similar color patterns would not matter to potential predators. Increasing evidence indicates that Batesian mimicry can involve nonvisual cues, such as olfaction, although such examples are less obvious to humans.

The kinds of butterflies that provide the models in Batesian mimicry are, not surprisingly, members of groups whose caterpillars feed on only one or a few closely related plant families. The plant families on which they feed are strongly protected by toxic chemicals. The model butterflies incorporate the poisonous molecules from these plants into their bodies. The mimic butterflies, in contrast, belong to groups in which the feeding habits of the caterpillars are not so restricted. As caterpillars, these butterflies feed on a number of different plant families that are unprotected by toxic chemicals.

One often-studied mimic among North American butterflies is the tiger swallowtail, whose range occurs throughout the eastern United States and into Canada (figure 57.14*a*). In areas in which the poisonous pipevine swallowtail occurs, female tiger swallowtails are polymorphic and one color form is extremely similar in appearance to the pipevine swallowtail.

The caterpillars of the tiger swallowtail feed on a variety of trees, including tulip, aspen, and cherry, and neither caterpillars nor adults are distasteful to birds. Interestingly, the Batesian mimicry seen in the adult tiger swallowtail butterfly does not extend to the caterpillars: Tiger swallowtail caterpillars are camouflaged on leaves, resembling bird droppings, but the pipevine swallowtail's distasteful caterpillars are very conspicuous.

Müllerian mimicry

Another kind of mimicry, **Müllerian mimicry,** was named for the German biologist Fritz Müller, who first described it in 1878. In Müllerian mimicry, several unrelated but protected animal species come to resemble one another (figure 57.14*b*). If animals that resemble one another are all poisonous or dangerous, they gain an advantage because a predator will learn more quickly to avoid them. In some cases, predator populations even evolve an innate avoidance of species; such evolution may occur more quickly when multiple dangerous prey look alike.

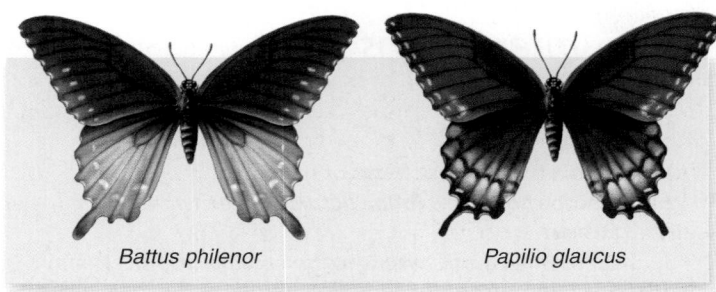

Battus philenor   *Papilio glaucus*

a. **Batesian mimicry:** Pipevine swallowtail butterfly (*Battus philenor*) is poisonous; Tiger swallowtail (*Papilio glaucus*) is a palatable mimic.

Heliconius erato   *Heliconius melpomene*

Heliconius sapho   *Heliconius cydno*

b. **Müllerian mimicry:** Two pairs of mimics; all are distasteful.

Figure 57.14 Mimicry. *a.* Batesian mimicry. Pipevine swallowtail butterflies (*Battus philenor*) are protected from birds and other predators by the poisonous compounds they derive from the food they eat as caterpillars and store in their bodies. Adult pipevine swallowtails advertise their poisonous nature with warning coloration. Tiger swallowtails (*Papilio glaucus*) are Batesian mimics of the poisonous pipevine swallowtail and are not chemically protected. *b.* Pairs of Müllerian mimics. *Heliconius erato* and *H. melpomene* are sympatric, and *H. sapho* and *H. cydno* are sympatric. All of these butterflies are distasteful. They have evolved similar coloration patterns in sympatry to minimize predation; predators need only learn one pattern to avoid.

In both Batesian and Müllerian mimicry, mimic and model must not only look alike but also act alike. For example, the members of several families of insects that closely resemble wasps behave surprisingly like the wasps they mimic, flying often and actively from place to place.

Learnings Outcomes Review 57.3

Predation is the consuming of one organism by another. High predation can drive prey populations to extinction; conversely, in the absence of predators, prey populations often explode and exhaust their resources. Defensive adaptations may evolve in prey species, such as becoming distasteful or poisonous, or having defensive structures, appearance, or capabilities.

■ *A nonpoisonous scarlet king snake has red, black, and yellow bands of color similar to that of the poisonous eastern coral snake. What type of mimicry is being exhibited?*

57.4 The Many Types of Species Interactions

Learning Outcomes

1. *Explain the different forms of symbiosis.*
2. *Describe how coevolution occurs between mutualistic partners.*
3. *Explain how the occurrence of one ecological process may affect the outcome of another occurring at the same time.*

Figure 57.15 Pollination by a bat. Many flowers have coevolved with other species to facilitate pollen transfer. Insects are widely known as pollinators, but they're not the only ones: birds, bats, and even small marsupials and lizards serve as pollinators for some species. Notice the cargo of pollen on the bat's snout.

The plants, animals, protists, fungi, and prokaryotes that live together in communities have changed and adjusted to one another continually over millions of years. We have already discussed competition and predation, but other types of ecological interactions commonly occur. For example, many features of flowering plants have evolved in relation to the dispersal of the plant's gametes by animals (figure 57.15). These animals, in turn, have evolved a number of special traits that enable them to obtain food or other resources efficiently from the plants they visit, often from their flowers. While doing so, the animals pick up pollen, which they may deposit on the next plant they visit, or seeds, which may be left elsewhere in the environment, sometimes a great distance from the parent plant.

Symbiosis involves long-term interactions

In symbiosis, two or more kinds of organisms interact in often elaborate and more-or-less permanent relationships. All symbiotic relationships carry the potential for coevolution between the organisms involved, and in many instances the results of this coevolution are fascinatingly complex.

Examples of symbiosis include lichens, which are associations of certain fungi with green algae or cyanobacteria. Another important example are mycorrhizae, associations between fungi and the roots of most kinds of plants. The fungi expedite the plant's absorption of certain nutrients, and the plants in turn provide the fungi with carbohydrates (both mycorrhizae and lichens are discussed in greater detail in chapter 31). Similarly, root nodules that occur in legumes and certain other kinds of plants contain bacteria that fix atmospheric nitrogen and make it available to their host plants.

In the tropics, leaf-cutter ants are often so abundant that they can remove a quarter or more of the total leaf surface of the plants in a given area in a single year (see figure 31.18). They do not eat these leaves directly; rather, they take them to underground nests, where they chew them up and inoculate them with the spores of particular fungi. These fungi are cultivated by the ants and brought from one specially prepared bed to another, where they grow and reproduce. In turn, the fungi constitute the primary food of the ants and their larvae. The relationship between leaf-cutter ants and these fungi is an excellent example of symbiosis. Recent phylogenetic studies using DNA and assuming a molecular clock (see chapter 23) suggest that these symbioses are ancient, perhaps originating more than 50 mya.

The major kinds of symbiotic relationships include (1) commensalism, in which one species benefits and the other neither benefits nor is harmed; (2) mutualism, in which both participating species benefit; and (3) **parasitism,** in which one species benefits but the other is harmed. Parasitism can also be viewed as a form of predation, although the organism that is preyed on does not necessarily die.

Commensalism benefits one species and is neutral to the other

In commensalism, one species benefits and the other is neither hurt nor helped by the interaction. In nature, individuals of one species are often physically attached to members of another. For example, epiphytes are plants that grow on the branches of other plants. In general, the host plant is unharmed, and the epiphyte that grows on it benefits. An example is Spanish moss, which hangs on trees in the southern United States. This plant and other members of its genus, which is in the pineapple family, grow on trees to gain access to sunlight; they generally do not harm the trees (figure 57.16).

Similarly, various marine animals, such as barnacles, grow on other, often actively moving sea animals, such as whales, and thus are carried passively from place to place. These "passengers" presumably gain more protection from predation than they would if they were fixed in one place, and they also reach new sources of food. The increased water circulation that these animals receive as their host moves around may also be of great importance, particularly if the passengers are filter feeders. Unless the number of these passengers gets too large, the host species is usually unaffected.

When commensalism may not be commensalism

One of the best known examples of symbiosis involves the relationships between certain small tropical fishes (clownfish) and sea anemones, shown in the first figure of this chapter. The fish have evolved the ability to live among the stinging tentacles of sea anemones, even though these tentacles would quickly paralyze other fishes that touched them. The clownfish feed on food particles left from the meals of the host anemone, remaining uninjured under remarkable circumstances.

On land, an analogous relationship exists between birds called oxpeckers and grazing animals such as cattle or ante-

Figure 57.17 Commensalism, mutualism, or parasitism? In this symbiotic relationship, oxpeckers definitely receive a benefit in the form of nutrition from the ticks and other parasites they pick off their host (in this case, an impala, *Aepyceros melampus*). But the effect on the host is not always clear. If the ticks are harmful, their removal benefits the host, and the relationship is mutually beneficial. If the oxpeckers also pick at scabs, causing blood loss and possible infection, the relationship may be parasitic. If the hosts are unharmed by either the ticks or the oxpeckers, the relationship may be an example of commensalism.

lopes (figure 57.17). The birds spend most of their time clinging to the animals, picking off parasites and other insects, carrying out their entire life cycles in close association with the host animals.

No clear-cut boundary exists between commensalism and mutualism; in each of these casees, it is difficult to be certain whether the second partner receives a benefit or not. A sea anemone may benefit by having particles of food removed from its tentacles because it may then be better able to catch other prey. Similarly, although often thought of as commensalism, the association of grazing mammals and gleaning birds is actually an example of mutualism. The mammal benefits by having parasites and other insects removed from its body, but the birds also benefit by gaining a dependable source of food.

On the other hand, commensalism can easily transform itself into parasitism. Oxpeckers are also known to pick not only parasites, but also scabs off their grazing hosts. Once the scab is picked, the birds drink the blood that flows from the wound. Occasionally, the cumulative effect of persistent attacks can greatly weaken the herbivore, particularly when conditions are not favorable, such as during droughts.

Figure 57.16 An example of commensalism. Spanish moss (*Tillandsia usneoides*) benefits from using trees as a substrate, but the trees generally are not affected positively or negatively.

Mutualism benefits both species

Mutualism is a symbiotic relationship between organisms in which both species benefit. Mutualistic relationships are of fundamental importance in determining the structure of biological communities.

Mutualism and coevolution

Some of the most spectacular examples of mutualism occur among flowering plants and their animal visitors, including insects, birds, and bats. During the course of flowering-plant evolution, the characteristics of flowers evolved in relation to the characteristics of the animals that visit them for food and, in the process, spread their pollen from individual to individual. At the same time, characteristics of the animals have changed, increasing their specialization for obtaining food or other substances from particular kinds of flowers.

Another example of mutualism involves ants and aphids. Aphids are small insects that suck fluids from the phloem of living plants with their piercing mouthparts. They extract a certain amount of the sucrose and other nutrients from this fluid, but they excrete much of it in an altered form through their anus. Certain ants have taken advantage of this—in effect, domesticating the aphids. Like ranchers taking cattle to fresh fields to graze, the ants carry the aphids to new plants and then consume as food the "honeydew" that the aphids excrete.

Ants and acacias: A prime example of mutualism

A particularly striking example of mutualism involves ants and certain Latin American tree species of the genus *Acacia*. In these species, certain leaf parts, called stipules, are modified as paired, hollow thorns. The thorns are inhabited by stinging ants of the genus *Pseudomyrmex*, which do not nest anywhere else (figure 57.18). Like all thorns that occur on plants, the acacia thorns serve to deter herbivores.

At the tip of the leaflets of these acacias are unique, protein-rich bodies called Beltian bodies, named after the 19th-century British naturalist Thomas Belt. Beltian bodies do not occur in species of *Acacia* that are not inhabited by ants, and their role is clear: they serve as a primary food for the ants. In addition, the plants secrete nectar from glands near the bases of their leaves. The ants consume this nectar as well, feeding it and the Beltian bodies to their larvae.

Obviously, this association is beneficial to the ants, and one can readily see why they inhabit acacias of this group. The ants and their larvae are protected within the swollen thorns, and the trees provide a balanced diet, including the sugar-rich nectar and the protein-rich Beltian bodies. What, if anything, do the ants do for the plants?

Whenever any herbivore lands on the branches or leaves of an acacia inhabited by ants, the ants, which continually patrol the acacia's branches, immediately attack and devour the herbivore. The ants that live in the acacias also help their hosts compete with other plants by cutting away any encroaching branches that touch the acacia in which they are living. They create, in effect, a tunnel of light through which the acacia can grow, even in the lush tropical rain forests of lowland Central America. In fact, when an ant colony is experimentally removed

Figure 57.18 Mutualism: Ants and acacias. Ants of the genus *Pseudomyrmex* live within the hollow thorns of certain species of acacia trees in Latin America. The nectaries at the bases of the leaves and the Beltian bodies at the ends of the leaflets provide food for the ants. The ants, in turn, supply the acacias with organic nutrients and protect the acacias from herbivores and shading from other plants.

from a tree, the acacia is unable to compete successfully in this habitat. Finally, the ants bring organic material into their nests. The parts they do not consume, together with their excretions, provide the acacias with an abundant source of nitrogen.

When mutualism may not be mutualism

As with commensalism, however, things are not always as they seem. Ant–acacia associations also occur in Africa; in Kenya, several species of acacia ants occur, but only a single species is found on any one tree. One species, *Crematogaster nigriceps*, is competitively inferior to two of the other species. To prevent invasion by these other ant species, *C. nigriceps* prunes the branches of the acacia, preventing it from coming into contact with branches of other trees, which would serve as a bridge for invaders.

Although this behavior is beneficial to the ant, it is detrimental to the tree because it destroys the tissue from which flowers are produced, essentially sterilizing the tree. In this case, what initially evolved as a mutualistic interaction has instead become a parasitic one.

Parasitism benefits one species at the expense of another

Parasitism is harmful to the prey organism and beneficial to the parasite. In many cases, the parasite kills its host, and thus the ecological effects of parasitism can be similar to those of predation. In the past parasitism was studied mostly in terms of its effects on individuals and the populations in which they live, but in recent years researchers have realized that parasitism can be an important factor affecting community structure.

External parasites

Parasites that feed on the exterior surface of an organism are external parasites, or ectoparasites (figure 57.19). Many instances of external parasitism are known in both plants and animals. **Parasitoids** are insects that lay eggs in or on living hosts. This behavior is common among wasps, whose larvae feed on the body of the unfortunate host, often killing it.

Internal parasites

Parasites that live within the body of their hosts, termed **endoparasites,** occur in many different phyla of animals and protists. Internal parasitism is generally marked by much more extreme specialization than external parasitism, as shown by the many protist and invertebrate parasites that infect humans.

The more closely the life of the parasite is linked with that of its host, the more its morphology and behavior are likely to have been modified during the course of its evolution (the same is true of symbiotic relationships of all sorts). Conditions within the body of an organism are different from those encountered outside and are apt to be much more constant. Consequently, the structure of an internal parasite is often simplified, and unnecessary armaments and structures are lost as it evolves (for example, see descriptions of tapeworms in chapter 33).

Parasites and host behaviors

Many parasites have complex life cycles that require several different hosts for growth to adulthood and reproduction. Recent research has revealed the remarkable adaptations of certain parasites that alter the behavior of the host and thus facilitate transmission from one host to the next. For example, many parasites cause their hosts to behave in ways that make them more vulnerable to their predators; when the host is ingested, the parasite is able to infect the predator.

Infected ant

Figure 57.20 Parasitic manipulation of host behavior. Due to a parasite in its brain, an ant climbs to the top of a grass blade, where it may be eaten by a grazing herbivore, thus passing the parasite from insect to mammal.

One of the most famous examples involves a parasitic flatworm, *Dicrocoelium dendriticum,* which lives in ants as an intermediate host, but reaches adulthood in large herbivorous mammals such as cattle and deer. Transmission from an ant to a cow might seem difficult because cows do not normally eat insects. The flatworm, however, has evolved a remarkable adaptation. When an ant is infected, one of the flatworms migrates to the brain and causes the ant to climb to the top of vegetation and lock its mandibles onto a grass blade at the end of the day, just when herbivores are grazing (figure 57.20). The result is that the ant is eaten along with the grass, leading to infection of the grazer.

Ecological processes have interactive effects

We have seen the different ways in which species can interact with one another. In nature, however, more than one type of interaction often occurs at the same time. In many cases, the outcome of one type of interaction is modified or even reversed when another type of interaction is also occurring.

Predation reduces competition

When resources are limiting, a superior competitor can eliminate other species from a community through competitive exclusion. However, predators can prevent or greatly reduce exclusion by lowering the numbers of individuals of competing species.

A given predator may often feed on two, three, or more kinds of plants or animals in a given community. The predator's choice depends partly on the relative abundance of the prey options. In other words, a predator may feed on species A when it is abundant and then switch to species B when A is rare. Similarly, a given prey species may become a primary source of food for increasing numbers of species as it becomes more abundant. In this way, superior competitors may be prevented from competitively excluding other species.

Figure 57.19 An external parasite. The yellow vines are the flowering plant dodder *(Cuscuta)*, a parasite that has lost its chlorophyll and its leaves in the course of its evolution. Because it is heterotrophic (unable to manufacture its own food), dodder obtains its food from the host plants it grows on.

Such patterns are often characteristic of communities in marine intertidal habitats. For example, in preying selectively on bivalves, sea stars prevent bivalves from monopolizing a habitat, opening up space for many other organisms (figure 57.21). When sea stars are removed from a habitat, species diversity falls precipitously, and the seafloor community comes to be dominated by a few species of bivalves.

Predation tends to reduce competition in natural communities, so it is usually a mistake to attempt to eliminate a major predator, such as wolves or mountain lions, from a community. The result may be a decrease in biological diversity.

Parasitism may counter competition

Parasites may affect sympatric species differently and thus influence the outcome of interspecific interactions. One classic experiment investigated interactions between two sympatric flour beetles, *Tribolium castaneum* and *T. confusum*, with and without a parasite, *Adelina*. In the absence of the parasite, *T. castaneum* is dominant, and *T. confusum* normally becomes extinct. When the parasite is present, however, the outcome is reversed, and *T. castaneum* perishes.

Similar effects of parasites in natural systems have been observed in many species. For example, in the *Anolis* lizards of St. Maarten mentioned previously, the competitively inferior species is resistant to lizard malaria (a disease related to human malaria), whereas the other species is highly susceptible. In places where the parasite occurs, the competitively inferior species can hold its own and the two species coexist; elsewhere, the competitively dominant species outcompetes and eliminates it.

Indirect effects

In some cases, species may not directly interact, yet the presence of one species may affect a second by way of interactions with a third. Such effects are termed indirect effects.

The desert rodents described earlier in the experiment with kangaroo rats eat seeds, and so do the ants in their community; thus, we might expect them to compete with each other. But when all rodents were removed from experimental enclosures and not allowed back in (unlike the previous experiment, no holes were placed in the enclosure walls), ant populations first increased but then declined (figure 57.22).

The initial increase was the expected result of removing a competitor. Why did it then reverse? The answer reveals the intricacies of natural ecosystems. Rodents prefer large seeds, whereas ants prefer smaller ones. Furthermore, in this system, plants with large seeds are competitively superior to plants with small seeds. The removal of rodents therefore led to an increase in the number of plants with large seeds, which reduced the number of small seeds available to ants, which in turn led to a decline in ant populations. In summary, the effect

Figure 57.21 Predation reduces competition. *a.* In a controlled experiment in a coastal ecosystem, Robert Paine of the University of Washington removed a key predator, sea stars *(Pisaster)*. *b.* In response, fiercely competitive mussels, a type of bivalve mollusk, exploded in population growth, effectively crowding out seven other indigenous species.

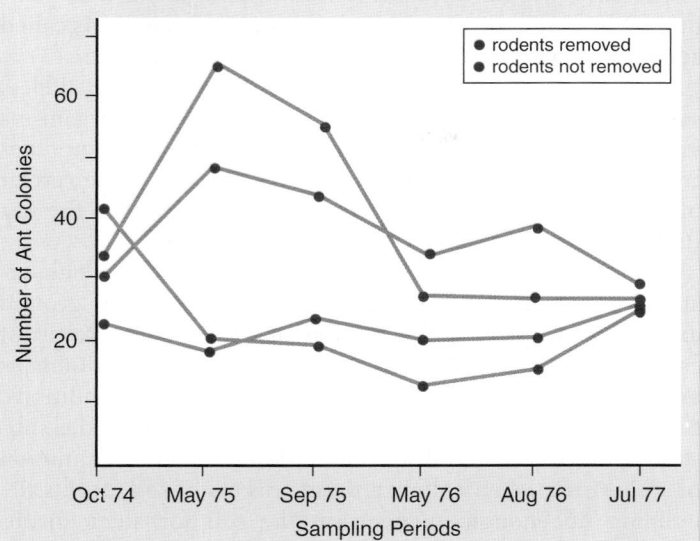

a.

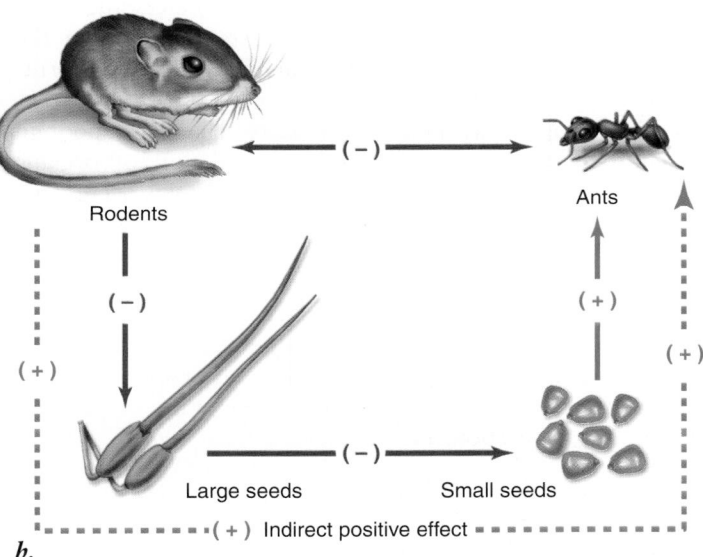

b.

Figure 57.22 Direct and indirect effects in an ecological community. *a.* In the enclosures in which kangaroo rats had been removed, ants initially increased in population size relative to the ants in the control enclosures, but then these ant populations declined. *b.* Rodents and ants both eat seeds, so the presence of rodents has a direct negative effect on ants, and vice versa. However, the presence of rodents has a negative effect on large seeds. In turn, the number of plants with large seeds has a negative effect on plants that produce small seeds, which the ants eat. Hence, the presence of rodents should increase the number of small seeds. In turn, the number of small seeds has a positive effect on ant populations. Thus, indirectly, the presence of rodents has a positive effect on ant population size.

? Inquiry question

How would you test the hypothesis that plant competition mediates the positive effect of kangaroo rats on ants?

of rodents on ants is complicated: a direct, negative effect of resource competition and an indirect, positive effect mediated by plant competition.

Keystone species have major effects on communities

Species whose effects on the composition of communities are greater than one might expect based on their abundance are termed **keystone species.** Predators, such as the sea star described earlier, can often serve as keystone species by preventing one species from outcompeting others, thus maintaining high levels of species richness in a community.

A wide variety of other types of keystone species also exist. Some species manipulate the environment in ways that create new habitats for others. Beavers, for example, change running streams into small impoundments, altering the flow of water and flooding areas (figure 57.23). Similarly, alligators excavate deep holes at the bottoms of lakes. In times of drought, these holes are the only areas where water remains, thus allowing aquatic species that otherwise would perish to persist until the drought ends and the lake refills.

Learning Outcomes Review 57.4

The types of symbiosis include mutualism, in which both participants benefit; commensalism, in which one benefits and the other is neutrally affected; and parasitism, in which one benefits at the expense of the other. Mutualistic species often undergo coevolution, such as the shape of flowers and the features of animals that feed on and pollinate them. Ecological interactions can affect many processes in a community; for example, predation and parasitism may lessen resource competition.

■ *How could the presence of a predator positively affect populations of a species on which it preys?*

Figure 57.23 Example of a keystone species. Beavers, by constructing dams and transforming flowing streams into ponds, create new habitats for many plant and animal species.

Ecological Succession, Disturbance, and Species Richness

Learning Outcomes

1. *Define succession and distinguish primary versus secondary.*
2. *Describe how early colonizers may affect subsequent occurrence of other species.*
3. *Explain how disturbance can either positively or negatively affect species richness.*

Even when the climate of an area remains stable year after year, communities have a tendency to change from simple to complex in a process known as **succession.** This process is familiar to anyone who has seen a vacant lot or cleared woods slowly become occupied by an increasing number of species.

Succession produces a change in species composition

If a wooded area is cleared or burned and left alone, plants will slowly reclaim the area. Eventually, all traces of the clear-

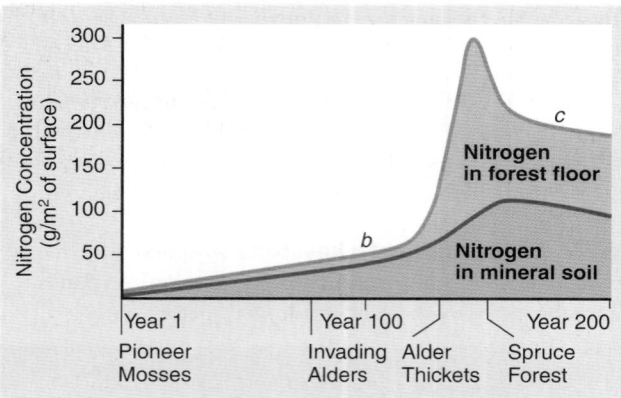

a.

ing will disappear, and the area will again be woods. This kind of succession, which occurs in areas where an existing community has been disturbed but organisms still remain, is called **secondary succession.**

In contrast, **primary succession** occurs on bare, lifeless substrate, such as rocks, or in open water, where organisms gradually move into an area and change its nature. Primary succession occurs in lakes and on land exposed after the retreat of glaciers, and on volcanic islands that rise from the sea (figure 57.24).

Primary succession on glacial moraines provides an example (see figure 57.24). On the bare, mineral-poor ground exposed when glaciers recede, soil pH is basic as a result of carbonates in the rocks, and nitrogen levels are low. Lichens are the first vegetation able to grow under such conditions. Acidic secretions from the lichens help break down the substrate and reduce the pH, as well as adding to the accumulation of soil. Mosses then colonize these pockets of soil, eventually building up enough nutrients in the soil for alder shrubs to take hold. Over a hundred years, the alders, which have symbiotic bacteria that fix atmospheric nitrogen (described in chapter 28), increase soil nitrogen levels, and their acidic leaves further lower soil pH. Eventually, spruce trees grow above the alders and shade them, crowding them out entirely and forming a dense spruce forest.

In a similar example, an *oligotrophic* lake—one poor in nutrients—may gradually, by the accumulation of organic matter, become *eutrophic*—rich in nutrients. As this occurs, the composition of communities will change, first increasing in species richness and then declining.

Why succession happens

Succession happens because species alter the habitat and the resources available in it in ways that favor other species. Three dynamic concepts are of critical importance in the process: establishment, facilitation, and inhibition.

Figure 57.24 Primary succession at Alaska's Glacier Bay.
a. Initially, the glacial moraine at Glacier Bay, Alaska, had little soil nitrogen *b.* The first invaders of these exposed sites are pioneer moss species with nitrogen-fixing, mutualistic microbes. *c.* Within 20 years, young alder shrubs take hold. Rapidly fixing nitrogen, they soon form dense thickets. *d.* Eventually spruce overgrow the mature alders, forming a forest.

b.

c.

d.

1. **Establishment.** Early successional stages are characterized by weedy, *r*-selected species that are tolerant of the harsh, abiotic conditions in barren areas (the preceding chapter discussed *r*-selected and *K*-selected species).

2. **Facilitation.** The weedy early successional stages introduce local changes in the habitat that favor other, less weedy species. Thus, the mosses in the Glacier Bay succession convert nitrogen to a form that allows alders to invade (see figure 57.24). Similarly, the nitrogen build-up produced by the alders, though not necessary for spruce establishment, leads to more robust forests of spruce better able to resist attack by insects.

3. **Inhibition.** Sometimes the changes in the habitat caused by one species, while favoring other species, also inhibit the growth of the original species that caused the changes. Alders, for example, do not grow as well in acidic soil as the spruce and hemlock that replace them.

Over the course of succession, the number of species typically increases as the environment becomes more hospitable. In some cases, however, as ecosystems mature, more *K*-selected species replace *r*-selected ones, and superior competitors force out other species, leading ultimately to a decline in species richness.

Succession in animal communities

The species of animals present in a community also change through time in a successional pattern. As the vegetation changes during succession, habitat disappears for some species and appears for others.

A particularly striking example occurred on the Krakatau islands, which were devastated by an enormous volcanic eruption in 1883. Initially composed of nothing but barren ash-fields, the three islands of the group experienced rapid successional change as vegetation became reestablished. A few blades of grass appeared the next year, and within 15 years the coastal vegetation was well established and the interior was covered with dense grasslands. By 1930, the islands were almost entirely forested (figure 57.25).

The fauna of Krakatau changed in synchrony with the vegetation. Nine months after the eruption, the only animal found was a single spider, but by 1908, 200 animal species were found in a 3-day exploration. For the most part, the first animals were grassland inhabitants, but as trees became established, some of these early colonists, such as the zebra dove and the long-tailed shrike (a type of predatory bird), disappeared and were replaced by forest-inhabiting species, such as fruit bats and fruit-eating birds.

Although patterns of succession of animal species have typically been caused by vegetational succession, changes in the composition of the animal community in turn have affected plant occurrences. In particular, many plant species that are animal-dispersed or pollinated could not colonize Krakatau until their dispersers or pollinators had become established. For example, fruit bats were slow to colonize Krakatau, and until they appeared, few bat-dispersed plant species were present.

Disturbances can play an important role in structuring communities

Traditionally, many ecologists considered biological communities to be in a state of equilibrium, a stable condition that resisted change and fairly quickly returned to its original state if disturbed by humans or natural events. Such stability was usually attributed to the process of interspecific competition.

In recent years, this viewpoint has been reevaluated. Increasingly, scientists are recognizing that communities are constantly changing as a result of climatic changes, species invasions, and disturbance events. As a result, many ecologists now invoke nonequilibrium models that emphasize change, rather than stability. A particular focus of ecological research concerns the role that disturbances play in determining the structure of communities.

Disturbances can be widespread or local. Severe disturbances, such as forest fires, drought, and floods, may affect large areas. Animals may also cause severe disruptions. Gypsy moths can devastate a forest by consuming all of the leaves on its trees. Unregulated deer populations may grow explosively, the deer

a. *b.*

Figure 57.25 Succession after a volcanic eruption. A major volcanic explosion in 1883 on the island of Krakatau destroyed all life on the island. *a.* This photo shows a later, much less destructive eruption of the volcano. *b.* Krakatau, forested and populated by animals.

overgrazing and so destroying the forest in which they live. On the other hand, local disturbances may affect only a small area, as when a tree falls in a forest or an animal digs a hole and uproots vegetation.

Intermediate disturbance hypothesis

In some cases, disturbance may act to increase the species richness of an area. According to the *intermediate disturbance hypothesis*, communities experiencing moderate amounts of disturbance will have higher levels of species richness than communities experiencing either little or great amounts of disturbance.

Two factors could account for this pattern. First, in communities where moderate amounts of disturbance occur, patches of habitat exist at different successional stages. Within the area as a whole, then, species diversity is greatest because the full range of species—those characteristic of all stages of succession—are present. For example, a pattern of intermittent episodic disturbance that produces gaps in the rain forest (as when a tree falls) allows invasion of the gap by other species (figure 57.26). Eventually, the species inhabiting the gap will go through a successional sequence, one tree replacing another, until a canopy tree species comes again to occupy the gap. But if there are many gaps of different ages in the forest, many different species will be coexisting, some in young gaps and others in older ones.

Second, moderate levels of disturbance may prevent communities from reaching the final stages of succession, in which a few dominant competitors eliminate most of the other species. In contrast, too much disturbance might leave the community continually in the earliest stages of succession, when species richness is relatively low.

Ecologists are increasingly realizing that disturbance is common, rather than exceptional, in many communities. As a result, the idea that communities inexorably move along a successional trajectory culminating in the development of a predictable end-state, or "climax," community is no longer widely accepted. Rather, predicting the state of a community in the future may be difficult because the unpredictable occurrence of disturbances will often counter successional changes. Understanding the role that disturbances play in structuring communities is currently an important area of investigation in ecology.

Figure 57.26 Intermediate disturbance. A single fallen tree created a small light gap in the tropical rain forest of Panama. Such gaps play a key role in maintaining the high species diversity of the rain forest. In this case, a sunlight-loving plant is able to sprout up among the dense foliage of trees in the forest.

Learning Outcomes Review 57.5

Communities change through time by a process termed succession. Primary succession occurs on bare, lifeless substrate; secondary succession occurs where an existing community has been disturbed. Early-arriving species alter the environment in ways that allow other species to colonize, and new colonizers may have negative effects on species already present. Sometimes, moderate levels of disturbance can lead to increased species richness because species characteristic of all levels of succession may be present.

■ *From a community point of view, would clear-cutting a forest be better than selective harvest of individual trees? Why or why not?*

Chapter Review

57.1 Biological Communities: Species Living Together

A community is a group of different species that occupy a given location.

Communities have been viewed in different ways.

The individualistic concept of a community is a random assemblage of species that happen to occur in a given place. The holistic concept of a community is an integrated unit composed of species that work together as part of a functional whole.

Communities change over space and time.

In accordance with the individualistic view, species generally respond independently to environmental conditions, and community composition gradually changes over space and time. However, in locations where conditions rapidly change, species composition may change greatly over short distances.

57.2 The Ecological Niche Concept

Fundamental niches are potential; realized niches are actual.

A niche is the total of all the ways a species uses environmental resources. The fundamental niche is the entire niche a species is capable of using if there are no intervening factors. The realized niche is the set of actual environmental conditions that allow establishment of a stable population.

Realized niches are usually smaller than fundamental niches because interspecific interactions limit a species' use of some resources.

Competitive exclusion can occur when species compete for limited resources.

The principle of competitive exclusion states that if resources are limiting, two species cannot simultaneously occupy the same niche; rather, one species will be eliminated.

Competition may lead to resource partitioning.

By using different resources (partitioning), sympatric species can avoid competing with each other and can coexist with reduced realized niches.

Detecting interspecific competition can be difficult.

Although experimentation is a powerful means of testing the hypothesis that species compete, practical limitations exist. Detailed knowledge of the ecology of species is important to evaluate the results of experiments and possible interactions.

57.3 Predator–Prey Relationships

Predation strongly influences prey populations.

Predation is the consuming of one organism by another, and includes not only one animal eating another, but also an animal eating a plant.

Natural selection strongly favors adaptations of prey species to prevent predation. In turn, sometimes predators evolve counter-adaptations, leading to an evolutionary "arms race."

Plant adaptations defend against herbivores.

Plants produce secondary chemical compounds that deter herbivores. Sometimes the herbivores evolve an ability to ingest the compounds and use them for their own defense.

Animal adaptations defend against predators.

Animal adaptations include chemical defenses and defensive coloration such as warning coloration or camouflage.

Mimicry allows one species to capitalize on defensive strategies of another.

In Batesian mimicry, a species that is edible or nontoxic evolves warning coloration similar to that of an inedible or poisonous species.

In Müllerian mimicry, two species that are both toxic evolve similar warning coloration.

57.4 The Many Types of Species Interactions

Symbiosis involves long-term interactions.

Many symbiotic species have coevolved and have permanent relationships.

Commensalism benefits one species and is neutral to the other.

Examples of commensal relationships include epiphytes growing on large plants and barnacles growing on sea animals.

Mutualism benefits both species.

One example is the case of ants and acacias, in which *Acacia* plants provide a home and food for a species of stinging ants that protect them from herbivores.

Parasitism benefits one species at the expense of another.

Many organisms have parasitic lifestyles, living on or inside one or more host species and causing damage or disease as a result.

Ecological processes have interactive effects.

Because many processes may occur simultaneously, species may affect one another not only through direct interactions but also through their effects on other species in the community.

Keystone species have major effects on communities.

Keystone species are those that maintain a more diverse community by reducing competition between species or by altering the environment to create new habitats.

57.5 Ecological Succession, Disturbance, and Species Richness

Succession produces a change in species composition.

Primary succession begins with a barren, lifeless substrate, whereas secondary succession occurs after an existing community is disrupted by fire, clearing, or other events.

Disturbances can play an important role in structuring communities.

Community composition changes as a result of local and global disturbances that "reset" succession.

Intermediate levels of such disturbance may maximize species richness in two ways: by creating a patchwork of different habitats harboring different species, and by preventing communities from reaching the final stage of succession, which may be dominated by only a few, competitively superior species.

Review Questions

UNDERSTAND

1. Studies that demonstrate that species living in an ecological community change independently of one another in space and time
   a. support the individualistic concept of ecological communities.
   b. support the holistic concept of ecological communities.
   c. suggest species interactions are the sole determinant of which species coexist in a community.
   d. None of the above

2. If two species have very similar realized niches and are forced to coexist and share a limiting resource indefinitely,
   a. both species would be expected to coexist.
   b. both species would be expected to go extinct.
   c. the species that uses the limiting resource most efficiently should drive the other species extinct.
   d. both species would be expected to become more similar to one another.

3. According to the idea of coevolution between predator and prey, when a prey species evolves a novel defense against a predator

    a. the predator is expected to always go extinct.

    b. the prey population should increase irreversibly out of control of the predator.

    c. the predator population should increase.

    d. evolution of a predator response should be favored by natural selection.

4. In order for mimicry to be effective in protecting a species from predation, it must

    a. occur in a palatable species that looks like a distasteful species.

    b. have cryptic coloration.

    c. occur such that mimics look and act like models.

    d. occur in only poisonous or dangerous species.

5. Which of the following is an example of commensalism?

    a. A tapeworm living in the gut of its host

    b. A clownfish living among the tentacles of a sea anemone

    c. An acacia tree and acacia ants

    d. Bees feeding on nectar from a flower

6. A species whose effect on the composition of a community is greater than expected based on its abundance can be called a

    a. predator.

    b. primary succession species.

    c. secondary succession species.

    d. keystone species.

7. When a predator preferentially eats the superior competitor in a pair of competing species

    a. the inferior competitor is more likely to go extinct.

    b. the superior competitor is more likely to persist.

    c. coexistence of the competing species is more likely.

    d. None of the above

8. Species that are the first colonists in a habitat undergoing primary succession

    a. are usually the fiercest competitors.

    b. help maintain their habitat constant so their persistence is ensured.

    c. may change their habitat in a way that favors the invasion of other species.

    d. must first be successful secondary succession specialists.

APPLY

1. Which of the following can cause the realized niche of a species to be smaller than its fundamental niche?

    a. Predation   c. Parasitism

    b. Competition   d. All of the above

2. The presence of a predatory species

    a. always drives a prey species to extinction.

    b. can positively affect a prey species by having a detrimental effect on competing species.

    c. indicates that the climax stage of succession has been reached.

    d. None of the above

3. Resource partitioning by sympatric species

    a. always occurs when species have identical niches.

    b. may not occur in the presence of a predator, which reduces prey population sizes.

    c. results in the fundamental and realized niches being the same.

    d. is more common in herbivores than carnivores.

4. Parasitism differs from predation because

    a. the presence of parasitism doesn't lead to selection for defensive adaptations in parasitized species.

    b. parasites and the species they parasitize never engage in an evolutionary "arms race."

    c. parasites don't have strong effects on the populations of the species they parasitize.

    d. None of the above

5. The presence of one species (A) in a community may benefit another species (B) if

    a. a commensualistic relationship exists between the two.

    b. The first species (A) preys on a predator of the second species (B).

    c. The first species (A) preys on a species that competes with a species that is eaten by the second species (B).

    d. All of the above

SYNTHESIZE

1. Competition is traditionally indicated by documenting the effect of one species on the population of another. Are there alternative ways to study the potential effects of competition on organisms that are impractical to study with experimental manipulations because they are too big or live too long?

2. Refer to figure 57.9. If the single prey species of *Paramecium* was replaced by several different potential prey species that varied in their palatability or ease of subduing by the predator (leading to different levels of preference by the predator) what would you expect the dynamics of the system to look like; that is, would the system be more or less likely to go to extinction?

3. Refer to figure 57.22. Are there alternative hypotheses that might explain the increase followed by the decrease in ant colony numbers subsequent to rodent removal in the experiment described in figure 57.22? If so, how would you test the mechanism hypothesized in the figure?

4. Refer to figure 57.7. Examine the pattern of beak size distributions of two species of finches on the Galápagos Islands. One hypothesis that can be drawn from this pattern is that character displacement has taken place. Are there other hypotheses? If so, how would you test them?

5. Is it possible that some species function together as an integrated, holistic community, whereas other species at the same locality behave more individualistically? If so, what factors might determine which species function in which way?

ONLINE RESOURCE

www.ravenbiology.com

Understand, Apply, and Synthesize—enhance your study with animations that bring concepts to life and practice tests to assess your understanding. Your instructor may also recommend the interactive eBook, individualized learning tools, and more.

Chapter 58

Dynamics of Ecosystems

Chapter Outline

58.1 Biogeochemical Cycles

58.2 The Flow of Energy in Ecosystems

58.3 Trophic-Level Interactions

58.4 Biodiversity and Ecosystem Stability

58.5 Island Biogeography

Introduction

The Earth is a relatively closed system with respect to chemicals. It is an open system in terms of energy, however, because it receives energy at visible and near-visible wavelengths from the Sun and steadily emits thermal energy to outer space in the form of infrared radiation. The organisms in ecosystems interact in complex ways as they participate in the cycling of chemicals and as they capture and expend energy. All organisms, including humans, depend on the specialized abilities of other organisms—plants, algae, animals, fungi, and prokaryotes—to acquire the essentials of life, as explained in this chapter. In chapters 58 and 59, we consider the many different types of ecosystems that constitute the biosphere and discuss the threats to the biosphere and the species it contains.

Biogeochemical Cycles

An ecosystem includes all the organisms that live in a particular place, plus the abiotic (nonliving) environment in which they live—and with which they interact—at that location. Ecosystems are intrinsically dynamic in a number of ways, including their processing of matter and energy. We start with matter.

The atomic constituents of matter cycle within ecosystems

During the biological processing of matter, the atoms of which it is composed, such as the atoms of carbon or oxygen, maintain their integrity even as they are assembled into new compounds and the compounds are later broken down. The Earth has an essentially fixed number of each of the types of atoms of biological importance, and the atoms are recycled.

Each organism assembles its body from atoms that previously were in the soil, the atmosphere, other parts of the abiotic environment, or other organisms. When the organism dies, its atoms are released unaltered to be used by other organisms or returned to the abiotic environment. Because of the cycling of the atomic constituents of matter, your body is likely during

your life to contain a carbon or oxygen atom that once was part of Julius Caesar's body or Cleopatra's.

The atoms of the various chemical elements are said to move through ecosystems in biogeochemical cycles, a term emphasizing that the cycles of chemical elements involve not only biological organisms and processes, but also geological (abiotic) systems and processes. Biogeochemical cycles include processes that occur on many spatial scales, from cellular to planetary, and they also include processes that occur on multiple timescales, from seconds (biochemical reactions) to millennia (weathering of rocks).

Biogeochemical cycles usually cross the boundaries of ecosystems to some extent, rather than being self-contained within individual ecosystems. For example, one ecosystem might import or export carbon to others.

In this section, we consider the cycles of some major elements along with the compound water. We also present an example of biogeochemical cycles in a forest ecosystem.

Carbon, the basis of organic compounds, cycles through most ecosystems

Carbon is a major constituent of the bodies of organisms because carbon atoms help form the framework of all organic compounds (see chapter 3); almost 20% of the weight of the human body is carbon. From the viewpoint of the day-to-day dynamics of ecosystems, carbon dioxide (CO_2) is the most significant carbon-containing compound in the abiotic environments of organisms. It makes up 0.03% of the volume of the atmosphere, meaning the atmosphere contains about 750 billion metric tons of carbon. In aquatic ecosystems, CO_2 reacts spontaneously with the water to form bicarbonate ions (HCO_3^-).

Figure 58.1 The carbon cycle. Photosynthesis by plants and algae captures carbon in the form of organic chemical compounds. Aerobic respiration by organisms and fuel combustion by humans return carbon to the form of carbon dioxide (CO_2) or bicarbonate (HCO_3^2). Microbial methanogens living in oxygen-free microhabitats, such as the mud at the bottom of the pond, might produce methane (CH_4), a gas that would enter the atmosphere and then gradually be oxidized abiotically to carbon dioxide (shown in green circled inset).

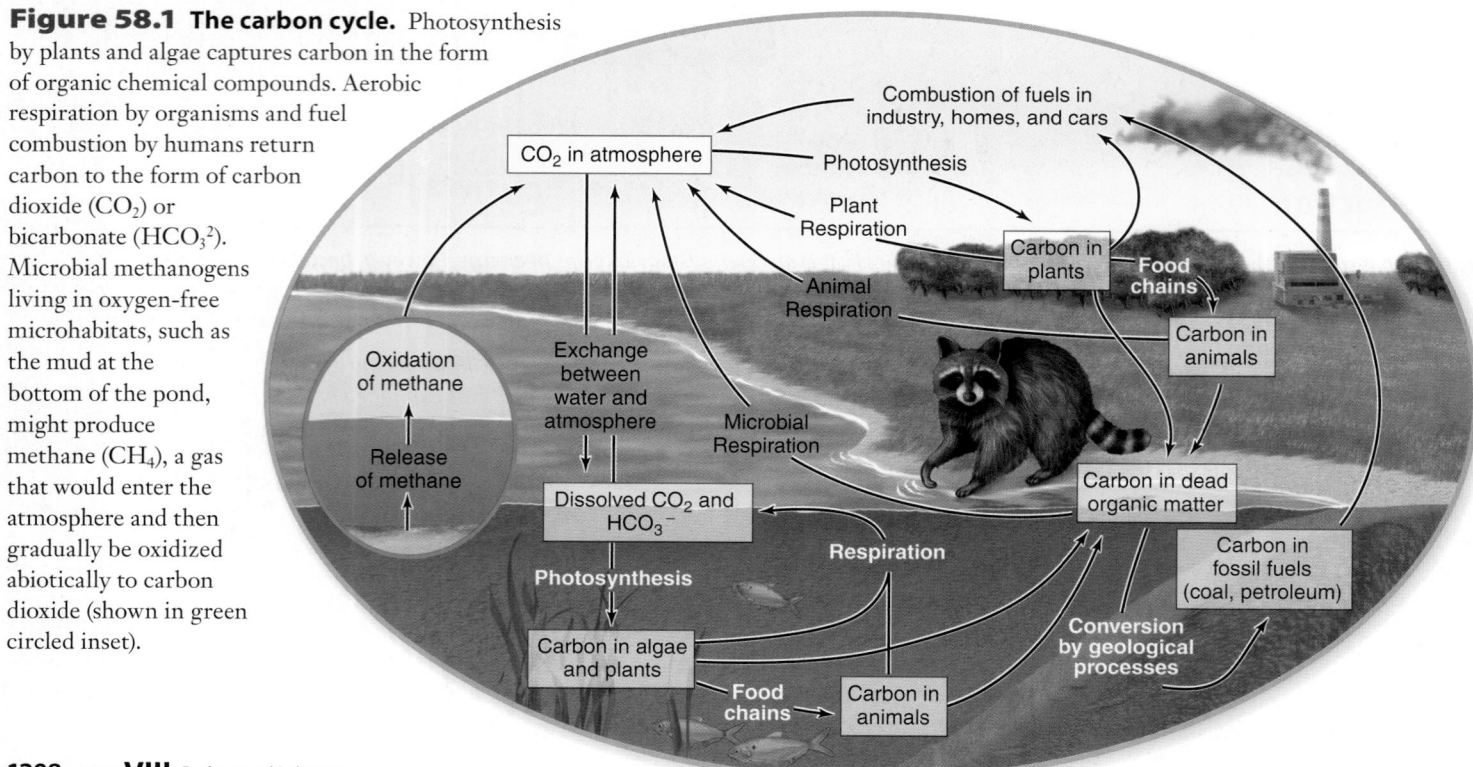

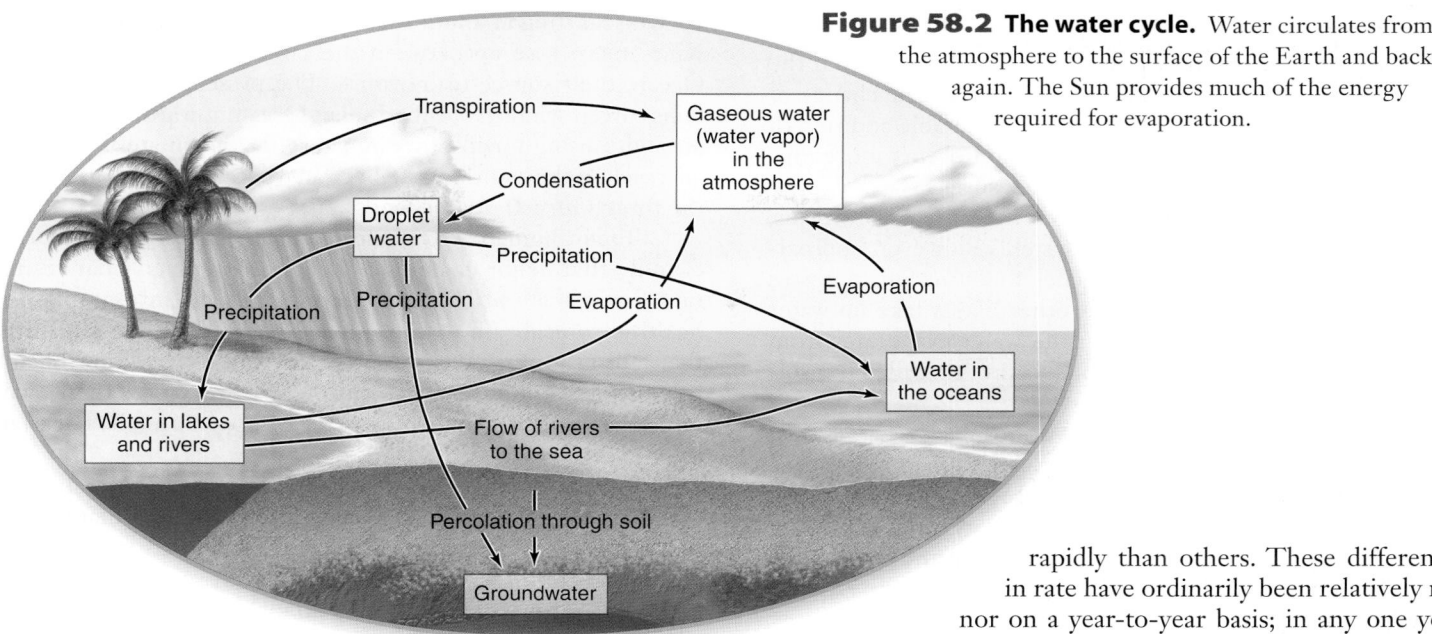

Figure 58.2 The water cycle. Water circulates from the atmosphere to the surface of the Earth and back again. The Sun provides much of the energy required for evaporation.

The basic carbon cycle

The carbon cycle is straightforward, as shown in figure 58.1. In terrestrial ecosystems, plants and other photosynthetic organisms take in CO_2 from the atmosphere and use it in photosynthesis to synthesize the carbon-containing organic compounds of which they are composed (see chapter 8). The process is sometimes called *carbon fixation;* fixation refers to metabolic reactions that make nongaseous compounds from gaseous ones.

Animals eat the photosynthetic organisms and build their own tissues by making use of the carbon atoms in the organic compounds they ingest. Both the photosynthetic organisms and the animals obtain energy during their lives by breaking down some of the organic compounds available to them, through aerobic cellular respiration (see chapter 7). When they do this, they produce CO_2. Decaying organisms also produce CO_2. Carbon atoms returned to the form of CO_2 are available once more to be used in photosynthesis to synthesize new organic compounds.

In aquatic ecosystems, the carbon cycle is fundamentally similar, except that inorganic carbon is present in the water not only as dissolved CO_2, but also as HCO_3^- ions, both of which act as sources of carbon for photosynthesis by algae and aquatic plants.

Methane producers

Microbes that break down organic compounds by anaerobic cellular respiration (see chapter 7) provide an additional dimension to the global carbon cycle. Methanogens, for example, are microbes that produce methane (CH_4) instead of CO_2. One major source of CH_4 is wetland ecosystems, where methanogens live in the oxygen-free sediments. Methane that enters the atmosphere is oxidized abiotically to CO_2, but CH_4 that remains isolated from oxygen can persist for great lengths of time.

The rise of atmospheric carbon dioxide

Another dimension of the global carbon cycle is that over long stretches of time, some parts of the cycle may proceed more rapidly than others. These differences in rate have ordinarily been relatively minor on a year-to-year basis; in any one year, the amount of CO_2 made by breakdown of organic compounds almost matches the amount of CO_2 used to synthesize new organic compounds.

Small mismatches, however, can have large consequences if continued for many years. The Earth's present reserves of coal were built up over geologic time. Organic compounds such as cellulose accumulated by being synthesized faster than they were broken down, and then they were transformed by geological processes into the fossil fuels. Most scientists believe that the world's petroleum reserves were created in the same way.

Human burning of fossil fuels today is creating large contemporary imbalances in the carbon cycle. Carbon that took millions of years to accumulate in the reserves of fossil fuels is being rapidly returned to the atmosphere, driving the concentration of CO_2 in the atmosphere upward year by year and helping to spur fears of global warming (see chapter 59).

The availability of water is fundamental to terrestrial ecosystems

The water cycle, seen in figure 58.2, is probably the most familiar of all biogeochemical cycles. All life depends on the presence of water; even organisms that can survive without water in resting states require water to regain activity. The bodies of most organisms consist mainly of water. The adult human body, for example, is about 60% water by weight. The amount of water available in an ecosystem often determines the nature and abundance of the organisms present, as illustrated by the difference between forests and deserts (see chapter 59).

Each type of biogeochemical cycle has distinctive features. A distinctive feature of the water cycle is that water is a compound, not an element, and thus it can be synthesized and broken down. It is synthesized during aerobic cellular respiration (see chapter 7) and chemically split during photosynthesis (see chapter 8). The rates of these processes are ordinarily about equal, and therefore a relatively constant amount of water cycles through the biosphere.

The basic water cycle

One key part of the water cycle is that liquid water from the Earth's surface evaporates into the atmosphere. The change of water from a liquid to a gas requires a considerable addition of thermal energy, explaining why evaporation occurs more rapidly when solar radiation beats down on a surface.

Evaporation occurs directly from the surfaces of oceans, lakes, and rivers. In terrestrial ecosystems, however, approximately 90% of the water that reaches the atmosphere passes through plants. Trees, grasses, and other plants take up water from soil via their roots, and then the water evaporates from their leaves and other surfaces through a process called transpiration (see chapter 38).

Evaporated water exists in the atmosphere as a gas, just like any other atmospheric gas. The water can condense back into liquid form, however, mostly because of cooling of the air. Condensation of gaseous water (water vapor) into droplets or crystals causes the formation of clouds, and if the droplets or crystals are large enough, they fall to the surface of the Earth as precipitation (rain or snow).

Groundwater

Less obvious than surface water, which we see in rivers and lakes, is water under ground—termed groundwater. Groundwater occurs in **aquifers,** which are permeable, underground layers of rock, sand, and gravel that are often saturated with water. Groundwater is the most important reservoir of water on land in many parts of the world, representing over 95% of all fresh water in the United States, for example.

Goundwater consists of two subparts. The upper layers of the groundwater constitute the water table, which is unconfined in the sense that it flows into streams and is partly accessible to the roots of plants. The lower, confined layers of the groundwater are generally out of reach to streams and plants, but can be tapped by wells. Groundwater is recharged by water that percolates downward from above, such as from precipitation. Water in an aquifer flows much more slowly than surface water, anywhere from a few millimeters to a meter or so per day.

In the United States, groundwater provides about 25% of the water used by humans for all purposes, and it supplies about 50% of the population with drinking water. In the Great Plains states, the deep Ogallala Aquifer is tapped extensively as a water source for agricultural and domestic needs. The aquifer is being depleted faster than it is recharged—a local imbalance in the water cycle—posing an ominous threat to the agricultural production of the area. Similar threats exist in many of the drier portions of the globe.

Changes in ecosystems brought about by changes in the water cycle

Water is so crucial for life that changes in its supply in an ecosystem can radically alter the nature of the ecosystem. Such changes have occurred often during the Earth's geological history.

Consider, for example, the ecosystem of the Serengeti Plain in Tanzania, famous for its seemingly endless grasslands occupied by vast herds of antelopes and other grazing animals. The semiarid grasslands of today's Serengeti were rain forests 25 MYA. Starting at about that time, mountains such as Mount Kilimanjaro rose up between the rain forests and the Indian Ocean, their source of moisture. The presence of the mountains forced winds from the Indian Ocean upward, cooling the air and causing much of its moisture to precipitate before the air reached the rain forests. The land became much drier, and the forests turned to grasslands.

Today, human activities can alter the water cycle so profoundly that major changes occur in ecosystems. Changes in rain forests caused by deforestation provide an example. In healthy tropical rain forests, more than 90% of the moisture that falls as rain is taken up by plants and returned to the air by transpiration. Plants, in a very real sense, create their own rain: The moisture returned to the atmosphere falls back on the forests.

When human populations cut down or burn the rain forests in an area, the local water cycle is broken. Water that falls as rain thereafter drains away in rivers instead of rising to form clouds and fall again on the forests. Just such a transformation is occurring today in many tropical rain forests (figure 58.3). Large areas in Brazil, for example, were transformed in the 20th century from lush tropical forest to semiarid desert, depriving many unique plant and animal species of their native habitat.

The nitrogen cycle depends on nitrogen fixation by microbes

Nitrogen is a component of all proteins and nucleic acids and is required in substantial amounts by all organisms; proteins are 16% nitrogen by weight. In many ecosystems, nitrogen is the chemical element in shortest supply relative to the needs of organisms. A paradox is that the atmosphere is 78% nitrogen by volume.

Figure 58.3 Deforestation disrupts the local water cycle. Tropical deforestation can have severe consequences, such as the extensive erosion in this area in the Amazon region of Brazil.

Nitrogen availability

How can nitrogen be in short supply if the atmosphere is so rich with it? The answer is that the nitrogen in the atmosphere is in its elemental form—molecules of nitrogen gas (N_2)—and the vast majority of organisms, including all plants and animals, have no way to use nitrogen in this chemical form.

For animals, the ultimate source of nitrogen is nitrogen-containing organic compounds synthesized by plants or by algae or other microbes. Herbivorous animals, for example, eat plant or algal proteins and use the nitrogen-containing amino acids in them to synthesize their own proteins.

Plants and algae use a number of simple nitrogen-containing compounds as their sources of nitrogen to synthesize proteins and other nitrogen-containing organic compounds in their tissues. Two commonly used nitrogen sources are ammonia (NH_3) and nitrate ions (NO_3^-). As described in chapter 39, certain prokaryotic microbes can synthesize ammonia and nitrate from N_2 in the atmosphere, thereby constituting a part of the nitrogen cycle that makes atmospheric nitrogen accessible to plants and algae (figure 58.4). Other prokaryotes turn NH_3 and NO_3^- into N_2, making the nitrogen inaccessible. The balance of the activities of these two sets of microbes determines the accessibility of nitrogen to plants and algae.

Microbial nitrogen fixation, nitrification, and denitrification

The synthesis of nitrogen-containing compounds from N_2 is known as **nitrogen fixation.** The first step in this process is the synthesis of NH_3 from N_2, and biochemists sometimes use the term *nitrogen fixation* to refer specifically to this step. After NH_3 has been synthesized, other prokaryotic microbes oxidize part of it to form NO_3^-, a process called **nitrification.**

Certain genera of prokaryotes have the ability to accomplish nitrogen fixation using a system of enzymes known as the nitrogenase complex (the *nif* gene complex; see chapter 28). Most of the microbes are free-living, but on land some are found in symbiotic relationships with the roots of legumes (plants of the pea family, Fabaceae), alders, myrtles, and other plants.

Additional prokaryotic microbes (including both bacteria and archaea) are able to convert the nitrogen in NO_3^- into N_2 (or other nitrogen gases such as N_2O), a process termed **denitrification.** Ammonia can be subjected to denitrification indirectly by being converted first to NO_3^- and then to N_2.

Nitrogenous wastes and fertilizer use

Most animals, when they break down proteins in their metabolism, excrete the nitrogen from the proteins as NH_3. Humans and other mammals excrete nitrogen as urea in their urine (see chapter 51); a number of types of microbes convert the urea to NH_3. The NH_3 from animal excretion can be picked up by plants and algae as a source of nitrogen.

Human populations are radically altering the global nitrogen cycle by the use of fertilizers on lawns and agricultural fields. The fertilizers contain forms of fixed nitrogen that crops can use, such as ammonium (NH_4) salts manufactured industrially from atmospheric N_2. Partly because of the production of fertilizers, humans have already doubled the rate of transfer of N_2 in usable forms into soils and waters.

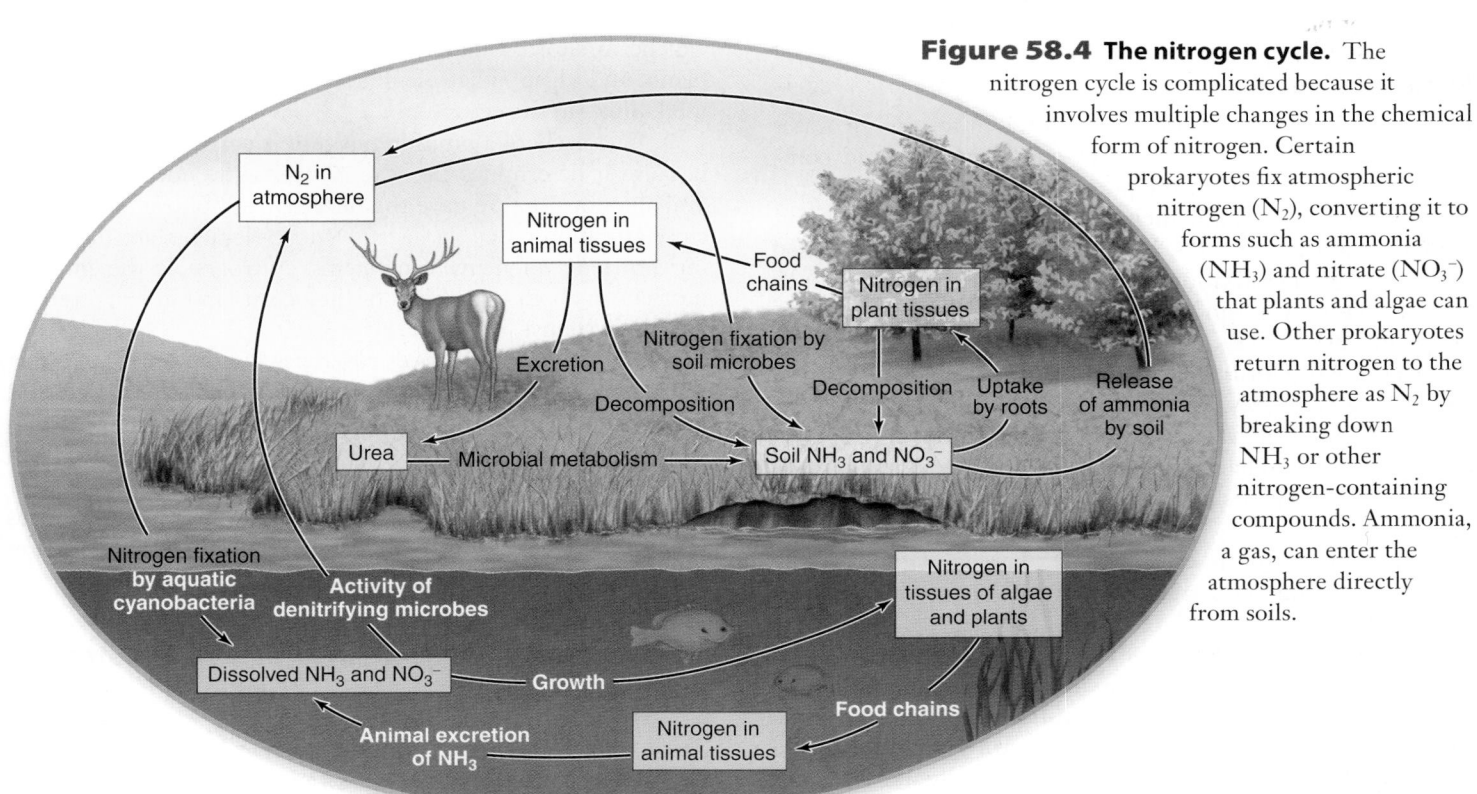

Figure 58.4 The nitrogen cycle. The nitrogen cycle is complicated because it involves multiple changes in the chemical form of nitrogen. Certain prokaryotes fix atmospheric nitrogen (N_2), converting it to forms such as ammonia (NH_3) and nitrate (NO_3^-) that plants and algae can use. Other prokaryotes return nitrogen to the atmosphere as N_2 by breaking down NH_3 or other nitrogen-containing compounds. Ammonia, a gas, can enter the atmosphere directly from soils.

Figure 58.5 The phosphorus cycle. In contrast to carbon, water, and nitrogen, phosphorus occurs only in the liquid and solid states and thus does not enter the atmosphere.

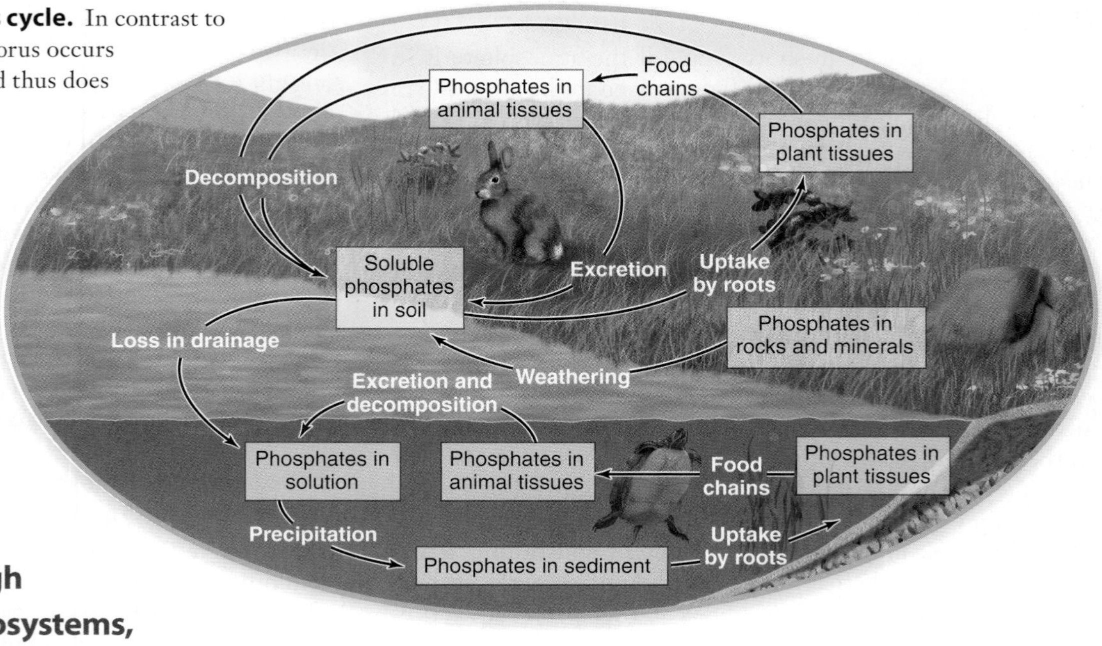

Phosphorus cycles through terrestrial and aquatic ecosystems, but not the atmosphere

Phosphorus is required in substantial quantities by all organisms; it occurs in nucleic acids, membrane phospholipids, and other essential compounds, such as adenosine triphosphate (ATP).

Unlike carbon, water, and nitrogen, phosphorus has no significant gaseous form and does not cycle through the atmosphere (figure 58.5). In this respect, the phosphorus cycle exemplifies the sorts of cycles also exhibited by calcium, silicon, and many other mineral elements. Another feature that greatly simplifies the phosphorus cycle compared with the nitrogen cycle is that phosphorus exists in ecosystems in just a single oxidation state, phosphate (PO_4^{3-}).

Phosphate availability

Plants and algae use free inorganic PO_4^{3-} in the soil or water for synthesizing their phosphorus-containing organic compounds. Animals then tap the phosphorus in plant or algal tissue compounds to build their own phosphorus compounds. When organisms die, decay microbes—in a process called phosphate remineralization—break up the organic compounds in their bodies, releasing phosphorus as inorganic PO_4^{3-} that plants and algae again can use.

The phosphorus cycle includes critical abiotic chemical and physical processes. Free PO_4^{3-} exists in soil in only low concentrations both because it combines with other soil constituents to form insoluble compounds and because it tends to be washed away by streams and rivers. Weathering of many sorts of rocks releases new PO_4^{3-} into terrestrial systems, but then rivers carry the PO_4^{3-} into the ocean basins. There is a large one-way flux of PO_4^{3-} from terrestrial rocks to deep-sea sediments.

Phosphates as fertilizers

Human activities have greatly modified the global phosphorus cycle since the advent of crop fertilization. Fertilizers are typically designed to provide PO_4^{3-} because crops might otherwise be short of it; the PO_4^{3-} in fertilizers is typically derived from crushed phosphate-rich rocks and bones. Detergents are an-

other potential culprit in adding PO_4^{3-} to ecosystems, but laws now mandate low-phosphate detergents in much of the world.

Limiting nutrients in ecosystems are those in short supply relative to need

A chain is only as strong as its weakest link. For the plants and algae in an ecosystem to grow—and to thereby provide food for animals—they need many different chemical elements. The simplest theory is that in any particular ecosystem, one element will be in shortest supply relative to the needs for it by the plants and algae. That element is the limiting nutrient—the weak link—in the ecosystem.

The cycle of a limiting nutrient is particularly important because it determines the rate at which the nutrient is made available for use. We gave the nitrogen and phosphorus cycles close attention precisely because those elements are the limiting nutrients in many ecosystems. Nitrogen is the limiting nutrient in about two-thirds of the oceans and in many terrestrial ecosystems.

Oceanographers have discovered in just the last 15 years that iron is the limiting nutrient for algal populations (phytoplankton) in about one-third of the world's oceans. In these waters, windborne soil dust seems often to be the chief source of iron. When wind brings in iron-rich dust, algal populations proliferate, provided the iron is in a usable chemical form. In this way, sand storms in the Sahara Desert, by increasing the dust in global winds, can increase algal productivity in Pacific waters (figure 58.6).

Biogeochemical cycling in a forest ecosystem has been studied experimentally

An ongoing series of studies at the Hubbard Brook Experimental Forest in New Hampshire has yielded much of the available information about the cycling of nutrients in forest ecosystems.

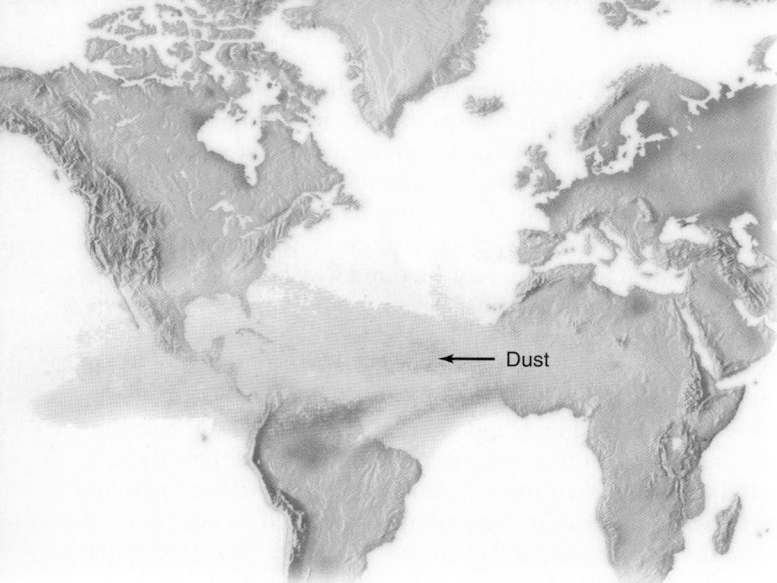

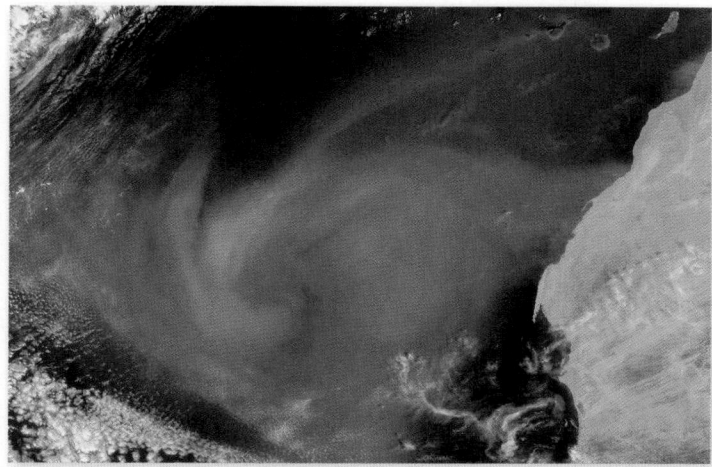

Figure 58.6 One world. Every year, millions of metric tons of iron-rich dust is carried westward by the trade winds from the Sahara Desert and neighboring Sahel area. A working hypothesis of many oceanographers is that this dust fertilizes parts of the ocean, including parts of the Pacific Ocean, where iron is the limiting nutrient. Land use practices in Africa, which are increasing the size of the north African desert, can thus affect ecosystems on the other side of the globe.

Hubbard Brook is the central stream of a large watershed that drains the hillsides of a mountain range covered with temperate deciduous forest. Multiple tributary streams carry water off the hillsides into Hubbard Brook.

Six tributary streams, each draining a particular valley, were equipped with measurement devices when the study was started. All of the water that flowed out of each valley had to pass through the measurement system, where the flow of water and concentrations of nutrients was quantified.

The undisturbed forests around Hubbard Brook are efficient at retaining nutrients. In a year, only small quantities of nutrients enter a valley from outside, doing so mostly as a result of precipitation. The quantities carried out in stream waters are small also. When we say "small," we mean the influxes and outfluxes represent just minor fractions of the total amounts of nutrients in the system—about 1% in the case of calcium, for example.

In 1965 and 1966, the investigators felled all the trees and cleared all shrubs in one of the six valleys and prevented regrowth (figure 58.7*a*). The effects were dramatic. The amount of water running out of that valley increased by 40%, indicating that water previously taken up by vegetation and evaporated into the atmosphere was now running off. The amounts of a number of nutrients running out of the system also greatly increased. For example, the rate of loss of calcium increased ninefold. Phosphorus, on the other hand, did not increase in the stream water; it apparently was locked up in insoluble compounds in the soil.

The change in the status of nitrogen in the disturbed valley was especially striking (figure 58.7*b*). The undisturbed forest in this valley had been accumulating NO_3^- at a rate of about 5 kg per hectare per year, but the deforested ecosystem lost NO_3^- at a rate of about 53 kg per hectare per year. The NO_3^- concentration in the stream water rapidly increased. The fertility of the valley decreased dramatically, while the run-off of nitrate generated massive algal blooms downstream, and the danger of downstream flooding greatly increased.

This experiment is particularly instructive at the start of the 21st century because forested land continues to be cleared worldwide (see chapter 59).

a.

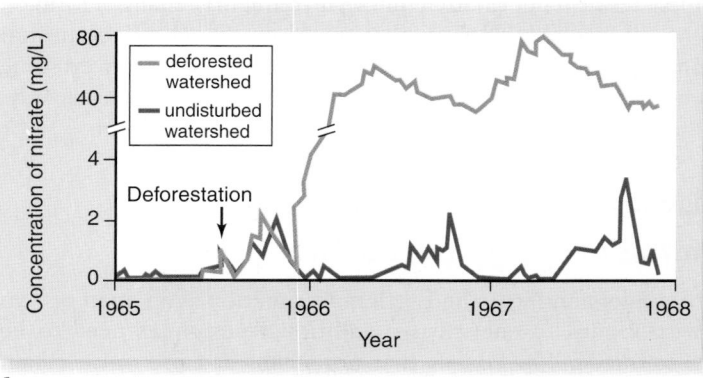

b.

Figure 58.7 The Hubbard Brook experiment. *a.* A 38-acre watershed was completely deforested, and the runoff monitored for several years. *b.* Deforestation greatly increased the loss of nutrients in runoff water from the ecosystem. The orange curve shows the nitrate concentration in the runoff water from the deforested watershed; the green curve shows the nitrate concentration in runoff water from an undisturbed neighboring watershed.

58.2 The Flow of Energy in Ecosystems

Learning Outcomes

1. **Describe the different trophic levels.**
2. **Distinguish between energy and heat.**
3. **Explain how energy moves through trophic levels.**

The dynamic nature of ecosystems includes the processing of energy as well as that of matter. Energy, however, follows very different principles than does matter. Energy is never recycled. Instead, radiant energy from the Sun that reaches the Earth makes a one-way pass through our planet's ecosystems before being converted to heat and radiated back into space, signifying that the Earth is an open system for energy.

Energy can neither be created nor destroyed, but changes form

Why is energy so different from matter? A key part of the answer is that energy exists in several different forms, such as light, chemical-bond energy, motion, and heat. Although energy is neither created nor destroyed in the biosphere (the First Law of Thermodynamics), it frequently changes form.

A second key point is that organisms cannot convert heat to any of the other forms of energy. Thus, if organisms convert some chemical-bond or light energy to heat, the conversion is one-way; they cannot cycle that energy back into its original form.

Living organisms can use many forms of energy, but not heat

To understand why the Earth must function as an open system with regard to energy, two additional principles need to be recognized. The first is that organisms can use only certain forms of energy. For animals to live, they must have energy specifically as chemical-bond energy, which they acquire from their foods. Plants must have energy as light. Neither animals nor plants (nor any other organisms) can use heat as a source of energy.

The second principle is that whenever organisms use chemical-bond or light energy, some of it is converted to heat; the Second Law of Thermodynamics states that a partial conversion to heat is inevitable. Put another way, animals and plants require chemical-bond energy and light to stay alive, but as they use these forms of energy, they convert them to heat, which they cannot use to stay alive and which they cannot cycle back into the original forms.

Fortunately for organisms, the Earth functions as an open system for energy. Light arrives every day from the Sun. Plants and other photosynthetic organisms use the newly arrived light to synthesize organic compounds and stay alive. Animals then eat the photosynthetic organisms, making use of the chemical-bond energy in their organic molecules to stay alive. Light and chemical-bond energy are partially converted to heat at every step. In fact, the light and chemical-bond energy are ultimately converted completely to heat. The heat leaves the Earth by being radiated into outer space at invisible, infrared wavelengths of the electromagnetic spectrum. For life to continue, new light energy is always required.

The Earth's incoming and outgoing flows of radiant energy must be equal for global temperature to stay constant. One concern is that human activities are changing the composition of the atmosphere in ways that impede the outgoing flow—the so-called *greenhouse effect*, which is described in the following chapter. Heat may be accumulating on Earth, causing global warming (see chapter 59).

Energy flows through trophic levels of ecosystems

In chapter 7, we introduced the concepts of autotrophs ("self-feeders") and heterotrophs ("fed by others"). **Autotrophs** synthesize the organic compounds of their bodies from inorganic precursors such as CO_2, water, and NO_3^- using energy from an abiotic source. Some autotrophs use light as their source of energy and therefore are **photoautotrophs;** they are the photosynthetic organisms, including plants, algae, and cyanobacteria. Other autotrophs are **chemoautotrophs** and obtain energy by means of inorganic oxidation reactions, such as the microbes that use hydrogen sulfide available at deep water vents (see chapter 59). All chemoautotrophs are prokaryotic. The photoautotrophs are of greatest importance in most ecosystems, and we focus on them in the remainder of this chapter.

Heterotrophs are organisms that cannot synthesize organic compounds from inorganic precursors, but instead live by taking in organic compounds that other organisms have made. They obtain the energy they need to live by breaking up some of the organic compounds available to them, thereby liberating chemical-bond energy for metabolic use (see chapter 7). Animals, fungi, and many microbes are heterotrophs.

When living in their native environments, species are often organized into chains that eat each other sequentially. For example, a species of insect might eat plants, and then a species of shrew might eat the insect, and a species of hawk might eat the shrew. Food passes through the four species in the sequence: plants $\longrightarrow$ insect $\longrightarrow$ shrew $\longrightarrow$ hawk. A sequence of species like this is termed a food chain.

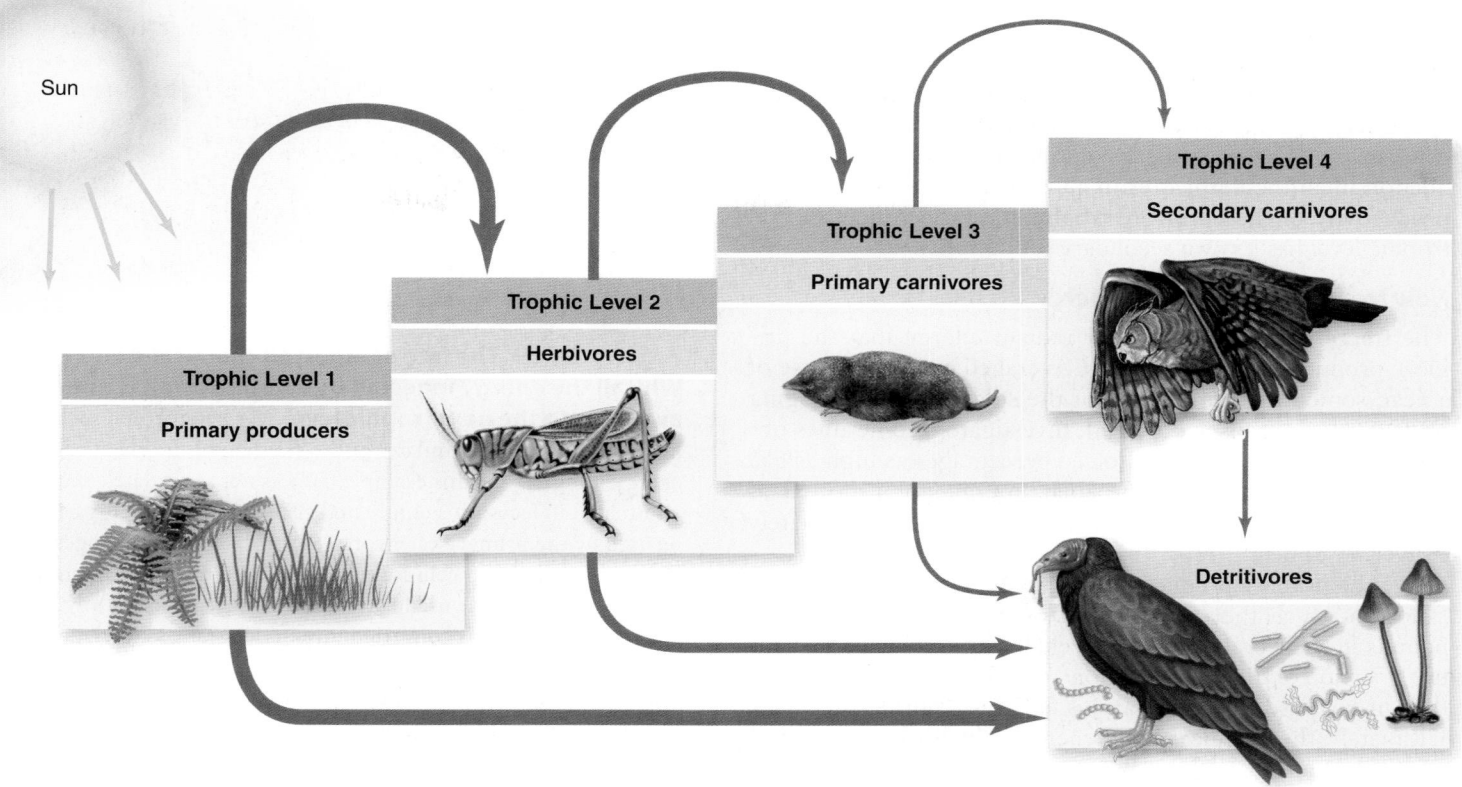

Figure 58.8 Trophic levels within an ecosystem. Primary producers such as plants obtain their energy directly from the Sun, placing them in trophic level 1. Animals that eat plants, such as plant-eating insects, are herbivores and are in trophic level 2. Animals that eat the herbivores, such as shrews, are primary carnivores and are in trophic level 3. Animals that eat the primary carnivores, such as owls, are secondary carnivores in trophic level 4. Each trophic level, although illustrated here by a particular species, consists of all the species in the ecosystem that function in a similar way in terms of what they eat. The organisms in the detritivore trophic level consume dead organic matter they obtain from all the other trophic levels.

In a whole ecosystem, many species play similar roles; there is typically not just a single species in each role. For example, the animals that eat plants might include not just a single insect species, but perhaps 30 species of insects, plus perhaps 10 species of mammals. To organize this complexity, ecologists recognize a limited number of feeding, or **trophic, levels** (figure 58.8).

Definitions of trophic levels

The first trophic level in an ecosystem, called the **primary producers,** consists of all the autotrophs in the system. The other trophic levels consist of the heterotrophs—the **consumers.** All the heterotrophs that feed directly on the primary producers are placed together in a trophic level called the **herbivores.** In turn, the heterotrophs that feed on the herbivores (eating them or being parasitic on them) are collectively termed **primary carnivores,** and those that feed on the primary carnivores are called **secondary carnivores.**

Advanced studies of ecosystems need to take into account that organisms often do not line up in simple linear sequences in terms of what they eat; some animals, for example, eat both primary producers and other animals. A linear sequence of trophic levels is a useful organizing principle for many purposes, however.

An additional consumer level is the **detritivore** trophic level. Detritivores differ from the organisms in the other trophic levels in that they feed on the remains of already-dead organisms; detritus is dead organic matter. A subcategory of detritivores is the **decomposers,** which are mostly microbes and other minute organisms that live on and break up dead organic matter.

Concepts to describe trophic levels

Trophic levels consist of whole populations of organisms. For example, the primary-producer trophic level consists of the whole populations of all the autotrophic species in an ecosystem. Ecologists have developed a special set of terms to refer to the properties of populations and trophic levels.

The **productivity** of a trophic level is the rate at which the organisms in the trophic level collectively synthesize new organic matter (new tissue substance). **Primary productivity** is the productivity of the primary producers. An important complexity in analyzing the primary producers is that not only do they synthesize new organic matter by photosynthesis, but they also break down some of the organic matter to release energy by means of aerobic cellular respiration (see chapter 7). The **respiration** of the primary producers, in this context, is the rate at which they break down organic compounds. **Gross primary productivity (GPP)** is simply the raw rate at which the primary producers synthesize new organic matter; **net primary productivity (NPP)** is the GPP minus the respiration of the primary producers. The NPP represents the organic matter available for herbivores to use as food.

The productivity of a heterotroph trophic level is termed **secondary productivity.** For instance, the rate that new organic matter is made by means of individual growth and reproduction in all the herbivores in an ecosystem is the secondary productivity of the herbivore trophic level. Each heterotroph trophic level has its own secondary productivity.

How trophic levels process energy

The fraction of incoming solar radiant energy that the primary producers capture is small. Averaged over the course of a year, something around 1% of the solar energy impinging on forests or oceans is captured. Investigators sometimes observe far lower levels, but also see percentages as high as 5% under some conditions. The solar energy not captured as chemical-bond energy through photosynthesis is immediately converted to heat.

The primary producers, as noted before, carry out respiration in which they break down some of the organic compounds in their bodies to release chemical-bond energy. They use a portion of this chemical-bond energy to make ATP, which they in turn use to power various energy-requiring processes. Ultimately, the chemical-bond energy they release by respiration turns to heat.

Remember that organisms cannot use heat to stay alive. As a result, whenever energy changes form to become heat, it loses much or all of its usefulness for organisms as a fuel source. What we have seen so far is that about 99% of the solar energy impinging on an ecosystem turns to heat because it fails to be used by photosynthesis. Then some of the energy captured by photosynthesis also becomes heat because of respiration by the primary producers. All the heterotrophs in an ecosystem must live on the chemical-bond energy that is left.

An example of energy loss between trophic levels

As chemical-bond energy is passed from one heterotroph trophic level to the next, a great deal of the energy is diverted all along the way. This principle has dramatic consequences. It means that, over any particular period of time, the amount of chemical-bond energy available to primary carnivores is far less than that available to herbivores, and the amount available to secondary carnivores is far less than that available to primary carnivores.

Why does the amount of chemical-bond energy decrease as energy is passed from one trophic level to the next? Consider the use of energy by the herbivore trophic level as an example (figure 58.9). After an herbivore such as a leaf-eating insect ingests some food, it produces feces. The chemical-bond energy in the compounds in the feces is not passed along to the primary carnivore trophic level. The chemical-bond energy of the food that is assimilated by the herbivore is used for a number of functions. Part of the assimilated energy is liberated by cellular respiration to be used for tissue repair, body movements, and other such functions. The energy used in these ways turns to heat and is not passed along to the carnivore trophic level. Some chemical-bond energy is built into the tissues of the herbivore and can serve as food for a carnivore. However, some herbivore individuals die of disease or accident rather than being eaten by predators.

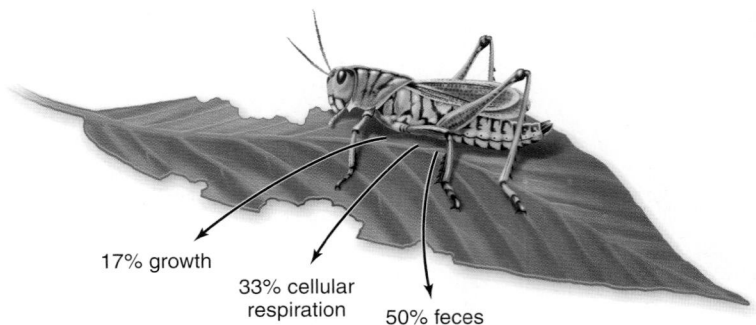

17% growth

33% cellular respiration

50% feces

Figure 58.9 The fate of ingested chemical-bond energy: Why all the energy ingested by a heterotroph is not available to the next trophic level. A heterotroph such as this herbivorous insect assimilates only a fraction of the chemical-bond energy it ingests. In this example, 50% is not assimilated and is eliminated in feces; this eliminated chemical-bond energy cannot be used by the primary carnivores. A third (33%) of the ingested energy is used to fuel cellular respiration and thus is converted to heat, which cannot be used by the primary carnivores. Only 17% of the ingested energy is converted into insect biomass through growth and can serve as food for the next trophic level, but not even that percentage is certain to be used in that way because some of the insects die before they are eaten.

In the end, of course, some of the initial chemical-bond energy acquired from the leaf is built into the tissues of herbivore individuals that are eaten by primary carnivores. Much of the initial chemical-bond energy, however, is diverted into heat, feces, and the bodies of herbivore individuals that carnivores do not get to eat. The same scenario is repeated at each step in a series of trophic levels (figure 58.10).

Ecologists figure as a rule of thumb that the amount of chemical-bond energy available to a trophic level over time is about 10% of that available to the preceding level over the same period of time. In some instances the percentage is higher, even as high as 30%.

Heat as the final energy product

Essentially all of the chemical-bond energy captured by photosynthesis in an ecosystem eventually becomes heat as the chemical-bond energy is used by various trophic levels. To see this important point, recognize that when the detritivores in the ecosystem metabolize all the dead bodies, feces, and other materials made available to them, they produce heat just like the other trophic levels do.

Productive ecosystems

Ecosystems vary considerably in their NPP. Wetlands and tropical rain forests are examples of particularly productive ecosystems (figure 58.11); in them, the NPP, measured as dry weight of new organic matter produced, is often around 2000 g/m²/year. By contrast, the corresponding figures for some other types of ecosystems are 1200 to 1300 for temperate forests, 900 for savanna, and 90 for deserts. (These general ecosystem types, termed *biomes*, are described in the following chapter.)

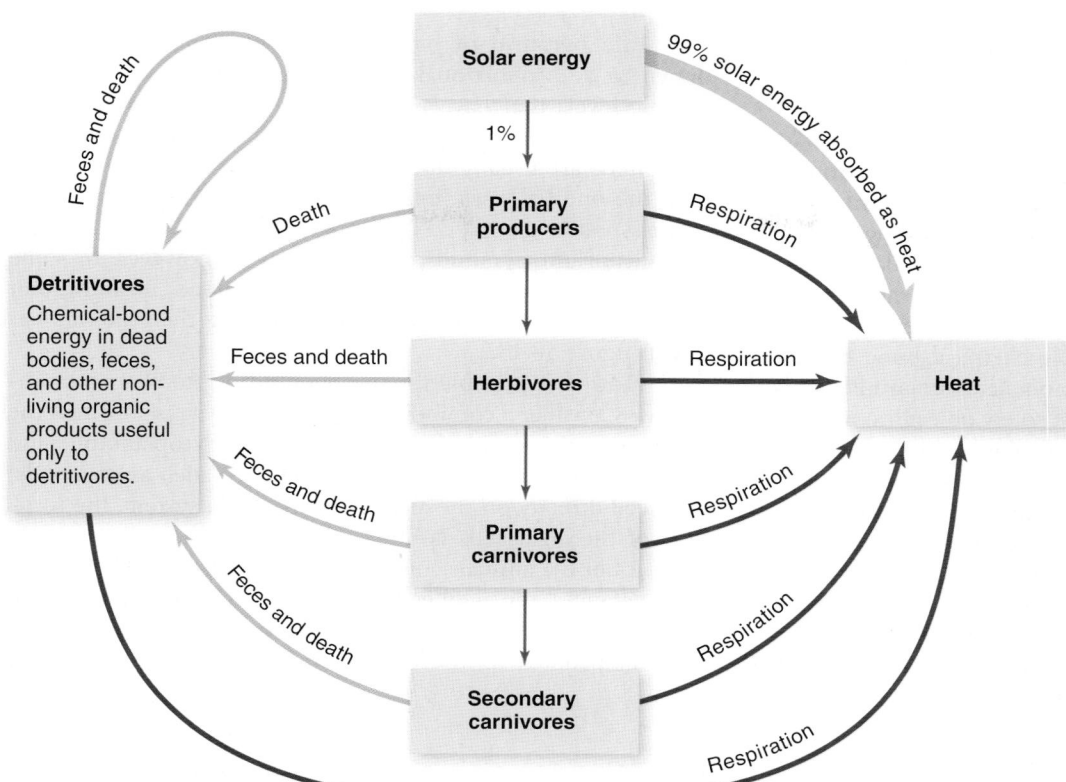

Figure 58.10 The flow of energy through an ecosystem. Blue arrows represent the flow of energy that enters the ecosystem as light and is then passed along as chemical-bond energy to successive trophic levels. At each step energy is diverted, meaning that the chemical-bond energy available to each trophic level is less than that available to the preceding trophic level. Red arrows represent diversions of energy into heat. Tan arrows represent diversions of energy into feces and other organic materials useful only to the detritivores. Detritivores may be eaten by carnivores, so some of the chemical-bond energy returns to higher trophic levels.

The number of trophic levels is limited by energy availability

The rate at which chemical-bond energy is made available to organisms in different trophic levels decreases exponentially as energy makes its way from primary producers to herbivores and then to various levels of carnivores. To envision this critical point, assume for simplicity that the primary producers in an ecosystem gain 1000 units of chemical-bond energy over a period of time. If the energy input to each trophic level is 10% of the input to the preceding level, then the input of chemical-bond energy to the herbivore trophic level is 100 units, to the

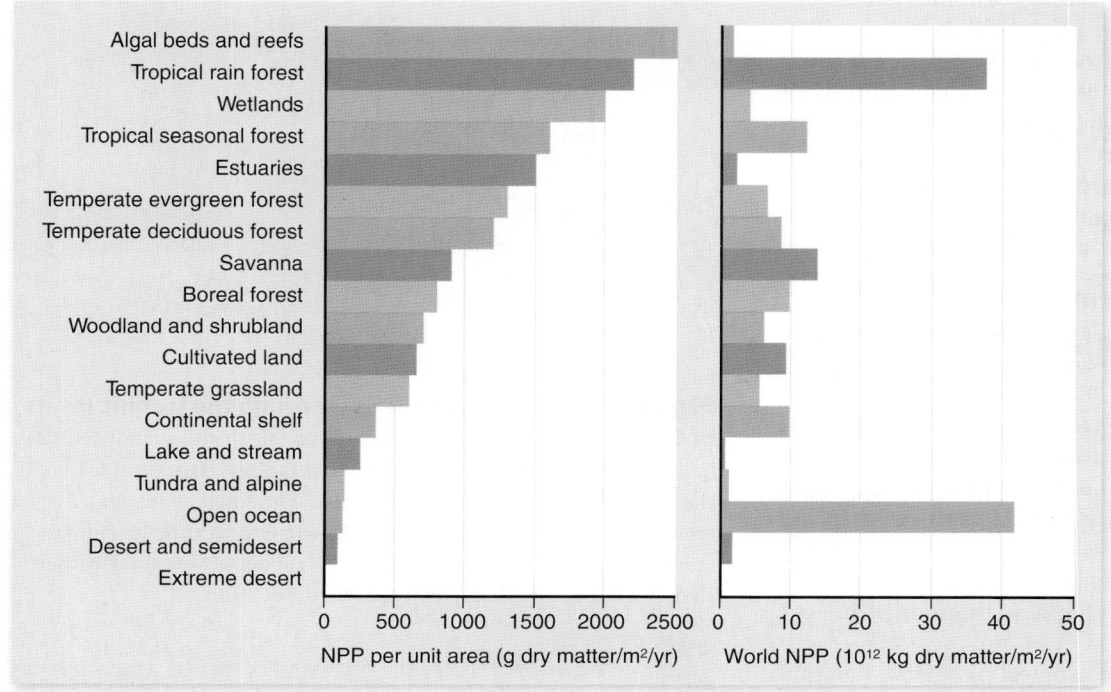

Figure 58.11 Ecosystem productivity per year. The first column of data shows the average net primary productivity (NPP) per square meter per year. The second column of data factors in the area covered by the ecosystem type; it is the product of the productivity per square meter per year times the number of square meters occupied by the ecosystem type worldwide. Note that an ecosystem type that is very productive on a square-meter basis may not contribute much to global productivity if it is an uncommon type, such as wetlands. On the other hand, a very widespread ecosystem type, such as the open ocean, can contribute greatly to global productivity even if its productivity per square meter is low.

Source: Data in: Begon, M., J.L. Harper, and C. R. Townsend, *Ecology* 3/e, Blackwell Science, 1996, page 715. Original source: Whittaker, R. H. *Communities and Ecosystems,* 2/e, Macmillan, London, 1975.

primary carnivores, 10 units, and to the secondary carnivores, 1 unit over the same period of time.

Limits on top carnivores

The exponential decline of chemical-bond energy in a trophic chain limits the lengths of trophic chains and the numbers of top carnivores an ecosystem can support. According to our model calculations, if an ecosystem includes secondary carnivores, only about one-thousandth of the energy captured by photosynthesis passes all the way through the series of trophic levels to reach these animals as usable chemical-bond energy. Tertiary carnivores would receive only one ten-thousandth. This helps explain why no predators subsist solely on eagles or lions.

The decline of available chemical-bond energy also helps explain why the numbers of individual top-level carnivores in an ecosystem tend to be low. The whole trophic level of top carnivores receives relatively little energy, and yet such carnivores tend to be big: They have relatively large individual body sizes and great individual energy needs. Because of these two factors, the population numbers of top predators tend to be small.

The longest trophic chains probably occur in the oceans. Some tunas and other top-level ocean predators probably function as third- and fourth-level carnivores at times. The challenge of explaining such long trophic chains is obvious, but the solutions are not well understood presently.

Humans as consumers: A case study

The flow of energy in Cayuga Lake in upstate New York (figure 58.12) helps illustrate how the energetics of trophic levels can affect the human food supply. Researchers calculated from the actual properties of this ecosystem that about 150 of each 1000 calories of chemical-bond energy captured by primary producers in the lake were transferred into the bodies of herbivores. Of these calories, about 30 were transferred into the bodies of smelt, small fish that were the principal primary carnivores in the system.

If humans ate the smelt, they gained about 6 of the 1000 calories that originally entered the system. If trout ate the smelt and humans ate the trout, the humans gained only about 1.2 calories. For human populations in general, more energy is available if plants or other primary producers are eaten than if animals are eaten—and more energy is available if herbivores rather than carnivores are consumed.

Ecological pyramids illustrate the relationship of trophic levels

Imagine that the trophic levels of an ecosystem are represented as boxes stacked on top of each other. Imagine also that the width of each box is proportional to the productivity of the trophic level it represents. The stack of boxes will always have the shape of a pyramid; each box is narrower than the one under it because of the inviolable rules of energy flow. A diagram of this sort is called a pyramid of energy flow or pyramid of productivity (figure 58.13a). It is an example of an ecological pyramid.

There are several types of ecological pyramids. Pyramid diagrams can be used to represent standing crop biomass or numbers of individuals, as well as productivity.

In a **pyramid of** biomass, the widths of the boxes are drawn to be proportional to standing crop biomass. Usually, trophic levels that have relatively low productivity also have relatively little biomass present at a given time. Thus, pyramids of biomass are usually upright, meaning each box is narrower than the one below it (figure 58.13b). An upright pyramid of biomass is not mandated by fundamental and inviolable rules like an upright pyramid of productivity is, however. In some ecosystems, the pyramid of biomass is **inverted,** meaning that at least one trophic level has greater biomass than the one below it (figure 58.13c).

How is it possible for the pyramid of biomass to be inverted? Consider a common sort of aquatic system in which the primary producers are single-celled algae (phytoplankton), and the herbivores are rice grain-sized animals (such as copepods) that feed directly on the algal cells. In such a system, the turnover of the algal cells is often very rapid: The cells multiply rapidly, but the animals consume them equally rapidly. In these circumstances, the algal cells never develop a large population size or large biomass. Nonetheless, because the algal cells are very productive, the ecosystem can support a substantial

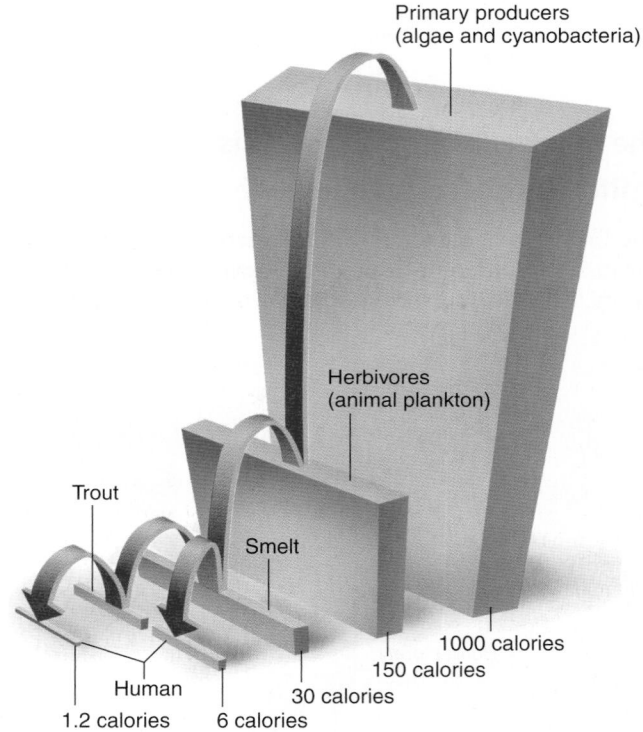

Primary producers (algae and cyanobacteria)

Herbivores (animal plankton)

Trout

Smelt

1000 calories

150 calories

Human

1.2 calories   6 calories   30 calories

Figure 58.12 Flow of energy through the trophic levels of Cayuga Lake. Autotrophic plankton (algae and cyanobacteria) fix the energy of the Sun, the herbivores (animal plankton) feed on them, and both are consumed by smelt. The smelt are eaten by trout. The amount of fish flesh produced per unit time for human consumption is at least five times greater if people eat smelt rather than trout, but people typically prefer to eat trout.

Inquiry question

? Why does it take so many calories of algae to support so few calories of humans?

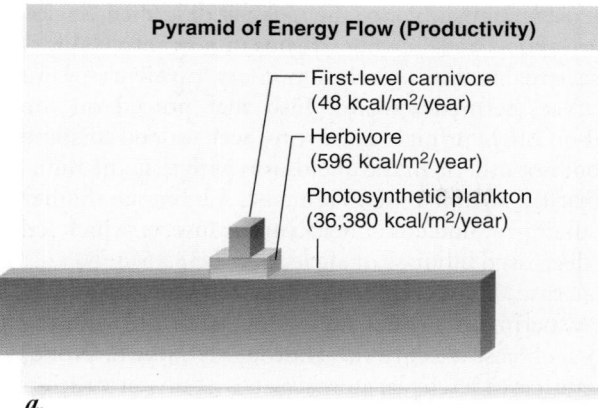

Pyramid of Energy Flow (Productivity)

First-level carnivore (48 kcal/m²/year)
Herbivore (596 kcal/m²/year)
Photosynthetic plankton (36,380 kcal/m²/year)

a.

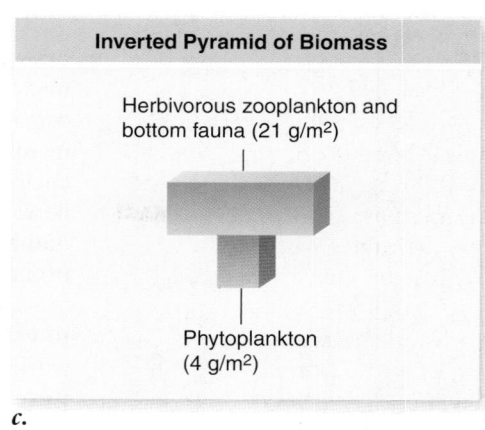

Inverted Pyramid of Biomass

Herbivorous zooplankton and bottom fauna (21 g/m²)

Phytoplankton (4 g/m²)

c.

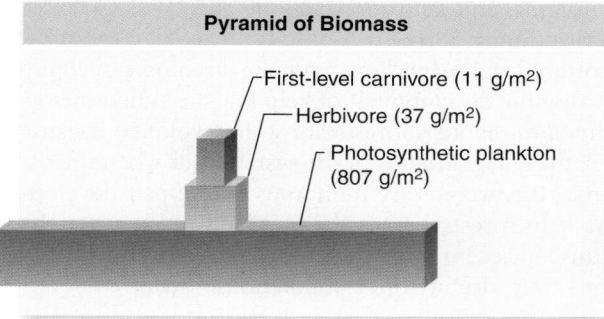

Pyramid of Biomass

First-level carnivore (11 g/m²)
Herbivore (37 g/m²)
Photosynthetic plankton (807 g/m²)

b.

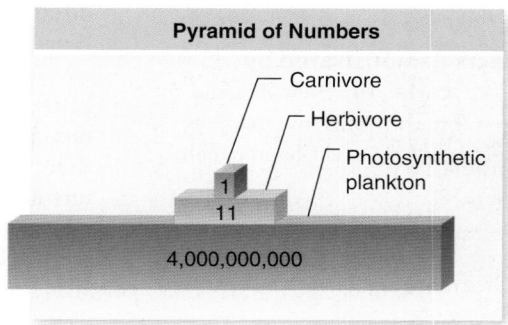

Pyramid of Numbers

Carnivore
Herbivore
Photosynthetic plankton

1
11
4,000,000,000

d.

Figure 58.13 Ecological pyramids. In an ecological pyramid, successive trophic levels in an ecosystem are represented as stacked boxes, and the widths of the boxes represent the magnitude of an ecological property in the various trophic levels. Ecological pyramids can represent several different properties. *a.* Pyramid of energy flow (productivity). *b.* Pyramid of biomass of the ordinary type. *c.* Inverted pyramid of biomass. *d.* Pyramid of numbers.

Inquiry question

? How can the existence of inverted pyramids of biomass be explained?

biomass of the animals, a biomass larger than that ever observed in the algal population.

In a pyramid of numbers, the widths of the boxes are proportional to the numbers of individuals present in the various trophic levels (figure 58.13*d*). Such pyramids are usually, but not always, upright.

Learning Outcomes Review 58.2

Trophic levels in an ecosystem include primary producers, herbivores, primary carnivores, and secondary carnivores. Detritivores consume dead or waste matter from all levels. As energy passes from one level to another, some is inevitably lost as heat, which cannot be reclaimed. Photosynthetic primary producers capture about 1% of solar energy as chemical-bond energy. As this energy is passed through the other trophic levels, some is diverted at each step into heat, feces, and dead matter; only about 10% is available to the next level.

■ *Describe the different ways that matter, such as carbon atoms, and energy move through ecosystems?*

58.3 Trophic-Level Interactions

Learning Outcomes

1. *Explain the meaning of trophic cascade.*
2. *Distinguish between top-down and bottom-up effects.*

The existence of food chains creates the possibility that species in any one trophic level may have effects on more than one trophic level. Primary carnivores, for example, may have effects not only on the animals they eat, but also, indirectly, on the plants or algae eaten by their prey. Conversely, increases in primary productivity may provide more food not just to herbivores, but also, indirectly, to carnivores.

The process by which effects exerted at an upper trophic level flow down to influence two or more lower levels is termed a **trophic cascade.** The effects themselves are called **top-down effects.** When an effect flows up through a trophic chain, such as from primary producers to higher trophic levels, it is termed a **bottom-up effect.**

Top-down effects occur when changes in the top trophic level affect primary producers

The existence of top-down effects has been confirmed by controlled experiments in some types of ecosystems, particularly freshwater ones. For example, in one study, sections of a stream were enclosed with a mesh that prevented fish from entering. Brown trout—predators on invertebrates—were added to some enclosures but not others. After 10 days, the numbers of invertebrates in the enclosures with trout were only two-thirds as great as the numbers in the no-fish enclosures (figure 58.14). In turn, the biomass of algae, which the invertebrates ate, was five times greater in the trout enclosures than the no-fish ones.

The logic of the trophic cascade just described leads to the expectation that if secondary carnivores are added to

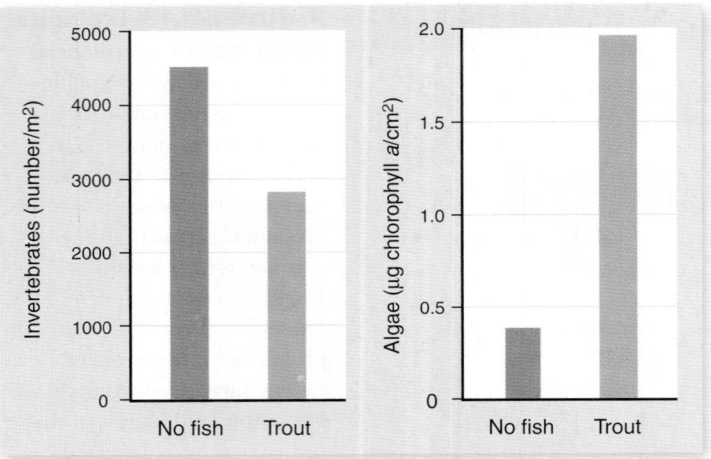

Figure 58.14 Top-down effects demonstrated by experiment in a simple trophic cascade. In a New Zealand stream, enclosures with trout had fewer herbivorous invertebrates (see the left-hand panel) and more algae (see the right-hand panel) than ones without trout.

Inquiry question

? Why do streams with trout have more algae?

enclosures, they would also cause cascading effects. The secondary carnivores would be predicted to keep populations of primary carnivores in check, which would lead to a profusion of herbivores and a scarcity of primary producers.

In an experiment similar to the one just described, enclosures were created in free-flowing streams in northern California. In these streams, the principal primary carnivores were damselfly larvae (termed *nymphs*). Fish that preyed on the nymphs and on other primary carnivores were added to some enclosures but not others. In the enclosures with fish, the numbers of damselfly nymphs were reduced, leading to higher numbers of their prey, including herbivorous insects, which led in turn to a decreased biomass of algae (figure 58.15).

Trophic cascades in large-scale ecosystems are not as easy to verify by experiment as ones in stream enclosures, and the workings of such cascades are not thoroughly known. Nonetheless, certain cascades in large-scale ecosystems are recognized by most ecologists. One of the most dramatic involves sea otters, sea urchins, and kelp forests along the West Coast of North America (figure 58.16).

The otters eat the urchins, and the urchins eat young kelps, inhibiting the development of kelp forests. When the otters are abundant, the kelp forests are well developed because there are relatively few urchins in the system. But when the otters are sparse, the urchins are numerous and impair development of the kelp forests. Orcas (killer whales) also enter the picture because in recent years they have started to prey intensively on the otters, driving otter populations down.

Human removal of carnivores produces top-down effects

Human activities are believed to have had top-down effects in a number of ecosystems, usually by the removal of top-level

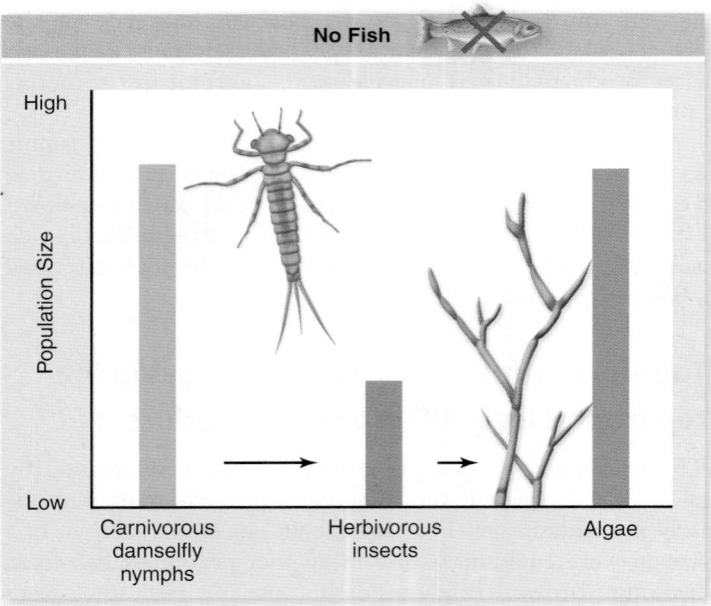
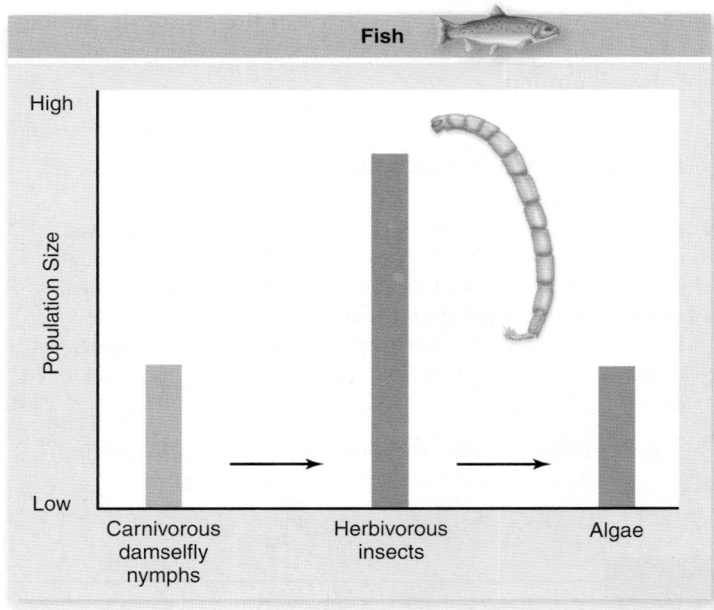

Figure 58.15 Top-down effects demonstrated by an experiment in a four-level trophic cascade. Stream enclosures with large, carnivorous fish *(on right)* have fewer primary carnivores, such as damselfly nymphs, more herbivorous insects (exemplified here by the number of chironomids, a type of aquatic insect), and lower levels of algae.

Inquiry question

? What might be the effect if snakes that prey on fish were added to the enclosures?

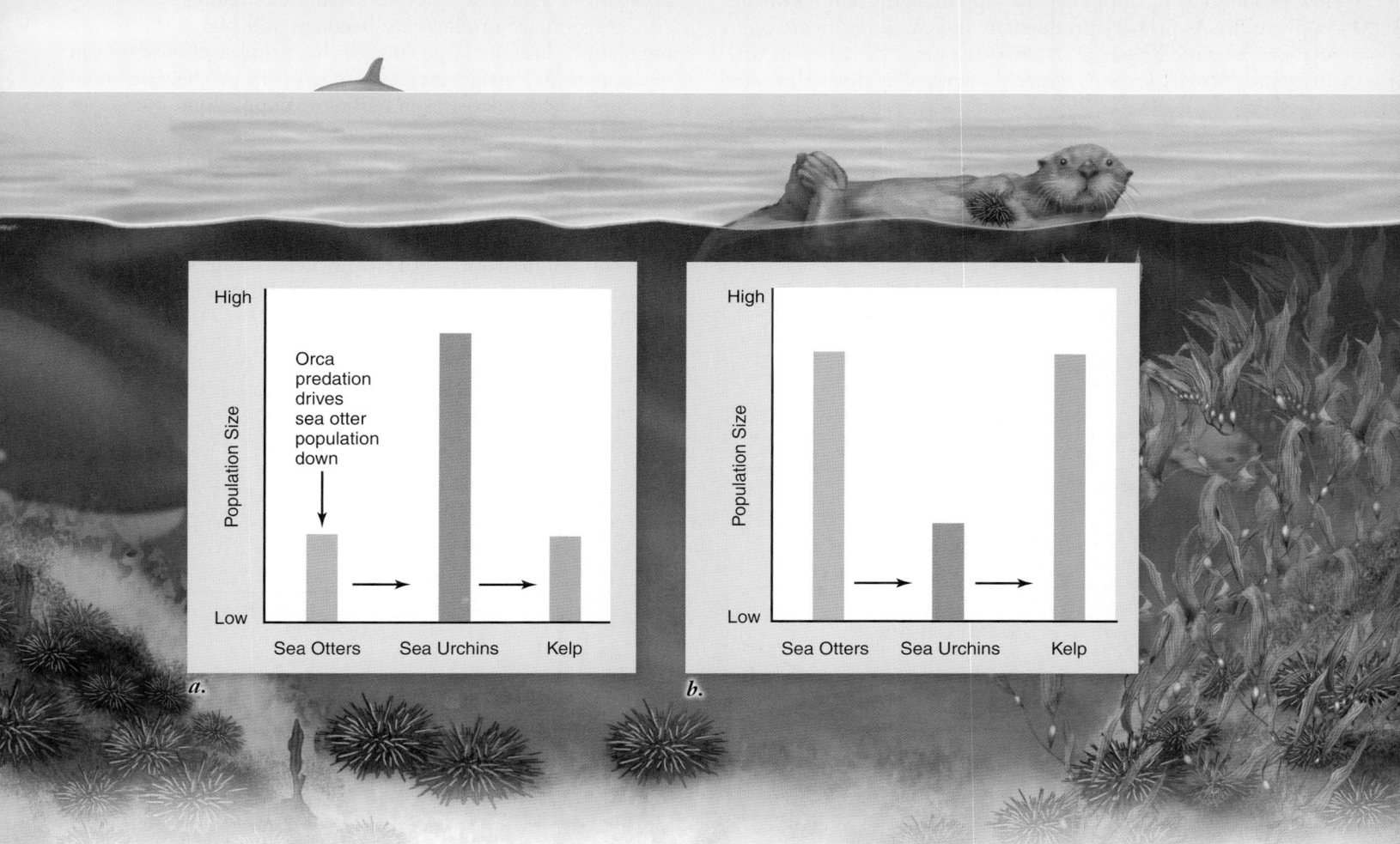

Figure 58.16 A trophic cascade in a large-scale ecosystem. Along the West Coast of North America, the sea otter/sea urchin/kelp system exists in two states: In the state shown in panel *a,* low populations of sea otters permit high populations of urchins, which suppress kelp populations; in the state shown in panel *b,* high populations of otters keep urchins in check, permitting profuse kelp growth. According to a recent hypothesis, a switch of orcas to preying on otters rather than other mammals is leading the ecosystem today to be mostly in the state represented on the left.

carnivores. The great naturalist Aldo Leopold posited such effects long before the trophic cascade hypothesis had been scientifically articulated when he wrote in *Sand County Almanac:*

"I have lived to see state after state extirpate its wolves. I have watched the face of many a new wolfless mountain, and seen the south-facing slopes wrinkle with a maze of new deer trails. I have seen every edible bush and seedling browsed, first to anemic desuetude, and then to death. I have seen every edible tree defoliated to the height of a saddle horn."

Many similar examples exist in which the removal of predators has led to cascading effects on lower trophic levels. Large predators such as jaguars and mountain lions are absent on Barro Colorado Island, a hilltop turned into an island by the construction of the Panama Canal at the beginning of the last century. As a result, smaller predators whose populations are normally held in check—including monkeys, peccaries (a relative of the pig), coatimundis, and armadillos—have become extraordinarily abundant. These animals eat almost anything they

find. Ground-nesting birds are particularly vulnerable, and many species have declined; at least 15 bird species have vanished from the island entirely.

Similarly, in the world's oceans, large predatory fish such as billfish and cod have been reduced by overfishing to an average of 10% of their previous numbers in virtually all parts of the world's oceans. In some regions, the prey of cod—such as certain shrimp and crabs—have become many times more abundant than they were before, and further cascading effects are evident at still lower trophic levels.

Bottom-up effects occur when changes to primary producers affect higher trophic levels

In predicting bottom-up effects, ecologists must take account of the life histories of the organisms present. A model of bottom-up effects thought to apply to a number of types of ecosystems is diagrammed in figure 58.17.

According to the model, when primary productivity is low, producer populations cannot support significant herbivore populations. As primary productivity increases, herbivore populations become a feature of the ecosystem. Increases in primary productivity are then entirely devoured by the herbivores, the populations of which increase in size while keeping the populations of primary producers from increasing.

As primary productivity becomes still higher, herbivore populations become large enough that primary carnivores can be supported. Further increases in primary productivity then does not lead to increases in herbivore populations, but rather to increases in carnivore populations.

Experimental evidence for the bottom-up effects predicted by the model was provided by a study conducted in enclosures on a river (figure 58.18). The enclosures excluded large fish (secondary carnivores). A roof was placed above each enclosure. Some roofs were clear, whereas others were tinted to various degrees, so that the enclosures differed in the amount of sunlight entering them.

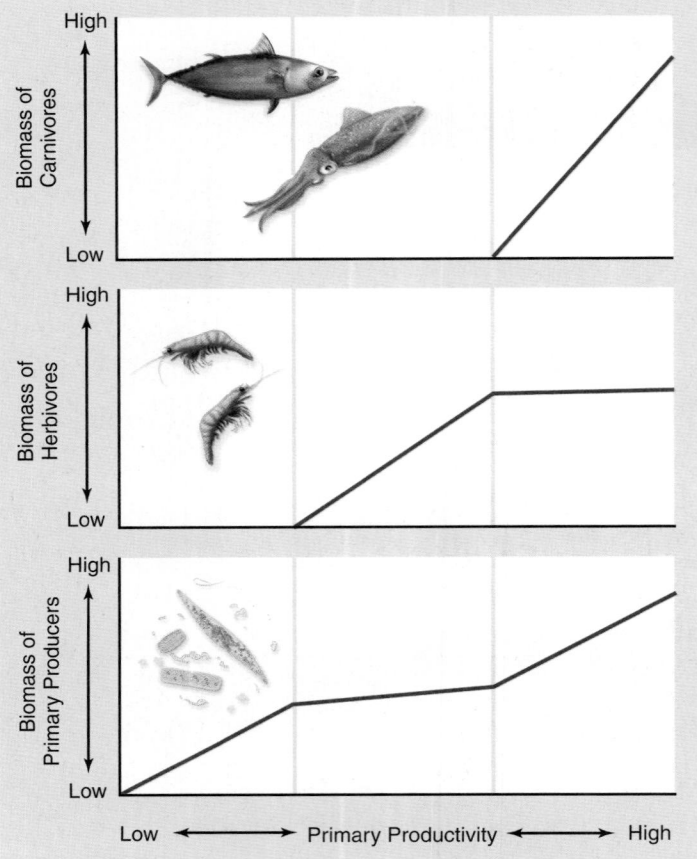

Figure 58.17 A model of bottom-up effects. At low levels of primary productivity, herbivore populations cannot obtain enough food to be maintained; without herbivory, the standing crop biomass of the primary producers such as these diatoms increases as their productivity increases. Above some threshold, increases in primary productivity lead to increases in herbivore populations and herbivore biomass; the biomass of the primary producers then does not increase as primary productivity increases because the increasing productivity is cropped by the herbivores. Above another threshold, populations of primary carnivores can be sustained. As primary productivity increases above this threshold, the carnivores consume the increasing productivity of the herbivores, so the biomass of the herbivore populations remains relatively constant while the biomass of the carnivore populations increases. The biomass of the primary producers is no longer constrained by increases in the herbivore populations and thus also increases with increasing primary productivity. A key to understanding the model is to maintain a distinction between the concepts of productivity and standing crop biomass.

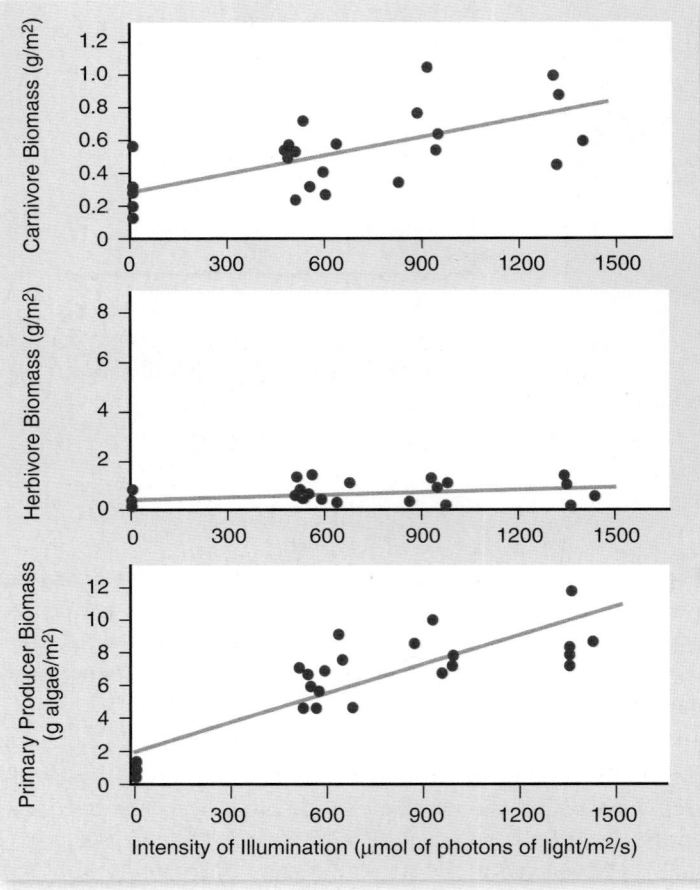

Figure 58.18 An experimental study of bottom-up effects in a river ecosystem. This system, studied on the Eel River in northern California, exhibited the patterns modeled by the red graphs of figure 58.17. Increases in the intensity of illumination led to increases in primary productivity and in the biomass of the primary producers. The biomass of the carnivore populations also increased. However, herbivore biomass did not increase much with increasing primary productivity because increases in herbivore productivity were consumed by the carnivores.

Inquiry question

? How is it possible for the biomass of the primary producers to stay relatively constant as the primary productivity increases?

Inquiry question

? Why is the amount of light an important determinant of carnivore biomass?

The primary productivity was highest in the enclosures with clear roofs and lowest in the ones with darkly tinted roofs. As primary productivity increased in parallel with illumination, the biomass of the primary producers increased, as did the biomass of the carnivores. However, the biomass of the trophic level sandwiched in between, the herbivores, did not increase much, as predicted by the model in figure 58.17 (see red graph lines).

Learning Outcomes Review 58.3

Populations of species at different trophic levels affect one another, and these effects can propagate through the levels. Top-down effects, termed trophic cascades, are observed when changes in carnivore populations affect lower trophic levels. Bottom-up effects are observed when changes in primary productivity affect the higher trophic levels.

■ *Could top-down and bottom-up effects occur simultaneously?*

58.4 Biodiversity and Ecosystem Stability

Learning Outcomes

1. *Define ecosystem stability.*
2. *Describe the effects of species richness on ecosystem function.*
3. *Name possible factors that contribute to species richness in the tropics.*

In the preceding chapter, we discussed *species richness*—the number of species present in a community. Ecologists have long debated the consequences of differences in species richness between communities. One theory is that species-rich communities are more stable—that is, more constant in composition and better able to resist disturbance. This hypothesis has been elegantly studied by David Tilman and colleagues at the University of Minnesota's Cedar Creek Natural History Area.

Species richness may increase stability: The Cedar Creek studies

Workers monitored 207 small rectangular plots of land (8–16 m²) for 11 years (figure 58.19a). In each plot, they counted the number of prairie plant species and measured the total amount of plant biomass (that is, the mass of all plants on the plot). Over the course of the study, plant species richness was related to community stability—plots with more species showed less year-to-year variation in biomass. Moreover, in two drought years, the decline in biomass was negatively related to species richness—that is, plots with more species were less affected by drought.

These findings were subsequently confirmed by an experiment in which plots were seeded with different numbers of

SCIENTIFIC THINKING

Question: *Does species richness affect the invasibility of a community?*

Hypothesis: *The rate of successful invasion will be lower in communities with greater richness.*

Experiment: *Add seeds from the same number of non-native plants to experimental plots that differ in the number of plant species.*

a.

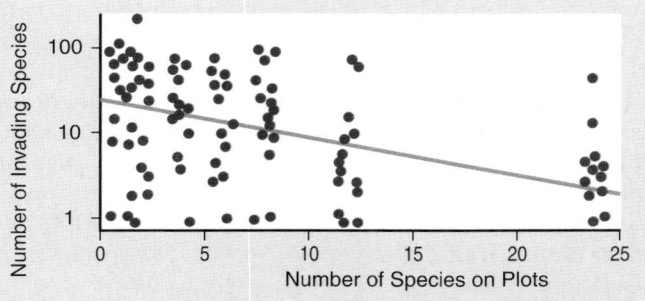
b.

Result: *Although the number of successful invasive species is highly variable, more species-rich plots on average are invaded by fewer species.*

Interpretation: *What might explain why so much variation exists in the number of successful invading species in communities with the same species richness?*

Figure 58.19 Effect of species richness on ecosystem stability. *a.* One of the Cedar Creek experimental plots. *b.* Community stability can be assessed by looking at the effect of species richness on community invasibility. Each dot represents data from one experimental plot in the Cedar Creek experimental fields. Plots with more species are harder to invade by nonnative species.

Inquiry question

? **How could you devise an experiment on invasibility that didn't rely on species from surrounding areas?**

species. Again, more species-rich plots had greater year-to-year stability in biomass over a 10-year period.

In a related experiment, when seeds of other plant species were added to different plots, the ability of these species to become established was negatively related to species richness (figure 58.19b). More diverse communities, in other words, are more resistant to invasion by new species, which is another measure of community stability.

Species richness may also affect other ecosystem processes. Tilman and colleagues monitored 147 experimental plots that varied in number of species to estimate how much growth was occurring and how much nitrogen the growing plants were taking up from the soil. They found that the more species a plot had, the greater the nitrogen uptake and total amount of biomass produced. In his study, increased biodiversity clearly appeared to lead to greater productivity.

Laboratory studies on artificial ecosystems have provided similar results. In one elaborate study, ecosystems covering 1 m² were constructed in growth chambers that controlled temperature, light levels, air currents, and atmospheric gas concentrations. A variety of plants, insects, and other animals were introduced to construct ecosystems composed of 9, 15, or 31 species, with the lower diversity treatments containing a subset of the species in the higher diversity enclosures. As with Tilman's experiments, the amount of biomass produced was related to species richness, as was the amount of carbon dioxide consumed, another measure of the productivity of the ecosystem.

Tilman's conclusion that healthy ecosystems depend on diversity is not accepted by all ecologists, however. Critics question the validity and relevance of these biodiversity studies, arguing that the more species are added to a plot, the greater the probability that one species will be highly productive. To show that high productivity results from high species richness per se, rather than from the presence of particular highly productive species, experimental plots have to exhibit "overyielding"; in other words, plot productivity has to be greater than that of the single most productive species grown in isolation.

Although this point is still debated, recent work at Cedar Creek and elsewhere has provided evidence of overyielding, supporting the claim that species richness of communities enhances community productivity and stability.

Species richness is influenced by ecosystem characteristics

A number of factors are known or hypothesized to affect species richness in a community. We discussed some in chapter 57, such as loss of keystone species and moderate physical disturbance. Here we discuss three more: primary productivity, habitat heterogeneity, and climatic factors.

Primary productivity

Ecosystems differ substantially in primary productivity (see figure 58.11). Some evidence indicates that species richness is related to primary productivity, but the relationship between them is not linear. In a number of cases, for example, ecosystems with intermediate levels of productivity tend to have the greatest number of species (figure 58.20a).

Why this is so is debated. One possibility is that levels of productivity are linked with numbers of consumers. Applying this concept to plant species richness, the argument is that at low productivity, there are few herbivores, and superior competitors among the plants are able to eliminate most other plant species. In contrast, at high productivity so many herbivores are present that only the plant species most resistant to grazing survive, reducing species diversity. As a result, the greatest numbers of plant species coexist at intermediate levels of productivity and herbivory.

Habitat heterogeneity

Spatially heterogeneous abiotic environments are those that consist of many habitat types—such as soil types, for example. These heterogeneous environments can be expected to accommodate more species of plants than spatially homogeneous environments. What's more, the species richness of animals can be expected to reflect the species richness of plants present. An

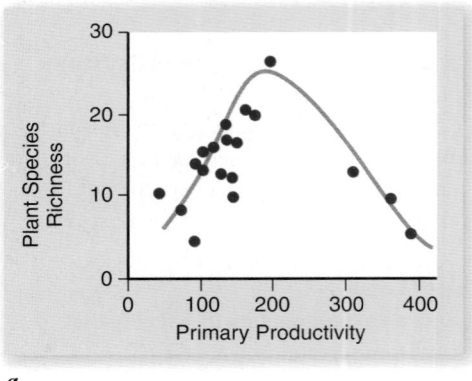
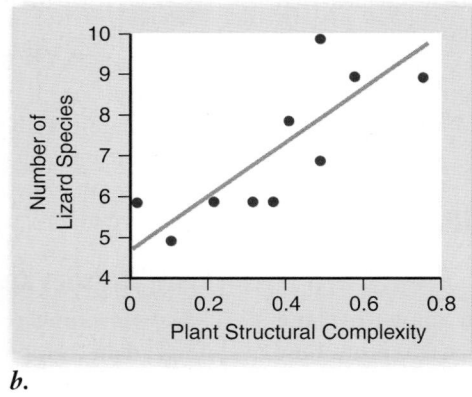
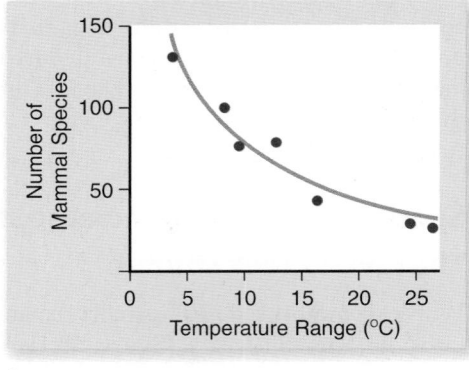

a.   b.   c.

Figure 58.20 Factors that affect species richness. *a. Productivity:* In plant communities of mountainous areas of South Africa, species richness of plants peaks at intermediate levels of productivity (biomass). *b. Spatial heterogeneity:* The species richness of desert lizards is positively correlated with the structural complexity of the plant cover in desert sites in the American Southwest. *c. Climate:* The species richness of mammals is inversely correlated with monthly mean temperature range along the West Coast of North America.

Inquiry question

? (a.) Why is species richness greatest at intermediate levels of productivity? (b.) Why do more structurally complex areas have more species? (c.) Why do areas with less variation in temperature have more species?

example of this latter effect is seen in figure 58.20b: The number of lizard species at various sites in the American Southwest mirrors the local structural diversity of the plants.

Climatic factors

The role of climatic factors is more difficult to predict. On the one hand, more species might be expected to coexist in a seasonal environment than in a constant one because a changing climate may favor different species at different times of the year. On the other hand, stable environments are able to support specialized species that would be unable to survive where conditions fluctuate. The number of mammal species at locations along the West Coast of North America is inversely correlated with the amount of local temperature variation—the wider the variation, the fewer mammalian species—supporting the latter line of argument (figure 58.20c).

Tropical regions have the highest diversity, although reasons are unclear

Since before Darwin, biologists have recognized that more different kinds of animals and plants inhabit the tropics than the temperate regions. For many types of organisms, there is a steady increase in species richness from the arctic to the tropics. Called a **species diversity cline,** this biogeographic gradient in numbers of species correlated with latitude has been reported for plants and animals, including birds (figure 58.21), mammals, and reptiles.

For the better part of a century, ecologists have puzzled over the species diversity cline from the arctic to the tropics. The difficulty has not been in forming a reasonable hypothesis of why more species exist in the tropics, but rather in sorting through these many reasonable hypotheses. Here, we consider five of the most commonly discussed suggestions.

Evolutionary age of tropical regions

Scientists have frequently proposed that the tropics have more species than temperate regions because the tropics have existed over long, uninterrupted periods of evolutionary time, whereas temperate regions have been subject to repeated glaciations. The greater age of tropical communities would have allowed complex population interactions to coevolve within them, fostering a greater variety of plants and animals.

Recent work suggests that the long-term stability of tropical communities has been greatly exaggerated, however. An examination of pollen within undisturbed soil cores reveals that during glaciations, the tropical forests contracted to a few small refuges surrounded by grassland. This suggests that the tropics have not had a continuous record of species richness over long periods of evolutionary time.

Increased productivity

A second often-advanced hypothesis is that the tropics contain more species because this part of the Earth receives more solar radiation than do temperate regions. The argument is that more solar energy, coupled to a year-round growing season, greatly increases the overall photosynthetic activity of tropical plants.

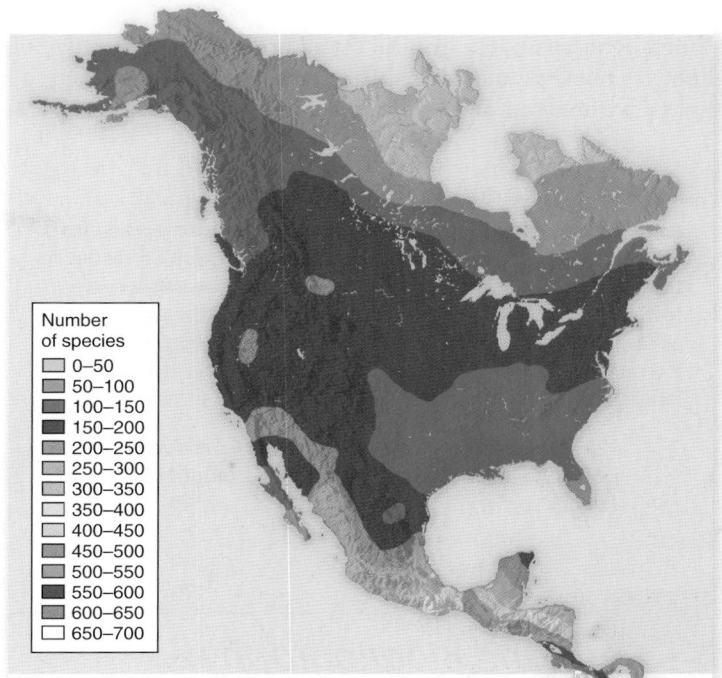

Figure 58.21 A latitudinal cline in species richness. Among North and Central American birds, a marked increase in the number of species occurs moving toward the tropics. Fewer than 100 species are found at arctic latitudes, but more than 600 species live in southern Central America.

If we visualize the tropical forest's total resources as a pie, and its species niches as slices of the pie, we can see that a larger pie accommodates more slices. But as noted earlier, many field studies have indicated that species richness is highest at intermediate levels of productivity. Accordingly, increasing productivity would be expected to lead to lower, not higher, species richness.

Stability/constancy of conditions

Seasonal variation, though it does exist in the tropics, is generally substantially less than in temperate areas. This reduced seasonality might encourage specialization, with niches subdivided to partition resources and so avoid competition. The expected result would be a larger number of more specialized species in the tropics, which is what we see. Many field tests of this hypothesis have been carried out, and almost all support it, reporting larger numbers of narrower niches in tropical communities than in temperate areas.

Predation

Many reports indicate that predation may be more intense in the tropics. In theory, more intense predation could reduce the importance of competition, permitting greater niche overlap and thus promoting greater species richness.

Spatial heterogeneity

As noted earlier, spatial heterogeneity promotes species richness. Tropical forests, by virtue of their complexity, create a variety of microhabitats and so may foster larger numbers of species. Perhaps the long vertical column of vegetation through which light passes in a tropical forest produces a wide range of light frequencies and intensities, creating a greater variety of light environments and so promoting species diversity.

Learning Outcomes Review 58.4

An ecosystem is stable if it remains relatively constant in composition and is able to resist disturbance. Experimental field studies support the conclusion that species-rich communities are better able to resist invasion by new species, as well as have increased biomass production at the primary level, although not all ecologists agree with these conclusions. Species richness is greatest in the tropics, and the reasons may include habitat variation, increased sunlight, and long-term climate and seasonal stability.

■ **What might be the effects on primary productivity if air pollution decreased the amount of sunlight reaching Earth's surface?**

58.5 Island Biogeography

Learning Outcomes

1. **Describe the species–area relationship.**
2. **Explain how area and isolation affect rates of colonization and extinction.**

One of the most reliable patterns in ecology is the observation that larger islands contain more species than do smaller islands. In 1967, Robert MacArthur of Princeton University and Edward O. Wilson of Harvard University proposed that this species–area relationship was a result of the effect of geographic area and isolation on the likelihood of species extinction and colonization.

The equilibrium model proposes that extinction and colonization reach a balance point

MacArthur and Wilson reasoned that species are constantly being dispersed to islands, so islands have a tendency to accumulate more and more species. At the same time that new species are added, however, other species are lost by extinction. As the number of species on an initially empty island increases, the rate of colonization must decrease as the pool of potential colonizing species not already present on the island becomes depleted. At the same time, the rate of extinction should increase—the more species on an island, the greater the likelihood that any given species will perish.

As a result, at some point, the number of extinctions and colonizations should be equal, and the number of species should then remain constant. Every island of a given size, then, has a characteristic equilibrium number of species that tends to persist through time (the intersection point in figure 58.22a)—though the species composition will change as some species become extinct and new species colonize.

MacArthur and Wilson's equilibrium model proposes that island species richness is a dynamic equilibrium between colonization and extinction. Both island size and distance from the mainland would affect colonization and extinction. We would expect smaller islands to have higher rates of extinction because their population sizes would, on average, be smaller. Also, we would expect fewer colonizers to reach islands that lie farther from the mainland. Thus, small islands far from the mainland would have the fewest species; large islands near the mainland would have the most (figure 58.22b).

The predictions of this simple model bear out well in field data. Asian Pacific bird species (figure 58.22c) exhibit a positive correlation of species richness with island size, but a negative correlation of species richness with distance from the source of colonists.

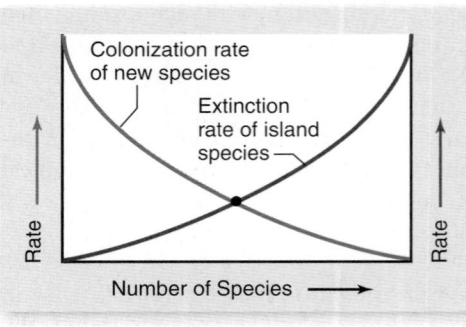

a.

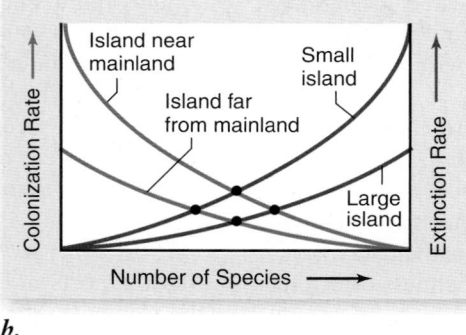

b.

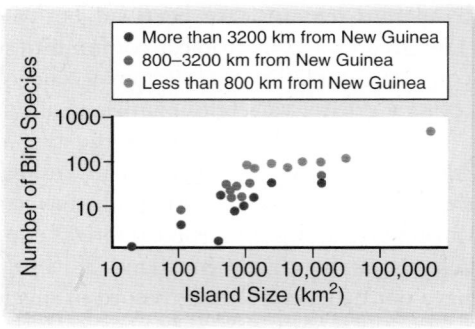

c.

Figure 58.22 The equilibrium model of island biogeography. *a.* Island species richness reaches an equilibrium (black dot) when the colonization rate of new species equals the extinction rate of species on the island. *b.* The equilibrium shifts depending on the rate of colonization, the size of an island, and its distance to sources of colonists. Species richness is positively correlated with island size and inversely correlated with distance from the mainland. Smaller islands have higher extinction rates, shifting the equilibrium point to the left. Similarly, more distant islands have lower colonization rates, again shifting the equilibrium point leftward. *c.* The effect of distance from a larger island, which can be the source of colonizing species, is readily apparent. More distant islands have fewer Asian Pacific bird species than do nearer islands of the same size.

The equilibrium model is still being tested

Wilson and Dan Simberloff, then a graduate student, performed initial studies in the mid-1960s on small mangrove islands in the Florida keys. These islands were censused, cleared of animal life by fumigation, and then allowed to recolonize, with censuses being performed at regular intervals. These and other such field studies have tended to support the equilibrium model.

Long-term experimental field studies, however, are suggesting that the situation is more complicated than MacArthur and Wilson envisioned. Their model predicts a high level of species turnover as some species perish and others arrive. But studies of island birds and spiders indicate that very little turnover occurs from year to year. Those species that do come and go, moreover, comprise a subset of species that never attain high populations. A substantial proportion of the species appear to maintain high populations and rarely go extinct.

These studies have been going on for a relatively short period of time. It is possible that over periods of centuries, the equilibrium model is a good description of what determines island species richness.

Learning Outcomes Review 58.5

The species–area relationship is an observation that an island of larger area contains more species. Species richness on islands appears to be a dynamic equilibrium between colonization and extinction. Distance from a mainland also affects the rates of colonization and extinction, and therefore fewer species would be found on small, isolated islands far from a mainland.

■ *Under what circumstances would a smaller island be expected to have more species than a larger island?*

Chapter Review

58.1 Biogeochemical Cycles

The atomic constituents of matter cycle within ecosystems.
The atoms of chemical elements move through ecosystems in biogeochemical cycles.

Carbon, the basis of organic compounds, cycles through most ecosystems.
The carbon cycle usually involves carbon dioxide, which is fixed through photosynthesis and released by respiration. Carbon is also present as bicarbonate ions and as methane. Burning of fossil fuels has created an imbalance in the carbon cycle (see figure 58.1).

The availability of water is fundamental to terrestrial ecosystems.
Water enters the atmosphere via evaporation and transpiration and returns to the Earth's surface as precipitation. It is broken down during photosynthesis and also produced during cellular respiration. Much of the Earth's water, including the groundwater in aquifers, is polluted, and human activities alter the water supply of ecosystems (see figure 58.2).

The nitrogen cycle depends on nitrogen fixation by microbes.
Nitrogen is usually the element in shortest supply even though N_2 makes up 78% of the atmosphere. Nitrogen must be converted into usable forms by nitrogen-fixing microorganisms. Human use of nitrates in fertilizers has doubled the available nitrogen (see figure 58.4).

Phosphorus cycles through terrestrial and aquatic ecosystems, but not the atmosphere.
Phosphorus, another limiting nutrient, is released by weathering of rocks; it flows into the oceans where it is deposited in deep-sea sediments. Humans also use phosphates as fertilizers (see figure 58.5).

Limiting nutrients in ecosystems are those in short supply relative to need.
The cycle of a limiting nutrient, such as nitrogen, determines the rate at which the nutrient is made available for use.

Biogeochemical cycling in a forest ecosystem has been studied experimentally.
Ongoing experiments indicate that severe disturbance of an ecosystem results in mineral depletion and runoff of water.

58.2 The Flow of Energy in Ecosystems

Energy can neither be created nor destroyed, but changes form.
Energy exists in forms such as light, stored chemical-bond energy, motion, and heat. In any conversion, some energy is lost.

Living organisms can use many forms of energy, but not heat.
The Second Law of Thermodynamics states that whenever organisms use chemical-bond or light energy, some of it is inevitably converted to heat and cannot be retrieved.

Energy flows through trophic levels of ecosystems.
Organic compounds are synthesized by autotrophs and are utilized by both autotrophs and heterotrophs. As energy passes from organism to organism, each level is termed a trophic level, and the sequence through progressive trophic levels is called a food chain (see figure 58.8).

The base trophic level includes the primary producers; herbivores that consume primary producers are the next level. They in turn are eaten by primarily carnivores, which may be consumed by secondary carnivores. Detritivores feed on waste and the remains of dead organisms.

Only about 1% of the solar energy that impinges on the Earth is captured by photosynthesis. As energy moves through each trophic level, very little (approximately 10%) remains from the preceding trophic level (see figure 58.10).

The number of trophic levels is limited by energy availability.
The exponential decline of energy between trophic levels limits the length of food chains and the numbers of top carnivores that can be supported.

Ecological pyramids illustrate the relationship of trophic levels.

Ecological pyramids based on energy flow, biomass, or numbers of organisms are usually upright. Inverted pyramids of biomass or numbers are possible if at least one trophic level has a greater biomass or more organisms than the level below it (see figure 58.13).

58.3 Trophic-Level Interactions

Top-down effects occur when changes in the top trophic level affect primary producers.

A trophic cascade, or top-down effect, occurs when a change exerted at an upper trophic level affects a lower level (see figure 58.15).

Human removal of carnivores produces top-down effects.

Removal of carnivores causes an increase in the abundance of species in lower trophic levels, such as an increase in deer populations when wolves or other predators are destroyed.

Bottom-up effects occur when changes to primary producers affect higher trophic levels.

An increase of producers may lead to the appearance or increase of herbivores; however, further increase in producers may then lead to increase in carnivores, without a comparable increase in herbivores (see figure 58.17).

58.4 Biodiversity and Ecosystem Stability

Species richness may increase stability: The Cedar Creek studies.

The Cedar Creek studies indicate that higher species richness results in less year-to-year variation in biomass and in greater resistance to drought and invasion by non-native species.

Species richness is influenced by ecosystem characteristics.

Primary production, habitat heterogeneity, and climatic factors all affect the number of species in an ecosystem (see figure 58.20).

Tropical regions have the highest diversity, although the reasons are unclear.

The higher diversity of tropical regions may reflect long evolutionary time, higher productivity from increased sunlight, less seasonal variation, greater predation that reduces competition, or spatial heterogeneity (see figure 58.21).

58.5 Island Biogeography

The species–area relationship reflects that larger islands contain more species than do smaller ones.

The equilibrium model proposes that extinction and colonization reach a balance point (see figure 58.22).

Smaller islands have fewer species because of higher rates of extinction. Islands near a mainland have more species than distant islands because of higher rates of colonization. An equilibrium is reached when the extinction rate balances the colonization rate.

The equilibrium model is still being tested.

Long-term studies are needed to clarify all the factors involved.

Review Questions

UNDERSTAND

1. Which of the statements about groundwater is *not* accurate?
   a. In the United States, groundwater provides 50% of the population with drinking water.
   b. Groundwaters are being depleted faster than they can be recharged.
   c. Groundwaters are becoming increasingly polluted.
   d. Removal of pollutants from groundwaters is easily achieved.

2. Photosynthetic organisms
   a. fix carbon dioxide.
   b. release carbon dioxide.
   c. fix oxygen.
   d. (a) and (b)
   e. (a) and (c)

3. Some bacteria have the ability to "fix" nitrogen. This means
   a. they convert ammonia into nitrites and nitrates.
   b. they convert atmospheric nitrogen gas into biologically useful forms of nitrogen.
   c. they break down nitrogen-rich compounds and release ammonium ions.
   d. they convert nitrate into nitrogen gas.

4. Which of the following statements about the phosphorus cycle is correct?
   a. Phosphorus is fixed by plants and algae.
   b. Most phosphorus released from rocks is carried to the oceans by rivers.
   c. Animals cannot get their phosphorus from eating plants and algae.
   d. Fertilizer use has not affected the global phosphorus budget.

5. As a general rule, how much energy is lost in the transmission of energy from one trophic level to the one immediately above it?
   a. 1%   c. 90%
   b. 10%   d. 50%

6. Inverted ecological pyramids of real systems usually involve
   a. energy flow.
   b. biomass.
   c. energy flow and biomass.
   d. None of the above

7. Bottom-up effects on trophic structure result from
   a. a limitation of energy flowing to the next higher trophic level.
   b. actions of top predators on lower trophic levels.

c. climatic disruptions on top consumers.
d. stability of detritivores in ecosystems.

8. Species diversity
   a. increases with latitude as you move away from the equator to the arctic.
   b. decreases with latitude as you move away from the equator to the arctic.
   c. stays the same as you move away from the equator to the arctic.
   d. increases with latitude as you move north of the equator and decreases with latitude as you move south of the equator.

9. The equilibrium model of island biogeography suggests all of the following *except*
   a. larger islands have more species than smaller islands.
   b. the species richness of an island is determined by colonization and extinction.
   c. smaller islands have lower rates of extinction.
   d. islands closer to the mainland will have higher colonization rates.

APPLY

1. Nitrogen is often a limiting nutrient in many ecosystems because
   a. there is much less nitrogen in the atmosphere than carbon.
   b. elemental nitrogen is very rapidly used by most organisms.
   c. nitrogen availability is being reduced by pollution due to fertilizer use.
   d. most organisms cannot use nitrogen in its elemental form.

2. Based on results from studies at Hubbard Brook Experimental Forest, what would be the predicted effect of clearing trees from a watershed?
   a. Increased loss of water and nutrients from a watershed
   b. Decreased loss of water and nutrients from a watershed
   c. Increased availability of phosphorus
   d. Increased availability of nitrate

3. According to the trophic cascade hypothesis, the removal of carnivores from an ecosystem may result in
   a. a decline in the number of herbivores and a decline in the amount of vegetation.
   b. a decline in the number of herbivores and an increase in the amount of vegetation.
   c. an increase in the number of herbivores and an increase in the amount of vegetation.
   d. an increase in the number of herbivores and a decrease in the amount of vegetation.

4. At Cedar Creek Natural History Area, experimental plots showed reduced numbers of invaders as species diversity of plots increased
   a. suggesting that low species diversity increases stability of ecosystems.
   b. suggesting that ecosystem stability is a function of primary productivity only.
   c. consistent with the theory that intermediate disturbance results in the highest stability.
   d. None of the above

SYNTHESIZE

1. Given that ectotherms do not utilize a large fraction of ingested food energy to maintain a high and constant body temperature (generate heat), how would you expect the food chains of systems dominated by ectothermic herbivores and carnivores to compare with systems dominated by endothermic herbivores and carnivores?

2. Given that, in general, energy input is greatest at the bottom trophic level (primary producers) and decreases with increasing transfers across trophic levels, how is it possible for many lakes to show much greater standing biomass in herbivorous zooplankton than in the phytoplankton they consume?

3. Ecologists often worry about the potential effects of the loss of species (e.g., due to pollution, habitat degradation, or other human-induced factors) on an ecosystem for reasons other than just the direct loss of the species. Using figure 58.17 explain why.

4. Explain several detailed ways in which increasing plant structural complexity could lead to greater species richness of lizards (figure 58.20*b*). Could any of these ideas be tested? How?

ONLINE RESOURCE

www.ravenbiology.com

Understand, Apply, and Synthesize—enhance your study with animations that bring concepts to life and practice tests to assess your understanding. Your instructor may also recommend the interactive eBook, individualized learning tools, and more.

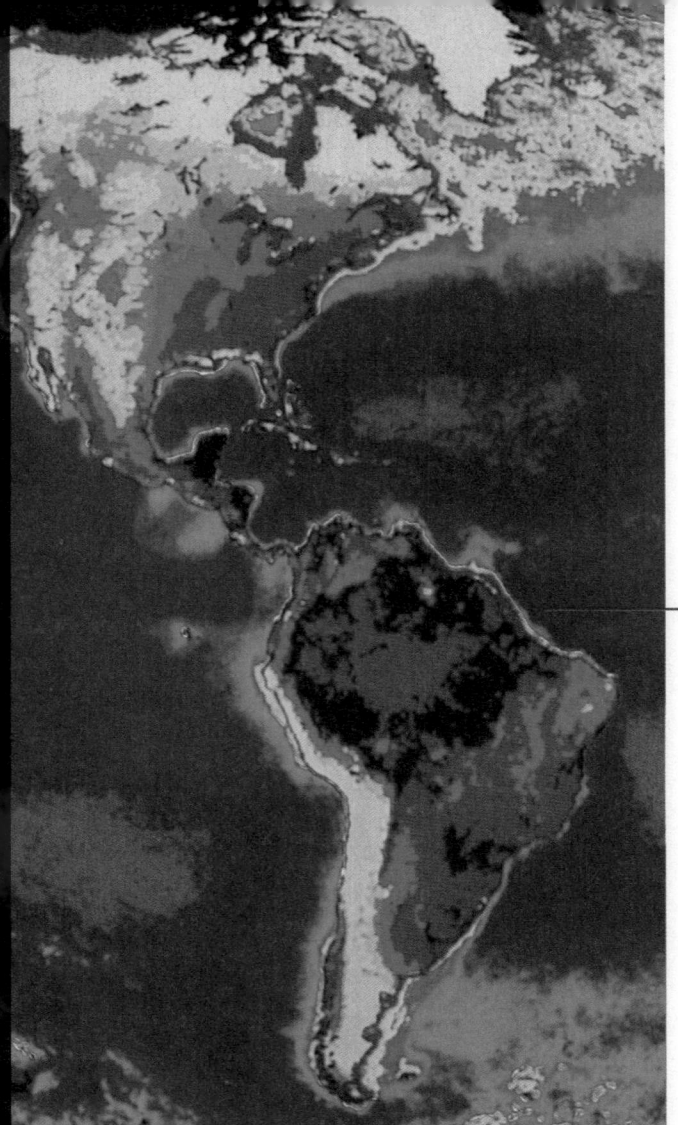

Chapter 59

The Biosphere

Chapter Outline

59.1 Ecosystem Effects of Sun, Wind, and Water

59.2 Earth's Biomes

59.3 Freshwater Habitats

59.4 Marine Habitats

59.5 Human Impacts on the Biosphere: Pollution and Resource Depletion

59.6 Human Impacts on the Biosphere: Climate Change

Introduction

The biosphere includes all living communities on Earth, from the profusion of life in the tropical rain forests to the planktonic communities in the world's oceans. In a very general sense, the distribution of life on Earth reflects variations in the world's abiotic environments, such as the variations in temperature and availability of water from one terrestrial environment to another. The figure on this page is a satellite image of the Americas, based on data collected over 8 years. The colors are keyed to the relative abundance of chlorophyll, an indicator of the richness of biological communities. Green and dark green areas on land are areas with high primary productivity (such as thriving forests), whereas yellow areas include the deserts of the Americas and the tundra of the far north, which have lower productivity.

59.1 Ecosystem Effects of Sun, Wind, and Water

Learning Outcomes

1. *Describe changes in wind and current direction with latitude.*
2. *Explain the Coriolis effect.*
3. *Describe how temperature changes with altitude and latitude.*

The great global patterns of life on Earth are heavily influenced by (1) the amount of solar radiation that reaches different parts of the Earth and seasonal variations in that radiation; and (2) the patterns of global atmospheric circulation and the resulting patterns of oceanic circulation. Local characteristics, such as soil types and the altitude of the land, interact with the global patterns in sunlight, winds, and water currents to determine the conditions under which life exists and thus the distributions of ecosystems.

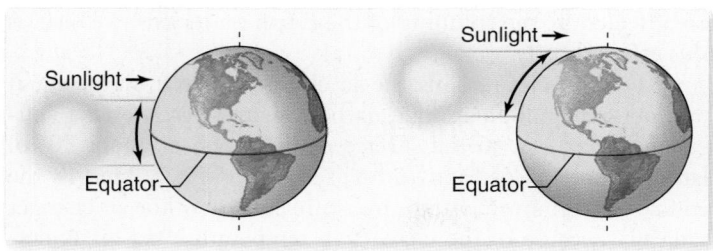

a.

Figure 59.1 Relationships between the Earth and the Sun are critical in determining the nature and distribution of life on Earth. *a.* A beam of solar energy striking the Earth in the middle latitudes of the northern hemisphere (or the southern) spreads over a wider area of the Earth's surface than an equivalent beam striking the Earth at the equator. *b.* The fact that the Earth orbits the Sun each year has a profound effect on climate. In the northern and southern hemispheres, temperature changes in an annual cycle because the Earth's axis is not perpendicular to its orbital plane and, consequently, each hemisphere tilts toward the Sun in some months but away from the Sun in others.

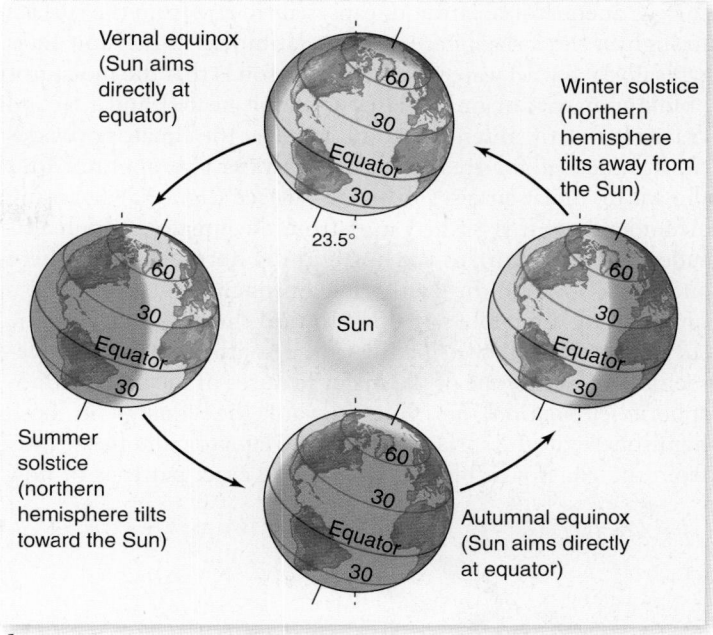

b.

Solar energy and the Earth's rotation affect atmospheric circulation

The Earth receives energy from the Sun at a high rate in the form of electromagnetic radiation at visible and near-visible wavelengths. Each square meter of the upper atmosphere receives about 1400 joules per second (J/sec), which is equivalent to the output of fourteen 100-watt (W) lightbulbs.

As the solar radiant energy passes through the atmosphere, its intensity and wavelength composition are modified. About half of the energy is absorbed within the atmosphere, and half reaches the Earth's surface. The gases in the atmosphere absorb some wavelengths strongly while allowing other wavelengths to pass freely through. As a result, the wavelength composition of the solar energy that reaches the Earth's surface is different from that emitted by the Sun. For example, the band of ultraviolet wavelengths known as UV-B is strongly absorbed by ozone (O_3) in the atmosphere, and thus this wavelength is greatly reduced in the solar energy that reaches the Earth's surface.

How solar radiation affects climate

Some parts of the Earth's surface receive more energy from the Sun than others. These differences have a great effect on climate.

A major reason for differences in solar radiation from place to place is the fact that Earth is a sphere, or nearly so (figure 59.1*a*). The tropics are particularly warm because the Sun's rays arrive almost perpendicular to the surface of the Earth in regions near the equator. Closer to the poles, the angle at which the Sun's rays strike, called the *angle of incidence*, spreads the solar energy out over more of the Earth's surface, providing less energy per unit of surface area. As figure 59.2 shows, the highest annual mean temperatures occur near the equator (0° latitude).

The Earth's annual orbit around the Sun and its daily rotation on its own axis are also important in determining patterns of

solar radiation and their effects on climate (figure 59.1*b*). The axis of rotation of the Earth is not perpendicular to the plane in which the earth orbits the Sun. Because the axis is tilted by approximately 23.5°, a progression of seasons occurs on all parts of the Earth, especially at latitudes far from the equator. The northern hemisphere, for example, tilts toward the Sun during some months but away during others, giving rise to summer and winter.

Global circulation patterns in the atmosphere

Hot air tends to rise relative to cooler air because the motion of molecules in the air increases as temperature increases, making it less dense. Accordingly, the intense solar heating of the Earth's

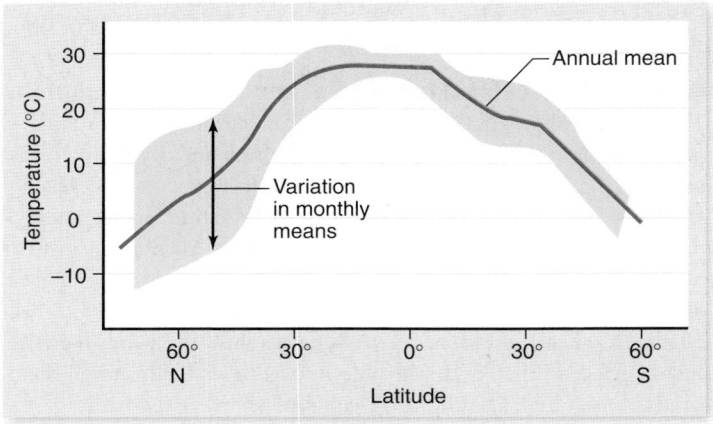

Figure 59.2 Annual mean temperature varies with latitude. The red line represents the annual mean temperature at various latitudes, ranging from near the North Pole at the left to near Antarctica at the right; the equator is at 0° latitude. At each latitude, the upper edge of the blue zone is the highest mean monthly temperature observed in all the months of the year, and the lower edge is the lowest mean monthly temperature.

surface at equatorial latitudes causes air to rise from the surface to high in the atmosphere at these latitudes. This rising air is typically rich with water vapor; one reason is that the moisture-holding capacity of air increases when it is heated, and a second reason is that the intense solar radiation at the equator provides the heat needed for great quantities of water to evaporate. After the warm, moist air rises from the surface (figure 59.3), rising air underneath it is pushed away from the equator at high altitudes (above 10 km), to the north in the northern hemisphere and to the south in the southern hemisphere. To take the place of the rising air, cooler air flows toward the equator along the surface from both the north and the south. These air movements give rise to one of the major features of the global atmospheric circulation: air flows toward the equator in both hemispheres at the surface, rises at the equator, and flows away from the equator at high altitudes. The exact patterns of flow

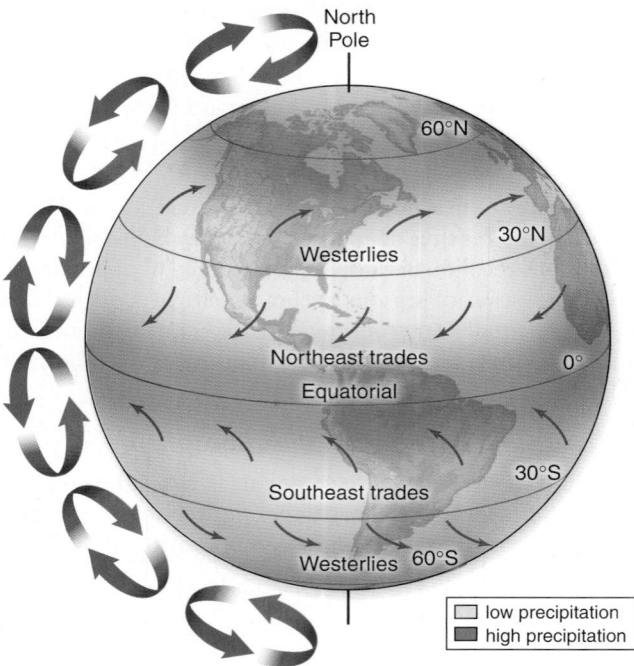

Figure 59.3 Global patterns of atmospheric circulation. The diagram shows the patterns of air circulation that prevail on average over weeks and months of time (on any one day the patterns might be dramatically different from these average patterns). Rising air that is cooled creates bands of relatively high precipitation near the equator and at latitudes near 60°N and 60°S. Air that has lost most of its moisture at high altitudes tends to descend to the surface of the Earth at latitudes near 30°N and 30°S, creating bands of relatively low precipitation. The red arrows show the winds blowing at the surface of the Earth; the blue arrows show the direction the winds blow at high altitude. The winds travel in curved paths relative to the Earth's surface because the Earth is rotating on its axis under them (the Coriolis effect). A terminological problem to recognize is that the formal names given to winds refer to the directions from which they come, rather than the directions toward which they go; thus, the winds between 30° and 60° are called Westerlies because they come out of the west. Unfortunately, oceanographers use the opposite approach, naming water currents for the directions in which they go.

are affected by the spinning of the Earth on its axis; we discuss this effect shortly.

For complex reasons, the air circulating up from the equator and away at high altitudes in both hemispheres tends to circulate back down to the surface of the Earth at about 30° of latitude, both north and south (see figure 59.3). During the course of this movement, the moisture content of the air changes radically because of the changes in temperature the air undergoes. Cooling dramatically decreases air's ability to hold water vapor. Consequently, much of the water vapor in the air rising from the equator condenses to form clouds and rain as the air moves upward. This rain falls in the latitudes near the equator, latitudes that experience the greatest precipitation on Earth.

By the time the air starts to descend back to the Earth's surface at latitudes near 30°, it is cold and thus has lost most of its water vapor. Although the air rewarms as it descends, it does not gain much water vapor on the way down. Many of the greatest deserts occur at latitudes near 30° because of the steady descent of dry air to the surface at those latitudes. The Sahara Desert is the most dramatic example.

The air that descends at latitudes near 30° flows only partly toward the equator after reaching the surface of the Earth. Some of it flows toward the poles, helping to give rise in each hemisphere to winds that blow over the Earth's surface from 30° toward 60° latitude. At latitudes near 60° air tends to rise from the surface toward high altitudes.

? Inquiry question

Why is it hotter at latitudes near 0°?

The Coriolis effect

If Earth did not rotate on its axis, global air movements would follow the simple patterns already described. Air currents—the winds—move across a rotating surface, however. Because the solid Earth rotates under the winds, the winds move in curved paths across the surface, rather than straight paths. The curvature of the paths of the winds due to Earth's rotation is termed the **Coriolis effect,** after the 19th-century French mathematician, Gaspard-Gustave Coriolis, who described it.

If you were standing on the North Pole, the Earth would appear to be rotating counterclockwise on its axis, but if you were at the South Pole, the Earth would appear to be rotating clockwise. This property of a rotating sphere, that its direction of rotation is opposite when viewed from its two poles, explains why the direction of the Coriolis effect is opposite in the two hemispheres. In the northern hemisphere, winds always curve to the right of their direction of motion; in the southern hemisphere, they always curve to the left.

The reason for these wind patterns is that the circumference of a sphere, the Earth, changes with latitude. It is zero at the poles and 38,000 km at the equator. Thus, land surface speed changes from about 0 to 1500 km per hour going from the poles to the equator. Air descending at 30° north latitude may be going roughly the same speed as the land surface below it. As it moves toward the equator, however, it is moving more slowly than the surface below it, so it is deflected to its right in the northern hemisphere and to its left in the southern hemisphere. In other words, in both the northern and southern hemispheres, the winds blow westward as well as toward the equator. The result (see figure 59.3) is that winds on both sides of the equator—called the Trade Winds—blow out of the east and toward the west.

Conversely, air masses moving north from 30° are moving more rapidly than underlying land surfaces and thus are deflected again to their right, which in this case is eastward. Similarly, in the southern hemisphere, air masses between 30° and 60° are deflected eastward, to the left. In both hemispheres, therefore, winds between 30° and 60° blow out of the west and toward the east; these winds are called Westerlies.

Global currents are largely driven by winds

The major ocean currents are driven by the winds at the surface of the Earth, which means that indirectly the currents are driven by solar energy. The radiant input of heat from the Sun sets the atmosphere in motion as already described, and then the winds set the ocean in motion.

In the north Atlantic Ocean (figure 59.4), the global winds follow this pattern: Surface winds tend to blow out of the east and toward the west near the equator, but out of the west and toward the east at midlatitudes (between 30° and 60°). Consequently, surface waters of the north Atlantic Ocean tend to move in a giant closed curve—called a **gyre**—flowing from North America toward Europe at midlatitudes, then re-

turning from Europe and Africa to North America at latitudes near the equator.

Water currents are affected by the Coriolis effect. Thus, the Coriolis effect contributes to this clockwise closed-curve motion. Water flowing across the Atlantic toward Europe at midlatitudes tends to curve to the right and enters the flow from east to west near the equator. This latter flow also tends to curve to its right and enters the flow from west to east at midlatitudes. In the south Atlantic Ocean, the same processes occur in a sort of mirror image, and similar clockwise and counterclockwise gyres occur in the north and south Pacific Ocean as well.

Regional and local differences affect terrestrial ecosystems

The environmental conditions at a particular place are affected by regional and local effects of solar radiation, air circulation, and water circulation, not just the global patterns of these processes. In this section we look at just a few examples of regional and local effects, focusing on terrestrial systems. These include rain shadows, monsoon winds, elevation, and presence of microclimate factors.

Rain shadows

Deserts on land sometimes occur because mountain ranges intercept moisture-laden winds from the sea. When air flowing

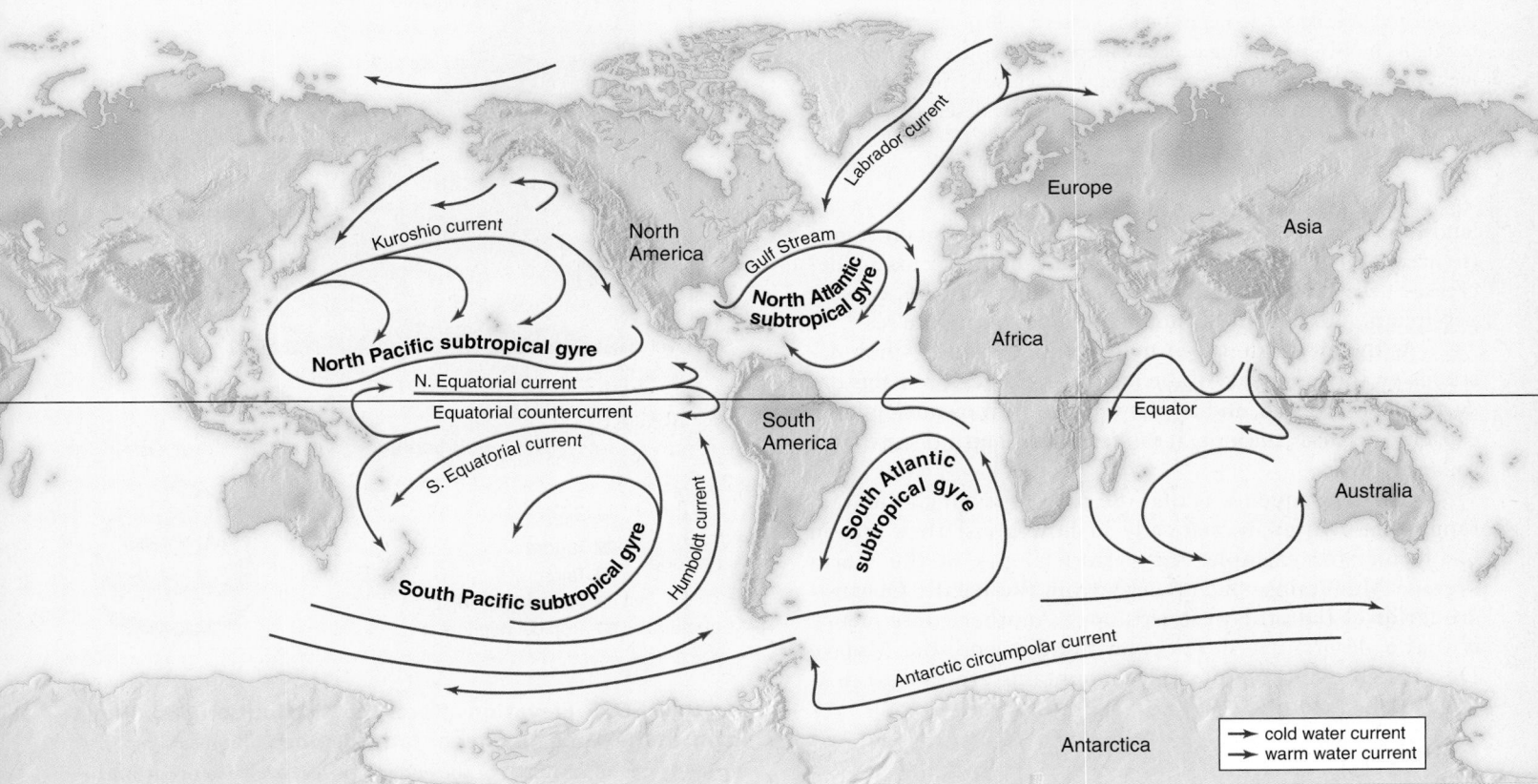

Figure 59.4 Ocean circulation. In the centers of several of the great ocean basins, surface water moves in great closed-curve patterns called gyres. These water movements affect biological productivity in the oceans and sometimes profoundly affect the climate on adjacent landmasses, as when the Gulf Stream brings warm water to the region of the British Isles.

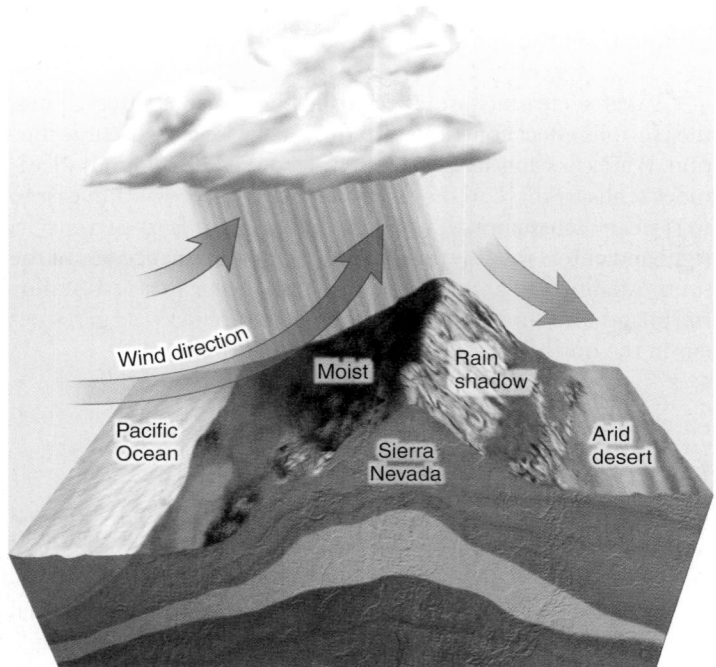

Figure 59.5 The rain shadow effect exemplified in California. Moisture-laden winds from the Pacific Ocean rise and are cooled when they encounter the Sierra Nevada Mountains. As the moisture-holding capacity of the air decreases at colder, higher altitudes, precipitation occurs, making the seaward-facing slopes of the mountains moist; tall forests occur on those slopes, including forests that contain the famous giant sequoias (*Sequoiadendron giganteum*). As the air descends on the eastern side of the mountain range, its moisture-holding capacity increases again, and the air picks up moisture from its surroundings. As a result, the eastern slopes of the mountains are arid, and rain shadow deserts sometimes occur.

landward from the oceans encounters a mountain range (figure 59.5), the air rises, and its moisture-holding capacity decreases because it becomes cooler at higher altitude, causing precipitation to fall on the mountain slopes facing the sea.

As the air—stripped of much of its moisture—then descends on the other side of the mountain range, it remains dry even as it is warmed, and as it is warmed its moisture-holding capacity increases, meaning it can readily take up moisture from soils and plants.

One consequence is that the two slopes of a mountain range often differ dramatically in how moist they are; in California, for example, the eastern slopes of the Sierra Nevada Mountains—facing away from the Pacific Ocean—are far drier than the western slopes. Another consequence is that a desert may develop on the dry side, the Mojave Desert being an example. The mountains are said to produce a rain shadow.

Monsoons

The continent of Asia is so huge that heating and cooling of its surface during the passage of the seasons causes massive regional shifts in wind patterns. During summer, the surface of the Asian landmass heats up more than the surrounding oceans,

but during winter the landmass cools more than the oceans. The consequence is that winds tend to blow off the water into the interior of the Asian continent in summer, particularly in the region of the Indian Ocean and western tropical Pacific Ocean. These winds reverse to flow off the continent out over the oceans in winter. These seasonally shifting winds are called the monsoons. They affect rainfall patterns, and their duration and strength can spell the difference between food sufficiency and starvation for hundreds of millions of people in the region each year.

Elevation

Another significant regional pattern is that in mountainous regions, temperature and other conditions change with elevation. At any given latitude, air temperature falls about 6°C for every 1000-m increase in elevation. The ecological consequences of the change of temperature with elevation are similar to those of the change of temperature with latitude (figure 59.6).

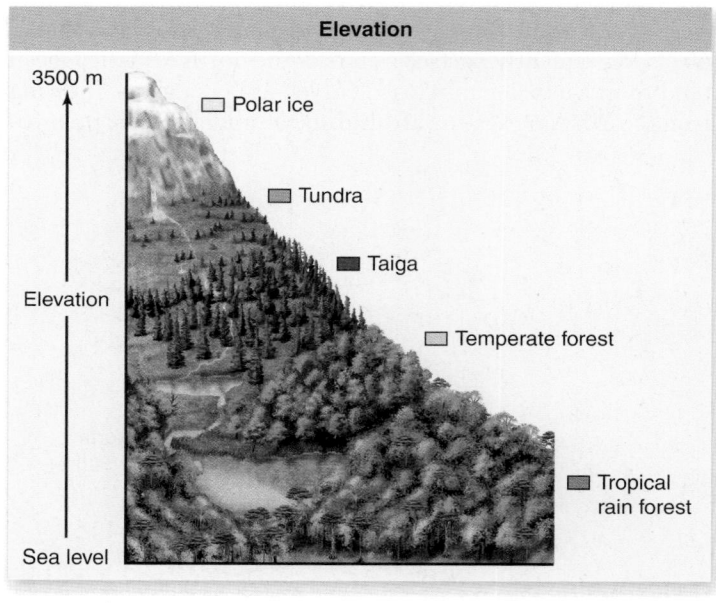

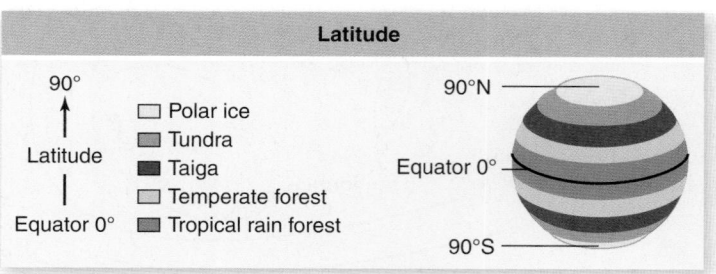

Figure 59.6 Elevation affects the distribution of biomes in much the same manner as latitude does. Biomes that normally occur far north of the equator at sea level also occur in the tropics at high mountain elevations. Thus, on a tall mountain in the tropics, one might see a sequence of biomes like the one illustrated above. In North America, a 1000-m increase in elevation results in a temperature drop equal to that of an 880-km increase in latitude.

Microclimates

Conditions also vary in significant ways on very small spatial scales. For example, in a forest, a bird sitting in an open patch may experience intense solar radiation, a high air temperature, and a low humidity, even while a mouse hiding under a log 10 feet away may experience shade, a cool temperature, and air saturated with water vapor. Such highly localized sets of climatic conditions are called microclimates.

In some cases, species avoid competing by adapting to use different microclimates. Sympatric salamanders, for example, may be specialized for the different levels of moisture found in different parts of the habitat.

Learning Outcomes Review 59.1

More intense solar heating of some global regions relative to others sets up global patterns of atmospheric circulation, which in turn cause global patterns of water circulation in the oceans. The Coriolis effect is caused by the Earth's spin beneath the moving air masses of the atmosphere. These patterns—plus seasonal changes—strongly affect the conditions that exist for living organisms in different parts of the world. In general, temperature declines as altitude or latitude increases.

■ *How would global air movement patterns be different if the Earth turned in the opposite direction?*

59.2 Earth's Biomes

Learning Outcomes

1. Define biome.
2. Explain the primary factors that determine which type of biome is found in a particular place.

Biomes are major types of ecosystems on land. Each biome has a characteristic appearance and is distributed over wide areas of land defined largely by sets of regional climatic conditions. Biomes are named according to their vegetational structures, but they also include the animals that are present.

As you might imagine from the broad definition given for biomes, there are a number of ways to classify terrestrial ecosystems into biomes. Here we recognize eight principal biomes: (1) tropical rain forest, (2) savanna, (3) desert, (4) temperate grassland, (5) temperate deciduous forest, (6) temperate evergreen forest, (7) taiga, (8) tundra.

Six additional biomes recognized by some ecologists are: polar ice, mountain zone, chaparral, warm moist evergreen forest, tropical monsoon forest, and semidesert. Other ecologists lump these six with the eight major ones. Figure 59.7 shows the distributions of all 14 biomes.

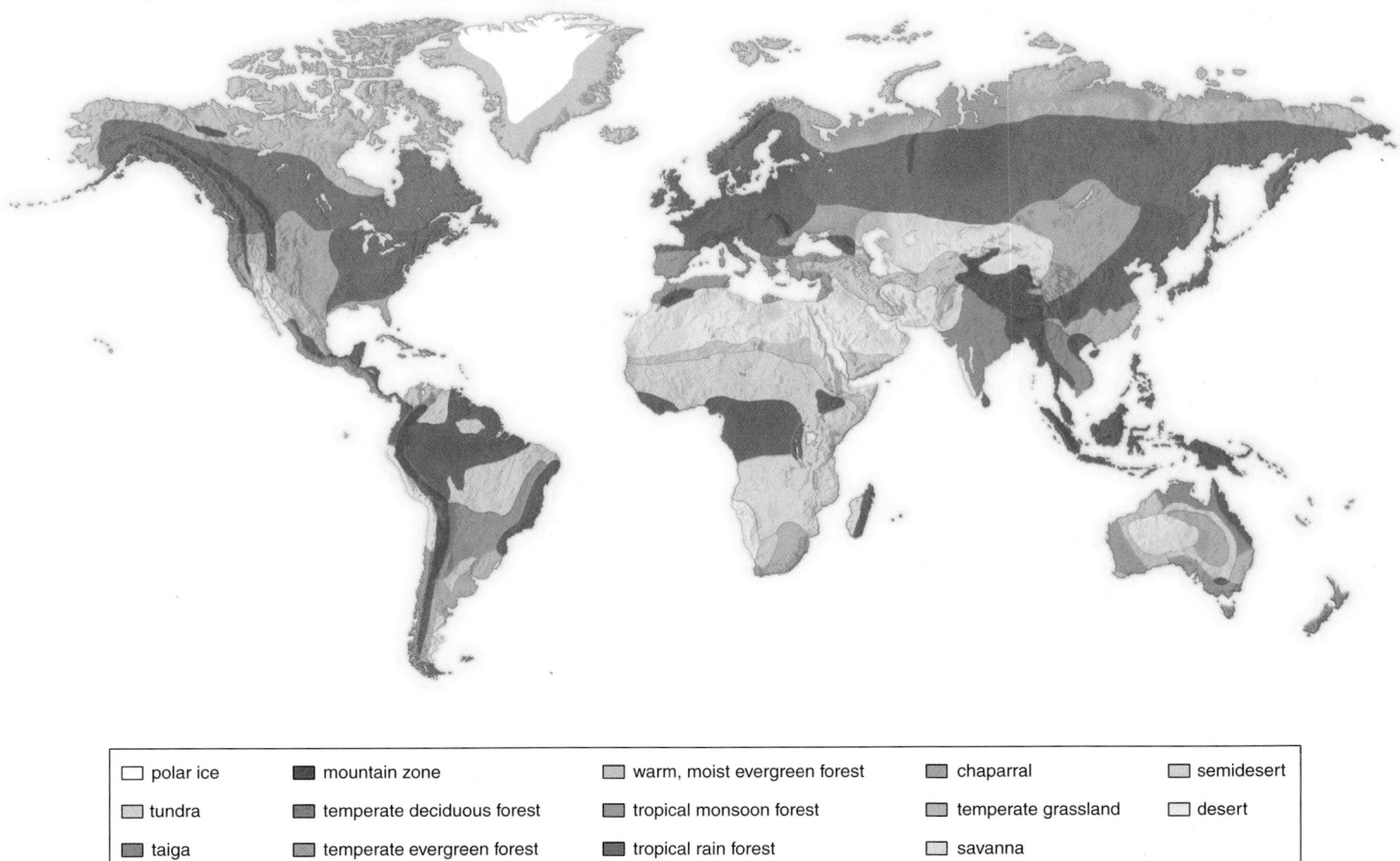

☐ polar ice	■ mountain zone	☐ warm, moist evergreen forest	☐ chaparral	☐ semidesert
☐ tundra	■ temperate deciduous forest	☐ tropical monsoon forest	■ temperate grassland	☐ desert
■ taiga	■ temperate evergreen forest	■ tropical rain forest	☐ savanna	

Figure 59.7 The distributions of biomes. Each biome is similar in vegetational structure and appearance wherever it occurs.

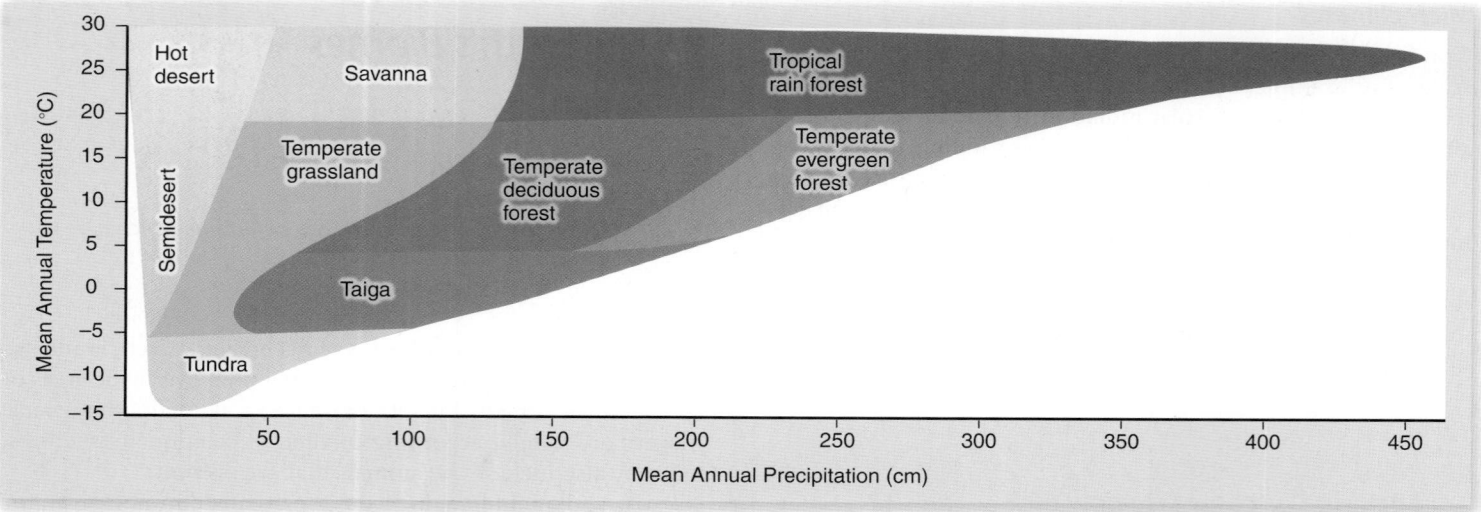

Figure 59.8 Predictors of biome distribution. Temperature and precipitation are quite useful predictors of biome distribution, although other factors sometimes also play critical roles.

Biomes are defined by their characteristic vegetational structures and associated climatic conditions, rather than by the presence of particular plant species. Two regions assigned to the same biome thus may differ in the species that dominate the landscape. Tropical rain forests around the world, for example, are all composed of tall, lushly vegetated trees, but the tree species that dominate a South American tropical rain forest are different from those in an Indonesian one. The similarity between such forests results from convergent evolution (see chapter 21).

Temperature and moisture often determine biomes

In determining which biomes are found where, two key environmental factors are temperature and moisture. As seen in figure 59.8, if you know the mean annual temperature and mean annual precipitation in a terrestrial region, you often can predict the biome that dominates. Temperature and moisture affect ecosystems in a number of ways. One reason they are so influential is that primary productivity is strongly correlated with them, as described in the preceding chapter (figure 59.9).

Different places that are similar in mean annual temperature and precipitation sometimes support different biomes, indicating that temperature and moisture are not the only factors that can be important. Soil structure and mineral composition (see chapter 39) are among the other factors that can be influential. The biome that is present may also depend on whether the conditions of temperature and precipitation are strongly seasonal or relatively constant.

Tropical rain forests are highly productive equatorial systems

Tropical rain forests, which typically require 140 to 450 cm of rain per year, are the richest ecosystems on land (figure 59.10).

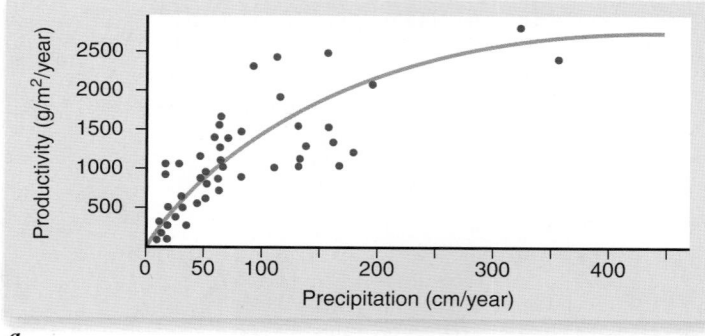

a.

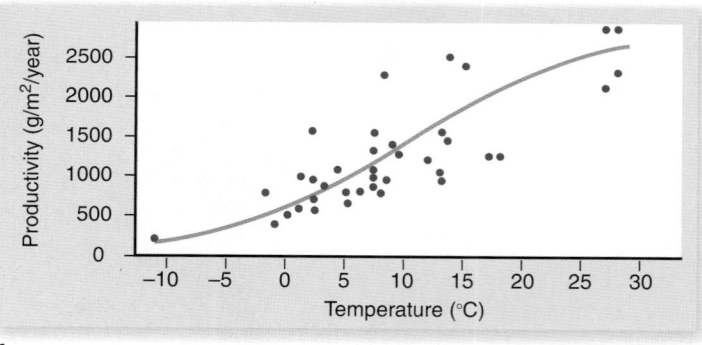

b.

Figure 59.9 The correlations of primary productivity with precipitation and temperature. The net primary productivity of ecosystems at 52 locations around the globe correlates significantly with (*a*) mean annual precipitation and (*b*) mean annual temperature.

? Inquiry question

Why might you expect primary productivity to increase with increasing precipitation and temperature?

Figure 59.10
Tropical rainforest.

They are very productive because they enjoy the advantages of both high temperature and high precipitation (see figure 59.9). They also exhibit very high biodiversity, being home to at least half of all the species of terrestrial plants and animals—over 2 million species! In a single square mile of Brazilian rain forest, there can be 1200 species of butterflies—twice the number found in all of North America. Tropical rain forests recycle nutrients rapidly, so their soils often lack great reservoirs of nutrients.

Savannas are tropical grasslands with seasonal rainfall

The **savannas** are tropical or subtropical grasslands, often dotted with widely spaced trees or shrubs. On a global scale, savannas often occur as transition ecosystems between tropical rain forests and deserts; they are characteristic of warm places where annual rainfall (50–125 cm) is too little to support rain forest, but not so little as to produce desert conditions.

Rainfall is often highly seasonal in savannas. The Serengeti ecosystem in East Africa is probably the world's most famous example of the savanna biome. In most of the Serengeti, no rain falls for many months of the year, but during other months rain is abundant. The huge herds of grazing animals in the ecosystem respond to the seasonality of the rain; a number of species migrate away from permanently flowing rivers only during the months when rain falls.

Deserts are regions with little rainfall

Deserts are dry places where rain is both sparse (annual rainfall often less than 25–40 cm) and unpredictable. The unpredictability means that plants and animals cannot depend on experi-

encing rain even once each year. As mentioned earlier, many of the largest deserts occur at latitudes near 30°N and 30°S because of global air circulation patterns (see figure 59.3). Other deserts result from rain shadows (see figure 59.5).

Vegetation is sparse in deserts, and survival of both plants and animals depends on water conservation. Many desert organisms enter inactive stages during rainless periods. To avoid extreme temperatures, small desert vertebrates often live in deep, cool, and sometimes even somewhat moist burrows. Some emerge only at night. Among large desert animals, camels drink large quantities of water when it is available and then conserve it so well that they can survive for weeks without drinking. Oryxes (large, desert-dwelling antelopes) survive opportunistically on moisture in leaves or roots that they dig up, as well as drinking water when possible.

Temperate grasslands have rich soils

Halfway between the equator and the poles are temperate regions where rich temperate grasslands grow. These grasslands, also called **prairies,** once covered much of the interior of North America, and they were widespread in Eurasia and South America as well.

The roots of perennial grasses characteristically penetrate far into the soil, and grassland soils tend to be deep and fertile. Temperate grasslands are often highly productive when converted to agricultural use, and vast areas have been transformed in this way. In North America prior to this change in land use, huge herds of bison and pronghorn antelope inhabited the temperate grasslands, migrating seasonally as resources changed over the course of the year. Natural temperate grasslands are one of the biomes adapted to periodic fire and therefore need fires to prosper.

Temperate deciduous forests are adapted to seasonal change

Mild but seasonal climates (warm summers and cold winters), plus plentiful rains, promote the growth of temperate deciduous forests in the eastern United States, eastern Canada, and Eurasia (figure 59.11). A deciduous tree is one that drops its leaves in the winter. Deer, bears, beavers, and raccoons are familiar animals of these forests.

Temperate evergreen forests are coastal

Temperate evergreen forests occur along coastlines with temperate climates, such as in the northwest of the United States. The dominant vegetation includes trees, such as spruces, pines, and redwoods, that do not drop their leaves (thus, they are *ever green*).

Taiga is the northern forest where winters are harsh

Taiga and tundra (described next) differ from other biomes in that both stretch in great unbroken circles around the entire globe (see figure 58.7). The taiga consists of a great band of northern forest dominated by coniferous trees (spruce, hemlock, and fir) that retain their needle-like leaves all year long.

Figure 59.11 Temperate deciduous forest.

The taiga is one of the largest biomes on Earth. The winters where taiga occurs are severely long and cold, and most of the limited precipitation falls in the summer. Many large herbivores, including elk, moose, and deer, plus carnivores such as wolves, bears, lynx, and wolverines, are characteristic of the taiga.

Tundra is a largely frozen treeless area with a short growing season

In the far north, at latitudes above the taiga but south of the polar ice, few trees grow. The landscape that occurs in this band, called tundra, is open, windswept, and often boggy. This enormous biome covers one-fifth of the Earth's land surface. Little rain or snow falls. **Permafrost**—soil ice that persists throughout all seasons—usually exists within a meter of the ground surface.

What trees can be found are small and mostly confined to the margins of streams and lakes. Large grazing mammals, including musk-oxen and reindeer (caribou), and carnivores such as wolves, foxes, and lynx, live in the tundra. Populations of lemmings (a small rodent native to the Arctic) rise and fall dramatically, with important consequences for the animals that prey on them.

Learning Outcomes Review 59.2

Major types of ecosystems called biomes can be distinguished in different climatic regions on land. These biomes are much the same wherever they are found on the Earth. Annual mean temperature and precipitation are effective predictors of biome type; however, the range of seasonal variation and the soil characteristics of a region also come into play.

■ *Why do different biomes occur at different latitudes?*

59.3 *Freshwater Habitats*

Learning Outcomes

1. *Define photic zone.*
2. *Explain what causes spring and fall overturns in lakes.*
3. *Distinguish between eutrophic and oligotrophic lakes.*

Of the major habitats, fresh water covers by far the smallest percentage of the Earth's surface: Only 2%, compared with 27% for land and 71% for ocean. The formation of fresh water starts with the evaporation of water into the atmosphere, which removes most dissolved constituents, much like distillation does. When water falls back to the Earth's surface as rain or snow, it arrives in an almost pure state, although it may have picked up biologically significant dissolved or particulate matter from the atmosphere.

Freshwater wetlands—marshes, swamps, and bogs—represent intermediate habitats between the freshwater and terrestrial realms. Wetlands are highly productive (see figure 58.11).

They also play key additional roles, such as acting as water storage basins that moderate flooding.

Primary production in freshwater bodies is carried out by single-celled algae (phytoplankton) floating in the water, by algae growing as films on the bottom, and by rooted plants such as water lilies. In addition, a considerable amount of organic matter—such as dead leaves—enters some bodies of fresh water from plant communities growing on the land nearby.

Life in freshwater habitats depends on oxygen availability

The concentration of dissolved oxygen (O_2) is a major determinant of the properties of freshwater communities. Oxygen dissolves in water just like sugar or salt does. Fish and other aquatic organisms obtain the oxygen they need by taking it up from solution. The solubility of oxygen is therefore critically important.

In reality, oxygen is not very soluble in water. Consequently, even when fresh water is fully aerated and at equilibrium with the atmosphere, the amount of oxygen it contains per liter is only 5%, or less, of that in air. This means that, in terms of acquiring the oxygen they need, freshwater organisms have a far smaller margin of safety than air-breathing ones.

Oxygen is constantly added to and removed from any body of fresh water. Oxygen is added by photosynthesis and by aeration from the atmosphere, and it is removed by animals and other heterotrophs. If a lot of decaying organic matter is present in a body of water, the oxygen demand of the decay microbes can be high and affect other life forms. Under conditions in which the rate of oxygen removal from water exceeds the rate of addition, the concentration of dissolved oxygen can fall so low that many aquatic animals cannot survive in it.

Lake and pond habitats change with water depth

Bodies of relatively still fresh water are called lakes if large and ponds if small. Water absorbs light passing through it, and the intensity of sunlight available for photosynthesis decreases sharply with increasing depth. In deep lakes, only water relatively near the surface receives enough light for phytoplankton to exhibit a positive net primary productivity (figure 59.12). Those waters are described as the photic zone.

The photic zone

The thickness of the photic zone depends on how much particulate matter is in the water. Water that is relatively free of particulate matter and clear allows light to penetrate to a depth of 10 m at sufficient intensity to support phytoplankton. Water that is thick with surface algal cells or soil from erosion may not allow light to penetrate very far before its intensity becomes too diminished for algal growth.

The supply of dissolved oxygen to the deep waters of a lake can be a problem because all oxygen enters any aquatic system near its surface. In the still waters of a lake, mixing between the surface and deeper layers may not occur except occasionally. When photosynthesis produces oxygen, it adds it to the photic zone of the lake near the surface. Thermal stratifica-

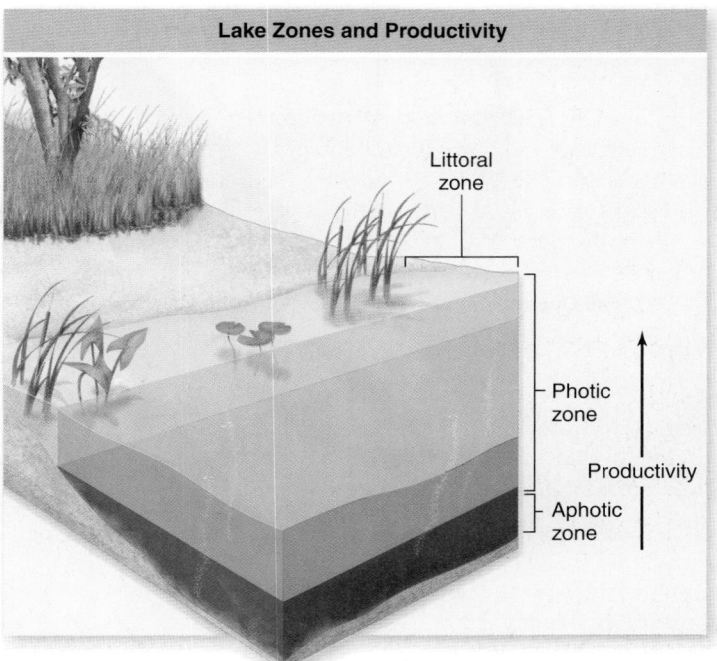

Figure 59.12 Light in a lake. The intensity of the sunlight available for photosynthesis decreases with depth in a lake. Consequently, only some of the upper waters—termed the photic zone—receive sufficient light for the net primary productivity of phytoplankton to be positive. The depth of the photic zone depends on how cloudy the water is. The shallows at the edge of a lake are called the littoral zone. They are well-illuminated to the bottom, so rooted plants and bottom algae can thrive there.

tion commonly affects how readily oxygen enters the deep waters from the surface waters.

Thermal stratification

Thermal stratification is characteristic of many lakes and large ponds. In summer, as shown at the bottom of figure 59.13, water warmed by the Sun forms a layer known as the *epilimnion* at the surface—because warm water is less dense than cold water and tends to float on top. Colder, denser water, called the *hypolimnion*, lies below. Between the warm and cold layers is a transitional layer, the thermocline. Although here we are focusing on fresh water, a similar thermal structuring of the water column occurs also in many parts of the ocean.

In a lake, thermal stratification tends to cut off the oxygen supply to the bottom waters; a consequence of the stratification is that the upper waters that receive oxygen do not mix with the bottom waters. The concentration of oxygen at the bottom may then gradually decline over time as the organisms living there use oxygen faster than it is replaced. If the rate of oxygen use is high, the bottom waters may run out of oxygen and become oxygen-free before summer is over. Oxygen-free conditions, if they occur, kill most (although not all) animals.

In autumn, the temperature of the upper waters in a stratified lake drops until it is about the same as the temperature of the deep waters. The densities of the two water layers become similar, and the tendency for them to stay apart is weakened.

Winter

0°
2°
4°
4°
4°
4°
4°

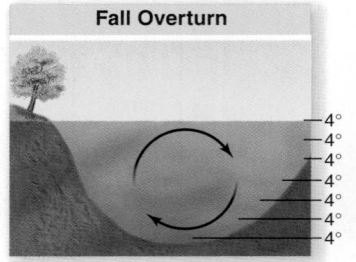

Fall Overturn

4°
4°
4°
4°
4°
4°
4°

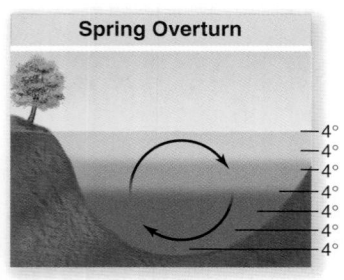

Spring Overturn

4°
4°
4°
4°
4°
4°
4°

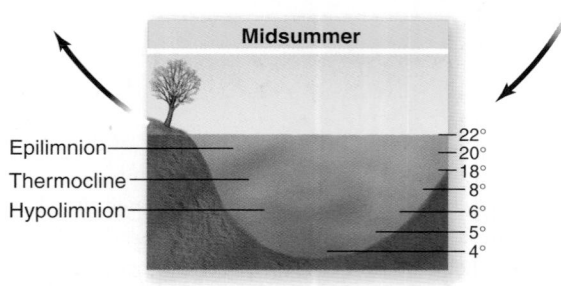

Midsummer

Epilimnion — 22°
20°
18°
Thermocline — 8°
6°
Hypolimnion — 5°
4°

Figure 59.13 **The annual cycle of thermal stratification in a temperate-zone lake.** During the summer (lower diagram), water warmed by the Sun (the epilimnion) floats on top of colder, denser water (the hypolimnion). The lake is also thermally stratified in winter (upper diagram) when water that is near freezing or frozen floats on top of water that is at 4°C (the temperature of greatest density for fresh water). Stratification is disrupted in the spring and fall overturns, when the lake is at an approximately uniform temperature and winds mix it from top to bottom.

Winds can then force the layers to mix, a phenomenon called the fall overturn (see figure 59.13). High oxygen concentrations are then restored in the bottom waters.

Chapter 2 discussed the unique properties of water. Fresh water is densest when its temperature is 4°C, and ice, at 0°, floats on top of this dense water. As a lake is cooled toward the freezing point with the onset of winter, the whole lake first reaches 4°C. Then, some water cools to an even lower temperature, and when it does, it becomes less dense and rises to the top. Further cooling of this surface water causes it to freeze into a layer of ice covering the lake. In spring, the ice melts, the surface water warms up, and again winds are able to mix the whole lake—the spring overturn.

Because temperature changes less over the course of the year in the tropics, many lakes there do not experience turnover. As a result, tropical lakes can have a permanent thermocline with depletion of oxygen near the bottom.

Lakes differ in oxygen and nutrient content

Bodies of fresh water that are low in algal nutrients (such as nitrate or phosphate) and low in the amount of algal material per unit of volume are termed *oligotrophic*. Such waters are often crystal clear. Oligotrophic streams and rivers tend to be high in dissolved oxygen because the movement of the flowing water aerates them; the small amount of organic matter in the water means that oxygen is used at a relatively low rate. Similarly, oligotrophic lakes and ponds tend to be high in dissolved oxygen at all depths all year because they also have a low rate of oxygen use. Because the water is relatively clear, light can penetrate the waters readily, allowing photosynthesis to occur through much of the water column, from top to bottom (figure 59.14).

Eutrophic bodies of water are high in algal nutrients and often populated densely with algae. They are more likely to be low in dissolved oxygen, especially in summer. In a eutrophic body of water, decay microbes often place high demands on the

Oligotrophic Lake

a.

Eutrophic Lake

b.

Figure 59.14 **Oligotrophic and eutrophic lakes.** *a.* Oligotrophic lakes are low in algal nutrients, have high levels of dissolved oxygen, and are clear. *b.* Eutrophic lakes have high levels of algal nutrients and low levels of dissolved oxygen. Light does not penetrate deeply in such lakes.

oxygen available because when thick populations of algae die, large amounts of organic matter are made available for decomposition. Moreover, light does not penetrate eutrophic waters well because of all the organic matter in the water; photosynthetic oxygen addition is therefore limited to just a relatively thin layer of water at the top.

Human activities have often transformed oligotrophic lakes into eutrophic ones. For example, when people overfertilize their lawns or fields, nitrate and phosphate from the fertilizers wash off into local water systems. Lakes that receive these nutrients become more eutrophic. A consequence is that the bottom waters are more likely to become oxygen-free during the summer. Many species of fish that are characteristic of oligotrophic lakes, such as trout, are very sensitive to oxygen deprivation. When lakes become eutrophic, these species of fish disappear and are replaced with species like carp that can better tolerate low oxygen concentrations. Lakes can return toward an oligotrophic state over time if steps are taken to eliminate the addition of excess nitrates, phosphates, and foreign organic matter such as sewage.

Learning Outcomes Review 59.3

The photic zone is the layer near the surface into which light penetrates. Photosynthesis can occur only in the photic zone. Thermal stratification is a major determinant of oxygen levels. In temperate lakes, mixing of different layers occurs when the layers reach the same temperature in spring and fall, and winds can cause the layers to mix. This overturn prevents oxygen depletion near the lake bottom. Eutrophic lakes are high in nutrients for algae but are low in dissolved oxygen; oligotrophic lakes are low in nutrients but high in dissolved oxygen at all depths.

■ *Why do tropical lakes often not experience seasonal turnover, and what effect is this likely to have on the ecosystems of these lakes?*

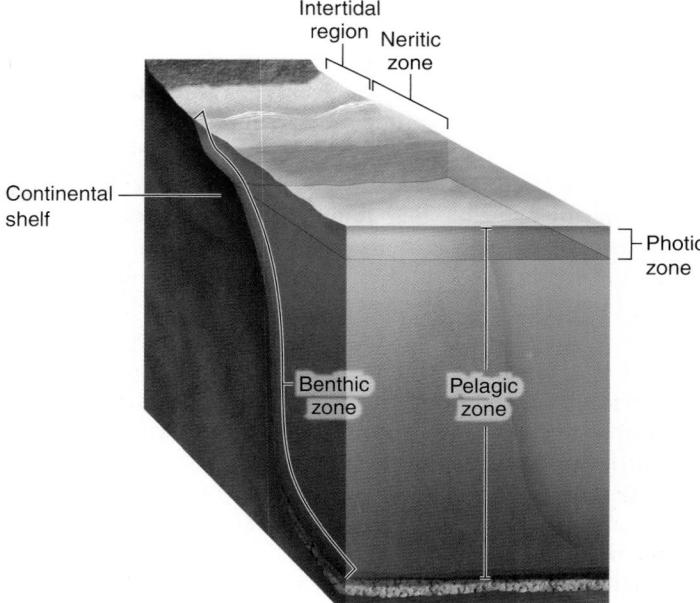

Figure 59.15 Basic concepts and terminology used in describing marine ecosystems. The continental shelf is the submerged edge of the continent. The waters over it are termed neritic and, on a worldwide average basis, are only 130 m deep at their deepest. The region where the tides rise and fall along the shoreline is called the intertidal region. The bottom is called the benthic zone, whereas the water column in the open ocean is called the pelagic zone. The photic zone is the part of the pelagic zone in which enough light penetrates for the phytoplankton to have a positive net primary productivity. The vertical scale of this drawing is highly compressed; whereas the outer edge of the continental shelf is 130 m deep, the open ocean in fact averages 35 times deeper (4000–5000 m deep).

59.4 Marine Habitats

Learning Outcomes

1. *Know the different marine habitats.*
2. *Explain why El Niño events occur.*

About 71% of the Earth's surface is covered by ocean. Near the coastlines of the continents are the continental shelves, where the water is not especially deep (figure 59.15); the shelves, in essence, represent the submerged edges of the continents. Worldwide, the shelves average about 80 km wide, and the depth of the water over them increases from 1 m to about 130 m as one travels from the coast toward the open ocean.

Beyond the continental shelves, the depth suddenly becomes much greater. The average depth of the open ocean is 4000 to 5000 m, and some parts—called trenches—are far deeper, reaching 11,000 m in the Marianas Trench in the western Pacific Ocean.

In most of the ocean, the principal primary producers are phytoplankton floating in the well-lit surface waters. A revolution is currently underway in scientific understanding of the limiting nutrients for ocean phytoplankton (see chapter 58). Primary production by the phytoplankton is presently understood to be nitrogen-limited in about two-thirds of the world's ocean, but iron-limited in about one-third. The principal known iron-limited areas are the great Southern Ocean surrounding Antarctica, parts of the equatorial Pacific Ocean, and parts of the subarctic, northeast Pacific Ocean. Where the water is shallow along coastlines, primary production is carried out not just by phytoplankton but also by rooted plants such as seagrasses and by bottom-dwelling algae, including seaweeds.

The world's ocean is so vast that it includes many different types of ecosystems. Some, such as coral reefs and estuaries, are high in their net primary productivity per unit of area (see figure 58.11), but others are low in productivity per unit area. Ocean ecosystems are of four major types: open oceans, continental shelf ecosystems, upwelling regions, and deep sea.

Open oceans have low primary productivity

In speaking of the open oceans, we mean the waters far from land (beyond the continental shelves) that are near enough to the surface to receive sunlight or to interact on a daily or weekly basis with those waters. We will discuss the deep sea separately later on.

The intensity of solar illumination in the open oceans drops from being high at the surface to being essentially zero at 200 m of depth; photosynthesis is limited to this level of the ocean. However, nutrients for phytoplankton, such as nitrate, tend to be present at low concentrations in the photic zone because over eons of time in the past, ecological processes have exported nitrate and other nutrients from the upper waters to the deep waters, and no vigorous forces exist in the open ocean to return the nutrients to the sunlit waters.

Because of the low concentrations of nutrients in the photic zone, large parts of the open oceans are low in primary productivity per unit area (see figure 58.11) and aptly called a "biological desert." These parts—which correspond to the centers of the great midocean gyres (see figure 59.4)—are often collectively termed the *oligotrophic ocean* (figure 59.16) in reference to their low nutrient levels and low productivity.

People fish the open oceans today for only a few species, such as tunas and some species of squids and whales. Fishing in the open oceans is limited to relatively few species for two reasons. First, because of the low primary productivity per unit of area, animals tend to be thinly distributed in the open oceans. The only ones that are commercially profitable to catch are those that are individually large or tend to gather together in tight schools. Second, costs for travelling far from land are high. All authorities agree that as we turn to the sea to help feed the burgeoning human population, we cannot expect the open ocean regions to supply great quantities of food.

Continental shelf ecosystems provide abundant resources

Many of the ecosystems on the continental shelves are relatively high in productivity per unit area. An important reason is that the waters over the shelves—termed the **neritic waters** (see figure 59.15)—tend to have relatively high concentrations of nitrate and other nutrients, averaged over the year.

Because the waters over the shelves are shallow, they have not been subject, over the eons of time, to the loss of nutrients into the deep sea, as the open oceans have. Over the shelves, nutrient-rich materials that sink hit the shallow bottom, and the nutrients they contain are stirred back into the water column by stormy weather. In addition, nutrients are continually replenished by run-off from nearby land.

Around 99% of the food people harvest from the ocean comes from continental shelf ecosystems or nearby upwelling regions. The shelf ecosystems are also particularly important to humankind in other ways. Mineral resources taken from the ocean, such as petroleum, come almost exclusively from the shelves. In addition, almost all recreational uses of the ocean, from sailing to scuba diving, take place on the shelves. The

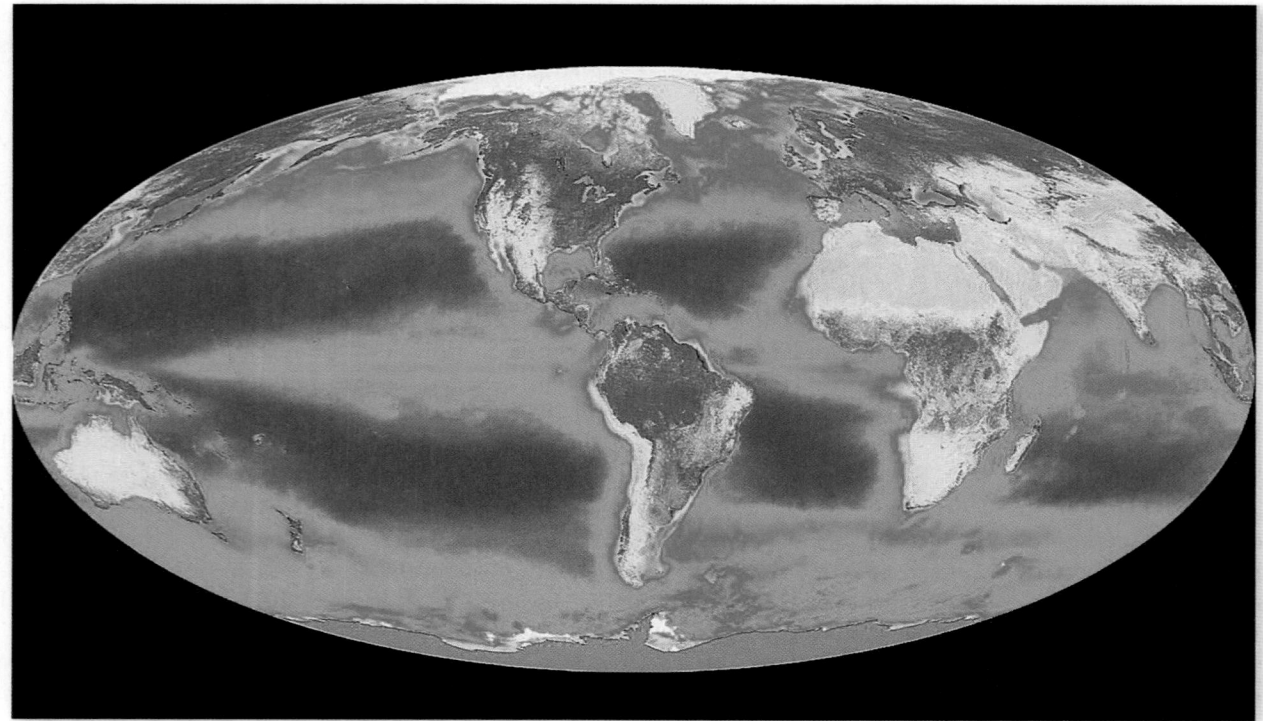

Figure 59.16 Major functional regions of the ocean. The regions classed as oligotrophic ocean (*colored dark blue*) are "biological deserts" with low productivity per unit area. Continental shelf ecosystems (*green at the edge of continents*) are typically medium to high in productivity. Upwelling regions (*yellow at the edge of continents*) are the highest in productivity per unit area and rank with the most productive of all ecosystems on Earth.

shelves feature prominently in these ways because they are close to coastlines and relatively shallow.

Estuaries

Estuaries are one of the types of shelf ecosystems. An estuary is a place along a coastline, such as a bay, that is partially surrounded by land and in which fresh water from streams or rivers mixes with ocean water, creating intermediate (brackish) salinities.

Estuaries, besides being bodies of water, include intertidal marshes or swamps. An **intertidal** habitat is an area that is exposed to air at low tide but under water at high tide. The marshes of the intertidal zone are called **salt marshes.** Intertidal swamps called **mangrove swamps** (dominated by trees and bushes) occur in tropical and subtropical parts of the world.

Estuaries are a vital and highly productive ecosystem—they provide shelter and food for many aquatic animals, especially the larvae and young, that people harvest for food. Estuaries are also important to a very large number of other animal species, such as migrating birds.

Banks and coral reefs

Other types of shelf ecosystems include banks and coral reefs. **Banks** are local shallow areas on the shelves, often extremely important as fishing grounds; Georges Bank, 100 km off the shore of Massachusetts, was formerly one of the most productive and famous; much of this area has been closed to fishing since the mid-1990s because of overexploitation.

Coral reef ecosystems occur in subtropical and tropical latitudes. Their defining feature is that in them, stony corals—corals that secrete a solid, calcified type of skeleton—build three-dimensional frameworks that form a unique habitat in which many other distinctive organisms live, including reef fish and soft corals (figure 59.17).

Figure 59.17 A coral reef ecosystem. Reef-building corals, which consist of symbioses between cnidarians and algae, construct the three-dimensional structure of the reef and carry out considerable primary production. Fish and many other kinds of animals find food and shelter, making these ecosystems among the most diverse. About 20% of all fish species occur specifically in coral reef ecosystems.

All the 700 or so species of reef-building corals are animal–algal symbioses; the animals are cnidarians, and dinoflagellate symbionts live within the cells of their inner cell layer (the gastrodermis). These corals depend on photosynthesis by the algal symbionts, and thus require clear waters through which sunlight can readily penetrate. Reef-building corals are threatened worldwide, as described later in this chapter.

Upwelling regions experience mixing of nutrients and oxygen

The upwelling regions of the ocean are localized places where deep water is drawn consistently to the surface because of the action of local forces such as local winds. The deep water is often rich in nitrate and other nutrients. Upwelling therefore steadily brings nutrients into the well-lit surface layers. Phytoplankton respond to the abundance of nutrients and light with prolific growth and reproduction. Upwelling regions have the highest primary productivity per unit area in the world's ocean.

The most famous upwelling region (see figure 59.16) is found along the coast of Peru and Ecuador, where upwelling occurs year-round. Another important upwelling region is the coastline of California, along which upwelling occurs during about half the year in the summer, explaining why swimmers find cold water at the beaches even in July and August.

Upwelling regions support prolific but vulnerable fisheries. Sardine fishing in the California upwelling region crashed a few decades ago, but previously was enormously important to the region, as Nobel Prize–winning author John Steinbeck chronicled in a number of his books, most notably *Cannery Row.*

El Niño Southern Oscillation (ENSO)

The phenomenon named El Niño first came to the attention of science in studies of the Peru–Ecuador upwelling region. In that region, every 2 to 7 years on an irregular and relatively unpredictable basis, the water along the coastline becomes profoundly warm, and simultaneously the primary productivity becomes unusually low.

Because of the low primary productivity, the ordinarily prolific fish populations weaken, and populations of seabirds and sea mammals that depend on the fish are stressed or plummet. The local people had named a mild annual warming event, which occurred around Christmas each year, "El Niño" (literally, "the child," after the Christ Child). Scientists adopted the term El Niño Southern Oscillation (ENSO) to refer to those dramatic warming events.

The immediate cause of El Niño took several decades to figure out, but research ultimately showed that the cause is a weakening of the east-to-west Trade Winds in the region. The Trade Winds ordinarily blow warm surface water to the west, away from the Peru–Ecuador coast. This thins the warm surface layer of water along the coast, so that deep water—cold but highly rich in nutrients—is drawn to the surface, leading to high primary production.

Weakening of the Trade Winds allows the warm surface layer to become thicker. Upwelling continues, but under such circumstances it merely recirculates the thick warm surface layer, which is nutrient-depleted.

After these fundamentals had been discovered, researchers in the 1980s realized that the weakening of the Trade Winds is actually part of a change in wind circulation patterns that recurs irregularly. One reason the Trade Winds blow east-to-west in ordinary times is that the surface waters in the western equatorial Pacific are warmer than those in the eastern equatorial Pacific; air rises from the warm western areas, creating low pressure at the surface there, and air blows out of the east into the low pressure. During an El Niño, the warmer the eastern ocean gets, the more similar it becomes to the western ocean, reducing the difference in pressure across the ocean. Thus, once the Trade Winds weaken a bit, the pressure difference that makes them blow is lessened, weakening the Trade Winds further. Warm water ordinarily kept in the west by the Trade Winds creeps progressively eastward at equatorial latitudes because of this self-reinforcing series of events. Ultimately, effects of El Niño occur across large parts of the world's weather systems, affecting sea temperatures in California, rainfall in the southwestern United States, and even systems as far distant as Africa.

One specific result is to shift the weather systems of the western Pacific Ocean 6000 km eastward. The tropical rainstorms that usually drench Indonesia and the Philippines occur when warm seawater abutting these islands causes the air above it to rise, cool, and condense its moisture into clouds. When the warm water moves east, so do the clouds, leaving the previously rainy areas in drought. Conversely, the western edge of Peru and Ecuador, which usually receives little precipitation, gets a soaking.

El Niño can wreak havoc on ecosystems. During an El Niño event, plankton can drop to 1/20 of their normal abundance in the waters of Peru and Ecuador, and because of the drop in plankton productivity, commercial fish stocks virtually disappear (figure 59.18). In the Galápagos Islands, for example, seabird and sea lion populations crash as animals starve due to the lack of fish. By contrast, on land, the heavy rains produce a

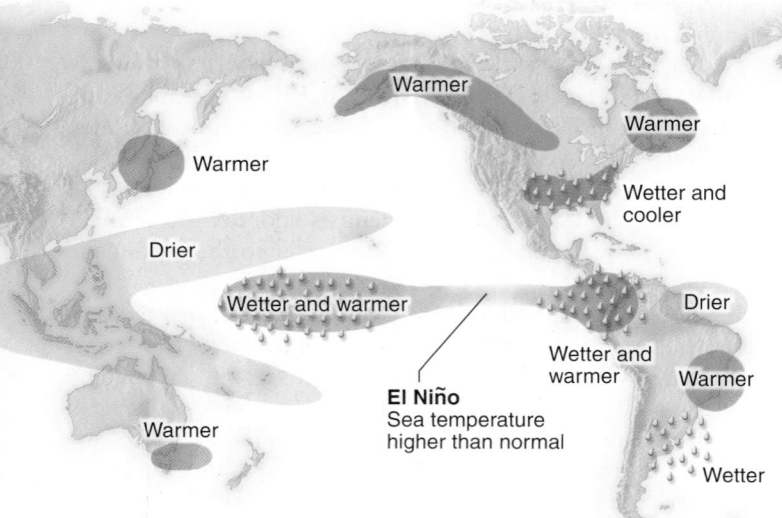

Figure 59.18 An El Niño winter. This diagram shows just some of the worldwide alterations of weather that are often associated with the El Niño phenomenon.

a. *b.*

Figure 59.19 Life in the deep sea. *a.* The luminous spot below the eye of this deep-sea fish results from the presence of a symbiotic colony of bioluminescent bacteria. Bioluminescence is a fairly common feature of mobile animals in the parts of the ocean that are so deep as to be dark. It is more common among species living part way down to the bottom than in ones living at the bottom. *b.* These large worms live along vents where hot water containing hydrogen sulfide rises through cracks in the seafloor crust. Much of the body of each worm is devoted to a colony of symbiotic sulfur-oxidizing bacteria. The worms transport sulfide and oxygen to the bacteria, which oxidize the sulfur and use the energy thereby obtained for primary production of new organic compounds, which they share with their worm hosts.

bumper crop of seeds, and land birds flourish. In Chile, similar effects on seed abundance propagate up the food chain, leading first to increased rodent populations and then to increased predator populations, a nice example of a bottom-up trophic cascade, as was discussed in chapter 58.

The deep sea is a cold, dark place with some fascinating communities

The deep sea is by far the single largest habitat on Earth, in the sense that it is a huge region characterized by relatively uniform conditions throughout the globe. The deep sea is seasonless, cold (2–5°C), totally dark, and under high pressure (400–500 atmospheres where the bottom is 4000–5000 m deep).

In most regions of the deep sea, food originates from photosynthesis in the sunlit waters far above. Such food—in the form of carcasses, fecal pellets, and mucus—can take as much as a month to drift down from the surface to the bottom, and along the way about 99% of it is eaten by animals living in the water column. Thus, the bottom communities receive only about 1% of the primary production and are food-poor. Nonetheless, a great many species of animals—most of them small-bodied and thinly distributed—are now known to live in the deep sea. Some of the animals are bioluminescent (figure 59.19*a*) and thereby able to communicate or attract prey by use of light.

Hydrothermal vent communities

The most astounding communities in the deep sea are the hydrothermal vent communities. Unlike most parts of the deep sea, these communities are thick with life (figure 59.19*b*), including large-bodied animals such as worms the size of baseball bats. The reason such a profusion of life can be supported is that these communities live on vigorous, local primary production rather than depending on the photic zone far above.

The hydrothermal vent communities occur at places where tectonic plates are moving apart, and seawater—circulating through porous rock—is able to come into contact with very hot rock under the seafloor. This water is heated to temperatures in excess of 350°C and, in the process, becomes rich in hydrogen sulfide.

As the water rises up out of the porous rock, free-living and symbiotic bacteria oxidize the sulfide, and from this reaction they obtain energy, which, in a manner analogous to photosynthesis, they use to synthesize their own cellular substance, grow, and reproduce. These sulfur-oxidizing bacteria are chemoautotrophs (see chapter 58). Animals in the communities either survive on the bacteria or eat other animals that do. The hydrothermal vent communities are among the few communities on Earth that do not depend on the Sun's energy for primary production.

Learning Outcomes Review 59.4

The oligotrophic ocean includes the open ocean and the deep sea, where little primary productivity occurs. Continental shelf ecosystems tend to be moderate to high in productivity; they include estuaries, salt marshes, fishing banks, and coral reefs. The highest levels of productivity are found in upwelling regions, such as those along the west coasts of North and South America, where prolific but vulnerable fisheries can be found. Periodic weakening of the Trade Winds in this region can prevent the upwelling of cold water and subsequently cause weather changes in an event termed El Niño.

■ **What sort of population cycles would you expect to see in regions that are affected by the ENSO?**

59.5 Human Impacts on the Biosphere: Pollution and Resource Depletion

Learning Outcomes

1. *Name the major human threats to ecosystems.*
2. *Differentiate between point-source pollution and diffuse pollution.*
3. *Explain the effect of deforestation.*

We all know that human activities can cause adverse changes in ecosystems. In discussing these, it is important to recognize that creative people can often come up with rational solutions to such problems.

An outstanding example is provided by the history of DDT in the United States. DDT is a highly effective insecti-cide that was sprayed widely in the decades following World War II, often on wetlands to control mosquitoes. During the years of heavy DDT use, populations of ospreys, bald eagles, and brown pelicans—all birds that catch large fish—plummeted. Ultimately, the use of DDT was connected with the demise of these birds.

Scientists established that DDT and its metabolic products became more and more concentrated in the tissues of animals as the compounds were passed along food chains (figure 59.20). Animals at the bottom of food chains accumulated relatively low concentrations in their fatty tissues. But the primary carnivores that preyed on them accumulated higher concentrations from eating great numbers, and the secondary carnivores accumulated higher concentrations yet. Top-level carnivores, such as the birds that eat large fish, were dramatically affected by the DDT. In these birds, scientists found that metabolic products of DDT disrupted the formation of eggshells. The birds laid eggs with such thin shells that they often cracked before the young could hatch.

Researchers concluded that the demise of the fish-eating birds could be reversed by a rational plan to clean ecosystems of DDT, and laws were passed banning its use. Now, three decades later, populations of ospreys, eagles, and pelicans are rebounding dramatically. For some people, a major reason to study science is the opportunity to be part of success stories of this sort.

Figure 59.20 Biological magnification of DDT concentration. Because all the DDT an animal eats in its food tends to accumulate in its fatty tissues, DDT becomes increasingly concentrated in animals at higher levels of the food chain. The concentrations at the right are in parts per million (ppm). Before DDT was banned in the United States, bird species that eat large fish underwent drastic population declines because metabolic products of DDT made their eggshells so thin that the shells broke during incubation.

DDT Concentration

25 ppm in predatory birds

2 ppm in large fish

0.5 ppm in small fish

0.04 ppm in zooplankton

0.000003 ppm in water

Freshwater habitats are threatened by pollution and resource depletion

Fresh water is not just the smallest of the major habitats, but also the most threatened. One of the simplest yet most ominous threats to fresh water is that burgeoning human populations often extract excessive amounts of water from rivers, lakes, or streams. The Colorado River, for example, is one of the greatest rivers in North America, originating with snow melt in the Rocky Mountains and flowing through Utah, Arizona, Nevada, California, and northern Mexico before emptying into the ocean. Today, water is pumped out of the river all along its way to meet the water needs of cities (even ones as distant as Los Angeles) and to irrigate crops. The river now frequently runs out of water and dries up in the desert, never reaching the sea. Worldwide, many crises in the supply of fresh water loom on the horizon.

Pollution: Point source versus diffuse

Pollution of fresh water is a global problem. Point-source pollution comes from an identifiable location—such as easily identified factories or other facilities that add pollutants at defined locations, such as an outfall pipe. Examples include sewage-treatment plants, which discharge treated effluents at specific spots on rivers, and factories that sometimes discharge water contaminated with heavy metals or chemicals. Laws and technologies can readily be brought to bear to moderate point-source pollution because the exact locations and types of pollution are well defined. In many countries, great progress has been made, but in other countries, often in the developing world, water pollution is still a major problem.

Diffuse pollution is exemplified by eutrophication caused by excessive run-off of nitrates and phosphates from lawn and agricultural field fertilization. When excessive nitrates and phosphates enter rivers and lakes, the character of the bodies of water is changed for the worse; the concentration of dissolved oxygen declines, and fish species such as carp take the place of more desirable species. The problem is exacerbated when rivers empty into the ocean. The eutrophication caused by the accumulation of chemicals can lead to enormous areas of water with no oxygen, causing massive die-offs of fish and other animals. The most famous such area, covering approximately 20,000 km² in 2008, occurs where the Mississippi River empties into the Gulf of Mexico, but other "dead zones" occur in places around the world.

The nitrates and phosphates that cause these problems originate on thousands of farms and lawns spread over whole watersheds, and they often enter fresh waters at virtually countless locations. The diffuseness of this sort of pollution renders it difficult to modify by simple technical fixes. Instead, solutions often depend on public education and political action.

Pollution from coal burning: Acid precipitation

A type of pollution that has properties intermediate between the point-source and diffuse types is the pollution that can arise from burning of coal for power generation. Although each smokestack is a point source, there are many stacks, and the smoke and gases from these stacks spread over wide areas.

Acid precipitation is one aspect of this problem. When coal is burned, sulfur in the coal is oxidized. The sulfur oxides, unless controlled, are spewed into the atmosphere in the stack smoke, and there they combine with water vapor to produce sulfuric acid. Falling rain or snow picks up the acid and is excessively acidic when it reaches the surface of the Earth (figure 59.21).

Mercury emitted in stack smoke is a second potential problem. Burning of coal can be one of the major sources of environmental mercury, a serious public health issue because just small amounts of mercury can interfere with brain development in human fetuses and infants.

Acid precipitation and mercury pollution affect freshwater ecosystems. At pH levels below 5.0, many fish species and other aquatic animals die, unable to reproduce. Thousands of lakes and ponds around the world no longer support fish because of pH shifts induced by acid precipitation. Mercury that falls from atmospheric emissions into lakes and ponds accumulates in the tissues of food fish. In the Great Lakes region of the United States, people—especially pregnant women—are advised to eat little or no locally caught fish because of its mercury content.

Forest ecosystems are threatened in tropical and temperate regions

Probably the single greatest problem for terrestrial habitats worldwide is deforestation by cutting or burning. There are many reasons for deforestation. In poverty-stricken countries, deforestation is often carried out diffusely by the general population; people burn wood to cook or stay warm, and they collect it from the local forests.

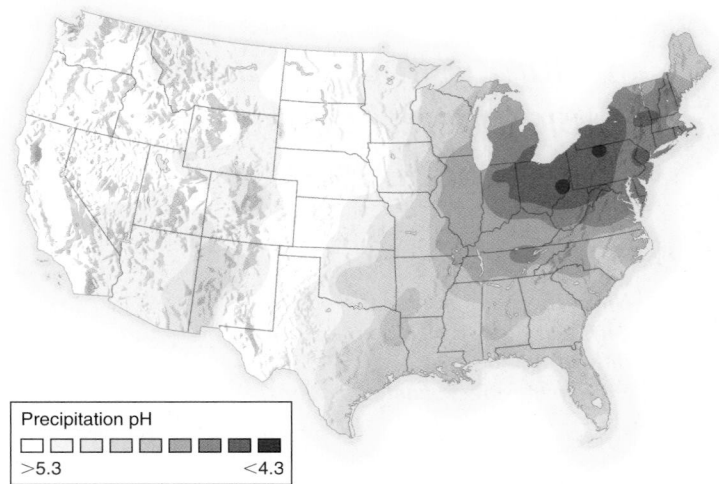

Precipitation pH
>5.3   <4.3

Figure 59.21 pH values of rainwater in the United States. pH values of less than 7 represent acid conditions; the lower the values, the greater the acidity. Precipitation in parts of the United States, especially in the Northeast, is commonly more acidic than natural rainwater, which has a pH of 5.6 or higher.

At the other extreme, corporations still cut large tracts of virgin forests in an industrialized fashion, often shipping the wood halfway around the world to buyers. Tropical hardwoods, such as mahogany, from Southeast Asian rain forests are shipped to the United States for use in furniture, and softwood logs are shipped from Alaska to East Asia for pulping and paper production. Forests are sometimes simply burned to open up land for farming or ranching (figure 59.22*a*).

Loss of habitat

The loss of forest habitat can have dire consequences. Particularly diverse sets of species depend on tropical rain forests for their habitat, for example. Thus, when rain forests are cleared, the loss of biodiversity can be extreme. Many tropical forest regions have been severely degraded, and recent estimates suggest that less than half of the world's tropical rain forests remain in pristine condition. All of the world's tropical rain forests will be degraded or gone in about 30 years at present rates of destruction.

Besides loss of habitat, deforestation can have numerous secondary consequences, depending on local contexts. In the Sahel region, South of the Sahara Desert in Africa, deforestation has been a major contributing factor in increased desertification. In the forests of the northeastern United States, as the Hubbard Brook experiment shows (see figure 58.7), deforestation can lead to both a loss of nutrients from forest soils and a simultaneous nutrient enrichment of bodies of water downstream.

Disruption of the water cycle

As discussed in chapter 58, cutting of a tropical rain forest often interrupts the local water cycle in ways that permanently alter the landscape. After an area of tropical rain forest is cleared, rain water often runs off the land to distant places, rather than being returned to the atmosphere immediately above by transpiration. This change may render conditions unsuitable for the rain forest trees that originally lived there. Then the poorly vegetated land—exposed and no longer stabilized by thick root systems—may be ravaged by erosion (figure 59.22*b*).

Acid rain

Deforestation can be a problem in temperate regions, as well as in the tropics. In addition, acid rain affects forests as well as lakes and streams; large tracts of trees in temperate regions have been adversely affected by acid rain. By changing the acidity of the soil, acid rain can lead to widespread tree mortality (figure 59.23).

Marine habitats are being depleted of fish and other species

Overfishing of the ocean has risen to crisis proportions in recent decades and probably represents the single greatest current problem in the ocean realm. The ocean is so huge that it has tended to be more immune than fresh water or terrestrial ecosystems to global human alteration. Nonetheless, the total world fish catch has been pushed to its maximum for over two decades, even as demand for fish has continued to rise. Fishing pressure is so excessive that 25% to 30% of the world's ocean

a.   *b.*

Figure 59.22 Destroying the tropical rain forests.
a. These fires are destroying a tropical rain forest in Brazil to clear it for cattle pasture. *b.* The consequences of deforestation can be seen on these middle-elevation slopes in Madagascar, which once supported tropical rain forest, but now support only low-grade pastures and permit topsoil to erode into the rivers (note the color of the water, stained brown by high levels of soil erosion). This sort of picture is seen in a number of places around the world, including Ecuador and Haiti as well as Madagascar.

fish stocks are presently officially rated as being overexploited, depleted, or in recovery; another 40% to 50% are rated as being maximally exploited.

Major cod fisheries in waters off of Nova Scotia, Massachusetts, and Great Britain have been closed to fishing in the past 15 years because of collapse (figure 59.24). Overfishing can

Figure 59.23 Damage to trees by acid precipitation at Clingman's Dome, Tennessee. Acid precipitation weakens trees and makes them more susceptible to pests and predators.

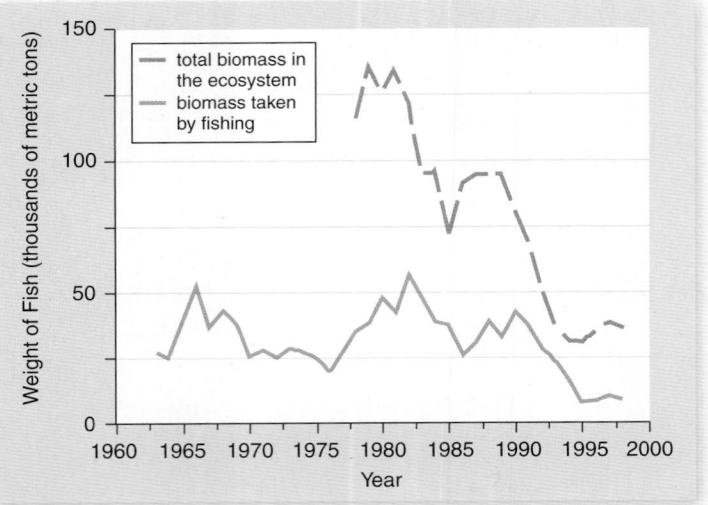

Figure 59.24 The collapse of a fishery. The red line shows the biomass of cod *(Gadus morhua)* in the Georges Bank ecosystem as estimated by the U.S. National Marine Fisheries Service based on data collected by scientific sampling. The biomass declined steeply between the 1970s and 1990s because of fishing pressure. As the years passed, commercial landings of cod *(blue line)* remained fairly constant, in part because ships worked harder and harder to catch cod, until catches fell precipitously toward zero and the fishery collapsed in the mid-1990s. Regulatory agencies closed the fishery in the mid-1990s to permit the cod to recover, but even in 2009 recovery of cod was weak at best, and production from the fishery was far below historical norms.

have disturbing indirect effects. In impoverished parts of Africa, poaching on primates and other wild mammals in national parks increases when fish catches decline.

Aquaculture: At present only a quick fix

Production of fish by aquaculture has grown steadily in the last two decades, and it is often viewed as a straightforward solution to the fisheries problem. But the dietary protein needs of many aquacultured fish, such as salmon, are met largely with wild-caught fish. In this case, exploitation has simply shifted to different species.

In addition, current aquaculture practices often damage natural ocean ecosystems. One example is the clearing of mangrove swamps along coasts to create shrimp and fish ponds, which are abandoned when their productivity declines. Research is needed to ameliorate these problems.

Pollution effects

As large as the ocean is, enough pollutants are being added that at the start of the 21st century, polluting materials are easily detectable on a global basis. An expedition to some of the most remote, uninhabited islands in the vast Pacific Ocean recently reported, for example, that considerable amounts of plastic could be found washed up on the beaches. Similarly, even the waters of the Arctic are laced with toxic chemicals; biopsy samples of tissue from Arctic killer whales *(Orcinus orca)* revealed extremely high levels of many chemicals, including pesticides

and a flame-retardant chemical often used in carpets. Nonetheless, because of the ocean's vastness, concentrations of pollutants are not at crisis levels in the ocean at large.

Destruction of coastal ecosystems

Second to overfishing, the greatest problem in the ocean realm is deterioration of coastal ecosystems. Estuaries along coastlines are often subject to severe eutrophication; since about 1970, for example, the bottom waters of the Chesapeake Bay near Washington, DC, have become oxygen-free each summer because of the decay of excessive amounts of organic matter.

Another coastal problem is destruction of salt marshes, which (like freshwater wetlands) are often perceived as disposable. Most authorities believe that the loss of salt marshes in the 20th century was a major contributing factor to the destruction of New Orleans by Hurricane Katrina in 2005; had the salt marshes and cypress swamps been present at their full extent, they would have absorbed a great deal of the flooding water and buffered the city from some of the storm's violence.

Stratospheric ozone depletion has led to an ozone "hole"

The colors of the satellite photo in figure 59.25*a* represent different concentrations of ozone (O_3) located 20 to 25 km above the Earth's surface in the stratosphere. Stratospheric ozone is depleted over Antarctica (purple region in the figure) to between one-half and one-third of its historically normal concentration, a phenomenon called the ozone hole.

Although depletion of stratospheric ozone is most dramatic over Antarctica, it is a worldwide phenomenon. Over the United States, the ozone concentration has been reduced by about 4%, according to the U.S. Environmental Protection Agency.

Stratospheric ozone and UV-B

Stratospheric ozone is important because it absorbs ultraviolet (UV) radiation—specifically the wavelengths called **UV-B**—from incoming solar radiation. UV-B is damaging to living organisms in a number of ways; for instance, it increases risks of cataracts and skin cancer in people. Depletion of stratospheric ozone permits more UV-B to reach the Earth's surface and therefore increases the risks of UV-B damage. Every 1% drop in stratospheric ozone is estimated to lead to a 6% increase in the incidence of skin cancer, for example. UV exposure also may be detrimental to many types of animals, such as amphibians (figure 59.26)

Ozone depletion and CFCs

The major cause of the depletion of stratospheric ozone is the addition of industrially produced chlorine- and bromine-containing compounds to the atmosphere. Of particular concern are chlorofluorocarbons (CFCs), used until recently as refrigerants in air conditioners and refrigerators, and in manufacturing. CFCs released into the atmosphere can ultimately liberate free chlorine atoms, which in the stratosphere catalyze the breakdown of ozone molecules (O_3) to form ordinary oxygen (O_2). Ozone is continually being made and broken down,

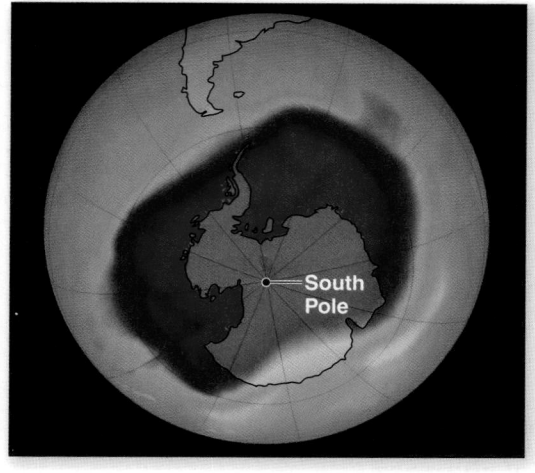

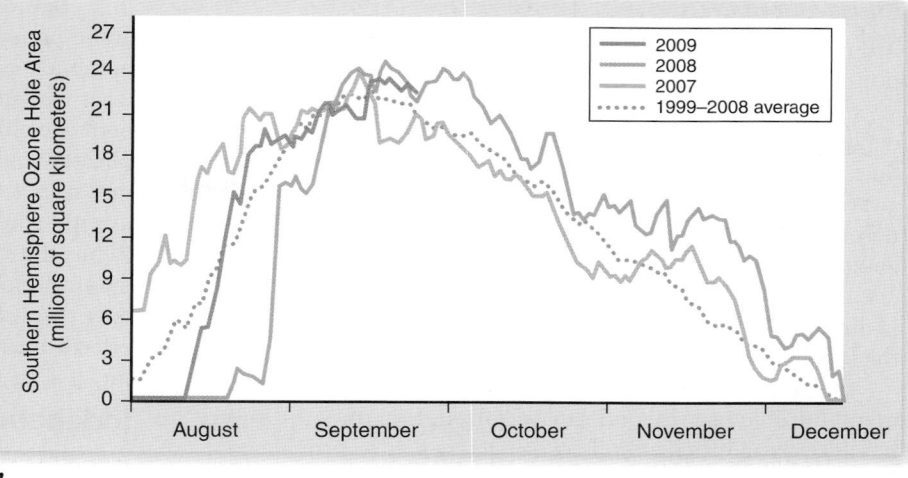

a.

b.

Figure 59.25 The ozone hole over Antarctica. NASA satellites currently track the extent of ozone depletion in the stratosphere over Antarctica each year. Every year since about 1980, an area of profound ozone depletion, called the ozone hole, has appeared in August (early spring in the southern hemisphere) when sunlight triggers chemical reactions in cold air trapped over the South Pole during the Antarctic winter. The hole intensifies during September before tailing off as temperature rises in November–December. *a.* In September, 2006, the 11.4 million-square-mile hole (*purple* in the satellite image shown) covered an area larger than the United States, Canada, and Mexico combined, the largest hole ever recorded. *b.* Concentrations of ozone-depleting chemical compounds in the atmosphere have probably peaked in the last few years and are expected to decline slowly over the decades ahead.

and free chlorine atoms tilt the balance toward a faster rate of breakdown.

The extreme depletion of ozone seen in the ozone hole is a consequence of the unique weather conditions that exist over Antarctica. During the continuous dark of the Antarctic winter, a strong stratospheric wind, the polar-night jet, develops and, blowing around the full circumference of the Earth, isolates the stratosphere over Antarctica from the rest of the atmosphere.

The Antarctic stratosphere stays extremely cold (–80°C or lower) for many weeks as a consequence, permitting unique types of ice clouds to form. Reactions associated with the particles in these clouds lead to accumulation of diatomic chlorine, Cl_2. When sunlight returns in the early Antarctic spring, the diatomic chlorine is photochemically broken up to form free chlorine atoms in great abundance, and the ozone-depleting reactions ensue.

SCIENTIFIC THINKING

Question: *Does exposure to UV radiation affect the survival of amphibian eggs?*

Hypothesis: *Direct UV exposure is detrimental to eggs.*

Experiment: *Fertilized eggs from several frog species are placed into enclosures in full sunlight. All enclosures have screens, some of which filter out UV radiation, whereas others do not affect UV transmission. Eggs are monitored to see whether they survive to hatching or whether they die.*

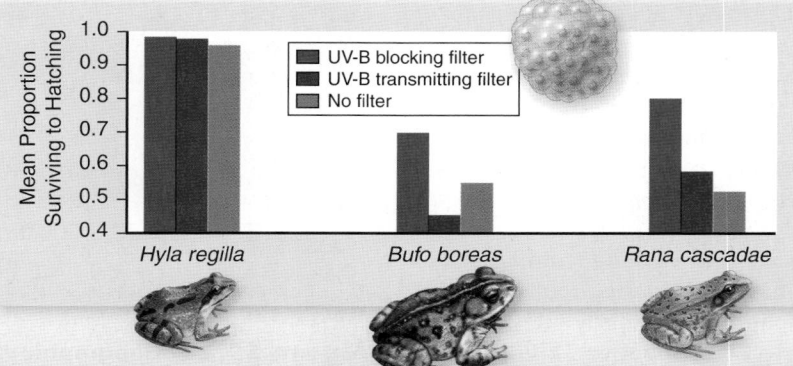

Result: *Egg survival was greatly decreased in two of three species in the enclosures where UV radiation was not filtered out, as compared to survival in the filtered enclosures. Therefore, the hypothesis is confirmed: UV exposure is detrimental to amphibian eggs.*

Further Questions: *What factors might explain why some species are affected by UV exposure and others are not? How could your hypotheses be tested?*

Figure 59.26 The effect of UV radiation on amphibian eggs.

Phase-out of CFCs

After research revealed the causes of stratospheric ozone depletion, worldwide agreements were reached to phase out the production of CFCs and other compounds that lead to ozone depletion. Manufacture of such compounds ceased in the United States in 1996, and there is now a great deal of public awareness about the importance of using "ozone-safe" alternative chemicals. The atmosphere will cleanse itself of ozone-depleting compounds only slowly because the substances are chemically stable. Nonetheless, the problem of ozone depletion is diminishing and is expected to be substantially corrected by the second half of the 21st century.

The CFC story is an excellent example of how environmental problems arise and can be solved. Initially, CFCs were heralded as an efficient and cost-effective way to provide cooling, a clear improvement over previous technologies. At that time, their harmful consequences were unknown. Once the problems were identified, international agreements led to an effective solution, and creative technological advances led to replacements that solved the problem at little cost.

Learning Outcomes Review 59.5

Pollution and resource depletion are the major human effects on the environment, with freshwater habitats being most threatened. Point-source pollution comes from identifiable locations, such as factories, whereas diffuse pollution comes from numerous sources, such as fertilized lawns. Deforestation is a major problem in that it destroys habitat, disrupts communities, depletes resources, and changes the local water cycle and weather patterns. Overfishing is the greatest problem in the oceans.

■ *Were CFCs an example of point-source or diffuse pollution? In general, how do efforts to combat pollution depend on their source?*

59.6 Human Impacts on the Biosphere: Climate Change

Learning Outcomes

1. *Explain the link between atmospheric carbon dioxide and global warming.*
2. *Describe the consequences of global warming on ecosystems and human health.*

By studying the Earth's history and making comparisons with other planets, scientists have determined that concentrations of gases in our atmosphere, particularly CO_2, maintain the average temperature on Earth about 25°C higher than it would be if these gases were absent. This fact emphasizes that the composition of our atmosphere is a key consideration for life on Earth. Unfortunately, human activities are now changing the composition of the atmosphere in ways that most authorities conclude will be damaging or, in the long run, disastrous.

Because of changes in atmospheric composition, the average temperature of the Earth's surface is increasing, a phenomenon called global warming. As you might imagine from what we said at the beginning of this chapter, changes in temperature alter global wind and water-current patterns in complicated ways. This means that as the average global temperature increases, some particular regions of the world warm to a lesser extent, whereas other regions heat up to a greater extent (figure 59.27). It also means that rainfall patterns are altered because global precipitation patterns depend on global wind patterns. Enormous computer models are used to calculate the effects predicted in all parts of the world.

Independent computer models predict global changes

The Intergovernmental Panel on Climate Change, which shared the 2007 Nobel Peace Prize with Al Gore for their work on global climate change, recently released its fourth assessment report. Based on a variety of different scenarios, computer models predicted that global temperatures would increase 1.1°C to 6.4°C (2.0–11.5°F) by the end of this century.

More ominous perhaps than temperature are some of the predictions for precipitation. For example, although northern Europe is expected to receive more precipitation than today, another recent studied predicted that parts of southern Europe will receive about 20% less, disrupting natural ecosystems, agriculture, and human water supplies. Some European countries may come out ahead economically, but others will come out behind, and political relationships among countries will likely change as some shift from being food exporters to the more tenuous role of requiring food imports.

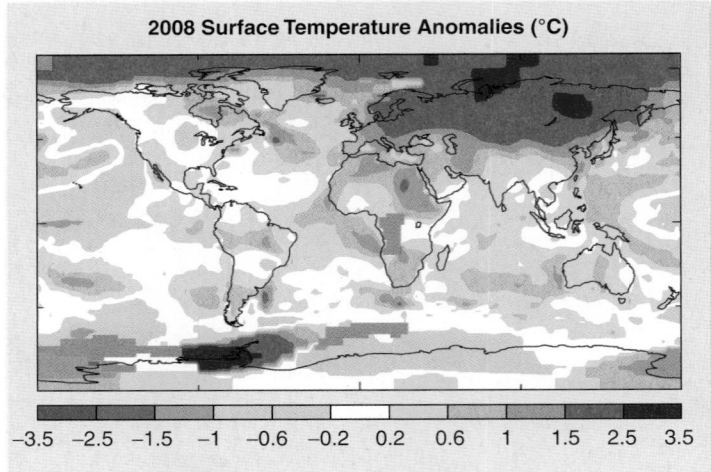

2008 Surface Temperature Anomalies (°C)

−3.5 −2.5 −1.5 −1 −0.6 −0.2 0.2 0.6 1 1.5 2.5 3.5

Figure 59.27 Geographic variation in global warming.
The 10 warmest years since record keeping began in 1880 all occur within the 12-year period 1997–2008, but some areas of the globe heated up more than others. Colors indicate how much warming occurred in 2008 relative to the mean temperature during a reference period (1951–1980) prior to full onset of the modern greenhouse effect.

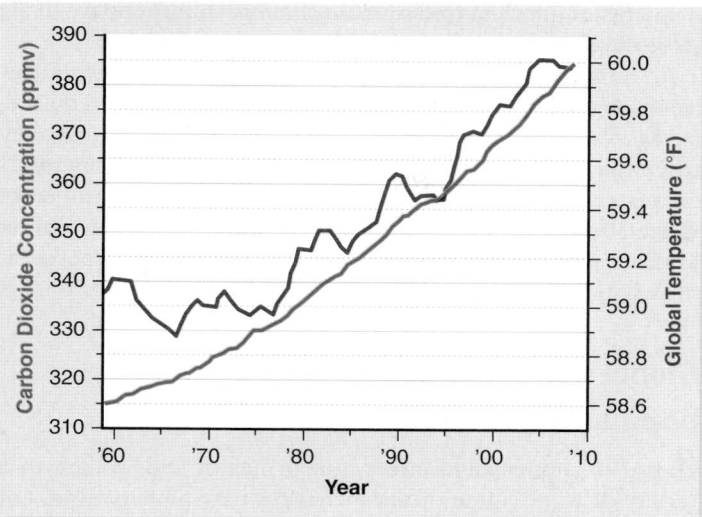

Figure 59.28 The greenhouse effect. The concentration of carbon dioxide in the atmosphere has increased steadily since the 1950s, as shown by the blue line. The red line shows the change in average global temperature over the same period.

Carbon dioxide is a major greenhouse gas

Carbon dioxide is the gas usually emphasized in discussing the cause of global warming (figure 59.28), although other atmospheric gases are also involved. A monitoring station on the top of the 13,700-foot (4200-m) Mauna Loa volcano on the island of Hawaii has monitored the concentration of atmospheric CO_2 since the 1950s. This station is particularly important because it is in the middle of the Pacific Ocean, far from the great continental landmasses where most people live, and it is therefore able to monitor the state of the global atmosphere without confounding influences of local events.

In 1958, the atmosphere was 0.031% CO_2. By 2004, the concentration had risen to 0.038%. All authorities agree that the cause of this steady rise in atmospheric CO_2 is the burning of coal and petroleum products by the increasing (and increasingly energy-demanding) human population.

How carbon dioxide affects temperature

The atmospheric concentration of CO_2 affects global temperature because carbon dioxide strongly absorbs electromagnetic radiant energy at some of the wavelengths that are critical for the global heat budget. As stressed in chapter 58, the Earth not only receives radiant energy from the Sun, but also emits radiant energy into outer space. The Earth's temperature will be constant only if the rates of these two processes are equal.

The incoming solar energy is at relatively short wavelengths of the electromagnetic spectrum: Wavelengths that are visible or near-visible. The outgoing energy from the Earth is at different, longer wavelengths. Carbon dioxide absorbs energy at certain of the important long-wave infrared wavelengths. This means that although carbon dioxide does not interfere with the arrival of radiant energy at short wavelengths, it retards the rate at which energy travels away from the Earth at long wavelengths into outer space.

Carbon dioxide is often called a greenhouse gas because its effects are analogous to those of a greenhouse. The reason that a glass greenhouse gets warm inside is that window glass is transparent to light but only slightly transparent to long-wave infrared radiation. Energy that strikes a greenhouse as light enters the greenhouse freely. Once inside, the energy is absorbed as heat and then re-radiated as long-wave infrared radiation. The infrared radiation cannot easily get out through the glass, and therefore energy accumulates inside.

Other greenhouse gases

Carbon dioxide is not the only greenhouse gas. Others include methane and nitrous oxide. The effect of any particular greenhouse gas depends on its molecular properties and concentration. For example, molecule-for-molecule, methane has about 20 times the heat-trapping effect of carbon dioxide; on the other hand, methane is less concentrated and less long-lived in the atmosphere than carbon dioxide.

Methane is produced in globally significant quantities in anaerobic soils and in the fermentation reactions of ruminant mammals, such as cows. Huge amounts of methane are presently locked up in Arctic permafrost. Melting of the permafrost could cause a sudden and large perturbation in global temperature by releasing methane rapidly.

Agricultural use of fertilizers is the largest source of nitrous oxide emissions, with energy consumption second and industrial use third.

Global temperature change has affected ecosystems in the past and is doing so now

Evidence for warming can be seen in many ways. For example, on a worldwide statistical basis, ice on lakes and rivers forms later and melts sooner than it used to; on average, ice-free seasons are now 2.5 weeks longer than they were a century ago. Also, the extent of ice at the North Pole has decreased substantially, and glaciers are retreating around the world (figure 59.29).

Figure 59.29 Disappearing glaciers. Mount Kilimanjaro in Tanzania in 1970 (*top*) and 2000 (*bottom*). Note the decrease in glacier coverage over three decades.

Global warming—and cooling—have occurred in the past, most recently during the ice ages and intervening warm periods. Species often responded by shifting their geographic ranges, tracking their environments. For example, a number of cold-adapted North American tree species that are now found only in the far north, or at high elevations, lived much farther south or at substantially lower elevations 10,000–20,000 years ago, when conditions were colder. Present-day global warming is having similar effects. For example, many butterfly and bird species have shifted northward in recent decades (figure 59.30).

Many migratory birds arrive earlier at their summer breeding grounds than they did decades ago. Many insects and amphibians breed earlier in the year, and many plants flower earlier. In Australia, recent research shows that wild fruit fly populations have undergone changes in gene frequencies in the past 20 years, such that populations in cool parts of the country now genetically resemble ones in warm parts.

Reef-building corals seem to have narrow margins of safety between the sea temperatures to which they are accustomed and the maximum temperatures they can survive. Global warming seems already to be threatening some corals by inducing mass "bleaching," a disruption of the normal and necessary symbiosis between the cnidarians and algal cells.

There are reasons to think that the effects of global warming on natural ecosystems today may, overall, be more severe than those of warming events in the distant past. One concern is that the rate of warming today is rapid, and therefore evolutionary adaptations would need to occur over relatively few generations to aid the survival of species. Another concern is that natural areas no longer cover the whole landscape but often take the form of parks that are completely surrounded by cities or farms. The parks are at fixed geographic locations and in general cannot be moved. If climatic conditions in a park become unsuitable for its inhabitants, the park will cease to perform its function. Moreover, the areas in which the park in-

habitants might then find suitable climatic conditions are likely to be developed, rather than being protected parks.

Similarly, as temperatures increase, many montane species have shifted to higher altitudes to find their preferred habitat. However, eventually they can shift no higher because they reach the mountain's peak. As the temperature continues to increase, the species' habitat disappears entirely. A number of Costa Rican frog species are thought to have become extinct for this reason. The same fate may befall many Arctic species as their habitat melts away.

Global warming affects human populations as well

Global warming could affect human health and welfare in a variety of ways. Some of these changes may be beneficial, but even if they are detrimental, some countries—particularly the wealthier ones—will be able to adjust. But poorer countries may not be able to transform as quickly, and some changes will require extremely costly countermeasures that even wealthy countries will be hard-pressed to afford.

Rising sea levels

During the second half of the 20th century, sea level rose at 2 to 3 cm per decade. The U.S. Environmental Protection Agency predicts that sea level is likely to rise two or three times faster in the 21st century because of two effects of global warming: (1) the melting of polar ice and glaciers, adding water to the ocean, and (2) the increase of average ocean temperature, causing an increase in volume because water expands as it warms. Such an increase would cause increased erosion and inundation of low-lying land and coastal marshes, and other habitats would also be imperiled. As many as 200 million people would be affected by increased flooding. Should sea levels continue to rise, coastal cities and some entire islands, such as the Maldives in the Indian Ocean, would be in danger of becoming submerged.

Other climatic effects

Global warming is predicted to have a variety of effects besides increased temperatures. In particular, the frequency or severity of extreme meteorological events—such as heat waves, droughts, severe storms, and hurricanes—is expected to increase, and El Niño events, with their attendant climatic effects, may become more common.

In addition, rainfall patterns are likely to shift, and those geographic areas that are already water-stressed, which are currently home to nearly 2 billion people, will likely face even graver water shortage problems in the years to come. Some evidence suggests that these effects are already evident in the increase in powerful storms, hurricanes, and the frequency of El Niño events over the past few years.

Effects on agriculture

Global warming may have both positive and negative effects on agriculture. On the positive side, warmer temperatures and increased atmospheric carbon dioxide tend to increase growth of some crops and thus may increase agricultural yields. Other crops, however, may be negatively affected. Furthermore, most

Figure 59.30 Butterfly range shift. The distribution of the speckled wood butterfly, *Pararge aegeria*, in Great Britain in 1970–1997 (green) included areas far to the north of the distribution in 1915–1939 (black).

crops will be affected by increased frequencies of droughts. Moreover, although crops in north temperate regions may flourish with higher temperatures, many tropical crops are already growing at their maximal temperatures, so increased temperatures may lead to reduced crop yields.

Also on the negative side, changes in rainfall patterns, temperature, pest distributions, and various other factors will require many adjustments. Such changes may come relatively easily for farmers in the developed world, but the associated costs may be devastating for those in the developing countries.

Effects on human health

Increasingly frequent storms, flooding, and drought will have adverse consequences on human health. Aside from their direct effect, such events often disrupt the fragile infrastructure of developing countries, leading to the loss of safe drinking water and other problems. As a result, epidemics of cholera and other diseases may be expected to occur more often.

In addition, as temperatures rise, areas suitable for tropical organisms will expand northward. Of particular concern are those organisms that cause human diseases. Many diseases currently limited to tropical areas may expand their range and become problematic in nontropical countries. Diseases transmitted by mosquitoes, such as malaria (see chapter 29), dengue fever, and several types of encephalitis, are examples. The distribution of mosquitoes is limited by cold; winter freezes kill many mosquitoes and their eggs. As a result, malaria only occurs in areas where temperatures are usually above 16°C, and yellow fever and dengue fever, transmitted by a different mosquito species from malaria, occur in areas where temperatures are normally above 10°C. Moreover, at higher temperatures, the malaria pathogen matures more rapidly.

Malaria already kills 1 million people every year; some projections suggest that the percentage of the human population at risk for malaria may increase by 33% by the end of the 21st century. Moreover, as predicted, malaria already appears to be on the move. By 1980, malaria had been eradicated from all of the United States except California, but in recent years it has appeared in a variety of southern, and even a few northern, states.

Dengue fever (sometimes called "breakbone fever" because of the pain it causes) is also spreading. Previously a disease restricted to the tropics and subtropics, where it infects 50 to 100 million people a year, it now occurs in the United States, southern South America, and northern Australia.

One of the most alarming aspects of these diseases is that no vaccines are available. Drug treatment is available (for malaria), but the parasites are rapidly evolving resistance and rendering the drugs ineffective. There is no drug treatment for dengue fever.

Solving the problem

The release of the IPCC's fourth assessment in 2007 may come to be seen as a turning point in humanity's response to climate change. Global warming is now recognized, even by former skeptics, as an ongoing phenomenon caused in large part by human actions. Even formerly recalcitrant governments now seem poised to take action, and corporations are recognizing the opportunities provided by the need to reverse human impacts. The resulting "green" technologies and practices are becoming increasingly common. With concerted efforts from citizens, corporations, and governments, the more serious consequences of global climate change hopefully can be averted, just as ozone depletion was reversed in the last century.

Learning Outcomes Review 59.6

Carbon dioxide is a significant greenhouse gas, meaning that it prevents heat from escaping the Earth so that temperatures rise. Global warming caused by changes in atmospheric composition—most notably CO_2 accumulation—may increase desertification and cause some habitats and species to disappear. Global warming may also melt ice caps and glaciers, altering coastlines as water levels rise. Violent weather events, disruption of water availability, and flooding of low-lying areas, as well as increased incidence of tropical diseases, may also occur.

■ *In what ways does global climate change pose different questions from those posed by ozone depletion?*

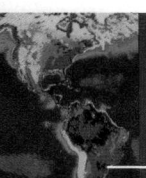

Chapter Review

59.1 Ecosystem Effects of Sun, Wind, and Water

Solar energy and the Earth's rotation affect atmospheric circulation.
The amount of solar radiation reaching the Earth's surface has a great effect on climate. The seasons result from changes in the Earth's position relative to the Sun (see figure 59.1). Hot air with its increased water content rises at the equator, then cools and loses its moisture, creating the equatorial rain forests (see figure 59.3).

As the drier cool air of the upper atmosphere moves away from the equator and then descends to Earth, it removes moisture from the Earth's surface and creates deserts on its way back to the equator.

Winds travel in curved paths relative to the Earth's surface because the Earth rotates on its axis (the Coriolis effect; see figure 59.3).

Global currents are largely driven by winds (see figure 59.4).
Four large circular gyres in ocean currents can be found, driven by wind direction. These also are influenced by the Coriolis effect.

Regional and local differences affect terrestrial ecosystems.
A rain shadow occurs when a range of mountains removes moisture from air moving over it from the windward side, creating a drier environment on the opposite side (see figure 59.5).

For every 1000-m increase in elevation, temperature drops approximately 6°C (see figure 59.6).

Microclimates are small-scale differences in conditions.

59.2 Earth's Biomes

Temperature and moisture often determine biomes.

Average annual temperature and rainfall, as well as the range of seasonal variation, determine different biomes. Eight major types of biomes are recognized.

Tropical rain forests are highly productive equatorial systems.

Savannas are tropical grasslands with seasonal rainfall.

Deserts are regions with little rainfall.

Temperate grasslands have rich soils.

Temperate deciduous forests are adapted to seasonal change.

Temperate evergreen forests are coastal.

Taiga is the northern forest where winters are harsh.

Tundra is a largely frozen treeless area with a short growing season.

59.3 Freshwater Habitats

Life in freshwater habitats depends on oxygen availability.

Oxygen is not very soluble in water. Oxygen is constantly added by photosynthesis of aquatic plants and removed by heterotrophs.

Lake and pond habitats change with water depth.

The photic zone, near the surface, is the zone of primary productivity; its depth varies with water clarity (see figure 59.12).

In the summer, the warmer water (epilimnion) floats on top of the colder water (hypolimnion). Freshwater lakes turn over twice a year as the temperature at the surface and at depth become the same, and the layers are set in motion by wind (see figure 59.13).

Lakes differ in oxygen and nutrient content.

Oligotrophic lakes have high oxygen and low nutrients, whereas eutrophic lakes are the opposite.

59.4 Marine Habitats

The ocean is divided into several zones: intertidal, neritic, photic, benthic, and pelagic zones (see figure 59.15).

Open oceans have low primary productivity.

Phytoplankton is the primary producer in open waters, and primary production is low due to low nutrient levels.

Continental shelf ecosystems provide abundant resources.

Neritic waters are found over continental shelves and have higher nutrient levels (see figure 59.15). Estuaries frequently contain rich intertidal zones. Other ecosystems include productive banks on continental shelves and symbiotic coral reef ecosystems.

Upwelling regions experience mixing of nutrients and oxygen.

In upwelling regions, local winds bring up nutrient-rich deep waters, creating the highest rates of primary production. El Niño events occur when Trade Winds weaken, restricting upwelling to surface waters rather than to the deeper nutrient-rich waters.

The deep sea is a cold, dark place with some fascinating communities.

The deep sea is the single largest habitat. Hydrothermal vent communities occur where tectonic plates are moving apart; chemoautotrophs living there obtain energy from oxidation of sulfur.

59.5 Human Impacts on the Biosphere: Pollution and Resource Depletion

Dangerous chemicals like DDT are biomagnified as energy moves up the food chain (see figure 59.20).

Freshwater habitats are threatened by pollution and resource depletion.

Point-source and diffuse pollution, acid precipitation, and overuse threaten freshwater habitats (see figure 59.21).

Forest ecosystems are threatened in tropical and temperate regions.

Deforestation leads to loss of habitat, disruption of the water cycle, and loss of nutrients. Acid rain has a major detrimental effect on forests as well as on lakes and streams (see figure 59.23).

Marine habitats are being depleted of fish and other species.

Many fisheries, such as the Georges Bank ecosystem, have collapsed and have not recovered.

Stratospheric ozone depletion has led to an ozone "hole."

Increased transmission of UV-B radiation is harmful to life. Global regulation of CFCs seems to be reversing ozone depletion.

59.6 Human Impacts on the Biosphere: Climate Change

Independent computer models predict global changes.

Carbon dioxide is a major greenhouse gas.

Carbon dioxide allows solar radiation to pass through the atmosphere but prevents heat from leaving the Earth, creating warmer conditions.

Global temperature change has affected ecosystems in the past and is doing so now.

If temperatures change rapidly, natural selection cannot occur rapidly enough to prevent many species from becoming extinct.

Global warming affects human populations as well.

Changing sea levels, increased frequency of extreme climatic events, direct and indirect effects on agriculture, and the expansion of tropical diseases can all affect human life.

UNDERSTAND

1. The Coriolis effect
   a. drives the rotation of the Earth.
   b. is responsible for the relative lack of seasonality at the equator.
   c. drives global wind circulation patterns.
   d. drives global wind and ocean circulation patterns.

2. What two factors are most important in biome distribution?
   a. Temperature and latitude
   b. Rainfall and temperature
   c. Latitude and rainfall
   d. Temperature and soil type

3. In a rain shadow, air is cooled as it rises and heated as it descends, often producing a wet and dry side because the water-holding capacity of the air
   a. is directly related to air temperature.
   b. is inversely related to air temperature.
   c. is unaffected by air temperature.
   d. produces changes in air temperature.

4. Thermal stratification in a lake
   a. is not modified by fall and spring overturn.
   b. leads to higher oxygen in deep versus surface waters.
   c. leads to higher oxygen in surface versus deep waters.
   d. is reduced when ice forms on the surface of the lake.

5. Oligotrophic lakes have
   a. low oxygen, and high nutrient availability.
   b. high oxygen, and high nutrient availability.
   c. high oxygen, and low nutrient availability.
   d. low oxygen, and low nutrient availability.

6. Deep-sea hydrothermal vent communities
   a. get their energy from photosynthesis in the photic zone near the surface.
   b. use bioluminescence to generate food.
   c. are built on the energy produced by the activity of chemoautotrophs that oxidize sulfur.
   d. contain only bacteria and other microorganisms.

7. Biological magnification occurs when
   a. pollutants increase in concentration in tissues at higher trophic levels.
   b. the effect of a pollutant is magnified by chemical interactions within organisms.
   c. an organism is placed under a dissecting scope.
   d. a pollutant has a greater than expected effect once ingested by an organism.

8. Which of the following is a point source of pollution?
   a. Lawns
   b. Smokestacks of coal-fired power plants
   c. Factory effluent pipe draining into a river
   d. Acid rain

APPLY

1. If the Earth were not tilted on its axis of rotation, the annual cycle of seasons in the northern and southern hemispheres
   a. would be reversed.   c. would be reduced.
   b. would stay the same.   d. would not exist.

2. Oligotrophic lakes can be turned into eutrophic lakes as a result of human activities such as
   a. overfishing of sensitive species, which disrupts fish communities.
   b. introducing nutrients into the water, which stimulates plant and algal growth.
   c. disrupting terrestrial vegetation near the shore, which causes soil to run into the lake.
   d. spraying pesticides into the water to control aquatic insect populations.

3. If a pesticide is harmless at low concentrations (such as, DDT) and used properly, how can it become a threat to nontarget organisms?
   a. Because after exposure to DDT, some species develop allergic reactions even at low levels of exposure
   b. Because DDT molecules can combine so that their concentration increases through time
   c. Because the concentration of chemicals such as DDT is increasingly concentrated at higher trophic levels
   d. Because global warming and exposure to UV-B radiation renders molecules such as DDT increasingly potent

4. If there are many greenhouse gases, why is only carbon dioxide considered a cause of global warming?
   a. The other gases do not cause global warming.
   b. Scientists are concerned about other causes; for example, release of methane from melting permafrost could have significant effects on global warming.
   c. Other gases occur in such low quantities that they have little effect on the climate.
   d. Carbon dioxide is the only gas that absorbs long-wavelength infrared radiation.

SYNTHESIZE

1. Discuss how figure 59.1 explains the pattern observed in figure 59.2.

2. Why are most of the Earth's deserts found at approximately 30° latitude?

3. If the world has experienced global warming many times in the past, why should we be concerned about it happening again now?

ONLINE RESOURCE

www.ravenbiology.com

Understand, Apply, and Synthesize—enhance your study with animations that bring concepts to life and practice tests to assess your understanding. Your instructor may also recommend the interactive eBook, individualized learning tools, and more.

Answer Key

CHAPTER 1

LEARNING OUTCOME QUESTIONS

1.1 No. The study of biology encompasses information/tools from chemistry, physics, geology, literally all of the "natural sciences."

1.2 A scientific theory has been tested by experimentation. A(n) hypothesis is a starting point to explain a body of observations. When predictions generated using the hypothesis have been tested it gains the confidence associated with a theory. A theory still cannot be "proved" however as new data can always force us to re-evaluate a theory.

1.3 No. Natural selection explains the patterns of living organisms we see at present, and allows us to work back in time, but it is not intended to explain how life arose. This does not mean that we can never explain this, but merely that natural selection does not do this.

1.4 Viruses do not fit well into our definition of living systems. It is a matter of controversy whether viruses should be considered "alive." They lack the basic cellular machinery, but they do have genetic information. Some theories for the origin of cells view viruses as being a step from organic molecules to cell, but looking at current organisms, they do not fulfill our definition of life.

INQUIRY QUESTIONS

Page 10 Reducing the factor by which the geometric progression increases (lowering the value of the exponent) reduces the difference between numbers of people and amount of food production. It can be achieved by lowering family size or delaying childbearing.

Page 11 A snake would fall somewhere near the bird, as birds and snakes are closely related.

UNDERSTAND

1. b   2. c   3. a   4. b   5. d   6. b   7. c   8. c

APPLY

1. d   2. d   3. c   4. d   5. d   6. d   7. a

SYNTHESIZE

1. For something to be considered living it would demonstrate organization, possibly including a cellular structure. The organism would gain and use energy to maintain homeostasis, respond to its environment, and to grow and reproduce. These latter properties would be difficult to determine if the evidence of life from other planets comes from fossils. Similarly, the ability of an alien organism to evolve could be difficult to establish.

2. a. The variables that were held the same between the two experiments include the broth, the flask, and the sterilization step.

   b. The shape of the flask influences the experiment because any cells present in the air can enter the flask with the broken neck, but they are trapped in the neck of the other flask.

   c. If cells can arise spontaneously, then cell growth will occur in both flasks. If cells can only arise from preexisting cells (cells in the air), then only the flask with the broken neck will grow cells. Breaking the neck exposes the broth to a source of cells.

   d. If the sterilization step did not actually remove all cells, then growth would have occurred in both flasks. This result would seem to support the hypothesis that life can arise spontaneously.

CHAPTER 2

LEARNING OUTCOME QUESTIONS

2.1 If the number of proton exceeds neutrons, there is no effect on charge; if the number of protons exceeds electrons, then the charge is (+).

2.2 Atoms are reactive when their outer electron shell is not filled with electrons. The noble gases have filled outer electrons shells, and are thus unreactive.

2.3 An ionic bond results when there is a transfer of electrons resulting in positive and negative ions that are attracted to each other. A covalent bond is the result of two atoms sharing electrons. Polar covalent bonds involve unequal sharing of electrons. This produces regions of partial charge, but not ions.

2.4 C and H have about the same electronegativity, and thus form nonpolar covalent bonds. This would not result in a cohesive or adhesive fluid.

2.5 Since ice floats, a lake will freeze from the top down, not the bottom up. This means that water remains fluid on the bottom of the lake allowing living things to overwinter.

2.6 Since pH is a log scale, this would be a change of 100 fold in $[H^+]$.

INQUIRY QUESTION

Page 30 The buffer works over a broad range because it ionizes more completely as pH increases; in essence, there is more acid to neutralize the greater amount of base you are adding. At pH4 none of the buffer is ionized. Thus below that pH, base raises the pH without the ameliorating effects of the ionization of the buffer.

UNDERSTAND

1. b   2. d   3. b   4. a   5. c   6. d   7. b

APPLY

1. c   2. b   3. a   4. c   5. d   6. Chemical reactions involve changes in the electronic configuration of atoms. Radioactive decay involves the actual decay of the nucleus producing another atom and emitting radiation.

SYNTHESIZE

1. A cation is an element that tends to lose an electron from its outer energy level, leaving behind a net positive charge due to the presence of the protons in the atomic nucleus. Electrons are only lost from the outer energy level if that loss is energetically favorable, that is, if it makes the atom more stable by virtue of obtaining a filled outer energy level (the octet rule). You can predict which elements are likely to function as cations by calculating which of the elements will possess one (or two) electrons in their outer energy level. Recall that each orbital surrounding an atomic nucleus can only hold two electrons. Energy level K is a single *s* orbital and can hold two electrons. Energy level L consists of another *s* orbital plus three *p* orbitals—holding a total of eight electrons. Use the atomic number of each element to predict the total number of electrons present. Examples of other cations would include: hydrogen (H), lithium (Li), magnesium (Mg), and beryllium (Be).

2. Silicon has an atomic number of 14. This means that there are four unpaired electrons in its outer energy level (comparable to carbon). Based on this fact, you can conclude that silicon, like carbon, could form four covalent bonds. Silicon also falls within the group of elements with atomic masses less than 21, a property of the elements known to participate in the formation of biologically important molecules. Interestingly, silicon is much more prevalent than carbon on Earth. Although silicon dioxide is found in the cell walls of plants and single-celled organisms called diatoms, silicon-based life has not been identified on this planet. Given the abundance of silicon on Earth you can conclude that some other aspect of the chemistry of this atom makes it incompatible with the formation of molecules that make up living organisms.

3. Water is considered to be a critical molecule for the evolution of life on Earth. It is reasonable to assume that water on other planets could play a similar role. The key properties of water that would support its role in the evolution of life are:

   • The ability of water to acts as a solvent. Molecules dissolved in water could move and interact in ways that would allow for the formation of larger, more complex molecules such as those found in living organisms.

   • The high specific heat of water. Water can modulate and maintain its temperature, thereby protecting the molecules or organisms within it from temperature extremes—an important feature on other planets.

- The difference in density between ice and liquid water. The fact that ice floats is a simple, but important feature of water environments since it allows living organisms to remain in a liquid environment protected under a surface of ice. This possibility is especially intriguing given recent evidence of ice-covered oceans on Europa, a moon of the planet Jupiter.

CHAPTER 3

LEARNING OUTCOME QUESTIONS

3.1 Hydrolysis is the reverse reaction of dehydration. Dehydration is a synthetic reaction involving the loss of water and hydrolysis is cleavage by addition of water.

3.2 Starch and glycogen are both energy storage molecules. Their highly branched nature allows the formation of droplets, and the similarity in the bonds holding adjacent glucoses together mean that the enzyme we have to break down glycogen allow us to break down starch. The same enzymes do not allow us to break down cellulose. The structure of cellulose leads to the formation of tough fibers.

3.3 The sequence of bases would be complementary. Wherever there is an A in the DNA there would be a U in the RNA, wherever there is a G in the DNA there would be a C in the RNA.

3.4 If an unknown protein has sequence similarity to a known protein, we can infer its function is also similar. If an unknown protein has known functional domains or motifs we can also use these to help predict function.

3.5 Phospholipids have a charged group replacing one of the fatty acids in a triglyceride. This leads to an amphipathic molecule that has both hydrophobic and hydrophilic regions. This will spontaneously form bilayer membranes in water.

UNDERSTAND

1.b   2.a   3.d   4.c   5.b   6.b   7.c   8.b

APPLY

1.c   2.d   3.b   4.d   5.b   6.b   7.d

SYNTHESIZE

1. The four biological macromolecules all have different structure and function. In comparing carbohydrates, nucleic acids and proteins, we can think of these as being polymers with different monomers. In the case of carbohydrates, the polymers are all polymers of the simple sugar glucose. These are energy storage molecules (with many C-H bonds) and structural molecules such as cellulose that make tough fibers.
   Nucleic acids are formed of nucleotide monomers, each of which consists of ribose, phosphate, and a nitrogenous base. These molecules are informational molecules that encode information in the sequence of bases. The bases interact in specific ways: A base pairs with T and G base pairs with C. This is the basis for their informational storage.
   Proteins are formed of amino acid polymers. There are 20 different amino acids, and thus an incredible number of different proteins. These can have an almost unlimited number of functions. These functions arise from the amazing flexibility in structure of protein chains.

2. *Nucleic Acids*—Hydrogen bonds are important for complementary base-pairing between the two strands of nucleic acid that make up a molecule of DNA. Complementary base-pairing can also occur within the single nucleic acid strand of a RNA molecule.
   Proteins—Hydrogen bonds are involved in both the secondary and tertiary levels of protein structure. The α helices and β-pleated sheets of secondary structure are stabilized by hydrogen bond formation between the amino and carboxyl groups of the amino acid backbone. Hydrogen bond formation between R-groups helps stabilize the three-dimensional folding of the protein at the tertiary level of structure.
   *Carbohydra*tes—Hydrogen bonds are less important for carbohydrates; however, these bonds are responsible for the formation of the fibers of cellulose that make up the cell walls of plants.
   Lipids—Hydrogen bonds are not involved in the structure of lipid molecules. The inability of fatty acids to form hydrogen bonds with water is key to their hydrophobic nature.

3. We have enzymes that can break down glycogen. Glycogen is formed from alpha-glucose subunits. Starch is also formed from alpha-glucose units, but cellulose is formed from beta-glucose units. The enzymes that break the alpha-glycosidic linkages cannot break the beta-glycosidic linkages. Thus we can degrade glycogen and starch but not cellulose.

CHAPTER 4

LEARNING OUTCOME QUESTIONS

4.1 The statement about all cells coming from preexisting cells might need to be modified. It would really depend on whether these Martian life forms were based on a similar molecular/cellular basis as terrestrial life.

4.2 Bacteria and archaea both tend to be single cells that lack a membrane-bounded nucleus, and extensive internal endomembrane systems. They both have a cell wall, although the composition is different. They do not undergo mitosis, although the proteins involved in DNA replication and cell division are not similar.

4.3 Part of what gives different organs their unique identities are the specialized cell types found in each. That does not mean that there will not be some cell types common to all (epidermal cells for example) but that organs tend to have specialized cell types.

4.4 They don't!

4.5 The nuclear genes that encode organellar proteins moved from the organelle to the nucleus. There is evidence for a lot of "horizontal gene transfer" across domains; this is an example of how that can occur.

4.6 It provides structure and support for larger cells, especially in animal cells that lack a cell wall.

4.7 Microtubules and microfilaments are both involved in cell motility, and in movement of substance around cells. Intermediate filaments do not have this dynamic role, but are more structural.

4.8 Cell junctions help to put together cells into higher level structures that are organized and joined in different ways. Different kinds of junctions can be used for different functional purposes.

INQUIRY QUESTIONS

Page 64 Stretch, dent, convolute, fold, add more than one nuclei, anything which would increase the amount of diffusion between the cytoplasm and the external environment.

Page 75 Both the cristae of mitochondria and the thylakoids of chloroplasts, where many of the reactions take place leading to the production of ATP, are highly folded. The convolutions allow for a large surface area increasing the efficiency of the mechanisms of oxidative phosphorylation.

Page 80 Ciliated cell in the trachea help to remove particulate matter from the respiratory tact where it can be expelled or swallowed and processed in the digestive tract.

UNDERSTAND

1.d   2.d   3.c   4.a   5.c   6.d   7.b

APPLY

1.c   2.b   3.b   4.b   5.c   6.b   7.a

SYNTHESIZE

1. Your diagram should start at the SER and then move to the RER, Golgi apparatus, and finally to the plasma membrane. Small transport vesicles are the mechanism that would carry a phospholipids molecule between two membrane compartments. Transport vesicles are small "membrane bubbles" composed of a phospholipid bilayer.

2. If these organelles were free-living bacteria, they would have the features found in bacteria. Mitochondria and chloroplasts do both have DNA but no nucleus, and they lack the complex organelles found in eukaryotes. At first glance, the cristae may seem to be an internal membrane system, but they are actually infoldings of the inner membrane. If endosymbiosis occurred, this would be the plasma membrane of the endosymbiont, and the outer membrane would be the plasma membrane of the engulfing cell. Another test would be to compare DNA in these organelles with current bacteria. This has actually shown similarities that make us confident of the identity of the endosymbionts.

3. The prokaryotic and eukaryotic flagella are examples of an analogous trait. Both flagella function to propel the cell through its environment by converting chemical energy into mechanical force. The key difference is in the structure of the flagella. The bacterial flagellum is composed of a single protein emerging from a basal body anchored within the cell's plasma membrane and using the potential energy of a proton gradient to cause a rotary movement. In contrast, the flagellum of the eukaryote is composed of

many different proteins assembled into a complex axoneme structure that uses ATP energy to cause an undulating motion.

4. Eukaryotic cells are distinguished from prokaryotic cells by the presence of a system of internal membrane compartments and membrane-bounded organelles such as mitochondria and chloroplasts. As outlined in Figure 4.19, the first step in the evolution of the eukaryotic cell was the infolding of the plasma membrane to create separate internal membranes such as the nuclear envelope and the endoplasmic reticulum. The origins of mitochondria and chloroplasts are hypothesized to be the result of a bit of cellular "indigestion" where aerobic or photosynthetic prokaryotes were engulfed, but not digested by the larger ancestor eukaryote. Given this information, there are two possible scenarios for the origin of *Giardia*. In the first scenario, the ancestor of *Giardia* split off from the eukaryotic lineage after the evolution of the nucleus, but before the acquisition of mitochondria. In the second scenario, the ancestor of *Giardia* split off after the acquisition of mitochondria, and subsequently lost the mitochondria. At present, neither of these two scenarios can be rejected. The first case was long thought to be the best explanation, but recently it has been challenged by evidence for the second case.

CHAPTER 5

LEARNING OUTCOME QUESTIONS

5.1 Cells would not be able to control their contents. Nonpolar molecules would be able to cross the membrane by diffusion, as would small polar molecules, but without proteins to control the passage of specific molecules, it would not function as a semipermeable membrane.

5.2 No. The nonpolar interior of the bilayer would not be soluble in the solvent. The molecules will organize with their nonpolar tails in the solvent, but the negative charge on the phosphates would repel other phosphates.

5.3 Transmembrane domains anchor protein in the membrane. They associate with the hydrophobic interior, thus they must be hydrophobic as well. If they slide out of the interior, they are repelled by water.

5.4 The concentration of the IV will be isotonic with your blood cell. If it were hypotonic, your blood cells would take on water and burst; if it were hypertonic, your blood cells would lose water and shrink.

5.5 Channel proteins are aqueous pores that allow facilitated diffusion. They cannot actively transport ions. Carrier proteins bind to their substrates and couple transport to some form of energy for active transport.

5.6 In all cases, there is recognition and specific binding of a molecule by a protein. In each case this binding is necessary for biological function.

INQUIRY QUESTIONS

Page 94 As the name suggests for the fluid mosaic model, cell membranes have some degree of fluidity. The degree of fluidity varies with the composition of the membrane, but in all membranes, phospholipids are able to move about within the membrane. Also, due to the hydrophobic and hydrophilic opposite ends of phospholipid molecules, phospholipid bilayers form spontaneously. Therefore, if stressing forces happen to damage a membrane, adjacent phospholipids automatically move to fill in the opening.

Page 95 Integral membrane proteins are those that are embedded within the membrane structure and provide passageways across the membrane. Because integral membrane proteins must pass through both polar and nonpolar regions of the phospholipid bilayer, the protein portion held within the nonpolar fatty acid interior of the membrane must also be nonpolar. The amino acid sequence of an intregral protein would have polar amino acids at both ends, with nonpolar amino acids comprising the middle portion of the protein.

UNDERSTAND

1. d   2. a   3. d   4. d   5. b   6. d   7. a

APPLY

1. c   2. b   3. d   4. c   5. d

SYNTHESIZE

1. Since the membrane proteins become intermixed in the absence of the energy molecule, ATP, one can conclude that chemical energy is not required for their movement. Since the proteins do not move and intermix when the temperature is cold, one can also conclude that the movement is temperature-sensitive. The passive diffusion of molecules also depends on tempera-

ture and does not require chemical energy; therefore, it is possible to conclude that membrane fluidity occurs as a consequence of passive diffusion.

2. The inner half of the bilayer of the various endomembranes becomes the outer half of the bilayer of the plasma membrane.

3. Lipids can be inserted into one leaflet to produce asymmetry. When lipids are synthesized in the SER, they can be assembled into asymmetric membranes. There are also enzymes that can flip lipids from one leaflet to the other.

CHAPTER 6

LEARNING OUTCOME QUESTIONS

6.1 At the bottom of the ocean, light is not an option as it does not penetrate that deep. However, there is a large source of energy in the form of reduced minerals, such as sulfur compounds, that can be oxidized. These are abundant at hydrothermal vents found at the junctions of tectonic plates. This supports whole ecosystems dependent on bacteria that oxidize reduced minerals available at the hydrothermal vents.

6.2 In a word: No. Enzymes only alter the rate of a reaction; they do not change the thermodynamics of the reaction. The action of an enzyme does not change the ΔG for the reaction.

6.3 In the text, it stated that the average person turns over approximately their body weight in ATP per day. This gives us enough information to determine approximately the amount of energy released:

100 kg = 1.0 x 10^5 g
$(1.0 \times 10^5 \text{ g})/(507.18 \text{ g/mol})=197.2$ mol
$(197.2 \text{ mol})(7.3 \text{ kcal/mol})=1{,}439$ kcal

6.4 This is a question that cannot be definitely answered, but we can give some reasonable conjectures. First, DNA's location is in the nucleus and not the cytoplasm, where most enzymes are found. Second, the double stranded structure of DNA is works well for information storage, but would not necessarily function well as an enzyme. Each base interacts with a base on the opposite strand, which makes for a very stable linear molecule, but does not encourage folding into the kind of complex 3-D shape found in enzymes.

6.5 Feedback inhibition is common in pathways that synthesize metabolites. In these anabolic pathways, when the end product builds up, it feeds back to inhibit its own production. Catabolic pathways are involved in the degradation of compounds. Feedback inhibition makes less biochemical sense in a pathway that degrades compounds as these are usually involved in energy metabolism, or recycling or removal of compounds. Thus the end product is destroyed or removed and cannot feed back.

INQUIRY QUESTION

Page 113 If ATP hydrolysis supplies more energy than is needed to drive the endergonic reaction, the overall process is exergonic. The reactions result in a net release of energy, so the ΔG for the overall process is therefore negative.

UNDERSTAND

1. b   2. a   3. b   4. a   5. d   6. b   7. d

APPLY

1. b   2. c   3. d   4. c   5. c   6. c

SYNTHESIZE

1. a. At 40°C the enzyme is at it optimum. The rate of the reaction is at its highest level.

   b. Temperature is a factor that influences enzyme function. This enzyme does not appear to function at either very cold or very hot temperatures. The shape of the enzyme is affected by temperature, and the enzyme's structure is altered enough at extreme temperatures that it no longer binds substrate. Alternatively, the enzyme may be denatured—that is a complete loss of normal three-dimensional shape at extreme temperatures. Think about frying an egg: What happens to the proteins in the egg?

   c. Everyone's body is slightly different. If the temperature optimum was very narrow, then the cells that make up a body would be vulnerable. Having a broad range of temperature optimums keeps the enzyme functioning.

2. a. The reaction rate would be slow because of the low concentration of the substrate ATP. The rate of reaction depends on substrate concentration.

b. ATP acts like a noncompetitive, allosteric inhibitor when ATP levels are very high. If ATP binds to the allosteric site, then the reaction should slow down.

c. When ATP levels are high, the excess ATP molecules bind to the allosteric site and inhibit the enzyme. The allosteric inhibitor functions by causing a change in the shape of the active site in the enzyme. This reaction is an example of feedback regulation because ATP is a final product of the overall series of reactions associated with glycolysis. The cell regulates glycolysis by regulating this early step catalyzed by phosphofructokinase; the allosteric inhibitor is the "product" of glycolysis (and later stages) ATP.

CHAPTER 7

LEARNING OUTCOME QUESTIONS

7.1 Cells require energy for a wide variety of functions. The reactions involved in the oxidation of glucose are complex and linking these to the different metabolic functions that require energy would be inefficient. Thus cells make and use ATP as a reusable source of energy.

7.2 The location of glycolysis does not argue for or against the endosymbiotic origin of mitochondria. If could have been located in the mitochondria previously and moved to the cytoplasm, or could have always been located in the cytoplasm in eukaryotes.

7.3 For an enzyme like pyruvate decarboxylase the complex reduces the distance for the diffusion of substrates for the different stages of the reaction. If there are any unwanted side reactions they are prevented. Finally the reactions occur within a single unit and thus can be controlled in a coordinated fashion. The main disadvantage is that since the enzymes are all part of a complex their evolution is more constrained than if they were independent.

7.4 At the end of the Krebs cycle, the electrons removed from glucose are all carried by soluble electron carriers. Most of these are in NADH and a few are in $FADH_2$. All of these are all fed into the electron transport chain under aerobic conditions where they are used to produce a proton gradient.

7.5 A hole in the outer membrane would allow protons in the intermembrane space to leak out. This would destroy the proton gradient across the inner membrane, stopping the phosphorylation of ADP by ATP synthase.

7.6 The inner membrane actually allows a small amount of leakage of protons back into the matrix, reducing the yield per NADH. The proton gradient can also be used to power other functions, such as the transport of pyruvate. The actual yield is also affected by the relative concentrations ADP, Pi, and ATP as the equilibrium constant for this reaction depends on this.

7.7 Glycolysis, which is the starting point for respiration from sugars is regulated at the enzyme phosphofructokinase. This enzyme is just before the 6-C skeleton is split into two 3-C molecules. The allosteric effectors for this enzyme include ATP and citrate. Thus the "end product" ATP, and an intermediate from the Krebs cycle, both feedback to inhibit the first part of this process.

7.8 The first obvious point is that the most likely type of ecosystem would be one where oxygen is nonexistent or limiting. This includes marine, aquatic, and soil environments. Any place where oxygen is in short supply is expected to be dominated by anaerobic organisms and respiration produces more energy than fermentation.

7.9 The short answer is no. The reason is two-fold. First the oxidation of fatty acids feeds acetyl units into the Krebs cycle. The primary output of the Krebs cycle is electrons that are fed into the electron transport chain to eventually produce ATP by chemiosmosis. The second reason is that the process of beta-oxidation that produces the acetyl units is oxygen dependent as well. This is because beta-oxidation uses FAD as a cofactor for an oxidation, and the $FADH_2$ is oxidized by the electron transport chain.

7.10 The evidence for the origins of metabolism is indirect. The presence of O_2 in the atmosphere is the result of photosynthesis, so the record of when we went from a reducing to an oxidizing atmosphere chronicles the rise of oxygenic photosynthesis. Glycolysis is a universal pathway that is found in virtually all types of cells. This indicates that it is an ancient pathway that likely evolved prior to other types of energy metabolism. Nitrogen fixation probably evolved in the reducing atmosphere that preceded oxygenic photosynthesis as it is poisoned by oxygen, and aided by the reducing atmosphere.

INQUIRY QUESTION

Page 142 During the catabolism of fats, each round of 2-oxidation uses one molecule of ATP and generates one molecule each of $FADH_2$ and NADH. For a 16-carbon fatty acid, seven rounds of 2-oxidation would convert the fatty acid into eight molecules of acetyl-CoA. The oxidation of each acetyl-CoA in the Krebs

cycle produces 10 molecules of ATP. The overall ATP yield from a 16-carbon fatty acid would be: a net gain of 21 ATP from 7 rounds of 2-oxidation [gain of 4 ATP per round minus 1 per round to prime reactions] + 80 ATP from the oxidation of 8 acetyl-CoAs = 101 molecules of ATP.

UNDERSTAND

1. d 2. d 3. c 4. c 5. a 6. d 7. c

APPLY

1. b 2. b 3. d 4. b 5. a 6. b 7. b

SYNTHESIZE

1.

Molecules	Glycolysis	Cellular Respiration
Glucose	*Is the starting material for the reaction*	*Does not directly use glucose; however, does use pyruvate derived from glucose*
Pyruvate	*The end product of glycolysis*	*The starting material for cellular respiration*
Oxygen	*Not required*	*Required for aerobic respiration, but not for anaerobic respiration*
ATP	*Produced through substrate-level phosphorylation*	*Produced through oxidative phosphorylation. More produced than in glycolysis*
CO_2	*Not produced*	*Produced during pyruvate oxidation and Krebs cycle*

2. The electron transport chain of the inner membrane of the mitochondria functions to create a hydrogen ion concentration gradient by pumping protons into the intermembrane space. In a typical mitochondrion, the protons can only diffuse back down their concentration gradient by moving through the ATP synthase and generating ATP. If protons can move through another transport protein then the potential energy of the hydrogen ion concentration gradient would be "lost" as heat.

3. If brown fat persists in adults, then the uncoupling mechanism to generate heat described above could result in weight loss under cold conditions. There is now some evidence to indicate that this may be the case.

CHAPTER 8

LEARNING OUTCOME QUESTIONS

8.1 Both chloroplasts and mitochondria have an outer membrane and an inner membrane. The inner membrane in both forms an elaborate structure. These inner membrane systems have electron transport chains that move protons across the membrane to allow for the synthesis of ATP by chemiosmosis. They also both have a soluble compartment in which a variety of enzymes carry out reactions.

8.2 All of the carbon in your body comes from carbon fixation by autotrophs. Thus, all of the carbon in your body was once CO_2 in the atmosphere, before it was fixed by plants.

8.3 The action spectrum for photosynthesis refers to the most effective wavelengths. The absorption spectrum for an individual pigment shows how much light is absorbed at different wavelengths.

8.4 Before the discovery of photosystems, we assumed that each chlorophyll molecule absorbed photons resulting in excited electrons.

8.5 Without a proton gradient, synthesis of ATP by chemiosmosis would be impossible. However, NADPH could still be synthesized because electron transport would still occur as long as photons were still being absorbed to begin the process.

8.6 A portion of the Calvin cycle is the reverse of glycolysis (the reduction of 3-phosphoglycerate to glyceraldehyde-3-phosphate).

8.7 Both C_4 plants and CAM plants fix carbon by incorporating CO_2 into the 4-carbon malate, then use this to produce high local levels of CO_2 for the Calvin cycle. The main difference is that in C_4 plants, this occurs in different cells, and in CAM plants this occurs at different times.

INQUIRY QUESTIONS

Page 150 Light energy is used in light-dependent reactions to reduce $NADP^+$ and to produce ATP. Molecules of chlorophyll absorb photons of light energy, but only within narrow energy ranges (specific wavelengths of light). When all chlorophyll molecules are in use, no additional increase in light intensity will increase the rate at which they can absorb light energy.

Page 154 Saturation levels should be higher when light intensity is greater, up to a maximum level. If it were possible to minimize the size of photosystems by reducing the number of chlorophyll molecules in each, then the saturation level would also increase.

Page 157 You could conclude that the two photosystems do not function sequentially.

UNDERSTAND

1. c   2. a   3. a   4. b   5. c   6. c   7. a   8. b

APPLY

1. d   2. b   3. c   4. c   5. d   6. b   7. a   8. a

SYNTHESIZE

1. In C_3 plants CO_2 reacts with ribulose 1,5-bisphosphate (RuBP) to yield 2 molecules of PGA. This reaction is catalyzed by the enzyme rubisco. Rubisco also catalyzes the oxidation of RuBP. Which reaction predominates depends on the relative concentrations of reactants. The reactions of the Calvin cycle reduce the PGA to G3P, which can be used to make a variety of sugars including RuBP. In C_4 and CAM plants, an initial fixation reaction incorporates CO_2 into malate. The malate then can be decarboxylated to pyruvate and CO_2 to produce locally high levels of CO_2. The high levels of CO_2 get around the oxidation of RuBP by rubisco. In C_4 plants malate is produced in one cell, then shunted into an adjacent cell that lacks stomata to produce high levels of CO_2. CAM plants fix carbon into malate at night when their stomata are open, then use this during the day to fuel the Calvin cycle. Both are evolutionary innovations that have arisen in hot dry climates that allow plants to more efficiently fix carbon and prevent desiccation.

2. Figure 8.19 diagrams this relationship. The oxygen produced by photosynthesis is used as a final electron acceptor for electron transport in respiration. The CO_2 that results from the oxidation of glucose (or fatty acids) is incorporated into organic compounds via the Calvin cycle. Respiration also produces water, while photosynthesis consumes water.

3. Yes. Plants use their chloroplasts to convert light energy into chemical energy. During light reactions ATP and NADPH are created, but these molecules are consumed during the Calvin cycle and are not available for the cell's general use. The G3P produced by the Calvin cycle stores the chemical energy from the light reactions within its chemical bonds. Ultimately, this energy is stored in glucose and retrieved by the cell through the process of glycolysis and cellular respiration.

CHAPTER 9

LEARNING OUTCOME QUESTIONS

9.1 Ligands bind to receptors based on complementary shapes. This interaction based on molecular recognition is similar to how enzymes interact with their ligands.

9.2 Hydrophobic molecule can cross the membrane and are thus more likely to have an internal receptor.

9.3 Intracellular receptors have direct effects on gene expression. This generally leads to effects with longer duration.

9.4 Ras protein occupies a central role in signaling pathways involving growth factors. A number of different kinds of growth factors act through Ras. So it is not surprising that this is mutated in a number of different cancers.

9.5 GPCRs are a very ancient and flexible receptor/signaling pathway. The genes encoding these receptors have been duplicated and then have diversified over evolutionary time so now there are many members of this gene family.

UNDERSTAND

1. b   2. b   3. c   4. d   5. b   6. d   7. c   8. a

APPLY

1. b   2. c   3. b   4. d   5. d   6. c

SYNTHESIZE

1. All signaling events start with a ligand binding to a receptor. The receptor initiates a chain of events that ultimately leads to a change in cellular

behavior. In some cases the change is immediate—for example, the opening of an ion channel. In other cases the change requires more time before it occurs, such as when the MAP kinase pathway becomes activated multiple different kinases become activated and deactivated. Some signals only affect a cell for a short time (the channel example), but other signals can permanently change the cell by changing gene expression, and therefore the number and kind of proteins found in the cell.

2. a. This system involves *both* autocrine and paracrine signaling because Netrin-1 can influence the cells within the crypt that are responsible for its production and the neighboring cells.

   b. The binding of Netrrin-1 to its receptor produces the signal for cell growth. This signal would be strongest in the regions of the tissue with the greatest amount of Netrin-1—that is, in the crypts. A concentration gradient of Netrin-1 exists such that the levels of this ligand are lowest at the tips of the villi. Consequently, the greatest amount of cell death would occur at the villi tips.

   c. Tumors occur when cell growth goes on unregulated. In the absence of Netrin-1, the Netrin-1 receptor can trigger cell death—controlling the number of cells that make up the epithelial tissue. Without this mechanism for controlling cell number, tumor formation is more likely.

CHAPTER 10

LEARNING OUTCOME QUESTIONS

10.1 The concerted replication and segregation of chromosomes works well with one small chromosome, but would likely not work as well with many chromosomes.

10.2 No.

10.3 The first irreversible step is the commitment to DNA replication.

10.4 Loss of cohesins would mean that the products of DNA replication would not be kept together. This would make normal mitosis impossible, and thus lead to aneuploid cells and probably be lethal.

10.5 The segregation of chromatids that lose cohesin would be random as they could not longer be held at metaphase attached to opposite poles. This would likely lead to gain and loss of this chromosome in daughter cells due to improper partitioning.

10.6 Tumor suppressor genes are genetically recessive, while proto-oncogenes are dominant. Loss of function for a tumor suppressor gene leads to cancer while inappropriate expression or gain of function lead to cancer with proto-oncogenes.

UNDERSTAND

1. d   2. b   3. b   4. b   5. a   6. c   7. b

APPLY

1. d   2. a   3. c   4. b   5. d   6. c   7. d

SYNTHESIZE

1. If Wee-1 were absent then there would be no way for the cell to phosphorylate Cdk. If Cdk is not phosphorylated, then it cannot be inhibited. If Cdk is not inhibited, then it will remain active. If Cdk remains active, then it will continue to signal the cell to move through the G_2/M checkpoint, but now in an unregulated manner. The cells would undergo multiple rounds of cell division without the growth associated with G_2. As a consequence, the daughter cells will become smaller and smaller with each division—hence the name of the protein!

2. Growth factor = ligand

   1. Ligand binds to receptor (the growth factor will bind to a growth factor receptor).
   2. A signal is transduced (carried) into the cytoplasm.
   3. A signal cascade is triggered. Multiple intermediate proteins or second messengers will be affected.
   4. A transcription factor will be activated to bind to a specific site on the DNA.
   5. Transcription occurs and the mRNA enters the cytoplasm.
   6. The mRNA is translated and a protein is formed.
   7. The protein functions within the cytoplasm—possibly triggering S phase.

   If you study Figure 10.22 you will see a similar pathway for the formation of S phase proteins following receptor–ligand binding by a growth factor. In this diagram various proteins in the signaling pathway become phosphorylated and then dephosphorylated. Ultimately, the Rb protein that regulated the transcription factor E2F becomes phosphorylated. This releases the E2F and allows it to bind to the gene for S phase proteins and cyclins.

3. Proto-oncogenes tend to encode proteins that function in signal transduction pathways that control cell division. When the regulation of these proteins is aberrant, or they are stuck in the "on" state by mutation, it can lead to cancer. Tumor suppressor genes, on the other hand, tend to be in genes that encode proteins that suppress instead of activate cell division. Thus loss of function for a tumor suppressor gene leads to cancer.

CHAPTER 11

LEARNING OUTCOME QUESTIONS

11.1 Stem cells divide by mitosis to produce one cell that can undergo meiosis, and another stem cell.

11.2 No. Keeping sister chromatids together at the first division is key to this is reductive division. Homologues segregate at the first division, reducing the number of chromosomes by half.

11.3 An improper disjunction at anaphase I would result in 4 aneuploid gametes: 2 with an extra chromosome and 2 that are missing a chromosome. Nondisjunction at anaphase II would result in 2 normal gametes and 2 aneuploid gametes: 1 with an extra chromosome and 1 missing a chromosome.

11.4 The independent alignment of homologous pairs at metaphase I and the process of crossing over. The first shuffles the genome at the level of entire chromosomes, and the second shuffles the genome at the level of individual chromosomes.

INQUIRY QUESTION

Page 217 No, at the conclusion of meiosis I each cell has a single copy of each homologue. So, even if the attachment of sister chromatids were lost after a meiosis I division, the results would not be the same as mitosis.

UNDERSTAND

1. c 2. d 3. a 4. b 5. b 6. a 7. b

APPLY

1. c 2. b 3. b 4. d 5. b 6. a

SYNTHESIZE

1. Compare your figure with Figure 11.8.
   a. There would be three homologous pairs of chromosomes for an organism with a diploid number of six.
   b. For each pair of homologues, you should now have a maternal and paternal pair.
   c. Many possible arrangements are possible. The key to your image is that it must show the homologues aligned pairwise—not single-file along the metaphase plate. The maternal and paternal homologues *do not* have to align on the same side of the cell. Independent assortment means that the pairs can be mixed.
   d. A diagram of metaphase II would not include the homologous pairs. The pairs have separated during anaphase of meiosis I. Your picture should diagram the haploid number of chromosomes, in this case three, aligned single-file along the metaphase plate. Remember that meiosis II is similar to mitosis.

2. The diploid chromosome number of a mule is 63. The mule receives 32 chromosomes from its horse parent (diploid 64: haploid 32) and another 31 chromosomes from its donkey parent (diploid 61: haploid 31). 32 + 31 = 63. The haploid number for the mule would be one half the diploid number $63 \div 2 = 31.5$. Can there be a 0.5 chromosome? Even if the horse and donkey chromosomes can pair (no guarantee of that) there will be one chromosome without a partner. This will lead to aneuploid gametes that are not viable.

3. Independent assortment involves the random distribution of maternal versus paternal homologues into the daughter cells produced during meiosis I. The number of possible gametes is equal to 2^n, where n is the haploid number of chromosomes. Crossing over involves the physical exchange of genetic material between homologous chromosomes, creating new combinations of genes on a single chromosome. Crossing over is a relatively rare event that affects large blocks of genetic material, so independent assortment likely has the greatest influence on genetic diversity.

4. Aneuploid gametes are cells that contain the wrong number of chromosomes. Aneuploidy occurs as a result of *nondisjunction*, or lack of separation of the chromosomes during either phase of meiosis.

a. Nondisjunction occurs at the point when the chromosomes are being pulled to opposite poles. This occurs during anaphase.
b. Use an image like Figure 11.8 and illustrate nondisjunction at anaphase I versus anaphase II

Anaphase I nondisjunction:

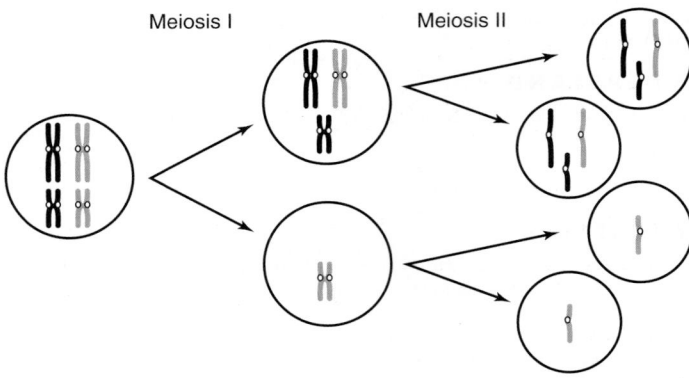

Meiosis I   Meiosis II

CHAPTER 12

LEARNING OUTCOME QUESTIONS

12.1 Both had an effect, but the approach is probably the most important. In theory, his approach would have worked for any plant, or even animal he chose. In practice, the ease of both cross and self-fertilization was helpful.

12.2 ⅓ of tall F_2 plants are true-breeding.

12.3 The events of meiosis I are much more important in explaining Mendel's laws. During anaphase I homologues separate and are thus segregated, and the alignment of different homologous pairs at metaphase I is independent.

12.4 Assuming independent assortment of all three genes, the cross is Aa Bb Cc × Aa Bb Cc and the prob(A_ B_ C_)=(¾) (¾) (¾)=27/64.

12.5 1:1:1:1 dom dom:dom rec:rec dom:rec rec.

12.6 6/16.

INQUIRY QUESTIONS

Page 223 The ability to control whether the plants self-fertilized or cross-fertilized was of paramount importance in Mendel's studies. Results due to cross-fertilization would have had confounding influences on the predicted number of offspring with a particular phenotype.

Page 227 Each of the affected females in the study had one unaffected parent, which means that each is heterozygous for the dominant trait. If each female marries an unaffected (recessive) male, each could produce unaffected offspring. The chance of having unaffected offspring is 50% in each case.

Page 228 Genetic defects that remain hidden or dormant as heterzygotes in the recessive state are more likely to be revealed in homozygous state among closely related individuals.

Page 235 Almost certainly, differences in major phenotypic traits of twins would be due to environmental factors such as diet.

UNDERSTAND

1. b 2. c 3. c 4. c 5. b 6. d

APPLY

1. b 2. c 3. b 4. a 5. c 6. d

SYNTHESIZE

1. The approach to solving this type of problem is to identify the possible gametes. Separate the possible gamete combinations into the boxes along the top and side. Fill in the Punnet square by combining alleles from each parent.
   a. A monohybrid cross between individuals with the genotype *Aa* and *Aa*

	A	*a*
A	AA	Aa
a	aA	aa

Phenotypic ratio: 3 dominant to 1 recessive

b. A dihybrid cross between two individuals with the genotype *AaBb*

	AB	*Ab*	*aB*	*ab*
AB	*AABB*	*AABb*	*AaBB*	*AaBb*
Ab	*AAbB*	*AAbb*	*AabB*	*Aabb*
aB	*aABB*	*aABb*	*aaBB*	*aaBb*
ab	*aAbB*	*aAbb*	*aabB*	*aabb*

Phenotypic ratio: 9 dominant dominant to 3 dominant recessive to 3 recessive dominant to 1 recessive recessive

Using Product Rule: Prob(A_ B_) = (¾)(¾) = 9/16

Prob(A_ bb) = (¾)(¼) = 3/16

Prob(aa B_) = (¼)(¾) = 3/16

Prob(aa bb) = (¼)(¼) = 1/16

c. A dihybrid cross between individuals with the genotype *AaBb* and *aabb*

	AB	*Ab*	*aB*	*ab*
ab	*aAbB*	*aAbb*	*aabB*	*aabb*

Using Product Rule: Prob(A_ B_) = (¼)(1) = 1/16

Prob(A_ bb) = (¼)(1) = 1/16

Prob(aa B_) = (¼)(1) = 1/16

Prob(aa bb) = (¼)(1) = 1/16

2. The segregation of different alleles for any gene occurs due to the pairing of homologous chromosomes, and the subsequent separation of these homologues during anaphase I. The independent assortment of traits, more accurately the independent segregation of different allele pairs, is due to the independent alignment of chromosomes during metaphase I of meiosis.

3. There seems to be the loss of a genotype as there are only 3 possible outcomes (2 yellow and 1 black). If the yellow gene has a dominant effect on coat color, but also causes lethality when homozygous, then this could explain the observations. So, a yellow mouse is heterozygous and crossing two yellow mice yields 1 homozygous yellow (dead):2 heterozygous (appears yellow):1 black. You could test this by crossing the yellow to homozygous black. You should get 1 yellow:1 black, and all black offspring should be true breeding, and all yellow should behave as above.

4. There are two genes involved, one of which is epistatic to the other. At one gene, there are two alleles: black and brown; at the other gene, there are two alleles: albino and colored. The albino gene is epistatic to the brown gene so when you are homozygous recessive for albino, you are albino regardless of whether you are black or brown at the other locus. This leads to the 4 albino in a Mendelian kind of crossing scheme.

Chapter 13

LEARNING OUTCOME QUESTIONS

13.1 Females would be all wild type; males would be all white eyed.

13.2 Yes, should be viable and appear female.

13.3 The mt-DNA could be degraded by a nuclease similar to how bacteria deal with invading viruses. Alternatively, the mt-containing mitochondria could be excluded from the zygote.

13.4 No, not by genetic crosses.

13.5 Yes. First division nondisjunction yields four aneuploid gametes while second division yields only two aneuploid gametes.

INQUIRY QUESTIONS

Page 244 There would probably be very little if any recombination so the expected assortment ratios would have been skewed from the expected 9:3:3:1.

Page 247 About 10% of the progeny would have been recombinants, based on the relationship of 1 cM (map unit or centimorgan) equals 1% recombination frequency. When gene loci are separated by greater distances, the frequency of recombination between them increases to the extent that the number of recombinant gametes roughly equals the number of parental gametes. In that instance, the genes would exhibit independent assortment. With a recombination frequency of only 10%, it is doubtful that it would have led Mendel to the concept of independent assortment.

Page 250 What has changed is the mother's age. The older the woman, the higher the risk she has of nondisjunction during meiosis. Thus, she also has a much greater risk of producing a child with Down syndrome.

Page 251 XY egg is fertilized by an X sperm. A normal X egg is fertilized by an XY sperm.

Page 253 Advanced maternal age, a previous child with birth defects, or a family history of birth defects.

UNDERSTAND

1. c 2. d 3. d 4. a 5. c 6. c 7. c

APPLY

1. c 2. b 3. c 4. b 5. c 6. b

SYNTHESIZE

1. Theoretically, 25% of the children from this cross will be color blind. All of the color blind children will be male and 50% of the males will be color blind.

2. Parents of heterozygous plant were: green wrinkled X yellow round
Frequency of recombinants is 36+29/1300=0.05
Map distance = 5 cM

3. Male calico cats are very rare. The coloration that is associated with calico cats is the product of X inactivation. X inactivation only occurs in females as a response to dosage levels of the X-linked genes. The only way to get a male calico is to be heterozygous for the color gene and to be the equivalent of a Klinefelters male (*XXY*).

Chapter 14

LEARNING OUTCOME QUESTIONS

14.1 The 20 different amino acid building blocks offers chemical complexity. This appears to offer informational complexity as well.

14.2 The proper tautomeric forms are necessary for proper base pairing, which is critical to DNA structure.

14.3 Prior to replication in light N there would be only one band. After one round of replication, there would be two bands with denatured DNA: one heavy and one light.

14.4 The 5′ to 3′ activity is used to remove RNA primers. The 3′ to 5′ activity is used to removed mispaired bases (proofreading).

14.5 A shortening of chromosome ends would eventually affect DNA that encodes important functions.

14.6 No. The number of DNA damaging agents, in addition to replication errors, would cause lethal damage (this has been tested in yeast).

INQUIRY QUESTIONS

Page 262 Because adenine always forms bonds with only thymine, and guanine forms bonds with only cytosine, adenine and thymine will always have the same proportions, and likewise with guanine and cytosine.

Page 265 The covalent bonds create a strong backbone for the molecule making it difficult to disrupt. Individual hydrogen bonds are more easily broken allowing enzymes to separate the two strands without disrupting the inherent structure of the molecule.

Page 269 DNA ligase is important in connecting Okazaki fragments during DNA replication. Without it, the lagging strand would not be complete.

Page 273 The linear structure of chromosomes creates the end problem discussed in the text. It is impossible to finish the ends of linear chromosomes using unidirectional polymerases that require RNA primers. The size of eukaryotic genomes also means that the time necessary to replicate the genome is much greater than in prokaryotes with smaller genomes. Thus the use of multiple origins of replication.

Page 275 Cells have a variety of DNA repair pathways that allow them to restore damaged DNA to its normal constitution. If DNA repair pathways are compromised, the cell will have a higher mutation rate. This can lead to higher rates of cancer in a multicellular organism such as humans.

UNDERSTAND

1. d 2. a 3. c 4. a 5. c 6. b 7. b

APPLY

1. c 2. b 3. c 4. c 5. a 6. b 7. d 8. c

SYNTHESIZE

1. a. If both bacteria are heat-killed, then the transfer of DNA will have no effect since pathogenicity requires the production of proteins encoded by the DNA. Protein synthesis will not occur in a dead cell.

    b. The nonpathogenic cells will be transformed to pathogenic cells. Loss of proteins will not alter DNA.

    c. The nonpathogenic cells remain nonpathogenic. If the DNA is digested, it will not be transferred and no transformation will occur.

2. The region could be an origin of replication. Origins of replication are adenine- and thymine-rich regions since only these nucleotides form two hydrogen bonds versus the three hydrogen bonds formed between guanine and cytosine, making it easier to separate the two strands of DNA.

    The RNA primer sequences would be 5′-ACUAUUGCUUUAUAA-3′. The sequence is antiparallel to the DNA sequence (review Figure 14.16) meaning that the 5′ end of the RNA is matching up with the 3′ end of the DNA. It is also important to remember that in RNA the thymine nucleotide is replaced by uracil (U). Therefore, the adenine in DNA will form a complementary base-pair with uracil.

3. a. *DNA gyrase* functions to relieve torsional strain on the DNA. If DNA gyrase were not functioning, the DNA molecule would undergo supercoiling, causing the DNA to wind up on itself, preventing the continued binding of the polymerases necessary for replication.

    b. *DNA polymerase III* is the primary polymerase involved in the addition of new nucleotides to the growing polymer and in the formation of the phosphodiester bonds that make up the sugar–phosphate backbone. If this enzyme were not functioning, then no new DNA strand would be synthesized and there would be no replication.

    c. *DNA ligase* is involved in the formation of phosphodiester bonds between Okazaki fragments. If this enzyme was not functioning, then the fragments would remain disconnected and would be more susceptible to digestion by nucleases.

    d. *DNA polymerase I* functions to remove and replace the RNA primers that are required for DNA polymerase III function. If DNA polymerase I was not available, then the RNA primers would remain and the replicated DNA would become a mix of DNA and RNA.

CHAPTER 15

LEARNING OUTCOME QUESTIONS

15.1 There is no molecular basis for recognition between amino acids and nucleotides. The tRNA is able to interact with nucleic acid by base pairing and an enzyme can covalently attach amino acids to it.

15.2 There would be no specificity to the genetic code. Each codon must specify a single amino acid, although amino acids can have more than one codon.

15.3 Transcription translation coupling cannot exist in eukaryotes where the two processes are separated in both space and time.

15.4 No. This is a result of the evolutionary history of eukaryotes but is not necessitated by genome complexity.

15.5 Alternative splicing offers flexibility in coding information. One gene can encode multiple proteins.

15.6 This tRNA would be able to "read" STOP codons. This could allow nonsense mutations to be viable, but would cause problems making longer than normal proteins. Most bacterial genes actually have more than one STOP at the end of the gene.

15.7 Attaching amino acids to tRNAs, bringing charged tRNAs to the ribosome, and ribosome translocation all require energy.

15.8 No. It depends on where the breakpoints are that created the inversion, or duplication. For duplications it also depends on the genes that are duplicated.

INQUIRY QUESTIONS

Page 281 One would expect higher amounts of error in transcription over DNA replication. Proofreading is important in DNA replication will be passed on to offspring as mutations. However, RNA's have very short life spans in the cytoplasm therefore mistakes are not permanent.

Page 284 The very strong similarity among organisms indicates a common ancestry of the code.

Page 285 The promoter acts a binding site for RNA polymerase. The structure of the promoter provides information as to both where to bind, but also the direction of transcription. If the two sites were identical, the polymerase would need some other cue for the direction of transcription.

Page 289 Splicing can produce multiple transcripts from the same gene.

Page 297 Wobble not only explains the number of tRNAs that are observed due to the increased flexibility in the 5′ position, it also accounts for the degeneracy that is observed in the Genetic Code. The degenerate base is the one in the wobble position.

UNDERSTAND

1. d 2. c 3. d 4. b 5. c 6. b 7. c

APPLY

1. d 2. c 3. b 4. b 5. c 6. b 7. b

SYNTHESIZE

1. the predicted sequence of the mRNA for this gene
    5′–GCAAUGGGCUCGGCAUGCUAAUCC–3′
    the predicted amino acid sequence of the protein
    5′–GCA AUG GGC UCG GCA UGC UAA UCC–3′
    Met-Gly-Ser-Ala-Cys-STOP

2. A frameshift essentially turns the sequence of bases into a "random" sequence. If you consider the genetic code, 3 of the 64 codons are STOP, so the probability of hitting a STOP in a random sequence is 3/64 or about 1 every 20 codons.

3. a. mRNA = 5′–GCA AUG GGC UCG GCA UUG CUA AUC C-3′
       The amino acid sequence would then be: Met-Gly-Ser-Ala-Leu-Iso-. There is no stop codon. This is an example of a frameshift mutation. The addition of a nucleotide alters the "reading frame," resulting in a change in the type and number of amino acids in this protein.

    b. mRNA = 5′–GCA AUG GGC UAG GCA UGC UAA UCC–3′
       The amino acid sequence would then be: Met-Gly-STOP.
       This is an example of a nonsense mutation. A single nucleotide change has resulted in the early termination of protein synthesis by altering the codon for Ser into a stop codon.

    c. mRNA = 5′–GCA AUG GGC UCG GCA AGC UAA UCC –3′
       The amino acid sequence would then be: Met-Gly-Ser-Ala-Ser-STOP. This base substitution has affected the codon that would normally encode Cys (UGC) and resulted in the addition of Ser (AGC).

4. The split genes of eukaryotes offers the opportunity to control the splicing process, which does not exist in prokaryotes. This is also true for poly adenylation in eukaryotes. In prokaryotes, transcription/translation coupling offers the opportunity for the process of translation to have an effect on transcription.

CHAPTER 16

LEARNING OUTCOME QUESTIONS

16.1 The control of gene expression would be more like humans (fellow eukaryote) than E. coli.

16.2 The two helices both interact with DNA, so the spacing between the helices is important for both to be able to bind to DNA.

16.3 The operon would be on all of the time (constitutive expression).

16.4 The loss of a general transcription factor would likely be lethal as it would affect all transcription. The loss of a specific factor would affect only those genes controlled by the factor.

16.5 These genes are necessary for the ordinary functions of the cell. That is, the role of these genes is in ordinary housekeeping and not in any special functions.

16.6 RNA interference offers a way to specifically affect gene expression using drugs made of siRNAs.

16.7 As there are many proteins in a cell doing a variety of functions, uncontrolled degradation of proteins would be devastating to the cell.

INQUIRY QUESTIONS

Page 308 The presence more than one gene in the operon allows for increased control over the elements of the pathway and therefore the product. A single regulatory system can regulate several adjacent genes.

Page 315 Regulation occurs when various genes have the same regulatory sequences, which bind the same proteins.

Page 324 Ubiqitin is added to proteins that need to be removed because they are nonfunctional or those that are degraded as part of a normal cellular cycle.

UNDERSTAND

1. c 2. d 3. a 4. c 5. b 6. c 7. b

APPLY

1. c 2. c 3. b 4. d 5. c 6. a 7. c

SYNTHESIZE

1. Mutations that affect binding sites for proteins on DNA will control the expression of genes covalently linked to them. Introducing a wild type binding site on a plasmid will not affect this. We call this being cis-dominant. Mutations in proteins that bind to DNA would be recessive to a wild type gene introduced on a plasmid.

2. Negative control of transcription occurs when the ability to initiate transcription is reduced. Positive control occurs when the ability to initiate transcription is enhanced. The *lac* operon is regulated by the presence or absence of lactose. The proteins encoded within the operon are specific to the catabolism (breakdown) of lactose. For this reason, operon expression is only required when there is lactose in the environment. Allolactose is formed when lactose is present in the cell. The allolactose binds to a repressor protein, altering its conformation and allowing RNA polymerase to bind. In addition to the role of lactose, there is also a role for the activator protein CAP in regulation of *lac*. When cAMP levels are high then CAP can bind to DNA and make it easier for RNA polymerase to bind to the promoter. The *lac* operon is an example of both positive and negative control.

   The *trp* operon encodes protein manufacture of tryptophan in a cell. This operon must be expressed when cellular levels of tryptophan are low. Conversely, when tryptophan is available in the cell, there is no need to transcribe the operon. The tryptophan repressor must bind tryptophan before it can take on the right shape to bind to the operator. This is an example of negative control.

3. Forms that control gene expression that are unique to eukaryotes include alternative splicing, control of chromatin structure, control of transport of mRNA from the nucleus to the cytoplasm, control of translation by small RNAs, and control of protein levels by ubiquitin- directed destruction. Of these, most are obviously part of the unique features of eukaryotic cells. The only mechanisms that could work in prokaryotes would be translational control by small RNAs and controlled destruction of proteins.

4. Mutation is a permanent change in the DNA. Regulation is a short-term change controlled by the cell. Like mutations, regulation can alter the number of proteins in a cell, change the size of a protein, or eliminate the protein altogether. The key difference is that gene regulation can be reversed in response to changes in the cell's environment. Mutations do not allow for this kind of rapid response.

CHAPTER 17

LEARNING OUTCOME QUESTIONS

17.1 *Eco*RI is a restriction enzyme that can be used to cut DNA at specific places. Ligase is used to "glue" together pieces of DNA that have been cut with the same restriction enzyme. The two enzymes make it possible to add foreign DNA into an *E. coli* plasmid.

17.2 A cDNA library is constructed from mRNA. Unlike the gene itself, cDNA does not include the introns or regulatory elements.

17.3 Multiple rounds of DNA replication allow for an exponential increase in copies of the DNA. A heat-stable DNA polymerase makes this possible.

17.4 The gene coding for a functional protein must be mutated. Recombination allows for the "knockout" gene to be specifically targeted.

17.5 The protein must be completely pure so that the patient does not have an immune response to proteins from another organism.

It is important that the protein have exactly the same structure when it is produced in a bacterial cell as in a human cell. Because post-translational modification is specific to eukaryotes, the human DNA may need to be modified before it is inserted in a bacterial genome to ensure the protein structure in identical to the human protein.

The protein may not be produced in every cell in a human. It is difficult to target the manufactured protein to only the cells where it is produced or needed. The protein could have unintended consequences in other cells in the patient's body.

17.6 The pollen from the plant with the recombinant gene might fertilize a closely related wild plant. If the offspring are viable, the recombinant gene will be introduced into the wild population.

INQUIRY QUESTIONS

Page 331 A bacterial artificial chromosome or a yeast artificial chromosome would be the best way to go as a plasmid vector only can stably hold up to 10 kb.

Page 332 No, cDNA is created using mRNA as a template, therefore, intron sequences would not be expressed.

Page 340 Yes, if you first used reverse transcriptase to make cDNA to amplify. This is called RT PCR.

UNDERSTAND

1. b 2. b 3. d 4. d 5. c 6. c 7. b 8. d 9. a

APPLY

1. d 2. c 3. d

SYNTHESIZE

1. Genes coding for each of the subunits would need to be inserted into different plasmids that are integrated into different bacteria. The cultures would need to be grown separately and the different protein subunits would then need to be isolated and purified. If the subunits can self assemble in vitro, then the protein could be functional. It could be difficult to establish just the right conditions for the assembly of the multiple subunits.

2. 5′–CTGATAGTCAGCTG–3′

CHAPTER 18

LEARNING OUTCOME QUESTIONS

18.1 Banding sites on karyotypes depend on dyes binding to the condensed DNA that is wrapped around protein. The dyes bind to some regions, but not all and are therefore not evenly spaced along the genome in the way that sequential base-pairs are evenly spaced.

18.2 Sequencing is not a perfect process and a small number of errors would occur. Also, the number of base-pairs that can be sequenced in an individual sequencing reaction is limited. Multiple copies of the genome need to be cut in different places and sequenced so that the overlapping pieces can be assembled into an overall genome sequence. If there were not multiple, overlapping sequences, it would not be possible to determine the order of the smaller pieces that are sequenced.

18.3 One possibility is that transposable elements can move within the genome and create new genetic variability, subject to natural selection.

18.4 From the transcriptome, it is possible to predict the proteins that may be translated and available for use in part of an organism at a specific time in development.

18.5 Yes. Additional protein could enhance the nutritional value of the potato for human consumption. One caveat would be that the increased level of protein not change the texture or flavor of potatoes that a consumer is expecting.

INQUIRY QUESTIONS

Page 354 Repetitive elements are one of the main obstacles to assembling the DNA sequences in proper order. There is one copy of *bcr* (see with green probe) and one copy of *abl* (seen with red probe).

The other *bcr* and *abl* genes are fused and the yellow color is the result of red plus green fluorescence combined.

Page 361 Repetitive elements are one of the main obstacles to assembling the DNA sequences in proper order because it is difficult to determine which sequences are overlapping.

Page 366 Proteins exhibit post-translational modification and the formation of protein complexes. Additionally a single gene can code for multiple proteins using alternative splicing.

Page 367 A proteome is all the proteins coded for by the genome, and the transcriptome is all the RNA present in a cell or tissue at a specific time.

Page 369 You may be able to take advantage of synteny between the rice and corn genome (see Figure 18.14). Let's assume that a drought-tolerance gene has already been identified and mapped in rice. Using what is known about synteny between the rice and corn genomes, you could find the region of the corn genome that corresponds to the rice drought-tolerance gene. This would narrow down the region of the corn genome that you might want to sequence to find your gene. A subsequent step might be to modify the corn gene that corresponds to the rice gene to see if you can increase drought tolerance.

UNDERSTAND

1. b   2. a   3. c   4. d   5. b   6. c   7. b   8. d

APPLY

1. b   2. a   3. d   4. b   5. c   6. d   7. d

SYNTHESIZE

1. The STSs represent unique sequences in the genome. They can be used to align the clones into one contiguous sequence of the genome based on the presence or absence of an STS in a clone. The contig, with aligned clones, would look like this:

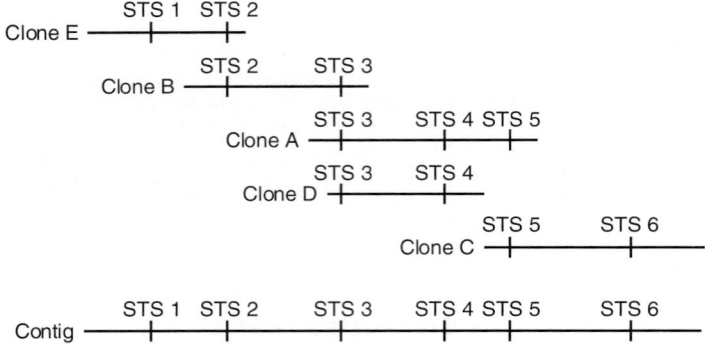

2. The anthrax genome has been sequenced. Investigators would look for differences in the genome between existing natural strains and those collected from a suspected outbreak. The genome of an infectious agent can be modified, or "weaponized," to make it more deadly. Also, single-nucleotide polymorphisms could be used to identify the source of the anthrax. In the case of the Florida anthrax outbreak it was determined that the source was a research laboratory.

CHAPTER 19

LEARNING OUTCOME QUESTIONS

19.2 The early cell divisions are very rapid and do not involve an increase in size between divisions. Interphase is greatly reduced allowing very fast cell divisions.

19.3 This requires experimentation to isolate cell from contact, which would prevent induction, or to follow a particular cells lineage.

19.4 The nucleus must be reprogrammed. What this means exactly on the molecular level is not clear, but probably involves changes in chromatin structure and methylation patterns.

19.5 Homeotic genes seem to have arisen very early in the evolutionary history of bilaterians. These have been duplicated and they have diversified with increasing morphological complexity.

19.6 Cell death can be a patterning mechanism. Your fingers were sculpted from a paddle-like structure by cell death.

INQUIRY QUESTION

Page 378 The *macho-1* gene product is a transcription factor that can activate the expression of several muscle-specific genes. Whether or not the fibroblast growth factor (FGF) signal is received from underlying endoderm precursor cells in the embryo determines how *macho-1* acts. If the FGF signal is present, it activates a Ras/MAP kinase pathway which, together with *macho-1*, either suppresses muscle genes or activates the transcription of mesenchyme genes. Without the FGF signal, *macho-1* alone triggers the transcription of muscle genes.

UNDERSTAND

1. b   2. d   3. c   4. d   5. b   6. c   7. b

APPLY

1. d   2. a   3. b   4. a   5. c   6. c   7. c

SYNTHESIZE

1. The horizontal lines of the fate map represent cell divisions. Starting with the egg, four cell divisions are required to establish a population of cells that will become nervous tissue. It takes another eight to nine divisions to produce the final number of cells that will make up the nervous system of the worm. It takes seven to eight rounds of cell division to generate the population of cells that will become the gonads. Once established, another seven to eight cell divisions are required to produce the actual gonad cells.

2. Not every cell in a developing embryo will survive. The process of apoptosis is responsible for eliminating cells from the embryo. In *C. elegans*, the process of apoptosis is regulated by three genes: *ced-3*, *ced-4*, and *ced-9*. Both *ced-3 and ced-4* encode proteases, enzymes that degrade proteins. Interestingly, the *ced-3* protease functions to activate gene expression of the *ced-4* protease. Together, these proteases will destroy the cell from the inside-out. The *ced-9* gene functions to repress the activity of the protease-encoding genes, thereby preventing apoptosis.

3. a. N-cadherin plays a specific role in differentiating cells of the nervous system from ectodermal cells. Ectodermal cells express E-cadherin, but neural cells express N-cadherin. The difference in cell-surface cadherins means that the neural cells lose their contact with the surrounding ectodermal cells and establish new contacts with other neural cells. In the absence of N-cadherin, the nervous system would not form. If you assume that E-cadherin expression is also lost (as would occur normally in development) then these cells would lose all cell–cell contacts and would probably undergo apoptosis.

   b. Integrins mediate the connection between a cell and its surrounding environment, the extracellular matrix (ECM). The loss of integrins would result in the loss of cell adhesion to the ECM. These cells would not be able to move and therefore, gastrulation and other developmental processes would be disrupted.

   c. Integrins function by linking the cell's cytoskeleton to the ECM. This connection is critical for cell movement. The deletion of the cytoplasmic domain of the integrin would not affect the ability of integrin to attach to the ECM, but it would prevent the cytoskeleton from getting a "grip." This deletion would likely result in a disruption of development similar to the complete loss of integrin.

4. Adult cells from the patient would be cultured with factors that reprogram the nucleus into pluripotent cells. These cells would then be grown in culture with factors necessary to induce differentiation into a specific cell type that could be transplanted into the patient. This would be easiest for tissue like a liver that regenerates, but could in theory be used for a variety of cell types.

CHAPTER 20

LEARNING OUTCOME QUESTIONS

20.1 Natural selection occurs when some individuals are better suited to their environment than others. These individuals live longer and reproduce more, leaving more offspring with the traits that enabled their parents to thrive. In essence, genetic variation within a population provides the raw material on which natural selection can act.

20.2 To determine if a population is in Hardy Weinberg equilibrium, one would first need to determine the actual allele frequencies, which can be calculated based on the actual genotype frequencies. After assigning variables p and q to the actual allele frequencies, one would then use the Hardy Weinberg equation, $p^2 + 2pq + q^2 = 1$ in order to determine the expected genotype frequencies. If the actual and expected genotype frequencies are the same (or, at least not significantly different) then it is safe to say that the population is in Hardy Weinberg equilibrium.

20.3 There are five mechanisms of evolution—natural selection, mutation, gene flow (migration), genetic drift, and nonrandom mating. Any of these mechanisms can alter allele frequencies within a population, although usually a change in allele frequency results from more than one mechanism working in concert (for example, mutation will introduce a beneficial new allele into the population, and natural selection will select for that allele such that its frequency increases over the course of two or more generations). Natural selection, the first mechanism and probably the most influential in bringing about evolutionary change, is also the only mechanism to produce adaptive change, that is, change that results in the population being better adapted to its environment. Mutation is the only way in which new alleles can be introduced—it is the ultimate source of all variation. Because it is a relatively rare event, mutation by itself is not a strong agent of allele frequency change; however, in concert with other mechanisms, especially natural selection, it can drastically change the allele frequencies in a population. Gene flow can introduce new alleles into a population from another population of the same species, thus changing the allele frequency within both the recipient and donor populations. Genetic drift is the random, chance factor of evolution—while the results of genetic drift can be negligible in a large population, small populations can see drastic changes in allele frequency due to this agent. Finally, nonrandom mating results in populations varying from Hardy Weinberg equilibrium not by changing allele frequencies but by changing genotype frequencies—nonrandom mating reduces the proportion of heterozygotes in a population.

20.4 Reproductive success relative to other individuals within an organism's population is referred to as that organism's fitness. Its fitness is determined by its longevity, mating frequency, and the number of offspring it produces for each mating. None of these factors is always the most important in determining reproductive success—instead it is the cumulative effects of all three factors that determines an individual's reproductive success. For example, an individual that has a very long life span but mates only infrequently might have lower fitness than a conspecific that lives only half as long but mates more frequently and with greater success. As seen with the water strider example in this section, traits that are favored for one component of fitness, say, for example, longevity, may be disadvantageous for other components of fitness, say, lifetime fecundity.

20.5 The dynamics among the different evolutionary mechanisms are very intricate, and it is often difficult, if not impossible, to discern which direction each process is operating within a population—it is much easier to simply see the final cumulative effects of the various agents of evolutionary change. However, there are cases in which more than one evolutionary process will operate in the same direction, with the resulting population changing, or evolving, more rapidly than it would have under only one evolutionary mechanism. For example, mutation may introduce a beneficial allele into a population; gene flow could then spread the new allele to other populations. Natural selection will favor this allele within each population, resulting in relatively rapid evolutionary adaptation of a novel phenotype.

20.6 In a population wherein heterozygotes had the lowest fitness, natural selection should favor both homozygous forms. This would result in disruptive selection, and a bimodal distribution of traits within the population. Over enough time, it could lead to a speciation event.

20.7 Directional selection occurs when one phenotype has an adaptive advantage over other phenotypes in the population, regardless of its relative frequency within the population. Frequency-dependent selection, on the other hand, results when either a common (positive frequency-dependent selection) or rare (negative frequency-dependent selection) has a selective advantage simply by virtue of its commonality or rarity. In other words, if a mutation introduces a novel allele into a population, directional selection may result in evolution because the allele is advantageous, not because it is rare.

20.8 Wild guppies have to balance natural selection, which, in the presence of a predator such as the pike cichlid, would tend to favor drab coloration, with sexual selection, wherein females prefer brightly colored males. Thus, in low-predation environments the male guppies tend to be brightly colored whereas in high-predation environments they are drably colored. Background color matching is a form of camouflage used by many species to avoid predation; again, however, in many cases this example of natural selection runs counter to sexual selection—males want to be inconspicuous to predators but attractive to potential mates. For example, to test the effects of predation on background color matching in a species of butterfly, one might raise captive populations of butterflies with a normal variation in coloration. After a few generations, add natural predators to half of the enclosures. After several generations, one would expect the butterflies in the predatory environment to have a high degree of background color matching in order to avoid predation, while the non-predatory environment would have promoted brightly-colored individuals where color would correlate with mating success.

20.9 Pleiotropic effects occur with many genes; in other words, a single gene has multiple effects on the phenotype of the individual. Whereas natural selection might favor a particular aspect of the pleiotropic gene, it might select against another aspect of the same gene; thus, pleiotropy often limits the degree to which a phenotype can be altered by natural selection. Epistasis occurs when the expression of one gene is controlled or altered by the existence or expression of another gene. Thus, the outcome of natural selection will depend not just on the genotype of one gene, but the other genotype as well.

INQUIRY QUESTIONS

Page 399 In the example of Figure 20.3, the frequency of the recessive white genotype is 0.16. The remaining 84 cats (out of 100) in the population are ho-

mozygous or heterozygous black. If the 16 white cats died, they will not contribute recessive white genes to the next generation. Only heterozygous black cats will produce white kittens in a 3:1 ratio of black to white. Homozygous × homozygous black and homozygous × heterozygous black cats will have all black kittens. Since there are 36 homozygous black cats and 48 heterozygous black cats, with a new total of 84 cats, the new frequency of homozygous black cats is 36/84 or 43%, with the heterozygous black cats now comprising 57% of the population. If $p^2 = 0.43$, then $p = 0.65$ (approximately), then $1-p = q$, and $q = 0.35$. The frequency of white kittens in the next generation, q^2, is 0.12 or 12%.

Page 405 Differential predation might favor brown toads over green toads, green toads might be more susceptible to disease, or green toads might be less able to tolerate variations in climate, among other possibilities.

Page 406 Since the intermediate-sized water strider has the highest level of fitness, it would be expected that the intermediate size would become more prevalent in the population. If the number of eggs laid per day was not affected by body size, the small water striders would be favored because of their tendency to live longer than their larger counterparts.

Page 407 Yes. The frequency of copper tolerance will decrease as distance from the mine increases.

Page 411 The proportion of flies moving toward light (positive phototropism) would again begin to increase in successive generations.

Page 411 The distribution of birth weights in the human population would expand somewhat to include more babies of higher and lower birth weights.

Page 413 Guppy predators evidently locate their prey using visual cues. The more colorful the guppy, the more likely it is to be seen and thus the more likely it will become prey.

Page 414 Thoroughbred horse breeders have been using selective breeding for certain traits over many decades, effectively removing variation from the population of thoroughbred horses. Unless mutation produces a faster horse, it remains unlikely that winning speeds will improve.

UNDERSTAND

1. a 2. b 3. d 4. a 5. d 6. a 7. d

APPLY

1. d 2. d 3. a

SYNTHESIZE

1. The results depend on coloration of guppies increasing their conspicuousness to predators such that an individual's probability of survival is lower than if it was a drab morph. In the laboratory it may be possible to conduct trials in simulated environments; we would predict, based on the hypothesis of predation, that the predator would capture more of the colorful morph than the drab morph when given access to both. Design of the simulated environment would obviously be critical, but results from such an experiment, if successful, would be a powerful addition to the work already accomplished.

2. On the large lava flows, where the background is almost entirely black, those individuals with black coloration within a population will have a selective advantage because they will be more cryptic to predators. On the other hand, on small flows, which are disrupted by light sand and green plants, dark individuals would be at an adaptive disadvantage for the same reason. You can read about this in chapter 21 (21.2); the black peppered moths had an advantage on the trees lacking lichen, but a disadvantage on lichen-covered trees.

3. Ultimately, genetic variation is produced by the process of mutation. However, compared with the speed at which natural selection can reduce variation in traits that are closely related to fitness, mutation alone cannot account for the persistence of genetic variation in traits that are under strong selection. Other processes can account for the observation that genetic variation can persist under strong selection. They include gene flow. Populations are often distributed along environmental gradients of some type. To the extent that different environments favor slightly different variants of phenotypes that have a genetic basis, gene flow among areas in the habitat gradient can introduce new genetic variation or help maintain existing variation. Similarly, just as populations frequently encounter different selective environments across their range (think of the guppies living above and below the waterfalls in Trinidad), a single population also encounters variation in selective environments across time (oscillating selection). Traits favored this year may not be the same as those favored next year, leading to a switching of natural selection and the maintenance of genetic variation.

CHAPTER 21

LEARNING OUTCOME QUESTIONS

21.1 No. If eating hard seeds caused individuals to develop bigger beaks, then the phenotype is a result of the environment, not the genotype. Natural selection can only act upon those traits with a genetic component. Just as a body builder develops large muscles in his or her lifetime but does not have well-muscled offspring, birds that develop large beaks in their lifetime will not necessarily have offspring with larger beaks.

21.2 An experimental design that would test this hypothesis could be as simple as producing enclosures for the moths and placing equal numbers of both morphs into each enclosure and then presenting predatory birds to each enclosure. One enclosure could be used as a control. One enclosure would have a dark background while the other would have a light background. After several generations, measuring the phenotype frequency of the moths should reveal very clear trends—the enclosure with the dark background should consist of mostly dark moths, the enclosure with the light background mostly light moths, and the neutral enclosure should have an approximately equal ratio of light to dark moths.

21.3 If the trait that is being artificially selected for is due to the environment rather than underlying genotype, then the individuals selected that have that trait will not necessarily pass it on to their offspring.

21.4 The major selective agent in most cases of natural selection is the environment; thus, climatic changes, major continental shifts, and other major geological changes would result in dramatic changes in selective pressure; during these times the rate and direction of evolutionary change would likely be affected in many, if not most, species. On the other hand, during periods of relative environmental stability, the selective pressure does not change and we would not expect to see many major evolutionary events.

21.5 The only other explanation that could be used to explain homologous characteristics and vestigial structures could be mutation. Especially in the case of vestigial structures, if one resulted from a mutation that had pleiotropic effects, and the other effects of the genetic anomaly were selected for, then the vestigial structure would also be selected for, much like a rider on a Congressional Bill.

21.6 Convergence occurs when distantly related species experience similar environmental pressures and respond, through natural selection, in similar ways. For example, penguins (birds), sharks (fish), sea lions (mammals) and even the extinct ichthyosaur (reptile) all exhibit the fusiform shape. Each of these animals has similar environmental pressures in that they are all aquatic predators and need to be able to move swiftly and agilely through the water. Clearly their most recent common ancestor does not have the fusiform body shape; thus the similarities are due to convergence (environment) rather than homology (ancestry). However, similar environmental pressures will not always result in convergent evolution. Most importantly, in order for a trait to appear for the first time in a lineage, there must have been a mutation; however, mutations are rare events, and even rarer is a beneficial mutation. There may also be other species that already occupy a particular niche; in these cases it would be unlikely that natural selection would favor traits that would increase the competition between two species.

21.7 It is really neither a hypothesis nor a theory. Theories are the building blocks of scientific knowledge, they have withstood the most rigorous testing and review. Hypotheses, on the other hand, are tentative answers to a question. Unfortunately, a good hypothesis must be testable and falsifiable, and stating that humans came from Mars is not realistically testable or falsifiable; thus, it is, in the realm of biological science, a nonsense statement.

INQUIRY QUESTIONS

Page 419 The figure demonstrates that the beak depth of offspring can be predicted by the average beak depth of the parent's bills. Thus, one would expect the offspring to have the same beak depth if their parents' mean beak depth is the same. This is only correct if males and females do not differ in beak depth. In species for which the sexes differ (such as height in humans), then one would need to know both the depth and the sex of the parents and the calculation would be more complicated.

Page 421 Such a parallel trend would suggest that similar processes are operating in both localities. Thus, one would conduct a study to identify similarities. In this case, both areas have experienced coincident reductions in air pollution, which most likely is the cause of the parallel evolutionary trends.

Page 422 Assuming that small and large individuals would breed with each other, then middle-sized offspring would still be born (the result of matings between small and large flies). Nonetheless, there would also be many small and large individuals (the result of small × small and large × large matings). Thus, the

frequency distribution of body sizes would be much broader than the distributions in the figures.

Page 426 This evolutionary decrease could occur for many reasons. For example, maybe *Nannippus* adapted to forested habitats and thus selection favored smaller size, as it had in the ancestral horses, before horses moved into open, grassland habitats. Another possibility is that there were many species of horses present at that time, and different sized horses ate different types of food. By evolving small size, *Nannippus* may have been able to eat a type of food not eaten by the others.

UNDERSTAND

1. d   2. b   3. b   4. a   5. b   6. b   7. b

APPLY

1. a   2. d   3. d

SYNTHESIZE

1. Briefly, they are:
   A. There must be variation among individuals within a population.
   B. Variation among individuals must be related to differences among individuals in their success in producing offspring over their lifetime.
   C. Variation related to lifetime reproductive success must have a genetic (heritable) basis.

2. Figure 21.2a shows in an indirect way that beak depth varies from year to year. Presumably this is a function of variation among individuals in beak size. However, the most important point of 21.2a is that it shows the result of selection. That is, if the three conditions hold, we might expect to see average beak depth change accordingly as precipitation varies from year to year. Figure 21.2b is more directly relevant to the conditions noted for natural selection to occur. The figure shows that beak size varies among individuals, *and* that it tends to be inherited.

3. The relationship would be given by a cloud of points with no obvious linear trend in any direction different from a zero slope. In other words, it would be a horizontal line through an approximately circular cloud of points. Such data would suggest that whether a parent(s) has a large or small beak has no bearing on the beak size of its offspring.

4. Assuming that small and large individuals would breed with each other, then middle-sized offspring would still be born (the result of matings between small and large flies). Nonetheless, there would also be many small and large individuals (the result of small × small and large × large matings). Thus, the frequency distribution of body sizes would be much broader than the distributions in the figures. In some experiments, reproductive isolation evolves in which small and large individuals evolve mating preferences that prevent them from interbreeding, leading to the production of two different-sized species. This would be a laboratory example of sympatric speciation. Most studies, however, have failed to produce such reproductive isolation; rather, a single population remains through time with great variation.

5. The evolution of horses was not a linear event; instead it occurred over 55 million years and included descendents of 34 different genera. By examining the fossil record, one can see that horse evolution did not occur gradually and steadily; instead several major evolutionary events occurred in response to drastic changes in environmental pressures. The fossil record of horse evolution is remarkably detailed, and shows that while there have been trends toward certain characteristics, change has not been fluid and constant over time, nor has it been entirely consistent across all of the horse lineages. For example, some lineages experienced rapid increases in body size over relatively short periods of geological time, while other lineages actually saw decreases in body size.

CHAPTER 22

LEARNING OUTCOME QUESTIONS

22.1 The Biological Species Concept states that different species are capable of mating and producing viable, fertile offspring. If sympatric species are unable to do so, they will remain reproductively isolated and thus distinct species. Along the same lines, gene flow between populations of the same species allow for homogenization of the two populations such that they remain the same species.

22.2 In order for reinforcement to occur and complete the process of speciation, two populations must have some reproductive barriers in place prior to sympatry. In the absence of this initial reproductive isolation we would expect rapid exchange of genes and thus homogenization resulting from gene flow. On the other hand, if two populations are already somewhat reproductively isolated (due to hybrid infertility or a prezygotic barrier such as behavioral isolation), then we would expect natural selection to continue improving the fitness of the non-hybrid offspring, eventually resulting in speciation.

22.3 Reproductive isolation that occurs due to different environments is a factor of natural selection; the environmental pressure favors individuals best suited for that environment. As isolated populations continue to develop, they accumulate differences due to natural selection that eventually will result in two populations so different that they are reproductively isolated. Reinforcement, on the other hand, is a process that specifically relates to reproductive isolation. It occurs when natural selection favors non-hybrids because of hybrid infertility or are simply less fit than their parents. In this way, populations that may have been only partly reproductively isolated become completely reproductively isolated.

22.4 Polyploidy occurs instantaneously; in a single generation, the offspring of two different parental species may be reproductively isolated; however, if it is capable of self-fertilization then it is, according to the Biological Species Concept, a new species. Disruptive selection, on the other hand, requires many generations as reproductive barriers between the two populations must evolve and be reinforced before the two would be considered separate species.

22.5 In the archipelago model, adaptive radiation occurs as each individual island population adapts to its different environmental pressures. In sympatric speciation resulting from disruptive selection, on the other hand, traits are selected for that are not necessarily best suited for a novel environment but are best able to reduce competition with other individuals. It is in the latter scenario wherein adaptive radiation due to a key innovation is most likely to occur.

22.6 It depends on what species concept you are using to define a given species. Certainly evolutionary change can be punctuated, but in times of changing environmental pressures we would expect adaptation to occur. The adaptations, however, do not necessarily have to lead to the splitting of a species—instead one species could simply change in accordance with the environmental changes to which it is subjected. This would be an example of non-branching, as opposed to branching, evolution; but again, whether the end-result organism is a different species from its ancestral organism that preceded the punctuated event is subject to interpretation.

22.7 Unlike the previous major mass extinction events, the current mass extinction is largely attributable to human activity, including but not limited to habitat degradation, pollution, and hunting.

INQUIRY QUESTIONS

Page 447 Speciation can occur under allopatric conditions because isolated populations are more likely to diverge over time due to drift or selection. Adaptive radiation tends to occur in places inhabited by only a few other species or where many resources in a habitat are unused. Different environmental conditions typical of adaptive radiation tend to favor certain traits within a population. Allopatric conditions would then generally favor adaptive radiation.

In character displacement, natural selection in each species favors individuals able to use resources not used by the other species. Two species might have evolved from two populations of the same species located in the same environment (sympatric species). Individuals at the extremes of each population are able to resources not used by the other group. Competition for a resource would be reduced for these individuals, possibly favoring their survival and leading to selection for the tendency to use the new resource. Character displacement tends to compliment sympatric speciation.

Page 452 If one area experiences an unfavorable change in climate, a mobile species can move to another area where the climate was like it was before the change. With little environmental change to drive natural selection within that species, stasis would be favored.

UNDERSTAND

1. a 2. c 3. a 4. b 5. a 6. a 7. d 8. b

APPLY

1. b 2. a 3. d 4. a 5. b 6. b

SYNTHESIZE

1. If hybrids between two species have reduced viability or fertility, then natural selection will favor any trait that prevents hybrid matings. The reason is that individuals that don't waste time, energy, or resources on such matings will have greater fitness if they instead spend the time, energy, and resources on mating with members of their own species. For this reason, natural selection

will favor any trait that decreases the probability of hybridization. By contrast, once hybridization has occurred, the time, energy, and resources have already been expended. Thus, there is no reason that less fit hybrids would be favored over more fit ones. The only exception is for species that invest considerable time and energy in incubating eggs and rearing the young; for those species, selection may favor reduced viability of hybrids because parents of such individuals will not waste further time and energy on them.

2. The biological species concept, despite its limitations, reveals the continuum of biological processes and the complexity and dynamics of organic evolution. At the very least, the biological species concept provides a mechanism for biologists to communicate about taxa and know that they are talking about the same thing! Perhaps even more significantly, discussion and debate about the meaning of "species" fuels a deeper understanding about biology and evolution in general. It is unlikely that we will ever have a single unifying concept of species given the vast diversity of life, both extinct and extant.

3. The principle is the same as in character displacement. In sympatry, individuals of the two species that look alike may mate with each other. If the species are not completely interfertile, then individuals hybridizing will be at a selective disadvantage. If a trait appears in one species that allows that species to more easily recognize members of its own species and thus avoid hybridization, then individuals bearing that trait will have higher fitness and that trait will spread through the population.

4. I would expect the two species to have more similar morphology when they are found alone (allopatry) than when they are found together (sympatry), assuming that food resources were the same from one island to the next. This would be the result of character displacement expected under a hypothesis of competition for food when the two species occur in sympatry. A species pair that is more distantly related might not be expected to show the pattern of character displacement since they show greater differences in morphology (and presumably in ecology and behavior as well), which should reduce the potential for competition to drive character divergence.

CHAPTER 23

LEARNING OUTCOME QUESTIONS

23.1 Because of convergent evolution; two distantly related species subjected to the same environmental pressures may be more phenotypically similar than two species with different environmental pressures but a more recent common ancestor. Other reasons for the possible dissimilarity between closely related species include oscillating selection and rapid adaptive radiations in which species rapidly adapt to a new available niche.

23.2 In some cases wherein characters diverge rapidly relative to the frequency of speciation, it can be difficult to construct a phylogeny using cladistics because the most parsimonious phylogeny may not be the most accurate. In most cases, however, cladistics is a very useful tool for inferring phylogenetic relationships among groups of organisms.

23.3 Yes, in some instances this is possible. For example, assume two populations of a species become geographically isolated from one another in similar environments, and each population diverges and speciation occurs, with one group retaining its ancestral traits and the other deriving new traits. The ancestral group in each population may be part of the same biological species but would be considered polyphyletic because to include their common ancestor would also necessitate including the other, more derived species (which may have diverged enough to be reproductively isolated).

23.4 Not necessarily; it is possible that the character changed since the common ancestor and is present in each group due to convergence. While the most recent common ancestor possessing the character is the most parsimonious, and thus the most likely, explanation, it is possible, especially for small clades, that similar environmental pressures resulted in the emergence of the same character state repeatedly during the course of the clade's evolution.

23.5 Hypothetically it is possible; however, the viral analyses and phylogenetic analyses have provided strong evidence that HIV emergence was the other way around; it began as a simian disease and mutated to become a human form, and that this has occurred several times.

INQUIRY QUESTIONS

Page 461 In parsimony analyses of phylogenies, the least complex explanation is favored. High rates of evolutionary change and few character states complicate matters. High rates of evolutionary change, such as occur when mutations arise in noncoding portions of DNA, can be misleading when constructing phylogenies. Mutations arising in noncoding DNA are not eliminated by natural selection in the same manner as mutations in coding (functional) DNA. Also, evolution of new character states can be very high in nonfunctional DNA and this can lead to genetic drift. Since DNA has only four nucleotides (four character states) it is highly likely that two species could evolve the same derived character at a particular base position. This leads to a violation of the assumptions of parsimony—that the fewest evolutionary events lead to the best hypothesis of phylogenetic relationships—and resulting phylogenies are inaccurate.

Page 462 The only other hypothesis is that the most recent common ancestor of birds and bats was also winged. Of course, this scenario is much less parsimonious (and thus much more unlikely) than the convergence hypothesis, especially given the vast number of reptiles and mammals without wings. Most phylogenies are constructed based on the rule of parsimony; in the absence of fossil evidence of other winged animals and molecular data supporting a closer relationship between birds and bats than previously thought, there is no way to test the hypothesis that bird and bat wings are homologous rather than analogous.

Page 471 If the victim had contracted HIV from a source other than the patient, the most recent common ancestor of the two strains would be much more distant. As it is, the phylogeny shows that the victim and patient strains share a relatively recent ancestor, and that the victim's strain is derived from the patient's strain.

UNDERSTAND

1. d 2. b 3. a 4. b 5. a 6. d 7. b 8. c

APPLY

1. c 2. d 3. d 4. a

SYNTHESIZE

1. Naming of groups can be variable; names provided here are just examples. Jaws—shark, salamander, lizard, tiger, gorilla, human (jawed vertebrates); lungs—salamander, lizard, tiger, gorilla, human (terrestrial tetrapods); amniotic membrane—lizard, tiger, gorilla, human (amniote tetrapods); hair—tiger, gorilla, human (mammals); no tail—gorilla, human (humanoid primate); bipedal—human (human).

2. It would seem to be somewhat of a conundrum, or potentially circular; choosing a closely related species as an outgroup when we do not even know the relationships of the species of interest. One way of guarding against a poor choice for an outgroup is to choose several species as outgroups and examine how the phylogenetic hypothesis for the group of interest changes as a consequence of using different outgroups. If the choice of outgroup makes little difference, then that might increase one's confidence in the phylogenetic hypotheses for the species of interest. On the other hand, if the choice makes a big difference (different phylogenetic hypotheses result when choosing different outgroups), that might at least lead to the conclusion that one cannot be confident in inferring a robust phylogenetic hypothesis for the group of interest without collecting more data.

3. Recognizing that birds are reptiles potentially provides insight to the biology of both birds and reptiles. For example, some characteristics of birds are clearly of reptilian origin, such as feathers (modified scales), nasal salt secreting glands, and strategies of osmoregulation/excretion (excreting nitrogenous waste products as uric acid) representing ancestral traits, that continue to serve birds well in their environments. On the other hand, some differences from other reptiles (again, feathers) seem to have such profound significance biologically, that they overwhelm similarities visible in shared ancestral characteristics. For example, no extant nonavian reptiles can fly, or are endothermic and these two traits have created a fundamental distinction in the minds of many biologists. Indeed, many vertebrate biologists prefer to continue to distinguish birds from reptiles rather than emphasize their similarities even though they recognize the power of cladistic analysis in helping to shape classification. Ultimately, it may be nothing much more substantial than habit which drives the preference of some biologists to traditional classification schemes.

4. In fact, such evolutionary transitions (the loss of the larval mode, and the re-evolution of a larval mode from direct development) are treated with equal weight under the simplest form of parsimony. However, if it is known from independent methods (for example, developmental biology) that one kind of change is less likely than another (loss versus a reversal), these should and can be taken into account in various ways. The simplest way might be to assign weights based on likelihoods; two transitions from larval development to direct development is equal to one reversal from direct development back to a larval mode. In fact, there are such methods, and they are similar in spirit to the statistical approaches used to build specific models of evolutionary change rather than rely on simple parsimony.

5. The structures are both homologous, as forelimbs, and convergent, as wings. In other words, the most recent common ancestor of birds, pterosaurs and bats had a forelimb similar in morphology to that which these organisms possess—it has similar bones and articulations. Thus, the forelimb itself among these organisms is homologous. The wing, however, is clearly convergent; the most recent common ancestor surely did not have wings (or all other mammals and reptiles would have had to have lost the wing, which violates the rule of parsimony). The wing of flying insects is purely convergent with the vertebrate wing, as the forelimb of the insect is not homologous with the vertebrate forelimb.

6. The biological species concept focuses on processes, in particular those which result in the evolution of a population to the degree that it becomes reproductively isolated from its ancestral population. The process of speciation as utilized by the biological species concept occurs through the interrelatedness of evolutionary mechanisms such as natural selection, mutation, and genetic drift. On the other hand, the phylogenetic species concept focuses not on process but on history, on the evolutionary patterns that led to the divergence between populations. Neither species concept is more right or more wrong; species concepts are, by their very nature, subjective and potentially controversial.

CHAPTER 24

LEARNING OUTCOME QUESTIONS

24.1 There should be a high degree of similarity between the two genomes because they are relatively closely related. There could be differences in the relative amounts of non-coding DNA. Genes that are necessary for bony skeletal development might be found in the bony fish. The cartilaginous fish might lack those genes or have substantial sequences in the genes needed for skeletal development in bony fish.

24.2 There would now be three copies of the chromosome from the same species. This would cause a problem for the cell during meiosis I as there would not be an even number of homologs of the chromosome to pair up and segregate.

24.3 Compare the sequence of the pseudogene with other species. If, for example, it is a pseudogene of an olfactory gene that is found in mice or chimps, the sequences will be much more similar than in a more distantly related species. If horizontal gene transfer explains the origins of the gene, there may not be a very similar gene in closely related species. You might use the BLAST algorithm discussed in chapter 18 to identify similar sequences and then construct a phylogenetic tree to compare the relationships among the different species.

24.4 A SNP can change a single amino acid in the coded peptide. If the new R group is very different, the protein may fold in a different way and not function effectively. SNPs in the *FOXP2* gene may, in part, explain why humans have speech and chimps do not. Other examples that you may remember from earlier in the text include cystic fibrosis and sickle cell anemia.

24.5 One approach would be to create a mutation in the non-coding gene and ask whether or not this changes the phenotype. You would need to be sure that both copies of the nonprotein-coding gene were "knocked out."

24.6 Much of the non-coding DNA could contain retrotransposons that replicate and insert the new DNA into the genome, enlarging the genome. Since the number of genes does not change, polyploidy is not a good explanation.

24.7 An effective drug might bind only to the region of the pathogen protein that is distinct from the human protein. The drug could render the pathogen protein ineffective without making the human ill. If the seven amino acids that differ are scattered throughout the genome, they might have a minimal effect on the protein and it would be difficult to develop a drug that could detect small differences. It's possible that the drug could inadvertently affect other areas of the protein as well.

24.8 One approach would be to create transgenic soy with additional protein coding genes.

INQUIRY QUESTIONS

Page 478 Meiosis in a 3n cell would be impossible because three sets of chromosomes cannot be divided equally between two cells. In a 3n cell, all three homologous chromosomes would pair in prophase I, then align during anaphase I. As the homologous chromosomes separate, two of a triplet might go to one cell while the third chromosome would go to the other cell. The same would be true for each set of homologues. Daughter cells would have an unpredictable number of chromosomes.

Page 479 Polyploidization seems to induce the elimination of duplicated genes. Duplicate genes code for the same gene product. It is reasonable that duplicate genes would be eliminated to decrease the redundancy arising from the translation of several copies of the same gene.

Page 484 Ape and human genomes show very different patterns of gene transcription activity, even though genes encoding proteins are over 99% similar between chimps and humans. Different genes would be transcribed when comparing apes with humans, and the levels of transcription would vary widely.

UNDERSTAND

1. c   2. d   3. d   4. b   5. b   6. a

APPLY

1. a   2. d   3. d   4. a

SYNTHESIZE

1. The two amino acid difference between the FOXP2 protein in humans and closely related primates must alter the way the protein functions in the brain. The protein affects motor function in the brain allowing coordination of larynx, mouth and brain for speech in humans. For example, if the protein affects transcription, there could be differences in the genes that are regulated by FOXP2 in humans and chimps.

2. Human and chimp DNA is close to 99% similar, yet our phenotypes are conspicuously different in many ways. This suggests that a catalogue of genes is just the first step to identifying the mechanisms underlying genetically influenced diseases like cancer or cystic fibrosis. Clearly, gene expression, which might involve the actions of multiple noncoding segments of the DNA and other potentially complex regulatory mechanics, are important sources of how phenotypes are formed, and it is likely that many genetically determined diseases result from such complex underlying mechanisms, making the gene identification of genomics just the first step; a necessary but not nearly sufficient strategy. What complete genomes do offer is a starting point to correlating sequence differences among humans with genetic disease, as well as the opportunity to examine how multiple genes and regulatory sequences interact to cause disease.

3. Phylogenetic analysis usually assumes that most genetic and phenotypic variation arises from descent with modification (vertical inheritance). If genetic and phenotypic characteristics can be passed horizontally (that is, not vertically through genetic lineages) then using patterns of shared character variation to infer genealogical relationships will be subject to potentially significant error. We might expect that organisms with higher rates of HGT will have phylogenetic hypotheses that are less reliable or at least are not resolved as a neatly branching tree.

CHAPTER 25

LEARNING OUTCOME QUESTIONS

25.1 A change in the promoter of a gene necessary for wing development might lead to the repression of wing development in a second segment of a fly in a species that has double wings.

25.2 No. This cichlid would need to reproduce and over time give rise to a line of cichlid's with extra-long jaws. Perhaps they would populate a different part of the lake and not reproduce with other cichlids. Over time they could become a new species. The extra-long jaw would have to offer some selective advantage or the trait would not persist in the population.

25.3 Yes, although this is not the only explanation. The coding regions could be identical but the promoter or other regulatory regions could have been altered by mutation, leading to altered patterns of gene expression. To test this hypothesis, the pitx1 gene should be sequenced in both fish and compared.

25.4 The pectoral fins are homoplastic because sharks and whales are only distantly related and pectoral fins are not found in whales' more recent ancestors.

25.5 The duplication could persist if a mutation in the duplicated gene prevented its expression or altered the coding region, and either a regulatory or a coding change could lead to a new function.

25.6 A phylogenetic analysis of paleoAP3 and its gene duplicates demonstrated that the presence of AP3 correlates with petal formation. The specific domain of AP3 that is necessary for petal development was identified by making gene constructs of the AP3 gene where the C terminus of the protein was eliminated or was replaced with the C terminus from the duplicate gene. The C terminus was shown to be essential for petal formation.

25.7 There is no need for eyes in the dark. Perhaps the fish expend less energy when eyes are not produced and that offered a selective advantage in cavefish. In a habitat with light, a mutation that resulted in a functional Pax6 would likely be selected for and over time more of the fish would have eyes. Keep in mind that the probability of a mutation restoring Pax6 function is very low, but real.

INQUIRY QUESTIONS

Page 495 Because there is a stop codon located in the middle of the CAL (cauliflower) gene coding sequence, the wild-type function of CAL must be concerned with producing branches rather than leaves. The wild type of *Brassica oleracea* consists of compact plants that add leaves rather than branches; branches are typical of the flowering heads of broccoli and cauliflower. Additional evolutionary events possibly include large flower heads, unusual head coloration, protective leaves covering flower heads, or head size variants, among other possibilities.

Page 501 Functional analysis involves the use of a variety of experiments designed to test the function of a specific gene in different species. By mixing and matching parts of the *AP3* and *PI* genes and introducing them into *ap3* mutant plants, it was found that the C terminus sequence of the *AP3* protein is essential for specifying petal function. Without the 3 region of the *AP3* gene, the *Arabidopsis* plant cannot make petals.

UNDERSTAND

1. c   2. b   3. a   4. a   5. b   6. d   7. b   8. c   9. c   10. d

APPLY

1. b   2. a   3. d   4. b

SYNTHESIZE

1. Mutations in the promoter region of other genes allowed them to be recognized by Tbx5, which led to transcriptional control of these genes by Tbx5.

2. Development is a highly conserved and constrained process; small perturbations can have drastic consequences, and most of these are negative. Given the thousands or hundreds of thousands of variables that can change in even a simple developmental pathway, most perturbations lead to negative outcomes. Over millions of years, some of these changes will arise under the right circumstances to produce a benefit. In this way, developmental perturbations are not different from what we know about mutations in general. Beneficial mutations are rare, but with enough time they will emerge and spread under specific circumstances.

   Not all mutations provide a selective advantage. For example, reduced body armor increases the fitness of fish in freshwater, but it was not selected for in a marine environment where the armor was important for protection from predators. The new trait can persist at low levels for a very long time until a change in environmental conditions results in an increase in fitness for individuals exhibiting the trait.

3. The latter view represents our current understanding. There are many examples of small gene families (such as, *Hox*, *MADS*) whose apparent role in generating phenotypic diversity among major groupings of organisms is in altering the expression of other genes. Alterations in timing (heterochrony) or spatial pattern of expression (homeosis) can lead to shifts in developmental events, giving rise to new phenotypes. Many examples are presented in the chapter, such as the developmental variants of two species of sea urchins, one with a normal larval phase, and another with direct development. In this case the two species do not have different sets of developmental genes, rather the expression of those genes differ. Another example that makes the same point is the evolution of an image forming eye. Recent studies suggest, in contrast to the view that eyes across the animal kingdom evolved independently multiple times, that image-forming eyes from very distantly related taxa (such as, insects and vertebrates) may trace back to the common origin of the *Pax6* gene. If that view is correct, then genes controlling major developmental patterns would seem to be highly conserved across long periods of time, with expression being the major form of variation.

4. Unless the Pax6 gene was derived multiple times, it is difficult to hypothesize multiple origins of eyes. Pax6 initiates eye development in many species. The variation in eyes among animals is a result of which genes are expressed and when after Pax6 initiates eye development.

5. Maize relies on paleoAP3 and PI for flower development while tomato has three genes because of a duplication of paleoAP3. This duplication event in the ancestor of tomato, but not maize, is correlated with independent petal origin.

6. The direct developing sea urchin has an ancestor that had one or more mutations in genes that were needed to regulate the expression of other genes needed for larval stage development. When those genes were not expressed, there was no larval development and the genes necessary for adult development were expressed.

CHAPTER 26

LEARNING OUTCOME QUESTIONS

26.1 The evidence would be that the organism reproduces and posses a system to pass on information from generation to generation (heredity), regulates its internal processes and can maintain homeostasis, grows and develops, has some sort of cellular organization, and can respond to some stimuli.

26.2 You can infer that both a squirrel and fox are in the class Mammalia but are in different orders. Thus they share many, but not all traits. They likely shared a common ancestor. However the taxonomic hierarchy does not show the evolutionary relationships among organisms the way a phylogeny would.

26.3 The viral genome would now be part of the infected cell's genome and the viral genes could be expressed. One example of this is the chicken pox virus.

26.4 Without atmospheric oxygen, organisms would still be anaerobic. There would be no cellular respiration and no mitochondria in cells. Organisms would not be as effective at producing energy and they may not have evolved to be as large as some life forms today because they couldn't meet the energy demands of the cells.

26.5 Insect vectors might carry DNA from moss to a flowering plant.

26.6 Closely related living organisms might have diverged from a common ancestor millions of years ago. Even though they are the closest living relatives, much evolutionary change could have occurred during the intervening years.

INQUIRY QUESTIONS

Page 515 A clade is an evolutionary unit consisting of a common ancestor and all of its descendants. Evidence suggests that the Archaea are very different from all other organisms, which justifies including the Archaea in a separate domain. Phylogenetically, each domain forms a clade.

Page 522 Comparisons of a single gene could result in an inaccurate phylogenetic tree because it fails to take into account the effects of horizontal gene transfer. For example, the clade of *Amborella trichopoda* is a sister clade to all other flowering plants, but roughly ⅔ of its mitochondrial genes are present due to horizontal gene transfer from other land plants, including more distantly-related mosses.

Page 522 To determine if a moss gene had a function you would employ functional analysis, using a variety of experiments, to test for possible functions of the moss gene in *Amborella*.

UNDERSTAND

1. b   2. c   3. c   5. The protists are a bit of a catchall and are not monophyletic. Organisms that were clearly eukarotic but did not fit with plants, fungi, or animals were placed in the protists   6. c   7. c   8. d

APPLY

1. Kindgom Fungi because some fungi have flagella and cell walls made of chitin. Fungi lack a nervous system   2. a   3. c   4. d   5. b   6. d

SYNTHESIZE

1. If the life is biochemically the same on one of these moons and Earth, then it is possible that life originated in one place and was moved to the other location by the action of meteorites and comets. As you have seen with convergent evolution, panspermia would still not be proven by such a finding. However, if the life was biochemically different it would suggest that life originated independently on the moons and Earth.

2.

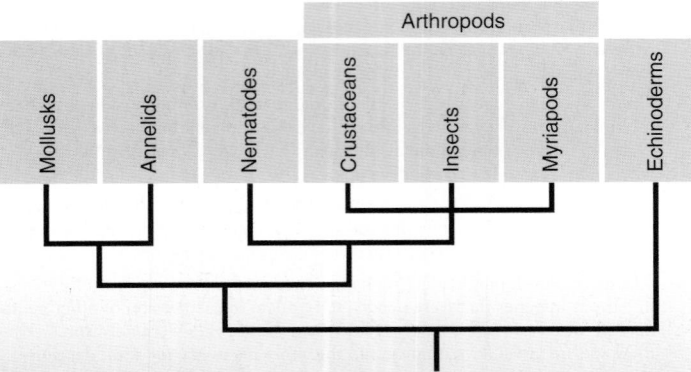

3. The most logical choice would be a species from the domain Archae. These are considered to be the oldest forms of life on our planet, and are known to have evolved to survive harsh environmental condition.

4. Morphology may be influenced by processes such as convergent evolution. However, DNA acts as a molecular record of a species' past. Combining what is being learned from both morphological and molecular data leads to more robust evolutionary hypotheses.

CHAPTER 27

LEARNING OUTCOME QUESTIONS

27.1 Viruses use cellular machinery for replication. They do not make all of the proteins necessary for complete replication.

27.2 A prophage carrying such a mutation could not be induced to undergo the lytic cycle.

27.3 This therapy, at present, does not remove all detectable viruses. This cannot be considered a true cure.

27.4 In addition to a high mutation rate, the influenza genome consists of multiple RNA segments that can recombine during infection. This causes the main antigens for the immune system to shift rapidly.

27.5 Prions carry information in their three-dimensional structure. This 3-D information is different from the essentially one-dimensional genetic information in DNA.

UNDERSTAND

1. c   2. b   3. c   4. d   5. b   6. d   7. b

APPLY

1. c   2. b   3. c   4. d   5. b   6. c   7. c   8. a

SYNTHESIZE

1. A set of genes that are involved in the response to DNA damage are normally induced by the same system. The protein involved destroys a repressor that keeps DNA repair genes unexpressed. Lambda has evolved to use this system to its advantage.

2. Since viruses require the replication machinery of a host cell to replicate, it is unlikely that they existed before the origin of the first cells.

3. This is a complex situation. Factors that act include the high mutation rate of the virus and the fact that the virus targets the very cells that mount an immune response. The influenza virus also requires a new vaccine every year due to rapids changes in the virus. The smallpox virus was a DNA virus that had antigenic determinants that did not change rapidly making a vaccine possible.

4. Emerging viruses are those that jump species and thus are new to humans. Recent examples include SARS and Ebola.

5. If excision of the lambda prophage is imprecise, then the phage produced will carry E. coli genes adjacent to the integration site.

CHAPTER 28

LEARNING OUTCOME QUESTIONS

28.1 Evidence would take the form of microfossils, evidence for altered isotopic ratios, or biomarkers such as hydrocarbons that do not arise by abiotic processes.

28.2 Archaea have ether linked instead of ester linked phospholipids; their cell wall is made of unique material.

28.3 Compare their DNA. The many metabolic tests we have used for years have been supplanted by DNA analysis.

28.4 Transfer of genetic information in bacteria is directional: from donor to recipient and does not involve fusion of gametes.

28.5 Prokaryotes do not have a lot of morphological features, but do have diverse metabolic functions.

28.6 Pathogens tend to evolve to be less virulent. If they are too good at killing, their lifestyle is an evolutionary dead end.

28.7 Rotating a crop that has a symbiotic association with nitrogen fixing bacteria will return nitrogen to the soil depleted by other plants.

INQUIRY QUESTION

Page 562 The simplest explanation is that the two STDs are occurring in different populations, and one population has rising levels of sexual activity, while the other has falling levels. However, the rise in incidence of an STD can reflect many parameters other than level of sexual activity. The virulence or infectivity of one or both disease agents may be changing, for example, or some aspect of exposed people may be changing in such a way as to alter susceptibility. Only a thorough public health study can sort this out.

UNDERSTAND

1. b 2. a 3. c 4. c 5. d 6. a 7. b

APPLY

1. c 2. b 3. b 4. c 5. d 6. b 7. a

SYNTHESIZE

1. The study of carbon signatures in rocks using isotopic data assumes that ancient carbon fixation involves one of two pathways that each show a bias towards incorporation of carbon 12. If this bias were not present, it is not possible to infer early carbon fixation by this pathway. This pathway could have arisen even earlier and we would have no way to detect it.

2. The heat killing of the virulent S strain of *Streptococcus* released the genome of the virulent smooth strain into the environment. These strains of *Streptococcus* bacteria are capable of natural transformation. At least some of the rough strain cells took up smooth strain genes that encoded the polysaccharide coat from the environment. These genes entered into the rough strain genome by recombination, and then were expressed. These transformed cells were now smooth bacteria.

3. The multiple antibiotics are not a bad idea if all of the bacteria are killed. In the case of some persistent infections, this is an effective strategy. However, it does provide very strong selective pressure for rare genetic events that produce multiple resistances in a single bacteria species. For this reason, it is not a good idea for it to be the normal practice. The more bacteria that undergo this selection for multiple resistance, the more likely it will arise. This is helped by patients not taking the entire course as bacteria may survive by chance and proliferate with each generation providing the opportunity for new mutations. This is also complicated by the horizontal transfer of resistance via resistance plasmids, and the existence of transposable genetic elements that can move genes from one piece of DNA to another.

4. Most species on the planet are incapable of fixing nitrogen without the assistance of bacteria. Without nitrogen, amino acids and other compounds cannot be synthesized. Thus a loss of the nitrogen fixing bacteria due to increased UV radiation levels would reduce the ability of plants to grow, severely limiting the food sources of the animals.

CHAPTER 29

LEARNING OUTCOME QUESTIONS

29.1 Mitochondria and chloroplasts contain their own DNA. Mitochondrial genes are transcribed within the mitochondrion, using mitochondrial ribosomes that are smaller than those of eukaryotic cells and quite similar to bacterial ribosomes. Antibiotics that inhibit protein translation in bacteria also inhibit protein translation in mitochondria. Also, both chloroplasts and mitochondria divide using binary fission like bacteria.

29.2 There are distinct clades in the Protista that do not share a common ancestor. The group of organisms commonly referred to as protists are actually a collection of a number of monophyletic clades.

Pseudopodia provide a large surface area and substantial traction for stable movement.

29.3 Undulating membranes would be effective on surfaces with curvature that may not always be smooth, including intestinal walls.

29.4 Contractile vacuoles collect and remove excess water from within the *Euglena*.

29.5 The *Plasmodium* often becomes resistant to new poisons and drugs.

29.6 While the gametophytes are often much smaller than the sporophytes, you could be most confident in your answer if you counted the chromosomes in the cells of each. The diploid sporophyte will have twice as many chromosomes as the haploid gametophyte.

29.7 Both the red and green algae obtained their chloroplasts through endosymbiosis, possibly of the same lineage of photosynthetic bacteria. The red and green algae had diverged before the endosymbiotic events and the history recorded in their nuclear DNA is a different evolutionary history than that recorded in the plastids derived through emdosymbiosis.

29.8 Comparative genomic studies of choanoflagellates and sponges would be helpful. Considering the similarities among a broader range of genes than just the conserved tyrosine kinase receptor would provide additional evidence.

29.9 It is unlikely that cellular and plasmodial slime molds are closely related. They both appear in the last section of this chapter because they have yet to be assigned to clades. The substantial differences in their cell biology are inconsistent with a close phylogenetic relationship.

INQUIRY QUESTION

Page 570 Red and green algae obtained chloroplasts by engulfing photosynthetic bacteria by primary endosymbiosis; chloroplasts in these cells have two membranes. Brown algae obtained chloroplasts by engulfing cells of red algae through secondary endosymbiosis; chloroplasts in cells of brown algae have four membranes. Counting the number of cell membranes of chloroplasts indicates primary or secondary endosymbiosis.

UNDERSTAND

1. b 2. a 3. b 4. c 5. d 6. b 7. a 8. c 9. b, c 10. a, d
11. d 12. a

APPLY

1. d 2. a 3. a

SYNTHESIZE

1. Cellular and plasmodial slime molds both exhibit group behavior and can produce mobile slime mold masses. However, these two groups are very distantly related phylogenetically.

2. The development of a vaccine, though challenging, will be the most promising in the long run. It is difficult to eradicate all the mosquito vectors and many eradication methods can be harmful to the environment. Treatments to kill the parasites are also difficult because the parasite is likely to become resistant to each new poison or drug. A vaccine would provide long-term protection without the need to use harmful pesticides or drugs where drug resistance is a real possibility.

3. For the first experiment, plate the cellular slime molds on a plate that has no bacteria. Spot cyclic-AMP and designated places on the plate and determine if the bacteria aggregate around the cAMP.

   For the second experiment, repeat the first experiment using plates that have a uniform coating of bacteria as well as plates with no bacteria. If the cellular slime molds aggregate on both plates, resource scarcity is not an issue. If the cells aggregate only in the absence of bacteria, you can conclude that the attraction to cAMP occurs only under starvation conditions.

CHAPTER 30

LEARNING OUTCOME QUESTIONS

30.1 Make sections and examine them under the microscope to look for tracheids. Only the tracheophytes will have tracheids.

Gametes in plants are produced by mitosis. Human gametes are produced directly by meiosis.

30.2 Chlorophytes have chloroplasts which are not found in choanoflagellates.

The lack of water is the major barrier for sperm that move through water to reach the egg. It is more difficult for sperm to reach the egg on land.

30.3 Moss are extremely desiccation tolerant and can withstand the lack of water. Also, freezing temperatures at the poles are less damaging when moss have a low water content.

30.4 The sporophyte generation has evolved to be the larger generation and therefore an effective means to transporting water and nutrients over greater distances would be advantageous.

30.5 There was substantial climate change during that time period. Glaciers had spread, then melted and retreated. Drier climates could have contributed to the extinction of large club mosses. Refer to chapter 26 for more information on changes in Earth's climate over geological time.

30.6 The silica can increase the strength of the hollow-tube stems and would also deter herbivores.

30.7 The pollen tube grows towards the egg, carrying the sperm within the pollen tube.

30.8 The ovule rests, exposed on the scale (a modified leaf).

30.9 Animals that consume the fruit disperse the seed over longer distances than wind can disperse seed. The species can colonize a larger territory more rapidly.

INQUIRY QUESTIONS

Page 592 The diploid sporophyte of *Ulva* produces sporangia in which meiosis occurs. The resultant haploid spores develop into either plus or minus strains of multicellular gametophytes which, in turn, produce haploid gametangia. The gametangia produce haploid gametes. Meiosis is involved in the formation of *Ulva* gametes, but not directly.

Page 596 Tracheophytes developed vascular tissue, enabling them to have efficient water- and food-conducting systems. Vascular tissue allowed tracheophytes to grow larger, possibly then able to out-compete smaller, nonvascular land plants. A protective cuticle and stomata that can close during dry conditions also conferred a selective advantage.

Page 610 Endosperm provides nutrients for the developing embryo in most flowering plants. The embryo cannot derive nutrition from soil prior to root development, therefore without endosperm, the embryo is unlikely to survive.

UNDERSTAND

1. d   2. d, c   4. c   5. a   6. c   7. b   8. d   9. a   10. d

APPLY

2. d   3. b   4. c   5. c   6. a   7. b   8. a   9. a

SYNTHESIZE

1. Moss has a dominant gametophyte generation while lycophytes have a dominant sporophyte generation. Perhaps a comparison of the two genomes would provide insight into the genomic differences associated with the evolutionary shift from dominant gametophyte to dominant sporophyte.

2. Answers to this question may vary. However, gymnosperms are defined as "naked" seed plants. Therefore, an ovule that is not completely protected by sporophyte tissue would be characteristic of a gymnosperm. To be classified as an angiosperm, evidence of flower structures and double fertilization are key characteristics, although double fertilization has been observed in some gnetophytes.

3. The purpose of pollination is to bring together the male and female gametes for sexual reproduction. Sexual reproduction is designed to increase the genetic variability of a species. If a plant allows self-pollination, then the amount of genetic diversity will be reduced, but this is a better alternative than not reproducing at all. This would be especially useful in species in which the individuals are widely dispersed.

4. The benefit is that by developing a relationship with a specific pollinator, the plant species increases the chance that its pollen will be brought to another member of its species for pollination. If the pollinator is a generalist, then the pollinator might not travel to another member of the same species, and pollination would not occur. The drawback is that if something happens to the pollinator (extinction or drop in population size) then the plant species would be left with either a reduced or nonexistent means of pollination.

CHAPTER 31

LEARNING OUTCOME QUESTIONS

31.1 In fungi mitosis results in duplicated nuclei, but the nuclei remain within a single cell. This lack of cell division following mitosis is very unusual in animals.
Hyphae are protected by chitin, which is not digested by fungal enzymes.

31.2 Microsporidians lack mitochondria which are found in *Plasmodium*.

31.3 Blastocladiomycetes are free-living and have mitochondria. Microsporidians are obligate parasites and lack mitochondria.

31.4 Zygospores are more likely to be produced when environmental conditions are not favorable. Sexual reproduction increases the chances of offspring with new combinations of genes that will have an advantage in a changing environment. Also, the zygospore can stay dormant until conditions improve.

31.5 Parasitism is a subset of symbiotic relationships. Symbiotic relationships refer to two or more organisms of different species living in close relationship to each other to the benefit of one, both or neither. In parasitism, only one member of the symbiosis benefits and that is at the expense of the other.

31.6 A dikaryotic cell has two nuclei, each with a single set of chromosomes. A diploid cell has a single nucleus with two sets of chromosomes.

31.7 Preventing the spread of the fungal infection using fungicides and good cultivation practices could help. If farmworkers must tend to infected fields, masks that filter out the spores could protect the workers.

31.8 The fungi that ants consumed may have originally been growing on leaves. Over evolutionary time, mutations that altered ant behavior so the ants would bring leaves to a stash of fungi would have been favored and the tripartite symbiosis evolved.

31.9 Wind can spread spores over large distances, resulting in the spread of fungal disease.

UNDERSTAND

1. c   2. d   3. a   4. d   5. b   6. d   7. d

APPLY

1. d   2. b   3. a   4. c   5. d

SYNTHESIZE

1. Fungi possess cell walls. Although the composition of these cell walls differs from that of the plants, cell walls are completely absent in animals. Fungi are also immobile (except for chytrids), and mobility is a key characteristic of the animals.

2. The mycorrhizal relationships between the fungi and plants allow plants to make use of nutrient poor soil. Without the colonization of land by plants, it is unlikely that animals would have diversified to the level they have achieved today. Lichens are important organisms in the colonization of land. Early land masses would have been composed primarily of barren rock, with little or no soil for plant colonization. As lichens colonize an area they begin the process of soil formation, which allows other plant

3. Antibiotics are designed to combat prokaryotic organisms and fungi are eukaryotic. In addition, fungi possess a cell wall that has a different chemical constitution (chitin) from that of prokaryotes.

CHAPTER 32

LEARNING OUTCOME QUESTIONS

32.1 The rules of parsimony state that the simplest phylogeny is most likely the true phylogeny. As there are living organisms that are both multicellular and unicellular, it stands to reason that the first organisms were unicellular, and multicellularity followed. Animals are also all heterotrophs; if they were the first type of life to have evolved, there would not have been any autotrophs on which they could feed.

32.2 Cephalization, the concentration of nervous tissue in a distinct head region, is intrinsically connected to the onset of bilateral symmetry. Bilateral symmetry promotes the development of a central nerve center, which in turn favors the nervous tissue concentration in the head. In addition, the onset of both cephalization and bilateral symmetry allows for the marriage of directional movement (bilateral symmetry) and the presence of sensory organs facing the direction in which the animal is moving (cephalization).

32.3 This allows systematists to classify animals based solely on derived characteristics. Using features that have only evolved once implies that the species that have that characteristic are more closely related to each other than they are to species that do not have the characteristic.

32.4 One hypothesis is that the rapid diversification in body plan was a biological response to the evolution of predation—the adaptation of traits that enabled predators to better find prey and prey to better elude predators. Another hypothesis is that the explosion of new body forms resulted from changes in the physical environment such as oxygen and mineral build up in the oceans.

UNDERSTAND

1. c   2. b   3. a   4. d   5. a   6. b   7. d   8. a   9. b   10. d   11. d

APPLY

1. d   2. b   3. Determinate development indicates that it is a protostome and the fact that it molts places it within the Ecdysozoa. The presence of jointed appendages makes it an arthropod.

SYNTHESIZE

1. The tree should contain platyhelminthes and nemetera on one branch, a second branch should contain nematodes, and a third branch should contain the annelids and the hemichordates. This does not coincide with the information in Figure 32.4. Therefore, some of the different types of body cavities have evolved multiple times, and the body cavities are not good characteristics to infer phylogenetic relationships.

2. Answers may vary depending on the classification used. Many students will place the Echinoderms near the Cnidaria due to radial symmetry; others will place them closer to the Annelids.

CHAPTER 33

LEARNING OUTCOME QUESTIONS

33.1 The cells of a truly colonial organism, such as a colonial protist, are all structurally and functionally identical; however, sponge cells are differentiated and these cells coordinate to perform functions required by the whole organism. Unlike all other animals, however, sponges do appear much like colonial organisms in that they are not comprised of true tissues, and the cells are capable of differentiating from one type to another.

33.2 The importance of triploblasty relates to the placement of ctenophores on the animal phylogenetic tree. Until recently, ctenophores have been considered diploblasts, with platyhelminthes as the first triploblasts. New evidence, however, indicates that ctenophores are actually triploblastic. In addition, molecular evidence suggests that this phylum belongs at the base of the animal phylogeny—thus implying that the ancestor to all animals was triploblastic.

33.3 Tapeworms are parasitic platyhelminthes that live in the digestive system of their host. Tapeworms have a scolex, or head, with hooks for attaching to the wall of their host's digestive system. Another way in which the anatomy of a tapeworm relates to its way of life is their dorsoventrally flattened body and corresponding lack of a digestive system. Tapeworms live in their food; as such they absorb their nutrients directly through the body wall, and their flat bodies facilitate this form of nutrient delivery.

33.4 *Ascaris lumbricoides*, the intestinal roundworm, infects humans when the human swallows food or water contaminated with roundworm eggs. The most effective ways of preventing the spread of intestinal roundworms is to increase sanitation, especially those in food handling, education, and cease using human feces as fertilizer. Not surprisingly, infection by these parasites is most common in areas without modern plumbing.

UNDERSTAND

1. c 2. a 3. b 4. b 5. d 6. d 7. c

APPLY

1. c 2. c 3. d

SYNTHESIZE

1. Answers may vary. Phylum Acoela represents a reclassification of the platyhelminthes and phylum Cycliophora represents an entirely new kingdom. Since we have most likely not discovered all of the noncoelomate invertebrate species on the planet, and we are utilizing new molecular tools to examine the relationships of existing phyla, it is unlikely that the modern phylogeny presented in section 33.2 is complete.

2. Since the population size of a parasitic species may be very small (just a few individuals), possessing both male and female reproductive structures would allow the benefits of sexual reproduction.

3. Answers may vary. However, it is known that the tapeworm is not the ancestral form of platyhelminthes; instead it has lost its digestive tract due to its role as an intestinal parasite. As an intestinal parasite, the tapeworm relies on the digestive system of its host to break down nutrients into their building blocks for absorption.

CHAPTER 34

LEARNING OUTCOME QUESTIONS

34.1 Cephalopods are the most active of all mollusks, and this increased level of activity necessitates a more efficient oxygen delivery system. The extensive series of blood vessels, and thus more efficient gas exchange, in the cephalopod circulatory system allows the animal to move more rapidly and over longer periods of time.

34.2 With a flow-through digestive tract, food moves in only one direction. This allows for specialization within the tract; sections may be specialized for

mechanical and chemical digestion, some for storage, and yet others for absorption. Overall, the specialization yields greater efficiency than does a gastrovascular cavity.

34.3 The main advantage is coordination. A nervous system that serves the entire body allows for coordinated movement and coordinated physiological activities such as reproduction and excretion, even if those systems themselves are segmented. Likewise, a body-wide circulatory system enables efficient oxygen delivery to all of the body cells regardless of the nature of the organism's individual segments.

34.4 Lophophorates are sessile suspension-feeding animals. Much of their body also remains submerged in the ocean floor. Thus, a traditional tubular digestive system would require either the mouth or the anus to be inaccessible to the water column—meaning the animal either could not feed or would have to excrete waste into a closed environment. The U-shaped gut allows them to both acquire nutrients from and excrete waste into their environment.

34.5 One of the defining features of the arthropods is the presence of a chitinous exoskeleton. As arthropods increase in size, the exoskeleton must increase in thickness disproportionately, in order to bear the pull of the animal's muscles. This puts a limit on the size a terrestrial arthropod can reach, as the increased bulk of the exoskeleton would prohibit the animal's ability to move. Water is denser than air and thus provides more support; for this reason aquatic arthropods are able to be larger than terrestrial arthropods.

34.6 Bilateral symmetry evolved relatively early in animal phylogeny, with the platyhelminthes. Echinoderms clearly branched off later in evolutionary history, as evidenced by deuterostome development, and yet, as adults they exhibit radial (or, more accurately, pentaradial) symmetry. This might be a confusing factor when determining the phylogeny of animals, if not for the bilateral form the echinoderm larvae take. The bilaterally symmetrical larvae suggest that the echinoderm ancestor is in fact bilaterally symmetrical, rather than radially symmetrical.

UNDERSTAND

1. c 2. b 3. a 4. d 5. d 6. b 7. c 8. d 9. d 10. a 11. a

APPLY

1. b 2. c 3. d 4. a

SYNTHESIZE

1. Clams and scallops are bivalves, which are filter feeders that siphon large amounts of water through their bodies to obtain food. They act as natural pollution-control systems for bays and estuaries. A loss of bivalves (from overfishing, predation, or toxic chemicals) would upset the aquatic ecosystem and allow pollution levels to rise.

2. Chitin is an example of convergent evolution since these organisms do not share a common chitin-equipped ancestor. Chitin is often used in structures that need to withstand the rigors of stress (chaetae, exoskeletons, zoecium, etc.).

CHAPTER 35

LEARNING OUTCOME QUESTIONS

35.1 Chordates have a truly internal skeleton (an endoskeleton), compared to the endoskeleton on echinoderms, which is functionally similar to the exoskeleton of arthropods. Whereas an echinoderm uses tube feet attached to an internal water vascular system for locomotion, a chordate has muscular attachments to its endoskeleton. Finally, chordates have a suite of four characteristics that are unique to the phylum—a nerve chord, a notochord, pharyngeal slits, and a postanal tail.

35.2 While mature and immature lancelets are similar in form, the tadpole-like tunicate larvae are markedly different from the sessile, vase-like adult form. Both tunicates and lancelets are chordates, but they differ from vertebrates in that they do not have vertebrae or internal bony skeletons.

35.3 The functions of an exoskeleton include protection and locomotion—arthropod exoskeletons, for example, provide a fulcrum to which the animals' muscles attach. In order to resist the pull of increasingly large muscles, the exoskeleton must dramatically increase in thickness as the animal grows larger. There is thus a limit on the size of an organism with an exoskeleton—if it gets too large it will be unable to move due to the weight and heft of its exoskeleton.

35.4 Lobe-finned fish are able to move their fins independently, whereas ray-finned fish must move their fins simultaneously. This ability to "walk" with their fins indicates that lobe-finned fish are most certainly the ancestors of amphibians.

35.5 The challenges of moving onto land were plentiful for the amphibians. First, amphibians needed to be able to support their body weight and locomote on land; this challenge was overcome by the evolution of legs. Second, amphibians needed to be able to exchange oxygen with the atmosphere; this was accomplished by the evolution of more efficient lungs than their lungfish ancestors as well as cutaneous respiration. Third, since movement on land requires more energy than movement in the water, amphibians needed a more efficient oxygen delivery system to supply their larger muscles; this was accomplished by the evolution of double-loop circulation and a partially divided heart. Finally, the first amphibians needed to develop a way of staying hydrated in a non-aquatic environment, and these early amphibians developed leathery skin that helped prevent desiccation.

35.6 Amphibians remain tied to the water for their reproduction; their eggs are jelly-like and if laid on the land will quickly desiccate. Reptile eggs, on the other hand, are amniotic eggs—they are watertight and contain a yolk, which nourishes the developing embryo, and a series of four protective and nutritive membranes.

35.7 There are two primary traits shared between birds and reptiles. First, both lay amniotic eggs. Second, they both possess scales (which cover the entire reptile body but solely the legs and feet of birds). Birds also share characteristics only with one group of reptiles—the crocodilians, such as a four-chambered heart.

35.8 The most striking convergence between birds and mammals is endothermy, the ability to regulate body temperature internally. Less striking is flight; found in most birds and only one mammal, the ability to fly is another example of convergent evolution.

35.9 Only the hominids comprise a monophyletic group. Prosimians, monkeys, and apes are all paraphyletic—they include the common ancestor but not all descendents: the clade that prosimians share with the common prosimian ancestor excludes all anthropoids, the clade that monkeys share with the common monkey ancestor excludes hominoids, and clade that apes share with the common ape ancestor excludes hominids.

UNDERSTAND

1. c 2. c 3. a 4. c 5. a 6. d 7. a 8. d

APPLY

1. c 2. c 3. b

SYNTHESIZE

1. Increased insulation would have allowed birds to become endothermic and thus to be active at times that ectothermic species could not be active. High body temperature may also allow flight muscles to function more efficiently.

2. Birds evolved from one type of dinosaurs. Thus, in phylogenetic terms, birds are a type of dinosaur.

3. Like the evolution of modern day horses, the evolution of hominids was not a straight and steady progression to today's *Homo sapiens.* Hominid evolution started with an initial radiation of numerous species. From this group, there was a evolutionary trend of increasing size, similar to what is seen in the evolution of horses. However, like in horse evolution, there are examples of evolutionary decreases in body size as seen in *Homo floresiensis.* Hominid evolution also reveals the coexistence of related species, as seen with *Homo neaderthalensis* and *Homo sapiens.* Hominid evolution, like horse evolution, was not a straight and steady progression to the animal that exists today.

CHAPTER 36

LEARNING OUTCOME QUESTIONS

36.1 Primary growth contributes to the increase in plant height, as well as branching. Secondary growth makes substantial contributions to the increase in girth of the plant, allowing for a much larger sporophyte generation.

36.2 Vessels transport water and are part of the xylem. The cells are dead with only the walls remaining. Cylinders of stacked vessels move water from the roots to the leaves of plants. Sieve tube members are part of the phloem and transport nutrients. Sieve tube members are living cells, but they lack a nucleus. The rely on neighboring companion cells to carry out some metabolic functions. Like vessels, sieve tube members are stacked to form a cylinder.

36.3 The energy of the cell is used primarily to elongate the cell. It would be difficult for a root hair to form in the region of elongation because its base would be pulled apart by the elongation of the cell wall.

36.4 Roots are constantly growing through soil where cells are damaged and sloughed off. The tips of stems do not encounter the same barriers and do not require the additional protection.

36.5 Both sides of the leaf are equally exposed to sunlight. In contrast, horizontal leaves have a top and a bottom. Palisade layers are tightly packed with minimum airspace between the cells which maximizes photosynthetic surface area.

INQUIRY QUESTION

Page 736 Three dermal tissue traits that are adaptive for a terrestrial lifestyle include: guard cells, trichomes, and root hairs. Guard cells flank an epidermal opening called a stoma and regulate its opening and closing. Stomata are closed when water is scarce, thus conserving water. Trichomes are hairlike outgrowths of the epidermis of stems, leaves, and reproductive organs. Trichomes help to cool leaf surfaces and reduce evaporation from stomata. Root hairs are epidermal extensions of certain cells in young roots and greatly increase the surface area for absorption.

UNDERSTAND

1. d 2. d 3. c 4. b 5. a 6. c 7 a 8. b

APPLY

1. a 2. c 3. d 4. c

SYNTHESIZE

1. Roots lack leaves with axillary buds at nodes, although there may be lateral roots that originated from deep within the root. The vascular tissue would have a different pattern in roots and stems. If there is a vascular stele at the core with a pericycle surrounded by a Casparian strip, you are looking at a root.

2. Lenticels increase gas exchange. In wet soil, the opportunity for gas exchange decreases. Lenticels could compensate for decreased gas exchange, which would be adaptive.

3. The tree is likely to die because the phloem and vascular cambium is located near the surface. Removing a ring of bark results in the loss of the vascular cambium and phloem, leading to starvation and death.

CHAPTER 37

LEARNING OUTCOME QUESTIONS

37.1 Only angiosperms have an endosperm which results from double fertilization. The endosperm is the nutrient source in angiosperms. Gymnosperm embryos rely on megagametophytic tissue sources for nutrients.

37.2 These seeds might be sensitive to temperature and require a period of cold before germinating.

37.3 Fruits with fleshy coverings, often shiny black or bright blue or red, normally are favored by birds or other vertebrates.

37.4 Retaining the seed in the ground might provide greater stability for the seedling until its root system is established.

INQUIRY QUESTIONS

Page 758 The root meristem never forms, although the shoot meristem is fully functional. This plant is missing the HOBBIT protein which normally allows auxin to induce the expression of a gene or genes needed for correct cell division to make a root meristem. Without the correct cell divisions, the meristem fails to form.

Page 758 The *MONOPTEROS* (*MP*) gene product cannot act as a transcription factor when it is bound by its repressor. With a *MP* protein that can no longer bind to its repressor, *MP* acts as a transcription factor and activates a root development gene. The phenotype of a plant with a mutation in the *MP* gene has roots.

Page 761 A monocot has a solitary cotyledon. Two cotyledons are illustrated here, thus the embryo is a eudicot.

Page 762 The prior sporophyte generation, as part of the ovary, is diploid. The degenerating gametophyte generation is haploid. The next sporophyte generation, the embryo, is diploid.

UNDERSTAND

1. c 2. a 3. d 4. a 5. d 6. b 7. a 8. c 9. c

APPLY

1. c 2. c 3. b 4. d 5. c

SYNTHESIZE

1. Place *Fucus* zygotes on a screen and shine a light from the bottom. If light is more important, the rhizoid will form towards the light, even though that is the opposite direction gravity would dictate. If gravity is more important, the rhizoid will form away from the direction of the light.

2. The endosperm has three times as many copies of each gene. If transcription occurs at a constant rate in both nutritive tissues, more will be produced in the endosperm because of the extra copies of the genes.

3. The seeds may need to be chilled before they can germinate. You can store them in the refrigerator for several weeks or months and try again. The surface of the seed may need to be scarified (damaged) before it can germinate. Usually this would happen from the effects of weather or if the seed goes through the digestive track of an animal where the seed coat is weakened by acid in the gut of the animal. You could substitute for natural scarification by rubbing your seeds on sand paper before germinating them. It is possible that your seed needs to be exposed to light or received insufficient water when you first planted it. You may need to soak your seed in water for a bit to imbibe it. Exposing the imbibed seed to sunlight might also increase the chances of germination.

CHAPTER 38

LEARNING OUTCOME QUESTIONS

38.1 Physical pressures include gravity and transpiration, as well as turgor pressure as an expanding cell presses against its cell wall. Increases in turgor pressure and other physical pressures are associated with increases water potential. Solute concentration determines whether water enters or leaves a cell via osmosis. The smallest amount of pressure on the side of the cell membrane with the greater solute concentration that is necessary to stop osmosis is the solute potential. Water potential is the sum of the pressure from physical forces and from the solute potential.

38.2 Proteins in the cell membrane allow diffusion to be selective. Other protein channels are involved in active transport across the membrane. Water moves through channels called aquaporins. For a review of membrane properties, see chapter 5.

38.3 The driving force for transpiration is the gradient between 100% humidity inside the leaf and the external humidity. When the external humidity is low, the rate of transpiration is high, limited primarily by the amount of water available for uptake through the root system.

The minerals are used for metabolic activities. Some minerals can move into the phloem and be transported to metabolically active areas of the plants, but others, including calcium, cannot be relocated after they leave the xylem.

38.4 Once carbon dioxide is dissolved in water, it can be transported to photosynthetically active cells where it is used in carbon fixation in the Calvin Cycle (see chapter 8 for a review of photosynthesis).

38.5 Physical changes in the roots in response to oxygen deprivation may prevent further transport of water in the xylem. Although the leaves may be producing oxygen, it is not available to the roots.

38.6 Phloem liquid is rich in organic compounds including sucrose and plant hormones dissolved in water. Fluid in the xylem consists of minerals dissolved in water.

INQUIRY QUESTIONS

Page 773 Before equilibrium, the solute potential of the solution is –0.5 MPa, and that of the cell is –0.2 MPa. Since the solution contains more solute than does the cell, water will leave the cell to the point that the cell is plasmolyzed. Initial turgor pressure (Ψ_p) of the cell = 0.05 MPa, while that of the solution is 0 MPa. At equilibrium, both the solution and the cell will have the same Ψ_w. $\Psi_{cell} = -0.2$ MPa + 0.5 MPa = 0.3 MPa before equilibrium is reached. At equilibrium, $\Psi_{cell} = \Psi_{solution}$ = –0.5MPa, thus $\Psi_{w\ cell}$ = –0.5 MPa. At equilibrium, the plasmolyzed cell Ψ_p = 0 MPa. Finally, using the relationship $\Psi_{W(cell)} = \Psi_p + \Psi_s$ and $\Psi_{W(cell)}$ = –0.5 MPa, $\Psi_{P(cel)}$ = 0 MPa, then $\Psi_{s(cell)}$ = –0.5 MPa.

Page 775 The fastest route for water movement through cells has the least hindrance, and thus is the symplast route. The route that exerts the most control over what substances enter and leave the cell is the transmembrane route, which is then the best route for moving nutrients into the plant.

Page 777 If a mutation increases the radius, r, of a xylem vessel threefold, then the movement of water through the vessel would increase 81-fold ($r^4 = 3^4 = 81$). A plant with larger diameter vessels can move much more water up its stems.

UNDERSTAND

1. a 2. c 3. d 4. a 5. c 6. d 7. b 8. a 9. b 10. b

APPLY

1. b 2. c 3. b 4. c 5. b

SYNTHESIZE

1. The solute concentration outside the root cells is greater than inside the cells. Thus the solute potential is more negative outside the cell and water moves out of the root cells and into the soil. Without access to water, your plant wilts.

2. Look for wilty plants since the rate of water movement across the membrane would decrease in the aquaporin mutants.

3. At the level of membrane transport, plants and animals are very similar. Plant cell walls allow plant cells to take up more water than most animal cells, which rupture without the supportive walls. At the level of epidermal cells there is substantial variation among animals. Amphibians exchange water across the skin. Plants have waterproof epidermal tissue but lose water through stomata. Humans sweat, but dogs do not. Some animals have adaptations for living in aquatic or high saline environment, as do plants. Vascular plants move vast amounts of water through the plant body via the xylem, using evaporation to fuel the transport. Animals with closed circulatory systems can move water throughout the organism and also excrete excess water through the urinary system, which is responsible for osmoregulation.

4. The rate of transpiration is greater during the day than the night. Since water loss first occurs in the upper part of the tree where more leaves with stomata are located, the decrease in water volume in the xylem would first be observed in the upper portion, followed by the lower portion of the tree.

5. Spring year 1—The new carrot seedling undergoes photosynthesis in developing leaves and the sucrose moves towards the growing tip.
   Summer year 1—The developing leaves are sources of carbohydrate, which now moves to the developing root and also the growing young tip.
   Fall year 1—The carrot root is now the sink for all carbohydrates produced by the shoot.
   Spring year 2—Stored carbohydrate in the root begins to move upwards into the shoot.
   Summer year 2—The shoot is flowering and the developing flowers are the primary sink for carbohydrates from the root and also from photosynthesis in the leaves.
   Fall year 2—Seeds are developing and they are the primary sink. The root reserves have been utilized and any remaining carbohydrates from photosynthesis are transported to developing seeds.

CHAPTER 39

LEARNING OUTCOME QUESTIONS

39.1 Alkaline soil can affect the availability of nutrients in the soil for uptake by a plant.

39.2 Magnesium is found in the center of the chlorophyll molecule. Without sufficient magnesium, chlorophyll deficiencies will result in decreased photosynthesis and decreased yield per acre.

39.3 Nitrogen is essential for all amino acids, the building blocks of protein. Without sufficient levels of proteins that function as enzymes, membrane transporters, transcription factors, and structural components, plant growth and reproduction will be limited.

39.4 Increasing the amount of available nitrogen in the soil is one strategy. This can be accomplished with chemically produced ammonia for fertilizing, intercropping with nitrogen-fixing legumes, or using organic matter rich in nitrogen for enriching the soil. Efforts to reduce the relative amounts of atmospheric carbon dioxide would also be helpful.

39.5 Large poplar trees that are not palatable to animals offer a partial solution. Fencing in areas that are undergoing phytoremediation is another possibility, but it would be difficult to isolate all animals, especially birds. Plants that naturally deter herbivores with secondary compounds, including some mustard species (*Brassica* species) could be effective for phytoremediation.

INQUIRY QUESTION

Page 797 At low and high temperature extremes, enzymes involved in plant respiration are denatured. Plants tend to acclimate to slower long-term changes in temperature, and rates of respiration are able to adjust. Short-term more dramatic changes might slow or halt respiration, especially if a temperature change is large enough to cause enzymes to denature.

UNDERSTAND

1. b 2. a 3. c 4. d 5. a 6. b 7. c 8. a

APPLY

1. c 2. a 3. a 4. d 5. The macronutrient potassium constitutes 0.5–6% of the dry weight. Let's assume that the potato is 90% water. The dry weight would be 10% of 1000 kg, or 100 kg. Next you calculate 0.5% of 100, which is 0.5 kg. You would do the same type of calculation for 6%.

The micronutrient problems would also use the estimate of 100 kg dry weight. The conversion you need to use is that 1 ppm is the same as 1 mg/kg. So, 4 ppm of copper is the same as 4 mg/kg. Multiply this by 100 kg of dry weight potato and you have 400 mg of copper. Since there are 1000 mg in a gram, 400 mg × 1 g/1000 mg = 0.4 g of copper in a ton of potato. The other micronutrient problems would be calculated in a similar manner.

SYNTHESIZE

1. Bacteria that are important for nitrogen fixation could be destroyed. Other microorganisms that make nutrients available to plants could also be destroyed.

2. Grow the tomatoes hydroponically in a complete nutrient solution minus boron and complete nutrient solution with varying concentrations of boron. Compare the coloration of the leaves, the rate of growth (number of new leaves per unit time), and number and size of fruits produced on plants in each treatment group. It would also be helpful to compare the dry weights of plants from each treatment group at the end of the study.

3. Other inputs include both the macronutrients and micronutrients. Nitrogen, potassium, and phosphorous are common macronutrients in fertilizers. Of course the plants also need to be watered.

CHAPTER 40

LEARNING OUTCOME QUESTIONS

40.1 The lipid-based compounds help to create a water impermeable layer on the leaves.

40.2 A drug prepared from a whole plant or plant tissue would contain a number of different compounds, in addition to the active ingredient. Chemically synthesized or purified substances contain one or more known substances in known quantities.

40.3 It is unlikely that wasps will kill all the caterpillars. When attacked by a caterpillar, the plant releases a volatile substance that attracts the wasp. But, the wasp has to be within the vicinity of the signal when the plant releases the signal. As a result, some caterpillars will escape detection by wasps.

40.4 The local death of cells creates a barrier between the pathogen and the rest of the plant.

INQUIRY QUESTION

Page 808 Ricin functions as a ribosome-binding protein that limits translation. A very small quantity of rice was injected into Markov's thigh from the modified tip of his assassin's umbrella. Without translation of proteins in cells, enzymes and other gene products are no longer produced, causing the victim's metabolism to shut down leading to death.

UNDERSTAND

1. d 2. b 3. b 4. d 5. c 6. a 7. c 8. a 9. d

APPLY

1. c 2. d 3. d 4. b 5. c 6. a

SYNTHESIZE

1. Humans learn quickly and plants with toxins that made people ill would not become a dietary mainstay. If there was variation in the levels of toxin in the same species in different areas, humans would likely have continued to harvest plants from the area where plants had reduced toxin levels. As domestication continued, seeds would be collected from the plants with reduced toxin levels and grown the following year.

2. For parasitoid wasps to effectively control caterpillars, sufficiently large populations of wasps would need to be maintained in the area where the infestation occurred. As wasps migrate away from the area, new wasps would need to be introduced. The density of wasps is critical because the wasp has to be in the vicinity of the plant being attacked by the caterpillar when the plant releases its volatile signal. Maintaining sufficient density is a major barrier to success.

3. If a plant is flowering or has fruits developing, the systemin will move towards the fruit or flowers, providing protection for the developing seed. If the plant is a biennial, such as a carrot plant, in its first year of growth, systemin will likely be diverted to the root or other storage organ that will reserve food stores for the plant for the following year.

CHAPTER 41

LEARNING OUTCOME QUESTIONS

41.1 Chlorphyll is essential for photosynthesis. Phytochromes regulate plant growth and development using light as a signal. Phytochrome mediated responses align the plant with the light environment so photosynthesis is maximized which is advantageous for the plant.

41.2 The plant would not have normal gravitropic responses. Other environmental signals, including light, would determine the direction of plant growth.

41.3 Folding leaves can startle an herbivore that lands on the plant. The herbivore leaves and the plant is protected.

41.4 During the winter months the leaves would cease photosynthesis except on a few warm days. If the weather warmed briefly, water would move into the leaves and photosynthesis would begin. Unfortunately, the minute the temperature dropped, the leaves would freeze and be permanently damaged. Come the spring, the leaves would not be able to function and the tree would die. It is to the trees advantage to shed it's leaves and grow new, viable leaves in the spring when the danger of freezing is past.

41.5 Abscisic acid could be isolated from root caps of several plants. The isolated abscisic acid could then be applied to the buds on stems of other plants of the same species. The growth of these buds (or lack of growth) could be compared with untreated controls to determine whether or not the abscisic acid had an effect.

INQUIRY QUESTIONS

Page 816 A number of red-light-mediated responses are linked to phytochrome action alone, including seed germination, shoot elongation, and plant spacing. Only some of the red-light-mediated responses leading to gene expression are dependent on the action of protein kinases. When phytochrome converts to the Pfr form, a protein kinase triggers phosphorylation that, in turn, initiates a signaling cascade that triggers the translation of certain light-regulated genes. Not all red-light-mediated responses are disrupted in a plant with a mutation in the protein kinase domain of phytochrome.

Page 819 Auxin is involved in the phototropic growth responses of plants, including the bending of stems and leaves toward light. Auxin increases the plasticity of plants cells and signals their elongation. The highest concentration of auxin would most likely occur at the tips of stems where sun exposure is maximal.

Page 827 A chemical substance, such as the hormone auxin, could trigger the elongation of cells on the shaded side of a stem, causing the stem to bend toward the light.

UNDERSTAND

1. c 2. a 3. d 4. d 5. b 6. d

APPLY

1. b 2. a 3. b 4. c 5. c 6. b 7. d

SYNTHESIZE

1. You are observing etiolation. Etiolation is an energy conservation strategy to help plants growing in the dark reach the light before they die. They don't green up until light becomes available, and they divert energy to internode elongation. This strategy is useful for potato shoots. The sprouts will be long so they can get to the surface more quickly. They will remain white until exposed to sunlight which will signal the production of chlorophyll.

2. Tropism refers to the growth of an organism in response to an environmental signal such as light. Taxis refers to the movement of an organism in response to an environmental signal. Since plants cannot move, they will not exhibit taxis, but they do exhibit tropisms.

3. Auxin accumulates on the lower side of a stem in a gravitropism, resulting in elongation of cells on the lower side. If auxin or vesicles containing auxin responded to a gravitational field, it would be possible to have a gravitropic response without amyloplasts.

4. Farmers are causing a thigmotropic response. In response to touch, the internodes of the seedlings will increase in diameter. The larger stems will be more resistant to wind and rain once they are moved to the field. The seedlings will be less likely to snap once they are moved to the more challenging environment.

CHAPTER 42

LEARNING OUTCOME QUESTIONS

42.1 Without flowering in angiosperms, sexual reproduction is not possible and the fitness of a plant drops to zero.

42.2 Set up an experiment in a controlled growth chamber with a day/night light regiment that promotes flowering. Then interrupt the night length with a brief exposure to light. If day length is the determining factor, the brief flash of light will not affect flowering. If night length is the determining factor, the light flash may affect the outcome. For example, if the plant requires a long night, interrupting the night will prevent flowering. If the plant flowers whether or not you interrupt the night with light, it may be a short night plant. In that case, you would want to set up a second experiment where you lengthen the night length. That should prevent the plant from flowering.

42.3   Flowers can attract pollinators, enhancing the probability of reproduction.

42.4   No because the gametes are formed by meiosis which allows for new combinations of alleles to combine. You may want to review Mendel's law of independent assortment.

42.5   When conditions are uniform and the plant is well adapted to those constant conditions, genetic variation would not be advantageous. Rather, vegetative reproduction will ensure that the genotypes that are well adapted to the current conditions are maintained.

42.6   A biennial life cycle allows an organism to store up substantial reserves to be used to support reproduction during the second season. The downside to this strategy is that the plant might not survive the winter between the two growing seasons and its fitness would be reduced to zero.

INQUIRY QUESTIONS

Page 843   Strict levels of CONSTANS (CO) gene protein are maintained according to the circadian clock. Phytochrome, the pigment that perceives photoperiod, regulates the transcription of CO. By examining posttranslational regulation of CO, it might be possible to determine whether protein levels are modulated by means other than transcription. An additional level of control might be needed to ensure that the activation of floral meristem genes coincides with the activation of genes that code for individual flower organs.

Page 846   Flower production employs up to four genetically-regulated pathways. These pathways ensure than the plant flowers when it has reached adult size, when temperature and light regimes are optimal, and when nutrition is sufficient to support flowering. All of these factors combine to ensure the success of flowering and the subsequent survival of the plant species.

Page 846   Once vernalization occurred and nutrition was optimal, flowering could occur in the absence of flower-repressing genes, even if the plant had not achieved adult size. Thus flowering might occur earlier than normal.

UNDERSTAND

1. a   2. c   3. a   4. d   5. d   6. c   7. d   8. c   9. b   10. c   11. a

APPLY

1. b   2. c   3. b   4. d   5. b

SYNTHESIZE

1.   Pointsettias are short day plants. The lights from the cars on the new highway interrupt the long night and prevent flowering.

2.   Spinach is a long day plant and you want to harvest the vegetative, not the reproductive parts of the plant. Spinach will flower during the summer as the days get longer. Only leaves will be produced during the spring. If you grow and harvest your spinach in the early spring, you will be able to harvest the leaves before the plant flowers and begins to senesce.

3.   Cross-pollination increases the genetic diversity of the next generation. But, self-pollination is better than no pollination. The floral morphology of columbine favors cross-pollination, but self-pollination is a backup option. Should this back up option be utilized, there is still one more opportunity for cross-pollination to override self-pollination because the pollen tube from the other plant can still grow through the style more rapidly than the pollen tube from the same plant.

4.   Potatoes grown from true seed take longer to produce new potatoes than potatoes grown from tubers. Seeds are easier to store between growing seasons and require much less storage space than whole potatoes. The seed-grown potatoes will have greater genetic diversity than the asexually propagated potato tubers. If environmental conditions vary from year to year, the seed grown potatoes may have a better yield because different plants will have an advantage under different environmental conditions. The tuber-grown potatoes will be identical. If conditions are optimal for that genotype, the tuber-grown potatoes will outperform the more variable seed-grown potatoes. But, if conditions are not optimal for the asexually propagated potatoes, the seed-grown potatoes may have the higher yield.

CHAPTER 43

LEARNING OUTCOME QUESTIONS

43.1   Organs may be made of multiple tissue types. For example, the heart contains muscle, connective tissue and epithelial tissue.

43.2   The epithelium in glandular tissue produces secretions, the epithelium has microvilli on the apical surface that increase surface area for absorption.

43.3   Blood is a form of connective tissue because it contains abundant extracellular material: the plasma.

43.4   The function of heart cell requires their being electrically connected. The gap junctions allow the flow of ions between cells.

43.5   Neurons may be a meter long, but this is a very thin projection that still can allow diffusion of materials along its length. They do require specialized transport along microtubules to move proteins from the cell body to the synapse.

43.6   The organ systems may overlap. Consider the respiratory and circulatory systems. These systems are interdependent.

43.7   Yes.

43.8   The distinction should be between the ability to generate metabolic heat to modulate temperature, and the lack of that ability. Thus ectotherms and endotherms have replaced cold-blooded and warm-blooded.

INQUIRY QUESTIONS

Page 880   After two minutes of shivering, the thoracic muscles have warmed up enough to engage in full contractions. The muscle contractions that allow the full range of motion of the wings utilize kinetic energy in the movement of the wings, rather than releasing the energy as heat, which occurred in the shivering response.

Page 882   Small mammals, with a proportionately larger surface area, dissipate heat readily, which is helpful in a warm environment, but detrimental in a cold environment. In cold conditions, small mammals must seek shelter or have adaptations, such as insulating hair, to maintain body temperature. Because of a greater volume and proportionately less surface area, large mammals are better adapted to cold environments since it takes much longer for them to lose body heat. Hot environments pose a greater challenge for them for the same reason.

UNDERSTAND

1. a   2. c   3. c   4. d   5. a   6. d   7. b   8. b

APPLY

1. b   2. b   3. c   4. c   5. d   6. a   7. c

SYNTHESIZE

1.   Yes, both the gut and the skin include epithelial tissue. A disease that affects epithelial cells could affect both the digestive system and the skin. For example, cystic fibrosis affects the ion transport system in epithelial membranes. It is manifested in the lungs, gut, and sweat glands.

2.   The digestive, circulatory, and respiratory systems are grouped together because they all provide necessary nutrients for the body. The digestive system is responsible for the acquisition of nutrients from food; the respiratory system provides oxygen and removes waste (carbon monoxide). The circulatory system transports nutrients to the cells of the body and removes metabolic wastes.

3.   Hunger is a negative feedback stimulus. Hunger stimulates an individual to eat which in turn causes a feeling of fullness that removes hunger. Hunger is the stimulus; eating is the response that removes the stimulus.

4.   The internal environment is constantly changing. As you move through your day, muscle activity raises your body temperature, but when you sit down to eat or rest, your temperature cools. The body must constantly adjust to changes in activity or the environment.

CHAPTER 44

LEARNING OUTCOME QUESTIONS

44.1   The somatic nervous system is under conscious control.

44.2   A positive current inwards (influx of Na^+) depolarizes the membrane while a positive current outward (efflux of K^+) repolarizes the membrane.

44.3   Tobacco contains the compound nicotine, which can bind some acetylcholine receptors. This leads to the classic symptoms of addiction due to underlying habituation involving changes to receptor numbers and responses.

44.4 Reflex arcs allow you to respond to a stimulus that is damaging before the information actually arises at your brain.

44.5 These two systems work in opposition. This may seem counterintuitive, but is the basis for much of homeostasis.

UNDERSTAND

1. a   2. c   3. a   4. a   5. d   6. d   7. a

APPLY

1. d   2. b   3. c   4. a   5. a   6. c   7. d

SYNTHESIZE

1. TEA blocks K^+ channels so that they will not permit the passage of K^+ out of the cell, thereby not allowing the cell to return to the resting potential. Voltage-gated Na^+ channels would still be functional and Na^+ would still flow into the cell but there would be no repolarization. Na^+ would continue to flow into the cell until an electrochemical equilibrium was reached for Na^+, which is + 60 mV. After the membrane potential reached + 60 mV, there would be no net movement of Na^+, but the membrane would also not be able to repolarize back to the resting membrane potential. The neuron would no longer be able to function.

   The effects on the postsynaptic cell would be somewhat similar if TEA were applied to the presynaptic cell. The presynaptic cell would depolarize and would continue to release neurotransmitter until it had exhausted its store of synaptic vesicles. As a result, the postsynaptic cell would be bombarded with neurotransmitters and would be stimulated continuously until the stores of presynaptic neurotransmitter were depleted. The postsynaptic cell however would recover, being able to repolarize its membrane, and return to the resting membrane potential.

2. Rising: Na^+ gates open, K^+ closed
   Falling: Na^+ inactivation gate closes, K^+ open
   Undershoot: Na^+ activation gate closed, inactivation gate open, K^+ gate closing.

3. Action potential arrives at the end of the axon.
   Ca^{2+} channels open.
   Ca^{2+} causes synaptic vesicles to fuse with the axon membrane at the synapse.
   Synaptic vesicles release their neurotransmitter.
   Neurotransmitter molecules diffuse across synaptic cleft.
   Postsynaptic receptor proteins bind neurotransmitter.
   Postsynaptic membrane depolarizes.
   If this were an inhibitory synapse, the binding of receptor protein and neurotransmitter would cause the postsynaptic membrane to hyperpolarize.

4. Cells exposed to a stimulus repeatedly may lose their ability to respond. This is known as habituation. Karen's postsynaptic cells may have decreased the number of receptor proteins they produce because the stimulatory signal is so abundant. The result is that it now takes more stimuli to achieve the same result.

CHAPTER 45

LEARNING OUTCOME QUESTIONS

45.1 When the log values of the intensity of the stimulus and the frequency of the resulting action potentials are plotted against each other, a straight line results; this is referred to as a logarithmic relationship.

45.2 Proprioceptors detect the stretching of muscles and subsequently relay information about the relative position and movement of different parts of the organism's body to the central nervous system. This knowledge is critical for the central nervous system; it must be able to respond to these data by signaling the appropriate muscular responses, allowing for balance, coordinated locomotion, and reflexive responses.

45.3 The lateral line system supplements the sense of hearing in fish and amphibian larvae by allowing the organism to detect minute changes in the pressure and vibrations of its environment. This is facilitated by the density of water; without an aquatic environment, the adult, terrestrial amphibian will no longer be able to make use of this system. On land, sound waves are more easily detectable by the sense of hearing than are vibratory or pressure waves by the similar structures of a lateral line.

45.4 Many insects, such as the housefly, have chemoreceptors on their feet with which they can detect the presence of edible materials as they move through their environment. These insects can thus "taste" what they are walking on, and when they encounter an edible substrate they can then descend their proboscis and consume the food.

45.5 Individuals with complete red-green color blindness (those who have no red cones or no green cones, as opposed to those who lack only some red or green cones) would be highly unlikely to be able to learn to distinguish these colors. In order for an individual to perceive the colors in the red-green area of the spectrum, both red and green cones are required; without both cones there is no reference point by which individuals could compare the signals between the retina and the brain. If there are other cues available, such as color saturation or object shape and size, individuals with a less severe form of color blindness may be able to learn to distinguish these colors. In the absence of other references, however, it would be very difficult for individuals with even partial red-green color blindness to distinguish these colors.

45.6 The body temperature of an ectothermic organism is not necessarily the same as the ambient temperature; for example, other reptiles may bask in the sun, wherein on a chilly day the sun may warm the animal's body temperature above the ambient temperature. In this situation, the heat-sensing organs of, for example, a pit viper would still be effective in hunting as it would be able to distinguish the differences between the environment and its ectothermic prey.

INQUIRY QUESTIONS

Page 921   As the injured fish thrashed around, it would produce vibrations, rapid changes in the pressure of the water. The lateral line system in fish consists of canals filled with sensory cells that send a signal to the brain in response to the changes in water pressure.

Page 927   Both taste and smell utilize chemoreceptors as sensory receptors, wherein the binding of specific proteins to the receptor induces an action potential which is sent as a sensory signal to the brain. The chemicals detected by both systems must first be dissolved in extracellular fluid before they can be detected. One major difference between the two systems is that the olfactory system does not route a signal through the thalamus; instead, action potentials are routed directly to the olfactory cortex. Another difference is that olfactory receptors occur in larger numbers—tens of millions, as opposed to tens or hundreds of thousands for taste receptors.

Page 929   In humans, the ganglion cells attach to the front of the retinal cells, thus forcing the optic nerve to disrupt the continuity of the retina, leading to the formation of a "blind spot". In mollusks, however, the ganglion cells attach to the back of the retina and thus the retina is uninterrupted, eliminating the blind spot.

UNDERSTAND

1. d   2. b   3. d   4. b   5. a   6. c   7. b   8. d   9. a

APPLY

1. c   2. a   3. c   4. b

SYNTHESIZE

1. When blood pH becomes acidic, chemoreceptors in the circulatory and the nervous systems notify the brain and the body responds by increasing the breathing rate. This causes an increase in the release of carbon dioxide through the lungs. Decreased carbon dioxide levels in the blood cause a decrease in carbonic acid, which, in turn, causes the pH to rise.

2. In order to reach the retina and generate action potentials on the optic nerve, light must first pass through the ganglion and bipolar cells to reach the rods and cones that synapse with the bipolar cells. The bipolar cells then synapse with ganglion cells. These in turn send action potentials to the brain. Because the retina comprises three layers, with the rods and cones located farthest from the pupil, light must travel to the deepest level to set off reactions that move up through the more superficial levels and result in optic signals.

3. Without gravity to force the otoliths down toward the hair cells, the otolith organ will not function properly. The otolith membrane would not rest on the hair cells and would not move in response to movement of the body parallel or perpendicular to the pull of gravity. Consequently, the hair cell would not bend and so would not produce receptor potentials. Because the astronauts can see, they would have an impression of motion—they can see themselves move in relation to objects around them—but with their eyes closed, they would not know if they were moving in relation to their surroundings. Because their proprioceptors would still function, they would be able to sense when they moved their arms or legs, but they would not have the sensation of their enter body moving through space.

   The semicircular canals would not function equally well in zero-gravity conditions. Although the fluid in the semicircular canals is still able to move around, some sensation of angular movement would most likely occur, but the full function of the semicircular canals requires the force of gravity to aid in the directional movement of the fluid in the canals.

CHAPTER 46

LEARNING OUTCOME QUESTIONS

46.1 Neurotransmitters are released at a synapse and act on the post synaptic membrane. Hormones enter the circulatory system and are thus delivered to the entire body.

46.2 The response of a particular tissue depends first on the receptors on its surface, and second on the response pathways active in a cell. There can be different receptor subtypes that bind the same hormone, and the same receptor can stimulate different response pathways.

46.3 This might lower the amount of GH in circulation. As a treatment, it may have unwanted side effects.

46.4 With two hormones that have antagonistic effects, the body can maintain a fine level of blood sugar.

46.5 Reducing blood volume should also reduce blood pressure.

UNDERSTAND

1. b 2. d 3. c 4. b 5. d 6. b 7. a

APPLY

1. a 2. c 3. c 4. b 5. b 6. b 7. b

SYNTHESIZE

1. If the target cell for a common hormone or paracrine becomes cancerous, it may become hypersensitive to the messenger. This may in turn cause over production of cells, which would result in tumor formation. By blocking the production of the hormone specific to that tissue (for example, breast or prostate tissue and sex steroids), it would be possible to slow the growth rate and decrease the size of the tumor.

2. The same hormone can affect two different organs in different ways because the second messengers triggered by the hormone have different targets inside the cell because the cells have different functions. Epinephrine affects the cells of the heart by increasing metabolism so that their contractions are faster and stronger. However, liver cells do not contract and so the second messenger in liver cells triggers the conversion of glycogen into glucose. That is why hormones are so valuable but also economical to the body. One hormone can be produced, one receptor can be made, and one second-messenger system can be used, but there can be two different targets inside the cell.

3. With hormones such as thyroxine, whose effects are slower and have a broader range of activity, a negative feedback system using one hormone adequately controls the system. However, for certain parameters that have a very narrow range and change constantly within that range, a regulatory system that uses up-and-down regulation is desirable. Too much or too little Ca^{2+} or glucose in the blood can have devastating effects on the body and so those levels must be controlled within a very narrow range. To rely on negative feedback loops would restrict the quick "on" and "off" responses needed to keep the parameters in a very narrow range.

CHAPTER 47

LEARNING OUTCOME QUESTIONS

47.1 There are three limitations terrestrial invertebrates experience due to an exoskeleton. First, animals with an exoskeleton can only grow by shedding, or molting, the exoskeleton, leaving them vulnerable to predation. Second, muscles that act upon the exoskeleton cannot strengthen and grow as they are confined within a defined space. Finally, the exoskeleton, in concert with the respiratory system of many terrestrial invertebrates, limits the size to which these animals can grow. In order for the exoskeleton of a terrestrial animal to be strong, it has to have a sufficient surface area, and thus it has to increase in thickness as the animal gets larger. The weight of a thicker exoskeleton would impose debilitating constraints on the animal's ability to move.

47.2 Vitamin D is important for the absorption of dietary calcium as well as the deposition of calcium phosphate in bone. Children undergo a great deal of skeletal growth and development; without sufficient calcium deposition their bones can become soft and pliable, leading to a condition known as rickets, which causes a bending or bowing of the lower limbs. In the elderly, bone remodeling without adequate mineralization of the bony tissue can lead to brittle bones, a condition known as osteoporosis.

47.3 First, unlike the chitinous exoskeleton, a bony endoskeleton is made of living tissue; thus, the endoskeleton can grow along with the organism. Second, because the muscles that act upon the bony endoskeleton are not confined within a rigid structure, they are able to strengthen and grow with increased use. Finally, the size limitations imposed by a heavy exoskeleton that covers the entire organism are overcome by the internal bony skeleton, which can support a greater size and weight without itself becoming too cumbersome.

47.4 Slow-twitch fibers are found primarily in muscles adapted for endurance rather than strength and power. Myoglobin provides oxygen to the muscles for the aerobic respiration of glucose, thus providing a higher ATP yield than anaerobic respiration. Increased mitochondria also increases the ATP productivity of the muscle by increasing availability of cellular respiration and thus allows for sustained aerobic activity.

47.5 Locomotion via alternation of legs requires a greater degree of nervous system coordination and balance; the animal needs to constantly monitor its center of gravity in order to maintain stability. In addition, a series of leaps will cover more ground per unit time and energy expenditure than will movement by alternation of legs.

INQUIRY QUESTIONS

Page 969 The idea is very similar; both quadrupeds and insects such as grasshoppers have flexors and extensors that exert antagonistic control over many of their muscles. The main different is in the structure rather than function—in a grasshopper, the muscles are covered by the skeletal elements, while in organisms with an endoskeleton, the muscles overlie the bony skeleton.

Page 974 Increasing the frequency of stimulation to a maximum rate will yield the maximum amplitude of a summated muscle contraction. The strength of a contraction increases because little or no relaxation time occurs between successive twitches.

Page 974 A rough estimate of the composition of calf muscle could be obtained by measuring the amount of time the calf muscle takes to reach maximum tension and compare that amount with the contraction speed of muscles of known fiber composition. Alternatively, a small sample of muscle could be extracted and examined for histological differences in fiber composition.

UNDERSTAND

1. d 2. b 3. c 4. a 5. c 6. a 7. b 8. a

APPLY

1. d 2. b 3. d 4. b 5. b 6. b

SYNTHESIZE

1. Although a hydrostatic skeleton might have advantages in terms of ease of transport and flexibility of movement, the exoskeleton would probably do a better job at protecting the delicate instruments within. This agrees with our observations of these support systems on Earth. Worms and marine invertebrates use hydrostatic skeletons, although arthropods ("hard bodies") use an exoskeleton. Worms are very flexible, but easily crushed.

2. The first 90 seconds of muscle activity are anaerobic in which the cells utilize quick sources of energy (creatine phosphate, lactic acid fermentation) to generate ATP. After that, the respiratory and circulatory systems will catch up and begin delivering more oxygen to the muscles which allows them to use aerobic respiration, which is a much more efficient method of generating ATP from glucose.

3. If acetylcholinesterase is inhibited, acetylcholine will continue to stimulate muscles to contract. As a result, muscle twitching, and eventually paralysis, will occur. In March 1995, canisters of Sarin were released into a subway system in Tokyo. Twelve people were killed and hundreds injured.

4. Natural selection is not goal-oriented. In other words, evolution does not anticipate environmental pressures and the structures that result from evolution by natural selection are those most well-suited the previous generations' environment. Since vertebral wing development occurred several times during evolution, it is probable that the animals in question—birds, pterosaurs, and bats—all encountered different evolutionary pressures during wing evolution.

CHAPTER 48

LEARNING OUTCOME QUESTIONS

48.1 The cells and tissues of a one-way digestive system are specialized such that ingestion, digestion, and elimination can happen concurrently, making it more efficient in terms of food processing and energy utilization. With a gastrovascular cavity, however, all of the cells are exposed to all aspects of digestion.

48.2 Voluntary processes include bringing food into the mouth (food capture), mastication, and the initiation of swallowing. Salivation and the swallowing reflex are involuntary.

48.3 The sandwich represents carbohydrate (bread), protein (chicken), and fat (mayonnaise). The breakdown of carbohydrates begins with salivary amylase in the mouth. The breakdown of proteins begins in the stomach with pepsinogen, and the emulsification of fats begins in the duodenum with the introduction of bile. So—it is the chicken that will begin its breakdown in the stomach.

48.4 Fats are broken down, by emulsification, into fatty acids and monoglycerides, both of which are nonpolar molecules. Nonpolar molecules are able to enter the epithelial cells by simple diffusion.

48.5 The success of any mutation depends upon the selective pressures that species is subjected to. Thus, if two different species are subjected to similar environmental conditions and undergo the same mutation, then, yes, the mutation should be similarly successful. If two species undergo the same mutation but are under different selective pressures, then the mutation may not be successful in both species.

48.6 The sight, taste, and, yes, smell of food are the triggers the digestive system needs to release digestive enzymes and hormones. The saliva and gastric secretions that are required for proper digestion and are triggered by the sense of smell would be affected by anosmia.

48.7 Any ingested compounds that might be dangerous are metabolized first by the liver, thus reducing the risk to the rest of the body.

48.8 Even with normal leptin levels, individuals with reduced sensitivity in the brain to the signaling molecule may still become obese.

INQUIRY QUESTIONS

Page 985 If the epiglottis does not properly seal off the larynx and trachea, food can accidentally become lodged in the airway, causing choking.

Page 986 The digestive system secretes a mucus layer that helps to protect the delicate tissues of the alimentary canal from acidic secretions.

Page 992 The amino acid sequences for lysozyme evolved convergently among ruminants and langur monkeys. Thus, if a phylogeny was constructed using solely the lysozyme molecular data, these species—ruminants and langur monkeys—would be adjacent to each other on the phylogenetic tree.

Page 997 GIP and CCK send inhibitory signals to the hypothalamus upon food intake. If the hypothalamus sensors did not work properly, leptin levels would increase; increased leptin levels would result in a loss of appetite.

UNDERSTAND

1. b 2. c 3. c 4. b 5. d 6. d 7. c

APPLY

1. d 2. b 3. c 4. c

SYNTHESIZE

1. Birds feed their young with food they acquire from the environment. The adult bird consumes the food but stores it in her crop. When she returns to the nest, she regurgitates the food into the mouths of the fledglings. Mammals on the other hand feed their young with milk that is produced in the mother's mammary glands. Young feed by latching onto the mother's nipples and sucking the milk. Mammals have no need for a crop in their digestive system because they don't feed their young in the same way as birds.

2. Leptin is produced by the adipose cells and serves as a signal for feeding behavior. Since low blood leptin levels signal the brain to initiate feeding, a treatment for obesity would need to raise leptin levels, thereby decreasing appetite.

3. The liver plays many important roles in maintaining homeostasis. Two of those roles are detoxifying drugs and chemicals and producing plasma proteins. A drop in plasma protein levels is indicative of liver disease, which in turn could be caused by abuse of alcohol or other drugs.

4. The selective pressures that guide the adaptation of mutated alleles within a population were the same in these two groups of organisms. Both ruminants and langur monkeys eat tough, fibrous plant materials which are broken down by intestinal bacteria. The ruminants and langurs then absorb the nutrients from the cellulose by digesting those bacteria; this is accomplished through the use of these adapted lysozymes. Normal lysozymes, found in saliva and other secretions, work in a relatively neutral pH environment. These intestinal lysozymes, however, needed to adapt to an acidic environment, which explains the level of convergence.

5. Whereas mammalian dentition is adapted to process different food types, birds are able to process different types of food by breaking up food particles

in the gizzard. Bird diets are comparably diverse to mammalian diets; some birds are carnivores, others are insectivores or frugivores, still others omnivores.

CHAPTER 49

LEARNING OUTCOME QUESTIONS

49.1 Fick's law states that the rate of diffusion (R) can be increased by increasing the surface area of a respiratory surface, increase the concentration difference between respiratory gases, and decreasing the distance the gases must diffuse: $R = \frac{DA \Delta p}{d}$. Continually beating cilia increase the concentration difference (Δp).

49.2 Countercurrent flow systems maximize the oxygenation of the blood by increasing Δp, thus maintaining a higher oxygen concentration in the water than in the blood throughout the entire diffusion pathway. The lamellae, found within a fish's gill filaments, facilitate this process by allowing water to flow in only one direction, counter to the blood flow within the capillary network in the gill.

49.3 Birds have a more efficient respiratory system than other terrestrial vertebrates. Birds that live or fly at high altitudes are subjected to lower oxygen partial pressure and thus have evolved a respiratory system that is capable of maximizing the diffusion and retention of oxygen in the lungs. In addition, efficient oxygen exchange is crucial during flight; flying is more energetically taxing than most forms of locomotion and without efficient oxygen exchange birds would be unable to fly even short distances safely.

49.4 There are both structural and functional differences in bird and mammalian respiration. Both mammals and birds have lungs, but only birds also have air sacs, which they use to move air in and out of the respiratory system, while only mammals have a muscular diaphragm used to move air and in and out of the lungs. Mammalian lungs are pliable, and gas exchange occurs within small closed-ended sacs in the mammalian lung called alveoli. In contrast, bird lungs are rigid, and gas exchange occurs in the unidirectional parabronchi. In addition, because air flow in mammals is bi-directional, there is a mixing of oxygenated and deoxygenated air, while the unidirectional air flow in birds increases the purity of the oxygen entering the capillaries. Mammalian respiration is less efficient than avian respiration; birds transfer more oxygen with each breath than do mammals. Finally, mammals only have one respiratory cycle whereas birds have two complete cycles.

49.5 Most oxygen is transported in the blood bound to hemoglobin (forming oxyhemoglobin) while only a small percentage is dissolved in the plasma. Carbon dioxide, on the other hand, is predominantly transported as bicarbonate (having first been combined with water to form carbonic acid and then dissociated into bicarbonate and hydrogen ions). Carbon dioxide is also transported dissolved in the plasma and bound to hemoglobin.

INQUIRY QUESTIONS

Page 1002 Capillaries, the tiniest of the cardiovascular vessels, are located near every cell of the body. Because of their small size and large number, the surface area for gas exchange through them is maximized. This capillary arrangement also works well with the tiny alveoli of the lungs which also provide a large surface area for gas exchange. Since capillaries are in intimate contact with alveoli, rapid gas exchange is enhanced.

Page 1012 Fick's law of diffusion states that for a dissolved gas, the rate of diffusion is directly proportional to the pressure difference between the two sides of the membrane and to the area over which the diffusion occurs. In emphysema, alveolar walls break down and alveoli increase in size, effectively reducing the surface area for gas exchange. Emphysema thus reduces the diffusion of gases.

Page 1013 Most veins have a bluish color and function to return oxygen-depleted blood to the heart. The pulmonary veins, however, are bright red because they return fully oxygenated blood from the lungs to the left atrium of the heart.

Page 1013 The difference in oxygen content between arteries and veins during rest and exercise shows how much oxygen was unloaded to the tissues.

Page 1014 Not really. A healthy individual still has a substantial oxygen reserve in the blood even after intense exercise.

Page 1014 It increases it. At any pH or temperature, the percentage of O_2 saturation falls (e.g. more O_2 is delivered to tissues) as pressure increases.

UNDERSTAND

1. c 2. d 3. d 4. d 5. b 6. a 7. d 8. c

APPLY

1. d   2. c   3. a   4. c   5. a   6. c

SYNTHESIZE

1. Fish gills have not only a large respiratory surface area but also a countercurrent flow system, which maintains an oxygen concentration gradient throughout the entire exchange pathway, thus providing the most efficient system for the oxygenation of blood. Amphibian respiratory systems are not very efficient. They practice positive pressure breathing. Bird lungs are quite effective, in that they have a large surface area and one-way air flow; mammals, on the other hand, have only a large surface area but no mechanism to ensure the maintenance of a strong concentration gradient.

2. During exercise, cellular respiration increases the amount of carbon dioxide released, thus decreasing the pH of the blood. In addition, the increased cellular respiration increases temperature, as heat is released during glucose metabolism. Decreased pH and increased temperature both facilitate an approximately 20% increase in oxygen unloading in the peripheral tissues.

3. Unicellular prokaryotic organisms, protists, and many invertebrates are small enough such that gas exchange can occur over the body surface directly from the environment. Only larger organisms, where most cells are not in direct contact with the environment with which gases must be exchanged, require specialized structures for gas exchange.

CHAPTER 50

LEARNING OUTCOME QUESTIONS

50.1 Following an injury to a vessel, vasoconstriction is followed by the accumulation of platelets at the site of injury and the subsequent formation of a platelet plug. This triggers a positive feedback enzyme cascade, attracting more platelets, clotting factors, and other chemicals, each of which continually attract additional clotting molecules until the clot is formed. The enzyme cascade also causes fibrinogen to come out of solution as fibrin, forming a fibrin clot that will eventually replace the platelet plug.

50.2 When the insect heart contracts, it forces hemolymph out through the vessels and into the body cavities. When it relaxes, the resulting negative pressure gradient, combined with muscular contractions in the body, draws the blood back to the heart.

50.3 The primary advantage of having two ventricles rather than one is the separation of oxygenated from deoxygenated blood. In fish and amphibians, oxygenated and deoxygenated blood mix, leading to less oxygen being delivered to the body's cells.

50.4 The delay following auricular allows the atrioventricular valves to close prior to ventricular contraction. Without that delay, the contraction of the ventricles would force blood back up through the valves into the atria.

50.5 During systemic gas exchange, only about 90% of the fluid that diffuses out of the capillaries returns to the blood vessels; the rest moves into the lymphatic vessels, which then return the fluid to the circulatory system via the left and right subclavian veins.

50.6 Breathing rate is regulated to ensure ample oxygen is available to the body. However, the heart rate must be regulated to ensure efficient delivery of the available oxygen to the body cells and tissues. For example, during exertion, respiratory rates will increase in order to increase oxygenation and allow for increased aerobic cellular respiration. But simply increasing the oxygen availability is not enough—the heart rate must also increase so that the additional oxygen can be quickly delivered to the muscles undergoing cellular respiration.

INQUIRY QUESTION

Page 1021 Erythropoietin is a hormone that stimulates the production of erythrocytes from the myeloid stem cells. If more erythrocytes are produced, the oxygen-carrying capacity of the blood is increased. This could potentially enhance athletic performance and is why erythropoietin is banned from use during the Olympics and other sporting events.

UNDERSTAND

1. a   2. b   3. c   4. a   5. c   6. d   7. c

APPLY

1. a   2. b   3. a   4. c   5. a

SYNTHESIZE

1. Antidiuretic hormone (ADH) is secreted by the posterior pituitary but has its target cells in the kidney. In response to the presence of ADH, the kidneys increase the amount of water reabsorbed. This water eventually returns to the plasma where it causes an increase in volume and subsequent increase in blood pressure. Another hormone, aldosterone, also causes an increase in blood pressure by causing the kidney to retain Na+, which sets up a concentration gradient that also pulls water back into the blood.

2. Blood includes plasma (comprised primarily of water with dissolved proteins) and formed elements (red blood cells, white blood cells, and platelets). Lymph is comprised of interstitial fluid and found only within the lymphatic vessels and organs. Both blood and lymph are found in organisms with closed circulatory systems. Hemolymph is both the circulating fluid and the interstitial fluid found in organisms with open circulatory systems.

3. Many argue that the evolution of endothermy was less an adaptation to maintain a constant internal temperature and more an adaptation to function in environments low in oxygen. If this is the case, then yes, it makes sense that the evolution of the four-chambered heart, an adaptation that increases the availability of oxygen in the body tissues and which would be highly beneficial in an oxygen-poor environment, and the evolution of endothermy were related. These two adaptations can also be looked at as related in that the more efficient heart would be able to provide the oxygen necessary for the increased metabolic activity that accompanies endothermy.

4. The SA node acts as a natural pacemaker. If it is malfunctioning, one would expect a slow or irregular heartbeat or irregular electrical activity between the atria and the ventricles.

CHAPTER 51

LEARNING OUTCOME QUESTIONS

51.1 Water moves towards regions of higher osmolarity.

51.2 The are both involved in water conservation.

51.3 This may have arisen independently in both the mammalian and avian lineages, or lost from the reptilian lineage.

51.4 Nitrogenous waste is a problem because it is toxic, and it is a result of degrading old proteins.

51.5 This would increase the osmolarity within the tubule system, and thus should decrease reabsorption of water. This would lead to loss of water.

51.6 Blocking aquaporin channels would prevent reabsorption of water from the collecting duct.

UNDERSTAND

1. d   2. a   3. c   4. c   5. d   6. d   7. d

APPLY

1. d   2. c   3. b   4. b   5. c   6. b

SYNTHESIZE

1a. Antidiuretic hormone (ADH) is produced in the hypothalamus and is secreted by the posterior pituitary. ADH targets the collecting duct of the nephron and stimulates the reabsorption of water from the urine by increasing the permeability of water in the walls of the duct. The primary stimulus for ADH secretion is an increase in the osmolarity of blood.

1b. Aldosterone is produced and secreted by the adrenal cortex in response to a drop in blood Na+ concentration. Aldosterone stimulates the distal convoluted tubules to reabsorb Na+, decreasing the excretion of Na+ in the urine. The reabsorption of Na+ is followed by Cl- and water, and so aldosterone has the net effect of retaining both salt and water. Aldosterone secretion however, is not stimulated by a decrease in blood osmolarity, but rather by a decrease in blood volume. A group of cells located at the base of the glomerulus, called the juxtaglomerular apparatus, detect drops in blood volume that then stimulates the renin-angiotensin-aldosterone system.

1c. Atrial natriuretic hormone (ANH) is produced and secreted by the right atrium of the heart, in response to an increase in blood volume. The secretion of ANH results in the reduction of aldosterone secretion. With the secretion of ANH, the distal convoluted tubules reduce the amount of Na+ that is reabsorbed, and likewise reduces the amount of Cl- and water that is reabsorbed. The final result is the reduction in blood volume.

His normal renal blood flow rate would be 21% of cardiac output, or 7.2 L/min $\times$ 0.21 = 1.5 L/min.

If John's kidneys are not affected by his circulatory condition, his renal blood flow rate should be about 1.5 L/min.

CHAPTER 52

LEARNING OUTCOME QUESTIONS

52.1   No, innate immunity shows some specificity for classes of molecules common to pathogens.

52.2   Hematopoetic stem cells.

52.3   T-cell receptors are rearranged to generate a large number of different receptors with specific binding abilities. Toll-like receptors are not rearranged, and recognize specific classes of molecules, not specific molecules.

52.4   Ig receptors are rearranged to generate many different specificities. TLR innate receptors are not rearranged and bind to specific classes of molecules.

52.5   Allergies are a case of the immune system overreacting while autoimmune disorders involve the immune system being compromised.

52.6   Diagnostic kits use monoclonal antibodies because they are against a single specific epitope of an antigen. They also use cells that can be grown in culture, and do not require immunizing an animal, bleeding them and then isolating the antibodies from their sera.

52.7   The main difference between Polio and influenza is the rate at which the viruses can change. The Polio virus is a RNA virus with a genome that consists of a single RNA. The viral surface proteins do not change rapidly allowing immunity via a vaccine. Influenza is an RNA virus with a high mutation rate, which means that surface proteins change rapidly. Influenza has a genome that consists of multiple RNAs, which allows recombination of the different viral RNA's during infection with different strains.

INQUIRY QUESTIONS

Page 1059   The viruses would be liberated into the body where they could infect numerous additional cells.

Page 1063   The antigenic properties of the two viruses must be similar enough that immunity to cowpox also enables protection against smallpox.

Page 1074   The common structure and mechanism of formation of B cell immunoglobulins (Igs) and T-cell receptors (TCRs) suggests a common ancestral form of adaptive immunity gave rise to the two cell lines existing today.

Page 1078   A high level of HCG in a urine sample will block the binding of the antibody to HCG-coated particles and prevent any agglutination.

Page 1079   Influenza frequently alters its surface antigens making it impossible to produce a vaccine with a long-term effect. Smallpox virus has a considerably more stable structure.

UNDERSTAND

1. b   2. a   3. b   4. c   5. c   6. b   7. c

APPLY

1. d   2. c   3. c   4. a. b., then d., then c   5. c   6. b   7. a

SYNTHESIZE

1. It would be difficult to advertise this lotion as immune-enhancing. The skin serves as a barrier to infection because it is oily and acidic. Applying a lotion that is watery and alkaline will dilute the protective effects of the skin secretions, thereby inhibiting the immune functions. Perhaps it is time to look for another job.

2. The scratch has caused an inflammatory response. Although it is very likely that some pathogens entered her body through the broken skin, the response is actually generated by the injury to her tissue. The redness is a result of the increased dilation of blood vessels caused by the release of histamine. This also increases the temperature of the skin by bringing warm blood closer to the surface. Leakage of fluid from the vessels causes swelling in the area of the injury, which can cause pressure on the pain sensors in the skin. All of these serve to draw defensive cells and molecules to the injury site, thereby helping to defend her against infection.

3. There are a number of ways that this could be done. However, one method would be to show that viral genetic material never appears within the cells of those who claim immunity. Another method would involve testing for the presence of interferon, which is released by cells in response to viral infection.

4. These data imply that innate immunity is a very ancient defense mechanism. The presence of these proteins in Cnidarians indicates that they arose soon after multicellularity.

CHAPTER 53

LEARNING OUTCOME QUESTIONS

53.1   Genetic sex determination essentially guarantees equal sex ratios; when sex ratios are not equal, the predominant sex is selected against because those individuals have more competition for mates. Temperature-dependent sex-determination can result in skewed sex ratios in which one sex or the other is selected against. Genetic sex determination, on the other hand, can provide much greater stability within the population, and consequently the genetic characteristics that provide that stability are selected for.

53.2   Estrous cycles occur in most mammals, and most mammalian species have relatively complex social organizations and mating behaviors. The cycling of sexual receptivity allows for these complex mating systems. Specifically, in social groups where male infanticide is a danger, synchronized estrous among females may be selected for as it would eliminate the ability of the male to quickly impregnate the group females. Physiologically, estrous cycles result in the maturation of the egg accompanying the hormones that promote sexual receptivity.

53.3   In mating systems where males compete for mates, sperm competition, a form of sexual selection, is very common. In these social groups, multiple males may mate with a given female, and thus those individuals who produced the highest number of sperm would have a reproductive advantage—a higher likelihood of siring the offspring.

53.4   The answer varies depending upon the circumstances. In a species that is very r-selected, in other words, one that reproduces early in life and often but does not invest much in the form of parental care, multiple offspring per pregnancy would definitely be favored by natural selection. In K-selected species where parental care is very high, on the other hand, single births might be favored because the likelihood of offspring survival is greater if the parental resources are not divided among the offspring.

53.5   The birth control pill works by hormonally controlling the ovulation cycle in women. By releasing progesterone continuously the pill prevents ovulation. Ovulation is a cyclical event and under hormonal control, thus it is easy for the process to be controlled artificially. In addition, the female birth control pill only has to halt the release of a single ovum. An analogous male birth control pill, on the other hand, would have to completely cease sperm production (and men produce millions of sperm each day), and such hormonal upheaval in the male could lead to infertility or other intolerable side effects.

INQUIRY QUESTIONS

Page 1085   The ultimate goal of any organism is to maximize its relative fitness. Small females are able to reproduce but once they become very large they would be better able to maximize their reproductive success by becoming male, especially in groups where only a few males mate with all of the females. Protandry might evolve in species where there is a limited supply of mates and relatively little space; a male of such a species in close proximity to another male would have higher reproductive success by becoming female and mating with the available male than by waiting for a female (and then having to compete for her with the other male).

Page 1088   The evolutionary progression from oviparity to viviparity is a complex process; requiring the development of a placenta or comparable structure. Once a complex structure evolves, it is rare for an evolutionary reversal to occur. Perhaps more importantly, there are several advantages to viviparity over oviparity, especially in cold environments where eggs are vulnerable to mortality due to cold weather (and predation). In aquatic reptiles such as sea snakes, viviparity allows the female to remain at sea and avoid coming ashore, where both she and her eggs would be exposed to predators.

Page 1094   Under normal circumstances, the testes produce hormones, testosterone and inhibin, which exert negative feedback inhibition on the hormones produced and secreted by the anterior pituitary (luteinizing hormone and follicle-stimulating hormone). Following castration, testosterone and inhibin are no longer produced and thus the brain will overproduce LH and FSH. For this reason, hormone therapy is usually prescribed following castration.

UNDERSTAND

1. c   2. d   3. d   4. d   5. b   6. c   7. a   8. c   9. a

APPLY

1. a   2. b   3. d   4. a

SYNTHESIZE

1. A mutation that makes *SRY* nonfunctional would mean that the embryo would lack the signal to form male structures during development. Therefore, the embryo would have female genitalia at birth.

2. Amphibians and fish that rely on external fertilization also have access to water. Lizards, birds, and mammals have adaptations that allow them to reproduce away from a watery environment. These adaptations include eggs that have protective shells or internal development, or both.

3. FSH and LH are produced by the anterior pituitary in both males and females. In both cases they play roles in the production of sex hormones and gametogenesis. However, FSH stimulates spermatogenesis in males and oogenesis in females, whereas LH promotes the production of testosterone in males and estradiol in females.

4. It could indeed work. The hormone hCG is produced by the zygote to prevent menstruation, which would in turn prevent implantation in the uterine lining. Blocking the hormone receptors would prevent implantation and therefore pregnancy.

5. Parthenogenic species reproduce from gametes that remain diploid. Sperm are haploid, whereas eggs do not complete meiosis (becoming haploid) until after fertilization. Therefore, only eggs could develop without DNA from an outside source. In addition, only eggs have the cellular structures needed for development. Therefore only females can undergo parthenogenesis.

CHAPTER 54

LEARNING OUTCOME QUESTIONS

54.1 Ca^{2+} ions act as second messengers and bring about changes in protein activity that result in blocking polyspermy and increasing the rate of protein synthesis within the egg.

54.2 In a mammal, the cells at the four-cell stage are still uncommitted and thus separating them will still allow for normal development. In frogs, on the other hand, yolk distribution results in displaced cleavage; thus, at the four-cell stage the cells do not each contain a nucleus which contains the genetic information required for normal development.

54.3 The cellular behaviors necessary for gastrulation differ across organisms; however, some processes are necessary for any gastrulation to occur. Specifically, cells must rearrange and migrate throughout the developing embryo.

54.4 No—neural crest cell fate is determined by its migratory pathway.

54.5 Marginal zone cells in both the ventral and dorsal regions express bone morphogenetic protein 4 (BMP4). The fate of these cells is determined by the number of receptors on the cell membrane to bind to BMP4; greater BMP4 binding will induce a ventral mesodermal fate. The organizer cells, which previously were thought to activate dorsal development, have been found to actually inhibit ventral development by secreting one of many proteins that block the BMP4 receptors on the dorsal cells.

54.6 Most of the differentiation of the embryo, in which the initial structure formation occurs, happens during the first trimester; the second and third trimesters are primarily times of growth and organ maturation, rather than the actual development and differentiation of structures. Thus, teratogens are most potent during this time of rapid organogenesis.

INQUIRY QUESTION

Page 1127 High levels of estradiol and progesterone in the absence of pregnancy would still affect the body in the same way. High levels of both hormones would inhibit the release of FSH and LH, thereby preventing ovulation. This is how birth control pills work. The pills contain synthetic forms of either both estradiol and progesterone or just progesterone. The high levels of these hormones in the pill trick the body into thinking that it is pregnant and so the body does not ovulate.

UNDERSTAND

1. d   2. b   3. d   4. c   5. d   6. b

APPLY

1. c   2. b   3. a   4. a   5. d   6. b   7. c

SYNTHESIZE

1. By starting with a series of embryos at various stages, you could try removing cells at each stage. Embryos that failed to compensate for the removal (evidenced by missing structures at maturity) would be those that lost cells after they had become committed; that is, when their fate has been determined.

2. Homeoboxes are sequences of conserved genes that play crucial roles in development of both mammals (Fifi) and *Drosophila* (the fruit fly). In fact, we know that they are more similar than dissimilar; research has demonstrated that both groups use the same transcription factors during organogenesis. The major difference between them is in the genes that are transcribed. Homeoboxes in mammals turn on genes that cause the development of mammalian structures, and those in insects would generate insect structures.

3. After fertilization, the zygote produces hCG, which inhibits menstruation and maintains the corpus luteum. At 10 weeks gestation, the placenta stops releasing hCG but it does continue to release estradiol and progesterone, which maintain the uterine lining and inhibit the pituitary production of FSH and LH. Without FSH and LH no ovulation and no menstruation occur.

4. Spemann and Mangold removed cells from the dorsal lip of one amphibian embryo and transplanted them to a different location on a second embryo. The transplanted cells caused cells that would normally form skin and belly to instead form somites and the structures associated with the dorsal area. Because of this and because the secondary dorsal structures contained both host and transplanted cells, Spemann and Mangold concluded that the transplanted cells acted as organizers for dorsal development.

CHAPTER 55

LEARNING OUTCOME QUESTIONS

55.1 Just as with morphological characteristics that enhance an individual's fitness, behavioral characteristics can also affect an individual's survivability and reproductive success. Understanding the evolutionary origins of many behaviors allows biologists insights into animal behavior, including that of humans.

55.2 A male songbird injected with testosterone prior to the usual mating season would likely begin singing prior to the usual mating season. However, since female mating behavior is largely controlled by hormones (estrogen) as well, most likely that male will not have increased fitness (and may actually have decreased fitness, if the singing stops before the females are ready to mate, or if the energetic expenditure from singing for two additional weeks is compensated by reduced sperm production).

55.3 The genetic control over pair-bonding in prairie voles has been fairly well-established. The fact that males sometimes seek extra-pair copulations indicates that the formation of pair-bonds is under not only genetic control but also behavioral control.

55.4 In species where males travel farther from the nest (and thus have larger range sizes), there should be significant sex differences in spatial memory. However, in species without sexual differences in range sizes should not express sex differences in spatial memory. To test the hypothesis you could perform maze tests on males and females of species with sex differences in range size as well as those species without range size differences between the sexes. (NOTE: such experiments have been performed and do support the hypothesis that there is a significant correlation between range size and spatial memory, so in species with sex differences in range size there are indeed sex differences in spatial memory. See Jones, CM et al., 2003. "The Evolution of Sex Differences in Spatial Ability." *Behavioral Neuroscience.* 117(3): 403-411)

55.5 Although there may be a link between IQ and genes in humans, there is most certainly also an environmental component to IQ. The danger of assigning a genetic correlation to IQ lies in the prospect of selective "breeding" and the emergence of "designer babies."

55.6 One experiment that has been implemented in testing counting ability among different primate and bird species is to present the animal with a number and have him match the target number to one of several arrays containing that number of objects. In another experiment, the animal may be asked to select the appropriate number of individual items within an array of items that equals the target number.

55.7 Butterflies and birds have extremely different anatomy and physiology and thus most likely use very different navigation systems. Birds generally migrate bi-directionally; moving south during the cold months and back north during the warmer months. Usually, then, migrations are multi-generational events and it could be argued that younger birds can learn migratory routes from older generations. Butterflies, on the other hand, fly south to breed and die. Their offspring must then fly north having never been there before.

55.8 In addition to chemical reproductive barriers, many species also employ behavioral and morphological reproductive barriers, such that even if a female moth is attracted by the pheromones of a male of another species, the two may be behaviorally or anatomically incompatible.

55.9 The benefits of territorial behavior must outweigh the potential costs, which may include physical danger due to conflict, energy expenditure, and the loss of foraging or mating time. In a flower that is infrequently encountered, the honeycreeper would lose more energy defending the resource than it could gain by utilizing the resource. On the other hand, there is usually low competitive pressure for highly abundant resources, thus the bird would expend unnecessary energy defending a resource to which its access is not limited.

55.10 The males should exhibit mate choice, as they are the sex with the greater parental investment and energy expenditure; thus, like females of most species, they should be the "choosier" sex.

55.11 Generally, reciprocal behaviors are low-cost while behaviors due to kin selection may be low- or high-cost. Protecting infants from a predator is definitely a high-risk / potentially high-cost behavior; thus it would seem that the behavior is due to kin selection. The only way to truly test this hypothesis, however, is to conduct genetic tests or, in a particularly well-studied population, consult a pedigree.

Living in a group is associated with both costs and benefits. The primary cost is increased competition for resources, while the primary benefit is protection from predation. Altruism toward kin is considered selfish because helping individuals closely related to you will directly affect your inclusive fitness. Most armies more closely resemble insect societies than vertebrate societies. Insect societies consist of multitudes of individuals congregated for the purpose of supporting and defending a select few individuals. One could think of these few protected and revered individuals as the society the army is charged with protecting. These insect societies, like human armies, are composed of individuals each "assigned" to a particular task. Most vertebrate societies, on the other hand, are less altruistic and express increased competition and aggression between group members. In short, vertebrate societies are comprised of individuals whose primary concern is usually their own fitness, while insect societies are comprised of individuals whose primary concern is the colony itself.

INQUIRY QUESTIONS

Page 1135 Selection for learning ability would cease, and thus change from one generation to the next in maze learning ability; would only result from random genetic drift.

Page 1136 Normal *fosB* alleles produce a protein that in turn affects enzymes that affect the brain. Ultimately, these enzymes trigger maternal behavior. In the absence of the enzymes, normal maternal behavior does not occur.

Page 1140 Peter Marler's experiments addressed this question and determined that both instinct and learning are instrumental in song development in birds.

Page 1148 Many factors affect the behavior of an animal other than its attempts to maximize energy intake. For example, avoiding predation is also important. Thus, it may be that larger prey take longer to subdue and ingest, thus making the crabs more vulnerable to predators. Hence, the crabs may trade off decreased energy gain for decreased vulnerability to predators. Many other similar explanations are possible.

Page 1150 A question that is the subject of much current research. Ideas include the possibility that males with longer tails are in better condition (because males in poor condition couldn't survive the disadvantage imposed by the tail). The advantage to a female mating with a male in better condition might be either that the male is less likely to be parasitized, and thus less likely to pass that parasite on to the female, or the male may have better genes, which in turn would be passed on to the offspring. Another possibility is the visual system for some reason is better able to detect males with long tails, and thus long-tailed males are preferred by females simply because the longer tails are more easily detected and responded to.

Page 1151 Yes, the larger the male, the larger the prenuptial gift, which provides energy that the female converts into egg production.

Page 1158 If more birds are present, then each one can spend less time watching for predators, and thus have more time for foraging.

UNDERSTAND

1. b 2. a 3. a 4. c 5. a 6. c 7. d 8. a 9. b 10. a
11. c 12. d

APPLY

1. Presumably, the model is basic, taking into account only size and energetic value of mussels. However, it may be that larger mussels are in places where shore crabs would be exposed to higher levels of predation or greater physiological stress. Similarly, it could be that the model underestimated time costs or energy returns as a function of mussel size. In the case of large mussels being in a place where shore crabs are exposed to costs not considered by the model, one could test the hypothesis in several ways. First, how are the sizes of mussels distributed in space? If they are completely interspersed that would tend to reject the hypothesis. Alternatively, if the mussels were differentially distributed such that the hypothesis was

reasonable, mussels could be experimentally relocated (change their distribution in space) and the diets would be expected to shift to match more closely the situation predicted by the model.

2. The four new pairs may have been living in surrounding habitat that was of lower quality, or they may have been individuals that could not compete for a limited number of suitable territories for breeding. Often, the best territories are won by the most aggressive or largest or otherwise best competitors, meaning that the new territory holders would likely have been less fierce competitors. If new residents were weaker competitors (due to aggression or body size), then the birds not removed would have been able to expand their territories to acquire even more critical resources.

3. The key here is that if the tail feathers are a handicap, then by reducing the handicap in these males should enhance their survival compared with males with naturally shorter tail feathers. The logic is simple. If the mail with long tail feathers is superior such that it can survive the negative effect of the long tail feathers, then that superior phenotype should be "exposed" with the removal or reduction of the tail feathers. Various aspects of performance could be measured since it is thought that the tail feathers hinder flying. Can males with shorter tails fly faster? Can males with shorter tails turn better? Ultimately, whether males with shorter tails survive better than males with un-manipulated tails can be measured.

4. Both reciprocity and kin selection explain the evolution of altruistic acts by examining the hidden benefits of the behavior. In both cases, altruism actually *benefits* the individual performing the act in terms of its fitness effects. If it didn't, it would be very hard to explain how such behavior could be maintained because actions that reduce the fitness of an individual should be selected against. Definition of the behavior reflects the apparent paradox of the behavior because it focuses on the cost and not the benefit that also accrues to the actor.

SYNTHESIZE

1. The best experiment for determining whether predatory avoidance of certain coloration patterns would involve rearing a predator without an opportunity to learn avoidance and subsequently presenting the predator with prey with different patterns. If the predator avoids the black and yellow coloration more frequently than expected then the avoidance is most likely innate. If the predator does not express any preference but upon injury from a prey with the specific coloration does begin to express a preference, then the avoidance is most likely learned. In this case, the learning would be operant conditioning; the predator has learned to associate the coloration with pain and thus subsequently avoids prey with that coloration. To measure the adaptive significance of black and yellow coloration, both poisonous (or stinging) and harmless prey species with the coloration and without the coloration pattern could be presented to predators; if predators avoid both the harmful and the harmless prey, the coloration is evolutionary significant.

2. In many cases the organisms in question are unavailable for or unrealistic to study in a laboratory setting. Model organisms allow behavioral geneticists to overcome this obstacle by determining general patterns and then applying these patterns and findings to other, similar organisms. The primary disadvantage of the model system is, of course, the vast differences that are usually found between groups of taxa; however, when applying general principles, in particular those of genetic behavioral regulation, the benefits of using a model outweigh the costs. Phylogenetic analysis is the best way to determine the scale of applicability when using model organisms.

3. Extra-pair copulations and mating with males that are outside a female's territory are, by and large, more beneficial than costly to the female. By mating with males outside her territory, she reduces the likelihood that a male challenging the owner of her territory would target her offspring; males of many species are infanticidal but would not likely attack infants that could be their own. Historical data have actually shown that in many cases, females are more attracted to infanticidal males if those males win territory prior to their infanticidal behavior.

CHAPTER 56

LEARNING OUTCOME QUESTIONS

56.1 It depends upon the type of species in question. Conformers are able to adapt to their environment by adjusting their body temperature and making other physiological adjustments. Over a longer period of time, individuals within a non-conforming species might not adjust to the changing environment but we would expect the population as a whole to adapt due to natural selection.

56.2 If the populations in question comprised a source-sink metapopulations, then the lack of immigration into the sink populations would, most likely, eventually result in the extinction of those populations. The source populations would likely then increase their geographic ranges.

56.3 It depends upon the initial sizes of the populations in question; a small population with a high survivorship rate will not necessarily grow faster than a large population with a lower survivorship rate.

56.4 A species with high levels of predation would likely exhibit an earlier age at first reproduction and shorter inter-birth intervals in order to maximize its fitness under the selective pressure of the predation. On the other hand, species with few predators have the luxury of waiting until they are more mature before reproducing and can increase the inter-birth interval (and thus invest more in each offspring) because their risk of early mortality is decreased.

56.5 Many different factors might affect the carrying capacity of a population. For example, climate changes, even on a relatively small scale, could have large effects on carrying capacity by altering the available water and vegetation, as well as the phenology and distribution of the vegetation. Regardless of the type of change in the environment, however, most populations will move toward carrying capacity; thus, if the carrying capacity is lowered, the population should decrease, and if the carrying capacity is raised, the population should increase.

56.6 A given population can experience both positive and negative density-dependent effects, but not at the same time. Negative density-dependent effects, such as low food availability or high predation pressure, would decrease the population size. On the other hand, positive density-dependent effects, such as is seen with the Allee effect, results in a rapid increase in population size. Since a population cannot both increase and decrease at the same time, the two cannot occur concurrently. However, the selective pressures on a population are on a positive-negative continuum, and the forces shaping population size can not only vary in intensity but can also change direction from negative to positive or positive to negative.

56.7 The two are closely tied together, and both are extremely important if the human population is not to exceed the Earth's carrying capacity. As population growth increases, the human population approaches the planet's carrying capacity; as consumption increases, the carrying capacity is lowered—thus, both trends must be reversed.

INQUIRY QUESTIONS

Page 1164 Very possibly. How fast a lizard runs is a function of its body temperature. Researchers have shown that lizards in shaded habitats have lower temperatures and thus lower maximal running speeds. In such circumstances, lizards often adopt alternative escape tactics that rely less on rapidly running away from potential predators.

Page 1169 Because of their shorter generation times, smaller species tend to reproduce more quickly, and thus would be able to respond more quickly to increased resources in the environment.

Page 1171 Based on the survivorship curve of meadow grass, the older the plant, the less likely it is to survive. It would be best to choose a plant that is very young to ensure the longest survival as a house plant. A survivorship curve that is shaped like a Type I curve, in which most individuals survive to an old age and then die would also lead you to select a younger plant. A type III survivorship curve, in which only a few individuals manage to survive to an older age, would suggest the selection of a middle-aged plant that had survived the early stages of life since it would also be more likely to survive to old age.

Page 1172 It depends on the situation. If only large individuals are likely to reproduce (as is the case in some territorial species, in which only large males can hold a territory), then a few large offspring would be favored; alternatively, if body size does not affect survival or reproduction, then producing as many offspring as possible would maximize the representation of an individual's genes in subsequent generations. In many cases, intermediate values are favored by natural selection.

Page 1174 Because when the population is below carrying capacity, the population increases in size. As it approaches the carrying capacity, growth rate slows down either from increased death rates, decreased birthrates, or both, becoming zero as the population hits the carrying capacity. Similarly, populations well above the carrying capacity will experience large decreases in growth rate, resulting either from low birthrates or high death rates, that also approach zero as the population hits the carrying capacity.

Page 1175 There are many possible reasons. Perhaps resources become limited, so that females are not able to produce as many offspring. Another possibility is that space is limited so that, at higher populations, individuals spend more time in interactions with other individuals and squander energy that otherwise could be invested in producing and raising more young.

Page 1176 The answer depends on whether food is the factor regulating population size. If it is, then the number of young produced at a given population size would increase and the juvenile mortality rate would decrease. However, if other factors, such as the availability of water or predators, regulated population size, then food supplementation might have no effect.

Page 1177 If hare population levels were kept high, then we would expect lynx populations to stay high as well because lynx populations respond to food availability. If lynx populations were maintained at a high level, we would expect hare populations to remain low because increased reproduction of hares would lead to increased food for the lynxes.

Page 1179 If human populations are regulated by density-dependent factors, then as the population approaches the carrying capacity, either birthrates will decrease or death rates will increase, or both. If populations are regulated by density-independent factors, then if environmental conditions change, then either both rates will decline, death rates will increase, or both.

Page 1179 The answer depends on whether age-specific birth and death rates stay unchanged. If they do, then the Swedish distribution would remain about the same. By contrast, because birthrates are far outstripping death rates, the Kenyan distribution will become increasingly unbalanced as the bulge of young individuals enter their reproductive years and start producing even more offspring.

Page 1181 Both are important causes and the relative importance of the two depends on which resource we are discussing. One thing is clear: The world cannot support its current population size if everyone lived at the level of resource consumption of people in the United States.

UNDERSTAND

1.b 2.c 3.a 4.b 5.d 6.b 7.c

APPLY

1.d 2.c 3.b 4.c

SYNTHESIZE

1. The genetic makeup of isolated populations will change over time based on the basic mechanisms of evolutionary change; for example, natural selection, mutation, assortative mating, and drift. These same processes affect the genetic makeup of populations in a metapopulation, but the outcomes are likely to be much more complicated. For example, if immigration between a source and a sink population is very high, then local selection in a sink population may be swamped by the regular flow of individuals carrying alleles of lower fitness from a source population where natural selection may not be acting against those alleles; divergence might be slowed or even stopped under some circumstances. On the other hand, if sinks go through repeated population declines such that they often are made up of a very small number of individuals, then they may lose considerable genetic diversity due to drift. If immigration from source populations is greater than zero but not large, these small populations might begin to diverge substantially from other populations in the metapopulation due to drift. The difference is that in the metapopulation, such populations might actually be able to persist and diverge, rather than just going extinct due to small numbers of individuals and no ability to be rescued by neighboring sources.

2. The probability that an animal lives to the next year should decline with age (Note that in Figure 55.11, all the curves decrease with age) so the cost of reproduction for an old animal would, all else being equal, be lower than for a young animal. The reason is that the cost of reproduction is measured by changes in fitness. Imagine a very old animal that has almost no chance in surviving to another reproductive event; it should spend all its effort on a current reproductive effort since its future success is likely to be zero anyway.

3. If offspring size does not affect offspring quality, then it is in the parent's interest to produce absolutely as many small offspring as possible. In doing so, it would be maximizing its fitness by increasing the number of related individuals in the next generation.

4. By increasing the mean generation time (increasing the age at which an individual can begin reproducing; age at first reproduction), keeping all else equal, one would expect that the population growth rate would be reduced. That comes simply from the fact of reducing the number of individuals that are producing offspring in the adult age classes; lower population birth rates would lead to a reduced population growth rate. As to which would have a larger influence, that is hard to say. If the change in generation time (increased age at first reproduction) had an overall larger effect on the total number of offspring an individual female had than a reduced fecundity at any age, then population growth rate would probably be more sensitive to the

change in generation time. Under different scenarios, the comparison of these two effects could become more complicated, however. Suffice it to say that population growth control can come from more than one source: fecundity and age at first reproduction.

CHAPTER 57

LEARNING OUTCOME QUESTIONS

57.1 The answer depends upon the habitat of the community in question. Some habitats are more hospitable to animals, and others to plants. The abundance of plants and animals in most habitats is also closely tied; thus the variation in abundance of one would affect the variation in abundance of the other.

57.2 It depends upon whether we are talking about fundamental niche or realized niche. Two species can certainly have identical fundamental niches and coexist indefinitely, because they could develop different realized niches within the fundamental niche. In order for two species with identical realized niches to coexist indefinitely, the resources within the niche must not be limited.

57.3 This is an example of Batesian mimicry, in which a non-poisonous species evolves coloration similar to a poisonous species.

57.4 In an ecosystem with limited resources and multiple prey species, one prey species could out-compete another to extinction in the absence of a predator. In the presence of the predator, however, the prey species that would have otherwise be driven to extinction by competitive exclusion is able to persist in the community. The predators that lower the likelihood of competitive exclusion are known as keystone predators.

57.5 Selective harvesting of individual trees would be preferable from a community point of view. According to the Intermediate Disturbance Hypothesis, moderate degrees of disturbance, as in selective harvesting, increase species richness and biodiversity more than severe disturbances, such as clear-cutting.

INQUIRY QUESTIONS

Page 1187 The different soil types require very different adaptations, and thus different species are adapted to each soil type.

Page 1191 The kangaroo rats competed with all the other rodent species for resources, keeping the size of other rodent populations smaller. In the absence of competition when the kangaroo rats were removed, there were more resources available which allowed the other rodent populations to increase in size.

Page 1192 This could be accomplished in a variety of ways. One option would be to provide refuges to give some *Paramecium* a way of escaping the predators. Another option would be to include predators of the *Didinium*, which would limit their populations (see Ecosystem chapter).

Page 1201 By removing the kangaroo rats from the experimental enclosures and measuring the effects on both plants and ants. At first, the number of small seeds available to ants increases due to the absence of rodents. However, over time, plants that produce large seeds outcompete plants that produce small seeds, and thus fewer small seeds are produced and available to ants; hence, ant populations decline.

UNDERSTAND

1. a 2. a 3. d 4. a 5. b 6. d 7. c 8. c

APPLY

1. d 2. b 3. d 4. d 5. d

SYNTHESIZE

1. Experiments are useful means to test hypotheses about ecological limitations, but they are generally limited to rapidly reproducing species that occur in relatively small areas. Alternative means of studying species' interactions include detailed studies of the mechanisms by which species might interact; sometimes, for long-lived species, instead of monitoring changes in population size, which may take a very long time, other indices can be measured, such as growth or reproductive rate. Another means of assessing interspecific interactions is to study one species in different areas, in only some of which a second species occurs. Such studies must be interpreted cautiously, however, because there may be many important differences between the areas in addition to the difference in the presence or absence of the second species.

2. Adding differentially preferred prey species might have the same effect as putting in a refuge for prey in the single species system. One way to think about it is that if a highly preferred species becomes rare due to removal by the predator, then a predator might switch to a less desirable species, even if it doesn't taste as good or is harder to catch, simply because it is still provides a better return than chasing after a very rare preferred species. While the predator has switched, there might be enough time for the preferred species to rebound. All of these dynamics will depend upon the time it takes a predator to reduce the population size of its prey relative to the time it takes for those prey populations to rebound once the predator pressure is removed.

3. Although the mechanism might be known in this system, hidden interactions might affect interpretations in many ways because ecological systems are complex. For example, what if some other activity of the rodents besides their reduction of large seeds leading to an increase in the number of small seeds was responsible for the positive effect of rodents on ants? One way to test the specific mechanism would be to increase the abundance of small seeds experimentally independent of any manipulation of rodents. Under the current hypothesis, an increase in ant population size would be expected and should be sustained, unlike the initial increase followed by a decrease seen when rodents are removed.

4. By itself, the pattern shown in Figure 56.7 suggests character displacement, but alternative hypotheses are possible. For example, what if the distribution of seeds available on the two islands where the species are found alone is different from that seen where they are found in sympatry? If there were no large and small seeds seen on Los Hermanos or Daphne, just medium-sized ones, then it would be hard to conclude that the bill size on San Cristobal has diverged relative to the other islands just due to competition. This is a general criticism of inferring the process of character displacement with just comparing the size distributions in allopatry and sympatry. In this case, however, the Galápagos system has been very well studied. It has been established that the size distribution of seeds available is not measurably different. Furthermore, natural selection-induced changes seen in the bill size of birds on a single island, in response to drought-induced changes in seed size lend further support to the role of competition in establishing and maintaining these patterns.

5. It is possible, as the definition of an ecosystem depends upon scale. In some ecosystems, there may be other, smaller ecosystems operating within it. For example, within a rainforest ecosystem, there are small aquatic ecosystems, ecosystems within the soil, ecosystems upon an individual tree. Research seems to indicate that most species behave individualistically, but there are some instances where groups of species do depend upon one another and do function holistically. We would expect this kind of dual community structure especially in areas of overlap between distinct ecosystems, where ecotones exist.

CHAPTER 58

LEARNING OUTCOME QUESTIONS

58.1 Yes, fertilization with natural materials such as manure is less disruptive to the ecosystem than is chemical fertilization. Many chemical fertilizers, for example, contain higher levels of phosphates than does manure and thus chemical fertilization has disrupted the natural global phosphorus cycle.

58.2 Both matter and energy flow through ecosystems by changing form, but neither can be created or destroyed. Both matter and energy also flow through the trophic levels within an ecosystem. The flow of matter such as carbon atoms is more complex and multi-leveled than is energy flow, largely because it is truly a cycle. The atoms in the carbon cycle truly cycle through the ecosystem, with no clear beginning or end. The carbon is changed during the process of cycling from a solid to a gaseous state and back again. On the other hand, energy flow is unidirectional. The ultimate source of the energy in an ecosystem is the sun. The solar energy is captured by the primary producers at the first trophic level and is changed in form from solar to chemical energy. The chemical energy is transferred from one trophic level to another, until only heat, low quality energy, remains.

58.3 Yes, there are certainly situations in ecosystems in which the top predators in one trophic chain affect the lower trophic levels, while within the same ecosystem the primary producers affect the higher trophic levels within another trophic chain.

58.4 It depends on whether the amount of sunlight captured by the primary producers was affected. Currently, only approximately 1% of the solar energy in Earth's atmosphere is captured by primary producers for photosynthesis. If less sunlight reached Earth's surface, but a correlating increase in energy capture accompanied the decrease in sunlight, then the primary productivity should not be affected.

58.5 The equilibrium model of island biogeography describes the relationship between species richness and not only island size but also distance from the mainland. A small island closer to the mainland would be expected to have more species than would a larger island that is farther from the mainland.

INQUIRY QUESTIONS

Page 1218 At each link in the food chain, only a small fraction of the energy at one level is converted into mass of organisms at the next level. Much energy is dissipated as heat or excreted.

Page 1219 In the inverted pyramid, the primary producers reproduce quickly and are eaten quickly, so that at any given time, a small population of primary producers exist relative to the heterotroph population.

Page 1220 Because the trout eat the invertebrates which graze the algae. With fewer grazers, there is more algae.

Page 1220 The snakes might reduce the number of fish, which would allow an increase in damselflies, which would reduce the number of chironomids and increase the algae. In other words, lower levels of the food chain would be identical for the "snake and fish" and "no fish and no snake" treatments. Both would differ from the enclosures with only fish.

Page 1222 Herbivores consume much of the algal biomass even as primary productivity increases. Increases in primary productivity can lead to increased herbivore populations. The additional herbivores crop the biomass of the algae even while primary productivity increases.

Page 1222 More light means more photosynthesis. More plant material means more herbivores, which translates into more predator biomass.

Page 1223 Introduce them yourself. For example, each spring, you could place a premeasured number of seeds of a particular invasive species in each plot. Such an experiment would have the advantage of more precisely controlling the opportunity for invasion, but also would be less natural, which is one of the advantages of the Cedar Creek study site: the plots are real ecosystems, interacting with their surrounding environment in natural ways.

Page 1224 (*a*) Perhaps because an intermediate number of predators is enough to keep numbers of superior competitors down. (*b*) Perhaps because there are more habitats available and thus more different ways of surviving in the environment. (*c*) Hard to say. Possibly more stable environments permit greater specialization, thus permitting coexistence of more species.

UNDERSTAND

1. d   2. d   3. b   4. a   5. a   6. b   7. a   8. a   9. c

APPLY

1. d   2. a   3. d   4. d

SYNTHESIZE

1. Because the length of food chains appears to be ultimately limited by the amount of energy entering a system, and the characteristic loss of usable energy (about 90%) as energy is transferred to each higher level, it would be reasonable to expect that the ectotherm-dominated food chains would be longer than the endotherm-dominated chains. In fact, there is some indirect evidence for this from real food chains, and it is also predicted by some advanced ecological models. However, whether in reality such is the case, is difficult to determine due to all of the complex factors that determine food chain length and structure. Moreover, there are many practical difficulties associated with measuring actual food chain length in natural systems.

2. It is critical to distinguish, as this chapter points out, between energy and mass transfer in trophic dynamics of ecosystems. The standing biomass of phytoplankton is not necessarily a reliable measure of the energy contained in the trophic level. If phytoplankton are eaten as quickly as they are produced, they may contribute a tremendous amount of energy, which can never be directly measured by a static biomass sample. The standing crop therefore, is an incomplete measure of the productivity of the trophic level.

3. As Figure 58.17 suggests, trophic structure and dynamics are interrelated and are primary determinants of ecosystem characteristics and behavior. For example, if a particularly abundant herbivore is threatened, energy that is abundant at the level of primary productivity in an ecosystem may be relatively unavailable to higher trophic levels (e.g., carnivores). That is, the herbivores are an important link in transducing energy through an ecosystem. Cascading effects, whether they are driven from the bottom up or from the top down are a characteristic of energy transfer in ecosystems, and that translates into the reality that effects on any particular species are unlikely to be limited to that species itself.

4. There are many ways to answer this question, but the obvious place to start is to think about the many ways plant structural diversity potentially affects animals that are not eating the plants directly. For example, plants may provide shelter, refuges, food for prey, substrate for nesting, among other

things. Therefore, increasing complexity might increase the ability of lizards to partition the habitat in more ways, allow more species to escape their predators or seek refuge from harsh physical factors (such as, cold or hot temperatures), provide a greater substrate for potential prey in terms of food resources, for instance. If we want to know the exact mechanisms for the relationship, we would need to conduct experiments to test specific hypotheses. For example, if we hypothesize that some species that require greater structural complexity in order to persist in a particular habitat, we could modify the habitat (reduce plant structure) and test whether species originally present were reduced in numbers or became unable to persist.

CHAPTER 59

LEARNING OUTCOME QUESTIONS

59.1 If the Earth rotated in the opposite direction, the Coriolis Effect would be reversed. In other words, winds descending between 30° north or 30° south and the equator would still be moving more slowly than the underlying surface so it would be deflected; however, they would be deflected to the left in the northern hemisphere and to the right in the southern hemisphere. The pattern would be reversed between 30° and 60° because the winds would be moving more rapidly than the underlying surface, and would thus be deflected again in the opposite directions from normal—to the left in the northern hemisphere and to the right in the southern hemisphere. All of this would result in Trade Winds that blew from west to east and "Westerlies" that were actually "Easterlies," blowing east to west.

59.2 As with elevation, latitude is a primary determinant of climate and precipitation, which together largely determine the vegetational structure of a particular area, which in turn defines biomes.

59.3 The spring and fall overturns that occur in freshwater lakes found in temperate climates result in the oxygen-poor water near the bottom of the lake getting re-mixed with the oxygen-rich water near the top of the lake, essentially eliminating, at least temporarily, the thermocline layer. In the tropics, there is less temperature fluctuation; thus the thermocline layer is more permanent and the oxygen depletion (and resulting paucity of animal life) is sustained.

59.4 Regions affected by the ENSO, or El Niño Southern Oscillation events, experience cyclical warming events in the waters around the coastline. The warmed water lowers the primary productivity, which stresses and subsequently decreases the populations of fish, seabirds, and sea mammals.

59.5 CFCs, or chlorofluorocarbons, are an example of point-source pollution. CFCs and other types of point-source pollutants are, in general, easier to combat because their sources are more easily identified and thus the pollutants more easily eliminated.

59.6 Global climate change and ozone depletion may be interconnected. However, while climate change and ozone depletion are both global environmental concerns due to the impact each has on human health, the environment, economics, and politics, there are some different approaches to combating and understanding each dilemma. Ozone depletion results in an increase in the ultraviolet radiation reaching the earth's surface. Global climate change, on the other hand, results in long-term changes in sea level, ice flow, and storm activity.

INQUIRY QUESTIONS

Page 1232 Because of the tilt of the Earth's axis and the spherical shape of the planet, the light (and heat) from the sun hits the equator and nearby latitudes more directly than it does at the poles.

Page 1236 Increased precipitation and temperature allows for the sustainability of a larger variety and biomass of vegetation, and primary productivity is a measure of the rate at which plants convert solar energy into chemical energy.

UNDERSTAND

1. d   2. b   3. a   4. c   5. c   6. c   7. a   8. c

APPLY

1. d   2. b   3. c   4. b

SYNTHESIZE

1. The Earth is tilted on its axis such that regions away from the equator receive less incident solar radiation per unit surface area (because the angle of incidence is oblique). The northern and southern hemispheres alternate between angling towards vs. away from the Sun on the Earth's annual orbit. These two facts mean that the annual mean temperature will decline as you move away from the equator, and that variation in the mean temperatures of

the northern and southern hemispheres will be complementary to each other; when one is hot, the other will be cold.

2. Energy absorbed by the Earth is maximized at the equator because of the angle of incidence. Because there are large expanses of ocean at the equator, warmed air picks up moisture and rises. As it rises, equatorial air, now saturated with moisture, cools and releases rain, the air falling back to Earth's surface displaced north and south to approximately 30°. The air, warming as it descends, absorbs moisture from the land and vegetation below, resulting in desiccation in the latitudes around 30°.

3. Even though there have been global climate changes in the past, conservation biologists are concerned about the current warming trend for two reasons. First, the warming rate is rapid, thus the selective pressures on the most vulnerable organisms may be too strong for the species to adapt. Second, the natural areas that covered most of the globe during past climatic changes are now in much more limited, restricted areas, thus greatly impeding the ability of organisms to migrate to more suitable habitats.

4. Two characteristics can lead to a phenomenon known as biological magnification. First, if a pesticide actually persists in the bodies of target species (that is, it doesn't degrade after having its effect), then depending on its chemical composition, it might actually be sequestered in the bodies of animals that eat the target species. Because large numbers of prey are consumed at each trophic level (due to the 10% rate of transfer of energy), large amounts of the pesticide may be passed up the food chain. So, persistence and magnification can lead to toxic exposures at the top of food chains.

Chapter 60

LEARNING OUTCOME QUESTIONS

60.1 Unfortunately, most of the Earth's biodiversity hotspots are also areas of the greatest human population growth; human population growth is accompanied by increased resource utilization and exploitation.

60.2 I would tell the shrimp farmers that if they were to shut down the shrimp farm and remediate the natural mangrove swamp on which their property sits, other, more economically lucrative businesses could be developed, such as timber, charcoal production, and offshore fishing.

60.3 Absolutely. The hope of conservation biologists is that even if a species is endangered to the brink of extinction due to habitat degradation, the habitat may someday be restored. The endangered species can be bred in captivity (which also allows for the maintenance of genetic diversity within the species) and either re-introduced to a restored habitat, or even introduced to another suitable habitat.

60.4 It depends upon the reason for the degradation of the habitat in the first place, but yes, in some cases, habitat restoration can approach a pristine state. For example, the Nashau River in New England was heavily polluted, but habitat restoration efforts returned it to a relatively pristine state. However, because habitat degradation affects so many species within the ecosystem, and the depth and complexity of the trophic relationships within the ecosystem are difficult if not impossible to fully understand, restoration is rarely if ever truly pristine.

INQUIRY QUESTIONS

Page 1260 Many factors affect human population trends, including resource availability, governmental support for settlement in new areas or for protecting natural areas, and the extent to which governments attempt to manage population growth.

Page 1262 The mangroves provide many economic services. For example, without them, fisheries become less productive and storm damage increases. However, because the people who benefit from these services do not own the mangroves, governmental action is needed to ensure that the value of what are economists call "common goods" is protected.

Page 1266 On smaller islands, populations tend to be smaller. As we discuss later in this chapter, small populations are vulnerable to many problems, which individually or in concert can heighten the risk of extinction.

Page 1269 As discussed in this chapter, populations that are small face many problems that can reinforce one another and eventually cause extinction.

Page 1274 As we discussed in chapter 21, allele frequencies change randomly in a process called genetic drift. The smaller the population size, the greater these random fluctuations will be. Thus, small populations are particularly prone to one allele being lost from a population due to these random changes.

UNDERSTAND

1. a   2. c   3. d   4. d   5. b   6. c

APPLY

1. d   2. d   3. a   4. d

SYNTHESIZE

1. Although it is true that extinction is a natural part of the existence of a species, several pieces of evidence suggest that current rates of extinction are much elevated over the natural background level and the disappearance is associated with human activities (which many of the most pronounced extinction events in the history of the Earth were not). It is important to appreciate the length of time over which the estimate of 99% is made. The history of life on Earth extends back billions of years. Certainly, clear patterns of the emergence and extinction of species in the fossil record extend back many hundreds of millions of years. Since the average time of species' existence is short relative to the great expanse of time over which we can estimate the percentage of species that have disappeared, the perception might be that extinction rates have always been high, when in fact the high number is driven by the great expanse of time of measurement. We have very good evidence that modern extinction rates (over human history) are considerably elevated above background levels. Furthermore, the circumstances of the extinctions may be very different because they are also associated with habitat and resource removal; thus potentially limiting the natural processes that replace extinct species.

2. The problem is not unique and not new. It represents a classic conflict that is the basic source of societal laws and regulations, especially in the management of resources. For example, whether or not to place air pollution scrubbers on the smoke stacks of coal-fired power plants is precisely the same issue. In this case, it is not ecosystem conversion, per se, but the fact that the businesses that run the power plants benefit from their operation, but the public "owns" and relies on the atmosphere is a conflict between public and private interests. Some of the ways to navigate the dilemma is for society to create regulations to protect the public interest. The problem is difficult and clearly does not depend solely on economic valuation of the costs and benefits because there can be considerable debate about those estimates. One only has to look at the global climate change problem to suggest how hard it will be to make progress in an expedient manner.

3. This is not a trivial undertaking, which is why, since the first concerns were raised in the late 1980s, it has taken nearly 15 years to collect evidence showing a decline is likely. Although progress has been made on identifying potential causes, much work remains to be done. Many amphibians are secretive, relatively long-lived, and subject to extreme population fluctuations. Given those facts about their biology, documenting population fluctuations (conducting censuses of the number of individuals in populations) for long periods of time is the only way to ultimately establish the likely fate of populations, and that process is time-consuming and costly.

4. Within an ecosystem, every species is dependent upon and depended upon by any number of other species. Even the smallest organisms, bacteria, are often specific about the species they feed upon, live within, parasitize, etc. So, the extinction of a single species anywhere in the ecosystem will affect not only the organisms it directly feeds upon and that directly feed upon it, but also those related more distantly. In the simplest terms, if, for example, a species of rodent goes extinct, the insects and vegetation upon which it feeds would no longer be under the same predation pressure and thus could grow out of control, outcompeting other species and leading to their demise. In addition, the predators of the rodent would have to find other prey, which would result in competition with those species' predators. And so on, and so on. The affects could be catastrophic to the entire ecosystem. By looking at the trophic chains in which a particular organism is involved, one could predict the affects its extinction would have on other species.

5. Population size is not necessarily a direct cause of extinction, but it certainly is an indirect cause. Smaller populations have a number of problems that themselves can lead directly to extinction, such as loss of diversity (and thus increased susceptibility to pathogens) and greater vulnerability to natural catastrophes.

A

ABO blood group A set of four phenotypes produced by different combinations of three alleles at a single locus; blood types are A, B, AB, and O, depending on which alleles are expressed as antigens on the red blood cell surface.

abscission In vascular plants, the dropping of leaves, flowers, fruits, or stems at the end of the growing season, as the result of the formation of a layer of specialized cells (the abscission zone) and the action of a hormone (ethylene).

absorption spectrum The relationship of absorbance vs. wavelength for a pigment molecule. This indicates which wavelengths are absorbed maximally by a pigment. For example, chlorophyll *a* absorbs most strongly in the violet-blue and red regions of the visible light spectrum.

acceptor stem The 3' end of a tRNA molecule; the portion that amino acids become attached to during the tRNA charging reaction.

accessory pigment A secondary light-absorbing pigment used in photosynthesis, including chlorophyll *b* and the carotenoids, that complement the absorption spectrum of chlorophyll *a*.

aceolomate An animal, such as a flatworm, having a body plan that has no body cavity; the space between mesoderm and endoderm is filled with cells and organic materials.

acetyl-CoA The product of the transition reaction between glycolysis and the Krebs cycle. Pyruvate is oxidized to acetyl-CoA by NAD+, also producing CO_2, and NADH.

achiasmate segregation The lining up and subsequent separation of homologues during meiosis I without the formation of chiasmata between homologues; found in *Drosophila* males and some other species.

acid Any substance that dissociates in water to increase the hydrogen ion (H+) concentration and thus lower the pH.

actin One of the two major proteins that make up vertebrate muscle; the other is myosin.

action potential A transient, all-or-none reversal of the electric potential across a membrane; in neurons, an action potential initiates transmission of a nerve impulse.

action spectrum A measure of the efficiency of different wavelengths of light for photosynthesis. In plants it corresponds to the absorption spectrum of chlorophylls.

activation energy The energy that must be processed by a molecule in order for it to undergo a specific chemical reaction.

active site The region of an enzyme surface to which a specific set of substrates binds, lowering the activation energy required for a particular chemical reaction and so facilitating it.

active transport The pumping of individual ions or other molecules across a cellular membrane from a region of lower concentration to one of higher concentration (i.e., against a concentration gradient); this transport process requires energy, which is typically supplied by the expenditure of ATP.

adaptation A peculiarity of structure, physiology, or behavior that promotes the likelihood of an organism's survival and reproduction in a particular environment.

adapter protein Any of a class of proteins that acts as a link between a receptor and other proteins to initiate signal transduction.

adaptive radiation The evolution of several divergent forms from a primitive and unspecialized ancestor.

adenosine triphosphate (ATP) A nucleotide consisting of adenine, ribose sugar, and three phosphate groups; ATP is the energy currency of cellular metabolism in all organisms.

adherins junction An anchoring junction that connects the actin filaments of one cell with those of adjacent cells or with the extracellular matrix.

ATP synthase The enzyme responsible for producing ATP in oxidative phosphorylation; it uses the energy from a proton gradient to catalyze the reaction $ADP + P_i \longrightarrow ATP$.

adenylyl cyclase An enzyme that produces large amounts of cAMP from ATP; the cAMP acts as a second messenger in a target cell.

adhesion The tendency of water to cling to other polar compounds due to hydrogen bonding.

adipose cells Fat cells, found in loose connective tissue, usually in large groups that form adipose tissue. Each adipose cell can store a droplet of fat (triacylglyceride).

adventitious Referring to a structure arising from an unusual place, such as stems from roots or roots from stems.

aerenchyma In plants, loose parenchymal tissue with large air spaces in it; often found in plants that grow in water.

aerobic Requiring free oxygen; any biological process that can occur in the presence of gaseous oxygen.

aerobic respiration The process that results in the complete oxidation of glucose using oxygen as the final electron acceptor. Oxygen acts as the final electron acceptor for an electron transport chain that produces a proton gradient for the chemiosmotic synthesis of ATP.

aleurone In plants, the outer layer of the endosperm in a seed; on germination, the aleurone produces α-amylase that breaks down the carbohydrates of the endosperm to nourish the embryo.

alga, pl. **algae** A unicellular or simple multicellular photosynthetic organism lacking multicellular sex organs.

allantois A membrane of the amniotic egg that functions in respiration and excretion in birds and reptiles and plays an important role in the development of the placenta in most mammals.

allele One of two or more alternative states of a gene.

allele frequency A measure of the occurrence of an allele in a population, expressed as proportion of the entire population, for example, an occurrence of 0.84 (84%).

allometric growth A pattern of growth in which different components grow at different rates.

allelopathy The release of a substance from the roots of one plant that block the germination of nearby seeds or inhibits the growth of a neighboring plant.

allopatric speciation The differentiation of geographically isolated populations into distinct species.

allopolyploid A polyploid organism that contains the genomes of two or more different species.

allosteric activator A substance that binds to an enzyme's allosteric site and keeps the enzyme in its active configuration.

allosteric inhibitor A noncompetitive inhibitor that binds to an enzyme's allosteric site and prevents the enzyme from changing to its active configuration.

allosteric site A part of an enzyme, away from its active site, that serves as an on/off switch for the function of the enzyme.

alpha (α) helix A form of secondary structure in proteins where the polypeptide chain is wound into a spiral due to interactions between amino and carboxyl groups in the peptide backbone.

alternation of generations A reproductive cycle in which a haploid (*n*) phase (the gametophyte), gives rise to gametes, which, after fusion to form a zygote, germinate to produce a diploid (2*n*) phase (the sporophyte). Spores produced by meiotic division from the sporophyte give rise to new gametophytes, completing the cycle.

alternative splicing In eukaryotes, the production of different mRNAs from a single primary transcript by including different sets of exons.

altruism Self-sacrifice for the benefit of others; in formal terms, the behavior that increases the fitness of the recipient while reducing the fitness of the altruistic individual.

alveolus, pl. **alveoli** One of many small, thin-walled air sacs within the lungs in which the bronchioles terminate.

amino acid The subunit structure from which proteins are produced, consisting of a central carbon atom with a carboxyl group (—COOH), an amino group (—NH₂), a hydrogen, and a side group (*R* group); only the side group differs from one amino acid to another.

aminoacyl-tRNA synthetase Any of a group of enzymes that attach specific amino acids to the correct tRNA during the tRNA-charging reaction. Each of the 20 amino acids has a corresponding enzyme.

amniocentesis Indirect examination of a fetus by tests on cell cultures grown from fetal cells obtained from a sample of the amniotic fluid or tests on the fluid itself.

amnion The innermost of the extraembryonic membranes; the amnion forms a fluid-filled sac around the embryo in amniotic eggs.

amniote A vertebrate that produces an egg surrounded by four membranes, one of which is the amnion; amniote groups are the reptiles, birds, and mammals.

amniotic egg An egg that is isolated and protected from the environment by a more or less impervious shell during the period of its development and that is completely self-sufficient, requiring only oxygen.

ampulla In echinoderms, a muscular sac at the base of a tube foot that contracts to extend the tube foot.

amyloplast A plant organelle called a plastid that specializes in storing starch.

anabolism The biosynthetic or constructive part of metabolism; those chemical reactions involved in biosynthesis.

anaerobic Any process that can occur without oxygen, such as anaerobic fermentation or H_2S photosynthesis.

anaerobic respiration The use of electron transport to generate a proton gradient for chemiosmotic synthesis of ATP using a final electron acceptor other than oxygen.

analogous Structures that are similar in function but different in evolutionary origin, such as the wing of a bat and the wing of a butterfly.

anaphase In mitosis and meiosis II, the stage initiated by the separation of sister chromatids, during which the daughter chromosomes move to opposite poles of the cell; in meiosis I, marked by separation of replicated homologous chromosomes.

anaphase-promoting complex (APC) A protein complex that triggers anaphase; it initiates a series of reactions that ultimately degrades cohesin, the protein complex that holds the sister chromatids together. The sister chromatids are then released and move toward opposite poles in the cell.

anchoring junction A type of cell junction that mechanically attaches the cytoskeleton of a cell to the cytoskeletons of adjacent cells or to the extracellular matrix.

androecium The floral whorl that comprises the stamens.

aneuploidy The condition in an organism whose cells have lost or gained a chromosome; Down syndrome, which results from an extra copy of human chromosome 21, is an example of aneuploidy in humans.

angiosperms The flowering plants, one of five phyla of seed plants. In angiosperms, the ovules at the time of pollination are completely enclosed by tissues.

animal pole In fish and other aquatic vertebrates with asymmetrical yolk distribution in their eggs, the hemisphere of the blastula comprising cells relatively poor in yolk.

anion A negatively charged ion.

annotation In genomics, the process of identifying and making note of "landmarks" in a DNA sequence to assist with recognition of coding and transcribed regions.

anonymous markers Genetic markers in a genome that do not cause a detectable phenotype, but that can be detected using molecular techniques.

antenna complex A complex of hundreds of pigment molecules in a photosystem that collects photons and feeds the light energy to a reaction center.

anther In angiosperm flowers, the pollen-bearing portion of a stamen.

antheridium, pl. antheridia A sperm-producing organ.

anthropoid Any member of the mammalian group consisting of monkeys, apes, and humans.

antibody A protein called immunoglobulin that is produced by lymphocytes in response to a foreign substance (antigen) and released into the bloodstream.

anticodon The three-nucleotide sequence at the end of a transfer RNA molecule that is complementary to, and base-pairs with, an amino-acid–specifying codon in messenger RNA.

antigen A foreign substance, usually a protein or polysaccharide, that stimulates an immune response.

antiporter A carrier protein in a cell's membrane that transports two molecules in opposite directions across the membrane.

anus The terminal opening of the gut; the solid residues of digestion are eliminated through the anus.

aorta (Gr. *aeirein*, to lift) The major artery of vertebrate systemic blood circulation; in mammals, carries oxygenated blood away from the heart to all regions of the body except the lungs.

apical meristem In vascular plants, the growing point at the tip of the root or stem.

apoplast route In plant roots, the pathway for movement of water and minerals that leads through cell walls and between cells.

apoptosis A process of programmed cell death, in which dying cells shrivel and shrink; used in all animal cell development to produce planned and orderly elimination of cells not destined to be present in the final tissue.

aposematic coloration An ecological strategy of some organisms that "advertise" their poisonous nature by the use of bright colors.

aquaporin A membrane channel that allows water to cross the membrane more easily than by diffusion through the membrane.

aquifers Permeable, saturated, underground layers of rock, sand, and gravel, which serve as reservoirs for groundwater.

archegonium, pl. archegonia The multicellular egg-producing organ in bryophytes and some vascular plants.

archenteron The principal cavity of a vertebrate embryo in the gastrula stage; lined with endoderm, it opens up to the outside and represents the future digestive cavity.

arteriole A smaller artery, leading from the arteries to the capillaries.

artificial selection Change in the genetic structure of populations due to selective breeding by humans. Many domestic animal breeds and crop varieties have been produced through artificial selection.

ascomycetes A large group comprising part of the "true fungi." They are characterized by separate hyphae, asexually produced conidiospores, and sexually produced ascospores within asci.

ascus, pl. asci A specialized cell, characteristic of the ascomycetes, in which two haploid nuclei fuse to produce a zygote that divides immediately by meiosis; at maturity, an ascus contains ascospores.

asexual reproduction The process by which an individual inherits all of its chromosomes from a single parent, thus being genetically identical to that parent; cell division is by mitosis only.

A site In a ribosome, the aminoacyl site, which binds to the tRNA carrying the next amino acid to be added to a polypeptide chain.

assembly The phase of a virus's reproductive cycle during which the newly made components are assembled into viral particles.

assortative mating A type of nonrandom mating in which phenotypically similar individuals mate more frequently.

aster In animal cell mitosis, a radial array of microtubules extending from the centrioles toward the plasma membrane, possibly serving to brace the centrioles for retraction of the spindle.

atom The smallest unit of an element that contains all the characteristics of that element. Atoms are the building blocks of matter.

atrial peptide Any of a group of small polypeptide hormones that may be useful in treatment of high blood pressure and kidney failure; produced by cells in the atria of the heart.

atrioventricular (AV) node A slender connection of cardiac muscle cells that receives the heartbeat impulses from the sinoatrial node and conducts them by way of the bundle of His.

atrium An antechamber; in the heart, a thin-walled chamber that receives venous blood and passes it on to the thick-walled ventricle; in the ear, the tympanic cavity.

autonomic nervous system The involuntary neurons and ganglia of the peripheral nervous system of vertebrates; regulates the heart, glands, visceral organs, and smooth muscle.

autopolyploid A polyploid organism that contains a duplicated genome of the same species; may result from a meiotic error.

autosome Any eukaryotic chromosome that is not a sex chromosome; autosomes are present in the same number and kind in both males and females of the species.

autotroph An organism able to build all the complex organic molecules that it requires as its own food source, using only simple inorganic compounds.

auxin (Gr. *auxein*, to increase) A plant hormone that controls cell elongation, among other effects.

auxotroph A mutation, or the organism that carries it, that affects a biochemical pathway causing a nutritional requirement.

avirulent pathogen Any type of normally pathogenic organism or virus that utilizes host resources but does not cause extensive damage or death.

axil In plants, the angle between a leaf's petiole and the stem to which it is attached.

axillary bud In plants, a bud found in the axil of a stem and leaf; an axillary bud may develop into a new shoot or may become a flower.

axon A process extending out from a neuron that conducts impulses away from the cell body.

B

b6–f complex *See* cytochrome *b6–f* complex.

bacteriophage A virus that infects bacterial cells; also called a *phage*.

Barr body A deeply staining structure, seen in the interphase nucleus of a cell of an individual with more than one X chromosome, that is a condensed and inactivated X. Only one X remains active in each cell after early embryogenesis.

basal body A self-reproducing, cylindrical, cytoplasmic organelle composed of nine triplets of microtubules from which the flagella or cilia arise.

base Any substance that dissociates in water to absorb and therefore decrease the hydrogen ion (H^+) concentration and thus raise the pH.

base-pair A complementary pair of nucleotide bases, consisting of a purine and a pyrimidine.

basidium, pl. **basidia** A specialized reproductive cell of the basidiomycetes, often club-shaped, in which nuclear fusion and meiosis occur.

basophil A leukocyte containing granules that rupture and release chemicals that enhance the inflammatory response. Important in causing allergic responses.

Batesian mimicry A survival strategy in which a palatable or nontoxic organism resembles another kind of organism that is distasteful or toxic. Both species exhibit warning coloration.

B cell A type of lymphocyte that, when confronted with a suitable antigen, is capable of secreting a specific antibody protein.

behavioral ecology The study of how natural selection shapes behavior.

biennial A plant that normally requires two growing seasons to complete its life cycle. Biennials flower in the second year of their lives.

bilateral symmetry A single plane divides an organism into two structural halves that are mirror images of each other.

bile salts A solution of organic salts that is secreted by the vertebrate liver and temporarily stored in the gallbladder; emulsifies fats in the small intestine.

binary fission Asexual reproduction by division of one cell or body into two equal or nearly equal parts.

binomial distribution The distribution of phenotypes seen among the progeny of a cross in which there are only two alternative alleles.

binomial name The scientific name of a species that consists of two parts, the genus name and the specific species name, for example, *Apis mellifera*.

biochemical pathway A sequence of chemical reactions in which the product of one reaction becomes the substrate of the next reaction. The Krebs cycle is a biochemical pathway.

biodiversity The number of species and their range of behavioral, ecological, physiological, and other adaptations, in an area.

bioenergetics The analysis of how energy powers the activities of living systems.

biofilm A complex bacterial community comprising different species; plaque on teeth is a biofilm.

biogeography The study of the geographic distribution of species.

biological community All the populations of different species living together in one place; for example, all populations that inhabit a mountain meadow.

biological species concept (BSC) The concept that defines species as groups of populations that have the potential to interbreed and that are reproductively isolated from other groups.

biomass The total mass of all the living organisms in a given population, area, or other unit being measured.

biome One of the major terrestrial ecosystems, characterized by climatic and soil conditions; the largest ecological unit.

bipolar cell A specialized type of neuron connecting cone cells to ganglion cells in the visual system. Bipolar cells receive a hyperpolarized stimulus from the cone cell and then transmit a depolarization stimulus to the ganglion cell.

biramous Two-branched; describes the appendages of crustaceans.

blade The broad, expanded part of a leaf; also called the lamina.

blastocoel The central cavity of the blastula stage of vertebrate embryos.

blastodisc In the development of birds, a disclike area on the surface of a large, yolky egg that undergoes cleavage and gives rise to the embryo.

blastomere One of the cells of a blastula.

blastopore In vertebrate development, the opening that connects the archenteron cavity of a gastrula stage embryo with the outside.

blastula In vertebrates, an early embryonic stage consisting of a hollow, fluid-filled ball of cells one layer thick; a vertebrate embryo after cleavage and before gastrulation.

Bohr effect The release of oxygen by hemoglobin molecules in response to elevated ambient levels of CO_2.

bottleneck effect A loss of genetic variability that occurs when a population is reduced drastically in size.

Bowman's capsule In the vertebrate kidney, the bulbous unit of the nephron, which surrounds the glomerulus.

β-oxidation The oxygen-dependent reactions where 2-carbon units of fatty acids are cleaved and combined with CoA to produce acetyl-CoA, which then enters the Krebs cycle. This occurs cyclically until the entire fatty acid is oxidized.

β sheet A form of secondary structure in proteins where the polypeptide folds back on itself one or more times to form a planar structure stabilized by hydrogen bonding between amino and carboxyl groups in the peptide backbone. Also known as a β-pleated sheet.

book lung In some spiders, a unique respiratory system consisting of leaflike plates within a chamber over which gas exchange occurs.

bronchus, pl. **bronchi** One of a pair of respiratory tubes branching from the lower end of the trachea (windpipe) into either lung.

bud An asexually produced outgrowth that develops into a new individual. In plants, an embryonic shoot, often protected by young leaves; buds may give rise to branch shoots.

buffer A substance that resists changes in pH. It releases hydrogen ions (H^+) when a base is added and absorbs H^+ when an acid is added.

C

C_3 photosynthesis The main cycle of the dark reactions of photosynthesis, in which CO_2 binds to ribulose 1,5-bisphosphate (RuBP) to form two 3-carbon phosphoglycerate (PGA) molecules.

C_4 photosynthesis A process of CO_2 fixation in photosynthesis by which the first product is the 4-carbon oxaloacetate molecule.

cadherin One of a large group of transmembrane proteins that contain a Ca^{2+}-mediated binding between cells; these proteins are responsible for cell-to-cell adhesion between cells of the same type.

callus Undifferentiated tissue; a term used in tissue culture, grafting, and wound healing.

Calvin cycle The dark reactions of C_3 photosynthesis; also called the Calvin–Benson cycle.

calyx The sepals collectively; the outermost flower whorl.

CAM plant Plants that use C_4 carbon fixation at night, then use the stored malate to generate CO_2 during the day to minimize dessication.

Cambrian explosion The huge increase in animal diversity that occurred at the beginning of the Cambrian period.

cAMP response protein (CRP) *See* catabolite activator protein (CAP)

cancer The unrestrained growth and division of cells; it results from a failure of cell division control.

capillary The smallest of the blood vessels; the very thin walls of capillaries are permeable to many molecules, and exchanges between blood and the tissues occur across them; the vessels that connect arteries with veins.

capsid The outermost protein covering of a virus.

capsule In bacteria, a gelatinous layer surrounding the cell wall.

carapace (Fr. from Sp. *carapacho*, shell) Shieldlike plate covering the cephalothorax of decapod crustaceans; the dorsal part of the shell of a turtle.

carbohydrate An organic compound consisting of a chain or ring of carbon atoms to which hydrogen and oxygen atoms are attached in a ratio of approximately 2:1; having the generalized formula $(CH_2O)_n$; carbohydrates include sugars, starch, glycogen, and cellulose.

carbon fixation The conversion of CO_2 into organic compounds during photosynthesis; the first stage of the dark reactions of photosynthesis, in which carbon dioxide from the air is combined with ribulose 1,5-bisphosphate.

carotenoid Any of a group of accessory pigments found in plants; in addition to absorbing light energy, these pigments act as antioxidants, scavenging potentially damaging free radicals.

carpel A leaflike organ in angiosperms that encloses one or more ovules.

carrier protein A membrane protein that binds to a specific molecule that cannot cross the membrane and allows passage through the membrane.

carrying capacity The maximum population size that a habitat can support.

cartilage A connective tissue in skeletons of vertebrates. Cartilage forms much of the skeleton of embryos, very young vertebrates, and some adult vertebrates, such as sharks and their relatives.

Casparian strip In plants, a band that encircles the cell wall of root endodermal cells. Adjacent cells' strips connect, forming a layer through which water cannot pass; therefore, all water entering roots must pass through cell membranes and cytoplasm.

catabolism In a cell, those metabolic reactions that result in the breakdown of complex molecules into simpler compounds, often with the release of energy.

catabolite activator protein (CAP) A protein that, when bound to cAMP, can bind to DNA and activate transcription. The level of cAMP is inversely related to the level of glucose, and CAP/cAMP in *E. coli* activates the *lac* (lactose) operon. Also called *cAMP response protein (CRP)*.

catalysis The process by which chemical subunits of larger organic molecules are held and positioned by enzymes that stress their chemical bonds, leading to the disassembly of the larger molecule into its subunits, often with the release of energy.

cation A positively charged ion.

cavitation In plants and animals, the blockage of a vessel by an air bubble that breaks the cohesion of the solution in the vessel; in animals more often called embolism.

CD4⁺ cell A subtype of helper T cell that is identified by the presence of the CD4 protein on its surface. This cell type is targeted by the HIV virus that causes AIDS.

cecum In vertebrates, a blind pouch at the beginning of the large intestine.

cell cycle The repeating sequence of growth and division through which cells pass each generation.

cell determination The molecular "decision" process by which a cell becomes destined for a particular developmental pathway. This occurs before overt differentiation and can be a stepwise process.

cell-mediated immunity Arm of the adaptive immune system mediated by T cells, which includes cytotoxic cells and cells that assist the rest of the immune system.

cell plate The structure that forms at the equator of the spindle during early telophase in the dividing cells of plants and a few green algae.

cell-surface marker A glycoprotein or glycolipid on the outer surface of a cell's membrane that acts as an identifier; different cell types carry different markers.

cell-surface receptor A cell surface protein that binds a signal molecule and converts the extracellular signal into an intracellular one.

cellular blastoderm In insect embryonic development, the stage during which the nuclei of the syncitial blastoderm become separate cells through membrane formation.

cellular respiration The metabolic harvesting of energy by oxidation, ultimately dependent on molecular oxygen; carried out by the Krebs cycle and oxidative phosphorylation.

cellulose The chief constituent of the cell wall in all green plants, some algae, and a few other organisms; an insoluble complex carbohydrate formed of microfibrils of glucose molecules.

cell wall The rigid, outermost layer of the cells of plants, some protists, and most bacteria; the cell wall surrounds the plasma membrane.

central nervous system (CNS) That portion of the nervous system where most association occurs; in vertebrates, it is composed of the brain and spinal cord; in invertebrates, it usually consists of one or more cords of nervous tissue, together with their associated ganglia.

central vacuole A large, membrane-bounded sac found in plant cells that stores proteins, pigments, and waste materials, and is involved in water balance.

centriole A cytoplasmic organelle located outside the nuclear membrane, identical in structure to a basal body; found in animal cells and in the flagellated cells of other groups; divides and organizes spindle fibers during mitosis and meiosis.

centromere A visible point of constriction on a chromosome that contains repeated DNA sequences that bind specific proteins. These proteins make up the kinetochore to which microtubules attach during cell division.

cephalization The evolution of a head and brain area in the anterior end of animals; thought to be a consequence of bilateral symmetry.

cerebellum The hindbrain region of the vertebrate brain that lies above the medulla (brainstem) and behind the forebrain; it integrates information about body position and motion, coordinates muscular activities, and maintains equilibrium.

cerebral cortex The thin surface layer of neurons and glial cells covering the cerebrum; well developed only in mammals, and particularly prominent in humans. The cerebral cortex is the seat of conscious sensations and voluntary muscular activity.

cerebrum The portion of the vertebrate brain (the forebrain) that occupies the upper part of the skull, consisting of two cerebral hemispheres united by the corpus callosum. It is the primary association center of the brain. It coordinates and processes sensory input and coordinates motor responses.

chaetae Bristles of chitin on each body segment that help anchor annelid worms during locomotion.

channel protein (ion channel) A transmembrane protein with a hydrophilic interior that provides an aqueous channel allowing diffusion of species that cannot cross the membrane. Usually allows passage of specific ions such as K^+, Na^+, or Ca^{2+} across the membrane.

chaperone protein A class of enzymes that help proteins fold into the correct configuration and can refold proteins that have been misfolded or denatured.

character displacement A process in which natural selection favors individuals in a species that use resources not used by other species. This results in evolutionary change leading to species dissimilar in resource use.

character state In cladistics, one of two or more distinguishable forms of a character, such as the presence or absence of teeth in amniote vertebrates.

charging reaction The reaction by which an aminoacyl-tRNA synthetase attaches a specific amino acid to the correct tRNA using energy from ATP.

chelicera, pl. chelicerae The first pair of appendages in horseshoe crabs, sea spiders, and arachnids—the chelicerates, a group of arthropods. Chelicerae usually take the form of pincers or fangs.

chemical synapse A close association that allows chemical communication between neurons. A chemical signal (neurotransmitter) released by the first neuron binds to receptors in the membrane of the second neurons.

chemiosmosis The mechanism by which ATP is generated in mitochondria and chloroplasts; energetic electrons excited by light (in chloroplasts) or extracted by oxidation in the Krebs cycle (in mitochondria) are used to drive proton pumps, creating a proton concentration gradient; when protons subsequently flow back across the membrane, they pass through channels that couple their movement to the synthesis of ATP.

chiasma An X-shaped figure that can be seen in the light microscope during meiosis; evidence of crossing over, where two chromatids have exchanged parts; chiasmata move to the ends of the chromosome arms as the homologues separate.

chitin A tough, resistant, nitrogen-containing polysaccharide that forms the cell walls of certain fungi, the exoskeleton of arthropods, and the epidermal cuticle of other surface structures of certain other invertebrates.

chlorophyll The primary type of light-absorbing pigment in photosynthesis. Chlorophyll *a* absorbs light in the violet-blue and the red ranges of the visible light spectrum; chlorophyll *b* is an accessory pigment to chlorophyll *a*, absorbing light in the blue and red-orange ranges. Neither pigment absorbs light in the green range, 500–600 nm.

chloroplast A cell-like organelle present in algae and plants that contains chlorophyll (and usually other pigments) and carries out photosynthesis.

choanocyte A specialized flagellated cell found in sponges; choanocytes line the body interior.

chorion The outer member of the double membrane that surrounds the embryo of reptiles, birds, and mammals; in placental mammals, it contributes to the structure of the placenta.

chorionic villi sampling A technique in which fetal cells are sampled from the chorion of the placenta rather than from the amniotic fluid; this less invasive technique can be used earlier in pregnancy than amniocentesis.

chromatid One of the two daughter strands of a duplicated chromosome that is joined by a single centromere.

chromatin The complex of DNA and proteins of which eukaryotic chromosomes are composed; chromatin is highly uncoiled and diffuse in interphase nuclei, condensing to form the visible chromosomes in prophase.

chromatin-remodeling complex A large protein complex that has been found to modify histones and DNA and that can change the structure of chromatin, moving or transferring nucleosomes.

chromosomal mutation Any mutation that affects chromosome structure.

chromosome The vehicle by which hereditary information is physically transmitted from one generation to the next; in a bacterium, the chromosome consists of a single naked circle of DNA; in eukaryotes, each chromosome consists of a single linear DNA molecule and associated proteins.

chromosomal theory of inheritance The theory stating that hereditary traits are carried on chromosomes.

cilium A short cellular projection from the surface of a eukaryotic cell, having the same internal structure of microtubules in a 9 + 2 arrangement as seen in a flagellum.

circadian rhythm An endogenous cyclical rhythm that oscillates on a daily (24-hour) basis.

circulatory system A network of vessels in coelomate animals that carries fluids to and from different areas of the body.

cisterna A small collecting vessel that pinches off from the end of a Golgi body to form a transport vesicle that moves materials through the cytoplasm.

cisternal space The inner region of a membrane-bounded structure. Usually used to describe the interior of the endoplasmic reticulum; also called the *lumen*.

clade A taxonomic group composed of an ancestor and all its descendents.

cladistics A taxonomic technique used for creating hierarchies of organisms that represent true phylogenetic relationship and descent.

class A taxonomic category between phyla and orders. A class contains one or more orders, and belongs to a particular phylum.

classical conditioning The repeated presentation of a stimulus in association with a response that causes the brain to form an association between the stimulus and the response, even if they have never been associated before.

clathrin A protein located just inside the plasma membrane in eukaryotic cells, in indentations called clathrin-coated pits.

cleavage In vertebrates, a rapid series of successive cell divisions of a fertilized egg, forming a hollow sphere of cells, the blastula.

cleavage furrow The constriction that forms during cytokinesis in animal cells that is responsible for dividing the cell into two daughter cells.

climax vegetation Vegetation encountered in a self-perpetuating community of plants that has proceeded through all the stages of succession and stabilized.

cloaca In some animals, the common exit chamber from the digestive, reproductive, and urinary system; in others, the cloaca may also serve as a respiratory duct.

clone-by-clone sequencing A method of genome sequencing in which a physical map is constructed first, followed by sequencing of fragments and identifying overlap regions.

clonal selection Amplification of a clone of immune cells initiated by antigen recognition.

cloning Producing a cell line or culture all of whose members contain identical copies of a particular nucleotide sequence; an essential element in genetic engineering.

closed circulatory system A circulatory system in which the blood is physically separated from other body fluids.

coacervate A spherical aggregation of lipid molecules in water, held together by hydrophobic forces.

coactivator A protein that functions to link transcriptional activators to the transcription complex consisting of RNA polymerase II and general transcription factors.

cochlea In terrestrial vertebrates, a tubular cavity of the inner ear containing the essential organs for hearing.

coding strand The strand of a DNA duplex that is the same as the RNA encoded by a gene. This strand is not used as a template in transcription, it is complementary to the template.

codominance Describes a case in which two or more alleles of a gene are each dominant to other alleles but not to each other. The phenotype of a heterozygote for codominant alleles exhibit characteristics of each of the homozygous forms. For example, in human blood types, a cross between an AA individual and a BB individual yields AB individuals.

codon The basic unit of the genetic code; a sequence of three adjacent nucleotides in DNA or mRNA that codes for one amino acid.

coelom In animals, a fluid-filled body cavity that develops entirely within the mesoderm.

coenzyme A nonprotein organic molecule such as NAD that plays an accessory role in enzyme-catalyzed processes, often by acting as a donor or acceptor of electrons.

coevolution The simultaneous development of adaptations in two or more populations, species, or other categories that interact so closely that each is a strong selective force on the other.

cofactor One or more nonprotein components required by enzymes in order to function; many cofactors are metal ions, others are organic coenzymes.

cohesin A protein complex that holds sister chromatids together during cell division. The loss of cohesins at the centromere allow the anaphase movement of chromosomes.

collenchyma cell In plants, the cells that form a supporting tissue called collenchyma; often found in regions of primary growth in stems and in some leaves.

colloblast A specialized type of cell found in members of the animal phylum Ctenophora (comb jellies) that bursts on contact with zooplankton, releasing an adhesive substance to help capture this prey.

colonial flagellate hypothesis The proposal first put forth by Haeckel that metazoans descended from colonial protists; supported by the similarity of sponges to choanoflagellate protists.

commensalism A relationship in which one individual lives close to or on another and benefits, and the host is unaffected; a kind of symbiosis.

community All of the species inhabiting a common environment and interacting with one another.

companion cell A specialized parenchyma cell that is associated with each sieve-tube member in the phloem of a plant.

competitive exclusion The hypothesis that two species with identical ecological requirements cannot exist in the same locality indefinitely, and that the more efficient of the two in utilizing the available scarce resources will exclude the other; also known as Gause's principle.

competitive inhibitor An inhibitor that binds to the same active site as an enzyme's substrate, thereby competing with the substrate.

complementary Describes genetic information in which each nucleotide base has a complementary partner with which it forms a base-pair.

complementary DNA (cDNA) A DNA copy of an mRNA transcript; produced by the action of the enzyme reverse transcriptase.

complement system The chemical defense of a vertebrate body that consists of a battery of proteins that become activated by the walls of bacteria and fungi.

complete digestive system A digestive system that has both a mouth and an anus, allowing unidirectional flow of ingested food.

compound eye An organ of sight in many arthropods composed of many independent visual units called ommatidia.

concentration gradient A difference in concentration of a substance from one location to another, often across a membrane.

condensin A protein complex involved in condensation of chromosomes during mitosis and meiosis.

cone (1) In plants, the reproductive structure of a conifer. (2) In vertebrates, a type of light-sensitive neuron in the retina concerned with the perception of color and with the most acute discrimination of detail.

conidia An asexually produced fungal spore.

conjugation Temporary union of two unicellular organisms, during which genetic material is transferred from one cell to the other; occurs in bacteria, protists, and certain algae and fungi.

consensus sequence In genome sequencing, the overall sequence that is consistent with the sequences of individual fragments; computer programs are used to compare sequences and generate a consensus sequence.

conservation of synteny The preservation over evolutionary time of arrangements of DNA segments in related species.

contig A contiguous segment of DNA assembled by analyzing sequence overlaps from smaller fragments.

continuous variation Variation in a trait that occurs along a continuum, such as the trait of height in human beings; often occurs when a trait is determined by more than one gene.

contractile vacuole In protists and some animals, a clear fluid-filled vacuole that takes up water from within the cell and then contracts, releasing it to the outside through a pore in a cyclical manner; functions primarily in osmoregulation and excretion.

conus arteriosus The anteriormost chamber of the embryonic heart in vertebrate animals.

convergent evolution The independent development of similar structures in organisms that are not directly related; often found in organisms living in similar environments.

cork cambium The lateral meristem that forms the periderm, producing cork (phellem) toward the surface (outside) of the plant and phelloderm toward the inside.

cornea The transparent outer layer of the vertebrate eye.

corolla The petals, collectively; usually the conspicuously colored flower whorl.

corpus callosum The band of nerve fibers that connects the two hemispheres of the cerebrum in humans and other primates.

corpus luteum A structure that develops from a ruptured follicle in the ovary after ovulation.

cortex The outer layer of a structure; in animals, the outer, as opposed to the inner, part of an organ; in vascular plants, the primary ground tissue of a stem or root.

cotyledon A seed leaf that generally stores food in dicots or absorbs it in monocots, providing nourishment used during seed germination.

crassulacean acid metabolism (CAM) A mode of carbon dioxide fixation by which CO_2 enters open leaf stomata at night and is used in photosynthesis during the day, when stomata are closed to prevent water loss.

crista A folded extension of the inner membrane of a mitochondrion. Mitochondria contain numerous cristae.

cross-current flow In bird lungs, the latticework of capillaries arranged across the air flow, at a 90° angle.

crossing over In meiosis, the exchange of corresponding chromatid segments between homologous chromosomes; responsible for genetic recombination between homologous chromosomes.

ctenidia Respiratory gills of mollusks; they consist of a system of filamentous projections of the mantle that are rich in blood vessels.

cuticle A waxy or fatty, noncellular layer (formed of a substance called cutin) on the outer wall of epidermal cells.

cutin In plants, a fatty layer produced by the epidermis that forms the cuticle on the outside surface.

cyanobacteria A group of photosynthetic bacteria, sometimes called the "blue-green algae," that contain the chlorophyll pigments most abundant in plants and algae, as well as other pigments.

cyclic AMP (cAMP) A form of adenosine monophosphate (AMP) in which the atoms of the phosphate group form a ring; found in almost all organisms, cAMP functions as an intracellular second messenger that regulates a diverse array of metabolic activities.

cyclic photophosphorylation Reactions that begin with the absorption of light by reaction center chlorophyll that excites an electron. The excited electron returns to the photosystem, generating ATP by chemiosmosis in the process. This is found in the single bacterial photosystem, and can occur in plants in photosystem I.

cyclin Any of a number of proteins that are produced in synchrony with the cell cycle and combine with certain protein kinases, the cyclin-dependent kinases, at certain points during cell division.

cyclin-dependent kinase (Cdk) Any of a group of protein kinase enzymes that control progress through the cell cycle. These enzymes are only active when complexed with cyclin. The cdc2 protein, produced by the *cdc2* gene, was the first Cdk enzyme discovered.

cytochrome Any of several iron-containing protein pigments that serve as electron carriers in transport chains of photosynthesis and cellular respiration.

cytochrome *b6–f* complex A proton pump found in the thylakoid membrane. This complex uses energy from excited electrons to pump protons from the stroma into the thylakoid compartment.

cytokinesis Division of the cytoplasm of a cell after nuclear division.

cytokine Signaling molecules secreted by immune cells that affect other immune cells.

cytoplasm The material within a cell, excluding the nucleus; the protoplasm.

cytoskeleton A network of protein microfilaments and microtubules within the cytoplasm of a eukaryotic cell that maintains the shape of the cell, anchors its organelles, and is involved in animal cell motility.

cytosol The fluid portion of the cytoplasm; it contains dissolved organic molecules and ions.

cytotoxic T cell A special T cell activated during cell-mediated immune response that recognizes and destroys infected body cells.

D

deamination The removal of an amino group; part of the degradation of proteins into compounds that can enter the Krebs cycle.

deductive reasoning The logical application of general principles to predict a specific result. In science, deductive reasoning is used to test the validity of general ideas.

dehydration reaction A type of chemical reaction in which two molecules join to form one larger molecule, simultaneously splitting out a molecule of water; one molecule is stripped of a hydrogen atom, and another is stripped of a hydroxyl group (—OH), resulting in the joining of the two molecules, while the H and —OH released may combine to form a water molecule.

dehydrogenation Chemical reaction involving the loss of a hydrogen atom. This is an oxidation that combines loss of an electron with loss of a proton.

deletion A mutation in which a portion of a chromosome is lost; if too much information is lost, the deletion can be fatal.

demography The properties of the rate of growth and the age structure of populations.

denaturation The loss of the native configuration of a protein or nucleic acid as a result of excessive heat, extremes of pH, chemical modification, or changes in solvent ionic strength or polarity that disrupt hydrophobic interactions; usually accompanied by loss of biological activity.

dendrite A process extending from the cell body of a neuron, typically branched, that conducts impulses toward the cell body.

deoxyribonucleic acid (DNA) The genetic material of all organisms; composed of two complementary chains of nucleotides wound in a double helix.

dephosphorylation The removal of a phosphate group, usually by a phosphatase enzyme. Many proteins can be activated or inactivated by dephosphorylation.

depolarization The movement of ions across a plasma membrane that locally wipes out an electrical potential difference.

derived character A characteristic used in taxonomic analysis representing a departure from the primitive form.

dermal tissue In multicellular organisms, a type of tissue that forms the outer layer of the body and is in contact with the environment; it has a protective function.

desmosome A type of anchoring junction that links adjacent cells by connecting their cytoskeletons with cadherin proteins.

derepression Seen in anabolic operons where the operon that encodes the enzymes for a biochemical pathway is repressed in the presence of the end product of the pathway and derepressed in the absence of the end product. This allows production of the enzymes only when they are necessary.

determinate development A type of development in animals in which each embryonic cell has a predetermined fate in terms of what kind of tissue it will form in the adult.

deuterostome Any member of a grouping of bilaterally symmetrical animals in which the anus develops first and the mouth second; echinoderms and vertebrates are deuterostome animals.

diacylglycerol (DAG) A second messenger that is released, along with inositol-1,4,5-trisphosphate (IP_3), when phospholipase C cleaves PIP_2. DAG can have a variety of cellular effects through activation of protein kinases.

diaphragm (1) In mammals, a sheet of muscle tissue that separates the abdominal and thoracic cavities and functions in breathing. (2) A contraceptive device used to block the entrance to the uterus temporarily and thus prevent sperm from entering during sexual intercourse.

diapsid Any of a group of reptiles that have two pairs of temporal openings in the skull, one lateral and one more dorsal; one lineage of this group gave rise to dinosaurs, modern reptiles, and birds.

diastolic pressure In the measurement of human blood pressure, the minimum pressure between heartbeats (repolarization of the ventricles). *Compare with* systolic pressure.

dicer An enzyme that generates small RNA molecules in a cell by chopping up double-stranded RNAs; dicer produces miRNAs and siRNAs.

dicot Short for dicotyledon; a class of flowering plants generally characterized as having two cotyledons, net-veined leaves, and flower parts usually in fours or fives.

dideoxynucleotide A nucleotide lacking —OH groups at both the 2′ and 3′ positions; used as a chain terminator in the enzymatic sequencing of DNA.

differentiation A developmental process by which a relatively unspecialized cell undergoes a progressive change to a more specialized form or function.

diffusion The net movement of dissolved molecules or other particles from a region where they are more concentrated to a region where they are less concentrated.

dihybrid An individual heterozygous at two different loci; for example *A/a B/b*.

dihybrid cross A single genetic cross involving two different traits, such as flower color and plant height.

dikaryotic In fungi, having pairs of nuclei within each cell.

dioecious Having the male and female elements on different individuals.

diploid Having two sets of chromosomes (2*n*); in animals, twice the number characteristic of gametes; in plants, the chromosome number characteristic of the sporophyte generation; in contrast to haploid (*n*).

directional selection A form of selection in which selection acts to eliminate one extreme from an array of phenotypes.

disaccharide A carbohydrate formed of two simple sugar molecules bonded covalently.

disruptive selection A form of selection in which selection acts to eliminate rather than favor the intermediate type.

dissociation In proteins, the reversible separation of protein subunits from a quaternary structure without altering their tertiary structure. Also refers to the dissolving of ionic compounds in water.

disassortative mating A type of nonrandom mating in which phenotypically different individuals mate more frequently.

diurnal Active during the day.

DNA-binding motif A region found in a regulatory protein that is capable of binding to a specific base sequence in DNA; a critical part of the protein's DNA-binding domain.

DNA fingerprinting An identification technique that makes use of a variety of molecular techniques to identify differences in the DNA of individuals.

DNA gyrase A topoisomerase involved in DNA replication; it relieves the torsional strain caused by unwinding the DNA strands.

DNA library A collection of DNAs in a vector (a plasmid, phage, or artificial chromosome) that taken together represent a complex mixture of DNAs, such as the entire genome, or the cDNAs made from all of the mRNA in a specific cell type.

DNA ligase The enzyme responsible for formation of phosphodiester bonds between adjacent nucleotides in DNA.

DNA microarray An array of DNA fragments on a microscope slide or silicon chip, used in hybridization experiments with labeled mRNA or DNA to identify active and inactive genes, or the presence or absence of particular sequences.

DNA polymerase A class of enzymes that all synthesize DNA from a preexisting template. All synthesize only in the 5′-to-3′ direction, and require a primer to extend.

DNA vaccine A type of vaccine that uses DNA from a virus or bacterium that stimulates the cellular immune response.

domain (1) A distinct modular region of a protein that serves a particular function in the action of the protein, such as a regulatory domain or a DNA-binding domain. (2) In taxonomy, the level higher than kingdom. The three domains currently recognized are Bacteria, Archaea, and Eukarya.

Domain Archaea In the three-domain system of taxonomy, the group that contains only the Archaea, a highly diverse group of unicellular prokaryotes.

Domain Bacteria In the three-domain system of taxonomy, the group that contains only the Bacteria, a vast group of unicellular prokaryotes.

Domain Eukarya In the three-domain system of taxonomy, the group that contains eukaryotic organisms including protists, fungi, plants, and animals.

dominant An allele that is expressed when present in either the heterozygous or the homozygous condition.

dosage compensation A phenomenon by which the expression of genes carried on sex chromosomes is kept the same in males and females, despite a different number of sex chromosomes. In mammals, inactivation of one of the X chromosomes in female cells accomplishes dosage compensation.

double fertilization The fusion of the egg and sperm (resulting in a 2n fertilized egg, the zygote) and the simultaneous fusion of the second male gamete with the polar nuclei (resulting in a primary endosperm nucleus, which is often triploid, 3n); a unique characteristic of all angiosperms.

double helix The structure of DNA, in which two complementary polynucleotide strands coil around a common helical axis.

duodenum In vertebrates, the upper portion of the small intestine.

duplication A mutation in which a portion of a chromosome is duplicated; if the duplicated region does not lie within a gene, the duplication may have no effect.

E

ecdysis Shedding of outer, cuticular layer; molting, as in insects or crustaceans.

ecdysone Molting hormone of arthropods, which triggers when ecdysis occurs.

ecology The study of interactions of organisms with one another and with their physical environment.

ecosystem A major interacting system that includes organisms and their nonliving environment.

ecotype A locally adapted variant of an organism; differing genetically from other ecotypes.

ectoderm One of the three embryonic germ layers of early vertebrate embryos; ectoderm gives rise to the outer epithelium of the body (skin, hair, nails) and to the nerve tissue, including the sense organs, brain, and spinal cord.

ectomycorrhizae Externally developing mycorrhizae that do not penetrate the cells they surround.

ectotherms Animals such as reptiles, fish, or amphibians, whose body temperature is regulated by their behavior or by their surroundings.

electronegativity A property of atomic nuclei that refers to the affinity of the nuclei for valence electrons; a nucleus that is more electronegative has a greater pull on electrons than one that is less electronegative.

electron transport chain The passage of energetic electrons through a series of membrane-associated electron-carrier molecules to proton pumps embedded within mitochondrial or chloroplast membranes. *See* chemiosmosis.

elongation factor (Ef-Tu) In protein synthesis in *E. coli*, a factor that binds to GTP and to a charged tRNA to accomplish binding of the charged tRNA to the A site of the ribosome, so that elongation of the polypeptide chain can occur.

embryo A multicellular developmental stage that follows cell division of the zygote.

embryonic stem cell (ES cell) A stem cell derived from an early embryo that can develop into different adult tissues and give rise to an adult organism when injected into a blastocyst.

emergent properties Novel properties arising from the way in which components interact. Emergent properties often cannot be deduced solely from knowledge of the individual components.

emerging virus Any virus that originates in one organism but then passes to another; usually refers to transmission to humans.

endergonic Describes a chemical reaction in which the products contain more energy than the reactants, so that free energy must be put into the reaction from an outside source to allow it to proceed.

endocrine gland Ductless gland that secretes hormones into the extracellular spaces, from which they diffuse into the circulatory system.

endocytosis The uptake of material into cells by inclusion within an invagination of the plasma membrane; the uptake of solid material is phagocytosis, and that of dissolved material is pinocytosis.

endoderm One of the three embryonic germ layers of early vertebrate embryos, destined to give rise to the epithelium that lines internal structures and most of the digestive and respiratory tracts.

endodermis In vascular plants, a layer of cells forming the innermost layer of the cortex in roots and some stems.

endomembrane system A system of connected membranous compartments found in eukaryotic cells.

endometrium The lining of the uterus in mammals; thickens in response to secretion of estrogens and progesterone and is sloughed off in menstruation.

endomycorrhizae Mycorrhizae that develop within cells.

endonuclease An enzyme capable of cleaving phosphodiester bonds between nucleotides located internally in a DNA strand.

endoplasmic reticulum (ER) Internal membrane system that forms a netlike array of channels and interconnections within the cytoplasm of eukaryotic cells. The ER is divided into rough (RER) and smooth (SER) compartments.

endorphin One of a group of small neuropeptides produced by the vertebrate brain; like morphine, endorphins modulate pain perception.

endosperm A storage tissue characteristic of the seeds of angiosperms, which develops from the union of a male nucleus and the polar nuclei of the embryo sac. The endosperm is digested by the growing sporophyte either before maturation of the seed or during its germination.

endospore A highly resistant, thick-walled bacterial spore that can survive harsh environmental stress, such as heat or dessication, and then germinate when conditions become favorable.

endosymbiosis Theory that proposes that eukaryotic cells evolved from a symbiosis between different species of prokaryotes.

endotherm An animal capable of maintaining a constant body temperature. *See* homeotherm.

energy level A discrete level, or quantum, of energy that an electron in an atom possesses. To change energy levels, an electron must absorb or release energy.

enhancer A site of regulatory protein binding on the DNA molecule distant from the promoter and start site for a gene's transcription.

enthalpy In a chemical reaction, the energy contained in the chemical bonds of the molecule, symbolized as *H*; in a cellular reaction, the free energy is equal to the enthalpy of the reactant molecules in the reaction.

entropy A measure of the randomness or disorder of a system; a measure of how much energy in a system has become so dispersed (usually as evenly distributed heat) that it is no longer available to do work.

enzyme A protein that is capable of speeding up specific chemical reactions by lowering the required activation energy.

enzyme–substrate complex The complex formed when an enzyme binds with its substrate. This complex often has an altered configuration compared with the nonbound enzyme.

epicotyl The region just above where the cotyledons are attached.

epidermal cell In plants, a cell that collectively forms the outermost layer of the primary plant body; includes specialized cells such as trichomes and guard cells.

epidermis The outermost layers of cells; in plants, the exterior primary tissue of leaves, young stems, and roots; in vertebrates, the nonvascular external layer of skin, of ectodermal origin; in invertebrates, a single layer of ectodermal epithelium.

epididymis A sperm storage vessel; a coiled part of the sperm duct that lies near the testis.

epistasis Interaction between two nonallelic genes in which one of them modifies the phenotypic expression of the other.

epithelium In animals, a type of tissue that covers an exposed surface or lines a tube or cavity.

equilibrium A stable condition; the point at which a chemical reaction proceeds as rapidly in the reverse direction as it does in the forward direction, so that there is no further net change in the concentrations of products or reactants. In ecology, a stable condition that resists change and fairly quickly returns to its original state if disturbed by humans or natural events.

erythrocyte Red blood cell, the carrier of hemoglobin.

erythropoiesis The manufacture of blood cells in the bone marrow.

E site In a ribosome, the exit site that binds to the tRNA that carried the previous amino acid added to the polypeptide chain.

estrus The period of maximum female sexual receptivity, associated with ovulation of the egg.

ethology The study of patterns of animal behavior in nature.

euchromatin That portion of a eukaryotic chromosome that is transcribed into mRNA; contains active genes that are not tightly condensed during interphase.

eukaryote A cell characterized by membrane-bounded organelles, most notably the nucleus, and one that possesses chromosomes whose DNA is associated with proteins; an organism composed of such cells.

eutherian A placental mammal.

eutrophic Refers to a lake in which an abundant supply of minerals and organic matter exists.

evolution Genetic change in a population of organisms; in general, evolution leads to progressive change from simple to complex.

excision repair A nonspecific mechanism to repair damage to DNA during synthesis. The damaged or mismatched region is excised, and DNA polymerase replaces the region removed.

exergonic Describes a chemical reaction in which the products contain less free energy than the reactants, so that free energy is released in the reaction.

exhalant siphon In bivalve mollusks, the siphon through which outgoing water leaves the body.

exocrine gland A type of gland that releases its secretion through a duct, such as a digestive gland or a sweat gland.

exocytosis A type of bulk transport out of cells in which a vacuole fuses with the plasma membrane, discharging the vacuole's contents to the outside.

exon A segment of DNA that is both transcribed into RNA and translated into protein. *See* intron.

exonuclease An enzyme capable of cutting phosphodiester bonds between nucleotides located at an end of a DNA strand. This allows sequential removal of nucleotides from the end of DNA.

exoskeleton An external skeleton, as in arthropods.

experiment A test of one or more hypotheses. Hypotheses make contrasting predictions that can be tested experimentally in control and test experiments where a single variable is altered.

expressed sequence tag (EST) A short sequence of a cDNA that unambiguously identifies the cDNA.

expression vector A type of vector (plasmid or phage) that contains the sequences necessary to drive expression of inserted DNA in a specific cell type.

exteroceptor A receptor that is excited by stimuli from the external world.

extremophile An archaean organism that lives in extreme environments; different archaean species may live in hot springs (thermophiles), highly saline environments (halophiles), highly acidic or basic environments, or under high pressure at the bottom of oceans.

F

5′ cap In eukaryotes, a structure added to the 5′ end of an mRNA consisting of methylated GTP attached by a 5′ to 5′ bond. The cap protects this end from degradation and is involved in the initiation of translation.

facilitated diffusion Carrier-assisted diffusion of molecules across a cellular membrane through specific channels from a region of higher concentration to one of lower concentration; the process is driven by the concentration gradient and does not require cellular energy from ATP.

family A taxonomic grouping of similar species above the level of genus.

fat A molecule composed of glycerol and three fatty acid molecules.

feedback inhibition Control mechanism whereby an increase in the concentration of some molecules inhibits the synthesis of that molecule.

fermentation The enzyme-catalyzed extraction of energy from organic compounds without the involvement of oxygen.

fertilization The fusion of two haploid gamete nuclei to form a diploid zygote nucleus.

fibroblast A flat, irregularly branching cell of connective tissue that secretes structurally strong proteins into the matrix between the cells.

first filial (F₁) generation The offspring resulting from a cross between a parental generation (P); in experimental crosses, these parents usually have different phenotypes.

First Law of Thermodynamics Energy cannot be created or destroyed, but can only undergo conversion from one form to another; thus, the amount of energy in the universe is unchangeable.

fitness The genetic contribution of an individual to succeeding generations. relative fitness refers to the fitness of an individual relative to other individuals in a population.

fixed action pattern A stereotyped animal behavior response, thought by ethologists to be based on programmed neural circuits.

flagellin The protein composing bacterial flagella, which allow a cell to move through an aqueous environment.

flagellum A long, threadlike structure protruding from the surface of a cell and used in locomotion.

flame cell A specialized cell found in the network of tubules inside flatworms that assists in water regulation and some waste excretion.

flavin adenine dinucleotide (FAD, FADH₂) A cofactor that acts as a soluble (not membrane-bound) electron carrier (can be reversibly oxidized and reduced).

fluorescent in situ hybridization (FISH) A cytological method used to find specific DNA sequences on chromosomes with a specific fluorescently labeled probe.

food security Having access to sufficient, safe food to avoid malnutrition and starvation; a global human issue.

foraging behavior A collective term for the many complex, evolved behaviors that influence what an animal eats and how the food is obtained.

founder effect The effect by which rare alleles and combinations of alleles may be enhanced in new populations.

fovea A small depression in the center of the retina with a high concentration of cones; the area of sharpest vision.

frameshift mutation A mutation in which a base is added or deleted from the DNA sequence. These changes alter the reading frame downstream of the mutation.

free energy Energy available to do work.

free radical An ionized atom with one or more unpaired electrons, resulting from electrons that have been energized by ionizing radiation being ejected from the atom; free radicals react violently with other molecules, such as DNA, causing damage by mutation.

frequency-dependent selection A type of selection that depends on how frequently or infrequently a phenotype occurs in a population.

fruit In angiosperms, a mature, ripened ovary (or group of ovaries), containing the seeds.

functional genomics The study of the function of genes and their products, beyond simply ascertaining gene sequences.

functional group A molecular group attached to a hydrocarbon that confers chemical properties or reactivities. Examples include hydroxyl (—OH), carboxylic acid (—COOH) and amino groups (—NH₂).

fundamental niche Also referred to as the hypothetical niche, this is the entire niche an organism could fill if there were no other interacting factors (such as competition or predation).

G

G₀ phase The stage of the cell cycle occupied by cells that are not actively dividing.

G₁ phase The phase of the cell cycle after cytokinesis and before DNA replication called the first "gap" phase. This phase is the primary growth phase of a cell.

G₁/S checkpoint The primary control point at which a cell "decides" whether or not to divide. Also called START and the restriction point.

G₂ phase The phase of the cell cycle between DNA replication and mitosis called the second "gap" phase. During this phase, the cell prepares for mitosis.

G₂/M checkpoint The second cell-division control point, at which division can be delayed if DNA has not been properly replicated or is damaged.

gametangium, pl. gametangia A cell or organ in which gametes are formed.

gamete A haploid reproductive cell.

gametocytes Cells in the malarial sporozoite life cycle capable of giving rise to gametes when in the correct host.

gametophyte In plants, the haploid (n), gamete-producing generation, which alternates with the diploid ($2n$) sporophyte.

ganglion, pl. ganglia An aggregation of nerve cell bodies; in invertebrates, ganglia are the integrative centers; in vertebrates, the term is restricted to aggregations of nerve cell bodies located outside the central nervous system.

gap gene Any of certain genes in *Drosophila* development that divide the embryo into large blocks in the process of segmentation; *hunchback* is a gap gene.

gap junction A junction between adjacent animal cells that allows the passage of materials between the cells.

gastrodermis In eumetazoan animals, the layer of digestive tissue that develops from the endoderm.

gastrula In vertebrates, the embryonic stage in which the blastula with its single layer of cells turns into a three-layered embryo made up of ectoderm, mesoderm, and endoderm.

gastrulation Developmental process that converts blastula into embryo with three embryonic germ layers: endoderm, mesoderm, and ectoderm. Involves massive cell migration to convert the hollow structure into a three-layered structure.

gene The basic unit of heredity; a sequence of DNA nucleotides on a chromosome that encodes a protein, tRNA, or rRNA molecule, or regulates the transcription of such a sequence.

gene conversion Alteration of one homologous chromosome by the cell's error-detection and repair system to make it resemble the sequence on the other homologue.

gene expression The conversion of the genotype into the phenotype; the process by which DNA is transcribed into RNA, which is then translated into a protein product.

gene pool All the alleles present in a species.

gene-for-gene hypothesis A plant defense mechanism in which a specific protein encoded by a viral, bacterial, or fungal pathogen binds to a protein encoded by a plant gene and triggers a defense response in the plant.

general transcription factor Any of a group of transcription factors that are required for formation of an initiation complex by RNA polymerase II at a promoter. This allows a basal level that can be increased by the action of specific factors.

generalized transduction A form of gene transfer in prokaryotes in which any gene can be transferred between cells. This uses a lytic bacteriophage as a carrier where the virion is accidentally packaged with host DNA.

genetic counseling The process of evaluating the risk of genetic defects occurring in offspring, testing for these defects in unborn children, and providing the parents with information about these risks and conditions.

genetic drift Random fluctuation in allele frequencies over time by chance.

genetic map An abstract map that places the relative location of genes on a chromosome based on recombination frequency.

genome The entire DNA sequence of an organism.

genomic imprinting Describes an exception to Mendelian genetics in some mammals in which the phenotype caused by an allele is exhibited when the allele comes from one parent, but not from the other.

genomic library A DNA library that contains a representation of the entire genome of an organism.

genomics The study of genomes as opposed to individual genes.

genotype The genetic constitution underlying a single trait or set of traits.

genotype frequency A measure of the occurrence of a genotype in a population, expressed as a proportion of the entire population, for example, an occurrence of 0.25 (25%) for a homozygous recessive genotype.

genus, pl. genera A taxonomic group that ranks below a family and above a species.

germination The resumption of growth and development by a spore or seed.

germ layers The three cell layers formed at gastrulation of the embryo that foreshadow the future organization of tissues; the layers, from the outside inward, are the ectoderm, the mesoderm, and the endoderm.

germ-line cells During zygote development, cells that are set aside from the somatic cells and that will eventually undergo meiosis to produce gametes.

gill (1) In aquatic animals, a respiratory organ, usually a thin-walled projection from some part of the external body surface, endowed with a rich capillary bed and having a large surface area. (2) In basidiomycete fungi, the plates on the underside of the cap.

globular protein Proteins with a compact tertiary structure with hydrophobic amino acids mainly in the interior.

glomerular filtrate The fluid that passes out of the capillaries of each glomerulus.

glomerulus A cluster of capillaries enclosed by Bowman's capsule.

glucagon A vertebrate hormone produced in the pancreas that acts to initiate the breakdown of glycogen to glucose subunits.

gluconeogenesis The synthesis of glucose from noncarbohydrates (such as proteins or fats).

glucose A common six-carbon sugar ($C_6H_{12}O_6$); the most common monosaccharide in most organisms.

glucose repression In *E. coli*, the preferential use of glucose even when other sugars are present; transcription of mRNA encoding the enzymes for utilizing the other sugars does not occur.

glycocalyx A "sugar coating" on the surface of a cell resulting from the presence of polysaccharides on glycolipids and glycoproteins embedded in the outer layer of the plasma membrane.

glycogen Animal starch; a complex branched polysaccharide that serves as a food reserve in animals, bacteria, and fungi.

glycolipid Lipid molecule modified within the Golgi complex by having a short sugar chain (polysaccharide) attached.

glycolysis The anaerobic breakdown of glucose; this enzyme-catalyzed process yields two molecules of pyruvate with a net of two molecules of ATP.

glycoprotein Protein molecule modified within the Golgi complex by having a short sugar chain (polysaccharide) attached.

glyoxysome A small cellular organelle or microbody containing enzymes necessary for conversion of fats into carbohydrates.

glyphosate A biodegradable herbicide that works by inhibiting EPSP synthetase, a plant enzyme that makes aromatic amino acids; genetic engineering has allowed crop species to be created that are resistant to glyphosate.

Golgi apparatus (Golgi body) A collection of flattened stacks of membranes in the cytoplasm of eukaryotic cells; functions in collection, packaging, and distribution of molecules synthesized in the cell.

G protein A protein that binds guanosine triphosphate (GTP) and assists in the function of cell-surface receptors. When the receptor binds its signal molecule, the G protein binds GTP and is activated to start a chain of events within the cell.

G protein-coupled receptor (GPCR) A receptor that acts through a heterotrimeric (three component) G protein to activate effector proteins. The effector proteins then function as enzymes to produce second messengers such as cAMP or IP_3.

gradualism The view that species change very slowly in ways that may be imperceptible from one generation to the next but that accumulate and lead to major changes over thousands or millions of years.

Gram stain Staining technique that divides bacteria into gram-negative or gram-positive based on retention of a violet dye. Differences in staining are due to cell wall construction.

granum (pl. grana) A stacked column of flattened, interconnected disks (thylakoids) that are part of the thylakoid membrane system in chloroplasts.

gravitropism Growth response to gravity in plants; formerly called geotropism.

ground meristem The primary meristem, or meristematic tissue, that gives rise to the plant body (except for the epidermis and vascular tissues).

ground tissue In plants, a type of tissue that performs many functions, including support, storage, secretion, and photosynthesis; may consist of many cell types.

growth factor Any of a number of proteins that bind to membrane receptors and initiate intracellular signaling systems that result in cell growth and division.

guard cell In plants, one of a pair of sausage-shaped cells flanking a stoma; the guard cells open and close the stomata.

guttation The exudation of liquid water from leaves due to root pressure.

gymnosperm A seed plant with seeds not enclosed in an ovary; conifers are gymnosperms.

gynoecium The aggregate of carpels in the flower of a seed plant.

H

habitat The environment of an organism; the place where it is usually found.

habituation A form of learning; a diminishing response to a repeated stimulus.

halophyte A plant that is salt-tolerant.

haplodiploidy A phenomenon occurring in certain organisms such as wasps, wherein both haploid (male) and diploid (female) individuals are encountered.

haploid Having only one set of chromosomes (n), in contrast to diploid ($2n$).

haplotype A region of a chromosome that is usually inherited intact, that is, it does not undergo recombination. These are identified based on analysis of SNPs.

Hardy-Weinberg equilibrium A mathematical description of the fact that allele and genotype frequencies remain constant in a random-mating population in the absence of inbreeding, selection, or other evolutionary forces; usually stated: if the frequency of allele a is p and the frequency of allele b is q, then the genotype frequencies after one generation of random mating will always be $p_2 + 2pq + q_2 = 1$.

Haversian canal Narrow channels that run parallel to the length of a bone and contain blood vessels and nerve cells.

heat A measure of the random motion of molecules; the greater the heat, the greater the motion. Heat is one form of kinetic energy.

heat of vaporization The amount of energy required to change 1 g of a substance from a liquid to a gas.

heavy metal Any of the metallic elements with high atomic numbers, such as arsenic, cadmium, lead, etc. Many heavy metals are toxic to animals even in small amounts.

helicase Any of a group of enzymes that unwind the two DNA strands in the double helix to facilitate DNA replication.

helix-turn-helix motif A common DNA-binding motif found in regulatory proteins; it consists of two α-helices linked by a nonhelical segment (the "turn").

helper T cell A class of white blood cells that initiates both the cell-mediated immune response and the humoral immune response; helper T cells are the targets of the AIDS virus (HIV).

hemoglobin A globular protein in vertebrate red blood cells and in the plasma of many invertebrates that carries oxygen and carbon dioxide.

hemopoietic stem cell The cells in bone marrow where blood cells are formed.

hermaphroditism Condition in which an organism has both male and female functional reproductive organs.

heterochromatin The portion of a eukaryotic chromosome that is not transcribed into RNA; remains condensed in interphase and stains intensely in histological preparations.

heterochrony An alteration in the timing of developmental events due to a genetic change; for example, a mutation that delays flowering in plants.

heterokaryotic In fungi, having two or more genetically distinct types of nuclei within the same mycelium.

heterosporous In vascular plants, having spores of two kinds, namely, microspores and megaspores.

heterotroph An organism that cannot derive energy from photosynthesis or inorganic chemicals, and so must feed on other plants and animals, obtaining chemical energy by degrading their organic molecules.

heterozygote advantage The situation in which individuals heterozygous for a trait have a selective advantage over those who are homozygous; an example is sickle cell anemia.

heterozygous Having two different alleles of the same gene; the term is usually applied to one or more specific loci, as in "heterozygous with respect to the W locus" (that is, the genotype is W/w).

Hfr cell An *E. coli* cell that has a high frequency of recombination due to integration of an F plasmid into its genome.

histone One of a group of relatively small, very basic polypeptides, rich in arginine and lysine, forming the core of nucleosomes around which DNA is wrapped in the first stage of chromosome condensation.

histone protein Any of eight proteins with an overall positive charge that associate in a complex. The DNA duplex coils around a core of eight histone proteins, held by its negatively charged phosphate groups, forming a nucleosome.

holoblastic cleavage Process in vertebrate embryos in which the cleavage divisions all occur at the same rate, yielding a uniform cell size in the blastula.

homeobox A sequence of 180 nucleotides located in homeotic genes that produces a 60-amino-acid peptide sequence (the homeodomain) active in transcription factors.

homeodomain motif A special class of helix-turn-helix motifs found in regulatory proteins that control development in eukaryotes.

homeosis A change in the normal spatial pattern of gene expression that can result in homeotic mutants where a wild-type structure develops in the wrong place in or on the organism.

homeostasis The maintenance of a relatively stable internal physiological environment in an organism; usually involves some form of feedback self-regulation.

homeotherm An organism, such as a bird or mammal, capable of maintaining a stable body temperature independent of the environmental temperature. *See* endotherm.

homeotic gene One of a series of "master switch" genes that determine the form of segments developing in the embryo.

hominid Any primate in the human family, Hominidae. *Homo sapiens* is the only living representative.

hominoid Collectively, hominids and apes; the monkeys and hominoids constitute the anthropoid primates.

homokaryotic In fungi, having nuclei with the same genetic makeup within a mycelium.

homologue One of a pair of chromosomes of the same kind located in a diploid cell; one copy of each pair of homologues comes from each gamete that formed the zygote.

homologous (1) Refers to similar structures that have the same evolutionary origin. (2) Refers to a pair of the same kind of chromosome in a diploid cell.

homoplasy In cladistics, a shared character state that has not been inherited from a common ancestor exhibiting that state; may result from convergent evolution or evolutionary reversal. The wings of birds and of bats, which are convergent structures, are examples.

homosporous In some plants, production of only one type of spore rather than differentiated types. *Compare with* heterosporous.

homozygous Being a homozygote, having two identical alleles of the same gene; the term is usually applied to one or more specific loci, as in "homozygous with respect to the W locus" (i.e., the genotype is W/W or w/w).

horizontal gene transfer (HGT) The passing of genes laterally between species; more prevalent very early in the history of life.

hormone A molecule, usually a peptide or steroid, that is produced in one part of an organism and triggers a specific cellular reaction in target tissues and organs some distance away.

host range The range of organisms that can be infected by a particular virus.

***Hox* gene** A group of homeobox-containing genes that control developmental events, usually found organized into clusters of genes. These genes have been conserved in many different multicellular animals, both invertebrates and vertebrates, although the number of clusters changes in lineages, leading to four clusters in vertebrates.

humoral immunity Arm of the adaptive immune system involving B cells that produce soluble antibodies specific for foreign antigens.

humus Partly decayed organic material found in topsoil.

hybridization The mating of unlike parents.

hydration shell A "cloud" of water molecules surrounding a dissolved substance, such as sucrose or Na$^+$ and Cl$^-$ ions.

hydrogen bond A weak association formed with hydrogen in polar covalent bonds. The partially positive hydrogen is attracted to partially negative atoms in polar covalent bonds. In water, oxygen and hydrogen in different water molecules form hydrogen bonds.

hydrolysis reaction A reaction that breaks a bond by the addition of water. This is the reverse of dehydration, a reaction that joins molecules with the loss of water.

hydrophilic Literally translates as "water-loving" and describes substances that are soluble in water. These must be either polar or charged (ions).

hydrophobic Literally translates as "water-fearing" and describes nonpolar substances that are not soluble in water. Nonpolar molecules in water associate with each other and form droplets.

hydrophobic exclusion The tendency of nonpolar molecules to aggregate together when placed in water. Exclusion refers to the action of water in forcing these molecules together.

hydrostatic skeleton The skeleton of most soft-bodied invertebrates that have neither an internal nor an external skeleton. They use the relative incompressibility of the water within their bodies as a kind of skeleton.

hyperosmotic The condition in which a (hyperosmotic) solution has a higher osmotic concentration than that of a second solution. *Compare with* hypoosmotic.

hyperpolarization Above-normal negativity of a cell membrane during its resting potential.

hypersensitive response Plants respond to pathogens by selectively killing plant cells to block the spread of the pathogen.

hypertonic A solution with a higher concentration of solutes than the cell. A cell in a hypertonic solution tends to lose water by osmosis.

hypha, pl. hyphae A filament of a fungus or oomycete; collectively, the hyphae constitute the mycelium.

hypocotyl The region immediately below where the cotyledons are attached.

hypoosmotic The condition in which a (hypoosmotic) solution has a lower osmotic concentration than that of a second solution. *Compare with* hyperosmotic.

hypothalamus A region of the vertebrate brain just below the cerebral hemispheres, under the thalamus; a center of the autonomic nervous system, responsible for the integration and correlation of many neural and endocrine functions.

hypotonic A solution with a lower concentration of solutes than the cell. A cell in a hypotonic solution tends to take in water by osmosis.

I

icosahedron A structure consisting of 20 equilateral triangular facets; this is commonly seen in viruses and forms one kind of viral capsid.

imaginal disk One of about a dozen groups of cells set aside in the abdomen of a larval insect and committed to forming key parts of the adult insect's body.

immune response In vertebrates, a defensive reaction of the body to invasion by a foreign substance or organism. *See* antibody and B cell.

immunoglobulin An antibody molecule.

immunological tolerance Process where immune system learns to not react to self-antigens.

in vitro mutagenesis The ability to create mutations at any site in a cloned gene to examine the mutations' effects on function.

inbreeding The breeding of genetically related plants or animals; inbreeding tends to increase homozygosity.

inclusive fitness Describes the sum of the number of genes directly passed on in an individual's offspring and those genes passed on indirectly by kin (other than offspring) whose existence results from the benefit of the individual's altruism.

incomplete dominance Describes a case in which two or more alleles of a gene do not display clear dominance. The phenotype of a heterozygote is intermediate between the homozygous forms. For example, crossing red-flowered with white-flowered four o'clocks yields pink heterozygotes.

independent assortment In a dihybrid cross, describes the random assortment of alleles for each of the genes. For genes on different chromosomes this results from the random orientations of different homologous pairs during metaphase I of meiosis. For genes on the same chromosome, this occurs when the two loci are far enough apart for roughly equal numbers of odd- and even-numbered multiple crossover events.

indeterminate development A type of development in animals in which the first few embryonic cells are identical daughter cells, any one of which could develop separately into a complete organism; their fate is indeterminate.

inducer exclusion Part of the mechanism of glucose repression in *E. coli* in which the presence of glucose prevents the entry of lactose such that the *lac* operon cannot be induced.

induction (1) Production of enzymes in response to a substrate; a mechanism by which binding of an inducer to a repressor allows transcription of an operon. This is seen in catabolic operons and results in production of enzymes to degrade a compound only when it is available. (2) In embryonic development, the process by which the development of a cell is influenced by interaction with an adjacent cell.

inductive reasoning The logical application of specific observations to make a generalization. In science, inductive reasoning is used to formulate testable hypotheses.

industrial melanism Phrase used to describe the evolutionary process in which initially light-colored organisms become dark as a result of natural selection.

inflammatory response A generalized nonspecific response to infection that acts to clear an infected area of infecting microbes and dead tissue cells so that tissue repair can begin.

inhalant siphon In bivalve mollusks, the siphon through which incoming water enters the body.

inheritance of acquired characteristics Also known as Lamarckism; the theory, now discounted, that individuals genetically pass on to their offspring physical and behavioral changes developed during the individuals' own lifetime.

inhibitor A substance that binds to an enzyme and decreases its activity.

initiation factor One of several proteins involved in the formation of an initiation complex in prokaryote polypeptide synthesis.

initiator tRNA A tRNA molecule involved in the beginning of translation. In prokaryotes, the initiator tRNA is charged with N-formylmethionine ($tRNA^{fMet}$); in eukaryotes, the tRNA is charged simply with methionine.

inorganic phosphate A phosphate molecule that is not a part of an organic molecule; inorganic phosphate groups are added and removed in the formation and breakdown of ATP and in many other cellular reactions.

inositol-1,4,5-trisphosphate (IP$_3$) Second messenger produced by the cleavage of phosphatidylinositol-4,5-bisphosphate.

insertional inactivation Destruction of a gene's function by the insertion of a transposon.

instar A larval developmental stage in insects.

integrin Any of a group of cell-surface proteins involved in adhesion of cells to substrates. Critical to migrating cells moving through the cell matrix in tissues such as connective tissue.

intercalary meristem A type of meristem that arises in stem internodes in some plants, such as corn and horsetails; responsible for elongation of the internodes.

interferon In vertebrates, a protein produced in virus-infected cells that inhibits viral multiplication.

intermembrane space The outer compartment of a mitochondrion that lies between the two membranes.

interneuron (association neuron) A nerve cell found only in the middle of the spinal cord that acts as a functional link between sensory neurons and motor neurons.

internode In plants, the region of a stem between two successive nodes.

interoceptor A receptor that senses information related to the body itself, its internal condition, and its position.

interphase The period between two mitotic or meiotic divisions in which a cell grows and its DNA replicates; includes G_1, S, and G_2 phases.

intracellular receptor A signal receptor that binds a ligand inside a cell, such as the receptors for NO, steroid hormones, vitamin D, and thyroid hormones.

intron Portion of mRNA as transcribed from eukaryotic DNA that is removed by enzymes before the mature mRNA is translated into protein. *See* exon.

inversion A reversal in order of a segment of a chromosome; also, to turn inside out, as in embryogenesis of sponges or discharge of a nematocyst.

ionizing radiation High-energy radiation that is highly mutagenic, producing free radicals that react with DNA; includes X-rays and γ-rays.

isomer One of a group of molecules identical in atomic composition but differing in structural arrangement; for example, glucose and fructose.

isosmotic The condition in which the osmotic concentrations of two solutions are equal, so that no net water movement occurs between them by osmosis.

isotonic A solution having the same concentration of solutes as the cell. A cell in an isotonic solution takes in and loses the same amount of water.

isotope Different forms of the same element with the same number of protons but different numbers of neutrons.

J

jasmonic acid An organic molecule that is part of a plant's wound response; it signals the production of a proteinase inhibitor.

K

karyotype The morphology of the chromosomes of an organism as viewed with a light microscope.

keratin A tough, fibrous protein formed in epidermal tissues and modified into skin, feathers, hair, and hard structures such as horns and nails.

key innovation A newly evolved trait in a species that allows members to use resources or other aspects of the environment that were previously inaccessible.

kidney In vertebrates, the organ that filters the blood to remove nitrogenous wastes and regulates the balance of water and solutes in blood plasma.

kilocalorie Unit describing the amount of heat required to raise the temperature of a kilogram of water by 1°C; sometimes called a Calorie, equivalent to 1000 calories.

kinase cascade A series of protein kinases that phosphorylate each other in succession; a kinase cascade can amplify signals during the signal transduction process.

kinesis Changes in activity level in an animal that are dependent on stimulus intensity. *See* kinetic energy.

kinetic energy The energy of motion.

kinetochore Disk-shaped protein structure within the centromere to which the spindle fibers attach during mitosis or meiosis. *See* centromere.

kingdom The second highest commonly used taxonomic category.

kin selection Selection favoring relatives; an increase in the frequency of related individuals (kin) in a population, leading to an increase in the relative frequency in the population of those alleles shared by members of the kin group.

knockout mice Mice in which a known gene is inactivated ("knocked out") using recombinant DNA and ES cells.

Krebs cycle Another name for the citric acid cycle; also called the tricarboxylic acid (TCA) cycle.

L

labrum The upper lip of insects and crustaceans situated above or in front of the mandibles.

lac **operon** In *E. coli*, the operon containing genes that encode the enzymes to metabolize lactose.

lagging strand The DNA strand that must be synthesized discontinuously because of the 5′-to-3′ directionality of DNA polymerase during replication, and the antiparallel nature of DNA. Compare *leading strand*.

larva A developmental stage that is unlike the adult found in organisms that undergo metamorphosis. Embryos develop into larvae that produce the adult form by metamorphosis.

larynx The voice box; a cartilaginous organ that lies between the pharynx and trachea and is responsible for sound production in vertebrates.

lateral line system A sensory system encountered in fish, through which mechanoreceptors in a line down the side of the fish are sensitive to motion.

lateral meristems In vascular plants, the meristems that give rise to secondary tissue; the vascular cambium and cork cambium.

Law of Independent Assortment Mendel's second law of heredity, stating that genes located on nonhomologous chromosomes assort independently of one another.

Law of Segregation Mendel's first law of heredity, stating that alternative alleles for the same gene segregate from each other in production of gametes.

leading strand The DNA strand that can be synthesized continuously from the origin of replication. Compare *lagging strand*.

leaf primordium, pl. primordia A lateral outgrowth from the apical meristem that will eventually become a leaf.

lenticels Spongy areas in the cork surfaces of stem, roots, and other plant parts that allow interchange of gases between internal tissues and the atmosphere through the periderm.

leucine zipper motif A motif in regulatory proteins in which two different protein subunits associate to form a single DNA-binding site; the proteins are connected by an association between hydrophobic regions containing leucines (the "zipper").

leucoplast In plant cells, a colorless plastid in which starch grains are stored; usually found in cells not exposed to light.

leukocyte A white blood cell; a diverse array of nonhemoglobin-containing blood cells, including phagocytic macrophages and antibody-producing lymphocytes.

lichen Symbiotic association between a fungus and a photosynthetic organism such as a green alga or cyanobacterium.

ligand A signaling molecule that binds to a specific receptor protein, initiating signal transduction in cells.

light-dependent reactions In photosynthesis, the reactions in which light energy is captured and used in production of ATP and NADPH. In plants this involves the action of two linked photosystems.

light-independent reactions In photosynthesis, the reactions of the Calvin cycle in which ATP and NADPH from the light-dependent reactions are used to reduce CO_2 and produce organic compounds such as glucose. This involves the process of carbon fixation, or the conversion of inorganic carbon (CO_2) to organic carbon (ultimately carbohydrates).

lignin A highly branched polymer that makes plant cell walls more rigid; an important component of wood.

limbic system The hypothalamus, together with the network of neurons that link the hypothalamus to some areas of the cerebral cortex. Responsible for many of the most deep-seated drives and emotions of vertebrates, including pain, anger, sex, hunger, thirst, and pleasure.

linked genes Genes that are physically close together and therefore tend to segregate together; recombination occurring between linked genes can be used to produce a map of genetic distance for a chromosome.

linkage disequilibrium Association of alleles for 2 or more loci in a population that is higher than expected by chance.

lipase An enzyme that catalyzes the hydrolysis of fats.

lipid A nonpolar hydrophobic organic molecule that is insoluble in water (which is polar) but dissolves readily in nonpolar organic solvents; includes fats, oils, waxes, steroids, phospholipids, and carotenoids.

lipid bilayer The structure of a cellular membrane, in which two layers of phospholipids spontaneously align so that the hydrophilic head groups are exposed to water, while the hydrophobic fatty acid tails are pointed toward the center of the membrane.

lipopolysaccharide A lipid with a polysaccharide molecule attached; found in the outer membrane layer of gram-negative bacteria; the outer membrane layer protects the cell wall from antibiotic attack.

locus The position on a chromosome where a gene is located.

long interspersed element (LINE) Any of a type of large transposable element found in humans and other primates that contains all the biochemical machinery needed for transposition.

long terminal repeat (LTR) A particular type of retrotransposon that has repeated elements at its ends. These elements make up 8% of the human genome.

loop of Henle In the kidney of birds and mammals, a hairpin-shaped portion of the renal tubule in which water and salt are reabsorbed from the glomerular filtrate by diffusion.

lophophore A horseshoe-shaped crown of ciliated tentacles that surrounds the mouth of certain spiralian animals; seen in the phyla Brachiopoda and Bryozoa.

lumen A term for any bounded opening; for example, the cisternal space of the endoplasmic reticulum of eukaryotic cells, the passage through which blood flows inside a blood vessel, and the passage through which material moves inside the intestine during digestion.

luteal phase The second phase of the female reproductive cycle, during which the mature eggs are released into the fallopian tubes, a process called ovulation.

lymph In animals, a colorless fluid derived from blood by filtration through capillary walls in the tissues.

lymphatic system In animals, an open vascular system that reclaims water that has entered interstitial regions from the bloodstream (lymph); includes the lymph nodes, spleen, thymus, and tonsils.

lymphocyte A type of white blood cell. Lymphocytes are responsible for the immune response; there are two principal classes: B cells and T cells.

lymphokine A regulatory molecule that is secreted by lymphocytes. In the immune response, lymphokines secreted by helper T cells unleash the cell-mediated immune response.

lysis Disintegration of a cell by rupture of its plasma membrane.

lysogenic cycle A viral cycle in which the viral DNA becomes integrated into the host chromosome and is replicated during cell reproduction. Results in vertical rather than horizontal transmission.

lysosome A membrane-bounded vesicle containing digestive enzymes that is produced by the Golgi apparatus in eukaryotic cells.

lytic cycle A viral cycle in which the host cell is killed (lysed) by the virus after viral duplication to release viral particles.

M

macroevolution The creation of new species and the extinction of old ones.

macromolecule An extremely large biological molecule; refers specifically to proteins, nucleic acids, polysaccharides, lipids, and complexes of these.

macronutrients Inorganic chemical elements required in large amounts for plant growth, such as nitrogen, potassium, calcium, phosphorus, magnesium, and sulfur.

macrophage A large phagocytic cell that is able to engulf and digest cellular debris and invading bacteria.

madreporite A sievelike plate on the surface of echinoderms through which water enters the water–vascular system.

MADS **box gene** Any of a family of genes identified by possessing shared motifs that are the predominant homeotic genes of plants; a small number of *MADS* box genes are also found in animals.

major groove The larger of the two grooves in a DNA helix, where the paired nucleotides' hydrogen bonds are accessible; regulatory proteins can recognize and bind to regions in the major groove.

major histocompatibility complex (MHC) A set of protein cell-surface markers anchored in the plasma membrane, which the immune system uses to identify "self." All the cells of a given individual have the same "self" marker, called an MHC protein.

Malpighian tubules Blind tubules opening into the hindgut of terrestrial arthropods; they function as excretory organs.

mandibles In crustaceans, insects, and myriapods, the appendages immediately posterior to the antennae; used to seize, hold, bite, or chew food.

mantle The soft, outermost layer of the body wall in mollusks; the mantle secretes the shell.

map unit Each 1% of recombination frequency between two genetic loci; the unit is termed a centimorgan (cM) or simply a map unit (m.u.).

marsupial A mammal in which the young are born early in their development, sometimes as soon as eight days after fertilization, and are retained in a pouch.

mass extinction A relatively sudden, sharp decline in the number of species; for example, the extinction at the end of the Cretaceous period in which the dinosaurs and a variety of other organisms disappeared.

mass flow hypothesis The overall process by which materials move in the phloem of plants.

mast cells Leukocytes with granules containing molecules that initiate inflammation.

maternal inheritance A mode of uniparental inheritance from the female parent; for example, in humans mitochondria and their genomes are inherited from the mother.

matrix In mitochondria, the solution in the interior space surrounded by the cristae that contains the enzymes and other molecules involved in oxidative respiration; more generally, that part of a tissue within which an organ or process is embedded.

medusa A free-floating, often umbrella-shaped body form found in cnidarian animals, such as jellyfish.

megapascal (MPa) A unit of measure used for pressure in water potential.

megaphyll In plants, a leaf that has several to many veins connecting it to the vascular cylinder of the stem; most plants have megaphylls.

mesoglea A layer of gelatinous material found between the epidermis and gastrodermis of eumetazoans; it contains the muscles in most of these animals.

mesohyl A gelatinous, protein-rich matrix found between the choanocyte layer and the epithelial layer of the body of a sponge; various types of amoeboid cells may occur in the mesohyl.

metacercaria An encysted form of a larval liver fluke, found in muscle tissue of an infected animal; if the muscle is eaten, cysts dissolves in the digestive tract, releasing the flukes into the body of the new host.

methylation The addition of a methyl group to bases (primarily cytosine) in DNA. Cytosine methylation is correlated with DNA that is not expressed.

meiosis I The first round of cell division in meiosis; it is referred to as a "reduction division" because homologous chromosomes separate, and the daughter cells have only the haploid number of chromosomes.

meiosis II The second round of division in meiosis, during which the two haploid cells from meiosis I undergo a mitosis-like division without DNA replication to produce four haploid daughter cells.

membrane receptor A signal receptor present as an integral protein in the cell membrane, such as GPCRs, chemically gated ion channels in neurons, and RTKs.

Mendelian ratio The characteristic dominant-to-recessive phenotypic ratios that Mendel observed in his genetics experiments. For example, the F_2 generation in a monohybrid cross shows a ratio of 3:1; the F_2 generation in a dihybrid cross shows a ratio of 9:3:3:1.

menstruation Periodic sloughing off of the blood-enriched lining of the uterus when pregnancy does not occur.

meristem Undifferentiated plant tissue from which new cells arise.

meroblastic cleavage A type of cleavage in the eggs of reptiles, birds, and some fish. Occurs only on the blastodisc.

mesoderm One of the three embryonic germ layers that form in the gastrula; gives rise to muscle, bone and other connective tissue, the peritoneum, the circulatory system, and most of the excretory and reproductive systems.

mesophyll The photosynthetic parenchyma of a leaf, located within the epidermis.

messenger RNA (mRNA) The RNA transcribed from structural genes; RNA molecules complementary to a portion of one strand of DNA, which are translated by the ribosomes to form protein.

metabolism The sum of all chemical processes occurring within a living cell or organism.

metamorphosis Process in which a marked change in form takes place during postembryonic development as, for example, from tadpole to frog.

metaphase The stage of mitosis or meiosis during which microtubules become organized into a spindle and the chromosomes come to lie in the spindle's equatorial plane.

metastasis The process by which cancer cells move from their point of origin to other locations in the body; also, a population of cancer cells in a secondary location, the result of movement from the primary tumor.

methanogens Obligate, anaerobic archaebacteria that produce methane.

microarray DNA sequences are placed on a microscope slide or chip with a robot. The microarray can then be probed with RNA from specific tissues to identify expressed DNA.

microbody A cellular organelle bounded by a single membrane and containing a variety of enzymes; generally derived from endoplasmic reticulum; includes peroxisomes and glyoxysomes.

microevolution Refers to the evolutionary process itself. Evolution within a species. Also called adaptation.

micronutrient A mineral required in only minute amounts for plant growth, such as iron, chlorine, copper, manganese, zinc, molybdenum, and boron.

microphyll In plants, a leaf that has only one vein connecting it to the vascular cylinder of the stem; the club mosses in particular have microphylls.

micropyle In the ovules of seed plants, an opening in the integuments through which the pollen tube usually enters.

micro-RNA (miRNA) A class of RNAs that are very short and only recently could be detected. *See also* small interfering RNAs (siRNAs).

microtubule In eukaryotic cells, a long, hollow protein cylinder, composed of the protein tubulin; these influence cell shape, move the chromosomes in cell division, and provide the functional internal structure of cilia and flagella.

microvillus Cytoplasmic projection from epithelial cells; microvilli greatly increase the surface area of the small intestine.

middle lamella The layer of intercellular material, rich in pectic compounds, that cements together the primary walls of adjacent plant cells.

mimicry The resemblance in form, color, or behavior of certain organisms (mimics) to other more powerful or more protected ones (models).

miracidium The ciliated first-stage larva inside the egg of the liver fluke; eggs are passed in feces, and if they reach water they may be eaten by a host snail in which they continue their life cycle.

missense mutation A base substitution mutation that results in the alteration of a single amino acid.

mitochondrion The organelle called the powerhouse of the cell. Consists of an outer membrane, an elaborate inner membrane that supports electron transport and chemiosmotic synthesis of ATP, and a soluble matrix containing Krebs cycle enzymes.

mitogen-activated protein (MAP) kinase Any of a class of protein kinases that activate transcription factors to alter gene expression. A mitogen is any molecule that stimulates cell division. MAP kinases are activated by kinase cascades.

mitosis Somatic cell division; nuclear division in which the duplicated chromosomes separate to form two genetically identical daughter nuclei.

molar concentration Concentration expressed as moles of a substance in 1 L of pure water.

mole The weight of a substance in grams that corresponds to the atomic masses of all the component atoms in a molecule of that substance. One mole of a compound always contains 6.023×10^{23} molecules.

molecular clock method In evolutionary theory, the method in which the rate of evolution of a molecule is constant through time.

molecular cloning The isolation and amplification of a specific sequence of DNA.

monocot Short for monocotyledon; flowering plant in which the embryos have only one cotyledon, the floral parts are generally in threes, and the leaves typically are parallel-veined.

monocyte A type of leukocyte that becomes a phagocytic cell (macrophage) after moving into tissues.

monoecious A plant in which the staminate and pistillate flowers are separate, but borne on the same individual.

monomer The smallest chemical subunit of a polymer. The monosaccharide α-glucose is the monomer found in plant starch, a polysaccharide.

monophyletic In phylogenetic classification, a group that includes the most recent common ancestor of the group and all its descendants. A clade is a monophyletic group.

monosaccharide A simple sugar that cannot be decomposed into smaller sugar molecules.

monosomic Describes the condition in which a chromosome has been lost due to nondisjunction during meiosis, producing a diploid embryo with only one of these autosomes.

monotreme An egg-laying mammal.

morphogen A signal molecule produced by an embryonic organizer region that informs surrounding cells of their distance from the organizer, thus determining relative positions of cells during development.

morphogenesis The development of an organism's body form, namely its organs and anatomical features; it may involve apoptosis as well as cell division, differentiation, and changes in cell shape.

morphology The form and structure of an organism.

morula Solid ball of cells in the early stage of embryonic development.

mosaic development A pattern of embryonic development in which initial cells produced by cleavage divisions contain different developmental signals (determinants) from the egg, setting the individual cells on different developmental paths.

motif A substructure in proteins that confers function and can be found in multiple proteins. One example is the helix-turn-helix motif found in a number of proteins that is used to bind to DNA.

motor (efferent) neuron Neuron that transmits nerve impulses from the central nervous system to an effector, which is typically a muscle or gland.

M phase The phase of cell division during which chromosomes are separated. The spindle assembles, binds to the chromosomes, and moves the sister chromatids apart.

M phase-promoting factor (MPF) A Cdk enzyme active at the G_2/M checkpoint.

Müllerian mimicry A phenomenon in which two or more unrelated but protected species resemble one another, thus achieving a kind of group defense.

multidrug-resistant (MDR) strain Any bacterial strain that has become resistant to more than one antibiotic drug; MDR *Staphylococcus* strains, for example, are responsible for many infection deaths.

multienzyme complex An assembly consisting of several enzymes catalyzing different steps in a sequence of reactions. Close proximity of these related enzymes speeds the overall process, making it more efficient.

multigene family A collection of related genes on a single chromosome or on different chromosomes.

muscle fiber A long, cylindrical, multinucleated cell containing numerous myofibrils, which is capable of contraction when stimulated.

mutagen An agent that induces changes in DNA (mutations); includes physical agents that damage DNA and chemicals that alter DNA bases.

mutation A permanent change in a cell's DNA; includes changes in nucleotide sequence, alteration of gene position, gene loss or duplication, and insertion of foreign sequences.

mutualism A symbiotic association in which two (or more) organisms live together, and both members benefit.

mycelium, pl. **mycelia** In fungi, a mass of hyphae.

mycorrhiza, pl. **mycorrhizae** A symbiotic association between fungi and the roots of a plant.

myelin sheath A fatty layer surrounding the long axons of motor neurons in the peripheral nervous system of vertebrates.

myofilament A contractile microfilament, composed largely of actin and myosin, within muscle.

myosin One of the two protein components of microfilaments (the other is actin); a principal component of vertebrate muscle.

N

natural killer cell A cell that does not kill invading microbes, but rather, the cells infected by them.

natural selection The differential reproduction of genotypes; caused by factors in the environment; leads to evolutionary change.

nauplius A larval form characteristic of crustaceans.

negative control A type of control at the level of DNA transcription initiation in which the frequency of initiation is decreased; repressor proteins mediate negative control.

negative feedback A homeostatic control mechanism whereby an increase in some substance or activity inhibits the process leading to the increase; also known as feedback inhibition.

nematocyst A harpoonlike structure found in the cnidocytes of animals in the phylum Cnidaria, which includes the jellyfish among other groups; the nematocyst, when released, stings and helps capture prey.

nephridium, pl. **nephridia** In invertebrates, a tubular excretory structure.

nephrid organ A filtration system of many freshwater invertebrates in which water and waste pass from the body across the membrane into a collecting organ, from which they are expelled to the outside through a pore.

nephron Functional unit of the vertebrate kidney; one of numerous tubules involved in filtration and selective reabsorption of blood; each nephron consists of a Bowman's capsule, an enclosed glomerulus, and a long attached tubule; in humans, called a renal tubule.

nephrostome The funnel-shaped opening that leads to the nephridium, which is the excretory organ of mollusks.

nerve A group or bundle of nerve fibers (axons) with accompanying neurological cells, held together by connective tissue; located in the peripheral nervous system.

nerve cord One of the distinguishing features of chordates, running lengthwise just beneath the embryo's dorsal surface; in vertebrates, differentiates into the brain and spinal cord.

neural crest A special strip of cells that develops just before the neural groove closes over to form the neural tube in embryonic development.

neural groove The long groove formed along the long axis of the embryo by a layer of ectodermal cells.

neural tube The dorsal tube, formed from the neural plate, that differentiates into the brain and spinal cord.

neuroglia Nonconducting nerve cells that are intimately associated with neurons and appear to provide nutritional support.

neuromuscular junction The structure formed when the tips of axons contact (innervate) a muscle fiber.

neuron A nerve cell specialized for signal transmission; includes cell body, dendrites, and axon.

neurotransmitter A chemical released at the axon terminal of a neuron that travels across the synaptic cleft, binds a specific receptor on the far side, and depending on the nature of the receptor, depolarizes or hyperpolarizes a second neuron or a muscle or gland cell.

neurulation A process in early embryonic development by which a dorsal band of ectoderm thickens and rolls into the neural tube.

neutrophil An abundant type of granulocyte capable of engulfing microorganisms and other foreign particles; neutrophils comprise about 50–70% of the total number of white blood cells.

niche The role played by a particular species in its environment.

nicotinamide adenine dinucleotide (NAD) A molecule that becomes reduced (to NADH) as it carries high-energy electrons from oxidized molecules and delivers them to ATP-producing pathways in the cell.

NADH dehydrogenase An enzyme located on the inner mitochondrial membrane that catalyzes the oxidation by NAD^+ of pyruvate to acetyl-CoA. This reaction links glycolysis and the Krebs cycle.

nitrification The oxidization of ammonia or nitrite to produce nitrate, the form of nitrogen taken up by plants; some bacteria are capable of nitrification.

nociceptor A naked dendrite that acts as a receptor in response to a pain stimulus.

nocturnal Active primarily at night.

node The part of a plant stem where one or more leaves are attached. *See* internode.

node of Ranvier A gap formed at the point where two Schwann cells meet and where the axon is in direct contact with the surrounding intercellular fluid.

nodule In plants, a specialized tissue that surrounds and houses beneficial bacteria, such as root nodules of legumes that contain nitrogen-fixing bacteria.

nonassociative learning A learned behavior that does not require an animal to form an association between two stimuli, or between a stimulus and a response.

noncompetitive inhibitor An inhibitor that binds to a location other than the active site of an enzyme, changing the enzyme's shape so that it cannot bind the substrate.

noncyclic photophosphorylation The set of light-dependent reactions of the two plant photosystems, in which excited electrons are shuttled between the two photosystems, producing a proton gradient that is used for the chemiosmotic synthesis of ATP. The electrons are used to reduce NADP to NADPH. Lost electrons are replaced by the oxidation of water producing O_2.

nondisjunction The failure of homologues or sister chromatids to separate during mitosis or meiosis, resulting in an aneuploid cell or gamete.

nonextreme archaea Archaean groups that are not extremophiles, living in more moderate environments on Earth today.

nonpolar Said of a covalent bond that involves equal sharing of electrons. Can also refer to a compound held together by nonpolar covalent bonds.

nonsense codon One of three codons (UAA, UAG, and UGA) that are not recognized by tRNAs, thus serving as "stop" signals in the mRNA message and terminating translation.

nonsense mutation A base substitution in which a codon is changed into a stop codon. The protein is truncated because of premature termination.

Northern blot A blotting technique used to identify a specific mRNA sequence in a complex mixture. *See* Southern blot.

notochord In chordates, a dorsal rod of cartilage that runs the length of the body and forms the primitive axial skeleton in the embryos of all chordates.

nucellus Tissue composing the chief pair of young ovules, in which the embryo sac develops; equivalent to a megasporangium.

nuclear envelope The bounding structure of the eukaryotic nucleus. Composed of two phospholipid bilayers with the outer one connected to the endoplasmic reticulum.

nuclear pore One of a multitude of tiny but complex openings in the nuclear envelope that allow selective passage of proteins and nucleic acids into and out of the nucleus.

nuclear receptor Intracellular receptors are found in both the cytoplasm and the nucleus. The site of action of the hormone–receptor complex is in the nucleus where they modify gene expression.

nucleic acid A nucleotide polymer; chief types are deoxyribonucleic acid (DNA), which is double-stranded, and ribonucleic acid (RNA), which is typically single-stranded.

nucleoid The area of a prokaryotic cell, usually near the center, that contains the genome in the form of DNA compacted with protein.

nucleolus In eukaryotes, the site of rRNA synthesis; a spherical body composed chiefly of rRNA in the process of being transcribed from multiple copies of rRNA genes.

nucleosome A complex consisting of a DNA duplex wound around a core of eight histone proteins.

nucleotide A single unit of nucleic acid, composed of a phosphate, a five-carbon sugar (either ribose or deoxyribose), and a purine or a pyrimidine.

nucleus In atoms, the central core, containing positively charged protons and (in all but hydrogen) electrically neutral neutrons; in eukaryotic cells, the membranous organelle that houses the chromosomal DNA; in the central nervous system, a cluster of nerve cell bodies.

nutritional mutation A mutation affecting a synthetic pathway for a vital compound, such as an amino acid or vitamin; microorganisms with a nutritional mutation must be grown on medium that supplies the missing nutrient.

O

ocellus, pl. **ocelli** A simple light receptor common among invertebrates.

octet rule Rule to describe patterns of chemical bonding in main group elements that require a total of eight electrons to complete their outer electron shell.

Okazaki fragment A short segment of DNA produced by discontinuous replication elongating in the 5′-to-3′ direction away from the replication.

olfaction The function of smelling.

ommatidium, pl. **ommatidia** The visual unit in the compound eye of arthropods; contains light-sensitive cells and a lens able to form an image.

oncogene A mutant form of a growth-regulating gene that is inappropriately "on," causing unrestrained cell growth and division.

oocyst The zygote in a sporozoan life cycle. It is surrounded by a tough cyst to prevent dehydration or other damage.

open circulatory system A circulatory system in which the blood flows into sinuses in which it mixes with body fluid and then reenters the vessels in another location.

open reading frame (ORF) A region of DNA that encodes a sequence of amino acids with no stop codons in the reading frame.

operant conditioning A learning mechanism in which the reward follows only after the correct behavioral response.

operator A regulatory site on DNA to which a repressor can bind to prevent or decrease initiation of transcription.

operculum A flat, bony, external protective covering over the gill chamber in fish.

operon A cluster of adjacent structural genes transcribed as a unit into a single mRNA molecule.

opisthosoma The posterior portion of the body of an arachnid.

oral surface The surface on which the mouth is found; used as a reference when describing the body structure of echinoderms because of their adult radial symmetry.

orbital A region around the nucleus of an atom with a high probability of containing an electron. The position of electrons can only be described by these probability distributions.

order A category of classification above the level of family and below that of class.

organ A body structure composed of several different tissues grouped in a structural and functional unit.

organelle Specialized part of a cell; literally, a small cytoplasmic organ.

orthologues Genes that reflect the conservation of a single gene found in an ancestor.

oscillating selection The situation in which selection alternately favors one phenotype at one time, and a different phenotype at a another time, for example, during drought conditions versus during wet conditions.

osculum A specialized, larger pore in sponges through which filtered water is forced to the outside of the body.

osmoconformer An animal that maintains the osmotic concentration of its body fluids at about the same level as that of the medium in which it is living.

osmosis The diffusion of water across a selectively permeable membrane (a membrane that permits the free passage of water but prevents or retards the passage of a solute); in the absence of differences in pressure or volume, the net movement of water is from the side containing a lower concentration of solute to the side containing a higher concentration.

osmotic concentration The property of a solution that takes into account all dissolved solutes in the solution; if two solutions with different osmotic concentrations are separated by a water-permeable membrane, water will move from the solution with lower osmotic concentration to the solution with higher osmotic concentration.

osmotic pressure The potential pressure developed by a solution separated from pure water by a differentially permeable membrane. The higher the solute concentration, the greater the osmotic potential of the solution; also called *osmotic potential.*

ossicle Any of a number of movable or fixed calcium-rich plates that collectively make up the endoskeleton of echinoderms.

osteoblast A bone-forming cell.

osteocyte A mature osteoblast.

outcrossing Breeding with individuals other than oneself or one's close relatives.

ovary (1) In animals, the organ in which eggs are produced. (2) In flowering plants, the enlarged basal portion of a carpel that contains the ovule(s); the ovary matures to become the fruit.

oviduct In vertebrates, the passageway through which ova (eggs) travel from the ovary to the uterus.

oviparity Refers to a type of reproduction in which the eggs are developed after leaving the body of the mother, as in reptiles.

ovoviviparity Refers to a type of reproduction in which young hatch from eggs that are retained in the mother's uterus.

ovulation In animals, the release of an egg or eggs from the ovary.

ovum, pl. **ova** The egg cell; female gamete.

oxidation Loss of an electron by an atom or molecule; in metabolism, often associated with a gain of oxygen or a loss of hydrogen.

oxidation–reduction reaction A type of paired reaction in living systems in which electrons lost from one atom (oxidation) are gained by another atom (reduction). Termed a *redox reaction* for short.

oxidative phosphorylation Synthesis of ATP by ATP synthase using energy from a proton gradient. The proton gradient is generated by electron transport, which requires oxygen.

oxygen debt The amount of oxygen required to convert the lactic acid generated in the muscles during exercise back into glucose.

oxytocin A hormone of the posterior pituitary gland that affects uterine contractions during childbirth and stimulates lactation.

ozone O_3, a stratospheric layer of the Earth's atmosphere responsible for filtering out ultraviolet radiation supplied by the Sun.

P

p53 gene The gene that produces the p53 protein that monitors DNA integrity and halts cell division if DNA damage is detected. Many types of cancer are associated with a damaged or absent *p53* gene.

pacemaker A patch of excitatory tissue in the vertebrate heart that initiates the heartbeat.

pair-rule gene Any of certain genes in *Drosophila* development controlled by the gap genes that are expressed in stripes that subdivide the embryo in the process of segmentation.

paleopolyploid An ancient polyploid organism used in analysis of polyploidy events in the study of a species' genome evolution.

palisade parenchyma In plant leaves, the columnar, chloroplast-containing parenchyma cells of the mesophyll. Also called *palisade cells.*

panspermia The hypothesis that meteors or cosmic dust may have brought significant amounts of complex organic molecules to Earth, kicking off the evolution of life.

papilla A small projection of tissue.

paracrine A type of chemical signaling between cells in which the effects are local and short-lived.

paralogues Two genes within an organism that arose from the duplication of one gene in an ancestor.

paraphyletic In phylogenetic classification, a group that includes the most recent common ancestor of the group, but not all its descendants.

parapodia One of the paired lateral processes on each side of most segments in polychaete annelids.

parasexuality In certain fungi, the fusion and segregation of heterokaryotic haploid nuclei to produce recombinant nuclei.

parasitism A living arrangement in which an organism lives on or in an organism of a different species and derives nutrients from it.

parenchyma cell The most common type of plant cell; characterized by large vacuoles, thin walls, and functional nuclei.

parthenogenesis The development of an egg without fertilization, as in aphids, bees, ants, and some lizards.

partial diploid (merodiploid) Describes an *E. coli* cell that carries an F′ plasmid with host genes. This makes the cell diploid for the genes carried by the F′ plasmid.

partial pressure The components of each individual gas—such as nitrogen, oxygen, and carbon dioxide—that together constitute the total air pressure.

passive transport The movement of substances across a cell's membrane without the expenditure of energy.

pedigree A consistent graphic representation of matings and offspring over multiple generations for a particular genetic trait, such as albinism or hemophilia.

pedipalps A pair of specialized appendages found in arachnids; in male spiders, these are specialized as copulatory organs, whereas in scorpions they are large pincers.

pelagic Free-swimming, usually in open water.

pellicle A tough, flexible covering in ciliates and euglenoids.

pentaradial symmetry The five-part radial symmetry characteristic of adult echinoderms.

peptide bond The type of bond that links amino acids together in proteins through a dehydration reaction.

peptidoglycan A component of the cell wall of bacteria, consisting of carbohydrate polymers linked by protein cross-bridges.

peptidyl transferase In translation, the enzyme responsible for catalyzing the formation of a peptide bond between each new amino acid and the previous amino acid in a growing polypeptide chain.

perianth In flowering plants, the petals and sepals taken together.

pericycle In vascular plants, one or more cell layers surrounding the vascular tissues of the root, bounded externally by the endodermis and internally by the phloem.

periderm Outer protective tissue in vascular plants that is produced by the cork cambium and functionally replaces epidermis when it is destroyed during secondary growth; the periderm includes the cork, cork cambium, and phelloderm.

peristalsis In animals, a series of alternating contracting and relaxing muscle movements along the length of a tube such as the oviduct or alimentary canal that tend to force material such as an egg cell or food through the tube.

peroxisome A microbody that plays an important role in the breakdown of highly oxidative hydrogen peroxide by catalase.

petal A flower part, usually conspicuously colored; one of the units of the corolla.

petiole The stalk of a leaf.

phage conversion The phenomenon by which DNA from a virus, incorporated into a host cell's genome, alters the host cell's function in a significant way; for example, the conversion of *Vibrio cholerae* bacteria into a pathogenic form that releases cholera toxin.

phage lambda (λ) A well-known bacteriophage that has been widely used in genetic studies and is often a vector for DNA libraries.

phagocyte Any cell that engulfs and devours microorganisms or other particles.

phagocytosis Endocytosis of a solid particle; the plasma membrane folds inward around the particle (which may be another cell) and engulfs it to form a vacuole.

pharyngeal pouches In chordates, embryonic regions that become pharyngeal slits in aquatic and marine chordates and vertebrates, but do not develop openings to the outside in terrestrial vertebrates.

pharyngeal slits One of the distinguishing features of chordates; a group of openings on each side of the anterior region that form a passageway from the pharynx and esophagus to the external environment.

pharynx A muscular structure lying posterior to the mouth in many animals; aids in propelling food into the digestive tract.

phenotype The realized expression of the genotype; the physical appearance or functional expression of a trait.

pheromone Chemical substance released by one organism that influences the behavior or physiological processes of another organism of the same species. Pheromones serve as sex attractants, as trail markers, and as alarm signals.

phloem In vascular plants, a food-conducting tissue basically composed of sieve elements, various kinds of parenchyma cells, fibers, and sclereids.

phoronid Any of a group of lophophorate invertebrates, now classified in the phylum Brachiopoda, that burrows into soft underwater substrates and secretes a chitinous tube in which it lives out its life; it extends its lophophore tentacles to feed on drifting food particles.

phosphatase Any of a number of enzymes that removes a phosphate group from a protein, reversing the action of a kinase.

phosphodiester bond The linkage between two sugars in the backbone of a nucleic acid molecule; the phosphate group connects the pentose sugars through a pair of ester bonds.

phospholipid Similar in structure to a fat, but having only two fatty acids attached to the glycerol backbone, with the third space linked to a phosphorylated molecule; contains a polar hydrophilic "head" end (phosphate group) and a nonpolar hydrophobic "tail" end (fatty acids).

phospholipid bilayer The main component of cell membranes; phospholipids naturally associate in a bilayer with hydrophobic fatty acids oriented to the inside and hydrophilic phosphate groups facing outward on both sides.

phosphorylation Chemical reaction resulting in the addition of a phosphate group to an organic molecule. Phosphorylation of ADP yields ATP. Many proteins are also activated or inactivated by phosphorylation.

photoelectric effect The ability of a beam of light to excite electrons, creating an electrical current.

photon A particle of light having a discrete amount of energy. The wave concept of light explains the different colors of the spectrum, whereas the particle concept of light explains the energy transfers during photosynthesis.

photoperiodism The tendency of biological reactions to respond to the duration and timing of day and night; a mechanism for measuring seasonal time.

photoreceptor A light-sensitive sensory cell.

photorespiration Action of the enzyme rubisco, which catalyzes the oxidization of RuBP, releasing CO_2; this reverses carbon fixation and can reduce the yield of photosynthesis.

photosystem An organized complex of chlorophyll, other pigments, and proteins that traps light energy as excited electrons. Plants have two linked photosystems in the thylakoid membrane of chloroplasts. Photosystem II passes an excited electron through an electron transport chain to photosystem I to replace an excited electron passed to NADPH. The electron lost from photosystem II is replaced by the oxidation of water.

phototropism In plants, a growth response to a light stimulus.

pH scale A scale used to measure acidity and basicity. Defined as the negative log of H^+ concentration. Ranges from 0 to 14. A value of 7 is neutral; below 7 is acidic and above 7 is basic.

phycobiloprotein A type of accessory pigment found in cyanobacteria and some algae. Complexes of phycobiloprotein are able to absorb light energy in the green range.

phycologist A scientist who studies algae.

phyllotaxy In plants, a spiral pattern of leaf arrangement on a stem in which sequential leaves are at a 137.5° angle to one another, an angle related to the golden mean.

phylogenetic species concept (PSC) The concept that defines species on the basis of their phylogenetic relationships.

phylogenetic tree A pattern of descent generated by analysis of similarities and differences among organisms. Modern gene-sequencing techniques have produced phylogenetic trees showing the evolutionary history of individual genes.

phylogeny The evolutionary history of an organism, including which species are closely related and in what order related species evolved; often represented in the form of an evolutionary tree.

phylum, pl. phyla A major category, between kingdom and class, of taxonomic classifications.

physical map A map of the DNA sequence of a chromosome or genome based on actual landmarks within the DNA.

phytochrome A plant pigment that is associated with the absorption of light; photoreceptor for red to far-red light.

phytoestrogen One of a number of secondary metabolites in some plants that are structurally and functionally similar to the animal hormone estrogen.

phytoremediation The process that uses plants to remove contamination from soil or water.

pigment A molecule that absorbs light.

pilus, pl. pili Extensions of a bacterial cell enabling it to transfer genetic materials from one individual to another or to adhere to substrates.

pinocytosis The process of fluid uptake by endocytosis in a cell.

pistil Central organ of flowers, typically consisting of ovary, style, and stigma; a pistil may consist of one or more fused carpels and is more technically and better known as the gynoecium.

pith The ground tissue occupying the center of the stem or root within the vascular cylinder.

pituitary gland Endocrine gland at the base of the hypothalamus composed of anterior and posterior lobes. Pituitary hormones affect a wide variety of processes in vertebrates.

placenta, pl. placentae (1) In flowering plants, the part of the ovary wall to which the ovules or seeds are attached. (2) In mammals, a tissue formed in part from the inner lining of the uterus and in part from other membranes, through which the embryo (later the fetus) is nourished while in the uterus and through which wastes are carried away.

plankton Free-floating, mostly microscopic, aquatic organisms.

plant receptor kinase Any of a group of plant membrane receptors that, when activated by binding ligand, have kinase enzymatic activity. These receptors phosphorylate serine or threonine, unlike RTKs in animals that phosphorylate tyrosine.

planula A ciliated, free-swimming larva produced by the medusae of cnidarian animals.

plasma The fluid of vertebrate blood; contains dissolved salts, metabolic wastes, hormones, and a variety of proteins, including antibodies and albumin; blood minus the blood cells.

plasma cell An antibody-producing cell resulting from the multiplication and differentiation of a B lymphocyte that has interacted with an antigen.

plasma membrane The membrane surrounding the cytoplasm of a cell; consists of a single phospholipid bilayer with embedded proteins.

plasmid A small fragment of extrachromosomal DNA, usually circular, that replicates independently of the main chromosome, although it may have been derived from it.

plasmodesmata In plants, cytoplasmic connections between adjacent cells.

plasmodium Stage in the life cycle of myxomycetes (plasmodial slime molds); a multinucleate mass of protoplasm surrounded by a membrane.

plasmolysis The shrinking of a plant cell in a hypertonic solution such that it pulls away from the cell wall.

plastid An organelle in the cells of photosynthetic eukaryotes that is the site of photosynthesis and, in plants and green algae, of starch storage.

platelet In mammals, a fragment of a white blood cell that circulates in the blood and functions in the formation of blood clots at sites of injury.

pleiotropy Condition in which an individual allele has more than one effect on production of the phenotype.

plesiomorphy In cladistics, another term for an ancestral character state.

plumule The epicotyl of a plant with its two young leaves.

point mutation An alteration of one nucleotide in a chromosomal DNA molecule.

polar body Minute, nonfunctioning cell produced during the meiotic divisions leading to gamete formation in vertebrates.

polar covalent bond A covalent bond in which electrons are shared unequally due to differences in electronegativity of the atoms involved. One atom has a partial negative charge and the other a partial positive charge, even though the molecule is electrically neutral overall.

polarity (1) Refers to unequal charge distribution in a molecule such as water, which has a positive region and a negative region although it is neutral overall. (2) Refers to axial differences in a developing embryo that result in anterior–posterior and dorsal–ventral axes in a bilaterally symmetrical animal.

polarize In cladistics, to determine whether character states are ancestral or derived.

pollen tube A tube formed after germination of the pollen grain; carries the male gametes into the ovule.

pollination The transfer of pollen from an anther to a stigma.

polyandry The condition in which a female mates with more than one male.

polyclonal antibody An antibody response in which an antigen elicits many different antibodies, each fitting a different portion of the antigen surface.

polygenic inheritance Describes a mode of inheritance in which more than one gene affects a trait, such as height in human beings; polygenic inheritance may produce a continuous range of phenotypic values, rather than discrete either–or values.

polygyny A mating choice in which a male mates with more than one female.

polymer A molecule composed of many similar or identical molecular subunits; starch is a polymer of glucose.

polymerase chain reaction (PCR) A process by which DNA polymerase is used to copy a sequence of interest repeatedly, making millions of copies of the same DNA.

polymorphism The presence in a population of more than one allele of a gene at a frequency greater than that of newly arising mutations.

polyp A typically sessile, cylindrical body form found in cnidarian animals, such as hydras.

polypeptide A molecule consisting of many joined amino acids; not usually as complex as a protein.

polyphyletic In phylogenetic classification, a group that does not include the most recent common ancestor of all members of the group.

polyploidy Condition in which one or more entire sets of chromosomes is added to the diploid genome.

polysaccharide A carbohydrate composed of many monosaccharide sugar subunits linked together in a long chain; examples are glycogen, starch, and cellulose.

polyunsaturated fat A fat molecule having at least two double bonds between adjacent carbons in one or more of the fatty acid chains.

population Any group of individuals, usually of a single species, occupying a given area at the same time.

population genetics The study of the properties of genes in populations.

positive control A type of control at the level of DNA transcription initiation in which the frequency of initiation is increased; activator proteins mediate positive control.

posttranscriptional control A mechanism of control over gene expression that operates after the transcription of mRNA is complete.

postzygotic isolating mechanism A type of reproductive isolation in which zygotes are produced but are unable to develop into reproducing adults; these mechanisms may range from inviability of zygotes or embryos to adults that are sterile.

potential energy Energy that is not being used, but could be; energy in a potentially usable form; often called "energy of position."

precapillary sphincter A ring of muscle that guards each capillary loop and that, when closed, blocks flow through the capillary.

pre-mRNA splicing In eukaryotes, the process by which introns are removed from the primary transcript to produce mature mRNA; pre-mRNA splicing occurs in the nucleus.

pressure potential In plants, the turgor pressure resulting from pressure against the cell wall.

prezygotic isolating mechanism A type of reproductive isolation in which the formation of a zygote is prevented; these mechanisms may range from physical separation in different habitats to gametic in which gametes are incapable of fusing.

primary endosperm nucleus In flowering plants, the result of the fusion of a sperm nucleus and the (usually) two polar nuclei.

primary growth In vascular plants, growth originating in the apical meristems of shoots and roots; results in an increase in length.

primary immune response The first response of an immune system to a foreign antigen. If the system is challenged again with the same antigen, the memory cells created during the primary response will respond more quickly.

primary induction Inductions between the three primary tissue types: mesoderm and endoderm.

primary meristem Any of the three meristems produced by the apical meristem; primary meristems give rise to the dermal, vascular, and ground tissues.

primary nondisjunction Failure of chromosomes to separate properly at meiosis I.

primary phloem The cells involved in food conduction in plants.

primary plant body The part of a plant consisting of young, soft shoots and roots derived from apical meristem tissues.

primary productivity The amount of energy produced by photosynthetic organisms in a community.

primary structure The specific amino acid sequence of a protein.

primary tissues Tissues that make up the primary plant body.

primary transcript The initial mRNA molecule copied from a gene by RNA polymerase, containing a faithful copy of the entire gene, including introns as well as exons.

primary wall In plants, the wall layer deposited during the period of cell expansion.

primase The enzyme that synthesizes the RNA primers required by DNA polymerases.

primate Monkeys and apes (including humans).

primitive streak In the early embryos of birds, reptiles, and mammals, a dorsal, longitudinal strip of ectoderm and mesoderm that is equivalent to the blastopore in other forms.

primordium In plants, a bulge on the young shoot produced by the apical meristem; primordia can differentiate into leaves, other shoots, or flowers.

principle of parsimony Principle stating that scientists should favor the hypothesis that requires the fewest assumptions.

prions Infectious proteinaceous particles.

procambium In vascular plants, a primary meristematic tissue that gives rise to primary vascular tissues.

product rule *See* rule of multiplication.

proglottid A repeated body segment in tapeworms that contains both male and female reproductive organs; proglottids eventually form eggs and embryos, which leave the host's body in feces.

prokaryote A bacterium; a cell lacking a membrane-bounded nucleus or membrane-bounded organelles.

prometaphase The transitional phase between prophase and metaphase during which the spindle attaches to the kinetochores of sister chromatids.

promoter A DNA sequence that provides a recognition and attachment site for RNA polymerase to begin the process of gene transcription; it is located upstream from the transcription start site.

prophase The phase of cell division that begins when the condensed chromosomes become visible and ends when the nuclear envelope breaks down. The assembly of the spindle takes place during prophase.

proprioceptor In vertebrates, a sensory receptor that senses the body's position and movements.

prosimian Any member of the mammalian group that is a sister group to the anthropoids; prosimian means "before monkeys." Members include the lemurs, lorises, and tarsiers.

prosoma The anterior portion of the body of an arachnid, which bears all the appendages.

prostaglandins A group of modified fatty acids that function as chemical messengers.

prostate gland In male mammals, a mass of glandular tissue at the base of the urethra that secretes an alkaline fluid that has a stimulating effect on the sperm as they are released.

protease An enzyme that degrades proteins by breaking peptide bonds; in cells, proteases are often compartmentalized into vesicles such as lysosomes.

proteasome A large, cylindrical cellular organelle that degrades proteins marked with ubiquitin.

protein A chain of amino acids joined by peptide bonds.

protein kinase An enzyme that adds phosphate groups to proteins, changing their activity.

protein microarray An array of proteins on a microscope slide or silicon chip. The array may be used with a variety of probes, including antibodies, to analyze the presence or absence of specific proteins in a complex mixture.

proteome All the proteins coded for by a particular genome.

proteomics The study of the proteomes of organisms. This is related to functional genomics as the proteome is responsible for much of the function encoded by a genome.

protoderm The primary meristem that gives rise to the dermal tissue.

proton pump A protein channel in a membrane of the cell that expends energy to transport protons against a concentration gradient; involved in the chemiosmotic generation of ATP.

proto-oncogene A normal cellular gene that can act as an oncogene when mutated.

protostome Any member of a grouping of bilaterally symmetrical animals in which the mouth develops first and the anus second; flatworms, nematodes, mollusks, annelids, and arthropods are protostomes.

pseudocoel A body cavity located between the endoderm and mesoderm.

pseudogene A copy of a gene that is not transcribed.

pseudomurien A component of the cell wall of archaea; it is similar to peptidoglycan in structure and function but contains different components.

pseudopod A nonpermanent cytoplasmic extension of the cell body.

P site In a ribosome, the peptidyl site that binds to the tRNA attached to the growing polypeptide chain.

punctuated equilibrium A hypothesis about the mechanism of evolutionary change proposing that long periods of little or no change are punctuated by periods of rapid evolution.

Punnett square A diagrammatic way of showing the possible genotypes and phenotypes of genetic crosses.

pupa A developmental stage of some insects in which the organism is nonfeeding, immotile, and sometimes encapsulated or in a cocoon; the pupal stage occurs between the larval and adult phases.

purine The larger of the two general kinds of nucleotide base found in DNA and RNA; a nitrogenous base with a double-ring structure, such as adenine or guanine.

pyrimidine The smaller of two general kinds of nucleotide base found in DNA and RNA; a nitrogenous base with a single-ring structure, such as cytosine, thymine, or uracil.

pyruvate A three-carbon molecule that is the end product of glycolysis; each glucose molecule yields two pyruvate molecules.

Q

quantitative trait A trait that is determined by the effects of more than one gene; such a trait usually exhibits continuous variation rather than discrete either–or values.

quaternary structure The structural level of a protein composed of more than one polypeptide chain, each of which has its own tertiary structure; the individual chains are called subunits.

R

radial canal Any of five canals that connect to the ring canal of an echinoderm's water–vascular system.

radial cleavage The embryonic cleavage pattern of deuterostome animals in which cells divide parallel to and at right angles to the polar axis of the embryo.

radial symmetry A type of structural symmetry with a circular plan, such that dividing the body or structure through the midpoint in any direction yields two identical sections.

radicle The part of the plant embryo that develops into the root.

radioactive isotope An isotope that is unstable and undergoes radioactive decay, releasing energy.

radioactivity The emission of nuclear particles and rays by unstable atoms as they decay into more stable forms.

radula Rasping tongue found in most mollusks.

reaction center A transmembrane protein complex in a photosystem that receives energy from the antenna complex exciting an electron that is passed to an acceptor molecule.

reading frame The correct succession of nucleotides in triplet codons that specify amino acids on translation. The reading frame is established by the first codon in the sequence as there are no spaces in the genetic code.

realized niche The actual niche occupied by an organism when all biotic and abiotic interactions are taken into account.

receptor-mediated endocytosis Process by which specific macromolecules are transported into eukaryotic cells at clathrin-coated pits, after binding to specific cell-surface receptors.

receptor protein A highly specific cell-surface receptor embedded in a cell membrane that responds only to a specific messenger molecule.

receptor tyrosine kinase (RTK) A diverse group of membrane receptors that when activated have kinase enzymatic activity. Specifically, they phosphorylate proteins on tyrosine. Their activation can lead to diverse cellular responses.

recessive An allele that is only expressed when present in the homozygous condition, but being "hidden" by the expression of a dominant allele in the heterozygous condition.

redia A secondary, nonciliated larva produced in the sporocysts of liver flukes.

regulatory protein Any of a group of proteins that modulates the ability of RNA polymerase to bind to a promoter and begin DNA transcription.

replicon An origin of DNA replication and the DNA whose replication is controlled by this origin. In prokaryotic replication, the chromosome plus the origin consist of a single replicon; eukaryotic chromosomes consist of multiple replicons.

replisome The macromolecular assembly of enzymes involved in DNA replication; analogous to the ribosome in protein synthesis.

reciprocal altruism Performance of an altruistic act with the expectation that the favor will be returned. A key and very controversial assumption of many theories dealing with the evolution of social behavior. *See* altruism.

reciprocal cross A genetic cross involving a single trait in which the sex of the parents is reversed; for example, if pollen from a white-flowered plant is used to fertilize a purple-flowered plant, the reciprocal cross would be pollen from a purple-flowered plant used to fertilize a white-flowered plant.

reciprocal recombination A mechanism of genetic recombination that occurs only in eukaryotic organisms, in which two chromosomes trade segments; can occur between nonhomologous chromosomes as well as the more usual exchange between homologous chromosomes in meiosis.

recombinant DNA Fragments of DNA from two different species, such as a bacterium and a mammal, spliced together in the laboratory into a single molecule.

recombination frequency The value obtained by dividing the number of recombinant progeny by the total progeny in a genetic cross. This value is converted into a percentage, and each 1% is termed a map unit.

reduction The gain of an electron by an atom, often with an associated proton.

reflex In the nervous system, a motor response subject to little associative modification; a reflex is among the simplest neural pathways, involving only a sensory neuron, sometimes (but not always) an interneuron, and one or more motor neurons.

reflex arc The nerve path in the body that leads from stimulus to reflex action.

refractory period The recovery period after membrane depolarization during which the membrane is unable to respond to additional stimulation.

reinforcement In speciation, the process by which partial reproductive isolation between populations is increased by selection against mating between members of the two populations, eventually resulting in complete reproductive isolation.

replica plating A method of transferring bacterial colonies from one plate to another to make a copy of the original plate; an impression of colonies growing on a Petri plate is made on a velvet surface, which is then used to transfer the colonies to plates containing different media, such that auxotrophs can be identified.

replication fork The Y-shaped end of a growing replication bubble in a DNA molecule undergoing replication.

repolarization Return of the ions in a nerve to their resting potential distribution following depolarization.

repression In general, control of gene expression by preventing transcription. Specifically, in bacteria such as *E. coli* this is mediated by repressor proteins. In anabolic operons, repressors bind DNA in the absence of corepressors to repress an operon.

repressor A protein that regulates DNA transcription by preventing RNA polymerase from attaching to the promoter and transcribing the structural gene. *See* operator.

reproductive isolating mechanism Any barrier that prevents genetic exchange between species.

residual volume The amount of air remaining in the lungs after the maximum amount of air has been exhaled.

resting membrane potential The charge difference (difference in electric potential) that exists across a neuron at rest (about 70 mV).

restriction endonuclease An enzyme that cleaves a DNA duplex molecule at a particular base sequence, usually within or near a palindromic sequence; also called a restriction enzyme.

restriction fragment length polymorphism (RFLP) Restriction enzymes recognize very specific DNA sequences. Alleles of the same gene or surrounding sequences may have base-pair differences, so that DNA near one allele is cut into a different-length fragment than DNA near the other allele. These different fragments separate based on size on electrophoresis gels.

retina The photosensitive layer of the vertebrate eye; contains several layers of neurons and light receptors (rods and cones); receives the image formed by the lens and transmits it to the brain via the optic nerve.

retinoblastoma susceptibility gene (*Rb*) A gene that, when mutated, predisposes individuals to a rare form of cancer of the retina; one of the first tumor-suppressor genes discovered.

retrovirus An RNA virus. When a retrovirus enters a cell, a viral enzyme (reverse transcriptase) transcribes viral RNA into duplex DNA, which the cell's machinery then replicates and transcribes as if it were its own.

reverse genetics An approach by which a researcher uses a cloned gene of unknown function, creates a mutation, and introduces the mutant gene back into the organism to assess the effect of the mutation.

reverse transcriptase A viral enzyme found in retroviruses that is capable of converting their RNA genome into a DNA copy.

Rh blood group A set of cell-surface markers (antigens) on the surface of red blood cells in humans and rhesus monkeys (for which it is named); although there are several alleles, they are grouped into two main types: Rh-positive and Rh-negative.

rhizome In vascular plants, a more or less horizontal underground stem; may be enlarged for storage or may function in vegetative reproduction.

rhynchocoel A true coelomic cavity in ribbonworms that serves as a hydraulic power source for extending the proboscis.

ribonucleic acid (RNA) A class of nucleic acids characterized by the presence of the sugar ribose and the pyrimidine uracil; includes mRNA, tRNA, and rRNA.

ribosomal RNA (rRNA) A class of RNA molecules found, together with characteristic proteins, in ribosomes; transcribed from the DNA of the nucleolus.

ribosome The molecular machine that carries out protein synthesis; the most complicated aggregation of proteins in a cell, also containing three different rRNA molecules.

ribosome-binding sequence (RBS) In prokaryotes, a conserved sequence at the 5' end of mRNA that is complementary to the 3' end of a small subunit rRNA and helps to position the ribosome during initiation.

ribozyme An RNA molecule that can behave as an enzyme, sometimes catalyzing its own assembly; rRNA also acts as a ribozyme in the polymerization of amino acids to form protein.

ribulose 1,5-bisphosphate (RuBP) In the Calvin cycle, the five-carbon sugar to which CO_2 is attached, accomplishing carbon fixation. This reaction is catalyzed by the enzyme rubisco.

ribulose bisphosphate carboxylase/oxygenase (rubisco) The four-subunit enzyme in the chloroplast that catalyzes the carbon fixation reaction joining CO_2 to RuBP.

RNA interference A type of gene silencing in which the mRNA transcript is prevented from being translated; small interfering RNAs (siRNAs) have been found to bind to mRNA and target its degradation prior to its translation.

RNA polymerase An enzyme that catalyzes the assembly of an mRNA molecule, the sequence of which is complementary to a DNA molecule used as a template. *See* transcription.

RNA primer In DNA replication, a sequence of about 10 RNA nucleotides complementary to unwound DNA that attaches at a replication fork; the DNA polymerase uses the RNA primer as a starting point for addition of DNA nucleotides to form the new DNA strand; the RNA primer is later removed and replaced by DNA nucleotides.

RNA splicing A nuclear process by which intron sequences of a primary mRNA transcript are cut out and the exon sequences spliced together to give the correct linkages of genetic information that will be used in protein construction.

rod Light-sensitive nerve cell found in the vertebrate retina; sensitive to very dim light; responsible for "night vision."

root The usually descending axis of a plant, normally below ground, which anchors the plant and serves as the major point of entry for water and minerals.

root cap In plants, a tissue structure at the growing tips of roots that protects the root apical meristem as the root pushes through the soil; cells of the root cap are continually lost and replaced.

root hair In plants, a tubular extension from an epidermal cell located just behind the root tip; root hairs greatly increase the surface area for absorption.

root pressure In plants, pressure exerted by water in the roots in response to a solute potential in the absence of transpiration; often occurs at night. Root pressure can result in guttation, excretion of water from cells of leaves as dew.

root system In plants, the portion of the plant body that anchors the plant and absorbs ions and water.

R plasmid A resistance plasmid; a conjugative plasmid that picks up antibiotic resistance genes and can therefore transfer resistance from one bacterium to another.

rule of addition The rule stating that for two independent events, the probability of either event occurring is the sum of the individual probabilities.

rule of multiplication The rule stating that for two independent events, the probability of both events occurring is the product of the individual probabilities.

rumen An "extra stomach" in cows and related mammals wherein digestion of cellulose occurs and from which partially digested material can be ejected back into the mouth.

S

salicylic acid In plants, an organic molecule that is a long-distance signal in systemic acquired resistance.

saltatory conduction A very fast form of nerve impulse conduction in which the impulses leap from node to node over insulated portions.

saprobes Heterotrophic organisms that digest their food externally (e.g., most fungi).

sarcolemma The specialized cell membrane in a muscle cell.

sarcomere Fundamental unit of contraction in skeletal muscle; repeating bands of actin and myosin that appear between two Z lines.

sarcoplasmic reticulum The endoplasmic reticulum of a muscle cell. A sleeve of membrane that wraps around each myofilament.

satellite DNA A nontranscribed region of the chromosome with a distinctive base composition; a short nucleotide sequence repeated tandemly many thousands of times.

saturated fat A fat composed of fatty acids in which all the internal carbon atoms contain the maximum possible number of hydrogen atoms.

Schwann cells The supporting cells associated with projecting axons, along with all the other nerve cells that make up the peripheral nervous system.

sclereid In vascular plants, a sclerenchyma cell with a thick, lignified, secondary wall having many pits; not elongate like a fiber.

sclerenchyma cell Tough, thick-walled cells that strengthen plant tissues.

scolex The attachment organ at the anterior end of a tapeworm.

scrotum The pouch that contains the testes in most mammals.

scuttellum The modified cotyledon in cereal grains.

second filial (F₂) generation The offspring resulting from a cross between members of the first filial (F_1) generation.

secondary cell wall In plants, the innermost layer of the cell wall. Secondary walls have a highly organized microfibrillar structure and are often impregnated with lignin.

secondary growth In vascular plants, an increase in stem and root diameter made possible by cell division of the lateral meristems.

secondary immune response The swifter response of the body the second time it is invaded by the same pathogen because of the presence of memory cells, which quickly become antibody-producing plasma cells.

secondary induction An induction between tissues that have already differentiated.

secondary metabolite A molecule not directly involved in growth, development, or reproduction of an organism; in plants these molecules, which include nicotine, caffeine, tannins, and menthols, can discourage herbivores.

secondary plant body The part of a plant consisting of secondary tissues from lateral meristem tissues; the older trunk, branches, and roots of woody plants.

secondary structure In a protein, hydrogen-bonding interactions between —CO and —NH groups of the primary structure.

secondary tissue Any tissue formed from lateral meristems in trees and shrubs.

Second Law of Thermodynamics A statement concerning the transformation of potential energy into heat; it says that disorder (entropy) is continually increasing in the universe as energy changes occur, so disorder is more likely than order.

second messenger A small molecule or ion that carries the message from a receptor on the target cell surface into the cytoplasm.

seed bank Ungerminated seeds in the soil of an area. Regeneration of plants after events such as fire often depends on the presence of a seed bank.

seed coat In plants, the outer layers of the ovule, which become a relatively impermeable barrier to protect the dormant embryo and stored food.

segment polarity gene Any of certain genes in *Drosophila* development that are expressed in stripes that subdivide the stripes created by the pair-rule genes in the process of segmentation.

segmentation The division of the developing animal body into repeated units; segmentation allows for redundant systems and more efficient locomotion.

segmentation gene Any of the three classes of genes that control development of the segmented body plan of insects; includes the gap genes, pair-rule genes, and segment polarity genes.

segregation The process by which alternative forms of traits are expressed in offspring rather than blending each trait of the parents in the offspring.

selection The process by which some organisms leave more offspring than competing ones, and their genetic traits tend to appear in greater proportions among members of succeeding generations than the traits of those individuals that leave fewer offspring.

selectively permeable Condition in which a membrane is permeable to some substances but not to others.

self-fertilization The union of egg and sperm produced by a single hermaphroditic organism.

semen In reptiles and mammals, sperm-bearing fluid expelled from the penis during male orgasm.

semicircular canal Any of three fluid-filled canals in the inner ear that help to maintain balance.

semiconservative replication DNA replication in which each strand of the original duplex serves as the template for construction of a totally new complementary strand, so the original duplex is partially conserved in each of the two new DNA molecules.

senescent Aged, or in the process of aging.

sensory (afferent) neuron A neuron that transmits nerve impulses from a sensory receptor to the central nervous system or central ganglion.

sensory setae In insect, bristles attached to the nervous system that are sensitive mechanical and chemical stimulation; most abundant on antennae and legs.

sepal A member of the outermost floral whorl of a flowering plant.

septation In prokaryotic cell division, the formation of a septum where new cell membrane and cell wall is formed to separate the two daughter cells.

septum, pl. septa A wall between two cavities.

sequence-tagged site (STS) A small stretch of DNA that is unique in a genome, that is, it occurs only once; useful as a physical marker on genomic maps.

seta, pl. setae (L., bristle) In an annelid, bristles of chitin that help anchor the worm during locomotion or when it is in its burrow.

severe acute respiratory syndrome (SARS) A respiratory infection with an 8% mortality rate that is caused by a coronavirus.

sex chromosome A chromosome that is related to sex; in humans, the sex chromosomes are the X and Y chromosomes.

sex-linked A trait determined by a gene carried on the X chromosome and absent on the Y chromosome.

Sexual dimorphism Morphological differences between the sexes of a species.

sexual reproduction The process of producing offspring through an alternation of fertilization (producing diploid cells) and meiotic reduction in chromosome number (producing haploid cells).

sexual selection A type of differential reproduction that results from variable success in obtaining mates.

shared derived character In cladistics, character states that are shared by species and that are different from the ancestral character state.

shoot In vascular plants, the aboveground portions, such as the stem and leaves.

short interspersed element (SINE) Any of a type of retrotransposon found in humans and other primates that does not contain the biochemical machinery needed for transposition; half a million copies of a SINE element called Alu is nested in the LINEs of the human genome.

shotgun sequencing The method of DNA sequencing in which the DNA is randomly cut into small fragments, and the fragments cloned and sequenced. A computer is then used to assemble a final sequence.

sieve cell In the phloem of vascular plants, a long, slender element with relatively unspecialized sieve areas and with tapering end walls that lack sieve plates.

signal recognition particle (SRP) In eukaryotes, a cytoplasmic complex of proteins that recognizes and binds to the signal sequence of a polypeptide, and then docks with a receptor that forms a channel in the ER membrane. In this way the polypeptide is released into the lumen of the ER.

signal transduction The events that occur within a cell on receipt of a signal, ligand binding to a receptor protein. Signal transduction pathways produce the cellular response to a signaling molecule.

simple sequence repeat (SSR) A one- to three-nucleotide sequence such as CA or CCG that is repeated thousands of times.

single-nucleotide polymorphism (SNP) A site present in at least 1% of the population at which individuals differ by a single nucleotide. These can be used as genetic markers to map unknown genes or traits.

sinus A cavity or space in tissues or in bone.

sister chromatid One of two identical copies of each chromosome, still linked at the centromere, produced as the chromosomes duplicate for mitotic division; similarly, one of two identical copies of each homologous chromosome present in a tetrad at meiosis.

small interfering RNAs (siRNAs) A class of micro-RNAs that appear to be involved in control of gene transcription and that play a role in protecting cells from viral attack.

small nuclear ribonucleoprotein particles (snRNP) In eukaryotes, a complex composed of snRNA and protein that clusters together with other snRNPs to form the spliceosome, which removes introns from the primary transcript.

small nuclear RNA (snRNA) In eukaryotes, a small RNA sequence that, as part of a small nuclear ribonucleoprotein complex, facilitates recognition and excision of introns by base-pairing with the 5′ end of an intron or at a branch site of the same intron.

sodium–potassium pump Transmembrane channels engaged in the active (ATP-driven) transport of Na^+, exchanging them for K^+, where both ions are being moved against their respective concentration gradients; maintains the resting membrane potential of neurons and other cells.

solute A molecule dissolved in some solution; as a general rule, solutes dissolve only in solutions of similar polarity; for example, glucose (polar) dissolves in (forms hydrogen bonds with) water (also polar), but not in vegetable oil (nonpolar).

solute potential The amount of osmotic pressure arising from the presence of a solute or solutes in water; measure by counterbalancing the pressure until osmosis stops.

solvent The medium in which one or more solutes is dissolved.

somatic cell Any of the cells of a multicellular organism except those that are destined to form gametes (germ-line cells).

somatic cell nuclear transfer (SCNT) The transfer of the nucleus of a somatic cell into an enucleated egg cell that then undergoes development. Can be used to make ES cells and to create cloned animals.

somatic mutation A change in genetic information (mutation) occurring in one of the somatic cells of a multicellular organism, not passed from one generation to the next.

somatic nervous system In vertebrates, the neurons of the peripheral nervous system that control skeletal muscle.

somite One of the blocks, or segments, of tissue into which the mesoderm is divided during differentiation of the vertebrate embryo.

Southern blot A technique in which DNA fragments are separated by gel electrophoresis, denatured into single-stranded DNA, and then "blotted" onto a sheet of filter paper; the filter is then incubated with a labeled probe to locate DNA sequences of interest.

S phase The phase of the cell cycle during which DNA replication occurs.

specialized transduction The transfer of only a few specific genes into a bacterium, using a lysogenic bacteriophage as a carrier.

speciation The process by which new species arise, either by transformation of one species into another, or by the splitting of one ancestral species into two descendant species.

species, pl. species A kind of organism; species are designated by binomial names written in italics.

specific heat The amount of heat that must be absorbed or lost by 1 g of a substance to raise or lower its temperature 1°C.

specific transcription factor Any of a great number of transcription factors that act in a time- or tissue-dependent manner to increase DNA transcription above the basal level.

spectrin A scaffold of proteins that links plasma membrane proteins to actin filaments in the cytoplasm of red blood cells, producing their characteristic biconcave shape.

spermatid In animals, each of four haploid (*n*) cells that result from the meiotic divisions of a spermatocyte; each spermatid differentiates into a sperm cell.

spermatozoa The male gamete, usually smaller than the female gamete, and usually motile.

sphincter In vertebrate animals, a ring-shaped muscle capable of closing a tubular opening by constriction (e.g., between stomach and small intestine or between anus and exterior).

spicule Any of a number of minute needles of silica or calcium carbonate made in the mesohyl by some kinds of sponges as a structural component.

spindle The structure composed of microtubules radiating from the poles of the dividing cell that will ultimately guide the sister chromatids to the two poles.

spindle apparatus The assembly that carries out the separation of chromosomes during cell division; composed of microtubules (spindle fibers) and assembled during prophase at the equator of the dividing cell.

spindle checkpoint The third cell-division checkpoint, at which all chromosomes must be attached to the spindle. Passage through this checkpoint commits the cell to anaphase.

spinnerets Organs at the posterior end of a spider's abdomen that secrete a fluid protein that becomes silk.

spiracle External opening of a trachea in arthropods.

spiral cleavage The embryonic cleavage pattern of some protostome animals in which cells divide at an angle oblique to the polar axis of the embryo; a line drawn through the sequence of dividing cells forms a spiral.

spiralian A member of a group of invertebrate animals; many groups exhibit spiral cleavage. Mollusks, annelids, and flatworms are examples of spiralians.

spliceosome In eukaryotes, a complex composed of multiple snRNPs and other associated proteins that is responsible for excision of introns and joining of exons to convert the primary transcript into the mature mRNA.

spongin A tough protein made by many kinds of sponges as a structural component within the mesohyl.

spongy parenchyma A leaf tissue composed of loosely arranged, chloroplast-bearing cells. *See* palisade parenchyma.

sporangium, pl. sporangia A structure in which spores are produced.

spore A haploid reproductive cell, usually unicellular, capable of developing into an adult without fusion with another cell.

sporophyte The spore-producing, diploid (*2n*) phase in the life cycle of a plant having alternation of generations.

stabilizing selection A form of selection in which selection acts to eliminate both extremes from a range of phenotypes.

stamen The organ of a flower that produces the pollen; usually consists of anther and filament; collectively, the stamens make up the androecium.

starch An insoluble polymer of glucose; the chief food storage substance of plants.

start codon The AUG triplet, which indicates the site of the beginning of mRNA translation; this codon also codes for the amino acid methionine.

stasis A period of time during which little evolutionary change occurs.

statocyst Sensory receptor sensitive to gravity and motion.

stele The central vascular cylinder of stems and roots.

stem cell A relatively undifferentiated cell in animal tissue that can divide to produce more differentiated tissue cells.

stereoscopic vision Ability to perceive a single, three-dimensional image from the simultaneous but slightly divergent two-dimensional images delivered to the brain by each eye.

stigma (1) In angiosperm flowers, the region of a carpel that serves as a receptive surface for pollen grains. (2) Light-sensitive eyespot of some algae.

stipules Leaflike appendages that occur at the base of some flowering plant leaves or stems.

stolon A stem that grows horizontally along the ground surface and may form adventitious roots, such as runners of the strawberry plant.

stoma, pl. stomata In plants, a minute opening bordered by guard cells in the epidermis of leaves and stems; water passes out of a plant mainly through the stomata.

stop codon Any of the three codons UAA, UAG, and UGA, that indicate the point at which mRNA translation is to be terminated.

stratify To hold plant seeds at a cold temperature for a certain period of time; seeds of many plants will not germinate without exposure to cold and subsequent warming.

stratum corneum The outer layer of the epidermis of the skin of the vertebrate body.

striated muscle Skeletal voluntary muscle and cardiac muscle.

stroma In chloroplasts, the semiliquid substance that surrounds the thylakoid system and that contains the enzymes needed to assemble organic molecules from CO_2.

stromatolite A fossilized mat of ancient bacteria formed as long as 2 BYA, in which the bacterial remains individually resemble some modern-day bacteria.

style In flowers, the slender column of tissue that arises from the top of the ovary and through which the pollen tube grows.

stylet A piercing organ, usually a mouthpart, in some species of invertebrates.

suberin In plants, a fatty acid chain that forms the impermeable barrier in the Casparian strip of root endoderm.

subspecies A geographically defined population or group of populations within a single species that has distinctive characteristics.

substrate (1) The foundation to which an organism is attached. (2) A molecule on which an enzyme acts.

subunit vaccine A type of vaccine created by using a subunit of a viral protein coat to elicit an immune response; may be useful in preventing viral diseases such as hepatitis B.

succession In ecology, the slow, orderly progression of changes in community composition that takes place through time.

summation Repetitive activation of the motor neuron resulting in maximum sustained contraction of a muscle.

supercoiling The coiling in space of double-stranded DNA molecules due to torsional strain, such as occurs when the helix is unwound.

surface tension A tautness of the surface of a liquid, caused by the cohesion of the molecules of liquid. Water has an extremely high surface tension.

surface area-to-volume ratio Relationship of the surface area of a structure, such as a cell, to the volume it contains.

suspensor In gymnosperms and angiosperms, the suspensor develops from one of the first two cells of a dividing zygote; the suspensor of an angiosperm is a nutrient conduit from maternal tissue to the embryo. In gymnosperms the suspensor positions the embryo closer to stored food reserves.

swim bladder An organ encountered only in the bony fish that helps the fish regulate its buoyancy by increasing or decreasing the amount of gas in the bladder via the esophagus or a specialized network of capillaries.

swimmerets In lobsters and crayfish, appendages that occur in lines along the ventral surface of the abdomen and are used in swimming and reproduction.

symbiosis The condition in which two or more dissimilar organisms live together in close association; includes parasitism (harmful to one of the organisms), commensalism (beneficial to one, of no significance to the other), and mutualism (advantageous to both).

sympatric speciation The differentiation of populations within a common geographic area into species.

symplast route In plant roots, the pathway for movement of water and minerals within the cell cytoplasm that leads through plasmodesmata that connect cells.

symplesiomorphy In cladistics, another term for a shared ancestral character state.

symporter A carrier protein in a cell's membrane that transports two molecules or ions in the same direction across the membrane.

synapomorphy In systematics, a derived character that is shared by clade members.

synapse A junction between a neuron and another neuron or muscle cell; the two cells do not touch, the gap being bridged by neurotransmitter molecules.

synapsid Any of an early group of reptiles that had a pair of temporal openings in the skull behind the eye sockets; jaw muscles attached to these openings. Early ancestors of mammals belonged to this group.

synapsis The point-by-point alignment (pairing) of homologous chromosomes that occurs before the first meiotic division; crossing over takes place during synapsis.

synaptic cleft The space between two adjacent neurons.

synaptic vesicle A vesicle of a neurotransmitter produced by the axon terminal of a nerve. The filled vesicle migrates to the presynaptic membrane, fuses with it, and releases the neurotransmitter into the synaptic cleft.

synaptonemal complex A protein lattice that forms between two homologous chromosomes in prophase I of meiosis, holding the replicated chromosomes in precise register with each other so that base-pairs can form between nonsister chromatids for crossing over that is usually exact within a gene sequence.

syncytial blastoderm A structure composed of a single large cytoplasm containing about 4000 nuclei in embryonic development of insects such as *Drosophila*.

syngamy The process by which two haploid cells (gametes) fuse to form a diploid zygote; fertilization.

synthetic polyploidy A polyploidy organism created by crossing organisms most closely related to an ancestral species and then manipulating the offspring.

systematics The reconstruction and study of evolutionary relationships.

systemic acquired resistance (SAR) In plants, a longer-term response to a pathogen or pest attack that can last days to weeks and allow the plant to respond quickly to later attacks by a range of pathogens.

systemin In plants, an 18-amino-acid peptide that is produced by damaged or injured leaves that leads to the wound response.

systolic pressure A measurement of how hard the heart is contracting. When measured during a blood pressure reading, ventricular systole (contraction) is what is being monitored.

T

3′ poly-A tail In eukaryotes, a series of 1–200 adenine residues added to the 3′ end of an mRNA; the tail appears to enhance the stability of the mRNA by protecting it from degradation.

T box A transcription factor protein domain that has been conserved, although with differing developmental effects, in invertebrates and chordates.

tagma, pl. **tagmata** A compound body section of an arthropod resulting from embryonic fusion of two or more segments; for example, head, thorax, abdomen.

Taq polymerase A DNA polymerase isolated from the thermophilic bacterium *Thermus aquaticus* (Taq); this polymerase is functional at higher temperatures, and is used in PCR amplification of DNA.

TATA box In eukaryotes, a sequence located upstream of the transcription start site. The TATA box is one element of eukaryotic core promoters for RNA polymerase II.

taxis, pl. **taxes** An orientation movement by a (usually) simple organism in response to an environmental stimulus.

taxonomy The science of classifying living things. By agreement among taxonomists, no two organisms can have the same name, and all names are expressed in Latin.

T cell A type of lymphocyte involved in cell-mediated immunity and interactions with B cells; the "T" refers to the fact that T cells are produced in the thymus.

telencephalon The most anterior portion of the brain, including the cerebrum and associated structures.

telomerase An enzyme that synthesizes telomeres on eukaryotic chromosomes using an internal RNA template.

telomere A specialized nontranscribed structure that caps each end of a chromosome.

telophase The phase of cell division during which the spindle breaks down, the nuclear envelope of each daughter cell forms, and the chromosomes uncoil and become diffuse.

telson The tail spine of lobsters and crayfish.

temperate (lysogenic) phage A virus that is capable of incorporating its DNA into the host cell's DNA, where it remains for an indeterminate length of time and is replicated as the cell's DNA replicates.

template strand The DNA strand that is used as a template in transcription. This strand is copied to produce a complementary mRNA transcript.

tendon (Gr. *tendon*, stretch) A strap of cartilage that attaches muscle to bone.

tensile strength A measure of the cohesiveness of a substance; its resistance to being broken apart. Water in narrow plant vessels has tensile strength that helps keep the water column continuous.

tertiary structure The folded shape of a protein, produced by hydrophobic interactions with water, ionic and covalent bonding between side chains of different amino acids, and van der Waal's forces; may be changed by denaturation so that the protein becomes inactive.

testcross A mating between a phenotypically dominant individual of unknown genotype and a homozygous "tester," done to determine whether the phenotypically dominant individual is homozygous or heterozygous for the relevant gene.

testis, pl. **testes** In mammals, the sperm-producing organ.

tetanus Sustained forceful muscle contraction with no relaxation.

thalamus That part of the vertebrate forebrain just posterior to the cerebrum; governs the flow of information from all other parts of the nervous system to the cerebrum.

therapeutic cloning The use of somatic cell nuclear transfer to create stem cells from a single individual that may be reimplanted in that individual to replace damaged cells, such as in a skin graft.

thermodynamics The study of transformations of energy, using heat as the most convenient form of measurement of energy.

thermogenesis Generation of internal heat by endothermic animals to modulate temperature.

thigmotropism In plants, unequal growth in some structure that comes about as a result of physical contact with an object.

threshold The minimum amount of stimulus required for a nerve to fire (depolarize).

thylakoid In chloroplasts, a complex, organized internal membrane composed of flattened disks, which contain the photosystems involved in the light-dependent reactions of photosynthesis.

Ti (tumor-inducing) plasmid A plasmid found in the plant bacterium *Agrobacterium tumefaciens* that has been extensively used to introduce recombinant DNA into broadleaf plants. Recent modifications have allowed its use with cereal grains as well.

tight junction Region of actual fusion of plasma membranes between two adjacent animal cells that prevents materials from leaking through the tissue.

tissue A group of similar cells organized into a structural and functional unit.

tissue plasminogen activator (TPA) A human protein that causes blood clots to dissolve; if used within 3 hours of an ischemic stroke, TPA may prevent disability.

tissue-specific stem cell A stem cell that is capable of developing into the cells of a certain tissue, such as muscle or epithelium; these cells persist even in adults.

tissue system In plants, any of the three types of tissue; called a system because the tissue extends throughout the roots and shoots.

tissue tropism The affinity of a virus for certain cells within a multicellular host; for example, hepatitis B virus targets liver cells.

tonoplast The membrane surrounding the central vacuole in plant cells that contains water channels; helps maintain the cell's osmotic balance.

topoisomerase Any of a class of enzymes that can change the topological state of DNA to relieve torsion caused by unwinding.

torsion The process in embryonic development of gastropods by which the mantle cavity and anus move from a posterior location to the front of the body, closer to the location of the mouth.

totipotent A cell that possesses the full genetic potential of the organism.

trachea, pl. **tracheae** A tube for breathing; in terrestrial vertebrates, the windpipe that carries air between the larynx and bronchi (which leads to the lungs); in insects and some other terrestrial arthropods, a system of chitin-lined air ducts.

tracheids In plant xylem, dead cells that taper at the ends and overlap one another.

tracheole The smallest branches of the respiratory system of terrestrial arthropods; tracheoles convey air from the tracheae, which connect to the outside of the body at spiracles.

trait In genetics, a characteristic that has alternative forms, such as purple or white flower color in pea plants or different blood type in humans.

transcription The enzyme-catalyzed assembly of an RNA molecule complementary to a strand of DNA.

transcription complex The complex of RNA polymerase II plus necessary activators, coactivators, transcription factors, and other factors that are engaged in actively transcribing DNA.

transcription factor One of a set of proteins required for RNA polymerase to bind to a eukaryotic promoter region, become stabilized, and begin the transcription process.

transcription bubble The region containing the RNA polymerase, the DNA template, and the RNA transcript, so called because of the locally unwound "bubble" of DNA.

transcription unit The region of DNA between a promoter and a terminator.

transcriptome All the RNA present in a cell or tissue at a given time.

transfection The transformation of eukaryotic cells in culture.

transfer RNA (tRNA) A class of small RNAs (about 80 nucleotides) with two functional sites; at one site, an "activating enzyme" adds a specific amino acid, while the other site carries the nucleotide triplet (anticodon) specific for that amino acid.

transformation The uptake of DNA directly from the environment; a natural process in some bacterial species.

transgenic organism An organism into which a gene has been introduced without conventional breeding, that is, through genetic engineering techniques.

translation The assembly of a protein on the ribosomes, using mRNA to specify the order of amino acids.

translation repressor protein One of a number of proteins that prevent translation of mRNA by binding to the beginning of the transcript and preventing its attachment to a ribosome.

translocation (1) In plants, the long-distance transport of soluble food molecules (mostly sucrose), which occurs primarily in the sieve tubes of phloem tissue. (2) In genetics, the interchange of chromosome segments between nonhomologous chromosomes.

transmembrane domain Hydrophobic region of a transmembrane protein that anchors it in the membrane. Often composed of α-helices, but sometimes utilizing β-pleated sheets to form a barrel-shaped pore.

transmembrane route In plant roots, the pathway for movement of water and minerals that crosses the cell membrane and also the membrane of vacuoles inside the cell.

transpiration The loss of water vapor by plant parts; most transpiration occurs through the stomata.

transposable elements Segments of DNA that are able to move from one location on a chromosome to another. Also termed *transposons* or *mobile genetic elements*.

transposition Type of genetic recombination in which transposable elements (transposons) move from one site in the DNA sequence to another, apparently randomly.

transposon DNA sequence capable of transposition.

trichome In plants, a hairlike outgrowth from an epidermal cell; glandular trichomes secrete oils or other substances that deter insects.

triglyceride (triacylglycerol) An individual fat molecule, composed of a glycerol and three fatty acids.

triploid Possessing three sets of chromosomes.

trisomic Describes the condition in which an additional chromosome has been gained due to nondisjunction during meiosis, and the diploid embryo therefore has three of these autosomes. In humans, trisomic individuals may survive if the autosome is small; Down syndrome individuals are trisomic for chromosome 21.

trochophore A specialized type of free-living larva found in lophotrochozoans.

trophic level A step in the movement of energy through an ecosystem.

trophoblast In vertebrate embryos, the outer ectodermal layer of the blastodermic vesicle; in mammals, it is part of the chorion and attaches to the uterine wall.

tropism Response to an external stimulus.

tropomyosin Low-molecular-weight protein surrounding the actin filaments of striated muscle.

troponin Complex of globular proteins positioned at intervals along the actin filament of skeletal muscle; thought to serve as a calcium-dependent "switch" in muscle contraction.

***trp* operon** In *E. coli*, the operon containing genes that code for enzymes that synthesize tryptophan.

true-breeding Said of a breed or variety of organism in which offspring are uniform and consistent from one generation to the next; for example. This is due to the genotypes that determine relevant traits being homozygous.

tube foot In echinoderms, a flexible, external extension of the water–vascular system that is capable of attaching to a surface through suction.

tubulin Globular protein subunit forming the hollow cylinder of microtubules.

tumor-suppressor gene A gene that normally functions to inhibit cell division; mutated forms can lead to the unrestrained cell division of cancer, but only when both copies of the gene are mutant.

turgor pressure The internal pressure inside a plant cell, resulting from osmotic intake of water, that presses its cell membrane tightly against the cell wall, making the cell rigid. Also known as *hydrostatic pressure*.

tympanum In some groups of insects, a thin membrane associated with the tracheal air sacs that functions as a sound receptor; paired on each side of the abdomen.

U

ubiquitin A 76-amino-acid protein that virtually all eukaryotic cells attach as a marker to proteins that are to be degraded.

unequal crossing over A process by which a crossover in a small region of misalignment at synapsis causes two homologous chromosomes to exchange segments of unequal length.

uniporter A carrier protein in a cell's membrane that transports only a single type of molecule or ion.

uniramous Single-branched; describes the appendages of insects.

unsaturated fat A fat molecule in which one or more of the fatty acids contain fewer than the maximum number of hydrogens attached to their carbons.

urea An organic molecule formed in the vertebrate liver; the principal form of disposal of nitrogenous wastes by mammals.

urethra The tube carrying urine from the bladder to the exterior of mammals.

uric acid Insoluble nitrogenous waste products produced largely by reptiles, birds, and insects.

urine The liquid waste filtered from the blood by the kidney and stored in the bladder pending elimination through the urethra.

uropod One of a group of flattened appendages at the end of the abdomen of lobsters and crayfish that collectively act as a tail for a rapid burst of speed.

uterus In mammals, a chamber in which the developing embryo is contained and nurtured during pregnancy.

V

vacuole A membrane-bounded sac in the cytoplasm of some cells, used for storage or digestion purposes in different kinds of cells; plant cells often contain a large central vacuole that stores water, proteins, and waste materials.

valence electron An electron in the outermost energy level of an atom.

variable A factor that influences a process, outcome, or observation. In experiments, scientists attempt to isolate variables to test hypotheses.

vascular cambium In vascular plants, a cylindrical sheath of meristematic cells, the division of which produces secondary phloem outwardly and secondary xylem inwardly; the activity of the vascular cambium increases stem or root diameter.

vascular tissue Containing or concerning vessels that conduct fluid.

vas deferens In mammals, the tube carrying sperm from the testes to the urethra.

vasopressin A posterior pituitary hormone that regulates the kidney's retention of water.

vector In molecular biology, a plasmid, phage or artificial chromosome that allows propagation of recombinant DNA in a host cell into which it is introduced.

vegetal pole The hemisphere of the zygote comprising cells rich in yolk.

vein (1) In plants, a vascular bundle forming a part of the framework of the conducting and supporting tissue of a stem or leaf. (2) In animals, a blood vessel carrying blood from the tissues to the heart.

veliger The second larval stage of mollusks following the trochophore stage, during which the beginning of a foot, shell, and mantle can be seen.

ventricle A muscular chamber of the heart that receives blood from an atrium and pumps blood out to either the lungs or the body tissues.

vertebrate A chordate with a spinal column; in vertebrates, the notochord develops into the vertebral column composed of a series of vertebrae that enclose and protect the dorsal nerve cord.

vertical gene transfer (VGT) The passing of genes from one generation to the next within a species.

vesicle A small intracellular, membrane-bounded sac in which various substances are transported or stored.

vessel element In vascular plants, a typically elongated cell, dead at maturity, which conducts water and solutes in the xylem.

vestibular apparatus The complicated sensory apparatus of the inner ear that provides for balance and orientation of the head in vertebrates.

vestigial structure A morphological feature that has no apparent current function and is thought to be an evolutionary relic; for example, the vestigial hip bones of boa constrictors.

villus, pl. villi In vertebrates, one of the minute, fingerlike projections lining the small intestine that serve to increase the absorptive surface area of the intestine.

virion A single virus particle.

viroid Any of a group of small, naked RNA molecules that are capable of causing plant diseases, presumably by disrupting chromosome integrity.

virus Any of a group of complex biochemical entities consisting of genetic material wrapped in protein; viruses can reproduce only within living host cells and are thus not considered organisms.

visceral mass Internal organs in the body cavity of an animal.

vitamin An organic substance that cannot be synthesized by a particular organism but is required in small amounts for normal metabolic function.

viviparity Refers to reproduction in which eggs develop within the mother's body and young are born free-living.

voltage-gated ion channel A transmembrane pathway for an ion that is opened or closed by a change in the voltage, or charge difference, across the plasma membrane.

W

water potential The potential energy of water molecules. Regardless of the reason (e.g., gravity, pressure, concentration of solute particles) for the water potential, water moves from a region where water potential is greater to a region where water potential is lower.

water–vascular system A fluid-filled hydraulic system found only in echinoderms that provides body support and a unique type of locomotion via extensions called tube feet.

Western blot A blotting technique used to identify specific protein sequences in a complex mixture. *See* Southern blot.

wild type In genetics, the phenotype or genotype that is characteristic of the majority of individuals of a species in a natural environment.

wobble pairing Refers to flexibility in the pairing between the base at the 5′ end of a tRNA anticodon and the base at the 3′ end of an mRNA codon. This flexibility allows a single tRNA to read more than one mRNA codon.

wound response In plants, a signaling pathway initiated by leaf damage, such as being chewed by a herbivore, and lead to the production of proteinase inhibitors that give herbivores indigestion.

X

X chromosome One of two sex chromosomes; in mammals and in *Drosophila*, female individuals have two X chromosomes.

xylem In vascular plants, a specialized tissue, composed primarily of elongate, thick-walled conducting cells, which transports water and solutes through the plant body.

Y

Y chromosome One of two sex chromosomes; in mammals and in *Drosophila*, male individuals have a Y chromosome and an X chromosome; the Y determines maleness.

yolk plug A plug occurring in the blastopore of amphibians during formation of the archenteron in embryological development.

yolk sac The membrane that surrounds the yolk of an egg and connects the yolk, a rich food supply, to the embryo via blood vessels.

Z

zinc finger motif A type of DNA-binding motif in regulatory proteins that incorporates zinc atoms in its structure.

zona pellucida An outer membrane that encases a mammalian egg.

zone of cell division In plants, the part of the young root that includes the root apical meristem and the cells just posterior to it; cells in this zone divide every 12–36 hr.

zone of elongation In plants, the part of the young root that lies just posterior to the zone of cell division; cells in this zone elongate, causing the root to lengthen.

zone of maturation In plants, the part of the root that lies posterior to the zone of elongation; cells in this zone differentiate into specific cell types.

zoospore A motile spore.

zooxanthellae Symbiotic photosynthetic protists in the tissues of corals.

zygomycetes A type of fungus whose chief characteristic is the production of sexual structures called zygosporangia, which result from the fusion of two of its simple reproductive organs.

zygote The diploid (2*n*) cell resulting from the fusion of male and female gametes (fertilization).

Photo Credits

Chapter 1
Opener: © Soames Summerhays/Natural Visions; 1.1d: © Dr. Donald Fawcett & Porter/Visuals Unlimited; 1.1e: © Lennart Nilsson/Albert Bonniers Förlag AB; 1.1f: © Ed Reschke; 1.1i-j: © Getty RF; 1.1k-l: © Volume 44/Getty RF; 1.1m: © Steve Harper/Grant Heilman Photography, Inc.; 1.1n: © Robert and Jean Pollock; 1.1o: NASA; 1.5: © Huntington Library/SuperStock; 1.11a: © Dennis Kunkel/Phototake; 1.11b: © Karl E. Deckart/Phototake; 1.12a: © Alan L. Detrick/Photo Researchers, Inc.; 1.12b: © DAVID M. DENNIS/Animals Animals - Earth Scenes; 1.12c: © Volume 46/Corbis RF; 1.12d: © Corbis RF; 1.12e: © Mediscan/Corbis; 1.12f: © Volume 15/Photodisc/Getty RF; 1.12g: © Corbis RF; 1.12h: © Tom Brakefield/Corbis; 1.12i: © Volume 44/Photodisc/Getty RF; 1.12j: © Volume 64/Corbis RF; 1.12k: © T.E. Adams/Visuals Unlimited; 1.12l: © Douglas P. Wilson/Frank Lane Picture Agency/Corbis; 1.12m: © R. Robinson/Visuals Unlimited; 1.12n: © Kari Lounatman/Photo Researchers, Inc.; 1.12o: © Dwight R. Kuhn; 1.12p: © Alfred Pasieka/Science Photo Library/Photo Researchers, Inc.

Chapter 2
Opener: Courtesy of IBM Zurich Research Laboratory. Unauthorized use not permitted; 2.2: Image Courtesy of Veeco Instruments, Inc.; 2.10a: © Glen Allison/Getty Images RF; 2.10b: © PhotoLink/Getty RF; 2.10c: © Jeff Vanuga/Corbis; 2.13: © Hermann Eisenbeiss/National Audubon Society Collection/Photo Researchers, Inc.

Chapter 3
Opener: © Jacob Halaska/Index Stock Imagery; 3.10b: © Asa Thoresen/Photo Researchers, Inc.; 3.10c: © J.Carson/Custom Medical Stock Photo; 3.11b: © J.D. Litvay/Visuals Unlimited; 3.12: © Scott Johnson/Animals Animals - Earth Scenes; 3.13a: © Driscoll, Youngquist & Baldeschwieler, Caltech/SPL/Photo Researchers, Inc.; 3.13b: © PhotoLink/Getty RF.

Chapter 4
Opener: © Dr. Gopal Murti/Photo Researchers, Inc.; Table 4.1a: © David M. Phillips/Visuals Unlimited; Table 4.1b: © Mike Abbey/Visuals Unlimited; Table 4.1c: © David M. Phillips/Visuals Unlimited; Table 4.1d: © Mike Abbey/Visuals Unlimited; Table 4.1e: © DR TORSTEN WITTMANN/Photo Researchers, Inc.; Table 4.1f: © Med. Mic. Sciences, Cardiff Uni./Wellcome Images; Table 4.1g: © Microworks/Phototake; Table 4.1h: © Stanley Flegler/Visuals Unlimited; p. 62 (plasma membrane): © Dr. Don W. Fawcett/Visuals Unlimited; 4.3: © Phototake; 4.4: Courtesy of E.H. Newcomb & T.D. Pugh, University of Wisconsin; 4.5a: © Eye of Science/Photo Researchers, Inc.; 4.8b: © Dr. Richard Kessel & Dr. Gene Shih/Visuals Unlimited; 4.8c: © John T. Hansen, Ph.D/Phototake; 4.8d: Reprinted by permission from Macmillan Publishers Ltd: Nature, 323, 560-564, "The nuclear lamina is a meshwork of intermediate-type filaments," Ueli Aebi, Julie Cohn, Loren Buhle, Larry Gerace, © 1986; 4.10c: © R. Bolender & D. Fawcett/Visuals Unlimited; 4.11c: © Dennis Kunkel/Phototake; 4.14: From "Microbody-Like Organelles in Leaf Cells," Sue Ellen Frederick and Eldon H. Newcomb, SCIENCE, Vol. 163: 1353-1355 © 21 March 1969. Reprinted with permission from AAAS; 4.15: © Dr. Henry Aldrich/Visuals Unlimited; 4.16c: © Dr. Donald Fawcett & Dr. Porter/Visuals Unlimited; 4.17c: © Dr. Jeremy Burgess/Photo Researchers, Inc.; 4.23a-b: © William Dentler, University of Kansas; 4.24a-b: © SPL/Photo Researchers, Inc.; 4.25: © BioPhoto Associates/Photo Researchers, Inc.; 4.27a: Courtesy of Daniel Goodenough; 4.27b-c: © Dr. Donald Fawcett/Visuals Unlimited.

Chapter 5
Opener: © Dr. Gopal Murti/Science Photo Library/Photo Researchers, Inc.; p. 91 (top)-5.3: © Don W. Fawcett/Photo Researchers, Inc.; 5.12a-c: © David M. Phillips/Visuals Unlimited; 5.15a: Micrograph Courtesy of the CDC/Dr. Edwin P. Ewing, Jr.; 5.15b: © BCC Microimaging, Inc., Reproduced with permission; 5.15c (top)-(bottom): © The Company of Biologists Limited; 5.16b: © Dr. Brigit Satir.

Chapter 6
Opener: © Robert Caputo/Aurora Photos; 6.3a-b: © Spencer Grant/PhotoEdit; 6.11b: © Professor Emeritus Lester J. Reed, University of Texas at Austin.

Chapter 7
Opener: © Creatas/PunchStock RF; 7.18a: © Wolfgang Baumeister/Photo Researchers, Inc.; 7.18b: National Park Service.

Chapter 8
Opener: © Corbis RF; 8.1: Courtesy Dr. Kenneth Miller, Brown University; 8.8a-b: © Eric Soder; 8.20: © Dr. Jeremy Burgess/Photo Researchers, Inc.; 8.22a: © John Shaw/Photo Researchers, Inc.; 8.22b: © Joseph Nettis/National Audubon Society Collection/Photo Researchers, Inc.; 8.24: © Clyde H. Smith/Peter Arnold Inc.

Chapter 9
Opener: RMF/Scientifica/Visuals Unlimited.

Chapter 10
Opener: © Stem Jems/Photo Researchers, Inc.; 10.2a-b: Courtesy of William Margolin; 10.4: © BioPhoto Associates/Photo Researchers, Inc.; 10.6: © CNRI/Photo Researchers, Inc.; 10.10: Image courtesy of S. Hauf and J-M. Peters, IMP, Vienna, Austria; 10.11a-g, 10.12: © Andrew S. Bajer, University of Oregon; 10.13a-b: © Dr. Jeremy Pickett-Heaps; 10.14a: © David M. Phillips/Visuals Unlimited; 10.14b: © Guenter Albrecht-Buehler, Northwestern University, Chicago; 10.15: © B.A. Palevits & E.H. Newcomb/BPS/Tom Stack & Associates.

Chapter 11
Opener: © Science VU/L. Maziarski/Visuals Unlimited; 11.3b: Reprinted, with permission, from the Annual Review of Genetics, Volume 6 © 1972 by Annual Reviews, www.annualreviews.org; 11.7a-h: © Clare A. Hasenkampf/Biological Photo Service.

Chapter 12
Opener: © Corbis RF; 12.1: © Norbert Schaefer/Corbis; 12.2: © David Sieren/Visuals Unlimited; 12.3: © Leslie Holzer/Photo Researchers, Inc.; 12.11: From Albert F. Blakeslee "CORN AND MEN: The Interacting Influence of Heredity and Environment—Movements for Betterment of Men, or Corn, or Any Other Living Thing, One-sided Unless They Take Both Factors into Account," Journal of Heredity, 5: 511-518, © 1914 Oxford University Press; 12.14: © DK Limited/Corbis.

Chapter 13
Opener: © Adrian T. Sumner/Photo Researchers, Inc.; 13.1a-b: © Cabisco/Phototake; p. 241: © BioPhoto Associates/Photo Researchers, Inc.; 13.3: © Bettmann/Corbis; p. 243(left): From Brian P. Chadwick and Huntington F. Willard, "Multiple spatially distinct types of facultative heterochromatin on the human inactive X chromosome," PNAS vol. 101 no. 50:17450-17455, Fig. 3 © 2004 National Academy of Sciences, U.S.A.; 13.4: © Kenneth Mason; 13.33: © Jackie Lewin, Royal Free Hospital/Photo Researchers, Inc.; 13.12: © Colorado Genetics Laboratory, University of Colorado Denver.

Chapter 14
Opener: © Volume 29/Getty RF; 14.5a-b: Courtesy of Cold Spring Harbor Laboratory Archives; 14.6: © Barrington Brown/Photo Researchers, Inc.; 14.11: From M. Meselson and F.W. Stahl/PNAS 44(1958):671; 14.16a-b: From Biochemistry by Stryer. © 1995, 1981, 1988, 1995 by Lupert Stryer. Used with permission of W.H. Freeman and Company; 14.20: © Dr. Don W. Fawcett/Visuals Unlimited.

Chapter 15
Opener: © Dr. Gopal Murti/Visuals Unlimited; 15.3: From R.C. Williams, PNAS 74(1977):2313;

Boldface page numbers correspond with **boldface terms** in the text. Page numbers followed by an "f" indicate figures; page numbers followed by a "t" indicate tabular material.

A

A band, 969
Aardvark, 525, 525f
ABC model, of floral organ specification, 846, 846f, 847f, 848, 848f
ABO blood group, 90t, 230t, 234-**235**, 235f, 1077
Abscisic acid, **779**, 779f, 826t, 836, 836f
Abscission, **823**-824, 823f
Abscission zone, 823, 823f
Absolute dating, 424
Absorption
    in digestive tract, 982, 989-990, 989f
    water and minerals in plants, 771f, 773-775, 774f-775f
Absorption spectrum,
    of photosynthetic pigments, **152**-154, 152f, 153f
Abstinence, 1100
Acacia, mutualism with ants, 809, 809f, 1198, 1198f
Acari (order), 682
Acceptor stem, **291**-292, 291f
Accessory digestive organs, 983f, 988-989, 988f-989f, 994-995, 995f
Accessory pigment, **152**, 153f
Accessory sex organs
    female, 1097-1098, 1098f
    male, 1092-1093, 1093f
Acetaldehyde, 35f
Acetic acid, 35f
Acetyl-CoA
    in Krebs cycle, 131, 132, 133f, 138, 138f
    from protein catabolism, 141f
    from pyruvate, 130, 130f
    uses of, 142
Acetylcholine, 897-898, 897f-898f, 909t, 910, 912, 912f, 973, 1034
Acetylcholine (ACh) receptor, 172, 893f, 912, 912f
Acetylcholinesterase (AChE), 898
Achiasmate segregation, **214**
Acid, **29**-30
Acid growth hypothesis, **830**, 831f
Acid precipitation, 1246, 1246f-1247f
Acid rain, 1247, 1247f
Acid soil, 789
Acini, **989**

Acoela, 644f, 660, 660f
Acoelomate, 637, 637f, 643, 644f, 656-660, 657f, 659f-661f
Acoelomorpha, 644f
Acromegaly, **950**
Acrosomal process, 1106
Acrosome, **1106**
ACTH, 947-948
Actin, 970f
Actin filament, **76**, 76f, **84**, 84f
Actinobacteria, 550f
Actinomyces, 550f, 561
Actinopoda (phylum), 583
Action potential, 893-895
    all-or-none law of, 894
    falling phase of, 893, 894f
    generation of, 893-895, 894f-895f
    propagation of, 894-895, 895f
    rising phase of, 893, 894f, 895, 895f
    undershoot phase of, 893, 894f
Action spectrum, **153**
    of chlorophyll, 153, 153f
Activation energy, **111**, 111f, 113-114
Activator, 117, 308, 313, 314-315, 314f-315f, 316-317
    allosteric, **117**
Active immunity, 1063
Active site, **114**, 114f
Active transport, across plasma membrane, **99**-102, 104t
Acute-phase protein, 1059
ADA-SCID, 345
Adaptation, speciation and, 443, 443f
Adapter protein, **176**, 178
Adaptive radiation, **446**-447, 446f-447f, 450, 450f
Adaptive significance, of behavior, 1148
Adaptive value, of egg coloration, 1147-1148, 1147f
Addiction, drug, 900-901, 900f
Adenine, 42, 42f, 259f, 260, 262
Adenohypophysis, **946**
Adenosine diphosphate. *See* ADP
Adenosine monophosphate. *See* AMP
Adenosine triphosphate. *See* ATP
Adenovirus, 531f
Adenylyl cyclase, **179**-180, 180f, 946
ADH. *See* Antidiuretic hormone
Adherens junction, **84**
Adhesion, 27, 27f
Adipose cells, **868**
Adipose tissue, **868**, 868f
ADP, 113, 113f
Adrenal cortex, 954, 954f
Adrenal gland, **953**-954, 954f
Adrenal medulla, 953-954, 954f

Adrenocorticotropic hormone (ACTH), 947-948
Adsorption, of virus to host, 533
Adventitious plantlet, 858
Adventitious root, **742**, 746f, 765f
Aerenchyma, **780**, 781f
Aerial root, 742, 743f
Aerobic capacity, 974
Aerobic metabolism, 129
Aerobic respiration, **124**, 126, 126f, 129, 136f
    ATP yield from, 137-138, 137f
    evolution of, 143
    regulation of, 138, 138f
Aesthetic value, of biodiversity, 1263
Afferent arteriole, 1046
Afferent neuron. *See* Sensory neuron
Aflatoxin, 630, 630f
African savanna, 1186f
African sleeping sickness, 574
African violet, 748f
Afrovenator, 709f
Age, at first reproduction, 1173
Age structure, of population, **1169**
Aging, telomerase and, 273
Agriculture
    applications of genetic engineering to, 346-349, 346f-348f
    applications of genomics to, 368-369, 368f-369f
    effect of global warming on, 1252-1253
    pollution due to, 1251
Agrobacterium tumefaciens, 346, 346f, 832, 833f
AIDS, 470-471, 531, 532t, 535-538, **1079**
    deaths in United States, 535
    gene therapy for, 345, 345t
Air pollution, monitoring with lichens, 627
Akiapolaau, 1270f
Alanine, 35f, 46, 47f
Alaskan near-shore habitat, 1271-1272, 1272f
Albinism, 227t, 228, 228f
Albumin, **1019**
Aldosterone, 954, **1035**, 1050, 1051, 1052f
Aleurone, 764f, **765**
Alfalfa plant bug, 803, 803f
Alkaptonuria, 227t, 279
Allantoin, **1044**
Allantois, **706**, 708f, 1089, 1116
Allee effect, **1176**
Allee, Warder, 1176

Allele, **225**
    multiple, 233t, 233-235, 235f
    temperature-sensitive, 235, 235f
Allele frequency, 397, **399**-400
    changes in populations, 398-400, 399f
Allelopathy, **807**, 807f
Allen's rule, 1164
Allergy, 1075, 1076f
Alligator, 707t, 711, 711f
Allometric growth, **1128**
Allomyces, 615t, 620, 621f
Allopatric speciation, **442**, 442f, 444-445, 444f
Allopolyploidy, **445**, 445f, 477, 477f, 479f
Allosteric activator, **117**
Allosteric enzymes, 117
Allosteric inhibitor, **117**, 117f
Allosteric site, **117**
Alpha helix, **48**
Alpha wave, 905
Alternate leaf, 744, 744f
Alternation of generations, 850
Alternative splicing, **290**, 320, 321f, 322f, 361, 361f
Altricial young, **1153**
Altruism, **1154**-1157, 1155f-1157f
    reciprocal, 1154-1155, 1155f
Alveolata, 515f, 570f, 576-579, 569f-579f
Alveoli, **1007**-1008, 1008f
Alveoli, of protists, 576, 576f
Alzheimer disease, 906-907
Amborella, 607, 607f
Amborella trichopoda, 521-522, 522f, 607, 607f
American basswood, 836f
American woodcock (*Scolopax minor*), 933
Amino acid, **44**
    abbreviations for, 47f
    catabolism of, 141, 141f
    chemical classes of, 46, 47f
    as neurotransmitters, 898-899
    in proteins, 36f, 44
    structure of, 44-46, 47f
    twenty common, 47f
Amino acid derivative, 939
Amino group, 35, 35f
Aminoacyl-tRNA synthetase, **291**-291, 291f-292f
Ammonia, 1044, 1045f
Amniocentesis, **252**, 252f
Amnion, 1089, 1116
Amniotic egg, **706**, 708f, 1089
Amniotic fluid, 1116
Amniotic membrane, 1116

Amoeba, 571, 583-584, 583f
slime mold, 585, 585f
Amoeba proteus, 583f
AMP, 112f, 113, 124
Amphibia (class), 698f, 703-706,
704f-705f
Amphibian, 641t, 698f, 703-706,
704f-705f
brain of, 903, 903f
characteristics of, 703, 703t
circulation in, 703, 1024, 1024f
classification of, 705-706, 705f
development in, 952, 952f
eggs of, 1249f
evolution of, 697, 703, 704-705,
704f-705f
fertilization in, 1088, 1088f-1089f
first, 704-705
gastrulation in, 1114, 1114f
heart of, 703, 1024, 1024f
invasion of land by, 704-705,
704f-705f
kidney of, 1043
legs of, 703, 704f
lungs of, 703, 1007, 1007f
nitrogenous wastes of, 1044, 1045f
nuclear transplant in, 380
orders of, 703t
population declines in, 1258t,
1264-1266, 1264f-1265f
prolactin in, 951
reproduction in, 704
respiration in, 703, 1004, 1003f-1004f
Amphioxus. See Branchiostoma
Ampullae of Lorenzini, **934**
Amygdala, **905**
Amylopectin, 40, 40f
Amyloplast, **75**, 739, 820, 820f
Amylose, 39, 40, 40f
Anabaena, 563
Anabolism, **117**
Anaerobic respiration, **124**, 139
Analogous structures, **11**, 11f, 498
Anaphase
meiosis I, 210, 211f, 212f, 214,
215, 216f-217f
meiosis II, 213f, 214, 217f
mitotic, 192f, 195f, **196-197**,
197f, 216f
Anaphase A, 195f, 197-198
Anaphase B, 195f, 197-198
Anaphase-promoting complex
(APC), **201**
Anatomical dead space, 1010
Ancestral characters, 458-459, 459f
Anchoring junction, 83f, **84**
Andrews, Tommie Lee, 336, 336f
Androecium, 608, 608f, 848-849
Androgen, 956
Aneuploidy, **214**, **250**, **481**
Angelman syndrome, 251-252
Angina pectoris, **1033**
Angiosperm. *See* Flowering plant
Angle of incidence, 1231
Animal(s)
body plan of, evolution of,
636-640, 636f-637f, 639f
classification of, 522-525, 640,
641t-642t, 643-645, 644f-645f

coevolution of plants and, 807
communication and, 1144-1147,
1144f-1147f
development in, 372-373,
373f, 635t
diversity in, 633-646
evolution of, 583, 645-646, 646f
fruit dispersal by, 762, 763f
gap junctions in, 83f, **84**
general features of, 634,
634t-635t
habitats of, 635t
movement in, 634t
multicellularity in, 634t
obtaining nutrients, 634t
phylogeny of, 640, 643-645,
644f-645f
pollination by, 852-854, 852f-853f
sexual life cycle in, 208, 208f
sexual reproduction in, 519, 635t
succession in animal communities,
1203, 1203f
transgenic, **342**
Animal breeding, thoroughbred
horses, 414, 414f
Animal cells
cell division in, 188f
cytokinesis in, 197, 197f
genetically modified
domesticated, 349
sexual life cycle in, 208, 208f
structure of, 66f, 80-81, 81f, 81t
Animal pole, 377, 377f, **1110**, 1110f
Animalia (kingdom), 13, 13f, 513f,
514, 515f, 517f, 518t, 640
Anion, **19**, 96
Annelid, 140, 643, 644f, 673-676,
673f-676f
body plan of, 673-674, 673f
classes of, 674-676
connections between
segments, 674
excretory system of, 674
segmentation in, 523, 523f,
639-640, 643, 673-674
Annelida (phylum), 641t, 643, 644f,
673-676, 673f-676f
Annotation, **359**
Annual plants, 859f, **860**
Anolis lizard
courtship display of, 443, 443f
dewlap of, 443, 443f
Anonymous marker, **248**, 248f
Anopheles mosquito, 358f, 475f,
487, 1079
Anoxygenic photosynthesis, 143,
148, 156
Ant
ant farmer-fungi symbiosis,
629, 629f
mutualism with acacias, 809, 809f,
1198, 1198f
social, 1158f
Antagonistic effector, 877-878, 877f
Anteater, 431f, 525, 525f
Antenna complex (photosynthesis),
154-**155**, 155f, 157
Antennal gland, 1041
Antennapedia complex, 388f, 389

Antennapedia gene, 388, 494
Anterior pituitary, **946**, 947-948,
948-951, 950f
Anther, **608**, 608f, 848f, **849**
Antheridium, **594**, 594f
Anthocyanin, 824
Anthophyta (phylum), 602t
Anthozoa (class), **654-655**, 654f
Anthrax, 554, 561t
Anthropoid, 721, 721f-722f
Antibiotic resistance, 558
Antibiotics, bacteria susceptibility
to, 64
Antibody, **1063**, 1068-1074,
1069f-1074f. *See also*
Immunoglobulin (Ig)
antigen-binding site on, 1070,
1070f-1071f
monoclonal, 1077-1078, 1078f
polyclonal, 1077
recombinant, 349
specificity of, 1069-1070, 1070f
Anticodon loop, **291-292**, 291f
Antidiuretic hormone (ADH), **947**,
947f, **1034**, 1049,
1050-1051, 1051f
Antigen, **1061**-1062, 1062f, 1074,
1074f, 1078f
Antigen-binding site, 1070,
1070f-1071f
Antigen drift, **1079**
Antigen-presenting cell, **1066**
Antigen shift, **1079**
Antigenic determinant, 1062
Antiparallel strands, in DNA,
262f, 263
Antiporter, **100**
Anura (order), 703, 703t,
705-706, 705f
Aorta, **1029**
Aortic body, **1011**, 1011f
Aortic valve, **1026**
AP gene, in plants, 499-500,
499f-500f
APC. *See* Anaphase-promoting
complex
Ape, 720t, 721-726
compared to hominids, 722
evolution of, 721-726
Aperture (pollen grain), 609
Apex, **730**
Aphasia, 906
Aphid, feeding on phloem, 782, 782f
Apical meristem, **731**, 732,
732f-733f, 832f
Apical surface, 866, 987
Apicomplexans, 576, 576f, 577-578
Aplysina longissima, 650f
Apoda (order), 703, 703t, 705f, 706
Apolipoprotein B, 320-321
Apomixis, **857**
Apoplast route, **775**, 775f
Apoptosis, **305**, 1067, 1067f
in development, 390-391, 391f
genetic control of, 390-391, 391f
mechanism of, 390-391
Appendicular locomotion, 975
Appendix, **990**, 990f
Aquaculture, 1248

Antennapedia gene, 388, 494
Aquaporin, **98**, 104t, 772, 773f, 1050
Aqueous solution, 97
Aquifer, **1210**
Aquifex, 515f, 516, 550f
Arabidopsis
aquaporins of, 772
auxin transport in, 830
columella cells in, 739
CONSTANS gene in, 843
det2 mutant in, 817, 817f
development in, 375, 499
embryonic flower mutant in,
841, 841f
genome of, 358f, 364, 475f,
476-477, 479f, 486, 489, 595
GLABROUS3 mutant in,
735, 735f
HOBBIT gene in, 757-758, 758f
hot mutants in, 825
KANADI gene in, 747f
LEAFY COTYLEDON
gene in, 759
LEAFY gene in, 841
MONOPTEROS gene in,
758, 758f
overexpression of flowering
gene in, 841f
PHABULOSA gene in, 747f
PHAVOLUTA gene in, 747f
phytochrome genes in, 815f, 816
scarecrow mutant in, 740, 740f,
820, 820f
SHOOTMERISTEMLESS gene in,
756, 757f
short root mutant, 820, 820f
small RNAs in, 317
suspensor mutant in, 755, 756f
thaliana, 755, 757f, 759
too many mouths mutant in,
734, 734f
touch responses in, 821
transposons in, 484
trichome mutation in, 734f
vernalization in, 844
WEREWOLF gene in,
739-740, 740f
WOODEN LEG gene in, 759, 759f
YABBY gene in, 747f
Arachidonic acid, 943
Araneae (order), 681-682, 682f
Arbuscular mycorrhizae, **622**,
628, 628f
Archaea (domain), 13, 13f, 483,
514, **515**, 515f, 516t, 517f, 518t,
547, 549f
Archaea (kingdom), **514**
Archaeal viruses, 533
Archaebacteria, 516, 549f.
See also Prokaryote
bacteria versus, 547
cell wall of, 64, 548-549
characteristics of, 516, 516t
gene architecture of, 549
membrane lipids of, 548, 549f
nonextreme, 516
plasma membrane of, 63-64, 548
Archaefructus, 607, 607f
Archaeopteryx, 425, 425f, 712, 712f,
714, 714f

Archegonium, **594**, 594f
Archenteron, **638**, 639f, 1114
Archosaur, 709, 709f
Aristotle, 512
Armadillo, 525, 525f
Armillaria, 614, 629f
Arousal, state of consciousness, 905
ART. *See* Assisted reproductive
  technology
Arteriole, **1030**
Arteriosclerosis, **1033**
Artery, **1030**, 1030f
Arthropod, 641t, 643, 644, 678-687,
  679f-687f
  body plan of, 679-681, 679f-681f
  circulatory system of, 680, 680f
  classification of, 523f, 524-525
  economic importance of, 678
  excretory system of, 680f, 681
  exoskeleton of, 679-680, 679f
  groups of, 679t
  jointed appendages of, 680
  locomotion in, 976
  molting in, 680
  nervous system of, 680, 681f,
    901f, 902
  respiratory system of, 680-681,
    681f, 1006
  segmentation in, 523, 523f,
    639-640, 679, 679f
  taste in, 926, 926f
Arthropoda (phylum), 635, 641t,
  644, 645f, 678-687,
  679f-687f, 685t
Artificial selection, **10**, 403, 422-423,
  422f-423f
  domestication, 422-423, 423f
  laboratory experiments, 422, 422f
Artificial transformation, 558
Ascaris, 208, 641t, 663
Ascocarp, **624**, 624f
Ascomycetes, 615, 615f, 624-625, 624f
Ascomycota (phylum), 615, 615f,
  615t, 623-624
Ascospore, **624**, 624f
Ascus, **624**, 624f
Asexual reproduction, **572**
  in ascomycetes, 624-625
  in plants, 857-859, 858f
  in protists, 572
  in sponges, 651
  in zygomycetes, 621, 621f
Aspen, 859
Aspergillus flavus, 630, 630f
Aspirin, 348, 943
Assemblage, **1186**
Assembly, of virus particle, **533**
Assisted reproductive technology
  (ART), 1102
Assortative mating, **402**
Aster (mitosis), **195**, 196f
Asteroidea (class), 689, 689f, 690
Asthma, **1012**
Atherosclerosis, 55, **1033**, 1033f
Atmosphere
  of early earth, 509
  reducing, 509
Atmospheric circulation, 1231-1233,
  1231f-1232f

Atom, 2f, **3**, **18**-19
  chemical behavior of, 20, 20f
  energy within, 21, 21f
  isotopes of, 19-20, 19f
  neutral, 19
  scanning tunneling microscopy
    of, 18f
  structure of, 18-20, 19f
Atomic mass, **18**-19
Atomic number, **18**
ATP, **43**-44, 44f
  energy storage molecule, 112-113
  production of , 113, 113f. *See also*
    ATP synthase
    in electron transport chain,
      124, 124f, 135-136,
      135f, 136f
    in glycolysis, 127, 127f, 129
    in Krebs cycle, 132, 131f, 133f
    in photosynthesis, 148, 149f,
      151, 156-160, 156f,
      158f-159f
  regulation of aerobic respiration,
    138, 138f
  role in metabolism, 125
  structure of, 44f, 112, 112f
  synthesis of, 125-126, 125f, 126f
  uses of
    in active transport, 100-102,
      100f, 101f
    in coupled transport,
      101-102, 101f
    in endergonic reactions, 113,
      113f, 125
    in muscle contraction,
      971, 971f
    in protein folding, 51, 51f
    in sodium-potassium pump,
      100-101, 100f
ATP cycle, 113, 113f
ATP-dependent remodeling factor,
  317, 317f
ATP synthase, **126**, 126f, 136, 136f,
  156, 158-160, 159f
Atrial natriuretic hormone, 956, 1051
Atrial peptide, **343**
  genetically engineered, 343
Atrioventricular (AV) node, 1027,
  1028f, 1034
Atrioventricular (AV) valve,
  1026, 1027f
Atrium, **1023**, 1023f
Attachment
  in HIV infection cycle, 536-537
  of virus to host, 533
Auditory tube, 922
Australopithecine, 722-723
  early, 723
Australopithecus, 722
Australopithecus afarensis, 724
Autocrine signaling, 169-170
Autoimmune disease, 1075
Autologous blood donation, 1077
Automated DNA sequencing,
  337f, 339
Autonomic nervous system, **888**, 889f,
  909, 909t, 910, 910f, 911f
Autophosphorylation, 175-176, 175f
Autopolyploidy, **445**, 445f, 477, 479f

Autosome, **241**
  nondisjunction involving,
    250-251, 250f
Autotroph, **123**, **558**, 559, **1214**
Aux/IAA protein, 829-830, 830f
Auxin
  cytokinin and, 832f
  discovery of, 825, 827-828,
    827f-828f
  effects of, 828, 829f
  gravitropism and, 819, 820
  mechanism of action of,
    828-830, 829f
  phototropism and, 829f
  synthetic, 829f, 830-831
  thigmotropism and, 821
Auxin binding protein, 829
Auxin receptor, 829
Auxin response factor (ARF), 829
AV node. *See* Atrioventricular node
AV valve. *See* Atrioventricular valve
Avascular bone, **966**
Avery, Oswald, 257
Aves (class), 699f, **712**-715,
  712f, 714f-715f
Avian cholera, 1061
Avian influenza, 539, 1079
Avirulent pathogen, **811**
Axial locomotion, 975
Axil, **744**
Axillary bud, 730f, **744**, 744f,
  802, 803f
Axon, 872, 873t
  conduction velocities of,
    895-896, 895t
  diameter of, 895
  myelinated, 895-896, 895f,
    895t, 896f
  unmyelinated, 895-896, 895f, 895t
Aznalcóllar mine spill (Spain),
  799-800, 799f
Azolla, 599

B

B cell, 1062t, **1063**, 1063f
B lymphocyte, 1063, **1063**
Babbitt, Bruce, 1275
Bacillary dysentery, 560
Bacillus, 550f, 552
Bacillus anthracis, 550f, 561t
Bacillus thuringiensis insecticidal
  protein, 347-348
Bacon, Francis, 5
Bacteria, 550f-551f. *See also*
  Prokaryote
  ancient, 546, 546f
  archaebacteria versus, 547
  cell wall of, 64, 548-549
  endosymbiotic, 568
  flagella of, 64f, 65, 548,
    553, 553f
  genetically engineered, 564
  Gram staining of, 552-553,
    552f-553f
  intestinal, 564
  photosynthetic, 63-64, 64f, 150,
    156, 156f, 547, 548, 569-570
  plasma membrane of, 63-64, 93, 548

Bacteria (domain), 13, 13f, 483, **515**,
  515-516, 515f, 516t, 547, 549f
Bacteria (kingdom), **514**, 517f, 518t
Bacterial artificial chromosome
  (BAC), 330-331, 356
Bacterial disease
  in humans, 558,
    560-563, 561t, 562f
  in plants, 560
Bacteriochlorophyll, 559
Bacteriophage, **258**, 528, 530-531,
  530f, 533-534, 534f
  cloning vector, 330, 331f
  Hershey-Chase experiment with,
    258-259, 258f
  induction of, 533-534
  lysogenic cycle of, 533-534, 534f
  lytic cycle of, 533, 534f
  temperate, **533**
  virulent, **533**
Bacteriophage lambda, 533
  cloning vector, 330, 331f
Bacteriophage T2, 531f
Bacteriophage T4, 530f, 533
Bacteriorhodopsin, 95, 95f
Bait protein, in DNA-binding hybrid,
  341, 341f
Ball-and-socket joint, **967**, 968f
Bank (fishing on continental
  shelf), **1243**
Barley, genome of, 363, 476, 479f
Barnacle, 683-684, 683f
  competition among species of,
    1188, 1188f
Barometer, 1006
Baroreceptor, 919, **1034**, 1035f
Barr body, **243**, 243f, 251
Barro Colorado Island, 1221
Basal body, **79**, 79f
Basal ganglia, 902t, 904
Basal metabolic rate (BMR), **995**
Basal surface, 866
Base, 29-**30**
Base-pairs, **262**, 262f
Base substitution, **299**, 300f
Basidiocarp, **623**, 623f
Basidiomycetes, 615, 615f,
  622-623, 623f
Basidiomycota (phylum), 615, 615f,
  615t, 622
Basidiospore, **622**, 623f
Basidium, **622**, 623f
Basophil, **1062**, 1062t
Bat, 525f, 717-718, 717f
  pollination by, 854, 1196f
  vampire, 1155, 1155f
Bates, Henry, 1195
Batesian mimicry, **1195**,
  1195f, 1196
Batrachochytrium dendrobatidis,
  619, 630
Beadle, George, 6, 279
Bean, 760, 760f, 765f, 822, 823f
Bee
  chromosome number in, 189t
  pollination by, 852, 852f-853f
  solitary, 852
Beetle, species richness in,
  469-470, 469f

Behavior, 1132-1159. *See also*
  specific types
  adaptation to environmental
    change, 1164, 1164f
  adaptive significance of, 1148
  altruism, 1154-1157, 1155f-1157f
  cognitive, 1141, 1141f-1142f
  communication and,
    1144-1147, 1144f-1147f
  development of, 1139-1141
  foraging, 1148-1149, 1148f
  innate, 1133, 1133f
  learning and, 1135, 1135f,
    1137-1138, 1138f, 1140
  migratory, 1142-1144,
    1142f-1143f
  reproductive strategies,
    1150-1154, 1150f-1153f
  study of, 1133-1134, 1133f
  territorial, 1149, 1149f
Behavioral ecology, 1147-1149, **1148**
Behavioral genetics, **1135-1137**,
  1135f-1137f
  in fruit flies, 1135-1136
  in mice, 1136, 1136f
Behavioral genomics, 369
Behavioral isolation, 438t, 439, 439f
*Bergey's Manual of Systematic
  Bacteriology*, 550
Beta wave, 905
β barrel, 50, 95, 95f
β-oxidation, **141**, 142f
β-pleated sheet, **48**, 95, 95f
β α β motif, 50, 50f
Betacyanin, 824
Bicarbonate, 30
bicoid gene, **384**, 385f, 386
Bicuspid valve, **1026**
Biennial plants, **860**
Bilateral symmetry, **636**-637,
  636f-637f
Bilaterally symmetrical flower, **499**,
  849-850, 849f
Bilateria, 644f, 656-660, 657f,
  659f-661f
Bile, 983, 988f
Bile pigments, 989
Bile salts, 989
Bilirubin, 1077
Binary fission, **187**, 187f
Binocular vision, 721, **933**
Binomial name, **512**
Biochemical pathway, **118**, 118f
  evolution of, 118
  regulation of, 118-119, 119f
Biodiversity, 4, 1223-1226. *See also*
  Species richness
  biodiversity crisis, 1257-1261,
    1257f-1260f
  conservation biology, 1256-1278
  economic value of, 1261-1263,
    1261f-1263f
  ethical and aesthetic values
    of, 1263
  factors responsible for extinction,
    1264-1275
Bioenergetics, **107**
Biofilm, **548**, 561-562
Biogenic amine, **899**

Biogeochemical cycle, 1208-1214,
  1208f-1213f
  in forest ecosystem,
    1212-1213, 1213f
Biogeography, **430**, 432
  island, 1226-1227, 1226f
  pattersn of species diversity,
    1225, 1225f
Bioinformatics, **359**, 364
Biological community, 3f, **4**,
  1186-1187, 1186f-1187f
Biological species concept, **437**-438,
  438t, 463
  weaknesses in, 440-441
Biomarker, 547
Biome, **1235**-1238, 1235f-1238f
  climate and, 1236, 1236f
  distribution of, 1235f
  predictors of biome distribution,
    1236, 1236f
Biopharming, 348-349
Bioremediation, 564
Biosphere, 3f, **4**, 1230-1253
  influence of human activity on,
    1245-1253
Biostimulation, 564
Bioterrorism, 368, 368t
Biotic potential, **1173**
Bipedalism, 722, 723-724
Bipolar cell, **930**, 931f
Biramous appendage, **524**, 524f
Birch (*Betula*), 854f
Bird, 641t, 699f, 712-715, 712f,
  714f-715f
  altruism in, 1156-1157, 1157f
  bones of, 712
  brain of, 903, 903f
  characteristics of, 712, 715
  circulation in, 715, 1025, 1025f
  cost of reproduction in,
    1171, 1172f
  declining populations of
    songbirds, 1268, 1268f
  digestive tract of, 984, 984f
  evolution of, 425, 424f-425f, 463,
    466, 467f, 712, 712f, 714, 714f
  eyes of, 933
  fertilization in, 1088-1089,
    1088f-1089f, 1112f
  gastrulation in, 1114-1115, 1115f
  habituation in, 1137
  kidney of, 1043-1044, 1044f
  locomotion in, 976-977, 977f
  magnetic field detection by, 934
  migration of, 1142-1143,
    1143f, 1252
  nitrogenous wastes of, 1044, 1045f
  orders of, 713t
  parental care in, 464
  pollination by, 852-854, 853f
  present day, 715
  respiration in, 715, 1008, 1009f
  selection and beak sizes, 409-410,
    410f, 418-419, 418f-419f
  sex chromosomes of, 241t
  territorial behavior in, 1149, 1149f
  thermoregulation in, 715
Bird flu, 539, 1079
Birdsong, 1140, 1140f, 1145, 1149

Birth control, 1098-1101, 1099f,
  1099t, 1101f
Birth control pill. *See* Oral
  contraceptives
1,3 Bisphosphoglycetate, 127, 128f
Bithorax complex, 388f, **388**-389, 494
Bivalent, 209
Bivalve mollusk, 667, 668f, 669
Bivalvia (class), 671, 671f
Black walnut (*Fuglans nigra*), 807, 807f
Blackman, F. F., 150
Bladder
  swim, **701**-702, 701f
  urinary, **1045**, 1046f
Bladderwort (*Utricularia*), 794
Blade, of leaf, 730f, **747**
BLAST algorithm, 359
Blastocladiomycetes, 619-620, 620f
Blastocladiomycota (phylum), 615,
  615f, 619
Blastocoel, **1110**
Blastoderm, **1114**, 1115f
Blastodisc, **1111**
Blastomere, 373, 373f, 1110, 1112
Blastopore, 392f, **635**, **638**,
  639f, 1114
Blastula, **635**, 1110
Bleaching (global warming), 1252
Blending inheritance, 399
Blinking, 908
Blood, 869t, 870, 1018-1021,
  1018f-1021f
  functions of, 1018-1019
  regulation of, 1034-1035, 1035f
Blood acidosis, 30
Blood alkalosis, 30
Blood cells, 1019f
Blood clotting, 1021, 1021f
Blood flow, 1034-1035
Blood group
  ABO, 90t, 233t, 234-**235**,
    235f, 397
  genetic variation in, 397-398
Blood plasma, 1019
Blood pressure
  measurement of,
    1029-1030, 1029f
  sensing, 919
Blood transfusion, 1077
Blood typing, 1077
Blood vessel, 1026-1030
  characteristics of, 1030-1033,
    1030f-1033f
  paracrine regulation of, 942-943
  tissue layers of, 1030, 1030f
Blue crab, 644f
Blue-footed booby, 439, 439f
Blue-light receptors, in plants,
  818, 818f
BMR. *See* Basal metabolic rate
Bobolink (*Dolichonyx oryzivorus*),
  1143, 1143f
Body cavity
  evolution of, 637f, 638
  kinds of, 638
Body plan
  animal, evolution of, 636-640,
    636f-637f, 639f
  of vertebrates, 864-865, 865f

Body position, sensing of, 924-925,
  924f-925f
Body size, metabolic heat and,
  881-882, 882f
Body temperature, regulation of.
  See Thermoregulation
Bohr effect, **1014**
Bohr, Niels, 18
Bohr shift, **1014**
Boll weevil (*Anthonomus grandis*),
  684f
Bolus, **985**
Bone, 869t, 870, 963-967
  avascular, **966**
  compact, 965f, **966**
  development of, 963-966, 964f
    endochondral, 965-966, 965f
    intramembranous, 963,
      964f, 965
  medullary, 965f, **966**
  remodeling of, 966-967,
    966f-967f
  spongy, 965f, **966**
  structure of, 965f, 966
  vascular, **966**
Bone morphogenetic protein 4 (BMP4),
  1124, 1124f
Bony fish, 701-702, 701f, 1004-1006,
  1004f, 1042
Book lung, **681**
Borrelia burgdorferi, 550f, 561t
Bottleneck effect, 402f, **403**, 403f
Bottom-up effect, **1219**,
  1221-1223, 1222f
Botulism, 550f, 554, 561t
Bowman's capsule, 1042,
  1047, 1047f
Box jellyfish, 655, 655f
Boysen-Jensen, Peter, 827
Brachiopoda (phylum), 642t, 643,
  644f, 676, 677-678, 677f-678f
Brachyury gene, 496-497, 497f
Bract, **749**
Bradykinin, 942
Brain, 902t
  of amphibians, 903, 903f
  of birds, 903, 903f
  divisions of, 902-903, 902t
  of fish, 902-903, 903f
  of mammals, 903, 903f
  primitive, 902
  of reptiles, 903, 903f
  size of, 903, 903f
  of vertebrates, 903f
Brainstem, 905
Branch point (nucleotide), 290, 290f
Branchial chamber, 1004
Branching diagrams, 457, 457f
Branching morphogenesis, **1118**
Branchiostoma, 696, 696f
  Hox genes in, 389
Branchless gene, in *Drosophila*, 1118
Brassica
  evolution of, 495, 495f
  genome of, 479f
Brassica juncea, 799
Brassinosteroid, 826t, 834, 834f
Bread mold, 279
Breakbone fever, 1253

Breathing, 1009-1012, 1010f-1012f
mechanics of, 1002,
1010-1011, 1010f
negative pressure, **1007**
positive pressure, **1007**
rate of, 1010-1011
regulation of, 1011-1012, 1011f
Brenner, Sydney, 282, 283, 299
Briggs, Winslow, 828, 829f
Bright-field microscope, 62t
Brittle star, 689, 689f, 690
Bronchi, 1007, 1008f
Brood parasite, **1140**, 1140f
Brown algae, 517f, 518, 569, 580,
580f, 581f
Brush border, 988
Bryophyte, 463f, 593-595, 593f-595f
Bryozoa (phylum), 641t, 643, 644f,
676-677, 677f
Bt crops, 347-348
Budding, virus release from
cells, 537
Buffer, **30**, 30f
Bulb (plant), 746, 746f
Bulbourethral gland, 1091f, 1092
Bulk transport, **102**
Bumblebee (*Bombus*), 852f
Bushmeat, 471
Buttercup (*Ranunculus*), 741f
alpine, New Zealand,
450-451, 450f
Butterfly, 807, 880
effect of global warming on,
1252, 1252f
eyespot on wings of, 498, 498f
metapopulations of, 1167, 1168f
mimicry in, 1195-1196, 1195f
Buttress root, 743, 743f

C

C_3 photosynthesis, **161**, **164**,
164f, 165f
C_4 photosynthesis,
164-165, 164f, 165f, 749
Cactus finch (*Geospiza scandens*),
9f, 418f, 441, 448, 448f
Cadherin, 83f, **84**, 84f, 391-392
Cadherin domain, 391
Caecilian, 703, 703t, 705f, 706
Caenorhabditis elegans
development in, 373, 374f,
390-391, 391f, 644, 662
small RNAs in, 317
transposons in, 484
CAL gene, 495, 495f
Calciferol. *See* Vitamin D
Calcitonin, 320, 321f, **952**-953
Calcitonin gene-related peptide
(CGRP), 320, 321f
Calcium
in fertilization, 1108, 1108f
homeostasis, 952-953, 953f
in muscle contraction,
972-973, 972f-973f
as second messenger,
181-182, 182f
California condor (*Gymnogyps
californianus*), 1276-1277

Callus (plant), 858f, 859
Calmoudulin, 45t, 181, 182f
Calorie, 108
Calvin cycle, 160-163, **161**, 161f
carbon fixation in, 160-163,
161f, 547
discovery of, 161
Calvin, Melvin, 161
Calyx, **848**
CAM plants, **164**, 165, 165f
Cambrian explosion, **645**-646, 646f
Camel, 525
cAMP. *See* Cyclic AMP
Campylobacter pylori, 562
Canaliculi, 870, **965**, 965f
Cancer, 175, **202**
of breast, 808
cell cycle control in, 202-204, 203f
of cervix, 541
hormonal responses in, 957
lung, **1012**, 1012f
telomerase and, 273
treatment of gene therapy, 345t
viruses and, 540-541
Candida, 630
Candida milleri, 625
CAP. *See* Catabolite activator protein
5′ Cap mRNA, **288**, 188f
Capillary, **1030**, 1030f, 1031
Capsid, viral, **529**, 529f
Capsule, of bacteria, 63f, 64, **553**
Captive breeding,
1276-1277, 1276f
Carbohydrates, 33, 36f, 37, **38**-41
catabolism of, 124, 138
function of, 37t
structure of, 36f
Carbon
chemistry of, 24, 34-37
isotopes of, 19, 19f
in plants, 790, 790t, 795-797,
795f-796f
prokaryotes need for, 559
Carbon-12, 19, 19f
Carbon-13, 19, 19f
Carbon-14, 19, 19f, 20
Carbon cycle, 1208-1209, 1208f
Carbon dioxide
atmospheric, 1209, 1252, 1251f
as electron acceptor, 139
from ethanol fermentation, 140
from Krebs cycle, 131-132, 133f
from pyruvate oxidation, 130, 130f
transport in blood,
1002-1015, 1015f
use in photosynthesis,
147-151, 149f
Carbon fixation, **148**, 151, 160-163,
161f, 546-547, 563, 1209
Carbonic acid, 30, 114
Carbonic anhydrase, 114
Carbonyl group, 35, 35f
Carboxyl group, 35, 35f, 44-46, 46f
Cardiac cycle, **1026**, 1027f
Cardiac muscle, **871**-872, 871t, 872f
Cardiac output, **1034**
Cardioaccelerator center, **1034**
Cardioinhibitory center, **1034**
Cardiovascular disease, 1033, 1033f

Carnivore, 525, 525f, **982**
digestive system of, 991f
human removal of, 1220-1221
primary, **1215**, 1215f
secondary, **1215**, 1215f
teeth of, 984, 984f
top, 1218
in trophic level ecosystem, **1215**,
1215f, 1218
Carnivorous plants, 793-794, 794f
Carotene, 153-154, 348, 348f
Carotenoid, 152f, **153**-154,
153f, 853
Carotid body, **1011**, 1011f
Carpel, 606, **608**, 608f, 848f, 849
Carrier protein, 90t, **96**, 97,
97f, 104t
Carrying capacity, **1174**
Cartilage, 869t, 870, 963
Cartilaginous fish, 698f, 700-701,
700f, 1043, 1065
Cassava (*Mannihot esculenta*),
805, 806t
Castor bean (*Ricinus communis*),
807, 807f
Cat
coat color in, 233t, 235, 235f,
243, 243f
ovary in, 1096f
Catabolism, **117**
of proteins and fats, 140-142,
141f, 142f
Catabolite activator protein (CAP),
310-311, 310f
Catalyst, **25**, 37, **111**-112, 111f
Catecholamine, 899
Caterpillar, 809
Cation, **19**, 96
Cattle, 475f, 525f
Caudal protein, **386**, 386f
Caudata. *See* Urodela (order)
Caudipteryx, 714, 714f
Cavitation, **777**, 777f
Cayuga Lake, 1218, 1218f
CD4 cells, **535**
cdc2 gene, 199
Cdc2 kinase, 200-201, 201f
Cdk. *See* Cyclin-dependent
protein kinase
Cdk1, 200
cDNA library, 332, 332f
Cech, Thomas J., 116
Cecum, **990**, 990f
Cedar Creek experimental fields,
1223-1224, 1223f
Cell(s)
earliest, 546, 546f
in hierarchical organization
of living things, 2f, **3**
as information-processing
systems, 14
origin of, 512, 546, 546f
shape of, 390
size of, 60, 61f
in prokaryotes, 548
structure of, 62-63, 62f
visualizing structure of, 60-62
Cell adhesion, 83-85

Cell adhesion protein, 93, 94f
Cell body, of neuron, 872, 873t,
889, 889f
Cell communication, 168-183
Cell cycle, **192**-198
duration of, 192-193, 201-202
genetic analysis of, 199
growth factors and, 202
Cell cycle control, 198-204
in cancer cells, 202-204, 203f, 204f
checkpoints, 200, 200f
history of investigation into,
198-200
in multicellular eukaryotes,
201-202, 202f
Cell death, 390-391, 391f
Cell determination, **375**, 1117
Cell division, 186-204. *See also*
Cell cycle
in animal cells, 188f
during development, 372,
373-375, 373f-374f, 390
in prokaryotes, 187-188, 188f, 548
in protists, 188f
in yeast, 188f
Cell identity, 82, 82t
Cell junction, 83-85, 83f, 84f, 85f
Cell-mediated immunity, **1063**,
1066-1068, 1066t, 1067f, 1069f
Cell membrane, 81t
Cell migration, in development,
391-392, 392f
Cell plate, 195f, **197**-198, 198f
Cell signaling
between cells
autocrine signaling, 169-170
by direct contact, 169,
169f, 170
endocrine signaling, 169,
169f, **170**
paracrine signaling, 169,
169f, **170**
synaptic signaling, 169,
169f, **170**
receptor proteins, 171-178
Cell surface
of prokaryotes, 553-554
of protists, 571
Cell surface marker, 63, 82, 82t, 90t,
91, 93, 94f
Cell surface receptor, 93, 94f,
171-173, 172f, 172t
Cell theory, **12**, 12f, 59-63
Cell wall, **63**, 63f
of archaebacteria, 64, 548
of bacteria, 64, 548, 552
of eukaryotes, 67f, 78t, 81t
of fungi, 616
of plant cells, 40, 67f, 80, 80f, 81t,
393, 393f, 731, 731f
primary, **80**, 80f
of prokaryotes, 63, 63f, 64, 81t,
548-549, 552-554, 552f-553f
secondary, **80**, 80f
Cellular blastoderm, **384**, 384f, 1110
Cellular immune response, 345
Cellular organization, as characteristic
of life, 2-3f, 3, 508, 508f
Cellular respiration, **123**

Cellular slime mold, 585, 585f
Cellulose, 37t, **39**, 40-41, 40f
    breakdown of, 41, 617, 620, 625
Celsius, 108
Centers for Disease Control
    (CDC), 368
Centipede, 641t, 679t, 686-687, 687f
Central chemoreceptor, **927**
Central Dogma, **280**, 280f
Central nervous system, **872**,
    901-909, 901f-908f
Central vacuole, **65**
Centriole, 66f, **76**-77, 77f, 81t
Centromere, 189f, 191, **193**, 193f, 211
Centrosome, 76-77
Cephalization, **637**
Cephalopod, 667-668, 668f
Cephalopoda (class), 668f, 671-672,
    671f-672f
Cercariae, 658, 659f
Cercomeromorpha (class),
    659-660, 660f
Cerebellum, **902**, 902t
Cerebral cortex, 902t, **904**, 904f,
    905f, 932-933
Cerebral hemisphere, **903**, 904f
Cerebrum, 902t, **903**
Cervical cap (birth control),
    1099t, 1100
cGMP. *See* Cyclic GMP (cGMP)
CGRP. *See* Calcitonin
    gene-related peptide
Chaetae, 673f, **674**
Chaetognatha (phylum), 642t,
    643, 645f
Chagas disease, 487, 488, 488f, 574
Chain terminator, 336
Chambered nautilus (*Nautilus
    pompilius*), 667, 667f, 671-672
Chancre, 562
Channel-linked receptor, 171-172,
    172f, 172t
Channel protein, **96**, 97f, 104t
Chaperone protein, **51**, 51f
Chara, 592, 592f
Character displacement, **447**,
    447f, 1190
Character state, **458**
Charales, 521, 521f, 592, 592f
Chargaff, Ertwin, 260
Chargaff's rules, 260
Charging reaction, tRNA, **292**, 292f
Charophyte, 589, **592**, 592f
Checkpoint, cell cycle, 198,
    200, 200f
Chelicerae, **681**
Chelicerata (class), 679t,
    681-682, 682f
Chelonia (order), 707t, 710, 710f
Chemical bond, 23, 25. *See also specific
    types of bonds*
Chemical defenses
    of animals, 1194, 1194f
    of plants, 1193
Chemical digestion, 982
Chemical messenger, 938-939, 938f
Chemical reaction, 25
    activation energy, 111-112, 111f
    energy changes in, 110-111, 111f

Chemical synapse, **170**, 896
Chemiosmosis, 134-136, 134f, 135f,
    136f, 137f, 156, 158-159
Chemoautotroph, **1214**
Chemoheterotroph, **559**
Chemolithoautotroph, **559**
Chemolithotroph, 548
Chemoreceptor, **916**,
    925-927, 926f-927f
    central, **927**
    internal, 927
    peripheral, **927**
Chewing, 967, 982, 984
"Chewing the cud," 991
Chiasmata, **210**, 211f, 215
    terminal, 211
Chicken, 189t
    clutch size in, 414
    development in, 1110f
    genome of, 482
Chicken pox, 529, 532t, 1061
Chief cells, 986, 986f
Chihuahua, 423f
Childbirth, 947, 1128, 1128f. *See also*
    Uterine contractions
    positive feedback during, 878f
Chilling, of plant, 825
Chimpanzee (*Pan*), 457, 457f
    chromosome number in, 189t
    cognitive behavior in, 1141, 1141f
    genome of, 362-363, 475f, 476,
        482, 482f, 484
Chiral molecule, 35, 35f
Chitin, 37t, **41**, 41f, 616, 962
Chiton, 668f, 670, 670f
Chitridiomycetes, **619**
Chlamydia, 561f
    heart disease and, 563
    sexually-transmitted disease,
        562-563, 562f
Chlamydia trachomatis, 561t, 562
Chlamydomonas, 244, 591, 591f, 595
Chloramphenicol, 554
Chlorella, 154
Chlorofluorocarbons, 1248-1250
Chlorophyll, **148**, 149f
    absorption spectra of, 152, 152f
    action spectrum of, **153**, 153f
    structure of, 152-153, 152f
Chlorophyll *a*, 152, 152f
Chlorophyll *b*, 152, 152f
Chlorophyta (phylum), 521, 521f, 582
Chlorophyte, 591-594, 591f-592f
Chloroplast, 67f, **74**-75, 74f, 78t,
    81t, 518t
    diversity of, 569
    DNA of, 74, 74f
    of euglenoids, 573-574, 574f
    genetic code in, 284
    genome of, 364
    maternal inheritance, 244
    origin of, 517, 517f,
        569-570, 569f
    photosynthesis, 147-165
Choanocyte, 641t, 650f, **651**
Choanoflagellate, 520, 571f, 583,
    583f, 644f
Cholecystokinin (CCK), **993**, 993f,
    994t, 996, 997, 997f

Cholera, 180, 534, 560, 561t
Cholesterol, 54
    in cardiovascular disease, 1033
    structure of, 54f
    uptake by cells, 103
Chondrichthyes (class), 699t,
    700-701, 700f
Chondroitin, 870
Chordata (phylum), 513f, 641t, 645f,
    693, 694-695, 695f
Chordate
    characteristics of, 694, 694f
    eyes of, 928f, 929
    nonvertebrate, 695-696,
        695f-696f
    segmentation in, 523, 523f,
        639-640
    vertebrate, 696-697, 697f-698f
Chorion, **706**, 708f, 1089
Chorionic villi sampling, 253, 253f
Chromatid, **191**, 191f, 193, 193f.
    See also Sister chromatid(s)
Chromatin, **68**, 68f, 190, 190f,
    316-317, 316f-317f
Chromatin-remodeling complex, **317**
Chromosomal mutation,
    300-301, 301f
Chromosomal theory of inheritance,
    240-241, 240f
    exceptions to, 244
Chromosome, **65**, 78t, 81t, 193
    artificial, 330-331, 356
    bacterial artificial chromosome
        (BAC), 330-331, 356
    banding patterns, 353, 354f
    discovery of, 189
    duplication of, 480f-481f, 481
    of eukaryotes, 65, 189-191,
        189f-191f, 189t, 548
    fusion of, 482
    homologous, **191**, 191f,
        209-210, 209f
    of prokaryotes, 548
    structure of, 189-191, 190f-191f
    yeast artificial chromosome
        (YAC), 331, 356
Chromosome number, 189, 189t,
    207-208
Chronic obstructive pulmonary
    disease (COPD), **1012**
Chrysalis, **686**
Chrysophyta (phylum), 580
Chylomicron, **990**
Chyme, **987**
Chymotrypsin, **988**
Chytrid, 615, 615f, **619**, 619f
Chytridiomycetes, 619
Chytridiomycosis, **630**, 630f
Chytridiomycota (phylum), 615, 615f,
    615t, 619-620, 619f
Cichlid fish
    Lake Barombi Mbo, 446
    Lake Malawi, 495-496, 496f
    Lake Victoria, 449-450, 449f, 1271
    pike cichlid, 412-413, 412f
Cigarette smoking. *See* Smoking
Cilia, 66f, 79-**80**, 79f, 80f. *See also*
    Ciliate
Ciliate, 284, 576, 579-580, 578f

Circadian rhythm, in plants, **818**,
    822, 823f
Circulatory system, **638**, **874**, 874f,
    1018-1035
    of amphibians, 703, 1024,
        1024f
    of annelids, 673f, 674
    of arthropods, 680, 680f
    of birds, 715, 1025, 1025f
    closed, **638**, 1022f, 1023
    of fish, 699, 1023, 1023f
    of invertebrates, 1022-1023,
        1022f
    of mammals, 1025, 1025f
    of mollusk, 669
    open, **638**, 1022f, 1023
    of reptiles, 709, 709f, 1024
    of vertebrates, 1023-1025,
        1023f-1025f
Cisternae, of Golgi body, **71**, 71f
Cisternal space, **69**
Citrate, 131, 132, 133f
Citrate synthetase, 138, 138f
Citric acid cycle. *See* Krebs cycle
Clade, **459**
Cladistics, **458**-461, 459f-460f
Cladogram, **459**, 459f
Cladophyll, 746f, 747
Clam, 666, 667, 668, 671, 671f
Clark's nutcracker (*Nucifraga
    columbiana*), 1138, 1138f
Class (taxonomic), **512**, 513f, 514
Classical conditioning, **1137**
Classification, **461**, 512-514
    of animals, 522-525, 640
    grouping organisms, 514-520
    of organisms, 512-514
    of prokaryotes, 549-550,
        549f-551f
    of protists, 520, 520f,
        570-571f, 571
    systematics and, 461-464,
        462f-464f
    of viruses, 519-520
Clean Air Acts, 421
Cleavage, **373**, 373f, 635t, 1106t,
    1110-1112, 1110f-1112f
    holoblastic, **1110**-1111,
        1111f, 1111t
    in insects, 1110
    in mammals, 1112, 1112f
    meroblastic, **1111-1112**,
        1111t, 1112f
    radial, **638**, 639f
    spiral, **638**, 639f, 643
Cleavage furrow, 195f, **197**, 197f
Climate. *See also* Global climate
    change, Global warming
    biomes and, 1236, 1236f
    effects on ecosystems, 1230-1235,
        1230f-1234f
    El Niño and, 1243-1244,
        1244f, 1252
    elevation and, 1234, 1234f
    human impact on climate change,
        1250-1253
    microclimate, 1235
    selection to match climatic
        conditions, 404

solar energy and, 1230-1235, 1231f-1232f
species richness and, 1224f, 1225
See also Global warming
Clinical trials, gene therapy, 345, 345t
Clitellata (class), 675-676, 675f-676f
Clitellum, 673f, 675
Clitoris, **1094**, 1094f
Clonal selection, **1063**
Clone, **330**
Clone-by-clone sequencing, **357**, 357f
Cloning
    DNA libraries, **331**-332, 331f
    host/vector systems, 330-331, 331f
    identifying specific DNA in complex mixtures, 332-333
    isolating specific clones from library, 333, 333f
    of plants, 858f, 859
    reproductive, **381**
    of sheep, 381, 381f
    therapeutic, **383**, 383f
Cloning vector, **330**
    expression vectors, **342**
    plasmids, 330, 331f
Clonorchis sinensis, 658, 659f
Closed circulatory system, **638**, 1022f, 1023
Clostridium botulinum, 550f, 561t
Clover, 842f
Club moss, 598, 601t
Clutch size, in birds, 414, 1172, 1172f
Cnidaria (phylum), 635t, 636, 636f, 637, 641t, 644f, 652-655, 652f-653f
    body plan of, 653, 653f
    body structure of, 652, 652f
    circulatory system of, 1022, 1022f
    classes of, 654-655
    digestive cavity of, 982, 982f
    life cycle of, 653, 653f
    nervous system of, 901-902, 901f
Coactivator, **174**, 314-315, 315f
Coal, 1246
Coastal ecosystem, destruction of, 1248
Cocaine, 900, 900f
Coccidioides posadasii, 625
Coccus, 552
Cochlea, 921f, **922**-923, 923f
Cocklebur, 842f
Coding strand, **280**, 285f, 286f
Codominance, 233t, **234**, 234f
Codon, **282**, 283t, 298f
    spaced or unspaced, 282-283
    start, **283**
    stop (nonsense), **283**, 296f, 297
Coelom, 637f, **638**
    formation of, 639, 639f
Coelomate, 637f
Coenzyme, **117**
Coevolution, **1193**
    mutualism and, 1198
    of plants and animals, 807, 1193-1194, 1193f, 1196
    predation and, 1193
Cofactor, **117**

Cognition, animal, 1141, 1141f-1142f
Cognitive behavior, **1141**
Cohesin, **191**, 191f, 193, 193f, 201
Cohesion, 26, 27f, 27t
Coleochaetales, 521, 521f, 592, 592f
Coleoptera (order), 684f, 685t
Coleoptile, 765, 765f
Coleorhiza, 765, 765f
Collagen, 45, 81, 81f, 392, 868, 868f, 870
Collar cell. *See* Choanocyte
Collared flycatcher, 442, 442f
Collecting duct, **1047**, 1047f
Collenchyma cells, **736**, 736f
Colloblast, **656**
Colon, **990**. *See also* Large intestine
Colon cancer, 990
Colonial flagellate hypothesis, for origin of metazoans, **645**
Colonization, human influence on, 1270-1271
Color blindness, 227t, 242, **933**
Color vision, 930, 930f
Coloration, warning, 1194, 1195f
Colorectal cancer. *See* Colon cancer
Columella root cap, 739, 739f
Columnar epithelium, 866, 867t
    pseudostratified, 867t
    simple, 866, 867t
Comb jelly, 641t, 656, 656f
Combination joint, **967**, 968f
Combined DNA Index System (CODIS), 355
Commensalism, 564, **626**, 1197, 1197f
Communicating junction, 83f, 84-85
Communication, animal, 1144-1147, 1144f-1147f
Community, 3f, **4**, **1186**-1187, 1186f-1187f
    across space and time, 1187, 1187f
    concepts of, 1186
    fossil records of, 1187
Community ecology, 1185-1204
Compact bone, 965f, **966**
Compaction, 1112
Companion cells, 738, 738f
Comparative anatomy, 11, 11f
Comparative biology, 464-470, 465f-469f
Comparative genomics, 362-363, 474-477, 475f, 500
    medical applications of, 487-488, 488f
Comparator, **876**
Compartmentalization
    in eukaryotes, 517, 518-519, 548
    in prokaryotes, 548
Competition
    among barnacle species, 1188, 1188f
    direct and indirect effects of, 1200-1201, 1201f
    effect of parasitism on, 1200
    experimental studies of, 1191-1192, 1191f
    exploitative, **1188**
    interference, **1188**

interspecific, **1188**, 1191, 1191f
    reduction by predation, 1199-1200, 1200f
    resource, 1190-1191, 1190f
    sperm, **1151**
Competitive exclusion, **1189**-1190, 1189f
Competitive inhibitor, **117**, 117f
Complement system, **1059-1060**
Complementary base-pairing, **43**, 43f, 262, 262f, 265, 265f
    base-pairs, 262, 262f
Complete flower, **848**, 848f
Complexity, as characteristic of life, 3
Compound, 23
Compound eye, 414, 414f, **680**, 680f, 681f
Compound leaf, **748**, 748f
Compsognathus, 714
Concentration gradient, 96, 100
Concurrent flow, 1005, 1005f
Condensation, 37
Condensin, **191**, 193, 201
Conditioning
    classical (pavlovian), **1137**
    operant, **1138**
Condom, 1099f, 1099t, 1100
Conduction (heat transfer), 880
Cone (eye), **930**, 930f, 931f
Confocal microscope, 62t
Confuciornis, 714f
Congression, 196
Conidia, **624**, 624f
Conifer, 602t, **603**, 603f, 607f
Coniferophyta (phylum), 602t
Conjugation, **554**
    in bacteria, 554-556, 555f
        gene transfer by, 555-556, 556f
    in ciliates, 579, 579f
Conjugation bridge, 555, 555f
Connective tissue, **864**, 868, 868f, 869t, 870
    dense, **868**, 869t
    dense irregular, 868
    dense regular, 868
    loose, **868**, 869t
    special, **868**, 870
Connell, Joseph, 1188
Consensus sequence, **357**
Conservation biology, 1256-1278
Conservation of synteny, **482**, 483f
Conservative replication, 263-265, 263f
CONSTANS gene, of *Arabidopsis*, 843
Constitutive heterochromatin, 359
Consumer, **1215**, 1215f
Consumption, of resources, 1181
Contig, **353**, 357
Continental drift, 432
Continental shelf, 1241f, 1242-1243
Continuous variation, 232, 233f
Contraception, 1098-1101, 1099f, 1099t, 1101f
Contractile root, 742, 743f
Contractile vacuole, 73, 99, 103
Control experiment, **6**
Controlling elements, 480
Conus arteriosus, **1023**, 1023f

Convection (heat transfer), 880
Convergent evolution, **430**, 430-432, 431f, 458, 464-465, 498-499, 498f, 502
Cooksonia, 596, 596f
COPD, **1012**
Coprophagy, 992
Copy numbers, 486
Coral, 636, 641t, 654
Coral reef, 654-655, **1243**, 1243f, 1252
Coriolis effect, **1232**-1233, 1232f
Cork, 745f
Cork cambium, **732**, 733f, 744, 745, 745f
Cork cells, 745
Corm, 746
Corn (*Zea mays*), 164, 369f, 743f, 765f, 836f
    artificial selection in, 422, 423f
    chromosome number in, 189t
    endosperm of, 760, 760f
    epistasis in, 236, 236f
    genome of, 363f, 475f, 476, 479f, 489
    grain color in, 233t, 235-236, 236f, 245-246, 245f
    oil content of kernels, 422
    recombination in, 245, 245f
    transgenic, 347
Cornea, **929**, 929f
Corolla, **848**, 848f
Coronary artery, **1029**
Corpus callosum, 902t, **903-904**, 904f
Corpus luteum, **1097**, 1097f
Correns, Carl, 240, 244
Cortex (plant), **741**, 741f, 744
Cortical granule, **1108**
Corticosteroid, 954
Corticotropin, 947
Corticotropin-releasing hormone (CRH), 949
Cortisol, 943f, 954
Corynebacterium diphtheriae, 534
Cost of reproduction, **1171**
Costa Rica, biosphere reserves in, 1277, 1277f
Cotransduction frequency, 556-557
Cotton
    genome of, 479f
    transgenic, 347
Cotyledon, **759**
Countercurrent flow, **1005**, 1005f
Countercurrent heat exchange, 881, 881f
Countertransport, 102
Coupled transport, 101-102, 101f, 104t
Courtship behavior/signaling, 439, 439f, 443, 443f, 1144f, 1145, 1152, 1152f
    of *Anolis* lizards, 443, 443f
    of blue-footed boobies, 439, 439f
    of lacewings, 439, 439f
Covalent bond, 23t, 24-25, 24f
Cowper's gland, 1091f, 1092
Cowpox, 1061
COX. *See* Cyclooxygenase
COX-2 inhibitor, 943

Crab, 641t, 682, 683, 683f
Cranial neural crest cells, 1120
Crassulacean acid metabolism, **164**
Crassulacean acid pathway, 165
Craton, 546
Crawling, cellular, 79
Crayfish, 683
Creighton, Harriet, 245-246, 245f
Cretinism, 952
CRH. *See* Corticotropin-releasing
    hormone
Cri-du-chat syndrome, 300
Crick, Francis, 259-263, 261f, 280,
    282, 283, 299
Crinoidea (class), 689f
Cro-Magnons, 725, 725f
Crocodile, 699f, 707t, 711,
    711f, 1025
    parental care in, 464, 465f
Crocodylia (order), 699f, 707t, 710f,
    711, 711f
Crop plant
    artificial selection in, 422, 423f
    breeding of, 489
    transgenic, 346-349
Cross-fertilization, 223, 223f
Cross-pollination, 223, 223f, 851
Crossing over, 209f, **210**, 210f, 211,
    212f, 215, 216f, 244-246, 245f
    multiple crossovers, 247, 247f
Crown gall, 832, 833f
CRP. *See* Cyclic AMP (cAMP)
    response protein
Crustacean, 679t, 682-684, 682f-683f
    body plan in, 682, 683f
    decapod, 683, 683f
    habitats of, 682
    reproduction in, 682-683
    sessile, 683-684, 683f
Ctenidia, **668**
Ctenophora (phylum), 642t, 643,
    644f, **656**, 656f
Cuboidal epithelium, 866, 867t
    simple, 866, 867t
Cubozoa (class), **655**, 655f
Cuenot, Lucien, 233
Culex, 686f
Cultivation, 788-789, 788f
Cutaneous respiration, **1006**
Cuticle, of plant, **734**
Cutin, **734**
Cuttlefish, 667, 668, 672
Cyanobacteria, 64, 64f, 143, 148,
    152, 517f, 547, 548, 554f, **559**,
    563. *See also* Lichen
Cyanogenic glycosides, 805,
    806t, 807
Cycad, 602t, 603, **605**, 605f, 607f
Cycadophyta (phylum), 602t,
    605, 605f
Cyclic AMP (cAMP), as second
    messenger, **173**, 179-181, 180f
Cyclic AMP (cAMP) response protein
    (CRP), **310**-311, 310f
Cyclic GMP (cGMP), 174, 932
    signal transduction in
        photoreceptors, 932, 932f
Cyclic photophosphorylation, 156,
    156f, 160

Cyclin, **199**-200, 199f, 373, 374f
    degradation of, 323
    discovery of, 199
Cyclin-dependent protein kinase
    (Cdk), **199**-200, 199f, 200f,
    201-202, 202f, 373, 374f, 375
Cycliophora (phylum), 642t, 644f,
    660, 661f
CYCLOIDIA gene, of snapdragons,
    499, 849-850, 849f
Cyclooxygenase-1 (COX-1), 943
Cyclooxygenase-2 (COX-2), 943
Cyclosome, 201
Cysteine, 35f
Cystic fibrosis, 51-52, 227t, 233,
    249t, 335, 484
    gene therapy for, 345, 345t
Cytochrome, 45t
Cytochrome b_{6-f} complex, **157**-158,
    158f, 159f
Cytochrome bc_1, 134, 134f
Cytochrome c, 134, 134f
Cytokine, **942**, **1067**-1068, 1069f
Cytokinesis, **192**, 192f, 194f, 195f,
    197, 212f-213f, 214
    in animal cells, 197, 197f
    in fungi, 198
    in plant cells, 197-198, 198f
Cytokinin, 826t, 831-832,
    831f-832f
    synthetic, 831f
Cytological maps, 353
Cytoplasm, **62**, 892t
Cytoplasmic receptor, 1057
Cytosine, 42, 42f, 259f, 260, 262
Cytoskeleton, **65**, 67f, 75-79, 76f, 78t
    attachments to, 93, 94f
Cytosol, **62**
Cytotoxic T cell, 1062t, **1066**-1067,
    1066t, 1067f

D

2,4-D, 829f, **830**
Dachshund, 423f
Dalton (unit of mass), 19
Dance language, of honeybees,
    1146, 1146f
Darevsky, Ilya, 1085
Dark-field microscope, 62t
Dark reaction, 150
Darwin, Charles, 399, 403, 412, 1156.
    See also Galápagos finch
    critics of, 432-433
    invention of theory of natural
        selection, 9-11
    Malthus and, 10
    On the Origin of Species, 8, 10, 397
    photograph of, 8f
    plant studies, 825, 827
    theory of evolution, 8-10, 397
    voyage on *Beagle*, 1, 1f, 8, 9f,
        10, 418
Darwin, Francis, 827
Dating, of fossils, 424, 424f
Day-neutral plant, 842f, **843**
DDT, 577-578, 1245, 1245f
Deamination, **141**
    of amino acids, 141, 141f

Decapentaplegic protein, in
    Drosophila, 1117, 1117f
Decapod crustacean, 683, 683f
Deciduous forest, temperate,
    1238, 1238f
Deciduous plant, 860
Decomposer, 563, **1215**
Decomposition, 563
Deductive reasoning, **4**-5, 5f
Deep sea, 1244-1245, 1244f
Deer, 525f
Defensin, **805**, 1057, 1057f
Deforestation, 1210, 1210f,
    1246-1247
Degeneracy, **284**
Dehydration reaction, **37**, 37f
Dehydrogenation, **123**
Deinococcus, 550f
Delamination, **1113**
Delayed hypersensitivity, 1076
Deletion, 282-283, **300**, 301f
Delta wave, 905
Demography, **1168**
Denaturation, of proteins, **52**-53, 52f
Dendrite, 872, 873t, **889**, 889f
Dendritic cell, **1062**-1063, 1062t
Dendritic spines, 889
Dengue fever, 1253
Denitrification, **1211**
Denitrifier, 563
Dense connective tissue, **868**, 869t
Dense irregular connective tissue, 868
Dense regular connective tissue, 868
Density-dependent effect, **1175**-1176,
    1175f-1176f
Density-independent effects,
    1176, 1176f
Dental caries, 561-562, 561t
Deoxyhemoglobin, **1013**
Deoxyribonucleic acid. *See* DNA
Dephosphorylation, of proteins, **170**
Depolarization, **892**-893, 893f
Derepression, **312**
Derived characters, **458**-459, 459f
    shared, 458, 463-464
Dermal tissue, of plants,
    731, 733-736, 734f-735f, 756,
    758, 803
Desert, **1237**
Desmosome, 83f, 84
Determinate development, **638**, 639f
Determination, **375**-377, 375f-376f
    molecular basis of, 376
    reversal of, 380-381
    standard test for, 375-376, 375f
Detritivore, **1215**, 1215f
Deuterostome, **523**, 523f, **638**, 639f,
    643, 644f, 645, 1114
Development
    in animals, 372-373, 373f, 635t,
        638, 639f
    apoptosis in, 390-391, 391f
    of behavior, 1139-1141
    in *Caenorhabditis elegans*, 373, 374f,
        390-391, 391f
    cell differentiation in, 375-379,
        375f-379f
    cell division in, 372, 373-375,
        373f-374f

    cell migration in, 391-392, 392f
    cellular mechanisms of, 373-393
    as characteristic of life, 3, 508
    defined, 372
    determination, **375**-377,
        375f-376f
    in *Drosophila*, 494
    evidence for, 428-429, 428f
    evolution of, 492-504, 497f
    of eye, 501-504, 501f-503f
    in frogs, 373f
    gene expression in, 304
    induction, **377**-378, 377f
    of limbs, 497-498, 497f
    morphogenesis, 373, **390**-393,
        391f-393f
    nuclear reprogramming, 380-383,
        380f-383f
    overview of, 372-373
    pattern formation, 373, 383-389,
        384f-388f
    in plants, 374-375
        morphogenesis, 392-393, 393f
    in sea urchins, 493, 493f
    in tunicates, 376f, 377
    of wings, 497, 497f
Dewlap, of *Anolis* lizard, 443, 443f
Diabetes insipidus, 98, 1050
Diabetes mellitus, 955
    treatment of, 955
    type I (insulin-dependent), 955
    type II (non-insulin-dependent),
        955
Diacylglycerol, 180f, **181**
Diagnostics, 1078-1079, 1078f
Diaphragm (birth control), 1099f,
    1099t, 1100
Diaphragm (muscle), **1009**, 1010f
Diapsid, 708f, **709**, 709f
Diastole, **1026**, 1027f
Diastolic pressure, **1029**, 1029f
Diatom, 571, 580-581, 581f
Diazepam, 899
Dicer, 319, 319f, 320
Dichlorophenoxyacetic acid (2,4-D),
    829f, **830**
Dichogamous plant, **855**
Dictyostelium discoideum, 180, 358f,
    585, 585f
Dideoxynucleotide, **336**-337, 337f
Didinium, 1192, 1192f
Diencephalon, 902t, 903
Diethystilbestrol (DES), 957
Differential-interference-contrast
    microscope, 62t
Differentiation, 14, 372-373,
    375-379, 375f-379f
Diffuse pollution, 1246
Diffusion, **96**-97, 96f, 104t
    facilitated, **96**-97,
        97f, 104t
    Frick's Law of, **1002**
Digestion, 123
    chemical, 982
    in insects, 686
    of plant material, 717
    in small intestine, 987, 988,
        988f-989f
    in stomach, 986-987

Digestive system, **874**, 874f, 981-998
  of birds, 984, 984f
  of carnivores, 991f
  of herbivores, 991f, 992
  of insectivores, 991f
  of invertebrates, 982, 982f
  of nematodes, 982, 982f
  of ruminants, 991, 992f
  types of, 982-983, 982f-983f
    variations in, 990-992,
      991f-992f
Digestive tract, 982f, 983
  layers of, 983, 983f
  neural and hormonal regulation
    of, 993, 993f, 994t
Dihybrid cross, **228**-229, 229f, 233t
Dihydroxyacetone phosphate, 128f
Dikaryon, 617, 623
Dikaryotic hyphae, **616**
Dinoflagellate, 576-577, 576f-577f
Dinosaur, 424f, 453, 462f, 697, 707t,
  708-709, 708f-709f
  feathered, 714
  parental care in, 464, 465f
Dioecious plant, **606**, 855
Dioxin, 831
Diphtheria, 534, 560, 561t
Diploblastic animal, 637, 643
Diploid (*2n*), **191**, 208, 208f,
  225, 1109
  partial, **556**
Diplomonads, 570f, **572**-573, 573f
Diplontic life cycle, **590**, 590f
Diptera (order), 684f, 685t
Direct contact, cell signaling by,
  169, 169f, 170
Directional selection, **410**-411,
  410f-411f
Disaccharide, **38**-39, 39f
Disassortative mating, **402**
Disease
  causes of, 487
  evolution of pathogens, 470-471,
    470f-471f
  pathogen-host genome
    differences, 487-488
Dispersive replication, 263f, 264, 265
Disruptive selection, **409**-410,
  410f, 445-446
Dissociation, of proteins, **53**
Distal convoluted tubule, **1047**,
  1047f, 1049-1050
Distal-less gene, 498, 498f, 524, 524f
Disturbances, biological, 1203,
  1204, 1204f
DNA, **12**-13, **41**-42,
  256-275. *See also* Gene
  analysis of, 334-341
  antiparallel strands, 262f, 263
  central dogma, **280**, 280f
  chromatin in, 68
  in chromosomes.
    See Chromosome
  cloning of. *See* Cloning
  coding strand, **280**, 285f, 286f
  complementary. *See* cDNA library
  double helix, 41-42, 41f, **43**, 43f,
    261-262, 261f, 262f

functions of, 37t
gel electrophoresis of,
  328-329, 329f
genetic engineering. *See* Genetic
  engineering
junk. *See* DNA, noncoding
major groove of, 262f
manipulation of, 327-349
methylation of, 252
minor groove of, 262f
of mitochondria, 74
noncoding, 359-360,
  485-486
of prokaryotes, 62
proof that it is genetic material,
  256-259, 257f-258f
protein-coding, 359
recombinant. *See* Recombinant
  DNA
replication of. *See* Replication
RNA versus, 43, 43f
segmental duplications, 481
sequencing of, 50, 336-337,
  336f-338f, 339. *See also*
    Genome sequencing
with sticky ends, 328, 328f
structural, 359, 360f
structure of, 37t, 42-43, 43f,
  259-263, 259f-262f
supercoiling of, **267**, 267f
template strand, 265, 265f
three-dimensional structure of,
  259-261, 259f-260f
topological state of, 267
in transformation.
  See Transformation
Watson-Crick DNA molecule,
  262f, 263
X-ray diffraction pattern of,
  260-261, 260f
DNA-binding motifs, in regulatory
  proteins, 306-307, 307f
DNA-binding proteins, 48
DNA fingerprint, **335**-336, 336f
DNA gyrase, **267**, 267f, 268t,
  269, 269f
DNA helicase, **267**, 268t, 269f
DNA library, **331**-332, 331f
DNA ligase, 268t, **269**, 269f-270f,
  328, 328f, 331f
DNA microarray, **364**
  analysis of cancer, 364
  preparation of, 364, 365f
DNA polymerase, **265**-266, 265f
  proofreading function of, 273
DNA polymerase delta, 271
DNA polymerase epsilon, 271
DNA polymerase I, **266**-267, 268t,
  269f-270f
DNA polymerase II, **266**-267
DNA polymerase III, 265f, **266**-270,
  268t, 268f-270f
  beta subunit of, 268, 268f
  processivity of, 268
  sliding clamp, 268, 268f-269f
DNA primase, 268-269, 268t,
  269f, 272
DNA rearrangement, 483,
  1072-1074, 1073f

DNA repair, 273-275, 274f
DNA sequence data, cladistics and,
  460, 460f
DNA vaccine, 344-**345**
DNA virus, 529, 529f, 531, 532t
Docking (protein on ER), 296f, 297
Dodder (*Cuscuta*), 742, 794
Dog
  Brachyury gene mutation in, 496
  breeds of, 422-423, 423f
  chromosome number in, 189t
  "Dolly" (cloned sheep), 381, 381f
Dolphin, evolution of, 425
Domain (protein), **50**-51, 51f
Domain (taxonomic), **513**, 513f
Domestication, 422-423, 423f
Dominant hemisphere,
  905-906, 906f
Dominant trait, **224**-228, 224f-225f
  codominance, 233t, **234**, 234f
  in humans, 227t
  incomplete dominance, 233t,
    234, 234f
Dopamine, **899**, 900, 1134
Dormancy
  in plants, 823-824, 823f-824f
  in seed, 824, 824f, 836, 836f
Dorsal body cavity, 864, 865f
Dorsal nerve cord, **1118**
Dorsal protein, 386-387, 387f
Dorsal root, **909**
Dorsal root ganglia, **909**, 910f
Dosage compensation, **243**
Double circulation, **1024**
Double covalent bond, 24, 24f
Double fertilization, 608, 609f, **610**,
  856-857, 856f-857f
Double helix, 41-42, 41f, **43**, 43f,
  261-261, 261f, 262f
Douche, 1100
Down, J. Langdon, 250
Down syndrome, **250**, 250f
  maternal age and, 250-251,
    250f, 252
  translocation, 250
Drought tolerance, in plants,
  780, 780f
Drugs
  for AIDS treatment,
    537-538, 537f
  drug addiction, 900-901, 900f
  drug development,
    487-488, 488f
  manufacture of illegal, 605
  nonsteroidal anti-inflammatory
    drug, 943
  pharmaceutical plants,
    1261-1262, 1261f
Duchenne muscular dystrophy,
  227t, 249t
Duck-billed platypus, 475f, 487,
  719f, 1090
Dugesia, 657f, 658
Duodenum, **987**, 988f
Duplication (mutation), **300**, 301f,
  480, 480f-481f, 481
Dwarfism, **950**
Dynactin complex, 77
Dynein, 77, 77f, 79

E

Ear
  sensing gravity and acceleration,
    924-925, 924f
  structure of, 920-922, 920f-922f
Ear popping, 922
Earth
  age of, 11
  atmosphere of early Earth, 509
  circumference of, 4-5, 5f
  formation of, 17
  orbit around sun, 1231, 1231f
  origin of life on, 509-510, 511f
  rotation of, 1231-1233,
    1231f-1232f
Earthworm, 641t, 675, 675f, 901f, 902
  circulatory system of, 1022f
  digestive system of, 982, 982f
  locomotion in, 962, 962f
  nephridia of, 1040, 1041f
Ebola virus, 529, 532t, **540**, 540f
Ecdysis, **680**
Ecdysone, **957**, 957f
Ecdysozoan, **523**-524, 523f, 643,
  644-645, 644f-645f
ECG. *See* Electrocardiogram
Echinoderm, 523f, 641t, 645,
  687-690, 688f-689f
  body plan of, 688-689, 688f
  classes of, 689-690
  development in, 687-688
  diversity in, 689f
  endoskeleton of, 688-689
  nervous system of, 901f
  regeneration in, 689
  reproduction in, 689
  respiration in, 1003f
  water-vascular system of, **688**, 689
Echinodermata (phylum), 641t, 645f,
  687-690, 688f-689f
Echinoidea (class), 689f, 690
Echolocation, **924**
Ecological footprint, **1181**-1182,
  1181f
Ecological isolation, 438, 438f, 438t
Ecological pyramid, 1218-1219, 1219f
  inverted, **1218**, 1219f
Ecological species concept, 441
Ecology
  behavioral, 1147-1149
  community, 1185-1204
  of fungi, 625-629, 626f-629f
  population, 1162-1182
Economic value, of biodiversity,
  1261-1263, 1261f-1263f
Ecosystem, 3f, **4**, 1208. *See also*
  specific types
  biogeochemical cycles in,
    1208-1214, 1208f-1213f
  climate effects on, 1230-1235,
    1230f-1234f
  disruption of ecosystems,
    1271, 1272f
  dynamics of, 1207-1227
  effect of global warming on,
    1251-1252, 1251f
  effect of human activity on,
    1245-1250

energy flow through, 1214-1219
stability of, 1223-1226, 1223f
trophic levels in, 1217-1223,
1218f-1222f
Ecotone, **1187**, 1187f
Ectoderm, **637**, 637f, 864,
1113, 1113f
Ectomycorrhizae, **628**, 628f
Ectoprocta, 641t, 644f
Ectotherm, **710**, 880-881
Edema, 994, **1032**
Edge effect, **1267**
EEG. *See* Electroencephalogram
Eel, 975, 975f
Effector, 876
antagonistic, 877-878, 877f
Effector protein, 179-182, 179f
Efferent arteriole, 1047
EGF. *See* Epidermal growth factor
Egg
amniotic, **706**, 708f
fertilization, 1106-1109, 1106t,
1107f-1109f
of frogs, 1109, 1109f
of reptiles, 706, 708f
Egg coloration, adaptive value of,
1147-1148, 1147f
Ejaculation, 1093
EKG. *See* Electrocardiogram
El Niño Southern Oscillation,
1243-1244, 1244f, 1252
Elasmobranch, 934, 1043
Elastin, 81, 81f, 392
Eldredge, Niles, 451
Electrical synapse, **896**
Electricity, detection of, 934
Electrocardiogram (ECG, EKG),
1028, 1028f
Electroencephalogram (EEG), 905
Electromagnetic receptor, **916**
Electromagnetic spectrum,
151, 151f
Electron, 18, **19**, 19f
in chemical behavior of atoms,
20, 20f
energy level of, 21, 21f
valence, **22**
Electron acceptor, 124, 124f,
139-140, 139f
Electron carriers, 124, 125f, 134-135
Electron microscope, 61, 61f, 62t
microscopy of plasma membrane,
91-92, 91f
scanning, 61, 62t, 91
transmission, 61, 62t, 91
Electron orbital, **19**, 20f
Electron transport chain, 124f, **125**,
132, 133f
ATP production in, 134-136, 134f,
135f, 136f
photosynthetic, 156
production of ATP by
chemiosmosis, 135-136, 135f
Electronegativity, **24**, 25t, 34
Electrophoresis, 398
Element, 18
inert, 22
in living systems, 22-23
periodic table, 22-23, 22f

Elephant, 525, 525f
Elephant seal, 403, 403f, 1002f
Elevation, climate and, 1234, 1234f
Elongation factor, **295**, 295f
EF-Tu, **295**, 295f
Embryo implantation, prevention of,
1100
Embryo (plant), **754**, 754f
Embryo sac, **850**, 850f, 851, 851f
Embryo transfer, 1102
Embryogenesis, 754f
Embryonic development
human, 429f
in plants, 754-760, 754f-760f
Embryonic flower mutant,
in *Arabidopsis*, 841, 841f
Embryonic stem cells, **342**-343,
342f-343f, 379, 379f
Emergent properties, **4**, 14
Emerging viruses, **540**
Emerson, R. A., 236
Emphysema, **1012**
Enantiomer, 35, 35f
Encephalitozoon cuniculi, 358f,
618, 618f
Endangered species
conservation biology, 1256-1278
preservation of, 1275-1276
Endemic species, 1258-1261,
1259f, 1260t
Endergonic reaction, **110**-111, 111f,
113, 113f
Endochondral development, of bone,
965-966, 965f
Endocrine gland, **866**, 938. *See also
specific glands*
Endocrine signaling, 169, 169f, **170**
Endocrine system, **873**, 874f,
937-957, **938**
Endocytosis, **102**, 102f, 104t
receptor-mediated, 102f,
103, 104t
Endoderm, **637**, 637f, 864,
1113, 1113f
Endodermis, **741**, 741f, 775
Endogenous opiate, 899
Endomembrane system, **65**, 69-73
Endonuclease, **266**
Endoparasite, **1199**
Endophyte, 626, 626f
Endoplasmic reticulum (ER), 65,
69-71, 78t, 81t
origin of, 568, 568f
proteins targeted to, 296f, 297
rough, **69**-70, 70f
smooth, **70**, 70f
Endorphin, **899**
Endoskeleton, **962**, **963**, 963f
of echinoderm, 688-689
of vertebrates, 696
Endosperm, **754**, 754f, 760, 760f
Endospore, **554**
Endosteum, **966**
Endosymbiont theory, 75, 75f,
568-569, 569f, 570
Endosymbiosis, **75**, 75f, **517**,
568-569, 569f
secondary, **569**
Endothelin, 942

Endothelium, 1030, 1030f
Endotherm, **710**, 715, 716, 876, 880,
881-882, 882f
Energy, 108. *See also specific types
of energy*
as characteristic of life, 3
feeding behavior and, 997, 997f
flow in living things, 3, 108-109
flow through ecosystem,
1214-1219
forms of, 108
laws of thermodynamics, 109-110
prokaryotes need for, 559
Energy expenditure, 995, 997
Energy level, **21**, 21f
Enhancement effect, 157, 157f
Enhancer, **313**-314, 314f
Enkephalin, **899**
Enteric bacteria, 551f
Enterobacteriaceae, 558
Enterogastrone, **993**
Enthalpy, **110**
Entropy, **110**, 110f
Environment
effect on enzyme function,
116-117, 116f
effect on gene expression, 233t,
235, 235f
individual responses to changes in,
1162-1163
limitations on population growth,
1173-1174, 1174f-1175f
Environmental Protection Agency
(EPA), U.S., 798
Environmental variation, coping with,
1163, 1163f
EnviroPig, 349
Enzymatic DNA sequencing,
336-337, 337f
Enzymatic receptor, 172-173,
172f, 172t
Enzyme, 44, 45t, 113-117
activation energy, 113-114
attached to membranes, 93, 94f
catalytic cycle of, 114, 115f
cofactors, **117**
defects in gene disorders, 279
digestive, 994t
genetic variation in, 398
inhibitors and activators of,
117, 117f
intracellular receptors as, 174
multienzyme complex,
115-116, 115f
nonprotein, 116
pH effect on, 52-53, 116-117, 116f
restriction, 328, 328f, 331f,
353, 353f
RNA, 116
temperature effect on, 52-53,
116, 116f
Enzyme-substrate complex, **114**, 114f
Eosinophil, **1062**, 1062t
Ephedra, 602t, 605, 760
Ephedrine, 605
Epidermal cells, of plants, **734**,
734f, 740
Epidermal growth factor (EGF),
202, 942

Epidermis, of plant, 731, **733**, 741f
Epididymis, **1092**
Epigenetic, **380**
Epilimnion, 1239
Epinephrine, 170, 182, **899**
Epiparasite, 628
Epiphyseal growth plate, 966
Epiphyses, **965**, 965f
Epistasis, 233t, 235-**236**, 236f, 414
Epithelial tissue, **864**, 865-866, 867t
columnar, 866, 867t
cuboidal, 866, 867t
keratinized, 866
regeneration of, 866
simple, 866
squamous, 866, 867t
stratified, 866
structure of, 866
Epithelium, **865**
EPSP. *See* Excitatory postsynaptic
potential
Equilibrium constant, 111
Equilibrium model, of island
biogeography, 1226-1227, 1226f
Equilibrium potential, **891**, 892t
Equisetum, 599, 599f
ER. *See* Endoplasmic reticulum
Eratosthenes, 4-5, 5f
Erythrocytes, 870, **1019**, 1019f
facilitated diffusion in, 97
membrane of, 90t
Erythropoiesis, **1021**
Erythropoietin, 956, **1021**
Escherichia coli (*E. coli*), 533, 1164
cell division in, 186-187, 188f
conjugation map of, 555, 555f,
556, 556f
DNA repair in, 274-275
harmful traits of, 558
introduction of foreign DNA into,
329-330
lac operon of, **308**, 309-310,
308f-310f
mutations in, 558
replication in, 266-270
Esophagus, 985-986, 986f
Essay on the Principle of Population
(Malthus), 10
Essential amino acids, 998
Essential nutrient, 997-998, 998t
in plants, 790t
EST. *See* Expressed sequence tag
Estrogen, 956, 1093t
Estrus, **1090**, 1097
Estuary, 1243
Ethanol, 35f
Ethanol fermentation, 140, 140f
Ethics
ownership of genomic
information, 369
of stem cell research, 379
value of biodiversity, 1263
Ethology, 1133-1134
Ethylene, 826t, 835-836, 835f
Etiolation, 817, 817f
Eucalyptus, 749
Euchromatin, **190**
Eudicot, 499, 607f, 608
leaf of, 741-742, 741f, 748, 748f

Euglena, 574, 575f
Euglenoid, **573**-574, 574f
Euglenozoa, 570f, 573-575, 574f
Eukarya (domain), 13, 13f, 483, 513f, **515**, 515f, 516f, 518-519, 549f
Eukaryote, 13, **545**
  cell division in, 187, 548
  cell structure in, 65-69, 66f, 67f, 68f, 81t
  cell wall of, 67f, 78t, 81t
  chromosomes of, 65, 78t, 189-191, 189f-191f, 189t, 548
  compartmentalization in, 517, 518-519, 548
  cytoskeleton of, 65, 75-79, 76f
  DNA of, 62
  endomembrane system of, 65, 69-71
  evolution of, 75, 75f, 188, 568-570, 568f-569f
  flagella of, 66f, 78t, 79-80, 79f, 80f, 81t, 548
  gene expression in, 305, 312-315, 313f-315f, 322f
  genome of, 358f
    gene organization in, 360t
    noncoding DNA in, 359-360
  initiation in, 295
  key characteristics of, 518-519, 518t
  origin of, 517-518, 517f, 568-570, 568f-570f
  plasma membrane of, 66f
  prokaryotes versus, 81t, 547-548
  promoters of, 287-288
  replication in, 271-273, 271f-272f
  ribosomes of, 68-69, 69f
  transcription factor in, 313-314, 314f
  transcription in, 287-289, 288f
  transcriptional control in, 305, 312-315, 322f
  translation in, 295
  vacuoles of, 81t
Eumetazoa (subkingdom), 640, 643, 644f, 652-656, 652f-656f
Euryarchaeota, 550f
Eusociality, 1156
Eutherian, **524**, 525f
Eutrophic lake, **1240**-1241, 1240f
Evaporation, 880
Evening primrose (*Oenothera biennis*), 852
Evergreen forest
  temperate, **1238**
  warm moist, 1235f, 1236
Evolution, 396-397. *See also* Coevolution
  of aerobic respiration, 143
  agents of, 401-405, 401f-405f
    interactions among, 406-407, 407f
  of amphibians, 697, 703, 704-705, 704f-705f
  of apes, 721-726
  of biochemical pathways, 118
  of birds, 424f-425f, 425, 463, 466, 467f, 712, 712f, 714, 714f

of *Brassica*, 495, 495f
of complex characters, 466, 467f
controversial nature of theory, 432-433
convergent, **430**, 430-432, 431f, 458, 464-465, 498-499, 498f, 502
Darwin's theory of, 8-10, 432
of development, 492-504
of diseases, 470-471, 470f-471f
of eukaryotes, 75, 75f, 188
evidence for, 417-433
  age of Earth, 11
  anatomical record, 428-430, 428f-430f
  biogeographical studies, 430
  comparative anatomy, 11, 11f
  convergence, 431-432, 431f
  development, 428-429, 428f
  experimental tests, 411-413, 412f-413f, 422, 22f
  fossil record, 10-11, 424-428, 424f-427f
  homologous structures, **428**, 428f
  imperfect structures, 429-430, 429f
  molecular biology, 11-12, 11f
  vestigial structures, **430**, 430f
of eye, 414, 414f, 429, 429f, 501-504, 501f-503f
of eyespot on butterfly wings, 498f
of fish, 698, 700-701, 700f, 702, 702f
of flight, 467f
of flowers, 469-470, 499, 848-850
of fruit, 606f
of gas exchange, 1002-1003, 1003f
gene flow and, 401, 401f, 406-407, 407f
genetic drift and, 401f, **402**-403, 402f, 406
genetic variation and, 396-397, 397f, 412, 412f
of genomes, 474-489
of glycolysis, 129, 143
of heart, 1026f
of homeobox genes, 389
of hominids, 722-724
of horses, 414, 414f, 426-428, 426f-427f
human impact on, 453
of humans. *See* Human evolution
on islands, 431-432, 431f, 444-445, 444f
of land plants, 521f, 571, 589-590
of leaf, 596-597, 597f
of life on earth, 511f
of mammals, 525f, 697, 698f, 718, 718f
marsupial-placental convergence, 430-431, 431f
of mitosis, 570
of mollusks, 667
mutation and, 301, 401, 401f, 406
natural selection. *See* Natural selection
of nitrogen fixation, 143
of oysters, 426

of photosynthesis, 139, 143, 156
of plants, 390
of primates, 721-726, 721f-726f
of prosimians, 721
rate of, 461
of reproductive isolation, 441-442, 442f
of reproductive systems, 1087-1088, 1088f
of reptiles, 697, 708-709, 708f-709f
of seed plants, 602-603, 603f
of shark, 701
of snakes, 425
of social system, 1157-1159
speciation and, 451-452, 451f
  in spurts, 451-452
of tobacco, 477f, 480, 480f
of vertebrate brain, 903f
of vertebrates, 697, 698f, 1121, 1121f
of whales, 425, 425f
of wheat, 478f
of wings, 497, 498, 976-977, 977f
Evolutionary adaptation, as characteristic of life, 3
Evolutionary age, species richness and, 1225
Evolutionary conservation, 14
Excision repair, **274**-275, 274f
Excitation-contraction coupling, **972**, 972f
Excitatory postsynaptic potential (EPSP), 898, 899-900, 899f
Excretion, by kidney, 1048
Excretory system
  annelids, 674
  of arthropods, 679f, 680f, 681
  of flatworms, 657-658, 657f
  of mollusks, 669
Exercise
  bone remodeling and, 967f
  effect on metabolic rate, 995
  muscle metabolism during, 974-975
Exergonic reaction, **110**-111, 111f
Exhalant siphon, **671**, 671f
Exocrine gland, **866**
Exocytosis, **103**, 103f, 104t
Exon, **289**, 289f
Exon shuffling, 290
Exonuclease, **266**, 268
Exoskeleton, 41, 41f, **679**-680, 679f, **962**-963, 963f
Experiment, 5f, **6**
  control, 6
  test, 6
Expiration, 1009-1011, 1010f
Exploitative competition, **1188**
Expressed sequence tag (EST), **361**, 361f
Expression vector, **342**
Extensor muscles, 969f
External fertilization, 1088, 1089f
External intercostal muscle, 1009
Exteroceptor, **916**
Extinction, 452-453, 452f
  conservation biology, 1256-1278
  disruption of ecosystems and, 1271, 1272f

  due to human activities, 1257-1258
  due to prehistoric humans, 1257-1258, 1257f
  factors responsible for, 1264-1275, 1264f-1274f
  genetic variation and, 1274
  habitat loss, 1264t, 1266-1268
  in historical time, 1258, 1258t
  introduced species and, 1264t, 1269-1271
  of Lake Victoria cichlid fish, 449-450, 449f, 1271
  loss of keystone species, 1272, 1273f
  mammals, extinct, 718t
  over time, 452-453
  overexploitation and, 1264t, 1268-1269
  population size and, 1273-1275, 1273f-1274f
  in prehistoric time, 1257-1258, 1257f
Extra-pair copulation, 1153-**1153**, 1153f
Extracellular fluid, 892t
Extracellular matrix, 80-81, 81f, **868**
Extracellular regulated kinase, 178f
Extraembryonic coelom, 1116
Extraembryonic membrane, **1116**, 1116f
Extraterrestrial life, 508-509, 509f
Extremophile, **516**, 547
Extrusion, 99
Eye, 928-933, 928f-933f
  compound, 414, 414f, 680, 680f, 681f
  development of, 501-504, 501f-503f, 1125f
  evolution of, 414, 414f, 429, 429f, 501-504, 501f-503f, 928-929, 928f
  focusing of, 929f
  of insects, 414, 414f, 501, 501f
  of mollusks, 429, 429f, 501, 501f
  of planarian, 501, 501f
  structure of, 929-930, 929f
  of vertebrates, 429, 429f, 501, 501f, 929-930, 929f
Eye color
  in fruit fly, 240-241, 240f
  in humans, 232-233, 233t
Eyeless gene, 342, 502, 502f

F

F plasmid, **554**-556, 555f
F plasmid transfer, 555, 555f
F_1 generation. *See* First filial generation
F_2 generation. *See* Second filial generation
Facilitated diffusion, **96**-97, 97f, 104t
Facilitation, 1203
Facultative symbiosis, **626**
FAD, **44**, 131
FADH
  in ATP yield, 137, 137f
  contributing electrons to electron transport chain, 134, 134f, 135
  from Krebs cycle, 131, 132, 133f

Fallopian tube, 1097, 1097f
Family (taxonomic), **512**, 513f, 513
Farsightedness, 929f
Fast-twitch muscle fiber, **974**, 974f
Fat(s), 37t
    absorption in small intestine, 989-990
    caloric content of, 53
    as energy-storage molecules, 54-55
    structure of, 53-54, 54f
Fatty acids, 36f, 55
    catabolism of, 141-142, 142f
    polyunsaturated, **53**, 54f
    saturated, **53**, 54f
    trans-fatty acids, 55
    unsaturated, **53**, 54f
Fatty acid desaturase, 93
Feather, 712, 712f
Feather star, 689
Feces, 990
Fecundity, **1169**
Feedback inhibition, 117, **118**-119, 119f
Female infertility, 1101
Female reproduction, hormonal control of, 1093t
Female reproductive system, 875f, **876**, 1090, 1090f, 1094-1098, 1094f-1098f
Fermentation, **124**, 129, 139-140, 140f
    ethanol, 140, 140f
Fern, 589f, 590, 598-601, **599**, 599f-600f, 601t
Ferredoxin, 158, 159f
Fertilization, **208**, 208f, 1087-1090, 1106-1109, 1106t, 1107f-1109f
    in amphibians, 1088, 1088f-1089f
    in birds, 1088-1089, 1088f-1089f
    double, 608, 609f, **610**, 856-857, 856f-857f
    external, 1088, 1089f
    in fish, 1087f, 1088, 1088f
    internal, 1087-1090, 1087f-1090f
    in plants, 605, 609, 609f, 610, 856-857, 856f-857f
    in reptiles, 1089-1090
Fertilization envelope, 1108
Fertilizer
    nitrogen, 1211
    phosphorus, 1212
    pollution from, 1251
Fever, **883**
Fiber, dietary, 990
Fibrin, **1021**
Fibrinogen, **1019**
Fibroblast growth factor, 378, 378f, **1118**
Fibronectin, 81, 81f, 392, 392f
Fiddlehead, 600, 600f
Filament (flower), **608**, 608f, 848f, **849**
Filial imprinting, **1139**
Filopodia, 1113
Filovirus, 532t, **540**, 540f
Filtration, 1040
    in kidney, 1045, 1046-1047, 1047f
Finch, Darwin's, 8, 9f
    beaks of, 408, 418-419, 418f, 1191, 1191f

Finger, grasping, 721
Firefly, 1145, 1145f
First filial generation, **224**-225, 225f, 228-229, 229f
First Law of Thermodynamics, **109**
Fish, 641t, 698-702, 698f-702f
    aquaculture, 1248
    armored, 699t
    bony, 701-702, 701f, 1004-1006, 1004f, 1042
    brain in, 902-903, 903f
    cartilaginous, 698f, 700-701, 700f, 1043, 1065
    characteristics of, 698-702
    circulation in, 699, 1023, 1023f
    depletion of, 1247-1248, 1248f
    evolution of, 698, 700-701, 700f, 702, 702f
    fertilization in, 1087f, 1088, 1088f
    hearing in, 920-921, 921f
    heart in, 1023, 1023f
    jawed, 699-700, 700f
    jawless, 700, 1065-1066
    kidney of
        cartilaginous fish, 1043
        freshwater fish, 1042, 1043f
        marine bony fish, 1042, 1043f
    lobe-finned, 698f, 699t, 702, 702f, 704f
    nitrogenous wastes of, 1045f
    path to land, 702, 702f
    predation on insects, 408, 408f
    prostaglandins in, 943
    ray-finned, 698f, 699t, 702, 702f
    respiration in, 1004-1006, 1003f-1005f
    spiny, 699t, 700
    swimming by, 975-976, 975f
    taste in, 926
    viviparous, 1087, 1087f
FISH. *See* Fluorescence in situ hybridization
Fitness, **405**-406, 406f, 414
5′ Cap mRNA, **288**, 288f
Flagella, **65**
    of bacteria, 64f, 65, 548, **553**, 553f
    of eukaryotes, 66f, 78t, 79-80, 79f, 80f, 81t, 548
    of prokaryotes, 63f, 65, 81t, 548, 552, **553**, 553f
    of protists, 572-573, 575f
Flame cells, **657**-658
Flatworm, 523f, 641t, 643, 657-660, 657f, 659f-660f
    classification of, 658-660
    digestive cavity of, 657, 657f, 982
    excretion and osmoregulation in, 657-658, 657f, 1040-1041, 1040f-1041f
    eyespot of, 657, 657f, 928, 928f
    free-living, 657, 658
    nervous system of, 657f, 658, 901f, 902
    reproduction in, 657f, 658
Flavin adenine dinucleotide. *See* FAD
Flavivirus, 531f, 532t
Flemming, Walther, 189, 207
Flesh-eating disease, 560
Flexor muscles, 969f

Flight skeleton, 712
Flipper, 710
Flooding, plant responses to, 780, 781f
Floral leaf, 749
Floral meristem identity gene, **846**, 846f
Floral organ identity gene, **846**, 846f-847f, 848
Florigen, 844
Flower
    complete, **848**
    evolution of, 469-470, 499, 848-850
    floral symmetry, 499
    incomplete, **848**
    initiation of flowering, 840-841, 840f
    male and female structures, separation of, 855-856
    morphology of, 848-849
    production of 842-848, 842f-848f
        autonomous pathway of, 845-846, 845f-846f
        flowering hormone, 844
        formation of floral meristems and floral organs, 846, 846f-847f, 848, 848f
        gibberellin-dependent pathway, 845
        light-dependent pathway, 842-844, 842f-843f
        phase change and, 840-841, 841f
        temperature-dependent pathway, 844
    shape of, 499
    structure of, 848-849, 848f
Flower color, 853-854, 853f
Flowering hormone, 844
Flowering plant, 589f, 602t, 606-610, 606f-610f
    angiosperm, **606**, 754f
    dichogamous, **855**
    dioecious, 855
    evolution of, 469-470
    fertilization in, 856-857, 856f-857f
    gamete formation in, 850-851, 850f-851f
    gene duplication in, 499-500, 499f-500f
    life cycle of, 608-610, 609f, 840f
    monoecious, **855**
    pollination. *See* Pollination
    trends in, 849-850, 849f
Fluid mosaic model, 89, 90f, 92-93
Fluidity, membrane, 92-93, 93f
Fluke, 658-659, 659f
Fluorescence in situ hybridization (FISH), **353**, 354f
Fluorescence microscope, 62t
Fly, eye development in, 502, 502f
Flying fox, declining populations of, 1272-1273, 1273f
Flying phalanger, 431f
Flying squirrel, 431f
Folic acid, 998t
Foliose, 627f

Follicle-stimulating hormone (FSH), 948, 1093, 1093t, 1094f
Food, caloric content of, 995
Food and Drug Administration (FDA), U.S., antiretroviral drugs, 537-538
Food energy, 995-997
Food intake, regulation of, 995-997
Food poisoning, 1079
Food preservation, 52-53
Food security, **792**
Food storage, in plants, 759-760, 760f
Food storage root, 742, 743f
Food supply, population cycles and, 1177
Foraging behavior, 1148-1149, 1148f
Foraminifera (phylum), 571, 584, 584f
Forebrain, 902f, 902t
    human, 903-905, 904f-905f
Forest ecosystem
    biogeochemical cycles in, 12-1213, 1213f
    effect of deforestation on, 1246-1247
Fork head gene, in *Drosophila*, 1117
fosB gene, 1136
Fossil record, 424-428, 424f-427f
    angiosperms, 606-607, 607f
    community, 1187
    early eukaryotic, 568, 568f
    evidence for evolution, 10-11, 424-428, 424f-427f, 432
    gaps in, 425, 432
    history of evolutionary change, 425-426, 425f
    microfossils, 546, 546f
Founder effect, 402-**403**
Four o'clock, flower color in, 233t, 234, 234f, 244
Fox, 423, 423f
FOXP2 gene, 485, 1147
Frameshift mutation, **283**, 299
Franklin, Rosalind, 260-261, 260f
Free energy, **110**
Free water, 98, 98f
Freeze-fracture microscopy, 91-92, 91f
Frequency-dependent selection, **407**-408, 408f
Freshwater habitat, 1238-1241, 1239f-1240f
    changes with water depth, 1239-1240, 1239f-1240f
    oxygen availability in, 1239
    pollution of, 1246, 1246f
Frick's Law of Diffusion, **1002**
Frog (*Rana*), 703, 703t, 705-706, 705f
    chromosome number in, 189t
    declining populations of, 1265, 1265f
    development in, 373f, 1110f, 1111f
    fertilization in, 1088-1089, 1089f-1090f, 1109, 1109f
    gastrulation in, 1114, 1114f
    hybridization between species of, 439, 440
Frond, 600, 600f
Frontal lobe, 904, 904f
Fructose, 38, 39f

Fructose 1,6-bisphosphate, 128f, 138, 138f
Fructose 6-phosphate, 128f, 138, 138f
Fruit, 597, **608**
    development of, 761-763, 762f-763f
    dispersal of, 762, 763f
    evolution of, 606f
    kinds of, 762, 763f
    ripening of, 835-836, 835f
Fruit fly (*Drosophila*)
    behavioral genetics in, 1135-1136
    body color in, 246-247, 246f
    branchless gene in, 1118
    bristle number in, 422, 422f
    development in, 494, 1117-1118, 1117f
    eye color in, 240-241, 240f
    eyeless gene from, 342
    gene expression of, 304f
    genetic map of, 246-247, 246f, 354
    genome of, 354, 358f, 362, 475f, 486
    Hawaiian, 443, 447, 447f
    heart development in, 1118, 1118f
    hedgehog signaling molecule in, 1124
    heterozygosity in, 398
    homeotic genes in, 5, 388, 388f
    homeotic mutations in, 307, 494
    meiosis in, 214
    Morgan's experiments with, 240-241, 240f, 354
    pattern formation in 383-389, 384f-388f
        forming the axis, 384-387, 385f-387f
        producing the body plan, 384f-385f, 387-388
    proteasome, 323f
    salivary gland development in, 1117-1118, 1117f
    segmentation in, 388-389, 388f
    selection for negative phototropism, 410-411, 411f
    sex chromosomes of, 241, 241t
    toll receptor in, 1056
    transposons in, 484
    wing traits in, 246-247, 246f
    X chromosome of, 241, 245
Fruticose lichen, 627f
FSH. *See* Follicle-stimulating hormone
FtsZ protein, 188, 188f
Fucus (zygote), 754, 755, 755f
Fumarate, 132, 133f
Funch, Peter, 660
Function, of living systems, 13
Functional genomics, **364**-366, 365f-366f, 484, 500
Functional group, **35**, 35f
Functional magnetic resonance imaging (fMRI), 1134, 1134f
Fundamental niche, **1188**, 1188f
Fungal disease, 626
    in animals, 630, 630f
    in humans, 630
    in plants, 629-630, 629f, 804-805, 804f

Fungal garden, of leafcutter ants, 629, 629f
Fungi, 614-630. *See also* Lichen; Mycorrhizae
    body of, 616, 616f
    carnivorous, 617-618, 617f
    cell types in, 614
    cytokinesis in, 198
    ecology of, 625-629, 626f-629f
    endophytic, 626, 626f
    genome of, 477
    key characteristics of, 615, 615t
    major groups of, 615, 615f, 615t
    mating type in, 177
    mitosis in, 616-618
    obtaining nutrients, 614, 617-618, 617f
    phylogeny of, 615, 615f, 615t
    reproduction in, 614, 617, 617f
    in rumen, 620
    in symbioses, 626-629
Fungi (kingdom), 13, 13f, 514, 517f, 518t
Fusarium, 630
Fusion protein, 341, 341f

G

G-protein, **173**, 179-183, 179f, 912, 912f, 946
G-protein-coupled receptor, 946
G-protein-linked receptor, 95, 172f, 172t, 173, **179**-183, 179f
G_0 phase, **192**-193, 202
G_1 phase, **192**, 192f, 202
G_1/S checkpoint, **200**, 200f, 201f
G_2/M checkpoint, **200**, 200f, 201f
G_2 phase, **192**, 192f
GA-TRXN protein, 833f
GABA, 898
GABA receptor, 899
Gal4 gene, 341, 341f
Galápagos finch, 8, 9f, 408, 418, 418f, 440-441, 448, 448f
Gallbladder, 988f, 989
Gallstones, 989
Gametangium, **590**
Gamete, **208**, 208f, 214, 1084
    plant, 850-851, 850f-851f
    prevention of fusion of, 438t, 440
Gametic intrafallopian transfer (GIFT), 1102
Gametophyte, **590**, 590f, 594f, 595, 608, 608f, 609, 850-851
Gametophytic self-incompatibility, 856, 856f
Ganglia, **909**, 910f
Ganglion cell, **930**, 931f
Gap genes, 385f, **387**
Gap junction, 83f, **84**
Gap phase, 192, 192f
Garden pea (*Pisum sativum*)
    chromosome number in, 189t
    flower color in, 224-228, 225f, 226f, 231-232, 231f
    genome of, 479
    Knight's experiments with, 222
    Mendel's experiments with 222-229, 222f-229f

    choice of garden pea, 223, 223f
    experimental design, 223
    seed traits in, 224-225, 229f
Garrod, Archibald, 278-279
Gas exchange, 1002-1003
    in animals, 1003f
    evolution of, 1001-1002, 1003f
    in lungs, 1009, 1010f
    in single cell organisms, 1003f
    in tissues, 1010f
Gastric inhibitory peptide (GIP), **993**, 993f, 994t, 996, 997, 997f
Gastric juice, **986**, 986f
Gastrin, **993**, 993f, 994t
Gastrodermis, **652**, 652f
Gastrointestinal tract. *See* Digestive tract
Gastropod, 668, 668f, 669, 670f
Gastropoda (class), 670-671, 670f
Gastrovascular cavity, 982, **1022**, 1022f
Gastrula, **635**
Gastrulation, **392**, 392f, 1106t, 1112-1116, 1113f-1116f, 1113t
    in amphibian, 1114, 1114f
    in birds, 1114-1115, 1115f
    in mammals, 1115, 1115f
    in sea urchins, 1113-1114, 1113f
Gated ion channel, 96, **892**, 893f, 917
Gause, Georgii, 1189
Gehring, Walter, 502
Gel electrophoresis of DNA, 328-329, 329f
Gene, 13, 225
    co-option of existing gene for new function, 496-497, 497f
    copy number, 486
    functional analysis of, 500-501
    inactivation of, 482
    nature of, 278-281
    one-gene/one-polypeptide hypothesis, 280
    pleiotropic effect of, 413
    in populations, 396-414
    segmental duplication, 481
Gene cloning, 330
Gene disorder
    enzyme deficiency in, 279
    important disorders, 227t
Gene disorder. *See* Genetic disorder
Gene duplication, 480, 480f-481f, 481, 499-500, 500f
Gene expression, **278**-301, 298f, 298t
    Central Dogma, **280**, 280f
    chromatin structure and, 316-317, 316f-317f
    control of, 14, 304-324
    in development, 1117
    environmental effects on, 233t, 235, 235f, 308-309
    in eukaryotes, 305, 312-315, 313f-315f, 322f
    in plants, 830f
    in polyploids, 480
    posttranscriptional control, 317-321, 318f-319f, 321f
    in prokaryotes, 305, 308-312, 308f-312f

    regulatory proteins, 305-307, 306f-307f
    RNA in, 281
    transcriptional control, 305, 308, 312-315, 313f-315f
    translational control, 321
Gene flow, **401**-402, 401f, 406-407, 407f
    interactions among evolutionary forces, 406-407, 407f
    speciation and, 442
Gene-for-gene hypothesis, **811**, 811f
Gene therapy, 345, 345t
General transcription factor, **313**, 313f
Generalized transduction, **556**-557, 557f
Generation time, **1168**, 1169f
Generative cell, 605, 609f, 610
Genetic code, 42-43, 43f, 282-284, 282f, 283t, 284f
    in chloroplasts, 284
    in ciliates, 284
    deciphering, 283
    degeneracy of, 283-284
    in mitochondria, 284
    triple nature of, 282-283, 282f
    universality of, 284
Genetic counseling, **252**-253
Genetic disorder, 249-253, 249t
    enzyme deficiency, 279
    gene therapy for, 345, 345t
    genetic counseling in, 252
    important disorders, 227t, 249t
    prenatal diagnosis of, 252-253, 252f-253f
Genetic drift, 401f, **402**-403, 402f, 406, 443
Genetic engineering, 341-343, 342f-343f
    agricultural applications of, 346-349, 346f-348f
    bacteria and, 564
    human proteins produced in bacteria, 343-344
    medical applications of, 343-345, 344f, 345t
    social issues raised by, 348
Genetic Information Nondiscrimination Act (GINA), 369
Genetic map, 244-248, 352-355, **353**
    of *Drosophila*, 246-247, 246f
    of humans, 247-248, 248f
    using recombination to make maps, 245f, 246-247, 246f
Genetic mosaic, **243**
Genetic recombination. *See* Recombination
Genetic relationships, 1155f
Genetic sex determination, 1086
Genetic template, **1140**
Genetic variation
    evolution and, 396-397, 397f, 412, 412f
    genes within populations, 396-414
    maintenance of, 407-409, 408f-409f
    in nature, 398, 398f

Genetics
population, **397**
of prokaryotes, 554-559, 555f-558f
reverse, **343**
Genome, 13. *See also specific organisms*
of chloroplasts, 364
conserved regions in, 362-363
downsizing of, 479, 479f
eukaryotic, 358f
gene organization in, 360t
noncoding DNA in, 359-360
evolution of, 474-489
finding genes in, 358-359
gene swapping evidence in, 483-484, 483f
human. *See* Human genome
of mitochondria, 364
of moss, 595
prokaryotic, 358f
rearrangement of, 482, 482f
size and complexity of, 358, 358f, 486
of virus, 529, 531
Genome map, 352-355, 353f-355f. *See also* Physical map
Genome sequencing, 356-358, 356f-357f
clone-by-clone method, **357**, 357f
databases, 358-359
shotgun method, **357**, 357f
using artificial chromosomes, 356
Genome-wide association (GWA) mapping, microarray analysis and, 364-365
Genomic imprinting, **251**-252, 381
Genomic library, **331**
Genomics, 352-369, 363f
agricultural applications of, 368-369, 368f-369f
applications of, 367-369, 368f-369f
behavioral, 369
comparative, 362-363, 363f, 474-477, 475f, 500
functional, **364**-366, 365f-366f
medical applications of, 368, 487-488, 488f
ownership of genomic information, 369
Genotype, **226**
Genotype frequency, 399f, **400**
Genus, 512, 513
Geographic distribution, variation within species, 437, 437f
Geographic isolation, 437t
Geography, of speciation, 444-446, 444f-445f
Germ cell, 1092
Germ layers, **864**, 1113
Germ-line cells, **208**, 208f
Germination, of seeds, 393, 393f, 610, **764**-766, 764f-766f, 817
GH. *See* Growth hormone
Ghrelin, 996
GHRH. *See* Growth hormone-releasing hormone (GHRH)
Giant clam (*Tridacna maxima*), 667, 667f

Giant redwood (*Sequoiadendron giganteum*), 859f
Giardia, 573, 573f
Gibberellin, 826t, 832-834, 833f-834f, 845
Gibbon (*Hylobates*), 457, 457f
Gibbs' free energy, 110
GIFT. *See* Gametic intrafallopian transfer
Gigantism, 950
Gill(s)
of fish, 699, 702, **1004**-1006, 1004f-1005f
internal, 699
Gill cover, 702
Gill filament, 1005
Ginkgo biloba, 605f, 606
Ginkgophyta (phylum), 602t, 603, 605f, 606, 607f
GIP. *See* Gastric inhibitory peptide
Girdling of tree, 738
GLABROUS3 mutant, in *Arabidopsis*, 735, 735f
Glacier, 1251, 1251f
Glaucoma, juvenile, 227-228, 227f
Gliding joint, **967**, 968f
Global climate change, 369f, 1187, 1209
crop production and, 795-797
Global warming, 1250-1253
carbon dioxide and, 1251, 1251f
computer models of, 1250
effect on humans, 1252-1253
effect on natural ecosystems, 1251-1252, 1251f
geographic variation in, 1250, 1250f
Globulin, **1019**
Glomeromycetes, 622
Glomeromycota (phylum), 615, 615f, 615t, 622
Glomerulus, 1042, 1042f, **1046**, 1047f
Glomus, 615, 615t
Glottis, 1007, 1008f
Glucagon, **955**, 994-995, 995f
Glucocorticoids, 954
Gluconeogenesis, **995**
Glucose
in aerobic respiration, 132
alpha form of, 38, 39, 39f
beta form of, 38, 39, 39f
blood, regulation of, 994-995, 995f
catabolism of, 124
oxidation of, 25, 124-125
polymers of, 40f
priming of, 127, 128f
reabsorption in kidney, 1048
structure of, 38, 38f, 39f
Glucose 6-phosphate, 128f
Glucose repression, **310**-311, 310f
Glucose transporter, 45t, 97, 101, 101f
Glutamate, 141, 141f, 898
Glyceraldehyde 3-phosphate, 127, 128f, 161f, 162
Glycerol, 53, 55, 55f
Glycerol phosphate, 35f
Glycine, 46, 47f

Glycogen, 37t, **40**, 40f
Glycogenolysis, **995**
Glycolipid, 71, 82, 90f, 90t, **91**
Glycolysis, **125**, 126f, 127-130, 127f, 128f, 129f, 138f
evolution of, 129, 143
Glycoprotein, **69**, 71, 81, 90f, 90t, **91**
Glycoprotein hormones, 948
Glyphosate, **346**, 347f
Gnathostomulida, 643
Gnathozoa, 643
Gnetophyta (phylum), 602t, 605-606, 605f, 607f
GnRH. *See* Gonadotropin-releasing hormone
Goblet cell, 866
Goiter, 949, 949f
Golden rice, 348, 348f
Golgi apparatus, **70**-71, 70f, 71f, 78t, 81t
Golgi body, **70**, 739
Golgi, Camillo, 70
Golgi tendon organs, **919**
Gonadotropin-releasing hormone (GnRH), 949, 1093, 1094f
Gonorrhea, 561t, 562, 562f
Gooseneck barnacle (*Lepas anatifera*), 683f
Gore, Al, 1250
Gorilla (*Gorilla*), 457, 457f, 482, 482f
Gould, Stephen Jay, 451
Gout, 1044
Graafian follicle, **1095**, 1096f
Graded potential, **892**-893, 893f
Gradualism, **451**, 451f
Gram-negative bacteria, **552**-553, 552f-553f
Gram-positive bacteria, 550f, **552**-553, 552f-553f
Gram stain, **552**-553, 552f-553f
Grana, **74**, 74f
Grant, Peter, 419, 441
Grant, Rosemary, 419, 441
Granular leukocytes, **1019**
Granulosa cell, **1095**
Grape, 834, 834f
Grass, 1237
Grasshopper, 1022f
Grassland, temperate, 1237
Gravitropism, **819**-820, 819f-820f
negative, 819f, 820
positive, 820
Gravity sensing, in plants, 819f, 820
Green algae, 463f, 517-518, 517f, 571, 589, 589f, 591-592, 591f-592f
Greenbriar (*Smilax*), 741f
Greenhouse gas, 1251, 1251f
Gregarine, 578, 578f
Greyhound dog, 422-423, 423f
Griffith, Frederick, 257, 257f, 329, 557
Gross primary productivity, **1215**
Ground finch, 448, 448f
large ground finch (*Geospiza magnirostris*), 9f, 418f, 448f
medium ground finch (*Geospiza fortis*), 419, 419f, 441, 448f
small ground finch (*Geospiza fuliginosa*), 441, 448f

Ground meristem, **732**, 733f, 741, 758
Ground substance, **868**
Ground tissue, **731**, 736-737, 736f, 756, 758
Groundwater, 1210
Growth, as characteristic of life, 3, 508
Growth factor, 202, 203f, **942**
cell cycle and, 202, 203f
characteristics of, 202, 203f
Growth factor receptor, 202
Growth hormone (GH), 948, 950-951, 950f
Growth hormone-inhibiting hormone (GHIH), 949
Growth hormone-releasing hormone (GHRH), 949
GTP, 132, 133f
Guanine, 42, 42f, 259f, 260, 262
Guano, 1044
Guard cells, **734**, 734f
Guppy, selection on color in, 412-413, 412f-413f
Gurdon, John, 380
Gurken protein, 386, 387f
Gustation, 926
Gut, 996
Guttation, **776**
Gymnopphiona. *See* Apoda (order)
Gymnosperm, **603**, 605f, 607f
Gynoecium, **608**, 608f, 849

H

H band, 969
H1N1 virus, 1079
H5N1 virus, 539, 1079
HAART therapy, 538
Haberlandt, Gottlieb, 831
Habitat destruction, 1266, 1266f
Habitat, economic value of, 1262, 1262f
Habitat fragmentation, 1267-1268, 1267f
Habitat loss, 1245-1247, 1245f-1247f, 1264t, 1266-1268, 1266f-1268f
Habitat occupancy, population dispersion and, 1167
Habituation, **900**, 1137
Haeckel, Ernst, 645
Haemophilus influenzae, 352, 352f, 353, 357
Hagfish, 698f, 699, 699t
Hair, 716
Hair cell, 921, 921f
Hair-cup moss (*Polytrichum*), 594f
Hairpin, 286, 286f
Haldane, J. B. S., 1155
Half-life, 19-20, 424
Halobacterium, 95f, 550f
Halophyte, **781**
Halorespiration, 564
Hamilton, William D., 1155-1156
Hamstring, 968, 969f
Handicap hypothesis, **1152**
Hansen disease (leprosy), 560, 561t
Hantavirus, **540**
Haplodiploidy, 1156

Haplodiplontic life cycle, **590**, 590f, 592, 596

Haploid (*n*), **191**, 208, 208f, 225

Haplotype, genomic, **361**, 362f

Hardy, Godfrey H., 399

Hardy-Weinberg equation, 399-400

Hardy-Weinberg equilibrium, **399**-400, 399f

Hardy-Weinberg principle, 399-400

Hashimoto thyroiditis, 1075

Hatfill, Steven J., 368

Haversian canals, 966

Haversian lamellae, 966

Haversian system, 965f, **966**

Hawaiian *Drosophila*, 443, 447, 447f

Hawaiian Islands, 1270, 1270f

hCG. *See* Human chorionic gonadotropin

Head, of vertebrates, 696, 697f

Hearing, 920-925, 920f-925f

Heart, **1023**
    of amphibians, 703, 1024, 1024f
    of birds, 1025, 1025f
    cardiac cycle, **1026**, 1027f
    contraction of, 1026
    development in *Drosophila*, 1118
    of fish, 1023, 1023f
    four-chambered, 1025, 1026-1030
    of mammals, 1025, 1025f
    of reptiles, 1024

Heart attack, **1033**

Heart disease, chlamydia and, 563

Heat, 108-**109**, 1216

Heat-losing center, 882

Heat of vaporization, **28**
    of water, 27t, 28

Heat shock protein (HSP), 825

Heat transfer, 879-880, 879f

Heavy chain (polypeptide), **1069**, 1070f

Heavy metal, phytoremediation for, 799-800, 799f

Hedgehog signaling molecule, in *Drosophila*, 1124

Helical virus, 530

Helicase, DNA, **267**, 268t, 269f

Helicobacter, 551f

Helicobacter pylori, 561t, 562, 987

Heliotropism, 822f

Helium, 23f

Helix-turn-helix motif, 50, 50f, **306**-307, 307f, 311

Helper T cell, 1062t, 1066, 1067-1068, 1069f

Hematopoiesis, **1021**, 1062-1063

Heme group, 1013

Hemidesmosome, 83f, 84

Hemiptera (order), 685t

Hemocyanin, **1013**

Hemoglobin, 45t, 49, 53, 531f, **1013**-1014, 1019
    affinity for oxygen, 1014, 1014f
    effect of pH and temperature on, 1014, 1014f
    evolution of, 11, 11f
    structure of, 46, 48, 49, 1013, 1013f

Hemolymph, 669, **1023**

Hemolytic disease of newborns (HDN), 1077

Hemophilia, 227t, 242-243, 242f, 249t

Hemorrhagic fever, 540

Hensen's node, 1124

Hepatitis B, 532t, 539

Hepatitis virus, 344, 539

Herbicide resistance, in transgenic plants, 346-347, 347f

Herbivore, **982**
    digestive system of, 991f, 992
    plant defenses against, 810, 810f, 1193-1194, 1193f
    teeth of, 984f
    in trophic level ecosystem, **1215**, 1215f

Heredity, 221-236. *See also* Gene *entries*
    as characteristic of life, 508
    mechanism as evidence for evolution, 11

Hermaphrodite, **658**, 1085, 1085f

Herpes simplex virus, 344, 531f, 532t

Herpes zoster, 529

Hershey-Chase experiment, 258-259, 258f

Heterochromatin, **190**

Heterochrony, **493**

Heterokaryon, **616**, 623

Heterotherm, 880

Heterotrimeric G protein, 179, 179f

Heterotroph, **123**, 139, 559, 634t

Heterozygosity, 398

Heterozygote, **225**, 227t, 399-400

Heterozygote advantage, **408**-409, 409f

Hexapoda (class), 679t, 684, 684f, 685t, 686, 686f

Hfr cells, **555**, 555f

Hibernation, 883

High-density lipoprotein (HDL), 54, 1033

Hill, Robin, 151

Hindbrain, 902, 902f, 902t

Hinge joint, **967**, 968f

Hippocampus, 902t, 903, 905

Hippopotamus, 525, 525f

Hirudinea (class), 676, 676f

Histogram, 232, 233f

Histone, **190**, 190f, 316-317, 316f

HIV. *See* Human immunodeficiency virus

HLA. *See* Human leukocyte antigen (HLA)

H.M.S. *Beagle* (Darwin's ship), 1, 1f, 8, 9f, 10, 418

HOBBIT gene, in *Arabidopsis*, 757-758, 758f

Holistic concept, of community, **1186**

Holoblastic cleavage, **1110**-1111, 1111f, 1111t

Holoenzyme, 284f, 285

Holothuroidea (class), 689f

Holt-Oram syndrome, 497

Homeobox, 389, 493, 646

Homeodomain, 307, 389

Homeodomain motif, **307**

Homeodomain protein, 14, 14f

Homeosis, **494**

Homeostasis, 14, 305, 876-878, 876f-878f
    calcium, 952-953, 953f
    as characteristic of life, 3, 508

Homeotherm, 880

Homeotic genes, **388**
    complexes, 388-389
    in *Drosophila*, 388, 388f
    evolution of, 389
    in mouse, 388f

Homeotic mutants, 388

Hominid, 482f, **722**-724, 723f
    compared to apes, 722
    evolution of, 722-724

Hominoid, **722**-723, 721f, 722f

Homo erectus, 724, 725

Homo floresiensis, 724, 724f

Homo (genus), 722, 724

Homo habilis, 724

Homo heidelbergensis, 725

Homo neanderthalensis, 725

Homo sapiens, 723, 724, 725, 726f

Homokaryotic hyphae, **616**

Homologous chromosomes, **191**, 191f, 209-210, 209f

Homologous recombination, 555

Homologous structures, **11**, 11f, **428**, 428f, 464, 465f, 497

Homologue, **191**, 211

Homoplasty, **459**-460, 460f, 464-465, 465f, 498

Homoptera (order), 684f, 685t

Homosporous plant, **596**

Homozygote, **225**, 227t

Honeybee (*Apis mellifera*)
    altruism in, 1156, 1156f
    dance language of, 1146, 1146f

Hooke, Robert, 12, 59

Horizontal gene transfer, **483**, 483f, 516, 521-522, 522f, 548

Hormonal control
    of digestive tract, 993, 993f, 994t, 997f
    of osmoregulatory functions, 1050-1052, 1051f-1052f

Hormone, 44, 45t, 169f, **170**, 938, 940t-941t. *See also* specific hormones
    chemical classes of, 939
    female reproductive hormones, 1093t
    hydrophilic, 939, 942, 942f, 945-946, 945f
    lipophilic, 939, 942, 942f, 943-945, 943f-944f
    male reproductive hormones, 1093, 1093t, 1094f
    plant. *See* Plant hormone
    protein, 45t
    steroid, 173-174, 173f
    treatment for infertility, 1102

Hormone-activated transcription factor, 944

Hormone response element, **944**

Horn (animal), 717

Hornwort, 463f, 589f, 595, 595f

Horse, 525, 525f, 865f
    chromosome number in, 189t
    evolution of, 414, 414f, 426-428, 426f-427f

    eyes of, 501f
    teeth of, 984f
    thoroughbred, 414, 414f

Horsetail, 189t, 596, 599, 599f, 601t

Host range, of virus, **529**

Host restriction, 328

Hot mutants, in *Arabidopsis*, 825

Hotspots, 1259-1261, 1259f-1260f, 1260t
    population growth in, 1260-1261, 1260f

Hox genes, **389**, 493, 494, 523f, 524, 639, 646, 756

Hubbard Brook Experimental Forest, 1212-1213, 1213f

Human
    birth weight in, 411, 411f
    cleavage in, 1112
    development in, 1125-1129, 1126f-1128f
    effect of global warming on, 1252-1253
    effect on biosphere, 1245-1250
    evolutionary relationships of, 457, 457f
    extinctions due to
        in historical time, 1258, 1258t
        in prehistoric times, 1257-1258, 1257f
    forebrain of, 903-905, 904f-905f
    gastrulation in, 1115
    genetic map of, 247-248, 248f
    influence on flower morphology, 850
    language of, 1147
    plant toxins, susceptibility to, 807-808, 807f
    sexual differentiation in, 1086
    skin of, 918, 918f
    survivorship curve for, 1170, 1170f-1171f
    teeth of, 717, 717f

Human chorionic gonadotropin (hCG), 1097

Human chromosomes, 189-191, 189-f, 189t, 190f, 241-243
    alterations in chromosome number, 250-251, 250f-251f
    artificial, 356
    chromosome number, 189t
    karyotype, 191f
    sex chromosomes, 241-243, 241t, 248f

Human disease
    bacterial, 558, 560-563, 561t, 562f
    effect of global warming on, 1253
    flukes, 658-659, 659f
    fungal, 630
    nematodes, 661f, 662-663
    viral, 539-541

Human evolution, 402, 457, 457f, 721-726, 721f-726f
    human races, 726, 726f

Human Gene Mutation Database, 250

Human genome, 4
    comparative genomics, 474-476, 475f
    gene swapping in, 484

segmental duplication in, 480f-481f, 481

single nucleotide, polymorphisms in, **248**

transposable elements in, 484

Human Genome Project, 253, 354, 357-358, 359

Human immunodeficiency virus (HIV), 531, 531f, 532t, 535-538, **1080**, 1080f

  effect on immune system, 535, 1080

  evolution of, 470-471, 470f-471f

    during infection, 537

  human effect of, 1080

  infection cycle of, 536-537, 536f, 1080

  latency period in humans, 535

  progression of, 1080

  testing for presence, 535

  tracking evolution of AIDS among individuals, 471, 471f

  transmission of, 535

  treatment of, 537-538, 537f

    blocking viral entry, 538

    combination therapy, 538

    HAART therapy, 538

    integrase inhibitors, 538

    protease inhibitors, 538

    reverse transcriptase inhibitors, 538

    vaccine therapy, 538

Human leukocyte antigen (HLA), **1066**

Human population

  in developing and developed countries, 1180-1181, 1180f, 1180t

  growth of, 1178-1182, 1179f-1181f, 1180t

    decline in growth rate, 1181

    exponential, 1178, 1179f

    future situation, 1180-1181

    in hotspots, 1260-1261, 1260f

  population pyramids, **1178**-1180, 1179f

Hummingbird, 852, 853f, 883

Humoral immunity, **1063**, 1068-1074, 1069-1074f

Humus, **787**

Hunchback protein, **386**, 386f

Huntington disease, 249, 249t, 300, 335, 898

Hyalin, 1108

Hybridization (between species), **222**, 437-438, 438f, 440-441

Hybridization (nucleic acid), **332**-333, 333f

Hybridoma cell, 1078

Hydra, 641t, 652f, 653, 655, 982f, 1022f

Hydration shell, 28, 29f

Hydrocarbon, 34

  in ancient rocks, 547

Hydrochloric acid, gastric, 986, 987

Hydrocortisone, 943f, 954

Hydrogen, 24, 24f

Hydrogen bond, 23t, **26**

  in proteins, 48, 48f

  structure of, 27f

  in water, 26, 26f

Hydrogen ion, 29-30

Hydrogenated oils, 55

Hydrolysis, **37**, 37f

Hydrophilic hormone, 939, 942, 942f, 945-946, 945f

Hydrophilic molecule, **28**

Hydrophobic exclusion, **28-29**

Hydrophobic interaction, 23t

Hydrophobic molecule, **28**

Hydroponics, 791, 791f

Hydrostatic skeleton, **962**, 962f

Hydrothermal vent, 1244-1245

Hydroxyapatite, 963

Hydroxyl group, 35, 35f, 43

Hydrozoa (class), **655**, 655f

Hymen, 1098

Hymenoptera (order), 684f, 685t

Hypercholesterolemia, 249t

Hyperosmotic solution, 98, 98f

Hyperpolarization, **892**-893, 893f

Hypersensitive response, in plants, **811**, 812f

Hypersensitivity, delayed, 1076

Hypertension, **1030**

Hyperthyroidism, 951

Hypertonic solution, **98**, 98f, 1039

Hyperventilation, **1010**-1011, 1012

Hyphae, **616**, 616f, 617

Hypolimnion, 1239

Hypoosmotic solution, 98, 98f

Hypophysectomy, 950

Hypophysis, **946**

Hypothalamohypophyseal portal system, 948

Hypothalamus, **876**, 882-883, 883f, 905

  control of anterior pituitary, 948-949, 948f

  production of neurohormones, 947

Hypothesis, 5-6, 5f

Hypothyroidism, 951

Hypotonic solution, **98**, 98f

Hyracotherium, 426-428, 426f

I

Ichthyosaur, 707t

Ichthyosauria (order), 707t

Ichthyostega, 704-705, 705f

Icosahedron, 530, 530f

ICSI. *See* Intracytoplasmic sperm injection

Ileum, **987**

Immune system, 875f, **876**, 1055-1080

  cells of, 1062t

  effect of HIV on, 1080

  organs of, 1064-1065, 1064f-1065f

  pathogens that invade, 1079-1080, 1080f

Immunity

  active, 1063, 1074f

  adaptive, 1061-1066, 1061f-1065f, 1062t

  cell-mediated, **1063**, 1066-1068, 1066t, 1067f, 1069f

  humoral, **1063**, 1068-1074, 1069f-1074f

  innate, 1056-1058, 1057f, 1068

  passive, 1063

Immunoglobulin A (IgA), 1071t, **1072**

Immunoglobulin D (IgD), 1071t, **1072**

Immunoglobulin E (IgE), 1071t, **1072**, 1075, 1076f

Immunoglobulin G (IgG), 1071f, 1071t, **1072**

Immunoglobulin (Ig), **1063**, 1063f. *See also* Antibody

  classes of, 1071-1072, 1071t

  diversity of, 1072-1074

  structure of, 1069-1070, 1070f

Immunoglobulin M (IgM), **1071**-1072, 1071f, 1071t

Immunohistochemistry, 61

Immunological tolerance, **1075**

Immunosuppression, 1080

Implantation, **1125**

Imprinting, **1139**

In situ hybridization, 353

In vitro fertilization, 1102

In vitro mutagenesis, **342**

Incomplete dominance, 233t, **234**, 234f

Incomplete flower, **848**, 848f

Incus, **921**

Independent assortment, **214**, **229**, 229f

Indeterminate development, **638**, 639f

Indian pipe (*Hypopitys uniflora*), 794, 794f

Individualistic concept, of community, 1186

Indoleacetic acid (IAA), **828**-829, 829f

Indolebutyric acid, **830**

Induced fit, 114, 114f

Inducer exclusion, **310**

Induction (development), **377**-378, 377f, 1117

  primary, **1124**

  secondary, **1124**, 1125f

Induction of phage, 533-534, 534f

Induction of protein, **308**

Inductive reasoning, **5**

Industrial melanism, 420-**421**, 420f-421f

  in peppered moth, 420-**421**, 420f-421f

Inert element, 22

Inferior vena cava, **1029**

Infertility, 1101

  female, 1101

  male, 1101

  treatment of, 1102

Inflammatory response, 1058-1059, 1060f

Influenza, 532t, 539

  bird flu, 539

Influenza virus, 529f, 531f, 532t, 539, 1079

  H subtypes, 539

  H1N1 strain, 1079

  H5N1 strain, 539, 1079

  N subtypes, 539

  origin of new strains, 539-540

  recombination in, 539

  types and subtypes of, 539

Infrared radiation, sensing of, 934, 934f

Ingen-Housz, Jan, 150

Ingression, **1113**

Inhalant siphon, **671**, 671f

Inheritance, patterns of, 221-236

Inhibiting hormone, **948**, 949

Inhibition, 1203

Inhibitor, **117**

  allosteric, **117**, 117f

  competitive, **117**, 117f

  noncompetitive, **117**, 117f

Inhibitory postsynaptic potential (IPSP), 899, 899f, 900

Initiation complex, 288, 288f, **294**, 294f, 313, 313f

Initiation factor, 294, 294f

Initiator tRNA, **294**, 294f

Innate behavior, 1133, 1133f

Innate releasing mechanism, 1133

Inner cell mass, **1112**, 1112f

Inner ear, **922**, 922f

Inorganic phosphate, **113**

Inositol phosphate, 180f, 181

Inositol triphosphate (IP$_3$/calcium) second messenger system, 179, 180f, 181, 181f

Inositol triphosphate (IP$_3$), **946**

Insect, 679t, 684-686, 684f, 685t, 686f

  Bt crops resistance to, 347-348

  chromosome number in, 189t

  cleavage in, 1110

  digestive system of, 686

  diversity among, 684f

  excretory organs in, 1041, 1041f

  external features of, 684, 685f, 686

  eyes of, 414, 414f, 501, 501f, 680, 680f, 681f, 928f

  fish predation on, 408, 408f

  hormones in, 956f, 957

  internal organization of, 686

  locomotion in, 976-977

  nitrogenous wastes of, 1044, 1045f

  orders of, 685t

  pheromones of, 686

  pollination by, 852, 852f-853f

  respiration in, 1003f

  selection for pesticide resistance in, 404-405, 405f

  sense receptors of, 686

  sex chromosomes of, 241, 241t

  social, 1157, 1158f

  taste in, 926, 926f

  thermoregulation in, 880, 880f

  wings of, 498-499, 498f, 684, 686f

Insectivore, digestive system of, 991f

Insectivorous leaf, 750

Insertion sequence (IS), 555, 555f

Insertional inactivation, 330

Instantaneous reaction, 110

Instinct, learning and, 1138, 1138f, 1140, 1140f

Insulin, 954-**955**, 955f, 994-995, 995f, 996

Insulin-like growth factor, 942, **950**
Insulin receptor, 176, 176f
Insulin receptor protein, 176
Integral membrane protein, 89, 90f, 94, 95f
Integrase inhibitor, 538
Integrin, **81**, 81f, 392, 392f
Integrin-mediated link, **84**
Integument (flower), **602**
Integumentary system, 875f, **876**
Intelligent design theory, against theory of evolution, 432-433
Intercalated disk, **871**, 1027
Interference competition, **1188**
Interferon, 1057-1058
Intergovernmental Panel on Climate Change, 795, 1250, 1253
Interior protein network, 90t, 91
Interleukin-1 (IL-1), **1059**
Intermediate filament, 76, 76f, 83f, **84**
Intermembrane space, of mitochondria, **74**
Internal chemoreceptor, 927
Internal fertilization, 1087-1090, 1087f-1090f
Internal membranes, of prokaryotes, 554, 554f
Internal organs, of vertebrates, 696, 697f
International Human Genome Sequencing Consortium, 357
Internet, 183
Interneurons, 873t, **888**, 888f
Internode, 730f, **744**, 744f
Interoceptor, **916**
Interoparity, **1173**
Interphase, **192**, 192f, 193-194, 193f-194f
Intersexual selection, 1150f, **1151**-1152
Interspecific competition, **1188**, 1191, 1191f
Intertidal region, 1241f, **1243**
Intestine, 982f. *See also* Large intestine; Small intestine
Intracellular receptor, 172t, 173-174, 173f
Intracytoplasmic sperm injection (ICSI), 1102
Intramembranous development, of bone, 963, 964f, 965
Intramolecular catalysis, 116
Intrasexual selection, **1151**, 1152f
Intrauterine device (IUD), 1099t, 1100
Intrinsic factor, **987**
Introduced species, 1264t, 1269-1271
    efforts to combat, 1271
    removing, 1276
Intron, **289**, 289f, 298t, 320, 321f, 359, 360t, 486
    distribution of, 290
Invaginate, **1113**
Inversion, **300**-301, 301f
Invertebrate, 635
    circulatory system of, 1022-1023, 1022f
    digestive system of, 982, 982f

marine, loss of larval stage, 468, 469f
osmoregulatory organs of, 1040-1041, 1040f-1041f
vision in, 928-929, 928f
Iodine, 949
Ion(s), 19
Ion channel, 90t, **96**-97, 97f, **171**, 172f, 172t, **891**
    chemically gated, 892
    gated, 96, **892**, 893f
    ligand-gated, 892
    stimulus-gated, **917**, 917f
    transient receptor potential, 918
    voltage-gated, **893**, 894f
Ionic bond, 23-24, 23f, 23t, 48, 48f
Ionic compound, 24
Ionization of water, 29
IP. *See* Inositol phosphate
IP₃. *See* inositol triphosphate
IPSP. *See* Inhibitory postsynaptic potential
Irreducible complexity argument, against theory of evolution, 433
IS. *See* Insertion sequence
Island
    biogeography of, 1226-1227, 1226f
    evolution on, 431-432, 431f, 444-445, 444f
    extinctions on, 1258, 1266, 1266f
Island biogeography, 1226-1227, 1226f
Island dwarfism, 724
Islets of Langerhans, 954-955, 988f, **989**
Isocitrate, 132, 133f
Isomer, **35**
    of sugars, 38, 39f
Isomotic regulation, 99
Isomotic solution, 98, 98f
Isoptera (order), 684f, 685t
Isotonic solution, **98**, 98f, 1039
Isotope, **19**, 19f
    radioactive, 19, 424, 424f
IUD. *See* Intrauterine device
Ivins, Bruce E., 368
Ivy, 744f

J

Jacob syndrome, 251
Jasmonic acid, **810**
Jaundice, 989
Jaws
    evolution of, 698, 700, 700f
    of fish, 699-700, 700f, 1065-1066
Jejunum, **987**
Jellyfish, 634t, 636, 641t, 655-656, 655f-656f
Jenner, Edward, 344, 1061, 1061f
Jimsonweed (*Datura stramonium*), 852
Joint, **967**
    movement at, 968, 968f-969f
    types of, 967, 968f
Jointed appendages, of arthropods, 680
Joule, 108
Juvenile glaucoma, 227-228, 227f
Juvenile hormone, **957**, 957f

K

K-selected population, **1177**, 1178t
KANADI gene, in *Arabidopsis*, 747f
Karyogamy, 622, 623f, 624, 624f
Karyotype, **191**, 191f
    human, 191f
Kaufmann, Thomas, 389
Keratin, 76, 866
Keratinized epithelium, 866
α-Ketoglutarate, 132, 133f, 141, 141f
α-Ketoglutarate dehydrogenase, 133f
Kettlewell, Bernard, 420-421
Key innovation, **446**
Key stimulus, 1133, 1133f
Keystone species, **1201**, 1201f
    loss of, 1272, 1273f
Khorana, H. Gobind, 283
Kidney, 956
    of amphibians, 1043
    of birds, 1043-1044, 1044f
    excretion in, 1048
    filtration in, 1046-1047, 1047f
    of fish
        cartilaginous fish, 1043
        freshwater fish, 1042, 1043f
        marine bony fish, 1042, 1043f
    hormonal regulation of, 1050-1052, 1051f-1052f
    of mammals, 1043-1044, 1044f, 1045-1050, 1046f-1050f
    reabsorption in, 1046, 1048, 1049f, 1050-1051, 1051f
    of reptiles, 1043
    secretion in, 1046, 1048
    of vertebrates, **1041**-1044, 1042f-1044f
Killer strain, *Paramecium*, 579
Killfish (*Rivulus hartii*), 412-413, 412f
Kilocalorie, 108, **995**
Kin selection, 1155-1157, 1155f-1156f
Kinase cascade, **176**-177, 177f, 178
Kinesin, 77, 77f
Kinetic energy, **108**, 108f
Kinetochore, 187f, 191f, **193**, 193f, 211, 211f, 216
Kinetoplastid, 574-575, 575f
Kingdom (taxonomy), **512**, 513f, 514
    evolutionary relationships among kingdoms, 517f
Kinocilium, **920**, 921f
Kinorhyncha (phylum), 640, 644f
Klinefelter syndrome, 251, 251f
Knee-jerk reflex, 908, 908f
Knight, T. A., 222
Knockout mice, **342**-343, 342f-343f
Kölreuter, Josef, 222
Komodo dragon (*Varanus komodoensis*), 1258-1259
Krebs, Charles, 1177
Krebs cycle, 118, 125, 126f, 130, 131-133, 131f, 133f, 141, 141f
    ATP production in, 132, 131f, 133f, 138, 138f
    products of, 133f
    reductive, 547
Kristensen, Reinhardt, 660
Kurosawa, Eiichi, 832-833

L

Labyrinth, **920**
lac operon, **308**, 309-310, 308f-310f
lac repressor, 45t, 309-310, 309f
Lacewing (*Chrysoperia*), courtship song of, 439, 439f
Lactation, 1128
Lactic acid fermentation, 140, 140f
Lactose, 39
Lactose intolerance, 39, 988
Lacunae, **870**
Lagging strand, 267f, **268**-269, 269f-270f
Lake, 1239-1241, 1239f-1240f
    eutrophic, **1240**-1241, 1240f
    oligotrophic, 1240, 1240f
    thermal stratification of, **1239**-1240, 1240f
Lake Victoria cichlid fish, 449-450, 449f, 1271
Lamarck, Jean-Baptiste, 397
Lamellae, 1005
Lamellipodia, 1113
Lamprey, 698f, 699, 699t
Lancelet, 696, 696f
Land plants
    evolution of, 521f, 571, 589-590
    innovations in, 597f
Langerhans, Paul, 954
Language, 905-906, 906f
Large intestine, 983, 983f, 990, 990f
Large offspring syndrome, 381
Larva
    loss in marine invertebrates, 468, 469f
    of snails, 466-468, 467f-468f
Larynx, **985**, 985f
Latent virus, 529
Lateral geniculate nuclei, **932**, 933f
Lateral line system, **701**, 920, 921f
Lateral meristem, **731**, 732, 733f
Lateral root cap, 739, 739f
LDL. *See* Low-density lipoprotein
Leading strand, 267f, **268**, 269f-270f, 272f
Leaf, 730f, 747-750, 747f-749f, 809, 809f
    abscission of, **823**-824, 823f-824f
    alternate, 744, 744f
    of carnivorous plant, 793-794
    compound, **748**, 748f
    establishing top and bottom of, 747, 747f
    evolution of, 596-597, 597f
    external structure of, 747-748, 747f-748f
    internal structure of, 748-749, 749f
    modified, 749-750
    opposite, 744, 744f
    pinnately compound, 748f
    simple, **748**, 748f
    transpiration of water from. *See* Transpiration
    whorled, 744, 744f
Leaf-cutter ant, 629, 629f
Leaflet, 748

LEAFY COTYLEDON gene,
in *Arabidopsis*, 759
LEAFY gene, in *Arabidopsis*, 841
Learning, 906
behavior and, 1135, 1135f,
1137-1138, 1138f, 1140, 1140f
Leber's hereditary optic neuropathy
(LHON), 244
Leech, 641t, 675-676, 676f
Leeuwenhoek, Anton van, 12, 59
Leg(s), of amphibians, 703, 704f
Leishmaniasis, 488, 574
Lens, **929**, 929f
Lenticel, 745, 746f
Leopard frog (*Rana*), postzygotic
isolation in, 440, 440f
Leopold, Aldo, 1221
Lepidoptera (order), 684f, 685t
Lepidosauria, 699f
Leprosy, 560, 561t
Leptin, 996, 996f
Lettuce, genome of, 479f
Leucine zipper motif, **307**, 307f
Leukocytes, 870, **1019**, 1058
granular, **1019**
nongranular, **1019**
Lewis, Edward, 388
Lichen, **626**-627, 627f
as air quality indicators, 627
foliose, 627f
fruticose, 627f
Life
characteristics of, 2-3
hierarchical organization of,
3-4, 3f
origin of. *See* Origin of life
science of, 2-4
Life cycle
of brown algae, 581f
of *Chlamydomonas*, 591f
of fern, 600, 600f
of flowering plant, 609f
of moss, 594f
of *Paramecium*, 579f
of pine, 604-605, 604f
of plants, 590, 590f, 608-610, 609f
of *Plasmodium*, 577f
of *Ulva*, 592f
Life history, 1171-1173, 1171f-1172f
Life table, **1169**-1170, 1170t
Ligand, **168**, 169f
Ligand-gated channel, 892
Light, cue to flowering in plants,
842-844, 842f-843f
Light chain (polypeptide),
1069, 1070f
Light-dependent reactions,
of photosynthesis, **148**, 149f, 150,
156-160, 156f-160f
Light-harvesting complex, 155,
155f, 157
Light-independent reactions,
of photosynthesis, **148**, 150, 150f
Light microscope, 61, 61f, 62t
Light-response genes, 815-816,
815f-816f
Lignin, **736**
Lily, 851f
Limb bud, 497

Limb, development of, 497-498, 497f
Limbic system, 900, 902t, **905**
LINE. *See* Long interspersed element
Lineus, 642t, 503, 672, 672f
Linkage disequilibrium, **361**
Linkage map. *See* Genetic map
Linnaeus, Carolus, 512
Lion (*Panthera leo*), 438, 438f, 984f
Lipase, **988**
Lipid(s), 33, 36f, 37, **53-56**. *See also*
Phospholipid
functions of, 37t, 53-56
membrane, 548, 549f
structure of, 53-56
Lipid bilayer, 56, 56f
Lipid raft, 91
Lipophilic hormone, 939, 942, 942f,
943-945, 943f-944f
Lipopolysaccharide, **553**, 553f, 1056
Little paradise kingfisher (*Tanysiptera
hydrocharis*), 444, 444f
Liver, 988f, **989**, 994
Liverwort, 463f, 589f, 590, 593, 593f
Lizard, 699f, 707t, 711, 711f
Llama, 525
Lobe-finned fish, 698f, 699t, 702,
702f, 704f
Lobster, 682, 683, 683f
Local anaphylaxis, 1075
Locomotion, 639, 975-977
in air, 976-977, 977f
appendicular, 975
axial, 975
on land, 976, 976f
in water, 975-976, 975f
Locomotor organelles,
of protists, 572
Logarithmic scale, 29
Long-day plant,
842-843, 842f
facultative, **843**
obligate, **843**
Long interspersed element (LINE),
360, 361f
Long-term depression (LTD),
906, 907f
Long-term memory, 906
Long-term potentiation (LTP),
906, 907f
Long terminal repeat (LTR),
360-361, 361f
Loop of Henle, 1044, **1047**, 1047f,
1048-1049
Loose connective tissue, **868**,
868f, 869t
Lophophore, 523f, 642t, **643**,
676-678, 677f-678f
Lophotrochozoan,
523-524, 523f, 643, 644f, 669
Lorenz, Konrad, 1139, 1139f, 1146
Loricifera (phylum), 642t, 644f
Low-density lipoprotein (LDL), 54,
103, 320-321, 1033
LTP. *See* Long-term potentiation
LTR. *See* Long terminal repeat
Lubber grasshopper (*Romalea
guttata*), 684f
Lumen, of endoplasmic reticulum, **69**
Luna moth (*Actias luna*), 684f

Lung(s), 1006-1008, 1007f-1009f
of amphibians, 703, 1007, 1007f
of birds, 1008, 1009f
of mammals,
1007-1008, 1008f
of reptiles, 1007
structure and function of,
1009, 1010f
Lung cancer, **1012**, 1012f
smoking and, 1012
Luteinizing hormone (LH), 948, 950,
1093, 1093t, 1094f
Lycophyta (phylum), 589f, 596, 597,
597f, 598, 598f, 601f
Lyme disease, 560, 561t
Lymph, **1032**
Lymph heart, **1032**
Lymphatic system, 875f, **876**,
1032-1033, 1032f
Lymphocyte, **1063**, 1063f,
1064, 1065f
Lysenko, T. D., 844
Lysogenic cycle, of bacteriophage,
533-534, 534f
Lysogeny, **533**
Lysosomal storage disorder, 71
Lysosome, **71**-72, 72f, 78t, 81t
Lysozyme, 1056
Lytic cycle, of bacteriophage, 258,
533, 534f

M

M phase. *See* Mitosis
M-phase-promoting factor (MPF),
198-199, 199f, **200**, 200f, 201
MacArthur, Robert, 1190, 1226
macho-1 gene, 377, 378, 378f
MacLeod, Colin, 257
Macrogymus, 620
Macromolecule, 2f, **33**, 36f, 37,
37f, 37t
Macronucleus, **578**, 578f
Macronutrients, in plants,
790-791, 790t
Macrophage, **1058**, 1058f
Madreporite, **689**
MADS-box genes, **389**, 493, 494,
499, 500, 500f
Magnetic field, sensing of, 934
Maidenhair tree (*Ginkgo biloba*),
605f, 606
Maize. *See* Corn (*Zea mays*)
Major groove, 262f,
305-**306**, 306f
Major histocompatibility complex
(MHC), **1064**, 1065f
MHC class I protein, **1066**, 1066t
MHC class II protein,
1066, 1066t
MHC proteins, 45t,
82-83, 1066
Malaria, 577-578, 577f, 808, 1253
drug development, 487-488, 488f
eradication of, 577
genome of, 475f
sickle cell anemia and, 250,
409, 409f
vaccine for, 578, 1079

Malate, 132, 133f
Male infertility, 1101
Male reproduction, hormonal
control of, 1093t
Male reproductive system, 875f, **876**,
1091-1094, 1091f-1094f, 1093t
Malleus, **921**
Malpighian tubule, 679f, 680f, **681**
MALT. *See* Mucosa-associated
lymphoid tissue
Malthus, Thomas, 10
Maltose, 39, 39f
Mammal, 641t, 698f, 716-720,
716f-719f
brain of, 903, 903f
characteristics of, 716-718,
716f-717f
circulatory system of,
1025, 1025f
classification of,
718-719, 718f
cleavage in, 1112, 1112f
digestion of plants by, 717
egg-laying. *See* Monotreme
evolution of, 525f, 697, 698f,
718, 718f
extinctions, 718t
flying, 717-718, 717f
gastrulation in, 1115, 1115f
kidney of, 1043-1044, 1044f,
1045-1050, 1046f-1050f
lungs of, 1007-1008, 1008f
marine, 720t
nitrogenous wastes of, 1044, 1045f
nuclear transplant in,
380-381, 381f
orders of, 720t
placental. *See* Placental mammal
pouched. *See* Marsupial
reproduction in, 1090f
respiration in, 1003f, 1007-1008,
1008f
saber-toothed, 465f
thermoregulation in, 716
Mammalia (class), 513f, 698f,
716-720, 716f-719f
Mammary gland, 716
Manatee, 430
Mandible, of crustaceans,
678-679, 679f
Mangold, Hilde, 1122
Mangrove, 780-781, 781f
Mangrove swamp, **1243**, 1248
Mannose-binding lectin (MBL)
protein, 1057, 1060
Mantle, **667**, 668f
Mantle cavity, 1004
MAP kinase. *See* Mitogen-activated
protein kinase
Marine habitat,
1241-1245, 1241f-1244f
human impacts on,
1247-1248, 1248f
Markers, cell, 63
Markov, Georgi, 808
Marler, Peter, 1140
Marrow cavity, **966**
Mars, life on, 509, 509f
Marsilea, 600

Marsupial, 525f, **719**, 719f, **1090**, 1090f, 1098
  marsupial-placental convergence, 430-431, 431f
  saber-toothed, 465f
Mass extinction, 452-453, 452f
Mast cell, **1062**, 1062t
Mastication, 967, 982, 984
Mastiff, 423f
Maternal inheritance, **244**
Maternity plant, 858
Mating
  assortative, **402**
  disassortative, **402**
  nonrandom, 401f, 402
  See also Courtship *entries*
Mating behavior, 439, 439f
  selection acting on, 443, 443f
  sexual selection and, 1151-1152, 1151f-1152f
Mating ritual, 439
Mating success, 405
Mating system, 1153-1154, 1153f
Mating type, in fungi, 177
Matrix
  extracellular. *See* Extracellular matrix
  of mitochondria, **74**
Matter, 18
Mauna kea silversword (*Argyroxiphium sandwicense*), 1259, 1259f
Mayr, Ernst, 437
Mccarty, Maclyn, 257
McClintock, Barbara, 245-246, 245f, 360, 480
MCS. *See* Multiple cloning site
Measles, 532t
Mechanical isolation, 438t, 439-440
Mechanoreceptor, **916**, 917-919, 918f-919f
Mediator, 314-315, 315f
Medicago truncatula, 479, 479f, 483f, 489
  genome of, 479f
Medicine
  antibodies in medical treatment, 1077-1079, 1078f
  applications of genetic engineering, 343-345, 344f, 345t
  applications of genomics to, 368, 368t, 487-488, 488f
Medulla oblongata, **902**, 902t
Medullary bone, 965f, **966**
Medullary cavity, 965f, 966
Medusa, **653**, 653f, 655, 655f
Meerkat (*Suricata suricata*), 1158, 1159f
Megakaryocyte, 1021
Megapascal, **770**
Megaphyll, **747**
Meiosis, **208**-218, 208f
  compared to mitosis, 215-218, 216f-217f
  errors in, 214
  sequence of events during, 209-214, 208f-213f

Meiosis I, **209**-210, 209f, 211f, 212f, 216, 216f, 217f
Meiosis II, **209**-210, 209f, 213f, 214
Meissner corpuscle, 918f
Melanin, **951**
Melanocyte-stimulating hormone (MSH), 948, 951, 997
Melanotropin-inhibiting hormone (MIH), 949
Melatonin, 956
Membrane(s), 88-104. *See also specific membranes*
Membrane attack complex, **1060**, 1060f
Membrane potential, 97, 890-891
Memory, 906
  long-term, 906
  short-term, 906
Mendel, Gregor, 11, 301, 399
  experiments with garden pea 222-229, 222f-229f
    experimental design, 223
  portrait of, 223f
  rediscovery of ideas, 232
Mendeleev, Dmitri, 22
Mendelian ratio, **225**
  modified, 236, 236f
Meninges, 907
Menstrual cycle, 1095-1097, 1095f-1096f
  follicular (proliferative) phase, **1095**-1096, 1095f
  luteal phase, 1095f, **1097**
  menstrual phase, 1097
  ovulation, 1095f, 1096-1097, 1096f
  secretory phase, **1097**
Menstruation, **1090**
Mercury pollution, 1246
Mereschkowsky, Konstantin, 568-569
Meristem, 374-**375**, 731-732, 731f
  apical, **731**, 732, 732f-733f, 832f
  floral, 846, 846f-847f
  ground, **732**, 733f, 741, 758
  lateral, **731**, 732, 733f
  primary, **732**, 758
Merkel cells, 918f, 919
Meroblastic cleavage, **1111-1112**, 1111t, 1112f
Merodiploid, **556**
Meselson-Stahl experiment, 264-265, 264f
Mesencephalon. *See* Midbrain
Mesenchyme, **963**
Mesoderm, **637**, 637f, 864, 1113, 1113f
Mesoglea, **653**, 653f
Mesohyl, **651**
Mesophyll, **748**-749
  palisade, 749, 749f
  spongy, 749, 749f
Messenger RNA (mRNA), 42, **69**, 281. *See also* Primary transcript
  degradation of, 321
  5′ cap, **288**, 288f
  making cDNA library, 332, 332f
  mature, **288**

  poly-A tail of, **289**, 289f
  posttranscriptional control in eukaryotes, 317-321, 318f-319f, 321f
  pre-mRNA splicing, 289-291, **290**, 290f
  translation. *See* Translation transport from nucleus, 321, 322f
Metabolic rate, 995
Metabolism, **117**, **508**
  biochemical pathways, 118-119, 118f
  evolution of, 142-143
  in prokaryotes, 559-560
Metamorphosis, **384**, 384f
Metaphase
  meiosis I, 211, 211f, 212f, 216f
  meiosis II, 213f, 214, 217f
  mitotic, 192f, 195f, **196**, 196f, 197f, 216f
Metaphase plate, 195f, 196, 211, 211f
Metazoa, 640, 644f
Metazoan, origin of, 645
Methane, 139, 1209, 1251
Methanococcus, 550f
Methanogen, 139, **516**, 517f
Methicilin-resistant *Staphylococcus aureus* (MRSA), 559
Methyl group, 35f
Methylation
  of DNA, 252, 316, 316f
  of histones, 316
MHC. *See* Major histocompatibility complex
Micelle, 56, 56f
Micro-RNA (miRNA), **281**, 318-319, 319f, 320, 360, 360t
Microarray
  DNA, **364**, 365f
  protein, **367**
Microbe-associated molecular pattern (MAMP), 1056
Microbody, **72**, 78t
Microclimate, 1235
Microfilament, 76
Microfossil, 546, 546f
Micrognathozoa, 642t, 643, 644f
Micronucleus, **578**, 578f
Micronutrients, in plants, **790**-791, 790t
Microorganism, 1056
Microphyll, **747**
Micropyle, **604**, 604f, 605, 608f
Microscope, 59-61
  invention of, 59
  resolution of, 60
  types of, 61, 62t
Microsporidia, 615, 615f, 618-619, 618f
Microtubule-organizing centers, 76
Microtubule(s), 76, 76f, 80, 81t, 188f
  kinetochore, 188f, 193, 193f
  spindle, 188f
Microvilli, 866, **987-988**, 988f
Midbrain, 902f, 902t, 903
Middle ear, **921**, 921f
Middle lamella, **80**, 80f, 198
Miescher, Friedrich, 259

Migration, 1142-1143, 1142f-1143f
  of birds, 1142-1143, 1143f, 1252
  of monarch butterfly, 1142, 1142f
  orientation and, 1142-1144, 1142f-1143f
MIH. *See* Melanotropin-inhibiting hormone
Milk, 1128
Milk let-down reflex, 1128
Milk snake (*Lampropeltis triangulum*), geographic variation in, 437f
Milk sugar, 39
Miller, Stanley L., 509
Miller-Urey experiment, 509-510, 510f
Millipede, 641t, 679t, 686-687, 687f
Mimicry
  Batesian, **1195**, 1195f, 1196
  Müllerian, **1195**-1196, 1195f
Mineral(s)
  absorption by plants, 771f, 773-775, 774f-775f
  in plants, 790t, 791, 791f
  in soil, 787-788, 787f
  transport in plants, 770-783
Minimal medium, 558
Miracidium, **658**, 659f
miRNA. *See* Micro-RNA
Missense mutation, **299**, 300f
Mite, 678, 682
Mitochondria, 73-75, **74**, 74f, 78t, 81t, 126f, 136f, 162f, 518t
  division of, 74
  DNA of, 74
  genome of, 364
  maternal inheritance, **244**
  origin of, 75, 75f, 517, 517f, 568-569, 569f
  ribosomes of, 74f
Mitogen-activated protein (MAP) kinase, **176**-177, 177f, 178, 182-183, 202, 203f
Mitosis, **189**, **192**, 192f, 193-194, 193f-194f
  compared to meiosis, 215-218, 216f-217f
  evolution of, 570
  in fungi, 616-618
Mitral valve, **1026**
Mobile genetic elements, 360
Model building, 7
Molar concentration, **29**
Mole, **29**
Molecular biology, 4
  central dogma of, **280**, 280f
Molecular clock, **461**
Molecular cloning, 330, 558. *See also* Cloning
Molecular formula, 24
Molecular hybridization, **332**-333, 333f
Molecular motor, 77, 77f, 79
Molecular record, evidence for evolution, 11-12, 11f
Molecule, 2f, **3**, 23, 24
Mollicutes, 64

Mollusca (phylum), 641t, 643, 644f, 666-672, 667f-672f
Mollusk, 523f, 641t, 643, 644f, 666-672, 667f-672f
  body plan of, 667-668, 668f
  circulatory system of, 669
  classes of, 670-672
  diversity among, 667, 667f
  economic significance of, 667
  evolution of, 667
  excretion in, 669
  eye of, 429, 429f, 501, 501f, 928f, 929
  feeding an prey capture in, 668-669, 669f
  locomotion in, 976
  nervous system of, 901f
  reproduction in, 669, 669f
  shell of, 668
Molting, in arthropods, 680
Molting hormone, **957**
Monarch butterfly (*Danaus plexippus*), migration of, 1142, 1142f
Monoamine oxidase-A (MAOA), 1137, 1141
Monoamine oxidase (MAO), 1137
Monoclonal antibody, 1077-1078, 1078f
Monocot, 607f, 608
  leaves of, 741f, 748, 748f, 749
Monocyte, **1062**, 1062t
Monoecious plant, **855**
Monogamy, 1153
Monohybrid cross, 224-228, 226f, 230-231
Monokaryotic hyphae, **616**, 622-623
Monomer, 36f, **37**
Mononucleosis, 532t
Monophyletic group, **461**-462, 462f, 464
MONOPTEROS gene, in *Arabidopsis*, 758, 758f
Monosaccharide, **38**, 38f, 39f
Monosomy, 189, **250**
Monotreme, 525f, **718**-719, 719f, **1090**
Monsoon, 1234
Moon snail, 669
Morgan, Thomas Hunt, 240, 245, 246, 301, 354
Morning after pill (birth control), 1100
Morphine, 805, 806t
Morphogen, **386**, 384, 385f, 386-387, 386f-387f, 1110, 1122
Morphogenesis, 373, **390**-393, 391f-393f
  in plants, 392-393, 393f, 759, 759f
Morphology, adaptation to environmental change, 1163, 1163f
Mortality, **1169**
Mortality rate, **1169**
Mosquito, 189t, 358f, 475f, 577-578, 577f, 684, 686f
Moss, 463f, 589f, 590, 594-595, 594f-595f
Moth, 853f, 880, 880f
Motif, protein, **50**, 50f

Motor effector, 888
Motor neurons, 873t, **888**, 888f
Motor protein, 77, 77f, 194, 971
Motor unit, **973**, 973f
Mouse (*Mus musculus*)
  behavioral genetics in, in 1136, 1136f
  Brachyury gene mutation in, 496
  chromosome number in, 189t
  coat color in, 404, 404f
  embryo of, 694f
  eye development in, 502, 502f
  genome of, 475f, 476, 487
  homeotic genes in, 388f
  knockout, **342**-343, 342f, 343f
  marsupial, 431f
  ob gene in, 996, 996f
Mouth, 984-985, 985f
Mouthparts
  of arthropods, 679t
  of insects, 684, 685f
MPF. *See* M-phase-promoting factor
mRNA. *See* Messenger RNA
MRSA, 559
MSH. *See* Melanocyte-stimulating hormone
Mucosa-associated lymphoid tissue (MALT), 1064, 1064f, **1065**, 1065f
Mucosa, of gastrointestinal tract, **983**, 983f
Mucus, 1056
Müller, Fritz, 1195
Müllerian mimicry, **1195**-1196, 1195f
Multicellular organism, 518t
  cell cycle control in, 201-202, 202f
Multicellularity
  in animals, 634t
  in eukaryotes, 519
  in protists, 572
Multidrug-resistant strains, **560**-561
Multienzyme complex, **115**-116, 115f, 130
Multigene family, 359
Multiple cloning site (MCS), 330
Multipotent stem cells, **379**
Muscle
  lactic acid accumulation in, 140, 140f
  metabolism during rest and exercise, 974-975
  organization of, 969f
Muscle contraction, 969-975, 969f-974f
  sliding filament model of, 969-971, 970f-971f
Muscle fatigue, **975**
Muscle fiber, **871**, 970f
  fast-twitch (type II), **974**, 974f
  slow-twitch (type I), **974**, 974f
  types of, 973-974
Muscle spindle, **919**, 919f
Muscle tissue, **864**, 864f, 870-872, 871t, 872f
Muscular dystrophy
  Duchenne, 227t, 249t
  gene therapy for, 345
Muscular system, 874f

Muscularis, of gastrointestinal tract, **983**, 983f
Musculoskeletal system, **873**, 961-977
Mushroom, 614, 614f, 615t, 616, 617, 617f, 623, 623f
Mussel, 667, 671
Mutagen, **273**
Mutation
  cancer and, 203f
  evolution and, 401, 401f, 406
  interactions among evolutionary forces, 406-407, 407f, 495-496
  kinds of, 299-301, 299f-301f
  in prokaryotes, 558-559
Mutualism, 564, **626**, 1197f-1198f, 1198
  coevolution and, 1198
  fungal-animal, 628-629, 629f
Mutually exclusive events, 230
Mycellium, **616**, 616f
  primary, 622
  secondary, 623
Mycobacterium tuberculosis, 560-561, 561t
  evasion of immune system, 1079-1080
  multidrug-resistant strains, **560**-561
Mycoplasma, 64
Mycorrhizae, **593**, **627**-628, 628f, 793
  arbuscular, **622**, 628, 628f
  ectomycorrhizae, **628**, 628f
Myelin sheath, 872, **890**, 890f
Myofibril, **871**, **969**, 969f
Myofilament, **969**, 969f
Myoglobin, **974**, 1014
Myosin, 44, 45t, **79**, 970, 970f, 971. *See also* Thick myofilament
Myriapoda (class), 679t, 686-687
Myriapods, 687f

N

NAA. *See* Naphthalene acetic acid
NAD$^+$, **44**, **123**-124, 123f
  as electron acceptor, 124, 125f
  regeneration of, 129-130, 129f
NADH, **123**
  in ATP yield, 137, 137f
  contributing electrons to electron transport chain, 132, 133f, 135
  as electron acceptor, 124, 125f
  from glycolysis, 126f, 127, 127f
  inhibition of pyruvate dehydrogenase, 138, 138f
  from Krebs cycle, 131-132, 131f
  in photosynthesis, 148, 149f, 151, 156-160, 158f-159f
  from pyruvate oxidation, 130, 130f
  recycling into NAD, 129-130, 129f
  structure of, 125f
NADH dehydrogenase, **134**, 134f
NADP reductase, 158, 159f
Nanog gene, 382
nanos gene, **384**, 385f, 386

Naphthalene acetic acid (NAA), 830
National Center for Biotechnology Information (NCBI), 355
Native lymphocyte, 1063
Natriuretic hormone, **1035**
Natural killer (NK) cell, **1058**, 1059f, 1062t
Natural selection, 8, **10**, 397, 403
  adaptation to environmental conditions, 1164
  ecological species concept and, 441
  evidence of, 418-421, 418f-421f
  evolution and, 9, 10, 404, 433
  experimental studies of, 411-413, 412f-413f
  invention of theory of, 9-11
  maintenance of variation in populations, 407-409, 408f-409f
  in speciation, 443
  testing predictions of, 10-12
Nauplius larva, **682**-683, 683f
Neanderthals, 725
Nearsightedness, 929f
Nectar, 608
Nectary, 608
Negative feedback loop, **876**, 877f, 949, 949f, 1175
Negative gravitropism, 819f, 820
Negative pressure breathing, **1007**
Negative-strand virus, 531
Neisseria gonorrhoeae, 561t, 562, 562f, 1080
Nematocyst, 641t, 652f, **653**-654
Nematoda (phylum), 641t, 643, 644, 645f, **661**-663, 662f
Nematode, 523f, 644-645. *See also* *Caenorhabditis elegans*
  circulatory system of, 1022f
  digestive system of, 982, 982f
  eaten by fungi, 617, 617f, 618
  plant parasites, 803-804, 803f-804f
Nemertea (phylum), 642t, 644f, 672-673, 672f
Neocallimastigo mycetes, 619, 620, **628**-629
Neocallimastix, 620
Neocallismastigo mycota (phylum), 615, 615f, 620
Neodermata (class), 658
Neonate, 1128
Neotyphodium, 626, 626f
Nephridia, **669**, 673f, 674, 1040, 1041f
Nephrogenic diabetes insipidus, 98
Nephron, **1042**, 1042f, 1046-1048
  organization of, 1042f
  structure and filtration, 1046-1048, 1047f
  transport processes in, 1048-1050, 1049f-1050f
Nephrostome, **669**, 1040
Neritic waters, 1241f, **1242**
Nerve, stimulation of muscle contraction, 972-973, 972f-973f
Nerve cord, dorsal, **694**, 694f, 695f

Nerve growth factor, 942
Nerve tissue, 871t, 872, 873t
Nervous system, 518t, **873**, 874f, 887-912
    of arthropods, 680, 680f, 901f, 902
    central, **872**, 901-909, 901f-908f
    of cnidarians, 901-902, 901f
    of earthworms, 901f, 902
    of echinoderms, 901f
    of flatworms, 657f, 658, 901f, 902
    of mollusks, 901f
    neurons and supporting cells, 889-890, 889f-890f
    peripheral, **872**, 888, 909-912, 909f-912f, 909t, 911t
Net primary productivity, **1215**
Neural crest, **696**, 1119-1121, 1119f-1121f
Neural groove, **1118**, 1119f
Neural plate, 1118
Neural tube, **1119**, 1119f
Neuroendocrine reflex, **947**
Neurofilament, 76
Neuroglia, **872**, 889
Neurohormone, **938-939**, 947
Neurohypophysis, **946**
Neuromuscular junction, **897**, 898f, 973, 973f
Neuron, **872**, 889-890, 889f-890f. *See also specific types of neurons*
Neuropeptide, **899**
Neuropeptide Y, 997
Neurospora
    Beadle and Tatum's experiment with, 279-280, 279f
    chromosome number in, 189t
    nutritional mutants in, 279-280
Neurotransmitter, 169f, **170**, 896-899, 897f, 898f
    in behavior, 1134
    drug addiction and, 900-901, 900f
Neurotropin, **942**
Neurulation, **392**, 1118-1119, 1119f
Neutron, 18, 19f
Neutrophil, **1058**, **1062**, 1062t
New World monkey, 721, 721f
New York City, watersheds of, 1262-1263, 1263f
New Zealand alpine buttercup, 450-451, 450f
Newton, Sir Isaac, 5, 7
Niche, **1188**
    competition for niche occupancy, 1188, 1188f
    fundamental, **1188**, 1188f
    niche overlap and coexistence, 1189-1190
    realized, **1188**, 1188f
    restrictions, 188-189
Nicolson, Garth J., 89
Nicotinamide adenine dinucleotide. *See* NAD⁺
Nicotinamide monophosphate. *See* NMP
Nicotine, 900-901
Nicotine receptor, 900

Nile perch, 1271, 1271f
Nirenberg, Marshall, 283
Nitric oxide
    as neurotransmitter, 899
    regulation of blood pressure flow by, **1035**
Nitrification, **1211**
Nitrogen
    electron energy levels for, 23f
    in plants, 792, 792f, 797
Nitrogen cycle, 1210-1211, 1211f
Nitrogen fixation, 563
    evolution from, 143
    in nitrogen cycle, **1211**, 1211f
    in plants, 792, 792f
Nitrogenous base, 42, 42f, 259-260, 259f
    tautomeric forms of, 261
Nitrogenous wastes, 1044, 1045f, 1211
Nitrous oxide, 1251
NMP, 124
No-name virus, 540
Noble gas, 22
Nocieptor, **918**
Node (plant stem), 730f, **744**, 744f
Nodes of Ranvier, 872, 889f, 890
Nodule (plant), **792**, 792f
Noncompetitive inhibitor, **117**, 117f
Noncyclic photophosphorylation, **157**-158, 158f
Nondisjunction, **250**-251, 250f-250f
    involving autosomes, 250-252, 250f
    involving sex chromosomes, 251, 251f
Nonequilibrium state, living systems in, 14
Nonextreme archaebacteria, **516**
Nongranular leukocytes, **1019**
Nonpolar covalent bond, **24-25**
Nonpolar molecule, 28-29
Nonrandom mating, 401f, 402
Nonsense mutation, **299**, 300f
Nonspecific repair mechanism, 274-275, 274f
Nonsteroidal anti-inflammatory drug (NSAID), 943, 1075
Nonvertebrate chordate, 695-696, 695f-696f
Norepinephrine, **899**
Normal distribution, 232, 233f
Northern blot, **335**
Northern elephant seal, 403, 403f
Norwalk virus, 349
Notochord, 497, 497f, 641t, **694**, 694f, 695f, 1118
NSAID. *See* Nonsteroidal anti-inflammatory drug
Nucellus, **604**, 604f, 608f
Nuclear envelope, 62, 65, 68, 68f, 188f, 194f, 195
Nuclear lamins, 68, 68f
Nuclear pore, **65**, 68f
Nuclear receptor, **174**
Nuclear receptor superfamily, 174
Nuclear reprogramming, 380, 382, 382f

Nucleic acids, 33, 37, **42**, 259. *See also* DNA; RNA
    functions of, 37t
    structure of, 36f, 41-44, 42f
    viruses and, 529, 529f
Nuclein, 259
Nucleoid, **62**, 63f, 187, 548
Nucleoid region, **554**
Nucleolus, **65**, 68, 68f, 78t
Nucleosome, **190**, 190f, 316
Nucleotide, 13, 37t, **42**, 42f, 259, 259f
    numbering carbon atoms in, 259-260, 259f
Nucleotide oligerization domain (NOD)-like receptor (NLR), 1057
Nucleus, cellular, **65**-68, 66f, 68f, 78t, 82t
    origin of, 568, 568f
    transplantation of
        in amphibians, 380
        cloning of animals, 380f, 381, 381f
    transport of RNA out of, 321, 322f
Nudibranch, 670-671, 670f
Nüsslein-Volhard, Christiane, 384
Nutrient
    essential, 997-998, 998t
    fungi obtaining nutrients, 614, 617-618, 617f
    limiting, 1212
    plant, 790-792, 790t, 791f
Nutrition, 518t
Nutritional deficiencies, in fish, 699
Nutritional mutants, in *Neurospora*, 279-280, 279f
Nutritional mutations, **279**
Nutritional strategies, in protists, 572

O

Oak (*Quercus*), 738, 841f
ob gene, in mice, 996, 996f
Obesity, 995
Obligate symbiosis, **626**
Ocean
    oligotrophic, 1242, 1242f
    open, 1242
Ocean circulation, 1233-1235, 1233f
Ocelli, **680**, 680f
Ocipital lobe, 904, 904f
Octet rule, 22, 23f, 24
Octopus, 641t, 667, 668, 671-672, 671f
Odonata (order), 685t
Offspring
    number of, 1172, 1172f
    parent-offspring interactions, 1139-1140, 1139f
    parental investment per offspring, 1172-1173, 1172f
    size of each, 1172, 1172f
Oil (fossil fuel), 1208f, 1209
    clean up of oil spill, 564
    oil-degrading bacteria, 564
Oil gland, 866, 1056
Oils (plants), 53, 55, 805
    in corn kernels, 422

Okazaki fragment, 268-269, 269f, 270f
Old World monkey, 721, 721f
Olfaction, 926
Olfactory receptor genes, 482
Oligodendrocyte, **890**
Oligosaccharin, 826t, 834-835
Oligotrophic lake, 1240, 1240f
Oligotrophic ocean, 1242, 1242f
Ommatidia, **680**, 681f
    phenotypic variation in, 414, 414f
Omnivore, **982**, 984f
On the Origin of Species (Darwin), 8, 10, 397
Oncogene, 175, **203**
One-gene/one-enzyme hypothesis, 6, 280
One-gene/one-polypeptide hypothesis, 6, **280**
Onychophora (phylum), 640, 642t, 645f
Oocyte
    primary, **1095**, 1096f
    secondary, 1096, 1096f
Oogenesis, 1096f
Oomycete, 580, 581-582
Open circulatory system, **638**, 1022f, 1023
Open reading frame (ORF), **359**
Operant conditioning, **1138**
Operator, **308**
Opercular cavity, 1004, 1004f
Operculum, **702**
Operon, **286**
Ophiuroidea (class), 689f, 690
Opisthosoma, **681**
Opossum, 189t
Opportunistic infections, 535
Opposite leaf, 744, 744f
Optic tectum, 903
Optimal foraging theory, **1148**
Optimum pH, 116, 116f
Optimum temperature, 116, 116f
Oral contraceptives, 1099f, 1099t, 1100
    risk involved with, 1100
Oral surface, **688**
Orangutan (*Pongo*), 457, 457f, 482f
Orbital of electron, **19**, 19f
Orchid, 849, 849f
Order (taxonomic), **512**, 513f, 514
Ordered complexity, as characteristic of life, 2-3
Organ, 2f, **3**, 864, 864f
Organ system, 3f, **3**, 864, 864f, 874f
Organelle, 2f, **3**, **62**, 65, 78t, 81t
Organic compound, 22-23
    fermentation use of, 139-140, 140f
Organic matter, in soil, 787, 787f
Organism, 3-4, 3f
Organizer, 1122-1125
Organogenesis, 1106t, 1116-1121, 1117f-1121f
oriC site, 266, 271
Orientation, migratory behavior and, 1142-1144, 1142f-1143f

Origin of life
508-510, 508f-511f
deep in Earth's crust, 509
extraterrestrial,
508-509, 509f
Miller-Urey experiment,
509-510, 510f
Origin of replication, 266, 266f,
271, 330
Ornithischia (order), 707t
Orthoptera (order), 684f, 685t
Oscillating selection, **408**
Osculum, 650f, **651**
Osmoconformer, **1039**
Osmolarity, 1038-1040,
1039, 1039f
Osmoregulator, **1039**-1040
Osmoregulatory functions,
of hormones, 1050-1052,
1051f-1052f
Osmoregulatory organs, 1040-1041,
1040f-1041f
Osmosis, 98, 98f, 104t, 770-**771**
Osmotic balance, 99,
1038-1040, 1039f
Osmotic concentration, **98**, 98f
Osmotic potential. *See* Solute
potential
Osmotic pressure, 98, 99f, 1039
Osmotic protein, 45t
Ossicle, **688**
Osteoblast, **963**
Osteocyte, **870**
Osteoporosis, 967
Ostracoderm, 699t, 700
Otolith, **920**
Outcrossing, 851, 855-856, 855f
Outer bark, 745
Outer ear, **921**
Outgroup, **458**-459
Outgroup comparison, 458
Ovary (plant), **608**, 608f, 848f, **849**
Overexploitation, 1264t,
1268-1269
Oviduct. *See* Fallopian tube
Oviparity, **1087**
Ovoviviparity, **1087**
Ovulation, **950**, 1095f, 1096-1097,
1096f, 1100
Ovule, **602**, 603f, 848f, **849**
Oxaloacetate, 131, 132, 133f
Oxidation, 21, **109**, 109f, 123, 123f
without oxygen, 139-140, 139f
Oxidation-reduction (redox) reaction,
109, 109f, 123-124, 123f
Oxidative phosphorylation,
126, 126f
Oxygen
atomic structure of, 19f, 24f
in freshwater ecosystem, 1239
oxidation without,
139-140, 139f
partial pressure, 1006-1007
from photosynthesis, 143
transport in blood, 1002-1015,
1003f, 1013f-1015f
Oxygenic photosynthesis, 148
Oxyhemoglobin,
1013-1014, 1013f

Oxytocin, **947**, 1093t
Oyster, 641t, 667
evolution of, 426
Ozone depletion,
1248-1249, 1249f
Ozone hole, 273,
1248-1250, 1249f

P

P53 gene, **202**-203, 203f
P53 protein, 203, 203f
Paal, Arpad, 827
Pacific giant octopus (*Octopus
dofleini*), 672f
Pacific yew (*Taxus brevifolia*),
806t, 808
Pacinian corpuscle, 918f
Pain receptor, 918
Pair-rule genes, 385f, **387**
Paired appendages, of fish, 699
Paired-like homeodomain
transcription factor 1(pitx1),
497-498
paleoAP3 gene, in plants,
499-500, 499f
Paleopolyploid, **477**
Palila, 1270f
Palindrome, 328
Palisade mesophyll, 749, 749f
Pancreas, 988-989, 988f
secretions of, 988-989
Pancreatic amylase, **988**
Pancreatic duct, 988, 988f
Pancreatic hormone,
954-955, 955f
Pancreatic juice, 983
Panspermia, **508**
Pantothenic acid. *See* Vitamin
B-complex vitamins
Papermaking, 738
Parabasalids, 570f,
572-573, 573f
Paracrine regulator, **938**, 942-943
Paracrine signaling, 169,
169f, **170**
Paramecium, 80f, 99, 578, 578f
competitive exclusion among
species of, 1189-1190, 1189f
killer strains of, 579
life cycle of, 579f
predation by *Didinium*,
1192, 1192f
Paramylon granule, 574f
Paraphyletic group, **462**, 462f,
464, 464f
Parapodia, **674**
Parasite, **626**
effect on competition, 1200
external, 1199, 1199f
internal, 1199
manipulation of host behavior,
1199, 1199f
Parasitic plant, 794, 794f
Parasitic root, 742, 743f
Parasitism, 564, 574, **1196**, 1197f,
1198-1199, 1199f
Parasitoid, **1199**, 1199f
Parasitoid wasp, 809, 809f

Parasympathetic division, 910,
911f, 911t
Parasympathetic nervous system, 888,
889f, 910
Parathyroid hormone (PTH),
953, 953f
Paratyphoid fever, 560
Parazoa, 640, 644f, 650-651, 650f
Parenchyma cells, **736**, 736f,
738, 741
Parent-offspring interactions,
1139-1140, 1139f
Parental investment, **1150**
Parietal cells, 986, 986f
Parietal lobe, 904, 904f
Parietal pleural membrane, **1009**
Parsimony, principle of,
459-460, 460f
Parthenogenesis, **1085**
Partial diploid, **556**
Partial pressure, **1006**-1007
Passeriformes (order), 713t,
715, 715f
Passive immunity, 1063
Passive transport, across plasma
membrane, 96-99, 104t
Pasteur, Louis, 6, 1061
Pathogen, **626**
avirulent, **811**
that invade immune system,
1079-1080, 1080f
Pathogen-associated molecular
pattern (PAMP), 1056
Pattern formation, 373, 383-389,
384f-388f
in *Drosophila*, 383-389, 384f-388f
in plants, 389
Pattern recognition receptor
(PFF), **1056**
Pauling, Linus, 48
Pavlov, Ivan, 1137
Pavlovian conditioning, **1137**
Pax6 gene, **502**-504, 502f-503f
PCNA. *See* Platelet-derived
growth factor
PCNA. *See* Proliferating cell
nuclear antigen
PCR. *See* Polymerase chain reaction
Peat moss (*Sphagnum*), 594-595
Pedigree analysis, **227**, 227f, 242-243,
242f, 252
Pedipalp, **681**
Peer review, 8
Pellicle, 574, 574f, 578, 578f
Pelvic inflammatory disease
(PID), 563
Pelycosaur, 708, 708f
Penguin, 1089f
Penicillin, 64, 70, 553
Penicillium, 624
Penis, 1091, 1093, 1093f
Pentaradial symmetry, **687**
Peppered moth (*Biston betularia*),
industrial melanism and, 420-421,
420f-421f
Pepsin, **986**
Pepsinogen, **986**
Peptic ulcer, 561t
Peptide, 939

Peptide bond, **46**, 46f, 296, 296f, 298f
Peptide hormones, **947**-948
Peptidoglycan, 64, **548**, 552,
552f-553f
Peptidyl transferase, **293**
Peregrine falcon (*Falco peregrinus*),
1276, 1276f
Perennial plants, **859**-860, 859f
Perforin, 1058
Pericardial cavity, **865**, 865f
Pericarp, 762
Pericentriolar material, **76**
Pericycle, **741**, 741f
Periderm, 745, 745f
Periodic table, 22-23, 22f
Peripheral chemoreceptor, **927**
Peripheral membrane protein, 89, 90f
Peripheral nervous system, **872**, 888,
909-912, 909f-912f, 909t, 911t
Peristalsis, **986**, 986f
Peritoneal cavity, 865
Peritubular capillary, **1047**, 1047f
Periwinkle, 744f
Permafrost, **1238**
Peroxisome, **72**-73, 72f
Peroxisome biogenesis disorders
(PBDs), 72
Pesticide resistance, in insects,
404-405, 405f
Petal, **608**, 608f
development of,
499-500, 499f-500f
Petiole, **747**
pH, 29-30
of blood, 1014, 1014f
effect on enzymes, 52,
116-117, 116f
pH scale, 29-30, 30f
of rainwater, 1246, 1246f
of soil, 789, 789f
of urine, 1048
PHABULOSA gene,
in *Arabidopsis*, 747f
Phage, **258**-259, 258f
Phage. *See* Bacteriophage
Phage conversion, **534**
in *Vibrio cholerae*, 534
Phagocytosis, 71, 102, 102f, **103**, 104t
Phagotroph, 572
Pharmaceuticals
applications of genetic
engineering, 348-349
from plants, 1261-1262, 1261f
Pharyngeal pouch, **694**, 694f
Pharyngeal slits, **694**, 695f
Pharynx, **662**, 662f, **694**
Phase change, in plants,
840-841, 841f
Phase-contrast microscope, 62t
PHAVOLUTA gene,
in *Arabidopsis*, 747f
Phenotype, **226**, 405, 408
Phenotype frequency, 399, 399f
Phenylketonuria, 249t
Pheromone, **439**, 620, 686, 938, 1145
Phloem, **596**, 738, 738f, 741f
primary, 733f, 741f, 742
secondary, 733f
transport in, 781-783, 782f, 783f

Phloem loading, **783**
Phlox, 852
Phoronida (phylum), 677-**678**, 678f
Phosphatase, **171**, 171f
Phosphate group, 35, 35f, 42, 42f, 55t, 259-260, 261f
Phosphodiester backbone, 261-262, 262f
Phosphodiester bond, 42, 42f, **260**, 260f, 261f
Phosphoenolpyruvate, 128f
Phosphofructokinase, 138, 138f
2-Phosphoglycerate, 128f
3-Phosphoglycerate, 128f
Phospholipase C, 179, 180f
Phospholipid, 37t, **55, 89**
  in membranes, 55-56, 55f, 89, 89f, 90t, 92-93
  structure of, 55, 55f, 89, 89f, 92
Phosphorus, fertilizer, 1212
Phosphorus cycle, 1212, 1212f
Phosphorylase kinase, 182, 182f
Phosphorylation cascade, 176, 177f
Phosphorylation, of proteins, **170**-171, 171f, 198-199, 200-201
Phosphotyrosine, 176
Photic zone, 1239, 1239f
Photoautotroph, **559, 1214**
Photoefficiency, 153
Photoelectric effect, **152**
Photoheterotroph, **559**
Photolyase, 274, 274f
Photomorphogenesis, **815**
Photon, **151**-152
Photoperiod, **842**-844, 842f-843f
Photopigment, 931
Photopsin, **930**
Photoreceptor, **928**
  sensory transduction in, 931-932, 932f
  in vertebrates, 930-931, 930f-931f
Photorepair, 274, 274f
Photorespiration, **163**-165, 163f-165f, 749, 795f-796f
Photosynthesis, 25, 108, 147-165
  anoxygenic, 143, 148
  in bacteria, 63-64, 64f, 150, 156, 156f
  C3, **161, 164,** 164f, 165f
  C4, **164**-165, 164f, 165f, 749
  Calvin cycle, 160-163, 161f
  carbon levels in plants and, 795-797
  discovery of, 149-151, 150f
  electron transport system in, 156
  evolution of, 139, 143, 156
  light-dependent reactions of, **148,** 149f, 150, 150f
  oxygen from, 143
  oxygenic, 148
  saturation of, 154, 154f
  soil and water in, 149-150
  summary of, 148-149, 148f, 149f
Photosynthetic pigments, 151-154
  absorption spectra of, 152-154, 152f, 153f

Photosystem, **148**-149, 149f
  architecture of, 154-155, 154f, 155f
  of bacteria, 156, 156f
  of plants, 156-158, 157f-159f
Photosystem I, **157,** 158f, 159f
Photosystem II, **157,** 158, 158f, 159f
Phototroph, **572**
Phototropin, **818,** 818f
Phototropism, 817-818, 817f
  auxin and, 829f
  negative, in *Drosophila*, 410-411, 411f
Phycobiliprotein, **154**
Phyla, animal, 640, 641t-642t
Phyllotaxy, **744**
Phylogenetic species concept (PSC), **463**-464, 464f
Phylogenetic tree, **12**
Phylogenetics
  comparative biology and, 464-470, 465f-469f
  disease evolution and, 470-471, 470f-471f
  plant origins and, 521, 521f
Phylogeny, **457,** 457f
  of animals, 640, 643-645, 644f-645f
  of fungi, 615f
  of vertebrates, 698f
Phylum, **512,** 513f, 514, 640
Physical map, **353,** 355, 355f
  correlation with genetic map, 355
  landmarks on, 335, 353
  types of, 353-354, 353f-354f
Physiology, adaptation to environmental change, 1163, 1163t
Phytoaccumulation, 798f
Phytoalexin, **811**
Phytochrome, **815**-816, 815f
  expression of light-response genes, 815-816, 816f
  in plant growth responses, 817
Phytoestrogen, 806t, **808**
Phytophthora infestans, 582
Phytoplankton, 1239
Phytoremediation, **797**-800, 798f-799f
  for heavy metals, 799-800, 799f
  for trichloroethylene, 798-799, 798f
  for trinitrotoluene, 799
Phytovolatilization, 798f
PI gene, in plants, 499-500, 499f-500f
PID. *See* Pelvic inflammatory disease
Pied flycatcher, 442, 442f
PIF. *See* Prolactin-inhibiting factor
Pigment, **151**
  photosynthetic pigments, 151-154, **152,** 151f, 152f, 153f
Pike cichlid (*Crenicichla alta*), 412-413, 412f
Pillbug, 682

Pilus, 63f, 534, **553**-554, 553f
Pine, 602t, 603-605, 603f-604f
Pine cone, 604
Pine needle, 604
Pineal gland, 956
Pinnately compound leaf, 748f
Pinocytosis, 102, 102f, **103,** 104t
Pinworm (*Enterobius*), 641t, 662-663
Pit organ, **934,** 934f
Pitcher plant (*Nepenthes*), 750, 793, 794f
Pith, 741f, 742, 744
Pituitary dwarfism, **950**
Pituitary gland, **946**-948, 947f
  anterior, **946,** 947-948, 948-951, 950f
  posterior, **946**-947
PKU. *See* Phenylketonuria
Placenta, **716,** 716f, 1112
  formation of, 1125
  functions of, 1125
  hormonal secretion by, 1126, 1127f
  structure of, 1126f
Placental mammal, **524,** 525f, 719, 719f, 1090, 1090f
  marsupial-placental convergence, 430-431, 431f
  orders of, 720t
Plague, 561t
Planarian, 982
  eyespot of, 501, 501f, 503
Plant(s). *See also* Flowering plant
  annual, 859f, **860**
  asexual reproduction in, 857-859, 858f
  biennial, **860**
  body plan in, 730-750
  C3, **164,** 164f, 165f
  C4, **164**-165, 164f, 165f, 749
  CAM, **164,** 165, 165f
  carnivorous, 793-794, 794f
  cell walls, 80
  chilling of, 825
  circadian rhythm in, 818, 822, 823f
  classification of, 463-464, 463f, 521f
  cloning of, 858f, 859
  coevolution of animals and, 807
  conducting tubes in, 466, 466f
  development in 374-375, 392-393, 393f
    embryonic, 754-760, 754f-760f
    establishment of tissue systems, 757f-758f, 758-759
    food storage, 759-760, 760f
    fruit formation, 761-763, 762f-763f
    morphogenesis, 392-393, 393f, 759, 759f
    seed formation, 760-761, 761f

  digestion of plants, mammals, 717
  dormancy in, 823-824, 823f-824f
  under drought stress, 780, 780f
  evolution of 390, 520-522, 521f-522f
    in land plants, 521f, 571, 589-590
  genome of, 476-479, 477f-479f, 486
  gravitropism in, **819**-820, 819f-820f
  heliotropism in, 822f
  heterozygosity in, 398
  leaves of, 747-750. *See also* Leaf
  life cycles of, 590, 590f
  life span of, 859-860, 859f
  nutritional adaptations in, 792-795, 792f-795f
  nutritional requirements in, 790-792, 790t, 791f
  organization of plant body, 730f
  parasitic, 794, 794f
  pattern formation in, 389
  perennial, **859**-860, 859f
  photomorphogenesis in, **815**
  photosynthesis in, 148-149, 148f
  photosystems of, 156-158, 157f-159f
  phototropism in, 817-818, 817f
  phytoremediation in, 797-800, 798f-799f
  plasmodesmata in, 67f, **84**-85, 85f
  polyploidy in, 479, 479f
  primary plant body, **732**
  primary tissues of, **732**
  reproduction in, 839-860
  responses to flooding, 780, 781f
  roots of, 739-743. *See also* Root
  saline conditions, under, 780-781, 781f
  secondary growth in, **732,** 745f
  secondary metabolites of, **805,** 806t, 808
  secondary plant body, **732**
  secondary tissues of, **732**
  sensory systems in, 814-836
  spacing of, 817
  stem of, 743-747, 743f-746f. *See also* Stem
  thermotolerance in, 825
  thigmotropism in, 821-822, 821f
  tissue culture, 859
  tissues of, 733-738, 734f-738f, 742f
  transgenic. *See* Transgenic plants
  transport in, 769-783
  turgor movement in, 821-822, 822f
  vacuole of plant cells, **73,** 73f, 81t
  vascular. *See* Vascular plant
  vegetative propagation of, 746-747
  wound response, **810,** 810f

Plant cells
    cell wall of, 67f, 80, 80f
    cytokinesis in, 197-198, 198f
    structure of, 67f, 81t
Plant defenses, 802-812
    against herbivores, 810, 810f,
      1193-1194, 1193f
    animals that protect plants,
      809, 809f
    pathogen-specific,
      810-811, 811f-812f
    physical defenses,
      802-805, 802f-804f
    toxins, 805-808, 805f, 806t,
      807, 807f
Plant disease, 802-812
    bacterial, 560
    fungal, 629-630, 629f,
      804-805, 804f
    nematodes, 803, 803f-804f
    viral, 810f
Plant hormone, 825-836
    functions of, 826t
    that guide plant growth, 825
    production and location of, 826t
    transport in phloem, 781-783,
      782f-783f
Plant receptor kinase, 175
Plantae (kingdom), 13, 13f, 514, 515f,
    517f, 518t, 521f
Plantlet, 858
Planula larva, 653, 655
Plasma cell, 1062t
Plasma membrane, 62-63, 67f, 78t
    active transport across,
      99-102, 104t
    of archaebacteria, 65, 548
    of bacteria, 548
    bulk transport across, 102-103
    components of, 90t, 92-93
    electron microscopy of, 91-92, 91f
    of eukaryotes, 66f, 78t
    fluid mosaic model, 89, 90f,
      92-93, 548
    passive transport across, 96-99
    of prokaryotes, 63-64, 63f, 548
    structure of, 62-63
Plasmid, 548
    antibiotic resistance genes on, 558
    cloning vector, 330, 331f
    conjugative, 554-556, 555f
    resistance, 558
Plasmodesmata, 67f,
    84-85, 85f, 592
Plasmodium, 577-578, 577f, 1079
Plasmodium falciparum, 409, 409f, 487,
    487f, 578
    genome of, 358f, 475f, 488
Plasmodium (slime mold),
    584-585, 585f
Plasmolysis, 771
Plastid, 75
Platelet, 202, 1021
Platelet-derived growth factor
    (PDGF), 175, 202
Platyhelminthes (phylum), 641t, 643,
    644f, 657-660, 657f, 659f, 902
Platyzoa, 643, 644f
Pleiotropic effect, 233, 233t, 413

Plesiomorphy, 459
Plesiosaur, 707t
Plesiosaura (order), 707t
Pleural cavity, 865, 865f, 1009
Plexus, 983, 983f
Pluripotent stem cells, 379, 1021
Pneumatophore, 742,
    743f, 781
Pneumocystis jiroveci, 630
Pneumonia, bacterial,
    560, 561f
Poa annua, 1169, 1170t
Poikilotherm, 880
Point mutation, 299
Point-source pollution, 1246
Polar body, 1096
Polar covalent bond, 25
Polar molecule, 25, 28
Polar nuclei, 851, 851f
Polarity, in development, 383
Polarized character states, 458-459
Polio, 531f, 532t
Pollen, 168, 609f
    dispersal of, 407, 407f
Pollen grain, 603, 604, 604f, 605,
    850, 851f
    formation of, 609, 609f,
      850-851, 850f
Pollen tube, 603, 604f, 609, 609f,
    610, 610f
Pollination, 604f, 608, 609-610, 610f,
    851-857, 852f-857f
    by animals, 852-854, 852f-853f
    by bats, 854, 1196f
    by bees, 852, 852f-853f
    by birds, 852-854, 853f
    by insects, 852, 852f-853f
    by wind, 852, 854, 854f
Pollinator, 851-852
Pollution, 1245-1250
    diffuse, 1246
    of freshwater habitats, 1246, 1246f
    habitat loss and, 1267
    of marine habitats, 1248
    phytoremediation, 797-800,
      798f-799f
    point-source, 1246
Poly-A tail, of mRNA, 289, 289f
Polyandry, 1153
Polychaeta (class), 674-675, 674f
Polychaete, 641t, 674-675,
    674f, 675f
Polyclonal antibody, 1077
Polydactyly, 227t, 403
Polygenic inheritance, 232-233,
    232f, 233t
Polymer, 36f, 37, 40f
Polymerase chain reaction (PCR),
    339-340, 340f
    applications of, 340
    procedure for, 339-340
Polymorphism
    in DNA sequence,
      335-336, 398-399
    in enzymes, 398, 398f
    single nucleotide, 248
Polynomial name, 512
Polynucleotides, 42

Polyp, of cnidarians, 653, 653f,
    655, 655f
Polypeptide, 36f, 46
Polyphyletic group, 462, 462f
Polyplacophora (class), 670, 670f
Polyploidy, 445, 477, 479f, 486, 1108
    alteration of gene expression, 480
    elimination of duplicated genes,
      480, 480f
    in evolution of flowering plants,
      479, 479f
    speciation through, 445, 445f
    synthetic polyploids, 478
    transposon jumping in, 480-481
Polysaccharide, 39
Polyspermy, 1108
Polyubiquitination, 323
Polyunsaturated fatty acid, 53, 54f
Polyzoa, 641t
Pond, 1239-1241, 1239f-1240f
Pons, 902, 902t
Popper, Karl, 7
Population, 3f, 4, 1165
    age structure of, 1168
    change through time, 1170
    human. *See* Human population
    metapopulations,
      1167-1168, 1168f
    survivorship curves for, 1170,
      1170f-1171f
Population cycle,
    1176-1177, 1177f
Population demography, 1168-1171,
    1169f-1171f
Population dispersion
    clumped spacing, 1167
    habitat occupancy and, 1167
    human effect on, 1166
    mechanisms of, 1166, 1166f
    randomly spaced, 1167
    uniformly spaced, 1167
Population genetics, 397
Population growth
    factors affecting growth rate,
      1168-1169, 1169f
    in hotspots, 1260-1261, 1260f
    limitations by environment,
      1173-1174, 1174f-1175f
Population pyramid,
    1178-1180, 1179f
Population range,
    1165-1166, 1165f-1166f
Population size
    density-dependent effects on,
      1175-1176, 1175f-1176
    density-independent effects on,
      1176, 1176f
    extinction of small populations,
      1273-1275, 1273f-1274f
    human, 1179f
Pore protein, 95, 95f
Porifera (phylum), 640, 641t, 643,
    644f, 650-651, 650f
Porphyrin ring, 152, 152f
Portuguese man-of-war, 655, 655f
Positive feedback loop, 878, 878f,
    950, 1176
Positive gravitropism, 820
Positive pressure breathing, 1007

Positive-strand virus, 531
Postanal tail, 694, 694f-695f
Posterior pituitary, 946-947
Postsynaptic cell, 896, 899-900, 899f
Posttranscriptional control, 317-321,
    318f-319f, 321f
    alternative splicing of primary
      transcript, 320, 321f, 322f
    RNA editing, 320-321
    small RNA's, 317-320, 318f-319f
Postzygotic isolating mechanisms,
    438, 438t, 440, 440f
Potassium channel, voltage-gated,
    893, 894f
Potato
    eye of, 858
    genome of, 479f
    Irish potato famine, 582
Potential energy, 21, 108, 108f
Power of Movement of Plants,
    The (Darwin), 827
Poxvirus, 531f
Prader-Willi syndrome, 251-252, 487
Prairie, 1237
Prairie chicken (*Tympanuchus cupido*
    pinnatus), 1274-1275, 1274f
Prairie dog
    (*Cynomys ludovivianus*), 1146f
Pre-mRNA splicing,
    289-291, 290, 290f
Precocial young, 1153
Predation, 1192
    evolution of prey population,
      412-413, 412f
    fish, 408, 408f
    population cycles and, 1177
    prey populations and, 1192-1193
    reduction of competition by,
      1199-1200, 1200f
    species richness and, 1225
Predator
    animal defenses against,
      1194, 1194f
    search image for prey, 407-408, 408f
    selection to avoid, 404, 404f
Predator avoidance, 404, 404f
Prediction, 5f, 6-7
Preganglionic neuron, 910
Pregnancy, high-risk, 252-253
Pressure-flow theory, of phloem
    transport, 782, 783f
Pressure potential, 772, 772f
Presynaptic cell, 896
Prey defense, 1137
Prey protein, in DNA-binding
    hybrid, 341, 341f
Prezygotic isolating mechanisms,
    438-440, 438f-439f, 438t
Priestly, Joseph, 149-150
Primary carnivore, 1215, 1215f
Primary induction, 1124
Primary lymphoid organs, 1064,
    1064f-1065f
Primary meristem, 732, 758
Primary mesenchyme cell, 1113
Primary motor cortex, 904, 905f
Primary mycelium, 622
Primary oocyte, 1095, 1096f
Primary phloem, 733f, 741f, 742

Primary plant body, **732**
Primary producer, **1215**, 1215f
Primary productivity, **1186**, **1215**, 1222-1223, 1222f, 1224, 1224f, 1236, 1236f
Primary somatosensoty cortex, **904**, 905f
Primary structure, of proteins, **46**, 49f
Primary succession, **1202**, 1202f
Primary tissue, **864**
    of plant, **732**
Primary transcript, **288**, 288f
Primary xylem, 733f, 737, 741-742, 741f
Primate, 525, 525f, **721**
    evolution of, 721-726, 721f-726f
    hunting for "bushmeat," 471
    language of, 1147, 1147f
Primer, for replication, 268-269
Primitive streak, **1115**
Primordium, **608**, 608f
Primosome, 269
Prion, **541**-542, 542f
Probability, 230-231
Procambium, **732**, 733f, 759
Processivity, of DNA polymerase III, 268
Prochloron, 64, 64f
Product of reaction, 25
Product rule, **230**
Productivity, **1215**
    primary, **1186**, **1215**, 1222-1223, 1222f, 1224, 1224f, 1236, 1236f
    secondary, **1216**
    species richness and, 1225
Progesterone, 956, 1093t
Proglottid, **659**-660, 660f
Progymnosperm, **602**
Prokaryote, 13, **62**, 545-564. *See also* Bacteria
    benefits of, 563-564
    cell division in, 187-188, 188f, 548
    cell organization of, 63-65, 63f
    cell size of, 548
    cell structure in, 551-554, 552f-554f
    cell walls of, 63, 63f, 64, 81t, 548-549, 552-554, 552f-553f
    classification of, 549-550, 549f-551f
    compartmentalization in, 548
    disease-causing, 561t
    diversity in, 547-550, 549f-550f
    DNA of, 62
    eukaryotes versus, 81t, 547-548
    first cells, 546, 546f
    flagella of, 63f, 65, 81t, 548, **553**, 553f
    gene expression in, 305, 308-312, 308f-312f, 549
    genetics of, 554-559, 555f-558f
    genome of, 358f
    internal membranes of, 554, 554f
    metabolic diversity in, 548
    metabolism in, 559-560

mutations in, 558-559
plasma membranes in, 63-64, 63f, 548
recombination in, 548
replication in, 187-188, 187f, 266-270, 266f-270f, 549
ribosomes of, 63, 63f, 554
shape of, 551-552
size of, 548
symbiotic, 563-564
transcription in, 284-287, 284f-287f
transcriptional control in, 305, 308-312, 308f-312f
unicellularity of, 548
Prolactin, 948, 951, 1093t
Prolactin-inhibiting factor (PIF), 949
Proliferating cell nuclear antigen (PCNA), 271
Prometaphase, 193f, 194f, **196**
Promoter, **285**, 285f
    in eukaryotes, 313-314, 313f
Proofreading function, of DNA polymerase, 273
Prop root, 742, 743f
Propane, 34
Prophage, 534, **534**, 557
Prophase
    meiosis I, 210-211, 212f, 214f
    meiosis II, 213f, 214, 217f
    mitotic, 192f, 194f, **195**, 216f
Proprioceptor, **919**
Prosimian, **721**, 721f-722f
Prosoma, **679**
Prostaglandin, 37t, 54, **943**
Prostate gland, **1092**
Protease, 45t, **323**, **816**
Protease inhibitor, 538
Proteasome, **323**-324, 323f-324f
Protective coloring, in guppies, 412-413, 412f-413f
Protective layer, 824
Protein, 33, 36f, 37, 433
    anchoring, 94
    catabolism of, 141, 141f, 142
    central dogma, **280**, 280f
    degradation of, 322-324, 323f-324f
    denaturation of, 52-53, 52f
    domains of, **50**-51, 51f
    folding of, 51-52, 51f
    functions of, 37t, 44-46, 45t, 46f
        prediction of, 366-367, 367f
    in membranes, 88, 93-95
        functions of, 93, 94f
        kinds of, 93, 94f
        movement of, 92-93, 93f
        structure of, 94-95, 95f
        transmembrane domains of, 94-95, 95f
    motifs of, **50**, 50f, 367, 367f
    nonpolar regions of, 46-49, 48f
    one-gene/one-polypeptide hypothesis, 6, **280**

phosphorylation of, **170**-171, 171f, 198-199, 200-201
polar regions of, 46-49, 48f
primary structure of, 46, 49f
quaternary structure of, 46, 49, 49f
renaturation of, 52f, 53
secondary structure of, 46, 48, 49f
structure of, 37t, 46-49
synthesis of. *See* Translation
tertiary structure of, 46, 48-49, 49f
transport within cells, 70-71, 71f, 296f, 297
ubiquitination of, 323-324, 323f
Protein-encoding gene, 359, 360t
Protein hormones, **948**
Protein kinase, 170, 171f, **173**, 176-177, 177f, 945
Protein kinase A, 180, 180f, 182, 182f
Protein kinase C, 181
Protein-protein interactions
    protein microarrays, 367
    two-hybrid system, 340-341, 341f
Proteobacteria, 551f
Proteoglycan, 81, 81f
Proteome, **366**
Proteomics, **366**-367
Prothoracicotropic hormone (PTTH), **957**
Protist, 512-513, 567-585
    asexual reproduction in, 572
    cell division in, 188f
    cell surface of, 571
    classification of, 520, 520f, 570-571f, 571
    cysts of, 571
    cytokinesis in, 197
    defining, 571-572
    flagella of, 572-573, 575f
    locomotor organelles of, 572
    nutritional strategies of, 572
Protista (kingdom), 13, 13f, **514**, 517f, 518t, 571, 644f
Proto-oncogene, **203**-204, 204f
Protoderm, **732**
Protogyny, 1085f
Proton, 18, 19f
Protonephridia, **1040**, 1040f
Protoplast, plant, 858f, 859
Protostome, **523**, **638**, 639f, 643-645, 644f
Proximal convoluted tubule, **1047**, 1047f, 1048
Prusiner, Stanley, 541
Pseudocoelom, 637f, **638**
Pseudocoelomate, 637f, 638, 643, 661-663, 661f-663f
Pseudogene, 359, 360, 360t, **482**
Pseudomonas fluorescens, 489
Pseudomurein, **548**, 552
Pseudostratified columnar epithelium, 867t
Psilotum, 599
Pterophyta (phylum), 596, 597, 597f, 598-601, 599f-600f, 601t
Pterosaur, 707t
Pterosauria (order), 707t

PTH. *See* Parathyroid hormone
Pufferfish (*Fugu rubripes*), genome of, 475f, 476, 486
Pulmocutaneous circuit, 1024
Pulmonary artery, 1024, **1028**
Pulmonary circulation, **1024**
Pulmonary valve, **1026**, 1027f
Pulmonary vein, 703, 1024, 1024f, **1029**
Pulvini, 822, 822f
Punctuated equilibrium, **451**, 451f
Punnett, R. C., 227
Punnett square, 226f, 226-**227**, 229, 229f, 400
Pupa, **686**
Purine, 42, 259f, **260**
Pvull, 328
Pyramid of energy flow, **1218**, 1219f
Pyrimidine, 42, 259f, **260**
Pyrogen, **883**
Pyruvate
    conversion to acetyl-CoA, 130, 130f
    from glycolysis, 126f, 128f, 130
    oxidation of, 130, 130f
Pyruvate dehydrogenase, 115, 115f, 130, 138, 138f
Pyruvate kinase, 128f

Q

Q_{10}, 878-879
Quantitative traits, **232**, 233f
Quaternary structure, of proteins, 46, **49**, 49f
Quiescent center, 739
Quinine, 806t, **808**

R

R plasmids, 558
R-selected population, **1177**, 1178t
Rabbit, 525f
Rabies, 349, 532t
Rabies virus, 531f
Race, human, 726, 726f
Radial canal, **688**
Radial cleavage, **638**, 639f
Radial symmetry, **636**, 636f
Radially symmetrical flower, **499**
Radiation (heat transfer), 879, 879f
Radicle, **764**, 765f
Radioactive decay, 19
    dating of fossils using, 424-425, 424f
Radioactive isotope, **19**
Radiolarian, 583-584, 584f
Radula, 641t, **668**-669, 669f
Rain forest
    loss of, 1246-1247, 1247f
    tropical, **1236**-1237, 1237f
Rain shadow, 1233-1234, 1234f
Ram ventilation, 1005
Rape case, 336, 336f
Raphe, 581, 581f
Ras protein, 176, **178**, 178f, 203f, 204f
Rat, genome of, 475f, 487
Raven, cognitive behavior in, 1141, 1142f

Ray-finned fish, 698f, 699t, 702, 702f
Ray (fish), 699t, 701
Ray initial, 738
Ray (parenchyma cells), 737-738
Reabsorption, **1040**-1041, 1046
   in kidney, 1046, 1048, 1049f,
     1050-1051, 1051f
Reactant, 25
Reaction center, **155**, 155f
Reading frame, **283**
Realized niche, **1188**, 1188f
Receptor kinase, 945, 945f
Receptor-mediated endocytosis, 102f,
   103, 104t
Receptor potential, 917
Receptor protein, 63, 90t, 93, 94f,
   168, 169f
   intracellular, 171-174, 172f,
     172t, 173f
Receptor tyrosine kinase, **174**-178,
   175f-178f, 182-183, 202
   autophosphorylation of,
     175-176, 175f
   inactivation of, 178
Recessive trait, **224**-228, 224f
   in humans, 227t
Reciprocal altruism, 1154-**1155**,
   1155f
Reciprocal cross, **223**
Recognition helix, 306
Recombinant DNA, **327**
   construction of, 327, 328, 328f
   introduction of foreign DNA into
     bacteria, 329-331, 331f
   in vaccine production,
     344-345, 344f
Recombination, **210**,
   245-247, 275
   in eukaryotes, 548
   homologous, 555
   in prokaryotes, 548
   using recombination to make
     maps, 245f, 246-247, 246f
   in viruses, 539
Recombination frequency, **246**
Recombination nodule, 211
Recruitment, **973**
Rectum, 990
Red algae, 463f, 517-518, 517f, 519,
   521f, 570, 570f, **582**, 582f, 589f
Red-bellied turtle (*Pseudemys
   rubriventris*), 710f
Red blood cell(s). *See* Erythrocytes
Red-eyed tree frog (*Agalychnis
   callidryas*), 705f
Red maple (*Acer rubrum*), 737f
Red tide, 576-577, 577f
Rediae, **658**, 659f
Redox, **109**, 109f, 123-124,
   123f, 124f
Reduction, **7**, 21, 109, 109f,
   123, 123f
Reduction division, 210
Reductionism, **7**
Reflex, **907**-908, 908f
Regeneration
   in echinoderms, 689
   of planarian eyespot, 501, 501f
   of ribbon worm eyespot, 503, 503f

Regulation, as characteristic
   of life, 508
Regulative development, 1112
Regulatory proteins, **305**, 305-307,
   306f-307f
   DNA-binding motifs in,
     306-307, 307f
Reinforcement, **442**, 442f
Relative dating, 424
Releasing hormone, **948**-949
REM sleep, 905
Remodeling, bone, 966-967,
   966f-967f
Renal cortex, **1045**, 1046f
Renal medulla, **1045**, 1046f
Renal pelvis, 1045
Renaturation, of proteins, 52f, 53
Replica plating, **558**
Replication, 263-266, 263f-265f
   conservative,
     263-265, 263f
   direction of, 265, 266f, 267,
     267f, 272f
   dispersive, 263f, 264, 265
   elongation stage of, 265-266
   enzymes needed for, 268t,
     269-270, 269f
   errors in, 273
   in eukaryotes, 271-273,
     271f-272f
   in HIV infection cycle, 537
   initiation stage of, 265-266, 271
   lagging strand, 267f, **268**-269,
     269f-270f
   leading strand, 267f, **268**,
     269f-270f, 272f
   Meselson-Stahl experiment,
     264-265, 264f
   Okazaki fragments, **268**-269,
     269f-270f
   in prokaryotes, 187-188, 187f,
     266-270, 266f-270f, 549
   rolling circle, 555, 555f
   semiconservative, 263-265, 263f
   semidiscontinuous,
     267-268, 267f
   suppression between meiotic
     divisions, 216
   termination stage of, 265-266, 269
   of virus, 530
Replication fork, **268**-269,
   269f-270f
Replication origin, 187-188, 187f
Replicon, **266**, 271
Replisome, 266f, **269**-270,
   269f-270f
Reporter gene, 341, 341f
Repression, **308**, 312
Repressor, **308**
Reproduction
   in amphibians, 704
   as characteristic of life, 3, 508
   cost of, 1171-1173, 1171f-1172f
   in crustaceans, 682-683
   in echinoderms, 689
   in fish, 701
   in flatworms, 657f, 658
   in fungi, 614, 617, 621
   in mollusks, 669, 669f

   in nematodes, 662
   in plants, 839-860
   in protists, 572
   reproductive events per
     lifetime, 1173
Reproductive cloning, **381**, 381f
Reproductive isolation, **437**,
   438, 438t
   evolution of, 441-442, 442f
Reproductive leaf, 749
Reproductive strategy, 1084-1086,
   1085f-1086f, **1150**-1154,
   1150f-1153f
Reproductive system, 875f, **876**,
   1084-1102
   evolution of, 1087-1088, 1088f
   female, 875f, **876**, 1090, 1090f,
     1094-1098, 1094f-1098f
   male, 875f, **876**, 1091-1094,
     1091f-1094f, 1093t
Reptile, 703t, 706-711, 708f-711f
   brain of, 903, 903f
   characteristics of, 706-707, 707t
   circulation in, 1024
   eggs of, 706, 708f
   evolution of, 697,
     708-709, 708f-709f
   fertilization in, 1089-1090
   heart of, 709, 709f, 1024
   kidney of, 1043
   lungs of, 1007
   nitrogenous wastes of,
     1044, 1045f
   orders of, 707f, 710-711,
     710f-711f
   present day, 709-710, 709f
   respiration in, 707
   skin of, 707
   skull of, 708f
   thermoregulation in, 710
Research, 7-8
Resolution (microscope), 60
Resource depletion, 1245-1250
Resource partitioning, **1190**-1191,
   1190f
Resources
   competition for limited,
     1189-1190, 1189f
   consumption of world's, 1181
Respiration, 123-126, **1215**
   aerobic. *See* Aerobic respiration
   in amphibians, 703, 1004,
     1003f-1004f
   in birds, 715, 1008, 1009f
   cutaneous, **1006**
   in echinoderms, 1003f
   in fish, 1004-1006, 1003f-1005f
   in insects, 1003f
   in mammals, 1003f,
     1007-1008, 1008f
Respiratory control center, 1011
Respiratory disease, 1012, 1012f
Respiratory system, **875**, 875f,
   1001-1015
   of arthropods, 680-681, 681f
Resting potential, **890**,
   891-892, 892f
Restoration ecology,
   1275-1276, 1275f

Restriction endonuclease, **327**-328,
   328f, 331f
Restriction fragment length
   polymorphism (RFLP) analysis,
   335, 335f
Restriction map, 328, 335, 353, 353f
Restriction site, **328**
Reticular-activating system, 905
Reticular formation, 905
Retina, **930**, 931f
Retinoblastoma susceptibility gene
   (*Rb*), **204**, 204f
Retrotransposon, 360, 486
Retrovirus, **280**, 529, 531
Reverse genetics, **343**
Reverse transcriptase, **280**, 332, 332f,
   531, 536f, 538
RFLP. *See* Restriction fragment
   length polymorphism analysis
Rh factor, 1077
Rh-negative individual, 1077
Rh-positive individual, 1077
Rheumatic fever, 560
Rhinoceros, 525
Rhizobium, 563, 792, 793f
Rhizoid, 594, 594f, 601
Rhizome, 600, 746, 746f, 858
Rhizopoda, 583, 583f
Rhizopus, 615t, 621f
Rhodophyta (phylum), 515f, 570f,
   582, 582f
Rhodopsin, **930**
Rhynchocephalia (order), 707t,
   710, 710f
Ribbon worm, 642t, 672-673, 672f
   regeneration of eyespot, 503, 503f
Ribonuclease, 52f, 53
Ribonucleic acid. *See* RNA
Ribosomal RNA (rRNA), **69**, **281**
Ribosome, 63, 78t, 81t
   A site on, **292**-293,
     293f-296f, 295
   E site on, **292**-293, 293f,
     294f, 296f
   of eukaryotes, 68-69, 69f, 78t
   free, 69
   functions of, 293
   membrane-associated, 69
   of mitochondria, 74f
   P site on, **292**-293, 293f-296f,
     295, 296
   of prokaryotes, 63, 293f, 554
   structure of, 293, 293f
   in translation, 293-297,
     294f-296f
Ribosome-binding sequence, **294**
Ribulose 1,5-bisphosphate (RuBP),
   161, 161f, 162
Ribulose bisphosphate carboxylase/
   oxygenase (rubisco), **161**,
   161f, 163
Rice (*Oryza sativa*), 368f
   genome of, 358f, 363, 363f, 475f,
     476-477, 479f, 486, 489
   golden, 348, 348f, 368
   transgenic, 348, 348f, 368
   world demand for, 368
Ricin, 807-808, 807f
Ricksettia, 517, 551f

Rig helicase-like receptor (RLR), 1057
RISC (enzyme complex), 318, 319f
RNA
    catalytic activity of, 116
    central dogma, **280**, 280f
    DNA versus, 43, 43f
    functions of, 37t
    in gene expression, 281
    micro-RNA, **281**, 318-319, 319f, 320
    small, 317-320, 318f-319f
    structure of, 37t, **41-42**
RNA editing, 320-321
RNA interference, 319-320, 319f, 322f
RNA polymerase, 266, 271, 281f, **285**
    core polymerase, 284f, 285
    in eukaryotes, 287-288
    holoenzyme, 284f, 285
    in prokaryotes, 284f, 285
RNA polymerase I, 270f
RNA polymerase II, 312, 313, 314-315, 313f-315f
RNA virus, 529, 529f, 531, 532t
RNAi gene therapy, 345
Rocky Mountain spotted fever, 560
Rod, **930**, 930f, 931f
Rodent, 525, 525f
Root, 596, 730f, 739-743, 739f-743f
    adventitious, 742, 746f, 765f
    gravitropic response in, 819f, 820
    modified, 742-743, 742f
    structure of, 739-743, 739f-741f
    tissues of, 730-731
Root cap, **739**, 739f
    columella, 739
    lateral, 739
Root hair, **735-736**, 735f, 739f, 741
Root pressure, **776**
Root system, **730**
Rosin, 604
Rossmann fold, 50
Rotifera (phylum), 642t, 643, 644f, 663, 663f
Rough endoplasmic reticulum, **69-70**, 70f
Roundworm, 641t, 644, **661**-663, 662f
rRNA. *see* Ribosomal RNA
Rubisco, **161**, 161f, 163
Ruffini corpuscle, 918f
Rule of addition, **230**
Rule of eight, 22, 23f
Rule of multiplication, **230**
Rumen, 564, 620
Ruminant, 991, 991f-992f
Rumination, 991
Runner, plant, 746, 746f, 858

S

S-layer, 553
S (synthesis) phase, **192**, 192f
SA node. *See* Sinoatrial node
Saber-toothed mammals, 464-465, 465f
Saccharomyces cerevisiae, 625, 625f
    genome of, 358f, 475f, 625

Saccule, **924**, 924f
Sager, Ruth, 244
Salamander, 703, 703t, 706, 982f
Salicylic acid, **810**
Salinity
    plant adaptations to, 780-781, 781f
    soil, 789
Saliva, 984
Salivary gland, 984-985
    development in *Drosophila*, 1117-1118, 1117f
Salmonella, 534, 551f, 560, 561t
    evasion of immune system, 1079
    type III system in, 560
Salt marsh, **1243**
Saltatory conduction, **896**, 896f
Sand dollar, 641t, 689, 689f, 690
Sanger, Frederick, 46, 336, 339
Saprolegnia, 582
Sarcomere, **969**, 970f, 971f
Sarcoplasmic reticulum, **972**, 972f
SARS. *See* Severe acute respiratory syndrome
Satiety factor, 996
Saturated fatty acid, **53**, 54f
Saturation, 97
Saurischia (order), 707t
Savanna, **1237**
Scaffold protein, 177, 177f
Scallop, 666, 667
Scanning electron microscope, 61, 62t, 91
Scar (leaf), 744, 744f
SCARECROW gene, in *Arabidopsis*, 740, 740f, 820, 820f
Scarlet fever, 560
Schistosomes, 659, 659f
Schistosomiasis, **659**
Schleiden, Matthias, 12, 60
Schwann cells, **890**, 890f
Schwann, Theodor, 12, 60
SCID. *See* Severe combined immunodeficiency disease
Science
    deductive reasoning in, 4-5
    definition of, 4
    descriptive, 4
    hypothesis-driven, 5-7
    inductive reasoning in, 5
Scientific method, 4, 7
Sclera, **929**, 929f
Sclerenchyma cells, **736-737**, 736f
SCN. *See* Suprachiasmatic nucleus
SCNT. *See* Somatic cell nuclear transfer
Scolex, **659**, 660f
Scouring rush. *See* Horsetail
Scrotum, 1091
Scutellum, **764**, 764f
Scyphozoa (class), **655**, 655f
Sea anemone, 636, 636f, 641t, 654, 654f
Sea cucumber, 641t, 689
Sea daisy, 689
Sea level, effect of global warming on, 1252
Sea lilly, 689

Sea slug, 641t, 670, 670f
Sea star, 641t, 689, 689f, 690
Sea turtle, 707t
Sea urchin, 641t, 689, 689f, 690
    development in, 493, 493f, 1110f
    gastrulation in, 1113-1114, 1113f
Sebaceous glands, 866, 1056
Second filial generation, **224**-225, 224f, 228-229, 229f
Second Law of Thermodynamics, **110**, 110f, 433, 879
Second messenger, **173**, 179-182, 180f
    calcium, 181-182, 182f
    cAMP, **173**, 179-181, 180f, 181f, 182
    cGMP, 174
    for hydrophilic hormones, 945-946, 945f
    IP3/calcium, 179, 180f, 181, 181f
Secondary carnivore, **1215**, 1215f
Secondary chemical compound, 1193
Secondary endosymbiosis, **569**
Secondary growth, in plants, **732**, 745f
Secondary induction, **1124**, 1125f
Secondary lymphoid organs, **1064-1065**, 1064f
Secondary metabolite, **805**, 806t, 808
Secondary mycelium, 623
Secondary oocyte, 1096, 1096f
Secondary phloem, 733f
Secondary plant body, **732**
Secondary productivity, **1216**
Secondary sexual characteristics, **1151**
Secondary structure, of proteins, 46, **48**, 49f
Secondary succession, **1202**
Secondary tissues, of plant, **732**
Secondary xylem, 733f, 737
Secretin, **993**, 994t
Secretion, **1041**
    in kidney, 1046, 1048
    in stomach, 986-987
Securin, 201
Seed, 392, 393f, 597, 602-603, 604f, 609f
    dispersal of, 1166, 1166f
    dormancy in, 824, 824f, 836, 836f
    formation of, 392, 393f, 604f, 605, 760-761, 761f
    germination of, 393, 393f, 610, 764-766, 764f-766f, 817
Seed bank, **764**
Seed coat, **760**
Seed plant, 596, 602t
    evolution of, 602-603, 603f
Seedcracker finch (*Pyrenestes ostrinus*), 409-410, 410f
Seedling
    growth of, 764-765, 764f-765f
    orientation of, 765
Segment polarity genes, 385f, **387**

Segmental duplication, 359, 360t, 480f-481f, 481
Segmentation (animals), **639-640**
    in arthropods, 523, 523f, 639-640, 679, 679f
    in chordates, 523, 523f, 639-640
    in *Drosophila* development, 388-389, 388f
    evolution of, 523-524, 523f, 639-640
    molecular details of, 524
Segmentation genes, 384f, **387**
Segregation of traits, **222**, **226**
Selectable marker, 330, 331f
Selection, 401f, **403-404**.
    See also Artificial selection; Natural selection
    to avoid predators, 404, 404f
    on color in guppies, 412-413, 412f-413f
    directional, **410-411**, 410f-411f
    disruptive, **409-410**, 410f
    frequency-dependent, 407-408, 408f
    interactions among evolutionary forces, 406-407, 407f
    limits of, 413-414, 414f
    to match climatic conditions, 404
    oscillating, **408**
    for pesticide and microbial resistance, 404-405, 405f
    sexual, 405
    stabilizing, 410f, **411**, 411f
Selective permeability, **96**
Selective serotonin reuptake inhibitor (SSRI), 899
Self-fertilization, **223**, 223f
Self-incompatibility, in plants, **856**, 856f
    gametophytic, 856, 856f
    sporophytic, 856, 856f
Self-pollination, 851, 854-855
Self versus nonself recognition, 1066
Semelparity, **1173**
Semen, 1092
Semicircular canal, 924f, **925**, 925f
Semiconservative replication, 263-265, 263f
Semidiscontinuous replication, 267-268, 267f
Semilunar valve, **1026**
Senescence, in plants, **860**
Sensitive plant (*Mimosa pudica*), 822, 822f
Sensitivity, as characteristic of life, 3, 508
Sensor, **876**
Sensory exploitation, **1152**
Sensory information, path of, 916f
Sensory neuron, 873t, **888**, 888f
Sensory organs, of flatworms, 657f, 658
Sensory receptor, 916-917, 916f-917f
Sensory setae, **686**
Sensory system, **873**
Sensory transduction, 917, 917f

Sensory transduction photoreceptor, 931-932, 932f
SEP genes, 846, 848, 848f
Sepal, **608**, 608f
Separase, 201
Separation layer, 824
Septation (cell division), **188**, 188f
September 11, 2001, events of, 368
Septum
    in binary fussion, **188**
    in fungal hyphae, 616, 616f
Sequence-tagged site (STS), **354**, 355f, 357
Sequential hermaphroditism, 1085, 1085f
Serosa, of gastrointestinal tract, **983**, 983f
Serotonin, **899**, 1134
Serotonin receptor, 321
Serum, **1019**
Sessile crustaceans, 683-684, 683f
Set point, 876
Severe acute respiratory syndrome (SARS), 532t, 540, 540f
Severe combined immunodeficiency disease (SCID), **345**, 345t
Sex chromosome, 240, **241**-243, 241t
    of birds, 241t
    of humans, 241-243, 241t, 248f
    of insects, 241t
    nondisjunction involving, 251, 251f
Sex combs reduced (scr) gene, 1117
Sex determination, 1086, 1086f
    genetic sex, 1086
    temperature-sensitive, 1086
Sex linkage, 240f, **241**
Sex steroid hormones, 956
Sexual dimorphism, **662**
Sexual reproduction, 207, **208**-218, 519, **572**, 1084-1086. *See also* Meiosis
    in animals, 635t
Sexual selection, 405, 1150-1154, 1150f, **1151**
Sexually transmitted disease (STD), 561t, 562-563, 562f, 1100
Shade leaf, 750
Shark, 699t, 700-701, 700f
    evolution of, 700
    teeth of, 700-701
Sheep, cloning of, 380f, 381, 381f
Shell, of mollusks, 667, 668, 670f, 671
Shigella, 560
Shingles, 529
Shipworm, 667
Shoot, 730, 730f, 743f
    elongation of, 817, 817f
    gravitropic response in, 819-820, 819f-820f
    tissues of, 730
Shoot system, **730**
SHOOT MERISTEMLESS gene, in *Arabidopsis*, 756, 757f
Shore crab, 1148, 1148f

Short-day plant, 842-843, 842f-843f
    facultative, **843**
    obligate, **843**
Short interspersed element (SINE), **360**, 361f, 363
Short root mutant, in *Arabidopsis*, 820, 820f
Short tandem repeat (STR), 354-355, 368
Short-term memory, 906
Shotgun cloning, 357
Shotgun sequencing, **357**, 357f
Shrimp, 682, 683
Shugoshin, 215
Sickle cell anemia, 49, 227t, 233, 233t, 249-250, 249f, 249t, 299, 299f, 335, 408-409
    malaria and, 250, 409, 409f
Sieve area, 738
Sieve cells, 738
Sieve plate, 738, 738f
Sieve tube, 738
Sieve-tube member, 738, 738f
Sigmoidal growth curve, **1174**
Sign stimulus, 1133, 1133f
Signal recognition particle (SRP), **281**, 296f, 297
Signal sequence, 296f, **297**
Signal transduction pathway, 14, 168, 169-**170**, 169f
    changes in pathways, 494
    in development, 494
Signaling molecule sonic hedgehog (Shh), 1124
Silent mutation, 299, 300f
Silkworm moth (*Bombyx mori*), 956f
Simberloff, Dan, 1227
Simian immunodeficiency virus (SIV), 470-471, 470f-471f
Simple epithelium, 866
    columnar, 866, 867t
    cuboidal, 866, 867t
    squamous, 866, 867t
Simple leaf, 748, 748f
Simple sequence repeats, **359**, 360t
Sin nombre virus, 540
SINE. *See* Short interspersed element
Singer, S. Jonathan, 89
Single-copy gene, 359
Single covalent bond, 24, 24f
Single nucleotide polymorphism (SNP), **248**, 361, 362f
    in human genome, 361
    single-base differences between individuals, 361-362
Single-strand-binding protein, 267, 268t, 269f-270f
Sink (plant carbohydrate), 782-783, 783f
Sinoatrial (SA) node, **1023**
Sinosauropteryx, 714f
Sinus venosus, **1023**, 1023f
Siphonaptera (order), 685t
siRNA. *See* Small interfering RNA
Sister chromatid, 191, 191f, 193, 193f, 209, 209f
Sister chromatid cohesion, 210-211, 214, 215-216
Sister clade, 469

SIV. *See* Simian immunodeficiency virus
6-PDG gene, 414
Skate, 699t, 701
Skeletal muscle, 870-871, 871t
Skeletal system, 874f, 962-963, 962f-963f
Skeleton
    hydrostatic, **962**, 962f
    types of, 962-963, 963f
Skin
    as barrier to infection, 1056
    of reptiles, 707
    sensory receptors in human skin, 918f
Skinner, B. F., **1138**
Skinner box, **1138**
Skull, 708f
Sleep, 905
Sleep movement, in plants, 822, 823f
Sliding clamp, DNA polymerase III, 268, 268f-269f
Slime mold, **584**-585, 585f
    cellular, 585, 585f
    plasmodial, 584-585, 585f
Slow-twitch muscle fiber, **974**, 974f
Slug (mollusk), 666, 667, 668, 670-671
Small interfering RNA (siRNA), 318, 319f, 320
Small intestine, 983, 983f, 988f, 990f
    absorption in, 989-990, 989f
    accessory organs to, 988-989, 988f-989f
    digestion in, 987, 988, 988f-989f
Small nuclear ribonucleoprotein (snRNP), **281**, 290, 290f
Smallpox, 344, 532t, 535, 1061
Smell, 926-927, 927f
Smoking, 1012
    cancer and, **1012**, 1012f
    cardiovascular disease and, 1033
    nicotine addiction, 901
Smooth endoplasmic reticulum, **70**, 70f
Smooth muscle, **870**, 871t
Snail, 641t, 666, 667, 668, 669, 670-671, 670f
    marine, larval disposal in, 466-468, 467f-468f
Snake, 699f, 707t, 711, 711f
    evolution of, 425, 429f
    sensing infrared radiation, 934, 934f
Snake venom, 45t, 433
Snapdragon, 499, 849, 849f
Snodgrass, Robert, 524
SNP. *See* Single nucleotide polymorphism
snRNP. *See* Small nuclear ribonucleoprotein
Social system
    communication in social group, 1146, 1146f
    evolution of, 1157-1159
Sodium, reabsorption in kidney, 1049, 1049f, 1050f, 1051, 1052f

Sodium channel, voltage-gated, **893**, 894f
Sodium chloride, 23-24, 23f, 29f
Sodium-potassium pump, 45t, 90t, 100-**101**, 100f, 104t, 890, 891f
Soil, **787**-789, 1163
    acid, 789
    air in, 787, 788f
    charges on soil particles, 787, 787f
    loss of, 788, 788f
    minerals in, 787-788, 787f
    organic matter in, 787, 787f
    saline, 789
    water content of, 787-788, 788f
    water potential of, 776-777, 787
Solar energy. *See also* Sunlight
    climate and, 1230-1235, 1231f-1232f
    distribution over Earth's surface, 1231, 1231f
    seasonal variation in, 1231, 1231f
    sunlight, 1163
Soldier fly (*Ptecticus trivittatus*), 684f
Solenoid, 190-191, 190f
Soluble receptor, 1057
Solute, 28, **97**
Solute potential, **772**, 772f
Solvent, 27t, 28, 29f, **97**
Somatic cell, **208**, 208f
Somatic cell nuclear transfer (SCNT), **381**
Somatic motor neuron, 973, 973f
Somatic nervous system, **888**, 889f, 909-910, 909t
Somatostatin, 949
Somite, **1119**, 1119f
Somitomere, **1119**
Song, bird's, 1140, 1140f, 1145, 1149
Songbirds, declining populations of, 1268, 1268f
Sorghum, 164
    genome of, 476, 479f
Sori, **601**
SOS response, 275
Sounds, navigation by, 923-924
Source-sink metapopulation, **1167**-1168, 1168f
Southern blot, 334f, **335**-336
Southern, Edwin M., 335
Soybean (*Glycine max*)
    genome of, 479, 479f, 483f
    phytoestrogens in soy products, 808
    transgenic, 347
Spatial heterogeneity, species richness and, 1224-1225, 1224f, 1225-1226
Spatial recognition, 906
Spatial summation, **900**
Special connective tissue, **868**, 870
Specialized transduction, **556**, 557
Speciation, **436**-453
    allopatric, **442**, 442f, 444-445, 444f
    gene flow and, 442
    genetic drift and, 443
    geography of, 444-446, 444f-445f

long-term trends in, 452-453, 452f
natural selection in, 443
polyploidy and, 445, 445f
reinforcement, **442**, 442f
sympatric, 437,
445-446, 445f
Species, 3f, **4**, 512, 513
endemic, 1258-1261, 1259f, 1260t
geographic variation within,
437, 437f
hotspots, 1259-1261,
1259f-1260f, 1260t
keystone, **1201**, 1201f,
1272, 1273f
nature of, 437
origin of, 436-453
sympatric, **437**
Species concept
biological, **437**-438, 438t, 463
ecological, 441
Species diversity cline, **1225**, 1225f
Species name, 512
Species richness, **469-470**, 469f,
1186. See also Biodiversity
climate and, 1224f, 1225
effects of, 1223-1224, 1223f
evolutionary age and, 1225
predation and, 1225
productivity and, 1224, 1224f
spatial heterogeneity and,
1224-1225, 1224f, 1225-1226
in tropics, 1225-1226, 1225f
Specific heat, **28**
of water, 27t, 28
Specific repair mechanism, 274, 274f
Specific transcription factor,
313, 313f
Spectrin, 90t, 91, 94
Speech, genetic basis of, 485
Spemann, Hans, 1122
Spemann organizer, 1122-1125,
1122f-1125f
Sperm, **1092**, 1092f
blockage of, 1100
destruction of, 1100
fertilization, 1106, 1106-1109,
1106t, 1107f-1109f
penetration of egg by, 1106,
1107f, 1109
Sperm competition, **1151**
Spermatid, **1092**
Spermatogenesis, 1091f
Spermatozoa, **1092**
Spermicide, 1099f, 1100
Sphincter, 986
Sphygmomanometer, 1029
Spicule, 650f, **651**
Spider, 641t, 681-682, 682f
poisonous, 682, 682f
Spinal cord, 902f, 907-909,
907f-908f
injury to, 909
Spinal muscular atrophy, 487
Spindle apparatus, 188f, **195**, 196
Spindle checkpoint, **200**, 200f, 201f
Spindle plaque, 617
Spine (plant), 749
Spinneret, **681**
Spiracle, 680f, **681**, 681f, 1006

Spiral cleavage, **638**, 639f, 643
Spiralia, 643, 644f, 669
Spirillum, 552
Spirochaete, 550f, 552
Spliceosome, 289-290, 290f
Sponge, 637, 641t, 643, 650-651,
651f, 901, 1022f
Spongin, 650f, **651**
Spongy bone, 965f, **966**
Spongy mesophyll, 749, 749f
Spontaneous
reaction, 110
Sporangiophore, **621**, 621f
Sporangium, **585**, 585f, **590**, 590f,
594, 594f, 600f
Spore
of fern, 599-600
of fungi, 617, 617f
of moss, 594, 594f
of plant, **590**, 590f
Spore mother cell, **590**, 590f
Sporocyst, **658**, 659f
Sporocyte. See Spore mother cell
Sporophyte, **590**, 590f, 594f, 595,
595f, 600f, 609f, 610
Sporophytic self-incompatibility,
856, 856f
Squamata (order), 707t, 710f,
711, 711f
Squid, 667, 668, 671-672
SRP. See Signal recognition particle
SSRI. See Selective serotonin
reuptake inhibitor
St. John's wort (*Hypericum perforatum*),
1188-1189
Stabilizing selection, 410f,
411, 411f
Stain, visualization of cell structure,
61-62
Stamen, **608**, 608f, **848-849**, 848f
Stanley, Wendell, 519
Stapes, **921**
Staphylococcus, 550f
Staphylococcus aureus, antibiotic
resistance in, 404-405, 558, 559
Star jelly, 655, 655f
Starch, 36f, 37t, **39-40**, 40f
Starfish. See Sea star
Starling (*Sturnus vulgaris*), migratory
behavior of, 1143, 1143f
START, in DNA synthesis,
199, 200
Start site, **285**
Starter culture, 625
Stasis, **451**
Statocyst, **924**
Staurozoa (class), 655, 655f
STD. See Sexually
transmitted disease
Ste5 protein, 177
Stegosaur, 707t
Stele, **741**
Stem, 596
gravitropic response in,
819-820, 819f
modified, 745-747, 746f
positive phototropism in,
817-818, 817f
structure of, 743-745, 743f-745f

Stem cells, **378**, 379f, 1020f, 1021
embryonic, **342-343**, 342f-343f,
379, 379f
ethics of stem cell research, 379
Stereoisomer, 35, 35f, 39, 39f
Sterilization (birth control),
1100-1101, 1101f
Steroid, 37t, 54, 55f, 939
Steroid hormone receptor, 173-174
Stickleback fish
courtship signaling in, 1144f, 1145
gene evolution in, 498
Stigma, of flower, **598**, 598f, 609
Stimulus, 916
Stimulus-gated ion channel,
917, 917f
Stimulus-response chain, 1144f, 1145
Stipule, 730f, 744, **747**
Stolon, 746, 746f, 858
Stomach, **986-987**, 986f
digestion in, 986-987
four-chambered, 991, 992f
secretion by, 986-987
Stomata, 163-165, 163f-164f, **589**,
734, 734f, 804f
opening and closing of, 778,
778f, 779f
STR. See Short tandem repeat
Stramenopile, 515f, 570f, 580-582,
580f-581f
Stratification (seed), **764**
Stratified epithelial membrane, **866**
Stratified epithelium, 866
pseudostratified columnar, 867t
squamous, 866, 867t
Stratospheric ozone depletion,
1248-1249, 1249f
Streptococcus, 550f, 560, 561t
Streptococcus mutans, 562
Streptococcus pneumoniae,
transformation in, 257-258, 257f
Streptococcus sobrinus, 562
Streptomyces, 550f
Streptophyta (phylum), 521, 521f
Streptophyte, **591**
Striated muscle, 870
Stroke, **1033**
Stroke volume, 1034
Stroma, 74, 74f, **148**,
148f, 149f
Stromatolite, **546**, 546f
Structural DNA, 359, 360t
Structural formula, 24
Structural isomer, 35
Structure, of living systems, 13
STS. See Sequence-tagged site
Sturtevant, Alfred, 354
Style, **608**, 608f
Stylet, **662**
Suberin, 741, **803**
Submucosa, of gastrointestinal tract,
983, 983f
Subspecies, **437**, 437f
Substance P, **899**
Substrate, **113**, 117f
Substrate-level phosphorylation,
125-126, 125f
Subunit vaccine,
344, 344f, 349

Succession, **1202**-1203
in animal communities,
1203, 1203f
in plant communities,
1202-1203, 1202f
primary, **1202**, 1202f
secondary, **1202**
Succinate, 132, 133f
Succinyl-CoA, 132, 133f
Suckers, plant, 858
Sucrose, 28, 39, 39f
transport in plants, 781, 782f
Sugar
isomers of, 38, 39f
transport in plants,
781-782, 782f
Sugarcane, 164, 189t, 363f
chromosome number in, 189t
genome of, 476, 479f
Sulfhydryl group, 35f
Sulfur bacteria, 139
Summation, **893**, 893f, **900**,
973, 974f
Sundew (*Drosera*), 750, 793, 794f
Sunflower (*Helianthus annuus*), 822f
genome of, 479f
Sunlight, 1163. See also Solar energy
in photosynthesis, 148, 150
regulation of stomatal opening
and closing, 778
Supercoiling, of DNA, **267**, 267f
Superior vena cava, **1029**
Suprachiasmatic nucleus (SCN), 956
Surface area-to-volume ratio, **60**, 60f
Surface marker. See Cell
surface marker
Surface tension, **26**, 27f
Survivorship, **1170**
Survivorship curve, 1170,
1170f-1171f
Suspensor, **754**
suspensor mutant, of *Arabidopsis*,
755, 756f
Sutherland, Earl, 945
Sutton, Walter, 240
Swallowing, 985, 985f
Sweet woodruff, 744f
Swim bladder, **701-702**, 701f
Swimmeret, **683**, 683f
Swimming, 975-976
by fish, 975-976, 975f
by terrestrial vertebrates, 976
Symbiosis, 75, **563**, 626
coevolution and, 1196
facultative, **626**
fungi in, 626-629
obligate, **626**
prokaryotes in, 563-564
Sympathetic chain, of ganglia,
910, 911f
Sympathetic division, 910, 911f, 911t
Sympathetic nervous system, 888,
889f, 910
Sympatric speciation, **437**,
445-446, 445f
Symplast route, **775**, 775f
Symplesiomorphy, **459**
Symporter, **100**
Synapomorphy, **459**

Synapse, **896**-901, 897f-900f
  chemical, **170**, 896
  electrical, **896**
  structure of, 896-897, 897f
Synapsid, **708**, 708f
Synapsis, **209**, 209f, 212f
Synaptic cleft, **896**, 897f
Synaptic integration, 900
Synaptic plasticity, 906
Synaptic signaling, 169, 169f, **170**, 897f
Synaptic vesicle, **896**
Synaptonemal complex, **209**, 209f
Syncytial blastoderm, **384**, 384f, 1110
Syngamy, **208**
Synteny, 363, 363f
  conservation of, **482**, 483f
Synthetic polyploid, **478**
Syphilis, 562, 562f
Systematics, 456-458, **457**, 457f
  classification and, 461-464, 462f-464f
Systemic acquired resistance, in plants, **811**, 812f
Systemic anaphylaxis, 1075
Systemic circulation, **1024**
Systemin, **810**
Systole, **1026**, 1027f
Systolic pressure, **1029**, 1029f

T

2, 4,5-T, 831
T box, **496**
T cell(s), 1020f, 1062, 1062t, **1063**, 1063f, 1068
  antigen recognition by, 1062f, 1066t
  cytotoxic, 1062t, **1066**-1067, 1066t, 1067f
  helper, 1062t, 1066, 1067-1068, 1069f
  HIV infection of, 531, 531f, 1080, 1080f
T-cell receptor (TCR), **1064**, 1065f, 1073-1074, 1074f
T-even phage, 533
T-Helper cells, **535**
T lymphocyte, **1063**, 1063f
T tubule. *See* Transverse tubule
Table salt. *See* Sodium chloride
Taenia saginata, 660, 660f
TAF. *See* Transcription-associated factor
Tagmata, **679**
Taiga, 1238
Tandem cluster, 359
Tandem duplication, 300
Tannin, 805
Tapeworm, 641t, 659-660, 660f
Taq polymerase, **339**-340, 340f
Tardigrada, 640, 642t, 645f
Taste, 926, 926f
Taste bud, 926, 926f, 984
Taste pore, 926
Tatum, Edward, 6, 279
Tautomer, of nitrogenous bases, 261

Taxol, 806t, **808**
Taxonomic hierarchy, 512-514, 513f
Taxonomy, **512**-514
Tay-Sachs disease, 71, 249t, 253
Tbx5 gene, 497, 497f
Teeth
  dental caries, 561-562, 561t
  of mammals, 717, 717f
  saber-toothed-ness, 464-465, 465f
  of sharks, 700-701
  of vertebrates, 984, 984f
Telencephalon, 902t, **903**
Telomerase, **272**-273, 272f
Telomere, **271**-272, 272f
  length of, 272
Telophase
  meiosis I, 212f, 214
  meiosis II, 213f, 214, 216f, 217f
  mitotic, 192f, 195f, **197**, 216f
Telson, **683**, 683f
Temperate deciduous forest, 1238, 1238f
Temperate evergreen forest, **1238**
Temperate grassland, 1237
Temperate virus, **533**
Temperature
  adaptation to specific range, 1162
  altitude and, 1234, 1234f
  annual mean, 1231, 1231f
  carbon dioxide and, 1251
  effect on chemical reactions, 25
  effect on enzyme activity, 52, 116, 116f
  effect on flower production, 844
  effect on oxyhemoglobin dissociation curve, 1014, 1014f
  effect on plant respiration, 797
  effect on transpiration, 779
  heat and water, 27t, 28
Temperature-sensitive sex determination, 1086
Template strand, 265, 265f, **280**, 285f, 286f
Temporal isolation, 438t, 439
Temporal lobe, 904, 904f
Temporal summation, **900**
Tendon, 968
Tendril, 730f, 746f, 747, 821
Tensile strength, **777**
Terminal bud, 744, 744f
Terminator, **285**, 286, 286f
Termite, 684f
Terpene, 37t, 54, 55f
Territorial behavior, 1149, 1149f
Tertiary follicle, **1095**
Tertiary structure, of proteins, 46, **48**-49, 49f
Test experiment, **6**
Test tube baby, 1102
Testcross, **231**-232, 231f, 232t, 241
Testes, 1091, 1091f, 1094f
Testosterone, 943f, 956, 1091, 1093t
Testudines, 699f
Tetanus (disease), 554, 560, **973**
Tetrad, 209
Tetrahedron, 26
Tetrapod, 497

Thalamus, 902t, **903**, 904-905
Theory, **7**, 432
Therapeutic cloning, **383**, 383f
Therapsid, 708, 708f
Theria, **718**
Thermal stratification, **1239**-1240, 1240f
Thermodynamics, **108**
  First Law of, **109**
  Second Law of, **110**, 110f, 433, 879
Thermogenesis, **882**
Thermophile, 139, 139f, 516, 517f, 550f
Thermoproteus, 550f
Thermoreceptor, **918**
Thermoregulation
  in birds, 715
  hypothalamus and mammalian, 882-883, 883f
  in insects, 880, 880f
  in mammals, 716
  negative feedback loop, 876, 877f
  regulating body temperature, 878-883
  in reptiles, 710
Thermotoga, 515f, 516
Thermotolerance, in plants, 825
Thick myofilament, 970-971, 970f-971f
Thigmomorphogenesis, **821**
Thigmonastic response, 821
Thigmotropism, **821**-822, 821f
Thin myofilament, 970-971, 970f-971f
Thiomargarita namibia, 548
Thoracic breathing, 707
Thorn-shaped treehopper (*Embonia crassiornis*), 684f
Threshold potential, **893**
Thrombocytes, 870. *See also* Platelet(s)
Thylakoid, **74**, 74f, 148, 148f, 149f, 160, 160f
Thymine, 42, 42f, 259f, 260
Thymine dimer, 274, 274f
Thymus, 956, **1064**, 1064f
Thyroid gland, 949, 949f, 951-953, 952f-953f
Thyroid hormone, **939**, 951, 952, 952f
Thyroid-stimulating hormone (TSH), 948, 949
Thyrotropin-releasing hormone (TRH), 949
Thyroxine, 943f, **949**, 952f
Ti plasmid, **346**, 346f
Tick, 560, 682
Tiger, 438, 438f
Tiger salamander (*Ambystoma tigrinum*), 705f
Tight junction, **83**-84, 83f
Tiktaalik, 704, 704f
Tinbergen, Niko, 1146, 1147-1148, 1147f
Tissue, 2f, **3**, 82, **635**, 864, 864f
  evolution of, 637
  primary, **732**, **864**
  secondary, **732**

Tissue culture, plant, 859
Tissue plasminogen activator, **343**
  genetically engineered, 343-344
Tissue systems (plant), **730**, 758-759
Tissue tropism, of virus, **529**
Tmespiteris, 599
TMV. *See* Tobacco mosaic virus
TNT. *See* Trinitrotoluene
Toad (*Bufo*), 703, 703t, 705-706
  hybridization between species of, 439, 440
Tobacco
  evolution of, 477f, 480, 480f
  genome of, 480, 480f
Tobacco hornworm (*Manduca sexta*), 805, 805f
Tobacco mosaic virus (TMV), 519-520, 519f, 529f
Tocopherol. *See* Vitamin E
Toe, grasping, 721
Toll-like receptor, 1056
Tomato (*Lycopersicon esculentum*)
  genome of, 479f
  wound response in, **810**, 810f
Tonicity, **1039**
Tonoplast, **73**
Too many mouths mutation, in *Arabidopsis*, 734, 734f
Tooth. *See* Teeth
Top-down effect, **1219**-1221, 1220f
Topoisomerase, **267**
Topsoil, **787**, 787f
Torpor, 883
Torsion, **670**
Tortoise, 707t, 710, 710f
Totipotent cells, **379**
Touch, receptors in human skin, 918-919, 918f
Toxin, plant, 805, 806t, 807-808, 807f
Toxoplasma gondii, 578, 578f
Trace elements, 998
Trachea, 1007, 1008f
Tracheae, **680**, 681f, 1006, 1118
Tracheid, **589**, 593, 737, 737f, 777
Tracheole, **680**-681, 681f
Tracheophyte, 589, 596-597
Trailing arbutus (*Epigaea repens*), 843
Trait, segregation of, **222**, **226**
Trans-fatty acids, 55
Transcription, 43, **280**, 280f, 280-281
  coupled to translation, 286-287, 287f
  DNA rearrangements and, 1073, 1073f
  elongation phase of, 285-286, 286f
  in eukaryotes, 287-289, 288f
  initiation of, 284f, 285, 288, 288f, 304-305, 322f
  posttranscriptional modifications, 288-289, 288f
  in prokaryotes, 284-287, 284f-287f
  termination of, 286, 286f, 288
Transcription-associated factor (TAF), 313, 313f

I-30 *index*

Transcription bubble, **285**-286, 285f, 286f

Transcription complex, 315, 315f

Transcription factor, 50, 202, 203f, **288**, 288f, 312-314
  cytoplasmic determinants, 376f, 377
  in development, 494, 494f, 497-498
  E2F, 203f
  in eukaryotes, 313-314, 314f
  FOXP2, 485
  general, **313**, 313f
  specific, **313**
  TFIID, 313, 313f
  translated regions of, 494

Transcription unit, **285**

Transcriptional control, 305
  in eukaryotes, 305, 312-315, 322f
  negative, **308**-310
  positive, **308**
  in prokaryotes, 305, 308-312, 308f-312f

Transcriptome, **366**

Transduction, 554, 556-557, 557f
  generalized, **556**-557, 557f
  sensory, 917, 917f
  specialized, **556**, 557

Transfer RNA (tRNA), 69, **281**, **291**-293
  binding to ribosomes, 292-293, 293f
  charged, 292, 292f
  initiator, **294**
  structure of, 291-292, 291f
  in translation, 293-297, 294f-296f

Transformation
  in bacteria, **257**, 554, 557-558, 558f
  introduction of foreign DNA into bacteria, 329-330
  in plants, 346, 346f

Transforming growth factor beta, 1122

Transforming principle, 257-258, 257f

Transfusion, of blood, 1077

Transgenic animals, 284f, **342**, 343f, 349

Transgenic organism, **330**, 365

Transgenic plants, 346-349, 365-366, 366f
  herbicide resistance in, 346-347, 347f, 366f
  social issues raised by, 348

Transient receptor potential ion channel (TRP), 918

Transition (mutation), 299

Translation, **280**, 281
  coupled to transcription, 286-287, 287f
  DNA rearrangements and, 1073, 1073f
  elongation stage of, 295-297, 294f-296f, 298f

initiation of, 293-295, 294f, 298f, 298t, 321
  "start" and "stop" signals, 283
  termination of, 296f, 297, 298f

Translation factor, 321

Translation repressor protein, **321**

Translational control, 321

Translocation (chromosome), 250, **300**, 300f

Translocation, Down syndrome, 250

Translocation (translation), 295f, 296

Transmembrane protein, 89, 90f, 90t, **94**-95, 95f

Transmembrane route, **775**, 775f

Transmissible spongiform encephalopathy (TSE), 541-542

Transmission electron microscope, 61, 62t, 91

Transpiration, **737**, 770
  environmental factors affecting, 779, 779f
  regulation of rate of, 778-779, 778f-779f

Transport protein, 44, 45t, 63, 93, 94f, 104t

Transposable element, **360**-361, 360t

Transposon, 360, 480-481
  dead, 361, 361f
  in *Drosophila*, 484
  in human genome, 484

Transverse tubule (T tubule), **972**, 972f

Transversion (mutation), 299

Tree finch (*Camarhynchus*), 448, 448f

Trematoda (class), 658-659, 659f

Treponema pallidum, 550f, 562

TRH. *See* Thyrotropin-releasing hormone

Trichinella, 661f, 662

Trichinosis, 661f, 662

Trichloroethylene (TCE), phytoremediation for, 798-799, 798f

Trichome, **734**-735, 735f, 766f

Trichomonas vaginalis, 573, 573f

Tricuspid valve, **1026**

Triglyceride, 36f, **53**, 54f

Trimester, 1125

Trinitrotoluene (TNT), phytoremediation for, 799

Triple covalent bond, 24, 24f

Triple expansion (mutation), 300

Triplet-binding assay, 283

Triploblastic animal, 637, 640, 643

Trisomy, 189, **250**, 250f

Trisomy 21. *See* Down syndrome

Trochophore, **643**, 669, 669f

Trophic cascade, **1219**-1220, 1220f, 1221f

Trophic level, 1214-**1215**, 1215f
  concepts to describe, 1215-1216
  defined, 1215

energy loss between levels, 1216, 1216f
  energy processing in, 1216
  number of levels, 1217-1218
  trophic level interactions, 1219-1223, 1220f-1222f

Trophoblast, **1112**, 1112f

Tropical ecosystem, 1225-1226
  species richness in, 1225-1226, 1225f

Tropical forest, destruction of, 1246-1247, 1247f

Tropical rain forest, **1236**-1237, 1237f
  loss of, 1246-1247, 1247f

Tropomyosin, **972**, 972f

Troponin, **972**, 972f

TRP ion channel. *See* Transient receptor potential ion channel

trp operon, **308**, 311-312, 311f

trp promoter, 311, 311f

trp repressor, 311-312, 311f

True-breeding plant, **222**, 225f

Trunk neural crest cells, 1120-1121, 1120f

Trypanosoma brucei, 488

Trypanosoma cruzi, 488, 574

Trypanosome, 574-575, 575f

Trypanosomiasis, 574

Trypsin, **988**

Tryptophan, 47f, 829f
  repressor, 311-312, 312f

TSE. *See* Transmissible spongiform encephalopathy

TSH. *See* Thyroid-stimulating hormone

Tuatara, 707t, 710, 710f

Tubal ligation, 1101f

Tuber, 746-747

Tuberculosis, 560-561, 561t

Tubeworm, 641t, 675, 675f

Tubulin, 76, 188, **194**

Tumor-suppressor gene, **203**, 203f, 204, 204f

Tundra, 1238

Tunicate, 695-696, 695f
  development in, 376f, 377

Turbellaria (class), 658

Turgor, 99

Turgor movement, 821-822, 822f

Turgor pressure, **99**, 772, 772f, 778, 779f, 782-783, 821-822

Turner syndrome, 251, 251f

Turpentine, 604

Turtle, 699f, 707t, 710, 710f

Tutt, J. W., 420, 421

Twin studies, 1141

Two-hybrid system, protein-protein interactions, 340-341, 341f

2,4-D, 829f, **830**

Tympanum, **686**

Type A flu virus, **539**

Type III secretion system, 560

Typhoid fever, 560, 561t

Typhus, 561t

Tyrannosaur, 707t

U

Ubiquinone, 134, 134f

Ubiquitin, 201, **323**-324, 323f

Ubiquitin ligase, 323, 323f

Ubiquitin-proteasome pathway, 324, 324f

Ulcer, 562, 987

Ultraviolet radiation, ozone layer and, 1248, 1249f

Ulva, 592, 592f

Unicellularity, of prokaryotes, 548

Uniporter, **100**

Unipotent stem cells, **379**

Uniramous appendage, **524**, 524f

Universal Declaration on the Human Genome and Human Rights, 369

Unsaturated fatty acid, **53**, 54f

Uracil, 42, 42f, 259f

Urea, **1044**, 1045f

Ureter, **1045**, 1046f

Urethra, **1045**, 1046f

Urey, Harold C., 509

Uric acid, **1044**, 1045f

Uricase, 1044

Urinary bladder, **1045**, 1046f

Urinary system, **875**, 875f

Urine, 1041, 1044, 1047-1048, 1056
  pH of, 1048

Urodela (order), 703, 703t, 705f, 706

Uropod, **683**, 683f

Uterine contractions, 878, 878f, 947, 1128, 1128f

Uterine tube. *See* Fallopian tube

Uterus, **1098**, 1098f

Utricle, **924**, 924f

UV-B, **1248**

uvr genes, 274-275, 274f

V

Vaccination, 1061

Vaccine
  DNA, 344-345
  HIV, 538
  malaria, 578, 1079
  production using recombinant DNA, 344-345, 344f
  subunit, **344**, 344f, 349

Vaccinia virus, 1061

Vacuole
  in ciliates, 578-579, 578f
  of eukaryotic cells, 81t
  of plant cells, **73**, 73f, 81t

Vaginal secretions, 1056

Valence electron, **22**

Vampire bat (*Desmodus rotundus*), 1155, 1155f

Van Beneden, Edouard, 207-208

van der Waals attractions, 23t, 48, 48f

Van Helmont, Jan Baptista, 149

Van Niel, C. B. (small v for van), 150-151

Vancomycin, 64

Vancomycin-resistant *Staphylococcus aureus* (VRSA), **559**
Vanilla orchid, 742
Variable region, of immunoglobulin, 1069-1070, 1070f
Variables, in hypotheses, 6
Varicella-zoster virus, 1061
Vas deferens, **1092**
Vasa recta, **1047**, 1047f
Vascular bone, **966**
Vascular cambium, **732**, 733f, 745, 745f
Vascular plant, 463f, 730, 730f
    extant phyla of, 596, 601t-602t
    features of, 596, 596f
Vascular tissue of plants, 596, **731**, 737-738, 737f-738f, 756, 759
Vasectomy, 1101f
Vasoconstriction, **1030**-1031, 1031f
Vasodilation, **1030**-1031, 1031f
Vasopressin, **1034**
Vector, cloning. *See* Cloning vector
Vegetal plate, **1113**
Vegetal pole, **1110**, 1110f
Vegetarian finch (*Platyspiza*), 418f, 448, 448f
Vegetative propagation, 746-747
Vegetative reproduction, in plants, **858**, 858f
Vein (blood vessel), **1030**, 1030f
Vein (leaf), **747**-748
Veliger, **669**, 669f
Velociraptor, 714, 714f
Venous pump, **1031**, 1031f
Venous valve, **1031**, 1031f
Venter, Craig, 357
Ventral body cavity, 864, 865f
Ventral root, **909**
Ventricle, **1023**, 1023f
Venule, **1030**, 1031, 1032f
Venus flytrap (*Dionaea muscipula*), 750, 793, 794f, 821, 830
Vernalization, 844
Vertebral column, 696, 697f
    of fish, 698-699
Vertebrate, **635**, 693-726
    characteristics of, 696-697, 697f-698f
    circulatory system of, 1023-1025, 1023f-1025f
    development in, 1118-1119, 1119f
    digestive system of, 982-983, 983f
    variations in, 990-992, 991f-992f
    evolution of, 697, 698f, 1121, 1121f
    eye in, 1125f
    fertilization and development in, 1087-1090, 1087f-1090f
    hearing in, 921-922, 921f, 923
    invasion of land by, 703-705, 704f-705f
    kidneys of, **1041**-1044, 1042f-1044f
    locomotion in, 976, 976f
    organization of body of, 864-865, 864f-865f
    photoreceptors of, 930-931, 930f-931f
    smell in, 926-927, 927f
    social systems of, 1157-1159, 1159f
    taste in, 926, 926f
    teeth of, 984, 984f
Vertical gene transfer, **483**
Vervet monkey (*Ceropithecus aethiops*), language of, 1147, 1147f
Vesicle, **65**
Vessel member, 737, 737f
Vessel (xylem), **605**, 777
Vestibular apparatus, **925**
Vestigial structure, **430**, 430f
Vibrio cholerae, 180, 548, 551f, 561t
    phage conversion in, 534
Victoria (Queen of England), 242-243, 242f
Villi, **987**, 988f
Vimentin, 76
Viridiplantae (kingdom), 519, 520, 521, 521f, 588, 590, 591
Virion, **528**, 530
Viroid, **542**
Virulent virus, **533**
Virus, 519f, 528-542
    bacteriophage. *See* Bacteriophage
    cancer and, 540-541
    classification of, 519-520
    disease-causing, 532t, 539-541
    DNA, 529, 529f, 532t
    emerging, **540**
    genome of, 529, 531
    host range of, **529**
    latent, 529
    recombination in, 539
    replication of, 530
    RNA, 529, 529f, 532t
    shape of, 519f, 529f, 530-531
    size of, 519, 519f, 531, 531f
    structure of, 529-531, 529f-531f, 532t
    temperate, **533**, 534f
    tissue tropism, **529**
    virulent, **533**, 534f
Viscera, 870
Visceral mass, **668**
Visceral muscle, 870
Visceral pleural membrane, **1009**
Vision, 928-933, 928f-933f
    binocular, 721, **933**
    color, 930, 930f
    nearsightedness and farsightedness, 929f
Visual acuity, 933
Vitamin, **997**-998, 998t
Vitamin A, 998t
Vitamin B-complex vitamins, 998t
Vitamin C, 998t
Vitamin D, 953, 953f, 998t
Vitamin E, 998t
Vitamin K, 992, 998t
Viviparity, **1087**, 1087f
Voltage-gated ion channel, **893**, 894f
    potassium channel, **893**, 894f
    sodium channel, **893**, 894f
Volvox, 591-592, 591f
Vomitoxin, 630
Von Frisch, Karl, 1146
VRSA, 559

W

Wadlow, Robert, 950, 950f
Wall cress. *See Arabidopsis*
Wallace, Alfred Russel, 10
Warbler finch (*Certhidea*), 418f, 448, 448f
Wasp, parasitoid, 809, 809f
Water, 1162
    absorption by plants, 773-775, 774f-775f
    adhesive properties of, 27, 27f
    cohesive nature of, 26, 27f, 27t
    forms of, 25-26, 26f
    heat of vaporization of, 27t, 28
    hydrogen bonds in, 26, 26f
    ionization of, 29
    lipids in, 56, 56f
    locomotion in, 975-976, 975f
    molecular structure of, 26, 26f
    osmosis, 97-99, 98f
    properties of, 27t, 28-29
    reabsorption in kidney, 1048, 1050-1051, 1051f
    soil, 787-788, 788f
    as solvent, 27t, 28, 29f
    specific heat of, 27t, 28
    transport in plants, 771f
Water cycle, 1209-1210, 1209f-1210f
    disruption by deforestation, 1247
Water-dispersed fruit, 762, 763f
Water mold, 581
Water potential, **770**-772, 772f, 774f
    calculation of, 771-772, 772f
    at equilibrium, 772, 773f
    gradient from roots to shoots, 776-777
    of soil, 787-788
Water storage root, 743, 743f
Water-vascular system, **688**, 688f, 689
Watersheds, of New York City, 1262-1263, 1263f
Waterwheel (*Aldrovanda*), 794, 794f
Watson, James, 259-263, 261f, 358
Weinberg, Wilhelm, 399
Welwitschia, 602t, 605, 605f
Wendell, Stanley, 519-520
Went, Frits, 827-828, 828f
WEREWOLF gene, in *Arabidopsis*, 740, 740f
Western blot, **335**
Whale, 525, 525f
    evolution of, 425, 425f, 430f
    overexploitation of, 1269, 1269f
Whaling industry, 1269, 1269f
Wheat (*Triticum*)
    chromosome number in, 189t
    evolution of, 478f
    genome of, 363, 363f, 476-477, 478f, 479f, 486
    transgenic, 366f
Whisk fern, 596, 598-599, 599f, 601t
White blood cells. *See* Leukocytes
White fiber, 974
White-fronted bee-eater (*Merops bullockoides*), 1156-1157, 1157f
Whooping cough, 560
Whorl (flower parts), **608**, 608f
Whorl (leaf pattern), 744, 744f
Wieschaus, Eric, 384
Wild geranium (*Geranium maculatum*), 849f
Wilkins, Maurice, 261
Wilson, Edward O., 1226-1227
Wind, pollination by, 852, 854, 854f
Window leaf, 749-750
Wing traits, in fruit fly, 246-247, 246f
Wings
    development of, 497, 497f, 976-977, 977f
    of insects, 498-499, 498f
Wnt pathway, **1123**
Wobble pairing, 296-**297**
Woese, Carl, 514
Wolf, 423f, 431f, 1163, 1163f
    captive breeding of, 1277
WOODEN LEG gene, in *Arabidopsis*, 759, 759f
Woody plant, 744, 744f
World Health Organization (WHO), 348, 560, 1079
Wound response, in plants, **810**, 810f

X

X chromosome, **241**, 241t
    of fruit fly, 241, 245
    human, 241-242, 248f
    inactivation of, 243, 243f
    nondisjunction involving, 251, 251f
X-SCID, 345
Xenopus, 1122, 1123
Xylem, **596**, 737-738, 737f, 741f
    primary, 733f, 737, 741-742, 741f
    secondary, 733f, 737
    vessels, **605**
    water and mineral transport through, 776-777, 776f-777f

Y

Y chromosome, 241-243, 241t
    nondisjunction involving, 251, 251f
YABBY gene, in *Arabidopsis*, 747f
YAC. *See* Yeast artificial chromosome
Yeast, 614, 625, 625f
    cell division in, 188f
    chromosome number in, 189t
    ethanol fermentation in, 140f
    genome of, 358f, 475f
Yeast artificial chromosome (YAC), 331, 356

Yellow fever, 531f, 532t
Yellowstone Park, return of wolves
to, 1277
Yersinia pestis, 559, 561t
Yersinia, type III system,
559-560
Yolk plug, **1114**, 1114f
Yolk sac, **706**, 708f

Z

Z diagram, 157, 158f
Z line, 969
Zebra mussel (*Dreissena polymorpha*),
667, 1270, 1270f
Zinc finger
motif, **307**

Zone cell of division,
739-740, 740f
Zone of elongation, **740**
Zone of maturation,
740-742, 740f, 741f
Zoospore, 582, 619, 619f, 620
Zygomycetes, 615, 615f, **620**,
621, 621f

Zygomycota (phylum), 615, 615f,
615t, 620-621, 621f
Zygosporangium, 621, 621f
Zygospore, 591f, **621**, 621f
Zygote, **208**, 208f, 373
fungi, 621, 621f
plant, 754, 754f,
755, 755f

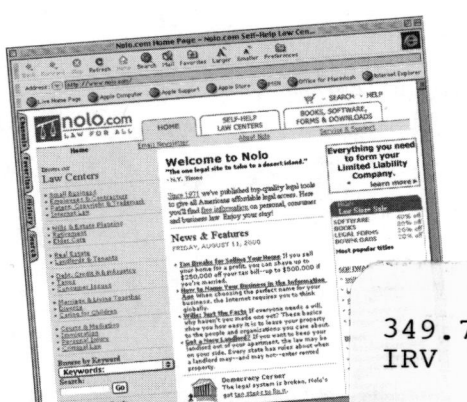

LEGAL INFORMATION
ONLINE ANYTIME

AT THE NOLO.COM SELF-

- Nolo's comprehensive L
  information on a variety of
- Nolo's Law Dictionary—le
- Auntie Nolo—if you've g
- The Law Store—over 25
  Downloadable Software,
- Legal and product updates
- Frequently Asked Question
- NoloBriefs, our free mon
- Legal Research Center, for
- Our ever-popular lawyer

UR
ASSLE"
ANTEE

ing you buy
Nolo for any
cheerfully re-
rchase price.
buts.

Quality LAW
FOR

Nolo's user-friendly products a

- A dozen in-house legal edito
  ensure that our products ar
- We continually update every
  to keep up with changes in t
- Our commitment to a more
  our work
- We appreciate & listen to yc
  return the card at the back of this book.

An Important Message to Our Readers

This product provides information and general advice about the law. But laws and procedures change frequently, and they can be interpreted differently by different people. For specific advice geared to your specific situation, consult an expert. No book, software or other published material is a substitute for personalized advice from a knowledgeable lawyer licensed to practice law in your state.

4th edition

Nolo's Encyclopedia of Everyday Law

Answers to Your Most Frequently Asked Legal Questions

**edited by Attorneys Shae Irving,
Kathleen Michon and Beth McKenna**

Keeping Up to Date

To keep its books up to date, Nolo issues new printings and new editions periodically. New printings reflect minor legal changes and technical corrections. New editions contain major legal changes, major text additions or major reorganizations. To find out if a later printing or edition of any Nolo book is available, call Nolo at 510-549-1976 or check our website at http://www.nolo.com.

To stay current, follow the "Update" service at our website: http://www.nolo.com/lawstore/ update/list.cfm. In another effort to help you use Nolo's latest materials, we offer a 35% discount off the purchase of the new edition of your Nolo book when you turn in the cover of an earlier edition.

This book was last revised in: May 2002.

Fourth Edition .... *May 2002*

Editors .... *Shae Irving, Kathleen Michon & Beth McKenna*

Cover .... *Jaleh Doane*

Book Design .... *Linda Marie Wanczyk & Jackie Mancuso*

Production .... *Susan Putney & Sarah Hinman*

Index .... *Nancy Mulvany*

Proofreader .... *Robert Wells*

Printer .... *Bertelsmann Services, Inc.*

Nolo's encyclopedia of everyday law : answers to your most frequently asked legal questions / edited by Shae Irving, Kathleen Michon, and Beth McKenna.- - 4th ed.

    p. cm.

Includes index.

ISBN 0-87337-830-X

  1. Law- -United States- -Popular works. 2. Law- -United States- -Miscellanea. I. Irving, Shae. II. Michon, Kathleen, 1966- III. McKenna, Beth.

KF387.N65 2002

349.73- -dc21   2002024251

QUANTITY SALES: FOR INFORMATION ON BULK PURCHASES OR CORPORATE PREMIUM SALES, PLEASE CONTACT THE SPECIAL SALES DEPARTMENT.

FOR ACADEMIC SALES OR TEXTBOOK ADOPTIONS, ASK FOR ACADEMIC SALES. 800-955-4775, Nolo, 950 PARKER ST., BERKELEY, CA, 94710.

Dedication

For Edward F. Dolan

Acknowledgments

First things first—thanks to Jake Warner for thinking up the project and providing the support to get it done. And thanks to all the Nolo editors who kept us (and the book) on track, particularly Robin Leonard, for rising above the call of duty, Mary Randolph for her eminent good judgment and Steve Elias for his relentless and contagious enthusiasm.

For diligent research help, we'd like to thank Ella Hirst, Naomi Starkman and Peri Pakroo. For helping manage the changes through draft after draft of the earlier editions, thanks go to Susan Cornell and Stephanie Harolde.

Jackie Mancuso made the book look great. Jaleh Doane, Susan Putney and Linda Marie Wanczyk brought their sharp minds and good humor to the design process, and made the whole thing even easier.

Finally, we're grateful to every Nolo author and editor whose fine work has shaped these pages. You'll find many of these talented folks listed in the Contributors section on the following page. But we want to give special thanks to:

Paul Bergman and Sara Berman-Barrett, authors of *Represent Yourself in Court* and *The Criminal Law Handbook*

David W. Brown, author of *How to Change Your Name* and *Beat Your Ticket: Go to Court and Win!*

Stephen Colwell and Ann Shulman, authors of *Trouble Free Travel...And What to Do When Things Go Wrong*

Frederick W. Daily, author of *Stand Up to the IRS, Tax Savvy for Small Business* and *Surviving an Audit*

James Evans, author of *Law on the Net* and *Government on the Net*

Cora Jordan, author of *Neighbor Law: Fences, Trees, Boundaries & Noise* and co-author (with Denis Clifford) of *Plan Your Estate*

Mimi E. Lyster, author of *Child Custody: Building Agreements That Work*

Joseph Matthews, author of *How to Win Your Personal Injury Claim* and co-author (with Dorothy Matthews Berman) of *Social Security, Medicare and Pensions*

Tanya Starnes, author of *Mad at Your Lawyer*

Fred S. Steingold, author of *The Legal Guide for Starting & Running a Small Business* and *The Employer's Legal Handbook.*

Contributors

Denis Clifford (Estate and Gift Taxes). Denis is the author of several Nolo books, including *Nolo's Will Book, The Quick & Legal Will Book, Plan Your Estate* (with Cora Jordan) and *The Partnership Book* (with Ralph Warner). A graduate of Columbia Law School, where he was an editor of *The Columbia Law Review,* Denis has practiced law in various ways, and is convinced that people can do much of their own legal work.

Amy DelPo (Workplace Rights, Travel, Retirement Plans). Amy has been an editor at Nolo since January 2000. She specializes in workers' rights, sexual harassment law, employment law, criminal law and civil litigation. She brings more than six years of criminal and civil litigation experience to her work at Nolo, having litigated cases in all levels of state and federal courts, including the California Supreme Court and the United States Supreme Court. Amy received her law degree with Honors from the University of North Carolina at Chapel Hill.

Stephen R. Elias (Patents, Copyrights, Trademarks, Criminal Law, Legal Research). Steve received a law degree from Hastings College of the Law in 1969. He has practiced law in California, Vermont and New York, working for a variety of programs delivering legal services to the poor. In 1980, he discovered Nolo and, referring to himself as a recovering lawyer, has never looked back. Steve has authored, co-authored or edited over 30 Nolo titles covering such topics as family law, patents, copyrights, trademarks and bankruptcy.

Lisa Guerin (Employers' Rights and Responsibilities). During her years as a law student at Boalt Hall School of Law at the University of California at Berkeley, Lisa worked for Nolo as a research and editorial assistant. After a stint as a staff attorney at the U.S. Court of Appeals for the Ninth Circuit, Lisa has worked primarily in the field of employment law, in both government and private practice. Lisa recently rejoined the staff at Nolo, where she is the co-author of *Nolo's Pocket Guide to California Law.*

Shae Irving (Durable Powers of Attorney for Finances, Wills and Estate Planning). Shae graduated from Boalt Hall School of Law at the University of California at Berkeley in 1993 and began working for Nolo in 1994. She has written extensively on durable powers of attorney and other estate planning issues. She edits many other Nolo titles, including *Plan Your Estate* and *Make Your Own Living Trust.*

Bethany K. Laurence (Small Businesses). Beth graduated from Hastings College of the Law at the University of California in 1993. She spent several years working for a corporate legal publisher before coming to Nolo. She joined Nolo's editorial staff in 1997 and has never been happier. Beth is the co-author of Nolo's *How to Create a Buy-Sell Agreement & Control the Destiny of Your Small Business* and the editor of several Nolo publications, including *The Small Business Start-Up Kit, Nolo's California Quick Corp* and *Nolo's Quick LLC.*

Robin Leonard (Your Money, Cars and Driving, Traveling, Spouses and Partners, Dealing With Your Lawyer). Robin specializes in debt, credit, bankruptcy and family law. She earned her law degree from Cornell Law School in 1985.

Robin is the author (or co-author) of many Nolo books, including *Money Troubles: Legal Strategies to Cope With Your Debts, How to File for Bankruptcy, Nolo's Pocket Guide to Family Law, Take Control of Your Student Loans* and *Credit Repair*.

Deanne Loonin (Your Money). Deanne works with Nolo on debt and credit issues. She is also a staff attorney with the National Consumer Law Center (NCLC) in Boston. Prior to joining Nolo and NCLC, she directed Bet Tzedek Legal Service's senior consumer fraud unit in Los Angeles. Deanne is the co-author of *Surviving Debt: A Guide for Consumers* (NCLC) and *Money Troubles* (Nolo).

Peter Lovenheim (Mediation). A 1979 graduate of Cornell Law School, Peter has been an active mediator since 1986 and is founder and president of a private dispute resolution service. He is the author of *Mediate, Don't Litigate* (McGraw-Hill), *Reading Between the Lines: New Stories From the Bible*, with co-editor David Katz (Jason Aronson), and *Mediate Your Dispute* (Nolo). Peter lives in Rochester, New York, with his wife and three children.

Anthony Mancuso (Nonprofit Corporations). Tony is a California attorney and the author of Nolo's best-selling corporate law series, including *How to Form Your Own Corporation* (California, Texas, New York and computer editions). He is also the author of Nolo's *Taking Care of Your Corporation* series and the book *How to Form a Nonprofit Corporation*. Tony is a jazz guitarist and a licensed helicopter pilot.

Beth McKenna (Criminal Law and Procedure, Changing Your Name). Beth received her law degree from Stanford Law

School. Before coming to Nolo, she worked as a public defender for five years, concentrating in appellate and habeas corpus law. She is Nolo's criminal law editor and is responsible for Nolo's best-selling *Quicken Lawyer Personal* software.

Kathleen Michon (Cars and Driving, Legal Research, Retirement Plans). Kathleen graduated cum laude from Northwestern University School of Law in 1993. Prior to joining Nolo's editorial staff, Kathleen was the Directing Attorney of Public Counsel's Consumer Rights Project. She is the editor of Nolo's debt and credit books, including *Credit Repair* and *Money Troubles*, and is a co-author of *How to File for Chapter 7 Bankruptcy*.

Shannon Miehe (Small Businesses, Dealing With the IRS). Shannon graduated from the University of Southern California Law School. She then spent several years representing small and mid-size entrepreneurial companies in connection with mergers, acquisitions and business formation issues. At Nolo, Shannon edits small business products, including *Legal Forms for Starting & Running a Small Business, The Partnership Book* and *How to Form Your Own California Corporation*.

Janet Portman (Landlords and Tenants). Janet received undergraduate and graduate degrees from Stanford University and a law degree from the University of Santa Clara. She was a public defender before coming to Nolo. Janet is Nolo's Publisher and the editor of several Nolo books, including *Legal Research: How to Find & Understand the Law* and *The Criminal Records Book*. She is the co-author of Nolo's *Every Landlord's Legal Guide, Every Tenant's Legal Guide* and *Renters' Rights*.

Mary Randolph (Deeds, Neighbors, Wills and Estate Planning). Mary has been editing and writing Nolo books and software for more than a decade. She earned her law degree from Boalt Hall School of Law at the University of California at Berkeley, and her undergraduate degree at the University of Illinois. She is the author of *Dog Law, The Deeds Book, 8 Ways to Avoid Probate* and other Nolo materials.

Barbara Kate Repa (Workplace Rights, Employers' Rights and Responsibilities, Funeral Planning and other Final Arrangements, Body and Organ Donations, Healthcare Directives, Older Americans, Traffic Accidents). Barbara Kate, a lawyer, has written several books for Nolo, including *Your Rights in the Workplace,* and *Sexual Harassment on the Job.*

Linda Robayo (Spouses and Partners, Parents and Children). Linda graduated from Boston College in 1989 and Seton Hall University School of Law in 1995. Linda practiced law with the Community Health Law Project and Ocean-Monmouth Legal Services in New Jersey for three years. She is currently a public relations executive for the Center for Reproductive Law and Policy in New York City. Linda has written articles for Nolo and has been published in national publications such as *Good Housekeeping* and *Mademoiselle.*

Spencer Sherman (Older Americans). Spencer has edited several Nolo books, including *Beat Your Ticket, Fight Your Ticket* (California Edition), *How to Get a Green Card* and *U.S. Immigration Made Easy.* A journalist for many years, he reported on legal issues in California and from the U.S. Supreme Court.

Marcia Stewart (Houses, Landlords and Tenants). Marcia is an expert on landlord-tenant law, buying and selling houses and other issues of interest to consumers. She is the co-author of Nolo's *Every Landlord's Legal Guide, Every Tenant's Legal Guide, Renters' Rights, Leases & Rental Agreements* and editor of Nolo's *LeaseWriter* software for landlords.

Richard Stim (Patents, Copyrights, Trademarks). Rich graduated from the University of San Francisco Law School in 1984 and worked in private practice for 16 years until joining Nolo as an editor in 2000. He is the author of *License Your Invention, Getting Permission, Music Law*, and is the co-author with David Pressman of *Nolo's Patents for Beginners.*

Ralph Warner (Courts and Mediation). Ralph is the co-founder and Publisher of Nolo. He is the author (or co-author) of a number of Nolo books, including *Every Landlord's Legal Guide, Everybody's Guide to Small Claims Court, The Partnership Book* and *Get a Life: You Don't Need a Million to Retire Well.* Ralph is a lawyer who became fed up with the legal system and as a result has dedicated his professional life to making law more accessible and affordable to all Americans.

Table of Contents

About This Book

Houses

1.2 *Buying a House*

1.9 *Selling Your House*

1.15 *Deeds*

Neighbors

2.2 *Boundaries*

2.3 *Fences*

2.4 *Trees*

2.6 *Views*

2.8 *Noise*

Landlords and Tenants

3.2 *Leases and Rental Agreements*

3.4 *Tenant Selection*

3.4 *Housing Discrimination*

3.6 *Rent and Security Deposits*

3.8 *Tenants' Privacy Rights*

3.9 *Repairs and Maintenance*

3.12 *Landlord Liability for Criminal Acts and Activities*

3.14 *Landlord Liability for Lead Poisoning*

3.15 *Landlord's Liability for Exposure to Asbestos and Mold*

3.16 *Insurance*

3.17 *Resolving Disputes*

Workplace Rights

4.2 *Fair Pay and Time Off*

4.9 *Workplace Health and Safety*

4.12 *Workers' Compensation*

4.17 *Age Discrimination*

4.21 *Sexual Harassment*

4.25 *Disability Discrimination*

4.29 *Losing or Leaving Your Job*

Small Businesses

5.2 *Before You Start*

5.8 *Legal Structures for Small Businesses*

5.15 *Nonprofit Corporations*

5.18 *Small Business Taxes*

5.24   *Home-Based Businesses*

5.29   *Employers' Rights & Responsibilities*

Patents

6.2   *Qualifying for a Patent*

6.7   *Obtaining a Patent*

6.9   *Enforcing a Patent*

6.12 *Putting a Patent to Work*

6.14 *How Patents Differ From Copyrights and Trademarks*

Copyrights

7.2   *Copyright Basics*

7.4   *Copyright Ownership*

7.6   *Copyright Protection*

7.10 *Copyright Registration and Enforcement*

Trademarks

8.2   *Types of Trademarks*

8.5   *Trademark Protection*

8.8   *Using and Enforcing a Trademark*

8.11 *Conducting a Trademark Search*

8.14 *Registering a Trademark*

8.18 *How Trademarks Differ From Patents and Copyrights*

Your Money

9.2   *Purchasing Goods and Services*

9.7   *Using Credit and Charge Cards*

9.11 *Using an ATM or Debit Card*

9.11 *Strategies for Repaying Debts*

9.18 *Dealing With the IRS*

9.22 *Debt Collections*

9.25 *Bankruptcy*

9.28 *Rebuilding Credit*

Cars and Driving

10.2 *Buying a New Car*

10.7 *Leasing a Car*

10.10 *Buying a Used Car*

10.12 *Financing a Vehicle Purchase*

10.13 *Insuring Your Car*

10.16 *Your Driver's License*

10.19 *If You're Stopped by the Police*

10.21 *Drunk Driving*

10.23 *Traffic Accidents*

11

Travel

11.2 *Airlines*

11.11 *Rental Cars*

11.16 *Hotels and Other Accommodations*

11.21 *Travel Agents*

11.25 *Travel Scams*

12

Wills and Estate Planning

12.2 *Wills*

12.8 *Probate*

12.9 *Executors*

12.13 *Avoiding Probate*

12.15 *Living Trusts*

12.18 *Estate and Gift Taxes*

12.22 *Funeral Planning and Other Final Arrangements*

12.25 *Body and Organ Donations*

13

Healthcare Directives and Powers of Attorney

13.2 *Healthcare Directives*

13.7 *Durable Powers of Attorney for Finances*

13.11 *Conservatorships*

14

Older Americans

14.2 *Social Security*

14.8 *Medicare*

14.12 *Pensions*

14.19 *Retirement Plans*

15

Spouses and Partners

15.2 *Living Together—Gay & Straight*

15.6 *Premarital Agreements*

15.8 *Marriage*

15.16 *Divorce*

15.26 *Domestic Violence*

15.29 *Changing Your Name*

16

Parents and Children

16.2	*Adopting a Child*
16.12	*Stepparent Adoptions*
16.14	*Adoption Rights: Birthparents, Grandparents and Children*
16.18	*Child Custody and Visitation*
16.25	*Child Support*
16.31	*Guardianship of Children*

17

Courts and Mediation

17.2	*Representing Yourself in Court*
17.13	*Small Claims Court*
17.21	*Mediation*
17.27	*Dealing With Your Lawyer*

18

Criminal Law and Procedure

18.2	*Criminal Law and Procedure: An Overview*
18.8	*If You Are Questioned by the Police*
18.10	*Searches and Seizures*
18.14	*Arrests and Interrogations*
18.17	*Bail*
18.20	*Getting a Lawyer*

Appendix: Legal Research

Glossary

About This Book

Whether we like it or not, the law touches our personal lives in many ways each day. We may not think much about the laws that affect us as we carry out simple tasks such as driving a car, making a telephone call or buying milk at the corner grocery store. But every now and again, we're sure to need an answer to a common legal question that arises in the course of daily life:

What can I do about my noisy neighbor?

WHAT ARE MY RIGHTS IF I'M FIRED FROM MY JOB?

Do I really need to make a will?

What should I do if I can't pay the child support I owe?

And so on.

This book provides answers to frequently asked questions about more than 100 subjects you might encounter in your personal life—topics that range from buying a house to getting a divorce, from paying your debts to starting and running a small business. Obviously, we can't answer every question on a particular subject, but we've answered many common ones to get you started. Throughout each chapter, you'll find resource boxes listing sources for more information about a particular subject.

In addition, for those of you who are computer savvy, each chapter contains a list of online sites that will help you learn more about a particular area of the law. Look for the "Online Help" icon as you read. And if you need more information about finding the law, The Legal Research Appendix contains a section that shows you how to do basic legal research—with a focus on searching the Internet.

Think of this book as a desk reference—a little encyclopedia that unpacks the law and puts it in your hands in a language you can understand. But remember that the law changes constantly as legislatures pass new laws and courts hand down their rulings. We will publish new, revised editions of this book periodically, but it will never be perfectly current. It's always your responsibility to be sure a law is up to date before you rely on it. Check the Legal Update Service on our website at http://www.nolo.com for the most current legal information affecting Nolo books & software.

Houses

1.2   *Buying a House*

1.9   *Selling Your House*

1.15 *Deeds*

Home is heaven for beginners.

—CHARLES H. PARKHURST

Buying or selling a house is a major undertaking. To do it right, you need to understand how houses are priced, financed and inspected; how to find and work with a real estate agent; how to protect your interests when negotiating a contract; and how legal transfer of ownership takes place. This chapter covers many of the basic issues that buyers, sellers and owners need to know.

Buying a House

Before you look for a house, it's essential to determine how much you can afford to pay and what your financing options are. You'll also need to decide whether you want to work with a real estate agent or broker, and finally, even if you think you've found your dream home, you'll need to master the ins and outs of house inspections. This section will help you find your way through the house-buying maze—and to your new front door.

I'm a first-time home buyer. Is there any easy way to determine how much house I can afford?

As a broad generalization, most people can afford to purchase a house worth about three times their total (gross) annual income, assuming a 20% down payment and a moderate amount of other long-term debts, such as car or student loan payments. With no other debts, you can probably afford a house worth up to four or even five times your annual income.

The most accurate way to determine whether you can afford a particular house is to total up the estimated monthly principal and interest payments plus one-twelfth of the yearly bill for property and homeowner's insurance. Now compare that to your gross monthly income. Lenders normally want you to make all monthly housing payments with 28%-38% of your monthly income—the percentage depends on the amount of your down payment, the interest rate on the type of mortgage you want, your credit history, the level of your long-term debts and other factors. A bank or other lender can help you determine how much house you can afford.

Or you can run the numbers yourself, using an online mortgage calculator such as those on the websites listed at the end of this chapter.

Once you've done the basic calculations, you can ask a lender or loan broker for a prequalification letter saying that loan approval for a specified amount is likely based on your income and credit history. Prequalifying lets you determine exactly how much you'll be able to borrow and how much you'll need for a down payment and closing costs.

Unless you're in a very slow market, with lots more sellers than buyers, you will want to do more than prequalify for a loan—you will want to be guaranteed for a specific loan amount. This means that the lender actually evaluates your financial situation, runs a credit check and preapproves you for a loan—rather than giving a general prequalification based on your own statement about your income and debts. Having lender preapproval for a loan makes you more attractive financially to sellers than simple loan prequalification and is crucial in competitive markets. Without it, you stand very little chance of your offer being accepted.

How important is my credit history in getting loan approval?

Your credit history has an important effect on the type and amount of loan lenders offer you. When reviewing loan applications and making financing decisions, lenders typically request your credit risk score from the credit bureaus. This score is a statistical summary of the information in your credit report and includes:

- your history of paying bills on time
- the level of your outstanding debts
- how long you've had credit
- your credit limit
- the number of inquiries for your credit report (too many can lower your score), and
- the types of credit you have.

The higher your credit score, the easier it will be to get a loan. If you routinely pay your bills late, you can expect a lower score, in which case a lender may either reject your loan application altogether or insist on a very large down payment or high interest rate to lower the lender's risk.

To avoid problems, always check your credit report and clean up your file if necessary—before, not after, you apply for a mortgage. For information on how to order your credit report, what to do if you find mistakes in your report and how to rebuild good credit, see *Rebuilding Credit* in Chapter 9, *Your Money*.

How can I find the best home loan or mortgage?

Many entities, including banks, credit unions, savings and loans, insurance companies and mortgage bankers make home loans. Lenders and terms change frequently as new companies appear, old ones merge and market conditions fluctuate. To get the best deal, compare loans and fees with at least a half-dozen lenders. Fortunately, mortgage rates and fees are usually published in the real estate sections of metropolitan newspapers and are widely available on the Internet.

Because many types of home loans are standardized to comply with rules established by the Federal National Mortgage Association (Fannie Mae) and other quasi-governmental corporations that purchase loans from lenders, comparison shopping is not difficult, especially if you go online.

Mortgage rate websites come in two basic flavors: those sites that don't offer loans (called "no-loan" sites) and those that do. No-loan sites don't broker or lend mortgage money, but are a great place to examine mortgage programs, learn mortgage lingo, understand underwriting, get questions answered about the loan qualification process, crunch numbers with online mortgage calculators and check your credit.

Many online mortgage sites also offer direct access to loans from one or more lenders. With multi-lender shopping sites, you simply enter the loan amount, property details and other information and you'll get current rates, APR, points, even settlement costs for each loan from dozens of lenders. If you choose to complete an application, mortgage shopping sites review your application, process the required documentation and ship your loan to the lender for further review and underwriting.

See the list of recommended websites at the end of this chapter for more information on mortgage websites.

If you don't want to shop for mortgages on your own, you can also work with a loan broker, someone who specializes in matching house buyers with an appropriate mortgage lender. Loan brokers usually collect their fee from the lender.

What are my other options for home loans?

You may also be eligible for a government-guaranteed loan, offered by:

- the Federal Housing Administration (FHA), an agency of the Department of Housing and Urban Development (HUD) (see http://www.hud.gov/mortprog.html)
- the U.S. Department of Veterans Affairs (see http://www.homeloans.va.gov), or
- a state or local housing agency.

Government loans usually have low down payment requirements and sometimes offer better-than-market interest rates as well.

Also, ask banks and other private lenders about any "first-time buyer programs" that offer low down payment plans and flexible qualifying guidelines to low and moderate income buyers with good credit.

Finally, don't forget private sources of mortgage money—parents, other relatives, friends or even the seller of the house you want to buy. Borrowing money privately is usually the most cost-efficient mortgage of all.

What's the difference between a fixed and an adjustable rate mortgage?

With a fixed rate mortgage, the interest rate and the amount you pay each month remain the same over the entire mortgage term, traditionally 15, 20 or 30 years. A number of variables are available, including five- and seven-year fixed rate loans with balloon payments at the end.

With an adjustable rate mortgage (ARM), the interest rate fluctuates as the interest rates in the economy fluctuate. Initial interest rates of ARMs are usually offered at a discounted ("teaser") rate which is lower than those for fixed rate mortgages. Over time, however, initial discounts are filtered out and ARM rates fluctuate as general interest rates go up or down. To avoid constant and drastic changes, ARMs typically regulate (cap) how much and how often the interest rate and/or payments can change in a year and over the life of the loan. A number of variations are available for adjustable rate mortgages, including hybrids that change from a fixed to an adjustable rate after a period of years.

A good loan officer or loan broker will walk you through all mortgage options and tradeoffs such as higher fees (or points) for a lower interest rate.

How do I decide whether to choose a fixed or an adjustable rate mortgage?

Because interest rates and mortgage options change often, your choice of a fixed or an adjustable rate mortgage should depend on the interest rates and mortgage options available when you're buying, how much you can afford in the short term, your view of the future (generally, high inflation will mean that ARM rates will go up and lower inflation means that they will fall), and how willing you are to take a risk. Very risk-averse people usually prefer the certainty of a fixed rate mortgage, rather than take a chance that an ARM might be cheaper in the long run. However, some people can't afford the relatively higher interest rates at which fixed rate mortgages usually begin.

Keep in mind that lenders not only lend money to purchase homes; they also lend money to refinance homes. If you take out a loan now, and several years from now interest rates have dropped, refinancing may be an option.

What's the best way to find and work with a real estate agent or broker?

Get recommendations from people who have purchased a house in the past few years and whose judgment you trust. Don't work with an agent you meet at an open house or find in the Yellow Pages or on the Internet unless and until you call references and thoroughly check the person out. The agent or broker you choose should be in the full-time business of selling real estate and should have the following five traits: integrity, business sophistication, experience with the type of services you need, knowledge of the area where you want to live and sensitivity to your tastes and needs.

All states regulate and license real estate agents and brokers. You may have different options as to the type of legal relationship you have with an agent or broker; typically, the seller pays the commission of the real estate salesperson who helps the buyer locate the seller's house. The commission is a percentage (usually 5% to 7%) of the sales price of the house. What this means is that your agent or broker has a built-in conflict of interest: Unless you've agreed to pay her separately, she won't get paid until you buy a home, and the more you pay for a house, the bigger her cut.

In short, when you evaluate the suitability of a house, it's not wise to rely principally on the advice of a person with a significant financial stake in your buying it. You need to be knowledgeable about the house-buying process, your ideal affordable house and neighborhood, your financing needs and options, your legal rights and how to evaluate comparable prices.

What's the best way to get information on homes for sale and details about the neighborhood?

Thanks to the Internet, you no longer have to rely solely on a real estate agent for information about homes for sale. You can scan online listings to see which homes are worth a visit, how much they cost and what amenities they offer. Virtual visits to new homes often include floor plans and photographs.

Once you identify a house you like, you can email the address or identification number to your agent, the listing agent or the owner (if it's a listing by a FSBO—For Sale By Owner) to obtain additional information or to set up an appointment to see the home in person.

The list of websites at the end of this chapter has some of the major national real estate listing sites. Your state or regional realty association or multiple listing service (MLS) may also have a website listing homes for sale. Major real estate companies, including ERA, RE/MAX, Coldwell Banker, Prudential and others often offer lists on their websites.

Finally, virtually all online editions of newspapers offer a homes-for-sale classifieds section that works much like an online listing site. On most newspaper sites, you can browse all the listings, or customize your search by typing in your criteria, such as price range, location and number of bedrooms and baths. Some of the best sites also include useful information on mortgage rates, schools and other community resources, financial calculators, links to sales data on comparable houses, home inspection services, real estate agents and other information of interest to local buyers. Check the Newspaper Association of America (http://www.naa.org) for a link to your newspaper. (Click on "Newspaper Links.")

Advice on relocation decisions and details about your new community and its services are also readily available online. For valuable information about cities, communities and neighborhoods, including schools, housing costs, demographics, crime rates and jobs, see the websites listed at the end of this chapter. Finally, keep in mind that the Internet is no substitute for your own legwork. Ask your friends and colleagues, walk and drive around neighborhoods, talk to local residents, read local newspapers, visit the local library and planning department and do whatever it takes to help you get a better sense of a neighborhood or city.

My spouse and I want to buy a $350,000 house. We have good incomes and can make high monthly payments, but we don't have $70,000 to make a 20% down payment. Are there other options?

Assuming you can afford (and qualify for) high monthly mortgage payments and have an excellent credit history, you should be able to find a low (10% to 15%) down payment loan for a $350,000 house. However, you may have to pay a higher interest rate and loan fees (points) than someone making a higher down payment. In addition, a buyer who puts less than 20% down should be prepared to purchase private mortgage insurance (PMI), which is designed to reimburse a mortgage lender up to a certain amount if a buyer defaults and the foreclosure sale price is less than the amount owed the lender (the mortgage plus the costs of the foreclosure sale).

PMI premiums are usually paid monthly and typically cost less than one-half of one percent of the mortgage loan. With the exception of some government and older loans, you can drop PMI once your equity in the house reaches 22% and you've made timely mortgage payments.

I want to buy a newly built house. Is there anything special I need to know?

The most important factor in buying a newly built house is not what you buy (that is, the particular model), but rather from whom you buy. New is not always better, especially if the house is slapped together in a hurry. Shop for an excellent builder—someone who builds quality houses, delivers on time and stands behind his or her work. To check out a particular builder, talk to existing owners in the development you're considering, or ask an experienced contractor to look at other houses the developer is building.

Many developers of new housing will help you arrange financing; some will also pay a portion of your monthly mortgage or subsidize your interest payments for a short period of time (called a "buydown" of the mortgage). As with any loan, be sure you comparison shop before arranging financing through a builder.

Also, be sure to negotiate the prices of any add-ons and upgrades, such as a spa or higher quality carpet. These can add substantially to the cost of a new home.

Is there anything else I need to know before buying a home in a development run by a homeowners' association?

When you buy a home in a new subdivision or planned unit development, chances are good that you also automatically become a member of an exclusive club—the homeowners' association, whose members are the people who own homes in the same development. The homeowners' association will probably exercise a lot of control over how you use and what you do to your property.

Deeds to houses in new developments almost always include restrictions—from the colors you can paint your house to the type of front yard landscaping you can do to where (and what types of vehicles) you can park in your driveway. Usually, these restrictions, called covenants, conditions and restrictions (CC&Rs), put decision-making rights in the hands of a homeowners' association. Before buying, study the CC&Rs carefully to see if they're compatible with your lifestyle. If you don't understand something, ask for more information and seek legal advice if necessary.

Usually, getting relief from overly restrictive CC&Rs after you move in isn't easy. You'll likely have to submit an application (with fee) for a variance, get your neighbors' permission and possibly go through a formal hearing. And if you want to make a structural change, such as building a fence or adding a room, you'll probably need formal permission from the association in addition to complying with city zoning rules.

How can I make sure that the house I'm buying is in good shape?

In some states, you may have the advantage of a law that requires sellers to disclose considerable information about the condition of the house. (See *Selling Your House*, below.) Regardless of whether the seller provides disclosures, however, you should have the property inspected for defects or malfunctions in the building's structure.

Start by conducting your own inspection. There are several useful do-it-yourself inspection books available to help you learn what to look for. Ideally, you should inspect a house before you make a formal written offer to buy it so that you can save yourself the trouble should you find serious problems.

If a house passes your inspection, hire a general contractor to check all major house systems from top to bottom, including the roof, plumbing, electrical and heating systems and drainage. This will take two or three hours and cost you anywhere from $200 to $500 depending on the location, size, age and type of home. You should accompany the inspector during the examination so that you can learn more about the maintenance and preservation of the house and get answers to any questions you may have, including which problems are important and which are relatively minor. Depending on the property, you may want to arrange specialized inspections for pest damage, hazards from floods, earthquakes and other natural disasters and environmental health hazards such as asbestos, mold and lead.

Professional inspections should be done after your written purchase offer has been accepted by the seller. (Your offer should be contingent upon the house passing one or more inspections.) To avoid confusion and disputes, be sure you get a written report of each inspection.

If the house is in good shape, you can proceed, knowing that you're getting what you paid for. If an inspector discovers problems—such as an antiquated plumbing system or a major termite infestation—you can negotiate with the seller to have him pay for necessary repairs and provide a home warranty (see *Selling Your House*, below). Finally, you can back out of the deal if an inspection turns up problems, assuming your contract is properly written to allow you to do so.

I'm making an offer to buy a house, but I don't want to lock myself into a deal that might not work out. How can I protect myself?

Real estate offers almost always contain contingencies—events that must happen within a certain amount of time (such as 30 days) in order to finalize the deal. For example, you may want to make your offer contingent on your ability to qualify for financing, the house passing certain physical inspections or even your ability to sell your existing house first. Be aware, however, that the more contingencies you place in an offer, the less likely the seller is to accept it. See *Selling Your House*, below, for more on real estate offers.

Strategies for Buying an Affordable House

To find a good house at a comparatively reasonable price, you must learn about the housing market and what you can afford, make some sensible compromises as to size and amenities and, above all, be patient. Here are some proven strategies to meet these goals:

Buy a fixer-upper cheap.

Buy a small house (with remodeling potential) and add on later.

Buy a house at an estate or probate sale.

Buy a house subject to foreclosure (when a homeowner defaults on his mortgage).

Buy a shared-equity house, pooling resources with someone other than a spouse or partner.

Rent out a room or two in the house.

Buy a duplex, triplex or house with an in-law unit.

Lease a house you can't afford now with an option to buy later.

Buy a limited-equity house built by a nonprofit organization.

Buy a house at an auction.

More Information About Buying a Home

100 Questions Every First-Time Home Buyer Should Ask, by Ilyce R. Glink (Times Books), is a substantial book designed to help first-time buyers through the maze of buying a house.

Your New House: The Alert Consumer's Guide to Buying and Building a Quality Home, by Alan & Denise Fields (Windsor Peak Press), offers valuable advice for those who want to buy or build a new home.

Inspecting a House, by Rex Cauldwell (Taunton Press), shows how to inspect a house in order to discover major problems such as a bad foundation, leaky roof or malfunctioning fireplace.

How to Buy a House in California, by Ralph Warner, Ira Serkes and George Devine (Nolo), explains all the details of the California house-buying process and contains tear-out contracts and disclosure forms.

Selling Your House

If you're selling a home, you need to time the sale properly, price the home accurately and understand the laws, such as disclosure requirements, that cover house transactions. These questions and answers will get you started.

I'm trying to decide whether to put my house on the market or wait a while. What are the best and worst times to sell?

Too many people rush to sell their houses and lose money because of it. Ideally, you should put your house on the market when there's a large pool of buyers—causing prices to go up. This may occur in the following situations:

- Your area is considered especially attractive—for example, because of the schools, low crime rate, employment opportunities, weather or proximity to a major city.
- Mortgage interest rates are low.
- The economic climate of your region is healthy and people feel confident about the future.
- There's a jump in house buying activity, as often occurs in spring.

Of course, if you have to sell immediately—because of financial reasons, a divorce, a job move or an imperative health concern—and you don't have any of the advantages listed above, you may have to settle for a lower price, or help the buyer with financing, in order to make a quick sale.

I want to save on the real estate commission. Can I sell my house myself without a real estate broker or agent?

Usually, yes. This is called a FSBO (pronounced "fizzbo")—For Sale By Owner. You must be aware, however, of the legal rules that govern real estate transfers in your state, such as who must sign the papers, who can conduct the actual transaction and what to do if and when any problems arise that slow down the transfer of ownership. You also need to be aware of any state-mandated disclosures as to the physical condition of your house. (See the discussion below.)

If you want to go it alone, be sure you have the time, energy and ability to handle all the details—from setting a realistic price to negotiating offers and closing the deal. Also, be aware that FSBOs are usually more feasible in hot or sellers' markets where there's more competition for homes, or when you're not in a hurry to sell. For more advice on FSBOs, including the involvement of attorneys and other professionals in the house transaction, contact your state department of real estate. Also, check online at http://www.owners.com for useful advice on selling a home without an agent.

If you're in California, check out *For Sale by Owner* by George Devine (Nolo). This book provides step-by-step advice on handling your own sale in California, from putting the house on the market to negotiating offers to transferring title.

Is there some middle ground where I can use a broker on a more limited (and less expensive) basis?

You might consider doing most of the work yourself—such as showing the house—and using a real estate broker's help with such crucial tasks as:

- setting the price of your house
- advertising your home in the local multiple listing service (MLS) of

homes for sale in the area, published by local boards of realtors, and

• handling some of the more complicated paperwork when the sale closes.

If you work with a broker in a limited way, you may be able to negotiate a reduction of the typical 5%-7% broker's commission, or you may be able to find a real estate agent who charges by the hour for specified services such as reviewing the sales contract.

How much should I ask for my house?

The key is to determine how much your property is actually worth on the market—called "appraising" a house's value. The most important factors used to determine a house's value are recent sales prices of similar properties in the neighborhood (called "comps").

Real estate agents have access to sales data for the area ("comp books") and can give you a good estimate of what your house should sell for. Many real estate agents will offer this service free, hoping that you will list your house with them. You can also hire a professional real estate appraiser to give you a documented opinion as to your house's value. Public record offices, such as the county clerk or recorder's office, may also have information on recent house sales. A few private companies offer detailed comparable sales prices online for many areas of the country, based on information from County Recorder's Offices and property assessors. See the list of recommended websites at the end of this chapter.

Finally, asking prices of houses still on the market can also provide guidance (adjusting for the fact that asking prices are typically 10% or more above the usual sales price). To find out asking prices, go to open houses and check newspaper real estate classified ads and online listings of homes for sale.

Preparing Your House for Sale

Making your house look as attractive as possible may put several thousand dollars in your pocket. Sweep the sidewalk; mow the lawn; put some pots of blooming flowers by the front door; clean the windows; fix chipped or flaking paint. Clean and tidy up all rooms; be sure the house smells good—hide the kitty litter box and bake some cookies. Check for loose steps, slick areas or unsafe fixtures, and deal with everything that might cause injury to a prospective buyer. Take care of real eyesores, such as a cracked window or overgrown front yard. Don't overlook small but obvious problems, such as a leaking faucet or loose doorknob. Find ways to improve the look of your house without spending much money—a new shower curtain and towels might really spruce up your bathroom.

Do I need to take the first offer that comes in?

Offers, even very attractive ones, are rarely accepted as written. More typically, you will respond with a written counteroffer accepting some, maybe even most, of the offer terms, but proposing certain changes. Most counteroffers correspond to these provisions of an offer:

- price—you want more money
- financing—you want a larger down payment
- occupancy—you need more time to move out
- buyer's sale of current house—you don't want to wait for this to occur
- inspections—you want the buyer to schedule them more quickly.

A contract is formed when either you or the buyer accept all of the terms of the other's offer or counteroffer in writing within the time allowed.

What are my obligations to disclose problems about my house, such as a basement that floods in heavy rains?

In most states, it is illegal to fraudulently conceal major physical defects in your property, such as your troublesome basement. And states are increasingly requiring sellers to take a pro-active role by making written disclosures on the condition of the property. California, for example, has stringent disclosure requirements.

California sellers must give buyers a mandatory disclosure form listing such defects as a leaky roof, faulty plumbing, deaths that occurred within the last three years on the property, even the presence of neighborhood nuisances, such as a dog that barks every night. In addition, California sellers must disclose potential hazards from floods, earthquakes, fires, environmental hazards and other problems in a Natural Hazard Disclosure Statement. California sellers must also alert buyers to the availability of a database maintained by law enforcement authorities on the location of registered sex offenders.

Generally, you are responsible for disclosing only information within your personal knowledge. While it's not usually required, many sellers hire a general contractor to inspect the property. The information will help you determine which items need repair or replacement and will assist you in preparing any required disclosures. An inspection report is also useful in pricing your house and negotiating with prospective buyers.

Full disclosure of any property defects will also help protect you from legal problems from a buyer who seeks to rescind the sale or sues you for damages suffered because you carelessly or intentionally withheld important information about your property.

Check with your real estate broker or attorney, or your state department of real estate, for disclosures required in your state and any special forms you must use. Also, be aware that real estate brokers are increasingly requiring that sellers complete disclosure forms, regardless of whether it's legally required.

Sellers Must Disclose Lead-Based Paint and Hazards

If you are selling a house built before 1978, you must comply with the federal Residential Lead-Based Paint Hazard Reduction Act of 1992 (42 U.S.Code § 4852d), also known as Title X (Ten). You must:

- disclose all known lead-based paint and hazards in the house
- give buyers a pamphlet prepared by the U.S. Environmental Protection Agency (EPA) called *Protect Your Family From Lead in Your Home*
- include certain warning language in the contract, as well as signed statements from all parties verifying that all disclosures (including giving the pamphlet) were made
- keep signed acknowledgments for three years as proof of compliance, and
- give buyers a ten-day opportunity to test the housing for lead.

If you fail to comply with Title X, the buyer can sue you for triple the amount of damages suffered—for example, three times the cost of repainting a house previously painted with lead-based paint.

For more information, contact the National Lead Information Center, 800-424-LEAD (phone) or http://www.epa.gov/lead/nlic.htm.

What are home warranties, and should I buy one?

Home warranties are service contracts that cover major housing systems—electrical wiring, built-in appliances, heating, plumbing and the like—for one year from the date the house is sold. Most warranties cost $300-$500 and are renewable. If something goes wrong with any of the covered systems after escrow closes, the repairs are paid for (minus a modest service fee)—and the new buyer saves money. Many sellers find that home warranties make their house more attractive and easier to sell.

Before buying a home warranty, be sure you don't duplicate coverage. You don't need a warranty for the heating system, for example, if your furnace is just six months old and still covered by the manufacturer's three-year warranty.

Your real estate agent or broker can provide more information on home warranties.

What is the "house closing"?

The house closing is the final transfer of the ownership of the house from the seller to the buyer. It occurs after both you and the buyer have met all the terms of the contract and the deed is recorded. (See *Deeds*, below). Closing also refers to the time when the transfer will occur, such as "The closing on my house will happen on January 27 at 10:00 a.m."

Do I need an attorney for the house closing?

This varies depending on state law and local custom. In some states, attorneys are not typically involved in residential property sales, and an escrow or title company handles the entire closing process. In many other states, particularly in the eastern part of the country, attorneys (for both buyer and seller) have a more active role in all parts of the house transaction; they handle all the details of offer contracts and house closings. Check with your state department of real estate or your real estate broker for advice.

I'm selling my house and buying another. What are some of the most important tax considerations?

The 1997 Taxpayer Relief Act contained a big break for homeowners. If you sell your home, you may exclude up to $250,000 of your profit (capital gain) from tax. For married couples filing jointly, the exclusion is $500,000.

The law applies to sales after May 6, 1997. To claim the whole exclusion, you must have owned and lived in your residence an aggregate of at least two of five years before the sale. You can claim the exclusion once every two years.

Even if you haven't lived in your home a total of two years out of the last five, you are still eligible for a partial exclusion of capital gains if you sold because of a change in employment, health or unforeseen circumstances. You get a portion of the exclusion, based on the percentage of the two-year period you lived in the house. To calculate it, take the number of months you lived there before the sale and divide it by 24.

For example, if you're an unmarried taxpayer who's lived in your home for 12 months, and you sell it for a $100,000 profit, the entire amount would be excluded from capital gains. Because you lived in the house for half of the two-year period, you could claim half the exclusion, or $125,000. (12/24 x $250,000 = $125,000.) That's enough to exclude your entire $100,000 gain.

For more information on current tax laws involving real estate transactions, contact the IRS at 800-829-1040 or check their website at http://www.irs.gov. Ask for Publication 523, *Selling Your Home*, and the general instructions for Form 2119, *Sale of Your Home*. If you're claiming the exclusion, you must file Form 2119 with your tax return.

Deeds

Castles in the air are the only property you can own without the intervention of lawyers. Unfortunately, there are no title deeds to them.

—J. FEIDOR REES

Remember playing Monopoly as a kid, where amassing deeds to property—those little color-coded cards—was all-important? Real-life deeds aren't nearly so colorful, but they're still very, very important. Here are some questions commonly asked about deeds.

What is a deed?

A deed is the document that transfers ownership of real estate. It contains the names of the old and new owners and a legal description of the property, and is signed by the person transferring the property.

Do I need a deed to transfer property?

Almost always. You can't transfer real estate without having something in writing. In some situations, a document other than a deed is used—for example, in a divorce, a court order may transfer real estate from the couple to just one of them.

I'm confused by all the different kinds of deeds—quitclaim deed, grant deed, warranty deed. Does it matter which kind of deed I use?

Probably not. Usually, what's most important is the substance of the deed: the description of the property being transferred and the names of the old and new owners. Here's a brief rundown of the most common types of deeds:

A *quitclaim* deed transfers whatever ownership interest you have in the property. It makes no guarantees about the extent of your interest. Quitclaim deeds are commonly used by divorcing couples; one spouse signs over all his rights in the couple's real estate to the other. This can be especially useful if it isn't clear how much of an interest, if any, one spouse has in property that's held in another spouse's name.

A *grant deed* transfers your ownership and implies certain promises—that the title hasn't already been transferred to someone else or been encumbered, except as set out in the deed. This is the most commonly used kind of deed, in most states.

A *warranty deed* transfers your ownership and explicitly promises the buyer that you have good title to the property. It may make other promises as well, to address particular problems with the transaction.

Does a deed have to be notarized?

Yes. The person who signs the deed (the person who is transferring the property) should take the deed to a notary public, who will sign and stamp it. The notarization means that a notary public has verified that the signature on the deed is genuine. The signature must be notarized before the deed will be accepted for recording (see the next question).

After a deed is signed and notarized, do I have to put it on file anywhere?

Yes. You should "record" (file) the deed in the land records office in the county where the property is located. This office goes by different names in different states; it's usually called the County Recorder's Office, Land Registry Office or Register of Deeds. In most counties, you'll find it in the courthouse.

Recording a deed is simple. Just take the signed, original deed to the land records office. The clerk will take the deed, stamp it with the date and some numbers, make a copy and give the original back to you. The numbers are usually book and page numbers, which show where the deed will be found in the county's filing system. There will be a small fee, probably about $5 a page, for recording.

What's a trust deed?

A trust deed (also called a deed of trust) isn't like the other types of deeds; it's not used to transfer property. It's really just a version of a mortgage, commonly used in some states.

A trust deed transfers title to land to a "trustee," usually a trust or title company, which holds the land as security for a loan. When the loan is paid off, title is transferred to the borrower. The trustee has no powers unless the borrower defaults on the loan; then the trustee can sell the property and pay the lender back from the proceeds, without first going to court.

More Information About Deeds

Deeds for California Real Estate, by Mary Randolph (Nolo), contains tear-out deed forms and instructions for transferring California real estate. For information about deeds in other states, check your local law library.

http://www.nolo.com

Nolo offers self-help information on a wide variety of legal topics, including real estate matters. The website also has several real estate calculators, including a Home Affordability calculator.

http://www.homefair.com/home

Homefair offers lots of information and calculators that will help you move and make relocation decisions. It's especially useful if you're deciding where to live based on home prices, schools, crime, salaries and other factors.

http://www.homeadvisor.com

Microsoft's Home Advisor helps with all aspects of buying or selling a home—from listings and financing to home improvements.

http://www.ashi.com

The American Society of Home Inspectors offers information on buying a home in good shape, including referrals to local home inspectors.

http://www.inman.com

Real estate columnist Brad Inman provides the latest real estate news. Also, see http://deadlinenews.com by real estate writer Brouderick Perkins.

http://www.realtylocator.com

Realty Locator provides over 100,000 real estate links nationwide, including property listings, agents, lenders, neighborhood data, real estate news and resources on everything from home improvement to mortgage calculators.

http://www.homepath.com

Fannie Mae, the nation's largest source of home mortgage loans, offers several useful home affordability mortgage calculators. It also provides a wide range of consumer information.

http://www.iOwn.com

iOwn allows you to compare rates from various lenders, prequalify and apply for a home loan. It includes detailed advice on choosing the best type of mortgage, determining how much house you can afford, selecting a real estate broker and evaluating the value of a house. Similar online mortgage sites are available at http://www.e-loan.com and http://www.homeadvisor.com.

http://www.hsh.com

HSH Associates publishes detailed information on mortgage loans available from lenders across the U.S.

http://www.realtor.com

The official website of the National Association of Realtors lists over one and a half million homes for sale throughout the United States and provides links to real estate broker websites and a host of related realty services.

http://www.homebuilder.com

The National Association of Homebuilders' website lists new homes and developments in major metropolitan areas.

http://www.owners.com

This site lists homes sold without a broker, also known as FSBOs (for sale by owner). It also provides useful information for anyone considering selling their home without a real estate agent.

http://www.homegain.com

HomeGain is geared toward home sellers. It provides an Agent Evaluator service to help you find a real estate agent, a Home Valuation tool to help price your home, calculators for a wide variety of tasks and other resources.

http://www.dataquick.com/consumer

For a modest fee, Dataquick.com (click on the "Neighborhood Report Center") provides details on houses—including purchase price, sales date, address, number of bedrooms and baths, square footage and property tax information.

Neighbors

2.2   *Boundaries*

2.3   *Fences*

2.4   *Trees*

2.6   *Views*

2.8   *Noise*

People have discovered that they can fool the devil, but they can't fool the neighbors.

—EDGAR WATSON HOWE

Years ago, problems between neighbors were resolved informally, perhaps with the help of a third person respected by both sides. These days, neighbors—who may not know each other well, if at all—are quicker to head for court. Usually, of course, lawsuits only exacerbate bad feelings and cost everyone money, and the courthouse should be the place of last, not first, resort. But knowing the legal ground rules is important; you may prevent small disputes from turning into big ones.

Boundaries

Most of us don't know, or care, exactly where our property boundaries are located. But if you or your neighbor wants to fence the property, build a structure or cut down a tree close to the line, you need to know where it actually runs.

How can I find the exact boundaries of my property?

You can hire a licensed land surveyor to survey the property and place official markers on the boundary lines. A simple survey usually costs about $500; if no survey has been done for a long time, or if the maps are unreliable and conflicting, be prepared to spend up to $1,000.

My neighbor and I don't want to pay a surveyor. Can't we just make an agreement about where we want the boundary to be?

You and the neighbor can decide where you want the line to be, and then make it so by signing deeds that describe the boundary. If you have a mortgage on the property, consult an attorney for help in drawing up the deeds. You may need to get the permission of the mortgage holder before you give your neighbor even a tiny piece of the land.

Once you have signed a deed, you should record (file) it at the county land records office, usually called the County Recorder's Office, Land Registry Office or something similar.

Deeds are discussed in more detail in Chapter 1.

What can I do if a neighbor starts using my property?

If a neighbor starts to build on what you think is your property, do something immediately. If the encroachment is minor—for instance, a small fence in the wrong place—you may think you shouldn't worry. But you're wrong. When you try to sell your house, a title company might refuse to issue insurance because the neighbor is on your land.

Also, if you don't act promptly, you could lose part of your property. When one person uses another's land for a long enough time, he can gain a legal right to continue to do so and, in some circumstances, gain ownership of the property.

Talk to your neighbor right away. Most likely, a mistake has been made because of a conflicting description in the neighbor's deed or just a mistaken assumption about the boundary line. If your neighbor is hostile and insists on proceeding, state that you will sue if necessary. Then send a firm letter—or have a lawyer send one on his or her letterhead. If the building doesn't stop, waste no time in having a lawyer get a judge's order to temporarily stop the neighbor until you can bring a civil lawsuit for trespass before the judge.

A Little Common Sense

If you are having no trouble with your property and your neighbors, yet you feel inclined to rush out to determine your exact boundaries just to know where they are, please ask yourself a question. Have you been satisfied with the amount of space that you occupy? If the answer is yes, then consider the time, money and hostility that might be involved if you pursue the subject.

If a problem exists on your border, keep the lines of communication open with the neighbor, if possible. Learn the law and try to work out an agreement. Boundary lines simply don't matter that much to us most of the time; relationships with our neighbors matter a great deal.

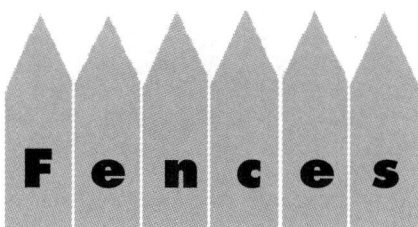

Local fence ordinances are usually strict and detailed. Most regulate height and location, and some control the material used and even appearance. Residents of planned unit developments and subdivisions are often subject to even pickier rules. On top of all this, many cities require you to obtain a building permit before you begin construction.

Fence regulations apply to any structure used as an enclosure or a partition. Usually, they include hedges and trees.

How high can I build a fence on my property?

In residential areas, local rules commonly restrict artificial (constructed) backyard fences to a height of six feet. In front yards, the limit is often four feet.

Height restrictions may also apply to natural fences—fences of bushes or trees—if they meet the ordinance's general definition of fences. Trees that are planted in a row and grow together to form a barrier are usually considered a fence. When natural fences are specifically mentioned in the laws, the height restrictions commonly range from five to eight feet.

If, however, you have a good reason (for example, you need to screen your house from a noisy or unsightly neighboring use, such as a gas station), you can ask the city for a one-time exception to the fence law, called a variance. Talk to the neighbors before you make your request, to explain your problem and get them on your side.

My neighbor is building a fence that violates the local fence law, but nothing's happening. How can I get the law enforced?

Cities are not in the business of sending around fence inspection teams, and as long as no one complains, a nonconforming fence may stand forever.

Tell the neighbor about the law as soon as possible. She probably doesn't know what the law is, and if the fence is still being built, may be able to modify it at a low cost. If she suggests that you mind your own business, alert the city. All it takes in most circumstances is a phone call to the planning or zoning department or the city attorney's office. The neighbor will be ordered to conform; if she doesn't, the city can fine her and even sue.

My neighbor's fence is hideous. Can I do anything about it?

As long as a fence doesn't pose a threat of harm to neighbors or those passing by, it probably doesn't violate any law just because it's ugly. Occasionally, however, a town or subdivision allows only certain types of new fences—such as board fences—in an attempt to create a harmonious architectural look. Some towns also prohibit certain materials—for example, electrically charged or barbed wire fences.

Even without such a specific law, if a fence is so poorly constructed that it is an eyesore or a danger, it may be prohibited by another law, such as a blighted property ordinance. And if the fence was erected just for meanness—it's high, ugly and has no reasonable use to the owner—it may be a "spite fence," and you can sue the neighbor to get it torn down.

The fence on the line between my land and my neighbor's is in bad shape. Can I fix it or tear it down?

Unless the property owners agree otherwise, fences on a boundary line belong to both owners when both are using the fence. Both owners are responsible for keeping the fence in good repair, and neither may remove it without the other's permission.

A few states have harsh penalties for refusing to chip in for maintenance after a reasonable request from the other owner. Connecticut, for example, allows one neighbor to go ahead and repair, and then sue the other owner for double the cost.

Of course, it's rare that a landowner needs to resort to a lawsuit. Your first step should be to talk to the neighbor about how to tackle the problem. Your neighbor will probably be delighted that you're taking the initiative to fix a fence that's already an eyesore and might deteriorate into a real danger.

Trees

WOODMAN, SPARE THAT TREE.

TOUCH NOT A SINGLE BOUGH:

IN YOUTH IT SHELTERED ME,

AND I'LL PROTECT IT NOW.

—GEORGE POPE MORRIS

We human beings exhibit some complicated, often conflicting, emotions over our trees. This is especially true when it comes to the trees in our own yards. We take ownership of our trees and their protection very seriously in this country, and this is reflected in the law.

Can I trim the branches of the neighbor's tree that hang over my yard?

You have the legal right to trim tree branches up to the property line. But you may not go onto the neighbor's property or destroy the tree itself.

Deliberately Harming a Tree

In almost every state, a person who intentionally injures someone else's tree is liable to the owner for two or three times the amount of actual monetary loss. These penalties protect tree owners by providing harsh deterrents to would-be loggers.

Most of a big oak tree hangs over my yard, but the trunk is on the neighbor's property. Who owns the tree?

Your neighbor. It is accepted law in all states that a tree whose trunk stands wholly on the land of one person belongs to that person.

If the trunk stands partly on the land of two or more people, it is called a boundary tree, and in most cases it belongs to all the property owners. All the owners are responsible for caring for the tree, and one co-owner may not remove a healthy tree without the other owners' permission.

My neighbor dug up his yard, and in the process killed a tree that's just on my side of the property line. Am I entitled to compensation for the tree?

Yes. The basic rule is that someone who cuts down, removes or hurts a tree without permission owes the tree's owner money to compensate for the harm done. You can sue to enforce that right—but you probably won't have to, once you tell your neighbor what the law is.

My neighbor's tree looks like it's going to fall on my house any day now. What should I do?

You can trim back branches to your property line, but that may not solve the problem if you're worried about the whole tree coming down.

City governments often step in to take care of, or make the owner take care of, dangerous trees. Some cities have ordinances that prohibit maintaining any dangerous condition—including a hazardous tree—on private property. To enforce such an ordinance, the city can demand that the owner remove the tree or pay a fine. Some cities will even remove such a tree for the owner. To check on your city's laws and policies, call the city attorney's office.

You might also get help from a utility company, if the tree threatens its equipment. For example, a phone company will trim a tree that hangs menacingly over its lines.

If you don't get help from these sources, and the neighbor refuses to take action, you can sue. The legal theory is that the dangerous tree is a "nuisance" because it is unreasonable for the owner to keep it and it interferes with your use and enjoyment of your property. You can ask the court to order the owner to prune or remove the tree. You'll have to sue in regular court (not small claims court) and have proof that the tree really does pose a danger to you.

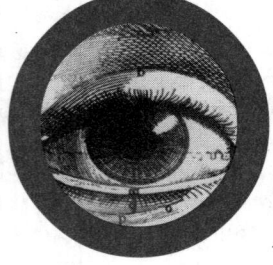

The privilege of sitting in one's home and gazing at the scenery is a highly prized commodity. And it can be a very expensive one. Potential buyers, sometimes overwhelmed by a stunning landscape, commit their life savings to properties, assuming that the view is permanent. Sometimes it is not.

If a neighbor's addition or growing tree blocks my view, what rights do I have?

Unfortunately, you have no right to light, air or view, unless it has been granted in writing by a law or subdivision rule. The exception to this general rule is that someone may not deliberately and maliciously block another's view with a structure that has no reasonable use to the owner.

This rule encourages building and expansion, but the consequences can be harsh. If a view becomes blocked, the law will help only if:

- a local law protects views
- the obstruction violates private subdivision rules, or
- the obstruction violates some other specific law.

How can a view ordinance help?

A few cities that overlook the ocean or other desirable vistas have adopted view ordinances. These laws protect a property owner from having his view (usually, the view that he had when he bought the property) obstructed by growing trees. They don't cover buildings or other structures that block views.

The ordinances allow someone who has lost a view to sue the tree owner for a court order requiring him to restore the view. A neighbor who wants to sue must first approach the tree owner and request that the tree be cut back. The complaining person usually bears the cost of trimming or topping, unless the tree was planted after the law became effective, or the owner refuses to cooperate.

Some view ordinances contain extensive limitations that take most of the teeth out of them. Some examples:

- Certain species of trees may be exempt, especially if they grew naturally.
- A neighbor may be allowed to complain only if the tree is within a certain distance from his or her property.
- Trees on city property may be exempt.

Cities Without View Ordinances

If, like most cities, your city doesn't have a view ordinance, you might find help from other local laws. Here are some laws that may help restore your view:

Fence Height Limits. If a fence is blocking your view, it may be in violation of a local law. Commonly, local laws limit artificial (constructed) fences in back yards to six feet high and in front yards to three or four feet. Height restrictions may also apply to natural fences, such as hedges.

Tree Laws. Certain species of trees may be prohibited—for example, trees that cause allergies or tend to harm other plants. Laws may also forbid trees that are too close to a street (especially an intersection), to power lines or even to an airport.

Zoning Laws. Local zoning regulations control the size, location and uses of buildings. In a single-family area, buildings are usually limited to 30 or 35 feet. Zoning laws also usually require a certain setback, or distance between a structure and the boundary lines. They also limit how much of a lot can be occupied by a structure. For instance, many suburban cities limit a dwelling to 40% to 60% of the property.

I live in a subdivision with a homeowners' association. Will that help me in a view dispute?

Often, residents of subdivisions and planned unit developments are subject to a detailed set of rules called Covenants, Conditions and Restrictions (CC&Rs). They regulate most matters that could concern a neighbor, including views. For example, a rule may state that trees can't obstruct the view from another lot, or simply limit tree height to 15 feet.

If someone violates the restrictions, the homeowners' association may apply pressure (for example, removing the privilege of using a swimming pool) or even sue. A lawsuit is costly and time-consuming, however, and the association may not want to sue except for serious violations of the rules.

If the association won't help, you can take the neighbor to court yourself, but be prepared for a lengthy and expensive experience.

I want to buy a house with a great view. Is there anything I can do to make sure I won't ever lose the view—and much of my investment?

First, ask the property owner or the city planning and zoning office if the property is protected by a view ordinance. Then check with the real estate agent to see if neighbors are subject to restrictions that would protect your view. Also, if the property is in a planned unit development, find out whether a homeowners' association actively enforces the restrictions.

Check local zoning laws for any property that might affect you. Could the neighbor down the hill add a second-story addition?

Finally, look very closely from the property to see which trees might later obstruct your view. Then go introduce yourself to their owners and explain your concerns. A neighbor who also has a view will probably understand your concern. If someone is unfriendly and uncooperative, you stand warned.

How to Approach a View Problem

Before you approach the owner of a tree that has grown to block your view, answer these questions:

- Does the tree affect the view of other neighbors? If it does, get them to approach the tree owner with you. Trimming costs may be divided among you.

- Which part of the tree is causing view problems for you—one limb, the top, one side of it?

- What is the least destructive action that could be taken to restore your view? Maybe the owner will agree to a limited and careful pruning.

- How much will the trimming cost? Be ready to pay for it. Remember that every day you wait and grumble is a day for the trees to grow and for the job to become more expensive. The loss of your personal enjoyment is probably worth more than the trimming cost, not to mention the devaluation of your property (which can be thousands of dollars).

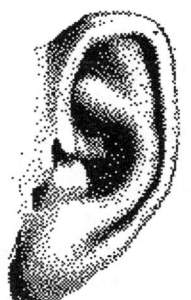

N o i s e

Nothing so needs reforming as other people's habits.

—MARK TWAIN

If you are a reasonable person and your neighbor is driving you wiggy with noise, the neighbor is probably violating a noise law.

Do I have any legal recourse against a noisy neighbor?

You bet. The most effective weapon you have to maintain your peace and quiet is your local noise ordinance. Almost every community prohibits excessive, unnecessary and unreasonable noise, and police enforce these laws.

Most laws designate certain "quiet hours"—for example, from 10 p.m. to 7 a.m. on weekdays, and until 8 or 9 a.m. on weekends. So running a power mower may be perfectly acceptable at 10 a.m. on Saturday, but not at 7 a.m. Many towns also have decibel level noise limits. When a neighbor complains, they measure the noise with electronic equipment. To find out what your town's noise ordinance says, ask at the public library or the city attorney's office.

If your neighbor keeps disturbing you, you can also sue, and ask the court for money damages or to order the neighbor to stop the noise ("abate the nuisance," in legal terms). For money damages alone, you can use small claims court. For a court order telling somebody to stop doing something, you'll have to sue in regular court.

Of course, what you really want is for the nuisance to stop. But getting a small claims court to order your neighbor to pay you money can be amazingly effective. And suing in small claims court is easy and inexpensive, and it doesn't require a lawyer.

Noise that is excessive and deliberate may also be in violation of state criminal laws against disturbing the peace or disorderly conduct. This means that, in very extreme circumstances, the police can arrest your neighbor. Usually, these offenses are punishable by fines or short jail sentences.

The neighbor in the apartment next to mine is very noisy. Isn't the landlord supposed to keep tenants quiet?

In addition to the other remedies all neighbors have, you have another arrow in your quiver: You can lean on the landlord to quiet the neighbor. Standard rental and lease agreements contain a clause entitled "Quiet Enjoyment." This clause gives tenants the right to occupy their apartments in peace, and also imposes upon them the responsibility not to disturb their neighbors. It's the landlord's job to enforce both sides of this bargain.

If the neighbor's stereo is keeping you up every night, the tenants are probably violating the rental agreement, and could be evicted. Especially if several neighbors complain, the landlord will probably order the tenant to comply with the lease or face eviction. For more information about your rights as a tenant, see Chapter 3.

Tips for Handling a Noise Problem

- Know the law and stay within it.
- Be reasonably tolerant of your neighbors.
- Assert your rights.
- Communicate with your neighbors—both the one causing the problem and others affected by it.
- Ask the police for help when it is appropriate.
- Use the courts when necessary.

My neighbor's dog barks all the time, and it's driving me crazy. What can I do?

Usually, problems with barking dogs can be resolved without resorting to police or courts. If you do eventually wind up in court, however, a judge will be more sympathetic if you made at least some effort to work things out first. Here are the steps to take when you're losing patience (or sleep) over a neighbor's noisy dog:

1. Ask your neighbor to keep the dog quiet. Sometimes owners are blissfully unaware that there's a problem. If the dog barks for hours every day—but only when it's left alone—the owner may not know that you're being driven crazy.

If you can establish some rapport with the neighbor, try to agree on specific actions to alleviate the problem: for example, that your neighbor will take the dog to obedience school or consult with an animal behavior specialist, or that the dog will be kept inside after 10 p.m. After you agree on a plan, set a date to talk again in a couple of weeks.

2. Try mediation. Mediators, both professional and volunteers, are trained to listen to both sides, identify problems, keep everyone focused on the real issues and suggest compromises. A mediator won't make a decision for you, but will help you and your neighbor agree on a resolution.

Many cities have community mediation groups which train volunteers to mediate disputes in their own neighborhoods. Or ask for a referral from:
- the small claims court clerk's office
- the local district attorney's office—the consumer complaint division, if there is one
- radio or television stations that offer help with consumer problems, or
- a state or local bar association.

For more information on mediation, see Chapter 17, *Courts and Mediation.*

3. Look up the law. In some places, barking dogs are covered by a specific state or local ordinance. If there's no law aimed specifically at dogs, a general nuisance or noise ordinance makes the owner responsible. Local law may forbid loud noise after 10 p.m., for example, or prohibit any "unreasonable" noise. And someone who allows a dog to bark after numerous warnings from police may be arrested for disturbing the peace.

To find out what the law is where you live, go to a law library and check the state statutes and city or county ordinances yourself. Look in the index under "noise," "dogs," "animals" or "nuisance." For more information on how to do this, see the Legal Research Appendix. Or call the local animal control agency or city attorney.

4. Ask animal control authorities to enforce local noise laws. Be persistent. Some cities have special programs to handle dog complaints.

5. Call the police, if you think a criminal law is being violated. Generally, police aren't too interested in barking dog problems. And summoning a police cruiser to a neighbor's house obviously will not improve your already-strained relations. But if nothing else works, and the relationship with your neighbor is shot anyway, give the police a try.

More Information About Neighbor Law

Neighbor Law: Fences, Trees, Boundaries & Noise, by Cora Jordan (Nolo), explains laws that affect neighbors and shows how to resolve common disputes without lawsuits.

Dog Law, by Mary Randolph (Nolo), is a guide to the laws that affect dog owners and their neighbors.

http://www.nolo.com

Nolo offers self-help information about a wide variety of legal topics, including neighbor law.

Landlords and Tenants

3.2	*Leases and Rental Agreements*
3.4	*Tenant Selection*
3.4	*Housing Discrimination*
3.6	*Rent and Security Deposits*
3.8	*Tenants' Privacy Rights*
3.9	*Repairs and Maintenance*
3.12	*Landlord Liability for Criminal Acts and Activities*
3.14	*Landlord Liability for Lead Poisoning*
3.15	*Landlord's Liability for Exposure to Asbestos and Mold*
3.16	*Insurance*
3.17	*Resolving Disputes*

Property has its duties as well as its rights.

–THOMAS DRUMMOND

Thirty years ago, custom, not law, controlled how most landlords and tenants interacted with each other. This is no longer true. Today, whether you focus on leases and rental agreements; habitability; discrimination; the amount, use and return of security deposits; how and when a landlord may enter a rental unit or a dozen other issues, both landlord and tenant must understand their legal rights and responsibilities.

Because landlord-tenant laws vary significantly depending on where you live, remember to check your state and local laws for specifics. A list of state landlord-tenant statutes is included at the end of this chapter. You can find and read the state statutes online. (See "Finding Statutes and Regulations Online" in the Legal Research Appendix.)

Leases and Rental Agreements

It's important to carefully read—and fully understand—the terms of your lease or rental agreement. This piece of paper is the contract that forms the legal basis for the landlord-tenant relationship.

Why is it important to sign a lease or rental agreement?

The lease or rental agreement is the key document of the tenancy. A thorough lease or rental agreement will set out important issues such as:
- the length of the tenancy
- the amount of rent and deposits the tenant must pay
- the number of people who can live on the rental property
- who pays for utilities
- whether the tenant may have pets
- whether the tenant may sublet the property
- the landlord's access to the rental property, and
- who pays attorney fees if there is a lawsuit.

Leases and rental agreements should always be in writing, even though oral agreements for less than a year are enforceable in most states. While oral agreements may seem easy and informal, they often lead to disputes. If a tenant and landlord later disagree about key agreements, such as whether the tenant can sublet, the result is all too likely to be a court argument over who said what to whom, when and in what context.

What's the difference between a rental agreement and a lease?

The biggest difference is the length of occupancy. A written rental agreement provides for a tenancy of a short period (often 30 days). The tenancy is automatically renewed at the end of this period unless the tenant or landlord ends it by giving written notice, typically 30 days. For these month-to-month rentals, the landlord can change the terms of the agreement with proper written notice, subject to any rent control laws. This notice is usually 30 days, but can be shorter in some states if the rent is paid weekly or bi-weekly or if the landlord and tenant agree. In some states, the notice period is longer.

A written lease, on the other hand, gives a tenant the right to occupy a rental unit for a set term—most often for six months or a year, but sometimes longer—as long as the tenant pays the rent and complies with other lease provisions. Unlike a rental agreement, when a lease expires it does not usually automatically renew itself. A tenant who stays on with the landlord's consent will generally be considered a month-to-month tenant (with the same terms and conditions that were present in the lease).

In addition, with a fixed-term lease, the landlord cannot raise the rent or change other terms of the tenancy during the lease, unless the changes are specifically provided for in the lease or the tenant agrees.

What happens if a tenant breaks a long-term lease?

As a general rule, a tenant may not legally break a lease unless the landlord significantly violates its terms—for example, by failing to make necessary repairs, or by failing to comply with an important law concerning health or safety. A few states have laws that allow tenants to break a lease because health problems or a job relocation require a permanent move. A tenant who begins active military service may break a lease after giving 30 day's notice.

A tenant who breaks a lease without a legally recognized cause will be responsible for the remainder of the rent due under the lease term. In most states, however, a landlord has a legal duty to try to find a new tenant as soon as possible—no matter what the tenant's reason for leaving—rather than charge the tenant for the total remaining rent due under the lease. At that point, the old tenants' responsibility for the rent will stop.

When can a landlord legally break a lease and end a tenancy?

Usually, a landlord may legally break a lease if a tenant significantly violates its terms or the law—for example, by paying the rent late, keeping a dog in violation of a no-pets clause in the lease, substantially damaging the property or participating in illegal activities on or near the premises, such as selling drugs.

Usually a landlord must first send the tenant a notice stating that the tenancy has been terminated. State laws set out very detailed requirements as to how a landlord must write and deliver (serve) a termination notice, depending on what the tenant has done wrong. The termination notice may state that the tenancy is over and warn the tenant that he or she must vacate the premises or face an eviction lawsuit. Or, the notice may give the tenant a few days to clean up his or her act—for example, pay the rent or find a new home for the dog. (If the tenant fixes the problem or leaves as directed, no one goes to court.) If a tenant doesn't comply with the termination notice, the landlord can file a lawsuit to evict the tenant.

Tenant Selection

Choosing tenants is the most important decision any landlord makes. To do it well, landlords need a reliable system that helps weed out tenants who will pay their rent late, damage the rental unit or cause legal or practical problems later.

What's the best way for landlords to screen tenants?

Savvy landlords should ask all prospective tenants to fill out a written rental application that asks for the following information:

- employment, income and credit history
- Social Security and driver's license numbers
- details on past evictions or bankruptcies, and
- references.

Before choosing tenants, landlords should check with previous landlords and other references; verify income, employment and bank account information; and obtain a credit report. The credit report is especially important because it will indicate whether a particular person has a history of paying rent or bills late, has gone through bankruptcy, has been convicted of a crime or has ever been evicted.

How can a landlord avoid discrimination lawsuits when choosing a tenant?

Fair housing laws specify clearly illegal reasons to refuse to rent to a tenant. (For details, see *Housing Discrimination*, below.) Landlords are legally free to choose among prospective tenants as long as their decisions comply with these laws and are based on legitimate business criteria. For example, a landlord is entitled to reject someone with a poor credit history, insufficient income to pay the rent or past behavior—such as damaging property—that makes the person a bad risk. A legally recognized occupancy policy limiting the number of people per rental unit—one that is clearly tied to health and safety—can also be a legal basis for refusing tenants.

Housing Discrimination

Not so long ago, a landlord could refuse to rent to an applicant, or could evict a tenant, for almost any reason. If a landlord didn't like your race or religion, or the fact that you had children, you might find yourself out on the street. But times have changed. To protect every American's right to be treated fairly and to help people find adequate housing, Congress and state legislatures passed laws prohibiting discrimination, most notably the federal Fair Housing Acts.

What types of housing discrimination are illegal?

The federal Fair Housing Act and Fair Housing Amendments Act prohibit landlords from choosing tenants on the basis of a group characteristic such as:

- race
- religion
- ethnic background or national origin
- sex
- age
- the fact that the prospective tenant has children (except in certain designated senior housing), or
- a mental or physical disability.

In addition, some state and local laws prohibit discrimination based on a person's marital status or sexual orientation. And some cities and counties have added other criteria, such as one's personal appearance.

On the other hand, landlords are allowed to select tenants using criteria that are based on valid business reasons, such as requiring a minimum income or positive references from previous landlords, as long as these standards are applied equally to all tenants.

Examples of Housing Discrimination

The Fair Housing Act and Amendments prohibit landlords from taking any of the following actions based on race, religion or any other protected category:

- advertising or making any statement that indicates a preference based on group characteristic, such as skin color
- falsely denying that a rental unit is available
- setting more restrictive standards, such as higher income, for certain tenants
- refusing to rent to members of certain groups
- refusing to accommodate the needs of disabled tenants, such as allowing a guide dog, hearing dog or service dog
- setting different terms for some tenants, such as adopting an inconsistent policy of responding to late rent payments, or
- terminating a tenancy for a discriminatory reason.

How does a tenant file a discrimination complaint?

A tenant who thinks that a landlord has broken a federal fair housing law should contact the U.S. Department of Housing and Urban Development (HUD), the agency which enforces the Fair Housing Act. To find the nearest office, call HUD's Fair Housing Information Clearinghouse at 800-343-3442, or check the HUD Website at http://www.hud.gov. HUD will provide a complaint form and will investigate and decide the merits of the claim. A tenant must file his or her complaint within one year of the alleged discriminatory act. HUD will typically appoint a mediator to negotiate with the landlord and reach a settlement (called a "conciliation"). If a settlement can't be reached, the fair housing agency will hold an administrative hearing to determine whether discrimination has occurred.

If the discrimination is a violation of a state fair housing law, the tenant may file a complaint with the state agency in charge of enforcing the law. In California, the Department of Fair Employment and Housing enforces the state's two fair housing laws.

Also, instead of filing a complaint with HUD or a state agency, tenants may file lawsuits directly in federal or state court. If a state or federal court or housing agency finds that discrimination has taken place, a tenant may be awarded damages, including any higher rent he or she had to pay as a result of being turned down, and damages for humiliation or emotional distress.

Rent and Security Deposits

Landlords may charge any dollar amount for rent, except in certain areas covered by rent control. Many states do, however, have rules as to when and how rent must be paid and how it may be increased.

Security deposits are more strictly regulated by state law. Most states dictate how much money a landlord can require, how the funds can be used—for example, to cover unpaid rent—and when and how the deposit must be returned.

What laws cover rent due dates, late rent and rent increases?

By custom, leases and rental agreements usually require rent to be paid monthly, in advance. Often rent is due on the first day of the month. However, it is legal for a landlord to require rent to be paid at different intervals or on a different day of the month. Unless the lease or rental agreement specifies otherwise, there is no legally recognized grace period—in other words, if a tenant hasn't paid the rent on time, the landlord can usually terminate the tenancy the day after it is due. Some landlords charge fees for late payment of rent or for bounced checks; these fees are usually legal if they are reasonable. The laws on late fees can be found in your state's landlord-tenant statutes, listed at the end of this chapter.

For month-to-month rentals, the landlord can raise the rent (subject to any rent control laws) with proper written notice, typically 30 days. With a fixed-term lease, the landlord may not raise the rent during the lease, unless the increase is specifically called for in the lease or the tenant agrees.

How Rent Control Works

Communities in only five states—California, the District of Columbia, Maryland, New Jersey and New York—have laws that limit the amount of rent landlords may charge. Rent control ordinances (also called rent stabilization, maximum rent regulation or a similar term) limit the circumstances and times rent may be increased. Many rent control laws require landlords to have a legal or just cause (that is, a good reason) to terminate a tenancy—for example, if the tenant doesn't pay rent or if the landlord wants to move a family member into the rental unit. Landlords and tenants in New York City, Newark, San Francisco and other cities with rent control should get a current copy of the ordinance and any regulations interpreting it. Check the phone book for the address and phone number of the local rent control board, or contact the mayor or city manager's office.

How much security deposit can a landlord charge?

All states allow landlords to collect a security deposit when the tenant moves in; the general purpose is to assure that the tenant pays rent when due and keeps the rental unit in good condition. Half the states limit the amount landlords can charge, usually not more than a month or two worth of rent—the exact amount depends on the state.

Many states require landlords to put deposits in a separate account, and some require landlords to pay tenants the interest on deposits.

What are the rules for returning security deposits?

The rules vary from state to state, but landlords usually have a set amount of time in which to return deposits, usually 14 to 30 days after the tenant moves out—either voluntarily or by eviction.

Landlords may normally make certain deductions from a tenant's security deposit, provided they do it correctly and for an allowable reason. Many states require landlords to provide a written itemized accounting of deductions for unpaid rent and for repairs for damages that go beyond normal wear and tear, together with payment for any deposit balance.

A tenant may sue a landlord who fails to return his or her deposit when and how required, or who violates other provisions of security deposit laws such as interest requirements. Often these lawsuits are brought in small claims court. If the landlord has intentionally and flagrantly violated the ordinance, in some states a tenant may recover the entire deposit—sometimes even two or three times this amount—plus attorney fees and other damages.

The rules for the keeping and return of security deposits can be found in state landlord-tenant statutes, listed at the end of this chapter.

Tenants' Privacy Rights

In most states, the tenant's duty to pay rent is conditioned on the landlord's proper repair and maintenance of the premises. This means that landlords have a legal responsibility to keep fairly close tabs on the condition of the property. To balance landlords' responsibilities with tenants' rights to privacy in their homes, laws in many states set rules about when and how landlords may legally enter rented premises.

Under what circumstances may a landlord enter rental property?

Typically, a landlord has the right to legally enter rented premises in cases of emergency, in order to make needed repairs (in some states, just to determine whether repairs are necessary) or to show the property to prospective new tenants or purchasers.

Several states allow landlords the right of entry during a tenant's extended absence (often defined as seven days or more) to maintain the property as necessary and to inspect for damage and needed repairs. In most cases, a landlord may not enter just to check up on the tenant and the rental property.

Must landlords provide notice of entry?

States typically require landlords to provide advance notice (usually 24 hours) before entering a rental unit. Without advance notice, a landlord or manager may enter rented premises while a tenant is living there only in an emergency, such as a fire or serious water leak, or when the tenant gives permission.

To find out how much notice a landlord must give a tenant before entering, check your state's landlord-tenant statutes, listed at the end of this chapter.

Is it legal for a landlord to answer questions about a tenant's credit?

Creditors, banks and prospective landlords may ask a landlord to provide credit or other information about a current or former tenant. A landlord who sticks to the facts that are relevant to the tenant's creditworthiness (such as whether the tenant paid rent on time) may respond to these inquiries without fear of legal difficulties initiated bt the tenant. To be extra careful, some landlords insist that tenants sign a release giving the landlord permission to respond to such requests.

Repairs and Maintenance

In 1863, an English judge wrote that "Fraud apart, there is no law against letting [leasing] a tumble-down house." But in 20th century America, it's no longer legal to be a slumlord. Landlords must repair and maintain their rental property or face financial losses and legal problems from tenants—who may withhold rent and pursue other legal remedies—and from government agencies that enforce housing codes.

What are the landlord's repair and maintenance responsibilities?

Under most state and local laws, rental property owners must offer and maintain housing that satisfies basic habitability requirements, such as adequate weatherproofing; available heat, water and electricity; and clean, sanitary and structurally safe premises. Local building or housing codes typically set specific standards, such as the minimum requirements for light, ventilation and electrical wiring. Many cities require the installation of smoke detectors in residential units and specify security measures involving locks and keys.

To find out more about state laws on repair and maintenance responsibilities, check your state's landlord-tenant statutes listed at the end of this chapter. Your local building or housing authority and health or fire department can provide information on local housing codes and penalties for violations.

What are a tenant's rights if the landlord refuses to maintain the property?

If a landlord doesn't meet his or her legal responsibilities, a tenant usually has several options, depending on the state. These options include:

- paying less rent
- withholding the entire rent until the problem is fixed
- making necessary repairs or hiring someone to make them and deducting the cost from the next month's rent
- calling the local building inspector, who can usually order the landlord to make repairs, or
- moving out, even in the middle of a lease.

A tenant who has lived under substandard conditions can also sue the landlord for a partial refund of rent paid during that time, and in some circumstances can sue for the discomfort, annoyance and emotional distress caused by the substandard conditions.

Tenants should check state and local laws and understand remedies available before taking any action, especially withholding rent.

What must tenants do to keep the rental property in good shape?

All tenants have the responsibility to keep their own living quarters clean and sanitary. A landlord can usually delegate his repair and maintenance tasks to the tenant in exchange for a reduction in rent. If the tenant fails to do the job well, however, the landlord is not excused from his responsibility to maintain habitability. In addition, tenants must carefully use common areas and facilities, such as lobbies, garages and pools.

Is a landlord liable if a tenant or visitor is injured on the rental property?

A landlord may be liable to the tenant—or others—for injuries caused by dangerous or defective conditions on the rental property. In order to hold the landlord responsible, the tenant must prove that the landlord was negligent and that the landlord's negligence caused an injury. To do this, the tenant must show that:

- the landlord had control over the problem that caused the injury
- the accident was foreseeable
- fixing the problem (or at least giving adequate warnings) would not have been unreasonably expensive or difficult
- a serious injury was the probable consequence of not fixing the problem

- the landlord failed to take reasonable steps to avert the accident
- the landlord's failure—his negligence—caused the tenant's accident, and
- the tenant was genuinely hurt.

For example, if a tenant falls and breaks his ankle on a broken front door step, the landlord will be liable if the tenant can show that:

- It was the landlord's responsibility to maintain the steps (this would usually be the case, because the steps are part of the common area, which is the landlord's responsibility).
- An accident of this type was foreseeable (falling on a broken step is highly likely).
- A repair would have been easy or inexpensive (fixing a broken step is a minor job).
- The probable result of a broken step is a serious injury (a fall certainly qualifies).
- The landlord failed to take reasonable measures to maintain the steps (this will be easy to prove if the step was broken for weeks, or even days, but less so if the step broke five minutes earlier and showed no previous signs of weakening).
- The broken step caused the injury (this is easy to prove if the tenant has a witness to the fall, but might be hard if there are no witnesses and the landlord claims that the tenant really injured himself somewhere else and is attempting to pin the blame on the landlord), and
- He is really hurt (in the case of a broken bone, this is easy to establish).

A tenant can file a personal injury lawsuit for medical bills, lost earnings, pain and other physical suffering, permanent physical disability and disfigurement and emotional distress. A tenant can also sue for property damage that results from faulty maintenance or unsafe conditions.

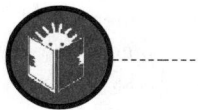

More Information on Personal Injury Lawsuits

How to Win Your Personal Injury Claim, by Joseph L. Matthews (Nolo), provides step-by-step details on how to understand what a claim is worth, prepare a claim for compensation, negotiate a fair settlement and manage a case even if a lawyer is not involved.

How can property owners minimize financial losses and legal problems related to repairs and maintenance?

Landlords who offer and maintain housing in excellent condition can avoid many problems. Here's how:

- Clearly set out responsibilities for repair and maintenance in the lease or rental agreement.
- Use a written checklist to inspect the premises and fix any problems before new tenants move in.
- Encourage tenants to immediately report plumbing, heating, weatherproofing or other defects or safety or security problems—whether in the tenant's unit or in common areas such as hallways and parking garages.
- Keep a written log of all tenant complaints and repair requests with details as to how and when problems were addressed.
- Handle urgent repairs as soon as possible. Take care of major inconveniences, such as a plumbing or heating problem, within 24 hours. For minor problems, respond in 48 hours. Always keep tenants informed as to when and how the repairs will be made and the reasons for any delays.
- Twice a year, give tenants a checklist on which to report potential safety hazards or maintenance problems that might have been overlooked. Use the same checklist to inspect all rental units once a year.

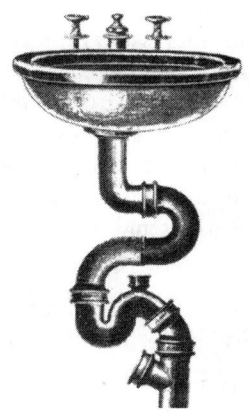

Landlord Liability for Criminal Acts and Activities

Can a law-abiding citizen end up financially responsible for the criminal acts of a total stranger? Yes—if it's a landlord who owns rental property where an assault or other crime occurred. Rental property owners are being sued with increasing frequency by tenants injured by criminals, with settlements and jury awards typically ranging from $100,000 to $1 million. What are the landlord's responsibilities for tenant safety and security?

Property owners are responsible for keeping their premises reasonably safe for tenants and guests. Landlords in most states now have at least some degree of legal responsibility to protect their tenants from would-be assailants and thieves and from the criminal acts of fellow tenants. Landlords must also protect the neighborhood from their tenants' illegal activities, such as drug dealing. These legal duties stem from building codes, ordinances, statutes and, most frequently, court decisions.

How can a landlord limit responsibility for crime committed by strangers on the rental property?

Effective preventive measures are the best response to possible liabilities from criminal acts and activities. The following steps will not only limit the likelihood of crime, but also reduce the risk that the property owner will be found responsible if a criminal assault or robbery does occur. A landlord should:

- Meet or exceed all state and local security laws that apply to the rental property, such as requirements for deadbolt locks on doors, good lighting and window locks.
- Realistically assess the crime situation in and around the rental property and neighborhood and design a security system that provides reasonable protection for the tenants—both in individual rental units and common areas such as parking garages and elevators. Local police departments, the landlord's insurance company and private security professionals can all provide useful advice on security measures. If additional security requires a rent hike, the landlord should discuss the situation with his or her tenants. Many tenants will pay more for a safer place to live.
- Educate tenants about crime problems in the neighborhood and describe the security measures provided and their limitations.
- Maintain the rental property and conduct regular inspections to spot and fix any security problems, such as broken locks or burned out exterior flood lights. Asking tenants for their suggestions as part of an ongoing repair and maintenance system is also a good idea.

• Handle tenant complaints about dangerous situations, suspicious activities or broken security items immediately. Failing to do this may saddle a landlord with a higher level of legal liability should a tenant be injured by a criminal act after a complaint is made.

The Costs of Crime

The money a landlord spends today on effective crime-prevention measures will pale in comparison to the costs that may result from crime on the premises. The average settlement paid by landlords' insurance companies for horrific crimes such as rape and assault is $600,000, and the average jury award (when cases go to trial) is $1.2 million.

What kind of legal trouble do landlords face from tenants who deal drugs on the property?

Drug-dealing tenants can cause landlords all kinds of practical and legal problems:

• It will be difficult to find and keep good tenants and the value of the rental property will plummet.
• Anyone who is injured or annoyed by drug dealers—be it other tenants or people in the neighborhood— may sue the landlord on the grounds that the property is a public nuisance that seriously threatens public safety or morals.
• Local, state or federal authorities may levy stiff fines against the landlord for allowing the illegal activity to continue.
• Law enforcement authorities may seek criminal penalties against the landlord for knowingly allowing drug dealing on the rental property.
• In extreme cases, the presence of drug dealers may result in the government confiscating the rental property.

How can a property owner avoid legal problems from tenants who deal drugs or otherwise break the law?

There are several practical steps landlords can take to avoid trouble from tenants and limit their exposure to any lawsuits that are filed:

• Screen tenants carefully and choose tenants who are likely to be law-abiding and peaceful citizens. Weed out violent or dangerous individuals to the extent allowable under privacy and anti-discrimination laws that may limit questions about a tenant's past criminal activity, drug use or mental illness.
• Keep the results of background checks that show that the tenants' rent appeared to come from legitimate sources (jobs and bank accounts).
• Don't accept a cash deposit or rental payments.
• Do not tolerate tenants' disruptive behavior. Include an explicit provision in the lease or rental agreement prohibiting drug dealing and other illegal activity by tenants or guests and promptly evict tenants who violate the clause.

- Be aware of suspicious activity, such as heavy traffic in and out of the rental premises.
- Respond to tenant and neighbor complaints about drug dealing on the rental property. Get advice from police immediately upon learning of a problem.
- Consult with security experts to do everything reasonable to discover and prevent illegal activity on the rental property.

Protecting Tenants From the Manager

Rental property owners should be particularly careful when hiring a property manager—the person who interacts with all tenants and has access to master keys. Landlords should scrupulously check a manager's background to the fullest extent allowed by law, and closely supervise his or her job performance. A tenant who gets hurt or has property stolen or damaged by a manager could sue the property owner for failing to screen the manager properly. If tenants complain about illegal acts by a manager, landlords should pay attention. Finally, property owners should make sure their insurance covers illegal acts of their employees.

Landlord Liability for Lead Poisoning

Landlords are increasingly likely to be held liable for tenant health problems resulting from exposure to lead and other environmental toxins, even if the landlord didn't cause—or even know about—the danger.

What are a landlord's legal responsibilities regarding lead in rental property?

Because of the health problems caused by lead poisoning, the Residential Lead-Based Paint Hazard Reduction Act was enacted in 1992. This law is commonly known as Title X (ten). Environmental Protection Agency (EPA) regulations implementing Title X apply to rental property built before 1978.

Under Title X, before signing or renewing a lease or rental agreement, and before undertaking any renovation, a landlord must give every tenant the EPA pamphlet, *Protect Your Family From Lead in Your Home,* or a state-approved version of this pamphlet. At the start of the tenancy, both the landlord and tenant must sign an EPA-approved disclosure form to prove that the landlord told the tenants about any known lead-based paint or hazards on the premises. Property owners must keep this disclosure form as part of their records for three years from the date that the tenancy begins.

A landlord who fails to comply with EPA regulations faces penalties of up to $10,000 for each violation. And a landlord who is found liable for tenant injuries from lead may have to pay three times what the tenant suffered in damages.

More Information on Lead Hazard Resources

Information on the evaluation and control of lead dust, and copies of *Protect Your Family From Lead in Your Home* may be obtained by calling the National Lead Information Center at 800-424-LEAD, or checking its website at http://www.epa.gov/opptintr/lead/nlic.htm. In addition, state housing departments have information on state laws and regulations governing the evaluation and control of lead hazards.

Are there any rental properties exempt from Title X regulations?

These properties are not covered by Title X:

- housing for which a construction permit was obtained, or on which construction was started, after January 1, 1978
- housing certified as lead-free by a state-accredited lead inspector
- lofts, efficiencies and studio apartments
- short-term vacation rentals of 100 days or less
- a single room rented in a residential dwelling
- housing designed for persons with disabilities, unless any child less than six years old lives there or is expected to live there
- retirement communities (housing designed for seniors, where one or more tenants is at least 62 years old), unless children under the age of six are present or expected to live there.

Landlord's Liability for Exposure to Asbestos and Mold

In addition to lead, property owners may be liable for tenant health problems caused by exposure to other environmental hazards, such as asbestos and mold.

Regulations concerning asbestos are issued by the Occupational Safety and Health Administration (OSHA). They set strict standards for the testing, maintenance and disclosure of asbestos in buildings constructed before 1981. For information call the nearest OSHA office or check OSHA's website at http://www.osha.gov.

Mold is the newest environmental hazard fueling lawsuits against rental property owners. Across the country, tenants have won multi-million-dollar cases against landlords for significant health problems—such as rashes, chronic fatigue, nausea, cognitive losses, hemorrhaging and asthma—allegedly caused by exposure to "toxic molds" in their building. In a typical case, the Delaware Supreme Court in May 2001 upheld a $1.4 million award to two tenants who suffered asthma and other health problems caused by mold that grew when the landlord refused to fix leaks in their apartment.

There are no federal or state laws or regulations covering permissible exposure to mold, though California has directed its Department of Health Services to study the issue. New York City's Department of Health has developed guidelines for indoor air quality, which landlords in New York City should follow. In fact, any landlord would be wise to consult them. You can read them online at http://www.ci.nyc.ny.us. San Francisco has added mold to its list of nuisances, thereby allowing tenants to sue landlords under private and public nuisance laws if they fail to clean up serious outbreaks (San Francisco Health Code §581).

Insurance

Both tenants and landlords need insurance to protect their property and bank accounts. Without adequate insurance, landlords risk losing hundreds of thousands of dollars of property from fire or other hazards. While tenants may not have as much at stake financially, they also need insurance—especially tenants with expensive personal belongings. Tenant losses from fire or theft are not covered by the landlord's insurance.

How can insurance help protect a rental property business?

A well-designed insurance policy can protect rental property from losses caused by many perils, including fire, storms, burglary and vandalism. (Earthquake and flood insurance are typically separate and, in some areas, mold may soon join the list.) A comprehensive policy will also include liability insurance, covering injuries or losses suffered by others as the result of defective conditions on the property.

Equally important, liability insurance covers the cost (mostly lawyer's bills) of defending personal injury lawsuits.

Here are some tips on choosing insurance:
- Purchase enough coverage to protect the value of the property and assets.
- Be sure the policy covers not only physical injury but also libel, slander, discrimination, unlawful and retalia-

tory eviction and invasion of privacy suffered by tenants and guests.

- Carry liability insurance on all vehicles used for business purposes, including the manager's car or truck if he or she will use it on the job.
- Make sure your policy is "occurence based," not "claims based." Here's the difference: under a claims-based policy, your policy must be in effect on the date you make the claim—even if it was in place when the incident leading to the claim occurred. Under an occurance-based arrangement, you can make the claim after the policy has ended—which is obviously to your advantage.

If you need more information, *The Legal Guide for Starting & Running a Small Business*, by Fred S. Steingold (Nolo), contains a detailed discussion of small business law, including how to insure your rental property.

What does renter's insurance cover?

The average renter's policy covers tenants against losses to their belongings occurring as a result of fire and theft, up to the amount stated on the face of the policy, such as $25,000 or $50,000.

Most renter policies include deductible amounts of $250 or $500. This means that if a tenant's apartment is burglarized, the insurance company will pay only for the amount of the loss over and above the deductible amount.

In addition to fire and theft, most renter's policies include personal li-

ability coverage ($100,000 is a typical amount) for injuries or damage caused by the tenant—for example, if a tenant's garden hose floods the neighbor's cactus garden, or a tenant's guest is injured on the rental property due to the tenant's negligence.

Renter's insurance is a package of several types of insurance designed to cover tenants for more than one risk. Each insurance company's package will be slightly different—types of coverage offered, exclusions, the dollar amounts specified and the deductible will vary. Tenants who live in a flood or earthquake-prone area will need to pay extra for coverage. Policies covering flood and earthquake damage can be hard to find; tenants should shop around until they find the type of coverage that they need. There's lots of information on the Web—type "renters' insurance" into your favorite search engine to learn more.

Resolving Disputes

Legal disputes—actual and potential—come in all shapes and sizes for landlords and tenants. Whether it's a disagreement over a rent increase, responsibility for repairs or return of a security deposit, rarely should lawyers and litigation be the first choice for resolving a landlord-tenant dispute.

How can landlords and tenants avoid disputes?

Both landlords and tenants should follow these tips to avoid legal problems:

- Know your rights and responsibilities under federal, state and local law.
- Make sure the terms of your lease or rental agreement are clear and unambiguous.
- Keep communication open. If there's a problem—for example, a disagreement about the landlord's right to enter a tenant's apartment—see if you can resolve the issue by talking it over, without running to a lawyer.
- Keep copies of any correspondence and make notes of conversations about any problems. For example, a tenant should ask for repairs in writing and keep a copy of the letter. The landlord should keep a copy of the repair request and note when and how the problem was repaired.

We've talked about the problem and still don't agree. What should we do next?

If you can't work out an agreement on your own, but want to continue the rental relationship, consider mediation by a neutral, third party. Unlike a judge, the mediator has no power to impose a decision but will simply work to help find a mutually acceptable solution to the dispute. Mediation is often available at little or no cost from a publicly funded program.

More Information About Mediation

For information on local mediation programs, call your mayor's or city manager's office, and ask for the staff member who handles "landlord-tenant mediation matters" or "housing disputes." That person should refer you to the public office, business or community group that handles landlord-tenant mediations.

You can learn more about mediation by reading Chapter 17 of this book, *Courts and Mediation*.

If mediation doesn't work, is there a last step before going to a lawyer?

If you decide not to mediate your dispute, or mediation fails, it's time to pursue other legal remedies. If the disagreement involves money, such as return of the security deposit, you can take the case to small claims court. A few states use different names for this type of court (such as "Landlord-Tenant Court"), but traditionally the purpose has been the same: to provide a speedy, inexpensive resolution of disputes that involve relatively small amounts of money.

Keep in mind that your remedy in small claims court may be limited to an award of money damages. The maximum amount you can sue for varies from $3,000 to $7,500, depending on your state.

You can find more information about small claims court in Chapter 17, *Courts and Mediation*.

Landlord-Tenant Statutory Codes

Here are some of the key statutes pertaining to landlord-tenant law in each state.

ALABAMA
Ala. Code §§ 35-9-1 to 35-9-100

ALASKA
Alaska Stat. §§ 34.03.010 to 34.03.380

ARIZONA
Ariz. Rev. Stat. Ann. §§ 12-1171 to 12-1183, §§ 33-1301 to 33-1381

ARKANSAS
Ark. Code Ann. §§ 18-16-101 to 18-16-306

CALIFORNIA
Cal. Civ. Code §§ 1925 to 1954, 1961 to 1962.7, 1995.010 to 1997.270

COLORADO
Colo. Rev. Stat. §§ 38-12-101 to 38-12-104, 38-12-301 to 38-12-302

CONNECTICUT
Conn. Gen. Stat. Ann. §§ 47a-1 to 47a-51

DELAWARE
Del. Code Ann. tit. 25, §§ 5101 to 7013

DIST. OF COLUMBIA
D.C. Code Ann. §§ 45-1401 to 45-1597, 45-2501 to 45-2593

FLORIDA
Fla. Stat. Ann. §§ 83.40 to 83.66

GEORGIA
Ga. Code Ann. §§ 44-7-1 to 44-7-81

HAWAII
Haw. Rev. Stat. §§ 521-1 to 521-78

IDAHO
Idaho Code §§ 6-301 to 6-324, §§ 55-201 to 55-313

ILLINOIS
765 Ill. Comp. Stat. §§ 705/0.01 to 740/5

INDIANA
Ind. Code Ann. §§ 32-7-1-1 to 37-7-9-10

IOWA
Iowa Code Ann. §§ 562A.1 to 562A.36

KANSAS
Kan. Stat. Ann. §§ 58-2501 to 58-2573

KENTUCKY
Ky. Rev. Stat. Ann. §§ 383.010 to 383.715

LOUISIANA
La. Rev. Stat. Ann. §§ 9:3201 to 9:3259; La. Civ. Code Ann. art. 2669 to 2742

MAINE
Me. Rev. Stat. Ann. tit. 14, §§ 6001 to 6046

MARYLAND
Md. Code Ann. [Real Prop.] §§ 8-101 to 8-604

MASSACHUSETTS
Mass. Gen. Laws Ann. ch. 186, §§ 1 to 21

MICHIGAN
Mich. Comp. Laws §§ 554.601 to 554.640

MINNESOTA
Minn. Stat. Ann. §§ 504B.001 to 504B.471

MISSISSIPPI
Miss. Code Ann. §§ 89-8-1 to 89-8-27

MISSOURI
Mo. Rev. Stat. §§ 441.005 to 441.880, §§ 535.150 to 535.300

MONTANA
Mont. Code Ann. §§ 70-24-101 to 70-25-206

NEBRASKA
Neb. Rev. Stat. §§ 76-1401 to 76-1449

NEVADA
Nev. Rev. Stat. Ann. §§ 118A.010 to 118A.520

NEW HAMPSHIRE
N.H. Rev. Stat. Ann. §§ 540:1 to 540:29, 540-A:1 to 540-A:8

NEW JERSEY
N.J. Stat. Ann. §§ 46:8-1 to 46:8-49

NEW MEXICO
N.M. Stat. Ann. §§ 47-8-1 to 47-8-51

NEW YORK
N.Y. Real Prop. Law §§ 220 to 238, Real Prop. Acts. §§ 701 to 853, Mult. Dwell. Law (all), Mult. Res. Law (all), Gen. Oblig. Law §§ 7-103 to 7-108

NORTH CAROLINA
N.C. Gen. Stat. §§ 42-1 to 42-14.2, 42-25.6 to 42-76

NORTH DAKOTA
N.D. Cent. Code §§ 47-16-01 to 47-16-41

OHIO
Ohio Rev. Code Ann. §§ 5321.01 to 5321.19

OKLAHOMA
Okla. Stat. Ann. tit. 41, §§ 1 to 136

OREGON
Or. Rev. Stat. §§ 90.100 to 90.450

PENNSYLVANIA
68 Pa. Cons. Stat. Ann. §§ 250.101 to 250.510-B

RHODE ISLAND
R.I. Gen. Laws §§ 34-18-1 to 34-18-57

SOUTH CAROLINA
S.C. Code Ann. §§ 27-40-10 to 27-40-910

SOUTH DAKOTA
S.D. Codified Laws Ann. §§ 43-32-1 to 43-32-29

TENNESSEE
Tenn. Code Ann. §§ 66-28-101 to 66-28-520

TEXAS
Tex. Prop. Code Ann. §§ 91.001 to 92.354

UTAH
Utah Code Ann. §§ 57-17-1 to 57-17-5, 57-22-1 to 57-22-6

VERMONT
Vt. Stat. Ann. tit. 9, §§ 4451 to 4468

VIRGINIA
Va. Code Ann. §§ 55-218.1 to 55-248.40

WASHINGTON
Wash. Rev. Code Ann. §§ 59.04.010 to 59.04.900, 59.18.010 to 59.18.911

WEST VIRGINIA
W. Va. Code §§ 37-6-1 to 37-6-30

WISCONSIN
Wis. Stat. Ann. §§ 704.01 to 704.45

WYOMING
Wyo. Stat. §§ 1-21-1201 to 1-21-1211, §§ 34-2-128 to 34-2-129

More Information About Landlord-Tenant Law

From the landlord's point of view:

Every Landlord's Legal Guide, by Marcia Stewart, Ralph Warner and Janet Portman (Nolo). This 50-state book provides extensive legal and practical information on leases, tenant screening, rent, security deposits, privacy, repairs, property managers, discrimination, roommates, liability, tenancy termination and much more. It includes more than 25 legal forms and agreements as tear-outs and on disk.

LeaseWriter (Nolo)(CD-ROM for Windows/Macintosh). This software program generates a customized legal residential lease or rental agreement, plus more than a dozen key documents and forms every landlord and property manager needs. It includes a database to track tenants and rental properties, and a log for rental payments, repairs and problems. The program gives you instant access to state-specific landlord-tenant information, and extensive online legal help.

From the tenant's point of view:

Every Tenant's Legal Guide, by Janet Portman and Marcia Stewart (Nolo). This book gives tenants in all 50 states the legal and practical information they need to deal with their landlords and protect their rights when things go wrong. It covers all important issues of renting, including signing a lease, getting a landlord to make needed repairs, fighting illegal discrimination, protecting privacy rights, dealing with roommates, getting the security deposit returned fairly, moving out and much more.

Renters' Rights, by Janet Portman and Marcia Stewart (Nolo). A concise, highly accessible guide for tenants in every state, loaded with tips and strategies.

For both landlords and tenants:

Everybody's Guide to Small Claims Court, by Attorney Ralph Warner (National and California Editions)(Nolo). The book explains how to evaluate your case, prepare for court and convince a judge you're right. It also tells you what remedies (money only, or enforcement of the lease) are available in your state.

How to Mediate Your Dispute, by Peter Lovenheim (Nolo), explains how to choose a mediator, prepare a case and navigate the mediation process.

Additionally, tenants' unions and rental property owners' associations are good sources of advice. Look in your telephone book's white pages for names of these organizations.

For tenants renting commercial property:

Leasing Space for Your Small Business, by Janet Portman and Fred. S. Steingold (Nolo). Gives commercial tenants the information they need to understand and negotiate a commercial lease, plus tips on finding suitable space, choosing and working with brokers and lawyers and bargaining effectively for the best terms and conditions.

http://www.nolo.com
Nolo offers self-help information about a wide variety of legal topics, including landlord-tenant law and provides links to federal and state statutes.

http://tenant.net
TenantNet provides information about landlord-tenant law, with a focus on tenants' rights. TenantNet is designed primarily for tenants in New York City, but the site offers information about the law in many other states. The site also provides the text of the federal fair housing law.

http://www.spl.org
The Seattle Public Library has links to many cities that have posted their ordinances (and often their rent control laws) online.

Workplace Rights

4.2	*Fair Pay and Time Off*
4.9	*Workplace Health and Safety*
4.12	*Workers' Compensation*
4.17	*Age Discrimination*
4.21	*Sexual Harassment*
4.25	*Disability Discrimination*
4.29	*Losing or Leaving Your Job*

I LIKE WORK; IT FASCINATES ME.

I CAN SIT AND LOOK AT IT FOR HOURS.

—JEROME K. JEROME

If you're like most workers, you have experienced occasional job-related problems or have questions about whether you are being fairly and legally treated on the job. Here are several common problems:

- You were not hired for a job and you have good reason to suspect it was because of your race, age, sex, sexual orientation or because you are disabled.
- Your employer promoted a less-qualified person—perhaps someone who is younger than you are—to fill a position you were promised.
- You are regularly forced to work overtime but are not given extra pay. Or, you are paid for working extra hours, but you do not receive a premium rate, such as time-and-a-half.
- You need to take a leave of absence from your job to care for a sick parent, but you are concerned that this will jeopardize your job or your eligibility for a promotion.
- You have been called to serve on a jury and wonder if your employer must pay you for this time.
- You have just been laid off and you want to know whether, if business at your company picks up in the future, you have any right to get your job back. You also want to know whether you're entitled to unemployment payments, or whether your employer owes you severance pay.

It is reassuring for many workers to learn that they do not face these issues alone. In recent years, a number of laws have been passed to protect your rights in the workplace. Federal laws now establish some basic guarantees for most workers—such as the right to be paid fairly and on time and to work free from discrimination. And state laws may place their own twists on your workplace rights—giving more protection than federal law, for example, or regulating whether or not you are entitled to time off work to vote.

Fair Pay and Time Off

*I do not like work
even when someone else does it.*

—MARK TWAIN

These days, most of us spend at least half of our waking hours working. Ideally, this time will be spent on jobs that are fulfilling. But whether or not we enjoy our work, the bottom line for almost all of us is to be paid fairly and on time. Fortunately, both state and federal laws protect this right.

I suspect my employer is bending some of the rules on paying employees. What are the legal controls on pay for work?

The most important and far-reaching law guaranteeing a worker's right to be paid fairly is the federal Fair Labor Standards Act or FLSA. The FLSA:

- defines the 40-hour workweek
- covers the federal minimum wage (currently $5.15 per hour)
- sets requirements for overtime, and
- places restrictions on child labor.

The FLSA is the single law most often violated by employers. But employers must also comply with other local, state or federal workplace laws that sometimes set higher standards on wages and hours. If a state law sets a higher—or more worker-friendly—standard, then your employer must follow it. So in addition to determining whether you are being paid properly under the FLSA, you may need to check other laws that apply to your situation. For example, many states have a higher minimum wage than mandated by federal law. Your employer must comply with whichever minimum wage is higher.

To learn about state and local labor laws that might apply to you, contact the local office of your state department of labor, which should be able to supply you with written materials setting forth your legal rights.

What is the current minimum wage?

The federal minimum wage is currently $5.15 per hour. But many states have their own minimum wage laws that require a higher rate of pay. For example, Rhode Island's minimum wage is $6.15 per hour. Employers must pay whichever minimum wage rate—federal or state—is higher. To find out the minimum wage rates in the 50 states, the District of Columbia, Puerto Rico and Guam, visit the U.S. Department of Labor's website at http://www.dol.gov/dol/esa/public/minwage/america.htm You can also contact your state labor department for information.

In addition, some cities and counties have enacted so-called "living

wage" ordinances. These can set the minimum wage that your employer must pay even higher. To find out if your area has a living wage ordinance, contact your local government offices.

My boss says that because I'm a supervisor, I am not legally entitled to overtime pay. Is this true?

It may be. Some employees are exempt from the overtime requirements of the FLSA—and the biggest and most abused exemption is for executive, administrative and professional workers. To qualify as an exempt executive, the employee must, among other things, supervise two full-time employees (or the equivalent). The definitions of administrative and professional employees have their own quirks. For example, employees categorized as professionals must perform work that is primarily intellectual. The definitions also change with the employee's salary level. For example, if the weekly salary of the executive, administrative or professional employee exceeds a certain minimum, fewer factors are required to qualify for the exemption.

Determining whether you truly are exempt from overtime requirements becomes even more complex when you factor in state law requirements. If you have a question about whether your particular job is exempt, it may be worth your while to go to the nearest law library and carefully read the Fair Labor Standards Act, 29 U.S.C. §§ 201 and following. You can also read this law online by visiting the U.S. Department of Labor site at http://www.dol.gov.

To learn about overtime laws in your state, contract your state department of labor.

I put in more than forty hours on the job each week, without overtime pay. Am I entitled to time off to compensate for this?

Most workers are familiar with compensatory or comp time—the practice of offering employees time off from work in place of cash payments for overtime. What comes as a shock to many is that the practice is illegal in most situations. Under the FLSA, only state or government agencies may legally allow their employees time off in place of wages (29 U.S.C. § 207(o)). Even then, comp time may be awarded only:

- according to the terms of an agreement arranged by union representatives, or
- if the employer and employee agree to the arrangement before work begins.

When compensatory time is allowed, it must be awarded at the rate of one and one-half times the overtime hours worked—and comp time must be taken during the same pay period that the overtime hours were worked.

Some states do allow private employers to give employees comp time instead of cash. But there are complex, often conflicting laws controlling how and when it may be given. A common control, for example, is that employees must voluntarily request in writing that comp time be given instead of overtime pay—before the extra hours are worked. Check with your state's labor department for special laws on comp time in your area.

Many employers and employees routinely violate the rules governing the use of compensatory time in place of cash overtime wages. However, such violations are risky. Employees can find themselves unable to collect money due them if a company goes out of business or they are fired. And employers can end up owing large amounts of overtime pay to employees as the result of a labor department prosecution of compensatory time violations.

Can my boss force me to work overtime?

Under the FLSA (which, you'll recall, is a federal law) your employer can force you to work overtime and can even fire you if you refuse to do so.

The FLSA does not limit the number of hours in a day or days in a week that an employer can schedule an employee to work. It only requires employers to pay non-exempt employees overtime (time and a half the worker's regular rate of pay) for any hours over 40 that the employee works in a week.

However, your state law may provide additional rights. Contact your state labor department to learn more.

Does my employer have to pay me overtime if I work more than eight hours in a day?

Under the FLSA, your employer does not have to pay you overtime if you work more than eight hours in any given day. The federal law is interested only in weeks, not days, so as long as you work less than 40 hours in a week, you aren't entitled to overtime.

In this area, however, it's definitely worth checking to see what your state law has to say on the subject. Some states, such as California, do require employers to pay overtime to employees who work more than eight hours in a day. Your employer must comply with whichever law—federal or state—is most beneficial to you.

I work as a waitress and make good tips. My boss says that because I get this extra money at work, he can pay me a wage that is lower than the hourly minimum wage. Is this true?

It depends on how much money you make in tips. Employers must pay all employees not less than the minimum wage.

But the matter of minimum wage becomes tricky when an employee routinely receives at least $30 per

month in tips. Under federal law, employers are allowed to credit half of those tips against the minimum wage requirement, which, under federal law, is currently $5.15 per hour. So, they can credit up to $2.12 an hour of the tips received toward their wage obligation and actually pay you only $2.13 an hour. However, the employer's offset must not exceed the tips the employee actually receives.

EXAMPLE

Alphonse is employed as a waiter and earns more than $10 per hour in tips. Denis, the restaurant's owner, is required to pay Alphonse at least $2.13 per hour on top of his tips for the first 40 hours worked in each week.

If business slows and Alphonse's tips dip to, say, $1 an hour, Denis may credit the tip amount toward Alphonse's hourly minimum wage. Denis must pay the additional salary required to make up the full amount of minimum wage Alphonse is owed: $5.15 an hour.

I am required to carry a beeper 24 hours a day, every day of the week for my job. I am occasionally called on my vacation, holidays and other days off. Am I entitled to be paid anything for on-call time?

Under federal law, vacation days, holidays and other paid days off work should be just that—days off work—and you are entitled to enjoy them free from the reins of your beeper. When your employer requires you to be on-call but does not require you to stay on the company's premises, the following two rules generally apply:

- On-call time that you control and use for your own enjoyment or benefit is not counted as payable time.
- On-call time over which you have little or no control and which you cannot use for your own enjoyment or benefit is payable time.

Disputes usually boil down to the slipperiness in the definition of control and use of time. If the occasional beep beckons you only to call in to give advice, but you are otherwise free to spend your time any way you want, your employer need only pay for the time you spend answering the beeper. However, if your employer insists that you be available to return to work on demand and puts constraints on your behavior between beeper calls—you cannot consume alcohol, or you must stay within a certain radius of work, for example—you may be entitled to compensation for your on-call time.

Similarly, if you receive five or six beeper calls on every day off, and if each of those beeps require you to come into the office or be in a specific place, then a court will likely see that your time isn't your own and will require that your employer compensate you.

And—as always—be sure to check with your state labor department to see if your state has different rules.

Independent Contractors Are Exempt

The Fair Labor Standards Act covers only employees, not independent contractors, who are considered independent business people. Whether a person is an employee for purposes of the FLSA, however, generally turns on whether that worker is employed by a single employer, and not on the sometimes more lax Internal Revenue Service definition of an independent contractor.

If nearly all of your income comes from one company, a court would probably rule that you are an employee of that company for purposes of the FLSA, regardless of whether other details of your worklife would appear to make you an independent contractor.

The FLSA was passed to clamp down on employers who cheated workers of their fair wages. As a result, employee status is broadly interpreted so that as many workers as possible come within the protections of the law. In recent cases determining close questions of employment status, growing numbers of courts have found workers to be employees rather than independent contractors.

Courts are more likely to find that workers are employees when:

- the relationship appears to be permanent
- the worker lacks bargaining power with regard to the terms of his or her employment, and
- the individual worker is economically dependent upon the business to which he or she gives service.

What laws ensure my right to take vacations?

Here's a surprising legal truth that most workers would rather not learn: No law requires employers to pay you for time off, such as vacation or holidays. This means that if you receive a paid vacation, it's because of custom, not law.

And just as vacation benefits are discretionary with each employer, so is the policy of how and when they accrue. For example, it is perfectly legal for an employer to require a certain length of employment—six months or a year are common—before an employee is entitled to any vacation time. It is also legal for employers to prorate vacations for part-time employees, or to deny them the benefit completely. Employers are also free to set limits on how much paid

time off employees may store up before it must be taken or is lost.

If your employer does have a policy of offering employees paid time off, however, it cannot discriminate in offering it—all employees must be subject to the same rules.

If I lose or leave my job, when will I receive my final paycheck?

Unfortunately, there is no easy answer to this question. Many state laws, but not all, mandate that a worker who is fired must be paid all accrued wages and promised vacation pay immediately. Furthermore, state laws often set short limits—generally 72 hours—as the time in which this payment must be made if an employee quits. But you'll need to check with your state's deparment of labor to learn the details of the law that applies to you.

Am I entitled to take time off from work if I get sick?

No law requires an employer to offer paid time off for illness. As with paid vacation time, however, an employer who offers paid sick time to some workers cannot discriminate by denying it to others.

Though you may not be entitled to paid time off, the Family and Medical Leave Act (FMLA), a federal law passed in 1993, gives workers some rights to unpaid leave for medical reasons. Under the FMLA, you may be eligible for up to 12 weeks of unpaid sick leave during any 12-month period. Your employer can count your accrued paid benefits—vacation, sick leave and personal leave days—toward the 12 weeks of leave allowed under the law. But many employers give employees the option of deciding whether or not to include paid leave time as part of their 12 weeks of sick leave.

The FMLA applies to all private and public employers with 50 or more employees—an estimated one-half of the workforce. To be covered under the law, you must have:

- been employed at the same workplace for a year or more, and
- worked at least 1,250 hours (about 24 hours a week) during the year preceding the leave.

There are a number of loopholes in the FMLA. Companies with fewer than 50 employees working at offices within a 75-mile radius are exempt from the FMLA—this means that small regional companies of even the largest corporations may not need to comply with the Act. The law also allows companies to exempt the highest paid 10% of employees. And finally, schoolteachers and instructors who work for educational agencies and private elementary or secondary schools may have restrictions on their FMLA leave.

Note, however, that a number of states have passed their own versions of family leave laws—and most of them give workers more liberal leave rights. A number of laws apply, for example, to smaller workplaces and

extend to workers who have been on the job only a short time. Check with your state's department of labor for more information.

What if a member of my family gets sick—can I take time off to care for him or her?

Possibly. Workers' rights under the Family and Medical Leave Act (FMLA)—or under your state's version of it—also apply if a member of your close family gets sick, or if you give birth to or adopt a child. The rights for new parents apply to both mothers and fathers in all situations—birth or adoption.

My employer refused to grant me the time off for sick leave guaranteed by the FMLA. What can I do?

The FMLA is enforced by the U.S. Department of Labor. If you have specific questions about this law, including how to file a claim against your employer for failing to comply, contact your local Department of Labor office. You should be able to find a listing under U.S. Government, Department of Labor, in the phone book. You can also find a list of local offices of the U.S. Department of Labor by visiting the agency's website at http://www.dol.gov.

You generally must file a claim under the FMLA within two years of an employer's violation. If the violation was willful (intentional), you'll have up to three years to file.

*More Information About
Wages, Hours and Time Off*

You can check into your employer's
wage and payment policies by calling
the local U.S. Labor Department, Wage
and Hour Division office, listed in the
federal government section of your
telephone directory.

Most of the exemptions to FLSA coverage are listed in federal statute, 29
U.S.C. §213. The most direct way to
become familiar with these exemptions is
to read about them in an annotated edition of the U.S. Code, which is what your
local law library (or even a large public
library) is most likely to have. You can
also find this law through Nolo's Legal
Research Center at http://
www.nolo.com/research/index.html.

Also, the United States Department of
Labor, 200 Constitution Avenue, NW,
Washington, DC 20210, 202-219-
7316, offers pamphlets describing
federal wage and hours laws and the
Family Medical Leave Act. Or, visit the
agency's website at http://www.dol.gov.

Workplace Health and Safety

Over the past 20 years, workers have
pushed strongly for laws to protect
their health and safety on the job.
And they have been somewhat successful. Several laws now establish
basic safety standards aimed at reducing the number of illnesses, injuries
and deaths in workplaces. Because
most workplace safety laws rely for
their effectiveness on employees who
are willing to report job hazards, most
laws also prevent employers from firing or discriminating against employees who report unsafe conditions to
proper authorities.

Do I have any legal rights if I feel that my workplace is unsafe or unhealthy?

The main federal law covering threats
to workplace safety is the Occupational
Safety and Health Act of 1970 (OSHA).
OSHA requires employers to provide
a workplace that is free of dangers
that could physically harm employees.

The law quite simply requires that
your employer protect you from "recognized hazards" in the workplace. It
does not specify or limit the types of
dangers covered. Instead, it includes
everything from equipment that
might cause a serious cut or bruise to
the unhealthy effects of long-term
exposure to radiation, chemicals or
airborne pollutants.

Most states now have their own OSHA laws, most of which offer protections similar to the federal law. A few states, including California, require all employers to fashion workplace safety plans. And Texas, big in its approach to most everything, has instituted a 24-hour hotline to receive complaints; the state prohibits employers from discriminating against those who call in.

How do I assert my rights to a safe workplace?

If you feel that your workplace is unsafe, your first action should be to make your supervisor aware of the danger. If your employer doesn't take prompt action, follow up in writing. Then, if you are still unsuccessful in getting your company to correct the safety hazard, you can file a complaint at the nearest OSHA office. Look under the U.S. Labor Department in the federal government section of your local telephone directory. You can also file a complaint online at http://www.osha.gov/as/opa/worker/index.html.

If you feel that a workplace hazard poses an imminent danger (which is a danger that could immediately cause death or serious physical harm), you should act immediately and call the agency's hotline at 800-321-OSHA.

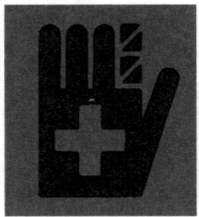

Preventing Additional Injuries

Workplace hazards often become obvious only after they cause an injury. For example, an unguarded machine part that spins at high speed may not seem dangerous until someone's clothing or hair becomes caught in it. But even after a worker has been injured, employers sometimes fail—or even refuse—to recognize that something that hurt one person is likely to hurt another.

If you have been injured at work by a hazard that should be eliminated before it injures someone else, take the following steps as quickly as possible after obtaining the proper medical treatment:

- Immediately file a claim for workers' compensation benefits so that your medical bills will be paid and you will be compensated for your lost wages and injury. In some states, the amount you receive from a workers' comp claim will be larger if a violation of a state workplace safety law contributed to your injury. (For more information about workers' compensation, see the next series of questions in this chapter.)

- Point out to your employer that a continuing hazard or dangerous condition exists. As with most workplace safety complaints, the odds of getting action will be greater if other employees join in your complaint.

- If your employer does not eliminate the hazard promptly, file a complaint with OSHA and any state or local agency that you think may be able to help.

You can obtain a list of state health and safety agencies on the OSHA website at http://www.osha.gov. For example, if your complaint is about hazardous waste disposal, you may be able to track down a specific local group that has been successful in investigating similar complaints in the past.

Does OSHA protect against the harmful effects of tobacco smoke in the workplace?

OSHA rules apply to tobacco smoke only in rare and extreme circumstances, such as when contaminants created by a manufacturing process combine with tobacco smoke to create a dangerous workplace air supply that fails OSHA standards. Workplace air quality standards and measurement techniques are so technical that typically only OSHA agents or consultants who specialize in environmental testing are able to determine when the air quality falls below allowable limits.

If OSHA won't protect me from secondhand tobacco smoke at work, is there anything I can do to limit or avoid exposure?

If your health problems are severely aggravated by co-workers' smoking, there are a number of steps you can take.

Check local and state laws. A growing number of local and state laws prohibit smoking in the workplace. Most of them also set out specific procedures for pursuing complaints. Your state's labor department should have up-to-date information about these. If you can't find local laws that prohibit smoking in workplaces, check with a national nonsmokers' rights group, such as Americans for Nonsmokers Rights, 2530 San Pablo Avenue, Suite J, Berkeley, CA 94702, 510-841-3032, http://www.no-smoke.org.

Ask your employer for an accommodation. Successful accommodations to smoke-sensitive workers have included installing additional ventilation systems, restricting smoking areas to outside or special rooms and segregating smokers and nonsmokers.

Consider income replacement programs. If you are unable to work out a plan to resolve a serious problem with workplace smoke, you may be forced to leave the workplace. But you may qualify for workers' compensation or unemployment insurance benefits. See *Losing or Leaving Your Job*, below.

More Information About Workplace Health and Safety

The Occupational Safety and Health Administration, 200 Constitution Avenue, NW, Washington, DC 20210, 202-693-1999, publishes pamphlets about workplace safety laws. You can also visit OSHA online at http://www.osha.gov.

Workers' Compensation

If you are injured on the job—or suffer a work-related illness or disease that prevents you from working—you may be eligible to receive benefits from your state workers' compensation program. You also may be entitled to free medical care. If your disability is classified as permanent or results in death, additional benefits may be available to you and your family. If you receive workers' compensation benefits, you lose your right to sue your employer for the injury.

Who pays workers' compensation benefits?

In most states, employers are required to purchase insurance for their employees from a workers' compensation insurance company—also called an insurance carrier. In some states, larger employers who are clearly solvent are allowed to self-insure or act as their own insurance companies, while smaller companies (with fewer than three or four employees) are not required to carry workers' compensation insurance at all. When a worker is injured, her claim is filed with the insurance company—or self-insuring employer—who pays medical and disability benefits according to a state-approved formula.

Are all on-the-job injuries covered by workers' compensation?

Most are. The workers' compensation system is designed to provide benefits to injured workers no matter whether an injury is caused by the employer's or employee's negligence. But there are some limits. Generally, injuries caused because an employee is intoxicated or using illegal drugs are not covered by workers' compensation. Coverage may also be denied in situations involving:

- self-inflicted injuries (including those caused by a person who starts a fight)
- injuries suffered while a worker was committing a serious crime
- injuries suffered while an employee was not on the job, and
- injuries suffered when an employee's conduct violated company policy.

If your employer's conduct is especially egregious (for example, your employer did something intentional or reckless that injured you), you may be allowed to bypass the workers' compensation system and sue your employer in court—for much larger amounts of money than you could cover through workers' compensation.

Does an injury have to have a definite date of onset in order to be covered?

Not necessarily. Your injury does not need to be caused by an accident—such as a fall from a ladder. Many workers, for example, receive compensation for repetitive stress injuries, including carpal tunnel syndrome and back problems, that are caused by overuse or misuse over a long period of time. You may also be compensated for some illnesses and diseases that are the gradual result of work conditions—for example, heart conditions, lung disease and stress-related digestive problems.

Are You Covered by Workers' Compensation?

Most workers are eligible for workers' compensation coverage, but every state excludes some workers. Exclusions often include:

- business owners
- independent contractors
- casual workers
- domestic employees in private homes
- farm workers
- maritime workers
- railroad employees, and
- unpaid volunteers.

Check the workers' compensation law of your state to see whether these exclusions affect you.

Federal government employees are also excluded from state workers' compensation coverage, but they receive workers' compensation benefits under a separate federal law.

Employees who aren't covered by workers' compensation usually must sue the employer for damages or, in some cases, they can sue the maker of a faulty piece of equipment.

Do I have to be injured at my workplace to be covered by workers' compensation?

No. As long as your injury is job-related, it's covered. For example, you'll be covered if you are injured while traveling on business, doing a work-related errand or even attending a required, business-related social function.

How do I claim workers' compensation benefits?

First, promptly report the work-related injury or sickness to your employer. Most states require that this be done within two to 30 days following an injury. If an injury occurs over time (for example, a breathing problem or carpal tunnel syndrome), you must report your condition soon after you discover it and realize that it is caused by your work.

Next, get the medical treatment you need and follow the doctor's instructions exactly. (This may include an "off-work order" or a "limited-duties work order.") Finally, file a claim with your workers' compensation carrier. Necessary forms must be provided by your employer. Ask someone in the personnel or benefits department.

Finally, make sure you save copies of all correspondence with your employer, its insurance carrier and your doctor concerning your workers' compensation claim.

What kind of benefits will I receive?

The workers' compensation system provides replacement income, medical expenses and sometimes vocational rehabilitation benefits—that is, on the job training, schooling or job placement assistance. The benefits paid through workers' compensation, however, are almost always limited to relatively modest amounts.

If you become temporarily unable to work, you'll usually receive two-thirds of your average wage up to a fixed ceiling. But because these payments are tax-free, if you received decent wages prior to your injury, you'll fare reasonably well in most states. You will be eligible for these wage-loss replacement benefits as soon as you've lost a few days of work because of an injury or illness that is covered by workers' compensation.

If you become permanently unable to do the work you were doing prior to the injury, or unable to do any work at all, you may be eligible to receive long-term or lump-sum benefits. The amount of the payment you may be entitled to receive varies greatly with the nature and extent of your injuries. If you anticipate a permanent work disability, contact your local workers' compensation office as soon as possible; these benefits are rather complex and may take a while to process.

Social Security Benefits for the Permanently Disabled

If you're permanently unable to return to work, you may qualify for Social Security Disability benefits. Social Security will, over the long run, provide more benefits than workers' compensation—but be forewarned that these benefits are hard to get. They are reserved for seriously injured workers. To qualify, your injury or illness:

- must prevent you from doing any "substantial gainful work," and
- must be expected to last at least twelve months, or to result in death.

If you think you may meet the above requirements, contact your local Social Security office. For more information about Social Security benefits, see Chapter 14.

Can I be treated by my own doctor and, if not, can I trust a doctor provided by my employer?

In some states, you have a right to see your own doctor if you make this request in writing before the injury occurs. More typically, however, injured workers are referred to a doctor or health plan recruited and paid for by their employer.

Your doctor's report will have a big impact upon the benefits you receive. While it's crucial that you tell the doctor the truth about both your injury and your medical history (your benefits may be denied based on fraud if you don't), be sure to clearly identify all possible job-related medical problems and sources of pain. In short, this is no time to downplay or gloss over the presence of a pain.

Keep in mind that a doctor paid for by your employer's insurance company is not your friend. The desire to get future business may motivate a doctor to minimize the seriousness of your injury or to identify it as a pre-existing condition.

If I am initially treated by an insurance company doctor, do I have a right to see my own doctor at some point?

State workers' compensation systems establish technical and often tricky rules in this area. Often, you have the right to ask for another doctor at the insurance company's expense if you clearly state you don't like the one the insurance company provides, although there is sometimes a waiting period before you can get a second doctor. Also, if your injury is serious, you usually have the right to a second opinion. And in some states, after you are treated by an insurance company's doctor for a certain period (90 days is typical), you may have the automatic right to transfer your treatment to your own doctor or health plan—with the cost being paid for by the workers' comp insurance company.

To understand your rights, contact your state worker's compensation office (also called industrial relations office). You can also get copy of your state's rules—or, if necessary, research your state workers' compensation laws and regulations in the law library. The Appendix contains information about how to do your own legal research.

Suppose I suffer an injury to a part of my body that had been injured previously—will I still be covered?

If the previous injury was also work-related, workers' compensation should provide full coverage. If it wasn't, you may receive lower-level benefits.

If your earlier injury occurred at a former job, it's generally up to your current employer's insurance company and your former employer to sort out who's responsible for paying your benefits—sometimes they will split the costs between them.

How do I find a good workers' compensation lawyer—and how much will it cost?

You usually don't need a lawyer unless you suffer a permanent disability, or all or part of your workers' compensation claim is denied. If one of these situations occurs, you'll probably want to do some research to familiarize yourself with your rights and duties. For example, many claims are denied based on a doctor's report claiming that you are not injured. If you dispute this, you may have a right to obtain a second doctor's opinion paid for by the workers' compensation insurer.

If your claim is denied, consider hiring an experienced workers' compensation lawyer to help you navigate the appeals process. The best way to find a good lawyer is often through word of mouth—talk to other injured workers or check with a local union or other workers' organization.

In most states, fees for legal representation in workers' compensation cases are limited to between 10% and 15% of any eventual award. Because these fees are relatively modest, workers' compensation lawyers customarily take on many clients and, as a result, do not have time to provide much individual attention. Most of your contacts with your attorney's office will be with paralegals and other support personnel. This is not a bad thing in itself, if the office is well run by support staff. Be sure that the office is able to stay on top of paperwork and filing deadlines, and that a knowledgeable person is available to answer your questions clearly and promptly.

What to Do When the Insurance Company Won't Pay

Some workers' compensation carriers take an aggressive stance and deny legitimate claims for workers' compensation. When this happens, it's often because the insurer claims you haven't been injured or, if you have, that it's not serious enough to qualify you for temporary or total disability. Commonly,

this is done after a private investigator hired by the insurance company follows you and obtains photographs showing you engaging in fairly strenuous physical activity, such as lifting a box or mowing the lawn, despite claiming a back injury.

If your legitimate benefits are denied, you should immediately file an appeal with your state appeals agency—called the industrial accidents board, the workers' compensation appeals board or something similar. You may also want to hire an attorney to help you press your claim.

If I receive workers' compensation, can I also sue my employer in court?

Generally, no. The workers' compensation system was established as part of a legal trade-off. In exchange for giving up the right to sue an employer in court, you get workers' compensation benefits no matter who was at fault. Before the workers' compensation system was passed, if you went to court, you stood to recover a large amount of money, but only if you could prove the injury was caused by your employer.

Today, you may be able to sue in court if your injury was caused by someone other than your employer (a visitor or outside contractor, for example) or if it was caused by a defective product (such as a flaw in the construction of the equipment you were working with).

You might even be able to sue your employer in court if your injury was caused by intentional, reckless or illegal conduct on your employer's part.

What if my employer tells me not to file a workers' compensation claim or threatens to fire me if I do?

In most states, it is a violation of the workers' compensation laws to retaliate against an employee for filing a workers' compensation claim. If this happens, immediately report it to your local workers' compensation office.

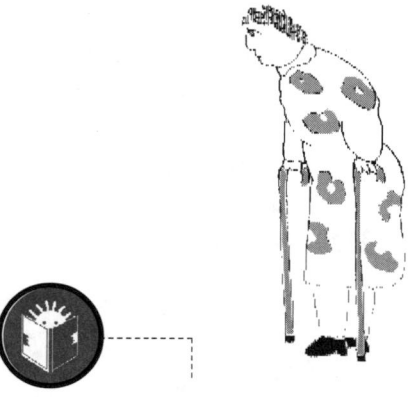

More Information About Workers' Compensation

How to Handle Your Workers' Compensation Claim, by Christopher Ball (Nolo), includes all forms and instructions for filing a workers' compensation claim in California. The book is also useful for people who live elsewhere, given the absence of self-help resources for other states; it provides a good overview of how the system works.

Age Discrimination

Young men think old men are fools, but old men know *young men are fools.*

—GEORGE CHAPMAN

Unfortunately, rather than value older workers' intelligence, experience and work ethic, some employers assume that older workers are "out of touch" or set in their ways. And, because older workers often earn higher salaries and have higher healthcare premiums than younger workers, some employers think they are too "expensive." For these reasons, some employers try to get rid of their more seasoned workers and are reluctant to hire older workers.

Fortunately, federal and state laws afford some protection to older workers who face discrimination in the workplace—and also help protect their pension rights when they leave.

My employer has just cut the workforce in half, singling out older workers. Is there any legal protection for us?

Possibly. The federal Age Discrimination in Employment Act (ADEA) provides that workers over the age of 40 cannot be arbitrarily discriminated against because of age in any employment decision. Perhaps the single most important rule under the ADEA is that no worker can be forced to retire.

Under the ADEA, there has to be a valid reason—not related to age—for all employment decisions, especially lay-offs. Examples of valid reasons would be poor job performance by the employee or an employer's economic trouble. If lay-offs have been announced or are in the wind, talk with other affected workers. If most people who are laid off are 40 or older, and the majority of workers kept on are younger, you may have the basis for an ADEA complaint or lawsuit. This is especially likely if the employer has hired younger workers to take the places of workers over 40.

Many states also have laws that prohibit age discrimination. To find out if your state has such a law, contact your state labor department or fair employment office.

Does the ADEA protect all workers from age discrimination?

Unfortunately not; there are limits on both the employees and the employers who are covered. The ADEA applies only to employees age 40 and older—and only to workplaces with 20 or more employees. The ADEA applies to federal employees, private sector employees and labor union employees. It does not, however, cover state employees.

There are several other exceptions to the broad protection of the ADEA:

- Executives or people "in high policy-making positions" can be forced to retire at age 65 if they would receive annual retirement pension benefits worth $44,000 or more.
- There are special exceptions for police and fire personnel, tenured university faculty and certain federal employees having to do with law enforcement and air traffic control. If you are in one of these categories, check with your personnel office or benefits plan office for details.
- An additional exception to the federal age discrimination law is made when age is an essential part of a particular job—referred to by the legal jargon of a "bona fide occupational qualification" (BFOQ). For example, if an employer who sets age limits on a particular job can prove that the limit is necessary because a worker's ability to adequately perform the particular job does, in fact, diminish after the age limit is reached, it's okay to discriminate. However, it has become more difficult for employers to prove a BFOQ because the law protects workers as young as age 40.

If I'm not protected by the ADEA, is an employer free to discriminate against me because of my age?

That depends on where you live. All states except Alabama and South Dakota have laws against age discrimination in employment, and those state laws often provide greater protection than the federal law. For example, several states provide age discrimination protection to workers before they reach age 40, and other states protect against the actions of employers with fewer than 20 employees. In addition, state laws against age discrimination do protect state employees, unlike the federal ADEA.

To find out more about the laws of your own state, contact your state labor department.

I've noticed a pattern where I work: Older workers tend to be laid off just before their pension rights lock in or vest. Is that legal?

Using various ploys like this one to cheat workers out of their promised pensions is a technique some employers use to save money. But it's not legal. The federal Older Workers Benefit Protection Act forbids

- using an employee's age as the basis for discrimination in benefits, and
- targeting older workers for their staff cutting programs.

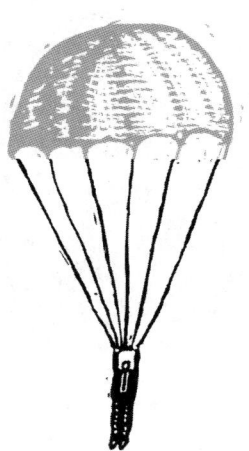

Can my employer force me to take early retirement?

No employer can require you to retire because of your age. An early retirement plan is legal only if it gives you a choice between two options: keeping things as they are or choosing to retire under a plan that leaves you better off than you previously were. This choice must be a genuine one; you must be free to reject the offer. In addition, if either choice leaves you worse off, the offer violates the Older Workers Benefit Protection Act.

How can I enforce my rights under the laws that protect against age discrimination?

If you believe that an employer has discriminated against you because of your age, you can file a complaint with the federal Equal Employment Opportunity Commission (EEOC) just as you would against any other workplace discrimination. Call 800-669-4000 to find the EEOC office nearest you. You can also find a list of EEOC regional offices on the agency's website at http://www.eeoc.gov. If the EEOC does not resolve your complaint to your satisfaction, you can consult an attorney for advice about filing a lawsuit.

In addition, you can file a complaint under your state age discrimination law, if your state has one. Contact your state labor department or fair employment office for details.

Like all fair employment laws, age discrimination laws require you to file a complaint within a specified amount of time, usually 180 days. Therefore, it is important for you to act as soon as you realize that you might be the victim of age discrimination. If you wait too long, you might lose your rights.

Out From Under the Golden Parachute

A growing number of employers ask older workers to sign waivers—also called releases or agreements not to sue. In return for signing the waivers, the employer offers the employee an incentive to leave the job voluntarily, such as a significant amount of severance pay. The Older Workers Benefit Protection Act places a number of restrictions on such waivers:

- Your employer must make the waiver understandable to the people who are likely to use it.
- The waiver may not cover any rights or claims that you discover are available after you sign it, and it must specify that it covers your rights under the ADEA.
- Your employer must offer you something of value (such as severance pay)—over and above what is already owed to you—in exchange for your signature on the waiver.
- Your employer must advise you, in writing, that you have the right to consult an attorney before you sign the waiver.

- If the offer is being made to a group or class of employees, your employer must inform you in writing how the class of employees is defined; the job titles and ages of all the individuals to whom the offer is being made; and the ages of all the employees in the same job classification or unit of the company to whom the offer is not being made.
- You must be given a fixed time in which to make a decision on whether or not to sign the waiver.

More Information About Age Discrimination

Several organizations offer help and information on age discrimination in employment. Among the most helpful are:

American Association of Retired Persons
601 E Street, NW
Washington, DC 20049
800-424-3410
http://www.aarp.org

AARP is a nonprofit membership organization of older Americans open to anyone age 50 or older. It offers a wide range of publications on retirement planning, age discrimination and employment-related topics. Networking and direct services are available through local chapters.

Older Women's League
666 Eleventh Street, NW, Suite 700
Washington, DC 20001
202-783-6686

The Older Women's League provides advice on discrimination and other issues facing elderly men and women.

Sexual Harassment

Sexual harassment on the job took a dramatic leap into public awareness in October 1991, when Professor Anita Hill made known her charges against Judge Clarence Thomas after his nomination to the U.S. Supreme Court. Many other incidents have erupted since then, including investigations into the Navy after the Tailhook incident and into government officials after Senator Bob Packwood was accused of harassing several female staffers. Paula Jones dominated headlines for months with her claim that President Clinton harassed her while a conventioneering governor. And more recently, Mitsubishi Motors agreed to pay a record $34 million settlement to hundreds of women harassed at its auto assembly plant.

Enforcement of the laws prohibiting sexual harassment has been stepped up in the last few years. But in workplaces across America, the issue is far from settled. Sexual harassment is still a daily problem for many workers, especially women.

What is sexual harassment?

In legal terms, sexual harassment is any unwelcome sexual advance or conduct on the job that creates an intimidating, hostile or offensive working environment. In real life, sexually harassing behavior ranges from repeated offensive or belittling jokes to a workplace full of offensive pornography to an outright sexual assault.

Are there laws that protect against sexual harassment on the job?

Yes. But surprisingly, those laws are fairly new. In 1980, the Equal Employment Opportunity Commission (EEOC) issued regulations defining sexual harassment and stating it was a form of sex discrimination prohibited by the Civil Rights Act, which had been originally passed in 1964. In 1986, the U.S. Supreme Court first ruled that sexual harassment was a form of job discrimination—and held it to be illegal.

Today, there is greater understanding that the Civil Rights Act prohibits sexual harassment at work. In addition, most states have their own fair employment practices laws that prohibit sexual harassment—many of them more strict than the federal law. To find out more about the federal prohibition against sexual harassment, contact the EEOC office nearest you. For a list of EEOC regional offices, call the main EEOC office at 800-669-4000 or refer to the agency's website at http://www.eeoc.gov.

To learn more about state laws prohibiting sexual harassment, contact your state labor department or state fair employment office. In addition, your local EEOC office should be able to give you information about the laws in your state.

Can a man be sexually harassed?

Yes, a man can be sexually harassed. The laws prohibiting sexual harassment on the job protect all workers, male and female, from being harassed on the basis of their gender.

But in the overwhelming majority of cases of sexual harassment, it's a male co-worker or supervisor who is harassing a female worker. No one is sure why this is so. Socialization probably plays a part: Men are more likely than women to find sexual advances flattering, women more likely to be perceived as the gatekeepers of sexual conduct. Economics probably enter, too. There are simply more women in the workforce than ever before—and at least some male workers feel the influx as a threat to their own livelihoods. Finally, sexual harassment is usually a power ploy, a way to keep some workers in lower-paid, less respected positions—or force them out of the workplace altogether.

Are gays and lesbians protected by the laws against sexual harassment?

Whether federal civil rights laws protect gays and lesbians is a hot question these days. The U.S. Supreme Court has not addressed the issue, so there is no definitive word on whether gays and lesbians can find shelter under the federal prohibition against sexual harassment in the workplace. A number of lower federal courts have considered the issue, however, and

they have proven to be quite hostile to the protection of gays and lesbians.

If you are gay or lesbian, you might find protection under a state law or a local ordinance. In addition, you might live in an area where the federal courts are more receptive to granting protection. To find out about what laws might protect you in your geographical area, contact the Lambda Legal Defense and Education Fund at 202-809-8585 or http://www.lambdalegal.org.

I'm being sexually harassed at work. What is the first thing I should do?

Tell the harasser to stop. Surprisingly often—some experts say up to 90% of the time—this works.

When confronted directly, harassment is especially likely to end if it is at a fairly low level: off-color jokes, inappropriate comments about your appearance, tacky cartoons tacked onto the office refrigerator or repeated requests for dates after you have said no.

But clearly saying you want the offensive behavior to stop does more than let the harasser know that the behavior is unwelcome. It is also a crucial first step if you later decide to take more formal action against the harasser, whether through your company's complaint procedure or through the legal system. And be sure to document what's going on by keeping a diary or journal; your case will be stronger if you can later prove that the harassment continued after you confronted the harasser.

What if the harassment doesn't stop even after I've confronted the harasser?

If confronting the harasser doesn't work, complain, complain, complain. Talk to your supervisor. Talk to the harasser's supervisor. If that doesn't work, talk to their supervisors, and so on. If your company has a complaint procedure in place, follow it. If your company has a human resources department, talk to someone there. And every step of the way, document your complaints. Save copies of all letters and e-mails. Take notes of all conversations. You have a right to a work environment free of sexual harassment, and you must be assertive about making that right work for you.

Of course, there will be times when you are afraid to complain about harassment, perhaps because the harasser is your supervisor or because the harasser has made threats against you. The laws against sexual harassment prohibit your employer from retaliating against you for complaining about sexual harassment. Although this fact might be cold comfort if you fear for your job or your safety, the fact is that the law can protect you only if you let someone with power at your workplace know about your problem. Be creative. If your supervisor is the one harassing you, go to his supervisor or go to a supervisor in another department.

Collect as much detailed evidence as possible about the harassment. Be sure to save any offensive letters, photographs, cards or notes you receive. And if you were made to feel uncomfortable because of jokes, pin-ups or cartoons posted at work, confiscate them—or at least make copies. An anonymous, obnoxious photo or joke posted on a bulletin board is not anyone else's personal property, so you are free to take it down and keep it as evidence. If that's not possible, photograph the workplace walls. Note the dates the offensive material was posted—and whether there were hostile reactions when you took it down or asked another person to do so.

Also, keep a detailed journal. Write down the specifics of everything that feels like harassment. Include the names of everyone involved, what happened, and where and when it took place. If anyone else saw or heard the harassment, note that as well. Be as specific as possible about what was said and done—and how it affected you, your health or your job performance.

If your employer has conducted periodic evaluations of your work, make sure you have copies. In fact, you may want to ask for a copy of your entire personnel file—before you tip your hand that you are considering taking action against a harassing co-worker. Your records will be particularly persuasive evidence if your evaluations have been good but after you complain, your employer retaliates by trying to transfer or fire you, claiming poor job performance.

If You're Afraid of Offending

The super-cautious advice—don't talk with co-workers about anything but business—is surely overkill. The better approach is to use common sense. There is plenty of room to be friendly and personable without behaving in a way that is likely to offend workers of either gender.

Some rough guides for evaluating your own workplace behavior:

- If you wouldn't say or do something in front of your spouse or parents, it's probably a poor idea to say or do it at work.
- Would you say or do it in front of a colleague of the same gender?
- How would you feel if your mother, wife, sister or daughter were subjected to the same words or behavior?
- How would you feel if a co-worker said or did the same things to you?
- Does it need to be said or done at all?

If you are truly concerned that your words or conduct may be offensive to a co-worker, there is one surefire way to find out: ask.

If the harassment still doesn't stop, what are my options short of filing a lawsuit or a complaint with a government agency?

If the harasser has ignored your oral requests to stop, or you are uncomfortable making the request, write a succint letter demanding an end to the behavior. If that doesn't end the harassment, you may want to take more forceful action. Consider giving a copy of your letter to the harasser's supervisor—along with a memo explaining that the behavior has become more outrageous.

If the harassment still does not abate—or if you believe the supervisor is sympathetic to the harassment or the harasser—send the letter to the next-ranked worker or official at your workplace. Include a cover letter in which you offer your own remedy for the situation—something realistic that might help end the discomfort, such as transferring the harasser to a more distant worksite. If it's your own supervisor who has been harassing you, consider asking to be assigned a different supervisor.

These days, most workplaces have specific written policies prohibiting sexual harassment. If you have followed the steps that seem reasonable to you but the harassment continues, your next option is to pursue any procedure your company has established for handling harassment.

What legal steps can I take to end the harassment?

If all investigation and settlement attempts fail to produce satisfactory results, one option is to file a civil lawsuit for damages either under the federal Civil Rights Act or under a state fair employment practices statute.

Even if you intend right from the beginning to file such a lawsuit, you sometimes must first file a claim with a government agency. For example, an employee pursuing a claim under the Civil Rights Act must first file a claim with the federal EEOC, and a similar complaint procedure is required under some state laws. The EEOC or state agency may decide to prosecute your case on its own, but that happens only occasionally.

More commonly, at some point, the agency will issue you a document referred to as a "right-to-sue" letter that allows you to take your case to court. When filing an action for sexual harassment, you will almost always need to hire a lawyer for help.

More Information About Sexual Harassment

Sexual Harassment on the Job, by William Petrocelli and Barbara Kate Repa (Nolo), explains what sexual harassment is and how to stop it.

9to5, National Association of Working Women
614 Superior Avenue, NW
Cleveland, OH 44113
216-566-9308 (general information)
800-522-0925 (hotline)
http://www.9to5.org

9to5 is a national nonprofit membership organization for working women. It provides counseling, information and referrals for problems on the job, including family leave, pregnancy disability, termination, compensation and sexual harassment. 9to5 also offers a newsletter and publications. There are local chapters throughout the country.

Disability Discrimination

Many individuals fortunate enough to be healthy in mind and body—and to be employed—lament the difficulties a workplace can impose. But for those with physical or mental disabilities, many workplaces can be truly daunting. Fortunately, the federal Americans with Disabilities Act (ADA), has helped to level the playing field a bit.

What laws protect disabled workers from workplace discrimination?

The Americans with Disabilities Act (ADA) prohibits employment discrimination on the basis of workers' disabilities. Generally, the ADA prohibits employers from:
- discriminating on the basis of virtually any physical or mental disability
- asking job applicants questions about their past or current medical conditions
- requiring job applicants to take medical exams, and
- creating or maintaining worksites that include substantial physical barriers to the movement of people with physical disabilities.

The ADA covers companies with 15 or more employees. Its coverage broadly extends to private employers, employment agencies and labor organizations. A precursor of the ADA, the Vocational Rehabilitation Act, prohibits discrimination against disabled workers in state and federal government.

In addition, many state laws protect against discrimination based on physical or mental disability.

Exactly whom does the ADA protect?

The ADA's protections extend to disabled workers—defined as people who:

- have a physical or mental impairment that substantially limits a major life activity
- have a record of impairment, or
- are regarded as having an impairment.

An impairment includes physical disorders, such as cosmetic disfigurement or loss of a limb, as well as mental and psychological disorders.

The ADA protects job applicants and employees who, although disabled as defined above, are still qualified for a particular job. In other words, they would be able to perform the essential functions of a job with some form of accommodation, such as wheelchair access, a voice-activated computer or a customized workspace. As with other workers, whether a disabled worker is deemed qualified for a given job depends on whether he or she has appropriate skill, experience, training or education for the position.

If I am disabled, how do I get my employer to accommodate my disability?

The first step is simple, but often skipped: Ask. The ADA places the burden on you, the employee, to in-

form the employer that you have a disability and that you need an accommodation for it. Indeed, the ADA forbids employers from asking employees whether they have a disability.

When you ask for an accommodation, you do not need to use formal legal language or even do it in writing (though it's always a good idea to document your request). Just tell your employer what your disability is and why you need an accommodation. If you aren't comfortable going to your employer and making this request yourself, you can ask a friend, family member, or representative to do it for you.

Once you request the accommodation, your employer should engage in an informal process of determining whether it can accommodate you and, if so, how. Remember that your employer may be concerned about cost or worried that other employees may incorrectly view you as getting "special treatment." The more helpful and understanding you can be during this process, the more likely it is that your employer will find a way to accommodate you.

As part of this process, your employer is allowed to ask you for documentation, or proof, of your disability. It is important that you comply with this request to the best of your ability; if you don't, then you will lose your right to an accommodation.

If an accommodation is not "reasonable" (see below for more explanation), your employer does not have to provide it. Nor does your employer have to provide you with the accommodation that you want, as long as it provides another one that is effective.

You don't have to accept a particular accommodation, but be prepared to defend your choice on the grounds that the accommodation isn't effective. If a court decides that the offered accommodation was reasonable, you may no longer be qualified for the job, and your employer can terminate you.

Accommodations Don't Need to Cost a Bundle

According to ergonomic and job accommodation experts, the cost of accommodating a particular worker's disability is often surprisingly low.

- 31% of accommodations cost nothing.
- 50% cost less than $50.
- 69% cost less than $500.
- 88% cost less than $1,000.

The Job Accommodation Network (JAN), which provides information about how to accommodate people with disabilities, gives the following examples of inexpensive accommodations:

- Glare on a computer screen caused an employee with an eye disorder to get eye fatigue. The problem was solved with a $39 antiglare screen.
- A deaf medical technician couldn't hear the buzz of a timer, which was necessary for laboratory tests. The problem was solved with an indicator light at a cost of $26.95.

To contact JAN, call 1-800-526-7234 or visit its website at http://janweb.icdi.wvu.edu.

How can I tell if a particular accommodation offered by my employer is reasonable?

The ADA points to several specific accommodations that are likely to be deemed reasonable—some of them changes to the physical set-up of the workplace, some of them changes to how or when work is done. They include:

- making existing facilities usable by disabled employees—for example, by modifying the height of desks and equipment, installing computer screen magnifiers or installing telecommunications devices for the deaf
- restructuring jobs—for example, allowing a ten-hour/four-day workweek so that a worker can receive weekly medical treatments
- modifying exams and training materials—for example, allowing more time for taking an exam, or allowing it to be taken orally instead of in writing
- providing a reasonable amount of additional unpaid leave for medical treatment
- hiring readers or interpreters to assist an employee, and
- providing temporary workplace specialists to assist in training.

These are just a few possible accommodations. The possibilities are limited only by an employee's and employer's imaginations—and the reality that might make one or more of these accommodations financially impossible in a particular workplace.

When can an employer legally claim that a particular accommodation is simply not feasible?

The ADA does not require employers to make accommodations that would cause them an undue hardship—a weighty concept defined in the ADA only as "an action requiring significant difficulty or expense."

The Equal Employment Opportunity Commission (EEOC), the federal agency responsible for enforcing the ADA, has set out some of the factors that will determine whether a particular accommodation presents an undue hardship on a particular employer:

- the nature and cost of the accommodation
- the financial resources of the employer (a large employer may be expected to foot a larger bill than a mom-and-pop business)
- the nature of the business (including size, composition and structure of the workforce), and
- accommodation costs already incurred in the workplace.

It is not easy for employers to prove that an accommodation is an undue hardship, as financial difficulty alone is not usually sufficient. Courts will look at other sources of money, including tax credits and deductions available for making some accommodations, as well as the disabled employee's willingness to pay for all or part of the costs.

Taking Action Under the ADA

The ADA is enforced by the Equal Employment Opportunity Commission (EEOC). To start an investigation of your claim, file a complaint at the local EEOC office. Call 800-669-4000 to find the office nearest you. Or refer to the agency's website at http://www.eeoc.gov.

If you live in a state with laws that protect workers against discrimination based on physical or mental disability, you can choose to file a complaint under your state's law, the ADA or both. To find out about state laws, contact your state labor department or fair employment office.

For additional information on the ADA, contact:

Office of the Americans
with Disabilities Act
Civil Rights Division
U.S. Department of Justice
P.O. Box 66118
Washington, DC 20035-6118
Hotline:
800-514-0301 (voice)
800-514-0383 (TTY)
http://www.usdoj.gov/
crt/ada/adahom1.htm

Losing or Leaving Your Job

Nothing is really work unless you would rather be doing something else.

—SIR JAMES A. BARRIE

The possibility of being laid off or fired looms large in the list of fears of most workers. Employers have traditionally had a free hand to hire and fire, but a number of recent laws and legal rulings restrict these rights.

For what reasons can I be fired?

Unfortunately, the answer to this question is: "It depends." Generally, the reasons for which you can be fired depend in large part on whether you have a contract for employment.

Determining whether you have an employment contract can be tricky. A contract can be oral or written, express or implied. Sometimes, a contract is a document labeled "Contract for Employment" that has a number of provisions and that is signed by you and your employer. Other times, it is an oral promise that your employer makes to you when you are hired that you will only be fired if you perform your job incompetently. Still other times, it is something that is implied from the peculiar circumstances of your employment, such as the amount of time you have worked for your employer, the way that your employer has treated other employees and provisions in your employee handbook.

If you do have a contract for employment, that generally (but not always) means that you can be fired only for "good cause," a legal concept that includes such things as incompetence, excessive absences and violation of work rules.

If you don't have a contract for employment (which is likely since the majority of employees in this country do not have employment contracts), then your employer can terminate you for any reason that isn't illegal (see below). For example, your employer can terminate you simply because she doesn't like you or because your work style does not fit in with the company or because you and your supervisor disagree too much on how your job should be done. Be aware, however, that sometimes these sorts of superficial reasons, such as "I just didn't like her" or "She didn't fit in with the rest of the office," can mask the real reason behind the termination, which is an illegal one.

Whether or not you have an employment contract, the law does place limits on your employer's ability to fire you. For example, employers do not have the right to discriminate against you illegally or to violate state or federal laws, such as those controlling wages and hours. Most state discrimination laws are quite broad. In addition to protecting against the traditional forms of discrimination based on race, color, religion, national origin and age, many also protect against discrimination based on sexual orientation, physical and mental disability, marital status and receiving public funds.

Separate state laws protect workers from being fired or demoted for taking advantage of laws protecting them from discrimination and unsafe workplace practices. And there are a number of other more complex reasons that may make it illegal for an employer to fire you—all boiling down to the fact that an employer must deal with you fairly and honestly.

I've just received a warning from my employer, and I suspect I will be fired soon. What should I do?

If you find yourself on the receiving end of a disciplinary notice you consider to be unfair, there are several steps you should take to avoid losing your job.

First, be sure you understand exactly what work behavior is being challenged. Check your company handbook to see if there is a clear policy against what you've done. If you are unclear, ask for a meeting with your supervisor or human resources staff to discuss the issue more thoroughly.

If you think that there might be some truth to what you are told, find out what you can do to improve the situation. Arrange a meeting with your supervisor and ask her what you can do to improve. Or you can make your own suggestions. For example, if your employer is unhappy with your

performance, consider requesting training or educational materials. If your employer thinks that you talk too much on company time, ask to move your workstation to a place where you won't be quite so tempted to talk. Make sure you document any meeting or communication with your supervisor regarding the discipline, your performance and strategies you can pursue to improve.

If you disagree with allegations that your work performance or behavior is poor, you may want to ask for the assessment in writing. You can then write a clarification and ask that it be inserted in your personnel file. But do this only if you feel your employer's assessment is clearly inaccurate; otherwise you may risk escalating a minor verbal reprimand into a more major incident that will be permanently recorded in your file. Before you sit down to write, take some time to reflect and perhaps discuss your situation with friends.

If you think you are likely to be fired, see if any policy in the employee handbook will buy you time—for example, the right to file an appeal— so the controversy can die down and, if necessary, you can change your work habits.

Finally, read between the lines to see whether your employer's action may be discriminatory or in other ways unfair. Look particularly at the timing. For example, if you were let go shortly before your rights in the company pension plan were permanently locked in or vested, the company may be guilty of age discrimination. Look also at uneven applications of discipline: Are women more often given substandard performance reviews or fired before they could be elevated to supervisor?

What can I do to protect any legal rights I might have before leaving my job?

Even if you decide not to challenge the legality of your firing, you will be in a much better position to enforce all of your workplace rights if you keep careful written records of everything that happens. For example, if you apply for unemployment insurance benefits and your former employer challenges that application, you will probably need to prove that you were dismissed for reasons that were not related to your misconduct.

There are a number of ways to document events. The easiest is to keep an employment diary where you record and date each significant work-related event such as performance reviews, commendations or reprimands, salary increases or decreases and even informal comments your supervisor makes to you about your work. Note the date, time and location for each event, which members of management were involved and whether or not witnesses were present. Whenever possible, back up your log with materials issued by your employer, such as copies of the employee handbook, memos, brochures, employee orientation videos and any written evaluations, commendations or criticisms of your work. In addition, if a problem develops, ask to see your personnel file and make a copy of all reports and reviews in it.

Am I entitled to severance pay if I'm fired?

No law requires an employer to provide severance pay. Nevertheless, some employers voluntarily offer one or two months' salary to employees who are laid off. A few are more generous to long-term employees, basing severance pay on a formula such as one month's pay for every year an employee worked for the company.

An employer may be legally obligated to give you some severance pay if you were promised it, as evidenced by:
- a written contract stating that severance will be paid
- a promise in an employee handbook of severance pay
- a long history of the company paying severance to other employees in your position, or
- an oral promise to pay you severance—although you may run into difficulties proving the promise existed.

My biggest concern about losing my job is losing health insurance coverage. Do I have any rights?

Ironically, workers have more rights to health insurance coverage after they lose their jobs than while employed. This is because of a 1986 law, the Consolidated Omnibus Budget Reconciliation Act (COBRA). Under COBRA, employers with 20 or more employees must offer them the option of continuing to be covered by the company's group health insurance plan at the workers' own expense for a specific period—often 18 months—

after employment ends. Family coverage is also included. In some other circumstances, such as the death of the employee, that employee's dependents can continue coverage for up to 36 months.

Another federal law, the Health Insurance Portability and Accountability Act, makes it easier for employees to change jobs without the fear of losing insurance coverage—and makes it easier for many employees to get coverage in the first place. The law imposes some restrictions on group health plans, including HMOs. Under this law:

- Employees with preexisting conditions may not be denied coverage under a new health insurance plan if they have been continuously covered for 12 months under another plan. Employees who do not have this prior coverage may be denied coverage based on a preexisting condition for only one year.

- No group health plan may discriminate in eligibility for coverage or premiums based on health status, physical or mental condition, claims experience, receipt of healthcare, medical history, genetic information, evidence of insurability or disability of the individual or dependents seeking coverage.

Getting Money When You're Out of Work

If you've lost your job, you may be desperately seeking income. It's best to act quickly to apply for unemployment and other possible benefits, as there is often a delay—in a few states, as long as six weeks—between the time you apply and the date on which you actually receive a check.

Here is a brief breakdown of what is covered by each of the three major income replacement programs.

Unemployment insurance. This program may provide some financial help if you lose your job, temporarily or permanently, through no fault of your own. Benefits will be less than your former pay and temporary—often lasting for about 26 weeks.

Workers' compensation. When you cannot work because of a work-related injury or illness, this program is designed to provide you with prompt replacement income. It may also pay the medical bills resulting from a workplace injury or illness; compensate you for a permanent injury, such as the loss of a limb; and provide death benefits to the survivors of workers who die from a workplace injury or illness. For more information, see the questions and answers on workers' compensation that appear earlier in this chapter.

Social Security disability insurance. This is intended to provide income to adults who, because of injury or illness, cannot work for at least 12 months. Unlike the workers' compensation program, it does not require that your disability be caused by a workplace injury or illness.

Also consider possible income from a private disability insurance program if you were paying for it through payroll withholdings, or if your employer paid for such premiums.

In addition, a few states offer disability benefits as part of their unemployment insurance programs. Typical program requirements mandate that you submit your medical records and show that you requested a leave of absence from your employer. Some may also require proof that you intend to return to your job when you recover. Call the local unemployment insurance and workers' compensation insurance offices to determine whether your state is one that maintains this kind of coverage.

http://www.nolo.com

Nolo offers self-help information about a wide variety of legal topics, including workplace rights.

http://www.eeoc.gov

The U.S. Equal Employment Opportunity Commission is the federal agency responsible for enforcing federal fair employment laws, including Title VII (which outlaws discrimination in employment based on race, gender, religion and national ori-

gin), the Equal Pay Act, the Age Discrimination in Employment Act and the Americans with Disabilities Act. The agency's website is a gold mine of information about these fair employment laws. Among other things, it includes information on your workplace rights, the text of the fair employment laws and instructions on how to file a charge against your employer.

http://www.dol.gov

The U.S. Department of Labor enforces many of the laws that govern your relationship with your employer, including wage and hour laws, health and safety laws and benefits laws. This website offers information about your rights under all of the laws enforced by the department, and it contains links to state labor department websites.

http://www.law.cornell.edu

The Legal Information Institute at Cornell Law School provides information about discrimination in the workplace, including relevant codes and regulations.

http://www.ahipubs.com

The Alexander Hamilton Institute serves up common sense packaged as FAQs about many aspects of employment, from benefits to safety and health concerns. The information is aimed at managers, but it's helpful for employees, too.

Small Businesses

5.2	Before You Start
5.8	Legal Structures for Small Businesses
5.15	Nonprofit Corporations
5.18	Small Business Taxes
5.24	Home-Based Businesses
5.29	Employers' Rights & Responsibilities

Business is never so healthy as when, like a chicken, it must do a certain amount of scratching for what it gets.

—HENRY FORD

For all sorts of personal and economic reasons, more Americans are starting and running their own businesses today than ever before. This trend has been helped by the increasing availability of powerful and affordable data storage and communications equipment, most notably the personal computer and the Internet. Because of this accessible technology, today's savvy small-time operator can often accomplish tasks that just a few decades ago could be tackled only by large corporations.

But not all change has been positive. When it comes to the law, the relatively informal world of just 40 years ago—where deals were often sealed with a handshake—has given way to a world where legal rules affect almost every small business relationship, including organizing the business, dealing with co-owners, hiring and supervising employees and relating to customers and suppliers. Staying on top of all these rules is as necessary as it is challenging. Fortunately, by using affordable, good quality self-help legal resources and getting additional help from a knowledgeable small business lawyer, you can master the laws you need to know to keep your business healthy.

Before You Start

Your imagination is your preview of life's coming attractions.

—ALBERT EINSTEIN

No matter what type of business you're thinking of starting, there are some practical and legal issues you'll face right away, including choosing a name and location for your business, deciding whether or not to hire employees, writing a business plan, choosing a legal structure (sole proprietorship, partnership, corporation or limited liability company), establishing a system for reporting and paying taxes and adopting policies to deal with your customers. This section addresses many of these concerns. As you read, don't be discouraged by the details. If you have chosen a business that you will truly enjoy and, after creating a tight business plan, are confident you'll make a decent profit, your big jobs are done. Furthermore, many people and affordable sources of information are available to help you cope with the practical details we discuss here.

I'm thinking of starting my own business. What should I do first?

Be sure you are genuinely interested in what the business does. If you aren't, you are unlikely to succeed in the long run—no matter how lucrative your work turns out to be. Yes, going into business with a firm plan to make a good living is important, but so, too, is choosing a business that fits your life goals in an authentic way. Here are a few things you might want to consider before you take the leap:

• Do you know how to accomplish the principal tasks of the business? (Don't open a transmission repair shop if you hate cars, or a restaurant if you can't cook.)

- If the business involves working with others, do you do this well? If not, look into the many opportunities to begin a one-person business.

- Do you understand basic business tasks, such as bookkeeping and how to prepare a profit-and-loss forecast and cash-flow analysis? If not, learn before—not after—you begin.

- Does the business fit your personality? If you are a shy introvert, stay away from businesses that require lots of personal selling. If you are easily bored, find a business which will allow you to deal with new material on a regular basis (publishing a newsletter, for example).

What should I keep in mind when choosing a name for my business?

First, assume that you will have competitors and that you will want to market your products or services under the name you choose. (This will make your name a trademark.) For marketing purposes, the best names are those that customers will easily remember and associate with your business. Also, if the name is memorable, it will be easier to stop others from using it in the future.

Most memorable business names are made-up words, such as Exxon and Kodak, or are somehow fanciful or surprising, such as Double Rainbow ice cream and Penguin Books. And some notable names are cleverly suggestive, such as The Body Shop (a store that sells personal hygiene products) and Accuride tires.

Names that tend to be forgotten by consumers are common names (names of people), geographic terms and names that literally describe some aspect of a product or service. For instance, Steve's Web Designs may be very pleasing to Steve as a name, but it's not likely to help Steve's customers remember his company when faced with competitors such as Sam's Web Designs and Sheri's Web Designs. Similarly, names like Central Word Processing Services or Robust Health Foods are not particularly memorable.

Of course, over time even a common name can become memorable through widespread use and advertising, as with Ben and Jerry's Ice Cream. And unusual names of people can sometimes be very memorable indeed, as with Fuddrucker's (restaurants and family entertainment centers).

Choosing a Domain Name

If your business will have a website, part of choosing your business name will be deciding on a domain name. Using all or part of your business name in your domain name will make your website easier for potential customers to find. But many domain names are already taken, so you'll want to see what's available before you settle on a business name. See *Conducting a Trademark Search* in Chapter 8, *Trademarks*, for more information on conducting name searches.

How do I find out whether I'm legally permitted to use the business name I've chosen?

Your first step depends on whether you plan to form a corporation or a limited liability company (LLC). If you do, you should check with the Secretary of State's office in your state to see whether your proposed name is the same or confusingly similar to an existing corporate or LLC name in your state. If it is, you'll have to choose a different name.

If you don't plan to incorporate or form an LLC, check with your county clerk to see whether your proposed name is already on the list maintained for fictitious or assumed business names in your county. In the few states where assumed business name registrations are statewide, check with your Secretary of State's office. (The county clerk should be able to tell you whether you'll need to check the name at the state level.) If you find that your chosen name or a very similar name is listed on a fictitious or assumed name register, you shouldn't use it.

If my proposed business name isn't listed on a county or state register, am I free to use it however I like?

Not necessarily. Even if you are permitted to use your chosen name as a corporate, LLC or assumed business name in your state or county, you might not be able to use the name as a trademark or service mark. To understand what all this is about, consider the potential functions of a business name:

- A business name may be a trade name that describes the business for purposes of bank accounts, invoices, taxes and the public.
- A business name may be a trademark or servicemark used to identify and distinguish products or services sold by the business (for example, Ford Motor Co. sells Ford automobiles, and McDonald's Corporation offers McDonald's fast food services).

While your corporate or assumed business name registration may legally clear the name for the first purpose, it doesn't speak to the second. For example, if your business is organized as a limited liability company or corporation, you may get the green light from your Secretary of State to use IBM Toxics as your business name (if no other corporation or LLC in your state is using it or something confusingly similar), but if you try to use that name out in the marketplace, you're asking for a claim of trademark violation from the IBM general counsel's office.

To find out whether you can use your proposed name as a trademark or servicemark, you will need to do what's known as a trademark search. See Chapter 8, *Trademarks*.

I've found out that the name I want to use is available. What do I need to do to reserve it for my business?

If you are forming a corporation or an LLC, every state has a procedure—operated by the Secretary of State's office—under which a proposed name can be reserved for a certain period of time, usually for a fee. Additional reservation periods can usually be purchased for additional fees. (For more information about corporations and LLCs, see *Legal Structures for Small Businesses*, below.)

If you are not forming a corporation or an LLC, then you may need to file a fictitious or assumed business name statement with the agency that handles these registrations in your state (usually the county clerk, but sometimes the Secretary of State). Generally speaking, you need to file a fictitious business name statement only if your business name does not include the legal names of all the owners.

If you plan to use your business name as a trademark or servicemark and your service or product will be marketed in more than one state (or across territorial or international borders), you can file an application with the U.S. Patent and Trademark Office to reserve the name for your use. See Chapter 8, *Trademarks*.

What should I keep in mind when choosing a location for my business?

Commercial real estate brokers are fond of saying the three most important factors in establishing a business are location, location and location. While true for some types of businesses—such as a retail sandwich shop that depends on lunchtime walk-in trade—for many, locating in a popular, high-cost area is a mistake. For example, if you design computer soft-

ware, repair tile, import jewelry from Indonesia or do any one of ten thousand other things that don't rely on foot traffic, your best bet is to search out convenient, low-cost, utilitarian surroundings. And even if yours is a business that many people will visit, consider the possibility that a low-cost, offbeat location may make more sense than a high-cost, trendy one.

What about zoning and other rules that restrict where a business may locate?

Never sign a lease without being absolutely sure you will be permitted to operate your business at that location. If the rental space is in a shopping center or other retail complex, this involves first checking carefully with management, because many have contractual restrictions (for example, no more than two pizza restaurants in the Mayfair Mall). If your business will be located in a non-shopping center area, you'll need to be sure that you meet applicable zoning rules, which typically divide a municipality into residential, commercial, industrial and mixed-use areas.

You'll also need to find out whether any other legal restrictions will affect your operations. For example, some cities limit the number of certain types of business—such as fast food restaurants or coffee bars—in certain areas, and others require that a business provide off-street parking, close early on weeknights, limit advertising signs or meet other rules as a condition of getting a permit. Fortunately, many cities have business development offices that help small business owners understand and cope with restrictions.

What is a business plan, and do I need to write one?

A business plan is a written document that describes the business you want to start and how it will become profitable. The document usually starts with a statement outlining the purpose and goals of your business and how you plan to realize them, including a detailed marketing plan. It should also contain a formal profit-and-loss projection and cash-flow analysis designed to show that if the business develops as expected, it will be profitable.

Your business plan enables you to explain your business prospects to potential lenders and investors in a language they can understand. Even more important, the intellectual rigor of creating a tight business plan will help you see whether the business you hope to start is likely to meet your personal and financial goals. Many times when budding entrepreneurs take an honest look at their financial numbers, they see that hoped-for profits are unlikely to materialize. Or, put another way, one of the most important purposes of writing a good business plan is to talk yourself out of starting a bad business.

I plan to sell products and services directly to the public. What do I need to know to comply with consumer protection laws?

Many federal and state laws regulate the relationship between a business and its customers. These laws cover such things as advertising, pricing, door-to-door sales, written and implied warranties and, in a few states, layaway plans and refund policies. You can find out more about consumer protection laws by contacting the Federal Trade Commission, 6th and Pennsylvania Avenue, NW, Washington DC 20850, 202-326-2222, http://www.ftc.gov, and by contacting your state's consumer protection agency.

Although it's essential to understand and follow the rules that protect consumers, most successful businesses regard them as only a foundation for building friendly customer service policies designed to produce a high level of customer satisfaction. For example, many enlightened businesses tell their customers they can return any purchase for a full cash refund at any time for any reason. Not only does this encourage existing customers to continue to patronize the business, but it can be a highly effective way to get customers to brag about the business to their friends.

Selling Goods and Services on Consignment

Many small business people, especially those who produce art, crafts and specialty clothing items, sell on consignment. In a consignment agreement, the owner of goods (in legal jargon, the consignor) puts the goods in the hands of another person or business—usually a retailer (the consignee)—who then attempts to sell them. If the goods are sold, the consignee receives a fee, which is usually a percentage of the purchase price, and the rest of the money is sent to the consignor. For example, a sculptor (the consignor) might place his or her work for sale at an art gallery (the consignee) with the understanding that if the artwork sells, the gallery keeps 50% of the sale price. Or a homeowner might leave old furniture with a resale shop that will keep one-third of the proceeds if the item sells. Typically, the consignor remains the owner of the goods until the consignee sells them.

As part of any consignment of valuable items, the consignor (owner) wants to be protected if the goods are lost or stolen while in the consignee's possession. The key here is to establish that the consignee has an insurance policy which will cover any loss. When extremely valuable items are being consigned, it's often appropriate for the cosignor to ask to be named as a co-insured so that she can receive a share of the insurance proceeds if a loss occurs.

If you're a consignee, check your insurance coverage. Before you accept the risk of loss or theft, make sure your business insurance policy covers you for loss of "personal property of others" left in your possession—and that the amount of coverage is adequate. Getting full reimbursement for the selling price of consigned goods may require an added supplement (called an endorsement) to your insurance policy. Check with your insurance agent or broker.

For a consignment contract, including detailed insrtructions and guidance, as well as small business forms and contracts, see Nolo's new business software, *Quicken Lawyer Business.*

More Information About Starting Your Small Business

Legal Guide for Starting & Running a Small Business, by Fred S. Steingold (Nolo), provides clear, plain-English explanations of the laws that affect business owners every day. It covers partnerships, corporations, limited liability companies, leases, trademarks, contracts, franchises, insurance, hiring and firing and much more.

Legal Forms for Starting & Running a Small Business, by Fred S. Steingold (Nolo), contains the forms and instructions you need to accomplish many routine legal tasks, such as borrowing money, leasing property and contracting for goods and services.

The Small Business Start-Up Kit, by Peri H. Pakroo (Nolo), shows you how to choose from among the basic types of business organizations, write an effective business plan, file the right forms in the right place, acquire good bookkeeping and accounting habits and get the proper licenses and permits.

Small Time Operator, by Bernard Kamoroff, C.P.A. (Bell Springs Publishing), is a good source of practical information on getting a small business off the ground—from business licenses, to taxes, to basic accounting. It includes ledgers and worksheets to get you started.

Quicken Lawyer Business, (software by Nolo), contains over 60 interactive forms and contracts that all small businesses should have, plus the text of five best-selling Nolo business titles.

Running a One-Person Business, by Claude Whitmyer and Salli Rasberry (Ten Speed Press), covers the nuts and bolts of doing business on your own: finances, time management, marketing and more.

How to Write a Business Plan, by Mike McKeever (Nolo), shows you how to write the business plan necessary to finance your business and make it work. It includes up-to-date sources of financing.

Guerrilla Marketing, by Jay Conrad Levinson (Houghton Mifflin), contains hundreds of ideas and strategies to help you market your business.

Marketing Without Advertising, by Michael Phillips and Salli Rasberry (Nolo), shows you how to generate sales and encourage customer relations without spending a lot of money on advertising.

Legal Structures for Small Businesses

There is no one legal structure that's best for all small businesses. Whether you're better off starting as a sole proprietor or choosing one of the more complicated organizational structures, such as a partnership, corporation or limited liability company (LLC), usually depends on several factors, in-

cluding the size and profitability of your business, how many people will own it and whether it will entail liability risks not covered by insurance.

If I'm the only owner, what's the easiest way to structure my business?

The vast majority of small business people begin as sole proprietors, because it's cheap, easy and fast. With a sole proprietorship, there's no need to draft an agreement or go to the trouble and expense of registering a corporation or limited liability company (LLC) with your state regulatory agency. All it usually entails is getting a local business license, and unless you are doing business under your own name, filing and possibly publishing a fictitious name statement.

If it's so simple, why aren't all businesses sole proprietorships?

There are several reasons why doing business as a sole proprietor is not appropriate for everyone. First, a sole proprietorship is possible only when a business is owned by one person or, in some cases, a husband and wife. Second, the owner of a sole proprietorship is personally responsible for all business debts, whereas limited liability companies and corporations normally shield their owners' assets from such debts. And finally, unlike a corporation (or a partnership or LLC that elects to be taxed as a corporation), which is taxed separately from its owners (something that can result in lower taxes for some small businesses—see below), a sole proprietor and her business are considered to be the same legal entity for tax purposes. This means you'll report all of the business's income, expenses and deductions on your individual tax return.

I'm starting my business with several other people. What are the advantages and disadvantages of forming a general partnership?

One big advantage of a general partnership is that you usually don't have to register it with your state and pay an often hefty fee, as you do to establish a corporation or limited liability company. And because a partnership is normally a "pass through" tax entity (the partners, not the partnership, are taxed on the partnership's profits), filing income tax returns is easier than it is for a regular corporation, where separate tax returns must be filed for the corporate entity and its owners. But because the business-related acts of one partner legally bind all others, it is essential that you go into business with a partner or partners you completely trust. It is also essential that you prepare a written partnership agreement establishing, among other things, each partner's share of profits or losses and day-to-day duties as well as what happens if one partner dies or retires.

Finally, a major disadvantage of doing business as a partnership is that all partners are personally liable for business debts and liabilities (for example, a judgment in a lawsuit).

While it's true that a good insurance policy can do much to reduce lawsuit worries and that many small, savvy businesses do not face debt problems, it's also true that businesses that face significant risks in either of these areas should probably organize themselves as a corporation or LLC in order to benefit from the limited liability these business structures provide.

What exactly is "limited liability"— and why is it so important?

Some types of businesses—corporations and limited liability companies are the most common—shield their owners from personal responsibility for business debts. For instance, if the business goes bankrupt, its owners are not usually required to use their personal assets to make good on business losses—unless they voluntarily assume responsibility. Other types of businesses—sole proprietorships and general partnerships—do not provide this shield, which means their owners are personally responsible for business liabilities. To see how this works, assume someone obtains a large court judgment against an incorporated business. Because corporate stockholders are not personally liable for business debts, their houses and other personal assets can't be taken to pay the judgment, even if the corporation files for bankruptcy. By comparison, if a sole proprietorship or partnership gets into the same kind of trouble, the houses, bank accounts and other valuable personal assets of the business's owners (and possibly their spouses) can be attached and used to satisfy the debt.

Why do so many small business owners choose not to take advantage of limited liability protection?

Many small businesses simply don't have major debt or lawsuit worries, so they don't need limited liability protection. For example, if you run a small service business (perhaps you are a graphic artist, management consultant or music teacher), your chances of being sued or running up big debts are low. And when it comes to liability for many types of debts, creating a limited liability entity makes little practical difference for newly formed businesses. Often, if you want to borrow money from a commercial lender or establish credit with a vendor, you will be required to pledge your personal assets or personally guarantee payment of the debt (waive limited liability status) should your business be unable to pay.

Finally, organizing your business to achieve limited liability status is no substitute for purchasing a good business insurance policy especially if your business faces serious and predictable financial risks (for instance, the risk that a customer may trip and fall on your premises or that your products may malfunction). After all,

without insurance, if a serious injury occurs, all the assets of your business—which will probably amount to a large portion of your net worth—can be grabbed to satisfy any resulting court judgment. It follows that even if you operate your business as a sole proprietorship, if you purchase comprehensive business insurance, your personal assets may not be at significant risk and you may therefore conclude you don't need limited liability status.

Given all its limitations, when is it wise for a small business person to seek limited liability status?

You should consider forming a business that offers its owners limited liability if:

- your business subjects you to a risk of lawsuits in an area where insurance coverage is unaffordable or incomplete, or
- your business will incur significant debts and is well established and has a good credit rating so that you no longer need to personally guarantee every loan or credit application.

The easiest and most popular way to gain limited liability status is to form a corporation or a limited liability company (LLC).

SMALL BUSINESS STRUCTURES: AN OVERVIEW

Type of Entity	Main Advantages	Main Drawbacks
Sole Proprietorship	Simple and inexpensive to create and operate	Owner personally liable for business debts and liabilities
	Owner reports profit or loss on his or her personal tax return	
General Partnership	Relatively easy and inexpensive to create and operate	Owners (partners) personally liable for business debts
	Owners (partners) report their share of profit or loss on their personal tax returns	Must prepare and file separate partnership tax return
Limited Partnership	Limited partners have limited personal liability for business debts as long as they don't participate in management	General partners personally liable for business debts
	General partners can raise cash without involving outside investors in management of business	More expensive to create than a general partnership
		Suitable mainly for companies that invest in real estate or other businesses
Regular Corporation	Owners have limited personal liability for business debts	More expensive to create than partnership or sole proprietorship
	Owners' fringe benefits (such as health insurance and pension plans) can be deducted as business expenses	Paperwork can seem burdensome to some owners
	Owners can split corporate profit among owners and corporation, sometimes paying a lower overall tax rate	Separate taxable entity that must prepare and file a separate corporate tax
S Corporation	Owners have limited personal liability for business debts	More expensive to create than partnership or sole proprietorship
	Owners report their share of corporate profit or loss on their personal tax returns	More paperwork than for a limited liability company, which offers some of the same advantages
	Owners can use corporate loss to offset income from other sources (such as another business in which they are active)	Income must be allocated to owners in proportion to their ownership interests
		Deductibility of fringe benefits limited for owners who own more than 2% of shares
Professional Corporation	Owners have no personal liability for malpractice of other owners	More expensive to create than partnership or sole proprietorship
		Paperwork can seem burdensome to some owners
		All owners must generally belong to, and often be licensed to practice in, the same profession
Nonprofit Corporation	Corporation doesn't pay income taxes	Full tax advantages available only to groups organized for charitable, scientific, educational, literary or religious purposes
	Contributions to charitable corporations are tax-deductible	
	Fringe benefits can be deducted as business expense	Property transferred to corporation stays there; if corporation ends, property must go to another nonprofit

Type of Entity	Main Advantages	Main Drawbacks
Limited Liability Company	All states except Massachusetts allow LLCs to be organized with only one member	More expensive to create than partnership or sole proprietorship
	Owners have limited personal liability for business debts even if they participate in management	
	Profit and loss can be allocated differently than ownership interests	Laws for creating LLCs in a few states may not reflect latest federal tax changes
	IRS rules now allow LLCs to choose between being taxed as partnership or corporation	
Professional Limited Liability Company	Same advantages as a regular limited liability company	Same as for a regular limited liability company
	Gives state-licensed professionals a way to enjoy those advantages	Members must all belong to the same profession
		At least one state (CA) does not permit professionals to organize as an LLC
Limited Liability Partnership	Mostly of interest to partners in old-line professions such as law, medicine and accounting	Unlike a limited liability company or a professional limited liability company, owners (partners) remain personally liable for many types of obligations owed to business creditors, lenders and landlords
	Owners (partners) aren't personally liable for the malpractice of other partners	
	Owners report their share of profit or loss on their personal tax returns	Not available in all states
		Often limited to a short list of professions

Is forming a corporation difficult?

No. As long as you and close associates and family members will own all of the stock and none of the stock will be sold to the public, the necessary documents—principally your articles of incorporation and corporate bylaws—can usually be prepared in a few hours.

While most states use the term "articles of incorporation" to refer to the basic document creating the corporation, some states (including Connecticut, Delaware, New York and Oklahoma) use the term "certificate of in-

corporation." Washington calls the document a "certificate of formation" and Tennessee calls it a "charter."

The first step is to check with your state's corporate filing office (usually either the Secretary of State or Department of Corporations) and conduct a trademark search to be sure the name you want to use is legally available.

You then fill in blanks in a pre-printed form (available from most states' corporate filing offices or websites) listing the purpose of your corporation, its principal place of business and the number and type of shares of stock. You'll file these documents with the appropriate office, along with a registration fee that will usually be between $200 and $1,000, depending on the state.

You'll also need to complete, but not file, corporate bylaws. These will outline a number of important corporate housekeeping details, such as when annual shareholder meetings will be held, who can vote and the manner in which shareholders will be notified if there is need for an additional "special" meeting.

Fortunately, a good self-help book can make it easy and safe to incorporate your business without a lawyer.

What about operating my corporation? Aren't ongoing legal formalities involved?

Assuming your corporation has not sold stock to the public, conducting corporate business is remarkably straightforward and uncomplicated. Often it amounts to little more than recording key corporate decisions (for example, borrowing money or buying real estate) and holding an annual meeting. Even these formalities can often be done by written agreement and don't usually necessitate a face-to-face meeting between the directors.

Doesn't forming a corporation mean income will be taxed twice—once at the corporate level and then again when dividends are paid to the corporation's owners (shareholders)?

Taxation of business is complicated; we'll be able to cover only the main points here. First, understand that most types of businesses—sole proprietorships and corporations that have qualified for subchapter S status, as well as partnerships and limited liability companies that have not elected to be taxed as regular, or C, corporations—are known as pass-through tax entities, meaning that all business profits and losses are reflected on the individual tax returns of the owners. For example, if a sole proprietor's convenience store turns a yearly profit of $85,000, this amount goes right on his personal tax return. By contrast, a regular profit corporation (and any partnership or LLC that elects to be taxed like a corporation) is a separate tax entity—meaning that the business files a tax return and pays its own taxes.

But the fact that a corporation is taxed separately from its owners doesn't always mean that profits will be taxed twice. That's because owners of most incorporated small businesses are also employees of those businesses; the money they receive in the form of salaries and bonuses is tax-deductible to the corporation as an ordinary and necessary business expense. If it pays surplus money to owners in the form of reasonable salaries, along with bonuses and other fringe benifits, a corporation does not have to show a profit, and therefore will pay no corporate income tax. In addition, most small corporations don't pay dividends, so the dividends aren't taxed twice.

Are there tax advantages to forming a corporation?

Frequently, yes. Corporations pay federal income tax at a lower rate than do most individuals for the first $75,000 of their profits—15% of the first $50,000 of profit and 25% of the next $25,000. By contrast, in a sole proprietorship or partnership, where the business owner(s) pay taxes on all profits at their personal income tax rates, up to 39.6% could be subject to federal income tax.

A corporation can often reduce taxes by paying its owner-employees a decent salary (which, of course, is tax-deductible to the corporation but taxable to the employee), and then retaining additional profits in the business (say, for future expansion). The additional profits will be taxed at the lower corporate tax rates. Under IRS rules, however, the maximum amount of profits most corporations are allowed to retain is $250,000, and some professional corporations are limited to $150,000.

Recently I've heard a lot about limited liability companies. How do they work?

For many years, small business people have been torn between operating as sole proprietors (or, if several people are involved, as partnerships) or incorporating. On the one hand, many owners are attracted to the tax-reporting simplicity of being a sole proprietors or partner. On the other, they desire the personal liability protection offered by incorporation. Until the mid 1990s it was possible to safely achieve these dual goals only by forming a corporation and then complying with a number of technical rules to gain S-corporation status from the IRS. Then the limited liability com-

pany (LLC) was introduced and slowly gained full IRS acceptance.

LLCs can have many of the most popular attributes of both partnerships (pass-through tax status) and corporations (limited personal liability for the owners). You can establish an LLC by filing a document called articles of organization with your state's corporate filing office (often the Secretary or Department of State).

While most states use the term "articles of organization" to refer to the basic document creating an LLC, some states (including Delaware, Mississippi, New Hampshire, New Jersey and Washington) use the term "certificate of formation." Two other states (Massachusetts and Pennsylvania) call the document a "certificate of organization."

Can any small business register as a limited liability company?

Most small businesses can be run as LLCs because limited liability companies are recognized by all states. And almost all states (except Massachusetts) now permit one-owner LLCs, which means that sole proprietors can easily organize their businesses as LLCs to obtain both limited liability and pass-through tax status.

Are there any drawbacks to forming a limited liability company?

Very few, beyond the fact that LLCs require a moderate amount of paperwork at the outset and a filing fee. You must file Articles of Organization with your state's Secretary of State, along with a filing fee that will range from a few hundred dollars in some states to almost $1,000 in others.

More Information About Choosing a Structure for Your Small Business

Legal Guide to Starting & Running a Small Business, by Fred S. Steingold (Nolo), explains what you need to know to choose the right form for your business and shows you what to do to get started.

Legal Forms for Starting & Running a Small Business, by Fred S. Steingold (Nolo), provides all the forms you'll need to get your business up and running, no matter what ownership structure you choose.

LLC Maker, by Anthony Mancuso (Nolo), is interactive software containing all the information and forms you'll need to set up an LLC on your own.

Form Your Own Limited Liability Company, by Anthony Mancuso (Nolo), explains how to set up an LLC in any state, without the aid of an attorney.

Incorporate Your Business, by Anthony Mancuso (Nolo), explains how to set up a corporation in any state.

How to Form Your Own Corporation (California and Texas editions), by Anthony Mancuso (Nolo), offers state-specific instructions and forms for creating a corporation in those states.

Nonprofit Corporations

In the long run you hit only what you aim at. Therefore, though you should fail immediately, you had better aim at something high.

—HENRY DAVID THOREAU

A nonprofit corporation is a group of people who join together to do some activity that benefits the public, such as running a homeless shelter, an artists' performance group or a low-cost medical clinic. Making an incidental profit from these activities is allowed under legal and tax rules, but the primary purpose of the organization should be to do good work, not make money. Nonprofit goals are typically educational, charitable or religious.

How do nonprofit organizations begin?

Most nonprofits start out as small, informal loosely structured organizations. Volunteers perform the work, and the group spends what little money it earns to keep the organization afloat. Formal legal papers (such as a nonprofit charter or bylaws) are rarely prepared in the beginning. Legally, groups of this sort are considered nonprofit associations, and each member can be held personally liable for organizational debts and liabilities.

Once a nonprofit association gets going and starts to make money, or wishes to obtain a tax exemption to attract public donations and qualify for grant funds, the members will formalize its structure. Usually the members decide to incorporate, but forming an unincorporated nonprofit association by adopting a formal association charter and operating bylaws is an alternative.

Most groups form a nonprofit corporation because it is the traditional form—the IRS and grant agencies are very familiar with it. Also, once incorporated, the individual members of the nonprofit are not personally liable for debts of the organization—a big legal advantage over the unincorporated association.

Will my association benefit from becoming a nonprofit corporation?

Here are some circumstances that might make it worth your while to incorporate and get tax-exempt status:

- *You want to solicit tax-deductible contributions.* Contributions to nonprofits are generally tax deductible for those who make them. If you want to solicit money to fund your venture, you'll make it more attractive to potential donors if their contributions are tax-deductible.
- *Your association makes a taxable profit from its activities.* If your association will generate any kind of income from its activities, it's wise to incorporate so that you and your associates don't have to pay income tax on this money.

- *You want to apply for public or private grant money.* Without federal tax-exempt status, your group is unlikely to qualify for grants.
- *Your members want some protection from legal liability.* By incorporating your association, you can generally insulate your officers, directors and members from liability for the activities they engage in on behalf of the corporation
- *Your advocacy efforts might provoke legal quarrels.* If, for instance, your association is taking aim at a powerful industry (such as tobacco companies), it might be worth incorporating so that your association's officers and directors will have some protection from the spurious lawsuits that are sure to come—and will also receive compensation for their legal fees.

Forming a nonprofit corporation brings other benefits as well, such as lower nonprofit mailing rates and local real estate and personal property tax exemptions.

Is forming a nonprofit corporation difficult?

Legally, no. To form a nonprofit corporation, one of the organization's founders prepares and files standard articles of incorporation—a short legal document that lists the name and the directors of the nonprofit plus other basic information. The articles are filed with the Secretary of State's office for a modest filing fee. After the articles are filed, the group is a legally recognized nonprofit corporation.

Is there more to forming a nonprofit than this simple legal task?

Taxwise, there is more. In addition to filing your articles, you will want to apply for and obtain federal and state nonprofit tax exemptions. If the formation of your organization depends on its nonprofit tax status, you'll likely want to know whether you'll qualify for tax exemption at the outset. Unfortunately, your corporation must be formed before you submit your federal tax exemption application. Why? Because the IRS requires that you submit a copy of your filed articles with the exemption application. Still, you should carefully review the tax exemption application before you submit your corporation papers. Doing so will give you a good idea of whether your organization will qualify for a tax exemption or not.

What type of tax exemption do most nonprofits get?

Most organizations obtain a federal tax exemption under Section 501(c)(3) of the Internal Revenue Code, for charitable, education, religious, scientific or literary purposes. States typically follow the federal lead and grant state tax-exempt status to nonprofits recognized by the IRS as 501(c)(3) organizations.

How can my organization get a 501(c)(3) tax exemption?

You'll need to get the IRS Package 1023 exemption application. This is a lengthy and technical application with many references to the federal tax code. Most nonprofit organizers need help in addition to the IRS instructions that accompany the form. But you can do it on your own if you have a good self-help resource by your side such as Nolo's *How to Form Your Own Nonprofit Corporation*, by Anthony Mancuso, which shows you, line by line, how to complete your application.

Are there any restrictions imposed on 501(c)(3) nonprofits?

You must meet the following conditions to qualify for a 501(c)(3) IRS tax exemption:

- The assets of your nonprofit must be irrevocably dedicated to charitable, educational, religious or similar purposes. If your 501(c)(3) nonprofit dissolves, any assets it owns must be transferred to another 501(c)(3) organization. (In your organizational papers, you don't have to name the specific organization that will receive your assets—a broad dedication clause will do.)

- Your organization cannot campaign for or against candidates for public office, and political lobbying activity is restricted.

- If your nonprofit makes a profit from activities unrelated to its nonprofit purpose, it must pay taxes on the profit (but up to $1,000 of unrelated income can be earned tax-free).

More Information About Nonprofit Corporations

How to Form a Nonprofit Corporation, by Anthony Mancuso (Nolo), shows you how to form a tax-exempt corporation in all 50 states. In California, look for *How to Form a Nonprofit Corporation in California*, also by Anthony Mancuso (Nolo).

The Law of Tax Exempt Organizations, by Bruce Hopkins (Wiley), is an in-depth guide to the legal and tax requirements for obtaining and maintaining a 501(c)(3) tax exemption and public charity status with the IRS.

Small Business Taxes

THE MAN WHO IS ABOVE HIS BUSINESS MAY ONE DAY FIND HIS BUSINESS ABOVE HIM.

—SAMUEL DREW

Taxes are a fact of life for every small business. Those who take the time to understand and follow the rules will have little trouble with tax authorities. By contrast, those who are sloppy or dishonest are likely to be dogged by tax bills, audits and penalties. The moral is simple: Meeting your obligations to report business information and pay taxes is one of the cornerstones of operating a successful business.

I want to start my own small business. What do I have to do to keep out of trouble with the IRS?

Start by learning a new set of "3 Rs"—recordkeeping, recordkeeping and (you guessed it) recordkeeping. IRS studies show that poor records—not dishonesty—cause most small business people to lose at audits or fail to comply with their tax reporting obligations, with resulting fines and penalties. Even if you hire someone to keep your records, you need to know how to supervise him—if he goofs up, you'll be held responsible.

I don't have enough money in my budget to hire a business accountant or tax preparer. Is it safe and sensible for me to keep my own books?

Yes, if you remember to keep thorough, current records. Consider using a check register-type computer program such as Quicken (Intuit) to track your expenses, and if you are doing your own tax return, use Intuit's companion program, Turbotax for Business. To ensure that you're on the right track, it's a good idea to run your bookkeeping system by a savvy small business tax professional, such as a CPA. With just a few hours of work, she should help you avoid most common mistakes and show you how to dovetail your bookkeeping system with tax filing requirements.

When your business is firmly in the black and your budget allows for it, consider hiring a bookkeeper to do your day-to-day payables and receivables. And hire an outside tax pro to handle your heavy-duty tax work—not only are the fees a tax-deductible business expense, but chances are your business will benefit if you put more of your time into running it and less into completing paperwork.

Recordkeeping Basics

Keep all receipts and canceled checks for business expenses. It will help if you separate your documents by category, such as:

- auto expenses
- rent
- utilities
- advertising
- travel
- entertainment, and
- professional fees.

Organize your documents by putting them into individual folders or envelopes, and keep them in a safe place. If you are ever audited, the IRS is most likely to zero in on business deductions for travel and entertainment, and car expenses. Remember that the burden will be on you—not the IRS—to explain your deductions. If you're feeling unsure about how to get started or what documents you need to keep, consult a tax professional familiar with recordkeeping for small businesses.

What is—and isn't—a tax-deductible business expense?

Just about any "ordinary, necessary and reasonable" expense that helps you earn business income is deductible. These terms reflect the purpose for which the expense is made. For example, buying a computer, or even a sound system, for your office or store is an "ordinary and necessary" business expense, but buying the same items for your family room obviously isn't. The property must be used in a "trade or business," which means it is used with the expectation of generating income.

In addition to the "ordinary and necessary" rule, a few expenses are specifically prohibited by law from being tax deductible—for instance, you can't deduct a bribe paid to a public official. Other deduction no-nos are traffic tickets and clothing you wear on the job, unless it is a required uniform. As a rule, if you think it is necessary for your business, it is probably deductible. Just be ready to explain it to an auditor.

Business Costs That Are Never Deductible

A few expenses are not deductible even if they are business related, because they violate public policy (IRC §162). These expenses include:

- any type of government fine, such as a tax penalty paid to the IRS, or even a parking ticket
- bribes and kickbacks
- any kind of payment made for referring a client, patient or customer, if it is contrary to a state or federal law, and
- expenses for lobbying and social club dues.

Thankfully, very few other business expenses are affected by these rules.

If I use my car for business, how much of that expense can I write off?

You must keep track of how much you use your car for business in order to figure out your deduction. (You'll also need to produce these records if you're ever audited.) Start by keeping a log showing the miles for each business use, always noting the purpose of the trip. Then, at the end of the year, you will usually be able to figure your deduction by using either the "mile-age method" (for the year 2001 you can take 34.5¢ per mile deduction for business usage) or the "actual expense" method (you can take the total you pay for gas and repairs plus depreciation according to a tax code schedule, multiplied by the percentage of business use). Figure the deduction both ways and use the method that benefits you most.

Can I claim a deduction for business-related entertainment?

You may deduct only 50% of expenses for entertaining clients, customers or employees, no matter how many martinis or Perriers you swigged. (Yes, this is a fairly recent change. In the old days you could write off 100% of every entertainment expense, and until a few years ago, 80%.)

The entertainment must be either directly related to the business (such as a catered business lunch) or "associated with" the business, meaning that the entertainment took place immediately before or immediately after a business discussion. Qualified business entertainment includes taking a client to a ball game, a concert or dinner at a fancy restaurant, or just inviting a few of your customers over for a Sunday barbecue at your home.

Parties, picnics and other social events you put on for your employees and their families are an exception to the 50% rule—such events are 100% deductible. Keep in mind that if you are audited, you must be able to show some proof that it was a legitimate business expense. So, keep a guest list and note the business (or potential business) relationship of each person entertained.

Commonly Overlooked Business Expenses

Despite the fact that most people keep a sharp eye out for deductible expenses, it's not uncommon to miss a few. Some overlooked routine deductions include:

- advertising giveaways and promotions
- audio and video tapes related to business skills
- bank service charges
- business association dues
- business gifts
- business-related magazines and books (like this one)
- casual labor and tips
- casualty and theft losses
- charitable contributions
- coffee service
- commissions
- consultant fees
- credit bureau fees
- education to improve business skills
- interest on credit cards for business expenses
- interest on personal loans used for business purposes
- office supplies
- online computer services related to business

- parking and meters
- petty cash funds
- postage
- promotion and publicity
- seminars and trade shows
- taxi and bus fare
- telephone calls away from the business.

Must some types of business supplies and equipment be fully deducted in the year they are purchased, but others deducted over several years?

Current expenses, which include the everyday costs of keeping your business going, such as office supplies, rent and electricity, can be deducted from your business's total income in the year you incurred them. But expenditures for things that will generate revenue in future years—for example, a desk, copier or car—must be "capitalized," that is, written off or "amortized" over their useful life—usually three, five or seven years—according to IRS rules. There is one important exception to this rule, discussed next.

Does this mean that, even if I buy business equipment this year, I must spread the deduction over a period of five years?

Not necessarily. Normally the cost of "capital equipment"—equipment that has a useful life of more than one year—must be deducted over a number of years, but there is one major exception. In 2002, Internal Revenue Code § 179 allowed you to deduct up to $24,000 worth of capital assets in any one year against your business income. Even if you buy the equipment on credit, with no money down, you can still qualify for this deduction. (The maximum deduction is slated to rise to $25,00 in 2003.)

Business Assets That Must Be Capitalized

Buildings

Cellular phones and beepers

Computer components and software

Copyrights and patents

Equipment

Improvements to business property

Inventory

Office furnishings and decorations

Small tools and equipment

Vehicles

Window coverings

A friend told me that corporations get the best tax breaks of any type of business, so I am thinking of incorporating my startup. What do you recommend?

There's a seed of truth in what your friend told you, but keep in mind that most tax benefits flow to profitable, established businesses, not to startups in their first few years. For example, corporations can offer more tax-flexible pension plans and greater medical deductions than sole proprietors, partnerships or LLCs, but few startups have the cash flow needed to take full advantage of this tax break. Similarly, the ability to split income between a corporation and its owners—thereby keeping income in lower tax brackets—is effective only if the business is solidly profitable. And incorporating adds state fees, as well as legal and accounting charges, to your expense load. So unless you are sure that substantial profits will begin to roll in immediately, hold off.

For more information about choosing the right structure for your business, see *Legal Structures for Small Businesses*, above.

I am thinking about setting up a consulting business with two of my business associates. Do we need to have partnership papers drawn up? Does it make any difference tax-wise?

If you go into business with other people and split the expenses and profits, under the tax code you are in partnership whether you have signed a written agreement or not. This means that you will have to file a partnership tax return every year, in addition to your individual tax return.

Even though a formal partnership agreement doesn't affect your tax status, it's essential to prepare one to establish all partners' rights and responsibilities vis-à-vis each other, as well as to provide for how profits and losses will be allocated to each partner. For more information about partnerships, see *Legal Structures for Small Businesses*, above.

I am a building contractor with a chance to land a big job. If I get it, I'll need to hire people quickly. Should I hire independent contractors or employees?

If you will be telling your workers where, when and how to do their jobs, you should treat them as employees, because that's how the IRS will classify them. Generally, you can treat workers as independent contractors only if they have their own businesses and offer their services to several clients—for example, a specialty sign painter with his own shop who you hire to do a particular job.

If in doubt, err on the side of treating workers as employees. While classifying your workers as independent contractors might save you money in the short run (you wouldn't have to pay the employer's share of payroll taxes or have an accountant keep records and file payroll tax forms), it may get you into big trouble if the IRS later audits you. (The IRS is very aware of the tax benefits of misclassifying an employee as an independent contractor and regularly audits companies who hire large numbers of independent contractors.) If your company is audited, the IRS may reclassify your "independent contractors" as employees—with the result that you are assessed hefty back taxes, penalties and interest.

I've heard that I can no longer claim a deduction for an office in my home. But I also see that the IRS has a form for claiming home office expenses. What's the story?

It's not as confusing as it sounds. A while back, the Supreme Court told a doctor who was taking work home from the hospital that he couldn't take a depreciation deduction for the space used at his condo. But this is quite different from maintaining a home-based business. If you run a business out of your home, you can usually claim a deduction for the portion of the home used for business. Also, you can deduct related costs—utilities, insurance, remodeling—whether you own or rent.

For more information about running a home-based business, see the next section.

I am planning a trip to Los Angeles to attend a trade show. Can I take my family along for a vacation and still be able to deduct the expenses?

If you take others with you on a business trip, you can deduct business expenses for the trip no greater than if you were traveling alone. If on the trip your family rides in the back seat of the car and stays with you in one standard motel room, then you can fully deduct your automobile and hotel expenses. You can also fully deduct the cost of your air tickets even if they feature a two-for-one or "bring along the family" discount. You can't claim a deduction for your family's meals or jaunts to Disneyland or Universal Studios, however. And if you extend your stay and partake in some of the fun after the business is over, the expenses attributed to the nonbusiness days aren't deductible, unless you extended your stay to get discounted airfare (the "Saturday overnight" requirement). In this case, your hotel room and your own meals would be deductible.

More Information About Small Business Taxes

Tax Savvy for Small Business, by Frederick W. Daily (Nolo), tells small business owners what they need to know about federal taxes and shows them how to make the right tax decisions.

Hiring Independent Contractors: The Employer's Legal Guide, by Stephen Fishman (Nolo), explains who qualifies as an independent contractor, describes applicable tax rules and shows employers how to set up effective working agreements with independent contractors.

Working for Yourself: Law & Taxes for Freelancers, Independent Contractors & Consultants, by Stephen Fishman (Nolo), is designed for the estimated 20 million Americans who are self-employed and offer their services on a contract basis.

Home-Based Businesses

As technology advances, it becomes more and more convenient and economical to operate a business from home. Depending on local zoning rules, as long as the business is small, quiet and doesn't create traffic or parking problems, it's usually legal to do so. But as with any other business endeavor, it pays to know the rules before you begin.

Is a home-based business legally different from other businesses?

No. The basic legal issues, such as picking a name for your business and deciding whether to operate as a sole proprietorship, partnership, limited liability company or corporation, are the same. Similarly, when it comes to signing contracts, hiring employees and collecting from your customers, the laws are identical whether you run your business from home or the top floor of a high-rise.

Are there laws that restrict a person's right to operate a business from home?

Municipalities have the legal right to establish rules about what types of activities can be carried out in different geographic areas. For example, laws and ordinances often establish zones for stores and offices (commercial zones), factories (industrial zones) and houses (residential zones). In some residential areas—especially in affluent communities—local zoning ordinances absolutely prohibit all types of business. In the great majority of municipalities, however, residential zoning rules allow small non-polluting home businesses, as long as the home is used primarily as a residence and the business activities don't negatively affect neighbors.

How can I find out whether residential zoning rules allow the home-based business I have in mind?

Get a copy of your local ordinance from your city or county clerk's office, the city attorney's office or your public library, and read it carefully. Zoning ordinances are worded in many different ways to limit business activities in residential areas. Some are extremely vague, allowing "customary home-based occupations." Others allow homeowners to use their houses for a broad—but, unfortunately, not very specific—list of business purposes (for example, "professions and domestic occupations, crafts or services"). Still others contain a detailed list of approved occupations, such as "law, dentistry, medicine, music lessons, photography, cabinet making."

If you read your ordinance and still aren't sure whether your business is okay, you may be tempted to talk to zoning or planning officials. But until you figure out what the rules and politics of your locality are, it may be best to do this without identifying and calling attention to yourself. (For example, have a friend who lives nearby make inquiries.)

The business I want to run from home is not specifically allowed or prohibited by my local ordinance. What should I do to avoid trouble?

Start by understanding that in most areas zoning and building officials don't actively search for violations. The great majority of home-based businesses that run into trouble do so when a neighbor complains—often because of noise or parking problems, or even because of the unfounded fear that your business is doing something illegal such as selling drugs.

It follows that your best approach is often to explain your business activities to your neighbors and make sure that your activities are not worrying or inconveniencing them. For example, if you teach piano lessons or do physical therapy from your home and your students or clients will often come and go, make sure your neighbors are not bothered by noise or losing customary on-street parking spaces.

Will the local ordinance regulating home-based businesses include rules about specific activities, such as making noise, putting up signs or having employees?

Quite possibly. Many ordinances—especially those which are fairly vague as to the type of business you can run from your home—restrict how you can carry out your business. The most frequent rules limit your use of on-street parking, prohibit outside signs, limit car and truck traffic and restrict the number of employees who can work at your house on a regular basis (some prohibit employees altogether). In addition, some zoning ordinances limit the percentage of your home's floor space that can be devoted to the business. Again, you'll need to study your local ordinance carefully to see how these rules will affect you.

If Municipal Officials Say No to Your Home-Based Business

In many cities and counties, if a planning or zoning board rejects your business permit appplication, you can appeal—often to the city council or county board of supervisors. While this can be an uphill battle, it is likely to be less so if you have the support of all affected neighbors. You may also be able to get an overly restrictive zoning ordinance amended by your municipality's governing body. For example, in some communities, people are working to amend ordinances that prohibit home-based businesses entirely or allow only "traditional home-based businesses" to permit businesses that rely on the use of computers and other hightech equipment.

I live in a planned development that has its own rules for home-based businesses. Do these control my business activities or can I rely on my city's home-based business ordinance, which is less restrictive?

In an effort to protect residential property values, most subdivisions, condos and planned unit developments create special rules—typically called Covenants, Conditions and Restrictions (CC&Rs)—that govern many aspects of property use. Rules pertaining to home-based businesses are often significantly stricter than those found in city ordinances. As long as the rules of your planned development are reasonably clear and consistently enforced, you must follow them.

I sell my consulting services to a number of businesses. Does maintaining a home office help me establish independent contractor status with the IRS?

No. An independent contractor is a person who controls both the outcome of a project and the means of accomplishing it, and who offers services to a number of businesses or individual purchasers. Although having an office or place of business is one factor the IRS looks at in determining whether an individual qualifies as an independent contractor, it makes no difference whether your office is located at home or in a traditional business setting.

Are there tax advantages to working from home?

Almost all ordinary and necessary business expenses (everything from wages to computers to paper clips) are tax deductible, no matter where they are incurred—in a factory or office, while traveling or at home.

But if you operate your business from home and qualify under IRS rules, you may be able to deduct part of your rent from your income taxes—or if you own your home, take a depreciation deduction.

You may also be eligible to deduct a portion of your total utility, home repair and maintenance, property tax and house insurance costs, based on the percentage of your residence you use for business purposes.

To qualify for home-office deductions, the IRS requires that two legal tests be met:

- you must use your business space regularly and exclusively for business purposes, and
- your home office must the be the principal place where you conduct your business. This rule is satisfied if your office is used for administrative or managerial activities, as long as these activities aren't often conducted at another business location. Alternatively, you must meet clients at home or use a separate structure on your property exclusively for business purposes.

Note that the amount of your deduction can't exceed your home-based business's total profit.

Insuring Your Home-Based Business

It's a mistake to rely on a homeowner's or renter's insurance policy to cover your home-based business. These policies often exclude or strictly limit coverage for business equipment and injuries to business visitors. For example, if your computer is stolen or a client or business associate trips and falls on your steps, you may not be covered.

Fortunately, it's easy to avoid these nasty surprises. Sit down with your insurance agent and fully disclose your planned business operation. You'll find that it's relatively inexpensive to add business coverage to your homeowner's policy—and it's a tax-deductible expense. But be sure to check prices—some insurance companies provide special cost-effective policies designed to protect both homes and home-based businesses.

How big will my home-office tax deduction be if my business qualifies under IRS rules?

To determine your deduction, you first need to figure out how much of your home you use for business as compared to other purposes. Do this by dividing the number of square feet used for your home business by the total square footage of your home. The resulting percentage of business usage determines how much of your rent (or, if you are a homeowner, depreciation), insurance, utilities and other expenses are deductible. But remember, the amount of the deduction can't be larger than the profit your home-based business generates. (Additional technical rules apply to calculating depreciation on houses you own to allow for the fact that the structure, but not the land, depreciates.) For more information, see IRS Publication 587, *Business Use of Your Home* (you can view it online at http://www.irs.gov).

Do I need to watch out for any tax traps when claiming deductions for my home office?

Claiming a home-office deduction increases your audit risk slightly, but this needn't be a big fear if you carefully follow the rules.

Keep in mind that if you sell your house, the depreciation portion of the home-based office deductions you have previously taken will be subject to tax in that year (up to a maximum of 25%), whether you made a profit or not. And you can't use the $250,000 per person "exclusion of profits" on the sale of a home to offset this tax. For example, if your depreciation deductions total $5,000 for the last seven years, you will be taxed on this amount in the year you sell your house. Despite this tax, it's generally wise to continue to take your home-office deductions each year. Especially for people who don't plan to sell their houses anytime soon, it's usually beneficial to receive a tax break today that you won't have to repay for many years. You can use your tax savings to help your business grow.

I have a full-time job, but I also operate a separate part-time business from home. Can I claim a tax deduction for my home-based business expenses?

Yes, as long as your business meets certain IRS rules. It makes no difference that you work only part-time at your home-based business or that you have another occupation. But your business must be more than a disguised hobby—it has to pass muster with the IRS as a real business.

The IRS defines a business as "any activity engaged in to make a profit." If a venture makes money—even a small amount—in three of five consecutive years, it is presumed to possess a profit motive. (IRC §183(d).) However, courts have held that some activities that failed to meet this three-profitable-years-out-of-five test still qualify as a business if they are run in a businesslike manner. When determining whether a nonprofitable venture qualifies for a deduction, courts may look at whether you kept thorough business records, had a separate business bank account, prepared advertising or other marketing materials and obtained any necessary licenses and permits (a business license from your city, for example).

More Information About Home-Based Business

Tax Savvy for Small Business, by Frederick W. Daily (Nolo), shows you how to take the home-office deduction, including depreciation and household expenses.

The Best Home Businesses for the 21st Century, by Paul & Sarah Edwards (J.P. Tarcher), profiles over 100 workable home-based businesses, including information about how each business works and what sets of skills and opportunities are necessary to succeed.

Working for Yourself: Law & Taxes for Freelancers, Independent Contractors & Consultants, by Stephen Fishman (Nolo), shows independent contractors how to meet business start-up requirements, comply with strict IRS rules and make sure they get paid in full and on time.

Employers' Rights & Responsibilities

At some point during your business venture, you may need to hire people to help you manage your workload. When you do, you'll be held accountable to a host of state and federal laws that regulate your relationship with your employees. Among the things you'll be expected to know and understand:

- proper hiring practices, including how to write appropriate job descriptions, conduct interviews and respect applicants' privacy rights
- wage and hour laws, as well as the laws that govern retirement plans, healthcare benefits and life insurance benefits
- workplace safety rules and regulations
- how to write an employee handbook and conduct performance reviews, including what you should and shouldn't put in an employee's personnel file
- how to avoid sexual harassment as well as discrimination based on gender, age, race, pregnancy, sexual orientation and national origin, and
- how to avoid trouble if you need to fire an employee.

This section provides you with an overview of your role as an employer. And you can find more guidance elsewhere in this book. Employee's rights—including questions and answers about wages, hours and workplace safety—are discussed in Chapter 4; pension plans are covered in Chapter 14.

First things first. How can I write advertisements that will attract the best pool of potential employees—without getting in legal hot water?

Many small employers get tripped up when summarizing a job in an advertisement. This can easily happen if you're not familiar with the legal guidelines. Nuances in an ad can be used as evidence of discrimination against applicants of a particular gender, age or marital status.

There are a number of pitfalls to avoid in job ads:

DON'T USE	USE
Salesman	Salesperson
College Student	Part-time Worker
Handyman	General Repair Person
Gal Friday	Office Manager
Married Couple	Two-Person Job
Counter Girl	Retail Clerk
Waiter	Wait Staff
Young	Energetic

Also, requiring a high school or college degree may be discriminatory in some job categories. You can avoid problems by stating that an applicant must have a "degree or equivalent experience."

Probably the best way to write an ad that meets legal requirements is to stick to the job skills needed and the basic responsibilities. Some examples:

"Fifty-unit apartment complex seeks experienced manager with general maintenance skills."

"Mid-sized manufacturing company has opening for accountant with tax experience to oversee interstate accounts."

"Cook trainee position available in new vegetarian restaurant. Flexible hours."

Help Wanted ads placed by federal contractors must state that all qualified applicants will receive consideration for employment without regard to race, color, religion, sex or national origin. Ads often express this with the phrase, "An Equal Opportunity Employer." To show your intent to be fair, you may want to include this phrase in your ad even if you're not a federal contractor.

Any tips on how to conduct a good, forthright interview—and again, avoid legal trouble?

Good preparation is your best ally. Before you begin to interview applicants for a job opening, write down a set of questions focusing on the job duties and the applicant's skills and experience. For example:

"Tell me about your experience in running a mailroom."

"How much experience did you have in making cold calls on your last job?"

"Explain how you typically go about organizing your workday."

"Have any of your jobs required strong leadership skills?"

By writing down the questions and sticking to the same format at all interviews for the position, you reduce the risk that a rejected applicant will later complain about unequal treatment. It's also smart to summarize the applicant's answers for your files—but don't get so involved in documenting the interview that you forget to listen closely to the applicant. And don't be so locked in to your list of questions that you don't follow up on something significant that an applicant has said, or try to pin down an ambiguous or evasive response.

To break the ice, you might give the applicant some information about the job—the duties, hours, pay range, benefits and career opportunities. Questions about the applicant's work history and experience that may be relevant to the job opening are always appropriate. But don't encourage the applicant to divulge the trade secrets of a present or former employer—especially a competitor. That can lead to a lawsuit. And be cautious about an applicant who volunteers such information or promises to bring secrets to the new position; such an applicant will probably play fast and loose with your own company's secrets, given the chance.

I've heard horror stories about employers who get sued for discriminating—both by employees and even by people they've interviewed but decided not to hire. What's the bottom line?

Federal and state laws prohibit you from discriminating against an employee or applicant because of race, color, gender, religious beliefs, national origin, disability—or age if the person is at least 40 years old. Also, many states and cities have laws prohibiting employment discrimination based on other characteristics, such as marital status or sexual orientation.

A particular form of discrimination becomes illegal when Congress, a state legislature or a city council decides that a characteristic—race, for example—bears no legitimate relationship to employment decisions. As an employer, you must be prepared to show that your hiring and promotion decisions have been based on objective criteria and that the more qualified applicant has always succeeded.

Still, when hiring, you can exercise a wide range of discretion based on business considerations. You remain free to hire, promote, discipline and fire employees and to set their duties and salaries based on their skills, experience, performance and reliability—factors that are logically tied to valid business purposes.

The law also prohibits employer practices that seem neutral, but may have a disproportionate impact on a particular group of people. Again, a policy is legal only if there's a valid business reason for its existence. For example, refusing to hire people who don't meet a minimum height and weight is permissible if it's clearly related to the physical demands of the particular job—felling and hauling huge trees, for instance. But applying such a requirement to exclude applicants for a job as a cook or receptionist wouldn't pass legal muster.

How can I check out a prospective employee without violating his or her right to privacy?

As an employer, you likely believe that the more information you have about job applicants, the better your hiring decisions will be. But make sure any information you seek will actually be helpful to you. It's often a waste of time and effort to acquire and review transcripts and credit reports—although occasionally they're useful. If you're hiring a bookkeeper, for example, previous job experience is much more important than the grades the applicant received in a community college bookkeeping program ten years ago. On the other hand, if the applicant is fresh out of school and has never held a bookkeeping job, a transcript may yield some insights. Similarly, if you're hiring a switchboard operator, information on a credit report would be irrelevant. But if you're filling a job for a bar manager who will be handling large cash receipts, you might want to see a credit report to learn if the applicant is in financial trouble.

To avoid claims that you've invaded a prospective employee's privacy, always obtain the applicant's written consent before you contact a former employer, request a credit report or send for high school or college transcripts.

Finally, it's usually not wise to resort to screening applicants through personality tests; laws and court rulings restrict your right to use them in most states.

Can I require job applicants to pass a drug test?

It depends on the laws of your state. Although many states allow employers to test all applicants for illegal drug use, some states allow testing only for certain jobs—those that require driving, carrying a weapon or operating heavy machinery, for ex-

ample. Before requiring any applicant to take a drug test, you should check with your state's department of labor to find out what the law allows.

In general, you will be on safest legal ground if you have a strong, legitimate reason for testing applicants—especially if your reason involves protecting the public's safety.

Is drug use a disability?

When it passed the Americans with Disabilities Act, Congress refused to recognize illegal drug use or current drug addiction as a disability. Therefore, if an applicant fails a legally administered drug test, you will not violate the ADA by refusing to hire that applicant.

However, the ADA does protect applicants who no longer use illegal drugs and have successfully completed (or are currently attending) a supervised drug rehabilitation program. Although you can require these applicants to take a drug test or show you proof of their participation in a rehabilitation program, you cannot refuse to hire them solely because they used to take illegal drugs.

How do I avoid legal problems when giving employee evaluations?

Be honest and consistent with your employees. If a fired employee initiates a legal action against you, a judge or jury will probably see those evaluations—and will want to see that you were consistent in word and deed. For example, a jury will sense that something is wrong if you consistently rate a worker's performance as poor or mediocre—but continue to hand out generous raises or perhaps even promote the person. The logical conclusion: You didn't take seriously the criticisms in your evaluation report, so you shouldn't expect the employee to take them seriously, either.

It's just as damaging to give an employee glowing praise in report after report—perhaps to make the employee feel good—and then to fire him or her for a single infraction. That strikes most people as unfair. And unfair employers often lose court fights, especially in situations where a sympathetic employee appears to have been treated harshly.

If your system is working, employees with excellent evaluations should not need to be fired for poor performance. And employees with poor performance shouldn't be getting big raises.

As a small employer, what should I keep in personnel files—and what right do employees have to see what's inside?

Create a file for each employee in which you keep all job-related information, including:
- job description
- job application
- offer of employment
- IRS form W-4, the Employee's Withholding Allowance Certificate
- receipt for employee handbook
- periodic performance evaluations
- sign-up forms for employee benefits
- complaints from customers and co-workers

- awards or citations for excellent performance
- warnings and disciplinary actions, and
- notes on an employee's attendance or tardiness.

Experts recommend keeping one separate file for all of your employees' INS I-9 Employment Eligibility Verification forms—the forms you have to complete for new employees demonstrating that they are authorized to work in the United States. There are two practical reasons for keeping these forms in their own file—and out of your workers' personnel files. First, this will limit the number of people who know an employee's immigration status. If you keep an employee's I-9 in her personnel file, anyone who reviews that file (a supervisor, human resources employee or payroll administrator) will know whether or not the employee is a citizen. This could lead to problems later, if the employee claims that she was discriminated against based on her immigration status. If you keep the forms in a separate file, fewer people will be aware of the employee's immigration status—and the employee will have a much tougher time trying to prove that important employment decisions were made on that basis.

Second, if the INS decides to audit you, they are entitled to see I-9 forms as they are kept in the normal course of business. If you keep these forms in each employee's personnel file, that means the government will rummage through all of these files—causing inconvenience for you and privacy concerns for your employees. On the other hand, if you keep your forms in a single folder, you can simply hand over that folder if the INS comes knocking.

Special Rules for Medical Records

The Americans with Disabilities Act (ADA) imposes very strict limitations on how you must handle information obtained from medical examinations and inquiries. You must keep the information in medical files that are separate from nonmedical records, and you must store the medical files in a separate locked cabinet. To further guarantee the confidentiality of medical records, designate a specific person to have access to those files.

The ADA allows very limited disclosure of medical information. Under the ADA, you may:

- inform supervisors about necessary restrictions on an employee's duties and about necessary accommodations
- inform first aid and safety workers about a disability that may require emergency treatment and about specific procedures that are needed if the workplace must be evacuated, and
- provide medical information required by government officials and by insurance companies that require a medical exam for health or life insurance.

Otherwise, don't disclose medical information about employees. Although the confidentiality provisions of the ADA protect only some disabled workers, some state's laws also require confidential handling of medical records. The best policy is to treat all medical information about all employees as confidential.

Many states have laws giving employees—and former employees—access to their own personnel files. How much access varies from state to state. Typically, if your state allows employees to see their files, you can insist that you or another supervisor be present to make sure nothing is taken, added or changed. Some state laws allow employees to obtain copies of items in their files, but not necessarily all items. For example, a law may limit the employee to copies of documents that he or she has signed, such as a job application. If an employee is entitled to a copy of an item in the file or if you're inclined to let the employee have a copy of any document in the file, you—rather than the employee—should make the copy.

Usually, you won't have to let the employee see sensitive items such as information assembled for a criminal investigation, reference letters and information that might violate the privacy of other people. In a few states, employees may insert rebuttals to information in their personnel files with which they disagree.

Am I required to offer my employees paid vacation, disability, maternity or sick leave?

No law requires you to offer paid vacation time or paid sick or disability leave to your employees. You could choose to offer none—although a policy like this could make it tough to attract high-quality employees in a competitive market. If you decide to adopt a policy that gives your employees paid vacation or sick time, you must apply the policy consistently to all employees. If you offer some employees a more attractive package than others, you are opening yourself up to claims of unfair treatment.

The same rules apply to pregnancy and maternity leave. No law requires employers to provide paid leave for employees during their pregnancy or immediately after they give birth. However, if you choose to offer paid vacation, sick or disability leave, you must allow pregnant women and women who have just given birth to make use of these policies. For example, a new mother who is physically unable to work following the birth of her child must be allowed to use paid disability leave if such leave is available to other employees.

Must I offer my employees unpaid leave?

There are two situations in which you might be legally required to offer unpaid leave to your employees. First, if the employee requesting leave qualifies as disabled under the Americans with Disabilities Act (see below for an explanation of the ADA), and requests the leave as a reasonable accommodation for the disability, you may be required to grant the leave request. For example, an employee who needs time off to undergo surgery or treatment for a disabling condition is probably entitled to unpaid leave, unless you can show that providing the leave would be an undue hardship to your business.

Second, your employees might be entitled to unpaid leave under the Family and Medical Leave Act (FMLA) or a similar state statute. See Chapter 4, *Workplace Rights*, for an explanation of when you must provide leave under the FMLA.

What am I legally required to do for my disabled employees?

The Americans with Disabilities Act (ADA) prohibits employers from discriminating against disabled applicants or employees. However, the ADA does not require employers to hire or retain workers who can't do their jobs. Only "qualified workers with disabilities"—employees who can perform all the essential elements of the job, with or without some form of accommodation from their employers—are protected by the law.

An employee is legally disabled if:

- He has a physical or mental impairment that substantially limits a major life activity (such as the ability to walk, talk, see, hear, breathe, reason or take care of oneself). Courts tend not to categorically characterize certain conditions as disabilities—instead, they consider the effect of the particular condition on the particular employee.
- He has a record or history of impairment, or

He is regarded by the employer as disabled, even if the employer is incorrect.

The ADA also requires employers to make reasonable accommodations for their disabled employees. This means you may have to provide some assistance or make some changes in the job or workplace to enable the worker to do their job. For example, an employer might lower the height of a workspace or install ramps to accommodate a worker in a wheelchair, provide voice-recognition software for a worker with a repetitive stress disorder or provide TDD telephone equipment for a worker with impaired hearing.

It is your employee's responsibility to inform you of his disability and request a reasonable accommodation—you don't have to be psychic to follow the law. Once an employee raises the issue, you must engage in a dialogue with the worker to try to figure out what kinds of accommodations might be effective and practical. Although you don't have to provide the precise accommodation your worker requests, you do have to work together to come up with a reasonable solution.

Employers don't have to provide an accommodation if it would cause their business to suffer "undue hardship"— essentially, if the cost or effect of the accommodation would be excessive. There are no hard and fast rules about when an accommodation poses an undue hardship. When faced with this issue, courts consider a number of factors, including:

- the cost of the accommodation
- the size and financial resources of the employer
- the structure of the employer's business, and
- the effect the accommodation would have on the business.

Employees With Mental Disabilities

The ADA applies equally to employees with physical disabilities and employees with mental or psychiatric disabilities. Therefore, workers who suffer from severe depression, bipolar disorder, schizophrenia, attention deficit disorder and other mental diseases or conditions may be covered by the ADA, if their condition meets the ADA's definition of a disability.

Workers with mental disabilities are also entitled to reasonable accommodations. For example, you might allow an employee whose anti-depressant medication makes her groggy in the morning to come in a few hours later, or provide an office with soundproofed walls to reduce distractions for an employee who suffers from attention deficit disorder.

One of my employees just told me that she was sexually harassed by a coworker. What should I do?

Most employers feel anxious when faced with complaints of sexual harassment. And with good reason: such complaints can lead to workplace tension, government investigations and even costly legal battles. If the complaint is mishandled, even unintentionally, an employer may unwittingly put itself out of business.

Here are some basics to keep in mind if you receive a complaint:

- *Educate yourself.* Do some research on the law of sexual harassment—learn what sexual harassment is, how it is proven in court and what your responsibilities are as an employer. An excellent place to start is *Sexual Harassment on the Job,* by William Petrocelli and Barbara Kate Repa (Nolo).
- *Follow established procedures.* If you have an employee handbook or other documented policies relating to sexual harassment, follow those policies. Don't open yourself up to claims of unfair treatment by bending the rules.
- *Interview the people involved.* Start by talking to the person who complained. Then talk to the employee accused of harassment and any witnesses. Get details: what was said or done, when, where and who else was there.
- *Look for corroboration or contradiction.* Usually, the accuser and accused offer different versions of the incident, leaving you with no way of knowing who's telling the truth. Turn to other sources for clues. For example, schedules, time cards and other attendance records (for trainings, meetings, and so on) may help you determine if each party was where they claimed to be. Witnesses may have seen part of the incident.

And in some cases, documents will prove one side right. It's hard to argue with an X-rated email.

- *Keep it confidential.* A sexual harassment complaint can polarize a workplace. Workers will likely side with either the complaining employee or the accused employee, and the rumor mill will start working overtime. Worse, if too many details about the complaint are leaked, you may be accused of damaging the reputation of the alleged victim or alleged harasser—and get slapped with a defamation lawsuit. Avoid these problems by insisting on confidentiality, and practicing it in your investigation.
- *Write it all down.* Take notes during your interviews. Before the interview is over, go back through your notes with the interviewee, to make sure you got it right. Write down the steps you have taken to learn the truth, including interviews you have conducted and documents you have reviewed. Document any action taken against the accused, or the reasons for deciding not to take action. This written record will protect you later, if your employee claims that you ignored her complaint or conducted a one-sided investigation.
- *Cooperate with government agencies.* If the accuser makes a complaint with a government agency (either the federal Equal Employment Opportunity Commission (EEOC) or an equivalent state agency), that agency may investigate. Try to provide the agency with the materials it requests,

but remember that the agency is gathering evidence that could be used against you later. This is a good time to consider hiring a lawyer to advise you.

- *Don't retaliate.* It is against the law to punish someone for making a sexual harassment complaint. The most obvious forms of retaliation are termination, discipline, demotion, pay cuts or threats of any of these actions. More subtle forms of retaliation may include changing the shift hours or work area of the accuser, changing the accuser's job responsibilities or reporting relationships and isolating the accuser by leaving her out of meetings and other office functions.

- *Take appropriate action against the harasser.* Once you have gathered all the information available, sit down and decide what you think really happened. If you conclude that some form of sexual harassment occurred, figure out how to discipline the harasser appropriately. Once you have decided on an appropriate action, take it quickly, document it and notify the accuser.

My employees' religious differences are causing strife in the workplace. What am I required to do?

This is a tricky area. An increasing number of employees are claiming religious discrimination. And unfortunately, the law in this delicate area is unclear.

First, make sure you aren't imposing your religious beliefs on others.

You have the legal right to discuss your own religious beliefs with an employee, if you're so inclined, but you can't persist to the point that the employee feels you're being hostile, intimidating or offensive. So if an employee objects to your discussion of religious subjects or you get even an inkling that your religious advances are unwelcome, back off. Otherwise, you may find yourself embroiled in a lawsuit or administrative proceeding.

If employees complain to you that a co-worker is badgering them with religious views, you have a right—if not a duty—to intervene, although you must, of course, use the utmost tact and sensitivity.

While you may feel that the best way to resolve these knotty problems is to simply banish religion from the workplace, that's generally not a viable alternative. You're legally required to accommodate the religious needs of employees—for example, allowing employees to pick and choose the paid holidays they would like to take during the year. You don't, however, need to do anything that would cost more than a minimum amount or that would cause more than minimal inconvenience.

Some of my employees insist they have a right to smoke during breaks and at lunch, and another group claims they'll quit if I allow smoking on the premises. I'm caught in the middle. What should I do?

It's well established that second-hand tobacco smoke can harm the health of nonsmokers. Consequently, in many states and municipalities, employers are legally required to limit smoking in the workplace. And a number of locales have specific laws that ban or limit smoking in public places; if your workplace falls within the legal definition of a public place—a bar, restaurant or hotel, for example—your legal rights and responsibilities will be clearly spelled out in the law.

A rule proposed by the Occupational Health and Safety Administration (OSHA) would allow only two choices: you'd have to either prohibit smoking in the workplace, or limit it to areas that are enclosed and ventilated directly to the outdoors. Under the rule, you couldn't require employees to enter the smoking areas when performing their normal job duties. This proposal is till under consideration.

Given the scientific facts and the general direction in which the law is moving, your safest legal course is to restrict smoking in the workplace—and a total ban may be the only practical solution. That's because in many modern buildings, it's too expensive—maybe even impossible—to provide a separate ventilation system for a smokers' room.

In addition to meeting the specific requirements of laws and regulations that limit or prohibit smoking in the workplace, be aware that you may be legally liable to nonsmoking employees if you don't take appropriate actions on their complaints.

It's been a bad year for my business—and it looks as though I may have to lay off some workers. Are there legal problems to avoid?

Generally, you're free to lay off or terminate employees because business conditions require it. But if you do cut back, don't leave your business open to claims that the layoffs were really a pretext for getting rid of employees for illegal reasons.

Be sensitive to how your actions may be perceived. If the layoff primarily affects workers of a particular race, or women or older employees, someone may well question your motives. It's better to spread the pain around; don't let the burden fall on just one group of employees.

How can I make sure that my employees don't reveal my company's trade secrets to a competitor—especially after they leave the company?

You should take two steps to protect your trade secrets from disclosure by former employees: always treat your trade secrets as confidential, and require any employee who will come in contact with your trade secrets to sign a nondisclosure agreement.

A trade secret is any information that provides its owner with a competitive advantage in the market, and is treated as a secret—that is, handled in a manner that can reasonably be expected to prevent others from learning about it. Examples of trade secrets might include recipes, manufacturing processes, customer or pricing lists and ideas for new products. If you own a trade secret, you have the legal right to prevent anyone from disclosing, copying or using it, and can sue anyone who violates these rights to your disadvantage.

Always keep your trade secrets confidential. For example, you should mark documents containing trade secrets "confidential" and limit their circulation, disclose trade secret material only to those employees with a real need to know, keep materials in a safe place and have a written policy which makes it clear that trade secrets are not to be revealed to outsiders.

In addition to taking steps to keep your trade secrets confidential, you should also require any employee who will come in contact with your trade secrets to sign a nondisclosure agreement, or NDA. An NDA is a contract in which the parties promise to keep confidential any trade secrets disclosed during the employment relationship. You can find more information and sample NDA forms in *Nondisclosure Agreements* by Stephen Fishman (Nolo).

What are my legal obligations to an employee who is leaving the company?

Surprisingly, your responsibility to your employees doesn't necessarily end when the employment relationship ends. Even after an employee quits or is fired, you must:

- Provide the employee's final paycheck in accordance with state law. Most states require that an employee receive this check fairly quickly, sometimes just a day or two after the last day of work.
- Provide severance pay. No law requires employers to provide severance pay (although a few states require employers to pay severance to workers fired in a plant closure). But if you promise it, you must pay it to all employees who meet your policy's requirements.
- Give information on continuation of health insurance, under a federal law called the Consolidated Omnibus Budget Reconciliation Act (COBRA). If you offer your employees health insurance, and your company has 20 or more employees, you must offer departing employees the option of continued coverage under the company's group health insurance plan, at the worker's expense, for a specified period.
- Allow former employees to view their personnel files. Most states provide employees and former employees with the legal right to see their personnel file, and to receive copies of some of the documents relating to their job. State laws vary as to how long employers must keep these records for former employees.

I have to give a reference for a former employee I had to fire. I don't want to be too positive about him, but I am also afraid he might sue me for unflattering remarks. Advice?

The key to protecting yourself is to stick to the facts and act in good faith.

You'll get in trouble only if you exaggerate or cover up the truth—or are motivated by a desire to harm your former employee.

Former employees who feel maligned can sue for defamation—called slander if the statements were spoken or libel if they were written. To win a defamation case, a former employee must prove that you intentionally gave out false information and that the information harmed his or her reputation. If you can show that the information you provided was true, the lawsuit will be dismissed.

And even if it turns out that the information provided is untrue, employers in most states are entitled to some protection in defamation cases. This protection is based on a legal doctrine called "qualified privilege." To receive the benefits, you must show that:

• you made the statement in good faith
• you and the person to whom you disclosed the information shared a common interest, and
• you limited your statement to this common interest.

The law recognizes that a former employer and a prospective employer share a common interest in the attributes of an employee. To get the protection of the qualified privilege, your main task is to stick to facts that you've reasonably investigated and to lay aside your personal feelings about the former employee.

A practical policy—and one that gives you a high degree of legal protection—is simply not to discuss an employee with prospective employers if you can't say something positive. Just tell the person inquiring that it's not your policy to comment on former workers.

Where an employee's record is truly mixed, it's usually possible to accent the positive while you try to put negative information into a more favorable perspective. If you do choose to go into detail, don't hide the bad news. In very extreme cases (in which the former employee committed a serious crime or engaged in dangerous wrongdoing), you could be sued by the new employer for concealing this information.

Do I have the same legal obligations to independent contractors as I do to employees?

Generally, an employer has more obligations, both legally and financially, to employees than to independent contractors. The workplace rights guaranteed to employees do not protect independent contractors, for the most part. And an employer must make certain contributions to the government on behalf of its employees, while independent contractors are expected to make these payments themselves.

Here are a number of rules that apply only to employees:

• *Anti-discrimination laws.* Most laws prohibiting employers from discriminating against employees or applicants for employment based such characteristics as race, gender, national origin, religion, age or disability do not protect independent contractors.

- *Wage and hour laws.* Independent contractors are not covered by laws governing the minimum wage, overtime pay and the like.
- *Medical and parental leave laws.* You are not required to offer independent contractors medical or parental leave.
- *Workers' compensation laws.* You do not have to provide workers' compensation for independent contractors.
- *Unemployment insurance.* You do not have to contribute to unemployment insurance for independent contractors.
- *Social Security contributions.* You are not required to make any Social Security payments on behalf of independent contractors.
- *Wage withholding.* You are not required to withhold state or federal income tax, or state disability insurance payments (where applicable) from the paychecks of independent contractors.

When can I classify a worker as an independent contractor?

Different government agencies use different tests to decide whether workers should be classified as independent contractors or employees. Generally, these tests are intended to figure out whether an independent contractor is truly a self-employed businessperson offering services to the general public. The more discretion a worker has to decide how, when and for whom to perform work, the more likely that the worker is an independent contractor. For example, an independent contractor might do similar work for other companies, provide the tools and equipment to do the job, decide how to do the job (including when, where and in what order to do the work) and hire employees or assistants to help out with big jobs. On the other hand, a worker who works only for you, under conditions determined by you, is more likely to be classified as an employee.

More Information About Employers' Rights and Responsibilities

The Employer's Legal Handbook, by Fred Steingold (Nolo), explains employers' legal rights and responsibilities in detail.

Dealing With Problem Employees, by Amy DelPo and Lisa Guerin (Nolo), offers employers advice and step-by-step instructions for handling problems in the workplace, from giving effective performance evaluations to firing employees who don't work out.

Everyday Employment Law: The Basics, by Lisa Guerin and Amy DelPo (Nolo), provides all the basic information, tips and real-world examples employers need to answer their employment law questions.

Information on independent contractors can be found in *Hiring Independent Contractors* by Stephen Fishman (Nolo).

For information on federal discrimination laws and lists of state resources, contact the Equal Employment Opportunity Commission, 1801 L St., NW,

Washington, DC, 20507, 800-669 3362, http://www.eeoc.gov.

For information on wage and hour laws, workers' compensation and family and medical leave, contact the Department of Labor, 200 Constitution Ave., NW, Washington, DC, 20210, 202-693-4650, http://www.dol.gov.

For a variety of helpful employment law resources—including fact sheets, sample policies and more—visit the website of CCH, Inc., at http://www.toolkit.cch.com.

General Sites for Small Businesses

http://www.nolo.com
Nolo offers free self-help information and small business books, software and forms on a wide variety of subjects, including starting and running your small business.

http://www.americanexpress. com/smallbusiness
The American Express Small Business Exchange helps you find information, resources and customers for your small business.

http://www.nfibonline.com
The National Federation of Independent Business provides news, workshops and action alerts for small business owners. The NFIB is the nation's largest advocacy organization for small and independent businesses.

http://www.sba.gov
The Small Business Administration provides information about starting, financing and expanding your small business.

http://smallbusiness.yahoo.com
Yahoo offers an abundance of links to resources for small business people.

Sites for Nonprofit Corporations

http://www.igc.org
The Institute for Global Communication offers an extensive list of links to resources for activism and nonprofit development.

http://www.boardsource.org
BoardSource, formerly the National Center for Nonprofit Boards, provides information and publications to help you run a successful nonprofit organization.

Sites for Independent Contractors and Home-Based Businesses

http://www.hoaa.com
The Home Office Association of America is a national association for home-based business people. It offers resources, ideas and benefits to help you run a more profitable business from home. The site also contains an extensive list of links to other sites of interest to the self-employed.

http://www.ssa.gov
The Social Security Administration provides lots of information on regulations and benefits for self-employed people.

Patents

6.2 *Qualifying for a Patent*

6.7 *Obtaining a Patent*

6.9 *Enforcing a Patent*

6.12 *Putting a Patent to Work*

6.14 *How Patents Differ From Copyrights and Trademarks*

To invent, you need a good imagination and a pile of junk.

—THOMAS EDISON

Many of us muse about the million-dollar idea: the invention that will make life easier for others and more lucrative for us. Most of these ideas never get off the ground, however; we decide it's not really worth the time and effort to create the perfect dog toothbrush, clothes hanger or juice squeezer. But every now and then we may hit on a winner—an idea worth developing, marketing and protecting. In these cases, we must turn to the patent laws for help.

This chapter addresses the basic legal issues that arise in the patent area, answering questions such as:

- What is a patent?
- When does a particular invention qualify for a patent?
- How do you get a patent in the U.S. or abroad?
- How are patent rights enforced?
- How can you profit from your patent?

Qualifying for a Patent

THERE IS NOTHING WHICH

PERSEVERING EFFORT AND UNCEASING

AND DILIGENT CARE CANNOT

ACCOMPLISH.

—SENECA

A patent is a document issued by the U.S. Patent and Trademark Office (PTO) that grants a monopoly for a limited period of time on the manufacture, use and sale of an invention.

What types of inventions can be patented?

The PTO issues three different kinds of patents: utility patents, design patents and plant patents.

Design patents last for 14 years from the date the patent issues. Plant and utility patents last for 20 years from the date of filing.

To qualify for a utility patent—by far the most common type of patent—an invention must be:

- a process or method for producing a useful, concrete and tangible result (such as a genetic engineering procedure, an investment strategy or computer software)
- a machine (usually something with moving parts or circuitry, such as a cigarette lighter, sewage treatment system, laser or photocopier)
- an article of manufacture (such as an eraser, tire, transistor or hand tool)
- a composition of matter (such as a chemical composition, drug, soap or genetically altered life form), or
- an improvement of an invention that fits within one of the first four categories.

Often, an invention will fall into more than one category. For instance, a laser can usually be described both as a process (the steps necessary to produce the laser beam) and a machine (a device that implements the steps to produce the laser beam). Regardless of the number of categories into which a particular invention fits, it can receive only one utility patent.

If an invention fits into one of the categories described above, it is known as "statutory subject matter" and has passed the first test in qualifying for a patent. But an inventor's creation must overcome several additional hurdles before the PTO will issue a patent. The invention must also:

- have some utility, no matter how trivial
- be novel (that is, it must be different from all previous inventions in some important way), and

• be nonobvious (a surprising and significant development) to somebody who understands the technical field of the invention.

For design patents, the law requires that the design be novel, nonobvious and nonfunctional. For example, a new shape for a car fender, bottle or flashlight that doesn't improve its functionality would qualify.

Finally, plants may qualify for a patent if they are both novel and nonobvious. Plant patents are issued less frequently than any other type of patent.

More Examples of Patentable Subject Matter

The following items are just some of the things that might qualify for patent protection: biological inventions; carpet designs; new chemical formulas, processes or procedures; clothing accessories and designs; computer hardware and peripherals; computer software; containers; cosmetics; decorative hardware; electrical inventions; electronic circuits; fabrics and fabric designs; food inventions; furniture design; games (board, box and instructions); housewares; jewelry; laser light shows; machines; magic tricks or techniques; mechanical inventions; medical accessories and devices; medicines; methods of doing business; musical instruments; odors; plants; recreational gear; and sporting goods (designs and equipment).

What types of inventions are not eligible for patent protection?

Some types of inventions will not qualify for a patent, no matter how interesting or important they are. For example, mathematical formulas, laws of nature, newly discovered substances that occur naturally in the world, and purely theoretical phenomena—for instance, a scientific principle like superconductivity without regard to its use in the real world—have long been considered unpatentable. This means, for example, that you can't patent a general mathematical approach to problem solving or a newly discovered pain killer in its natural state.

In addition, the following categories of inventions don't qualify for patents:

• processes done entirely by human motor coordination, such as choreographed dance routines or a method for meditation

• most protocols and methods used to perform surgery on humans

• printed matter that has no unique physical shape or structure associated with it

• unsafe new drugs

• inventions useful only for illegal purposes, and

• nonoperable inventions, including "perpetual motion" machines (which are presumed to be non-operable because to operate they would have to violate certain bedrock scientific principles).

Can computer software qualify for patent protection?

Yes. Even though you can't get a patent on a mathematical formula per se, you may be able to get protection for a specific application of a formula. Thus, software may qualify for a patent if it produces a useful, concrete and tangible result. For example, the PTO will not issue a patent on the complex mathematical formulae that are used in space navigation, but will grant a patent for the software and machines that translate those equations and make the space shuttle go where it's supposed to go.

Can a business method qualify for a utility patent?

A business method is a series of steps that express some business activity, for example, a method of calculating an interest rate or a system for evaluating employee performance. Before 1988, the PTO rarely granted patents for methods of doing business. Then, in 1988, the United States Court of Appeals for the Federal Circuit changed this. (*State Street Bank & Trust Co. v. Signal Financial Group, Inc.* 149 F.3d 1368 (Fed. Cir. 1998).) The court ruled that patent laws were intended to protect business methods, so long as the method produced a "useful, concrete and tangible result."

In the six months following the *State Street* ruling, patent filings for business methods increased by 40%. In response to the development of these new methods, the PTO created a new classification for such applications: "Data processing: financial, business practice, management or cost/price determination."

Is it possible to obtain a patent on forms of life?

Forms of life, from bacteria to cows, that are genetically altered to have new and useful characteristics or behaviors may qualify for utility patents. Also patentable are sequences of DNA that have been created to test genetic behaviors and the methods used to accomplish this sequencing. With the advent of cloning techniques and the ability to mix genes across species—for example, the human immune system genetic code transplanted into a mouse for testing purposes—the question of what life forms can and cannot be patented promises to be a subject of fierce debate for years to come.

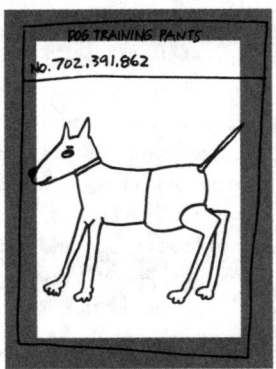

What makes an invention novel?

In the context of a patent application, an invention is considered novel when it is different from all previous inventions (called "prior art") in one or more of its constituent elements. When deciding whether an invention is novel, the PTO will consider all prior art that existed as of the date the inventor files a patent application on the invention, or if necessary, as of the date the inventor can prove he or she first built and tested the invention. If prior art is uncovered, the invention may still qualify for a patent if the inventor can show that he or she conceived of the invention before the prior art existed and was diligent in building and testing the invention or filing a patent application on it.

An invention will flunk the novelty test if it was described in a published document or put to public use more than one year prior to the date the patent application was filed. This is known as the one-year rule.

When is an invention considered nonobvious?

To qualify for a patent, an invention must be nonobvious as well as novel. An invention is considered nonobvious if someone who is skilled in the particular field of the invention would view it as an unexpected or surprising development.

For example, in August of 2000, Future Enterprises invents a portable high quality virtual reality system. A virtual reality engineer would most likely find this invention to be truly surprising and unexpected. Even though increased portability of a computer-based technology is always expected in the broad sense, the specific way in which the portability is accomplished by this invention would be a breakthrough in the field and thus unobvious. Contrast this with a bicycle developer who uses a new, light but strong metal alloy to build his bicycles. Most people skilled in the art of bicycle manufacturing would consider the use of the new alloy in the bicycle to be obvious, given that lightness of weight is a desirable aspect of high-quality bicycles.

Knowing whether an invention will be considered nonobvious by the PTO is difficult because it is such a subjective exercise—what one patent examiner considers surprising, another may not. In addition, the examiner will usually be asked to make the nonobviousness determination well after the date of the invention, because of delays inherent in the patent process. The danger of this type of retroactive assessment is that the examiner may unconsciously be affected by the intervening technical improvements. To avoid this, the examiner generally relies only on the prior-art references (documents describing previous inventions) that existed as of the date of invention.

As an example, assume that in 2003, Future Enterprises' application for a patent on the 2000 invention is being examined in the Patent and Trademark Office. Assume further that by 2003, you can find a portable virtual reality unit in any consumer electronics store for under $200. The patent examiner will have to go back to the time of the invention to fully appreciate how surprising and unexpected it was when it was first conceived, and ignore the fact that in 2003 the technology of the invention is very common.

What makes an invention useful?

Patents may be granted for inventions that have some type of usefulness (utility), even if the use is humorous, such as a musical condom or a motorized spaghetti fork. However, the invention must work—at least in theory. Thus, a new approach to manufacturing superconducting materials may qualify for a patent if it has a sound theoretical basis—even if it hasn't yet been shown to work in practice. But a new drug that has no theoretical basis and which hasn't been tested will not qualify for a patent.

Remember that to qualify for a design or plant patent, the other two types of patents obtained in the U.S., the inventor need not show utility

Are You the First?

As discussed previously, patents are awarded only on new and nonobvious inventions. How can an inventor find out whether his or her invention is really new? The place to start is to see whether it has ever been patented. Although a number of great inventions have never received a patent, most have. A quick spin through the patent database can provide a good headstart on finding out just how innovative an invention really is.

The Internet can be used for free access to patents issued since 1971. The U.S. Patent and Trademark Office (http://www.uspto.gov) provides free online databases where you simply type in words which describe your invention—called keywords.

Commercial fee-based databases often offer more choices than the free USPTO site. Below are some fee-based patent databases and a brief description of their contents.

- **MicroPatent** (http://www.micropatent.com). You can search U.S. and Japanese patents from 1976 to the present, International patents issued under the Patent Cooperation Treaty (PCT) from 1983 and European patents from 1988.

- **Delphion** (http://www.delphion.com). You can search U.S patents from 1971 to the present and full-text patents from the European Patent Office, the World Intellectual Property Organization PCT collection and abstracts from Derwent world patent index.

- **LEXPAT** (http://www.lexis-nexis.com). You can search U.S. patents from 1971 to the present. In addition, the LEXPAT library offers extensive prior-art searching capability of technical journals and magazines.
- **QPAT** (http://www.qpat.com) and **Questel/Orbit** (http://www.questel.orbit.com). You can search U.S. patents from 1974 to the present and full-text European patents from 1987 to the present.

Sometimes an inventor needs to search for patents issued before 1971. All patents since the founding of the United States count when deciding whether an invention is sufficiently new to deserve a patent. And if the invention involves timeless technology (another way to core an apple), these pre-1971 patents are as important as those that were issued later.

A great resource for complete patent searching—from the first patent ever issued to the latest—is a network of special libraries called Patent and Trademark Depository Libraries (PTDLs). Every state but Connecticut has at least one. While a complete patent search can be done for free in these libraries, many of them also offer computer searches for a reasonable fee. Consult the PTO website at http://www.uspto.gov to find the PTDL nearest you.

Obtaining a Patent

Many times a day I realize how much my own outer and inner life is built upon the labors of my fellow men, both living and dead, and how earnestly I must exert myself in order to give in return as much as I have received.

—ALBERT EINSTEIN

Because a patent grants the inventor a monopoly on his or her invention for a relatively long period of time, patent applications are rigorously examined by the Patent and Trademark Office (PTO). Typically, a patent application travels back and forth between the applicant and the patent examiner until both sides agree on which aspects of an invention the patent will cover, if any. This process typically takes between one and two years.

If an agreement is reached, the PTO "allows" the application and publishes a brief description of the patent in a weekly publication called the *Official Gazette.* If no one objects to the patent as published, and the applicant pays the required issuance fee, the PTO provides the applicant with a document called a patent deed, which we colloquially refer to as a patent. The patent deed consists primarily of the information submitted in the patent application, as modified during the patent examination process.

What information is typically included in a patent application?

There is no such thing as an automatic patent through creation or usage of an invention. To receive patent protection, an inventor must file an application, pay the appropriate fees and obtain a patent. To apply for a U.S. patent, the inventor must file the application with a branch of the U.S. Department of Commerce known as the U.S. Patent and Trademark Office, or PTO. A U.S. patent application typically consists of:

- an Information Disclosure Statement—that is, an explanation of why the invention is different from all previous and similar developments (the "prior art")
- a detailed description of the structure and operation of the invention (called a patent specification) that teaches how to build and use the invention
- a precise description of the aspects of the invention to be covered by the patent (called the patent claims)
- all drawings that are necessary to fully explain the specification and claims
- a Patent Application Declaration—a statement under oath that the information in the application is true, and
- the filing fee.

In addition, small inventors often include a declaration asking for a reduction in the filing fee.

Understanding the Provisional Patent Application

Often inventors want to have a patent application on file when they go out to show their invention to prospective manufacturers because it will discourage ripoffs. Also, inventors like to get their invention on record as early as possible in case someone else comes up with the same invention. To accomplish both these goals, an inventor may file what is known as a Provisional Patent Application (PPA). The PPA need only contain a complete description of the structure and operation of an invention and any drawings that are necessary to understand it—it need not contain claims, formal drawings, a Patent Application Declaration or an Information Disclosure Statement.

An inventor who files a regular patent application within one year of filing a PPA can claim the PPA's filing date for the regular patent application. If the regular patent application includes any new matter (technical information about the invention) that wasn't in the PPA, the inventor won't be able to rely on the PPA's filing date for the new matter. The PPA's filing date doesn't affect when the patent on the invention will expire; it still expires 20 years from the date the regular patent application is filed. So, the PPA has the practical effect of delaying examination of a regular patent application and extending—up to one year—the patent's expiration date.

What happens if there are multiple applications for the same invention?

If a patent examiner discovers that another pending application involves the same invention and that both inventions appear to qualify for a patent, the patent examiner will declare that a conflict (called an interference) exists between the two applications. In that event, a hearing is held to determine who is entitled to the patent.

Who gets the patent depends on such variables as who first conceived the invention and worked on it diligently, who first built and tested the invention and who filed the first provisional or regular patent application. Because of the possibility of a patent interference, it is wise to document all invention-related activities in a signed and witnessed inventor's notebook so that you can later prove the date the invention was conceived and the steps you took to build and test the invention or quickly file a patent application.

How are U.S. patents protected abroad?

Patent rights originate in the U.S. Constitution and are implemented exclusively by federal laws passed by Congress. These laws define the kinds of inventions that are patentable and the procedures that must be followed to apply for, receive and maintain patent rights for the duration of the patent.

All other industrialized countries offer patent protection as well. While patent requirements and rules differ from country to country, several international treaties (including the Patent Cooperation Treaty and the Paris Convention) allow U.S. inventors to obtain patent protection in other countries that have adopted the treaties if the inventors take certain required steps, such as filing a patent application in the countries on a timely basis and paying required patent fees.

Enforcing a Patent

Once a patent is issued, it is up to the owner to enforce it. If friendly negotiations fail, enforcement involves two basic steps:

- making a determination that the patent is being illegally violated (infringed), and
- filing a federal court action to enforce the patent.

Because enforcing a patent can be a long and expensive process, many patent infringment suits that could have been filed, aren't. Instead, the patent owner often settles with the infringer. Frequently, an infringer will pay a reasonable license fee that allows the infringer to continue using the invention.

What constitutes infringement of a patent?

To decide whether an inventor is violating a patent, it is necessary to carefully examine the patent's claims (most patents contain more than one of these terse statements of the scope of the invention) and compare the elements of each claim with the elements of the accused infringer's device or process. If the elements of a patent claim match the elements of the device or process (called "reading on" or "teaching" the device or process), an infringement has occurred. Even if the claims don't literally match the infringing device, it is possible that a court would find an infringement by applying what's known as the "doctrine of equivalents," that is, the invention in the patent and the allegedly infringing device or process are sufficiently equivalent in what they do and how they do it to warrant a finding of infringement.

For example, Steve invents a tennis racket with a score keeper embedded in the racket handle's end. The invention is claimed as a tennis racket handle that combines grasping and score keeping functions. Steve receives a patent on this invention. Later, Megan invents and sells a tennis racket with a transparent handle that provides a more sophisticated score keeping device than Steve's racket. Even though Megan's invention improves on Steve's invention in certain respects, it will most likely be held to be an infringement of Steve's invention, for one of two reasons:

• Megan's invention teaches the same elements as those claimed in Steve's patent (a tennis racket handle with two functions), or

• when considering what it is and how it works, Megan's invention is the substantial equivalent of Steve's invention (the doctrine of equivalents).

What remedies are available for patent infringement?

A patent owner may enforce his patent by bringing a patent infringement action (lawsuit) in federal court against anyone who uses his invention without permission. If the lawsuit is successful, the court will take one of two approaches. It may issue a court order (called an injunction) preventing the infringer from any further use or sale of the infringing device, and award damages to the patent owner. Or, the court may work with the parties to hammer out an agreement under which the infringing party will pay the patent owner royalties in exchange for permission to use the infringing device.

Bringing a patent infringement action can be tricky, because it is possible for the alleged infringer to defend by proving to the court that the patent is really invalid (most often by showing that the PTO made a mistake in issuing the patent in the first place). In a substantial number of patent infringement cases, the patent is found invalid and the lawsuit dismissed, leaving the patent owner in a worse position than before the lawsuit.

When does patent protection end?

Patent protection usually ends when the patent expires. For all utility patents filed before June 8, 1995, the patent term is 17 years from date of issuance. For utility patents filed on or after June 8, 1995, the patent term is 20 years from the date of filing. For design patents, the period is 14 years from date of issuance. For plant patents, the period is 17 years from date of issuance.

A patent may expire if its owner fails to pay required maintenance fees. Usually this occurs because attempts to commercially exploit the underlying invention have failed and the patent owner chooses to not throw good money after bad.

Patent protection ends if a patent is found to be invalid. This may happen if someone shows that the patent application was insufficient or that the applicant committed fraud on the PTO, usually by lying or failing to disclose the applicant's knowledge about prior art that would legally prevent issuance of the patent. A patent may also be invalidated if someone shows that the inventor engaged in illegal conduct when using the patent—such as conspiring with a patent licensee to exclude other companies from competing with them.

Once a patent has expired, the invention described by the patent falls into the public domain: It can be used by anyone without permission from the owner of the expired patent. The basic technologies underlying television and personal computers are good examples of valuable inventions that are no longer covered by in-force patents.

The fact that an invention is in the public domain does not mean that subsequent developments based on the original invention are also in the public domain. Rather, new inventions that improve public domain technology are constantly being conceived and patented. For example, televisions and personal computers that roll off today's assembly lines employ many recent inventions that are covered by in-force patents.

The Life of an Invention

Although most inventors are concerned with the rights a patent grants during its monopoly or in-force period (from the date the patent issues until it expires), the law actually recognizes five "rights" periods in the life of an invention. These five periods are as follows:

1. Invention conceived but not yet documented. When an inventor conceives an invention but hasn't yet made any written, signed, dated and witnessed record of it, the inventor has no rights whatsoever.

2. Invention documented but patent application not yet filed. After making a proper signed, dated and witnessed documentation of an invention, the inventor has valuable rights against any inventor who later conceives the same invention and applies for a patent. The invention may also be treated as a "trade secret"—that is, kept confidential. This gives the inventor the legal right to sue and recover damages against anyone who immorally learns of the invention—for example, through industrial spying.

3. Patent pending (patent application filed but not yet issued). During the

patent pending period, including the one-year period after a provisional patent application is filed, the inventor's rights are the same as they are in Period 2, above, with one exception. Effective December 2000, if the patent owner intends to also file for a patent abroad, the PTO will publish the application 18 months after the earliest claimed filing date. Under the new 18-month publication statute, an inventor whose application is published prior to issuance may obtain royalties from an infringer from the date of publication, provided the application later issues as a patent and the infringer had actual notice of the published application. Otherwise, the inventor has no rights whatsoever against infringers—only the hope of a future monopoly, which doesn't commence until a patent issues.

By law, the PTO must keep all patent applications secret until the application is published or the patent issues, whichever comes first. The patent pending period usually lasts from one to three years.

4. In-force patent (patent issued but hasn't yet expired). After the patent issues, the patent owner can bring and maintain a lawsuit for patent infringement against anyone who makes, uses or sells the invention without permission. The patent's in-force period lasts from the date it issues until it expires. Also, after the patent issues, it becomes a public record or publication that prevents others from getting patents on the same or similar inventions—that is, it becomes "prior art" to anyone who

files a subsequent patent application.

5. Patent expired. After the patent expires, the patent owner has no further rights, although infringement suits can still be brought for any infringement that occurred during the patent's in-force period as long as the suit is filed within the time required by law. An expired patent remains a valid "prior-art reference" forever.

Putting a Patent to Work

OUR ASPIRATIONS ARE OUR

POSSIBILITIES.

—ROBERT BROWNING

On its own, a patent has no value. Value arises only when a patent owner takes action to realize commercial gain from his or her monopoly position. There are several basic approaches to making money from a patent.

How can an inventor make money with a patent?

Some inventors start new companies to develop and market their patented inventions. This is not typical, however, because the majority of inventors would rather invent than run a business. More often, an inventor makes arrangements with an existing company to develop and market the invention. This arrangement usually takes the form of a license (contract) under which the developer is authorized to commercially exploit the invention in exchange for paying the patent owner royalties for each invention sold. Or, in a common variation of this arrangement, the inventor may sell all the rights to the invention for a lump sum.

What does it mean to license an invention?

A license is written permission to use an invention. A license may be exclusive (if only one manufacturer is licensed to develop the invention) or nonexclusive (if a number of manufacturers are licensed to develop it). The license may be for the duration of the patent or for a shorter period of time.

The developer itself may license other companies to market or distribute the invention. The extent to which the inventor will benefit from these sub-licenses depends on the terms of the agreement between the inventor and the developer. Especially when inventions result from work done in the course of employment, the employer-business usually ends up owning the patent rights, and receives all or most of the royalties based on subsequent licensing activity. (See the next question.)

In many cases, a developer will trade licenses with other companies—called cross-licensing—so that companies involved in the trade will benefit from each other's technology. For example, assume that two computer companies each own several patents on newly developed remote-controlled techniques. Because each company would be strengthened by being able to use the other company's inventions as well as its own, the companies will most likely agree to swap permissions to use their respective inventions.

Can inventors who are employed by a company benefit from their inventions?

Typically, inventor-employees who invent in the course of their employment are bound by employment agreements that automatically assign all rights in the invention to the employer. While smart research and development companies give their inventors bonuses for valuable inventions, this is a matter of contract rather than law.

If there is no employment agreement, the employer may still own rights to an employee-created invention under the "employed to invent" doctrine. How does this rule apply? If an inventor is employed—even without a written employment agreement—to accomplish a defined task, or is hired or directed to create an invention, the employer will own all rights to the subsequent invention.

If there is no employment agreement and the inventor is not employed to invent, the inventor may retain the right to exploit the invention, but the employer is given a nonexclusive right to use the invention for its internal purposes (called shop rights). For example, Robert is a machinist in a machine shop and invents a new process for handling a particular type of metal. If Robert isn't employed to invent and hasn't signed an employment agreement giving the shop all rights to the invention, Robert can patent and exploit the invention for himself. The shop, however, would retain the right to use the new process without having to pay Robert.

How Patents Differ From Copyrights and Trademarks

While it is possible to invent definitions that draw clear lines between the areas of patent, copyright and trademark (the three major types of intellectual property protection), there are complications when it comes to certain innovative designs. In some cases, a design may be subject to patent, trademark and copyright protection all at the same time.

How do patents differ from copyrights?

With the exception of innovative designs, patents are closely associated with things and processes which are useful in the real world. Almost at the opposite end of the spectrum, copy-

right applies to expressive arts such as novels, fine and graphic arts, music, phonorecords, photography, software, video, cinema and choreography. While it is possible to get a patent on technologies used in the arts, it is copyright that keeps one artist from stealing another artist's creative work.

An exception to the general rule that patents and copyright don't overlap can be found in product designs. It is theoretically possible to get a design patent on the purely ornamental (nonfunctional) aspects of the product design and also claim a copyright in this same design. For example, the stylistic fins of a car's rear fenders may qualify for both a design patent (because they are strictly ornamental) and copyright (as to their expressive elements). In practice, however, a product is usually granted one type of protection or the other—not both.

For more information about copyright law, see Chapter 7.

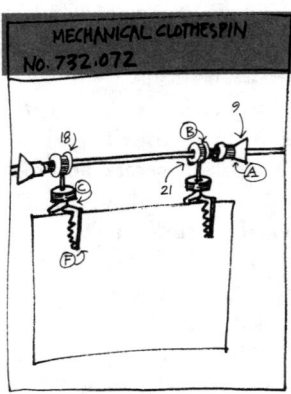

What's the difference between patent and trademark?

Generally speaking, patents allow the creator of certain kinds of inventions that contain new ideas to keep others from making commercial use of those ideas without the creator's permission. Trademark, on the other hand, is not concerned with how a new technology is used. Rather, it applies to the names, logos and other devices—such as color, sound and smell—that are used to identify the source of goods or services and distinguish them from their competition.

Generally, patent and trademark laws do not overlap. When it comes to a product design, however—say, jewelry or a distinctively shaped musical instrument—it may be possible to obtain a patent on a design aspect of the device while invoking trademark law to protect the design as a product identifier. For example, a surfboard manufacturer might receive a patent for a surfboard design that mimics the design used in a popular surfing film. Then, if the design is intended to be—and actually is—used to distinguish the particular type of surfboard in the marketplace, trademark law may kick in to protect the appearance of the board.

For more information about trademarks, see Chapter 8.

More Information About Patents

Patent It Yourself, by David Pressman (Nolo), takes you step by step through the process of getting a patent without hiring a patent lawyer. Patent It Yourself software (for Windows) is also available.

Patent Searching Made Easy, by David Hitchcock (Nolo), shows you how to search the U.S. Patent Database on the internet and in the library.

How to Make Patent Drawings Yourself, by Jack Lo and David Pressman (Nolo), takes you step by step through the process of making your own patent drawing.

License Your Invention, by Richard Stim (Nolo), walks you through the process of realizing your invention's commercial potential.

Patent, Copyright & Trademark, by Stephen Elias and Richard Stim (Nolo), provides concise definitions and examples of the important words and phrases commonly used in patent law.

Nolo's Patents for Beginners, by David Pressman and Richard Stim (Nolo), is a primer that explains all of the essential patent principles in plain English.

http://www.nolo.com

Nolo offers self-help information about a wide variety of legal topics, including patent law.

http://www.uspto.gov

The U.S. Patent and Trademark Office is the place to go for recent policy and statutory changes and transcripts of hearings on various patent law issues. The U.S. Patent and Trademark Office maintains a seachable electronic database of the front page of all patents issued since 1971. This site is an excellent way to initiate a search for relevant patents. Also, the USPTO has announced that it is putting the full U.S. patent database online for free searching near the end of 1998.

http://www.inventionconvention.com

The National Congress of Inventor Organizations (NCIO) maintain this invention website that includes links, trade show information, and advice for inventors.

http://www.patentcafe.com

The Patent Café is an inventor resource that provides software, inventor kits and advice on patent searching, patent attorneys and marketing.

http://www.sci3.com

Sc{I}³ provides in-depth patent searching services, patent-related products and seminars.

http://www.spi.org

The Software Patent Institute lets you search for previous software developments that may affect whether your software qualifies for a patent.

Copyrights

7.2   *Copyright Basics*

7.4   *Copyright Ownership*

7.6   *Copyright Protection*

7.10 *Copyright Registration and Enforcement*

People seldom improve when they have no other model but themselves to copy after.

—OLIVER GOLDSMITH

It has long been recognized that everyone benefits when creative people are encouraged to develop new intellectual and artistic works. When the United States Constitution was written in 1787, the framers took care to include a copyright clause (Article I, Section 8) giving Congress the power to "promote the Progress of Science and useful Arts" by passing laws that give creative people exclusive rights in their own artistic works for a limited period of time.

Copyright laws are not designed to enrich creative artists, but to promote human knowledge and development. These laws encourage artists in their creative efforts by giving them a mini-monopoly over their works—called a copyright. But this monopoly is limited when it conflicts with the overriding purpose of encouraging people to create new works of scholarship or art.

This chapter introduces you to copyright law and guides you through the first steps of creating, owning and protecting a copyright. To learn about how copyrights differ from—and work with—patents and trademarks, see Chapters 6 and 8.

Copyright Basics

IT IS NECESSARY TO ANY ORIGINALITY

TO HAVE THE COURAGE TO BE AN

AMATEUR.

—WALLACE STEVENS

Copyright is a legal device that gives the creator of a work of art or literature, or a work that conveys information or ideas, the right to control how that work is used. The Copyright Act of 1976—the federal law providing for copyright protection—grants authors a bundle of exclusive rights over their works, including the right to reproduce, distribute, adapt or perform them.

An author's copyright rights may be exercised only by the author—or by a person or entity to whom the author has transferred all or part of her rights. If someone wrongfully uses the material covered by a copyright, the copyright owner can sue and obtain compensation for any losses suffered.

What types of creative work does copyright protect?

Copyright protects works such as poetry, movies, video games, videos, DVDs, plays, paintings, sheet music, recorded music performances, novels, software code, sculptures, photographs, choreography and architectural designs.

To qualify for copyright protection, a work must be "fixed in a tangible medium of expression." This means that the work must exist in some physical form for at least some period of time, no matter how brief. Virtually any form of expression will qualify as a tangible medium, including a computer's random access memory (RAM), the recording media that capture all radio and television broadcasts and the scribbled notes on the back of an envelope that contain the basis for an impromptu speech.

In addition, the work must be original—that is, independently created by the author. It doesn't matter if an author's creation is similar to existing works, or even if it is arguably lacking in quality, ingenuity or aesthetic merit. So long as the author toils without copying from someone else, the results are protected by copyright.

Finally, to receive copyright protection, a work must be the result of at least some creative effort on the part of its author. There is no hard and fast rule as to how much creativity is enough. As one example, a work must be more creative than a telephone book's white pages, which involve a straightforward alphabetical listing of telephone numbers rather than a creative selection of listings.

Does copyright protect an author's creative ideas?

No. Copyright shelters only fixed, original and creative expression, not the ideas or facts upon which the expression is based. For example, copyright may protect a particular song, novel or computer game about a romance in space, but it cannot protect the underlying idea of having a love affair among the stars. Allowing authors to monopolize their ideas would thwart the underlying purpose of copyright law, which is to encourage people to create new work.

For similar reasons, copyright does not protect facts—whether scientific, historical, biographical or news of the day. Any facts that an author discovers in the course of research are in the public domain, free to all. For instance, anyone is free to use information included in a book about how the brain works, an article about the life and times of Neanderthals or a TV documentary about the childhood of President Clinton—provided that they express the information in their own words.

Facts are not protected even if the author spends considerable time and effort discovering things that were previously unknown. For example, the author of the book on Neanderthals takes ten years to gather all the necessary materials and information for her work. At great expense, she travels to hundreds of museums and excavations around the world. But after the book is published, any reader is free to use the results of this ten-year research project to write his or her own book on Neanderthals—without paying the original author.

How long does a copyright last?

For works published after 1977, the copyright lasts for the life of the author plus 70 years. However, if the work is a work for hire (that is, the work is done in the course of employment or has been specifically commissioned) or is published anonymously or under a pseudonym, the copyright lasts between 95 and 120 years, depending on the date the work is published.

All works published in the United States before 1923 are in the public domain. Works published after 1922, but before 1964, are protected for 95 years from the date of publication if a renewal was filed with the Copyright Office during the 28th year after publication. If no renewal was filed, such works are in the public domain in the U.S. Works published during 1964-1977 are protected for 95 years whether or not a renewal was filed. If the work was created, but not published, before 1978, the copyright lasts for the life of the author plus 70 years. However, even if the author died over 70 years ago, the copyright in an unpublished work lasts until December 31, 2002. And if such a work is published before 2003, the copyright lasts until December 31, 2047.

Is the Work Published?

In the complicated scheme of copyright laws, which law applies to a particular work depends on when that work is published. A work is considered published when the author makes it available to the public on an unrestricted basis. This means that it is possible to distribute or display a work without publishing it if there are significant restrictions placed on what can be done with the work and when it can be shown to others. For example, Andres Miczslova writes an essay called "Blood Bath" about the war in Bosnia, and distributes it to five human rights organizations under a non exclusive license that places restrictions on their right to disclose the essay's contents. "Blood Bath" has not been "published" in the copyright sense. If Miczslova authorizes posting of the essay on the Internet, however, it would likely be considered published.

Copyright Ownership

HE WHO CAN COPY, CAN DO.

—LEONARDO DA VINCI

A copyright is initially owned by a creative work's author or authors. But under the law, a person need not actually create the work to be its "author" for copyright purposes. A protectible work created by an employee as part of his or her job is initially owned by the employer—that is, the employer is considered to be the work's author. Such works are called "works made for hire." Works created by nonemployees (independent contractors) may also be works made for hire if they sign written agreements to that effect and the work falls within one of eight enumerated categories.

Like any other property, a copyright can be bought and sold. Transfers of copyright ownership are unique in one respect, however: Authors or their heirs have the right to terminate any transfer of copyright ownership 35 to 40 years after it is made.

What are the exceptions to the rule that the creator of a work owns the copyright?

Copyrights are generally owned by the people who create the works of expression, with some important exceptions:

- If a work is created by an employee in the course of his or her employment, the employer owns the copyright.
- If the work is created by an independent contractor and the independent contractor signs a written agreement stating that the work shall be "made for hire," the commissioning person or organization owns the copyright only if the work is (1) a part of a larger literary work, such as an article in a magazine or a

poem or story in an anthology; (2) part of a motion picture or other audiovisual work, such as a screenplay; (3) a translation; (4) a supplementary work such as an afterword, an introduction, chart, editorial note, bibliography, appendix or index; (5) a compilation; (6) an instructional text; (7) a test or answer material for a test; or (8) an atlas. Works that don't fall within one of these eight categories constitute works made for hire only if created by an employee within the scope of his or her employment.

- If the creator has sold the entire copyright, the purchasing business or person becomes the copyright owner.

Who owns the copyright in a joint work?

When two or more authors prepare a work with the intent to combine their contributions into inseparable or interdependent parts, the work is considered joint work and the authors are considered joint copyright owners. The most common example of a joint work is when a book or article has two or more authors. However, if a book is written primarily by one author, but another author contributes a specific chapter to the book and is given credit for that chapter, then this probably wouldn't be a joint work because the contributions aren't inseparable or interdependent.

The U.S. Copyright Office considers joint copyright owners to have an equal right to register and enforce the copyright. Unless the joint owners make a written agreement to the contrary, each copyright owner has the right to commercially exploit the copyright, provided that the other copyright owners get an equal share of the proceeds.

Can two or more authors provide contributions to a single work without being considered a joint authors?

Yes. If at the time of creation, the authors did not intend their works to be part of an inseparable whole, the fact that their works are later put together does not create a joint work. Rather, the result is considered a collective work. In this case, each author owns a copyright in only the material he or she added to the finished product. For example, in the 1950s, Vladimir writes a famous novel full of complex literary allusions. In the 1980s, his publisher issues a student edition of the work with detailed annotations written by an English professor. The student edition is a collective work. Vladimir owns the copyright in the novel, but the professor owns the annotations.

What rights do copyright owners have under the Copyright Act?

The Copyright Act of 1976 grants a number of exclusive rights to copyright owners, including:

- reproduction right—the right to make copies of a protected work
- distribution right—the right to sell or otherwise distribute copies to the public

• right to create adaptations (called derivative works)—the right to prepare new works based on the protected work, and
• performance and display rights—the rights to perform a protected work (such as a stageplay) or to display a work in public.

This bundle of rights allows a copyright owner to be flexible when deciding how to realize commercial gain from the underlying work; the owner may sell or license any of the rights.

Can a copyright owner transfer some or all of his specific rights?

Yes. When a copyright owner wishes to commercially exploit the work covered by the copyright, the owner typically transfers one or more of these rights to the person or entity who will be responsible for getting the work to market, such as a book or software publisher. It is also common for the copyright owner to place some limitations on the exclusive rights being transferred. For example, the owner may limit the transfer to a specific period of time, allow the right to be exercised only in a specific part of the country or world or require that the right be exercised only through certain media, such as hardcover books, audiotapes, magazines or computers.

If a copyright owner transfers all of his rights unconditionally, it is generally termed an "assignment." When only some of the rights associated with the copyright are transferred, it is known as a "license." An exclusive license exists when the transferred rights can be exercised only by the owner of the license (the licensee), and no one else—including the person who granted the license (the licensor). If the license allows others (including the licensor) to exercise the same rights being transferred in the license, the license is said to be nonexclusive.

The U.S. Copyright Office allows buyers of exclusive and non-exclusive copyright rights to record the transfers in the U.S. Copyright Office. This helps to protect the buyers in case the original copyright owner later tries to transfer the same rights to another party.

Copyright Protection

Probably the most important fact to grasp about copyright protection is that it automatically comes into existence when the protected work is created. However, the degree of protection that copyright laws extend to a protected work can be influenced by later events.

What role does a copyright notice play?

Until 1989, a published work had to contain a valid copyright notice to receive protection under the copyright laws. But this requirement is no longer in force—works first published after March 1, 1989 need not include a copyright notice to gain protection under the law.

But even though a copyright notice is not required, it's still important to include one. When a work contains a valid notice, an infringer cannot claim in court that he or she didn't know it was copyrighted. This makes it much easier to win a copyright infringement case and perhaps collect enough damages to make the cost of the case worthwhile. And the very existence of a notice might discourage infringement.

Finally, including a copyright notice may make it easier for a potential infringer to track down a copyright owner and legitimately obtain permission to use the work.

What is a valid copyright notice?

A copyright notice should contain:
- the word "copyright"
- a "c" in a circle (©)
- the date of publication, and
- the name of either the author or the owner of all the copyright rights in the published work.

For example, the correct copyright for the fifth edition of *The Copyright Handbook*, by Stephen Fishman (Nolo), is *Copyright © 2001 by Stephen Fishman.*

International Copyright Protection

Copyright protection rules are fairly similar worldwide, due to several international copyright treaties, the most important of which is the Berne Convention. Under this treaty, all member countries—and there are more than 100, including virtually all industrialized nations—must afford copyright protection to authors who are nationals of any member country. This protection must last for at least the life of the author plus 50 years, and must be automatic, without the need for the author to take any legal steps to preserve the copyright.

In addition to the Berne Convention, the GATT (General Agreement on Tariffs and Trade) treaty contains a number of provisions that affect copyright protection in signatory countries. Together, the Berne Copyright Convention and the GATT treaty allow U.S. authors to enforce their copyrights in most industrialized nations, and allow the nationals of those nations to enforce their copyrights in the U.S.

When can I use a work without the author's permission?

When a work becomes available for use without permission from a copyright owner, it is said to be "in the public domain." Most works enter the public domain because their copyrights have expired.

To determine whether a work is in the public domain and available for use without the author's permission, you first have to find out when it was published. Then you can apply the periods of time set out earlier in this chapter. (See *How long does a copyright last?*, above.) If the work was published between 1923 and 1963, however, you must check with the U.S. Copyright Office to see whether the copyright was properly renewed. If the author failed to renew the copyright, the work has fallen into the public domain and you may use it.

The Copyright Office will check renewal information for you, at a charge of $65 per hour. (Call the Reference & Bibliography Section at 202-707-6850.) You can also hire a private copyright search firm to see if a renewal was filed. Finally, you may be able to conduct a renewal search yourself. The renewal records for works published from 1950 to the present are available online at http://lcweb.loc.gov/copyright. Renewal searches for earlier works can be conducted at the Copyright Office in Washington DC or by visiting one of the many government depository libraries throughout the country. Call the Copyright Office for more information.

With one important exception, you should assume that every work is protected by copyright unless you can establish that it is not. As mentioned above, you can't rely on the presence or absence of a copyright notice (©) to make this determination, because a notice is not required for works published after March 1, 1989. And even for works published before 1989, the absence of a copyright notice may not affect the validity of the copyright—

for example, if the author made diligent attempts to correct the situation.

The exception is for materials put to work under the "fair use rule." This rule recognizes that society can often benefit from the unauthorized use of copyrighted materials when the purpose of the use serves the ends of scholarship, education or an informed public. For example, scholars must be free to quote from their research resources in order to comment on the material. To strike a balance between the needs of a public to be well informed and the rights of copyright owners to profit from their creativity, Congress passed a law authorizing the use of copyrighted materials in certain circumstances deemed to be "fair"— even if the copyright owner doesn't give permission.

Often, it's difficult to know whether a court will consider a proposed use to be fair. The fair use statute requires the courts to consider the following questions in deciding this issue:

- Is it a competitive use? If the use potentially affects the sales of the copied material, it's probably not fair.

- How much material was taken compared to the entire work of which the material was a part? The more someone takes, the less likely it is that the use is fair.

- How was the material used? Did the defendant change the original by adding new expression or meaning? Did the defendant add value to the original by creating new information, new aesthetics, new insights and understandings? If the use was transformative, this weighs in favor of a fair use finding. Criticism, comment, news reporting, research, scholarship and nonprofit educational uses are also likely to be judged fair uses. Uses motivated primarily by a desire for a commercial gain are less likely to be fair use.

As a general rule, if you are using a small portion of somebody else's work in a noncompetitive way and the purpose for your use is to benefit the public, you're on pretty safe ground. On the other hand, if you take large portions of someone else's expression for your own purely commercial reasons, the rule usually won't apply.

If You Want to Use Material on the Internet

Each day, people post vast quantities of creative material on the Internet—material that is available for downloading by anyone who has the right computer equipment. Because the information is stored somewhere on an Internet server, it is fixed in a tangible medium and potentially qualifies for copyright protection. Whether it does, in fact, qualify depends on other factors that you would have no way of knowing about, such as when the work was first published (which affects the need for a copyright notice), whether the copyright in the work has been

renewed (for works published before 1964), whether the work is a work made for hire (which affects the length of the copyright) and whether the copyright owner intends to dedicate the work to the public domain.

As a general rule, it is wise to operate under the assumption that all materials are protected by either copyright or trademark law unless conclusive information indicates otherwise. A work is not in the public domain simply because it has been posted on the Internet (a popular fallacy) or because it lacks a copyright notice (another fallacy). As a general rule permission is needed to reproduce copyrighted materials including photos, text, music and artwork. It's best to track down the author of the material and ask for permission.

The most useful sources for finding information and obtaining permission are copyright collectives or clearinghouses. These are organizations that organize and license works by their members. For example, the Copyright Clearinghouse (http://www.copyright.com), and icopyright (http://www.icopyright.com) provide permissions for written materials. You can use an Internet search engine to locate other collectives for music, photos and artwork.

The only exception to this advice is for situations where you want to use only a very small portion of text for educational or nonprofit purposes. (See the previous question for a discussion of the "fair use rule.")

Copyright Registration and Enforcement

Although every work published after 1989 is automatically protected by copyright, you can strengthen your rights by registering your work with the U.S. Copyright Office. This registration makes it possible to bring a lawsuit to protect your copyright if someone violates (infringes) it. The registration process is straightforward and inexpensive, and can be done without a lawyer.

Why register your work with the U.S. Copyright Office?

You must register your copyright with the U.S. Copyright Office before you are legally permitted to bring a lawsuit to enforce it.

You can register a copyright at any time, but filing promptly may pay off in the long run. "Timely registration"—that is, registration within three months of the work's publication date or before any copyright infringement actually begins—makes it much easier to sue and recover money from an infringer. Specifically, timely registration creates a legal presumption that your copyright is valid, and allows you to recover up to $100,000 (and possibly lawyer's fees) without having to prove any actual monetary harm.

How do you register a copyright?

You can register your copyright by filing a simple form and depositing one or two samples of the work (depending on what it is) with the U.S. Copyright Office. There are different forms for different types of works—for example, form TX is for literary works while form VA is for a visual art work. Forms and instructions may be obtained from the U.S. Copyright Office by telephone, (202) 707-9100, or online at http://www.loc.gov/copyright. Registration currently costs $30 per work. If you're registering several works that are part of one series, you may be able to save money by registering the works together (called "group registration").

How are copyrights enforced? Is going to court necessary?

If someone violates the rights of a copyright owner, the owner is entitled to file a lawsuit in federal court asking the court to:

- issue orders (restraining orders and injunctions) to prevent further violations
- award money damages if appropriate, and
- in some circumstances, award attorney fees.

Whether the lawsuit will be effective and whether damages will be awarded depends on whether the alleged infringer can raise one or more legal defenses to the charge. Common legal defenses to copyright infringement are:

- too much time has elapsed between the infringing act and the lawsuit (the statute of limitations defense)
- the infringement is allowed under the fair use doctrine (discussed above)
- the infringement was innocent (the infringer had no reason to know the work was protected by copyright)
- the infringing work was independently created (that is, it wasn't copied from the original), or
- the copyright owner authorized the use in a license.

If someone has good reason to believe that a use is fair—but later finds herself on the wrong end of a court order—she is likely to be considered an innocent infringer at worst. Innocent infringers usually don't have to pay any damages to the copyright owner, but do have to cease the infringing activity or pay the owner for the reasonable commercial value of that use.

More Information About Copyrights

The Copyright Handbook: How to Protect & Use Written Works, by Stephen Fishman (Nolo), is a complete guide to the law of copyright. The book includes forms for registering a copyright.

Copyright Your Software, by Stephen Fishman (Nolo), explains copyright protection for computer software and include all the forms and instructions necessary for registering a software copyright.

Patent, Copyright & Trademark, by Stephen Elias and Richard Stim (Nolo), provides concise definitions and examples of the important words and phrases commonly used in copyright law.

Getting Permission: How to License & Clear Copyrighted Materials Online & Off, by Richard Stim (Nolo), spells out how to obtain permission to use art, music, writing or other copyrighted works and includes a variety of permission and licensing agreements.

The Public Domain: How to Find & Use Copyright-Free Writings, Music, Art & More, by Stephen Fishman (Nolo), is an authoritative book devoted to what is and is not protected by copyright law.

http://www.nolo.com
Nolo offers self-help information about a wide variety of legal topics, including copyright law.

http://lcweb.loc.gov/copyright
The U.S. Copyright office offers regulations, guidelines, forms and links to other helpful copyright sites.

http://fairuse.stanford.edu
This is one of the leading websites for measuring fair use. It provides academic fair use links and guidelines.

http://www.benedict.com
The Copyright Website has articles, good links and slick design. Best of all, you can examine actual examples from real cases.

http://www.ipmall.fplc.edu
The Intellectual Property Mall provided by the Franklin Pierce Law Center is a source of ever-changing links and information about copyrights, trademarks and patents.

8

Trademarks

8.2   *Types of Trademarks*

8.5   *Trademark Protection*

8.8   *Using and Enforcing a Trademark*

8.11   *Conducting a Trademark Search*

8.14   *Registering a Trademark*

8.18   *How Trademarks Differ From Patents and Copyrights*

A good name lost is seldom regained.
—JOEL HAWES

Most of us encounter many trademarks each day; we might eat Kellogg's cornflakes for breakfast, drive our Ford car to work and sit down at an IBM computer. But as we go about our daily tasks, we rarely think about the laws behind the familiar words and images that identify the products and services we use.

Trademark law consists of the legal rules that govern how businesses may:
- distinguish their products or services in the marketplace to prevent consumer confusion, and
- protect the means they've chosen to identify their products or services against use by competitors.

This chapter will introduce you to trademark law and answer common questions about choosing, using and protecting a trademark.

Types of Trademarks

The term trademark is commonly used to describe many different types of devices that label, identify and distinguish products or services in the marketplace. The basic purpose of all these devices is to inform potential customers of the origin and quality of the underlying products or services.

What is a trademark?

A trademark is a distinctive word, phrase, logo, graphic symbol, slogan or other device that is used to identify the source of a product and to distinguish a manufacturer's or merchant's products from others. Some examples are Nike sports apparel, Gatorade beverages and Microsoft software. In the trademark context, "distinctive" means unique enough to help customers recognize a particular product in the marketplace. A mark may either be inherently distinctive (the mark is unusual in and of itself, such as Milky Way candy bars) or may become distinctive over time because customers come to associate the mark with the product or service (for example, Beef & Brew restaurants).

Consumers often make their purchasing choices on the basis of recognizable trademarks. For this reason, the main thrust of trademark law is to make sure that trademarks don't overlap in a manner that causes customers to become confused about the source of a product. However, in the case of trademarks that have become famous—for example, McDonald's—the courts are willing to prohibit a wider range of uses of the trademark (or anything close to it) by anyone other than the famous mark's owner. For instance, McDonald's was able to prevent the use of the mark McSleep by a motel chain because McSleep traded on the McDonald's mark reputation for a particular type of service (quick, inexpensive, standardized). This type of sweeping protection is authorized by federal and state statutes (referred to as antidilution laws) designed to prevent the weakening of a famous mark's reputation for quality.

What is a servicemark?

For practical purposes, a servicemark is the same as a trademark—but while trademarks promote products, servicemarks promote services and events. As a general rule, when a business uses its name to market its goods or services in the yellow pages, on signs or in advertising copy, the name qualifies as a servicemark. Some familiar servicemarks: Jack in the Box (fast food service), Kinko's (photocopying service), ACLU (legal service), Blockbuster (video rental service), CBS's stylized eye in a circle (television network service) and the Olympic Games' multicolored interlocking circles (international sporting event).

What is a certification mark?

A certification mark is a symbol, name or device used by an organization to vouch for products and services provided by others—for example, the "Good Housekeeping Seal of Approval." This type of mark may cover characteristics such as regional origin, method of manufacture, product quality and service accuracy. Some other examples of certification marks: Stilton cheese (a product from the Stilton locale in England), Carneros wines (from grapes grown in the Carneros region of Sonoma/Napa counties) and Harris Tweeds (a special weave from a specific area in Scotland).

What is a collective mark?

A collective mark is a symbol, label, word, phrase or other mark used by members of a group or organization to identify goods, members, products or services they render. Collective marks are often used to show membership in a union, association or other organization.

The use of a collective mark is restricted to members of the group or organization that owns the mark. Even the group itself—as opposed to its members—cannot use the collective mark on any goods it produces. If the group wants to identify its product or service, it must use its own trademark or servicemark.

EXAMPLE

The letters "ILGWU" on a shirt label is the collective mark that identifies the shirt as a product of a member of the International Ladies Garment Workers Union. If, however, the ILGWU wanted to start marketing its own products, it could not use the ILGWU collective mark to identify them; the union would have to get a trademark of its own.

What is trade dress?

In addition to a label, logo or other identifying symbol, a product may come to be known by its distinctive packaging—for example, Kodak film or the Galliano liquor bottle—and a service by its distinctive decor or shape, such as the decor of Gap clothing stores. Collectively, these types of identifying features are commonly termed "trade dress." Because trade dress often serves the same function as a trademark or service-mark—the identification of goods and services in the marketplace—trade dress can be protected under the federal trademark laws and in some cases registered as a trademark or servicemark with the Patent and Trademark Office.

What kinds of things can be considered trademarks or service marks?

Most often, trademarks are words or phrases that are clever or unique enough to stick in a consumer's mind. Logos and graphics that become strongly associated with a product line or service are also typical. But a trademark or servicemark can also consist of letters, numbers, a sound, a smell, a color, a product shape or any other nonfunctional but distinctive aspect of a product or service that tends to promote and distinguish it in the marketplace. Titles, character names or other distinctive features of movies, television and radio programs can also serve as trademarks or servicemarks when used to promote a service or product. Some examples of unusual trademarks are the pink color of housing insulation manufactured by Owens-Corning and the shape of the Absolut vodka bottle.

What's the difference between a business name and a trademark or servicemark?

The name that a business uses to identify itself is called a "trade name." This is the name the business uses on its stock certificates, bank accounts, invoices and letterhead. When used to identify a business in this way—as an entity for nonmarketing purposes— the business name is given some protection under state and local corporate and fictitious business name registration laws, but it is not considered a trademark or entitled to protection under trademark laws.

If, however, a business uses its name to identify a product or service produced by the business, the name will then be considered a trademark or servicemark and will be entitled to protection if it is distinctive enough. For instance, Apple Computer Corporation uses the trade name Apple as a trademark on its line of computer products.

Although trade names by themselves are not considered trademarks for purposes of legal protection, they may still be protected under federal and state unfair competition laws against a confusing use by a competing business.

If my trade name is registered with the Secretary of State as a corporate name, or placed on a fictitious business name list, can I use it as a trademark?

Not necessarily. When you register a corporate name with a state agency or place your name on a local fictitious business name register, there is no guarantee that the name has not already been taken by another business as a trademark. It is only the trade name aspect of the name that is affected by your registration. This means that before you start using your business name as a trademark, you will need to make sure it isn't already being used as a trademark by another company in a context that precludes your using it. For more information about trademark searches, see *Conducting a Trademark Search,* below.

Trademark Protection

If a trademark or servicemark is protected, the owner of the mark can:

- prevent others from using it in a context where it might confuse consumers, and
- recover money damages from someone who used the mark knowing that it was already owned by someone else.

Trademark law also protects famous marks by allowing owners to sue to prevent others from using the same or similar mark, even if customer confusion is unlikely.

Not all marks are entitled to an equal amount of protection, however—and some aren't entitled to any protection at all.

What laws offer protection to trademark owners?

The basic rules for resolving disputes over who is entitled to use a trademark come from decisions by federal and state courts (the common law). These rules usually favor the business that first used the mark where the second use would be likely to cause customer confusion. A number of additional legal principles used to protect owners against improper use of their marks derive from federal statutes known collectively as the Lanham Act (Title 15 U.S.C. §§ 1051 to 1127). And all states have statutes that govern the use and protection of marks within the state's boundaries.

In addition to laws that specifically protect trademark owners, all states have laws that protect one business against unfair competition by another business, including the use by one business of a name already used by another business in a context that's likely to confuse customers.

What types of marks are entitled to the most legal protection?

Trademark law grants the most legal protection to the owners of names, logos and other marketing devices that are distinctive—that is, memorable because they are creative or out of the ordinary, or because they have become well known to the public through their use over time or because of a marketing blitz.

Inherently Distinctive Marks

Trademarks that are unusually creative are known as inherently distinctive marks. Typically, these marks consist of:

- unique logos or symbols (such as the McDonald's Golden Arch and the IBM symbol)
- made-up words or words that have no dictionary meaning such as *Exxon* or *Kodak* (called "fanciful" or "coined" marks)
- words that are surprising or unexpected in the context of their usage, such as Time Magazine or Diesel for a bookstore (called "arbitrary marks"), and

- words that cleverly connote qualities about the product or service, such as Slenderella diet food products (called "suggestive or evocative marks").

Which marks receive the least protection?

Trademarks and servicemarks consisting of common or ordinary words are not considered inherently distinctive and receive less protection under federal and state laws. Typical examples of trademarks using common or ordinary words are:

- people's names, such as Pete's Muffins or Smith Graphics
- geographic terms, such as Northern Dairy or Central Insect Control, and
- descriptive terms—that is, words that attempt to literally describe the product or some characteristic of the product, such as Rapid Computers, Clarity Video Monitors or Ice Cold Ice Cream.

However, nondistinctive marks may be come distinctive through use over time or through intensive marketing efforts.

What about Ben and Jerry's Ice Cream? Even though Ben and Jerry are common names, isn't the Ben and Jerry's trademark entitled to maximum protection?

Absolutely. Even if a mark is not inherently distinctive, it may become distinctive if it develops great public recognition through long use and exposure in the marketplace. A mark that becomes protected in this way is said to have acquired a "secondary

meaning." In addition to Ben and Jerry's, examples of otherwise common marks that have acquired a secondary meaning and are now considered to be distinctive include Sears (department stores) and Park 'n Fly (airport parking services.)

What cannot be protected under trademark law?

There are five common situations in which there is no trademark protection. In any of these situations the intended trademark cannot be registered and the owner has no right to stop others from using a similar name. Generally, when speaking of what *cannot* be protected under trademark law, we are referring to the standards established under the Lanham Act (the federal statute that provides for registration of marks and federal court remedies in case a mark is infringed).

- *Nonuse.* An owner may lose trademark protection if she "abandons" a trademark. This can happen in many ways. The most common is when the mark is no longer used in commerce and there is sufficient evidence that the owner intends to discontinue its use. Under the Lanham Act, a trademark is presumed to be abandoned after three years of nonuse. But, if the owner can prove that she intended to resume commercial use of the mark, she will not lose trademark protection.

- *Generics and genericide.* A generic term describes a type of goods or services; it is not a brand name. Examples of generic terms are "computer," "eyeglasses" and "eBook." Consumers are used to seeing a generic term used in conjunction with a trademark (for example, Avery labels or Hewlett-Packard printers). On some occasions, a company invents a new word for a product (for example, Kleenex for a tissue) that functions so successfully as a trademark that the public eventually comes to believe that it is the name of the goods. This is called genericide. When that happens, the term loses its trademark protection. Other famous examples of genericide are "aspirin," "yo-yo," "escalator," "thermos" and "kerosene".

- *Confusingly similar marks.* A mark will not receive trademark protection if it is so similar to another existing trademark that it causes confusion among consumers. This standard, known as likelihood of confusion, is a foundation of trademark law. Many factors are weighed when considering "likelihood of confusion." The most important are: the similarity of the marks, the similarity of the goods, the degree of care exercised by the consumer when making the pur-

chase, the intent of the person using the similar mark and any actual confusion that has occurred.

- *Weak marks.* A weak trademark will not be protected unless the owner can prove that consumers are aware of the mark. There are three types of weak marks: descriptive marks, geographic marks that describe a location and marks that are primarily surnames (last names). When an applicant attempts to register a weak mark, the PTO will permit the applicant to submit proof of distinctiveness or to move the application from the Principal Register to the Supplemental Register. (See Registering a Trademark, below, for more information about the different benefits offered these registers.)

- *Functional features.* Trademark law, like copyright law, will not protect functional features. Generally, a functional feature is something that is necessary for the item to work. The issue usually arises with product packaging or shapes. For instance, the unique shape of the Mrs. Butterworth bottle is not a functional feature because it is not necessary for the bottle to work. Therefore, it is eligible for trademark protection.

Are Internet domain names— names for sites on the World Wide Web—protected by trademark law?

Domain name registration, by itself, does not permit you to stop another business from using the same name for its business or product. Instead, it gives you only the right to use that specific Internet address. To protect your domain name as a trademark, the name must meet the usual trademark standards. That is, the domain name must be distinctive or must achieve distinction through customer awareness, and you must be the first to use the name in connection with your type of services or products. An example of a domain name that meets these criteria and has trademark protection is Amazon.com. Amazon.com was the first to use this distinctive name for online retail sales and the name has been promoted to customers through advertising and sales.

Using and Enforcing a Trademark

Generally, a trademark is owned by the business that first uses it in a commercial context—that is, attaches the mark to a product or uses the mark when marketing a product or service. A business may also obtain trademark protection if it files for trademark registration before anyone else uses the mark. (Trademark registration is discussed in more detail in the series of questions, *Registering a Trademark,* below.)

Once a business owns a trademark, it may be able to prevent others from using that mark, or a similar one, on their goods and services.

More specifically, what does it mean to "use" a trademark?

In trademark law, "use" means that the mark is at work in the marketplace, identifying the underlying goods or services. This doesn't mean that the product or service actually has to be sold, as long as it is legitimately offered to the public under the mark in question. For example, Robert creates a website where he offers his new invention—a humane mousetrap—for sale under the trademark "MiceFree." Even if Robert doesn't sell any traps, he is still "using" the trademark as long as "MiceFree" appears on the traps or on tags attached to them and the traps are ready to be shipped when a sale is made. Similarly, if Kristin, a trademark attorney, puts up a website to offer her services under the servicemark Trademark Queen, her servicemark will be in use as long as she is ready to respond to customer requests for her advice.

How can a business reserve a trademark for future use?

It is possible to acquire ownership of a mark by filing an "intent-to-use" (ITU) trademark registration application with the U.S. Patent and Trademark Office before someone else has actually started using the mark. The filing date of this application will be considered the date of first use of the mark if the applicant actually uses the mark within the required time limits—six months to three years after the PTO approves the mark, depending on whether the applicant seeks and pays for extensions of time.

For more information about trademark registration, see *Registering a Trademark*, below.

When can the owner of a trademark stop others from using it?

Whether the owner of a trademark can stop others from using it depends on such factors as:

- whether the trademark is being used on competing goods or services (goods or services compete if the sale of one is likely to affect the sale of the other)
- whether consumers would likely be confused by the dual use of the trademark, and
- whether the trademark is being used in the same part of the country or is being used on related goods (goods that will probably be noticed by the same customers, even if they don't compete with each other).

In addition, under federal and state laws known as "antidilution statutes," a trademark owner may go to court to prevent its mark from being used by someone else if the mark is famous and the later use would dilute the mark's strength—that is, weaken its reputation for quality (called tarnishment) or render it common through overuse in different contexts.

Antidilution statutes can apply even if there is no way customers would be likely to confuse the source of the goods or services designated by the later mark with the famous mark's owner. For instance, consumers would not think that Microsoft Bakery is associated with Microsoft, the software company, but

Microsoft Bakery could still be forced to choose another name under federal and state antidilution laws.

How does a trademark owner prevent others from using the mark?

Typically, the owner will begin by sending a letter, called a "cease and desist letter," to the wrongful user, demanding that it stop using the mark. If the wrongful user continues to infringe the mark, the owner can file a lawsuit to stop the improper use. The lawsuit is usually filed in federal court if the mark is used in more than one state or country, and in state court if the dispute is between purely local marks. In addition to preventing further use of the mark, a trademark owner can sometimes obtain money damages from the wrongful user.

When can a trademark owner get money from someone who has infringed the owner's mark?

If a trademark owner proves in federal court that the infringing use is likely to confuse consumers and that it suffered economically as a result of the infringement, the competitor may have to pay the owner damages based on the loss. And if the court finds that the competitor intentionally copied the owner's trademark, or at least should have known about the mark, the competitor may have to give up the profits it made by using the mark as well as pay other damages, such as punitive damages, fines or attorney fees. On the other hand, if the trademark's owner has not been damaged, a court has discretion to allow the competitor to continue to use the trademark under limited circumstances designed to avoid consumer confusion.

Do people have the right to use their last names as marks even if someone else is already using them for a similar business?

It depends on the name. A mark that is primarily a surname (last name) does not qualify for protection under federal trademark law unless the name becomes well known as a mark through advertising or long use. If this happens, the mark is said to have acquired a "secondary meaning."

If a surname acquires a secondary meaning, it is off limits for all uses that might cause customer confusion, whether or not the name is registered. Sears, McDonald's, Hyatt, Champion, Howard Johnson's and Calvin Klein are just a few of the hundreds of surnames that have become effective and protected marks over time.

Also, a business that tries to capitalize on the name of its owner to take advantage of an identical famous name being used as a trademark may be forced, under the state or federal antidilution laws, to stop using the name. This may happen if the trademark owner files a lawsuit.

"TM" and ®: What do they mean?

Many people like to put a "TM" (or "SM" for servicemark) next to their mark to let the world know that they are claiming ownership of it. However, it is not legally necessary to provide this type of notice; the use of the mark itself is the act that confers ownership.

The "R" in a circle (®) is a different matter entirely. This notice may not be put on a mark unless it has been registered with the U.S. Patent and Trademark Office—and it should accompany a mark after registration is complete. Failure to put the notice on a registered trademark can greatly reduce the possibility of recovering significant damages if it later becomes necessary to file a lawsuit against an infringer.

Conducting a Trademark Search

If you want to find out whether the trademark you've chosen for your products or services is available, you'll need to conduct a trademark search— an investigation to discover potential conflicts between your desired mark and any existing marks. Ideally, the search should be done before you begin to use a mark; this will help you avoid the expensive mistake of infringing a mark belonging to someone else.

Why do I need to conduct a trademark search?

The consequences of failing to conduct a reasonably thorough trademark search may be severe, depending on how widely you intend to use your mark and how much it would cost you to change it if a conflict later develops. If the mark you want to use has been federally registered by someone else, a court will presume that you knew about the registration— even if you did not. You will be precluded from using the mark in any context where customers might become confused. And if you do use the mark improperly, you will be cast in

the role of a "willful infringer." Willful infringers can be held liable for large damages and payment of the registered owner's attorney fees; they can also be forced to stop using the mark altogether.

My business is local. Why should I care what name or mark someone else in another part of the country is using?

Most small retail or service-oriented business owners well know the mantra for success: location, location, location. But as the Internet takes firm hold in the late 1990s, the concept of location, while still central to business success, takes on a whole new meaning. Instead of being rooted in physical space, businesses are now required to jockey for locations in the virtual or electronic space known as the Internet.

Vast numbers of businesses—even local enterprises—are putting up their own websites, creating a new potential for competition (and confusion) in the marketplace. Because of this, every business owner must pay attention to whether a proposed name or mark has already been taken by another business, regardless of the location or scope of that business.

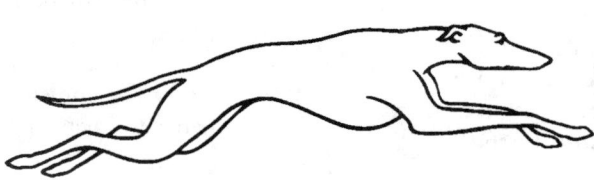

Can I do my own trademark search?

Yes. Although the most thorough trademark searches are accomplished by professional search firms such as Thomson & Thomson, it is also possible to conduct a preliminary online trademark search to determine if a trademark is distinguishable from other federally registered trademarks. You can accomplish this with the PTO's trademark databases (http://www.uspto.gov), which provide free access to records of federally registered marks or marks that are pending. In addition, privately owned fee-based online trademark databases often provide more current PTO trademark information. Below are some private fee-based online search companies:

Saegis (http://www.thomson-thomson.com). Provides access to all Trademarkscan databases (state, federal and international trademark databases), domain name databases, common law sources on the Internet and access to newly filed United States federal trademark applications. Saegis also provides access to Dialog services, discussed next.

Dialog (http://www.dialog.com). Provides access to Trademarkscan databases including state and federal registration and some international trademarks and provides common law searching of news databases.

MicroPatent (http://www.micropatent.com). Provides access to federal and state trademarks.

Trademark.com (http://www.trademark.com). Provides access to current federal registration information.

Trademark Register (http://www.trademarkregister.com). Provides access to current federal registration information.

Marks on Line (http://www.marksonline.com). This is a comprehensive trademark link site providing access to federal registration information and a listing of state and international trademark offices.

LEXIS/NEXIS (http://www.lexis-nexis.com). LEXIS provides access to federal and state registrations. You can also search for non-registered trademarks through its NEXIS news services. The PTO uses NEXIS to evaluate descriptive and generic terms.

You can also visit one of the Patent and Trademark Depository Libraries available in every state. These libraries offer a combination of hardcover directories of federally registered marks and an online database of both registered marks and marks for which a registration application is pending. To find the Patent and Trademark Depository Library nearest you, consult the PTO website at http://www.uspto.gov.

You should also search for marks that have not been registered.

This is important because an existing mark, even if it's unregistered, would preclude you from:

- registering the same or a confusingly similar mark in your own name, and
- using the mark in any part of the country or commercial transaction where customers might be confused.

You can search for unregistered marks in the Patent and Trademark Depository Libraries and on the Internet. In the libraries, use the available product guides and other materials. On the Internet, look for online shopping websites and review the inventory for items similar to yours. For example, go to eToys (http://www.etoys.com) to find hundreds of trademarked toys. You can also search for unregistered marks by using an Internet search engine. Enter your proposed name in the search field of an Internet search engine (such as Alta Vista). You will get a report of every instance that the name appears on Web pages indexed by that engine. Because no search engine is 100% complete, you should do this same search on a several different search engines.

How can I find out whether a mark I want to use is already being used as a domain name (the name of a site on the World Wide Web)?

Every website is identified by a unique phrase known as a "domain name." For example, the domain name for Nolo is Nolo.com. Because so much business is now being done online, most people will want to be able to use their proposed mark as a domain name so that their customers can easily locate them on the Web.

The easiest way to find out if a domain name is already in use is to check with one of the dozens of online companies that have been approved to register domain names. You can access a listing of these registrars through InterNIC's site at http://www.internic.net or ICANN's site at http://www.icann.org. ICANN is the organization that oversees the process of approving domain name registrars.

Would it be better to have a professional firm conduct my trademark search?

Many people do prefer to pay a professional search firm to handle a trademark search. This can make sense if your financial plans justify an initial outlay of several hundred dollars, the minimum cost for a thorough professional search for both registered and unregistered marks. Depending on the search firm, you may also get a legal opinion as to whether your proposed mark is legally safe to use in light of existing registered and unregistered marks. Obtaining a legal opinion may provide important protection down the road if someone later sues you for using the mark.

How do I find a professional search firm?

There are many trademark search services in the United States. Here are three of the most well known:

The Sunnyvale Center on Innovation, Invention and Ideas (Sc[i]3) (http://www.sci3.com). Sc[i]3 (pronounced "sigh-cubed") is one of three Patent and Trademark Depository Libraries—the others are in Detroit and Houston—that have formed partnerships with the U.S. Patent and Trademark Office. Under this partnership,

Sc[i]3 is encouraged to offer a variety of information services—including trademark searches—for very reasonable fees.

Trademark Express (http://www.tmexpress.com). Trademark Express is a private company that, in addition to other trademark-related services, offers a full choice of trademark searches.

Thomson & Thomson (http://www.thomson-thomson.com). Thomson & Thomson is the trademark search service of choice for the legal professional.

If you don't like doing business at a distance, you can find trademark search services in your area by looking in the Yellow Pages of the nearest good-sized city under "trademark consultants" or "information brokers." If that yields nothing, consult the advertisements in a local legal journal or magazine. Finally, you can find a good list of trademark search firms at http://www.ggmark.com.

Registering a Trademark

It is possible to register certain types of trademarks and servicemarks with the U.S. Patent and Trademark Office (PTO). Federal registration puts the rest of the country on notice that the trademark is already taken, and makes it easier to protect a mark against would-be copiers.

How does a mark qualify for federal registration?

To register a trademark with the PTO, the mark's owner first must put it into use "in commerce that Congress may regulate." This means the mark must be used on a product or service that crosses state, national or territorial lines or that affects commerce crossing such lines—for example, a catalog business or a restaurant or motel that caters to interstate or international customers. Even if the owner files an intent-to-use (ITU) trademark application (ITU applications are discussed in the previous set of questions), the mark will not actually be registered until it is used in commerce.

Once the PTO receives a trademark registration application, the office must answer the following questions:

- Is the trademark the same as or similar to an existing mark used on similar or related goods or services?
- Is the trademark on the list of prohibited or reserved names?
- Is the trademark generic—that is, does the mark describe the product itself rather than its source?
- Is the trademark too descriptive (not distinctive enough) to qualify for protection?

If the answer to each question is "no," the trademark is eligible for registration and the PTO will continue to process the application.

I know the PTO won't register a mark if it's not distinctive or already in use. But are there other types of marks that are ineligible for federal registration?

Yes. The PTO won't register any marks that contain:

- names of living persons without their consent
- the U.S. flag
- other federal and local governmental insignias
- the name or likeness of a deceased U.S. President without his widow's consent
- words or symbols that disparage living or deceased persons, institutions, beliefs or national symbols, or
- marks that are judged immoral, deceptive or scandalous.

As a general rule the PTO takes a liberal view of the terms immoral and scandalous and will rarely refuse to register a mark on those grounds.

If the PTO decides that a mark is eligible for federal registration, what happens next?

Next, the PTO publishes the trademark in the *Official Gazette* (a publication of the U.S. Patent and Trademark Office). The *Gazette* states that the mark is a candidate for registration; this provides existing trademark owners with an opportunity to object to the registration. If someone objects, the PTO will schedule a hearing to resolve the dispute.

Is it possible to federally register a mark made up of common or ordinary words?

Yes, if the combination of the words is distinctive. But even if the entire mark is judged to lack sufficient distinctiveness, it can be placed on a list called the Supplemental Register. (Marks that are considered distinctive—either inherently or because they have become well known—are placed on a list called the Principal Register.) Marks on the Supplemental Register receive far less protection than do those on the Principal Register. The benefits granted by each type of registration are discussed in more detail in the next question.

What are the benefits of federal trademark registration?

It depends on which register carries the mark. Probably the most important benefit of placing a mark on the Principal Register is that anybody who later initiates use of the same or a confusingly similar trademark may be presumed by the courts to be a "willful infringer" and therefore liable for large money damages.

Placing a trademark on the Supplemental Register produces significantly fewer benefits, but still provides notice of ownership. This notice makes it far less likely that someone will use that identical mark; the fear of being sued for damages should keep potential infringers away. Also, if the trademark remains on the Supplemental Register for five years—meaning that the registration isn't canceled for some reason—and the mark remains in use during that time, it may be moved to the Principal Register under the secondary meaning rule (secondary meaning will be presumed).

Even if a mark is not registered, it is still possible for the owner to sue the infringer under a federal statute which forbids use of a "false designation of origin" (Title 15 U.S.C. § 1125). It is usually much easier to prove the case and collect large damages, however, if the mark has been registered.

How long does federal registration last?

Once a trademark or servicemark is placed on the Principal Register, the owner receives a certificate of registration good for an initial term of ten years. The registration may lapse before the ten-year period expires, however, unless the owner files a form within six years of the registration date (called the Section 8 Declaration) stating that the mark is either still in use in commerce or that the mark is not in use for legitimate reasons.

The Section 8 Declaration is usually combined with a Section 15 Declaration, which effectively renders the trademark incontestable except for limited reasons.

The original registration may be renewed indefinitely for additional ten-year periods if the owner files the required renewal applications (called a Section 9 Affidavit) with the U.S. Patent and Trademark Office. A Section 8 Declaration must also be filed at the time of trademark renewal.

Failure to renew a registration does not void all rights to the mark, but if the owner fails to re-register, the special benefits of federal registration will be lost.

What happens if there is a conflict between an Internet domain name and an existing trademark?

The answer depends on the nature of the conflict. There are three reasons why a conflict may develop between the owner of a trademark and the owner of a domain name:

The domain name registrant is a cybersquatter. If a domain name is registered in bad faith—for example, the name is registered with the intent of selling it back to a company with the same name—the domain name can be taken away under federal law or under international arbitration rules for domain name owners. A victim of cybersquatting in the U.S. can now sue under the provisions of the Anticybersquatting Consumer Protection Act (ACPA) or can fight the cybersquatter using an international arbitration system created by the Internet Corporation of Assigned Names and Numbers (ICANN). The ICANN arbitration system is usually faster and less expensive than suing under the ACPA. In addition, it does not require an attorney. For information on the ICANN policy visit the organization's website at http:// www.icann.org.

The domain name infringes an existing trademark. If a domain name is likely to confuse consumers because it is similar to an existing trademark, the owner of the federally owned trademark can sue for infringement in federal court. For example, it's likely that the Adobe company, makers of graphics software, would be able to prevent another software company from using the domain name of www.adoobie.com.

The domain name dilutes a famous trademark. If a domain name dilutes the power of a famous trademark, the trademark owner can sue under federal laws to stop the continued use. Dilution occurs when the domain name blurs or tarnishes the reputation of a famous trademark. For example, Gucci could probably prevent a company from using the domain name "guccigoo.com" for the purpose of selling baby diapers.

Can a business register its mark at the state level?

It is possible to register a mark with the state trademark agency, although the state registration does not offer the same level of protection provided by federal law. The main benefit of state registration is that it notifies anyone who checks the list that the mark is owned by the registrant. This fact will lead most would-be users of the same mark to choose another one rather than risk a legal dispute with the registered mark's owner. If the mark is also federally registered, this notice is presumed and the state registration isn't necessary. If, however, the mark is used only within the state and doesn't qualify for federal registration, state registration is a good idea.

How to Register Your Trademark

For most trademarks already in use, federal registration is a relatively straightforward process. You use a simple two-sided form provided by the PTO to:

- describe your mark
- state when it was first used
- describe the products or services on which the mark will be used, and
- suggest the classification under which the mark should be registered (there are approximately 40 classifications for goods and services; the PTO can help you figure out which one is right for your mark).

In addition, your form must be accompanied by:

- a "drawing" of your mark (for word marks, this simply involves setting the mark out in the middle of a page in capital letters)
- samples of how your proposed mark is being used, and
- the registration fee—currently $325.

On its website, http://www.uspto.gov, the PTO offers two electronic registration options. PrinTEAS lets you fill in the form online but requires you to print out and mail in a hardcopy. eTEAS lets you both fill in and file the form online.

If you are applying to register your mark on the basis of its intended use (See *How can a business reserve a trademark for future use?*, above), then you needn't provide the samples or the date of first use, but you can't complete your registration until you put your mark into actual use and file some additional paperwork with the PTO.

The PTO offers a free booklet containing plain English instructions for filling out this form, and also provides help on its website: http://www.uspto.com. For more information about registering your trademark, see the resource list at the end of this chapter.

How Trademarks Differ From Patents and Copyrights

Trademarks are often mentioned in the same breath as copyrights and patents. While they do sometimes apply to the same thing, they're more often defined by their differences. It's important to understand how trademark law differs from other laws protecting creative works (collectively called "intellectual property laws"); rules and benefits depend on the type of intellectual property at issue.

How does trademark differ from copyright?

Copyright protects original works of expression, such as novels, fine and graphic arts, music, phonorecords, photography, software, video, cinema and choreography by preventing people from copying or commercially exploiting them without the copyright owner's permission. But the copyright laws specifically do not protect names, titles or short phrases. That's where trademark law comes in. Trademark protects distinctive words, phrases, logos, symbols, slogans and any other devices used to identify and distinguish products or services in the marketplace.

There are, however, areas where both trademark and copyright law may be used to protect different aspects of the same product. For example, copyright laws may protect the artistic aspects of a graphic or logo used by a business to identify its goods or services, while trademark may protect the graphic or logo from use by others in a confusing manner in the marketplace. Similarly, trademark laws are often used in conjunction with copyright laws to protect advertising copy. The trademark laws protect the product or service name and any slogans used in the advertising, while the copyright laws protect the additional creative written expression contained in the ad.

For more information about copyright law, see Chapter 7, *Copyrights*.

What's the difference between patent and trademark?

Patents allow the creator of certain kinds of inventions that contain new ideas to keep others from making commercial use of those ideas without the creator's permission. For example, Tom invents a new type of hammer that makes it very difficult to miss the nail. Not only can Tom keep others from making, selling or using the precise type of hammer he invented, but he may also be able to apply his patent monopoly rights to prevent people from making commercial use of any similar type of hammer during the time the patent is in effect (20 years from the date the patent application is filed).

Generally, patent and trademark laws do not overlap. When it comes to a product design, however—say, jewelry or a distinctively shaped musical instrument—it may be possible to obtain a patent on a design aspect of the device while invoking trademark law to protect the design as a product identifier. For instance, an auto manufacturer might receive a design patent for the stylistic fins that are part of a car's rear fenders. Then, if the fins were intended to be—and actually are—used to distinguish the particular model car in the marketplace, trademark law may kick in to protect the appearance of the fins.

For more information about patent law, see Chapter 6, *Patents*.

More Information About Trademarks

Trademark: Legal Care for Your Business & Product Name, by Stephen Elias (Nolo), shows you how to choose a legally strong business and product name, register the name with state and federal agencies and sort out any name disputes that arise.

Patent, Copyright & Trademark, by Stephen Elias and Richard Stim (Nolo), provides concise definitions and examples of the important words and phrases commonly used in trademark law.

Domain Names: How to Choose & Protect a Great Name for Your Website, by Stephen Elias & Patricia Gima (Nolo). This how-to book provides information on selecting, registering and protecting a domain name.

McCarthy on Trademarks and Unfair Competition, by J. Thomas McCarthy (Clark Boardman Callaghan), is a book intended for lawyers that provides an exhaustive treatment of trademark law.

Trademark Law—A Practitioners Guide, by Siegrun D. Kane (Practicing Law Institute), is a good overview of trademark law written for lawyers.

Trademark Registration Practice, by James E. Hawes (Clark Boardman Callaghan), a book for trademark lawyers, provides the ins and outs of registering a trademark with the U.S. Patent and Trademark Office.

The following associations of trademark lawyers offer a number of helpful publications. Write or call for a list of available materials.

International Trademark Association (INTA)
1133 Avenue of the Americas
New York, NY 10036
212-768-9887
http://www.inta.org

American Intellectual Property Law Association (AIPLA)
2001 Jefferson Davis Highway, Suite 203
Arlington, VA 22202
703-415-0780
http://www.aipla.org

http://www.nolo.com

Nolo Press offers self-help information about a wide variety of legal topics, including trademarks.

http://www.marksonline.com

This comprehensive trademark site provides trademark searching services, news and links as well as domain name information. It's easy to navigate, contains lots of practical information for trademark owners and includes links to state and federal trademark offices.

http://www.inta.org

The International Trademark Association (INTA) provides trademark services, publications and online resources.

http://www.uspto.gov

The U.S. Patent and Trademark Office provides new trademark rules and regulations and, as of August 1998, is expected to put the federal registered trademark database online.

http://www.sci3.com

The Sunnyvale Center for Invention, Innovation and Ideas (a Patent and Trademark Depository Library), provides information about their excellent, low-cost trademark search service conducted by the Center's librarians.

http://www.ggmark.com

This site, maintained by a trademark lawyer, provides basic trademark information and a fine collection of links to other trademark resources.

9

Your Money

9.2   *Purchasing Goods and Services*

9.7   *Using Credit and Charge Cards*

9.10   *Using an ATM or Debit Card*

9.11   *Strategies for Repaying Debts*

9.18   *Dealing With the IRS*

9.22   *Debt Collections*

9.25   *Bankruptcy*

9.28   *Rebuilding Credit*

Too many people spend money they haven't earned, to buy things they don't want, to impress people they don't like.

—WILL ROGERS

America's economy is driven by consumer spending. When we open any newspaper or magazine, turn on the radio or television, or take a drive across town, we're bombarded with ads urging us to spend our hard-earned dollars. And so we do. We pull out our cash, checks, credit cards, and increasingly, debit cards.

What the ads don't tell you is what to do when things go wrong—for example, when the item you buy is defective, when you lose your credit card, when you need extra time to pay or when you fall behind and the bill collectors start calling.

Fortunately, many federal (and some state) laws provide some protections to consumers; this chapter describes some of those that are most important. While no law substitutes for common sense, comparison shopping and avoiding offers that sound too good to be true, if you do face problems as a consumer, many laws can help.

Purchasing Goods and Services

I did not have three thousand pairs of shoes: I had one thousand and sixty.

—IMELDA MARCOS

While 19th century business relationships were governed by the doctrine "caveat emptor" or "let the buyer beware," the notion that a buyer-seller arrangement should be fair gained ground in the 20th century. As a result, you now have a right to receive nondefective goods and services that meet a minimum standard.

When I buy something, is it covered by a warranty?

Generally, yes. A warranty (also called a guarantee) is an assurance about the quality of goods or services you buy, and is intended to give you recourse if something you purchase fails to live up to what you were promised.

Some warranties are implied and some are expressed. Virtually everything you buy comes with two implied warranties—one for "merchantability" and one for "fitness." The implied warranty of merchantability is an assurance that a new item will work if you use it for a reasonably expected purpose. For used items, the warranty of merchantability is a promise that the product will work as expected, given its age and condition. The implied warranty of fitness applies when you buy an item with a specific (even unusual) purpose in mind. If you communicated your specific needs to the seller, the implied warranty of fitness assures you that the item will fill your need.

Most expressed warranties state something such as "the product is warranted against defects in materials or workmanship" for a specified time. Most either come directly from the manufacturer or are included in the sales contract you sign with the seller. But an expressed warranty may also be in an advertisement or on a sign in the store ("all dresses 100% silk"), or it may even be an oral description of a product's features.

How long does a warranty last?

In most states, an implied warranty lasts forever. In a few states, however, the implied warranty lasts only as long as any expressed warranty that comes with a product. In these states, if there is no expressed warranty, the implied warranty lasts forever.

Can a seller avoid a warranty by selling a product "as is"?

The answer depends on whether the warranty is express or implied (see the previous questions for an explanation of implied and express warranties) and in what state you live. Sellers cannot avoid express warranties by claiming the product is sold "as is." On the other hand, if there is no express warranty, sellers can sometimes avoid an implied warranty by selling the item

"as is." Some states prohibit all "as is" sales. And in all states, the buyer must know that the item is sold "as is" in order for the seller to avoid an implied warranty.

How do I enforce a warranty if something is wrong with what I bought?

Most of the time, a defect in an item will show up immediately and you can ask the seller or manufacturer to fix or replace it. If the seller won't, or tries only once and the fixed or replaced item is still defective, you can withhold payment (or refuse to pay a credit card charge). If you are uncomfortable doing this or have already paid for the item, call the seller and try to work out an arrangement. If the seller refuses, try to mediate the dispute through a community or Better Business Bureau mediation program. (For more information about mediation, see Chapter 17.)

If you can't get anywhere informally, you can sue. In most states, if the seller or manufacturer won't make good under a warranty you must sue within four years of when you discovered the defect.

Do I have any recourse if the item breaks after the warranty expires?

Usually not. But in most states, if the item gave you some trouble while it was under the warranty and you had it repaired by someone authorized by the manufacturer to make repairs, the manufacturer must extend your original warranty for the amount of time the item sat in the shop. If you think you're entitled to an extension, call the manufacturer and ask to speak to the department that handles warranties.

You may have other options as well. If your product was trouble-free during the warranty period, the manufacturer may offer a free repair for a problem that arose after the warranty expired if the problem is widespread. Many manufacturers have secret "fix it" lists—items with defects that don't affect safety and therefore don't require a recall, but that the manufacturer will repair for free. It can't hurt to call and ask.

I just bought a stereo system and the salesclerk tried to sell me an extended warranty contract. Should I have bought it?

Probably not. Merchants encourage you to buy extended warranties (also called service contracts) because they are a source of big profits for stores, which pocket up to 50% of the amount you pay.

Rarely will you have the chance to exercise your rights under an extended warranty. Name-brand electronic equipment and appliances usually don't break down during the first few years (and if they do they're covered by the original warranty), and often have a lifespan well beyond the length of the extended warranty.

I think I was the victim of a scam. Can I get my money back?

Federal and state laws prohibit "unfair or deceptive trade acts or practices." If

you think you've been cheated, *immediately* let the appropriate government offices know. Although any government investigation will take some time, these agencies often have the resources to go after unscrupulous merchants. And, the more agencies you notify, the more likely someone will take notice of your complaint and act on it.

Unfortunately, government agencies are rarely able to get you your money back. If the business is a reputable one, however, it may refund your money when a consumer fraud law enforcement investigator shows up. It certainly can't hurt to complain.

If you can't get relief from a government agency, consider suing the company in small claims court. *Everybody's Guide to Small Claims Court*, by Ralph Warner (Nolo), provides extensive information on how to sue in small claims court.

How to File a Complaint for Fraud

The National Fraud Information Center, a project of the National Consumer's League, can help you if you've been defrauded. NFIC provides:

- assistance in filing a complaint with appropriate federal agencies
- recorded information on current fraud schemes
- tips on how to avoid becoming a fraud victim, and
- direct ordering of consumer publications in English or Spanish.

You can contact NFIC at P.O. Box 65868, Washington, DC 20035, 800-876-7060, 202-737-5084 (TTD), http://www.fraud.org.

Also contact your local prosecutor to find out if it investigates consumer fraud complaints. Finally, contact any local newspaper, radio station or television station "action line." Especially in metropolitan areas, these folks often have an army of volunteers ready to pursue consumer complaints.

I received some unordered merchandise in the mail and now I'm getting billed. Do I have to pay?

You don't owe any money if you receive an item you never ordered. It's considered a gift. If you get bills or collection letters from a seller who sent you something you never ordered, write to the seller stating your intention to treat the item as a gift. If the bills continue, insist that the seller send you proof of your order. If this doesn't stop the bills, notify the state consumer protection agency in the state where the merchant is located.

If you sent for something in response to an advertisement claiming a "free" gift or "trial" period, but are now being billed, be sure to read the fine print of the ad. It may say something about charging shipping and handling; or worse, you may have inadvertently joined a club or subscribed to a magazine. Write the seller, offer to return the merchandise and state that you believe the ad was misleading.

I just signed a contract to have carpeting installed in my house and I changed my mind. Can I cancel?

Possibly. Under the Federal Trade Commission's "Cooling Off Rule," you have until midnight of the third business day after a contract was signed to cancel either of the following:

- door-to-door sales contracts for more than $25, or
- a contract for more than $25 made anywhere other than the seller's normal place of business—for instance, at a sales presentation at a hotel or restaurant, outdoor exhibit, computer show or trade show (other than public car auctions and craft fairs).

Do I have the right to cancel any other kinds of contracts?

The federal Truth in Lending Act lets you cancel some loans up until midnight of the third business day after you signed the contract. It applies only to loans for which you pledged your home as security, as long as the loan is not a first mortgage. For example, the Act applies to home improvement loans and second mortgages. If the lender never notified you of the three-day right to cancel, you have even longer to cancel your loan.

In addition, many states have laws that allow you to cancel written contracts covering the purchase of certain goods or services within a few days of signing, including contracts for dance or martial arts lessons, credit repair services, health club memberships, dating services, weight loss programs, time share properties and hearing aids. In a few states, you can also cancel a contract if you negotiated the transaction in a language other than English but the seller did not give you a copy of the contract in that language. Call your state consumer protection agency (check directory assistance in your state capital) to find out what contracts, if any, are covered in your state.

I ordered some clothes through a catalogue and there's a delay in shipping. Can I cancel my order?

If you order goods by mail, phone, computer or fax (other than photo development, magazine subscriptions, seeds or plants), the Federal Trade Commission's "Mail or Telephone Order Rule" requires that the seller ship to you within the time promised or, if no time was stated, within 30 days.

If the seller cannot ship within those time frames, the seller must send you a notice with a new shipping date and offer you the option of canceling your order and getting a refund, or accepting the new date. If you opt for the second deadline, but the seller can't meet it, it must send a notice requesting your signature to agree to yet a third date. If you don't return the notice, the seller must automatically cancel your order and refund your money. The seller must issue the refund promptly—within seven days if you paid by check or money order and within one billing cycle if you charged your purchase.

Do I have the right to a cash refund after I make a purchase?

Generally, no. A seller isn't required to offer refunds or exchanges, though many do.

But at least four states do have laws governing refund policies:

- *California*. Sellers who do not allow a full cash or credit refund (or an equal exchange) within seven days of purchase must post the store's refund-credit-exchange policy. If the seller fails to post the policy, you may return the goods, for a full refund, within 30 days of your purchase.

- *Florida*. If the seller has no refund policy, such a statement must be posted in the store. If a "no refund" isn't posted, you may return unused goods in the original packaging within seven days for a full refund.

- *New York*. Sellers with a no refund policy must post it. If a seller does not post a policy, you're entitled to a choice of cash or credit refund within 20 days if goods are not used or damaged.

- *Virginia*. Sellers must post their refund or exchange policies unless they give a full cash refund (or full credit) within 20 days after purchase.

More Information About Purchasing Goods and Services

Everybody's Guide to Small Claims Court, by Ralph Warner (Nolo), has extensive information on pursuing your rights in the event a seller or manufacturer won't make good on a warranty.

The Direct Marketing Association is a membership organization made up of mail-order companies and other direct marketers. If you have a complaint about a particular company, contact Mail-Order Action Line, c/o DMA, 1111 19th Street, NW, Suite 1100, Washington, DC 20036, 202-955-5030, http://www.the_dma.org. DMA may contact the mail-order company and try to resolve your problem.

Using Credit and Charge Cards

American adults hold approximately two billion total credit and charge cards—an average of nine cards per person. Buying on credit has become a cornerstone of the American economy. But buying on credit can be very expensive—the interest rate on bank credit cards averages about 18%; on gasoline company and department store cards, it's over 20%. Only charge cards (also called travel and entertainment cards), such as American Express and Diners Club, don't generally impose interest. Of course, charge cards usually require that you pay off the entire balance each month.

My credit card debt is consuming my life. How can I cut credit card costs?

If you have more than one card, pay down the balances with the highest interest rates and then use (or obtain) a card with a low rate. Because there is great competition among credit card issuers, you might get a rate reduction simply by asking for one from your current credit card company.

Which Cards Should You Keep?

When you think about the costs of using your credit cards, you may decide that you're better off canceling most of them. If so, you'll have to choose which cards to keep. If you don't carry a monthly balance, keep a card with no annual fee, but make sure it has a grace period. If you carry a balance each month, get rid of the cards that come with the worst of the following features:

- High interest rates.
- Unfair interest calculations. Avoid cards that charge interest on the average daily balance, not the balance due. Here's why. Let's say you pay $1,200 of your $1,500 balance in January. If your bank uses the average daily

balance method, in February it will charge you interest on the $1,500 average daily balance from January, not on the $300 you still owe.

- No grace periods. This means you pay interest from the time of purchase until the time of payment even if you pay your balance in full.

- Nuisance fees. Get rid of cards with late payment fees, over-the-limit fees, inactivity fees, fees for not carrying a balance or for carrying a balance under a certain amount or a flat monthly fee that's a percentage of your credit limit.

I'm always getting credit card offers with low interest rates in the mail. Should I sign up and transfer the balance from my current card to the new card?

It depends. Check the fine print of the offer. Many credit card companies offer a "teaser" rate—a low rate that lasts for a short period of time. Once the "teaser" period is over, a much higher rate kicks in. Also be sure to consider any annual fees, grace periods and nuisance fees (see Which Cards Should You Keep?, above) before you switch.

I can't afford the minimum payment required on my statement. Can I pay less?

Most card companies insist that you make the monthly minimum payment, which is usually 2% to 2.5% of the outstanding balance. If you can convince the card issuer that your financial situation is desperate, the issuer may cut your payments in half. In some cases, the issuer may waive

payments altogether for a few months. This courtesy is usually extended only to people who have never made late payments.

Bear in mind that paying nothing or very little on your credit card should be a temporary solution only. The longer you pay only a small amount, the quicker your balance will increase due to interest charges.

My checking account and Visa card are from the same bank. Can the bank take money out of my checking account to cover my missed credit card payments?

No. A bank that takes money out of a deposit account to cover a missed credit card payment violates the federal Truth in Lending Act. You can sue for damages—the amount taken out of your account and any other damages you suffer, such as lost interest or bounced-check fees.

My wallet was stolen. Will I have to pay charges that the thief made using my credit cards?

No. Federal law limits your liability for unauthorized charges made on your credit or charge card after it has been lost or stolen. If you notify the card issuer within a reasonable time after you discover the loss or theft (usually 30 days), you're not responsible for any charges made after the notification, and are liable for only the first $50 of charges made before you notified the card issuer. In practice, card issuers rarely even charge the $50.

I purchased an item using my credit card and it fell apart. Can I refuse to pay?

Maybe. Under federal law, you must first attempt in good faith to resolve the dispute with the merchant. If that fails, you can withhold payment on non-seller-issued cards only if the purchase was for more than $50 and was made within your home state or within 100 miles of your home. This limitation applies only if you used a card not issued by the seller, such as a MasterCard. There is no $50, 100-mile or in-state limitation if you use a seller's card, such as your Sears card.

The 100-mile limitation is easy to calculate when purchases are made in person. But if you order through the mail, over the telephone or using your computer, the law is unclear as to where the purchase took place. Your best bet is to claim that the purchase was made in the state where you live (even if the catalogue company is on the other side of the country) because you placed the order from home.

My credit card billing statement contains an error. What should I do?

Immediately write a letter to the customer service department of the card issuer. Give your name, account number, an explanation of the error and the amount involved. Enclose copies of supporting documents, such as receipts showing the correct amount of the charge. You must act quickly—the issuer must receive your letter within 60 days after it mailed the bill to you.

Under the federal Fair Credit Billing Act, the issuer must acknowledge receipt of your letter within 30 days, unless it corrects the bill within that time. Furthermore, the issuer must, within two billing cycles (but in no event more than 90 days), correct the error or explain why it believes the amount to be correct.

During the two-billing-cycle/90-day period, the issuer cannot report the amount to credit bureaus or other creditors as delinquent. The issuer can charge you interest on the amount you dispute during this period, but if it later agrees that you were correct, it must drop the interest accrued.

Must I give my phone number when I use a credit card?

Most often, no. Several states, including California, Delaware, Georgia, Kansas, Massachusetts, Minnesota, Nevada, New Jersey, New York, Oregon, Pennsylvania, Rhode Island and Wisconsin, bar merchants from recording personal information when you use a credit card. Furthermore, merchant agreements with Visa and MasterCard prohibit them from requiring a customer to furnish a phone number when paying with Visa or MasterCard.

I took out a cash advance using my credit card, and feel I was gouged. What are all those fees?

Cash advances usually come with the following fees:

- *Transaction fees.* Most banks charge a transaction fee of up to 4% for taking a cash advance.

- *No grace period.* Most banks charge interest from the date the cash advance is posted, even if you pay it back in full when your bill comes.
- *Interest rates.* The interest rate is often higher on cash advances than it is on ordinary credit card charges.

Using an ATM or Debit Card

A bank is a place where they lend you an umbrella in fair weather and ask for it back when it begins to rain.

—ROBERT FROST

Banks issue ATM cards to allow customers to withdraw money, make deposits, transfer money between accounts, find out their balances, get cash advances and even make loan payments at all hours of the day or night.

Debit cards combine the functions of ATM cards and checks. Debit cards are issued by banks, but can be used at stores. When you pay with a debit card, the money is automatically deducted from your checking account.

What are the advantages of using an ATM or debit card?

There are generally two advantages:
- You don't have to carry your checkbook and identification, but you can make purchases directly from your checking account.
- You pay immediately—without running up interest charges on a credit card bill.

Are there disadvantages?

Yes. You don't have the 20- to 25-day delay in paying the bill. Also, you don't have the right to withhold payment (the money is immediately removed from the account) in the event of a dispute with the merchant over goods or services. Finally, many banks charge transaction fees when you use an ATM or debit card at locations other than those owned by the bank.

Do I have to pay if there's a mistake on my statement or receipt?

Although ATM statements and debit receipts don't usually contain errors, mistakes do happen. If you find an error, you have 60 days from the date of the statement or receipt to notify the bank. Always call first and follow up with a letter. If you don't notify the bank within 60 days, it has no obligation to investigate the error and you're out of luck.

The bank has ten business days from the date of your notification to investigate the problem and tell you the result. If the bank needs more time, it can take up to 45 days, but only if it deposits the disputed amount of money into your account. If the bank later determines that there was no error, it can take the money back, but it must first send you a written explanation.

If Your ATM Card Is Lost or Stolen

If your ATM or debit card is lost or stolen (never, never, never keep your personal identification number—PIN—near your card), call your bank immediately, and follow up with a confirming letter. Under the federal Electronic Fund Transfers Act, your liability is:

- $0—after you report the card missing
- up to $50—if you notify the bank within two business days after you realize the card is missing (unless you were on extended travel or in the hospital)
- up to $500—if you fail to notify the bank within two business days after you realize the card is missing (unless you were on extended travel or in the hospital) , but do notify the bank within 60 days after your bank statement is mailed to you listing the unauthorized withdrawals
- unlimited—if you fail to notify the bank within 60 days after your bank statement is mailed to you listing the unauthorized withdrawals.

In response to consumer complaints about the possibility of unlimited liability, Visa and MasterCard now cap the liability on debit cards at $50. A few states have capped the liability for unauthorized withdrawals on an ATM or debit card at $50 as well. And some large debit card issuers won't charge you anything if unauthorized withdrawals appear on your statement.

More Information About Credit, Charge, ATM and Debit Cards

Money Troubles: Legal Strategies to Cope With Your Debts, by Robin Leonard and Deanne Loonon (Nolo), contains extensive information on credit, charge, ATM and debit card laws and practical usage tips.

The Federal Deposit Insurance Corporation, 550 17th Street, NW, Washington, DC 20429, 877-275-3342, http://www.fdic.gov, publishes free pamphlets, including *Fair Credit Billing.*

The Federal Trade Commission, CRC-240, Washington, DC 20580, 877-FTC-HELP (382-4357), http://www.ftc.gov, publishes free pamphlets, including *Billing Errors, Fair Credit Billing, Lost or Stolen Credit and ATM Cards* and *Solving Credit Problems.*

Strategies for Repaying Debts

If you think nobody cares if you're alive, try missing a couple of car payments.

—Earl Wilson

The recent economic downturn has left many folks in financial trouble. Many others never reaped any benefit from the previous economic boom and have struggled with debt for an even longer time. Today, many people are either unemployed or forced to work harder than ever (often in more than one job), earning less, saving little and struggling with debt. If this story sounds familiar to you, you're not alone. Here are some specific suggestions for dealing with debts.

I feel completely overwhelmed by my debts and don't know where to begin. What should I do?

Take a deep breath and realize that for the most part, your creditors want to help you. Whether you're behind on your bills or are afraid of getting behind, call your creditors. Let them know what's going on—job loss, reduction in hours, medical problem or whatever—and ask for help. Suggest possible solutions such as a temporary reduction of your payments, skipping a few payments and tacking them on at the end of a loan or paying them off over a few months, dropping late fees and other charges or even rewriting a loan. If you need help negotiating with your creditors, consider contacting a nonprofit debt counseling organization, such as Myvesta.org (http://www.myvesta.org) or a local Consumer Credit Counseling Service office (to find the office nearest you, contact the National Foundation for Consumer Credit at 800-388-2227 or visit http://www.nfcc.org).

I'm afraid I might miss a car payment—should I just let the lender repossess?

No. Before your car payment is due, call the lender and ask for extra time. If you're at least a few months into the loan and haven't missed any payments, the lender will probably let you miss one or two months' payments and tack them on at the end. If you don't pay or make arrangements with the lender, the lender can repossess without warning, although many will warn you and give you a chance to pay what's due.

If your car is repossessed, you can get it back by paying the entire balance due and the cost of repossession or, in some cases, by paying the cost of the repossession and the missed payments, and then making payments under your contract. If you don't get the car back, the lender will sell it at an auction for far less than it's worth. You'll owe the lender the difference between the balance of your loan and what the sale brings in. The amount is usually in the thousands.

If you are far behind on your car payments and can't catch up, think hard about whether you can really afford the car. If you decide to give up your car, there are two options that are almost always better than waiting for the dealer to repossess it. First, if you act quickly, you can sell the car yourself and use the proceeds to pay off the loan (or most of the loan). You'll get more for the car if you sell it yourself than the dealer will by selling it at an auction after repossession—which means you'll be able to pay off more of the loan. Or, you can voluntarily "surrender" your car to the dealer before repossession. This will save you expensive repossession costs and attorneys' fees. Because it also makes life easier for the dealer, try to negotiate a deal. Many dealers will agree to waive any deficiency balance or promise not to report the default or repossession to credit bureaus.

How soon after I miss a house payment will the bank begin foreclosure proceedings?

This varies from state to state and lender to lender, but most lenders don't start foreclosure proceedings until you've missed four or five payments. Before taking back your house, a lender would usually rather rewrite the loan, suspend principal payments for a while (have you pay interest only), reduce your payments or even let you miss a few payments and spread them out over time.

If your loan is owned by one of the giant U.S. government mortgage holders, Fannie Mae or Freddie Mac, foreclosure could come even more slowly. Fannie Mae and Freddie Mac often work with homeowners to avoid foreclosure when a loan is delinquent.

If your loan is insured by a federal agency such as the Department of Housing and Urban Development (HUD), the Federal Housing Administration (FHA), the Veterans Administration (VA) or the Farmers Home Administration (FmHA), the lender may be required to try to help you avoid foreclosure. Contact the federal agency to find out more.

Might I be better off just selling my house?

You're certainly better off selling the house than having it go to foreclosure. If you can find a buyer who will offer to pay at least what you owe your lender, take the offer. If the offer is for less than what you owe your lender, your lender can block the sale. But many lenders will agree to a "short sale"—where the sale brings in less than you owe the lender and the lender agrees to forego the rest. Some lenders require documentation of any financial or medical hardship you are experiencing before agreeing to a short sale.

Can I just walk away from the house?

If you get no offers for your house or the lender won't approve a short sale, you can walk away from your house. To do this, you transfer your ownership interest in your home to the lender – called a deed in lieu of foreclosure. Keep in mind that with a deed in lieu, you won't get any cash back, even if you have lots of equity in your home. The deed in lieu may also appear on your credit report as a negative mark. If you opt for a deed in lieu, try to get concessions from the lender – after all, you are saving it the expense and hassle of foreclosing on your home. For example, ask the lender to eliminate negative references on your credit report or give you more time to stay in the house.

Beware of the IRS

IRS regulations could cost you money if you settle a debt or if a creditor writes off money you owe. The rules state that if a creditor agrees to forego a debt you owe, you must treat the amount you didn't pay as income. Similarly, if a creditor ceases collection efforts, declares a debt uncollectible and reports it as a tax loss to the IRS, you must treat this amount as income. This includes any amount owed after a house foreclosure or property repossession, or on a credit card bill.

The rule applies to a debt or part of a debt for $600 or more forgiven by any bank, credit union, savings and loan or other financial institution. The institution must send you and the IRS a Form 1099-C at the end of the tax year. These forms report that income, which means that when you file your tax return for the tax year in which your debt was forgiven, the IRS will make sure that you report the amount on the Form 1099-C as income.

There are five exceptions to this rule stated in the Internal Revenue Code, three of which apply to consumers. Even if the financial institution issues a Form 1099-C or 1099-A, you do not have to report the income if:

- the cancellation of the debt is intended as a gift (this would be unusual)
- you discharge the debt in bankruptcy, or
- you were insolvent before the creditor agreed to waive the debt.

The Internal Revenue Code does not define what is meant by insolvent. Generally it means that your debts exceed the value of your assets. To figure out whether or not you are insolvent, you will have to total up your assets and your debts, including the debt that was forgiven or written off.

Let's say your assets are worth $35,000 and your debts total $45,000. You are insolvent to the tune of $10,000. If a creditor forgives or writes off debts up to that amount, you will not have to include the Form 1099-C income on your tax return.

On the other hand, let's say your assets and debts are $35,000 and $45,000 respectively, but your creditor forgives or writes off a $14,000 debt. Now, you can ignore $10,000 of the Form 1099-C income (the amount you are insolvent), but you will have to report $4,000 on your tax return.

My utility bill was huge because of a very cold winter. Do I have to pay it all at once?

Maybe not. Many utility companies offer customers an amortization program. This means that if your bills are higher in certain months than others, the company averages your yearly bills so you can spread out the large bills. Also, if you are elderly, disabled or earn a low income, you may be eligible for reduced rates—ask your utility company.

I'm swamped with student loans and can't afford my payments. What can I do to avoid default?

First, know that you're right to do all you can to avoid default, rather than ignoring your loans and hoping they'll just go away. If you default, the amount you owe will probably skyrocket because the government can add a hefty collections fee—often up to 25% of the principal.

To avoid default, contact the companies that service your student loans and tell them why you can't make your payments. You may be eligible for a deferment or forbearance—ways of postponing repayment. In very limited circumstances, you may be able to cancel a loan. Also talk to your loan holders about flexible payment options—many now offer payments geared to borrowers' incomes.

In addition, consider consolidating your student loans. You can consolidate federal student loans through the government's direct lending program or through a private loan servicing company, such as Sallie Mae or USA Group. With loan consolidation, you can lower your monthly payments by extending your repayment period; you may also be able to lower your interest rate. Most loan consolidators offer flexible repayment options based on your income, and you may be able to consolidate even if one or more of your loans is in default. Types of loans eligible for consolidation, repayment options and interest rates vary slightly from lender to lender. Contact loan servicers for more information:

- Federal Direct Consolidation Loan Center: 800-557-7392, http://www.ed.gov/DirectLoan/consolid.html
- Sallie Mae: 800-340-1086, http://www.Salliemae.com
- USA Group: 888-272-5543, http://www.usagroup.com.

Finally, if you can prove that repayment would cause you extreme hardship, you may be able to discharge your student loans in bankruptcy.

I defaulted on a student loan a long time ago and I just received collection letters. I can't afford very much, but I can pay something. Any suggestions?

The Higher Education Act allows you to rehabilitate your student loan by making "reasonable and affordable" payments based on your income and expenses. The holder cannot insist on a monthly minimum. If you make six consecutive monthly payments on time, you will become eligible to apply for new federal student loans or grants if you want to return to school. You must continue to make the monthly payments, however, until you make at least 12 consecutive payments. Then your loans will come out of default. The default notation will come off your credit report, and if you return to school, you can apply for an in-school deferment to postpone your payments.

If you do not return to school, after you make 12 consecutive monthly payments, the holder of your loan will sell it back to a regular loan servicing company. (This is called loan rehabilitation.) Your new loan servicer will put you on a standard ten-year repayment plan, which may cause your monthly payments to increase dramatically. If you can't afford them, you will need to apply for a deferment (if you are eligible) or request a flexible repayment option.

I paid off my student loan a long time ago, but the Department of Education recently wrote me saying I still owe it. Help!

You need documentation. First, contact your school and ask for its Department of Education report showing the loan's status. Then, think about ways you can show that you paid the loan: Do you have canceled checks or old bank statements? Can you get microfiche copies of checks from your bank or a government regulatory agency if your bank is out of business? Does an old roommate remember seeing you write a check every month? Can you get old credit reports (check with lenders from whom you've borrowed in years past) which may show a payment status on an old loan? Get old tax returns (from the IRS, if necessary) showing that you itemized the interest deduction on student loan payments back when that was permitted. The last holder of the loan might have a copy of the signed promissory note. Any of these things will help you prove to the Department of Education that you paid your loan.

To find out more about the status of your loan, visit the Department of Education's website at http://www.ed.gov or the National Student Loan Data System's website at http://www.nslds.ed.gov. Or call 800-4-FED-AID or the student loan ombudsman at 877-557-2575.

When can a creditor garnish my wages, place a lien on my house, seize my bank account or take my tax refund?

For the most part, a creditor must sue you, obtain a court judgment and then solicit the help of a sheriff or other law enforcement officer to garnish wages. Even then, the maximum the creditor can take is 25% of your net pay—and you can protest that amount in court if you can't live on only 75% of your wages.

In two situations your wages may be garnished without your being sued:

- Most federal administrative agencies (including the IRS and the Department of Education) can garnish your wages to collect debts owed to that agency.
- Up to 50% of your wages can be garnished to pay child support or alimony (even more if you don't currently support any dependents or if you are in arrears).

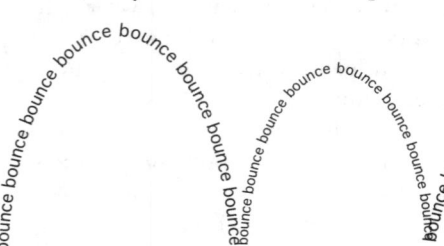

To place a lien on your house or empty your bank account, almost all creditors must first sue you, get a judgment and then use a law enforcement officer. A few creditors, such as an unpaid contractor who worked on your house, can put a lien on your house without suing. And again, the IRS is an exception—it can place a lien or empty your bank account without suing first.

Your tax refund can never be taken unless the Treasury Department receives such a request from the IRS, the Department of Education or a child support collection agency.

If You Bounce a Check

In every state, writing a bad check is a crime. Aggressive district attorneys don't hesitate to prosecute, especially given that an estimated 450 million rubber checks are written each year. If you are prosecuted, you may be able to avoid a trial if your county has a "diversion" program where you attend classes for bad check writers. You must pay the tuition and make good on the bad checks you wrote.

Even if you escape criminal prosecution, you'll be charged a bad check "processing" fee by your bank. Many banks charge as much as $20 or $30. In addition, most creditors who receive a bad check can sue for damages. Before suing you, the creditor usually must first make a written demand that you make good on the bad check. If you don't pay up within approximately 30 days, the creditor can sue you. Damages recoverable by the merchant vary from state to state, but are often a minimum of $50, and in most states more like a few hundred or a thousand dollars.

Can I go to jail for not paying my debts?

Debtor's prisons were eliminated in the U.S. by 1850. In a few unusual situations, however, you could be jailed: you willfully violate a court order, especially an order to pay child support; you are convicted of willfully refusing to pay income taxes; or you are about to conceal yourself or your property to avoid paying a debt for which a creditor has a judgment against you.

More Information About Repaying Debts

Money Troubles: Legal Strategies to Cope With Your Debts, by Robin Leonard and Deanne Loonin (Nolo), explains your legal rights and offers practical strategies for dealing with debts and creditors.

Take Control of Your Student Loans, by Robin Leonard and Deanne Loonin (Nolo), provides strategies for repaying your loans, dealing with loan collectors and getting out of default.

The Ultimate Credit Handbook, by Gerri Detweiler (Penguin Books), provides tips on doubling your credit and cutting your debt.

Surviving Debt: A Guide for Consumers, by Gary Klein, Deanne Loonin and Jonathan Sheldon (National Consumer Law Center), contains tips on dealing with debt collectors and repaying debts.

Myvesta.org, 800-680-3328, http://www.myvesta.org, offers free publications, recommended books, a forum for posting your debt questions, information on obtaining your credit report and special programs to help you get out of debt.

National Foundation for Consumer Credit, 800-388-2227, http://www.nfcc.org, can put you in contact with the CCCS office located nearest you.

The Federal Student Aid Information Center, 800-4-FED-AID, (433-3243) provides information about federal student loan programs.

The Federal Trade Commission, CRC-240, Washington, DC 20580, 877-FTC-HELP (382-4357), http://www.ftc.gov, publishes nearly 50 free pamphlets on debts and credit. Go to the FTC website and click on "Consumer Preotection," or call or write and ask for a complete list.

Dealing With the IRS

Of all debts men are least willing to pay the taxes.

—RALPH WALDO EMERSON

No three letters bring more fear to the average American than IRS. Yet, at one time or another in our lives, nearly everyone will owe a tax bill they can't pay, need extra time to file a tax return or even get audited. This section suggests several strategies for dealing with the government's largest bureaucracy.

How long should I keep my tax papers?

Keep anything related to your tax return—W-2 and 1099 forms, receipts and canceled checks for deductible items—for at least three years after you file. The IRS usually has three years from the day you file your return to audit you. For example, if you filed your 1997 tax return on April 15, 1998, keep those records until at least April 16, 2001. To be completely safe, you should keep your records for six years. The reason is that the IRS can audit you up to six years after you file if the IRS believes you underreported your income by 25% or more.

One last caution: Keep records showing purchase costs and sales figures for real estate, stocks or other investments for at least three years after you sell these assets. This is because you must be able to show your taxable gain or loss to an auditor.

If I can't pay my taxes, should I file a return anyway?

Absolutely. The consequences of filing and not paying are less severe than those for simply not filing. If you don't file a tax return, the IRS will assess a penalty of up to 25% of the tax due, plus interest. In addition, the IRS could criminally charge you for failing to file a return (although it isn't likely to). By contrast, if you file a return but can't pay, you'll only be on the hook for interest and penalties of 6%–12% on any amounts you owe.

Who has access to my IRS files?

The federal Privacy Act of 1976 declares tax files to be "confidential." This was an attempt by Congress to correct the abuses of power uncovered in the Watergate scandal. Even IRS officials cannot rummage willy-nilly through your tax files unless they are involved in some kind of case involving you and your taxes. Consequently, individuals, businesses and credit reporting agencies do not have access to your tax information unless you authorize its release to the IRS in writing.

The privacy law has exceptions, however, and IRS security is sometimes lax. Your IRS files are shared with other federal and state agencies that can demonstrate a "need to know." This usually occurs when your affairs are being investigated by a law enforcement agency. In fairness to the IRS, most leakage of information is the result of sloppiness by other federal or state agencies granted access to IRS files. Furthermore, computer hackers have broken into IRS and government databases and retrieved private tax information. While violation of the Privacy Act is a crime, violators are rarely prosecuted.

Do many people cheat on their taxes? And what will happen to me if I cheat on mine?

No one really knows how many people cheat the IRS, but several years ago an independent poll found that 20% of Americans admitted to cheating. This is somewhat in line with government studies showing that

82% of us faithfully file and pay our taxes every year. The IRS claims that most cheating is by self-employed small business people who do not have taxes withheld by their employers. Arguably, cheating by the self-employed approaches 100% if you count small violations like mailing a personal letter with a business-bought stamp.

If you are caught in some major cheating, the government can (but rarely does) throw you in jail. Fewer than 1,500 individuals are jailed in the U.S. for tax crimes each year, many of whom also are charged with drug crimes. That is really not many people, considering there are over 200 million American adults.

The IRS would much prefer collecting money to putting anyone in prison. More likely, if you're caught cheating, you'll be assessed heavy penalties, and will probably be audited for several years.

I am faced with a tax bill that I can't pay. Am I completely at the IRS's mercy, or do I have some options?

There are six ways to deal with a tax bill you can't pay:

- Borrow from a financial institution, family or friends and pay the tax bill in full.
- Negotiate a monthly payment plan with the IRS. This will include interest and penalty charges.
- File for Chapter 13 bankruptcy to set up a payment plan for your debts, including your taxes.

- Find out whether you can wipe out the debt in a Chapter 7 bankruptcy (only certain tax debts are dischargeable).
- Make an offer in compromise by filing IRS Form 656, *Offer in Compromise*. That is, ask the IRS to accept less than the full amount due.
- Ask the IRS to designate your debt temporarily uncollectible if you are out of work or your income is very low. This will buy you time to get back on your feet before dealing with the IRS. Interest and penalties will continue to accrue.

Tax Avoidance Schemes Don't Work

Dozens of tax avoidance schemes emerge every decade. Some promoters are very persuasive, particularly if you are predisposed to believing that it's possible to opt out of the tax system. Sad to say, these promoters are all snake-oil salesmen, the most successful of whom make millions peddling their products at expensive "seminars" and through underground publications. One recent scheme involves holding your assets in multiple family trusts, limited partnerships and offshore banks. While these artifices may put your assets beyond the reach of your creditors, they won't beat the IRS.

I made a mistake on my tax return and am now being billed for the taxes, plus interest and penalties. Do I have to pay it all?

Maybe not. The IRS must charge you interest on your tax bill, but penalties are discretionary. The IRS abates (cancels) one-third of all penalties it charges. The trick is to convince the IRS that you had "reasonable cause" (a good excuse) for failing to observe the tax law. Examples that might work include:

- serious illness or a death in the family
- destruction of your records by a flood, fire or other catastrophe
- wrong advice from the IRS over the phone
- bookkeeper or accountant error, or
- your being in jail or out of the country at the time the tax return was due.

You can ask anyone at the IRS to cancel a penalty, in person or over the phone. And, you can ask for a penalty to be canceled even if you already paid it. The best way to get the IRS's attention is to use IRS Form 843, *Claim for Refund and Request for Abatement*. Send this form to your IRS Service Center.

Can the IRS take my house if I owe back taxes?

The IRS can seize just about anything you own—including your home and pension plans. There is a list of items exempt by federal law from IRS seizures, but it is hardly generous, and doesn't include your residence. More-over, state homestead protection laws don't apply to the IRS. With that said, the good news is that the federal Taxpayer Bill of Rights discourages the IRS from taking homes of people who owe back taxes. In addition, the IRS doesn't like the negative public-ity generated when it takes a home, unless of course it is the home of a notorious public enemy.

Nevertheless, if the IRS collection division has tried—and failed—to get any cooperation from a tax debtor (for example, if the debtor has not an-swered correspondence or returned phone calls, or has made threats, lied about her income or hidden her as-sets), the IRS may go after a residence as a last resort. An IRS tax collector can't make the decision on his own—it must come from top IRS personnel.

If the IRS lets you know that it plans to take your house, your Congressperson may be able to inter-vene and put some pressure on the IRS to stop the seizure. And, if the seizure would add you and your family to the ranks of the homeless, you can contact your local IRS Problems Resolution Office to plead that the seizure would create a substantial hardship.

In the unhappy event the IRS does seize your home, all may not be lost. The IRS must sell the home at public auction, usually held about 45 days after the seizure. Then, the high bid-der at auction must wait 180 days to get clear title. In this interim period you have the right to redeem (buy back) the home by coming up with the bid price plus interest.

What are my chances of getting through an audit without owing additional taxes?

Although only about 1% of all tax returns are audited, the IRS has a pretty high success rate. Fewer than 15% of all IRS audit victims make a clean getaway. This is primarily be-cause the IRS's sophisticated com-puter selection process makes it likely that the agency will audit returns in which "adjustments" are almost a certainty.

If you receive an audit notice, focus on limiting the damage rather than getting off scot-free. Most adjust-ments made following an audit result from poor taxpayer records, so make sure you have organized documenta-tion to back up your deductions, ex-emptions and other claims. Ignore the tales about dumping a box of receipts on the auditor's desk in the hope that she will throw up her hands and let you off rather than go through the mess. It doesn't work like that. If you have any significant worries, get a tax pro to represent you or to help you navigate through the perilous audit waters.

Can I challenge the IRS if I get audited and don't agree with the result?

Yes, you do not have to accept any audit report. In most cases, you can appeal by sending a protest letter to the IRS within 30 days after receiving the audit report. If you request an appeals consideration, you will be granted a meeting with an appeals officer who is not part of the IRS division that performed your audit. See IRS Publication 5, *Your Appeal Rights and How to Prepare a Protest If You Don't Agree.*

If your appeal fails, you still can file a petition in Tax Court. This is a fairly inexpensive and simple process if the audit bill is for less than $50,000. If it's for more, you will most likely need the help of a tax attorney.

Generally, it pays to contest an audit report by appealing and going to court. About half the people who challenge their audit report succeed in lowering their tax bill.

More Information About Dealing With the IRS

Stand Up to the IRS, by Frederick W. Daily (Nolo), explains your legal rights and offers practical strategies for dealing with the IRS.

Surviving an Audit, by Frederick W. Daily (Nolo), provides a wealth of information for minimizing the damage when you are audited.

Debt Collections

Laws prohibit debt collectors from using abusive or deceptive tactics to collect a debt. Unfortunately, many collectors ignore the rules and don't play fair. In addition, creditors and debt collectors have powerful collection tools once they have won a lawsuit for the debt. Here are some frequently asked questions and answers to help you deal with debt collectors.

Collection agencies have been calling me all hours of the day and night. Can I get them to stop contacting me?

It's against the law for a bill collector who works for a collection agency (as opposed to working in the collections department of the creditor itself) to call you at an unreasonable time. The law presumes that calls before 8 a.m. or after 9 p.m. are unreasonable. But other hours may be unreasonable too, such as daytime hours for a person who works nights. The law, the federal Fair Debt Collection Practices Act (FDCPA), also bars collectors from calling you at work if you ask them not to, harassing you, using abusive language, making false or misleading statements, adding unauthorized charges and many other practices. Under the FDCPA, you can demand that the collection agency stop contacting you, except to tell you that collection efforts have ended or that the creditor or collection agency will sue you. You must put your request in writing.

I'm also getting calls from the collections department of a local merchant I did business with. Can I tell that collector to stop contacting me?

Usually not. The FDCPA applies only to bill collectors who work for collection agencies. While many states have laws prohibiting all debt collectors— including those working for the creditor itself—from harassing, abusing or threatening you, these laws don't give you the right to demand that the collector stop contacting you. There is at least one exception: Residents of New York City can use a local consumer protection law to write any bill collector and say, "Leave me alone." A few states, including Colorado and Massachusetts, prohibit all collectors from calling you at work if you tell them not to.

A bill collector insisted that I wire the money I owe through Western Union. Am I required to do so?

No, and it could be expensive if you do. Many collectors, especially when a debt is more than 90 days past due, will suggest several "urgency payment" options, including:

• *Sending money by express or overnight mail.* This will add at least $10 to your bill; a first class stamp is fine.

• *Wiring money through Western Union's Quick Collect or American Express's Moneygram.* This is another $10 down the drain.

• *Putting your payment on a credit card.* You'll never get out of debt if you do this.

You Can Run, But You Can't Hide

In this technological age, it's easy to run from collectors—but hard to hide. Collectors use many different resources to find debtors. They may contact relatives, friends, neighbors and employers, posing as long-lost friends to get these people to reveal your new whereabouts. In addition, collectors often get information from post office change of address forms, state motor vehicle registration information, voter registration records, former landlords and banks.

Can a collection agency add interest to my debt?

In most cases, yes. But only if either:
• the original agreement allows for additional interest during collection proceedings, or
• state law authorizes the addition of interest.
Virtually all states do allow this interest.

A collection agency sued me and won. Will I still get calls and letters demanding payment?

Probably not. Before obtaining a court judgment, a bill collector generally has only one way of getting paid: demand payment. This is done with calls and letters. You can ignore the phone calls and throw out your mail, and the collector can't do much else short of suing you. Once the collector (or creditor) sues and gets a judgment, however, you can expect more aggressive collection actions. If you have a job, the collector will try to garnish up to 25% of your net wages. The collector may also try to seize any bank or other deposit accounts you have. If you own real property, the collector will probably record a lien, which will have to be paid when you sell or refinance your property. Even if you're not currently working or have no property, you're not home free. Depending on the state, court judgments can last up to 20 years and, in many states, can be renewed so they last even longer.

What can I do if a bill collector violates the FDCPA?

Document the violation as soon as it occurs. Write down what happened, when it happened and who witnessed it. In some states, you can tape record phone conversations with debt collectors without their knowledge. But beware. In about a dozen states, this is illegal. Instead, try to have a witness present (or on another phone extension) the next time you talk to the collector.

Then file a complaint with the Federal Trade Commission (the address and phone number are at the end of this section). Next, complain to your state consumer protection agency. Fi-

nally, send a copy of your complaint to the creditor who hired the collection agency. If the violations are severe enough, the creditor may stop the collection efforts.

Also, you can sue a collection agency (and the creditor that hired the agency) in small claims court for violating the FDCPA. You are less likely to win if you can prove only a few minor violations. If the violations are outrageous, you can sue the collection agency and creditor in regular civil court. One Texas jury awarded a debtor $11 million when a debt collector made death and bomb threats against her and her husband that frightened them so much they moved out of the county.

More Information About Debt Collections

Money Troubles: Legal Strategies to Cope With Your Debts, by Robin Leonard and Deanne Loonin (Nolo), explains your legal rights and offers practical strategies for dealing with debts and creditors.

The Federal Trade Commission, CRC-240, Washington, DC 20580, 877-FTC-HELP (382-4357), http://www.ftc.gov, publishes free pamphlets on debts and credit, including a couple on the Fair Debt Collections Practices Act. It also takes complaints about collection agencies.

Bankruptcy

*Where everything is bad it
must be good to know the worst.*

—FRANCIS HERBERT BRADLEY

If you are seriously in debt, you might consider filing for bankruptcy. Here are some common questions and answers designed to help you understand the bankruptcy process and what bankruptcy can and cannot do for you.

What exactly is bankruptcy?

Bankruptcy is a federal court process designed to help consumers and businesses eliminate their debts or repay them under the protection of the bankruptcy court. Bankruptcy's roots can be traced to the Bible. (Deuteronomy 15:1-2 —"Every seventh year you shall practice remission of debts. This shall be the nature of the remission: Every creditor shall remit the due that he claims from his neighbor; he shall not dun his neighbor or kinsman.")

Aren't there different kinds of bankruptcy?

Yes. Bankruptcies can generally be described as "liquidation" or "reorganization."

Liquidation bankruptcy is called Chapter 7. Under Chapter 7 bankruptcy, a consumer or business asks the bankruptcy court to wipe out (discharge) the debts owed. Certain debts cannot be discharged—these are discussed below. In exchange for the discharge of debts, the business assets or the consumer's nonexempt property

are sold—that is, liquidated—and the proceeds are used to pay off creditors. The property a consumer might lose is discussed below.

In any reorganization bankruptcy, you file a plan with the bankruptcy court proposing how you will repay your creditors. Some debts must be repaid in full; others you pay only a percentage; others aren't paid at all. Some debts you have to pay with interest; some are paid at the beginning of your plan and some at the end.

There are several types of reorganization bankruptcy. Consumers with secured debts under $871,550 and unsecured debts under $290,525 can file for Chapter 13. Family farmers can file for Chapter 12. Consumers with debts in excess of the Chapter 13 debt limits or businesses can file for Chapter 11—a complex, time-consuming and expensive process.

What generally happens in consumer bankruptcy cases?

In a Chapter 7 case, you file several forms with the bankruptcy court listing income and expenses, assets, debts and property transactions for the past two years. The cost to file is $200, which may be waived for people who receive public assistance or live below the poverty level. A court-appointed person, the trustee, is assigned to oversee your case. About a month after filing, you must attend a "meeting of creditors" where the trustee reviews your forms and asks questions. Despite the name, creditors rarely attend. If you have any nonexempt property, you must give it (or its value in cash) to the trustee. The meeting lasts about five minutes. Three to six months later, you receive a notice from the court that "all debts that qualified for discharge were discharged." Then your case is over.

Chapter 13 is a little different. You file the same forms plus a proposed repayment plan, in which you describe how you intend to repay your debts over the next three, or in some cases five, years. The cost to file is $185 (it cannot be waived but it can be paid in installments), and a trustee is assigned to oversee the case. Here, too, you attend the meeting of creditors, but often one or two creditors attend this meeting, especially if they don't like something in your plan. After the meeting of the creditors, you attend a hearing before a bankruptcy judge who either confirms or denies your plan. If your plan is confirmed, and you make all the payments called for under your plan, any remaining balance on a dischargeable debt will be wiped out at the end of your case (see "Nondischargeable Debts," below, to learn which debts will have balances that are not wiped out at the end of the case).

Nondischargeable Debts

The following debts are nondischargeable in both Chapter 7 and Chapter 13. If you file for Chapter 7, these will remain when your case is over. If you file for Chapter 13, these debts will have to be paid in full during your plan. If they are not, the balance will remain at the end of your case:

• debts you forget to list in your

bankruptcy papers, unless the creditor learns of your bankruptcy case
• child support and alimony
• debts for personal injury or death caused by your intoxicated driving
• student loans, unless it would be an undue hardship for you to repay
• fines and penalties imposed for violating the law, such as traffic tickets and criminal restitution
• recent income tax debts and all other tax debts, and
• debts you couldn't discharge in a previous bankruptcy because that bankruptcy was dismissed due to your fraud or other bad acts.

In addition, the following debts may be declared nondischargeable by a bankruptcy judge in Chapter 7 if the creditor challenges your request to discharge them. These debts may be discharged in Chapter 13. You can include them in your plan—at the end of your case, the balance is wiped out:
• debts you incurred on the basis of fraud, such as lying on a credit application
• credit purchases of $1,150 of more for luxury goods or services made within 60 days of filing
• loans or cash advances of $1,150 or more taken within 60 days of filing
• debts from willful or malicious injury to another person or another person's property
• debts from embezzlement, larceny or breach of trust, and
• debts you owe under a divorce decree or settlement unless after bankruptcy you would still not be able to afford to pay them or the benefit you'd receive by the discharge outweighs any detriment to your ex-spouse (who would have to pay them if you discharge them in bankruptcy).

What property might I lose if I file for bankruptcy?

You lose no property in Chapter 13. In Chapter 7, you select property you are eligible to keep from either a list of state exemptions or exemptions provided in the federal Bankruptcy Code. Most debtors use the exemptions provided by their state.

Exemptions are generally as follows:

- *Equity in your home, called a homestead exemption.* Under the Bankruptcy Code, you can exempt up to $17,425. Some states have no homestead exemption; others allow debtors to protect all or most of the equity in their home.
- *Insurance.* You usually get to keep the cash value of your policies.
- *Retirement plans.* Pensions which qualify under the Employee Retirement Income Security Act (ERISA) are fully protected in bankruptcy. So are many other retirement benefits; often, however, IRAs and Keoghs are not.
- *Personal property.* You'll be able to keep most household goods, furniture, furnishings, clothing (other than furs), appliances, books and musical instruments. You may be limited up to $1,000 or so in how much jewelry you can keep. Most states let you keep a vehicle with more than $2,400 of equity. And many states give you a "wild card" amount of money—often $1,000 or more—that you can apply toward any property.
- *Public benefits.* All public benefits, such as welfare, Social Security and unemployment insurance, are fully protected.
- *Tools used on your job.* You'll probably be able to keep up to a few thousand dollars worth of the tools used in your trade or profession.
- *Wages.* In most states, you can protect at least 75% of earned but unpaid wages.

Why choose Chapter 13 over Chapter 7?

Although the overwhelming number of people who file for bankruptcy choose Chapter 7, there are several reasons why people select Chapter 13:

- You cannot file for Chapter 7 bankruptcy if you received a Chapter 7 or Chapter 13 discharge within the previous six years.
- You have valuable nonexempt property.
- You're behind on your mortgage or car loan. In Chapter 7, you'll have to give up the property or pay for it in full during your bankruptcy case. In Chapter 13, you can repay the arrears through your plan, and keep the property by making the payments required under the contract.
- You have debts that cannot be discharged in Chapter 7.
- You have codebtors on personal (nonbusiness) loans. In Chapter 7, the creditors will go after your codebtors for payment. In Chapter 13, the creditors may not seek payment from your codebtors for the duration of your case.
- You feel a moral obligation to repay your debts or you want to learn money management.

*More Information
About Bankruptcy*

How to File for Chapter 7 Bankruptcy, by Stephen Elias, Albin Renauer, Robin Leonard and Kathleen Michon (Nolo), is a complete guide to filing for Chapter 7 bankruptcy, including all the forms you need.

Nolo's Law Form Kit: Personal Bankruptcy, by Stephen Elias, Albin Renauer, Robin Leonard and Kathleen Michon (Nolo), contains all the forms and instructions necessary for filing a Chapter 7 bankruptcy.

Chapter 13 Bankruptcy: Repay Your Debts, by Robin Leonard (Nolo), contains the forms and instructions necessary to file your own Chapter 13 bankruptcy or successfully work with a lawyer.

Bankruptcy: Is It the Right Solution to Your Debt Problems?, by Robin Leonard (Nolo), provides tools to help you decide if filing for bankruptcy is for you and, if so, which type is best.

Will Bankruptcy Law Change for the Worse?

In March 2001, the U.S. Congress passed legislation that would make it difficult—or impossible—for some people to file for bankruptcy. The House and Senate were scheduled to meet in September 2001 to work out differences between their respective versions of the bill. That meeting was cancelled due to the events of September

11. At the time this book went to print, Congressional committees were once again discussing whether a final version of the legislation could be hammered out. However, the future of the legislation is uncertain. Many experts believe that the legislation is no longer a priority, especially given the recent downturn in the economy and rising unemployment.

The legislation is very unfriendly to debtors. Among other things, it would prohibit some people from filing for bankruptcy, add to the list of debts that people cannot get rid of in bankruptcy and make it harder for people to come up with manageable repayment plans.

To learn more about the legislation, check Legal Updates on Nolo's website (http://www.nolo.com).

Rebuilding Credit

People who have been through a financial crisis—bankruptcy, repossession, foreclosure, history of late payments, IRS lien or levy or something similar—may think they will never get credit again. Not true. Following some simple steps, you can rebuild your credit in just a couple of years.

What's the first step in rebuilding credit?

To avoid getting into financial problems in the future, you must understand your flow of income and expenses. Some people call this making a budget. Others find the term budget too restrictive and use the term "spending plan." Whatever you call it, spend at least two months writing down every expenditure you make. At each month's end, compare your total expenses with your income. If you're overspending, you have to cut back or find more income. As best you can, plan how you'll spend your money each month. If you have trouble putting together your own budget, consider getting help from a nonprofit group, such as Myvesta.org or your local Consumer Credit Counseling Service, which provides budgeting help for free or at a low cost.

Okay, I've made my budget. What do I do next?

Now it's time to clean up your credit report. Credit reports are compiled by credit bureaus—private, for-profit companies that gather information about your credit history and sell it to banks, mortgage lenders, credit unions, credit card companies, department stores, insurance companies, landlords and even a few employers.

Credit bureaus get most of their data from creditors. They also search court records for lawsuits, judgments and bankruptcy filings. And they go through county records to find recorded liens (legal claims against property).

To create a credit file for a given person, a credit bureau searches its computer files until it finds entries that match the name, Social Security number and any other available identifying information. All matches are gathered together to make the report.

Noncredit data in a credit report usually includes names you previously used, past and present addresses, Social Security number, employment history, marriages and divorces. Your credit history includes the names of your creditors, type and number of each account, when each account was opened, your payment history for the previous 24–36 months, your credit limit or the original amount of a loan, and your current balance. The report will show if an account has been turned over to a collection agency or is in dispute.

How to Get Your Credit Report

There are three major credit bureaus—Equifax, Trans Union and Experian. The federal Fair Credit Reporting Act (FCRA) entitles you to a copy of your credit report, and you can get one for free if any of the following are true:

- you were denied credit because of information in your credit report and you request a copy within 60 days of being denied credit
- you receive public assistance
- you are unemployed and plan to apply for a job within 60 days, or
- you believe your file contains errors due to fraud.

Residents of Colorado, Georgia, Maryland, Massachusetts, New Jersey and Vermont are entitled to a free copy of their report once a year from each credit bureau.

If you don't qualify for a free report, you'll have to pay about $8.50 (less in some states) to obtain one. Write to Equifax (P.O. Box 740241, Atlanta, GA 30374, 800-685-1111, http://www.equifax.com), Trans Union (Consumer Disclosure Center, P.O. Box 1000, Chester, PA 19022, 800-888-4213, http://www.tuc.com) or Experian (P.O. Box 2002, Allen, TX 75013, 888-397-3742, http://www.experian.com).

Send the following information:
- your full name (including generations such as Jr., Sr., III)
- your birth date
- your Social Security number
- your spouse's name (if relevant)
- your telephone number, and
- your current address and addresses for the previous five years.

What should I do if I find mistakes in my report?

As you read through your report, make a list of everything out of date:
- Lawsuits, paid tax liens, accounts sent out for collection, late payments and any other adverse information older than seven years.
- Bankruptcies older than ten years from the discharge or dismissal. (Credit bureaus often list Chapter 13 bankruptcies for only seven years, but they can stay for as many as ten.)
- Credit inquiries (requests by companies for a copy of your report) older than two years.

Next, look for incorrect or misleading information, such as:
- incorrect or incomplete name, address, phone number, Social Security number or employment information
- bankruptcies not identified by their specific chapter number
- accounts not yours or lawsuits in which you were not involved
- incorrect account histories—such as late payments when you paid on time
- closed accounts listed as open—it may look as if you have too much open credit, and
- any account you closed that doesn't say "closed by consumer."

After reviewing your report, complete the "request for reinvestigation" form the credit bureau sent you or send a letter listing each item that is incorrect or too old to be reported. Once the credit bureau receives your request, it must investigate the items you dispute and contact you within 30 days. If you don't hear back within 30 days, send a follow-up letter.

If you are right, or if the creditor who provided the information can no longer verify it, the credit bureau must remove the information from your report. Often credit bureaus will remove an item on request without an investigation if rechecking the item is more bother than it's worth.

If the credit bureau insists that the information is correct, call the bureau to discuss the problem:
- Experian: 888-397-3742
- Trans Union: 800-916-8800
- Equifax: 800-685-1111

If you don't get anywhere with the credit bureau, contact the creditor directly and ask that the information be removed. Write to the customer service department, vice president of marketing and president or CEO. If the information was reported by a collection agency, send the agency a copy of your letter, too.

If the creditor will not remove the information, remind the creditor that under the 1997 amendments to the Fair Credit Reporting Act, the creditor must do the following:

- refrain from reporting information they know is incorrect
- refrain from ignoring information they know contradicts what they have on file, and
- provide credit bureaus with correct information when that information becomes available.

If a credit bureau is including the wrong information in your report, or you want to explain a particular entry, you have the right to put a brief explanatory statement in your report. The credit bureau must give a copy of your statement—or a summary—to anyone who requests your report. Be clear and concise; use the fewest words possible.

I've been told that I need to use credit to rebuild my credit. Is this true?

Yes. The one type of positive information creditors like to see in credit reports is credit payment history. If you have a credit card, use it every month. (Make small purchases and pay them off to avoid interest charges.) If you don't have a credit card, apply for one. If your application is rejected, try to find a cosigner or apply for a secured card—where you

deposit some money into a savings account and then get a credit card with a line of credit close to the amount you deposited. But beware. Don't apply for new credit before getting back on your feet. Defaulting on new credit will only make matters worse.

What else can I do to rebuild my credit?

After you've cleaned up your credit report, work on getting positive information into your record. Here are two suggestions:

- If your credit report is missing accounts you pay on time, send the credit bureaus a recent account statement and copies of canceled checks showing your payment history. Ask that these be added to your report. The credit bureau doesn't have to add anything, but often will.
- Creditors like to see evidence of stability, so if any of the following information is not in your report, send it to the bureaus and ask that it be added: your current employment, your previous employment (especially if you've been at your current job fewer than two years), your current residence, your telephone number (especially if it's unlisted), your date of birth and your checking account number. Again, the credit bureau doesn't have to add these, but often will.

How long does it take to rebuild credit?

If you follow the steps outlined above, it will take about two years to rebuild your credit to the point that you won't be turned down for a major credit card or loan. After approximately four years, you may be able to qualify for a mortgage.

More Information About Rebuilding Your Credit

Credit Repair, by Robin Leonard and Deanne Loonin (Nolo), is a quick guide to lawfully rebuilding your credit. It contains several strategies for improving credit, sample credit reports with explanations on how to read them and the text of the federal and many state credit reporting laws.

Money Troubles: Legal Strategies to Cope With Your Debts, by Robin Leonard and Deanne Loonin (Nolo), explains your legal rights and offers practical strategies for dealing with debts and creditors, including rebuilding your credit.

The Federal Trade Commission, CRC-240, Washington, DC 20580, 877-FTC-HELP (382-4357), http://www.ftc.gov, publishes free pamphlets on debts and credit, including *Building a Better Credit Record*, *Cosigning a Loan*, *Fair Credit Reporting* and *Fix Your Own Credit Problems and Save Money*.

The Federal Deposit Insurance Corporation, 550 17th Street, NW, Washington, DC 20429, 877-275-3342, 800-925-4618 (TDD), http://www.fdic.gov, publishes free pamphlets about credit, including *Fair Credit Reporting*.

http://www.nolo.com
Nolo offers self-help information about a wide variety of legal topics, including advice about consumer law, debts and credit.

http://www.fraud.org
The National Fraud Information Center helps you file a complaint with federal agencies if you've benn defrauded. It also offers information on how to avoid becoming the victim of a scam.

http://www.financenter.com
The FinanCenter provides financial advice and includes a calculator to help you compare various financing alternatives when you're making a budget or considering a major purchase, such as a home or automobile. The cool graphics alone make visiting this site worthwhile.

http://www.bbb.org
The Better Business Bureau provides general information on their programs and services, including alerts, warnings and updates about businesses. You can also find information about filing a complaint against a business and using the BBB's dispute resolution program.

http://www.lawguru.com
The Internet Law Library provides the texts of finance, economic and consumer protection laws including the federal bankruptcy code and bankruptcy rules, banking laws, Fed-

eral Trade Commission publications and selected state consumer protection laws.

http://www.pueblo.gsa.gov

The Consumer Information Center provides the latest in consumer news as well as many publications of interest to consumers, including the Consumer Information Catalog.

http://www.fdic.gov
http://www.ftc.gov

Both the Federal Deposit Insurance Corporation and the Federal Trade Commission offer consumer protection rules, guides and publications.

http://www.irs.ustreas.gov

The Internal Revenue Service provides tax information, forms and publications.

http://www.agin.com/lawfind

This site provides an extensive list of online bankruptcy-related materials, including other online bankruptcy sites.

Cars and Driving

10.2	**Buying a New Car**
10.7	**Leasing a Car**
10.10	**Buying a Used Car**
10.12	**Financing a Vehicle Purchase**
10.13	**Insuring Your Car**
10.16	**Your Driver's License**
10.19	**If You're Stopped by the Police**
10.21	**Drunk Driving**
10.23	**Traffic Accidents**

WHEN SOLOMON SAID THAT THERE WAS
A TIME AND A PLACE FOR EVERYTHING
HE HAD NOT ENCOUNTERED THE PROBLEM
OF PARKING AN AUTOMOBILE.

—BOB EDWARDS

Together, Americans own more than 137 million automobiles—that's at least one car for every 1.7 people in the country. It is not surprising that this average is well above that for the rest of the world, where there is approximately one car for every 12 people. Plainly, Americans love their cars—or at least the mobility they provide. For the privilege of owning and operating a vehicle, we pay an average of more than $8,000 per year. We also expend plenty of time and energy figuring out which cars to buy, how to insure and maintain them, and how to keep out of trouble on the road. This chapter provides answers to many of your questions about owning a car and driving responsibly.

Buying a New Car

These days, the average new car costs more than $20,000. For that amount of money, you would hope for a hassle-free buying experience and a safe and reliable product. Unfortunately, new car buyers are frequently overwhelmed with the pressure to buy immediately or spend more than planned, and worse—the product you bring home might be plagued with problems ranging from annoying engine "pings," to frequent stalls, to safety hazards such as poor acceleration or carbon monoxide leaks.

I want to get a good deal on a new car. What make and model should I buy?

There are several good resources to help you comparison shop when you're looking for a new car. *Consumer Reports* magazine publishes an annual car-buying issue that compares price, features, service history, resale value and reliability. Other helpful sources of information are *Motor Trend* magazine and *The Car Buyer's Art*, by Darrell Parrish (Book Express). Finally, many websites provide price and feature information. To start, try http://www.autosite.com, http://www.carwizard.com or http://www.carprices.com.

When deciding which car to buy, resist the urge to buy more car than you can afford—and don't talk yourself into a more expensive car by financing it for four or five years. You'll pay a bundle in interest that way.

Do you have any tips for negotiating with a car dealer?

Negotiating price with a dealer is almost never a pleasant experience. And, if you don't do it well, you are likely to pay hundreds or thousands of dollars more for a car. Here are some tips for getting the best deal.

- Know which car you want (or a few you are interested in), which features you want and what you can afford to pay before you walk into the dealership. Then, stick to your guns.
- Know the dealer's cost for the car before you start negotiating. Then,

use this figure as the starting point from which you negotiate up. The dealer invoice price is how much the dealer paid for the car. Many websites list dealer invoice prices. But the dealer's final cost is often even lower, because manufacturers offer dealers behind-the-scenes financial incentives. To find out the car's true cost to the dealer, you can order a report from *Consumer Reports* (http://www.consumerreports.org or 800-888-8275) for about $12.

- Don't buy in a hurry. You need time to compare prices. And usually, the longer you take and the more times you walk away, the lower the price will go.
- Order your new car if the one you want is not on the lot. Cars on the lot frequently have options you don't want, which jack up the price.
- Don't make a deposit on a vehicle before the dealership has accepted your offer.
- If a rebate is offered, negotiate the price as if the rebate didn't exist. And have the rebate sent to your home—don't allow the dealership to "apply" it to the amount you owe. Rebates come from the manufacturer and shouldn't be a reason to pay the dealer more for the car.
- Don't discuss the possibility of a trade-in until you fix the price for your new car.
- Don't trade in your old vehicle without doing your homework. A dealer will give you the low *Kelley Blue Book* value, at most. (The *Kelley*

Blue Book lists wholesale and retail prices for cars by year and model. You can find it in libraries, bookstores or online at http://www.kbb.com.) Take a look at classified ads to get an idea of how much you could get if you sold your car yourself. Or, order a used car price report from *Consumer Reports* magazine (http://www.consumerreports.org or 800-258-1169). Don't accept less than what you can get on the street. Or, forget the trade-in and sell your old car yourself.

- You might want to read up on the sales tactics dealerships use to get you to pay top dollar. Armed with this information, you will be better able to deflect the tactics and get a good deal. There are lots of books on this subject. Two of the best are *Don't Get Taken Every Time,* by Remar Sutton (Penguin Books), and *So...You Wanna Buy a Car,* by Bruce Fuller and Tony Whitney (Self-Counsel Press).

What other information do I need to know before I buy my new car?

Be sure you know the following before you sign any contract:

- what the warranty covers and how long it lasts
- how you might lose warranty coverage (such as driving off-road)
- whether an extended warranty is available to you, and if so, the following:
  - what it will cost
  - what it covers
  - how long it lasts
  - whether it duplicates coverage provided by the manufacturer's warranty
  - how likely it is that you'll need it (whether the covered parts have a history of problems)
- the vehicle's estimated miles per gallon for city and highway driving, and
- the dealer's suggested maintenance schedule.

Is there anything I should do when my new car is delivered?

Yes. Before signing a receipt and paying for your new vehicle, do the following:

- Check the vehicle against your order, item by item. Make sure all features are included.
- Inspect the vehicle for damage. Some new vehicles are damaged during manufacturing or in transit. For this reason, never take delivery of a new vehicle at night. Even in good artificial light, it's hard to see nicks or dents. You'll also miss subtle changes in paint that may indicate the car was damaged in transit and was repainted.
- Test drive the vehicle and pay attention to odd noises, smells or vibrations.
- Make sure the warranty matches what the dealer agreed to.

If I change my mind after I buy a new car, do I have the right to cancel the contract?

No. Unfortunately, many people think they have a right to change their mind, drive the car back to the dealer a day or two after buying, and cancel the contract. But the truth is, the dealer doesn't have to take the car back and probably won't, and you'll be stuck with a car you no longer want or cannot afford. Never buy a car unless you are absolutely certain you want it and can afford it.

This misunderstanding is so widespread that one state—California—requires the following to be included in new car contracts:

California law does not provide for a "cooling off" or other cancellation period for vehicle sales. Therefore, you cannot later cancel this contract simply because you change your mind, decide the vehicle costs too much, or wish you had acquired a different vehicle. After you sign below, you may only cancel this contract with the agreement of the seller or for legal cause, such as fraud.

Soon after I brought my new car home, it started having problems. How do I know if it's a lemon?

An estimated 150,000 vehicles each year (or 1% of new cars) are lemons. Although the precise definition of a

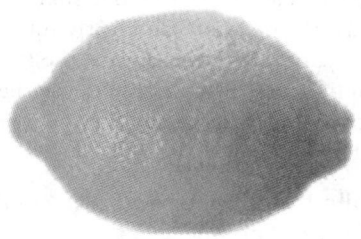

lemon varies by state, in general, a new car is a lemon if a number of attempts have been made to repair a "substantial defect" and the car continues to have this defect. A substantial defect is one that impairs the car's use, value or safety, such as faulty brakes or turn signals. Minor defects, such as loose radio and door knobs, don't qualify.

In all states, the defect must occur within a certain period of time (usually 1 or 2 years) or within a certain number of miles (usually 12,000 or 24, 000). And you must usually meet one of the following standards for repair attempts:

- the defect is a serious safety defect involving brakes or steering and remains unfixed after one repair attempt

- the defect is not a serious safety defect and remains unfixed after three or four repair attempts (the number depends on the state), or

- the vehicle is in the shop for a certain number of days (usually 30) in a one year period.

How to Find Your State's Lemon Law

If you want to find out if your car qualifies as a lemon in your state, get a copy of your state's lemon law. If you have access to the Internet, http://www.autopedia.com has links to each state's lemon law. Or, see this book's Appendix on Legal Research for information on how to find the law in the library. For a summary of each state's lemon law, check out *Return to Sender*, by Nancy Barron (National Consumer Law Center). You can order the book from NCLC at http://www.consumerlaw.org or 617-523-8089.

What should I do if my new car is a lemon?

If your new car meets the lemon law requirements for your state (see the previous question), every state gives you the right to obtain a refund or replacement vehicle from the manufacturer. The process for getting this relief is different in each state. In all states, you must first notify the manufacturer of the defect. If you're not offered a satisfactory settlement, most states require you to go to arbitration before going to court. Automakers use the following types of arbitration programs:

- in-house programs run by the auto makers
- programs set up by the Better Business Bureau's Auto Line
- programs run by the American Automobile Association or the National Automobile Dealer's Association, and
- programs run through a state consumer protection agency.

You probably won't get to choose which program to use—the manufacturer selects it. If you do have a choice, however, know that consumers who appear before a state consumer protection agency usually fare much better than those who use a manufacturer's in-house program or a private arbitration program run by the BBB, AAA or NADA.

What happens at a lemon law arbitration?

At the arbitration hearing, the arbitrator hears both sides of the dispute. The arbitrator has approximately 60 days to decide if your car is a lemon and if you're entitled to a refund or a replacement. Consumers who bring substantial documentation to the hearing tend to do better than those with little evidence to back up their claims. The types of documentation that can help include:

- brochures and ads about the vehicle —an arbitration panel is likely to make the manufacturer live up to its claims
- vehicle service records showing how often you took the car into the shop, and

- any other documents showing your attempts to get the dealer to repair your car, including old calendars and phone records.

It is important to take the arbitration seriously and be as prepared as possible. Although usually you can appeal a bad arbitration decision in court, the decision can greatly influence your case. For example, the manufacturer may be able to use the decision as evidence against you.

If I continue to drive my car while I wait for a decision, will it hurt my case?

Because it often takes a long time to get relief, most lemon laws allow you to keep using your car while pursuing a claim. But keep in mind that some courts may look less favorably on your case if you are able to drive your car. And of course, you should never drive your car if it is unsafe to do so.

"Secret" Warranty Adjustments

Many automobile manufacturers have "secret warranty," or warranty adjustment, programs. Under these programs, a manufacturer makes repairs for free on vehicles with persistent problems after a warranty expires in order to avoid a recall and bad press. According to the Center for Auto Safety, at any given time there are a total of 500 secret adjustment warranty programs available through automobile manufacturers. The

Center for Auto Safety's website, at http://www.autosafety.org, and the Car Talk site, at http://www.cartalk.cars.com/Got-a-car/lemon, have information about many of these programs.

Unfortunately, consumers aren't told of these warranty adjustments unless they come forward after the warranty has expired, complain about a problem and demand that the manufacturer repair it.

A few states, including California, Connecticut, Virginia and Wisconsin, require manufacturers to tell eligible consumers when they adopt a secret warranty adjustment, usually within 90 days of adopting the program.

What if I don't like the arbitrator's decision?

If you don't like the ruling, you can usually sue the manufacturer in court. You may want to do this if you have substantial "consequential" damages—that is, damages that resulted from owning the lemon, such as the cost of renting a car while your lemon was in the shop or time off from work every time your car broke down.

More Information About Lemons

If you think your new car is a lemon, an excellent book to help you sort out your rights and remedies is *Return to Sender*, by Nancy Barron (National Consumer Law Center). You can order the book from NCLC at http://www.consumerlaw.org or 617-523-8089.

Leasing a Car

More than one-third of new car owners lease, rather than purchase, their vehicles. Although leasing isn't for everyone, some people swear by it. Before you sign on the dotted line, be sure you know what you're getting into.

What are the advantages of leasing a new car?

There are three main reasons people lease, rather than buy, a new vehicle:
- People who like to drive a new car every few years will pay much less by leasing than if they buy. They also don't have to deal with getting rid of their old car—they just turn it in at the end of the lease period.
- Lease payments are lower than loan payments for any given car.
- Leasing gives people the opportunity to drive a more expensive car than they could afford to buy.

Are there any obvious disadvantages to leasing?

Yes—there are many.
- If you continually lease your cars, you will have never-ending car payments. If you look forward to paying off your car and owning it free and clear, don't lease.
- If you decide to buy the car at the lease-end, you'll pay several thousands of dollars more than if you had bought initially. For example, if you buy a car, paying $500 a month for four years, you'll pay a total of $24,000. You might be able to lease it for only $400 a

month (total payments of $19,200), but you'll probably have to pay another $8,000 to keep it—and if you finance that $8,000, you'll pay even more.

- Most leases charge you as much as 25¢ a mile if you exceed the annual mileage limit—usually between 12,000 and 15,000 miles. If you plan to do extensive driving, leasing probably isn't for you.

- It's very, very expensive to break a lease early. If you no longer want, or can afford, to keep your car—for example, because you lost your job or your financial situation changed—you are stuck.

- If you lease a lemon, the leasing company has to do the complaining (remember, you don't own the car) in order to get redress.

Are all leasing costs disclosed up front?

Not necessarily. While the federal Consumer Leasing Act requires lease agreements to include a statement of costs (such as the number and amount of regular payments), insurance requirements, the penalty for defaulting, and whether you'll have a balloon payment at the end, many lease agreements are ambiguously drafted, with key provisions buried in the fine print.

Even the revised regulations—which strengthened the existing disclosures and added others—do not eliminate all of the abuses. For example, the revised law does not obligate a dealer to disclose the interest rate that's been built into your pay-

ments. If you want to lease, you'll have to be a diligent consumer willing to read all the fine print. Also, ask a lot of questions and demand that the answers be put in writing.

Is there any way to find out the interest rate on a lease?

Yes. Ask the dealer for something called the "leasing factor." Multiply that factor by 24 and you'll get the approximate interest rate.

Are there any good leasing deals?

Yes—especially those heavily advertised by car manufacturers. Those deals usually offer low monthly payments or a high value for the vehicle at the end (so that you're not paying for a lot of depreciation during the lease term), and offer to lock-in the price you'd have to pay at lease-end if you want to keep the vehicle.

To get these good deals, you cannot deviate from the advertised terms. If you want air conditioning, a larger engine or any other feature that's not in the ad, the dealer will throw out the entire lease offer and you'll wind up paying a bundle.

Another way to get a good deal is to explore financing your lease through someone other than the dealer. A number of independent companies offer leases—look for these companies in your telephone Yellow Pages under "Automotive—Leasing." Also, if you belong to a credit union or AAA, ask about the possibility of financing your lease through them. Such deals are still in their infancy, but are catching on.

When buying a new car, I usually shop in the fall when dealers are trying to get rid of old inventory. Does this strategy work for leasing?

In general, no. Because dealers have lost money on cars sitting in their lots, they often increase the monthly lease payments to make up for lost revenue.

If I do lease a vehicle, who pays for maintenance and repairs?

Your lease agreement will specify who must pay. In addition, the agreement should come with a manufacturer's warranty. Ideally, it will cover the entire length of the lease and the number of miles you are likely to drive.

Most lease agreements obligate you to pay for "excessive wear and tear." This means that when you return the vehicle at lease-end, the dealer could charge you to fix anything deemed "excessive." You should insist that the dealer specify in writing exactly what is meant by "excessive" before you sign the lease contract.

Finally, look for a deal that includes "gap" insurance. If the vehicle is stolen or totaled, gap insurance will pay the difference between what you owe under the lease and what the dealer can recover on the vehicle (assuming it's not stolen)—a difference that could amount to thousands of dollars.

Can I cancel my lease agreement early?

Probably not, unless you're willing to pay a substantial penalty. If you want to cancel your lease, look carefully at the provision describing what happens if you default or want to terminate the lease early. The provision may state that you'll owe an enormous sum of money, or may use a complex formula to calculate what you owe.

While the federal Consumer Leasing Act gives you the right to cancel the lease if the termination formula is so complex that you can't easily figure out how much you owe, this will be hard for you to assert with success. Because of successful consumer lawsuits, lawyers for car manufacturers have rewritten lease contracts to avoid most of the ambiguities.

Even so, if you can't understand the formula, write to the dealer stating that you want to terminate the lease early but that the termination provision of the lease agreement is ambiguous. State further that you know you are entitled to sue for damages because of the dealer's failure to use a reasonable formula. Finally, state that you are willing to waive your right to sue if the dealer will waive the balance you owe.

If you can't get the dealer to drop his claim that you owe money, try to negotiate to reduce your payments or to extend them over time.

More Information About Leasing a Car

Both the Federal Trade Commission (at http://www.ftc.gov) and the Federal Reserve Board (at http://federalreserve.gov) publish brochures to help you understand your rights when leasing a car.

Buying a Used Car

HORSEPOWER WAS A WONDERFUL

THING WHEN ONLY HORSES HAD IT.

—ANONYMOUS

While buying a used car might be the only way you can afford a new set of wheels, it's a transaction ripe with potential disaster. We probably all know someone who bought a used car—assured that "my grandmother drove it once a week for ten years to church and the grocery store"—only to have it need $5,000 of work shortly after bringing it home.

How do I go about finding a used car?

It's best if you have some idea of the make, model and year that you're interested in. There are many good sources to help you compare cars. *Consumer Reports* magazine publishes an annual car-buying issue, comparing price, features, service histories, resale values and reliability. Other sources of information are *Motor Trend* magazine and *Used Cars,* by Darrell Parrish (Book Express). Once you've made this preliminary decision, look at the listings in your local newspaper. Don't forget weekly advertising papers or local automobile publications as well. Call any mechanics that you trust to see if they know of any available vehicles. Finally, check with car dealers; they often have used cars that people have traded in.

How much should I spend on a used car?

Check the wholesale and retail values of the cars that interest you. Bookstores and libraries have copies of the *Kelley Blue Book* (which lists wholesale and retail prices), or you can find it online at http://www.kbb.com. Lenders and insurance companies should be able to give you the same information.

For a small fee (about $10), *Consumer Reports* (http://www.consumerreports.org or 800-258-1169) will tell you how much a particular car is worth, taking into consideration the car's mileage, condition and additional equipment (such as power windows or compact disc player). The report also provides information about the car's reliability. You can also get most of this information from the *Kelley Blue Book* website at http://www.kbb.com.

Once you know the vehicle's wholesale and retail values, you'll want to pay wholesale (the lower number) and the seller will want to charge retail (the higher number). You'll probably settle somewhere in between. Your final price will depend on a number of factors, including the condition of the car and the person from whom you buy it.

The Buyers Guide

Federal law requires an automobile dealer to post a Buyers Guide in every used car it offers for sale (motorcycles and most recreational vehicles are exempt from this requirement). Among other things, the Buyers Guide tells you whether the vehicle is sold "as is" or with a warranty and describes the warranty. Be sure to get the Buyers Guide when you buy a used car and make sure it reflects any changes to warranty coverage that you negotiated with the dealer. The Buyers Guide becomes part of the sales contract—if the dealer refuses to make good on the warranty, you'll need it as proof of your original agreement.

Obviously, price isn't the only factor to consider when buying a used car. What else do I need to know?

With used cars, reliability is as important as price. You should do the following:

- Have the car checked out by a mechanic you trust.
- Have the car inspected by a diagnostic center. These businesses will check virtually every aspect and component of a car. They're more expensive—but more thorough—than a mechanic.
- Ask for copies of the maintenance records for the life of the car.
- From your state motor vehicle department, find out all previous owners, the mileage each time it was sold and all states (other than where you live) where the car has been registered. If this information doesn't match up or looks fishy, don't buy the car.
- Do your own visual inspection— you'll want to look for oddities that might indicate damage (such as scratches or new paint).

Also, look at the vehicle identification number (VIN) on the lower left-hand side of the front windshield. If it shows any signs of tampering, the car may be stolen. And finally, if you're buying the car from a private party (as opposed to a car dealer), make sure the person selling the car actually holds title. Ask to see the seller's driver's license (or other form of ID) and the title certificate for the vehicle.

Will a warranty protect me if I get a bad deal on a used car?

If you're buying a used car from a dealer, the dealer will probably offer you an extended warranty. Before buying, be sure you know exactly what is covered and what isn't, and for how long. You'll also need to know the type of problems the car has had in the past, and what types of problems that particular make of car is likely to have in the future. It makes no sense to buy an extended warranty that doesn't cover emissions, for example, if the type of car you're buying is likely to have emission problems in a year or so.

If you're buying a car from a private party, check to see if the car is still under a factory warranty or if the original owner purchased an extended warranty—and whether either of these warranties can be transferred to you as the new owner.

Used Car "Lemon Laws"

Arizona, California, Connecticut, Washington D.C., Florida, Hawaii, Iowa, Massachusetts, Maryland, Maine, Minnesota, New Hampshire, New Jersey, New York and Ohio have lemon laws or warranty coverage for used cars. If you're in one of these states and you buy a used car that turns out to be defective, contact your state attorney general or department of consumer affairs for the details of the law and how you can get redress under it. You can also obtain a copy of most of these laws by visiting http://www.autopedia.com.

Financing a Vehicle Purchase

If you are like most people, you don't have a large sum of cash to plunk down for a new or used car. This means you'll have to finance your

purchase. Of course, after you spend time shopping for a car and negotiating a good deal, the last thing you'll want to do is haggle over financing terms. But if you don't shop around for the best financing deal and read the finance contract carefully, you could end up paying lots more for a loan than you should.

I want to buy a car, but I'm not sure how to finance my purchase. Do you have any general advice?

Clearly, if you can pay for the purchase outright you'll save money by not paying any interest charges. But if you don't happen to have $20,000 lying around and need to borrow money to buy your new car, consider the following sources:

• *The car dealer.* Many offer generous terms—for example, interest at 1.5% or 2%—especially in the early fall when dealers are anxious to clear out stock to make room for new models. Be careful that these low-interest loans don't require you to buy upgraded features—such as air conditioning or rust protection—or credit insurance. And don't assume you are getting the best deal around. Always compare dealer terms to those of banks and credit unions.

• *Banks you do business with.* Dealer financing isn't your only option. Before you buy, contact the banks where you have your savings, checking, credit card or business accounts. Ask about the going rate for car loans. Also ask about discount rates for loans tied to your other accounts.

- *Credit unions.* If you're a member of a credit union (or are eligible to join one), be sure to investigate its car loans. Historically, credit unions have offered some of the best loan terms.

Regardless of who finances the contract, if you want a good interest rate but have a poor credit history, you'll need to either put a substantial amount down or get a cosigner.

Do You Need Credit Insurance?

Many dealers and lenders will ask you to buy credit insurance—insurance that will pay off your loan if you die or become disabled. Before you add this cost to your contract, consider whether you really need it. Remember, you can always sell the car and use the proceeds to pay off the loan. In fact, most financial experts say credit insurance is unnecessary and advise consumers not to buy it. If you do decide you want this protection, you can almost always buy this type of insurance from an outside source at a much better price.

If I borrow money for the purchase, what should the lender tell me about my loan?

If you get a car loan from a bank, credit union or car dealer, the federal Truth in Lending Act requires that the lender disclose, in writing, impor-

tant information about your loan, including:

- your right to a written itemization of the amount borrowed
- the total amount of the loan
- the monthly finance charge
- the annual percentage rate (APR)
- the number, amount and due dates of all payments, and
- whether any late payment fee or penalty may be imposed.

Insuring Your Car

Certainly those so inclined can have lots of fun imagining possible needs for insurance.

—HAYDEN CURRY

Most states require that every registered vehicle or licensed driver have some vehicle liability insurance. But even where it's not required by law, most drivers have some liability coverage. Before you buy auto insurance, you must decide how much coverage you need and what types of coverage are appropriate for you. And of course, you'll want to find ways to cut your insurance costs.

Who is usually covered under an auto insurance liability policy?

An auto insurance liability policy usually covers the following people no matter what car they are driving:

- *Named insured*—the person or people named in the policy.
- *Spouse*—a spouse not named in the policy, unless he or she does not live with the named insured.
- *Other relative*—anyone living in the household with the named insured who is related by blood, marriage or adoption, usually including a legal ward or foster child.

Auto insurance liability policies also cover anyone driving the insured vehicle with permission. Someone who steals the car is not covered.

Which vehicles are normally covered under an auto insurance liability policy?

- *Named vehicles*—an accident in a nonnamed vehicle is covered only if a named insured (see above) was driving.
- *Added vehicles*—any vehicle with which the named insured replaces the original named vehicle, and any additional vehicle the named insured acquires during the policy period (you may be required to notify the company of the new or different vehicle within 30 days after you acquire it).
- *Temporary vehicles*—any vehicle, including a rental vehicle, that substitutes for an insured vehicle that is out of use because it needs repair or service, or has been destroyed.

What kinds of damage are covered under an auto insurance liability policy?

Liability insurance covers money owed when a driver is at fault for hurting another person or damaging another car. Coverage includes medical costs for diagnosis and treatment of injuries, property damage, loss of use of damaged property, expenses incurred (such as the cost of renting a replacement vehicle), lost income and costs of defending a lawsuit.

In addition, an injured person is entitled to a certain amount of "general damages," also referred to as pain and suffering.

What is collision coverage?

Collision coverage pays for property damage to your vehicle resulting from a collision.

What is comprehensive coverage?

Comprehensive coverage pays for property damage to your vehicle resulting from anything other than a collision, such as a theft or a break-in.

What is uninsured motorist coverage?

If you have an accident with an uninsured vehicle or hit-and-run driver, the place to turn for compensation for your injuries is the uninsured motorist (UM) coverage of your own vehicle insurance policy. Normally, UM covers only bodily injury and not property damage to your vehicle. Vehicle damage would be covered by the collision coverage of your own policy.

What are the limits on my ability to collect under an uninsured motorist provision?

UM coverage usually limits your ability to collect as follows:

- If your accident involves a hit-and-run driver, you must notify the police within 24 hours of the accident.
- If your accident involves a hit-and-run driver, the driver's car must have actually hit you—being forced off the road by a driver who disappears is not sufficient.
- Your UM coverage will be reduced by any amounts you receive under other insurance coverage, such as your personal medical insurance or any applicable workers' compensation coverage.
- If you or a relative are injured by an uninsured motorist while you are in someone else's car, your UM coverage will be secondary to the UM coverage of that other car's owner.

What is no-fault automobile insurance?

Under no-fault insurance, each person's own insurance company pays for his or her medical bills and lost wages—up to certain dollar amounts —regardless of who was at fault.

About half the states have some form of no-fault law, often referred to in policies as Personal Injury Protection (PIP). The advantage of no-fault insurance is prompt payment of medical bills and lost wages without any arguments about who caused the accident. But most no-fault insurance provides extremely limited coverage:

- No-fault pays benefits for medical bills and lost income only. It provides no compensation for pain, suffering, emotional distress, inconvenience or lost opportunities.

- No-fault coverage does not pay for medical bills and lost income higher than the PIP limits of each person's policy. PIP benefits often fail to reimburse fully for medical bills and lost income.
- No-fault often does not apply to vehicle damage; those claims are paid under the liability insurance of the person at fault, or by your own collision insurance.

When No-Fault Benefits Aren't Enough

All no-fault laws permit an injured driver to file a liability claim, and lawsuit if necessary, against another driver who was at fault in an accident. The liability claim permits an injured driver to obtain compensation for medical and income losses above what the PIP benefits have paid, as well as compensation for pain, suffering and other general damages.

Whether and when you can file a liability claim for further damages against the person at fault in your accident depends on the specifics of the no-fault law in your state. In some states, you can always file a liability claim for all damages in excess of your PIP benefits. In others you must meet a monetary threshold, a serious injury threshold, or both, before you can file a liability claim.

My auto insurance rates seem to keep going up. How can I cut some of the cost?

Here are a few suggestions for ways to reduce your premiums:

- Shop around for insurance. Just because your current company once offered you the best deal doesn't mean it's still competitive.
- Increase your deductibles.
- Reduce your collision or comprehensive coverage on older cars.
- Find out what discounts are available from your company (or from a different company). Discounts are often given to people who:
  - use public transit or carpool to work
  - take a class in defensive driving (especially if you are older)
  - own a car with safety features such as airbags or anti-lock brakes
  - install anti-theft devices
  - are students with good academic records
  - have no accidents or moving violations, or
  - have multiple insurance policies with the same company—such as automobile and homeowner's insurance.
- Find out which vehicles cost more to insure. If you're looking to buy a new car, call your insurance agent and find out which cars are expensive to repair, targeted by thieves or involved in a higher rate of accidents. These vehicles all have higher insurance rates.
- Consolidate your policies. Most of the time you will pay less if all owners or drivers who live in the same household are on one policy or at least are insured with the same company.

More Information About Insuring Your Car

How to Insure Your Car, by The Merritt Editors (Merritt Publishing), is a step-by-step guide to buying the right kind of auto insurance at a price you can afford.

Your Driver's License

To a teenager, a driver's license seems magical—a ticket to freedom. For the rest of us, driver's licenses aren't much more than scraps of paper or plastic bearing bad pictures. But every now and then a question may arise about a license: Is it still good if I move to another state? What if I take a trip to a foreign country? And how do I know if I'm in danger of losing my license?

State laws governing how you can get, use and lose your driver's license vary tremendously. We can't answer every question here, but we do discuss some of the bigger issues that arise in connection with driving privileges.

Is my driver's license good in every state?

If you have a valid license from one state, you may use it in other states that you visit. But if you make a permanent move to another state, you'll have to take a trip to the local department of motor vehicles to apply for a new license. Usually, you must do this within 30 days after moving to the new state. Most states will issue your new license without requiring tests, though some may ask you to take a vision test and a written exam covering basic driving rules.

In some situations, you may be unsure as to whether you need to apply for a new license. If you make frequent business trips to another state, or even if you attend school in a state away from home, there's no need to get another driver's license. But when you set up housekeeping in the new state and pay taxes there as well, it's time to apply.

Young Drivers Who Cross State Lines

Adults who visit another state may rely on their driver's licenses, but the same may not be true for young drivers. The driving age varies significantly from state to state (from 15 to 21), and a state that makes people wait longer to drive may not honor a license from a state that issues licenses to younger folks. For example, if you are 16 and legally allowed to drive in your home state, but travel to another state where the legal age limit for driving is 17, you may not be permitted to drive in that state. A young driver who plans to drive in another state where the legal limit is above his or her age should call that state's department of motor vehicles to find out what the rules are.

If I get a ticket in another state, will it affect my license?

Forty-eight states belong either to an agreement called the "Driver's License Compact" or to the "Non-Resident Violator Compact." (The only states that don't are Michigan and Wisconsin.) When you get a ticket in one of these states, the department of motor vehicles will relay the information to your state—and the violation will affect your driving record as if the ticket had been issued in your home state.

Can I use my license in a foreign country?

Many countries, including the United States, have signed an international agreement allowing visitors to use their own licenses in other nations. Before traveling to another country, contact its consulate office or embassy to find out whether your license will be sufficient. Look in the telephone book under the name of the country. Or, visit the U.S. State Department website at http://www.travel.state.gov.

In addition, you may want to obtain an International Driver's Permit, issued by the American Automobile Association. This document translates the information on your driver's license into ten languages. Many countries require the permit, not because it meets their requirements for a license, but because it is a ready-made copy of the important information on your American license.

Finally, if you intend to stay in another country for an extended period of time, you should check with the consulate to find out whether you'll need to apply for a license in that country. Every country will have its own rules about when a "visit" turns into something more permanent.

When can my driver's license be suspended or revoked?

Driving a car is considered a privilege—and a state won't hesitate to take it away if a driver behaves irresponsibly on the road. A state may temporarily suspend your driving privileges for a number of reasons, including:

- driving under the influence of alcohol or drugs
- refusing to take a blood-alcohol test
- driving without liability insurance
- speeding
- reckless driving
- leaving the scene of an injury accident
- failing to pay a driving-related fine
- failing to answer a traffic summons, or
- failing to file an accident report.

In addition, many states use a "point" system to keep track of a driver's moving violations: Each moving violation is assigned a certain number of points. If a driver accumulates too many points within a given period of time, the department of motor vehicles suspends the license.

If you have too many serious problems as a driver, your state may take away (revoke) your license altogether. If this happens, you'll have to wait a certain period of time before you can apply for another license. Your state may deny your application if you have a poor driving record or fail to pass required tests.

Finally, a few states revoke or refuse to renew the driver's licenses of parents who owe back child support. (See Chapter 16, *Parents and Children*, for more information.)

My elderly friend is becoming unsafe at the wheel. Will her license be taken away?

The number of drivers over 65 years old has more than doubled in the last 20 years. At present, there are 13 million older drivers; by the year 2020 there will be 30 million. Studies show that, as a group, older drivers drive less than younger drivers, but they have more accidents per mile.

Elderly, unsafe drivers who continue to drive despite the advice of family and friends often do not come to the attention of the state until the inevitable—the driver is stopped for erratic driving or, worse, is involved in an accident. A few states try to screen out unsafe older drivers by requiring more frequent written tests. But the added tests are expensive and don't always identify unsafe driving habits.

All licensing departments accept information from police officers, families and physicians about a driver's abilities. If a licensing agency moves to cancel someone's license as the result of an officer's observations, an accident or the report of family members or a doctor, the driver usually has an opportunity to protest.

What will happen if I'm caught driving with a suspended or revoked license?

You'll probably be arrested. Driving with a suspended or revoked license is usually considered a crime that carries a heavy fine and possibly even jail time. At worst, it may be a felony; you'll end up in state prison or with an obligation to perform many hours of community service. The penalties will probably be heaviest if the suspension or revocation was the result of a conviction for driving under the influence of alcohol or drugs (DUI).

The Whole Truth and Nothing but the Truth

Many states will ask you specific questions regarding your health when you renew your driver's license. For example, you might receive a questionnaire that asks you whether you have ever had seizures, strokes, heart problems, dizziness, eyesight problems or other medical troubles. If you have medical problems and answer the questions truthfully, an examiner may question you further and may even deny you a license. If you don't tell the truth, you may get your license—but you're setting yourself up for big legal trouble if you are in an accident caused by one of these impairments. It's not that different from driving a car when you know the brakes are bad: If you go out on the road with defective equipment that you know about (including the driver), you greatly increase the chance that you will be held responsible if the defect causes an accident.

If You're Stopped by the Police

Most of us know the fear of being pulled over by the police. An officer may stop your car for any number of reasons, including an equipment defect (such as a burned-out headlight), expired registration tags, a moving violation or your car's resemblance to a crime suspect's car. You may also have to stop if you encounter a police roadblock or sobriety checkpoint.

What should I do if a police officer pulls me over?

Remain as calm as possible, and pull over to the side of the road as quickly and safely as you can. Roll down your window, but stay in the car—don't get out unless the officer directs you to do so. It's a good idea to turn on the interior light, turn off the engine, put your keys on the dash and place your hands on top of the steering wheel. In short, make yourself visible and do nothing that can be mistaken for a dangerous move. For example, don't reach for a purse or backpack or open the glove box unless you've asked the officer's permission, even if you are just looking for your license

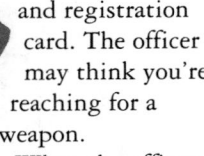

and registration card. The officer may think you're reaching for a weapon.

When the officer approaches your window, you may want to ask (with all the politeness you can muster) why you were stopped. If you are at all concerned that the person who stopped you is not actually a police officer (for example, if the car that pulled you over is unmarked), you should ask to see the officer's photo identification along with her badge. If you still have doubts, you can ask that the officer call a supervisor to the scene or you can request that you be allowed to follow the officer to a police station.

If an officer pulls me over for a traffic violation, can she search me or my car?

In most cases, no. Just because an officer has a justifiable reason for making a traffic stop—and even if she issues you a valid ticket for a traffic violation—that does not automatically give the officer authority to search you or your car. If the officer has a reasonable suspicion (based on observable facts, and not just a "hunch") that you are armed and dangerous or involved in criminal activity, then the officer can do a "pat-

down" search of you, and can search the passenger compartment of your car. The officer can also frisk any purses, bags or other objects within the car that might reasonably contain a weapon. The officer does have the authority, however, to ask you and any passengers to exit the car during a traffic stop.

If my car is towed and impounded, can the police search it?

Yes. If your car is impounded, the police are allowed to conduct a thorough search of it, including its trunk and any closed containers that they find inside. This is true even if your car was towed after you parked it illegally, or if the police recover your car after it is stolen.

The police are required, however, to follow fair and standardized procedures when they search your car, and may not stop you and impound your car simply to perform a search.

I was pulled over at a roadblock and asked to wait and answer an officer's questions. Is this legal?

Yes, as long as the police use a neutral policy when stopping cars (such as stopping all cars or stopping every third car) and minimize any inconvenience to you and the other drivers. The police can't single out your car unless they have good reason to believe that you've broken the law.

Drunk Driving

If you're caught while driving drunk or under the influence of drugs, you'll face serious legal penalties. Many states will put you in jail, even for a first offense, and almost all will impose hefty fines. If you're convicted more than once, you may also lose your driver's license.

How drunk or high does someone have to be before he can be convicted of driving under the influence?

In most states, it's illegal to drive a car while "impaired" by the effects of alcohol or drugs (including prescription drugs). This means that there must be enough alcohol or drugs in the driver's body to prevent him from thinking clearly or driving safely. Many people reach this level well before they'd be considered "drunk" or "stoned."

How can the police find out whether a driver is under the influence?

Police typically use three methods of determining whether a driver has had too much to be driving:

- *Observation.* A police officer will pull you over if he notices that you are driving erratically—swerving, speeding, failing to stop or even driving too slowly. Of course, you may have a good explanation for your driving (tiredness, for example), but an officer is unlikely to buy your story if he smells alcohol on your breath or notices slurred words or unsteady movements.

- *Sobriety tests.* If an officer suspects that you are under the influence, he will probably ask you to get out of the car and perform a series of balance and speech tests, such as standing on one leg, walking a straight line heel-to-toe or reciting a line of letters or numbers. The officer will look closely at your eyes, checking for pupil enlargement or constriction, which can be evidence of intoxication. If you fail these tests, the officer may arrest you or ask you to take a chemical test.

- *Blood-alcohol level.* The amount of alcohol in your body is understood by measuring the amount of alcohol in your blood. This measurement can be taken directly, by drawing a sample of your blood, or it can be calculated by applying a mathematical formula to the amount of alcohol in your breath or urine. Some states give you a choice of whether to take a breath, blood or urine test—others do not. If you test at or above the level of intoxication for your state (.08 to .10 percent blood-alcohol concentration, depending on the state), you are presumed to be driving under the influence unless you can convince a judge or jury that your judgment was not impaired and you were not driving dangerously. In many states, this level is even lower for young drivers. (In California, the level is .05% for drivers under 21.) Defense attorneys often question the validity of the conversion formula when driver's alcohol levels are based on breath or urine tests.

The New National Drunk Driving Standard

On October 23, 2000, President Clinton signed a new law encouraging states to pass laws that define drunk driving as having a blood alcohol concentration (BAC) of .08%. Many states currently set the level for drunk driving at .10% BAC. States have until October 1, 2003 to change their laws to meet the federal standard. Otherwise, they'll lose a portion of their federal highway funds.

Do I have to take a blood, breath or urine test if asked to do so by the police?

No, but it may be in your best interests to take the test. Many states will automatically suspend your license if you refuse to take a chemical test. And if your drunk driving case goes to trial, the prosecutor can tell the jury that you wouldn't take the test, which may lead the jury members to conclude that you refused because you were, in fact, drunk or stoned.

Am I entitled to talk to an attorney before I decide which chemical test to take?

The answer depends on where you live. In California, for example, you don't have the right to speak with an attorney first. But many other states allow you to talk to your lawyer before you take a chemical test.

If I am pulled over, does the officer have to read me my rights before he asks me how much I had to drink?

No. During a traffic stop, an officer does not have to read you your rights until you are under arrest. (See Chapter 18 for a description of Miranda rights.) Determining whether you are "under arrest" can be tricky—you can be under arrest even before a police officer says you are. But if an officer is just asking you questions at the side of the road or even if you are detained in the officer's car for a few minutes, you are probably not under arrest. Keep in mind that you don't have to answer an officer's questions, whether you are under arrest or not—and whether or not the officer has read your rights to you. Of course, sometimes it is wise to do so, as long as you don't say anything that can be used against you.

When to Get a Lawyer

Defending against a charge of drunk driving is tricky business. To fight this charge, you need someone who understands scientific and medical concepts, and can question tough witnesses, including scientists and police officers. If you want to challenge your DUI charge, you're well advised to hire an attorney who specializes in these types of cases.

Traffic Accidents

Anyone who drives or rides in a car long enough is likely to be involved in at least a minor fender-bender. Anyone who rides a bicycle or motorcycle knows the roads are even more dangerous for two-wheelers. And on our crowded streets, pedestrians, too, are often involved in accidents with buses, cars and bikes. Knowing a few laws of the road, and the best steps to take when an accident occurs, can help ease the pain of any accident that occurs—and help make any insurance claims process less painful, too.

What should I do if I'm involved in a traffic accident?

The most important thing to do is document the entire situation by taking careful notes soon after the accident. Good notes (rather than relying on your memory) will help with the claim process—and increase your chances of receiving full compensation for your injuries and damage to your vehicle.

Write things down as soon as you can: begin with what you were doing and where you were going, the people you were with, the time and the weather. Include every detail of what you saw, heard and felt. Be sure to include everything that others—those involved in the accident or witnesses—said about the accident.

Finally, make daily notes of the effects of your injuries. Always include pain, discomfort, anxiety, loss of sleep or other problems which are not as visible or serious as other injuries.

Reporting to the DMV

In many states, you must report a vehicle accident resulting in physical injury or a certain amount of property damage to the state department of motor vehicles. Check with your insurance agent or your local department of motor vehicles to find out the time limits for filing this report; you often have just a few days. Be sure to ask whether you'll need any specific form for the report.

If you must file a report, and the report asks for a statement about how the accident occurred, give only a very brief statement—and admit no responsibility for the accident. Similarly, if the official form asks what your injuries are, list every injury and not just the most serious or obvious. An insurance company may later gain access to the report, and if you have admitted some fault in it, or failed to mention an injury, you might run into some trouble explaining yourself.

What determines who is responsible for a traffic accident?

Figuring out who is at fault in a traffic accident is a matter of deciding who was careless. Each state has a set of traffic rules (which apply to automobiles, motorcycles, bicycles and pedestrians) that tell people how they are supposed to drive and provide guidelines for measuring liability.

Sometimes it is obvious that one driver violated a traffic rule which caused the accident—for example, one driver runs a stop sign and crashes into another. In other situations, whether or not there was a violation will be less obvious. A common example is a crash that occurs when drivers merge into a single lane of traffic. And at other times, neither driver violated a traffic rule, although one driver may still have been careless.

Finding Your State's Traffic Rules

The traffic rules are contained in each state's Vehicle Code. You can usually obtain a simplified version of these rules—often called the "Rules of the Road"—from the department of motor vehicles (DMV). Most DMV offices also have the complete Vehicle Code. Or, you can find the Vehicle Code in a public library, law library or the Internet. (See this book's Appendix on Legal Research for more information on how to find state laws.)

What if the cause of the accident is not clear?

It is sometimes difficult to say that one particular act caused an accident. This is especially true if what you claim the other driver did is vague or seems minor. But if you can show that the other driver made several minor driving errors or committed several minor traffic violations, you can argue

that the combination of those actions caused the accident.

Special Rules for No-Fault Policyholders

Almost half the states have some form of no-fault auto insurance, also called Personal Injury Protection. (See *Insuring Your Car*, above.)

In general, no-fault coverage eliminates injury liability claims and lawsuits in smaller accidents in exchange for direct payment by the injured person's own insurance company of medical bills and lost wages—up to certain dollar amounts—regardless of who was at fault for the accident. Usually, no-fault does not cover vehicle damage; those claims are still handled by filing a liability claim against the one who is responsible for the accident, or by looking to your own collision insurance.

Who is liable if my car is rear-ended in a crash?

The driver who hit you from behind is almost always at fault, regardless of your reason for stopping. Traffic rules require that a driver travel at a speed at which she can stop safely if a vehicle ahead stops suddenly. In rear-end accidents, the vehicle damage provides strong proof of liability. If the other car's front end and your car's rear end are both damaged, there is no doubt that you were struck from behind.

In some situations, both you and the car behind you are stopped when a third car runs into the car behind you, pushing it into the rear of your car. In that case, the driver of the third car is at fault and you should file a claim against her insurance.

Are there any other clear patterns of liability in traffic accidents?

A car making a left turn is almost always liable to a car coming straight in the other direction. According to traffic rules, a car making a left turn must wait until it can safely complete the turn before moving in front of oncoming traffic. There may be exceptions to this rule if:

- the car going straight was going too fast (this is usually difficult to prove)
- the car going straight went through a red light, or
- the left-turning car began its turn when it was safe but something unexpected happened which made it have to slow down or stop its turn.

Police Reports: Powerful Evidence

If the police responded to the scene of your accident, they probably made a written accident report (particularly if someone was injured).

Sometimes a police report will plainly state that a driver violated a specific Vehicle Code section and that the violation caused the accident. It may even indicate that the officer issued a citation. Other times, the report merely describes or briefly mentions negligent driving.

Any mention in a police report of a Vehicle Code violation or other evidence of careless driving will provide support for your claim that the other driver was at fault.

online help help online help online help

http://www.nolo.com
Nolo offers self-help information about a wide variety of legal topics, including what to do if you're in an accident.

http://www.kbb.com
Kelley Blue Book can give you the resale and wholesale values of your vehicle, as well as new car prices.

http://www.edmunds.com

Edmund's offers information about buying a new car, including reviews, comparisons, prices and strategies.

http://www.bbb.org

The Better Business Bureau offers tips on buying new and used cars, including financing suggestions.

http://www.autopedia.com

Autopedia is an encyclopedia of automotive-related information. In addition to articles on many topics, it includes links to each state's lemon law.

http://www.consumerreports.org

Consumer Reports provides articles on how to buy or lease a car and, for a small fee, a price service for both new and used cars.

http://www.nhtsa.dot.gov

The National Highway Traffic Safety Administration provides recall notices, service bulletins, defect investigations, consumer complaints and other data about vehicle problems.

http://www.leaseguide.com

Automobile Leasing: The Art of the Deal offers information about leasing a car, including frequently asked questions, an auto consumer's lease kit and tips for getting a good deal.

http://www.insure.com

The Insurance News Network provides information about choosing auto insurance, including an interactive experts forum.

http://www.dui.com

The Driver Performance Institutes provide information about driving under the influence.

http://www.motorists.org

This national organization for motorists offers lots of information on fighting traffic tickets.

Travel

11.2	*Airlines*
11.11	*Rental Cars*
11.16	*Hotels and Other Accommodations*
11.21	*Travel Agents*
11.25	*Travel Scams*

Travel is the frivolous part of serious lives, and the serious part of frivolous ones.

—MADAME SWETCHINE

Each year, Americans spend billions of dollars on traveling. And though most of us fondly recall our annual vacations—the trip to Europe after graduating from college or our children's faces the first time they visited a Disney theme park—we often share with one another the horror stories: The plane that took off

16 hours late, the rental company that charged $1,000 for returning the car with a slight scratch or the tour company that went out of business the night before the trip. The questions and answers in this chapter are designed to help your travels go more smoothly—and to let you know your rights should you encounter troubles along the way.

Airlines

The terrorist attacks on September 11, 2001, fundamentally changed airline travel. If you haven't flown since the attacks, you might be surprised to see armed national guard troops in the gate area, security guards inspecting passengers' shoes and food and people becoming irate when they learn that they must leave personal items, such as grandpa's antique pocket knife or Aunt Lucy's silver knitting needles, behind because they pose a "security risk."

Although some changes are consistent across airlines and airports because they are mandated by the federal Aviation Security Act or by the Federal Aviation Administration, other changes will depend on a number of factors, including which airline you are using, which airports you will be flying into and out of and whether your flight is domestic or international. Prudent travelers will do a little homework to find out about such things as permissible personal items, necessary identification and number and size of bags.

Of course, a lot of things haven't changed. Airlines still overbook flights and bump passengers. Ticket prices are still a confusing game of luck. And baggage still gets lost—much too often.

What personal items can I no longer bring with me in my carry-on baggage?

According to the Federal Aviation Administration, you cannot bring any of the following items onto the plane with you—either on your person or in your carry-on baggage:

- knives of any length, composition or description (including steak knives and plastic knives)
- all cutting and puncturing instruments, including pocketknives, carpet knives, box cutters, ice picks, straight razors, metal scissors and metal nail files

- corkscrews
- athletic equipment that could be used as a weapon, such as baseball/softball bats, golf clubs, pool cues, ski poles and hockey sticks
- fireworks, such as signal flares, sparklers or other explosives
- flammable liquids or solids, such as fuel, paints, lighter refills and matches
- certain dangerous household items, such as drain cleaners and solvent
- pressure containers, such as spray cans, butane fuel, scuba tanks, propane tanks, CO2 cartridges and self-inflating rafts
- weapons, such as firearms, ammunition, gunpowder, mace, tear gas or pepper spray
- dry ice, gasoline-powered tools, wet-cell batteries, camping equipment with fuel, radioactive materials (except limited quantities), poisons and infectious substances.

Some personal care items—such as perfume and aerosol hairspray—contain hazardous materials. You may take those on board with you if they total no more than 70 ounces. The contents of each container cannot exceed 16 fluid ounces.

Although "strike-anywhere" matches, lighters with flammable liquid reservoirs and lighter fluid are forbidden, you may carry ordinary matches and lighters on your person.

You may carry dry ice for packing perishables so long as it doesn't weigh more than four pounds and so long as the package is vented.

If you need to carry with you medically necessary items such as needles and syringes, you should contact the airline in advance to find out what kind of documentation (such as a prescription) you will need to get the items through security.

The best thing you can do is a careful appraisal of your items and put into checked baggage anything that looks remotely threatening—or call your airline to find out its position on the item.

Can my family still accompany me to the gate when I fly?

No. As of the printing of this book, regulations from the Federal Aviation Administration required that only passengers with proof of travel be allowed beyond security checkpoints and into the gate area. If you would like to accompany a minor or a passenger who needs extra assistance, contact your airline in advance to find out what procedures you have to follow.

How do airlines calculate fares?

The price of most airfares is determined by complicated computer programs which calculate how many passengers are likely to book seats on any given flight. But rather than fly with empty seats, an airline might offer discount fares. Ticket prices may also be affected by competition with other airlines that offer discounted prices. The result is that passengers on the same flight could be paying as many as a dozen different fares.

Benefits and Risks of E-Tickets

E-tickets aren't really tickets at all, but are reservations for air travel that are kept in the airline's computer system instead of being printed on paper. Prior to the September 11 terrorist attacks, all you needed to travel on an e-ticket was a photo ID and credit card. Although the Federal Aviation Administration still allows airlines to use e-tickets, you're going to need more than just your driver's license to get into the gate area and onto the plane. The documentation rules vary by airline, so check with your carrier before going to the airport to make sure you have what you need. Most airlines require a photo ID, credit card and e-ticket receipt or confirmation email.

If you are booked on a single airline and are flying in the United States, you will most likely have little trouble using your e-ticket. In fact, many find e-tickets to be convenient, since there's no paper ticket to keep track of or use.

E-tickets are not foolproof, however, especially if you are traveling internationally. Many countries require that you show some sort of ticket to gain access to a boarding area, and sometimes your e-ticket receipt and itinerary is not enough. In addition, some countries require that you present a roundtrip ticket at the point of entry—they want you to visit, but they don't want you to stay. If you have an e-ticket, you might have trouble convincing officials that you have booked passage out of their country. If you are traveling internationally by e-ticket, carry your itinerary and receipt with you.

On the domestic front, if your flight is canceled, your airline must first print a paper ticket before it can put you on another airline's flight. This can be time consuming. And, if your airline goes on strike, other airlines that might honor a paper ticket won't accept your e-ticket. If you have an e-ticket and an airline strike is imminent, exchange your e-ticket for a paper ticket as soon as possible.

What's all that fine print on the back of my airline ticket?

The back of all standard airline tickets has at least 11 paragraphs of fine print under the heading "Conditions of Contract." In Paragraph 3 you'll find a statement that various "applicable tariffs" and the "Carrier's Conditions of Carriage and Related Regulations" are incorporated into the contract. This means that each airline has filed with the U.S. Department of Transportation a series of statements about its obligations to its passengers and its limitations of liability. These tariffs and conditions are the terms of your contract with the airline.

The Conditions of Carriage cover everything from the number of bags you can check to the type of compensation you receive if your flight is delayed or canceled. Boarding priority, check-in requirements and most of the other fine-print terms that describe an airline's rights and responsibilities to its passengers are set forth in the Conditions of Carriage.

Conditions of Carriage vary from airline to airline. Although most airline tickets look identical, the subtle differences in the hidden terms can make a substantial difference in your rights as a passenger. You can obtain a summary of the hidden terms and conditions of most major airlines' contracts by requesting a copy of *United States Air Carriers, Conditions of Contract, Summary of Incorporated Terms (Domestic Air Transportation)* from the Air Transport Association, Distribution Center, P.O. Box 511, Annapolis, MD, 20701. Enclose a $65 check payable to ATAA. You can also call the ATAA at 800-497-3326.

Are there restrictions on my airline ticket?

Before the substantial deregulation of the airline industry in the 1980s, unused tickets were almost as good as cash—tickets could be cashed in, traded and even used on other airlines. This is still true for many full-fare, unrestricted tickets.

Most tickets, however, carry some sort of restrictions. Today, tickets usually have any or all of the following features:

- *Nontransferable*. A nontransferable ticket can be used only by the passenger whose name appears on the face of the ticket. If the names on the ID and the ticket do not match, the airline can confiscate the ticket. If a ticket is nontransferable but refundable, however, you may be able to cash in the old ticket and buy a new one with the new passenger's name.

- *Nonrefundable*. A nonrefundable ticket means you cannot get your money back if you decide not to travel. But each airline has exceptions. If you cannot make a flight for which you have a nonrefundable ticket, you may be able to apply the ticket toward a future flight or exchange it for credit toward future travel. If the fare has dropped on a flight for which you have a nonrefundable ticket, you may be able to get "re-ticketed." In either situation, you will probably have to pay a fee to make the change.

- *Penalties*. Often, there are penalties for canceling or making changes.

Do airlines offer discounted tickets or let you change a ticket if you need to travel because of death or serious illness?

In certain exceptional cases, the airlines will allow nonrefundable tickets to be refunded if you need to cancel because of the illness or death of your traveling companion or a close relative. Similarly, an airline may offer a discounted fare (sometimes minor, sometimes generous) when a close relative becomes seriously ill or dies and you need to travel without any advanced planning. Who must be ill or have died for you to obtain a "bereavement fare" varies among airlines —for example, some airlines will give a discounted fare to attend the funeral of a parent, child, sibling, spouse or in-laws only, while other airlines include nonmarital partners and their immediate family members.

What should I do if I lose my ticket?

Contact the airline immediately. You will be required to fill out a lost-ticket application. The airline will either issue a replacement ticket (after you sign an agreement to reimburse it for the cost of the replacement ticket if someone uses your lost ticket) or force you to purchase a replacement ticket at the currently available fare (often outrageously expensive because you don't get any advance purchase discounts). In addition, you usually have to pay some sort of service charge or penalty for issuing a replacement ticket.

After waiting three months to a year, the airline will issue you a refund for the price of your replacement ticket if your lost ticket was not used during that time.

Am I entitled to be compensated if the airline overbooks and I get bumped off the flight?

If a flight is overbooked, the airline is required to ask passengers to volunteer to take a later flight. Normally, the airline will offer some kind of incentive such as a free domestic or international round-trip ticket. If an insufficient number of passengers volunteer to be bumped from a flight, the airline must begin involuntary bumping. Generally, passengers with the most recent reservations or those who checked in the latest are the first to be bumped.

If you are bumped, you are entitled to compensation if you have a confirmed reservation (your ticket has an "ok" or "hk" in the Status column) and the scheduled plane has a seating capacity of more than 60 passengers. Even if you meet both of these requirements, the airline might refuse to compensate you if any of the following is true:

- You did not comply with the airline's ticketing, check-in and reconfirmation requirements.
- You are not acceptable for transportation under the airline's usual rules and practices—for example, you are drunk.
- The entire flight was canceled.
- A smaller aircraft was substituted for safety or operational reasons.
- You refuse an offer to take a seat in a different section (class) of the aircraft at no extra charge.

- The airline offers to place you on another flight or flights scheduled to reach your final destination within one hour of the scheduled arrival of the original flight.

Am I entitled to compensation if my flight is delayed, diverted or canceled?

A flight is considered on-time if it arrives at its destination within 15 minutes of the scheduled arrival time. Generally, a 15-minute delay will not affect your schedule very much. Longer delays can have serious consequences, particularly if you cannot make a connecting flight.

If your trip is delayed because of overbooking, the rules discussed in the previous question apply. If the delay is caused by any other reason, your rights depend on whether it's a domestic or international flight.

Domestic flights. Generally, airlines are not obliged to provide any compensation if the delay, diversion or cancellation was caused by factors outside of the airline's control, such as bad weather or air traffic congestion at a particular airport. On the other hand, airlines are required to compensate you for problems deemed in their control, such as mechanical difficulties or late-arriving crew members. The offered compensation can vary substantially among airlines—full-service airlines are likely to offer more generous terms, such as meals, hotels, alternate transportation or even emergency toiletries in the event of an overnight delay, while budget or no-frills airlines may offer little, if any, compensation.

International flights. Recovering damages for an international flight delay is very difficult if the delay was caused by anything other than the airline's overbooking. Under an international treaty called the Warsaw Convention, an airline can escape liability for damages caused by flight delay if it can show that it took all necessary measures to avoid the damage or that it was impossible to take such measures.

If your international flight is delayed, you may be able to persuade the airline that it should cover direct costs caused by the delay, such as meal, hotel or telephone expenses. To back up your argument, you can quote Article 19 of the Warsaw Convention which states: "The Carrier shall be liable for damages occasioned by delay in the transportation by air of passengers, baggage or goods."

Compensation for Involuntarily Bumping

(Flights Within or Leaving U.S.)

Scheduled Arrival of New Flight	Domestic Flights	International Flights (Departing From the U.S.)
New flight scheduled to arrive less than one hour after original flight	No compensation	No compensation
New flight scheduled to arrive between one and two hours after original flight	Value of ticket segment, $200 maximum	Value of ticket segment, $200 maximum
New flight scheduled to arrive more than two hours after original flight (domestic only)	Twice the value of ticket segment, $400 maximum	N/A
New flight scheduled to arrive more than four hours after original flight (international only)	N/A	Twice the value of ticket segment, $400 maximum

Compensation for Involuntarily Bumping

(Flight Departing European Union Country)

Scheduled Duration or Distance of Original Flight	Arrival at Destination	Compensation
Less than two hours or 3,500 kilometers	Within two hours of originally scheduled arrival	75 ECUs (approximately $50)
Less than two hours or 3,500 kilometers	More than two hours late	150 ECUs (approximately $100)
Over two hours or over 3,500 kilometers	Within two hours of originally scheduled arrival	150 ECUs (approximately $100)
Over two hours or over 3,500 kilometers	More than two hours late	300 ECUs (approximately $200)

Am I entitled to compensation if my baggage is lost or damaged?

The airlines' treatment of baggage is a constant source of passenger complaints. At some point, nearly every airline passenger has waited for what seemed like an eternity for his or her baggage to show up on the baggage carousel. Many passengers can identify with the old suitcase commercial which showed a gorilla jumping up and down on the passenger's bags and throwing the passenger's suitcase around a room.

To be fair, most of the time baggage does arrive, in good shape, on the same flight you were on. When your luggage is damaged, delayed or lost, however, the results can be disastrous. The best way to protect yourself from the most serious losses is to follow one simple rule: *Never* put anything valuable or irreplaceable (such as jewelry), or that you might urgently need (such as medications), in checked baggage. Your compensation will rarely cover your actual loss.

Domestic flights. An airline can limit the amount it must pay if baggage is lost, damaged or delayed to $1,250 per passenger. You can get around this limit by declaring at check-in a higher value for the baggage, up to the airline's maximum, which is likely to be between $2,500 and $5,000. If you declare a higher value, the airline will charge you a fee based on a percentage of the declared value. The airline then becomes liable up to the declared value if it loses, damages or delays delivery of the baggage, un-less the airline can prove that the actual loss was lower than the declared value.

International flights. The Warsaw Convention provides the rules under which liability for lost, delayed or damaged baggage is determined; these rules will not work to your advantage. Damages are calculated based on the weight of the baggage, regardless of the real value of the baggage or its contents. The Warsaw Convention states that the value for lost or damaged baggage is $9.07 per pound (or $20 per kilogram).

If your bag was weighed before the flight, then the value is determined by multiplying the weight of the bag times $9.07. For example, a 20-pound bag would be valued at $181.40. If your bags were not weighed, the airline will generally assume that all of your bags weighed a total of 70 pounds, and will reimburse you $634.90.

To add insult to injury, an airline can completely avoid responsibility for lost or damaged baggage if it can prove "that the damage was occasioned by error in piloting, in the handling of the aircraft or in navigation" and that, in all other respects, "the airline and its agents have taken all necessary measures to avoid the damage." It is difficult to understand why an airline should not be liable for your lost or damaged baggage if one of its pilots mishandles the airplane. On the other hand, if a pilot seriously mishandles the plane, your baggage may be the least of your concerns.

Are there any legal protections for the credits I earn in a frequent flyer program?

While frequent flyer programs can provide you with some travel bargains, understand that there are few legal protections for the credits you earn. Under the rules of almost all frequent flyer programs, the airline can change award levels, have credits expire or even cancel the whole program without warning.

Does it pay to belong to more than one frequent flyer program?

Some travelers will pay more for their tickets if they receive frequent flyer credit or will take an indirect or inconvenient flight on an airline in order to get frequent flyer credit. One way to avoid this frequent flyer trap is to join more than one program. Although you can get travel awards faster by concentrating your travel on one airline, you may get better fares and connections if you don't restrict yourself in that way. When you compare tickets, keep in mind that frequent flyer miles are worth approximately 2¢ per mile; use that figure to help calculate which option is best. The 2¢ per mile estimate was calculated by dividing the average cost of a domestic round trip ticket (approximately $500) by the number of frequent flyer miles needed for such a ticket (25,000 miles).

Can I trade or sell my frequent flyer awards?

You can use your frequent flyer awards or give them to anyone you choose, but you cannot sell or trade them. Despite this clear limitation, frequent flyer awards are often bartered. Many of the deeply discounted tickets advertised in newspapers are actually tickets obtained by agents using purchased frequent flyer awards. Because airlines require you to present a photo ID when you check in and are traveling on a ticket obtained through a frequent flyer program, it is difficult to use these purchased coupons.

I have a ticket on an airline that seems headed for bankruptcy. What can I do?

When an airline goes bankrupt, you technically become one of the airline's creditors in bankruptcy. If you file a claim in the bankruptcy court, there is a chance you will recover some very small percentage of the value of the ticket, but more likely you will recover nothing at all.

In the past, most airlines would honor a bankrupt airline's ticket and allow you on a substitute flight. But these days, given the competitive nature of the airline industry, this is rarely done. Sometimes, as a gesture of good will (and a way of luring new customers), an airline will offer a special discounted fare for passengers holding tickets on a bankrupt airline. If you have a ticket on a bankrupt airline and are a frequent flyer on another airline, try to negotiate free or discounted travel using the bankrupt airline's ticket. Trip cancellation or trip interruption insurance can sometimes cover the cost of a replacement ticket.

If you have an e-ticket, run fast to the nearest ticket counter for your airline and exchange it for a paper ticket. Any airline nice enough to accept passengers from a bankrupt airline will accept only those passengers with paper tickets.

Rental Cars

A TOURIST IS A FELLOW WHO TRAVELS THOUSANDS OF MILES SO HE CAN BE PHOTOGRAPHED STANDING IN FRONT OF HIS CAR.

—EMILE GANEST

Whether on business or vacation, you may need to rent a car for at least part of your trip. This section outlines some of your basic rights as a renter. Most laws related to rental cars were enacted by state legislatures or derived from cases interpreting those state laws.

Do I have any recourse if the rental car company doesn't provide me with the type of car I reserved?

If you have guaranteed payment and the company does not have the car you reserved available for you, the company must do everything it can to find you a different car from its fleet. Theoretically, the company must find you a car from another rental car company if it has no suitable substitute, but in practice this rarely happens. If the alternate car found for you is more expensive, you should not have to pay the difference.

If you haven't put down a deposit or guarantee, the company is still required to have a car available. But rental car companies often overbook to cover no-shows, which means that the class of car you reserved won't be available. The rental car company will usually provide you with a larger, more expensive car and tell you it is giving you a "free upgrade." Most renters are happy to accept the upgrade to a larger, more expensive car. If you accept a smaller, cheaper car than the one you reserved, the rental company is obliged to charge you the lower rate. If you refuse to accept a substitute car, you will probably have difficulty getting compensation afterward—you had a duty to reduce your damages by accepting a car that was a reasonable substitute for the car you reserved.

What if the company fails to provide any car at all?

A company's overbooking may mean that no cars are available when you arrive. Your only real alternatives may be to find a substitute rental car at a different company or to take a taxi and seek reimbursement from the original car rental company. In addition, the rental car company may offer you future discounts.

My son was told he couldn't rent a car because he's only 20. Is that legal?

Yes. Most major companies refuse to rent a car to someone who is under 21, or in some cases 25, unless that person is an employee using a corporate account or is military personnel traveling on orders. Companies that do rent to people as young as 21 usually charge an additional fee for drivers between 21 and 24.

This discrimination is not illegal. Rental car companies can do business with whomever they choose, as long as they do not discriminate based on race, religion, national origin, sex or other categories protected under civil rights laws.

Do I need a credit card to rent a car?

Most rental car companies require a major credit card as a way to secure a deposit from you at the time of rental, although you can use the card or cash when you actually pay for the car. The company will check your credit limit and "freeze" an amount slightly greater than your estimated rental charges against your card, meaning that this amount is not available for you to charge. This freeze can last for several days after you return the car, even once the actual amount is charged or you pay with cash.

If you don't have a credit card, you can get a prepaid voucher through your travel agent by paying for the rental car first at the travel agency and bringing the voucher to the rental counter. The voucher may not cover taxes, surcharges, additional drivers, upgrades and other charges, so be sure to find out exactly what is included with the voucher before you pick up the car. Many companies require you to present a credit card or provide some other form of deposit even if you are using a voucher, so call ahead to find out.

Can a rental car company charge a penalty if I don't show up or if I cancel my reservation?

Nearly all rental car companies charge penalties for four-wheel drives, minivans, convertibles and other specialty rentals if you fail to cancel a reservation in advance or are a no-show. Some companies are testing similar policies on their standard rental cars.

Can a rental car company screen me based on my driving record?

Yes, and many companies now screen drivers when they rent in vacation-popular destinations such as Arizona, California, Florida, Nevada, New York, Virginia and Washington, DC. Sales agents conduct screening checks by entering your license number into a computer program that calls up your driver's record as reported by your state department of motor vehicles. If your record doesn't meet the screening criteria of the rental company, the agent will refuse to rent you a car.

Instead of screening you, some rental car companies may require you to sign a statement that you have an acceptable driving record. This shifts the responsibility for providing accurate information away from the company and to you. If you have an accident and signed a statement that turns out to be incorrect, the rental car company could use it against you by claiming that you acted in violation of the rental agreement.

Screening Standards

Generally, a rental car company that screens drivers will deny you a vehicle if, during the past 36-month period, you:

- were caught driving with a suspended or invalid license
- had one instance of drunk driving, hit-and-run, driving a stolen car or other serious offense
- had three moving violations, or
- were at fault in two accidents.

The standards adopted by each rental car company vary and are subject to change, so you need to inquire about the specific rental screening standards of any company you are considering using.

If your driving record is questionable, do the following:

- Call your motor vehicle department to see if your state makes driver records available. If it doesn't, then relax and don't worry about being screened.
- If your state makes driver records available, when you call to reserve a rental car, ask if the company screens driving records and whether it maintains a nationwide blacklist.
- Get your driver record evaluated by a screening company. Several companies evaluate driving records to determine in advance whether drivers will be disqualified from renting. TML Information Services, the leading evaluator of vehicle records for rental car companies, operates a program for drivers from states that make driver record data available online. For around $11 (less for AAA members), you can get an evaluation of your driving record against the criteria for screening risky drivers used by six major rental car companies. You can reach TML on the Web at http://web2.tml.com or by phone at 800-743-7891.
- If you don't want to pay for an evaluation, get a copy of your driving record from the motor vehicle agency in your state (allow plenty of time), obtain the screening criteria of the rental car companies you are considering and make an evaluation on your own.
- If you are traveling for business, rent from a company that has a liability agreement with your employer—the screening company may overlook items that would otherwise disqualify you.

Finally, if you are disqualified by a screening system, have someone you are traveling with rent the car and do the driving.

How do rental car companies establish rental rates?

Car rental fees are set by each company and vary depending on the location of the rental office, time period the car will be rented, season, car model, special promotions or vacation packages, and your eligibility for discounts. In addition, because many rental car companies have franchises, the rates and policies of the central office may vary substantially from those of a local office. There is nothing illegal about these multiple prices, and there is nothing to stop you from asking about special fares when you rent or for a reduction after the rental if you learn that a better rate was available but was not offered to you. Although the company is not obligated to offer you the lower price, it may do so to maintain good customer relations.

Can the rental car company tack on other fees?

Yes, but the company must tell you about the fees before you rent. Here are the most common fees you're likely to encounter:

- *Mileage charges.* While many companies offer unlimited mileage, mileage charge policies change frequently, and you should ask each time you rent.
- *Fees for renting at an airport.* Renting at an airport may be more expensive than renting at an urban or suburban location because airports and local governments often add surcharges and taxes to rental car rates.
- *Additional driver fees.* Most rental car companies charge extra for anyone who drives the car other than the person who signs the rental agreement. Often, additional driver charges are waived for your spouse, immediate family member or business associate.
- *Young driver fees.* As indicated above, many rental car companies add a daily surcharge for any driver aged 21 to 24.
- *Child safety seat fees.* All states require children under a certain age to be placed in child car seats. If you don't bring your own seat, you will be required to rent one, usually at a cost of $3-$5 per day or $25 per week. You may be charged more for one-way rentals, and you may be required to make an extra deposit for the seat if you are paying cash for the car rental.
- *Vehicle drop-off fees.* Many rental car companies charge high rates for dropping off a car at a location other

than where you rented, unless the drop-off location is within the same metropolitan area as where you picked up the vehicle. Charges for picking up the car in one city and dropping it off in another can be as high as $1,000.

- *Refueling charges.* Most companies require you to return the rental car with a full tank of gas. If you can't or you forget, you'll be forced to pay the company's inflated price per gallon.

Do I have to take the rental car insurance offered to me?

No, and chances are you shouldn't. Each year, travelers in the U.S. spend more than $1 billion on rental car insurance, much of it unneeded or unwanted. A few states, including California, Texas and Indiana, require rental car companies to inform you that the rental car insurance may duplicate your personal automobile policy. But still, rental car insurance options are complex, confusing and rife with potential rip-offs.

When faced with a rental car insurance policy, adopt this basic strategy:
- determine what coverage you already have through your automobile insurance or credit cards— many gold cards issued by Visa and MasterCard provide rental car insurance coverage; American Express offers coverage as well
- find out what insurance options the rental car company offers, and
- don't fall prey to hardball sales tactics—buy only what you need.

What is loss damage waiver? Is it insurance?

Loss damage waiver, or LDW (also known as collision damage waiver, or CDW), has gotten substantial press in recent years due primarily to its high cost and to complaints by consumers of pressure from rental car companies to purchase unnecessary LDW.

Rental car companies claim that they are not selling insurance, and that LDW is simply a waiver of the company's right to collect from you if the rental car is damaged or stolen while under your control. In most rental contracts, the rental company shifts all responsibility for collision damage or other loss to you; the effect of purchasing LDW is to shift responsibility back to the rental car company. But three aspects of LDW make its value suspect:
- the high pressure or deceptive sales tactics used to sell LDW
- the high price for LDW—especially when you may already be protected by your own insurance or credit card, and
- the number of exclusions (loopholes) in LDW coverage that allow the company to charge you even if you purchased LDW to protect yourself.

Should You Purchase Loss Damage Waiver?

Purchasing loss damage waiver (LDW) may be a prudent choice for you if:
- You're in a foreign country and your auto insurance or credit card coverage

does not include foreign rentals.
- You have no personal car insurance and do not want to rely on credit card coverage alone.
- Your personal auto insurance is insufficient to cover a rental vehicle.
- You can't afford to carry any credit charges until the credit card company reimburses you.
- Your rental car isn't covered under your insurance or your credit card coverage (this may be the case if you rent an antique or exotic car).

What should I know before I rent a car in a foreign country?

Although the laws governing car rentals differ in every country, here are some general rules.

First, most countries will accept your valid state driver's license with another form of photo ID. Some countries may also require an International Driver's Permit (available through AAA offices). Check with an AAA travel office before you travel. You don't need to take a test to get an International Driver's Permit; all it does is explain (in a number of languages) the type of license you have, any limitations that apply and when it will expire.

Second, your personal automobile insurance policy may have restrictions or limitations on driving in foreign countries. Check your coverage, including the terms of your credit card policy, before you rent in a foreign country.

Third, in some countries, the police will take your license if you are in-

volved in an accident or stopped for a moving violation, and will not return it until you have paid any applicable fine. Get receipts for all payments you make, and report any mistreatment or apparent scams to the American embassy or consulate in that country.

Fourth, certain European countries track traffic violations with street cameras that photograph cars at intersections. The police trace the drivers using the license plate number of the car and request payment from the rental car company for the ticket. The rental car company is within its rights to collect the fine from you, even if the company is informed of the violation after you have returned and paid for the car.

Hotels and Other Accommodations

When you travel, you have the choice of many different types of accommodations: hotels, motels, inns, bed and breakfasts, rental houses and other lodging. With some minor variations, the laws governing most types of accommodations are similar. To simplify matters, we use the term "hotel" to cover all types of accommodations. In addition, the following information only applies to hotels in the United States unless we indicate otherwise.

Must a hotel provide me with a room, assuming there's a vacancy?

Generally, yes. The most basic legal principal concerning hotels is the "duty to receive." Created hundreds of years ago under the common law of England, the duty to receive required hotel keepers to accept and take care of any traveler who presented himself as a paying customer, as long as the inn had room. Although this basic duty to receive has been modified somewhat by state laws, it is still the basis for many of the fundamental obligations that a hotel has to its guests.

A hotel can say "no" only if it reasonably believes that you will:

• not pay for your room
• injure or annoy other guests, or
• physically damage or otherwise harm the hotel (including giving it a bad reputation).

If you arrive drunk and disorderly, threaten another guest or appear to want to use the room for prostitution, you'll probably be turned away.

Must a hotel honor my prepaid or guaranteed reservation?

A prepaid or guaranteed reservation is one where you give the hotel a credit card number and the hotel promises to have a room for you no matter when you show up, even if it's midnight or 3:00 a.m. If you have a guaranteed reservation and the hotel does not hold a room for you, the hotel has breached a contract and must do everything it can to find you a room—even if that means sending you to another hotel. If you guaranteed your reservation with a credit or debit card, the hotel may be required under the terms of its agreement with the card issuer to:

• pay for your first night's stay at an alternate hotel
• provide free transportation to the alternate hotel
• pay for a three-minute phone call to let your family or office know where you'll be staying, and
• forward all incoming calls to your new hotel.

Be sure to request these services. In all cases, if your alternate lodging is more expensive, the hotel should pay the difference.

Is a guaranteed reservation the same as a confirmed reservation?

If you have not paid for the reservation in advance or guaranteed it, but have received a "confirmed reservation" from the hotel, the hotel must keep a room for you unless you haven't met the conditions of the reservation. For example, it is common for a hotel to say, "We will hold the room for you until 6:00 p.m." or, "We will hold the room for you if we receive a written confirmation and deposit" by a certain date. If you do not fulfill these obligations, then the hotel does not have to hold the room for you. If you do meet your obligations and the hotel doesn't have a room for you, it must do its best to find you comparable lodging.

Do I have the right to a particular room?

Generally, no. A hotel manager can put you anywhere or move you from one room to another, as long as it is not done in a discriminatory way. The only exception is if you've reserved a certain room, like the honeymoon suite for your honeymoon.

If it's crucial for you to have a particular room, make sure the hotel management knows in advance and that you receive written confirmation for your reservation of that particular room. If the room you reserved is occupied by other guests, the management may, but is not obligated to, move those guests to another room. (A hotel can satisfy its obligation to you simply by providing a room comparable to the one you reserved.) If the room is uninhabitable (say, a water pipe breaks), then the hotel is excused from providing that particular room.

Do I have a right to privacy in my room?

If you are using your room in a normal way, not engaging in illegal acts or disturbing other guests, then you have a limited right of privacy in your room. But if the hotel management believes that you are carrying out illegal activities (such as dealing drugs), it is entitled to enter and search your room, even without your permission. The hotel management cannot, however, authorize the police to search your room without your permission or a search warrant.

The hotel management also has the right to enter your room to clean or perform needed maintenance, or if necessary, to stop you from disturbing other guests (for example, if you are playing the television very loudly) or destroying hotel property.

It is generally considered a violation of your privacy if the hotel tells an outside person the number of your room. The hotel can tell an inquirer whether you are a guest at the hotel and can connect any caller to your room. If you wish to maintain complete privacy, you must make it clear to the management that you are not to be contacted by anyone and that no one is to be told whether or not you are staying at the hotel.

Why do hotel room rates vary so much?

There is no set formula for determining what amount a hotel can charge, although rates must be "reasonable." Many states require hotels to post the maximum charge for a room in a conspicuous place in each room (usually on the back of the door). Although the hotel may not charge more than this maximum rate (often referred to as the "rack rate"), it certainly may rent the room for less.

Always check your hotel bill to see whether it matches the rate you were quoted when you reserved the room. Frequently, additional charges will be tacked on. Some, such as visitor fees or "bed taxes," may be mandated by local or state law and are probably legitimate.

Other fees, such as service charges or telephone charges, may not be legitimate. A hotel cannot legally charge you more than the rate it quoted to you when you made your reservation, unless you approve the charges in advance. Many states have laws requiring that all additional charges be posted or approved in writing by guests.

Ask About Discount Rates

When you reserve a hotel room, you may be able to get a reduced price simply by asking about discounts available to the following people:

- corporate employees—many hotels have negotiated rates with large corporations that are 10%-30% lower than their standard rates and these rates are generally available to anyone who asks for them (although an occasional desk clerk will ask for a business card or other ID)
- seniors
- families with children
- AAA members
- members of certain professional associations (like the American Medical Association or American Bar Association)
- guests paying with certain credit cards
- members of frequent flyer or frequent guest programs, or
- federal and state government employees.

I paid a lot for a room that fell way short of my expectations. Is there anything I can do?

Sometimes you may find yourself in a hotel room that looks nothing like the one described to you or pictured in an advertisement or brochure. If the advertisement or description was intentionally deceptive, the hotel may be guilty of fraud. The law generally allows a limited amount of exaggeration or "puffing" in advertisements, but it does not allow intentional deception. When you find yourself in such a situation, your best bet is to talk to the manager immediately—he may be able to reduce your room charge or move you to a better room. If the problem is with the entire hotel, however (for example, it's in a very dangerous neighborhood), you're better off requesting a refund and finding other accommodations.

If your hotel room is unclean or unsanitary, report it to the manager and the housekeeping department immediately. If they are unable to clean your room to your satisfaction, request a new room or a refund. Should you end up in a serious dispute over the cleanliness of a room, the health

and safety codes for the city or state where the hotel is located may provide the best support for your argument. Report any serious violation to local health authorities, not only to bolster your claims, but as a service to future guests. Take photographs of the offending conditions if you can.

I fell and hurt myself on a hotel's premises. Do I have any recourse against the hotel?

A hotel may be liable if you slip or trip and fall on the hotel premises—for example, on spilled food or drink in a hotel bar or restaurant, on snow and ice that has not been cleared from a walkway, or on moist tile floors or other slick surfaces. You might also be hurt because of a design or building flaw (such as steps that are too steep) or the hotel's failing to light an area properly.

Does a hotel have any special obligation to protect its guests around the swimming pool?

Because swimming pools create a potentially dangerous situation, hotels must be especially vigilant in designing, maintaining and controlling access to them. Disclaimers such as "swim at your own risk" are unlikely to protect a hotel from liability if it didn't use sufficient care to protect its guests, such as failing to install a fence around a pool. This is true even if you are drunk. Most courts require hotels to anticipate that children, inebriated guests and others might find their ways into the pool if safeguards don't keep them out.

Is the hotel responsible if I am the victim of a crime at or near the hotel?

A hotel cannot be held liable for crimes committed on or near the hotel unless it should have anticipated the crime (for example, the hotel is in a very high crime area) and could have prevented it, either by providing sufficient warnings or taking better security measures. In such situations, the hotel's general duty to warn you about dangerous conditions may extend to a duty to warn about crime in or around the hotel. Furthermore, the hotel's actions—such as failure to install proper locks on windows and doors, provide adequate lighting in parking areas or take adequate measures to ensure that passkeys are not used by criminals—may make the hotel at least partially liable.

Is the hotel responsible if my belongings are stolen?

Traditionally, hotels were liable for virtually all loss or theft of a guest's property. Today, however, most states limit a hotel's liability if it takes certain steps to protect your belongings. For cash, jewelry and other valuables, a hotel is required to provide a safe. Most states require the hotel to tell you that the safe is available, that the hotel has limited liability for valuables left in the safe and that the hotel may have no liability if you do not place valuables in the safe.

The limitation of liability also includes a limitation for clothing and other personal goods you bring to the hotel. While you are not required to check expensive suits or mink stoles at the front desk as valuables, clothing and expensive luggage often exceed the amount of the hotel's maximum liability.

Generally, these limited liability laws were passed to protect hotels from forces beyond their control, such as fire or theft. If the hotel fails to use reasonable care to protect your valuables (for example, it leaves the safe unlocked), it will probably be liable for the full value of your loss.

Is the hotel liable if my car is damaged, broken into or stolen?

Traditionally, hotels were strictly liable for protecting your means of transportation. This meant caring for your horses, saddles, tack and the rest. These days, hotels are required to use reasonable care to protect your car. Many state laws set a monetary limit for loss or damage to a vehicle or its contents. But even in these states, negligence by the hotel—including the valet—could make the hotel liable for damage it should have foreseen.

Whether the contents of a car parked at a hotel are the hotel's responsibility is not clear. They do not fall into the traditional categories of

goods within the hotel or transportation. The hotel is most likely to be liable when you pay for parking, a valet or other employee takes your car, retains the keys and is informed of the value of the contents of the car.

What if I don't check out when I say I will?

In most states, renting a hotel room gives you what is called a "revocable license" to use the room. This right is much more limited than the rights a tenant has when renting an apartment. Formal eviction proceedings don't have to be brought if you overstay your welcome. The hotel can simply change the lock (easy to do today because hotels often use preprogrammed entry cards, not keys) and pack up your items.

Travel Agents

One of the most common disruptions of marital bliss is the choice of where to spend a vacation. What this country needs is an ocean in the mountains.

—PAUL SWEENEY

At some point you're likely to rely on a travel agent—someone authorized to sell travel services to the public—to help you make decisions about where, when and how to travel. A travel agent's legal responsibilities vary depending on the role the agent plays in helping with your plans.

Does a travel agent work for me or for the travel industry?

A travel agent generally owes his highest duty to a travel supplier, such as an airline or tour operator, not you. This is because the travel supplier and the travel agent have an ongoing relationship—the agent represents the supplier and is compensated for providing business to the supplier.

You may feel that a travel agent should be "your" agent and should look out for your best interests, rather than the interests of travel suppliers. A good agent will take on this role, knowing that good customer service will lead to repeat business. In addition, the law is changing in this area, and sometimes a travel agent may be considered your agent as well. In most cases, however, the travel agent will owe you the normal duty owed by a salesperson to a customer, but no more.

Does a travel agent have any special responsibility when making a reservation for me?

If a travel agent fails to make a reservation for you—or delays in making a reservation for you—and you lose money because of it, the agent is responsible to you if the failure to make the reservation or the delay was his fault. For example, if the flight you want to take has seats available when you call your agent, but the agent delays in making your reservation, the flight sells out and you have to take a more expensive flight, the agent would be liable to you for the difference. On the other hand, if the flight was already sold out when you called the agent, the agent is not liable because his inability to make a reservation is not his fault.

When making a reservation, a travel agent must do his best to match the reservation to your specific requirements and limitations. If your travel agent makes the wrong reservation and you have a ticket on a plane destined for somewhere you don't want to go, the agent is probably responsible for paying the additional cost of getting you to your proper destination. If the agent books you into the wrong hotel or reserves the wrong type of rental car, he should compensate you for the difference between the value you would have received had the agent made the reservation properly and what you did receive as a result of the agent's mistake.

Is a travel agent responsible for confirming my reservation?

Generally, no. You must confirm your own reservations.

However, if your travel agent uses a tour operator or wholesaler who in turn makes your reservations, the agent probably has an obligation to verify your reservations with the various travel suppliers independently. The travel agent should not assume that a tour operator or wholesaler is reliable. Be sure to check with your travel agent about who is responsible for confirming your reservations.

My travel agent charged me the wrong amount for my ticket. What should I do?

If you overpay because of a travel agent's mistake, the travel agent must reimburse you for the difference between the amount you paid and the actual fare. You must consider the proper fare at the time you reserved and paid for your ticket, not when a subsequent fare change was made.

If a travel agent charges you less than the actual cost of your ticket, you are not entitled to travel for less than the established fare. The travel supplier may require you to pay the additional amount due before you travel. Whether you can recover the difference from your travel agent depends on the circumstances. If you knew the correct price and agreed to it, and the travel agent simply hit the wrong key on the computer, you are not entitled to any compensation from the travel agent. On the other hand, if you didn't know the correct price and made your decision based upon what the agent told you, then you probably can recoup the difference if your reliance on the travel agent's statement was reasonable. (If you were told that a $999 flight was $799, your reliance would probably be reasonable. If, however, you were told that a $999 flight was $9.99, you'd be out of luck.)

Is a travel agent responsible for researching airlines, hotels and other suppliers?

Travel agents do not have to thoroughly investigate suppliers. In general, they are required only to stay current with reasonably available information, such as what is in trade journals and magazines. The most important types of information are often the supplier's reputation, track record and financial condition. A travel agent must provide this type of information, as well as any specific experience that the travel agent has had with that supplier, if it would likely affect your decision to use the supplier.

If a travel agent books you on a flight that has already been canceled or in a hotel that has not been built, you have a fairly strong argument that the agent was negligent and failed to undertake a basic investigation. If, however, a tour operator suddenly goes out of business or a hotel closes between the time you make your reservation and the time you arrive, the agent's responsibility is less clear.

Must a travel agent warn me of any travel risks?

If a travel agent knows of a substantial risk to you, such as an airline that is bankrupt but continuing to fly, the travel agent has an obligation to warn you of that risk, with the following limitations:

- A travel agent does not have to warn you about risks that are obvious and apparent, such as the risk that the car you rent from "Rent-a-Wreck" may not be in the best condition.
- A travel agent is not required to be a fortune teller, particularly concerning factors out of the agent's control. An agent might be liable for promoting a "sun and fun" vacation in India during monsoon season, but the agent does not have a duty to warn you about all possible conditions—such as unannounced strikes, political conditions or bad weather—that could affect your enjoyment of the journey.
- A travel agent does not have to point out disclaimers or other legal elements of an agreement between you and the travel supplier, although a helpful travel agent might do so.

How are travel agents paid?

When a travel agent issues a ticket or makes other travel arrangements for you, he generally receives a commission from the travel supplier. This commission may range from 7% to 15% of the price you pay, but it is usually about 10%.

Do any professional associations regulate travel agents?

No. Travel agents have to meet very few formal requirements. Most travel agents do belong to one or more professional associations, however, and each association has a code of ethics that requires its members to remain knowledgeable of developments within the travel industry and to refrain from engaging in misleading sales practices. Membership in a professional association is voluntary, however, and if an agent violates the code of ethics, you have little recourse within the association.

If you have a complaint about a travel agent, ask someone in his office if he belongs to a professional association. If he does, contact the association as follows:

American Society of Travel Agents (ASTA)
1101 King Street, Suite 200
Alexandria, VA 22314
703-739-2782
703-684-8319 (fax)
http://www.astanet.com

International Airlines Travel Agent Network (IATAN)
300 Garden City Plaza, Suite 342
Garden City, NY 11530
516-663-6000
516-747-4462 (fax)
http://www.iatan.org

Institute of Certified Travel Agents (ICTA)
148 Linden Street
Wellesley, MA 02482
800-542-4282
800-FAX-ICTA
http://www.icta.com

The association can tell you if the agent is a member in good standing. In some cases, an association may be able to help you if you have a complaint against one of their members. For example, ASTA has a mediation program to help resolve disputes between travel agents and their clients.

Travel Scams

Each year, fraud costs American consumers over $100 billion. One out of every seven cases of fraud involves travel, with most travel scams being carried out over the telephone or by mail. Travel fraud knows no socioeconomic boundaries—scam artists ply their wares in every travel market. This section describes some common travel scams to help you avoid becoming part of these grim statistics.

Are there any general rules to follow to avoid being the victim of a travel scam?

As with most things in life, if the offer sounds too good to be true, it probably is. That being said, here are some signs to watch out for:

- The solicitation says that you were "specially selected" or "awarded" a trip or prize, but you haven't entered any contest.
- You must make a payment to collect your prize.
- The salesperson uses high pressure sales tactics or insists on an immediate decision.
- You must disclose your income, Social Security number, bank account number or other private information.
- The company offers great bargains, but refuses to put the details in writing unless you pay first.
- The salesperson makes vague references to "all major airlines" or "all major hotels," without saying which ones you will use.

- You must wait more than 60 days before taking the trip or receiving the prize. (Most scam victims pay for their "prize" on their credit card; scam artists know that you must dispute any credit card charge within 60 days. If they force you to wait more than 60 days, you can't challenge the charge.)
- The caller asks for your credit card number over the phone.
- The company requests a direct bank deposit or certified check, or offers to send a courier to your home to pick up your check.
- The deal cannot be booked through a travel agent.
- You must call a 900 number.
- The company cannot provide the names of references, or the references you call repeat nearly verbatim the claims of the travel provider.

Use a Credit Card Whenever Possible

Although using a credit card is not a surefire way to protect yourself, if you act quickly, you can dispute the charge and avoid paying for a scam. The Fair Credit Billing Act gives you 60 days from the date you receive your bill—not the date of your travel—to contest a charge. Some credit cards offer more extended coverage; a few even give members up to a year to contest a charge.

Some kids at my daughter's college lost money when they signed up for a trip that was canceled at the last minute. How can my daughter avoid becoming the next victim?

Many fly-by-night travel operations pitch specifically to students through telemarketing and other hard-sell tactics, hoping to take advantage of inexperienced travelers on a tight budget who are looking to save money.

Students should find out whether the tour company meets the standards set by the Council on Standards for International Educational Travel (CSIET). To qualify, tour operators must submit a review signed by an independent certified public accountant as well as extensive documentation concerning government regulations for student exchanges, promotions and student insurance.

The *Advisory List of International Educational Travel and Exchange Programs*, an annually updated booklet listing companies that meet the standards, is available from CSIET by writing to 212 S. Henry Street, Alexandria, VA 22314. The booklet costs $17.50 (Virginia residents must also pay a 4.5% sales tax) for orders placed within the United States, and $22.50 for orders placed overseas. Call 703-739-9050 for more information or log onto the organization's website at http://www.csiet.org.

We just returned from Hawaii, where we were constantly solicited to buy a timeshare. Are these deals as good as they sound?

Probably not. An estimated 94% of all timeshare owners never intended to buy in the first place; they are swept away by high pressure sales pitches and cleverly disguised promotions.

The idea behind a timeshare is simple: For a one-time price plus an annual maintenance fee, you can buy the right to use a given vacation property for a certain amount of time (typically one week) each year. What you may not be told is the extent to which the annual maintenance fee will increase over time—one timeshare owner in Hawaii saw her annual maintenance fees climb 76% in six years. Timeshare operators also may force owners to pay unexpected "special assessment fees," sometimes as high as $1,000. While a timeshare has the potential to be a satisfactory arrangement, it often yields a variety of pitfalls and frustrations for the unwary purchaser.

A Typical Timeshare Sales Pitch

A new camera, a half-price parasail ride, a free day's rental car, a free gourmet meal—you name it, timeshare salespeople have offered it. Many timeshare developers lure tourists to sales presentations by selling tours and activities at highly discounted prices, but provide only vague disclosure of what is required to qualify for the discount deal.

In the usual scenario, the catch for the gift is that you must sit through a presentation about a timeshare vacation property. The presentations vary, but most include high-pressure sales pitches that drone on for hours and leave visitors desperate to get out. Timeshare salespeople frequently go over the advertised time allotted for their presentation and are not responsive if you complain. They sometimes refuse to give the promised gift or discount if you don't buy. Although it may be illegal to not give you the gift or discount, few consumers complain—they just want out.

I've been told that I shouldn't buy a timeshare because it will be hard to sell it later. Is this true?

Very likely, yes. Timeshare owners face a couple of traps when they try to sell. The first hurdle is the lack of a strong resale market. Although statistics vary, all studies show that there are many more timeshare owners wanting to sell than there are buyers.

Another problem is the likelihood that you will lose money on the sale of a timeshare. The original price of a timeshare may have included premiums of up to 40% to cover sales costs. As a result, a resale will yield as little as 60% of the original purchase price—plus you will have to pay a commission to the broker (often as high as 20%) who sells the property for you.

Is it possible to get out of a timeshare after signing a contract?

Maybe. Nearly 30 states have "cooling-off" laws; these let you get out of a timeshare contract if you act within a few days after signing (three to ten, depending on the state). If there is no cooling-off period, or you change your mind after the time has passed, your only recourse may be a formal lawsuit. Timeshare sellers are accustomed to handling claims from unhappy buyers and are unlikely to refund your money unless forced to do so.

Suing a Timeshare Operator

There are several types of claims you might bring against a slippery timeshare seller. The first, breach of contract, involves promises explicitly made and set forth in the sales agreements. If the size, location, condition or some other important fact about the timeshare is materially different from what you agreed to in the sales contract, you may have a basis for claiming breach of the contract. But beware: These contracts are carefully drawn up by the timeshare sellers' attorneys and are likely to cover almost any contingency—scrutinize carefully before signing.

You may also bring claims based on tactics used and promises made before you agreed to purchase your timeshare. These claims may be covered under state laws prohibiting unfair business practices or those designed to prevent fraudulent inducement. In both cases, the idea is that the seller used unfair sales tactics or lies to get you to buy the timeshare. You will have to show:

- what the seller said or did
- why it was misleading
- that you wouldn't have bought the timeshare if the seller hadn't used the misleading tactics or promises, and
- that you suffered some monetary loss because of the purchase.

Timeshare sales contracts usually include clauses that disclaim any promises made during the sales pitch. The contract you sign will ask you to agree that you are making the purchase only on the basis of the representations in that contract. Prospective purchasers who notice differences between what is in the contract and what was promised by the salesperson are likely to be told that the contract is only "legal jargon." This is *not* true. If a timeshare salesperson will not put a promise in writing, don't go through with the sale. You will be forced to argue afterwards that you relied on that promise, even though you signed a contract that explicitly says you did not rely on any promises.

If you are the victim of a timeshare scam, you can ask for two things. First, you can ask to rescind the contract. You would get your money back, and the seller would regain title to the timeshare. If the seller (or court) refuses this, you must prove monetary damages, the largest of which is the difference between the amount you paid for the timeshare and its actual value. As you can imagine, it can be quite difficult to determine the actual value of a timeshare, although the amount you could obtain by reselling it is one possible indicator.

I received a vacation certificate in the mail. How can I figure out if it's legitimate?

First, review the tips at the beginning of this section. Then, if you note any of the following on a travel certificate, treat it with maximum skepticism and send it to the recycling bin:

- words such as "Certificate of Guarantee" and a spread-winged eagle or other prominent symbol designed to convey a sense of legitimacy
- a variety of possible vacation destinations, with no designated dates or price
- exciting descriptions of what you will do, such as "gala cruise," "glittering casino action," "moonlight dancing" or "resort accommodations," with no designated company names
- a phrase in the fine print indicating you were chosen "using credit and

purchasing criteria to select individuals interested in the many benefits of travel," or

- fine print language stating that the receipt of one portion of the offer (for example, the airline ticket) is dependent on purchase of something else (such as hotel accommodations).

How can I find out if a cheap airfare offered by a charter airline is legitimate?

Although many charter companies provide legitimate low-cost travel options, their reliability is far from uniform. Over the past few years, many charter operations have collapsed, leaving consumers in the lurch—and some that are still in business pose financial risks for current customers.

The Department of Transportation (DOT) regulates the manner in which charter operators must handle consumer funds. Among other things, the regulations require charter operators to post a bond or deposit consumer funds in an escrow account. Nonetheless, charter operators have found ways to shirk the rules; they may fail to deposit passenger funds into escrow accounts or divert funds that have already been deposited.

DOT regulations require sellers of charter flights to file a prospectus with the DOT, explaining how their business is organized. To find out whether a low-fare carrier has at least done this, call DOT's Consumer Affairs Office at 202-366-2220 and ask for the carrier's prospectus number.

Where to Report a Travel Scam

If you are the victim of any kind of travel scam, contact one or more of the following agencies or associations:

STATE AND LOCAL GOVERNMENT AGENCIES

State consumer protection office. Call directory assistance in your state capital and ask for the number for your state attorney general, and the division or department of consumer affairs or consumer protection.
Local prosecutor. Call the nearest district attorney or state attorney's office and ask whether there is a consumer fraud division.
State licensing board. Some states are starting to license travel providers. Ask your state attorney general if travel providers are licensed in your state.

FEDERAL GOVERNMENT AGENCIES

Federal Trade Commission. One mission of the FTC is consumer protection. Although the agency generally does not involve itself in individual disputes, your complaint, comment, or inquiry can help the agency spot a pattern of law violations that requires action. Your input can also help the agency recognize and tell people about larger trends affecting consumers. You can file a complaint with the FTC by writing to FTC, CRC-240, Washington, D.C. 20580; by calling 202-326-2222; or by completing a complaint form online at http://www.ftc.gov/ftc/consumer.htm. The FTC also has a number of guides and resources that might assist you.

Federal Communications Commission. If you were defrauded by a telemarketer or phone solicitor, or sucked in when a travel service provider aired a fraudulent ad on radio or television, contact the FCC, 445 12th St. SW, Washington, DC 20554, 202-225-5322, http://www.fcc.gov.

U.S. Department of Justice, Criminal Division, Fraud Section. The Fraud Section directs the federal law enforcement effort against fraud and white collar crime. You can reach the Fraud Section by phone at 202-514-7023, by fax at 202-514-7021 or online at http://www.usdoj.gov/criminal/fraud.html.

U.S. Department of Transportation. If you have a consumer concern or complaint regarding air services, you can contact the U.S. Department of Transportation's Aviation Consumer Protection Division at U.S. Department of Transportation, Room 4107, C-75, Washington, DC 20590; 202-366-2220; http://www.dot.gov/airconsumer.

U.S. Postal Service. If you were cheated by anyone who used the U.S. mail, file a complaint with the U.S. Postal Inspection Service. To do so, contact your local inspector's office or complete a complaint form online at http://www.framed.usps.com/postalinspectors.

PRIVATE ORGANIZATIONS

National Fraud Information Center. NFIC can help you file a complaint with the appropriate federal agency, give you tips on how to avoid becoming the victim of a scam or send you consumer publications. You can reach NFIC as follows: 800-876-7060 (voice), 202-835-0767 (fax), 202-347-3189 (electronic bulletin board), 202-737-5084 (TTD) or http://www.fraud.org. Or you can write to NFIC, c/o National Consumer's League, 1701 K Street, NW, Suite 1201, Washington, DC 20006.

American Society of Travel Agents (ASTA). If you have a complaint concerning an ASTA member, contact ASTA, 1101 King Street, Alexandria, VA 22314, 703-739-2782, 703-684-8319 (fax), http://www.astanet.com. You can also request a free copy of *Avoiding Travel Problems.*

United States Tour Operators Association (USTOA). If you have a complaint concerning a USTOA member or a question about USTOA's consumer protection plan, contact USTOA, 342 Madison Avenue, Suite 1522, New York, NY 10173, 212-549-6599, 212-599-6744 (fax), http://www.ustoa.com.

Better Business Bureau (BBB). You can provide a public service to other travelers by filing a complaint with all offices of the BBB where the scammer operates. In addition, the National Council of Better Business Bureaus operates a nationwide system for settling consumer disputes through mediation and arbitration. So, if you can find the company, you might be able to get some recourse through a BBB. Check http://www.bbb.org.

How can I tell whether a deeply discounted airfare is legitimate?

Deceptive airline advertising is so frequent that you may have already learned to read between the lines and scan the fine print to get the real picture. If you are not so savvy, watch out for the following:

- Deceptive two-for-one offers. The airline promises two tickets for the price of one, but then requires you to buy a ticket in a class that costs the same, if not more, than two tickets at some other published fare.
- Misleading discounts. Some airfare promotions advertise drastic price reductions in airfares without specifying the base fare from which the discounts are calculated. Furthermore, airlines usually advertise ticket prices at half their true cost. The fine print explains that the fare is "each way, based on round-trip purchase," despite the fact that you cannot buy a one-way ticket at the price shown.

- Phantom "sale" seats. The classic airline bait-and-switch tactic is to promote low airfares for a given route and then fail to disclose the strict limitations on the availability of seats. The airline may try to sell you a higher-priced seat or may offer a reasonable number of low-fare seats for the first few days of the promotion, and then retract the seats for the duration of the ad campaign.
- Frequent flyer deceptions. Airlines continue to severely limit the number of seats that they allocate to frequent flyers, especially for business and first class seats. As a result, frequent flyer customers may have a difficult time getting the seats they've earned.

More Information About Your Rights as a Traveler

Trouble-Free Travel ... and What to Do When Things Go Wrong, by Attorneys Stephen Colwell and Ann Shulman (Nolo), helps you anticipate and avoid hassles while traveling, and shows you how to deal with airlines, tour operators, rental car companies, hotels and other travel providers should problems arise.

http://www.nolo.com

Nolo offers self-help information about a wide variety of legal topics, including travel law.

http://www.dot.gov

The U.S. Department of Transportation offers information and tips for resolving travel problems.

http://www.travelocity.com

Travelocity can help you plan your entire trip, from finding the cheapest airfare to choosing your activities.

http://www.bbb.org

The Better Business Bureau provides information on resolving disputes through mediation and arbitration.

http://www.air-transport.org

The Air Transport Association of America allows you to order most major airlines' conditions of contract, the hidden terms of your ticket.

http://travel.state.gov

The Bureau of Consular Affairs provides extensive information on travelers' security, applying for a passport, foreign countries' entry requirements, international adoptions and how U.S. consulates can help you overseas.

http://www.cdc.gov/travel

The Centers for Disease Control and Prevention offers travel information on health risks in foreign countries and appropriate precautions to take.

http://www.faa.gov

The Federal Aviation Administration provides information and tips on air travel, including a fact sheet called Fly Smart.

http://www.sath.org

The Society for the Advancement of Travel for the Handicapped offers information to assist disabled people preparing to take a trip.

http://www.customs.ustreas.gov

The U.S. Customs Service provides publications including guides for returning U.S. residents and import restrictions.

Wills and Estate Planning

12.2	Wills
12.8	Probate
12.9	Executors
12.13	Avoiding Probate
12.15	Living Trusts
12.18	Estate and Gift Taxes
12.22	Funeral Planning and Other Final Arrangements
12.25	Body and Organ Donations

It's not that I'm afraid to die. I just don't want to be there when it happens.

—WOODY ALLEN

The first thing that comes to many people's minds when they think of estate planning is property: Who gets what you own when you die? But estate planning encompasses much more—for example, minimizing probate court costs and estate taxes, deciding who will care for your minor children if you can't, appointing people to handle your medical and financial affairs if necessary, and expressing your wishes regarding memorial services and burial. While none of us relish the thought of thinking about these things, taking some time to do so now can save your loved ones a great deal of money, pain and confusion later on.

This chapter answers often-asked questions about estate planning, from basic wills to organ donation. Along the way we consider probate and the many ways to avoid it, methods for eliminating or reducing death taxes, and funeral planning. For information about arranging for someone to make your medical and financial decisions should you become unable to handle them yourself, see the next chapter, *Living Wills and Powers of Attorney.*

Wills

Though most Americans are aware that they need a will, the majority—about 70% of us—don't have one. There are lots of reasons we put off making our wills, from fear of lawyers' fees to fear of death. But writing a will doesn't have to be expensive, or even terribly complicated. And once it's done, you can rest a little easier, knowing that your wishes are known and will be followed after your death.

What happens if I die without a will?

If you don't make a will or use some other legal method to transfer your property when you die, state law will determine what happens to your property. (This process is called "intestate succession.") Your property will be distributed to your spouse and children or, if you have neither, to other relatives according to a statutory formula. If no relatives can be found to inherit your property, it will go into your state's coffers. Also, in the absence of a will, a court will determine who will care for your young children and their property if the other parent is unavailable or unfit.

Do I need a lawyer to make my will?

Probably not. Making a will rarely involves complicated legal rules, and most people can draft their own will with the aid of a good self-help book or software program. If you know what you own and whom you care about, and you have a good clear, plain-English resource to guide you, you should be fine.

But you shouldn't approach the task of will drafting absolutely determined not to consult a lawyer. If you have questions that aren't answered by the resource you're relying on, a lawyer's services are warranted. Even so, you don't have to turn over the whole project; you can simply ask your questions and then finish making your own will.

For example, you may want to consult a lawyer if:

- You have questions about your will or other options for leaving your property.
- You expect to leave a very large amount of assets—over $1 million—that will be subject to estate taxes unless you engage in tax planning. (But first look at a good self-help resource that discusses tax-saving strategies.)
- You own a small business and have questions as to the rights of surviving owners or your ownership share.
- You must make arrangements for long-term care of a beneficiary—for example, a disabled child.
- You fear someone will contest your will on grounds of fraud, or claim that you were unduly influenced or weren't of sound mind when you signed it.
- You wish to leave no property, or very little property, to your spouse. It's usually not possible to do this unless you live in a community property state where your spouse already owns half of most assets acquired after marriage. (See *Can I disinherit relatives I don't like?*, below.) But a lawyer can explain exactly what your spouse is entitled to claim from your estate.

Also, some people simply feel more comfortable having a lawyer review their will, even though their situation has no apparent legal complications.

I don't have much property. Can't I just make a handwritten will?

Handwritten wills, called "holographic" wills, are legal in about 25 states. To be valid, a holographic will must be written, dated and signed in the handwriting of the person making the will. Some states allow will writers to use a fill-in-the-blanks form if the rest of the will is handwritten and the will is properly dated and signed.

If you have very little property, and you want to make just a few specific bequests, a holographic will is better than nothing if it's valid in your state. But generally, we don't recommend them. Unlike regular wills, holographic wills are not usually witnessed, so if your will goes before a probate court, the court may be unusually strict when examining it to be sure it's legitimate. It's better to take a little extra time to write a will that will easily pass muster when the time comes.

Making Your Will Legal

Any adult of sound mind is entitled to make a will. (And if you're reading this book, you're of sound mind.) Beyond that, there are just a few technical requirements:

- The will must be typewritten or computer generated (unless it is a valid handwritten will, as discussed above).
- The document must expressly state that it's your will.

- You must date and sign the will.
- The will must be signed by at least two, or in some states three, witnesses. They must watch you sign the will, though they don't need to read it. Your witnesses must be people who won't inherit anything under the will.

You don't have to have your will notarized. In many states, though, if you and your witnesses sign an affidavit (sworn statement) before a notary public, you can help simplify the court procedures required to prove the validity of the will after you die.

Do I need to file my will with a court or in public records somewhere?

No. A will doesn't need to be recorded or filed with any government agency, although it can be in a few states. Just keep your will in a safe, accessible place and be sure the person in charge of winding up your affairs (your executor) knows where it is.

Can I use my will to name somebody to care for my young children, in case my spouse and I both die suddenly?

Yes. If both parents of a child die while the child is still a minor, another adult—called a "personal guardian"—must step in. You and the child's other parent can use your wills to nominate someone to fill this position. To avert conflicts, you should each name the same person. If a guardian is needed, a judge will appoint your nominee unless the judge concludes that it is not in the best interest of your children.

The personal guardian will be responsible for raising your children until they become legal adults. Of course, you should have complete confidence in the person you nominate, and you should be certain that your nominee is willing to accept the responsibility of raising your children should the need actually arise.

I'm raising a child on my own. Do I have to name the other biological parent as personal guardian, or can I name someone who I think will do a better job?

If one parent dies, the other usually takes responsibility for raising the child. But if you and the other parent have parted ways, you may feel strongly that he or she shouldn't have custody if something happens to you. A judge will grant custody to someone else only if the surviving parent:
- has legally abandoned the child by not providing for or visiting the child for an extended period, or
- is clearly unfit as a parent.

In most cases, it is difficult to prove that a parent is unfit, absent serious problems such as chronic drug or alcohol use, mental illness or a history of child abuse.

If you honestly believe the other parent is incapable of caring for your child properly, or simply won't assume the responsibility, you should write a letter explaining why and attach it to your will. The judge will take it into account, and may appoint the person you choose as guardian instead of the other parent.

How to Leave Property to Young Children

Except for property of little value, the law requires that an adult manage property inherited by children until they turn 18. You can use your will to name someone to manage property inherited by minors, thus avoiding the need for a more complicated court-appointed guardianship. There are many ways to structure a property management arrangement. Here are four of the simplest and most useful:

Name a custodian under the Uniform Transfers to Minors Act

The Uniform Transfers to Minors Act (UTMA) is a law that has been adopted in every state except South Carolina and Vermont. Under the UTMA, you can choose someone, called a custodian, to manage property you are leaving to a child. If you die when the child is under the age set by your state's law—18 in a few states, 21 in most, 25 in several others—the custodian will step in to manage the property. An UTMA custodianship must end by the age specified by your state's law (18, 21 or up to 25). At that time, your child receives what's left of the trust property outright. If, however, you want to extend property management beyond the age set by your state, you may want to use one of the next three methods.

Set up a trust for each child

You can use your will to name someone (called a trustee) who will handle any property the child inherits until the child reaches the age you specify. When the child reaches the age you specified, the trustee ends the trust and gives whatever is left of the trust property to the child.

Set up a pot trust for your children

If you have more than one child, you may want to set up just one trust for all of them. This arrangement is usually called a pot trust. In your will, you establish the trust and appoint a trustee. The trustee doesn't have to spend the same amount on each child; instead, the trustee decides what each child needs, and spends money accordingly. When the youngest child reaches a certain age, usually 18, the trust ends. At that time, any property left in the trust will be distributed as you direct in the trust document.

Name a property guardian

If you wish, you can simply use your will to name a property guardian for your child. Then, if at your death your child needs the guardian, the court will appoint the person you chose. The property guardian will manage whatever property the child inherits, from you or others, if there's no other mechanism (a trust, for example) to handle it.

Can I disinherit relatives I don't like?

It depends on whom you want to disinherit. If it's anyone other than your spouse or child, the rule is very simple: Don't mention that person in your will, and he or she won't receive any of your property. Rules for spouses and children are somewhat more complex.

Spouses. It is not usually possible to disinherit your spouse completely. If you live in a community property state (Arizona, California, Idaho, Louisiana, Nevada, New Mexico, Texas, Washington or Wisconsin), your spouse automatically owns half of all the property and earnings (with a few exceptions) acquired by either of you during your marriage. You can, however, leave your half of the community property, and your separate property (generally considered to be all property you owned before marriage or received via gift or inheritance during marriage), to anyone you choose.

In all other states, there is no rule that property acquired during marriage is owned by both spouses. To protect spouses from being disinherited, these states give your spouse a legal right to claim a portion of your estate, no matter what your will provides. But keep in mind that these provisions kick in only if your spouse challenges your will. If your will leaves your spouse less than the statutory share and he or she doesn't object, the document will be honored as written.

If you don't plan to leave at least half of your property to your spouse in your will and have not provided for him or her generously outside your will, you should consult a lawyer—unless your spouse willingly consents in writing to your plan.

Children. Generally, it's legal to disinherit a child. Some states, however, protect minor children against the loss of a family residence. For example, the Florida Constitution prohibits the head of a family from leaving his residence to anyone other than a spouse if he is survived by a spouse or minor child.

Most states have laws—called "pretermitted heir" statutes—to protect children of any age from being accidentally disinherited. If a child is neither named in your will or specifically disinherited, these laws assume that you accidentally forgot to include that child. In many states, these laws apply only to children born after you made your will, but in a few states they apply to any child not mentioned in your will. The overlooked child has a right to the same share of your estate as he or she would have received if you'd left no will. The share usually depends on whether you leave a spouse and on how many other children you have, but it is likely to be a significant percentage of your property. In some states, these laws apply not only to your children, but also to any of your grandchildren by a child who has died.

To avoid any legal battles after your death, if you decide to disinherit a child, or the child of a deceased child, expressly state this in your will. And if you have a new child after you've made your will, remember to make a new will to include, or specifically disinherit, that child.

What happens to my will when I die?

After you die, your executor (the person you appointed in your will) is responsible for seeing that your wishes are carried out as directed by your will. The executor may hire an attorney to help wind up your affairs, especially if probate court proceedings are required. Probate and executors are discussed in more detail in the next three sets of questions.

Make Your Will and Records Accessible

Your executor's first task is to locate your will, and you can help by keeping the original in a fairly obvious place. Here are some suggestions:

• Store your will in an envelope on

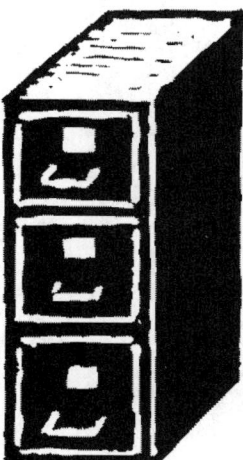

which you have typed your name and the word "Will."
• Place the envelope in a fireproof metal box, file cabinet or home safe. An alternative is to place the original in a safe deposit box. But before

doing that, learn the bank's policy about access to the box after your death. If, for instance, the safe deposit box is in your name alone, the box can probably be opened only by a person authorized by a court, and then only in the presence of a bank employee. An inventory may even be required if any person enters the box or for state tax purposes. All of this takes time, and in the meantime, your document will be locked away from those who need access to it.

Finally, wherever you choose to keep your will, make sure your executor (and at least one other person you trust) knows where to find it.

What if someone challenges my will after I die?

Very few wills are ever challenged in court. When they are, it's usually by a close relative who feels somehow cheated out of his or her rightful share of the deceased person's property.

Generally speaking, only spouses are legally entitled to a share of your property. Your children aren't entitled to anything unless you unintentionally overlooked them in your will. (See *Can I disinherit relatives I don't like?,* above.)

To get an entire will thrown out as invalid, someone must go to court and prove that it suffers from a fatal flaw: the signature was forged, you weren't of sound mind when you made the will or you were unduly influenced by someone.

More Information About Wills

Quicken Lawyer Personal (Nolo) (software), lets you create a valid will and many other important estate planning documents.

The Quick & Legal Will Book, by Denis Clifford (Nolo), contains forms and instructions for creating a basic will.

Nolo's Simple Will Book, by Denis Clifford (Nolo), contains a detailed discussion of wills and all the forms you need to create one.

Probate

THERE IS ONLY ONE WAY YOU CAN

BEAT A LAWYER IN A DEATH CASE.

THAT IS TO DIE WITH NOTHING.

THEN YOU CAN'T GET A LAWYER

WITHIN TEN MILES OF YOUR HOUSE.

—WILL ROGERS

When a person dies, someone must step in to wind up the deceased person's affairs. Bills must be paid, property must be accounted for and items must be passed on to the people chosen by the deceased person. If state law requires that all this be handled through court proceedings, the process can take many months.

What is probate?

Probate is a legal process that includes:

- proving in court that a deceased person's will is valid (usually a routine matter)
- identifying and inventorying the deceased person's property
- having the property appraised
- paying debts and taxes, and
- distributing the remaining property as the will directs.

Typically, probate involves paperwork and court appearances by lawyers, who are paid from estate property that would otherwise go to the people who inherit the deceased person's property. Property left by the will cannot be distributed to beneficiaries until the process is complete.

Probate rarely benefits your beneficiaries, and it certainly costs them money and time. Probate makes sense only if your estate will have complicated problems, such as many debts that can't easily be paid from the property you leave.

Property That Avoids Probate

Not all property has to go through probate. Most states allow a certain amount of property to pass free of probate, or through a simplified probate procedure. In California, for example, you can pass up to $100,000 of property without probate, and there's a simple transfer procedure for any property left to a surviving spouse.

In addition, property that passes outside of your will—say, through joint tenancy or a living trust—is not subject to probate. For a discussion of the most popular probate-avoidance methods, see *Avoiding Probate*, below.

Who is responsible for handling probate?

In most circumstances, the executor named in the will takes this job. If there isn't any will, or if the will maker fails to name an executor, the probate court names someone (called an administrator) to handle the process—most often the closest capable relative, or the person who inherits the bulk of the deceased person's assets.

If no formal probate proceeding is necessary, the court does not appoint an estate administrator. Instead, a close relative or friend serves as an informal estate representative. Normally, families and friends choose this person, and it is not uncommon for several people to share the responsibilities of paying debts, filing a final income tax return and distributing property to the people who are supposed to get it.

Executors

An executor is the person you name in your will to handle your property after death. The executor must be prepared to carry out a long list of tasks, prudently and promptly.

How do I choose an executor?

The most important factor in naming an executor is trust. The person you choose should be honest, with good organizational skills and the ability to keep track of details. If possible, name someone who lives nearby and who is familiar with your financial matters; that will make it easier to do chores like collecting mail and locating important records and papers.

Many people select someone who will inherit a substantial amount of their property. This makes sense, because a person with an interest in how your property is distributed is likely to do a conscientious job of managing your affairs after your death. He or she may also come equipped with knowledge of where your records are kept and an understanding of why you want your property left as you have directed.

Whomever you select, make sure the person is willing to do the job. Discuss the position with the person you've chosen before you make your will.

Are there restrictions on whom I may choose as my executor?

Your state may impose some restrictions on who can act as executor. You can't name a minor, a convicted felon or someone who is not a U.S. citizen. Most states allow you to name someone who lives in another state, but some require that out-of-state executors be a relative or a primary beneficiary under your will. Some states also require that nonresident executors obtain a bond (an insurance policy that protects your beneficiaries in the event of the executor's wrongful use of your estate's property) or an in-state resident to act as the executor's representative. These complexities underscore the benefits of naming someone who lives nearby. If you feel strongly about naming an executor who lives out of state, be sure to familiarize yourself with your state's rules.

Is it difficult to serve as executor?

Serving as an executor can be a tedious job, but it doesn't require special financial or legal knowledge. Common sense, conscientiousness and honesty are the main requirements. An executor who needs help can hire lawyers, accountants or other experts and pay them from the assets of the deceased person's estate.

Essentially, the executor's job is to protect the deceased person's property until all debts and taxes have been paid, and see that what's left is transferred to the people who are entitled to it. The law does not require an executor to be a legal or financial expert or to display more than reasonable prudence and judgment, but it does require the highest degree of honesty, impartiality and diligence. This is called a "fiduciary duty"—the duty to

act with scrupulous good faith and candor on behalf of someone else.

Does the person named in a will as executor have to serve?

No. When it comes time, an executor can accept or decline this responsibility. And someone who agrees to serve can resign at any time. That's why many wills name an alternate executor, who takes over if necessary. If no one is available, the court will appoint someone to step in.

Does the executor get paid?

Obviously, the main reason for serving as an executor is to honor the deceased person's request. But the executor is also entitled to payment. The exact amount is regulated by state law and is affected by factors such as the value of the deceased person's property and what the probate court decides is reasonable under the circumstances. Commonly, close relatives and close friends (especially those who are inheriting a substantial amount anyway) don't charge the estate for their services.

Is a lawyer necessary?

Not always. An executor should definitely consider handling the paperwork without a lawyer if he or she is the main beneficiary, the deceased person's property consists of common kinds of assets (house, bank accounts, insurance), the will seems straightforward and good self-help materials are at hand. Essentially, shepherding a case through probate court requires shuffling a lot of papers. In the vast majority of cases, there are no disputes that require a decision by a judge. So the executor may never see the inside of a courtroom, but will certainly become familiar with the court clerk's office. The executor may even be able to do everything by mail. Doing a good job requires persistence and attention to tedious detail, but not necessarily a law degree.

If, however, the estate has many types of property, significant tax liability or potential disputes among inheritors, an executor may want some help.

There are two ways for an executor to get help from a lawyer:

- Hire a lawyer to act as a "coach," answering legal questions as they come up. The lawyer might also do some research, look over documents before the executor files them or prepare an estate tax return.
- Turn the probate over to the lawyer. If the executor just doesn't want to deal with the probate process, a lawyer can do everything. The lawyer will be paid out of the estate. In most states, lawyers charge by the hour ($150–$200 is common) or charge a lump sum. But in a few places, including Arkansas, California, Delaware, Hawaii, Iowa, Missouri, Montana and Wyoming, state law authorizes the lawyer to take a certain percentage of the gross value of the deceased person's estate unless the executor makes a written agreement calling for less. An executor can probably find a competent lawyer who will agree to a lower fee.

If an executor doesn't want to hire a lawyer, is there any other way to get help?

Lawyers aren't the only source of information and assistance. Here are some others:

- *The court*. Probate court clerks will probably answer basic questions about court procedure, but they staunchly avoid saying anything that could possibly be construed as "legal advice." Some courts, however, have lawyers on staff who look over probate documents; they may point out errors in the papers and explain how to fix them.
- *Other professionals*. For certain tasks, an executor may be better off hiring an accountant or appraiser than a lawyer. For example, a CPA may be a big help on some estate tax matters.
- *Paralegals*. In many law offices, lawyers delegate all the probate paperwork to paralegals (nonlawyers who have training or experience in preparing legal documents). Now, in some areas of the country, experienced paralegals have set up shop to help people directly with probate paperwork. These paralegals don't offer legal advice; they just prepare documents as the executor instructs them, and file them with the court. To find a probate paralegal, an executor can look in the Yellow Pages under "Typing Services," "Legal Document Preparers," or "Attorney Services." The executor should hire someone only if that person has substantial experience in this field and provides references that check out.

An Executor's Duties

Executors have a number of duties, depending on the complexity of the deceased person's estate. Typically, an executor must:

Decide whether or not probate court proceedings are needed. If the deceased person's property is worth less than a certain amount (it depends on state law), formal probate may not be required.

Figure out who inherits property. If the deceased person left a will, the executor will read it to determine who gets what. If there's no will, the administrator will have to look at state law (called "intestate succession" statutes) to find out who the deceased person's heirs are.

Decide whether or not it's legally permissible to transfer certain items immediately to the people named to inherit them, even if probate is required for other property.

If probate is required, file the will (if any) and all required legal papers in the local probate court.

Find the deceased person's assets and manage them during the probate process, which may take up to a year. This may involve deciding whether to sell real estate or securities owned by the deceased person.

Handle day-to-day details, such as terminating leases and credit cards, and notifying banks and government agencies—such as Social Security, the post office, Medicare and the Department of Veterans Affairs—of the death.

Set up an estate bank account to hold money that is owed to the deceased person—for example, paychecks or stock dividends.

Pay continuing expenses—for example, mortgage payments, utility bills and homeowner's insurance premiums.

Pay debts. As part of this process, the executor must officially notify creditors of the probate proceeding, following the procedure set out by state law.

Pay taxes. A final income tax return must be filed, covering the period from the beginning of the tax year to the date of death. State and federal estate tax returns may also be required, depending on how much property the deceased person owned at death and to whom the property was left.

Supervise the distribution of the deceased person's property to the people or organizations named in the will.

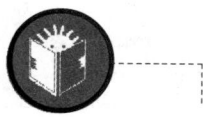

*More Information
About Executors and Probate*

The Executor's Handbook, by Theodore E. Hughes and David Klein (Facts On File), is a general but useful guide to an executor's duties. It's not a how-to book, but it discusses many aspects of the executor's job, including funerals, wills, the probate court process, simplified procedures for small estates and managing assets.

Social Security, Medicare and Government Pensions, by Joseph Matthews (Nolo), explains how to make claims for survivors benefits from the Social Security Administration, Federal Civil Service and the Veterans Administration.

How to Probate an Estate in California, by Julia Nissley (Nolo), leads you through the California probate process step by step. It contains tear-out copies of all necessary court forms, and instructions for filling them out. Although the forms are used only in California, the book contains much information that would be valuable background in any state.

Avoiding Probate

Because probate is time-consuming, expensive and usually unnecessary, many people plan in advance to avoid it. There are a number of ways to pass property to your inheritors without probate. Some of these probate-avoidance methods are quite simple to set up; others take more time and effort.

Should I plan to avoid probate?

Whether to spend your time and effort planning to avoid probate depends on a number of factors, most notably your age, your health and your wealth. If you're young and in good health, a simple will may be all you need—adopting a complex probate avoidance plan now may mean you'll have to redo it as your life situation changes. And if you have very little property, you might not want to spend your time planning to avoid probate. Your property may even fall under your state's probate exemption; most states have laws that allow a certain amount of property to pass free of probate, or through a simplified probate procedure.

But if you're older (say, over 50), in ill health or own a significant amount of property, you'll probably want to do some planning to avoid probate.

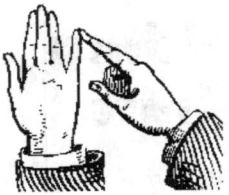

How to Avoid Probate

No one probate-avoidance method is right for all people. Which methods, if any, you should use depends on your personal and financial situation. Here are some common techniques to consider:

Pay-on-death designations

Designating a pay-on-death beneficiary is a simple way to avoid probate for bank accounts, government bonds, individual retirement accounts and, in most states, stocks and other securities. In a few states, you can even transfer your car through such an arrangement. All you need to do is name someone to inherit the property at your death. You retain complete control of your property when you are alive, and you can change the beneficiary if you choose. When you die, the property is transferred to the person you named, free of probate.

Joint tenancy

Joint tenancy is a form of shared ownership where the surviving owner(s) automatically inherits the share of the owner who dies. Joint tenancy is often a good choice for couples who purchase property together and want the survivor to inherit. (Many states also have a very similar type of ownership, called "ten-ancy by the entirety," just for married couples.) Adding another owner to property you already own, however, can create problems. The new co-owner can sell or borrow against his or her share. Also, there are negative tax consequences of giving appreciated property to a joint tenant shortly before death.

A living trust

A revocable living trust is a popular probate-avoidance device. You create the trust by preparing and signing a trust document. Once the trust is created, you can hold property in trust, without giving up any control over the trust property. When you die, the trust property can be distributed directly to the beneficiaries you named in the trust document, without the blessing of the probate court. Living trusts are discussed in more detail in the next set of questions.

Insurance

If you buy life insurance, you can designate a specific beneficiary in your policy. The proceeds of the policy won't go through probate unless you name your own estate as the beneficiary.

Gifts

Anything you give away during your life doesn't have to go through probate. Making nontaxable gifts (up to $11,000 per recipient per year, or to a tax-exempt entity) can also reduce eventual federal estate taxes. So if you can afford it, a gift-giving program can save on both probate costs and estate taxes.

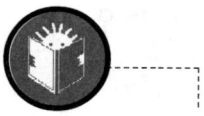

More Information
About Avoiding Probate

8 Ways to Avoid Probate, by Mary Randolph (Nolo), explains eight simple and inexpensive methods of sparing your family the hassle and expense of probate after your death.

Plan Your Estate, by Denis Clifford and Cora Jordan (Nolo), offers an in-depth discussion of almost all aspects of estate planning, including probate avoidance.

Living Trusts

If you're considering setting up a living trust to avoid probate, there's no shortage of advice out there—much of it contradictory. Personal finance columnists, lawyers, your Uncle Harry—everybody's got an opinion.

Whether or not a living trust is right for you depends on exactly what you want to accomplish and how much paperwork you're willing to put up with. Living trusts work wonderfully for many people, but not everyone needs one.

What is a living trust?

A trust is an arrangement under which one person, called the trustee, holds legal title to property on behalf of another. You can be the trustee of your own living trust, keeping full control over all property held in trust.

There are many kinds of trusts. A "living trust" (also called an "inter vivos" trust by lawyers who can't give up Latin) is simply a trust you create while you're alive, rather than one that is created at your death under the terms of your will.

All living trusts are designed to avoid probate. Some also help you save on death taxes, and others let you set up long-term property management.

Why do I need a living trust?

If you don't take steps to avoid probate, after your death your property will probably have to detour through probate court before it reaches the people you want to inherit it. In a nutshell, probate is the court-supervised process of paying your debts and distributing your property to the people who inherit it. (For more information see *Probate* and *Executors*, above.)

The average probate drags on for months before the inheritors get anything. And by that time, there's less for them to get: In many cases, about 5% of the property has been eaten up by lawyer and court fees. The exact amount depends on state law and the rates of the lawyer hired by the executor.

Don't Forget Your Will!

Even if you make a living trust, you still need a will. Here's why:

A will is an essential back-up device for property that you don't transfer to your living trust. For example, if you acquire property shortly before you die, you may not think to transfer ownership of it to your trust—which means that it won't pass under the terms of the trust document. But in your back-up will, you can include a clause that names someone to get any property that you don't leave to a particular person or entity.

If you don't have a will, any property that isn't transferred by your living trust or other probate-avoidance device (such as joint tenancy) will go to your closest relatives in an order determined by state law. These laws may not distribute property in the way you would have chosen.

How does a living trust avoid probate?

Property held in a living trust before your death doesn't go through probate. The successor trustee—the person you appointed to handle the trust after your death—simply transfers ownership to the beneficiaries you named in the trust. In many cases, the whole process takes only a few weeks, and there are no lawyer or court fees to pay. When the property has all been transferred to the beneficiaries, the living trust ceases to exist.

Is it expensive to create a living trust?

The expense of a living trust comes up front. Lawyers have figured out that they can charge high fees—much higher than for wills, documents usually of comparable complexity—for living trusts. They commonly charge upwards of $1,000 to draw up a simple trust. If you're going to hire a lawyer to draw up your living trust, you might pay as much now as your heirs would have to pay for probate after your death—which means the trust offers no net savings.

But you don't have to pay a lawyer to create a living trust. With a good self-help book or software program, you can create a valid Declaration of Trust (the document that creates a trust) yourself. If you run into questions that a self-help publication doesn't answer, you may need to consult a lawyer, but you probably won't need to turn the whole job over to an expensive expert.

Isn't it a hassle to own property in a trust?

Making a living trust work for you does require some crucial paperwork. For example, if you want to leave your house through the trust, you must sign a new deed showing that you now own the house as trustee of your living trust. And in a few states, you may need to use special language in your trust document to avoid wrinkles in your state's income tax laws. This paperwork can be tedious, but the hassles are fewer these days because living trusts are becoming quite commonplace.

Is a trust document ever made public, like a will?

A will becomes a matter of public record when it is submitted to a probate court, as do all the other documents associated with probate—inventories of the deceased person's assets and debts, for example. The terms of a living trust, however, need not be made public.

Does a trust protect property from creditors?

Holding assets in a revocable trust doesn't shelter them from creditors. A creditor who wins a lawsuit against you can go after the trust property just as if you still owned it in your own name.

After your death, however, property in a living trust can be quickly and quietly distributed to the beneficiaries (unlike property that must go through probate). That complicates matters for creditors; by the time they find out about your death, your property may already be dispersed, and the creditors have no way of knowing exactly what you owned (except for real estate, which is always a matter of public record). It may not be worth the creditor's time and effort to try to track down the property and demand that the new owners use it to pay your debts.

On the other hand, probate can offer a kind of protection from creditors. During probate, known creditors must be notified of the death and given a chance to file claims. If they miss the deadline to file, they're out of luck forever.

I'm young and healthy. Do I really need a trust now?

Probably not. At this stage in your life, your main estate planning goals are probably making sure that in the unlikely event of your early death, your property is distributed how you want it to be and, if you have young children, that they are cared for. You don't need a trust to accomplish those ends; writing a will, and perhaps buying some life insurance, would be simpler.

Can a living trust save on estate taxes?

A simple probate-avoidance living trust has no effect on taxes. More complicated living trusts, however, can greatly reduce your federal estate tax bill. Federal estate taxes are collected only from large estates—so few people need to worry about them. (See *Estate and Gift Taxes*, below.)

One tax-saving living trust is designed primarily for married couples with children. It's commonly called an AB trust, though it goes by many other names. For more information about how an AB trust works, see the next set of questions, *Estate and Gift Taxes*.

More Information About Living Trusts

Quicken Lawyer Personal (Nolo) (software), lets you make a basic probate-avoidance trust or tax-saving AB trust using your computer.

Make Your Own Living Trust, by Denis Clifford (Nolo), contains forms and instructions for preparing two kinds of living trusts: a basic probate avoidance trust and a tax-saving AB trust.

Plan Your Estate, by Denis Clifford and Cora Jordan (Nolo), is a detailed guide to estate planning, including information about living trusts.

Estate and Gift Taxes

In this world nothing can be said to be certain, except death and taxes.

—BENJAMIN FRANKLIN

It's a universal truth that you can't take it with you. But will your inheritors have to pay for what you leave behind? Most people who consider estate planning are understandably concerned with estate and inheritance taxes. The good news is that most people's estates won't have to pay any death taxes—federal or state.

Will my estate have to pay taxes after I die?

Most don't. The federal government imposes estate taxes only if your property is worth more than a certain amount at your death. All property left to a spouse is exempt from the tax, as long as the spouse is a U.S. citizen. And estate taxes won't be assessed on any property you leave to a tax-exempt charity.

Currently, the amount that you can leave that is exempt from estate tax is scheduled to rise steadily until 2010, at which time the estate tax will no longer be imposed at all. But unless Congress extends the estate tax repeal, the tax will pop up again in 2011 (with a $1 million exemption).

THE ESTATE TAX EXEMPTION

YEAR	AMOUNT
2002, 2003	$1 million*
2004, 2005	$1.5 million
2006, 2007, 2008	$2 million
2009	$3.5 million
2010	Estate tax repealed
2011	$1 million unless Congress extends repeal

*There is a special $1.3 million exemption for family farms and other businesses that stay in the family; it will become superfluous when the individual exemption hits $1.5 million in 2004.

Don't some states also impose death taxes?

A handful of states impose death taxes. These taxes are of two types: inheritance taxes and estate taxes.

Inheritance taxes are paid by your inheritors, not your estate. Typically, how much they pay depends on their relationship to you. For example, Nebraska imposes a 15% tax if you leave $25,000 to a friend, but only 1% if you leave the money to your child. But tax rates vary from state to state. If you live in Connecticut, your child wouldn't owe any taxes on a $25,000 inheritance, but your friend would owe 9%.

STATES THAT IMPOSE INHERITANCE TAXES

Connecticut (phased out by 2005)	Nebraska
	New Hampshire
Indiana	New Jersey
Iowa	Ohio
Kentucky	Oklahoma
Louisiana (phased out by 2004)	Pennsylvania
	Tennessee
Maryland	

State estate taxes are similar to the estate tax imposed by the federal government. Your estate must pay this tax no matter who your beneficiaries are. The good news is that every state except Ohio has abolished these taxes, at least in effect. In the rest, the state takes part of the money that you owe to the feds; it's a matter for accountants and tax preparers, but doesn't increase the tax bill.

You can find a listing of your state's death tax laws in Nolo's *Plan Your Estate*, by Denis Clifford and Cora Jordan.

What are the rates for federal estate taxes?

The estate tax rate starts at 37%. The maximum rate is 50% in 2002 and will drop to 45% in 2009, the year before the estate tax is repealed.

Are there ways to avoid federal estate taxes?

Yes, although there are fewer ways than many people think, or hope, there are.

The most popular method is frequently used by married couples with grown children. It's called an AB trust, though it's sometimes known as a "credit shelter trust," "exemption trust," "marital life estate trust" or "marital bypass trust." Spouses put their property in the trust, and then, when one spouse dies, his or her half of the property goes to the children—with the crucial condition that the surviving spouse gets the right to use it for life and is entitled to any income it generates. When the second spouse dies, the property goes to the children outright. Using this kind of trust keeps the second spouse's taxable estate half the size it would be if the property were left entirely to the spouse, which means that estate taxes may be avoided altogether.

Unlike a probate-avoidance revocable living trust, an AB trust controls what happens to property for years after the first spouse's death. A couple who makes one must be sure that the surviving spouse will be financially and emotionally comfortable receiving only the income from the money or property placed in trust, with the children as the actual owners of the property.

How an AB Trust Works: An Example

Ellen and Jack have been married for nearly 50 years. They have one grown son, Robert, who is 39. Ellen and Jack create an AB trust and transfer all their major items of property to it. They name each other as life beneficiaries, and Robert as the final beneficiary.

Ellen dies first. The trust splits into two parts: Trust A, which is irrevocable, contains Ellen's share of the property. Trust B is Jack's trust, and it stays revocable as long as he is alive.

The property in Trust A legally belongs to Robert, but with one very important condition: His father, Jack, is entitled to use the property, and collect any income it generates, for the rest of his life. When Jack dies, the property will go to Robert free and clear.

Now let's take a look at the tax savings:

Ellen's half of the trust property is worth $600,000 when she dies.

At Ellen's death

Taxable estate $600,000

Estate tax $0

(because of the personal exemption)

At Jack's death

Taxable estate $600,000

Estate tax $0

If Ellen had left all her property to Jack outright, his estate would have been worth $1.2 million at his death—which would have resulted in thousands of dollars of estate tax if they died before 2004.

Are there other ways to save on estate taxes?

Yes. Common ones include what's called a "QTIP" trust, which enables a surviving spouse to postpone estate taxes that would otherwise be due when the other spouse dies. And there are many different types of charitable trusts, which involve making a sizable gift to a tax-exempt charity. Some of them provide both income tax and estate tax advantages.

Can I avoid paying state death taxes?

If your state imposes death taxes, there probably isn't much you can do. But if you live in two states—winter here, summer there—your inheritors may save on death taxes if you can make your legal residence in the state with lower, or no, death taxes.

Can't I just give all my property away before I die and avoid estate taxes?

No. The government long anticipated this one. If you give away more than

$11,000 per year to any one person or noncharitable institution, you are assessed federal "gift tax," which applies at the same rate as the estate tax. There are, however, a few exceptions to this rule. You can give an unlimited amount of property to your spouse, unless your spouse is not a U.S. citizen, in which case you can give away up to $110,000 per year free of gift tax. Any property given to a tax-exempt charity avoids federal gift taxes. And money spent directly for someone's medical bills or school tuition is exempt as well.

The federal gift tax will not be repealed in 2010 with the estate tax. Instead, it will survive, but with a $1 million exemption. In other words, you'll still be able to give away $1 million in taxable gifts (and most ordinary gifts aren't taxable) without owing any tax.

But I've heard that people save on estate taxes by making gifts. How?

You can achieve substantial estate tax savings by making use of the annual gift tax exclusion for gifts to people and nonexempt organizations. If you give away $11,000 a year for four years, you've removed $44,000 from your taxable estate. And each member of a couple has a separate exclusion. So a couple can give $22,000 a year to a child free of gift tax. If you have a few children, or other people you want to make gifts to (such as your sons- or

daughters-in-law), you can use this method to significantly reduce the size of your taxable estate over a few years.

Consider a couple with combined assets worth $1.2 million and three children. Each year they give each child $22,000 tax free, for a total of $66,000 per year. In seven years, the couple has given away $456,000 and has reduced their estate to far below the federal estate tax threshold.

Of course, there are risks with this kind of gift-giving program. The most obvious is that you are legally transferring your wealth. Gift giving to reduce eventual estate taxes must be carefully evaluated to see if you can comfortably afford to give away your property during your lifetime.

More Information About Estate and Gift Taxes

9 Ways to Avoid Estate Taxes, by Mary Randolph and Denis Clifford (Nolo), presents the major methods you can use to avoid or reduce federal estate taxes.

Plan Your Estate, by Denis Clifford and Cora Jordan (Nolo), is a detailed guide to estate planning, including all major methods of reducing or avoiding estate and gift taxes.

Funeral Planning and Other Final Arrangements

Many of us are squeamish when it comes to thinking and talking about death, particularly our own. But there are many good reasons to spend some time considering what you want to have happen to your body after death, including any ceremonies and observances you'd like.

Why should I leave written instructions about my final ceremonies and the disposition of my body?

Letting your survivors know your wishes saves them the difficulties of making these decisions at a painful time. And many family members and friends find that discussing these matters ahead of time is a great relief—especially if a person is elderly or in poor health and death is expected soon.

Planning some of these details in advance can also help save money. For many people, death goods and services cost more than anything they bought during their lives except homes and cars. Some wise comparison shopping in advance can help ensure that costs will be controlled or kept to a minimum.

Why not leave these instructions in my will?

A will is not a good place to express your death and burial preferences for one simple reason: Your will probably won't be located and read until several weeks after you die—long after decisions must be made.

A will should be reserved for directions on how to divide and distribute your property and, if applicable, who should get care and custody of your children if you die while they're still young.

What happens if I don't leave written instructions?

If you die without leaving written instructions about your preferences, state law will determine who will have the right to decide how your remains will be handled. In most states, the right—and the responsibility to pay for the reasonable costs of disposing of remains—rests with the following people, in order:

- spouse
- child or children
- parent or parents
- the next of kin, or
- a public administrator, who is appointed by a court.

Disputes may arise if two or more people—the deceased person's children, for example—share responsibility for a fundamental decision, such as whether the body of a parent should be buried or cremated. But such disputes can be avoided if you are willing to do some planning and to put your wishes in writing.

What details should I include in a final arrangements document?

What you choose to include is a personal matter, likely to be dictated by custom, religious preference or simply your own whims. A typical final arrangements document might include:

- the name of the mortuary or other institution that will handle burial or cremation
- whether or not you wish to be embalmed
- the type of casket or container in which your remains will be buried or cremated, including whether you want it present at any after-death ceremony
- the details of any ceremony you want before the burial or cremation
- who your pallbearers will be if you wish to have some
- how your remains will be transported to the cemetery and gravesite
- where your remains will be buried, stored or scattered
- the details of any ceremony you want to accompany your burial, interment or scattering, and
- the details of any marker you want to show where your remains are buried or interred.

What services can I expect from a mortuary?

Most mortuaries or funeral homes are equipped to handle many of the details related to disposing of a person's remains. These include:

- collecting the body from the place of death
- storing the body until it is buried or cremated

- making burial arrangements with a cemetery
- conducting ceremonies related to the burial
- preparing the body for burial, and
- arranging to have the body transported for burial.

Where can I turn for help in making final arrangements?

From an economic standpoint, choosing the institution to handle your burial is probably the most important final arrangement that you can make. For this reason, many people join memorial or funeral societies, which help them find local mortuaries that will deal honestly with their survivors and charge reasonable prices.

Society members are free to choose whatever final arrangements they wish. Most societies, however, emphasize simple arrangements over the costly services often promoted by the funeral industry. The services offered by each society differ, but most societies distribute information on options and explain the legal rules that apply to final arrangements.

If you join a society, you will receive a form that allows you to plan for the goods and services you want—and to get them for a predetermined cost. Many societies also serve as watchdogs, making sure that you get and pay for only the services you choose.

The cost for joining these organizations is low—usually from $20 to $40 for a lifetime membership, although some societies periodically charge a small renewal fee.

To find a funeral or memorial society near you, look in the Yellow Pages of your telephone book under Funeral Information and Advisory Services, or contact the Funeral Consumers Alliance (contact information is below).

If you don't want to join a society, you can look for a mortuary or funeral home on your own. You'll have to shop around to find the institution that best meets your needs in terms of style, proximity and cost.

Beware of Prepayment Plans

Shopping around for the most suitable and affordable funeral goods and services is a wise idea. Be extremely cautious, however, about paying in advance—often called prepaying—for them.

Although there are a number of legal controls on how the funeral industry can handle and invest funds earmarked for future services, there are many reported instances of mismanaged or stolen funds. A great many other abuses go unreported by family members too embarrassed or too grief-stricken to complain.

There are additional pitfalls. When mortuaries go out of business, the consumer who has prepaid is often left without funds and without recourse. Also, many individuals who move to a new locale during their lifetimes are dismayed to find that their prepayment funds are nonrefundable or that there is a substantial financial penalty for withdrawing or transferring them. In addition, money paid now may not cover inflated costs of the future, meaning that survivors will be left to cover the substantially higher costs.

If you are interested in setting aside a fund of money to pay for your final arrangements, a more prudent approach for most people is to set up a trust or savings account earmarked to pay for your final arrangements. Most banks and savings institutions will do so for a very slight charge. You can easily withdraw or transfer the funds during your life, if need be. At your death, the trusted individual or institution you name in the bank documents can take over and spend the money as you have directed.

More Information About Final Arrangements

The Funeral Consumers Alliance, a nonprofit organization, can help you locate a funeral or memorial society near you. Call 802-482-3437 or reach FCA online at http://www.funerals.org.

Quicken Lawyer Personal (Nolo) (software) lets you use your computer to create a final arrangements document, in addition to a valid will, living trust, healthcare directives, a durable power of attorney for finances, and other documents.

Body and Organ Donations

In addition to making other arrangements for your funeral and burial or cremation, you may want to arrange to donate some or all of your body organs. You must make these arrangements separately and document your wishes on a special form.

How can I arrange to donate my body for scientific research or study after my death?

Arrangements for whole body donations must usually be made while you are alive, although some medical schools will accept a cadaver through arrangements made after death.

The best place to contact to arrange a whole body donation is the nearest medical school. If you live in a state with no medical school or one that has very strict requirements for whole body donations, you may wish to find out more about your body donation options from the National Anatomical Service at 800-727-0700. You can also find information online at http://www.livingbank.org.

How can I arrange to donate my body organs for others to use after my death?

The principal method for donating organs is by indicating your intent to do so on a uniform donor card. Once signed, this card identifies you to medical personnel as a potential organ donor. You can get a donor card or form from most hospitals, the county or state office of the National Kidney Foundation or a community eye bank.

In most states, you can also obtain an organ donation card from the department of motor vehicles. Depending on where you live, you can check a box, affix a stamp or seal or attach a separate card to your license, indicating your wish to donate one or more organs.

Even if you have not signed a card or other document indicating your intent to donate your organs, your next of kin can approve a donation after you die. If you fill out an organ donor card, make sure you tell family members you have done so. Even if you have indicated an intent to donate your organs, an objection by your next of kin will often defeat your intention; medical personnel usually do not proceed in the face of an objection from relatives. The best safeguard is to discuss your wishes with close friends and relatives, emphasizing your strong feelings about donating your body for research or teaching.

http://www.nolo.com
Nolo offers extensive self-help information about wills and estate planning.

http://www.estateplanninglinks.com
This site contains a very thorough list of websites that cover almost every imaginable estate planning issue.

Healthcare Directives and Powers of Attorney

13.2   *Healthcare Directives*

13.7   *Durable Powers of Attorney for Finances*

13.11   *Conservatorships*

There is no mortal whom sorrow and disease do not touch.

—EURIPIDES

Many of us fear that we may someday become seriously ill and unable to handle our own affairs. Who would act on our behalf to pay bills, make bank deposits, watch over investments and deal with the paperwork that accompanies collecting insurance and government benefits? Who would make arrangements for our medical care and see that our wishes for treatment are carried out?

Preparing a few simple documents—healthcare directives and a durable power of attorney for finances—can ease these worries by ensuring that your affairs will stay in the hands of the trusted people you choose. This chapter answers your questions about these documents and how they work, as well as what happens if a court appoints a conservator—that is, the person who will manage your affairs if you haven't drafted legally valid instructions naming someone to take over.

Healthcare Directives

Nearly 80% of Americans die in a hospital or other care facility. The doctors who work in these facilities are generally charged with preserving a patient's life through whatever means are available. This may or may not be what you would like in the way of treatment. Healthcare directives give you the opportunity to write out your wishes in advance and ensure some legal respect for them if ever you are unable to speak for yourself.

What is a healthcare directive?

A healthcare directive is a straightforward legal document that sets out your wishes about what medical treatment should be withheld or provided if you become unable to communicate those wishes.

The directive creates a contract with the attending doctor. Once the doctor receives a properly signed and witnessed directive, she is under a duty either to honor its instructions or to make sure you are transferred to the care of another doctor who will.

Many people mistakenly believe that healthcare directives are used only to instruct doctors to withhold life-prolonging treatments. In fact, some people want to reinforce that they would like to receive all medical treatment that is available—and a healthcare directive is the proper place to say so.

A Healthcare Directive by Any Other Name

Depending upon the state, your healthcare directive may go by one of several different names: Advance Healthcare Directive, Medical Directive, Directive to Physicians, Declaration Regarding Healthcare, Designation of Healthcare Surrogate or Patient Advocate Designation. A healthcare directive may also be called a "living will," but it bears no relation to the conventional will or living trust used to leave property at death.

What is a durable power of attorney for healthcare? Doesn't that do the same thing as a healthcare directive?

A durable power of attorney for healthcare—called a healthcare proxy in some states—gives another person authority to make medical decisions for you if you are unable to make them for yourself. Unlike a healthcare directive, this document doesn't necessarily state what type of treatment you want to receive. You can leave those decisions to your proxy if you feel comfortable doing so. Depending on the requirements imposed by your state law, you may need to make one or two documents to express your wishes for medical care. For example, your healthcare directive may contain a clause appointing a proxy (sometimes called an attorney-in-fact, agent or representative) to be certain your wishes are carried out as you've directed. Or you may create two separate documents: a directive explaining the treatment you want to receive, and a durable power of attorney appointing someone to oversee your directive and make other medical decisions for you, if you wish.

If you don't know anyone you trust enough to name as your healthcare proxy, it is still important to complete and finalize a healthcare directive recording your wishes. That way, your doctors will still be obligated to give you the medical care you want.

What happens if I don't have any healthcare documents?

If you have not completed a healthcare directive to express your wishes or a durable power of attorney to appoint someone to make healthcare decisions on your behalf, the doctors who attend you will use their own discretion in deciding what kind of medical care you will receive.

When a question arises about whether surgery or some other serious procedure is authorized, doctors may turn for consent to a close relative—spouse, parent or adult child. Friends and unmarried partners, although they may be most familiar with your wishes for your medical treatment, are rarely consulted, or are purposefully left out of the decision-making process. (This is slowly changing. In at least a couple of states—California and Vermont—

same-sex domestic partners may be given priority in making medical decisions for a partner who is incapacitated.)

Problems arise when partners and family members disagree about what treatment is proper. In the most complicated scenarios, these battles over medical care wind up in court, where a judge, who usually has little medical knowledge and no familiarity with you, is called upon to decide the future of your treatment. Such legal battles—which are costly, time consuming and usually painful to those involved—are unnecessary if you have the foresight to use a formal document to express your wishes for your healthcare.

When Your Healthcare Directive Takes Effect

Your healthcare directive takes effect when your doctor determines that you lack the ability, or capacity, to make your own healthcare decisions. Essentially, lacking capacity means that:

- you can't understand the nature and consequences of the healthcare choices that are available to you, and
- you are unable to communicate your own wishes for care, either orally, in writing or through gestures.

Practically speaking, this means that if you are so ill or injured that you cannot express your healthcare wishes in any way, your directive will spring immediately into effect. If, however, there is some question about your ability to understand your treatment choices and communicate clearly, your doctor (with the input of your healthcare proxy or close relatives) will decide whether it is time for your healthcare directive to become operative.

In some states, it is possible to give your healthcare proxy the authority to manage your healthcare immediately. If your state allows this option, you may prefer to make an immediately effective directive for any of several reasons, including:

- Allowing your proxy to put your document into effect quickly, without first having a doctor confirm that you are incapacitated. This may be particularly important if you are not under the care of a doctor with whom you have an established, trusting relationship.
- Keeping control in the hands of your proxy. You may feel that your proxy, not a doctor, is the best person to decide that you can no longer direct your own medical care.
- Asking your proxy to step in early and make decisions for you even if you still have the capacity to make your own choices. You may want this if illness, exhaustion or other circumstances leave you feeling that you'd like someone you trust to deal with your doctors and make treatment decisions for you.

Making an immediately effective document will not give your proxy the authority to override what you want in terms of treatment; you will always be able to dictate your own medical care if you have the ability to do so. And even when you are no longer capable of making your own decisions, your proxy must always act in your best interests and try diligently to follow any healthcare wishes you've expressed in your healthcare directive or otherwise.

Finally, to ensure that your document takes effect and your wishes are followed if your need for care arises unexpectedly, you should place copies of your healthcare documents with several people, including your regular doctor, your healthcare proxy and at least one other trusted relative or friend.

Whom should I choose as a healthcare proxy?

The person you name as your healthcare proxy should be someone you trust—and someone with whom you feel confident discussing your wishes. While your proxy need not agree with your wishes for your medical care, you should believe that he respects your right to get the kind of medical care you want.

The person you appoint to oversee your healthcare wishes could be a spouse or partner, relative or close friend. Keep in mind that your proxy may have to fight to assert your wishes in the face of a stubborn medical establishment—and against the wishes of family members who may be driven by their own beliefs and interests, rather than yours. If you foresee the possibility of a conflict in enforcing your wishes, be sure to choose a proxy who is strong willed and assertive.

While you need not name someone who lives in the same state as you do, proximity may be an important factor.

The reality is that the person you name may be called upon to spend weeks or months near your bedside, making sure medical personnel abide by your wishes for your healthcare. If you name someone who lives far away, make sure that person is willing to travel and stay with you a while. The job of proxy may demand it.

You should not choose your doctor or an employee of a hospital or nursing home where you receive treatment. In fact, the laws in many states prevent you from naming such a person. In a few instances, this legal constraint may frustrate your wishes. For example, you may wish to name your spouse or partner as your representative, but if he or she works as a hospital employee, that alone may bar you from naming that person. If the law in your state bans your first choice, you will have to name another person to serve.

What if I really don't know anyone I trust to supervise my medical care?

Naming a healthcare proxy is an optional part of completing your healthcare directive. It is better not to name anyone than to name someone who is not comfortable with the directions you leave—or who is not likely to assert your wishes strongly.

Medical personnel are still technically bound to follow your written wishes for your healthcare—or to find someone who will care for you in the way you have directed. It is far better to put your wishes for final healthcare in writing than to let the lack of a representative stand in the way.

What types of medical care should I consider when completing my healthcare documents?

Technological advances mean that currently unfathomable procedures and treatments will become available, and treatments that are now common will become obsolete. Also, the treatments that are available vary drastically with region, depending on the sophistication and funding levels of local medical facilities.

While putting together your healthcare directive, the best that you can do is to become familiar with the kinds of medical procedures that are most commonly administered to patients who are seriously ill. These include:

- blood and blood products
- cardiopulmonary resuscitation (CPR)
- diagnostic tests
- dialysis
- drugs
- respirators, and
- surgery.

Can I provide instructions in my healthcare documents about pain medication, or about food and water?

The laws of most states assume that people want relief from pain and discomfort and specifically exclude pain-relieving procedures from definitions of life-prolonging treatments that may be withheld. Some states also exclude food and water (commonly called nutrition and hydration) from their definitions of life-prolonging treatments. But there is some controversy about whether providing food and water, or drugs to make a person comfortable, will also have the effect of prolonging life. Some people are so adamant about not having their lives prolonged when they are comatose or likely to die soon that they choose to direct that all food, water and pain relief be withheld, even if the doctor thinks those procedures are necessary. Under the U.S. Constitution, you are allowed to leave these instructions even if your state's law is restrictive; your doctors are legally bound to follow your wishes.

On the other hand, some people feel concerned about how much pain or discomfort they may experience during a final illness; these people are willing to have their lives prolonged rather than face the possibility that discomfort or pain would go untreated. Obviously, it's a very personal choice; you're free to leave the instructions that feel right for you.

Where can I get a healthcare directive form?

There are a number of ways to find the proper healthcare documents for your state; you don't need to consult a lawyer to obtain or prepare them.

Here are some likely sources for forms and instructions:

- local senior centers
- local hospitals (ask to speak with the patient representative; by law, any hospital that receives federal funds must provide patients with appropriate forms for directing healthcare)
- your regular physician
- your state's medical association
- Partnership for Caring, 1620 I Street NW, Suite 202, Washington DC 20006, 800-989-9455 or 202-296-8071. You can order the forms for a small fee, or you can download them for free from the organization's website at http://www.partnershipforcaring.org.
- *Quicken Lawyer Personal* software from Nolo walks you step-by-step through the process of writing your own healthcare directive. In addition, you can use the program to prepare a valid will, living trust, durable power of attorney for finances and other important legal documents.
- *Medical Directives and Powers of Attorney for California,* by Shae Irving (Nolo), provides complete forms and instructions to help California residents prepare healthcare documents.

Make Your Documents Legal

There are a few requirements you must meet to make a valid healthcare directive. In most states, you must be 18 years old, though a few states allow parents to make healthcare directives for their minor children. All states require that the person making a healthcare directive be able to understand what the document means, what it contains and how it works.

Also, every state requires that you sign your documents. If you are physically unable to sign them yourself, you can direct another person to sign them for you.

You must sign your documents, or have them signed for you, in the presence of witnesses or a notary public—sometimes both, depending on your state's law. The purpose of this additional formality is so that there is at least one other person who can confirm that you were of sound mind and of legal age when you made the documents.

Durable Powers of Attorney for Finances

A durable power of attorney for finances is a simple, inexpensive and reliable way to arrange for someone to make your financial decisions should you become unable to do so yourself. It's also a wonderful thing to do for your family members. If you do become incapacitated, the durable power of attorney will likely appear as a minor miracle to those close to you.

How does a durable power of attorney work?

When you create and sign a power of attorney, you give another person legal authority to act on your behalf. This person is called your attorney-in-fact or, sometimes, your agent. The word attorney here means anyone authorized to act on another's behalf; it's most definitely not restricted to lawyers.

A "durable" power of attorney stays valid even if you become unable to handle your own affairs (incapacitated). If you don't specify that you want your power of attorney to be durable, it will automatically end if you later become incapacitated.

When does a durable power of attorney take effect?

There are two kinds of durable powers of attorney for finances: those that take effect immediately and those that never take effect unless a doctor (or two, in a couple of states) declares that you can no longer manage your financial affairs. Which kind you should make depends, in part, on when you want your attorney-in-fact to start handling tasks for you.

If you want someone to take over some or all of your affairs now, you should make your document effective as soon as you sign it. Then, your attorney-in-fact can begin helping you with your financial tasks right away—and can continue to do so if you later become incapacitated.

On the other hand, you may feel strongly that your attorney-in-fact should not take over unless you are incapacitated. In this case, you have two options. If you trust your attorney-in-fact to act only when it's absolutely necessary, you can go ahead and make an immediately effective document. Legally, your attorney-in-fact will then have the authority to act on your behalf—but won't do so unless he or she ever decides that you can't handle your affairs yourself.

If you're uncomfortable giving your attorney-in-fact authority now, you can add language to your durable power of attorney to make what's known as a "springing" document. It won't take effect until a physician examines you and declares, in writing, that you can't manage your finances. (In Alaska and New Mexico, two physicians must examine you and certify that you are incapacitated.)

There are some real inconveniences involved in creating a springing power of attorney. First, the process of obtain-

ing the doctor's statements can be time-consuming and complicated for your attorney-in-fact, and may delay the handling of your affairs. Second, some people may be reluctant to accept a springing power of attorney, even though your attorney-in-fact has obtained the required doctors' statements and your document is perfectly legal. A bank, for example, might question whether you have, in fact, become incapacitated. These hassles could further disrupt the handling of your finances. For these reasons, it's wise to think carefully before you make a springing document. If you truly trust your attorney-in-fact, you may find that it makes more sense to create a document that takes effect immediately and then make clear to your attorney-in-fact when to take action.

How do I create a durable power of attorney for finances?

To create a legally valid durable power of attorney, all you need to do is properly complete and sign a fill-in-the-blanks form that's a few pages long. Some states have their own forms.

After you fill out the form, you must sign it in front of a notary public. In some states, witnesses must also watch you sign the document. If your attorney-in-fact will have authority to deal with your real estate, you must put a copy on file at the local land records office. (In just two states, North and South Carolina, you must record your power of attorney for it to be durable.)

Some banks, title companies, insurance companies, brokerage companies and other financial institutions have their own durable power of attorney forms. If you want your attorney-in-fact to have an easy time with these institutions, you may need to prepare two (or more) durable powers of attorney: your own form and forms provided by the institutions with which you do business.

What happens if I don't have a durable power of attorney for finances?

If you become incapacitated and you haven't prepared a durable power of attorney for finances, a court proceeding is probably inescapable. Your spouse, closest relatives or companion will have to ask a court for authority over at least some of your financial affairs.

If you are married, your spouse does have some authority over property you own together—to pay bills from a joint bank account, for example. There are significant limits, however, on your spouse's right to sell property owned by both of you.

If your relatives go to court to get someone appointed to manage your financial affairs, they must ask a judge to rule that you cannot take care of your own affairs—a public airing of a very private matter. And like any court proceeding, it can be expensive if your relatives must hire a lawyer. Depending on where you live, the person appointed is called a conservator, guardian of the estate, committee or curator. When this person is appointed, you lose the right to control your own money and property.

The appointment of a conservator is usually just the beginning of court proceedings. Often the conservator must:

- post a bond—a kind of insurance policy that pays if the conservator steals or misuses property
- prepare (or hire a lawyer or accountant to prepare) detailed financial reports and periodically file them with the court, and
- get court approval for certain transactions, such as selling real estate or making slightly risky investments.

A conservatorship isn't necessarily permanent, but it may be ended only by the court. Conservatorships are discussed in more detail in the next set of questions.

The Attorney-in-Fact's Duties

Commonly, people give an attorney-in-fact broad power over their finances. But you can give your attorney-in-fact as much or as little power as you wish. You may want to give your attorney-in-fact authority to do some or all of the following:

- use your assets to pay your everyday expenses and those of your family
- buy, sell, maintain, pay taxes on and

mortgage real estate and other property
- collect benefits from Social Security, Medicare or other government programs or civil or military service
- invest your money in stocks, bonds and mutual funds
- handle transactions with banks and other financial institutions
- buy and sell insurance policies and annuities for you
- file and pay your taxes
- operate your small business
- claim property you inherit or are otherwise entitled to
- transfer property into your living trust
- represent you in court or hire someone to represent you, and
- manage your retirement accounts.

Whatever powers you give the attorney-in-fact, the attorney-in-fact must act in your best interests, keep accurate records, keep your property separate from his or hers and avoid conflicts of interest.

I have a living trust. Do I still need a durable power of attorney for finances?

A revocable living trust can be useful if you become incapable of taking care of your financial affairs. That's because the person who will distribute trust property after your death (the successor trustee) can also, in most cases, take over management of the trust property if you become incapacitated.

Few people, however, transfer all their property to a living trust, and the successor trustee has no authority over property that the trust doesn't own. So a living trust isn't a complete substitute for a durable power of attorney for finances.

Can my attorney-in-fact make medical decisions on my behalf?

No. A durable power of attorney for finances does not give your attorney-in-fact legal authority to make medical decisions for you.

You can, however, prepare a durable power of attorney for healthcare, a document that lets you choose someone to make medical decisions on your behalf if you can't. In most states, you'll also want to write out your wishes in a healthcare directive, which will tell your doctors your preferences about certain kinds of medical treatment and life-sustaining procedures if you can't communicate your wishes.

Healthcare documents are discussed in more detail in the previous section of this chapter.

When does the durable power of attorney end?

It ends at your death. That means that you can't give your attorney-in-fact authority to handle things after your death, such as paying your debts, making funeral or burial arrangements or transferring your property to the people who inherit it. If you want your attorney-in-fact to have authority to wind up your affairs after your death, use a will to name that person as your executor.

Your durable power of attorney also ends if:
- You revoke it. As long as you are mentally competent, you can revoke a durable power of attorney at any time.
- A court invalidates your document. This happens rarely, but a court may declare your document invalid if it concludes that you were not men-

tally competent when you signed it, or that you were the victim of fraud or undue influence.

- You get a divorce. In a handful of states, including Alabama, California, Colorado, Illinois, Indiana, Minnesota, Missouri, Pennsylvania, Texas, Washington and Wisconsin, if your spouse is your attorney-in-fact and you divorce, your ex-spouse's authority is automatically terminated. In any state, however, it is wise to revoke your durable power of attorney after a divorce and make a new one.

- No attorney-in-fact is available. A durable power of attorney must end if there's no one to serve as attorney-in-fact. To avoid this problem, you can name an alternate attorneys-in-fact in your document.

More Information About Durable Powers of Attorney for Finances

Quicken Lawyer Personal (software from Nolo) walks you step by step through the process of writing your own durable power of attorney for finances. You can also use the program to prepare a valid will, living trust, healthcare directive and other useful legal documents.

Medical Directives & Powers of Attorney in California, by Shae Irving (Nolo), provides complete forms and instructions to help California residents prepare a durable power of attorney for finances.

Conservatorships

A conservatorship is a legal arrangement in which an adult has the court-ordered authority and responsibility to manage another adult's financial affairs. Many states use the terms "conservator" and "guardian" interchangeably, or use other terms such as "custodian" or "curator." In this book, we use the term "guardian" for a person who makes personal decisions for a child or an incapacitated adult, and "conservator" for someone who takes care of financial matters for an incapacitated adult. The adult who needs help is called the "conservatee."

If you need information about guardianships for children, see Chapter 16, *Parents and Children*.

When is a conservatorship necessary?

A conservatorship is permitted only when someone is so incapacitated that he cannot manage his own financial affairs. Generally, conservatorships are established for people who are in comas, suffer from advanced stages of Alzheimer's disease or have other serious illnesses or injuries.

Conservatorships are rarely needed for people who have made—or can knowingly sign—financial documents, such as a durable power of attorney for finances. (See the previous set of questions.)

Adults May Need Guardians, Too

In addition to help with finances, an incapacitated adult may also need assistance with personal matters, such as medical decisions (if the adult has not prepared a healthcare directive) and decisions about where the adult will live and what his or her daily activities will be. If a court appoints someone to take care of these things, that person is usually called a "guardian" or "conservator of the person." The incapacitated adult is often called the "ward." An incapacitated adult may need a guardian or a conservator, or both. The same person can be appointed to take both jobs. As with conservators, guardians are supervised and held accountable to a court.

What are the advantages of a conservatorship?

Conservatorships are subject to court supervision, which provides a powerful safeguard for an incapacitated adult's property. To prevent a conservator from mismanaging the property of the person she is helping (the conservatee), most courts require the conservator to provide periodic reports and accountings that give details about the conservatee's assets and how the conservatee's money was spent. Many courts also require the conservator to seek permission before making major decisions about the conservatee's property, such as whether to sell real estate.

What are the downsides to a conservatorship?

Conservatorships are time consuming and expensive; they often require court hearings and the ongoing assistance of a lawyer. The paperwork can also be a hassle because, as mentioned above, the conservator must keep detailed records and file court papers on a regular basis.

In addition, a conservator must usually post a bond (a kind of insurance policy that protects the conservatee's estate from mishandling). The bond premiums are paid by the conservatee's estate—and are an unnecessary expense if the conservator is competent and trustworthy.

Occasionally, however, a conservator will mismanage a conservatee's assets. Common abuses range from reckless handling of the conservatee's assets to outright theft. Although each state has rules and procedures designed to prevent mishandling of assets, few have the resources to keep an eye on conservators and follow through if they spot trouble. Many cases of incompetence or abuse go unnoticed.

Finally, a conservatorship can be emotionally trying for the conservatee. All court proceedings and documents are public records, which can be embarrassing for someone who values independence and privacy.

How are conservators compensated for their services?

The conservatee's estate must reimburse the conservator for necessary expenses and must usually pay for the conservator's services—if these payments are "reasonable" in the eyes of a court. Generally, payments are made to professional or public conservators, but a family member who has been appointed conservator may also seek compensation by making a request to the court.

Are there ways to block a conservatorship?

Before a court approves a conservatorship, notice must be given to the proposed conservatee and his close family members. Anyone—including the proposed conservatee, family members and friends—may object to the conservatorship in general, or to the specific choice of conservator. The person who wants to block the conservatorship must file papers with the court, inform all interested parties (the proposed conservatee, family members and possibly close friends) and attend a legal hearing. The final decision is up to a judge.

The best way to avoid a conservatorship is to prepare a durable power of attorney for finances before a health crisis occurs. That way, someone you've hand-picked will be able to step in and make decisions for you if necessary. (For information about preparing a durable power of attorney, see the previous set of questions.)

How does a judge choose a conservator?

When a conservatorship petition is filed in court, a judge must decide whom to appoint. Often, just one person is interested in taking on the role of conservator—but sometimes several family members or friends vie for the position. If no one suitable is available to serve as conservator, the judge may appoint a public or other professional conservator.

When appointing a conservator, a judge follows certain preferences established by state law. Most states give preference to the conservatee's spouse, adult children, adult siblings or other blood relatives—and a couple of states give priority to a registered domestic partner. But a judge has some flexibility; he may use his discretion to pick the person he thinks is best for the job. Without strong evidence of what the conservatee would have wanted, however, it is unlikely that a nonrelative would be appointed over a relative. Because of this, conservatorship proceedings may cause great heartache if an estranged relative is chosen as conservator over the conservatee's partner or close friend.

Who financially supports the conservatee?

If the conservatee has the means, money for his support will come from his own assets. But a conservator should seek all financial benefits and coverage for which the conservatee may qualify. These benefits may include Social Security, medical insurance, Veterans Administration benefits, pension and retirement benefits, disability benefits, public assistance and Supplemental Security Income. When needed, close family members (including the conservator) often contribute their own money to help support a conservatee.

When does a conservatorship end?

A conservator must care for the conservatee's finances until the court issues an order relieving her from responsibility. This ordinarily happens when:

- the conservatee dies
- the conservatorship estate is used up
- the conservatee regains the ability to handle her own finances, or
- the conservator becomes unable or unwilling to handle the responsibilities. In this situation, the conservatorship itself does not end, but someone else takes over the conservator's duties.

More Information About Conservatorships

The Conservatorship Book, by Lisa Goldoftas & Carolyn Farren (Nolo), contains forms and instructions for getting a conservator appointed in California, without a lawyer. For information about conservatorships in other states, visit your local law library.

http://www.nolo.com

Nolo offers self-help information on a wide variety of legal topics, including healthcare directives, powers of attorney and conservatorships.

http://www.partnershipfor caring.org

Partnership for Caring offers information and publications about healthcare directives, as well as state-specific forms that you can download for free.

Many sites offer state-specific information about durable powers of attorney for finances and conservatorships. If you need more information about your state's laws, you can use an online search engine to hunt for a site that will help you. See the Legal Research Appendix for more information on how to do this.

14

Older Americans

14.2   *Social Security*

14.8   *Medicare*

14.12   *Pensions*

14.19   *Retirement Plans*

To be seventy years young is sometimes far more cheerful and hopeful than to be forty years old.

—OLIVER WENDELL HOLMES, JR.

For many older Americans, the final years are no longer the Golden Years. Worries over limited incomes—and the real threat of being financially ruined by any extended bout with the medical system—crowd out thoughts of leisure and fulfillment.

There is help available for supplementing limited incomes and covering medical care in your later years, but you have to take some initiative to find it. It also helps if you have the good fortune and foresight to do some early planning.

Social Security

Social Security is the general term that describes a number of related programs —retirement, disability, dependents and survivors benefits. These programs together provide workers and their families with some money when their normal flow of income shrinks because of retirement, disability or death.

Unfortunately, the government's original goal of providing financial security through these programs is becoming increasingly remote. The combination of rapidly rising living costs, stagnating benefit amounts and penalties for older people who continue to work make the amount of support offered by Social Security less adequate with each passing year. This shrinking of the Social Security safety net makes it that much more important that you know how to get the maximum benefits to which you are entitled.

How much can I expect to get in Social Security benefits?

There is no easy answer to this question. The amount of benefits to which you are entitled under any Social Security program is not related to need, but is based on the income you have earned through years of working. In most jobs, both you and your employer have paid Social Security taxes on the amounts you earned. Since 1951, Social Security taxes have also been paid on reported self-employment income. Social Security keeps a record of these earnings over your working lifetime, and pays benefits based upon the average amount earned.

Who is eligible to collect benefits?

The specific requirements vary depending on the type of benefits, the age of the person filing the claim and, if you are claiming as a dependent or survivor, the age of the worker. There is a general requirement, however, that everyone must meet to receive one of these Social Security benefits: The worker on whose earnings record the benefit is to be paid must have worked in "covered employment" for a sufficient number of years —that is, earned what Social Security calls work credits—by the time he or she claims retirement benefits, becomes disabled or dies. To find out about your eligibility, call the Social Security Administration, 800-772-1213, or visit the Social Security website at http://www.ssa.gov to request a Social Security Statement.

Note that Social Security eligibility rules have recently changed for some specific types of workers, including federal, state and local government workers; workers for nonprofit organizations; members of the military; household workers; and farm workers. If you have been employed for some time as one of these types of workers, check with the Social Security Administration for special rules that may affect your eligibility.

Social Security Benefits: A Guide to the Basics

Four basic categories of Social Security benefits are paid based upon the record of your earnings: retirement, disability, dependents and survivors benefits.

Retirement benefits. You may choose to begin receiving retirement benefits at any time after you reach age 62; the amount of benefits will increase for each year you wait until age 70. The increase in delayed benefits varies from 4% to 8%, depending on the year in which you were born. But no matter how long you wait to begin collecting benefits, the amount you receive will probably be only a small percentage of what you were earning.

Because so many variables are thrown into the mix in computing benefit amounts—some of them based on your individual work record and retirement plans, some of them based on changes and convolutions in Social Security rules—it is impossible to give you what you want most: a solid estimate of the amount that will appear on your retirement benefit check. For a 65-year-old single person first claiming retirement benefits in 2002, the average monthly benefit is about $900; $1,500 for a couple. But these numbers are just averages. Benefits change yearly as the cost of living changes.

Disability benefits. If you are under 65 but have met the work requirements and are considered disabled under the program's medical guidelines, you can receive benefits roughly equal to what your retirement benefits would be.

Dependents benefits. If you are the spouse of a retired or disabled worker who qualifies for retirement or disability benefits, you and your minor or disabled children may be entitled to benefits based on the worker's earning record. This is true whether or not you actually depend on your spouse for your support.

Survivors benefits. If you are the surviving spouse of a worker who qualified for retirement or disability benefits, you and your minor or disabled children may be entitled to benefits based on your deceased spouse's earnings record.

How are my benefit amounts calculated?

The amount of any benefit is determined by a formula based on the average of your yearly reported earnings in covered employment since you began working. To further complicate matters, Social Security computes the average of earnings differently depending on your age. If you reached age 62 or became disabled on or before December 31, 1978, the computation is simple: Social Security averages the actual dollar value of your total past earnings—and bases the amount of your monthly benefits on that amount.

If you turned 62 or became disabled on or after January 1, 1979, Social Security divides your earnings into two categories: earnings from before 1951 are credited with their actual dollar amount, up to a maximum of $3,000 per year; and from 1951 on, yearly limits are placed on earnings credits, no matter how much you actually earned in those years.

How can I find out what I've earned so far?

The Social Security Administration keeps a running computer account of your earnings record and work credits, tracking both through your Social Security number. The Administration mails out copies of individual Social Security records on what is called a Social Security Statement. The statement is mailed to everyone age 40 and over who is not currently receiving Social Security benefits.

If you are age 40 or over but have not received your statement, or you are under age 60 and want to check your statement now, you can request a copy by filing out a simple form, SSA 7004, called a Request for Social Security Statement, available at your local Social Security office. If you cannot easily get to your local office, you can request a copy of the form, in either Spanish or English, by calling 800-772-1213.

Request Your Earnings and Benefit Statement Online

You can request your Social Security Statement online, without having to fill out and request a written form. The Administration reportedly responds to online requests much more quickly than it does to mailed requests, so using this format may shave weeks off the time it takes to get your estimate.

Go to the Social Security Administration's site at http://www.ssa.gov. On the homepage, click on *Social Security Statement*.

If You Find an Error

Some government-watchers estimate that the Social Security Administration makes mistakes on at least 4% of the total official earnings records it keeps. It is always wise for you to check the SSA's work. Make sure that the Social Security number noted on your earnings statement is your own. Also make sure the earned income amounts listed on the agency's records mesh with your own records of earnings as listed on your income tax forms or pay stubs.

When you have evidence of your covered earnings in the year or years for which you think Social Security has made an error, call Social Security's helpline at 800-772-1213, Monday through Friday from 7 a.m. to 7 p.m. This is the line that takes all kinds of Social Security questions and it is often swamped, so be patient. It is best to call early in the morning or late in the afternoon, late in the week or late in the month. Have all your documents handy when you speak with a representative.

If you would rather speak with someone in person, call your local Social Security office and make an appointment to see someone there, or drop into the office during regular business hours. If you drop in, be prepared to wait, perhaps as long as an hour or two, before you get to see a representative. Bring with you two copies of your benefits statement and the evidence that supports your claim of higher income. That way, you can leave one copy with the Social Security worker. Write down the name of the person with whom you speak so that you can reach the same person when you follow up.

The process to correct errors is slow. It may take several months to have the changes made in your record. And once Social Security confirms that it has corrected your record, go through the process of requesting another benefits statement to make sure the correct information is in your file.

Can I collect more than one type of benefit at a time?

No. You may qualify for more than one type of Social Security benefit, but you can collect just one. For example, you might be eligible for both retirement and disability, or you might be entitled to benefits based on your own retirement as well as on that of your retired spouse. You can collect whichever one of these benefits is higher, but not both.

Can I claim spousal benefits if I'm divorced?

You are eligible for dependent's benefits if both you and your former spouse have reached age 62, your marriage lasted at least ten years and you have been divorced for at least two years. This two-year waiting period does not apply if your former spouse was already collecting retirement benefits before the divorce.

You can collect benefits as soon as your former spouse is eligible for retirement benefits. He or she does not actually have to be collecting those benefits for you to collect your dependent's benefits.

If you are collecting dependent's benefits on your former spouse's work record and then marry someone else, you lose your right to those benefits. You may, however, be eligible to collect dependent's benefits based on your new spouse's work record. If you divorce again, you can return to collecting benefits on your first spouse's record, or on your second spouse's record if you were married for at least ten years the second time around.

Can I keep a job even after I start collecting retirement benefits?

Yes—and many people do just that. But if you plan on working after retirement, be aware that the money you earn may cause a reduction in the amount of your Social Security benefits. The amount of income you're allowed to earn without losing a portion of your benefits depends on your age and yearly changes in the amounts allowed.

If you are under full retirement age and you earn income over the year's limit, your Social Security retirement benefits are reduced by one dollar for every two dollars over the limit. In 2002, the limit on earned income was $11,280 per year.

How do I claim my Social Security benefits?

You can apply for benefits at your local Social Security office, by phone or though the Internet at http://www.ssa.gov.

A Social Security worker in your local office is usually the best source of information and assistance for filing your claim. Most sizable cities have at least one Social Security office; in major urban areas, there will be several. Locate the office closest to you in your telephone directory under the listing for U.S. Government, Social Security Administration, or under U.S. Government, Department of Health and Human Services, Social Security Administration. If you have trouble finding an office nearby, call the Social Security Administration at 800-772-1213, or use the agency's website at http://www.ssa.gov.

If illness or disability prevents you from visiting your local office, call for accommodations. The most important thing is to act promptly and apply for the benefits to which you are entitled.

Social Security workers should also be able to answer general questions about benefits and rules over the phone—including what type of paperwork must be completed and what documentation is required to claim each kind of benefit.

What do I do if I feel I've been wrongly denied my benefits?

If your application for benefits is denied, you may not be completely out of luck. A substantial percentage of decisions are changed on appeal. For example, almost half of all disability appeals, which are by far the most common, are favorably changed during the appeal process.

There are four possible levels of appeal following any Social Security decision. The first is called reconsideration; it is an informal review that takes place in the local Social Security office where your claim was filed. The second level is a hearing before an administrative law judge; this is an independent review of what the local Social Security office has decided, made by someone outside the local office. The third level is an appeal to the Social Security national appeals council in Washington, DC. And the final level is filing a lawsuit in federal court.

Appealing a Social Security claim need not be terribly difficult, so long as you properly organized and prepared your original claim. In many situations, the appeal is simply another opportunity to explain why you qualify for a benefit. In other cases, you'll need to present a few more pieces of information that better explain your situation to Social Security personnel.

Begin your appeal by completing a simple, one-page form you can get from the Social Security office. It is called a Request for Reconsideration. You'll be asked for basic information such as your name and Social Security number. Then you will need to state, very briefly, the reasons why you think you were unfairly denied benefits or were allotted lower benefits than you believe you earned. When you submit your form, you can attach other material you want the administrators to consider, such as recent medical records or a letter from a doctor or employer about your ability to work. You must send in the completed Request for Reconsideration within 60 days after you of receive written notice of Social Security's decision denying you benefits.

Sign Up Three Months Before Your Birthday

If you need to receive benefit payments at the youngest eligibility age, file your claim three months before the birthday on which you will become eligible. This will give Social Security time to process your claim so that you will receive the benefits on time. If you file a claim later, you cannot get benefits retroactively for months during which you were eligible but before you applied.

Anyone who is eligible for Social Security benefits is also eligible for Medicare coverage at age 65. (For more information about Medicare, see the next series of questions.) Even if you are not going to claim Social Security benefits at age 65—because your benefit amount will be higher if you wait—you should sign up for Medicare coverage three months before your 65th birthday. There is no reason to delay signing up for Medicare, and waiting until after your 65th birthday will delay coverage.

More Information About Social Security

Social Security, Medicare and Government Pensions, by Joseph Matthews with Dorothy Matthews Berman (Nolo), explains Social Security rules and offers strategies for dealing with the Social Security system.

The Social Security Administration, 800-772-1213, answers general questions about eligibility and applications over the phone. It also operates a helpful website at http://www.ssa.gov.

In every state, there is a department or commission on aging that gives information and provides advice about problems with Social Security claims. Check the phone book under Aging or Elderly for the service in your state.

Medicare

Give me health and a day and I will make the pomp of emperors ridiculous.

—RALPH WALDO EMERSON

Over the last several decades, Medicare has been carving an inroad into the mountain of consumer health care costs. At present, the Medicare system provides some coverage for almost 40 million people, most of them seniors. Medicare pays for most of the cost of hospitalization and much other medical care for older Americans—about half of all medical costs for people over 65.

Despite its broad coverage, Medicare does not pay for many types of medical services, and pays only a portion of the costs of other services. To take maximum advantage of the benefits Medicare does provide, to protect yourself against the gaps in Medicare coverage and to understand the current political debate about the program's future, you must become well informed about how the Medicare system works.

What is Medicare?

Medicare is a federal government program that helps older and some disabled people pay their medical bills. The program is divided into two parts: Part A and Part B. Part A is called hospital insurance and covers most of the costs of a stay in the hospital, as well as some follow-up costs after time in the hospital. Part B, medical insur-ance, pays some of the cost of doctors and outpatient medical care.

Medicare, Medicaid: What's the Difference?

People are sometimes confused about the differences between Medicare and Medicaid. Medicare was created to address the fact that older citizens have medical bills significantly higher than the rest of the population, while they have less opportunity to earn enough money to cover those bills. Eligibility for Medicare is not tied to individual need. Rather, it is an entitlement program; you are entitled to it because you or your spouse paid for it through Social Security taxes.

Medicaid, on the other hand, is a federal program for low-income, financially needy people, set up by the federal government and administered differently in each state.

Although you may qualify and receive coverage from both Medicare and Medicaid, there are separate eligibility requirements for each program; being eligible for one program does not necessarily mean you are eligible for the other. Also, Medicaid pays for some services for which Medicare does not.

Who is eligible for Medicare Part A coverage?

There are two types of eligibility for Medicare Part A hospital insurance. Most people age 65 and over are covered for free, based on their work records or on their spouse's work records. People over 65 who are not eligible for free Medicare Part A coverage can enroll in it and pay a monthly fee for the same coverage—at least $175 per month according to current rules. The premium increases by 10% for each year after your 65th birthday during which you are not enrolled.

If you enroll in paid Part A hospital insurance, you must also enroll in Part B medical insurance, for which you pay an additional monthly premium.

Inpatient Care Generally Covered by Part A

The following list gives you an idea of what Medicare Part A does, and does not, cover during your stay in a participating hospital or skilled nursing facility. Remember, though, even when Part A pays for something, there are significant financial limitations on its coverage.

Medicare Part A hospital insurance covers:

- a semi-private room (two to four beds per room); a private room if medically necessary
- all meals, including special, medically required diets
- regular nursing services
- special care units, such as intensive care and coronary care
- drugs, medical supplies and appliances furnished by the facility, such as casts, splints or a wheelchair; also, outpatient drugs and medical supplies if they permit you to leave the hospital or facility sooner
- hospital lab tests, X-rays and radiation treatment billed by the hospital
- operating and recovery room costs
- blood transfusions; you pay for the first three pints of blood, unless you arrange to have them replaced by an outside donation of blood to the hospital, and
- rehabilitation services, such as physical therapy, occupational therapy and speech pathology provided while you are in the hospital or nursing facility.

Medicare Part A hospital insurance does not cover:

- personal convenience items such as television, radio or telephone
- private duty nurses, or
- a private room, unless medically necessary.

How much of my bill will Medicare Part A pay?

All rules about how much Medicare Part A pays depend on how many days of inpatient care you have during what is called a benefit period or spell of illness. The benefit period begins the day you enter the hospital or skilled nursing facility as an inpatient—and continues until you have been out for 60 consecutive days. If you are in and out of the hospital or nursing facility several times but have not stayed out completely for 60 consecutive days, all your inpatient bills for that time will be figured as part of the same benefit period. Medicare Part A pays only certain amounts of a hospital bill for any one benefit period—and the rules are slightly different depending on whether the care facility is a hospital, psychiatric hospital, skilled nursing facility or care received at home or through a hospice. For example, you must pay an initial deductible—currently $812 per benefit period—before Medicare will pay anything.

What kinds of costs does Medicare Part B cover?

Part B is medical insurance. It is intended to help pay doctor bills for treatment in or out of the hospital. It also covers many other medical expenses you incur when you are not in the hospital, such as the costs of necessary medical equipment and tests.

The rules of eligibility for Part B medical insurance are much simpler than for Part A: If you are age 65 or over and are either a U.S. citizen, or a U.S. lawful permanent resident who has been here for five consecutive years, you are eligible to enroll in Medicare Part B medical insurance. This is true whether or not you are eligible for Part A hospital insurance.

Types of Services Covered by Medicare Part B

Part B medical insurance is intended to cover basic medical services provided by doctors, clinics and laboratories. The lists of services specifically covered and not covered are long, and do not always make a lot of common sense. To maximize your benefits, learn what is and is not covered.

Part B insurance pays for:

- doctors' services (including surgery) provided at a hospital, doctor's office or your home
- some screening tests, such as colorectal cancer screening, mammograms and PAP smears
- medical services provided by nurses, surgical assistants or laboratory or X-ray technicians
- services provided by pathologists or radiologists while you're an inpatient at a hospital
- outpatient hospital treatment, such as emergency room or clinic charges, X-rays, tests and injections

- an ambulance, if medically required for a trip to or from a hospital or skilled nursing facility
- medicine administered to you at a hospital or doctor's office
- medical equipment and supplies, such as splints, casts, prosthetic devices, body braces, heart pacemakers, corrective lenses after a cataract operation, oxygen equipment, wheelchairs and hospital beds
- some kinds of oral surgery
- some of the cost of outpatient physical and speech therapy
- manual manipulation of out-of-place vertebrae by a chiropractor
- part-time skilled nursing care, physical therapy and speech therapy provided in your home, and
- limited counseling by a clinical psychologist or social worker or mental health day treatment.

How much of my bill will Medicare Part B pay?

When all your medical bills are added up, you will see that Medicare pays, on average, for only about half the total. There are three major reasons why Part B medical insurance pays for so little.

First, Medicare does not cover a number of major medical expenses, such as routine physical examinations, medications, glasses, hearing aids, dentures and a number of other costly medical services.

Second, Medicare only pays a portion of what it decides is the proper amount—called the approved charges—for medical services. When Medicare decides that a particular ser-

vice is covered and determines the approved charges for it, Part B medical insurance usually pays only 80% of those approved charges; you are responsible for the remaining 20%.

Note, however, that there are now several types of treatments and medical providers for which Medicare Part B pays 100% of the approved charges rather than the usual 80%. These categories of care include: home health care, clinical laboratory services and flu and pneumonia vaccines.

Finally, the approved amount may seem reasonable to Medicare, but it is often considerably less than what doctors actually charge. If your doctor or other medical provider does not accept assignment of the Medicare charges, you are personally responsible for the difference.

Free Prescription Drugs

You may be able to avoid the outrageous cost of prescription drugs by asking your doctor for samples of the drugs. Pharmaceutical companies, in an effort to push their particular brand of drugs, send free samples to doctors, and many doctors are willing to dispense those drugs to you free of charge.

But many doctors forget what they have in the way of samples, or simply do not offer samples unless asked. Ask your doctor if he or she has samples of the drug you need, explaining that it will be very hard on your pocketbook if you have to purchase them. Don't count on this method to cover your long-term need for a particular drug, however.

States With Limits on Billing

Several states—Connecticut, Massachusetts, Minnesota, New York, Ohio, Pennsylvania, Rhode Island and Vermont—have passed balance billing or charge-limit laws. These laws forbid a doctor from billing patients for the balance of the bill above the amount Medicare approves. The patient is still responsible for the 20% of the approved charge not paid by Medicare Part B.

The specifics of these patient protection laws vary from state to state: Some forbid balance billing to any Medicare patient, others apply the restriction only to patients with limited incomes or assets. To find out the rules in your state, call the following agencies:

Connecticut Medical Assignment Program: 800-443-9946

Massachusetts Office of Elder Affairs: 800-882-2003

Minnesota Board of Aging, Ombudsman: 800-657-3591

New York State Office for the Aging: 800-342-9871

Ohio State Department of Health: 800-899-7127

Pennsylvania State Department of Aging: 717-783-8975

Rhode Island Department of Elderly Affairs: 800-322-2880

Vermont Department of Aging and Disabilities: 800-642-5119

More Information About Medicare

Social Security, Medicare and Government Pensions, by Joseph Matthews with Dorothy Matthews Berman (Nolo), further explains Medicare rules and offers strategies for dealing with the Medicare system.

The Medicare Handbook, available from the Social Security Administration, 800-772-1213, provides a complete list of Medicare benefits.

Pensions

Some employers set up pension plans for employees as part of compensation for work. Although no law requires employers to offer these retirement funds, they are a crucial part of many labor negotiations and individual job decisions.

Since the 1980s, however, the number and scope of pension plans—and the number of workers covered by them—have been steadily shrinking. Workers are far more frequently laid off or let go, and as they lose their jobs, they also lose the pension benefits that go with longtime employment.

What is a pension plan?

A pension is an agreement between you, your employer and, sometimes, your union. Under the agreement, your employer contributes a certain amount of money to a retirement fund during the years you work. With some plans, you must contribute as well. Then, when you retire, you begin to receive money from the fund. Most people begin to collect retirement money at age 65, but many pension plans pay a smaller amount at younger ages.

Pensions come in several shapes and sizes, but most plans can be divided into two basic categories: defined benefit and defined contribution plans.

What's the difference between "defined benefit" and "defined contribution" plans?

Under a defined benefit plan, you receive a definite, predetermined amount of money when you retire or become disabled. The amount you receive is based on your years of service with a particular employer. Most often, your monthly benefit is a fixed amount of money for each year of service. For example, a plan may pay $20 per month for each year of service. If you worked 20 years for that company, your pension would be $400 per month until you die or payments end, as specified in your individual plan.

Payments under a defined benefit plan may also be calculated on a percentage of your salary over the years. In such plans, the benefit is figured by taking your average salary over all the years you worked, multiplying that average by the fixed percentage established by the pension plan, and then multiplying that total by the number of years you worked for the company.

EXAMPLE

Bob's average salary over 20 years' employment with one employer was $20,000 per year. The company's pension plan used 1% of yearly salary as the pension base. Bob's pension would be calculated by taking 1% of his average salary of $20,000, which is $200. That amount would then be multiplied by Bob's 20 years of service, for a yearly pension of $4,000.

Defined contribution plans, on the other hand, do not guarantee any particular pension amount upon retirement. They guarantee only that the employer will pay into the pension fund a certain amount every month, or every year, for each employee. The employer usually pays a fixed percentage of an employee's wages or salary, although sometimes the amount is a fraction of the company's profits, with the size of each employee's pension share depending on the amount of wage or salary. Payments end at the employee's death, or as specified in the individual plan. Some plans, for example, pay benefit amounts to survivors for a specified number of years.

Who is entitled to pension benefits?

If your employer offers a pension, you must be permitted to participate in that plan if you are age 21 or older and have worked for the company for at least one year. One year means a total of 1,000 hours at work in a 12-month period beginning your first day of work; that is an average of 20 hours a week for 50 weeks.

To participate in a plan simply means that your time at the job will be counted toward qualifying for retirement benefits, and the employer must begin paying into your pension account if the plan requires ongoing employer contributions. But this does not necessarily mean that you will receive a pension; that question is governed by a different set of rules.

What does it mean to have "vested" pension benefits?

Every pension plan establishes a level of accumulated benefits—years of employment—after which you have a legal right to receive a pension at retirement. This is true whether or not you continue to work for that employer up to retirement age. When your accumulated benefits reach this level, they are called vested benefits.

There are good reasons to understand how and when your benefits become vested. Before retiring or changing jobs, you will want to know whether your pension rights have vested. Also, in many pension plans there are different levels of vesting, so you must learn what those levels are to know how much of a pension to count on, and when is the best time to leave the job.

Do I sacrifice my pension rights if I take early retirement?

Many pension plans allow you to choose reduced benefits if you have not quite reached retirement age. Full retirement benefits are usually offered at age 65, although a very few plans still offer full benefits earlier. Early retirement age is usually between 60 and 65.

If your pension plan offers early retirement, it must also offer an early retirement survivor annuity. The annuity gives your spouse, or in some plans another named survivor, a right to collect pension money if you die before normal retirement age. For your survivor to collect this annuity, you must have reached either the company's early retirement age, or have reached an age ten years before the plan's normal retirement age, whichever is later. In practical terms, this means you must have reached at least age 55.

Can I lose pension benefits if the company I work for changes hands?

When a company is sold or reorganized, it often changes the rules of its pension plan. But if your pension benefits have vested under an existing plan, you cannot legally be deprived of any of those benefits when the plan's rules change. The law does not protect you, however, if your pension rights have not yet vested at the time of the change.

Under federal law, if the company you work for is taken over by a new company which keeps the existing pension plan, your years of service continue to accumulate and the benefits you receive must at least equal the benefits you would have received under the old plan. The law does not, however, obligate a new company to continue paying into the existing pension plan. If the existing plan is discontinued, your benefits under that plan will not increase even though you continue to work. If the new company institutes its own pension plan, however, your continued work may accumulate credits under that plan, eventually entitling you to a second pension. These rules do not protect you from changes in a pension plan which occurred prior to 1974.

Know Your Rights

Your employer must provide a Summary Plan Description that explains how your pension plan works and describes your benefit choices. Your plan description should explain rules regarding participation, benefit accrual, vesting, pay-out options, retirement ages and claim procedures. If the plan changes, you are entitled to an updated Summary Plan Description from the personnel or pension plan administrator's office where you work, or from your union's pension office.

In addition to the general plan description, you are entitled to a statement of your personal benefit account that explains the benefits you have accrued and tells you what benefits have vested, or when they will vest. Not all employers provide this statement regularly; you may have to make a written request for it. You are also entitled to a copy of your benefit statement if you leave your job.

Each pension plan must make a yearly report to the federal government about the investments of the money in the plan fund. You should be able to see a copy of the latest annual report or to obtain a copy at minimal expense from your pension plan administrator's office.

And any time you have a question about your pension plan, you may make a written request for clarification to the plan administrator. If the administrator's office does not give you a satisfactory answer, direct your questions to the local area office of the federal government's Labor-Management Services Administration. You can find its number in the government listings of the white pages of the telephone book under United States Government, Department of Labor.

Do I have any rights to a spouse's pension if we divorce?

The answer depends on what state you live in and what agreement you and your spouse reach. Because pension benefits are deferred compensation for work already done, in community property states (Arizona, California, Idaho, Louisiana, Nevada, New Mexico, Texas, Washington and Wisconsin) and many other states, the portion of the pension earned during marriage is considered marital property and is subject to division at divorce.

Valuing a pension in order to divide it before the pension holder retires is not easy. Pensions are evaluated by people called actuaries, who figure out what a pension is worth by estimating the following:
• when the pension holder will retire
• when the pension holder will die

The Envelope, Please: Will I Get All the Money at Once?

Pension plans pay retirement benefits in a number of different ways. Frequently, a single plan will offer several payment options. The form of payment not only determines when you receive benefits, but also how much in total you receive and whether your spouse or other survivor can continue to get benefits after you die.

Lump-sum payment. Many defined contribution plans offer to pay you the entire amount accumulated in your pension account at retirement. If you need the money immediately to meet living expenses, this is an obvious choice. Also, this entire pension amount can serve as, or add to, an investment in a business, home or other property. Or, if you are investment savvy, you may feel that you can get a greater return on the money than the alternatives offered by your pension plan.

Simple life annuity. Annuities pay a fixed amount of benefits every year (although most annuities actually pay monthly) for the life of the person who is entitled to them. In a simple life annuity, when the person receiving the annuity dies, the benefits stop. There is no final lump sum payment and no provision to pay benefits to a spouse or other survivor. If you are relatively healthy when you claim your retirement, a simple life annuity may pay you more over the years than a lump sum pension plan.

Continuous annuity. Some plans offer an annuity that pays monthly installments for the life of the retired worker, and also provide a smaller continuing annuity for the worker's spouse or other survivor after the worker's death. If the worker dies within a specified time after retiring—usually five or ten years—the annuity will be paid to the surviving spouse or other beneficiary for the rest of the period set out in the annuity plan. A retiring worker who chooses this option will receive less in monthly pension benefits—usually about 10% less—than would be paid under a simple life annuity.

Joint and survivor annuity. A pension plan that pays benefits in any annuity form is required to offer a worker the choice of a joint and survivor annuity in addition to whatever other form of annuity is offered. This form of annuity pays monthly benefits as long as the retired worker is alive, and then continues to pay the worker's spouse for life. Some pension plans also permit a survivor annuity to be paid to a nonspouse beneficiary, but the law does not require that such a benefit be offered. A worker who chooses the joint and survivor annuity will receive slightly less in pension benefits than under a simple annuity plan; how much less is determined by the age of the worker's spouse or other named beneficiary. The younger the beneficiary—that is, the longer the pension is likely to be paid—the lower the benefits. The amount the survivor receives is usually half of the retired worker's pension amount, although a few plans provide for larger survivor payments.

- what salary the pension holder will have at retirement, and
- what inflation and interest rates are likely to do between now and when the pension holder retires.

Divorcing couples have several options when dividing pension rights. You can:

- *Agree to keep rights to your own pension plans.* This eliminates the need to value the pensions and minimizes your future financial ties.
- *Give up your individual interest in your spouse's pension plan in exchange for receiving money or some other property of equal value.* This requires that you value the pension, but minimizes your future financial ties.
- *Divide the value of your pension rights so that each takes a future share.* This requires that you value the pension. Furthermore, you stay financially tied to your ex-spouse because you won't get your share of the benefits until your ex-spouse is eligible to retire. You run the risk of your ex-spouse leaving the job before vesting or before the pension builds up.

Do I have any legal protection if my pension fund is mismanaged?

Since 1974, when the Employee Retirement Income Security Act (ERISA) was passed, at least some of the worst sorts of disappearing pension acts have been halted. To protect pension rights, ERISA:

- sets minimum standards for pension plans, guaranteeing that pension

rights cannot be unfairly denied or taken from a worker

- provides some protection for workers in the event certain types of pension plans cannot pay the benefits to which workers are entitled, and
- requires that employers provide full and clear information about employees' pension rights, including the way pension benefits accumulate, how the company invests pension funds and when and how pension benefits can be collected.

What if the pension fund simply runs out of money?

Under ERISA, there is some protection against such pension fund collapse. The Pension Benefit Guaranty Corporation (PBGC), a public, nonprofit insurance fund, provides some limited coverage against bankrupt pension funds. Should a pension fund be unable to pay all its obligations to its retirees, the PBGC may pay some of the pension fund's unfulfilled obligations.

If you have a question about termination of benefits because of failure of your pension plan or the sale or end of your employer's company, write or call the Pension Benefit Guaranty Corporation, 1200 K Street, NW, Washington, DC 20005-4026, 202-326-4000, 800-400-7242, 800-877-8339 (TDD). You can also use the PBGC website at http://www.pbgc.gov.

How do I claim my pension benefits?

Although ERISA does not spell out one uniform claim procedure for all pension

How do I claim my pension benefits?

Although ERISA does not spell out one uniform claim procedure for all pension plans, it does establish some rules which must be followed when you retire and want to claim your benefits. All pension plans must have an established claim procedure and all participants in the plan must be given a summary of the plan which explains that procedure. When your claim is filed, you must receive a decision on the claim, in writing, within a "reasonable time." The decision must state specific reasons for the denial of any claimed benefits and must explain the basis for determining the benefits which are granted.

What do I do if my claim is denied or if I disagree with the amount I receive?

If you disagree with either the amount of your benefits or the method in which they are to be paid, you have 60 days from the date you receive a written notice of the amount and method to file a written appeal. Your plan summary explains where and how to file the appeal. If you are considering an appeal, or have filed one, you have the right to examine the pension plan's files and records regarding your pension account, and you can present written materials that correct or contradict information in those files.

Within 60 days of filing your appeal, the pension plan administrators must file a written response to your claim. If your appeal is denied, you have a legal right to press your claim in either state or federal court.

More Information About Pension Plans

Social Security, Medicare and Government Pensions, by Joseph L. Matthews with Dorothy Matthews Berman (Nolo), contains detailed information about pension plans and shows you how to maximize your pension benefits.

Get a Life: You Don't Need a Million to Retire Well, by Ralph Warner (Nolo), discusses strategies for creating a satisfying and enjoyable retirement, including pension plans.

Divorce and Money, by Violet Woodhouse (Nolo), guides you through the difficult process of dividing retirement funds in the event of a divorce.

You can also get information and assistance regarding your rights under pension plans from the independent, nongovernment Pension Rights Center, 918 16th Street, NW, Suite 704, Washington, DC 20006-2902, 202-296-3778, 202-833-2472 (fax).

Retirement Plans

In decades past, most Americans relied on retirement income from pension plans and Social Security benefits. However, that is changing rapidly. Today, the Social Security program is weaker than ever before, and many employers offer retirement plans such as 401(k)s instead of pensions. In addition, many Americans are turning to other devices, such as individual retirement accounts (IRAs), to save for the future.

Why should I set up a retirement plan?

The obvious reason to create a retirement plan is so that you'll have enough income to support yourself when you're no longer working. But retirement plans offer other important benefits as well.

Retirement plans were created by the U.S. Congress several decades ago to encourage working people to save for their later years—and they come with significant tax incentives. Contributions to most types of retirement plans are tax deductible.

Also, if you have the opportunity to participate in a retirement plan—such as a 401(k) plan—at work, your employer may make contributions to the plan in addition to your own contributions. A decision not to participate may mean that you're turning down a gift of additional investment dollars.

But of course it's not all good news. Retirement plans carry some restrictions, too. For example, there are limits on how much you or your employer can contribute to a retirement plan each year. And there are often penalties if you withdraw money before retirement.

What is a qualified retirement plan?

A qualified plan is simply one that is described in Section 401(a) of the Tax Code. A qualified plan must be established by an employer or a self-employed individual. The most common type of qualified plan is a profit sharing plan. Profit sharing plans include 401(k)s. Most likely, if you are covered by a retirement plan at work, it is a qualified plan.

In general, contributions to qualified plans are not taxed until you withdraw money from the plan. In addition, any contributions an employer makes on an employee's behalf are tax deductible for the employee. Employee contributions are also tax deductible.

What is a 401(k) plan?

401(k) plans are deferred compensation savings and investment programs—financial structures into which employees can place a certain amount of their wages and defer the taxes on them until retirement. An employee makes contributions by diverting a portion of his or her salary into the plan. Employers can, but do not have to, contribute a set amount per year to the employee's account. Contributions to the plan are tax deductible. The income and profits that come from investing the contributions are not taxed either. However, when the employee starts making withdrawals (usually at retirement), the money is subject to income tax.

Why are 401(k) plans so popular?

Employers like 401(k) plans because they are less expensive to fund than other types of retirement plans. This is because all or most of the plan contributions are usually made by the employee, not the employer.

Employees like 401(k) plans because they can save for retirement while simultaneously reducing their current income tax bill. And, because 401(k) plans allow employees to contribute more each year than do individual retirement plans, such as IRAs, the savings can be substantial. The ability to withdraw money early in certain circumstances is also an attractive feature for many employees. In addition, 401(k) plans offer a certain amount of flexibility. For example, an employee can usually change the amount of salary deferred into the plan if his or her circumstances change. And employees can typically make their own investment decisions.

What is an Individual Retirement Account (IRA)?

An IRA, or Individual Retirement Account, is a retirement plan governed by Section 408 of the Tax Code. The rules are different than those for qualified plans. The most significant difference is that, unlike qualified plans, which must be established by employers, some IRAs (such as traditional and Roth IRAs) can only be established by individuals. However, this doesn't hold true for all IRAs. Other types, such as SEPs and SIMPLE IRAs, are for businesses only and must be established by an employer.

What is the difference between a traditional and Roth IRA?

There are two big differences between traditional and Roth IRAs. Those differences determine who can contribute to the plan and what type of tax benefit you receive.

Anyone can establish a traditional IRA, regardless of income. For most people, the money deposited into a traditional IRA each year is tax deductible. (People who earn very high salaries can't deduct the value of their contributions.) For anyone who opens a traditional IRA, the income and profits earned on contributions is not taxed. But when you withdraw money from your account, those funds are subject to income taxes.

The Roth IRA, created by the 1997 Taxpayer Relief Act, is a whole different animal. Workers who earn high incomes cannot contribute to Roth IRAs. For those who can establish a Roth IRA, contributions are not tax deductible. Income accumulates tax free, however, as long as the contributions stay in the account for at least five years. Most important, withdrawals are not taxed.

I am self-employed. Can I set up a retirement plan?

Although self-employed people cannot open 401(k) accounts, they can take advantage of many other types of retirement plans. These fall into three broad categories: individual plans, employer IRAs and Keogh plans.

- *Individual plans.* Self-employed workers can always establish and contribute to a traditional or Roth IRA.
- *Employer IRAs.* Self-employed workers can take advantage of a category of IRAs designed for employers: SIMPLE IRAs and SEPs. SEPs and SIMPLE IRAs permit larger contributions (and, therefore, bigger tax deductions) than do traditional and Roth IRAs.
- *Keogh plans.* A Keogh plan is a qualified plan for self-employed individuals. Keoghs differ somewhat from qualified plans established by companies. For example, contribution limits for Keoghs are lower than for other qualified plans.

Can I contribute to a traditional or Roth IRA if I am already contributing to another retirement plan?

Usually, yes. Anyone can contribute to a traditional or Roth IRA, even if they are already contributing to another retirement plan. For example, if you contribute to a 401(k) plan at work, you can also establish a traditional or Roth IRA. Or, if you are self-employed and contribute to a Keogh, you can also set up a traditional or Roth IRA.

What does it mean to be "vested" in my retirement plan?

If you are vested in your company's retirement plan, you can take it with you when you leave your job. If you are 50% vested, you can take 50% of it with you when you go. In the case of a 401(k) plan, you are always 100% vested in the salary you contribute to the plan.

Is my retirement plan protected from creditors?

Most employer plans are safe from creditors, thanks to the Employee Retirement Income Security Act of 1974, commonly known as ERISA. ERISA requires all plans under its control (generally, qualified plans) to include provisions that prohibit the assignment of plan assets to a creditor. The U.S. Supreme Court has also ruled that ERISA plans are protected from creditors even when you are in bankruptcy.

Unfortunately, Keogh plans that cover only you—or you and your partners, but not employees—are not governed or protected by ERISA. Neither are IRAs, whether traditional, Roth, SEP or SIMPLE.

But even though IRAs are not automatically protected from creditors under federal law, many states have put safeguards in place that specifically protect IRA assets from creditors' claims, whether or not you are in bankruptcy. Also, some state laws contain protective language that is broad enough to protect single-participant Keoghs, as well.

More Information About Retirement Plans

IRAs, 401(k)s & Other Retirement Plans: Taking Your Money Out, by Twila Slesnick and John C. Suttle (Nolo), explains the different types of retirement plans—including 401(k)s and other profit-sharing plans, self-employed plans (Keoghs), IRAs and tax-deferred annuities—and the taxes and penalties that can deplete your nest egg.

Creating Your Own Retirement Plan: IRAs & Keoghs for the Self-employed, by Twila Slesnick and John Suttle (Nolo), provides self-employed people with the information they need to choose, establish and administer a retirement plan.

http://www.nolo.com

Nolo offers self-help information about a wide variety of legal topics, including issues affecting older Americans.

http://www.aarp.org

The American Association of Retired Persons offers helpful information on a range of issues for older people—including family, health, money matters, housing and crime prevention.

http://www.aoa.dhhs.gov/ elderpage.html

The Administration on Aging's ElderPage provides directories of resources that can help with aging isssues—along with a host of articles covering topics such as retirement planning, housing alterations and Medicare fraud.

http://www.pbgc.gov

The Pension Benefit Guaranty Corporation (PBGC) was established to protect pension benefits, primarily by giving financial assistance to some types of plans that have become insolvent. Its site provides information on pension rights and benefits, including what to expect if your pension plan changes hands and how to appeal an adverse pension decision.

Spouses and Partners

LOVE IS LOVE'S REWARD.

—JOHN DRYDEN

15.2	*Living Together— Gay & Straight*
15.6	*Premarital Agreements*
15.8	*Marriage*
15.16	*Divorce*
15.26	*Domestic Violence*
15.29	*Changing Your Name*

We all know how the story goes: Boy meets girl, boy and girl fall in love, get married and live happily ever after. And sometimes boy meets boy or girl meets girl—but the fairy tale hopes remain largely unchanged.

What we often don't see are the details: Where do boy and girl get a marriage license, and do they need blood tests first? What should girl and girl do if they can't get married, but they want to buy a house together? And what if the fairy tale turns into a nightmare, and one partner wants to end it?

Our intimate relationships aren't always the stuff of childhood tales, and there are a lot of real-world concerns—emotional and practical—that need attention every day. The questions and answers in this chapter are designed to help you with some of the legal tasks and troubles that may surface during the course of your relationship. Keep in mind that the laws in this area vary, sometimes dramatically, from state to state. We've put together a good overview to get you started, but be certain to confirm your state's law before you act on any of the information given here.

Living Together —Gay & Straight

Many laws are designed to govern and protect the property ownership rights of married couples. But no such laws exist for unmarried couples. If you and your partner are unmarried, you must take steps to protect your relationship and define your property rights. You will also face special concerns if you are raising children together.

My partner and I don't own much property. Do we really need a written contract covering who owns what?

If you haven't been together long and don't own much, it's really not necessary. But the longer you live together, the more important it is to prepare a written contract making it clear who owns what—especially if you begin to accumulate a lot of property. Otherwise, you might face a serious (and potentially expensive) battle if you split up and can't agree on how to divide what you've acquired. And when things are good, taking the time to draft a well-thought-out contract helps you clarify your intentions.

My partner makes a lot more money than I do. Should our property agreements cover who is entitled to her income and the items we purchase with it?

Absolutely. Although each person starts out owning all of his or her job-related income, many states allow this to be changed by an oral contract or even by a contract implied from the circumstances of how you live. These types of contracts often lead to misunderstandings during a breakup. For example, absent a written agreement stating whether income will be shared or kept separate, one partner might falsely claim the other promised to split his income 50-50. Although this can be tough to prove in court, the very fact that a lawsuit can be brought creates a huge problem. For obvious reasons, it's an especially good idea to make a written agreement if a person with a big income is living with and supporting someone with little or no income.

What is palimony? And should we make any agreements about it?

Palimony is a phrase coined by journalists—not a legal concept—to describe the division of property or alimony-like support paid to one partner in an unmarried couple by the other after a break up. Members of unmarried couples are not legally entitled to such payments unless they have an agreement. In the famous case of *Marvin v. Marvin*, the California Supreme Court ruled that a person who cohabitated and later sued for support could argue that an *implied* contract existed between the parties. To avoid a cry for palimony, it's best to include in a written agreement whether or not one person will make payments to the other.

Buying a House? Make an Agreement

It's particularly important to make a written property agreement if you buy a house together; the large financial and emotional commitments involved are good reasons to take extra care with your plans.

Your contract should cover at least four major areas:

How is title (ownership) listed on the deed? One choice is as "joint tenants with rights of survivorship," meaning that when one of you dies, the other automatically inherits the whole house. Another option is "tenants in common," meaning that when one of you dies, that share of the house goes to whomever is named in a will or trust, or goes to blood relatives if the deceased partner left no estate plan.

How much of the house does each of you own? If it's not 50-50, is there a way for the person who owns less than half to increase his share—for example, by fixing up the house or making a larger share of the mortgage payment?

What happens to the house if you break up? Will one of you have the first right to stay in the house (perhaps to care for a young child) and buy the other out, or will the house be sold and the proceeds divided?

If one of you has a buyout right, how will the house be appraised and how long will the buyout take? Most people agree to use the realtor they used to buy the house to appraise it, and then give the buying partner one to five years to pay off the other.

My partner and I have a young son, and I'm thinking of giving up my job to become a full-time parent. How might I be compensated for my loss of income?

This is a personal—not a legal—question. If you and your partner decide that compensation is fair, there are many ways to arrange it. For example, you could make an agreement stating that if you break up while you're still providing childcare, your partner will pay an agreed-upon amount to help you make the transition to a new situation. Or, you might agree in writing that your partner will pay you a salary during the time you stay at home, including Social Security and other required benefits.

Am I liable for the debts of my partner?

Not unless you have specifically undertaken responsibility to pay a particular debt—for example, as a cosigner or if the debt is charged to a joint account. By contrast, husbands and wives are generally liable for all debts incurred during marriage, even those incurred by the other person. The one exception for unmarried couples applies if you have registered as domestic partners in a city where the domestic partner ordinance states that you agree to pay for each other's "basic living expenses" (food, shelter and clothing).

If one of us dies, how much property will the survivor inherit?

Nothing, unless the deceased partner made a will or used another estate planning device such as a living trust or joint tenancy agreement, or, if under the terms of a contract (such as a contract to purchase household furnishings together), the survivor already owns part of the property. This is unlike the legal situation married couples enjoy, where a surviving spouse automatically inherits a major portion of a deceased spouse's property. The bottom line is simple: To protect the person you live with, you must specifically leave her property using a will, living trust or other legal document.

If I am injured or incapacitated, can my partner make medical or financial decisions on my behalf?

Not unless you have executed a document called a "durable power of attorney" giving your partner the specific authority to make those decisions. Without a durable power of attorney, huge emotional and practical problems can result. For example, the fate of a severely ill or injured person could be in the hands of a biological relative who disapproves of the relationship and who makes medical decisions contrary to what the ill or injured person wants. It is far better to prepare the necessary paperwork so the loving and knowing partner will be the primary decision-maker. For more information about durable powers of attorney, see Chapter 13, *Living Wills and Powers of Attorney.*

If my partner and I live together long enough, won't we have a common law marriage?

Probably not. A common law marriage can occur only when:
- a straight couple (common law marriages don't apply to same-sex couples) lives together in one of the few states that still recognize common law marriages
- for a significant period of time (not defined in any state)
- holding themselves out as a married couple—typically this means using the same last name, referring to the other as "my husband" or "my wife" and filing a joint tax return, and
- intending to be married.

Unless all four are true, there is no common law marriage. When one exists, the couple must go through a formal divorce to end the relationship.

Parenting Concerns of Unmarried Couples

All unmarried couples face unique concerns when they raise children together.

- Straight couples who have children together should take steps to ensure that both are recognized as the legal parents. Both parents should be listed on the birth certificate, and at a minimum the father should sign a statement of paternity. Even better, both parents should sign a statement of parentage acknowledging the father's paternity.

- All unmarried couples face potential obstacles when adopting together because all states favor married couples as adoptive parents.

For more information about adoption by unmarried couples, see Chapter 16, *Parents and Children*.

- Members of unmarried couples who have children from former marriages face the potential prejudice of an ex-spouse or a judge called on to make a custody determination. In most states, this is a much greater concern for lesbian and gay parents than for straight ones, as judges (with the exception of a few states which also come down hard on unmarried couples) tend to be more tolerant of opposite-sex cohabitation than same-sex cohabitation. Many judges prefer to place children with a parent who is heterosexual and married, if that's an option.

States That Recognize Common Law Marriage

Alabama

Colorado

District of Columbia

Iowa

Kansas

Montana

New Hampshire*

Oklahoma

Pennsylvania

Rhode Island

South Carolina

Texas

Utah

*For inheritance purposes only.

More Information About Living Together

Living Together: A Legal Guide for Unmarried Couples, by Attorneys Ralph Warner, Toni Ihara & Frederick Hertz (Nolo), explains the legal rules that apply to unmarried couples and includes sample contracts governing jointly owned property.

A Legal Guide for Lesbian & Gay Couples, by Hayden Curry, Denis Clifford and Frederick Hertz (Nolo), sets out the law and contains sample agreements for same-sex couples.

Premarital Agreements

Love reasons without reason.

—WILLIAM SHAKESPEARE

Before a couple marries, the parties may make an agreement concerning certain aspects of their relationship. This agreement might cover their responsibilities and property rights during marriage—for example, how the mortgage gets paid and who will stay home to take care of the kids. But more likely it will determine how property will be divided, and whether alimony will be paid, in the event the couple later divorces. These agreements are also called antenuptial or prenuptial agreements.

Are premarital agreements legal?

Courts usually uphold premarital agreements unless one person shows that the agreement:

- promotes divorce (for example, by providing for a large award of alimony in the event of divorce),
- was written and signed with the intention of divorcing, or
- was created unfairly (for example, one spouse giving up all of the rights in his spouse's future earnings without the advice of an attorney).

Courts will not uphold agreements that deal with nonmonetary issues. For example, you can't sue your spouse for failure to take out the garbage, even if your premarital agreement says that he or she must do so every Tuesday night.

Should my fiancé and I make a premarital agreement?

Whether you should make a premarital agreement depends on your circumstances and on the two of you as individuals. Some couples choose to make a premarital agreement as a way of clarifying their intentions and expectations, as well as their rights should they later split up.

On the other hand, some couples make premarital agreements to circumvent what a court might decide in the event of a divorce. Often this happens when one partner has property that he or she wishes to keep if the marriage ends—for example, a considerable income or a family business. Perhaps most frequently, premarital agreements are made by individuals who have children or grandchildren from prior marriages. In this case, a partner may use a premarital agreement to ensure that the bulk of his or her property passes to the children or grandchildren, rather than the current spouse.

Are there rules about what can or cannot be included in a premarital agreement?

A law called the Uniform Premarital Agreement Act provides legal guidelines for people who wish to make agreements prior to marriage regarding the following: ownership, management and control of property; property disposition on separation, divorce and death; alimony; wills; and life insurance beneficiaries.

States that haven't adopted the Act (or which have made some changes to it) have other laws, which often differ from the Act in minor ways. One important difference is that a few states, including California, do not allow premarital agreements to modify or eliminate the right of a spouse to receive court-ordered alimony at divorce. Other states have their own quirky laws—Maine, for example, voids all premarital agreements one and one-half years after the parties to the contract become parents, unless the agreement is renewed in writing.

In every state, whether covered by the Act or not, couples are prohibited from making binding provisions about child support payments. Also, agreements are not enforceable if one person proves the agreement was negotiated unconscionably or involuntarily. Premarital agreements are effective only upon a marriage and should always be in writing.

States That Have Adopted the Uniform Premarital Agreement Act

Arizona	Montana
Arkansas	Nebraska
California	Nevada
Connecticut	New Mexico
Delaware	North Carolina
District of Columbia	North Dakota
Hawaii	Oregon
Idaho	Rhode Island
Illinois	South Dakota
Indiana	Texas
Iowa	Utah
Kansas	Virginia
Maine	Wisconsin

Can my fiancé and I make our premarital agreement without a lawyer?

You can look up the laws for your state and write your agreement yourselves. Unfortunately, however, there's no good self-help resource for writing premarital agreements, and if you make a mistake, a court may find your agreement unenforceable. If you'd like to draft a contract on your own, we recommend that you have an attorney skilled in family or contract law (preferably both) look it over to make sure you've followed the law to the letter.

I've been living with someone for several years and we've decided to get married. Will our existing property agreement be enforceable even after we are married?

Probably not. To be enforceable, contracts made before marriage must be made in contemplation of marriage. This means that unless your living together contract is made shortly before your marriage, when you both plan to be married, a court will disregard it.

If you want to convert your living together contract into a premarital agreement, follow these steps:

- Use your upcoming marriage as an opportunity to take another look at your agreement, and make any agreed-upon updates and changes.
- Rewrite your agreement. Call it a premarital or prenuptial agreement, and state that it is made in contem-

plation of marriage and does not take effect until you marry.

- Because there is no good self-help resource in this area, and because even a small mistake can result in your agreement later being held unenforceable, have your agreement checked out by a lawyer.
- Sign the document in front of a notary.

Marriage

THERE IS MORE OF GOOD NATURE
THAN OF GOOD SENSE AT THE BOTTOM
OF MOST MARRIAGES.

—HENRY DAVID THOREAU

Marriage is the legal union of two people. When you are married, your responsibilities and rights toward your spouse concerning property and support are defined by the laws of the state in which you live. The two of you may be able to modify the rules set up by your state, however, if you desire to do so.

Your marriage can only be terminated by a court granting a divorce or an annulment.

What are the legal rights and benefits conferred by marriage?

Marriage entails many rights and benefits, including the rights to:

- file joint income tax returns with the IRS and state taxing authorities

- create a "family partnership" under federal tax laws, which allows you to divide business income among family members (this will often lower the total tax on the income)
- create a marital life estate trust (this type of trust is discussed in Chapter 12—see *Estate and Gift Taxes*)
- receive spouse's and dependent's Social Security, disability, unemployment, veterans', pension and public assistance benefits
- receive a share of your deceased spouse's estate under intestate succession laws
- claim an estate tax marital deduction
- sue a third person for wrongful death and loss of consortium
- sue a third person for offenses that interfere with the success of your marriage, such as alienation of affection and criminal conversation (these lawsuits are available in only a few states)
- receive family rates for insurance
- avoid the deportation of a noncitizen spouse
- enter hospital intensive care units, jails and other places where visitors are restricted to immediate family
- live in neighborhoods zoned for "families only"
- make medical decisions about your spouse in the event of disability, and
- claim the marital communications privilege, which means a court can't force you to disclose the contents of confidential communications between you and your spouse during your marriage.

Requirements for Marriage

You must meet certain requirements in order to marry. These vary slightly from state to state, but essentially require that you:

- are one man and one woman
- are at least the age of consent (usually 18, though sometimes you may marry younger with your parents' consent)
- are not too closely related to your intended spouse
- have the mental capacity—that is, you must understand what you are doing and what consequences your actions may have
- are sober at the time of the marriage
- are not married to anyone else
- get a blood test, and
- obtain a marriage license.

What's the difference between a "marriage license" and a "marriage certificate"?

A marriage license is the piece of paper that authorizes you to get married and a marriage certificate is the document that proves you are married.

Typically, couples obtain a marriage license, have the wedding ceremony and then have the person who performed the ceremony file a marriage certificate in the appropriate county office within a few days. (This may be the office of the county clerk, recorder or registrar, depending on where you live.) The married couple will be sent a certified copy of the marriage certificate within a few weeks after the ceremony.

Most states require both spouses, the person who officiated and one or two witnesses to sign the marriage certificate; often this is done just after the ceremony.

Where can we get a marriage license?

Usually, you may apply for a marriage license at any county clerk's office in the state where you want to be married. (In some circumstances, you must apply in the county or town where you intend to be married—this depends on state law.) You'll probably have to pay a small fee for your license, and you may also have to wait a few days before it is issued.

In some states, even after you get your license you'll have to wait a short period of time—one to three days—before you tie the knot. Often, this waiting period can be waived in special circumstances. Licenses are good for 30 days to one year, depending on the state. If your license expires before you get married, you can apply for a new one.

For more specific information about marriage license laws in your state, see *Marriage Licenses and Blood Tests*, below.

Do all states require blood tests? And why are they required?

Many states—but not all—require blood tests for couples planning to marry (see the chart below). But the trend is to eliminate these tests. Keep this in mind as you check the chart below. Your state's requirements may have changed since the publication of this book.

Blood tests are to find out whether either partner has a venereal disease or rubella (measles). The tests may also disclose the presence of genetic disorders such as sickle cell anemia or Tay-Sachs disease. You will not be tested for HIV, but in some states, the person who tests you will provide you with information about HIV and AIDS. In most states, the blood test may be waived for people over 50 and for other reasons, including pregnancy or sterility.

If either partner tests positive for a venereal disease, what happens depends on the state where you are marrying. Some states may refuse to issue you a marriage license. Other states may allow you to marry as long as you both know that the disease is present.

MARRIAGE LICENSES AND BLOOD TESTS

State	Blood tests required	Waiting period between applying for and receiving license	How soon you can marry after receiving license	When license expires
Alabama	Yes	None	Immediately	30 days
Alaska	No	3 days	Immediately	3 months
Arizona	No	None	Immediately	1 year
Arkansas	No	None	Immediately	No provision
California	No	None	Immediately	90 days
Colorado	No	None	Immediately	30 days
Connecticut	Yes	None	Immediately	65 days
Delaware	No	None	24 hours; 96 hours if both parties are nonresidents	30 days
District of Columbia	Yes	3 days	Immediately	No provision
Florida	No	None; 3 days if couple have not attended marriage preparation class	Immediately	60 days
Georgia	Yes	None	Immediately	No provision
Hawaii	No	None	Immediately	30 days
Idaho	No	None	Immediately	No expiration period
Illinois	No	None	1 day	60 days
Indiana	Yes	None	Immediately	60 days
Iowa	No	3 days	Immediately	No provision
Kansas	No	3 days	Immediately	6 months
Kentucky	No	None	Immediately	30 days
Louisiana	No	None	3 days	30 days
Maine	No	3 days	Immediately	90 days
Maryland	No	None	48 hours	6 months
Massachusetts	Yes	3 days	Immediately	60 days
Michigan	No	3 days	Immediately	33 days
Minnesota	No	5 days	Immediately	6 months
Mississippi	Yes	3 days	Immediately	No provision

MARRIAGE LICENSES AND BLOOD TESTS

State	Blood tests required	Waiting period between applying for and receiving license	How soon you can marry after receiving license	When license expires
Missouri	No	3 days	Immediately	30 days
Montana	Yes	None	Immediately	180 days
Nebraska	No	None	Immediately	1 year
Nevada	No	None	Immediately	1 year
New Hampshire	No	3 days	Immediately	90 days
New Jersey	No	72 hours	Immediately	30 days
New Mexico	No	None	Immediately	No provision
New York	No	None	24 hours	60 days
North Carolina	No	None	Immediately	60 days
North Dakota	No	None	Immediately	60 days
Ohio	No	None	Immediately	60 days
Oklahoma	Yes	None	Immediately	30 days
Oregon	No	None	3 days	60 days
Pennsylvania	No	3 days	Immediately	60 days
Rhode Island	No	None	Immediately	3 months
South Carolina	No	24 hours	Immediately	No provision (but counties may impose expiration periods)
South Dakota	No	None	Immediately	20 days
Tennessee	No	None	Immediately	30 days
Texas	No	None	3 days	31 days
Utah	No	None	Immediately	30 days
Vermont	No	None	Immediately	60 days
Virginia	No	None	Immediately	60 days
Washington	No	None	3 days	60 days
West Virginia	No	None	Immediately	60 days
Wisconsin	No	5 days	Immediately	30 days
Wyoming	No	None	Immediately	No expiration period

Who can perform a marriage ceremony?

Nonreligious ceremonies—called civil ceremonies—must be performed by a judge, justice of the peace or court clerk who has legal authority to perform marriages, or by a person given temporary authority by a judge or court clerk to conduct a marriage ceremony. Religious ceremonies must be conducted by a clergy member—for example, a priest, minister or rabbi. Native American weddings may be performed by a tribal chief or by another official, as designated by the tribe.

Are there requirements about what the ceremony must include?

Usually, no special words are required as long as the spouses acknowledge their intention to marry each other. Keeping that in mind, you can design whatever type of ceremony you desire.

It is customary to have witnesses to the marriage, although they are not required in all states.

What is a common law marriage?

In twelve states and the District of Columbia, heterosexual couples can become legally married if they:

• live together for a long period of time
• hold themselves out to others as husband and wife, and
• intend to be married.

These marriages are called common law marriages. Contrary to popular belief, even if two people cohabit for a certain number of years, if they don't intend to be married and hold themselves out as married, there is no common law marriage.

When a common law marriage exists, the spouses receive the same legal treatment given to formally married couples, including the requirement that they go through a legal divorce to end the marriage.

To find out whether your state recognizes common law marriages, see the list on page 15.6.

Does any state recognize same-sex marriage?

No state yet recognizes same-sex marriages. Some states have passed laws specifically barring same-sex marriages, and the number of states with such laws are increasing. And even states without an explicit "no-same-sex-marriage" law on the books do not allow same-sex couples to enter into legal marriage.

Despite all this, however, there is some good news to report. In the 1990s, there were two landmark cases that advanced the cause of legally recognized same-sex partnerships: the Hawaii case of *Baehr v. Miike*, and the Vermont case of *Baker v. State*.

In the Hawaii case, three same-sex couples sued the state, arguing that its failure to issue marriage licenses to them violated the Equal Rights Amendment to the state constitution. The Hawaii Supreme Court—while not explicitly finding in favor of same-sex marriage—ruled that the couples' lawsuit raised legitimate gender-discrimination concerns under the state constitution, and sent the case back to lower court. After a trial in the lower court, that judge ruled that the same-sex marriage ban was invalid. The state appealed. While that appeal was pending, Hawaii voters passed a constitutional amendment banning same-sex marriage. This new law effectively ended the case.

Although in the end Hawaii did not permit same-sex marriage, when the case was pending the "threat" of legalized gay marriage was in the air. The furor unleashed by the Hawaii case caused many state legislators to pass laws banning same-sex marriage. The federal government also got caught up in the hysteria, passing the "Defense of Marriage Act" (DOMA) in 1996. DOMA prohibits the federal government from recognizing same-sex marriages or denies federal benefits (such as income tax, immigration and Social Security) to spouses in same-sex marriages. Furthermore, in anticipation of a time when some forward-thinking state might allow full legal marriage for a same-sex couple, DOMA permits states to ignore a same-sex marriage entered into in another state.

Hawaii's Compromise: The Reciprocal Beneficiaries Law

In an effort to prevent Hawaii courts from allowing same-sex marriage, the state legislature passed the Reciprocal Beneficiaries Law of 1997. Couples who sign up as reciprocal beneficiaries gain many of the rights and benefits granted by the state to married couples. Although not quite the victory that the same-sex marriage movement had hoped for, it was still groundbreaking because it was the first statewide domestic partnership law passed in the United States. (For more on domestic partnerships, see "California's New Domestic Partnership Law,".)

Any two individuals over the age of 18 who are not permitted to marry under Hawaii law are eligible to register with the state as reciprocal beneficiaries. Rights and benefits extended to reciprocal beneficiaries include hospital visitation rights, the ability to sue for wrongful death, and property and inheritance rights similar to those enjoyed by married couples. Unlike couples registered under Vermont's civil union law (see below), reciprocal beneficiaries in Hawaii are not granted access to family court—which governs issues like divorce, alimony and child support for married couples.

The website of Hawaii's Vital Records Office has information about how to register as reciprocal beneficiaries, at http://www.state.hi.us/doh/records/rbrfaq.htm.

Across the county in Vermont, the state supreme court issued a landmark decision in *Baker v. State* (1999). The Vermont Supreme Court ruled that prohibiting same-sex marriage violated the Vermont constitution because it denied same-sex couples the rights granted straight couples. But instead of ordering the government to issue marriage licenses to gay and lesbian couples, the court left it up to the state legislature to remedy the situation.

In response to the court's order in *Baker v. State*, the legislature passed a law creating the civil union registration system. Under this system, same-sex couples can register their civil union, and they are then subject to all state laws applying to married couples. (For more details, see "The Vermont Civil Union Law," below.)

It is too soon to tell what effect the Vermont civil union statute will have on the nation. The statute allows couples who aren't Vermont residents to register their civil unions, but it is doubtful that other states will recognize their status. Although the federal constitution requires each state to give "full faith and credit" to the laws of other states—such that a heterosexual marriage or divorce in one state is recognized in another—the federal Defense of Marriage Act (DOMA) was passed with the express purpose of undercutting that guarantee in the case of same-sex marriages. At the same time, because DOMA abridges the rights guaranteed under the full faith and credit clause it seems ripe for a constitutional challenge.

The recent years have been marked by a rapid succession of victories and disappointments in the fight to legalize same-sex marriage. The best we can tell you at this point is: "Stay tuned." And you can always check the website of the Lambda Legal Defense and Education Fund's Marriage Project for the latest news, at www.lambdalegal.org.

The Vermont Civil Union Law

In 1999, the Vermont legislature passed the Vermont Civil Union law, which went into effect on July 1, 2000. While this law doesn't legalize same-sex marriages, it does provide gay and lesbian couples with many of the same advantages including:

- use of family laws such as annulment, divorce, child custody, child support, alimony, domestic violence, adoption and property division
- the right to sue for wrongful death, loss of consortium and any other tort or law related to spousal relationships
- medical rights such as hospital visitation, notification and durable power of attorney
- family leave benefits
- joint state tax filing, and
- property inheritance without a will.

These rights apply only to couples residing in Vermont. Even for Vermont residents, this new civil union law does not provide same-sex couples with rights and benefits provided by federal law; for example, same-sex couples cannot take advantage of Social Security benefits, immigration privileges and the marriage exemption to federal estate tax. Couples from outside Vermont can come to Vermont and be joined in civil union, but it appears unlikely that any other state will recognize the union.

To read Vermont's official state guide on the new law, visit http://www.sec.state.vt.us/pubs/civilunions.htm.

California's New Domestic Partnership Law

A comprehensive new domestic partnership law took effect in California in January 2002. With this new law, California, along with Hawaii and Vermont, is in the forefront of states offering legal protections to same-sex couples.

Under the California law, a registered domestic partner may now:

- adopt a partner's child using the stepparent adoption process—a faster and less expensive process than second-parent adoption
- sue for wrongful death of a partner
- make healthcare decisions for a partner who becomes incapacitated
- use sick leave to care for an ill domestic partner or the child of a domestic partner
- relocate with a partner without losing eligibility for unemployment benefits
- apply for disability benefits on behalf of an injured or incapacitated partner, and
- deduct the cost of a domestic partner's health insurance or other benefit from state income taxes.

Same-sex partners must register with the California Secretary of State's office (http://www.ssa.ca.gov) to be eligible for the rights and benefits extended under this law.

Divorce

THERE IS NO DISPARITY

IN MARRIAGE LIKE UNSUITABLILITY

OF MIND AND PURPOSE.

—CHARLES DICKENS

Divorce is the legal termination of a marriage. In some states, divorce is called dissolution or dissolution of marriage. A divorce usually includes division of marital property and, if necessary, arrangements for child custody and support. It leaves both people free to marry again.

How does an annulment differ from a divorce?

Like a divorce, an annulment is a court procedure that dissolves a marriage. But an annulment treats the marriage as though it never happened. For some people, divorce carries a stigma, and they would rather their marriage be annulled. Others prefer an annulment because it may be easier to remarry in their church if they go through an annulment rather than a divorce.

Grounds for annulment vary slightly from state to state. Generally, an annulment may be obtained for one of the following reasons:

- *misrepresentation or fraud*—for example, a spouse lied about the capacity to have children, stated that she had reached the age of consent or failed to say that she was still married to someone else
- *concealment*—for example, concealing an addiction to alcohol or drugs, conviction of a felony, children from a prior relationship, a sexually transmitted disease or impotency
- *refusal or inability to consummate the marriage*—that is, refusal or inability of a spouse to have sexual intercourse with the other spouse, or
- *misunderstanding*—for example, one person wanted children and the other did not.

These are the grounds for civil annulments; within the Roman Catholic church, a couple may obtain a religious annulment after obtaining a civil divorce, in order for one or both spouses to remarry.

Most annulments take place after a marriage of a very short duration—a few weeks or months, so there are usually no assets or debts to divide or children for whom custody, visitation and child support are a concern. When a long-term marriage is annulled, however, most states have provisions for dividing property and debts, as well as determining custody, visitation, child support and alimony. Children of an annulled marriage are *not* considered illegitimate.

When are married people considered separated?

Many people are confused about what is meant by "separated"—and it's no wonder, given that there are four different kinds of separations:

Trial separation. When a couple lives apart for a test period, to decide whether or not to separate permanently, it's called a trial separation. Even if they don't get back together, the assets they accumulate and debts they incur during the trial period are usually considered jointly owned. A trial separation is a personal choice, not a legal status.

Living apart. Spouses who no longer reside in the same dwelling are said to be living apart. In some states, living apart without intending to reunite changes the spouses' property rights. For example, some states consider property accumulated and debts incurred between living apart and divorce to be the separate property or debt of the person who accumulated or incurred it.

Permanent separation. When a couple decides to split up, it's often called a permanent separation. It may follow a trial separation, or may begin immediately when the couple starts living apart. In most states, all assets received and most debts incurred after permanent separation are the separate property or responsibility of the spouse incurring them. In some states, assets and debts are joint until the divorce papers are filed, regardless of when you separate.

Legal separation. A legal separation results when the parties separate and a court rules on the division of property, alimony, child support, custody and visitation—but does not grant a divorce. The money awarded for support of the spouse and children under these circumstances is often called separate maintenance (as opposed to alimony and child support). You can get a legal separation in all but 12 states: Delaware, Florida, Georgia, Maryland, Mississippi, New Hampshire, New Jersey, Ohio, Pennsylvania, Texas, Vermont and Washington.

What is a "no-fault" divorce?

"No-fault" divorce describes any divorce where the spouse suing for divorce does not have to prove that the other spouse did something wrong. All states allow divorces regardless of who is at "fault."

To get a no-fault divorce, one spouse must simply state a reason recognized by the state. In most states, it's enough to declare that the couple cannot get along (this goes by such names as "incompatibility," "irreconcilable differences" or "irremediable breakdown of the marriage"). In nearly a dozen states, however, the couple must live apart for a period of months or even years in order to obtain a no-fault divorce.

Is a no-fault divorce the only option even when there has been substantial wrongdoing?

In 18 states, yes. The other states allow a spouse to select either a no-fault divorce or a fault divorce. Why choose a fault divorce? Some people don't want to wait out the period of separation required by their state's law for a no-fault divorce. And in some states, a spouse who proves the other's fault may receive a greater share of the marital property or more alimony.

The traditional fault grounds are:
- cruelty (inflicting unnecessary emotional or physical pain)—this is the most frequently used ground
- adultery
- desertion for a specified length of time
- confinement in prison for a set number of years, and
- physical inability to engage in sexual intercourse, if it was not disclosed before marriage.

What happens in a fault divorce if both spouses are at fault?

Under a doctrine called "comparative rectitude," a court will grant the spouse least at fault a divorce when both parties have shown grounds for divorce. Years ago, when both parties were at fault, neither was entitled to a divorce. The absurdity of this result gave rise to the concept of comparative rectitude.

Can a spouse successfully prevent a court from granting a divorce?

One spouse cannot stop a no-fault divorce. Objecting to the other spouse's request for divorce is itself an irreconcilable difference that would justify the divorce.

A spouse can prevent a fault divorce, however, by convincing the court that he or she is not at fault. In addition, several other defenses to a divorce may be possible:

- *Collusion.* If the only no-fault divorce available in a state requires that the couple separate for a long time and the couple doesn't want to wait, they might pretend that one of them was at fault in order to manufacture a ground for divorce. This is collusion because they are cooperating in order to mislead the judge. If, before the divorce, one spouse no longer wants a divorce, he could raise the collusion as a defense.
- *Condonation.* Condonation is someone's approval of another's activities. For example, a wife who does not object to her husband's adultery may be said to condone it. If the wife sues her husband for divorce, claiming he has committed adultery, the husband may argue as a defense that she condoned his behavior.
- *Connivance.* Connivance is the setting up of a situation so that the other person commits a wrongdoing. For example, a wife who invites her husband's lover to the house and then leaves for the weekend may be said to have connived his adultery. If the wife sues her husband for divorce, claiming he has committed adultery, the husband may argue as a defense that she connived—that is, set up—his actions.
- *Provocation.* Provocation is the inciting of another to do a certain act. If a spouse suing for divorce claims that the other spouse abandoned her, her spouse might defend the suit on the ground that she provoked the abandonment.

Keep in mind that although these defenses exist, most courts will eventually grant the divorce. This is because of the strong public policy against forcing people to stay married against their will.

GROUNDS FOR DIVORCE

State	Fault grounds	No-fault grounds (other than separation)	Separation	Length of separation
Alabama	x	x	x	2 years
Alaska	x	x		
Arizona		x		
Arkansas	x		x	18 months
California		x		
Colorado		x		
Connecticut	x	x	x[1]	18 months
Delaware	x	x[2]		
District of Columbia	x		x	6 months if separation is mutual; otherwise 1 year
Florida		x		
Georgia	x	x		
Hawaii		x	x	2 years
Idaho	x	x	x	5 years
Illinois	x	x[3]	x[3]	2 years
Indiana		x		
Iowa		x		
Kansas	x	x		
Kentucky		x[4]		
Louisiana	x		x	180 days
Maine	x	x		
Maryland	x		x	12 months if both parties agree; otherwise 2 years
Massachusetts	x	x		
Michigan		x		
Minnesota		x		
Mississippi	x	x		
Missouri	x	x		
Montana		x	x	180 days

State	Fault grounds	No-fault grounds (other than separation)	Separation	Length of separation
Nebraska		x		
Nevada		x	x	1 year
New Hampshire	x	x		
New Jersey	x		x	18 months
New Mexico	x	x		
New York	x		x	1 year
North Carolina	x		x	1 year
North Dakota	x	x		
Ohio	x	x[5]	x	1 year
Oklahoma	x	x		
Oregon		x		
Pennsylvania	x	x	x	2 years
Rhode Island	x	x	x	3 years
South Carolina	x		x	1 year
South Dakota	x	x		
Tennessee	x	x	x[6]	2 years
Texas	x	x	x	3 years
Utah	x	x	x	3 years
Vermont	x		x	6 months
Virginia	x		x[7]	1 year
Washington		x		
West Virginia	x	x	x	1 year
Wisconsin		x	x	12 months
Wyoming		x		

[1]Separation-based divorce must also allege incompatibility.

[2]No-fault divorce requires a 6-month separation.

[3]Must allege irretrievable breakdown and separation for no-fault divorce; if both parties consent, two years may be reduced to six months.

[4]No-fault divorce requires a 60-day separation.

[5]No-fault divorce will be denied if one party contests ground of incompatibility.

[6]Separation-based divorce allowed only if there are no minor children.

[7]May be reduced to six months if there are no minor children.

Do you have to live in a state to get a divorce there?

All states except Alaska, South Dakota and Washington require a spouse to be a resident of the state for a certain length of time (30 days to one year, depending on the state) before filing for a divorce there. Someone who files for divorce must offer proof that he has resided there for the required length of time.

Can one spouse move to a different state or country to get a divorce?

If one spouse meets the residency requirement of a state or country, a divorce obtained there is valid, even if the other spouse lives somewhere else. The courts of all states will recognize the divorce.

Any decisions the court makes regarding property division, alimony, custody and child support, however, may not be valid unless the nonresident spouse consented to the jurisdiction of the court or later acts as if the foreign divorce was valid—for example, by paying court-ordered child support.

I'M A GREAT HOUSEKEEPER.

I GET DIVORCED. I KEEP THE HOUSE.

—ZSA ZSA GABOR

How is property divided at divorce?

It is common for a divorcing couple to decide about dividing their property and debts themselves, rather than leave it to the judge. But if a couple cannot agree, they can submit their property dispute to the court, which will use state law to divide the property.

Division of property does not necessarily mean a physical division. Rather, the court awards each spouse a percentage of the total value of the property. Each spouse gets items whose worth adds up to his or her percentage.

Courts divide property under one of two schemes: equitable distribution or community property.

- *Equitable distribution.* Assets and earnings accumulated during marriage are divided equitably (fairly). In practice, often two-thirds of the assets go to the higher wage earner and one-third to the other spouse. Equitable distribution principles are followed everywhere except the community property states listed just below.

- *Community property.* In Arizona, California, Idaho, Louisiana, Nevada, New Mexico, Texas, Washington and Wisconsin, all property of a married person is classified as either community property, owned equally by both spouses, or the separate property of one spouse. At divorce, community property is generally divided equally between the spouses, while each spouse keeps his or her separate property (that property which is accumulated prior to the divorce or acquired by gift or inheritance. In Alaska, couples can agree in writing to have their property treated as if they lived in a community property state.

DURATIONAL RESIDENCY REQUIREMENTS FOR DIVORCE

The durational residency requirement is the length of time a person filing for divorce must live in that state before he or she can file court papers.

State	No Length of Residency Specified	30 days	6 Weeks	60 Days	3 Months or 90 Days	6 Months or 180 Days	12 Months or 1 year
Alabama						x	
Alaska	x						
Arizona					x		
Arkansas				x			
California						x	
Colorado					x		
Connecticut							x
Delaware						x	
District of Columbia						x	
Florida						x	
Georgia						x	
Hawaii						x	
Idaho			x				
Illinois					x		
Indiana						x	
Iowa							x
Kansas				x			
Kentucky						x	
Louisiana						x	
Maine						x	
Maryland							x
Massachusetts							x
Michigan						x	
Minnesota						x	
Mississippi						x	
Missouri					x		
Montana					x		
Nebraska							x
Nevada			x				
New Hampshire							x

State	No Length of Residency Specified	30 days	6 Weeks	60 Days	3 Months or 90 Days	6 Months or 180 Days	12 Months or 1 year
New Jersey							x[1]
New Mexico						x	
New York							x
North Carolina						x	
North Dakota						x	
Ohio						x	
Oklahoma							
Oregon						x	
Pennsylvania						x	
Rhode Island							x
South Carolina[2]					x		
South Dakota	x						
Tennessee						x	
Texas						x	
Utah					x		
Vermont						x	
Virginia						x	
Washington	x						
West Virginia							x[3]
Wisconsin						x	
Wyoming				x			

[1]Required for all grounds but adultery.

[2]If only one spouse is a resident of South Carolina, the requirement is one year.

[3]If marriage occurred in West Virginia, there is no length of time required so long as one party lives in West Virginia. But if the marriage was entered into outside of West Virginia, one party to the divorce must be a one-year West Virginia resident.

Very generally, here are the rules for determining what's community property and what isn't:

Community property includes all earnings during marriage and everything acquired with those earnings. All debts incurred during marriage, unless the creditor was specifically looking to the separate property of one spouse for payment, are community property debts.

Separate property of one spouse includes gifts and inheritances given just to that spouse, personal injury awards received by that spouse and the proceeds of a pension that vested (that is, the pensioner became legally entitled to receive it) before marriage. Property purchased with the separate funds of a spouse remain that spouse's separate property. A business owned by one spouse before the marriage remains his or her separate property during the marriage, although a portion of it may be considered community property if the business increased in value during the marriage or both spouses contributed to its worth.

Property purchased with a combination of separate and community funds is part community and part separate property, so long as a spouse is able to show that some separate funds were used. Separate property mixed together with community property generally becomes community property.

My spouse and I are thinking of using a divorce mediator. Is there anything we should know before we begin the process?

More and more couples are turning to mediation in order to negotiate divorce agreements. Mediation almost always takes less time, is less expensive and results in a more solid agreement than using a lawyer to take the case to court. Of course, every divorcing spouse should know and understand his or her legal rights before agreeing to a settlement, even one reached through mediation. You might want to consult a lawyer or do some independent legal research early in the process and then have a lawyer review the agreement before signing. (See Chapter 17, *Courts and Mediation*, for general information on mediation and Chapter 16, *Parents and Children*, for more information on mediating disputes about child custody and visitation.)

I've heard some divorces take months or even years to become final. Is there a way I can get child support and access to the family's more reliable car during this time?

If you've already decided to obtain a divorce, and you have financial or child-rearing concerns, you may benefit from a *pendente lite* action, which literally means "pending the litigation." In a *pendente lite* procedure, a court may sign orders providing for temporary alimony, child support and asset distribution if appropriate. A lawyer is usually involved because the paperwork can be complicated. A *pendente lite* order lasts until it is modified by the final divorce judgment and can even act to set the tone for the final divorce order if situations such as custody and money arrangements are functioning satisfactorily during the time the divorce is being settled.

More Information About Divorce

How to Do Your Own Divorce in California, by Charles Sherman (Nolo Occidental), contains step-by-step instructions for obtaining a California divorce without a lawyer.

How to Do Your Own Divorce in Texas, by Charles Sherman (Nolo Occidental), contains step-by-step instructions for obtaining a Texas divorce without a lawyer.

Do Your Own Divorce in Oregon, by Robin Smith (Nolo), provides easy-to-use forms and step-by-step instructions for handling a non-contested divorce in Oregon.

Using Divorce Mediation: Save Your Money & Your Sanity, by Katherine E. Stoner (Nolo), provides divorcing couples with all the information they need to work with a neutral third party to resolve differences and find solutions.

Divorce & Money: How to Make the Best Financial Decisions During Divorce, by Violet Woodhouse with Dale Fetherling (Nolo), explains the financial aspects of divorce and how to divide property fairly.

Annulment: Your Chance to Remarry Within the Catholic Church, by Joseph P. Zwack (Harper & Row), explains how to get a religious annulment.

Domestic Violence

Domestic violence occurs more often than most of us realize. Those who are abused range in age from children to the elderly, and come from all backgrounds and income levels. The majority of those subjected to domestic violence are women abused by men, but women also abuse other women, men abuse men and women abuse men. If you're being hurt at home, the first rule of advice is to get away from the abuser and go to a safe place where he or she cannot find you. Then, find out about your options for getting help.

What kind of behavior is considered domestic violence?

Domestic violence can take a number of forms, including:

- physical behavior such as slapping, punching, pulling hair or shoving
- forced or coerced sexual acts or behavior such as unwanted fondling or intercourse, or jokes and insults aimed at sexuality
- threats of abuse—threatening to hit, harm or use a weapon on another, or to tell others confidential information, and
- psychological abuse—attacks on self-esteem, controlling or limiting another's behavior, repeated insults and interrogation.

Typically, many kinds of abuse go on at the same time in a household.

Finding a Safe Place

Many communities have temporary homes called battered women's shelters where women and their children who are victims of domestic violence may stay until the crisis passes or until they are able to find a permanent place to relocate. The best way to find these shelters is to consult the local police, welfare department, neighborhood resource center or women's center. You can also look in your phone book under Crisis Intervention Services, Human Service Organizations, Social Service Organizations, Family Services, Shelters or Women's Organizations. In some states, the police are required to provide an apparent battering victim a list of referrals for emergency housing, legal services and counseling services.

If you're having trouble finding resources in your area, you can contact the National Domestic Violence Hotline, 800-799-SAFE (7233), 800-787-3224 (TTY), http://www.ndvh.org.

If I leave, how can I make sure the abuser won't come near me again?

The most powerful legal tool for stopping domestic violence is the temporary restraining order (TRO). A TRO is a decree issued by a court that requires the perpetrator to stop abusing you. The order may require, for example, that the perpetrator stay away from the family home, where you work or go to school, your children's school and other places you frequent (such as a particular church). The order will also prohibit further acts of violence.

Many states make it relatively easy for you to obtain a TRO. In New York, California and some other states, for example, the court clerk will hand you a package of forms and will even assist you in filling them out. In other areas, nonlawyers may be available to help you complete the forms. When you've completed your forms, you'll go before a judge to show evidence of the abuse, such as hospital or police records or photo-

graphs. You can also bring in a witness, such as a friend or relative, to testify to the abuse. Judges are often available to issue TROs after normal business hours because violence certainly occurs at times other than between 9 a.m. and 5 p.m.

Programs for Abusive Men

A number of programs have been established to help abusive men change their behavior. You can get more information from the following organizations:

Men Overcoming Violence (MOVE)
1385 Mision Street, Suite 300
San Francisco, CA 94103
415-626-6683
http://www.menovercomingviolence.org

Abusive Men Exploring New Directions (AMEND)
2727 Bryant Street, Suite 350
Denver, CO 80211
303-832-6363
http://www.amendonline.org

Men Stopping Violence
1020 DeKalb Avenue, Suite 25
Atlanta, GA 30307
404-688-1376
http://www.menstoppingviolence.org

In my community, judges don't issue TROs after 5 p.m. How can I get protection?

Contact your local police department. In many communities, the police can issue something called an emergency protective order when court is out of session. An emergency protective order usually lasts only for a brief period of time, such as a weekend or a holiday, but otherwise it is the same as a temporary restraining order. On the next business day, you will need to go to court to obtain a TRO.

Are TROs and emergency protective orders only available when the abuser is a spouse?

No, in most states, the victim of an abusive live-in lover, even of the same sex, can obtain a TRO or emergency protective order. In a few states, the victim of any adult relative, an abusive lover (non-live-in) or even a roommate can obtain such an order. In some states, if non-romantic victims and abusers do not live in the same household, the domestic violence laws do not apply. However, in this situation, other criminal laws may come into play. To learn about your state's rule, contact a local crisis intervention center, social service organization or battered women's shelter.

Help for Abused Gay Men and Lesbians

The following organizations provide information and support for battered gay men and lesbians:

Go to this site, http://www.rainbow domesticviolence.itgo.com, for research and links on domestic violence in the gay and lesbian community.

The National Domestic Violence Hotline, at 800-799-SAFE is a national toll-free number that provides information to callers (gay and straight) about shelters and assistance programs in their area. You can also check out the hotline's website at http://www.ndvh.org.

The Lambda Gay & Lesbian Anti-Violence Project (AVP), has a website at http://www.lambda.org, and their address is P.O. Box 31321, El Paso, TX 79931-0321. The telephone number for the Lambda Anti-Violence Project is 916-562-GAYS.

The New York City Gay & Lesbian Anti-Violence Project maintains a website at http://www.avp.org, and their 24-hour hotline number is 212-714-1141.

San Francisco's Community United Against Violence has a hotline at 415-333-HELP, and their website address is http://www.cuav.org.

Massachusetts residents can contact the Gay Men's Domestic Violence Project at 800-832-1901. Their website is located at http://www.gmdvp.org.

What should I do once I have a TRO?

Register it with the police located in the communities in which the abuser has been ordered to stay away from you—where you live, work, attend school or church and where your children go to school. Call the appropriate police stations for information about how to register your order.

What if the abuse continues even if I have a TRO?

Obviously, a piece of paper cannot stop an enraged spouse or lover from acting violent, although many times it is all the deterrent the person needs.

If the violence continues, contact the police. They can take immediate action and are far more willing to intervene when you have a TRO than when you don't. Of course, if you don't have a TRO or it has expired, you should also call the police—in all states, domestic violence is a crime and you don't have to have a TRO for the police to investigate.

The police should respond to your call by sending out officers. In the past, police officers were reluctant to arrest abusers, but this has changed in many communities where victims' support groups have worked with police departments to increase the number of arrests. You can press criminal charges at the police department, and ask for criminal prosecution. Documentation is crucial if you want to go this route. Be sure to insist that the officer responding to your call makes an official report and takes photo-graphs of any bodily injuries, no matter how slight. Also, get the report's prospective number before the officer leaves the premises.

If you do press charges, keep in mind that only the district attorney decides whether or not to prosecute. If you don't press charges, however, the chance is extremely low that the district attorney will pursue the matter. But in some states, if the injury is severe, the prosecuter may decide to pursue the case and urge your cooperation.

Getting Legal Help

If you want to take legal action against your abuser or you need other legal help related to domestic abuse, the following organizations can refer you to assistance programs in your area:

The National Coalition Against Domestic Violence (NCADV), 303-839-1852, http:www.ncadv.org.

The National Domestic Violence Hotline, 800-799-SAFE (7233), 800-787-3224 (TTY), http://www.ndvh.org.

Changing Your Name

You may be thinking of changing your name for any number of reasons —perhaps you're getting married or divorced, or maybe you just don't like the name you've got, and you want one that suits you better. Whatever the reason, you'll be glad to know that name changes are common—and usually fairly easy to carry out.

I'm a woman who is planning to be married soon. Do I have to take my husband's name?

No. When you marry, you are free to keep your own name, take your husband's name or adopt a completely different name. Your husband can even adopt your name, if that's what you both prefer. Give some careful thought to what name feels best for you. You can save yourself considerable time and trouble by making sure you are happy with your choice of name before you change any records.

Can my husband and I both change our names—to a hyphenated version of our two names or to a brand new name?

Yes. Some couples want to be known by a hyphenated combination of their last names, and some make up new names that combine elements of each. For example, Ellen Berman and Jack Gendler might become Ellen and Jack Berman-Gendler or, perhaps, Ellen and Jack Bergen. You can also pick a name that's entirely different from the names you have now, just because you like it better.

What if I do want to take my husband's name? How do I make the change?

If you want to take your husband's name, simply start using the name as

soon as you are married. Use your new name consistently, and be sure to change your name on all of your identification, accounts and important documents. To change some of your identification papers—your Social Security card, for example—you'll need a certified copy of your marriage certificate, which you should receive within a few weeks after the marriage ceremony.

For a list of people and institutions to contact about your name change, see *Changing Identification and Records*, below.

I took my husband's name when I married, but now we're getting divorced, and I'd like to return to my former name. How do I do that?

In most states, you can request that the judge handling your divorce make a formal order restoring your former or birth name. If your divorce decree contains such an order, that's all the paperwork you'll need. You'll probably want to get certified copies of the order as proof of the name change—check with the court clerk for details. Once you have the necessary documentation, you can use it to have your name changed on your identification and personal records.

If your divorce papers don't show your name change, you can still resume your former name without much fuss. In most states, you can simply begin using your former name consistently, and have it changed on all your personal records (see *Changing*

Identification and Records, below). If you're returning to a name you had before marriage, you're not likely to be hassled about the change. A few states have more stringent laws, however, and you'll have to apply to a court for an order approving your name change. Contact your local court clerk's office to find out whether you'll need a court order.

After my husband and I are divorced and I return to my former name, can I change the last name of my children as well?

Traditionally, courts ruled that a father had an automatic right to have his child keep his last name if he continued to actively perform his parental role. But this is no longer true. Now a child's name may be changed by court petition when it is in the best interest of the child to do so. When deciding to grant a name change, courts consider many factors, such as the length of time the father's name has been used, the strength of the mother-child relationship and the need of the child to identify with a new family unit (if the change involves remarriage). The courts must balance these factors against the strength and importance of the father-child relationship. What this all boils down to is that it's up to a judge to decide which name is in the child's best interest.

Keep in mind that even if you do change your children's last name, you won't be changing the paternity—that is, the court's recognition that he is their father, and the rights and obligations that come with that recognition. Nor will a name change affect the rights or duties of either parent regarding visitation, child support or rights of inheritance. Changes such as these occur only if the parental roles are altered by court order—for example, a new custody decree or a legal adoption.

I just don't like my birth name and I want to change it. Can I choose any name I want?

There are some restrictions on what you may choose as your new name. Generally, the limits are as follows:

- You cannot choose a name with fraudulent intent—meaning you intend to do something illegal. For example, you cannot legally change your name to avoid paying debts, keep from getting sued or get away with a crime.
- You cannot interfere with the rights of others, which generally means capitalizing on the name of a famous person.
- You cannot use a name that would be intentionally confusing. This might be a number or punctuation—for example, "10," "III" or "?".
- You cannot choose a name that is a racial slur.
- You cannot choose a name that could be considered a "fighting word," which includes threatening or obscene words, or words likely to incite violence.

That's "Mr. Three" to You

Minnesota's Supreme Court once ruled that a man who wanted to change his name to the number "1069" could not legally do so, but suggested that "Ten Sixty-Nine" might be acceptable (*Application of Dengler*, 287 N.W.2d. 637 (1979)).

Do I have to file forms in court to change my birth name?

Maybe not. In all but a handful of states, you can legally change your name by usage only. A name change by usage is accomplished by simply using a new name in all aspects of your personal, social and business life. No court action is necessary, it costs nothing and it is legally valid. (Minors and prison inmates are generally exceptions to this rule.)

Practically speaking, however, an official court document may make it much easier to get everyone to accept your new name. Because many people and agencies do not know that a usage name change is legal, they may want to see something in writing signed by a judge. Also, certain types of identification—such as a new passport or a birth certificate attachment—are not readily available if you change your name by the usage method.

If it's available in your state, you may want to try the usage method and see how it goes. If you run into too many problems, you can always file a court petition later.

You can find out whether your state requires a court order by contacting your local clerk of court. Or, if the court clerk doesn't give you enough information, you can look at your state's statutes in a local law library—start in the index under "Name" or "Change of Name," or ask the reference librarian for help.

How do I implement my name change?

Whether you have changed your name by usage or by court order, the most important part of accomplishing your name change is to let others know you've taken a new name. Although it may take a little time to contact government agencies and businesses, don't be intimidated by the task—it's a common procedure.

The practical steps of implementing a name change are:

- *Advise officials and businesses.* Contact the various government and business agencies with which you deal and have your name changed on their records. See *Changing Identification and Records*, below.

- *Enlist help of family and friends.* Tell your friends and family that you've changed your name and you now want them to use only your new one. It may take those close to you a while to get used to associating you with a new sound. Some of them might even object to using the new name, perhaps fearing the person they know so well is becoming someone else. Be patient and persistent.

- *Use only your new name.* If you are employed or in school, go by your new name there. Introduce yourself to new acquaintances and business contacts with your new name.

If you've made a will or other estate planning document (such as a living trust), it's best to replace it with a new document using your new name. Your beneficiaries won't lose their inheritances if you don't, but changing the document now will avoid confusion later.

Finally, remember to change your name on other important legal papers—for example, powers of attorney, living wills and contracts.

Changing Identification and Records

To complete your name change, you'll need to tell others about it. Contact the people and institutions you deal with and ask what type of documentation they require to make your name change official in their records. Different institutions may have very different rules; some may need only your phone call, others may require special forms or a copy of a court document.

It's generally recommended that you first acquire a driver's license, then a Social Security card in your new name. Once you have those pieces of identification, it's usually fairly simple to acquire others or have records changed to reflect your new name.

Here are the people and institutions to notify of your name change:
- friends and family
- employers
- schools
- post office
- Department of Motor Vehicles
- Social Security Administration
- Department of Records or Vital Statistics (issuers of birth certificates)
- banks and other financial institutions
- creditors and debtors
- telephone and utility companies
- state taxing authority
- insurance agencies
- registrar of voters
- passport office
- Public Assistance (welfare) office, and
- Veterans Administration.

Many government agencies provide instructions on how to register a name change with the agency via their websites. (For information on how to find government websites, see the Legal Research Appendix.) For example, you can download the form for changing your name on your Social Security card at http://www.ssa.gov/online/ss-5.html.

What should I do if I have a hard time getting my new name accepted?

Some people and institutions may be reluctant to accept your new name—particularly if you've changed it without a court order. If you live in a state where no court order is required, however, you should be able to persuade them to make the change.

Start by providing documentation that shows both the old and new names. If you've recently obtained a passport, it may be helpful because it can show your old name as well as the new name as an AKA ("also known as").

If you're stonewalled, you may want to gently, but forcefully, give a rundown of state law that supports your position. (You can research the law for your state at your local law library or on the Internet. See the Legal Research Appendix.) If the person with whom you are dealing remains uncooperative, ask to speak to his or her supervisor. Be confident that you have the legal right to change your name, even if the people you're dealing with don't know your rights. Keep going up the ladder until you get results. If you have trouble at the local office of a government agency, contact the main office. If you come up against a seemingly impossible situation, get the help of your local elected official.

Finally, if you run into more trouble than you're prepared to deal with, consider going to court and getting a signed order from a judge. It costs more and will take a little time, but an official document will certainly make it easier to handle people and institutions who refuse to accept your new name.

More Information About Changing Your Name

How to Change Your Name in California, by Lisa Sedano (Nolo), provides complete information on how to change your name in California.

Local law libraries are good sources of information for name changes. Look under "Name" or "Change of Name" in the index of your state's statutes, or ask the reference librarian for help. You can also research state laws on the Internet. See the Legal Research Appendix for more information.

http://www.nolo.com

Nolo offers self-help information about a wide variety of legal topics, including relationships between spouses and partners.

http://samesexlaw.com

Same Sex Law provides information affecting lesbian and gay couples.

http://www.lectlaw.com

The 'Lectric Law Library's Lawcopedia on Family Law offers articles and other information on a wide variety of family law issues, including articles about living together.

http://divorceonline.com

The American Divorce Information Network provides FAQs, articles and information on a wide range of divorce issues.

http://www.ncadv.org

The National Coalition Against Domestic Violence offers help, information and links for those affected by domestic violence.

Parents and Children

16.2	Adopting a Child
16.12	Stepparent Adoptions
16.14	Adoption Rights: Birthparents, Grandparents and Children
16.18	Child Custody and Visitation
16.25	Child Support
16.31	Guardianship of Children

A child of five could understand this.
Fetch me a child of five.

—GROUCHO MARX

Raising children is a big job, and an emotional subject even when family relationships are well established and running smoothly. An adoption, divorce or guardianship proceeding adds extra stress, requiring us to juggle law, economics and our highly charged feelings. Be reassured, however, that there are many people who can help you find your way through family law proceedings, including knowledgeable lawyers, mediators, counselors and therapists. In this chapter, we get you started by answering many of your questions about the laws that affect parents and their children.

Adopting a Child

Adoption is a court procedure by which an adult legally becomes the parent of someone who is not his or her biological child. Adoption creates a parent-child relationship recognized for all purposes—including child support obligations, inheritance rights and custody. The birthparents' legal relationship to the child is terminated, unless a legal contract allows them to retain or share some rights or the adoption is a stepparent adoption, in which case only the parent without custody loses parental rights.

This section discusses the general legal procedures and issues involved in adopting a child, including the advantages and disadvantages of various types of adoption and some of the special concerns of single people or unmarried couples (gay and straight) who want to adopt a child. Stepparent adoptions and the rights of relatives are discussed later in this chapter.

Who can adopt a child?

As a general rule, any adult who is found to be a "fit parent" may adopt a child. Married or unmarried couples may adopt jointly, and unmarried people may adopt a child through a procedure known as a single-parent adoption.

Some states have special requirements for adoptive parents. A few of these require an adoptive parent to be a certain number of years older than the child. And some states require the adoptive parent to live in the state for a certain length of time before they are allowed to adopt. You will need to check the laws of your state to see whether any special requirements apply to you. And keep in mind that if you're adopting through an agency, you may have to meet strict agency requirements in addition to any requirements under state law.

Even if you find no state or agency barriers to adopting a child, remember that some people or couples are likely to have a harder time adopting than others. A single man or a lesbian couple may not legally be prohibited from adopting, but may have a harder time finding a placement than would a married couple. This is because all states look to the "best interests of the child" as their bottom line, and will judge the various characteristics of the parent or couple—often factoring in biases about who makes a good parent—when making a placement determination.

I'm single, but I'd like to adopt a child. What special concerns will I face?

As a single person, you may have to wait longer to adopt a child, or be flexible about the child you adopt. Agencies often "reserve" healthy infants and younger children for two-parent families, putting single people at the bottom of their waiting lists. And birthparents themselves often want their children to be placed in a two-parent home.

If you're a single person wishing to adopt, you should be prepared to make a good case for your fitness as a parent. You can expect questions from case workers about why you haven't married, how you plan to support and care for the child on your own, what will happen if you do marry and other questions that will put you in the position of defending your status as a single person. To many single adoptive parents, such rigorous screening doesn't seem fair, but it is common.

Agencies serving children with special needs may be a good option for singles, as such agencies often cast a wider net when considering adoptive parents. Of course, you shouldn't take a child unless you feel truly comfortable with the idea of raising him or her—but being flexible will make the obstacles to single-parent adoptions easier to overcome.

My long-term partner and I prefer not to get married, but we'd like to adopt a child together. Will we run into trouble?

There is no specific prohibition against unmarried couples adopting children—sometimes called two-parent adoptions. Like singles, however, you may find that agencies are biased towards married couples. You may have a longer wait for a child, or you may have to expand your ideas about what kind of child you want.

Is it still very difficult for lesbians and gay men to adopt children?

Only Florida, Utah and Mississippi specifically prohibit lesbians and gay men from adopting children. But that doesn't mean it's easy to adopt in other states. Alabama's Supreme Court in 1998, for example, awarded custody to a father because it found the mother's lesbian relationship "was neither legal in this state, nor moral in the eyes of most of its citizens." The same is true in other states—even if a state adoption statute does not specifically mention sexual orientation, it may become an issue in court, and some judges will use it to find a prospective adoptive parent to be unfit.

On the other hand, many gay men and lesbians have been able to adopt children, and an increasing number of states are allowing gay and lesbian couples to adopt jointly. Beginning in Alaska in 1985, joint adoptions by gay and lesbian couples have been granted in California, Colorado, Delaware, the District of Columbia, Illinois, Indiana, Maryland, Massachusetts, Michigan, Minnesota, New Jersey, New York, Oregon, Rhode Island, Pennsylvania, Texas, Vermont and Washington. While Connecticut does not allow same-sex partners to jointly adopt a child, the state passed a law in October 2001 that permits a biological parent to agree to his or her partner's adoption of his or her biological child.

Keep in mind that the legal landscape in all areas affecting gays and lesbians is changing rapidly. Just as a legislature might make it easier for gays and lesbians to adopt, a court decision to the contrary might provide quite a different result. One encouraging sign is the American Academy of Pediatrics' February 2002 report that supports second-parent adoptions by gay or lesbian parents. The Academy takes the position that children born to or adopted by gay or lesbian adults "deserve the security of two legally recognized parents." Lesbians and gay men will need an experienced attorney to handle an adoption. But you can do your own homework: The National Center for Lesbian Rights (address and phone number listed below) provides information for gay men and lesbians who want to adopt.

California's Domestic Partners and Stepparent Adoption

California's new domestic partnership law, which took effect January 2002, grants a new legal protection for gays and lesbians who want to adopt their partners' biological child. Under the new law, a registered domestic partner may adopt a partner's child using the stepparent adoption process—a faster and less expensive process than second-parent adoption. See "Stepparent Adoptions" below.

Same-sex partners must register with the California Secretary of State's office (http://www.ssa.gov) to be eligible for the rights and benefits extended under this new law.

Can I adopt a child whose race or ethnic background is different from mine?

Usually, yes. You do not need to be the same race as the child you want to adopt, although some states do give preference to prospective adoptive parents of the same race or ethnic background as the child. Adoptions of Native American children are governed by federal law—the Indian Child Welfare Act—which outlines specific rules and procedures that must be followed when adopting a Native American child.

Whose consent is needed for an adoption to take place?

For any adoption to be legal, the birthparents must consent to the adoption unless their parental rights have been legally terminated for some other reason, such as a finding that he or she is an unfit parent. All states prohibit birthparents from giving their consent to an adoption until after the child's birth, and some states require even more time—typically three to four days after the birth—before the parents are allowed to consent. This means that birthparents can legally change their minds about putting their child up for adoption at any point before the child is born.

Types of Adoption

Agency Adoptions. Agency adoptions involve the placement of a child with adoptive parents by a public agency, or by a private agency licensed or regulated by the state. Public agencies generally place children who have become wards of the state because they were orphaned, abandoned or abused. Private agencies are often run by charities or social service organizations. Children placed through private agencies are usually brought to an agency by parents that have or are expecting a child that they want to give up for adoption.

Independent Adoptions. In an independent or private adoption, a child is placed with adoptive parents without the assistance of an agency. Some independent adoptions consist of direct arrangement between the birthparents and the adoptive parents, while others are arranged through an intermediary such as a lawyer, doctor or clergyperson. Whether or not an intermediary is used, a lawyer is essential because of the legal complexities involved. Most states allow independent adoptions, though many regulate them quite carefully. Independent adoptions are not allowed in Connecticut, Delaware, Massachusetts or Minnesota.

Identified Adoptions. An identified, or designated, adoption is one in which the adopting parents locate a birthmother (or the other way around) and then ask an adoption agency to handle the rest of the adoption process. In this way, an identified adoption is a hybrid of an independent and an agency adoption. Prospective parents are spared the waiting lists of agencies by finding the birthparents themselves, but reap the other benefits of agencies, such as their experience with legal issues and their counseling services. Identified adoptions provide an alternative to parents in states that ban independent adoptions.

International Adoptions. In an international adoption, the adoptive parents take responsibility for a child who is a citizen of a foreign country. In addition to satisfying the adoption requirements of both the foreign country and the parents' home state in the U.S., the parents must obtain an immigrant visa for the child through the U.S. Immigration and Naturalization Service. The INS has its own rules for international adoptions, such as the requirement that the adoptive parents be either married or, if single, at least 25 years old. The INS also requires adoptive parents to complete several forms and submit a favorable home study report. Finally, you must apply for U.S. citizenship for the child; it is not granted automatically.

Relative Adoptions. When a child is related to the adoptive parent by blood or marriage, the adoption is a relative adoption. The most common example of this type of adoption is a stepparent adoption, in which a parent's new spouse adopts a child from a previous partner. Grandparents often adopt their grandchildren if the parents die while the children are minors. These adoptions are usually easier and simpler than nonrelative adoptions.

What are some of the advantages and disadvantages of an agency adoption?

Using an agency to manage your adoption can be helpful for a number of reasons. Agencies are experienced in finding children, matching them with parents and satisfying the necessary legal requirements. Agencies will do most of the legwork of an adoption, from finding a birthparent to finalizing the papers, and they'll walk adoptive parents through many of the crucial steps in between, such as conducting the home study, obtaining the necessary consents and advising parents on the state's specific legal requirements.

One key advantage of an agency adoption is the extensive counseling that agencies provide throughout the process. Typically, counseling is available for adoptive parents, birthparents and the children (if they are older). Careful counseling can help everyone involved weather the emotional, practical and legal complexities that are likely to arise during the adoption.

Finally, many agencies specialize in certain kinds of children; this may be helpful if you want, for example, to adopt an infant, a child of a different race from yours or a child with special medical needs. Some agencies also offer international adoption services.

On the down side, private agencies are often extremely selective when choosing adoptive parents. This is because they have a surplus of people who want to adopt and a limited number of available children. Most agencies have long waiting lists of prospective parents, especially for healthy, white infants. Agencies weed out parents using criteria such as age limits, marital status, income, health, religion, family size, personal history (including criminal conduct) and residency requirements.

Additionally, agencies often wait to place the child in the adoptive home until all necessary consents have been given and become final. Because of this, a child may be placed in foster care for a few days or weeks, depending on the situation and the state's law. This delay concerns many adoptive parents who want the child to have a secure, stable home as soon as possible. Some agencies get around this by placing infants immediately through a type of adoption known as a "legal risk placement": If the birthmother decides she wants her child back before her rights have been legally terminated, the adoptive parents must let the child go.

Public agencies often have many children ready to be adopted, but they often specialize in older or special needs children. If you want a newborn, a public agency might not be able to help you. Also, public agencies often do not provide many other services such as the much-needed counseling that private agencies offer. Generally, they don't have as many resources as private agencies.

How do I find an adoption agency?

There are an estimated 3,000 adoption agencies in the United States,
public and private. If you live in a state like California or New York, you'll have more options than if you live in a less populated state. But wherever you live, you'll probably have to do some searching to find an agency that meets your needs and is able to work with you. You can call a national adoption organization for referrals to get you started. The addresses and phone numbers of several organizations are listed at the end of this section.

Be persistent with the agencies you contact. If they tell you that there are no children, ask whether there is a waiting list. Then ask other questions such as: Is the waiting list for child placement or a home study? How do they determine who may file an application? Can you fill out an application now? If not, when can you? Do they hold orientation meetings? If so, when will the next one be held? Ask if you can speak with other parents in circumstances similar to yours who have adopted through the agency. These parents may provide valuable information about the service they received from the agency, how long the process took and whether they were ultimately happy with the outcome. Screen the agencies as much as they screen you.

How can I check on the reputation of an adoption agency?

As discussed above, you can and should speak with other parents who have adopted through the agency. In addition, you should check out the agency's accreditation. Start with the licensing department of your state. It can tell you whether the agency has been cited for licensing violations, or whether the licensing office has received any complaints about the agency. You can also request a copy of the state's rules governing agencies so that you understand the standards to which your agency is held.

The staff at your state's department of social services may also be able to give you information about the agency. Finally, you can check your state or local department of consumer affairs to see if it handles complaints about adoption agencies.

Are agency adoptions very expensive?

They can be. Agencies charge fees to cover the birthmother's expenses as allowed by state law; these expenses may include medical costs, living expenses during the pregnancy and costs for counseling. Add to this the agency's staff salaries and overhead—and charges can mount up quickly.

Many agencies charge a flat fee for adoptions, while others add the birthmother's expenses to a fixed rate for the agency's services. Some agencies use a sliding scale that varies with adoptive parents' income levels, usually with a set minimum and maximum fee. You can expect to pay between $1,000 and $6,000 to adopt a young child, and $10,000 or more to adopt a newborn. Some agencies charge a lower rate for handling special needs adoptions.

Public agencies generally do not charge fees for placing children in adoptive homes.

What are the costs involved in an independent adoption?

Because each situation is unique, fees for independent adoptions vary widely. Prospective parents must generally cover the costs of finding a birthmother, all costs related to the pregnancy and birth, and the legal costs involved in the adoption process. Some states also include the birthmother's living expenses during the pregnancy. Expenses such as hospital bills, travel costs, phone bills, home study fees, attorneys' fees and court costs can often surpass $10,000.

You Can't Buy a Baby

It is illegal in all states to buy or sell a baby. All states, however, allow adoptive parents to pay certain "reasonable" costs that are specifically related to the adoption process. Each state has its own laws defining the expenses that may be paid by adoptive parents in any kind of adoption proceeding—agency or independent. If you pursue an independent adoption, you must adhere to these laws when you give any money to the birthmother. And agencies are regulated to make sure that they charge adoptive parents only for the costs that the state allows.

Most states allow the adoptive parents to pay the birthmother's medical expenses, counseling costs and attorney fees. Some states allow payments to cover the birthmother's living expenses such as food, housing and transportation during pregnancy. Most states require all payments to be itemized and approved by a court before the adoption is finalized. Be sure to know and understand your state's laws, because providing or accepting prohibited financial support may subject you to criminal charges. Furthermore, the adoption itself may be jeopardized if you make improper payments.

What should I keep in mind when deciding whether to pursue an independent adoption?

Birth and adoptive parents are sometimes attracted to independent adoptions because they allow control over the entire adoption process. Rather than relying on an agency as a go-between, the birthparent and adoptive parents can meet, get to know each other and decide for themselves whether the adoption should take place. Independent adoptions also avoid the long waiting lists and restrictive qualifying criteria that are often involved in agency adoptions. Plus, independent adoptions usually happen much faster than agency adoptions, often within a year of beginning the search for a child.

One major drawback to independent adoptions is that they are illegal in some states, currently Connecticut, Delaware, Massachusetts and Minnesota. States that do allow independent adoptions sometimes regulate them in other ways—for example, by prohibiting adoptive parents from advertising for birthmothers. Be sure to check your state's laws before you proceed.

Another concern is that birthparents might not receive adequate counseling during the adoption process. This may leave your agreement more vulnerable to unraveling. Furthermore, some states extend the period in which birthparents may revoke their consent for independent adoptions; this places your agreement at additional risk.

Finally, independent adoptions are a lot of work. Adoptive parents often spend enormous amounts of time—and money—just finding a birthmother, not to mention the efforts required to follow through and bring the adoption to a close. Some parents decide afterwards that the energy and expense needed to adopt independently are just too much, and they hire an agency to do the work for their next adoption.

Open Adoptions

An open adoption is one in which there is some degree of contact between the birthparents and the adoptive parents—often this includes contact with the child as well. There is no one standard for open adoptions; each family works out the arrangement that works best for them. Some adoptive parents consider meeting the birthparents just once before the birth of the child, while others form ongoing relationships which may include written correspondence or visits.

Open adoptions often help reduce stress and worry by eliminating the power of the unknown: Rather than fearing the day that a stranger will come knocking on their door to ask for the child back, adoptive parents are reassured by knowing the birthparents personally and dealing with them directly. This openness can be beneficial to the child as well, who will grow up with fewer questions—and misconceptions—than might a child of a "closed" adoption.

If you want your adoption to be open and decide to use an agency, be sure to find out their policies on open placements. Some agencies offer only closed or "semi-open" adoptions, and will not provide identifying information about birth or adoptive parents even if both families want the adoption to be open. On the other hand, independent adoptions—where allowed—permit any degree of openness desired by the birth and adoptive families.

What's a home study?

All states require adoptive parents to undergo an investigation to make sure that they are fit to raise a child. Typically, the study is conducted by a state agency or a licensed social worker who examines the adoptive parents' home life and prepares a report that the court will review before allowing the adoption to take place. Some states do not require a report to be submitted to a court. These states allow the agency or social worker to decide whether the prospective par-

ents are fit to adopt. Common areas of inquiry include:

- financial stability
- marital stability
- lifestyles
- other children
- career obligations
- physical and mental health, and
- criminal history.

In recent years, the home study has become more than just a method of investigating prospective parents: It serves to educate and inform them as well. The social worker helps to prepare the adoptive parents by discussing issues such as how and when to talk with the child about being adopted, and how to deal with the reaction that friends and family might have to the adoption.

Can I adopt a child from another country?

You can adopt a foreign child through an American agency which specializes in intercountry adoptions—or you can adopt directly. If you prefer a direct adoption, you will have to adhere not only to the adoption laws of your state, but also to U.S. immigration laws and the laws of the country where the child is born. It will be a complex process, so be prepared for some tangles. Do as much research as you can before you fly off to find a child; the more you know about the chosen country's adoption system ahead of time, the better off you'll be when you get there.

U.S. immigration laws require that prospective adoptive parents be married or, if single, at least 25 years old. The adoptive parents must file a Petition to Classify Orphan as an Immediate Relative (INS form I-600) with the Immigration and Naturalization Service which shows either that the child's parents have died, disappeared or have abandoned the child, or that one remaining parent is not able to care for the child and consents to the child's adoption and immigration to the U.S. If there are two known parents, the child will not qualify as an orphan under any circumstances.

Along with the I-600, you will need to submit a number of other documents, including a favorable home study report. If the INS approves the petition, and there are no disqualifying factors such as a communicable disease, the child can be issued an immigrant visa.

Much of the paperwork for an intercountry adoption can be completed even before you have identified a specific child to adopt. Advance preparation is a valuable option because the INS paperwork often takes a long time to process, and may hold up the child's arrival in the U.S. even after all foreign requirements have been met.

Finally, be sure to check your own state laws for any preadoption requirements. Some states, for instance, require you to submit the written consent of the birthmother before they approve the entry of the child into the state. Some experts recommend that parents who adopt overseas readopt the child in their own state in order to make sure that the adoption fully conforms to state law.

For more information about intercountry adoptions, see the resource list at the end of this section.

What should my adoption petition say?

A standard adoption petition will generally include five pieces of information:

1) the names, ages and address of the adoptive parents
2) the relationship between the adoptive parents and the child to be adopted
3) the legal reason that the birthparents' rights are being terminated (usually that they consented to the termination)
4) a statement that the adoptive parents are the appropriate people to adopt the child, and
5) a statement that the adoption is in the child's best interests.

Typically, the written consent of the birthparents or the court order terminating their parental rights is also filed along with the petition. Adoptive parents also often include a request for an official name change for the child.

Do I need an attorney to handle the adoption of my child?

If you do not use an agency, yes. And even if you do use an agency, you will probably need to hire a lawyer to draft the adoption petition and to represent you at the hearing. Although there is no legal requirement that a lawyer be involved in an adoption, the process can be quite complex and should be handled by someone with experience and expertise. When seeking a lawyer, find out how many adoptions he or she has handled, and whether any of them were contested or developed other complications.

When is an adoption considered final?

All adoptions—agency or independent—must be approved by a court. The adoptive parents must file a petition to finalize the adoption proceeding; there will also be an adoption hearing.

Before the hearing, anyone who is required to consent to the adoption must receive notice. Usually this includes the biological parents, the adoption agency, the child's legal representative if a court has appointed one and the child himself if he is old enough (12 to 14 years in most states).

At the hearing, if the court determines that the adoption is in the child's best interest, the judge will issue an order approving and finalizing the adoption. This order, often called a final decree of adoption, legalizes the new parent-child relationship and usually changes the child's name to the name the adoptive parents have chosen.

Stepparent Adoptions

The majority of adoptions in the United States are stepparent adoptions, in which the biological child of one parent is formally adopted by that parent's new spouse. This type of adoption may occur when one biological parent has died or has left the family after a divorce, and the remaining parent remarries. While most stepparents do not formally adopt their stepchildren, if they do, they obtain the same parental rights as biological parents. This section discusses some of the issues that arise when a stepparent adopts a stepchild.

My new spouse wants to adopt my son from a previous marriage. Are there special adoption rules for stepparents?

Generally speaking, a stepparent adoption is much easier to complete than a nonrelative adoption. The procedure is generally the same as for any adoption, but specific steps are sometimes waived or streamlined. For instance, waiting periods, home studies and even the adoption hearing are sometimes dispensed with in a stepparent adoption.

In all stepparent adoptions, however, your ex-spouse will need to consent to the adoption because she is the other legally recognized parent of the child. If your former spouse refuses to consent, the adoption will not be allowed unless his or her parental rights are terminated for some other reason—abandonment or unfitness, for example.

My new husband has a great relationship with my 10-year-old son and wants to adopt him. My son communicates about once or twice a year with his real father, who will consent to the adoption. Is adoption the right thing to do?

Stepparent adoptions can be complicated when the noncustodial biological parent is still alive and in contact with the child. There may be no legal reason why the adoption cannot take place, but the emotional impact of the adoption also needs to be considered.

If an adoption will bring stability to your new family and help your son feel more secure, it may be the right choice. But no matter how well your son gets along with your new husband, he may feel conflicting loyalties between his adoptive father and his real father, and this may be hard for him to handle. Generally speaking, the less contact your son has with his real father, the more sense it makes for an adoption to take place.

Besides the impact on the child (which should be of primary importance), also make sure your ex-husband understands that giving consent to the adoption means giving up all parental rights to his son, including any right to visit him or make decisions for him regarding issues such as medical treatment or education. In addition, he would no longer be responsible for child support once his parental rights were terminated.

In addition, your new husband should be aware that if he adopts your son, and you and he divorce, he will be responsible for paying child support. Of course, he will also be entitled to visitation or custody.

I had my daughter when I was unmarried, and we haven't heard from her father for several years. I'm now married to another man, and he wants to adopt my daughter. Do I have to find her biological father and get his consent to the adoption before it can take place?

As in any adoption, the adoption cannot take place until the absent parent either gives consent or has his parental rights terminated for some other reason. That being said, there are a few specific ways to proceed with an adoption when one biological parent is out of the picture.

First, it is possible to go forward without a biological parent's consent if you can prove that the absent parent has not exercised any parental rights and convince the court that it's appropriate to legally terminate that parent-child relationship. Most states' laws allow parental rights to be terminated when a parent has willfully failed to support the child or has abandoned the child for a period of time, usually a year. Generally, abandonment means that the absent parent hasn't communicated with the child or supported the child financially.

If the absent parent is a father, another common way to terminate his parental rights is to show that he is not, legally speaking, the presumed father of the child. Most states have statutes establishing who the presumed father of a child is in certain situations. In this case, you won't have to prove that the father has abandoned the child. You simply must show that he does not meet the legal definition of presumed father. For instance, in all states, a man who is married to a woman at the time she gives birth is legally presumed to be the child's father. Another way of establishing presumed fatherhood in many states is by marrying the mother after the child has been born and being named as the father on the child's birth certificate.

If you can show that the father doesn't meet any of the tests in your state for presumed fatherhood, the court may terminate his rights and allow you to proceed without his consent. If, however, the father meets one of the state's tests for presumed fatherhood, you'll need either to obtain the father's consent to the adoption, or to have his rights terminated by proving abandonment, willful failure to support the child or parental unfitness.

Adoption Rights: Birthparents, Grandparents and Children

The rights of parents to raise and care for their children have traditionally received strong legal protection. Courts have long recognized that the bond between parents and children is a profound one, and the law will not interfere with that bond except in the most carefully defined circumstances. Since adoption generally involves creating a parent-child relationship where there previously was none—and sometimes negating someone's parental rights in the process—balancing the legal rights of the parties involved can sometimes be difficult. This section discusses how the legal rights of birthparents, grandparents and children can be affected by the adoption process.

Are birthparents allowed to change their minds and take children back even after they've been placed in the adoptive parents' home?

Even after the birthparents have consented to an adoption and the child is living in the adoptive home, many states set aside a period of time during which the birthparents can change their minds. Depending on the state, the birthparents have the right to withdraw consent weeks or even months after the placement. Though it can be nervewracking—and sometimes devastating—for the adoptive parents who have begun to care for the child, it's important that they understand that birthparents have this right. Adoptive parents should find out how long their state allows for birthparents to legally withdraw consent.

The birthmother of the baby we were going to adopt just decided she wants to keep her child. She's eight months pregnant, and we've paid all of her medical bills during her pregnancy. Can we get our money back?

Unless the mother agrees to pay you back, you're probably out of luck. Especially with independent adop-

tions, paying a birthmother's allowable costs is a risk for adoptive parents. Birthparents often change their minds, and courts will not force them to pay back the expenses paid by the adoptive parents.

My girlfriend is pregnant and I'm the father. I want to keep the baby, but she wants to give it up for adoption. Can she do that?

No. If you acknowledge that you're the father of the child, your consent is needed before the baby can be adopted. The rights of fathers have gotten much more attention in recent years and are now more strongly protected by the law. Some court rulings have held that father's homes must be strongly considered as best for the child. It's important to understand, however, that fathers' rights vary greatly from state to state, and the law in this area is far from settled. If you don't want to see your baby adopted, you should be sure to acknowledge paternity and make it clear to the mother that you won't allow your parental rights to be terminated.

My husband and I found an expectant mother who wants us to adopt her baby. But her mother is trying to talk her out of giving up the child. Can a grandparent legally object to an adoption?

No. The parents of a birthmother don't have any legal right to stop her from giving up the baby. Also, grandparents won't necessarily be favored as adoptive parents over nonrelative parents. (One big exception to this rule is the adoption of Native American children, where a special federal law applies.)

That said, however, grandparents often hold a lot of sway over birthparents, and in many cases have convinced them at the last minute not to give up their babies. If you know that the grandparents are actively trying to talk the birthmother out of the adoption, you should know that there's an increased risk that the adoption might fall through. In this situation, it's especially important to keep in close touch with the birthmother and make extra efforts to encourage open communication. You'll have to judge for yourself how confident you feel about proceeding with a birthmother whose family is opposed to the adoption.

I was adopted as a baby. Now I'm 25 and I want to find my birthparents. Do I have a legal right to obtain my birth records?

In most adoptions, the original birth records and other case documents are "sealed" by the court that finalizes the adoption, which means that no one can see them without the court's permission. But as attitudes toward adoption have become more open, states have adopted a variety of ways for adopted children to find their birthparents, some of which do not require the unsealing of records.

Only a few states offer adult adopted children open access to original birth certificates. More popular is a system called "search and consent," in which an adopted child has an

agency contact the birthparent, who then indicates whether or not he or she agrees to be identified. If the birthparent consents, then the agency provides the information to the child. The most common system is a mutual consent registry, used in about 25 states, in which birthparents and adopted children provide identifying information about themselves to the registry. If a birthparent and his or her adopted child both appear within a register, the agency in charge of the register will share the information with each of them, enabling them to contact each other.

If one of these options isn't available or doesn't work for you, it may be possible to obtain your birth records. Generally, a court will unseal a record for "good cause," such as a need for medical or genetic information.

The best way to start your search is to contact a local adoption agency that knows your state's laws and procedures for contacting birthparents. The National Adoption Information Clearinghouse and the North American Council on Adoptable Children are good sources for referrals to local agencies. (See the end of this section for contact information.)

Another useful tool in searching for birthparents is the Internet. Dozens of organizations and services designed to help adopted children find their birth families have cropped up on the Web. A good place to start is Yahoo!'s adoption category, located at http:// www.yahoo.com/Society_and_Culture/ Families/Parenting/Adoption.

More Information About Adopting a Child

The Adoption Resource Book, by Lois Gilman (HarperPerennial), is a comprehensive guide for anyone considering adoption.

National Council for Single Adoptive Parents, P.O. Box 55, Wharton, NJ 07885, is a clearinghouse for single people seeking information about adoption. The Committee publishes *The Handbook for Single Adoptive Parents*

The National Adoption Information Clearinghouse, 330 C St., NW Washington, DC 20447, 703-352-3488, 888-251-0075 (toll-free), http://www.calib.com/naic. NAIC provides free information about adoption as well as referrals to local agencies and support groups.

A Legal Guide for Lesbian & Gay Couples, by Attorneys Hayden Curry, Denis Clifford and Frederick Hertz (Nolo). Contains a chapter that covers adoption, as well as other issues such as foster parenting and guardianships.

The National Center for Lesbian Rights, 870 Market Street, Suite 570, San Francisco, CA 94102, 415-392-6257, http://www.nclrights.org, provides help to gay men and lesbians who want to adopt.

The National Federation for Open Adoption Education, c/o The Independent Adoption Center, 391 Taylor Boulevard, Suite 100, Pleasant Hill, CA 94523, 925-827-2229, http://www.adoption help.org, can refer you to agencies with expertise in open adoptions.

The North American Council on Adoptable Children (NACAC), 970 Raymond Ave., Suite 106, St. Paul, MN 55114, 651-644-3036, http://www.nacac.org, can provide you with information about adoption resources in your local area.

Adopt International: Everything You Need to Know to Adopt a Child from Abroad, by O. Robin Sweet & Patty Bryan (Noonday Press), is a good source of information for prospective parents considering an international adoption.

How to Adopt Your Stepchild in California, by Frank Zagone & Attorney Mary Randolph (Nolo), explains everything you need to know and do to adopt a stepchild in California.

The United States Immigration and Naturalization Service, 425 I Street, Washington, DC 20536, http://www.ins.gov, publishes a pamphlet called *The Immigration of Adopted and Prospective Adoptive Children* (M-249N), as well as other forms you will need for an international adoption.

U.S. Immigration Made Easy, by Laurence Canter & Martha Siegel (Nolo), contains a chapter on international adoptions, including the necessary INS forms.

Child Custody and Visitation

YOU CAN'T SHAKE HANDS

WITH A CLENCHED FIST.

—INDIRA GHANDI

When parents separate or divorce, the term "custody" often serves as shorthand for "who gets the children" under the divorce decree or judgment. In many states, custody is split into two types: physical custody and legal custody. Physical custody refers to the responsibility of taking care of the children, while legal custody involves making decisions that affect their interests (such as medical, educational and religious decisions). In states that don't distinguish between physical and legal custody, the term "custody" implies both types of responsibilities.

For information on finding your state's law, see the Legal Research Appendix. Also, the Legal Information Institute, at http://www.cornell.edu/topics/child_custody.html, has an excellent summary of child custody laws, cases and resources.

Does custody always go to just one parent?

No. Courts frequently award at least some aspects of custody to both parents, called "joint custody." Joint custody usually takes at least one of three forms:

- joint physical custody (children spend a relatively equal amount of time with each parent)
- joint legal custody (medical, educational, religious and other decisions about the children are shared), or
- both joint legal and joint physical custody.

In every state, courts are willing to order joint legal custody, but about half the states are reluctant to order joint physical custody unless both parents agree to it and they appear to be sufficiently able to communicate and cooperate with each other. In New Hampshire and New Mexico, courts automatically award joint legal custody unless the children's best interests—or a parent's health or safety—would be compromised. Many other states expressly allow their courts to order joint custody even if one parent objects to such an arrangement.

Can someone other than the parents have physical or legal custody?

Sometimes neither parent can suitably assume custody of the children, perhaps because of substance abuse or a mental health problem. In these situations, others may be granted custody of the children or be given a temporary guardianship or foster care arrangement by a court.

What factors do courts take into account when deciding who gets custody of the children?

A court gives the "best interests of the child" the highest priority when deciding custody issues. What the best interests of a child are in a given situation depends upon many factors, including:

- the child's age, gender, mental and physical health
- the mental and physical health of the parents
- the lifestyle and other social factors of the parents, including whether the child is exposed to secondhand smoke and whether there is any history of child abuse
- the love and emotional ties between the parent and the child, as well as the parent's ability to give the child guidance
- the parent's ability to provide the child with food, shelter, clothing and medical care
- the child's established living pattern (school, home, community, religious institution)
- the quality of the schools attended by the children
- the child's preference, if the child is above a certain age (usually about 12), and
- the ability and willingness of the parent to foster healthy communication and contact between the child and the other parent.

Assuming that none of these factors clearly favors one parent over the other, most courts tend to focus on which parent is likely to provide the children a stable environment. With younger children, this may mean awarding custody to the parent who has been the child's primary caregiver. With older children, this may mean giving custody to the parent who is best able to foster continuity in education, neighborhood life, religious institutions and peer relationships.

Are mothers more likely to be awarded custody over fathers?

In the past, most states provided that custody of children of "tender years" (about five and under) had to be awarded to the mother when parents divorced. This rule is now rejected in most states, or relegated to the role of tie-breaker if two fit parents request custody of their preschool children. Most states require their courts to determine custody on the basis of what's in the children's best interests without regard to the sex of the parent.

As it turns out, most divorcing parents agree that the mother will have custody after a separation or divorce, and that the father will exercise reasonable visitation. This sometimes happens because fathers presume that mothers will be awarded custody or because the mother is more tenacious in seeking custody. In still other situations, the parents agree that the mother has more time, a greater inclination or a better understanding of the children's daily needs.

Are there special issues if a gay or lesbian parent is seeking custody or visitation rights?

Only the District of Columbia has a law on its books stating that a parent's sexual orientation cannot be the sole factor in making a custody or visitation award. In a few states—including Alaska, California, New Mexico and Pennsylvannia—the highest court has ruled that a parent's homosexuality, in and of itself, cannot be grounds for an automatic denial of custody. But trial courts in many other states—including Alabama, Arizona, Connecticut, Delaware, Florida, Illinois, Indiana, Iowa, Kentucky, Maine, Maryland, Massachusetts, Michigan, New Jersey, New York, North Dakota, Ohio, Oregon, South Carolina, Tennessee, Utah, Vermont, Washington, West Virginia, Wisconsin and Wyoming—have ruled that judges must find that a parent's sexual orientation would harm the child before it can be used as the basis for denying custody or visitation.

In reality, a lesbian or gay parent faces a difficult struggle when trying to gain custody in most American courtrooms, especially if that parent lives with a partner. The trend in the late 1990s—particularly in southeastern states—has been to deny many lesbian mothers and gay fathers custody of their children. For example, in June 2001 the Arkansas Supreme Court ruled that a mother could have custody of her two children only if her same-sex partner moved out of the home they shared. It is fair to say that many, if not most, judges are ignorant about, prejudiced against or suspicious of, gay and lesbian parents. Only a few judges understand that a parent's sexual orientation, alone, does not effect the best interests of the children. But judges often use the best-interests standard to deny a gay or lesbian parent custody.

My partner and I broke up after eight years. During that time I was artificially inseminated and we raised the child together. Now she wants visitation. Is that possible even if she isn't related by blood to my child?

The trend in the last two years in states such as Massachusetts, New Jersey and Pennsylvania has been for courts to grant the non-biological former partner visitation if the ex-partner acted as a parent or in loco parentis. A court decides whether the former partner assumed a parental role toward the child by examining such factors as caretaking responsibilities (to ensure they were more than babysitting duties), time spent with the child, the length of the relationship with the child, what the child called the parental figure and even whether the former couple presented themselves as a family to the outside world.

Is race ever an issue in custody or visitation decisions?

The U.S. Supreme Court has ruled it unconstitutional for a court to consider race when a noncustodial parent petitions for a change of custody. In that case, a white couple had divorced, and the mother had been awarded custody of their son. She remarried an African-American man and moved to a predominantly African-American neighborhood. The father filed a request for modification of custody based on the changed circumstances. A Florida court granted the modification, but the U.S. Supreme Court reversed, ruling that societal stigma, especially a racial one, cannot be the basis for a custody decision. (*Palmore v. Sidoti*, 466 U.S. 429 (1984)).

When a court awards physical custody to one parent and "visitation at reasonable times and places" to the other, who determines what's reasonable?

The parent with physical custody is generally in the driver's seat regarding what is reasonable. This need not be bad if the parents cooperate to see that the kids spend a maximum amount of time with each parent. Unfortunately, it all too often translates into very little visitation time with the noncustodial parent, and lots of bitter disputes over missed visits and inconvenience. To avoid such problems, many courts now prefer for the parties to

work out a fairly detailed parenting plan (known as a parenting agreement) which sets the visitation schedule and outlines who has responsibility for decisions affecting the children.

The judge in my divorce case has mentioned a parenting agreement. What is that?

A parenting agreement is a detailed, written agreement between a divorcing couple that describes how they will deal with visitation, holiday schedules, vacation, religion, education and other issues related to their child. More and more, courts are encouraging the use of parenting agreements during divorce proceedings. Often, if couples have discussed and agreed upon how to deal with issues affecting their children—rather than having the judge make an independent ruling on those issues—they are more likely to stick to the terms of the agreement.

I have sole custody of my children. My ex-spouse, who lives in another state, has threatened to go to court in his state and get the custody order changed. Can he do that?

All states and the District of Columbia have enacted a statute called the Uniform Child Custody Jurisdiction Act (UCCJA), which sets standards for when a court may make a custody determination and when a court must defer to an existing determination from another state. Having the same law in all states helps standardize how custody decrees are treated. It also helps solve many problems created by kidnapping or disagreements over custody between parents living in different states.

In general, a state may make a custody decision about a child only if it meets one of these tests (in order of preference):

- The state is the child's home state. This means the child has resided in the state for the six previous months, or was residing in the state but is absent because a parent took the child to another state. (A parent who wrongfully removed or retained a child in order to create a "home state" will be denied custody.)

- The child has significant connections in the state with people such as teachers, doctors and grandparents and, in the words of the UCCJA, "substantial evidence in the state concerning the child's care, protection, training and personal relationships." (A parent who wrongfully removed or retained a child in order to create "significant connections" will be denied custody.)

- The child is in the state and either has been abandoned or is in danger of being abused or neglected if sent back to the other state.

- No other state can meet one of the above three tests, or a state that can meet at least one test has declined to make a custody decision.

If a state cannot meet one of these tests, the courts of that state cannot make a custody award, even if the child is present in the state. In the event more than one state meets the above standards, the law specifies that only one state may make custody decisions. This means that once a state makes a custody award, any other state must keep its hands off the matter.

Under what circumstances can custody and visitation orders be changed within the state where they were obtained?

After a final decree of divorce or other order establishing custody and visitation (such as a paternity decree) is filed with a court, parents may agree to modify the custody or visitation terms. This modified agreement (also called a "stipulated modification") may be made without court approval. If one parent later reneges on the agreement, however, the other person may not be able to enforce it unless the court has approved the modification. Thus, it is generally advisable to obtain a court's blessing before relying on such agreements. Courts usually approve modification agreements unless it appears that they are not in the best interests of the child.

If a parent wants to change an existing court order and the other parent won't agree to the change, he or she must file a motion (a written request) asking the court that issued the order to modify it. Usually, courts will modify an existing order only if the parent asking for the change can show a "substantial change in circumstances." This requirement encourages stability of arrangements and helps prevent the court from becoming overburdened with frequent and repetitive modification requests. Here are some examples of a substantial change in circumstances:

- *Geographic move.* If a custodial parent makes a significant move, or the move will seriously disrupt the stability of the child's life, the move may constitute a changed circumstance that justifies the court's modification of a custody or visitation order. Some courts switch custody from one parent to the other, although the increasingly common approach is to ask the parents to work out a plan under which both parents may continue to have significant contact with their children. If no agreement is reached, what the court will do depends on where you live. Courts in some states will permit the move unless it is shown that the child will be adversely affected. In other states, the court will carefully examine the best interests of the child—looking at factors such as switching schools and distance from relatives—and make a decision about which parent should have custody.

- *Change in lifestyle.* Changes in custody or visitation orders may be obtained if substantial changes in a parent's lifestyle threatens or harms the child. If, for example, a custodial parent begins working at night and leaving a nine-year-old child alone, the other parent may request a change in custody. Similarly, if a noncustodial parent begins drinking heavily or taking drugs, the custodial parent may file a request for modification of the visitation order (asking, for example, that visits occur when the parent is sober, or in the presence of another adult). What constitutes a lifestyle sufficiently detrimental to warrant a change in custody or visitation rights varies tremendously depending on the state and the particular judge deciding the case.

Custodial Interference

In most states, it's a crime to take a child from his or her parent with the intent to interfere with that parent's physical custody of the child (even if the taker also has custody rights). This crime is commonly referred to as "custodial interference." In most states, the parent deprived of custody may sue the taker for damages, as well as get help from the police to have the child returned.

If a parent without physical custody (who may or may not have visitation rights) removes a child from—or refuses to return a child to—the parent with physical custody, it is considered kidnapping or child concealment in addition to custodial interference. Federal and state laws have been passed to prosecute and punish parents guilty of this type of kidnapping, which is a felony in over 40 states.

In many states, interfering with a parent's custody is a felony if the child is taken out of state. Many states, however, recognize good-cause defenses, such as where the taker acted to prevent imminent bodily harm to herself or himself, or to the child. In addition, some states let a parent take a child out of state if the parent is requesting custody in court and has notified the court or police of the child's location.

I've heard that mediation is the best approach to solving disagreements about child custody and visitation. Is this true?

Mediation is a nonadversarial process where a neutral person (a mediator) meets with disputing persons to help them settle a dispute. The mediator does not have power to impose a solution on the parties, but assists them in creating an agreement of their own. (In a few states, however, the mediator may be asked by the court to make a recommendation if the parties cannot reach an agreement.)

There are several important reasons why mediation is a superior method to litigation for resolving custody and visitation disputes:

- Mediation usually does not involve lawyers or expert witnesses (or their astronomical fees).
- Mediation usually produces a settlement after five to ten hours of mediation over a week or two. (Child custody litigation can drag on for months or even years.)
- Mediation enhances communication between the couple and makes it much more likely that they will be able to cooperate after the divorce or separation when it comes to raising their children. Experts who have studied the effects of divorce on children universally conclude that when divorcing or separating parents can cooperate, the children suffer far less.

How to Find a Family Law Mediator

Several states require mediation in custody and visitation disputes and a number of others allow courts to order mediation. In these situations, the court will direct the parents to the mediator and will pay for the services. Parents can also find and pay for the mediator themselves. With increasing frequency, family law attorneys are offering mediation services for child custody and other divorce-related disputes, as are a number of nonlawyer community mediators. Two resources for finding a family law mediator in your area are:

Academy of Family Mediators
5 Militia Drive
Lexington, MA 02421
718-674-2663
718-674-2690 (fax)
http://www.mediators.org

Society of Professionals in Dispute Resolution (SPIDR)
1527 New Hampshire Avenue, NW
Third Floor
Washington, DC 20036
202-667-9700
202-265-1968 (fax)
http://www.spidr.org

Things are so bitter between my ex and me that it's hard to see us sitting down together to work things out. How can mediation possibly work?

Mediators are very skilled at getting parents who are bitter enemies to cooperate for the sake of their children. The more parents can agree on the details of separate parenting, the better it will be for them and their children. And mediators are skilled at getting the parents to recognize this fact and then move forward towards negotiating a sensible parenting agreement. If there is a history of abuse or if the parents initially cannot stand to be in the same room with each other, the mediator can meet with each parent separately and ferry messages back and forth until agreement on at least some issues is reached. At this point, the parties may be willing to meet face to face.

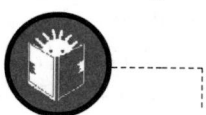

More Information About Child Custody

Child Custody: Building Parenting Agreements That Work, by Mimi Lyster (Nolo), shows separating or divorcing parents how to create a win-win custody agreement.

National Center for Lesbian Rights, 870 Market Street, Suite 570, San Francisco, CA 94102, 415-392-6257, http://www.nclrights.org, provides legal information, referrals and assistance to lesbian and gay parents.

National Congress for Fathers and Children, 9454 Wilshire Boulevard, Suite 207, Beverly Hills, CA 90212, 800-733-3237 or 310-247-6051, http://www.ncfc.net, provides information and assistance for fathers.

Child Support

Children have more need of models than of critics.

—JOSEPH JOUBERT

Child support is an emotional subject. Parents who are supposed to receive it on behalf of their children often do not. Parents who are supposed to pay it often cannot, or choose not to for a variety of reasons that are not legally recognized. It is the children who suffer the most when child support levels are inadequate or obligations are not met. Therefore, the trend in all states is to increase child support levels and the ways child support obligations can be enforced.

How long must parents support their children?

Biological parents and adoptive parents must support a child until:
- the child reaches the age of majority (and sometimes longer if the child has special needs or is in college)
- the child is on active military duty
- the parents' rights and responsibilities are terminated (for example, when a child is adopted), or

- the child has been declared emancipated by a court. (Emancipation can occur when a minor has demonstrated freedom from parental control or support and an ability to be self-supporting.)

How are child support obligations affected by a divorce or separation?

When one parent is awarded sole custody of a child, the other parent typically is required to fulfill his or her child support obligation by making payments to the custodial parent. The custodial parent, however, meets his or her support obligation through the custody itself. When parents are awarded joint physical custody in a divorce, the support obligation of each is often based on the ratio of each parent's income to their combined incomes, and the percentage of time the child spends with each parent.

Are fathers who never married the mother still required to pay child support?

The short answer to this question is yes. When a mother is not married, however, it's not always clear who the father is. An "acknowledged father" is any biological father of a child born to unmarried parents for whom paternity has been established by either the admission of the father or the agreement of the parents. Acknowledged fathers are required to pay child support.

Additionally, a man who never married may be presumed to be the father of a child if he welcomes the child into his home and openly holds the child out as his own. In some states, the presumption of paternity is considered conclusive, which means it cannot be disproved, even with contradictory blood tests.

The obligation to pay child support does not depend on whether a court ordered it. Where most unmarried fathers encounter this principle is when the mother seeks public assistance. Sooner or later the welfare department will ask the court to order the father to reimburse it, based on his support obligation and income during the period in question. Sometimes this happens many years later, and the father is required to pay thousands of dollars in back support that he never knew he owed.

Do fathers have the same right to child support as mothers?

Yes. If you're a father with custody, you have the right to ask for child support. Each parent has a duty to support his or her children, and that duty doesn't discriminate between genders.

Is a stepparent obligated to support the children of the person to whom he or she is married?

No, unless the stepparent legally adopts the children.

Calculating Child Support

Each state has guidelines for calculating child support, based on the parents' incomes and expenses. These guidelines vary considerably from state to state. In addition, in some states judges have considerable leeway in setting the actual amount, as long as the general state guidelines are followed. But an increasing number of states impose very strict guidelines that leave the judges very little latitude.

In most states, the guidelines in effect specify factors which must be considered in determining who pays child support, and how much. These factors usually include:

- the needs of the child—including health insurance, education, day care and special needs
- the income and needs of the custodial parent
- the paying parent's ability to pay, and
- the standard of living of the child before divorce or separation.

How does the court determine the amount I am able to pay for child support?

When determining your ability to pay child support, the court looks at your net income. This is your gross income from all sources—such as wages, investment income, rents from real property or public benefits—less any mandatory deductions. Mandatory deductions include income taxes, Social Security payments and healthcare costs. In most states, courts don't consider other types of automatic deductions from your paycheck (such as wage attachments or credit union payments) or debt obligations (such as loan or credit card payments) when figuring net income. This is because the law places a high priority on child support. Courts would rather see other debts go unpaid than have a child suffer from inadequate support. One exception is other child support obligations. In some states, courts allow you to deduct the amount of child support you pay for other children from your gross income.

Some courts consider reasonable expenses you incur for the necessaries of life—for example, rent, mortgage, food, clothing and healthcare. But, this usually does not include costs for tuition, eating in restaurants or entertainment. Again, the theory is that support of your children should come before these types of personal expenses. In a growing number of states, courts will not consider any personal expenses when determining your ability to pay support.

Can the court base its child support order on what I am able to earn as opposed to what I'm actually earning?

In most states, the judge is authorized to examine a parent's ability to earn as well as what she is actually earning, and order higher child support if there is a discrepancy. Actual earnings are an important factor in determining a person's ability to earn, but are not conclusive where there is evidence that a person could earn more if she chose to do so.

For example, assume a parent with an obligation to pay child support leaves his current job and enrolls in medical or law school, takes a job with lower pay but good potential for higher pay in the future or takes a lower-paying job that provides better job satisfaction. In each of these situations, a court may base the child support award on the income from the original job (ability to earn) rather than on the new income level (ability to pay). The basis for this decision would be that the children's current needs take priority over the parent's career plans and desires.

On the other hand, several courts have ruled that a parent's imprisonment entitles the parent to a reduction or suspension of child support where there is no showing that the imprisonment resulted from an attempt to avoid paying the support.

What happens if a parent falls behind on his or her child support payments?

Each installment of court-ordered child support is to be paid according to the date set out in the order. When a person does not comply with the order, the overdue payments are called arrearages or arrears. Judges have become very strict about enforcing child support orders and collecting arrearages. While the person with arrears can ask a judge for a downward modification of future payments, the judge will usually insist that the arrearage be paid in full, either immediately or in installments. In fact, judges in most states are prohibited by law from retroactively modifying a child support obligation.

EXAMPLE
Joe has a child support obligation of $300 per month. Joe is laid off of his job, and six months pass before he finds another one with comparable pay. Although Joe could seek a temporary decrease on the grounds of diminished income, he lets the matter slide and fails to pay any support during the six-month period. Joe's ex-wife later brings Joe into court to collect the $1,800 arrearage; Joe cannot obtain a retroactive ruling excusing him from making the earlier payments.

In addition, back child support cannot be cancelled in a bankruptcy proceeding. This means that once it is owed, it will always be owed, until paid.

My ex-spouse is refusing to pay court-ordered child support. How can I see to it that the order is enforced?

Under the Child Support Enforcement Act of 1984, the district attorneys (or state's attorneys) of every state must help you collect the child support owed by your ex. Sometimes this means that the D.A. will serve your ex with papers requiring him to meet with the D.A. and arrange a payment schedule, and telling him that if he refuses to meet or pay, he could go to jail. If your ex has moved out of state, you or the D.A. can use legal procedures to locate him and seek payment.

Federal and state parent locator services can also assist in locating missing parents.

Federal laws permit the interception of tax refunds to enforce child support orders. Other methods of enforcement include wage attachments, seizing property, suspending the business or occupational license of a payer who is behind on child support or—in some states—revoking the payer's driver's license. Your state's D.A. may employ any one of these methods in an attempt to help you collect from your ex.

If you and your ex live in different states, you may use the Revised Uniform Reciprocal Enforcement of Support Act (RURESA) to seek payment. Under that law, the court in the state where you live contacts a court in your ex-spouse's state, which in turn requires him to pay. This procedure will be provided to you free of charge. Unfortunately, however, it often falls short of its stated goals due to the complexity of the process and the low priority frequently assigned to these cases by the courts and law enforcement officers which are involved.

In 1992, Congress passed the Child Support Recovery Act (CSRA) which makes it a federal crime for a parent to willfully refuse to make support payments to a parent who lives in another state. This statute has been challenged on constitutional grounds (beyond the authority of Congress), and its enforcement is spotty.

In recent years, the federal government has taken an even more aggressive approach. In 1996, with legal amendments in 1998, the Financial Institution Data Match (FIDM) was established. FIDM permits state child support agencies to contact local banks, loan institutions and credit unions in order to search for, identify and freeze the accounts and assets of delinquent child support payers. While many states implement the FIDM system, the process is not automatic. Most states require a minimum delinquency. Colorado, for example, requires $5,000 in outstanding child support payments, while Mississippi requires $250. Other states go by the number of months the payments are late (in Nebraska it's three months and in Arizona it's one year). It is best to contact your county's child support agency and find out if you qualify for the FIDM program.

As a last resort, the court that has issued the child support order can hold your ex in contempt and, in the absence of a reasonable explanation for the delinquency, impose a jail term. This contempt power is exercised sparingly in most states, primarily because most judges would rather keep the payer out of jail where he has a chance of earning the income necessary to pay the support.

I think our existing child support order is unfair. How can I change it?

You and your child's other parent may agree to modify the child support terms, but even an agreed-upon modification for child support must be approved by a judge to be legally enforceable.

If you and your ex can't agree on a change, you must request the court to hold a hearing in which each of you can argue the pros and cons of the proposed modification. As a general rule, the court will not modify an existing order unless the parent proposing the modification can show changed circumstances. This rule encourages stability of arrangements and helps prevent the court from becoming overburdened with frequent and repetitive modification requests.

Depending on the circumstances, a modification may be temporary or permanent. Examples of the types of changes that frequently support temporary modification orders are:

- a child's medical emergency
- the payer's temporary inability to pay (for instance, because of illness or an additional financial burden such as a medical emergency or job loss), or
- temporary economic or medical hardship on the part of the recipient parent.

A permanent modification may be awarded under one of the following circumstances:

- either parent receives additional income from remarriage

- changes in the child support laws
- job change of either parent
- cost of living increase
- disability of either parent, or
- needs of the child.

A permanent modification of a child support order will remain in effect until support is no longer required or the order is modified at a later time—again, because of changed circumstances.

Do I have to pay child support if my ex keeps me away from my kids?

Yes. Child support should not be confused with custody and visitation. Every parent has an obligation to support his or her children. With one narrow exception, no state allows a parent to withhold support because of disputes over visitation. The exception? If the custodial parent disappears for a lengthy period so that no visitation is possible, a few courts have ruled that the noncustodial parent's duty to pay child support may be considered temporarily suspended.

No matter what the circumstances, if you believe that your ex is interfering with your visitation rights, the appropriate remedy is to go back to court to have your rights enforced or modified rather than stop making support payments.

More Information
About Child Support

The following organizations can give you information about enforcing child support orders:

National Child Support
Enforcement Association
Hall of the States
444 N. Capitol Street, Suite 414
Washington, DC 20001-1512
202-624-8180
http://www.ncsea.org

Federal Office of Child Support
Enforcement (OCSE)
370 L'Enfant Promenade, SW
Washington, DC 20447
202-401-9383
http://www.acf.dhhs.gov

Guardianship of Children

A guardianship is a legal arrangement in which an adult has the court-ordered authority and responsibility to care for a child (someone under 18 in most states) or an incapacitated adult. This section focuses on guardianships of children.

A guardianship may be necessary if a child's parents die, or if the child has been abandoned, is not receiving adequate care or is being abused in some way.

What does a guardian do?

Typically, a guardian takes care of a child's personal needs, including shelter, education and medical care. A guardian may also provide financial management for a child, though sometimes a second person (often called a "conservator" or "guardian of the estate") is appointed for this purpose.

What is the difference between a guardianship and an adoption?

An adoption permanently changes the relationship between the adults and child involved. The adopting adults legally become the child's parents. The biological parent (if living) gives up all parental rights and obligations to the child, including the responsibility to pay child support. If a biological parent dies without a will, the child has no right to inherit.

Although a guardianship establishes a legal relationship between a child and adult, it does not sever the legal relationship between the biological parents and the child. For example, the biological parents are legally required to provide financial support for the child. And if a biological parent dies without a will, the child has certain automatic inheritance rights.

May I be appointed guardian if the child's parents object?

It depends on how a judge sees the situation. You'll need to start by filing guardianship papers in court. A court investigator will likely interview you, the child and his or her parents and make a recommendation to the judge. The judge will then review the case and decide whether to appoint you. As a general rule, guardianships are not granted unless:

- the parents voluntarily consent
- the parents have abandoned the child, or
- a judge finds that it would be detrimental to the child for his or her parents to have custody.

If a child lives with me, do I need a guardianship?

You won't need a guardianship if the child is only staying with you for a few weeks or months. But anyone who anticipates caring for a child for a period of years will probably need a legal guardianship. Without this legal arrangement, you may have trouble registering the child in school, arranging for medical care and obtaining benefits on the child's behalf. In addition, you'll have no right to keep the child if his parents want him back—even if you think they're not capable of caring for him properly.

If You Want to Avoid a Formal Guardianship

An adult who has physical custody of a child may have strong reasons to avoid becoming a legal guardian—for example:

- The caretaker expects that the child's parents will not consent to a legal guardianship.
- Dynamics between family members are such that filing for a guardianship might set off a battle for legal custody. (This would be especially likely where a stepparent and one natural parent care for a child.)
- The caretaker doesn't want his or her personal life scrutinized in court or by a court-appointed investigator.

Some adults try to slide by and raise children (often grandchildren or other relatives) without any legal court authorization. If you go this route, you could run into problems with institutions that want authority from a parent or court-appointed legal guardian. Some communities and institutions are, however, very accommodating of people who are bringing up someone else's children. California, for example, has created a form that gives a nonparent permission to enroll a child in school and make medical decisions on his or her behalf without going to court. Research the laws for your state, or talk to a knowledgeable family law attorney, to find out whether there are ways for you to care for a child short of becoming a legal guardian.

When does a guardianship end?

A guardianship ordinarily lasts until the earliest of these events:

- the child reaches legal age
- the child dies
- the child's assets are used up—if the guardianship was set up solely for the purpose of handling the child's finances, or
- a judge determines that a guardianship is no longer necessary.

Even if a guardianship remains in force, a guardian may step down from his or her role with permission from the court. In that case, a judge will appoint a replacement guardian.

Who financially supports a child under a guardianship?

Unless a court terminates the biological parents' rights (uncommon in most guardianship situations), the parents are responsible for supporting their child. In practice, however, financial support often becomes the guardian's responsibility. The guardian may choose to pursue financial benefits on the child's behalf, such as public assistance and Social Security.

Any funds the guardian receives for the child must be used for that child's benefit. Depending on the amount of money involved, the guardian may be required to file periodic reports with a court showing how much money was received for the child and how it was spent.

Are You Prepared to Be a Guardian?

An obvious but important question to ask yourself before you take any steps to establish a guardianship is whether you're truly prepared for the job.

- Do you want the ongoing responsibilities of a legal guardianship—including potential liability for the child's actions?
- If you're managing the child's finances, are you willing to keep careful records, provide a court with periodic accountings and go to court when you need permission to handle certain financial matters?
- What kind of personal relationship do you have with the child? Do you want to act as the legal parent of this child for the duration of the guardianship?
- Will the guardianship adversely affect you or your family because of your own children, health situation, job, age or other factors?
- Do you have the time and energy to raise a child?
- What is the financial situation? If the child will receive income from Social Security, public assistance programs, welfare, a parent or the estate of a deceased parent, will this be enough to provide a decent level of support? If not, are you able and willing to spend your own money to raise the child?
- Do you anticipate problems with the child's relatives—including parents—who may suddenly reappear and contest the guardianship? (This is rare, but it can happen.)

• What kind of relationship do you have with the child's parents? Will they support the guardianship, or will they more likely be hostile, antagonistic or interfering?

It's smart to consider your options carefully before initiating a guardianship proceeding. After honestly answering the questions above, you may need to rethink your plans.

Is it true that parents may need a guardianship of their own child?

It's strange but true: Sometimes parents need to establish a particular type of guardianship—called a "guardianship of the estate"—to handle their own child's finances—even if the child lives with them. This situation usually arises when significant amounts of property (at least $5,000 in most states) are given directly to a child.

Understandably, institutions and lawyers are reluctant to turn assets over to parents when they were intended for a child. A guardianship of the estate relieves the institution from liability, and the parents are directly accountable to a court to show how funds are spent and invested.

The Thompsons lived next door to an elderly widow, who was extremely fond of their small daughter. When the widow died, she left her house to little Suzy Thompson. The lawyer handling the
widow's estate suggests that Suzy's parents go to court to establish a guardianship of their child's estate. The house is then transferred into the name of Suzy's guardianship estate, which her parents manage until she reaches adulthood.

While this system is effective in protecting children's assets from unscrupulous parents, setting up a formal guardianship of the estate involves time and money that well-meaning parents sometimes find burdensome. For this reason, all states have passed laws to make it easier to give money or property to children. These laws provide simple, inexpensive procedures by which gifts to minors (typically up to $10,000) can be managed by their parents without setting up a formal guardianship of the estate. The gift-giver must simply name, in his or her will or in a trust document, someone to manage the gift until the child reaches adulthood. No court involvement is required. (For more information about leaving property to children, see Chapter 12, *Wills and Estate Planning*.)

I have young children, and I'm worried about who will care for them if something happens to me. How can I name a guardian?

You can use your will to name a guardian for your children. The specifics are discussed in Chapter 12 of this book, *Wills and Estate Planning*.

More Information About Guardianships

The Guardianship Book for California, by Lisa Goldoftas and David Brown (Nolo), contains all forms and instructions necessary to become a child's guardian in California.

For information about guardianships in other states, visit your local law library.

http://www.nolo.com

Nolo offers self-help information about a wide variety of legal topics, including laws that affect parents and their children.

http://www.calib.com/naic

The National Adoption Information Clearinghouse provides information about adoption as well as referrals to local agencies and support groups.

http://www.adoption.com

This site provides information about adoption agencies, international adoption and many other adoption issues.

http://www.divorceonline.com

Divorce Online provides general information, including articles about mediation and child custody. The site also gives answers to frequently asked family law questions.

http://www.law.cornell.edu

The Legal Information Institute at Cornell Law School provides links to many of the family laws available on the Web, including laws governing adoption, child custody and children's rights.

Courts and Mediation

17.2   *Representing Yourself in Court*

17.13   *Small Claims Court*

17.21   *Mediation*

17.27   *Dealing With Your Lawyer*

NINETY PERCENT OF OUR LAWYERS SERVE

TEN PERCENT OF OUR PEOPLE. WE ARE

OVER-LAWYERED AND UNDER-REPRESENTED.

—JIMMY CARTER

The average citizen's ability to gain access to the American justice system has long been determined by economic status. The wealthy can afford experienced lawyers—the legal system's gatekeepers—while most others are frozen out. Fortunately, a number of initiatives are being developed to level the legal playing field. Although still too few, and often too limited in the size and types of disputes they can consider, mediators, expanded small claims courts and family courts that make nonlawyers welcome are all part of the changing landscape. So, too, are Internet-based legal information sites, which increasingly provide legal information as well as low-cost forms and instructions necessary to complete routine legal tasks. Together they give hope that all Americans will have improved access to our legal system in the years ahead.

Representing Yourself in Court

A MAN WAS ARRESTED IN NEW YORK FOR IMPERSONATING A LAWYER OVER A LENGTHY PERIOD OF TIME. ASSISTANT MANHATTAN DISTRICT ATTORNEY BRIAN ROSNER SAID ONE JUDGE TOLD HIM:

"I should have suspected he wasn't a lawyer. He was always so punctual and polite."

With lawyers' fees often running in excess of $200 an hour, it often makes sense to represent yourself in a small civil (noncriminal) lawsuit. The task may seem daunting, but if you have a good self-help resource to guide you and, if possible, someone who knows the ropes to coach you when you need help, you really can act as your own lawyer—safely and efficiently.

Is it ever truly sensible to appear in court without a lawyer?

When it comes to small claims court, which is designed to be accessible to nonlawyers—yes, of course. But sometimes it's also a good idea to represent yourself in a more formal court proceeding. Hiring a lawyer rarely makes economic sense for disputes that in-

volve less than $50,000 and often costs more than it's worth for disputes in the $50,000–$100,000 range. In these dollar ranges, representing yourself may be your only reasonable option.

Are you saying that for small cases, the cost of hiring a lawyer is too high, given the amount at stake?

With most lawyers charging hefty hourly fees, and any contested court case racking up at least dozens of hours of attorney time, it is obvious that attorney fees can quickly dwarf what is at stake in many disputes. But the problem is really more fundamental: No matter what the size of the case, many people don't have the kind of money it takes to pay a lawyer's hourly rate in the first place. This means that unless the case is for a personal injury or another type of dispute that lawyers will handle for a contingency fee (a percentage of the total recovery)—or the lawyer quotes a reasonable fixed fee to deal with the dispute from start to finish—the person will either have to go it alone or give up the lawsuit altogether.

Free Legal Help

Before you decide to represent yourself, you may want to explore the possibility of getting help at no cost to you. Here are several instances in which you may be able to get an attorney to represent you for free. If none of these matches your situation, or if you simply wish to represent yourself, you'll also want to explore whether your court offers pro per assistance either in person or on the Internet.

If you face criminal charges.

If you've been charged with a crime and cannot afford to hire your own lawyer, you have a constitutional right to an attorney at government expense. At your request, an attorney, often from a public defender's office, can be appointed to represent you when you are formally charged in court with a criminal offense.

If you've been injured.

If you have been significantly injured and it appears that someone else is at least partially at fault, many lawyers will agree to represent you on a "contingency fee" basis. This means that you pay attorney's fees only when and if the attorney recovers money for you, in which case the attorney takes an agreed-upon percentage of that total as fees. Be aware, however, that even if a lawyer takes your case on a contingency fee basis, you still have to agree to pay costs, which can add up to several thousand dollars. Costs, which will sometimes be advanced by a lawyer, include court filing fees,

court reporters' fees, expert witness fees and jury fees. The good news is that if you win your case, the judge will usually order your adversary to pay you back for these costs.

If you qualify for legal aid.

If you can't afford an attorney, you may qualify for free legal assistance. Legal aid lawyers are government-funded lawyers who represent people with low incomes in a variety of legal situations, including eviction defense, denial of unemployment compensation or other benefits, and consumer credit problems. If you think you might qualify, look in your telephone directory or ask a local attorney, lawyer referral service or elected representative for the nearest legal aid office.

If your claim involves an issue of social justice.

If your dispute involves a social justice issue, an attorney or nonprofit organization with an interest in that issue may represent you on a free or "pro bono" (for the public good) basis. For example, if your claim involves sexual harassment by an employer, abuse by a spouse or partner, discrimination in housing or employment, freedom of speech or religion or environmental pollution, you may find an attorney or nonprofit organization willing to represent you pro bono. Help is much more likely to be forthcoming if your claim raises new and important issues of law. Call a local bar association or a private organization that deals with the kind of problem you face, such as the American Civil Liberties Union, the NAACP Legal Defense Fund, the Natural Resources Defense Council, the National Women's Law Center or the Lambda Legal Defense and Education Fund (gay and lesbian rights).

If your claim involves a divorce, child custody or support, domestic violence or other family law problem.

Increasingly, family courts are providing plain English information and simplified forms to self-represented litigants. Many have established comprehensive family law centers right at the courthouse, where trained staff help nonlawyers successfully achieve their goals.

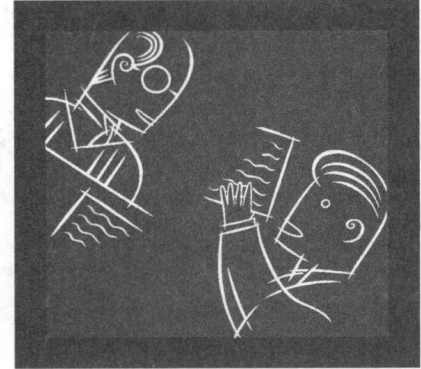

Court Information Online

Courts in all 50 states have begun posting legal information and useful forms and instructions on the Internet. Generally, small claims and family (divorce) courts provide the most helpful information, but in some areas all courts are striving to become more accessible. Here's how to find court websites:

- Nolo's Legal Research Center (http://www.nolo.com/research/index.html) links to federal, state and local courts around the country. It also provides access to information about small claims court in many states.

- The National Center for State Courts (http://www.ncsconline.org) lists state and local court websites.

- State Court Locator (http://vls. law.vill. edu/locator/statecourt) from the Villanova University School of Law provides links to state courts and opinions.

- The Federal Judiciary's website (http://www.uscourts.gov/links.htm) lists federal court websites.

If I do decide to represent myself, how can I possibly cope with all the picky procedural rules and complex legal language?

Essentially, you have two choices. Get the dispute diverted to mediation (see Mediation, below), where things are done in plain English and procedural rules are kept to a minimum, or take the time to learn how to navigate a formal court proceeding. As with learning any other bureaucratic process, doing this will take some effort, but it is far from impossible. Fortunately, Nolo publishes an excellent primer, *Represent Yourself in Court*, by Paul Bergman and Sara Berman-Barrett, which covers all the basics.

Will I really be able to learn everything I need to know to represent myself competently?

Again, the basics of how to bring or defend a case aren't difficult. But trying to get on top of every nuance of procedure and strategy is tricky. That's why Nolo suggests a two-pronged approach: learn how to handle routine representation tasks yourself while hiring a lawyer as a self-help law coach to provide advice on strategy and tactics as needed. In many situations, hiring a lawyer to coach your self-help efforts will cost only about 10%-20% of what it would cost to hire the lawyer to do the entire job.

How to Find a Lawyer Coach

Ten years ago, trying to find a lawyer who would help you find your own way through the legal system was next to impossible. Today, given the surplus of personal service lawyers and a gradual change for the better in the profession's attitude towards self-helpers, it's much easier. Because law is an increasingly specialized field, however, you'll want to find someone who is knowledgeable about your type of problem—not just any lawyer. Try to get a referral from someone else who has recently worked with lawyers in the area of your legal concern. For example, if you're opening a small business and want to find an appropriate lawyer to provide occasional guidance, you might talk to the owners of excellent local businesses to see whom they work with. Once you have a few names, make and pay for a first appointment (lawyers will respect you far more if you don't beg for a free consultation). Come right out and ask the lawyer if she is prepared to help you help yourself. If you're persistent, you're likely to find a lawyer who meets your needs. Another approach is to use one of several Internet sites, such as http://LegalOpinion.com or the LawExpress service on Nolo's website (http://www.nolo.com), which for a very reasonable fee allow you to ask a lawyer experienced in your field of interest questions by telephone without obligating yourself to full-scale representation.

I'm trying to decide whether to sue someone—for example, a contractor who goofed up my expensive remodeling project. What are my first steps?

You need to be able to answer yes to three fundamental questions in order to decide whether it's worthwhile to go forward:
• Do I have a good legal case?
• Can I prove my case?
• Can I collect when I win?

If the answer to any of these questions is no, you probably won't want to sue.

How hard is it to collect a court judgment?

That depends on your opponent. Most reputable businesses and individuals will pay you what they owe. But if your opponent tries to stiff you, collecting what you are owed can be a costly time-consuming struggle. Unfortunately, the court won't collect your money for you or even provide much help; it will be up to you to identify the assets you can grab.

Normally, if an individual is working or owns valuable property—such as land or investments—collection is less difficult; you can instruct your local law enforcement agency (usually the sheriff, marshal or constable) to garnish her wages or attach her non-exempt property. The same is true of a successful business, especially one which receives cash directly from customers; you can authorize your local sheriff or marshal to collect your judgment right out of the cash register. And in many states, if you are su-

ing a contractor or other business person with a state license, you can apply to have the license suspended until the judgment is paid.

But if you can't identify any collection source—for example, you're dealing with an unlicensed contractor of highly doubtful solvency—think twice before suing. A judgment will be of no value to you if the business or individual is insolvent, goes bankrupt or disappears.

How do I decide if I have a good case?

Lawyers break each type of lawsuit ("cause of action," in attorney-speak) into a short list of required elements. As long as you know what the elements are for your type of lawsuit, it's usually fairly easy to determine whether your case is legally sound. For example, a lawsuit against a contractor for doing substandard construction would be for breach of contract (the contractor agreed either orally or in writing to do the job properly). The legal elements for this type of lawsuit are:

Contract formation. You must show that you have a legally binding contract with the other party. If you have a written agreement, this element is especially easy to prove. Without a written contract, you will have to show that you had an enforceable oral (spoken) contract, or that an enforceable contract can be implied from the circumstances of your situation.

Performance. You must prove that you did what was required of you under the terms of the contract. Assuming you have made agreed-upon payments and otherwise met the terms of the agreement, you'll have no problems with this element.

Breach. You must show that the party you plan to sue failed to meet her contractual obligations. This is usually the heart of the case—you'll normally need to prove that the contractor failed to do agreed-upon work or did work of poor quality.

Damages. You must show that you suffered an economic loss as a result of the other party's breach of contract. Assuming the work must be redone or finished, this element is also easy to prove.

The legal elements for other types of lawsuits are different. You can find outlines for most in *Represent Yourself in Court,* by Attorneys Paul Bergman and Sara J. Berman-Barrett (Nolo).

Is it difficult to prepare the paperwork to initiate a lawsuit?

Actually, it's often fairly easy—especially if you learn how to do the necessary legal research and prepare drafts of the papers, restricting your lawyer's role to that of checking your work. Initiating a lawsuit is especially straightforward in states such as California and Michigan, where court clerks provide preprinted fill-in-the-blanks forms for many types of lawsuits. But even in states where lawsuits are filed the old-fashioned way, using paragraphs of appropriate legal jargon on numbered legal paper, the actual wording you'll need is almost always available word for word from lawyer "forms books" or CD-ROMs.

And increasingly states themselves are making forms available free on their own websites. (See "Court Information Online," above.) These information sources, which are routinely used by lawyers, are available at most larger law libraries and are usually fairly easy for the nonlawyer to understand.

I've filed my lawsuit. What do I need to do next?

Before a case gets scheduled for trial, a number of things need to happen, including meetings with your opponent and paperwork designed to reduce or narrow disputed issues. Court rules that cover many of these—for example, whether and when a settlement conference must take place, when papers must be filed and how to place a case on the court's trial calendar—should be available from the court clerk and, increasingly, on the Web (see Court Information Online, above). Unfortunately, many clerks are not willing to provide help beyond handing out a copy of often confusing written rules. To get a plain English overview of the pretrial process, see Nolo's *Represent Yourself in Court,* by Attorneys Paul Bergman & Sara J. Berman-Barrett.

In addition to procedural maneuverings, most larger lawsuits involve a search for information about the facts of the case, called "discovery." This process is left largely up to you and the other parties to the lawsuit. For example, one type of discovery consists of your taking the deposition (oral statement) of the other party or one or more witnesses to find out what he or she is likely to say at trial. Additional types of discovery consist of interrogatories (written questions to the other party), a request to produce documents or a request that the other party admit certain facts (stipulations).

What are the advantages and disadvantages of taking a deposition?

Depositions, which normally consist of face-to-face questioning of the other party or a witness before trial, have several big advantages as compared to the other types of discovery mentioned above:

- You can learn a great deal about your adversary's case, so as to avoid surprise in the courtroom.
- You can offer a deposition transcript into evidence at trial if the deponent (the person questioned) is unavailable to give live testimony. This rule explains why you might consider deposing a helpful witness who may not be available to testify at the time of trial.
- If an adversary's witness whose deposition you have taken testifies significantly differently at trial than at the deposition, you can read the inconsistent deposition testimony into the trial record to impeach (attack) the deponent's credibility.

EXAMPLE

You have sued your former employer for violating state law by firing you for missing work because you served on a jury in a lengthy trial. Before trial you take the *deposition of your former supervisor, Paul Chepick. At the deposition, Chepick testified that your work performance had been satisfactory before you took off for jury duty. At trial, Chepick testifies that you were fired not because of your jury service, but because of a number of work-related problems. Because Chepick's deposition testimony contradicts his trial testimony, you could read the deposition testimony into the record at trial to call his believability into question.*

- As compared to conducting discovery by asking written questions (interrogatories), depositions allow for more flexibility in questioning because you hear a deponent's answer before you ask the next question. For example, assume that a deponent unexpectedly refers to an important business meeting that you had no idea had taken place. In a deposition, you can immediately follow up the remark with questions about what took place during this meeting.
- You can take anyone's deposition. You can depose your adversary, an employee who works for your adversary, a bystander who witnessed a key event, an expert witness hired by your opponent—or even your opponent's attorney! By contrast, you can send written questions (interrogatories) only to your opponent, not to witnesses.
- You elicit the testimony of an individual deponent. While your adversary's lawyer will probably attend the deposition and can consult with the deponent during recesses (breaks in the testimony), it

is the deponent who has to answer the questions. By contrast, attorneys often play a major role in preparing the answers to written interrogatories and usually advise clients how to answer them in a way that provides you with as little information as possible.

- You can use a deposition to learn and ask about documents (or other tangible items) by simply using a Notice of Deposition (to depose your opponent) or a subpoena duces tecum (to depose a nonparty witness). In either case you can list items you want the deponent to bring to the deposition.

Unfortunately, deposing an adversary or a witness who supports your adversary also has some disadvantages. Weigh these considerations very carefully before you decide to take a deposition:

- Depositions are the most expensive discovery tool. Even if you are representing yourself (and therefore not paying an attorney to take or attend a deposition), you must pay a court reporter to transcribe the testimony and prepare a written transcript. While costs vary somewhat by locality, it's not unusual for a court reporter to charge up to $5.00 per page of transcript. A day of deposition testimony fills up about 150 pages, meaning that a day-long deposition may cost you around $750. If you win your case, however, the judge may order your adversary to pay your deposition costs.
- If you are involved in a lawsuit against a good-sized business or

governmental entity and haven't investigated thoroughly enough to know which witnesses are most likely to have important information, you may end up paying dearly to depose a witness whose main answers are, "I don't know." By contrast, written interrogatories give you access to "corporate knowledge." This means that when you send interrogatories to an adversary that is a business or other entity, any employee with knowledge has to contribute to the answers.

- Effective deposition questioning is a difficult skill, even for many attorneys. You have to pose questions carefully in order to be confident that you know how adverse witnesses will testify at trial. If questions are vague or you forget to cover a topic, you won't be prepared for your opponent's evidence at trial or be able to show that a witness has changed a story and therefore should not be believed.
- Your adversary's lawyer can be present at a deposition. The attorney may throw you off track by objecting to your questions. Also, an adversary's attorney can help witnesses "refresh their recollections" during recesses. Finally, seeing you in action will allow the attorney to estimate your own credibility, and by listening to your questions often learn as much about your case as you learn about your adversary's.
- If you depose an adverse witness who becomes unavailable for trial, you enable the adversary to offer the deposition transcript into evidence at trial.

How do I take a deposition?

Start by checking your local court rules (see Court Information Online, above). Then read Nolo's Deposition Handbook, by Paul Bergman and Albert Moore, which contains detailed instructions on how to ask and answer questions. Pay particular attention to the time window for taking depositions and understand exactly how to notify a person whose deposition you want to take. Under all rules, you'll need to select a date and location for the deposition, arrange and pay for a court reporter's presence (many are listed in phone books), and give the deponent and opposing counsel (or your self-represented adversary) at least ten days' written notice. Even better, as a courtesy, talk to all the necessary people ahead of time to try to arrange a mutually convenient date and location.

If you want to depose a "non-party witness" (someone other than your adversary), you'll probably have to serve the witness with an official court form called a "Subpoena re Deposition." If you want the non-party witness to bring documents to the deposition, use instead a form carrying the fancy title "Subpoena Duces Tecum re Deposition." (These forms should be available from a court clerk.) List the documents you want the witness to bring along, and state briefly how they pertain to the case.

Once the deposition has been scheduled, follow these tips to learn as much information as you can:

• Prepare a list of questions before you take a witness's deposition. You need not slavishly follow the list, but having one to refer to should prevent you from forgetting important topics.

• Bring (or subpoena) copies of any written statements about the case that the deponent has previously given. For example, bring the police report if the witness gave a statement to a police officer who included it in the report, or the witness's own declaration (statement under oath) if one was attached to a document filed in court. Ask the deponent to amplify on and fill any holes in a statement's contents, then check to see if the deponent in any way contradicts a prior statement. If so, you might ask the witness to repeat the contradictory statement. That way, if you impeach (attack the credibility of) the witness at trial, the witness cannot easily wriggle out by saying, "I made a careless mistake during my deposition."

• Bring copies of any other documents about which you want to question the witness, regardless of whether the witness wrote the document or has any connection to it. For example, you may want to know whether the witness ever saw a document, the date on which the witness saw it or whether the witness is aware of the information in the document.

• Review and bring along all paperwork relating to the case organized chronologically, including the complaint, answer and any motions or court rulings. These documents can help if an issue arises concerning the relevance of your questions.

When my case finally makes it to the courtroom, I'm afraid I won't know what to say, when to say it or even where to stand. How can I learn what to do?

It's not hard to learn how to conduct yourself in court. This is especially true if your trial is before a judge without a jury, because when dealing with a self-represented person many judges make an effort to simplify jargon and procedure. And there are several practical steps you can take to learn the ropes:

- Attend a few trials involving similar issues. You'll see that it won't be that difficult to present your story and evidence to a judge.
- Carefully read a self-help book such as Nolo's Represent Yourself in Court, by Attorneys Paul Bergman and Sara J. Berman-Barrett, which explains what you'll need to do in great detail. For example, you'll want to prepare and practice a brief but thorough opening statement to tell the judge what your case is about.
- Prepare a Trial Notebook which outlines each major aspect of your trial and what you need to do and say at each point. For example, based on taking the other side's deposition or asking written questions (interrogatories), you probably have a pretty good idea what she will say when she testifies. Clearly, it's a good idea to use your Trial Notebook to prepare a carefully

crafted outline of what you plan to ask her in court. Similarly, because you will know before trial who else will testify for the other side, your Trial Notebook should contain a well-organized list of points you want to cover when you have a chance to question (cross-examine) them.

A Typical Trial

Allowing for many possible variations, most trials begin with each side making an opening statement—each party presents an overview of his case, including what he expects to prove. The next stage is direct examination, during which the plaintiff (the person who filed the suit) presents her testimony about what happened and supports it with witnesses' statements and other relevant evidence. After each of the plaintiff's witnesses testifies, the defendant gets a chance to cross-examine them. In doing so, the defendant attempts to produce testimony favorable to his version of events and to cast doubt on the reliability or credibility of the plaintiff's witnesses. Finally, each side gets to make a closing argument explaining to the judge or jury why they should win.

What types of evidence win trials?

As mentioned above, in addition to having a legally sound case, you need to be able to prove it before a judge or jury. Technically, this means establishing each required legal element of your cause of action by a preponderance (more than 50%) of the evidence. (See above, "How do I decide if I have a good case?") Practically, it usually means focusing on one or two disputed elements of a case (did your remodeling contractor breach the contract by using substandard materials, doing poor work or installing equipment not called for in the contract?). Unfortunately, too many self-represented litigants try to rely primarily on their own oral rendition of events and overlook the need to back this up with tangible evidence. Depending on the key issues that must be proved, this normally means presenting things like photos, contracts, cost estimates to redo the work or government records. In addition, it typically involves presenting witnesses who either saw or heard what happened (overheard a boss demanding sex with a subordinate) or are qualified to render an expert opinion on a key aspect of the case (a master tile layer who will testify that the installation of the tile floor in your kitchen was botched).

What about actually examining (presenting) witnesses? I'm more than a little intimidated by having to act like Perry Mason.

And well you should be. It's not easy being an actor, especially one who died years ago. But fortunately, appearing in a routine court proceeding isn't that difficult, as long as you know the basic rules. For instance, when you present the testimony of eyewitnesses or expert witnesses, you

do so by asking a series of questions. First you need to establish that your eyewitness has personal knowledge of the event in question, or that an expert witness is qualified to render an opinion on the issues in dispute. This normally means you must show that your eyewitness personally observed, heard, smelled, touched or tasted whatever he is testifying to—for example, that your witness was on the spot and overheard the contractor you are suing talking to someone about the details of your garage job. Or in the case of an expert witness, her opinion is based on a careful and accurate review of the facts of the case. Second, you must learn to ask questions that allow that person to explain whatever it is he knows that supports your case without putting words into his mouth (called "leading the witness"). You can learn the basic techniques of how to question a witness and how to object to any improper questions asked by reading a good self-help book.

You've said a lot about trials before judges. Don't I have a right to have my civil case heard by a jury?

For some types of cases, such as those involving child support or custody, or a request for an injunction (to stop the city from cutting down a tree, for example), you are not entitled to a jury trial. And in some courts, the parties in all small civil cases must first try to resolve the case between themselves via mediation before initiating any type of trial. But in most civil cases, including those involving personal injury, breach of contract, professional malpractice, libel or slander, you are entitled to a jury trial if you want one.

You may, however, want to think twice before you request a jury trial; it will be more complicated and harder to handle a case before a jury on your own than it would be to represent yourself before a judge. Not only can it be tricky to participate in the jury selection process, but formal procedural and evidentiary rules will almost surely be more rigorously enforced when a jury is involved. In short, most who go it alone are better off avoiding this added level of complexity by trying their case in front of a judge. But, of course, the other party has a say, too, and if that person demands a jury, so be it.

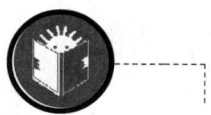

More Information About Representing Yourself in Court

Represent Yourself in Court: How to Prepare & Try a Winning Case, by Paul Bergman and Sara J. Berman-Barrett (Nolo). We have mentioned this book a number of times because it is quite simply the only publication that competently explains all aspects of a civil court trial, including how to determine if you have a good case, line up persuasive witnesses,

present effective testimony in court, cross-examine opponents and even pick a jury.

Nolo's Deposition Handbook, by Paul Bergman and Albert Moore (Nolo), thoroughly covers the deposition process. Whether you are represented by a lawyer or self-representing, it explains how to prepare for your deposition, how to respond to questions and how to cope with the tricks lawyers may use to influence your testimony. It also contains an excellent chapter on deposing expert witnesses.

The Criminal Law Handbook, by Paul Bergman and Sara J. Berman-Barrett (Nolo), tells you what you'll want to know if you or someone you love has been charged with a crime.

The Lawsuit Survival Guide, by Joseph Matthews (Nolo), is designed to help people who are represented by a lawyer understand what's going on in their case and better manage their own lawyer.

Small Claims Court

Small claims court judges resolve disputes involving relatively modest amounts of money. The people or businesses involved normally present their cases to a judge or court commissioner under rules that encourage a minimum of legal and procedural formality. The judge then makes a decision (a judgment) reasonably promptly. Although procedural rules dealing with when and where to file and serve papers are established by each state's laws and differ in detail, the basic approach to properly preparing and presenting a small claims case is remarkably similar everywhere.

How much can I sue for in small claims court?

The limit is normally between $2,000 and $10,000, depending on your state. For instance, the maximum is $5,000 in California, $7,500 in Minnesota, $3,000 in New York and $3,500 in Vermont. (See the chart below for your state's limit.)

Can any kind of case be resolved in small claims court?

No. Small claims courts primarily resolve small monetary disputes. In a few states, however, small claims courts may also rule on a limited range of other types of legal disputes, such as evictions or requests for the return of an item of property (restitution). You cannot use small claims court to file a divorce, guardianship, name change or bankruptcy, or to ask for emergency relief (such as an injunction to stop someone from doing an illegal act).

When it comes to disputes involving money, you can usually file in small claims court based on any legal theory that would be allowed in any other court—for example, breach of contract, personal injury, intentional harm or breach of warranty. A few states do, however, limit or prohibit small claims suits based on libel, slander, false arrest and a few other legal theories.

Finally, suits against the federal government or a federal agency, or even against a federal employee for actions relating to his or her employ-ment cannot be brought in small claims court. Suits against the federal government normally must be filed in a federal District Court or other federal court, such as Tax Court or the Court of Claims. Unfortunately, there are no federal small claims procedures available except in federal Tax Court.

Are there time limits in which a small claims court case must be filed?

Yes. States establish rules called "statutes of limitations" which dictate how long you may wait to initiate a lawsuit after the key event giving rise to the lawsuit occurs or, in some instances, is discovered. Statutes of limitations rules apply to all courts, including small claims.

You'll almost always have at least one year to sue (measured from the event or, sometimes, from its discovery). Often, you'll have much longer. But if you're planning to sue a state or local government agency, however, you'll usually need to file a formal claim with that agency within three to six months of the incident. Only after your initial timely complaint is denied are you eligible to file in small claims court.

SMALL CLAIMS COURT LIMITS FOR THE 50 STATES

Alabama	$3,000
Alaska	$7,500
Arizona	$2,500 (Small Claims Division); $5,000 (Regular Justice Court)
Arkansas	$5,000
California	$5,000 (A plaintiff may not file a claim over $2,500 more than twice a year. The limit for suits involving a surety company is $4,000.)
Colorado	$7,500
Connecticut	$3,500 (No limit for landlord-tenant cases involving security deposit claims)
Delaware	$15,000
District of Columbia	$5,000
Florida	$5,000
Georgia	$15,000
Hawaii	$3,500
Idaho	$4,000
Illinois	$5,000 (Small Claims); ($2,500 Cook County Pro Se Branch)
Indiana	$3,000 ($6,000 in Marion and Allen Counties)
Iowa	$4,000
Kansas	$1,800
Kentucky	$1,500
Louisiana	$3,000
Maine	$4,500
Maryland	$2,500
Massachusetts	$2,000
Michigan	$3,000
Minnesota	$7,500
Mississippi	$2,500
Missouri	$3,000
Montana	$3,000
Nebraska	$2,400
Nevada	$5,000

New Hampshire	$5,000
New Jersey	$2,000 (Small Claims Court); $10,000 (Special Civil Part, Superior Court)
New Mexico	$7,500
New York	$3,000
North Carolina	$4,000
North Dakota	$5,000
Ohio	$3,000
Oklahoma	$4,500
Oregon	$5,000
Pennsylvania	$8,000 (Small Claims Court); $10,000 (Philadelphia Municipal Court)
Rhode Island	$1,500
South Carolina	$7,500
South Dakota	$8,000
Tennessee	$15,000 ($25,000 in Shelby and Anderson Counties)
Texas	$5,000
Utah	$5,000
Vermont	$3,500
Virginia	$1,000 (Small Claims Court); $3,000 (General District Court); $15,000 (Circuit Court); no limits on eviction suits in General District Court
Washington	$4,000
West Virginia	$5,000
Wisconsin	$5,000 (no limit on eviction suits)
Wyoming	$3,000 (Small Claims Court); $7,000 (County Circuit Court)

If some time has passed since the incident giving rise to your lawsuit occurred—for example, after the breach of a written contract or a personal injury—you may need to do a little research to determine whether you can still file your claim. Check your state's legal code under the index heading "statute of limitations." See the Legal Research Appendix for information on how to do this in the library or online.

Where should I file my small claims lawsuit?

Assuming the other party lives or does business in your state, rules normally require that you sue in the small claims court district closest to that person's residence or headquarters. In some instances, you also may be able to sue in the location (court district) where a contract was signed or a personal injury occurred (such as an auto accident). Check with your small claims clerk for detailed rules.

If a defendant has no contact with your state, you'll generally have to sue in the state where the defendant lives or does business. Because most major corporations operate in all states, it's easy to sue most of them almost anywhere. But small businesses typically only conduct business in one or a few states, meaning you have to sue there.

If You Want to Avoid Going to Court

If you are anxious to recover what's owed to you, but you want to avoid the trouble of bringing a lawsuit, you have a couple of options to consider. First, even if you've been rudely turned down in the past, ask for your money at least once more. This time, make your demand in the form of a straightforward letter that briefly reviews the key facts of the dispute and concludes with the statement that you'll file in small claims court in ten days unless payment is promptly received. Unlike a conversation, where the other party may assume you'll never follow up, a polite but direct demand letter is like tossing a cup of cold water in his or her face in that it lets the person know you're serious about getting paid. Because many individuals and small business people have a strong aversion to appearing at a public trial (including the time and inconvenience it will take), making it clear you are prepared to file a lawsuit can be effective in getting the other party to talk settlement.

If your letter does cause your adversary to offer a settlement, be ready to agree to reasonable compromise. There are three reasons for this advice. First, studies show that in small claims cases, the prevailing party rarely gets everything she sues for. Second, by compromising, you save the time and anxiety inherent in preparing and presenting your case in court. And finally, when cases are settled, payment is normally made or forthcoming, meaning that you avoid potential collection problems.

Many states offer, and a few require, community- or court-based mediation designed to help parties who have not already settled their small claims dispute on their own. Mediation often works best where the parties have an interest in staying on good terms, as is generally the case with neighbors, family members or small business people who have done business together for many years. In addition, many defendants are open to arriving at a mediated settlement to avoid having an official court judgment appear on their record. For these and other reasons, resolving small disputes through mediation can be remarkably successful. In Maine, for example, where mediation is required before a small claims suit may be resolved in a courtroom, over half of the cases settle. For more information about mediation, see the next series of questions.

Will I get paid if I win the lawsuit?

Not necessarily. The court may decide in your favor, but it won't handle collection for you. So before you sue, always ask, "Can I collect if I win?" If not, think twice before suing.

Worrying about whether or not you can get paid is reasonable, because some people and businesses are "judgment proof"—that is, they have little money or assets and aren't likely to acquire much in the foreseeable future. In short, if they don't pay voluntarily, you may be out of luck. Ask yourself whether the person you're suing has a steady job, valuable real property or investments. If so, it should be reasonably easy to collect by garnishing his wages if you win. If not, try to identify another collection source, such as a bank account, before going forward. For people who seem to have no job or assets, ask whether they are likely to be more solvent in

the future, since court judgments are good for 10 to 20 years in many states and can usually be renewed for longer periods. Consider whether the person might inherit money, graduate from college and get a good job, or otherwise have an economic turn around not too far down the road.

If I'm sued in small claims court but the other party is really at fault, can I countersue?

In some states, you can and must countersue if your claim arises out of the same event or transaction, or risk forever waiving that claim. In other states, "counterclaims" are not mandatory and you can sue separately later. No matter what the technical rules, you'll normally want to countersue promptly.

If the amount you sue for is under the small claims limit, your case will probably remain in that court. If, however, you want to sue for more, check with your small claims clerk for applicable rules. Often, you'll need to have the case transferred to a different court that has the power to handle cases where more money is at stake.

What should I do to prepare my small claims case?

Whether you are a plaintiff (the person suing) or the defendant (person being sued), the key is to realize that it's often what you bring with you to court to back up your story—not what you say—that determines whether you'll win or lose. This makes sense if you understand that the judge has no idea who you are and whether your oral (spoken) testimony is reliable. After all, your opponent is likely to claim that the "true story" is exactly the reverse of your version.

It follows that your chances of winning will greatly increase if you carefully collect and present convincing evidence. Depending on the facts of your case, a few of the evidentiary tools you can use to convince the judge you are right include eyewitnesses, photographs, letters from experts, or an advertisement you relied on which falsely hyped a product or service and written contracts.

What's the best way to present my case to a judge?

First, understand that the judge is busy and has heard dozens of stories like yours. To keep the judge's attention, get to the point fast by describing the event that gave rise to your claim. Immediately follow up by stating how much money you are requesting. To be able to do this efficiently, it's best to practice in advance. Here is an example of a good start: "Your Honor, my car was damaged on December 10, 2002, when the defendant ran a red light at Rose and Hyacinth Streets in the town of Saginaw and hit my front fender. I have a canceled check to show it cost me $1,927 to fix the fender."

After you have clearly stated the key event and the amount of your loss, double back and tell the judge the events that led up to your loss. For example, you might next explain that you were driving below the speed limit and had entered the intersection when the light was green, and when the defendant came barreling through the red light, you did your best to avoid her car. Then it would be time to present any eyewitnesses, police reports or other evidence that backs up your version of events.

A Court Without Lawyers?

In a handful of states, including California, Michigan and Nebraska, you must appear in small claims court on your own. In most states, however, you can be represented by a lawyer if you like. But even where it's allowed, hiring a lawyer is rarely cost-efficient. Most lawyers charge too much given the relatively modest amounts of money involved in small claims disputes. Happily, several studies show that people who represent themselves in small claims cases usually do just as well as those who have a lawyer.

Will witnesses need to testify in person?

If possible, it's best to have key witnesses speak their piece in court. But if this isn't convenient, a clearly written memo or letter will be allowed under the rules of most small claims courts. (Be sure to check your state's rules—the Legal Research Appendix explains how.) Have the witness start the statement by establishing who he or she is. ("My name is John Lomax. I've owned and managed Reo's Toyota

Repair Service for the last 17 years.")
In clear, unemotional language, the
witness should explain what he or she
observed or heard. ("I carefully
checked Mary Wilson's engine and
found that it has been rebuilt improperly, using worn-out parts.") Finally,
the witness should try to anticipate
any questions a reasonable person
might ask and provide the answers.
("Although it can take a few days to
get new parts for older engines, such
as the one Mary Wilson owned, it is
easy and common practice to do so.")

If I lose my case in small claims court, can I appeal?

The answer depends on the state in
which you live. In some, either party
may appeal within a certain period of
time, usually between 10 and 30 days,
and obtain a complete new trial in a
formal court. In other states, appeals
must be based solely on the contention that the small claims judge made
a legal mistake, and not on the facts of
the case. And some states have their
own unique rules. In California, for
example, a defendant may appeal to
the Superior Court within 30 days. A
plaintiff may not appeal at all, although she can make a motion to correct clerical errors or to correct a decision based on a legal mistake.

To find the appeals rules for your
state, call your local small claims
court clerk or refer to the Legal Research Appendix for information on
how to get them in the library or
online.

More Information About Small Claims Court

*Everybody's Guide to Small Claims
Court,* by Ralph Warner (Nolo), explains
how to evaluate your case, prepare for
court and convince a judge you're right.
It also contains a useful section on trying
to negotiate or mediate a compromise
with the other party without going to
court. Best of all, it explains the most
useful courtroom techniques and tactics to
convincingly present evidence, witnesses
and your own testimony.

Collect Your Court Judgment, by Gini
Graham Scott, Stephen Elias and Lisa
Goldoftas (Nolo), explains 19 legal ways
to collect after you win a lawsuit in
California. It also shows you how to
locate debtors and their assets.

Mediation

*I'd rather jaw, jaw, jaw, than
war, war, war.*

—WINSTON CHURCHILL

If you're involved in a legal dispute,
you may be able to settle it without
going to court. One way to do this is
to work out a solution with the help
of a mediator—a neutral third person.
Unlike a judge or an arbitrator, a mediator will not take sides or make a
decision, but will help each party
evaluate goals and options in order to
agree on a solution that works for
everyone. One exception to this rule is
made for child custody mediations in
a few states such as California, where a
mediator has the power to recommend
a solution to a judge if the parties
cannot agree.

When you reach an agreement with
an opposing party through mediation,
you can make it legally binding by
writing down your decisions in the
form of an enforceable contract.

What kinds of cases can
be mediated?

Most civil (noncriminal) disputes can
be mediated, including those involving contracts, leases, small business
ownership, employment and divorce.
For example, a divorcing couple
might engage in mediation to work
out a mutually agreeable child custody agreement. Similarly, estranged
business partners might choose mediation to work out an agreement to
divide their business. Nonviolent
criminal matters, such as claims of
verbal or other personal harassment,
can also be successfully mediated.

Finally, you may want to consider
mediation if you get into a scrape
with a neighbor, roommate, spouse,
partner or co-worker. Mediation can
be particularly useful in these areas
because it is designed to identify and
cope with divisive interpersonal issues
not originally thought to be part of
the dispute. For example, if one
neighbor sues another for making outrageous amounts of noise, the court
will usually deal with only that issue—and by declaring neighbor A the
winner and neighbor B a loser, may
worsen long-term tensions. In mediation, however, each neighbor will be
invited to present all issues in dispute.
It may turn out that overly loud
neighbor B was being obnoxious in
part because neighbor A's dog constantly pooped on his lawn or A's
son's pickup blocked a shared driveway. In short, since mediation is designed to surface and solve all problems, it's a far better way to restore
long-term peace to the neighborhood,
home or workplace.

How long does mediation take?

People who mediate through programs offered by small claims court
are often able to settle their disputes
in an hour or less. Slightly more complicated cases such as consumer
claims, small business disputes or
auto accident claims are usually resolved after a half day or, at most, a
full day of mediation. Cases with mul-

tiple parties often last longer: Add at least an hour of mediation time for each additional party. Major business disputes—those involving lots of money, complex contracts or ending a partnership—may last several days or more.

Private divorce mediation, where a couple aims to settle all the issues in their divorce—property division and alimony, as well as child custody, visitation and support—may require half a dozen or more mediation sessions spread over several weeks or a couple of months.

How is mediation different from arbitration?

A mediator normally has no authority to render a decision; it's up to the parties themselves—with the mediator's help—to work informally toward their own agreement. An arbitrator, on the other hand, conducts a contested hearing between the parties and then, acting as a judge, rends a legally binding decision. The arbitrator's decision-making power may, however, be limited based on a written agreement between the parties. For example, the parties may agree in advance that the arbitrator is limited to making an award of monetary damages of between $200,000 and $500,000. Arbitration, which has long been used to resolve commercial and labor disputes, typically resembles a court hearing—with witnesses called and evidence taken.

The 6 Stages of Mediation

While mediation is a less formal process than going to court, it is more structured than many people imagine. A full-scale mediation typically involves at least six distinct stages, as discussed below. However, in some small claims, child custody and other publicly funded mediation procedures, time constraints mean that some of these stages end up being combined.

Mediator's Opening Statement

After the disputants are seated at a table, the mediator introduces everyone, explains the goals and rules of the mediation and encourages each side to work cooperatively toward a settlement.

Disputants' Opening Statements

Each party is invited to tell, in his or her own words, what the dispute is about and how he or she has been affected by it, and to present some general ideas about resolving it. While one person is speaking, the other is not allowed to interrupt.

Joint Negotiation

After caucuses, the mediator may bring the parties back together to negotiate directly.

Joint Discussion

The mediator may try to get the parties talking directly about what was said in the opening statements. This is the time to determine what issues need to be addressed.

Closure

This is the end of the mediation. If an agreement has been reached, the mediator may put its main provisions in writing as the parties listen. The mediator may ask each side to sign the written summary of agreement or suggest they take it to lawyers for review. If the parties want to, they can write up and sign a legally binding contract. If no agreement was reached, the mediator will review whatever progress has been made and advise everyone of their options, such as meeting again later, going to arbitration or going to court.

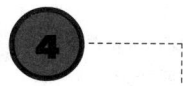

Private Caucuses

Often considered the guts of mediation, the private caucus is a chance for each party to meet privately with the mediator (usually in a nearby room) to discuss the strengths and weaknesses of his or her position, and propose new ideas for settlement. The mediator may caucus with each side just once, or several times, as needed. In mediation procedures sponsored by small claims courts and other public agencies, where time is short, this step may be shortened or skipped, with the parties encouraged to move on to joint negotiation.

Why should I consider having my case mediated?

If you've given up on negotiating a settlement of your dispute directly with the other party, mediation may be the most painless and efficient way to solve it. Compared to a lawsuit, mediation is swift, confidential, fair and low cost. Mediation sessions are usually scheduled within a few weeks or, at most, a couple of months from the time of a request—and most sessions last only a few hours or a day, depending on the type of case. In contrast, lawsuits often take many months, or even years, to resolve. Another advantage of mediation is confidentiality. With very few exceptions (for example, where a criminal act or child abuse is involved), what you say during mediation cannot legally be revealed outside the mediation proceedings or used later in a court of law.

Another huge advantage of mediation is that it will nearly always save you money. In many parts of the country, nonprofit community mediation centers or mediators employed by a small claims or other court handle relatively minor consumer, neighborhood, workplace and similar disputes for free or for a nominal charge. Private dispute resolution companies tackle more complex cases for a fraction of the cost of bringing a lawsuit. A half-day mediation of a personal injury claim, for example, may cost each side about $500-$1,000. By comparison, a full-scale court battle could cost $50,000 or more, sometimes much more.

Finally, consider that agreements reached through mediation are more likely to be carried out than those imposed by a judge. When folks go to court, the losing party is almost always angry and often prone to look for ways to violate the letter or spirit of any judgment. In contrast, a number of studies show that people who have freely arrived at their own solu-

tions through mediation are significantly more likely to follow through.

What Will It Cost?

In nearly all cases, mediating is far less expensive than going to court. Actual fees will vary depending on the type of case and who does the mediating. Here are some examples to consider.

Neighborhood dispute. Three neighbors are involved in a dispute over disruptive children. Mediation is provided by hundreds of nonprofit community mediation centers in the United States.

Typical length of mediation: full day
Typical fees per party: $10-$50 (fees usually waived for financial hardship)

Personal injury claim. A passenger in a car suffers leg and spine fractures when the driver hits a telephone pole. The passenger and the driver's insurance company cannot agree on the amount of compensation for these injuries. Mediation is conducted by a private dispute resolution company.

Typical length of mediation: half day
Typical fees per party: $600-$1,000

Business contract dispute. Ace Computer Supply sues Big Computer, Inc. for $5 million when Big C rejects parts which Ace claims conform to contract specifications. Just before the trial is to begin, the parties decide to try mediation. Mediation is provided by a private dispute resolution company.

Typical length of mediation: four days
Typical fees per party: $8,000

Divorce mediation. A divorcing couple with a house, two cars, bank accounts, pension plans and three minor children are trying to reach an agreement out of court as to the division of their property and the custody and visitation of their children. Mediation is provided by an independent divorce mediator in private practice.

Typical length of mediation: six two-hour sessions over two months, plus five hours to prepare a written agreement

Typical cost for couple: $2,000-$3,000 (split 50-50)

How can I be sure mediation will produce a fair result?

Remember that in mediation, you and the opposing parties will work to craft a solution to your own dispute. Unless you freely agree, there will be no final resolution. This approach has several advantages over going to court:

- Obscure legal precedents or the whim of a judge will not dictate the solution.
- If your dispute harbors undiscovered or undisclosed issues, mediation, unlike a structured court battle, offers the opportunity and flexibility to ferret them out.
- Because mediation does not force disputants to undergo the fear and sometimes paranoia of the courtroom—where a judge or jury can stun either party with a big loss—people who choose mediation tend to be more relaxed and less defensive, making it far easier to arrive at a compromise.

A piece of paper,
blown by the wind
into a law court may in the end
only be drawn out by two oxen.

—CHINESE PROVERB

How can I find a good mediator?

Much depends on the type of dispute you're involved in. Many cities have community mediation centers which do an excellent job of handling most types of routine disputes (consumer problems, neighbor disputes, landlord-tenant fights). For more complicated disputes (business termination, personal injury, breach of contract) it is often better to turn to a private mediation center. Two good online sources of information are the American Arbitration Association, http://www.adr.org and the Mediation Information and Resource Center, http://www.mediate.com. Private divorce mediations are usually handled by sole practitioners or small local mediation groups. Get a list from the phone book and check references carefully.

Are there some cases that should not be mediated?

All parties to a dispute must agree to mediate, so if one party refuses or isn't competent to participate, a dispute cannot be mediated. In addition, mediation may also not be the best choice if:

- One of the parties is attempting to set a legal precedent that interprets or defines the law according to its own point of view. Legal precedents cannot be set in mediation because mediation agreements do not establish who is "right" or "wrong," and are usually not made public.
- A person believes he or she can win a huge verdict against a big company (or even a small company with a big bank account or plenty of insurance). Because of the tendency toward compromise in mediation, hitting a legal "jackpot" is more likely in a jury trial.
- One person feels intimidated or intellectually overwhelmed by the other, in which case it's hard to arrive at a true meeting of the minds. It's often possible, however, to remedy a "power imbalance" by arranging for the more vulnerable person to participate with an advisor—perhaps a lawyer.

If I choose mediation, will I still need a lawyer?

In most mediations, it's not necessary to have a lawyer participate directly. This is because the parties are trying to work together to solve their problem—not trying to convince a judge or arbitrator of their point of view—and because mediation rules are few and straightforward. If your case involves substantial property or legal rights, however, you may want to consult with a lawyer before the mediation to discuss the legal consequences of possible settlement terms. You may

also want to condition any agreement you make on a lawyer's approval.

More Information About Mediation

How to Mediate Your Dispute, by Peter Lovenheim (Nolo), thoroughly explains the mediation process and shows you how to choose a mediator, prepare a case and conduct yourself during a mediation.

Using Divorce Mediation: Save Your Money & Your Sanity, by Katherine E. Stoner (Nolo), provides divorcing couples with all the information they need to work with a neutral third party to resolve differences and find solutions. By choosing mediation, couples can avoid court battles, save money, get through a divorce quickly and minimize negative effects on children.

Child Custody: Building Agreements That Work, by Mimi Lyster (Nolo), provides a step-by-step method for overcoming obstacles and putting together a practical parenting agreement that everyone—especially the children—can live with.

When Push Comes to Shove: A Practical Guide to Resolving Disputes, by Karl Slaikeu (Jossey-Bass), is a how-to mediation guide for lawyers, managers and human resource professionals.

Dealing With Your Lawyer

May your life be filled
with lawyers.

—MEXICAN CURSE

For any number of reasons, you may be frustrated with a lawyer you hired to do legal work for you. Perhaps your lawyer has failed to keep you informed about your case, to meet deadlines, to do what you believe is quality work or to involve you in decision making. Maybe your lawyer has sent you a bill for far more than you believe is reasonable. Or perhaps nothing specific is wrong, but you have simply concluded that you and your lawyer are not a good fit. The questions below look at the reasons for most complaints against attorneys and offer suggestions as to what you can do about them.

I've lost confidence in my lawyer. Can I fire him?

You have the right to end a relationship with a lawyer at any time. If you are paying for the lawyer's services, by all means insist on working with someone in whom you have full confidence. But if the lawyer you don't like is representing you on a contingency fee basis (for a percentage of any recovery), it is often better not to fire him unless his services really are substandard and you have a better lawyer lined up or feel you can handle the

case yourself. That's because unless lots of money is involved it can often be hard to find a second lawyer who will agree to pick up your case in the middle. Changing lawyers under a contingency fee arrangement usually means any eventual fee will have to be split between the two lawyers—and may mean the second lawyer has to clean up after the first.

I fired my lawyer, but I need my file. How do I get it?

Ask, or sign an authorization allowing any new attorney to get it. Even if you have a fee dispute with your former lawyer or you simply have not paid him, you are entitled to your file. If you have decided to represent yourself, demand that the lawyer turn your file over to you. If the lawyer refuses, contact your state's bar association for help.

I'm pretty sure my lawyer screwed up my case. Can I sue her for malpractice?

Unfortunately, it is very hard to win a malpractice case. Malpractice means that the lawyer failed to use the ordinary skill and care that would be used by other lawyers in handling a similar problem or case under similar circumstances.

To win a malpractice case against an attorney, you must prove four basic things:

- duty—that the attorney owed you a duty to act properly
- breach—that the attorney breached the duty, was negligent, made a

mistake or did not do what she agreed to do
- causation—that this conduct caused you damages, and
- damages—that you suffered financial losses as a result.

Causation may be your biggest hurdle. To win a malpractice case, you must prove not only that your lawyer made a mistake, but that you would have won the underlying case that the lawyer mishandled. (This second part is not required in Ohio.) Then, you will have to show that if you had won the underlying case, you would have been able to collect from the defendant. For example, let's say you were hit by a car when you were walking across the street, and you hired a lawyer who didn't file the lawsuit on time, with the result that your claim was legally dead. You sue for malpractice and can easily prove the lawyer's negligence and the driver's liability. But to win the malpractice case against your lawyer, however, you'd also have to show that the driver had the ability to pay your claim. If you can't show that the driver had assets which could have been used to pay the judgment, you won't win your malpractice case, even though the lawyer clearly blew it and the driver was clearly at fault.

My Lawyer Won't Call Me Back!

If your lawyer fails to return phone calls, it isn't malpractice, but it's a sure sign of trouble. Try to find out why your lawyer isn't calling you back. (He may be busy, rude, sick or procrastinating.) As you do this, examine the possibility that your lawyer may be avoiding you for a good reason—you may be too demanding. A good way to deal with this situation is to write or fax the lawyer a polite but straightforward letter explaining your difficulty in communicating and asking for a phone call or meeting to re-establish or restore your relationship. If this doesn't work, consider firing the lawyer and/or filing a formal complaint with your state's attorney regulatory agency.

My lawyer seems to have stopped working on my case. Is this malpractice?

The longer your attorney ignores you and your case, the more likely it is to amount to malpractice. You should act quickly to see that your case is properly handled and get another lawyer if necessary. Writing or faxing a letter expressing your concerns and asking for a meeting is a good first step.

My case was thrown out of court because my lawyer did no work. Is this grounds to sue my lawyer?

Maybe. Your lawyer is responsible for whatever money you could have won had the case been properly handled. Your difficulty will be in proving not only that your lawyer mishandled the case, but that if handled correctly, you could have won and collected a judgment.

My lawyer originally said my case was worth six figures and now suggests that I settle for peanuts. Can I sue the lawyer for the difference?

No. It's possible that newly discovered facts mean your case is worth less than first thought. Or, your lawyer may have initially given you an optimistic estimate of the value of your case to encourage you to hire her. In either case, this does not amount to malpractice. To find out, get your file from your lawyer and get a second opinion as to the value of your case. If another reputable lawyer believes you are being advised to settle for too little, consider changing lawyers.

Can I sue my lawyer for settling my case without my authorization?

Yes, but you would have to prove that the settlement your lawyer entered into was for less than your case was worth.

Big Bills

If you receive an unexpectedly large bill, your lawyer may have overcharged you. In this situation, you have six options:

- You can pay the entire bill and vow not to go near that attorney again.
- You can pay the part of the bill you think is reasonable with a letter explaining why you are refusing to pay the rest.
- You can refuse to pay any of the bill until the lawyer agrees to accept less as full payment.
- In most states and situations, you can request fee arbitration from a state or local bar association, usually before a panel made up of local lawyers and perhaps one or two nonlawyers. Arbitration is a process where a supposedly neutral decisionmaker resolves your fee dispute. But when it comes to disputes over legal fees, you will normally want to follow this approach only if it is "nonbinding," meaning that you are free to reject the arbitrator's decision. That's because whenever an arbitration is conducted by a panel dominated by lawyers, you are likely to get a biased result.
- You can pay the bill and file a complaint with your state attorney disciplinary agency.
- You can pay the bill and sue your attorney for a refund.

While weighing these options, keep in mind that a lawyer who has not been paid has far more motive to settle for a reasonable amount than does a lawyer who has already received half of your fee. So, even if you believe your attorney is entitled to part of the big bill, it often makes sense to try to arrive at a mutually acceptable compromise before you pull out your checkbook.

I saw my lawyer playing tennis with the opposing lawyer. Is this a breach of attorney ethics?

No. There is nothing ethically wrong with opposing attorneys playing tennis, bridge, golf or enjoying other common social interactions. If they talk about your case (on the tennis court or anywhere else), however, and your lawyer lets slip something that you said in confidence, that would be a clear violation of your attorney's duty to you.

Even though socializing with the opposing counsel isn't a violation of ethical rules, in the real world it can obviously make a big difference how you found out about it. If your lawyer told you he occasionally played tennis with the opposing attorney when you first discussed your case, you clearly had a chance to hire another lawyer if it bothered you. But you'll likely feel differently if you head to the tennis court to relax with a friend after being grilled by the opposing attorney at your deposition, only to run into your lawyer playing tennis with the same "barracuda" who just tried to eat you for lunch. But instead of firing your lawyer on the spot, it makes more sense to make an appointment to clarify his relationship with your adversary's lawyer.

I'm worried that my lawyer may have misused money I paid as a retainer. What should I do?

If you seriously suspect your lawyer has misused any money he holds for you in trust, complain to your state's attorney regulatory agency right away. Although regulation of lawyers is lax in most states, complaints about stealing clients' money are almost always taken seriously, so you should get a prompt response. All states except Maine and New Mexico have funds to reimburse clients when lawyers are caught stealing.

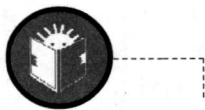

More Information About Dealing With Your Lawyer

Mad at Your Lawyer, by Attorney Tanya Starnes (Nolo), is a comprehensive guide, available as a downloadable electronic book from http://www.nolo.com, on what to do if you have a problem with your lawyer.

The Lawsuit Survival Guide: A Client's Companion to Litigation, by Joseph Matthews (Nolo), is a step-by-step guide for people who are involved in a lawsuit.

http://www.nolo.com
Nolo offers self-help information about a wide variety of legal topics, including representing yourself in court, small claims court, mediation and how to handle problems with your lawyer.

http://www.nolo.com/ lawcenter/statute/index.cfm
Nolo's Legal Research Center links to federal, state and local courts around the country. It also provides access to information about small claims court in many states.

http://www.legalethics.com
The Internet Ethics Site provides links to all states' rules of professional conduct and some states' ethics opinions.

http://www.ncsconline.org
The National Center for State Courts' website provides links to state and local court websites. These sites often contain helpful legal information, court forms and instructions.

http://www.uscourts.gov
The Federal Judiciary's website provides links to federal court websites.

18

Criminal Law and Procedure

18.2   *Criminal Law and Procedure: An Overview*

18.8   *If You Are Questioned by the Police*

18.10   *Searches and Seizures*

18.14   *Arrests and Interrogations*

18.17   *Bail*

18.20   *Getting a Lawyer*

IT IS A LESS EVIL THAT SOME CRIMINALS

SHOULD ESCAPE THAN THAT THE GOVERNMENT

SHOULD PLAY AN IGNOBLE PART.

—OLIVER WENDELL HOLMES

The word "criminal" reflects our society's belief that certain acts are unacceptable and that people who commit these acts should be punished. Because we place a high value on freedom, however, our state and federal constitutions make it difficult for the government to take that freedom away from us. As a result—and perhaps as a price—the court system often appears to protect the criminal rather than the victim, and to unduly favor defendants who are blessed with clever attorneys. On the other hand, if the system doesn't place a heavy burden on government prosecutors, we risk sending innocent people to jail and we make it easier for our government to slide into totalitarian practices. One thing is sure: No matter what type of system we have for prosecuting and punishing people who commit crimes, it will always be a matter of great controversy.

Caution!

The material in this chapter is designed to give you a general overview of several important criminal law topics. As you read, keep in mind that the criminal justice system differs in many small but important ways from state to state, county to county and even court to court. This means that some of the material in this chapter may not be applicable in your area.

In addition, the many different players in the criminal justice system—police, prosecutors, defense attorneys and judges—frequently adapt the law to their own uses and contexts. What this gap between theory and practice may mean in a particular case can only be understood by someone who knows the players and who is familiar with how they go about their jobs. Usually, this person would be a local private criminal defense attorney or public defender.

Because we cannot precisely describe the law in your state and what is likely to happen in your case, consider this chapter a place to get started. To get more specific and reliable information, do some research or consult a knowledgeable criminal defense attorney. For a more in-depth treatment of the topics addressed here as well as other aspects of the criminal justice system—including lineups, arraignments, defenses, plea bargains and sentencing—see *The Criminal Law Handbook*, by Paul Bergman and Sara Berman-Barrett (Nolo).

Criminal Law and Procedure: An Overview

A crime is any behavior that is punishable by imprisonment or fine (or both). State legislatures have an almost unlimited ability to decide which behaviors are considered crimes, and often their decisions do more than simply define socially unacceptable behaviors—they also reflect the values and judgments of the legislators. For example, most state legislatures define welfare fraud as a crime, and welfare recipients who cheat can end up in jail. On the other hand, no state legislature defines deliberate overcharging by an attorney or other professional as a crime.

While state legislatures have broad powers to decide what constitutes crime, Congress can define behavior as a crime only if the U.S. Constitution authorizes Congress to regulate that type of behavior in the first place. For example, the Constitution gives Congress the power to "regulate commerce . . . among the several States." Congress, therefore, can make many activities—such as racketeering—illegal, if the actions cross state lines or affect commerce that does.

Who decides how the criminal justice system works?

Though legislators have relatively unfettered power to decide whether a certain behavior should be a crime, many rules limit the ways in which the state or federal government can prosecute someone for a crime. These restrictions start with the U.S. Constitution's Bill of Rights, which provides basic protections—such as the right to refuse to testify against oneself, the right to confront one's accusers and the right to a trial by jury—for people charged with crimes. State constitutions may increase (but not take away from) the federal protections. Federal and state legislatures can pass laws governing how criminal procedures work in their jurisdictions, but these laws cannot reduce the protections offered by the federal and state constitutions.

The interplay between constitutional provisions and legislative enactments is regulated by our courts. Courts decide whether or not a particular legislative rule, court practice or police action is permissible under federal and state constitutional law. What may seem like a slight variation from one case to another can be, in the eyes of a court, the determining factor that leads to a vastly different result. For example, a police officer is frisking a suspect on the street and feels a hard object in the suspect's pocket. Suspecting that the object is a possible weapon, the officer reaches into the pocket and finds both a cardboard cigarette box and a packet of heroin. This action by the police officer—reaching into the pocket—would be deemed a permissible search under the rulings of most courts (to protect the officer's safety), and the heroin could be admitted into court as evidence. However, if the object felt by the officer was soft and obviously not a weapon, then reaching into the suspect's pocket might be deemed an illegal search, in which case the heroin couldn't be used as evidence.

What's the difference between a felony and a misdemeanor?

Most states break their crimes into two major groups—felonies and misdemeanors. Whether a crime falls into one category or the other depends on the potential punishment. If a law provides for imprisonment for longer than a year, it is usually considered a felony. If the potential punishment is for a year or less, then the crime is considered a misdemeanor. In some states, certain crimes, called "wobblers," may be considered either a misdemeanor or a felony, because under some conditions the punishment may be imprisonment for less than a year, and in other situations, the criminal may go to prison for a year or more.

Behaviors punishable only by fine are usually not considered crimes at all, but infractions—for example, traffic tickets. But a legislature may on occasion punish behavior only by fine and still provide that it is a misdemeanor—such as possession of less than an ounce of marijuana for personal use in California.

How can I tell from reading a criminal statute whether I'm guilty of the crime it defines?

All criminal statutes define crimes in terms of required acts and a required state of mind, usually described as the actor's "intent." These requirements are known as the "elements" of the offense. A prosecutor must convince a judge or jury that the person charged with the crime (the defendant) did the acts and had the intent described in the statute. For example, commercial burglary is commonly defined as entering a structure (such as a store) belonging to another person, with the intent to commit petty or grand theft (that is, to steal) or any felony. To convict a person of this offense, the prosecutor would have to prove three elements:

1. The defendant entered the structure.
2. The structure belonged to another person.
3. At the time the defendant entered the structure, he intended to commit petty or grand theft or any felony.

You will have to do the same when you read the law. Parse the crime into its required elements to see if each applies in your situation.

What is the presumption of innocence?

All people accused of a crime are legally presumed to be innocent until they are convicted, either in a trial or as a result of pleading guilty. This presumption means not only that the prosecutor must convince the jury of the defendant's guilt, but also that the defendant need not say or do anything in his own defense. If the prosecutor can't convince the jury that the defendant is guilty, the defendant goes free.

The presumption of innocence, coupled with the fact that the prosecutor must prove the defendant's guilt beyond a reasonable doubt (see below), theoretically makes it difficult for the government to put people behind bars.

What does it mean to prove guilt "beyond a reasonable doubt"?

The prosecutor must convince the judge or jury hearing the case that the defendant is guilty "beyond a reasonable doubt." This standard is meant to be hard to meet. (By contrast, in non-criminal cases, such as an accident or breach of contract, a plaintiff has to prove her case only by a preponderance of the evidence—just over 50%.) As a practical matter, the high burden of proof in criminal cases means that judges and jurors are supposed to resolve all doubts about the meaning of the evidence in favor of the defendant. With such a high standard imposed on the prosecutor, a defendant's most common defense is often to argue that there is reasonable doubt—that is, that the prosecutor hasn't done a sufficient job of proving that the defendant is guilty.

If I'm accused of a crime, am I guaranteed a trial by a jury?

Yes. The U.S. Constitution gives the right to be tried by a jury to a person accused of any crime where the maximum punishment is 6 months or more in jail. Some states (for example, California) guarantee a right to a jury trial for any misdemeanor or felony charge, even where the maximum possible sentence is less than 6 months. This right has long been interpreted to mean a 12-person jury that must arrive at a unanimous decision to convict or acquit. (In most states, a lack of unanimity is called a "hung jury" and the defendant will go free unless the prosecutor decides to retry the case. In Oregon and Louisiana, however, juries may convict or acquit on a vote of ten to two.) The potential jurors must be selected randomly from the community, and the actual jury must be selected by a process which allows the judge and lawyers to screen out biased jurors. In addition, a lawyer may eliminate several potential jurors simply because he feels that these people would not be sympathetic to his side—but these decisions may not be based on the juror's personal characteristics, such as race, sex, religion or national origin.

If I do not have any witnesses who will testify on my behalf, can I still win at trial?

Yes. Defendants often go to trial without having anyone testify for them. This strategy allows the defendant's lawyer to focus on cross-examining the prosecution witnesses in order to poke holes in the prosecutor's case—thereby creating reasonable doubt. Defense attorneys rely on a variety of arguments to discredit the prosecutor's witnesses. Some common arguments include:

- Prosecution witnesses are biased against the defendant and therefore are lying or grossly exaggerating.
- Prosecution witnesses are mistaken in their observations because the lighting was bad, they were under the influence of drugs or alcohol or they were too far away.
- Evidence from police laboratories is unreliable because the machines were not properly maintained or the

technicians were not properly trained.

- Prosecution witnesses are lying to get a good deal on the criminal charges they themselves are facing (witnesses are often criminals who have been offered a deal if they testify against the defendant).

What these arguments have in common is that they do not depend on defense evidence. Rather, they rely on the presumption of innocence and prosecutor's failure to overcome it by proving guilt beyond a reasonable doubt.

I am confused about why a defendant would choose not to testify. If I were innocent, why wouldn't I want to take the stand and tell my story?

A criminal defendant has a right not to testify, and jurors will be told that they cannot assume anything negative if the defendant decides to keep quiet. Of course, some jurors do make assumptions—and they cast their votes accordingly. On the other hand, there are some excellent reasons why a defendant might remain silent in court:

- If the defendant has previously been convicted of a crime, the prosecutor may be able to bring this fact out— but only if the defendant testifies. Evidence of a previous crime may cause some jurors to think that the defendant is guilty of the current crime, too.
- If the defendant testifies, the prosecutor may be able to bring out other information that tarnishes the

defendant's reputation and discredits his testimony.

- Some defendants have a poor demeanor when speaking in public. A judge or jury may not believe a defendant who, though telling the truth, is a nervous witness and makes a bad impression.
- The defendant may have a perfectly good story which would nevertheless sound fishy to the average jury in that particular locale.

What is self-defense—and how can a defendant prove it?

Self-defense is a common defense asserted by someone charged with a crime of violence, such as battery (striking someone), assault with a deadly weapon or murder. The defendant admits that she did in fact commit the crime, but claims that it was justified by the other person's threatening actions. The core issues in most self-defense cases are:

- Who was the aggressor?
- Was the defendant's belief that self-defense was necessary a reasonable one?
- If so, was the force used by the defendant also reasonable?

Self-defense is rooted in the belief that people should be allowed to protect themselves from physical harm. This means that a person does not have to wait until she is actually struck to act in self-defense. If a reasonable person would think that she is about to be physically attacked, she has the right to strike first and prevent the attack. But she cannot use more force than is reasonable—if she does, she may be guilty of a crime even though some force was justifiable.

When can a defendant win an acquittal on grounds of insanity?

The insanity defense is based on the principle that punishment is justified only if the defendant is capable of controlling his or her behavior and understanding that what he or she has done is wrong. Because some people suffering from a mental disorder are not capable of knowing or choosing right from wrong, the insanity defense prevents them from being criminally punished.

Despite its ancient origins (England, 1505), the insanity defense remains controversial. Victim-oriented critics point out that a person killed by an insane person is just as dead as a person killed by someone who is sane, and argue that people should be punished for the harm they cause regardless of their mental state. Critics also question the ability of psychiatrists, judges and jurors to determine whether a person suffers from a mental disorder, and to link mental disorders to the commission of crimes.

The insanity defense is an extremely complex topic; many scholarly works are devoted to explaining its nuances. Here are some major points of interest:

• Despite popular perceptions to the contrary, defendants rarely enter pleas of "not guilty by reason of insanity." On the few occasions that the defendant does raise it, judges and jurors rarely support it.

• Because neither the legal system nor psychiatrists can agree on a single meaning of insanity in the criminal law context, various definitions are employed. The most popular definition is the "McNaghten rule," which defines insanity as "the inability to distinguish right from wrong." Another common test is known as "irresistible impulse": A person who acts out of an irresistible impulse knows that an act is wrong, but because of mental illness, cannot control his actions.

• Defendants found not guilty by reason of insanity are not automatically set free. They are usually confined to a mental institution, and not released until their sanity is established. These defendants can spend more time in a mental institution than they would have spent in prison had they been convicted.

• An insanity defense normally rests on the testimony of a psychiatrist, who testifies for the defendant after examining him and his past history, and the facts of the case. Courts appoint psychiatrists at government expense to assist poor defendants who cannot afford to hire their own psychiatrists. The prosecution will normally hire another psychiatrist, who may offer an opinion different from the defense psychiatrist.

Competency to Stand Trial

Aside from insanity as a defense to criminal charges, the question may arise as to whether a defendant is mentally capable of facing a trial. Defendants cannot be prosecuted if they suffer from a mental disorder that prevents them from understanding the proceedings and assisting in the preparation of their defense. Based on a defendant's unusual behavior, a judge, prosecutor or defense attorney may ask that trial be delayed until the defendant has been examined and her ability to understand the proceedings has been determined in a court hearing. If a judge finds that a defendant doesn't understand what's going on, the defendant will probably be placed in a mental institution until her competence is re-established. At that time, the trial will be held.

Can a defendant go free because he was drunk or high on drugs when he committed a crime?

Defendants who commit crimes under the influence of drugs or alcohol sometimes argue that their mental functioning was so impaired that they cannot be held accountable for their actions. Generally, however, voluntary intoxication does not excuse criminal conduct. People know (or should know) that alcohol and drugs affect mental functioning, and thus they should be held legally responsible if they commit crimes as a result of their voluntary use.

Some states allow an exception to this general rule. If the defendant is accused of committing a crime that requires what's known as "specific intent" (intending the precise consequences, as well as intending to do the physical act that leads up to the consequences), the defendant can argue that he was too drunk or high to have formed that intent. This is only a partial defense, however, because it doesn't entirely excuse the defendant's actions. In this situation, the defendant will usually be convicted of another crime that doesn't require proof of a specific intent—for example, assault with a deadly weapon instead of assault with the intent to commit murder.

If You Are Questioned by the Police

There is plenty of law at the end of a nightstick.

—GROVER A. WHALEN

If a police officer wants to stop and question you, whether or not you must comply depends on the circumstances and the reasons the officer has for questioning you. This section explores some of the common questions people have about their rights and responsibilities when approached by a law enforcement officer.

If an officer wants to stop me while I'm walking on the street and I know I've done nothing wrong, should I comply?

A police officer may interfere with your freedom of movement only if he has observed unusual activity suggesting that criminal activity is afoot and that you are involved. Even if the officer is mistaken, however, you do not have the right to keep walking. As long as the officer has a good faith belief in your connection to criminal activity, he is allowed to detain you. Stopping you is one thing, however. It doesn't mean that you must answer all of his questions. (See below.)

If You Run Away

It is not unusual for people who are approached by the police to run away. Some courts have recognized that people of color, in particular, have a well-founded fear of unfair treatment at the hands of the police, and that many people will avoid contact with the police not because they are guilty of a crime, but because they reasonably believe that they may be mistreated or unjustly accused. Other courts view evasive behavior as evidence of guilt, however, and allow the police to rely on the attempt to run away as grounds for a detention.

If I am legally stopped by a police officer on the street, can he search me?

Yes and no. A police officer is permitted to briefly frisk your outer clothing for weapons if the officer reasonably fears for his safety. If a frisk is later challenged in court as being unreasonable, a judge will usually uphold it.

A frisk is different than a search in that a search may be conducted for evidence of a crime or contraband (an illegal item), and may be much more intrusive than a frisk. An officer may not search you unless he has good cause to believe that you committed a crime or that you're hiding an illegal item. (See *Searches and Seizures*, below.)

How a Frisk Becomes a Legal Search—And Possibly an Arrest

When frisking a person for weapons, the police are attuned not only to the feel of possible weapons under clothing, but also to the feel of packaged drugs. Although a frisk may not turn up a weapon, it may turn up a suspicious package which the officer knows is commonly used to carry illegal drugs or some other illegal substance. A discovery like that may create sufficient cause for a more intensive search of the person's clothing. The lesson here is that a frisk often leads to a search. And if a search produces an illegal substance, it may result in an arrest.

If I am questioned by a police officer after being stopped on the street, do I have to respond to the questions?

The general rule is that you don't have to answer any questions that the police ask you. This rule comes from the Fifth Amendment to the U.S. Constitution, which protects you against self-incrimination. As with all rules, however, there is an exception. Many local and state governments have anti-loitering laws that require people to account for their presence if the police have a reasonable suspicion that they are loitering. Once the police have asked all of their questions about loitering, however, you don't have to answer any others—such as questions about a crime in the neighborhood.

A defense lawyer's most sacred piece of advice is this: Don't talk to the police about a crime unless you clearly weren't involved and you want to help the police solve it.

Searches and Seizures

Most people instinctively understand the concept of privacy. It's the freedom to decide which details of your life are public and which are not. At the same time, most of us acknowledge that society is served when the police, in appropriate circumstances, are allowed to look for and seize contraband, stolen goods and evidence of a crime.

In an attempt to balance our desires for privacy against the legitimate needs of the police, the Fourth Amendment of the U.S. Constitution prohibits "unreasonable" searches and seizures by state or federal law officers. Generally, this means that the police may conduct a search of your home, barn, car, boat, office, personal or business documents, bank account records, trash barrel or any other property if:

- the police can show that it is more likely than not that a crime has occurred and that if they are allowed to search, they will probably find evidence or contraband (this requirement is called "probable cause"), and

- a judge agrees there is probable cause and issues a search warrant, or the police are permitted to search without a warrant because of the particular circumstances involved (the warrant requirement).

So, for a search to be legal under the constitution, the police must have both probable cause to conduct the search and a search warrant (although the warrant requirement has many exceptions, some of which we discuss below).

When is a police investigation considered a search?

A police investigation is not a search unless it intrudes on a person's privacy. In other words, if a person did not have a "legitimate expectation of privacy" in the place or thing searched, no "search" has occurred, at least not for the purpose of determining whether the Fourth Amendment has been violated.

Courts ask two questions to determine whether a person had a legitimate expectation of privacy in the place or things searched:

- Did the person expect some degree of privacy?
- Is the person's expectation reasonable—that is, one that society is willing to recognize?

For example, a person who uses a public restroom expects that no one will spy on her, and most people—including judges and juries—would consider that expectation to be reasonable. Therefore, if the police install a hidden video camera in a public restroom, the action is considered a search and must meet the Fourth Amendment's requirement of reasonableness.

On the other hand, if the police glance into a car and see a weapon on the front seat, it is not a search because it is unlikely that a person would think that the front seat of a car is a private place. And even if he did, society is not generally willing to extend the protections of privacy to the front seat of an automobile.

How Private Is Your Property?

Generally, if the police are able to view contraband or evidence on your property without actually entering it, they have not conducted a search. In other words, you cannot have a reasonable expectation of privacy in an area that can legitimately be seen from outside your property. This means that the police can use what they have seen as the basis for getting a warrant to come in and take a closer look. Or, if the situation calls for prompt action (the need to stop a drug deal, for instance), they may enter without a warrant.

Law enforcement officers are allowed to take aerial photographs or come close enough to overhear your conversations— these actions are not considered searches. On the other hand, without a warrant or an exception to the rule requiring a warrant, officers are not allowed to use sophisticated equipment, such as thermal imaging devices, to discover what is on your property or to eavesdrop on your conversations. In general, if the investigation method is highly artificial and high-tech, it's likely to be considered a search. Where the line is drawn, however, is not clear or consistent from state to state.

What is a search warrant?

A search warrant is a kind of permission slip, signed by a judge, that allows the police to enter private property to look for particular items. It is addressed to the owner of the property, and tells the owner that a judge has decided that it is reasonably likely that certain contraband, or evidence of criminal activities, will be found in specified locations on the property.

As a general rule, the police are supposed to apply for a warrant before conducting a search of private property; any search that is conducted without a warrant is presumed to be unreasonable—even if there was "probable cause" to conduct the search. This means that the police officers will later have to justify the search—and why a warrant wasn't obtained first—if the defendant challenges it in court.

What does it take to get a search warrant?

A judge will issue a search warrant after the police have convinced her that:

- it is more likely than not that a crime has taken place, and
- items connected to the crime are likely be found in a specified location on the property.

To convince the judge of these facts, the police tell the judge what they know about the situation. Usually, the information given to the judge is based either on the officers' own observations or on the second-hand observations of an informant.

The police are limited in their ability to use secondhand information. As a general rule, the information must be reliable given the circumstances. A judge will normally deem information to be reliable if it is corroborated by police observation. For example, a citizen's tip that a suspect regularly delivers drugs to a certain location would be corroborated if an officer observes that suspect's routine. But corroboration is not necessary in every case. Sometimes a judge will issue a warrant if the source of the information is known to the police and has provided trustworthy information in the past.

What are the police allowed to do after they obtain a search warrant?

Once the police have a search warrant, they are entitled to enter the designated property to search for the items listed on the warrant. Legally, the search is supposed to be confined to the specific areas described in the warrant. For example, if the search warrant includes only the living room, the search should not extend into the kitchen, bathroom or bedroom. But there are exceptions to this limitation which are frequently used to justify broader searches. For example, the police may search beyond the terms of the warrant in order to:

- ensure their safety and the safety of others
- prevent the destruction of evidence
- discover more about possible evidence or contraband that is in plain view elsewhere on the property, or
- hunt for evidence or contraband that, as a result of their initial search, they believe exists in another location on the property.

For instance, although a warrant might be issued for the search of a house, the sound of a shotgun being loaded in the backyard would justify expanding the search to the yard in order to protect the officers; similarly, a search limited to the ground floor might legitimately expand to the upstairs if the police, searching for illegal drugs, hear toilets being flushed above. And the police can always seize evidence or illegal items if they are in plain view or are discovered while the officers are searching for the items listed in the warrant.

Do the police always need a warrant to conduct a search?

No. In many situations, police may legally conduct a search without first obtaining a warrant.

- *Consent searches.* If the police ask your permission to search your home, purse, briefcase or other property, and you agree, the search is considered consensual, and they don't need a warrant. The police typically obtain a person's consent by threatening to detain her while they obtain the warrant.

- *Searches that accompany an arrest.* When a person is placed under arrest, the police may search the person and the immediate surroundings for weapons that might be used to harm the officer. If the person is taken to jail, the police may search to make sure that weapons or contraband are not brought into the jail. (This is called an inventory search.) Inventory searches also frequently involve a search of the arrested person's car (if it is being held by the police) and personal effects on the theory that the police need a precise record of the person's property to avoid claims of theft.

- *Searches necessary to protect the safety of the public.* The police don't need a warrant if they have a reasonable fear that their safety, or that of the public, is in imminent danger. For example, an officer who suspected a bomb-making operation while walking his beat might be justified in entering immediately and seizing the ingredients. And in the famous O.J. Simpson case, the police justified their entry onto O.J. Simpson's property on the grounds that they feared for the safety of other family members.

- *Searches necessary to prevent the imminent destruction of evidence.* A police officer does not need to obtain a warrant if she has observed illegal items (such as weapons or contraband) and believes that the items will disappear unless the officer takes prompt action. This exception arises most frequently when the police spot contraband or weapons in a car. Because cars are moved so frequently, the officer is justified in searching the entire vehicle, including the trunk, without obtaining a warrant—if the officer has probable cause. On the other hand, if the police learn about a marijuana-growing operation from a neighbor, they usually would need a warrant, as it is unlikely that the growing plants and other evidence of the operation will disappear quickly enough to justify a warrantless search.

- *"Hot pursuit" searches.* Police may enter private dwellings to search for criminals who are fleeing the scene of a crime.

Can my roommate—or my landlord—give the police permission to search my apartment?

The police may search your apartment if the person in charge of the premises gives permission. If you and your roommate share common areas (such as the kitchen and living room), your roommate can authorize a search of those areas. But your roommate cannot give permission to search your separate bedroom.

Similarly, your landlord cannot give permission to search your apartment. Although the landlord owns the property, your monthly check guarantees your privacy at home. This is true even if you are behind in your rent or your landlord has sued to evict you. Until the landlord has a court order that permits him to enter and retake the premises, he cannot enter without your permission. (But keep in mind that many states allow a landlord to enter for inspections, which usually require advance notice of a day or two.) If the police can point to circumstances that would justify immediate entry, however—such as the sound of a ferocious fight or the smell of burning marijuana—they may enter without permission from anyone.

Arrests and Interrogations

I HAVEN'T COMMITTED A CRIME.

WHAT I DID WAS FAIL TO COMPLY

WITH THE LAW.

–DAVID DINKINS

An arrest occurs when a police officer armed with an arrest warrant utters the magic words "you're under arrest," or when a police officer's actions cause you to believe that you are not free to leave. The restraint must be more than a mere detention on the street (discussed above). Although in most situations the police will take you to the police station for booking (photographs and fingerprinting), it is also possible for an officer to arrest and book you at the crime scene, and then release you when you give a written promise to appear in court at a later time.

After the police arrest you, they will often question you in order to find out more about the crime, your role in it and whether there may be other suspects. There are several Constitutional protections that you may invoke during police interrogations.

When do the police need a warrant to make an arrest?

As long as the police have good reason (called "probable cause") to believe that a crime has been committed and that the person they want to arrest committed the crime, they can, with just one exception, make an arrest without asking a judge for a warrant.

The exception? There are few places where the adage "a man's home is his castle" still applies, and an arrest at home is one of them. The police must have a warrant to arrest a person at home if the arrest is for a nonserious offense—such as a simple assault— and there is no fear that the person they want to arrest will destroy evidence or cause harm to the public.

How do the police obtain an arrest warrant?

An officer must present sworn evidence to a judge that a crime has occurred and that the police have probable cause to believe that the crime was committed by the person they want to arrest. If the judge agrees, she will issue a warrant. The police are then entitled to seize the person wherever they can find him.

If the police make an illegal arrest, is the arrested person set free?

No. But if a search of the person or her immediate surroundings is conducted during the arrest and turns up incriminating evidence, the evidence may be kept out of the person's trial on the grounds that it is "fruit of the poisonous tree"—that is, the evidence was found as the result of an improper arrest. Also, if the illegally arrested person makes any statements to the police after being arrested, the statements may not be used as evidence. This is true whether or not the arrested person was "read their rights." (See below.)

Can a person who is charged with a crime be forced to give bodily samples?

Yes. You might think that being forced to give bodily samples—such as blood, hair or fingernail clippings—is a violation of the U.S. Constitution's protection against self-incrimination, found in the Fifth Amendment. But the U.S. Supreme Court thinks otherwise. It has ruled that the Fifth Amendment protects communications only, and that bodily samples are physical evidence and therefore not covered by the Constitution.

If I'm arrested, do the police have to "read me my rights"?

No. They don't need to read your rights unless they want to question you. However, if they don't read you your rights, they can't use anything you say as evidence against you at trial. What are these rights? Popularly known as the *Miranda* warning (ordered by the U.S. Supreme Court in *Miranda v. Arizona*), your rights consist of the familiar litany invoked by T.V. police immediately upon arresting a suspect:

- You have the right to remain silent.
- If you do say anything, what you say can be used against you in a court of law.
- You have the right to consult with a lawyer and have that lawyer present during any questioning.
- If you cannot afford a lawyer, one will be appointed for you if you so desire.
- If you choose to talk to the police officer, you have the right to stop the interview at any time. (This part of the warning is usually omitted from the screenplay.)

It doesn't matter whether an interrogation occurs in a jail or at the scene of a crime, on a busy downtown street or in the middle of an open field: If you are in custody (deprived of your freedom of action in any significant way), the police must give a *Miranda* warning if they want to question you and use your answers as evidence at trial. If you are not in police custody, however, no *Miranda* warning is required. This exception most often comes up when the police stop someone on the street to question them about a recent crime and the person blurts out a confession before the police have an opportunity to deliver the warning.

Will a judge dismiss my case if I was questioned without a *Miranda* warning?

No. Many people mistakenly believe that a case will be thrown out of court if the police fail to give *Miranda* warnings to the arrested person. What *Miranda* actually says is that a warning is necessary if the police interrogate a suspect and want to use any of her responses as evidence. If the police fail to give you a *Miranda* warning, nothing you say in response to the questioning can be used as evidence to convict you. In addition, under the "fruit of the poisonous tree" rule, if the police find evidence as a result of an interrogation that violates the *Miranda* rule, that evidence is also inadmissible at trial. For example, if you tell the police where a weapon is hidden and it turns out that you gave this information in response to improper questioning, the police will not be able to use the weapon as evidence unless the police can prove that they would have found the weapon without your statements. If there is sufficient other evidence to convict you beyond any statements you made

to the police, you can still be convicted even when the police don't give *Miranda* warnings.

What's the best way to assert my right to remain silent if I am being questioned by the police?

If you're taken into custody by the police, you don't have to use any magic words to let police officers know that you want to remain silent. You can simply say nothing in response to police questions. Or, after an officer gives you a *Miranda* warning, you can stop the questioning by saying something like:

- I want to talk to an attorney.
- I won't say anything until I talk to an attorney.
- I don't have anything to say.
- I don't want to talk to you anymore.
- I claim my *Miranda* rights.

If the police continue to question you after you have asserted your right to remain silent, they have violated *Miranda*. As a result, anything you say after that point—and any evidence gleaned from that conversation—should not be admissible at your trial. Once you've invoked your right to silence, however, the best course is to remain silent, instead of counting on a judge to keep out your statements further down the line.

How heavy handed can the police get when asking questions?

Information that you voluntarily disclose to a police officer (after you have been properly warned) is generally admissible at trial. The key word is "voluntary." Police officers are not allowed to use physical force or psychological coercion to get you to talk to them. The days of the rubber hose, protracted grilling under bright lights and severe sleep deprivation are hopefully over. If police officers obtain information through any of these illegal means, the information cannot be used by the prosecutor at trial regardless of whether you invoked your *Miranda* rights. In addition, under the rule known as "the fruit of the poisonous tree," any evidence that the police obtain as the result of a coerced statement is equally inadmissible.

Reality Check: Cops Usually Win a Swearing Contest

Defendants often claim that police officers coerced them into talking. And it's just as common for police officers to say that the defendants spoke voluntarily. If the police physically coerce a defendant into talking, the defendant can support his coercion claims with photos of marks and bruises. But it may be difficult to provide clear evidence of police brutality, and a defendant cannot usually offer independent evidence to support his claims of psychological coercion. Judges, believing that defendants have a greater motivation to lie than do police officers, usually side with the police and conclude that no coercion took place.

Bail

Those who expect to reap the blessings of freedom must . . . undergo the fatigue of supporting it.

—THOMAS PAINE

Many people, especially those arrested for minor misdemeanors, are given citations at the scene of an arrest telling them when to appear in court, and are immediately released. Others, however, are put in jail. Often, a person's first thought upon landing in jail is how to get out—and fast. The usual way to do this is to "post bail." This section answers common questions about the bail system, including its version of Monopoly's "Get Out of Jail Free" card—called release O.R.

What does it mean to "post bail"?

Bail is cash or a cash equivalent that an arrested person gives to a court to ensure that he will appear in court when ordered to do so. If the defendant appears in court at the proper time, the court refunds the bail. But if the defendant doesn't show up, the court keeps the bail and issues a warrant for the defendant's arrest.

Bail can take any of the following forms:

- cash or check for the full amount of the bail
- property worth the full amount of the bail
- a bond—that is, a guaranteed payment of the full bail amount, or
- a waiver of payment on the condition that the defendant appear in court at the required time, commonly called "release on one's own recognizance" or simply "O.R."

Who decides how much bail I have to pay?

Judges are responsible for setting bail. Because many people want to get out of jail immediately and, depending on when you are arrested, it can take up to five days to see a judge, most jails have standard bail schedules which specify bail amounts for common crimes. You can get out of jail quickly by paying the amount set forth in the bail schedule.

Are there are restrictions on how high my bail can be?

The Eighth Amendment to the U. S. Constitution requires that bail not be excessive. This means that bail should not be used to raise money for the government or to punish a person for being suspected of committing a crime. The purpose of bail is to give an arrested person her freedom until she is convicted of a crime, and the amount of bail must be no more than is reasonably necessary to keep her from fleeing before a case is over.

So much for theory. In fact, many judges set an impossibly high bail in particular types of cases (such as those involving drug sales or rape) to keep a suspect in jail until the trial is over. Although bail set for this purpose—called preventative detention—is thought by many to violate the Constitution, no court has stopped the practice.

What can I do if I can't afford to pay the bail listed on the bail schedule?

If you can't afford the amount of bail on the bail schedule, you can ask a judge to lower it. Depending on the state, your request must be made either in a special bail-setting hearing or when you appear in court for the first time, usually called your arraignment.

How soon can I appear before a judge?

In federal court, a person taken to jail must be brought "without unnecessary delay before the nearest available . . . magistrate." Most states have similar rules. In no event should more than 48 hours elapse (not counting weekends and holidays) between the time of booking and bringing you to court. Unfortunately, these rules are rarely enforced because the police can simply release the suspect when the time is up and then immediately re-arrest him.

How do I pay for bail?

There are two ways to pay your bail. You may either pay the full amount of the bail or buy a bail bond. A bail bond is like a check held in reserve: It represents your promise that you will appear in court when you are supposed to. You pay a bond seller to post a bond (a certain sum of money) with the court, and the court keeps the bond in case you don't show up. You can usually buy a bail bond for about 10% of the amount of your bail; this premium is the bond seller's fee for taking the risk that you won't appear in court.

A bail bond may sound like a good deal, but buying a bond may cost you more in the long run. If you pay the full amount of the bail, you'll get that money back (less a small administrative fee) if you make your scheduled court appearances. On the other hand, the 10% premium you pay to a bond seller is nonrefundable. In addition, the bond seller may require "collateral." This means that you (or the person who pays for your bail bond) must give the bond seller a financial interest in some of your valuable property. The bond seller can cash in this interest if you fail to appear in court.

Nevertheless, if you can't afford your bail and you don't have a friend or relative that can help out, a bond seller may be your only option. You can find one by looking in the Yellow Pages; you're also likely to find bond sellers' offices very close to any jail.

Finally, be ready to pay in cash, a money order or a cashier's check. Jails and bond sellers usually do not take credit cards or personal checks for bail.

Is it true that a defendant who proves his reliability can get out of jail on his word alone?

Sometimes. This is generally known as releasing someone "on his own recognizance," or "O.R." A defendant released O.R. must simply sign a promise to show up in court. He doesn't have to post bail. A defendant commonly requests release on his own recognizance at his first court appearance. If the judge denies the request, he then asks for low bail.

In general, defendants who are released O.R. have strong ties to a community, making them unlikely to flee. Factors that may convince a judge to grant an O.R. release include the following:

- The defendant has other family members (most likely parents, a spouse or children) living in the community.
- The defendant has resided in the community for many years.
- The defendant has a job.
- The defendant has little or no past criminal record, or any previous criminal problems were minor and occurred many years earlier.
- The defendant has been charged with previous crimes and has always appeared as required.

Getting a Lawyer

JUSTICE OFT LEANS TO THE SIDE

WHERE YOUR PURSE HANGS.

—DANISH PROVERB

If you are accused of a crime, you will probably face the possibility of going to jail. This fact alone will most likely drive you to look for a good lawyer. Unfortunately, private criminal defense lawyers don't come cheap, and you may not be able to afford one. This doesn't mean you'll be completely at the mercy of the government, however. The U.S. Constitution guarantees you the right to be represented by an attorney if the state is trying to deprive you of your liberty. This means that a court may be required to appoint a lawyer to represent you for free—or for a fee you can afford. This section discusses the role of private and court-appointed attorneys in the criminal process and offers suggestions for finding a private attorney if you can afford one.

How can I get a court to appoint a lawyer for me?

Normally, if you want a court to appoint a lawyer for you at government expense, you must:

- ask the court to appoint a lawyer, and
- provide details about your financial situation.

Typically, your first opportunity to ask the court to appoint a lawyer for you will be at your first court appearance, normally called your arraignment or bail hearing. The judge will probably ask you whether you are represented by a lawyer. If you're not, the judge will then ask whether you want to apply for court-appointed counsel. If you say yes, some courts will appoint a lawyer right on the spot and finish your arraignment. Other courts will delay your case and appoint a lawyer only after reviewing and approving your economic circumstances.

Each state (or even county) makes its own rules as to who qualifies for a free lawyer. Also, the seriousness of the charge may affect a judge's decision as to whether you are eligible for free legal assistance. For example, a judge may recognize that a wage-earner can afford the cost of representation for a minor crime, but not for a crime involving a complicated and lengthy trial.

If you don't qualify for free help but can't afford the full cost of a private lawyer, you may still obtain the services of a court-appointed attorney. Most states provide for "partial indigency," which means that at the conclusion of the case, the judge will require you to reimburse the state or county for a portion of the costs of representation.

Do I need a lawyer at my arraignment?

In most criminal courts the arraignment is where you first appear before a judge and enter a plea of guilty or not guilty to the offense charged. Assuming you enter a plea of not guilty, which almost every defendant does at this early stage, the court will then:

- set a date for the next procedural event in your case
- consider any bail requests that you or the prosecutor make
- appoint your lawyer, and
- ask you to waive time—that is, give up your right to have the trial or other statutory proceedings occur within specified periods of time.

Most people can handle this proceeding without a lawyer. However, if you can get the court to appoint a lawyer for you without postponing the arraignment, or you are able to arrange for private representation before your arraignment, it's always better to have a lawyer.

If I'm poor, will a judge appoint a public defender to represent me?

Because most criminal defendants are unable to afford their own attorneys, many states have public defender's offices. Typically, each local office has a Chief Public Defender and a number of Assistant Public Defenders (P.D.s). P.D.s are fully-licensed lawyers whose sole job is to represent poor defendants in criminal cases. Because they appear daily in the same courts, P.D.s can gain a lot of experience in a short

period of time. And because they work daily with the same cast of characters, they learn the personalities (and prejudices) of the judges, prosecutors and local law enforcement officers—important information to know when assessing a case and conducting a trial.

My county doesn't have a public defender's office. How will the court provide an attorney for me?

In areas that don't have a public defender's office, the court maintains a list of attorneys and appoints them on a rotating basis to represent people who can't afford to hire their own lawyers.

Do public defenders provide the same quality of representation as regular lawyers?

Despite the increasingly severe financial constraints on their offices, public defenders often provide representation that is at least as competent as that provided by private defense attorneys. A 1992 study conducted by the National Center for State Courts concluded that P.D.s and private lawyers achieve approximately equal results. For example, in the nine counties surveyed in the study, 76% of P.D. clients were convicted, compared to 74% of clients with private lawyers.

Despite these good points, public defenders are often asked to perform too much work for not enough money, which can cut into their abilities to be effective.

How can I get a second opinion on my public defender's advice?

Like all attorneys, public defenders are ethically obligated to vigorously defend their clients' interests. Undoubtedly, most lawyers live up to their ethical duties. But defendants who think that their court-appointed attorneys are not representing them adequately can buy advice from a private defense attorney. Even a low-income person may be able to pay for a short "second opinion" consultation.

How can I find a private defense lawyer?

Recently arrested people often need to talk to a lawyer as soon as possible. The most urgent priority is often getting a lawyer to help arrange release and provide some information about what's to come in the days ahead.

If you have been represented by a criminal defense lawyer in the past, that is usually the lawyer to call—as long as you were satisfied with his services. If you have no previous experience with criminal defense lawyers, you can look to the following sources for a referral:

- *Lawyers you know.* Most lawyers do civil (noncriminal) work, such as divorces, drafting wills, filing bankruptcies or representing people hurt in accidents. If you know any attorney that you trust, ask him to recommend a criminal defense lawyer. (Some lawyers who do civil work can also represent clients in criminal matters, at least for the limited purpose of arranging for release from jail following an arrest.)

- *Family members or friends.* Someone close to you may know of a criminal defense lawyer or may have time to look for one.

- *Martindale-Hubbell.* Martindale-Hubbell directories identify lawyers according where they work and the type of law they practice. All law libraries have Martindale-Hubbell books; many general public libraries have them as well. If you have access to the World Wide Web, you can also find Martindale-Hubble online at http://www.martindale.com.

- *Courthouses.* You can visit a local courthouse and sit through a few criminal hearings. If a particular lawyer impresses you, ask for her card after the hearing is over, and then call for an appointment.

Should I expect a lawyer to guarantee a good result?

Toasters come with guarantees; attorneys don't. Steer clear of lawyers who guarantee satisfactory outcomes. A lawyer who guarantees a good result may simply be trying a hard-sell tactic to induce you to hire her.

What is a private lawyer likely to cost?

It's impossible to give a definitive answer. Attorneys set their own fees, which vary according to a number of factors:

- *The complexity of a case.* Most attorneys charge more for felonies than for misdemeanors because felonies carry greater penalties and are likely to involve more work for the attorney.

- *The attorney's experience.* Generally, less experienced attorneys set lower fees than their more experienced colleagues.
- *Geography.* Just as gasoline and butter cost more in some parts of the country than others, so do lawyers.

According to a survey of readers reported in the February, 1996 issue of *Consumer Reports*, the median legal fee charged by lawyers in criminal cases was $1,500. Many defendants can expect to pay more than this, however. A defendant charged with a misdemeanor should not be surprised by a legal fee in the neighborhood of $3,000–$5,000; an attorney may want $15,000–$25,000 in a felony case. And most attorneys want all or a substantial portion of the fee paid up front.

Can I arrange for a contingency fee in a criminal case?

No. A contingency fee is an arrangement where the lawyer gets paid only if he wins the case. These arrangements are not allowed in criminal cases.

Can I change lawyers if I'm unhappy with the one I hired?

Generally, defendants who hire their own attorneys have the right to fire them at any time, without court approval. A defendant doesn't have to show "good cause" or even justify the firing. After firing a lawyer, a defendant can hire another lawyer or perhaps even represent herself. Of course, changing lawyers will probably be costly. In addition to paying the new lawyer, the defendant will have to pay the original lawyer whatever portion of the fee the original lawyer has earned.

Limits on Your Right to Change Lawyers

Your right to change lawyers is limited by the prosecutor's right to keep cases moving on schedule. If you want to change attorneys on the eve of trial, for example, your new attorney is likely to agree to represent you only if the trial is delayed so she can prepare. The prosecutor may oppose delay, possibly because witnesses won't be available to testify later on. In these circumstances, the judge is likely to deny your request to change lawyers.

What if I'm not happy with my court-appointed lawyer? Can I get a new one?

Probably not. Defendants with court-appointed lawyers often ask for new ones. Sometimes the problems are the same as those that would be encountered with any retained lawyer: inability to communicate, personality conflicts or dissatisfaction with the strategy. In addition, clients who are represented by court-appointed lawyers often assume that the representation is substandard.

Requests for a new court-appointed lawyer are rarely granted. A defendant would have to prove that the representation is truly incompetent.

Why do some defendants choose to represent themselves?

Defendants choose to represent themselves for a variety of reasons:

- Some defendants can afford to hire a lawyer, but don't do so because they think the likely punishment is not severe enough to justify the expense.
- Some defendants believe (often mistakenly) that an attorney who represented them previously was ineffective, and figure they can do just as well on their own.
- Some defendants believe that lawyers are part of an overall oppressive system and seek to make a political statement by representing themselves.
- Some defendants want to take responsibility for their own destiny.
- Some defendants who are in jail can gain privileges through self-representation, such as access to the jail's law library. Also, not bound by lawyers' ethical codes, self-represented defendants can delay proceedings and sometimes wreak havoc on an already overloaded system by repeatedly filing motions.

How can I tell whether I should represent myself or not?

The most obvious rule is that the less severe the charged crime, the more sensible it is to represent yourself. Defendants charged with minor traffic offenses should rarely hire an attorney, while defendants charged with serious felonies should rarely be without one. The most difficult decisions involve misdemeanors such as drunk driving, possession of drugs or shoplifting. Hiring an attorney in these situations may be wise because jail time and a fine are possibilities, and convictions may carry hidden costs, such as more severe punishment for a second conviction or vastly increased insurance rates. On the other hand, first time offenders charged with nonviolent crimes are not usually sentenced to jail, and judges and prosecutors often offer standard deals to all defendants, whether or not they are represented by an attorney. Thus, the most critical piece of information that defendants should try to learn before deciding whether to hire an attorney is what the punishment is likely to be if they are convicted.

How to Find Out What Your Punishment Is Likely to Be

It can be difficult to learn about judges' common sentencing practices. Typical sentences aren't usually listed in statutes or court rules, unless you're being sentenced in federal court (and even in that case, the federal sentencing code is incredibly technical, so likely punishment can be difficult to figure out). If you want to find out what your punishment is likely to be if you're convicted, you might take the following steps:

- Pay a private defense attorney for an hour of consultation. An experienced defense attorney can often make accurate predictions as to likely punishment.
- Ask a relative or close friend who is or who knows an attorney for informal, unpaid advice.
- Call the public defender's office, and ask if they have an "attorney of the day" or "duty attorney" who can answer your questions.

Can I represent myself and pay a lawyer to advise me as I go?

Yes. If you're thinking about representing yourself, you might want to seek out an attorney willing to serve as a "legal coach." The goal of hiring a legal coach is to combine a lawyer's knowledge with your own time. Because you pay for the lawyer's help only occasionally, the cost of a legal coach can be far less than turning the entire case over to a private attorney.

Not all attorneys are willing to serve as legal coaches. Some are worried about their liability if they give wrong advice based on incomplete information; others do not want to be involved with a case unless they are in control of it. Thus, if you're considering going it alone and you think you'll want a lawyer's help, you should try to line up your legal coach before you make your final decision.

More Information About Crimes and Criminal Procedure

There are many books and publications devoted to the explanation of state and federal criminal law and procedure. Although most of them are written for lawyers, nonlawyers will find them useful, too. Since the practice of criminal law is so intimately tied to state and local laws, we cannot list every resource here. Your best bet is to go to your local law library and ask for practice manuals or digests on the subject. See the Appendix on Legal Reseach for more information on finding state law and practice manuals and digests.

http://nolo.com
Nolo's website offers self-help information about a wide variety of legal topics, including criminal law and procedure.

http://www.findlaw.com
Most states have put their statutes, including their criminal and criminal procedure codes, on the Internet. You can find links to these laws at the FindLaw site.

Appendix: Legal Research

A.2   *Learning About a Particular Area of the Law*

A.4   *Finding a Specific Law*

A.8   *Finding Answers to Specific Legal Questions*

A.10   *Finding Legal Forms*

Legal research is how you learn about the law. It is not a skill reserved exclusively for lawyers; you can find the answers to your legal questions if you are armed with a little bit of patience and a good road map.

The best legal research method depends on what you need to find out. Usually, people want to research the law in order to accomplish one of the following things:

• understand a particular area of the law

• find and read a statute, regulation, ordinance, court decision or piece of pending legislation (usually called a bill)

• find the answer to a specific legal question, or

• find a legal form.

This appendix explains how to do legal research in each of these situations.

Learning About a Particular Area of the Law

Many people need to understand an area of the law before making an important decision. For example, you might want to know:

• What laws are involved when selling a business?

• What's the difference between a living trust and a living will?

• What effect does divorce have on pensions earned during marriage?

Questions like these can be answered without regard to your specific circumstances; they involve a general understanding of the law. To find this type of information about a legal topic, you should turn to legal background materials.

Legal background materials are books, articles and encyclopedia entries in which experts summarize and explain the basic principles of a legal subject area, such as bankruptcy, landlord-tenant law or criminal law. These materials come in many forms and can be found in law libraries or, sometimes, on the Internet.

How to Find a Law Library

Most counties have law libraries in the government buildings or courthouses at the county seat. These libraries are open to the public. County libraries are a good place to go if you're looking for your state's laws.

Law schools also maintain libraries for their students and staff. Although public access to some law school libraries is restricted, many are willing to extend help to non-students. If you are looking for material from other states or countries, a law school library is the best place to start.

Finally, don't limit yourself to law libraries. Most major public libraries in urban areas contain both local and state laws.

Here are a number of legal background resources that you may find useful:

- *Self-Help Law Books.* Self-help law books, such as those published by Nolo, are written in plain English for a non-lawyer audience. They are an excellent starting point for cracking any legal area that is new to you. Law libraries, public libraries and bookstores (including Nolo's online bookstore at http://www.nolo.com) often carry self-help law books.

- *Organizations and Advocacy Groups.* Many non-profit and professional organizations or advocacy groups—such as tenants' rights groups, the American Association of Retired People (AARP) and local business groups—publish articles or booklets on particular legal topics. Think about what groups might have the information you need and then look for them in the Yellow Pages or on the Web.

- *Legal Encyclopedias.* You can often find a good introduction to your topic in a legal encyclopedia. The legal encyclopedias most commonly found in law libraries are *American Jurisprudence* and *Corpus Juris.* Many states have legal encyclopedias that are state-specific—for example, *Texas Jurisprudence.*

- *The "Nutshell" Series.* Another good introduction to legal topics is the "Nutshell" series, as in *Torts in a Nutshell* and *Intellectual Property in a Nutshell*, published by West Group. These books are available in most law libraries.

- *Treatises.* If you have the time and patience to delve deeply into a subject, you can find comprehensive books—generally known as treatises—on virtually every legal topic. For example, if you want to know about some aspect of trademark law, you could use *McCarthy on Trademarks*, a multi-volume treatise on all aspects of trademark law.

- *West's Legal Desk Reference.* This book, by Statsky, Hussey, Diamond and Nakamura, lists background materials both by state and legal topic. In addition, *West's Legal Desk Reference* provides keywords and phrases that will help you use the indexes to other resources you may need during your research.

- *Internet Resources.* Nolo's Legal Encyclopedia, available free at http://www.nolo.com, explains many common legal issues in plain English. The other major legal websites (listed below) also provide helpful information and links to specific areas of the law. Finally, many government agency sites provide legal information, such as state marriage license requirements or downloadable publications on different legal topics. For example, if you visit the Federal Judiciary's website at http://www.uscourts.gov, you can download Bankruptcy Basics, a pamphlet providing a good overview of bankruptcy. To find government agencies online, see Finding Court and Government Agency Websites, below.

The Best Legal Websites

In addition to our own website at http://www.nolo.com, Nolo's favorite legal websites are:

- **FindLaw**
  http://www.findlaw.com
- **The National Federation of Paralegal Associations** http://www.paralegals.org/LegalResources/home.html
- **The World Wide Web Virtual Library** http://www.law.indiana.edu/v-lib
- **American Association of Law Libraries: Legal Research Links** http://www.aallnet.org/research
- **The Library of Congress Guide to Law Online** http://loc.gov/law/guide
- **The Legal Information Institute at Cornell Law School** http://www.law.cornell.edu

Finding a Specific Law

There are many reasons why you might need to find a specific statute, regulation, ordinance or court decision. For example, you might learn from the newspaper about new state laws governing overtime wages and want to read the laws themselves. Or perhaps the city building department has referred you to a particular city ordinance that covers zoning laws in your neighborhood. Whatever the reason, the research involved in finding a specific law or court decision is relatively straightforward. The steps depend on what type of law you seek.

City or County Laws

You can usually get copies of city or county laws (often called "ordinances") from the office of the city or county clerk. The main branch of your public library is also likely to have a collected set of these laws. Once you get there, ask the reference librarian for help.

Many local ordinances are also available on the Web. The best place to start is Municipal Codes Online, maintained by the Seattle Public Library at http://www.spl.org/selectedsites/municode.html.

State or Federal Statutes and Regulations

Rules established by state and federal governments are called statutes and regulations. Federal statutes are passed by the United States Congress, while state statutes are passed by state legislatures. Regulations are issued by state or federal administrative agencies (such as the U.S. Department of Transportation or the State Department of Health) for the purpose of implementing and enforcing statutes.

You can find statutes and regulations in the library or on the Internet. You can also use legal background materials to point the way to the statute or regulation you seek.

Finding statutes and regulations at the library. State and federal statutes and regulations can be found at a law library or the main branch of a public library. Depending on the state, statutes are compiled in books called codes, revised statutes, annotated statutes or compiled laws. For example, the federal statutes are contained in a series called *United States Code*, and the Vermont statutes are found in a series called *Vermont Statutes Annotated*. (The term "annotated" means that the statutes are accompanied by information about their history and court decisions that have interpreted them.) Once you've located the books you need, search for the specific statute by its citation (if you know it) or by looking up keywords in the index.

And after you find a law in the statute books, it's important to look at the update pamphlet in the front or back of the book (called the "pocket part") to make sure your statute hasn't been amended or deleted. Since pocket parts are published only once per year, brand new statutes often have not yet made it to the pocket part. Law libraries subscribe to services and periodicals that update these books on a more frequent basis than the pocket parts. You can ask the law librarian to point you toward the materials you need.

Most federal regulations are published in the *Code of Federal Regulations* (*C.F.R.*), a well-indexed set of books organized by subject. If you don't have a citation for the regulation you seek, check the index. To make sure

the regulation is current, look at the monthly pamphlet that accompanies the books, called *C.F.R.-L.S.A. (List of C.F.R. Sections Affected).*

State regulations are harder to find. If you know which agency publishes the regulation you want, call or visit to get copies. Many states also keep a portion of their regulations in a series of books called the "Administrative Code." Check the table of contents. If the regulation is not in an Administrative Code, look for loose-leaf manuals published by the individual agency. If you find a regulation in the Administrative Code or loose-leaf manual, you should still call the agency to make sure the regulation hasn't recently changed.

Finding statutes and regulations online. You can find federal statutes, the entire *Code of Federal Regulations* and most state statutes by visiting Nolo's Legal Research Center at http://www.nolo.com/research/index.html. Your best bet for state regulations is FindLaw at http://www.findlaw.com. FindLaw also offers federal statutes and regulations, and state statutes.

If you are looking for a brand-new statute online, you may have to search for recently enacted legislation (see below), since there is often a delay between the time a statute is passed and the time it is included in the overall compilation of laws. The good legal websites listed earlier in this appendix also offer state and federal statutes.

Almost every state maintains its own website for pending and recently enacted legislation. These sites contain not only the most current version of a bill, but also its history. To find your state's website, see Finding Court and Government Agency Websites, below. Finally, the United States Congress maintains a website at http://thomas.loc.gov that contains all pending federal bills.

Using background materials to find statutes and regulations.
When looking for a particular statute or regulation (whether it be state or federal), you may want to consult background materials, which often include relevant laws. For example, *Collier on Bankruptcy*, the leading bankruptcy treatise, contains a complete set of the federal bankruptcy laws. Even if the background resource does not include the text of the statutes or regulations, it will provide citations to the relevant laws and the books in which they are found.

Finding Court and Government Agency Websites

Many courts and government agencies provide statutes and case law, plus other useful information such as forms, answers to frequently asked questions and downloadable pamphlets on various legal topics. To find to your state's website, open your browser and type in http://www.state.<your state's postal code>.us. Your state's postal code is the two-letter abbreviation you use for mailing addresses. For example, NY is the postal code for New York, so to find New York's state website, type in http://www.state.ny.us.

Nolo's Legal Research Center (http://www.nolo.com/research/index.html) provides links to courts across the country and access to small claims court information for most states. You can also find local, state and federal court websites on the National Center for State Courts' website at http://www.ncsconline.org. The federal judiciary's website at http://www.uscourts.govlists federal court websites.

State Case Law

State case law consists of the rules established by courts in court decisions (or "court opinions"). Court decisions do one of two things. First, courts interpret statutes, regulations and ordinances so that we know how they apply in real-life situations. Second, courts make rules that are not found in statutes, regulations or ordinances. These rules are called the "common law."

Finding state cases in the library. State cases are found in a series of books called reporters. For example, California cases are contained in the *California Reporter*. You can also find state cases in books known as "regional reporters." These volumes contain cases from several states in a geographical region. For example, the *Atlantic Reporter* contains cases from several eastern states, including Delaware and Maryland.

If you have a case citation, which is the number of the volume and page where the case appears (for example,

21 Cal.App.3d 446), you simply locate the correct series of books (in the above example, it would be the California Appellate Reports, 3rd Series), select the appropriate volume (here it's volume 21) and open the book to the indicated page (in the example, page 446). If you don't have a citation but know the name of one or both of the parties in the case—for instance, in the case named *Jones v. Smith*, Jones and Smith are the names of the parties—you can use a "case digest." Look for the parties' names in the digest's Table of Cases. If you don't know the name of the case or the citation, then it will be very difficult to find the case in the law library.

Finding state cases on the Web. If the case is recent (within the last few years), you may be able to find it for free on the Internet. A good place to start is FindLaw at http:// www.findlaw.com. Also, many state websites now publish recent cases. See Finding Court and Government Agency Websites, above, for information on how to find your state's website.

If the case is older, you can still find it on the Internet, but you will probably have to pay a private company for access to its database. VersusLaw at http:// www.versusLaw.com maintains an excellent library of older state court cases. You can do unlimited research on VersusLaw for $8.95 per month. You can also get state cases online through the Lexis and Westlaw databases. (For more information, see Using Westlaw and Lexis to Do Legal Research on the Web, below.)

Federal Case Law

Federal case law consists of the rules established by federal courts. Like state cases, you can find federal case law in both the library and on the Web.

Finding federal cases in the library. Cases decided by the U.S. Supreme Court are published in three different series of reporters. All three contain the same cases. The names of these series are:
- *United States Reports*
- *Supreme Court Reporter*; and
- *Supreme Court Reports: Lawyers' Edition.*

Well-stocked law libraries also have cases from other federal courts, including the Federal Circuit Courts of Appeal (federal appellate courts), U.S. District Courts (federal trial courts) and specialized courts such as bankruptcy or tax court.

To find a case in the Supreme Court reporters or any of the volumes containing other federal cases, follow the guidelines for finding state cases by citation or case name, above.

Finding U.S. Supreme Court cases on the Web. Nolo's Legal Research Center, available at http:// www.nolo.com/research/index.html, provides U.S. Supreme Court cases decided within the last hundred years.

Finding other federal cases on the Web. FindLaw, at http:// www.findlaw.com, contains cases decided by the Federal Circuit Courts of Appeal within the last four or five years, some bankruptcy opinions and very recent tax court cases. The Cornell Law School Legal Information

Institute at http://www.law.cornell.edu provides access to all federal appellate court cases, some District Court cases and some bankruptcy opinions. VersusLaw (explained above) also has some U.S. District Court cases and some bankruptcy opinions. If you can't find the case you're looking for on one of these websites, your best bet is to use Westlaw or Lexis.

Using Lexis and Westlaw to Do Legal Research on the Web

Lexis and Westlaw are the chief electronic legal databases which contain the full text of many of the legal resources found in law libraries, including almost all reported cases from state and federal courts, all federal statutes, the statutes of most states, federal regulations, law review articles, commonly used treatises and practice manuals.

Although Westlaw and Lexis databases are available over the Internet, subscriptions are pricey. However, both offer some free and some fee-based services to non-subscribers that are both helpful and reasonably priced (between $9 and $10 per document). To find out more about these services, visit Westlaw at http://www.westlaw.com or Lexis at http://www.lexis.com.

Finding Answers to Specific Legal Questions

It's one thing to track down information on a recent case or statute or to read up on general information about a legal topic. It's quite another to confidently answer a question about how the law might apply to your own situation, such as:

- I live in North Carolina, and I've been charged with second offense drunk driving. My passenger was injured as a result of the accident. What penalties do I face?
- My brother is the executor of our parents' estate, and I don't like how he's handling things. What can I do?
- Can I run a home school in my state (North Dakota) if I've been convicted of a felony?

These are the types of questions that people have traditionally asked lawyers. To answer such questions, you often need to look at all the legal resources we have mentioned thus far. You must also make sure that the law you find is current. If you want to undertake this type of legal research on your own, we recommend that you use a comprehensive legal research guide that wallks you through the process step-by-step. (See the list of resources at the end of this appendix.) Here, we can provide just a brief overview of what you'll need to do.

When seeking the answer to a specific legal question, your ultimate goal is to predict, as near as possible, how a judge would rule if presented with the issues and facts of your case. The closer your facts are to the facts in previous cases or the more directly a statute applies to your situation, the more likely you'll be able to predict what a judge would decide. Sometimes, your question is so basic that the answer is easy to find. But often, a statute won't address each facet of your situation and the facts of other cases won't match up 100%. Because of this, legal research cannot always provide a definitive answer, although it can often give you a good idea of what the answer will be. (That's why lawyers often hem and haw when asked a legal question.)

Basic or Common Legal Questions

It should be fairly easy to find an answer if your legal question is a common one—such as "What is the filing fee for a Chapter 7 bankruptcy?" or "Can the state garnish my wages if I fall behind on child support payments?" These types of questions usually rely on general legal information—rather than the nuances of your particular circumstances. You should begin your research by consulting one or more of the background resources discussed above. You might focus on organizations, advocacy groups or government agencies that are likely to have the answer you need. For example, a local tenants' rights group might provide pamphlets with fre-

quently asked questions about evictions. Or, the Association of American Retired Persons (AARP) may be able to tell you what the current estate tax rate is. You can often find this kind of information online.

Complex Legal Questions

If you can't get an answer to your legal question from a background resource—usually because your question involves unique facts related to your situation—you'll need to do more detailed research. But don't forget what the background materials have taught you. Remember that background resources can give you an important overview of your legal topic and also provide cites to relevant statutes and cases.

To proceed further, first search for statutes, regulations or ordinances that address your question. If you find relevant statutes, look for cases that have interpreted them. To do this at a law library, you can:

- look at the summaries of cases that follow the statute in an annotated code book
- use *Shepard's Citations for Statutes* (a book that provides a complete list of cases that mention a particular statute, regulation or constitutional provision), and
- search for cases in "case digests" (books that list cases by subject).

If you can't find a relevant statute or other legislative enactment, you need to look for case law only. To do this at a law library, you can:

- read any relevant cases mentioned in the background materials

- search in case digests by subject area or keywords
- if you find a relevant case, read the cases that it mentions, and
- if you find a relevant case, use *Shepard's Citations for Cases* to find more cases on point. (*Shepard's* provides a complete list of cases that mention your case.)

Making Sure the Law is Up to Date

Because law changes rapidly, you must make sure that the principles stated in your cases and statutes are still valid. A case may no longer be helpful to you if a more recent case has questioned its reasoning, ruled a different way or expressly stated that your case is no longer good law. Likewise, you should check to make sure your statute has not been changed or eliminated.

Updating your research in the library. If you are using the law library, there are a few things you should do to make sure your research is up to date.

- *Background Resources.* If you use background materials, be sure to check the pocket part; it contains changes and new developments in the law.
- *Statutes.* Books containing statutes and regulations also contain pocket parts. Be sure to check these as well. Also check law library periodicals that contain more recent statutory updates.
- *Cases.* You can check the validity of every case you find by using *Shepards' Citations for Cases. Shepards'* will list every case that mentions your case, and tell you the reasons

why it was mentioned. For example, it might show that a later case overruled your case, which means your case is no longer valid.

Updating your research on the Web. On the Internet, the updating process is easier, but often more expensive.

- *Statutes.* If you're checking a state statute, visit your state's website for current legislative developments. (See Finding Court and Government Agency Websites, above.) If you need federal information, track Congress' legislative developments through Nolo's website at http://www.nolo.com/research/index.html or by visiting http://thomas.loc.gov. You can also get the most recent version of a statute for a fee through Westlaw or Lexis. (See Using Westlaw and Lexis to Do Legal Research on the Web, above.)
- *Cases.* You can check the validity of cases through fee-based services. Try KeyCite at http://www.keycite.com or VersusLaw at http://www.versuslaw.com.

Finding Legal Forms

If you must take care of a legal matter, chances are good that you'll need to use a form of some sort—that is, a pre-formatted document that contains standard ("boilerplate") language addressing your specific situation. Leases, wills, trusts, sales agreements and employment contracts are just a few examples of the thousands of legal forms that are used in the course of our daily personal and business affairs.

What Form Do You Need?

Figuring out what form you need is usually simple—someone will tell you. For example, suppose you are handling your own divorce and when you try to file the papers, the clerk says you are missing a "disclosure" form. If the court can't give it to you, you'll have to find it on your own. Or, suppose you are trying to sell your car and the buyer says she wants a bill of sale. Again, you'll have to track one down.

If you haven't been directed toward a particular form, but want to undertake a procedure and suspect that it requires forms, you should find a resource that explains the procedure or transaction. Many of these resources will provide the necessary forms and explain how to fill them in.

Keep in mind that some forms used by courts and government agencies are "mandatory." This means that you have to use their form, and not a similar form that you or someone else has designed, even if your version contains the same information. If you need a form for a court or government agency, it's wise to ask the clerk whether the court has a mandatory form.

Finding the Form You Need

Fortunately, forms are readily available from many sources. Here are the best ways to get them.

- *Stationery Stores.* Many large stationery stores sell legal forms. However, these forms usually don't come with legal instructions, so you may need some help filling them in.
- *Self-Help Legal Materials.* Self-help legal materials, including those published by Nolo, are a good place to find legal forms. Because self-help law materials are written for non-lawyers, the forms are usually accompanied by detailed instructions in plain English. You can find self-help legal materials in bookstores, law libraries and on the Internet.
- *Law Libraries.* Most law libraries have a large collection of books that contain forms for almost every legal transaction imaginable. They usually contain step-by-step instructions for completing the forms and highlight areas where the boilerplate language might not be appropriate.
- *Government Forms on the Web.* Many federal, state, county and municipal courts offer forms on their websites. (See Finding Court and Government Agency Websites, above.) Often, these forms are accompanied by instructions and an overview of the relevant law. Also, FindLaw at http://www.findlaw.com provides lists of government forms, specific subject matter forms, form collections and indexes. Many of these forms are not accompanied by instructions. So, unless you already know what you are doing, you may have to search for additional information to assist you in filling them out.

More Information About Legal Research

Legal Research: How to Find & Understand the Law, by Stephen Elias and Susan Levinkind (Nolo), is an easy-to-read book that provides step-by-step instructions on how to find legal information, both in the law library and online. It includes examples, exercises (with answers) and sample legal memos.

Gilbert's Law Summaries: Legal Research, Writing and Analysis, by Peter Honigsberg (Harcourt Brace Legal and Professional Publications), is a no-nonsense guide to commonly used law library resources.

http://www.nolo.com/research/index.html

Nolo's Legal Research Center provides links to courts across the country and access to small claims information in many states. It also contains U.S. Supreme Court cases and federal and state statutes.

http://www.spl.org/selectedsites/municode.html

Municipal Codes Online, maintained by the Seattle Public Library, provides the text of many local ordinances around the country.

http://www.ncsconline.org

The National Center for State Courts provides links to local, state and federal court websites.

http://www.uscourts.gov

The federal judiciary's website provides links to federal court websites.

http://www.versuslaw.com

VersusLaw allows you to search online for state and federal statutes and cases for a low monthly fee.

http://findlaw.com

FindLaw's extensive database allows you to search for state and federal statutes and cases and provides links to many courts around the country.

401(k) plan A deferred compensation savings program in which employees invest part of their wages, sometimes with added employer contributions, to save on taxes. Income taxes on the amounts invested and earned are not due until the employee withdraws money from the fund, usually at retirement.

A

AB trust A trust that allows couples to reduce or avoid estate taxes. If property is held in an AB trust, when the first spouse dies, his or her half of the property goes to the beneficiaries named in the trust with the condition that the surviving spouse has the right to use the property for life and is entitled to any income it generates. This keeps the property out of the surviving spouse's estate, reducing the likelihood that estate tax will be due when the surviving spouse dies.

acquittal A decision by a judge or jury that a defendant in a criminal case is not guilty of a crime.

adjustable rate mortgage (ARM) A mortgage loan with an interest rate that fluctuates in accordance with a designated market indicator—such as the weekly average of one-year U.S. Treasury Bills—over the life of the loan.

administration (of an estate) The court-supervised distribution of a deceased person's property.

adoption A court procedure by which an adult becomes the legal parent of someone who is not his or her biological child.

annuity A purchased policy that pays a fixed amount of benefits every year for the life of the person who is entitled to those benefits under the policy.

annulment A court procedure that dissolves a marriage and treats it as if it never happened.

appeal A written request to a higher court to modify or reverse the judgment of a trial court or intermediate level appellate court.

appellate court A higher court that reviews the decision of a lower court when a losing party files an appeal.

arbitration A procedure for resolving disputes out of court using one or more neutral third parties—called the arbitrator or arbitration panel.

arraignment A court appearance in which a criminal defendant is formally charged with a crime and asked to respond by entering a plea, most commonly guilty, not guilty or "nolo contendere."

arrest A situation in which the police detain someone in a manner that would lead any reasonable person to believe that he or she is not free to leave.

arrest warrant A document issued by a judge or magistrate that authorizes the police to arrest someone.

articles of incorporation A document filed with state authorities to form a corporation.

assault The crime of attempting to physically harm another person in a way that makes the person under attack feel immediately threatened. Actual physical contact is not necessary.

attorney-in-fact A person named in a written power of attorney document to act on behalf of the person who signs the document, called the principal.

audit An examination of the financial records of a person, business or organization, typically undertaken to clean up careless or improper bookkeeping, or to verify that proper records are being kept. Audits are also conducted by the IRS in order to determine whether a person or business owes taxes.

B

bail The money paid to the court, usually at arraignment or shortly thereafter, to ensure that an arrested person who is released from jail will show up at all required court appearances.

bail bond Money posted for a defendant who cannot afford bail. The defendant pays a certain portion (usually 10%) of the bond as a fee.

balloon payment A large final payment due at the end of a loan, typically a home or car loan, to pay off the amount your monthly payments didn't cover.

bankruptcy trustee A person appointed by a bankruptcy court to oversee the case of a person or business that has filed for bankruptcy.

battery The crime of making physical contact with someone with the intention to harm him or her. Unintentional harmful contact is not battery, no mater how careless the behavior or how severe the injury.

beneficiary A person or organization that is legally entitled to receive benefits through a legal device, such as a will, trust or life insurance policy.

bylaws The rules that govern the internal affairs or actions of a corporation.

C

C corporation Common business slang to describe a corporation whose profits are taxed separately from its owners under Subchapter C of the Internal Revenue Code.

capital gains The profit on the sale of a capital asset, such as stock or real estate.

capitalized interest Accrued interest that is added to the principal balance of a loan while you are not making payments or when your payments are insufficient to cover both the principal and interest due.

case A term that most often refers to a lawsuit—for example, "I filed my small claims case." "Case" also refers to a written decision by a court.

certification mark A name, symbol or other device used by an organization to vouch for the quality of products and services provided by others.

child support Money paid by a parent to support his or her children until the children reach the age of majority or become emancipated—usually by marriage, by entry into the armed forces or by living independently.

circuit court In many states, the name used for the principal trial court. In the federal system, the name

for the appellate courts, which are organized into thirteen circuits.

civil case A noncriminal lawsuit in which an individual, business or government entity sues another to protect, enforce or redress private rights. There are hundreds of varieties of civil cases. A few examples include lawsuits involving breach of contract, probate, divorce, negligence and copyright violations.

collateral Property that guarantees payment of a secured debt.

collection agency A company hired by a creditor to collect a debt.

collective mark A name, symbol or other device used by members of a group or organization to identify the goods or services it provides.

collision damage waiver See "loss damage waiver."

collision insurance coverage A component of car insurance that pays for damages to the insured vehicle that result from a collision with another vehicle or object.

common law The system of rules that is established by court decisions and not by statutes, regulations or ordinances.

community property A method used in some states for defining the ownership of property acquired and the responsibility for debts incurred during marriage. In states with community property laws, all earnings during marriage and all property acquired with those earnings are considered community property. Likewise, all debts incurred during marriage are community property debts.

common law marriage In some states, a type of marriage in which couples can become legally married by living together for a long period of time, representing themselves as a married couple and intending to be married.

conservator Someone appointed by a judge to oversee the affairs of an incapacitated person. A conservator may also be called a guardian, committee or curator.

constitution The system of fundamental laws and principals that lay down the nature, functions and limitations of a government body. The United States Constitution is the supreme law of the United States. States also have constitutions. State constitutions can give people *more* rights than does the U.S. Constitution, but cannot give people *fewer* rights than those found in the U.S. Constitution.

contingency fee A method of paying a lawyer for legal representation by which, instead of an hourly or per job fee, the lawyer receives a percentage of the money his or her client obtains after settling or winning the case.

cooling-off rule A rule that allows you to cancel certain contracts within a specified time period (typically three days) after signing.

copyright A legal device that provides the owner the right to control how a creative work is used.

corporation A legal structure authorized by state law that allows a business to organize as a separate legal entity from its owners, thereby shielding them from personal liability from business debts and obligations, and allowing the business to take advantage of corporate tax rules.

counterclaim A defendant's court papers that claim that the plaintiff— not the defendant—committed legal wrongs, and that as a result it is the defendant who is entitled to money damages or other relief. In some states, a counterclaim is called a cross-complaint.

covenants, conditions & restrictions (CC&Rs) Restrictions governing the use of real estate, usually enforced by a homeowners' association and passed on to the new owners of property.

credit bureau A private, profit-making company that collects and sells information about a person's credit history.

credit insurance Insurance that pays off a loan if the person who owes the money dies or becomes disabled.

credit report An account of your credit history, prepared by a credit bureau.

creditor A person or entity (such as a bank) to whom a debt is owed.

crime A type of behavior that has been defined by the state or federal government as deserving of punishment. The punishment for a crime may include imprisonment.

custody (of a child) The legal authority to make decisions affecting a child's interests (legal custody) and the responsibility of taking care of the child (physical custody).

cybersquatting Buying a domain name that reflects the name of a business or famous person with the intent of selling the name back to the business or celebrity for a profit.

death taxes Taxes levied at death, based on the value of property left behind. Federal death taxes are called estate taxes. Some states also levy death taxes, sometimes called inheritance taxes, on people who inherit property.

debit card A card issued by a bank that can be used to withdraw cash at a bank like an ATM card, and can be used at stores to pay for goods and services in place of a check. A debit card automatically deducts money from your checking account at the time of the transaction.

debtor A person or entity (such as a bank) who owes money.

deductible Something that is taken away or subtracted. Under an insurance policy, for example, the deduct-

ible is the maximum amount that an insured person must pay toward his own losses before he can recover from the insurer.

deed A document that transfers ownership of real estate.

deed in lieu of foreclosure A method of avoiding foreclosure where the lender accepts ownership of the property in place of the money owed on the mortgage.

default The failure to perform a legal duty. For example, a default on a mortgage or car loan happens when a borrower fails to make the loan payments on time, fails to maintain adequate insurance or violates some other provision of the agreement.

defendant The person against whom a lawsuit is filed. In certain states, and in certain types of lawsuits, the defendant is called the respondent.

defined benefit plan A type of pension plan that pays a definite, predetermined amount of money when the worker retires or becomes disabled. The amount received is based on length of service with a particular employer.

defined contribution plan A type of pension plan that does not guarantee any particular pension amount upon retirement. Instead, the employer pays into the pension fund a certain amount every month, or every year, for each employee.

dependents benefits A type of Social Security benefit available to the spouse and minor or disabled children of a retired or disabled worker who qualifies for either retirement or disability benefits under the program's rigorous qualification guidelines.

design patent A patent issued on a new design, used for purely aesthetic reasons, that does not affect the functioning of the underlying device.

deposition A tool used in pretrial case investigation (called "discovery") where one party questions the other party or a witness in the case. All questions be answered under oath and be recorded by a court reporter, who creates a deposition transcript.

disability benefits Money available from Social Security to benefit those under 65 who qualify because of their work and earnings record and who meet the program's medical guidelines defining disability.

dischargeable debts Debts that can be erased by going through bankruptcy.

discovery A formal investigation—governed by court rules—that is conducted before a trial. Discovery allows one party to question other parties and sometimes witnesses and to force others to disclose documents or other physical evidence.

district court In federal court and, in some states, the name of the main trial court.

dissolution A term used instead of divorce in some states.

divorce The legal termination of marriage.

doing business as (DBA) A situation in which a business owner operates a company under a name different from his or her real name.

domain name A combination of letters and numbers that identifies a specific website on the Internet, followed by an identifier such as .com or .org.

down payment A lump sum cash payment made by a buyer when he or she purchases a major piece of property, such as a car or house.

durable power of attorney A power of attorney that remains in effect if the maker becomes incapacitated. If a power of attorney is not specifically made durable, it automatically expires upon incapacity.

durable power of attorney for finances A legal document that gives someone authority to manage the maker's financial affairs if he or she becomes incapacitated.

durable power of attorney for healthcare A legal document that names someone to make medical decisions if the person who makes the document is unable to express his or her wishes for care.

E

emergency protective order Any court-issued order meant to protect a person from harm or harassment. This type of order is a stop-gap measure, usually lasting only for a weekend or holiday.

escrow A document (such as a grant deed to real property) or sum of money that, by agreement of parties to a transaction, is held by a neutral third party until certain conditions are met. Once the conditions are met, the third party releases the funds or document from escrow.

estate Generally, all the property a person owns when he or she dies.

estate taxes Taxes imposed by the federal government on property as it passes from the dead to the living. Some states also impose "inheritance taxes" on the people who inherit the property.

eviction Removal of a tenant from rental property by a law enforcement officer.

evidence The many types of information presented to a judge or jury designed to convince them of the truth or falsity of the key facts in a case. Evidence may include testimony of witnesses, documents, photographs, items of damaged property, government records, videos or laboratory reports.

executor The person named in a will to handle the property of someone who has died.

exempt property The items of property you are allowed to keep if a creditor wins a lawsuit against you or if you file for Chapter 7 bankruptcy.

express warranty A guarantee made by a seller about the quality of goods or services provided. An express warranty is explicitly stated, either orally or in writing.

extended warranty contract Warranty coverage on an item that takes effect after the warranty coverage provided by the manufacturer or seller expires.

federal court A branch of the United States government with power derived directly from the U.S. Constitution. Federal courts decide cases involving the U.S. Constitution, federal law and some cases where the parties are from different states.

felony A serious crime, usually punishable by a prison term of more than one year or, in some cases, by death.

fictitious business name The name under which a business operates or by which it is commonly known. See also "doing business as."

fixed rate mortgage A mortgage loan that has an interest rate that remains constant throughout the life of the loan, so that the amount you pay each month remains the same over the entire mortgage term.

for sale by owner (FSBO) A type of house sale in which the owner acts alone, without a real estate broker.

forbearance Voluntarily refraining from doing something, such as asserting a legal right. For example, a creditor may forbear on its right to collect a debt by temporarily postponing or reducing the borrower's payments.

foreclosure The forced sale of real estate to pay off a home loan on which the owner of the property has defaulted.

G

garnishment A court-ordered process that takes property from a person to satisfy a debt. For example, a creditor may garnish a debtor's wages if the debtor loses a lawsuit filed by the creditor.

general partnership A business that is owned and managed by two or more people (called partners or general partners) who are personally liable for all business debts.

gift taxes Federal taxes assessed on any gift, or combination of gifts, from one person to another that exceeds $10,000 in one year. There are some exceptions to this tax.

grace period A period of time during which you are not required to make payments on a debt.

grant deed A deed containing an implied promise that the person transferring the property actually owns the title and that it is not encumbered in any way, except as described in the deed.

guarantor A person who makes a legally binding promise to either pay another person's debt or perform another person's duty if that person defaults or fails to perform.

guardian An adult who has been given the legal right by a court to control and care for someone known as a "ward." The ward may be either a minor child or an incapacitated adult. The guardian may make personal decisions on behalf of the ward (a "personal guardian"), manage the ward's property (a "property guardian" or "guardian of the estate"), or both.

guardian of the estate See "guardian."

guardianship A legal relationship created by a court between a guardian and his ward—either a minor child or an incapacitated adult. The guardian has a legal right and duty to care for the ward.

H

healthcare directive A legal document that allows the maker to set out written wishes for medical care—and to name a person to make sure those wishes are carried out. A healthcare directive may also be called a living will, advance directive or directive to physicians.

healthcare proxy A person named in a healthcare directive or durable power of attorney for healthcare to make medical decisions for the person who signed the document, called the principal. A healthcare proxy may also be known as an attorney-in-fact, agent or patient advocate.

holographic will A will that is completely handwritten, dated and signed by the person making it. Holographic wills are generally not witnessed.

home warranty A service contract that covers a major housing system— for example, plumbing or electrical wiring—for a set period of time from the date a house is sold. The warranty guarantees repairs to the covered system and is renewable.

homeowners' association An organization of neighbors concerned with managing the common areas of a subdivision or condominium complex. The homeowners' association is also responsible for enforcing any covenants, conditions and restrictions that apply to the property.

hung jury A jury unable to come to a final decision, resulting in a mistrial.

I

implied warranty A guarantee about the quality of goods or services purchased. An implied warranty is not written down or explicitly spoken, but is provided to consumers by law.

implied warranty of fitness An implied warranty that applies when you buy an item for a specific purpose. If you notify the seller of your specific needs, this warranty guarantees that the item will function to meet those needs.

implied warranty of habitability A legal doctrine that requires landlords to offer and maintain livable premises for their tenants.

implied warranty of merchantability An implied warranty that a new item will work for its specified purpose.

independent contractor A self-employed person, as defined by the IRS. The key to the definition is that, unlike employees, independent contractors retain control over how they do their work. The person or company paying the independent contractor controls only the outcome—the product or service.

individual retirement account (IRA) A savings or brokerage account to which a person may contribute up to a specified amount of earned income each year. There are several types of IRAs. The most common are traditional contributory IRAs and Roth IRAs. With a traditional contributory IRA, contributions and interest earned are not taxed until the participant withdraws funds at retirement. With Roth IRAs, contributions are taxed, but most distributions (investment returns and withdrawals at retirement) are not.

infraction A minor violation of the law that is punishable only by a fine—for example, a traffic or parking ticket.

infringement (of copyright, patent or trademark) The violation of a patent, copyright or trademark owner's rights. Usually, this occurs when someone uses or benefits from a patented or copyrighted work or a trademark or servicemark, without the owner's permission.

inheritance taxes Taxes levied by some states on people who inherit property (compare with "estate taxes"). Sometimes referred to as "death taxes."

interrogatories Written questions that one party to a lawsuit asks an opposing party. Interrogatories are designed to discover key facts about an opponent's case, and are a common part of pretrial case investigation.

interest A commission that a borrower pays to a bank or other creditor for lending the borrower money or extending credit. An interest rate represents the annual percentage that is added to the balance of a loan or credit line. This means that if your loan has an interest rate of 8%, the creditor adds 8% to the balance each year.

intestate succession The method by which property is distributed when a person dies without a valid will. Usually, the property is distributed to the closest surviving relatives.

irrevocable trust A permanent trust. Once the trust is created, it cannot be revoked, amended or changed in any way.

J

joint custody An arrangement by which parents who do not live together share the upbringing of a child. Joint custody can be joint legal custody (in which both parents have a say in decisions affecting the child) joint physical custody (in which the child spends a significant amount of time with both parents) or both.

joint tenancy A way for two or more people to share ownership of real estate or other property. When property is held in joint tenancy and one owner dies, the other owners automatically receive the deceased owner's share.

judgment A final court ruling resolving the key questions in a lawsuit and determining the rights and obligations of the opposing parties.

judgment-proof A term used to describe a person from whom nothing can be collected because he or she has little income and no property, or is protected from collection of the judgment by law—for example, a law preventing the collection of exempt property.

jury A group of people selected to apply the law, as stated by a judge, to the facts of a case and render a decision, called the verdict.

jury nullification A decision made by a jury to acquit a defendant who has violated a law that the jury believes is unjust or wrong.

L

landlord The owner of any real estate, such as a house, apartment building or land, that is leased or rented to another person, called the tenant.

lease An oral or written agreement between two people concerning the use by one of the property of the other. A person can lease either real estate (such as an apartment or business property) or personal property (such as a car or a boat).

legal custody The right and obligation to make decisions about a child's upbringing, including schooling and medical care. Compare "physical custody."

legislature The branch of government that has the responsibility and power to make laws. A state legislature makes state laws and the federal legislature (the U.S. Congress) makes federal laws.

lemon A car that gives you serious trouble soon after you buy it.

liability (1) The state of being liable—that is, legally responsible for an act or omission. (2) Something for which a person is liable. For example, a debt is often called a liability.

liability insurance A contract that provides compensation to third parties who are injured or whose property is damaged due to the fault of the insurance policyholder.

license (of invention, copyright or trademark) A contract giving written permission to use an invention, creative work or trademark.

lien The right of a secured creditor to take a specific item of property if the borrower doesn't pay a debt.

life estate A property interest that provides the right to live in or use, but not own, a specific piece of real estate until death.

life insurance A contract under which an insurance company agrees to pay money to a designated beneficiary upon the death of the policyholder. In exchange, the policyholder pays a regularly scheduled fee, known as the insurance premiums.

limited liability The maximum amount a business owner can lose if the business is subject to debts, claims or other liabilities. One of the primary advantages of forming a corporation or limited liability company (LLC) is that the business owners stand to lose only the amount of money invested in the business—creditors can't come after an owner's personal assets.

limited liability company (LLC) A business ownership structure that offers limited personal liability for business obligations and a choice of how the business will be taxed: either as a separate entity or as a partnership-like structure in which profits are taxed on the owners' personal income tax returns.

limited liability partnership (LLP)
A type of partnership recognized in a majority of states that protects a partner from personal liability for negligent acts committed by other partners or by employees not under his or her direct control.

limited partnership A business structure that allows some partners (called limited partners) to enjoy limited personal liability for partnership debts while other partners (called general partners) have unlimited personal liability. Limited partners are usually passive investors; they are not allowed to make day-to-day business decisions.

living trust A trust created during the trustmaker's life to avoid probate after death. Property transferred into the trust during life passes directly to the trust beneficiaries after death, without probate.

living will See "healthcare directive."

loan broker A person who specializes in matching home buyers with appropriate mortgage lenders.

loan consolidation Combining a number of loans into a single new loan.

loss damage waiver (LDW)
Rental car insurance that makes the rental car company responsible for damage to or theft of a rental car. Also called a "collision damage waiver."

M

malpractice (by an attorney) The delivery of substandard services by a lawyer. Generally, malpractice occurs when a lawyer fails to provide the quality of service that should reasonably be expected in the circumstances, with the result that the lawyer's client is harmed.

marital property Most of the property accumulated by spouses during a marriage, called "community property" in some states.

marriage license A document that authorizes a couple to get married, usually available from the county clerk's office in the state where the marriage will take place.

marriage certificate A document that provides proof of a marriage, typically issued to newlyweds a few weeks after they file for the certificate in a county office.

mediation A dispute resolution method designed to help warring parties resolve their dispute without going to court. In mediation, a neutral third party (the mediator) meets with the opposing sides to help them find a mutually satisfactory solution.

Medicare A federal program that provides health insurance to elderly and disabled people.

Medicaid A federal program that provides health insurance program for financially needy people. The program is administered by each state.

meeting of creditors A meeting held with a bankruptcy trustee about a month after a debtor files for bankruptcy.

Miranda warning A warning that the police must give to a suspect before conducting an interrogation; otherwise, the suspect's answers may not be used as evidence in a trial. Also known as "reading a suspect his rights."

misdemeanor A crime, less serious than a felony, punishable by no more than one year in jail.

mortgage A loan in which the borrower puts up the title to real estate as security (collateral) for the loan. If the borrower doesn't pay back the debt on time, the lender can foreclose on the real estate and have it sold to pay off the loan.

N

no-fault divorce Any divorce in which the spouse who wants to split up does not have to accuse the other of wrongdoing, but can simply state that the couple no longer gets along.

no-fault insurance Car insurance laws that require the insurance company of each person involved in an accident to pay for the medical bills and lost wages of its insured, up to a certain amount, regardless of who was at fault.

nolo contendere A plea entered by the defendant in response to being charged with a crime. A defendant who pleads nolo contendere neither admits nor denies that he or she committed the crime, but agrees to a punishment (usually a fine or jail time).

nondischargeable debts Debts that cannot be erased by filing for bankruptcy.

nondisclosure agreement A legally binding contract in which a person or business promises to treat specific information as a trade secret and not disclose it to others without proper authorization.

nonexempt property The property that a debtor risks losing to creditors when he or she files for Chapter 7 bankruptcy or when a creditor sues the debtor and wins a judgment.

nonprofit corporation A business structure that allows people to come together to obtain support for an organization (such as a club) or for some public purpose (such as a hospital or environmental organization). Nonprofits receive benefits—for instance, reduced filing fees and tax exemptions—that are not available to regular corporations.

nonrefundable ticket An airline ticket for which you cannot get your money back if you decide not to travel.

nontransferable ticket An airline ticket that can be used only by the passenger whose name appears on the ticket.

notarize The act of certification by a notary public that establishes the authenticity of a signature on a legal document.

notary public A licensed public officer who administers oaths, certifies documents and performs other specified functions.

nuisance Something that interferes with the use of property by being irritating, offensive, obstructive or dangerous. Nuisances include a wide range of conditions, from a chemical plant's noxious odors to a neighbor's dog barking.

open adoption An adoption in which there is some degree of contact between the birthparents and the adoptive parents and sometimes with the child as well.

order A decision issued by a court. It can be a simple command—for example, ordering a recalcitrant witness to answer a proper question during a trial—or it can be a complicated and reasoned decision made after a hearing, directing that a party either do or refrain from some act.

ordinance A law passed by a county or city government.

own recognizance (OR) A way for a criminal defendant to get out of jail, without paying bail, by promising to appear in court when next required to be there. Only those defendants with strong ties to the community, such as a steady job, local family and no history of failing to appear in court, are good candidates for "OR" release.

parenting agreement A detailed written agreement between a divorcing couple that describes how they will deal with visitation, holiday schedules, vacation, education, religion and other issues related to their child.

partnership When used without a qualifier such as "limited" or "limited liability," this term usually refers to a legal structure called a general partnership: a business that is owned and managed by two or more people who are personally liable for all business debts.

party A person, corporation or other legal entity that files a lawsuit (a plaintiff or petitioner) or defends against one (a defendant or respondent).

patent A legal monopoly, granted by the U.S. Patent and Trademark Office (PTO), for the use, manufacture and sale of an invention.

pay-on-death (POD) designation A way to avoid probate for bank accounts, government bonds, individual retirement accounts and, in many states, securities or a car. A pay-on-death designation is created when the property owner names someone on the ownership document—such as the registration card for a bank account—

to inherit the property at the owner's death.

pension A retirement fund for employees paid for or contributed to by an employer as part of a package of compensation for the employees' work.

personal property All property other than land and buildings attached to land. Cars, bank accounts, wages, securities, a small business, furniture, insurance policies, jewelry, patents, pets and season baseball tickets are all examples of personal property.

petition A formal written request made to a court, asking for an order or ruling on a particular matter.

petitioner A person who initiates a lawsuit. The term is a synonym for plaintiff, and it is used almost universally in some states and in others for certain types of lawsuits, most commonly divorce and other family law cases.

physical custody The right and obligation of a parent to have his child live with him. Compare "legal custody."

plaintiff The person, corporation or other legal entity that initiates a lawsuit. In certain states and for some types of lawsuits, the term "petitioner" is used instead of "plaintiff."

plant patent A patent issued for new strains of asexually reproducing plants.

plea The defendant's formal answer to criminal charges. Typically defendants enter one of the following pleas: guilty, not guilty or nolo contendere.

plea bargain A negotiation between the defense and prosecution (and sometimes the judge) that settles a criminal case. The defendant typically pleads guilty to a lesser crime (or fewer charges) than originally charged, in exchange for a guaranteed sentence that is shorter than what the defendant could face if convicted at trial.

pocket part The paper supplement found in the front or back of a book of laws—such as state statutes—that contains annual changes to the law that are not included in the hardcover version of the book.

pot trust A trust for children—typically established in a will or living trust—in which the trustee decides how to spend money on each child, taking money out of the trust to meet each child's specific needs.

power of attorney A document that gives another person (called the "attorney-in-fact" or "agent") legal authority to act on behalf of the person who makes the document, called the principal.

premarital agreement An agreement made by a couple before marriage that controls certain aspects of their relationship, usually the management and ownership of property, and sometimes whether alimony will be paid if the couple later divorces.

preponderance of the evidence
A legal "standard of proof" in which a jury is instructed to find for the party that, on the whole, has the stronger evidence, however slight that edge may be. This standard is used in most civil cases.

private mortgage insurance (PMI) Insurance that reimburses a mortgage lender if the buyer defaults on the loan and the foreclosure sale price is less than the amount owed the lender (the mortgage plus the costs of the sale).

pro per A term derived from the Latin in propria, meaning "for one's self," used in some states to describe a person who handles her own case without a lawyer. In other states, the term "pro se" is used.

pro se See "pro per."

probable cause The amount and quality of information a judge must have before she will sign a warrant allowing the police to conduct a search or arrest a suspect. If the police have presented reliable information that convinces the judge that it's more likely than not that a crime has occurred and the suspect is involved, the judge will conclude that there is "probable cause" and will issue the warrant.

probate The court process following a person's death that includes: proving the authenticity of the deceased person's will, appointing someone to handle the deceased person's affairs, identifying and inventorying the de-ceased person's property, paying debts and taxes, identifying heirs and distributing the deceased person's property.

property guardian See "guardian."

prosecutor A lawyer who works for the local, state or federal government to bring and litigate criminal cases.

provisional patent application (PPA) An interim patent application that has the legal effect of providing the inventor with an early filing date for her invention. The PPA does not take the place of a regular patent application, but it does confer patent pending status on the underlying invention.

public defender A lawyer appointed by the court and paid by the county, state, or federal government to represent clients who are charged with violations of criminal law and are unable to pay for their own defense.

QTIP trust A marital trust for wealthy couples designed to reduce estate taxes. The surviving spouse receives only a "life estate" in the trust property, which passes to the trust's final beneficiaries after the surviving spouse's death. No estate taxes are assessed on the trust property until surviving spouse dies.

quitclaim deed A deed that transfers whatever ownership interest the transferor has in a particular property. The deed does not guarantee anything about what is being transferred.

R

real estate agent A foot soldier of the real estate business who shows houses and does most of the other nitty-gritty tasks associated with selling real estate in exchange for a commission on the sale.

real estate broker A real estate professional one step up from a real estate agent. A broker has more training and can supervise agents.

real property Another term for real estate. It includes land and things permanently attached to the land, such as trees, buildings, and stationary mobile homes.

recording The process of filing a copy of a deed or other document concerning real estate with the land records office for the county in which the land is located. Recording creates a public record of changes in ownership for all property in the state.

regulation A law issued by a state or federal administrative agency for the purpose of implementing and enforcing a statute.

rent control Laws that limit the amount of rent landlords may charge, and that state when and by how much the rent can be raised. Most rent control laws also require a landlord to provide a good reason, such as repeatedly late rent, for evicting a tenant.

rental agreement A contract, either oral or written, between a landlord and tenant that sets forth the terms of a tenancy.

renter's insurance Insurance that covers those who rent residential property against losses to their belongings that occur as a result of fire or theft.

repossession A creditor's taking of property that has been pledged as collateral for a loan. Lenders most often repossess cars when the buyer has missed loan payments and has not attempted to work with the lender to resolve the problem.

request for admissions A procedure in which one party to a lawsuit asks the opposing party to admit that certain facts are true. This occurs in the pretrial case-investigation phase of a lawsuit, known as "discovery."

request to produce (documents or things) A procedure in which one party to a lawsuit asks an opposing party to turn over certain documents or physical objects. Like a "request for admissions," this procedure is part of the pretrial case-investigation phase of a lawsuit, called "discovery."

respondent A term used instead of "defendant" in some states—especially for divorce and other family law cases—to identify the party who is being sued.

restraining order A court order directing a person not to do something, such as make contact with another specified person, enter the family home or remove a child from the state.

Roth IRA See "individual retirement account."

ruling Any decision a judge makes during the course of a lawsuit.

S

S corporation A term that describes a corporation organized under Subchapter S of the Internal Revenue Code in which shareholders enjoy limited liability status but are taxed on their individual tax returns in the same way as sole proprietors or owners of a partnership.

search warrant An order signed by a judge that directs the owners of private property to allow the police to enter and search for items named in the warrant.

secret warranty program A program under which a car manufacturer will make repairs for free on vehicles with persistent problems, even after the warranty has expired, in order to avoid a recall and the accompanying bad press.

secured debt A debt on which a creditor has a lien. The creditor can initiate a foreclosure or repossession to take the property identified by the lien, called the collateral, to satisfy the debt if the borrower defaults.

security deposit A payment required by a landlord to ensure that a tenant pays rent on time and keeps the rental unit in good condition.

sentence Punishment in a criminal case. A sentence can range from a fine and community service to life imprisonment or death.

separate property In community property states, property owned and controlled entirely by one spouse in a marriage.

service mark A word, phrase, logo, symbol, color, sound or smell used by a business to identify a service and distinguish it from those of its competitors.

service contract Another term for "extended warranty contract."

settlement An agreement resolving a dispute between the parties in a lawsuit without a trial.

severance pay Funds, usually amounting to one or two months' salary, frequently offered by employers to workers who are laid off.

sexual harassment Unwelcome sexual advances or conduct on the job that creates an intimidating, hostile or offensive working environment.

shared custody See "joint custody."

shareholder An owner of a corporation whose ownership interest is represented by shares of stock in the corporation. Also called a "stockholder."

short sale (of a house) The sale of a house in which the proceeds fall short of what the owner still owes on the mortgage. Many lenders will agree to accept the proceeds of a short sale and forgive the rest of what is owed on the mortgage if the owner cannot make the mortgage payments.

sick leave Time off work for illness.

small claims court A state court that resolves disputes involving relatively small amounts of money. Adversaries usually appear without lawyers—in fact, some states forbid lawyers in small claims court.

Social Security The general term that describes a number of related programs administered by the federal government, including retirement, disability, dependents and survivors benefits. These programs operate together to provide workers and their families with some monthly income when their normal flow of income shrinks because of the retirement, disability or death of the person who earned that income.

sole custody An arrangement in which only one parent has physical and legal custody of a child and the other parent has visitation rights.

sole proprietorship A business owned and managed by one person—or, in some circumstances, a husband and wife. Business profits are reported and taxed on the owner's personal tax return and the owner is personally liable for all business debts.

state court A court that decides cases involving state law or the state constitution. State courts have jurisdiction to consider disputes involving individual defendants who reside in that state or have minimum contacts with the state, such as using its highways, owning real property in the state or doing business in the state.

statute A written law passed by Congress or a state legislature and signed into law by the President or a state governor.

statute of limitations The legally prescribed time limit in which a lawsuit must be filed.

subpoena A court order that requires a witness to appear in court. Subpoenas may be issued at the request of a party to a lawsuit. Also spelled "subpena."

subpoena duces tecum A type of subpoena, usually issued at the request of a party to a lawsuit, by which a court orders a witness to produce certain documents at a deposition or trial.

Supreme Court The United States Supreme Court is this country's highest court, which has the final power to decide cases involving the interpretation of the U.S. Constitution, certain legal areas set forth in the Constitution (called federal questions) and federal laws. It can also make final decisions in certain lawsuits between parties from different states. Most states also have a supreme court, which is the final arbiter of the state's constitution and state laws. In several states, this court uses a different name.

surviving spouse A widow or widower.

survivors benefits An amount of money available to the surviving spouse and minor or disabled children of a deceased worker who qualified for Social Security retirement or disability benefits.

T

temporary restraining order (TRO) An order that tells one person to stop harassing or harming another, issued after the aggrieved party appears before a judge.

tenant Anyone, including a corporation, who rents real property, with or without a house or structure, from the owner (called the landlord). A tenant may also be called the "lessee."

timeshare The right to use a given vacation property for a certain amount of time. Usually, a person with a timeshare pays a one-time lump sum and annual maintenance fees.

trade dress The distinctive packaging or design of a product that promotes the product and distinguishes it from other products in the marketplace.

trade name The official name of a business, the one it uses on its letterhead and bank account when not dealing with consumers.

trade secret In most states, a formula, pattern, physical device, idea, process, compilation of information or other information that provides a business with a competitive advantage, and that is treated in a way that can reasonably be expected to prevent the public or competitors from learning about it.

trademark A word, phrase, logo, symbol, color, sound or smell used by a business to identify a product and distinguish it from those of its competitors. Compare "trade dress," "service mark," "certification mark" and "collective mark."

treatise An extensive book or series of books written about a particular legal topic.

trial court The first court to hear the issues of fact and law presented by the parties to a lawsuit.

trust A legal device used to manage property—whether real or personal—established by one person for the benefit of another. A third person, called the trustee, manages the trust.

trust deed The most common method of financing real estate purchases in California (most other states use mortgages). The trust deed transfers title to the property to a trustee—often a title company—who holds it as security for a loan. When the loan is paid off, the title is transferred to the borrower.

trustee The person who manages assets owned by a trust under the terms of the trust document. A trustee's purpose is to safeguard the trust and distribute trust income or principal as directed in the trust document.

U

unemployment insurance (UI) A program run jointly by federal and state governments that provides money benefits for a specified time—usually 26 weeks—after an employee has been laid off or fired from a job for reasons other than serious misconduct. In some instances, an employee who quits a job for a good reason (for example, because she was being sexually harassed at work) can also collect unemployment insurance benefits.

uninsured motorist coverage The portion of car insurance that provides compensation for any injuries resulting from an accident with an uninsured motorist or a hit-and-run driver.

unlawful detainer An eviction lawsuit.

utility patent A patent issued for inventions that perform useful functions. Most patents issued by the U.S. Patent and Trademark Office (PTO) are utility patents.

V

visitation rights The right to see a child regularly, typically awarded by a court to the parent who does not have physical custody of his or her child.

W

warranty A guarantee by a seller to stand by its product or services by making repairs or offering replacements if something goes wrong. See "express warranty" and "implied warranty."

warranty deed A seldom-used type of deed that contains express assurances about the legal validity of the title being transferred.

will A document in which a person specifies what is to be done with his or her property at death, names an executor to oversee the distribution of that property and names a guardian for his or her young children.

witness A person who testifies under oath at a deposition or trial, providing firsthand or expert evidence. In addition, the term also refers to someone who watches another person sign a document and then adds his name to confirm that the signature is genuine; this is called "attesting."

workers' compensation A program that provides replacement income and medical expenses to employees who are injured or become ill due to job duties.

Z

zoning The laws dividing cities into different areas according to use, from single-family residences to industrial plants. Zoning ordinances control the size, location, and use of buildings within these different areas.

Index

A

Abatement of tax penalties, 9/20
AB trust, 12/19-20
Abusive men, programs for, 15/27
Accidents (traffic), 10/23-25
Accommodation and the ADA, 4/26-28
Accommodations while traveling, 11/16-21
ADA (Americans with Disabilities Act), 4/25-26
    employers and, 5/35-36
    illegal drug use and addiction, 5/32
    medical record disclosure, 5/34
Adjustable rate mortgages, 1/4-5
Adopted child's right to birth records, 16/16
Adopting a child, 16/2-17
    home study, 16/10
    legal rights, 16/14-16
    open adoptions, 16/9-10
    stepparent adoptions, 16/12-14
    types of adoptions, 16/5-6
    who can adopt, 16/2
Advance Healthcare Directive. *See* Healthcare
    directives
Advertising for jobs, 5/29-30
Affordable houses, strategies for finding, 1/9
Age and rental cars, 11/12
Age discrimination, 4/17-20
Age Discrimination in Employment Act (ADEA),
    4/17-18
Agency adoptions, 16/5, 16/6-8
Airline tickets, 11/3-6
Airline travel, 11/2-11
Air Transport Association, 11/5
American Association of Retired Persons (AARP),
    4/20
American Intellectual Property Law Association,
    8/19

Americans for Nonsmokers Rights, 4/11
Americans with Disabilities Act. *See* ADA
Amortizing business assets, 5/21-22
Annuities, pension benefits, 14/16
Annulment of marriage, 15/16-17
Anticybersquatting Consumer Protection Act
    (ACPA), 8/16
Antidilution statutes, trademarks and, 8/9
Appraising a house, 1/11
Arbitration
    lemon law arbitration, 10/6-7
    mediation compared to, 17/22
ARMs, 1/4-5
Arraignment, criminal cases, 18/21
Arrests and interrogations by police, 18/14-17
Asbestos exposure, landlord liability, 3/15-16
"As is" product, 9/3
Assignment of copyright, 7/6
ATM cards, 9/10-11
Attorney-in-fact, duties of, 13/9-10
Attorneys
    and adoptions, 16/11-12
    billing by, 17/29-30
    changing attorneys, 17/27, 18/23
    as coaches, 17/5
    contingency fee representation, 17/3
    criminal cases, 18/20-25
    dealing with, 17/27-30
    DUI charges, 10/22
    executors and, 12/10-11
    family law mediators, 16/24
    finding, 18/22
    house sale and, 1/14
    malpractice by, 17/27-29
    premarital agreements, 15/8
    social justice issues and pro bono representa-
        tion, 17/3-4

wills and, 12/2-3
workers' compensation claims, 4/15-16
Auto insurance, 10/13-16
Autos. *See* Cars and driving
Avoiding probate, 12/13-15

B

Bail, 18/17-19
Bankruptcy, 9/25-28
airline tickets and, 11/10-11
Battered women's shelters, finding, 15/26-27
Berne Convention, copyright protection, 7/7
BFOQ (bona fide occupational qualification), 4/18
Bill collection agencies, 9/22-24
Birthparents and adoption rights, 16/15, 16/16
Blood-alcohol levels, 10/21-22
Blood tests for marriage license, 15/10-12
Body and organ donations, 12/25
Bona fide occupational qualification (BFOQ), 4/18
Books. *See* Reference books
Bouncing checks, 9/17
Boundaries, 2/2-3
fences on, 2/4
Breaking a lease, 3/3-4
Bumping from flights, compensation for, 11/6-7, 11/8
Businesses. *See* Small businesses
Business expenses, and tax deductions, 5/19-24
Business methods, patents for, 6/4
Business names
choosing, 5/3-5
See also Trade names
Business plan development, 5/6
Buyers Guide, required for used car sales, 10/11
Buying a house, 1/2-9
Buying a new car, 10/2-7
Buying a used car, 10/10-12
Buying goods and services, 9/2-7

C

California
domestic partnership law, 15/16, 16/4
no "cooling off" period for vehicle sales, 10/4
real estate disclosures, 1/12
refund policy laws, 9/6
See also State laws

Canceled flights, compensation for, 11/7
Cancelling contracts for goods or services, 9/5-6
Capital equipment and taxes, 5/21-22
Carry-on baggage, forbidden items, 11/2-3
Cars and driving, 10/2-26
buying a new car, 10/2-7
buying a used car, 10/10-12
driver's license, 10/16-19
drunk driving, 10/21-22
expenses for business use, 5/20
financing a purchase, 10/12-13
insurance, 10/13-16
leasing, 10/7-10
payment problems, 9/12-13
police traffic stops, 10/19-20
rental cars, 11/11-16
repossession of car, 9/12-13
traffic accidents, 10/23-25
Case law research, A/6-8
Cash advance fees, 9/9-10
CC&Rs, 1/7
home-based business and, 5/26
view disputes, 2/7
Center for Auto Safety, 10/6-7
Challenges to wills, 12/7
Changing your name, 15/29-34
Chapter 7 and 11. *See* Bankruptcy
Charge and credit cards, 9/7-10
Charter airlines, discount airfares and, 11/29
Cheating on taxes, 9/19
Check bouncing, 9/17
Child custody and visitation, 16/18-25
Children. *See* Parents and children
Child support, 16/25-31
calculating, 16/27-28
enforcement, 16/28-29
pendente lite action, 15/25
Child Support Enforcement Act, 16/28-29
Child Support Recovery Act, 16/29
Civil Rights Act, sexual harassment and, 4/21
Civil Union Law, 15/15
Closing, sale of house, 1/13-14
COBRA and health insurance benefits, 4/31-32, 5/40
Collecting court judgments, 17/6, 17/18
Collection agencies, 9/22-24

Collective marks, 8/3
   See also Trademarks
Collective works and copyright, 7/5
Collision coverage, auto insurance, 10/14
Collision damage waiver (CDW), 11/15-16
Common law marriage, 15/4, 15/6, 15/13
Community property, divorce and, 15/22, 15/24-25
Competency to stand trial, 18/8
Comprehensive coverage, auto insurance, 10/14
"Comps" and pricing your house, 1/11
Comp time, 4/4
Computer software, patents for, 6/4
Conditions of Carriage, airline tickets, 11/5
Conditions of Contract, airline tickets, 11/4-5
Confirmed hotel reservations, 11/17-18
Consent searches, 18/13
Conservatorships, 13/11-14
Consignment sales, 5/6-7
Consumer protection laws, small business and, 5/6
Consumer Reports, 10/3, 10/10
Contingency fee representation, 17/3, 17/27
"Cooling Off Rule," 9/5
   not available for cars in California, 10/4
Copyright Clearinghouse, 7/9
Copyright Office
   registration information, 7/10
   renewal searches, 7/8
Copyrights, 7/1-12
   duration of, 7/3-4
   enforcement of, 7/10-11
   notice for, 7/6-7
   ownership of, 7/4-6
   patents compared to, 6/14
   permissions, obtaining, 7/9
   protections, 7/6-9
   registration of, 7/10
   trademarks compared to, 8/18
   transfer of rights, 7/6
   works protected by, 7/2-3
Corporations
   advantages and drawbacks, 5/11
   forming and running, 5/12-14
   naming of, 5/4-5
   taxes and, 5/22

Council on Standards for International Education Travel, 11/26
Counteroffer of seller, 1/12
Court system
   depositions, 17/8-11
   discovery process, 17/7-11
   free sources for legal help, 17/2-4
   information online, 17/4
   judgment collections, 17/6
   self-representation, 17/2-13
   small claims court, 17/13-20
   trial process, 17/11-13
   websites for, A/6
Covenants, conditions and restrictions. *See* CC&Rs
Credit and charge cards, 9/7-10
   guaranteed hotel reservation, 11/17
   rental car insurance, 11/15
   and rental cars, 11/12
Credit history
   landlords and, 3/8
   loan approval and, 1/3
   mistakes in credit report, 9/30-31
   obtaining your credit report, 9/29-30
   rebuilding your credit, 9/28-32
Credit insurance for vehicle purchase, 10/13
Creditors
   retirement plans and, 14/21
   and trust property, 12/17
Credit reports. *See* Credit history
Criminal acts and activities, landlord liability, 3/12-14
Criminal law and procedure, 18/1-25
   arrests and interrogations, 18/14-17
   attorneys and representation, 18/20-25
   bail, 18/17-19
   competency to stand trial, 18/8
   felony, 18/4
   insanity defense, 18/7
   jury trial, right to, 18/5
   misdemeanor, 18/4
   police questioning, 18/8-10
   presumption of innocence, 18/4
   public defenders, 17/3, 18/21-22
   searches and seizures, 18/10-14
   self-defense, 18/6-7
   self-representation, 18/24, 18/25

sentencing, 18/24-25
Custodial interference, 16/23
Custody and visitation, 16/18-25
Cybersquatting, 8/16

D

Damaged baggage, compensation for, 11/9
Dangerous trees, 2/5-6
Death
    airline tickets and, 11/5-6
    dying without a will, 12/2
    funerals and other final arrangements,
      12/22-24
Debit cards, 9/10-11
Debt collections, 9/22-24
Debt counseling organizations, 9/12
Debtor's prisons, 9/17
Debt repayment strategies, 9/11-18
Deeds, 1/15-16
    deed in lieu of foreclosure, 9/13
    property boundaries and, 2/2
Defaulting on student loan, 9/15
"Defense of Marriage Act" (DOMA), 15/14, 15/15
Defined benefit/defined contribution plans, 14/13
Delayed or diverted flights, compensation for,
    11/7
Delphion, 6/6
Dependents benefits, 14/3
Depositions, 17/8-11
Dept. of Education, student loan status
    information, 9/16
Design patents, 6/2, 6/3
Dialog, 8/12
Dilution of trademark, domain name and, 8/17
Direct Marketing Association, 9/7
Disability benefits, 4/14, 14/3
Disability discrimination, 4/25-28
Disciplinary notice to employee, 4/30-31
Disclosure, and selling a home, 1/12-13
Discount airfares, 11/31
Discovery process, 17/7-11
Discrimination
    advertising for jobs, 5/30
    age discrimination, 4/17-20
    complaint filing with HUD, 3/5-6
    disability discrimination, 4/25-28

housing discrimination, 3/4-6
    job interviews and, 5/31
    religious discrimination claims, 5/38
Disinheriting relatives, 12/6-7
Dispute resolution, landlords and tenants, 3/17-18
Disputing credit card bills, 9/9
Divorce, 15/16-26
    changing your name and, 15/30-31
    custody and visitation, 16/18-25
    grounds for, 15/20-21
    parenting agreements, 16/21
    pension benefits and, 14/15, 14/17
    property division, 15/22, 15/24-25
    Social Security spousal benefits, 14/5
    state residency requirements, 15/22, 15/23-24
DNA sequences, patents for, 6/4
Doctors and workers' compensation claims,
    4/14-15
Dogs, barking and noise disputes, 2/10-11
Domain names
    choosing, 5/3
    cybersquatting, 8/16
    registrars for, 8/13
    trademark conflicts, 8/16-17
    trademark protection for, 8/7-8
Domestic partnership law, 15/16, 16/4
Domestic violence, 15/26-29
Down payment for home, 1/6-7
Driver's license, 10/16-19
Driver's License Compact states, 10/17
Driving. *See* Cars and driving
Driving record, screening by rental car
    company, 11/12-13
Drug dealing, landlord's liability, 3/13-14
Drug tests for job applicants, 5/32
Drunk driving, 10/21-22
DUI driving, 10/21-22
Durable powers of attorney
    for finances, 13/7-11
    for healthcare, 13/2-3
Duration
    conservatorship, 13/14
    copyright, 7/3-4
    durable power of attorney for finances,
      13/10-11
    guardianship of child, 16/33

patent protection, 6/10-11

trademark protection, 8/16

warranties for products, 9/3

E

Early retirement. *See* Retirement

Earnings and benefit statement, Social Security, 14/4

Educational travel, 11/26

EEOC offices, 4/19, 4/21, 4/28

Elderly people. *See* Older Americans

Emergency protective orders, 15/27-28

"Employed to invent" doctrine, 6/13-14

Employee evaluations, 5/32-33

Employee Retirement Income Security Act (ERIS), 14/17-18

Employers' rights & responsibilities, 5/29-42

ADA and, 5/35-36

employee evaluations, 5/32-33

hiring issues, 5/29-32

independent contractors and, 5/41-42

inventions of employees and, 6/13-14

laying off workers, 5/39

medical records, 5/34

personnel files, 5/33-34

references for fired worker, 5/40-41

religious discrimination claims, 5/38

sexual harassment complaint handling, 5/36-38

smoking issues, 5/38-39

time off for employees, 5/34-35

trade secret protection, 5/39-40

See also Workplace rights

Encroachment, 2/2

Entertainment, as business expense, 5/20

EPA pamphlet about lead, 1/13, 3/14, 3/15

Equal Employment Opportunity Commission (EEOC), 4/19, 4/21, 4/28

Equifax, 9/29, 9/30

ERISA and pension plans, 14/17-18

Error on credit card bills, 9/9

Estate and gift taxes, 12/18-21

Estate planning. *See* Wills and estate planning

E-tickets (airline), 11/4

Exchange programs, 11/26

Exclusion for house sales, 1/14

Executors, 12/9-13

Experian, 9/29, 9/30

Extended warranty contracts, 9/4

F

Fair Credit Reporting Act (FCRA), 9/29, 9/31

Fair Debt Collection Practices Act (FDCPA), 9/22-23, 9/24

Fair Housing Acts, discrimination and, 3/4-5

Fair Housing Information Clearinghouse, 3/5

Fair Labor Standards Act (FLSA), 4/2-3

comp time and, 4/4

independent contractor exemption from, 4/6-7

overtime requirements, 4/3-4

Fair pay and time off, 4/2-9

Fair use and copyright, 7/8-9

Family and Medical Leave Act (FMLA), 4/7-8, 5/35

Family law mediators, 16/24

Fare calculations for air travel, 11/3

Fault divorce, 15/18-19

FDCPA, 9/22-23, 9/24

Federal Deposit Insurance Corp. (FDIC), 9/11, 9/32

Federal Direct Consolidation Loan Center, 9/15

Federal Student Aid Information Center, 9/18

Federal Trade Commission, 5/6

bill collector complaint filing, 9/24

credit and ATM card information, 9/11

debt and credit information, 9/18

rebuilding credit, 9/32

Felony, 18/4

Fences, 2/3-4

FHA loans, 1/4

Fictitious business name registration, 5/5

FIDM program, 16/29

Filing procedures

accident report to DMV, 10/23

ADA complaints, 4/28

age discrimination complaints, 4/19-20

copyright registration, 7/10

fictitious business name registration, 5/5

FMLA claims, 4/8

fraud complaints, 9/4-5

housing discrimination complaints, 3/5-6

marriage certificate, 15/10
patent applications, 6/8
sexual harassment complaints, 4/24-25
Social Security benefit claims, 14/6, 14/7
trademark registration, 8/17-18
workers' compensation claims, 4/13
Final arrangements, 12/22-24
Final paycheck, time for receiving, 4/7
Financial Institution Data Match program, 16/29
Financial issues, 9/2-33
    ATM or debit cards, 9/10-11
    bankruptcy, 9/25-28
    car financing, 10/12-13
    credit and charge cards, 9/7-10
    debt collections, 9/22-24
    debt repayment strategies, 9/11-18
    the IRS and, 9/18-22
    purchasing goods and services, 9/2-7
    rebuilding credit, 9/28-32
    See also Wills and estate planning
Firing of employee, 4/29-30
Fixed rate mortgages, 1/4-5
FLSA. *See* Fair Labor Standards Act
FMLA (Family and Medical Leave Act), 4/7-8,
    5/35
Foreclosure, 9/13
Foreign countries
    international adoptions, 16/5-6, 16/10-11
    international copyright protection, 7/7
    rental cars and, 11/16
    U.S. driver's license and, 10/17-18
For Sale By Owner (FSBO), 1/6, 1/10
401(k) plans, 14/19-20
Fraud complaints, 9/4-5
    See also Scams
Free sources for legal help, 17/2-4
Frequent flyer programs, 11/10
FSBO (For Sale By Owner), 1/6, 1/10
FTC. *See* Federal Trade Commission
Funeral Consumers Alliance, 12/24
Funerals and other final arrangements, 12/22-24
Funeral societies, 12/23-24

G

Garnishment of wages, 9/16-17
GATT, copyright protection, 7/7

Gay Men's Domestic Violence Project, 15/28
Gays and lesbians
    adopting a child, 16/3-4
    California's domestic partnership law, 15/16
    child custody and visitation, 16/20, 16/25
    domestic violence and, 15/28
    Hawaii's Reciprocal Beneficiaries Law, 15/14
    living together, 15/2-6
    same-sex marriage, 15/13-14
    sexual harassment of, 4/22
    Vermont's Civil Union Law, 15/15
General partnerships, 5/9, 5/11, 5/22
Gift and estate taxes, 12/18-21
Gifts and probate avoidance, 12/14
Government-guaranteed loans, 1/4
Grandparents and adoption rights, 16/15-16
Grant deeds, 1/15
Guaranteed hotel reservation, 11/17
Guardianships
    of children, 16/31-35
    for children in will, 12/4, 12/5
    guardianship of the estate, 16/34
    See also Conservatorships

H

Handwritten wills, 12/3
Hawaii
    Reciprocal Beneficiaries Law, 15/14
    See also State laws
Health and safety in the workplace, 4/9-11
Healthcare directives, 13/2-7
Health insurance and leaving a job, 4/31-32
Health Insurance Portability and Accountability
    Act, 4/32
Hedges as fences, 2/3, 2/7
Height restrictions on fences, 2/3, 2/7
Hiring issues for employers, 5/29-32
Holographic wills, 12/3
Home-based businesses, 5/24-29
    tax advantages, 5/27
    tax deduction for office, 5/23, 5/28-29
Homeowners' associations, 1/7
    See also CC&Rs
Homestead exemption, in bankruptcy, 9/27
Home study inquiry for adoption, 16/10
Hotels and other accommodations, 11/16-21

Houses
    agreements for unmarried couples, 15/3
    buying, 1/2-9
    deeds for, 1/15-16
    payment problems, 9/13
    seizure by IRS, 9/20-21
    selling, 1/9-14
Housing discrimination, 3/4-6

I

ICANN, 8/13
    cybersquatting and arbitration, 8/16
icopyright, 7/9
Identified adoptions, 16/5
Illness
    airline tickets and, 11/5-6
    lacking a healthcare directive and, 13/3
Immigration and Naturalization Service
    I-9 forms and recordkeeping for employers, 5/33-34
    international adoptions and, 16/10-11
Incapacity
    healthcare directives and, 13/3-4
    power of attorney for finance and, 13/7-8
    unmarried couples and, 15/4
Independent adoptions, 16/5, 16/9
Independent contractors
    employee rules that do not apply, 5/41-42
    exempt from FLSA, 4/6-7
    home office and status as, 5/27
    IRS classification of, 5/23
    retirement plans for, 14/21
    works made for hire, 7/4-5
Indoor air quality guidelines, 3/16
Information resources. *See* Resources and websites
Infringement
    domain name and trademark infringement, 8/16-17
    patent infringement, 6/9-10
    trademark infringement, 8/9-10
Inherently distinctive marks, 8/5-6
Inheritance taxes, 12/19
    See also Estate and gift taxes
Injury prevention in the workplace, 4/10

INS. *See* Immigration and Naturalization Service
Insanity defense, 18/7
Inspection of house, 1/8
Insurance
    car insurance, 10/13-16
    consignment goods, 5/7
    credit insurance for vehicle purchase, 10/13
    health insurance and leaving a job, 4/31-32
    home-based business, 5/27
    and probate avoidance, 12/14
    rental cars and, 11/15-16
    for rental property, 3/16-17
    renter's insurance, 3/17
    unemployment insurance, 4/32
    workers' compensation insurance, 4/12
"Intent-to-use" trademark registration application, 8/8-9
Interest
    collection agencies adding to debt, 9/23
    rates on car leases, 10/8
    rates on credit cards, 9/7-8
Internal Revenue Service. *See* IRS
International Driver's Permit, 11/16
International legal issues. *See* Foreign countries
International Trademark Association, 8/19
Internet resources. *See* Resources and websites
InterNIC, 8/13
Interrogations and arrests by police, 18/14-17
Intestate succession, 12/2
Inventions. *See* Patents
IRAs, 14/20-21
IRS
    audits by, 9/21-22
    debt write off issues, 9/14
    failure to file, 9/18
    home-based business information, 5/28
    house sale information, 1/14
    inability to pay taxes, 9/19-20
    nonprofits and 501(c)(3) exemption, 5/17-18
    penalties, abatement of, 9/20
    privacy of tax files, 9/19
    record retention period, 9/18
    seizure of house by, 9/20-21
    See also Taxes
ITU trademark registration application, 8/8-9

J

Job Accommodation Network, 4/27
Job interview procedures, 5/30-31
Joint copyright ownership, 7/5
Joint tenancy, as probate avoidance, 12/14
Judgment collection, 17/6, 17/18
Jury trial, right to, 18/5

K

Kelley Blue Book, 10/3, 10/10
Keogh plans, 14/21
Kidnapping and custodial interference, 16/23
Killing a tree, 2/5

L

Lambda Anti-Violence Project, 15/28
Lambda Legal Defense and Education Fund, 4/22
Landlord liability
    asbestos exposure, 3/15-16
    criminal acts and activities, 3/12-14
    lead poisoning, 3/14-15
    mold exposure, 3/15-16
    personal injuries, 3/10-11
Landlord-tenant laws, 3/2-22
Law libraries, A/2
Lawyers. *See* Attorneys
Laying off workers, 5/39
Lead-based paint hazard
    disclosure about, 1/13, 3/14-15
    landlord liability for, 3/14-15
Leases and rental agreements, 3/2-4
Leasing a car, 10/7-10
Legal forms, locating, A/10-11
Legal research, A/1-12
    background resources, A/2-4
    case law research, A/6-8
    forms, locating, A/10-11
    law libraries, A/2
    specific questions, finding answers to, A/8-10
    statute and regulation research, A/4-6
Lemon cars, 10/5-7
    used cars, 10/12
Lesbians. *See* Gays and lesbians
Lexis, A/8
LEXIS/NEXIS, 8/12
LEXPAT, 6/7

Liability for debts, unmarried couples, 15/4
Liability of hotel, personal injuries, 11/20
Liability of landlord. *See* Landlord liability
Liability policy, auto insurance, 10/13-14
License agreements
    copyright transfers and, 7/6
    for patents, 6/13
Life forms, patents for, 6/4
Life-prolonging treatments, healthcare
    directives and, 13/5-6
Limited liability company, 5/9-10
    advantages and drawbacks, 5/12, 5/14-15
    naming of, 5/4-5
Limited liability partnership, 5/12
Limited partnerships, 5/11
Liquidation bankruptcy, 9/25
Living together, 15/2-6
Living trusts, 12/15-18
    durable power of attorney for finances and,
        13/10
    as probate avoidance, 12/14
Living wage ordinances, 4/3
"Living will". *See* Healthcare directives
LLC. *See* Limited liability company
Loan consolidators for student loans, 9/15
Loans and mortgages, 1/2-9
Location for your business, 5/5-6
Loss damage waiver (LDW), 11/15-16
Lost items
    airline tickets, 11/6
    ATM/debit cards, 9/11
    baggage, 11/9
    credit/charge cards, 9/8
    See also Stolen items
Lump-sum payments, pension benefits, 14/16

M

Maintenance of rental property, 3/9-11
Malpractice by attorney, 17/27-29
Marks on Line, 8/12
Marriage, 15/8-16
    changing your name and, 15/30
    legal requirements for, 15/9
    legal rights conferred by, 15/8-9
    premarital agreements, 15/6-8
    See also Divorce; Parents and children

Marriage certificate, 15/10

Marriage license, 15/10-12

Martindale-Hubbell directories, 18/22

Mediation, 17/21-26

    arbitration compared to, 17/22

    child custody and visitation disputes, 16/24-25

    cost of, 17/24-25

    divorce mediator, 15/25

    landlord-tenant disputes, 3/18

    stages of, 17/22-23

Medicaid, 14/8

Medical Directive. *See* Healthcare directives

Medical procedures, healthcare directives and, 13/5

Medical record disclosure, 5/34

Medicare, 14/8-12

Memorial or funeral societies, 12/23-24

Men

    programs for abusive men, 15/27

    sexual harassment of, 4/22

Mental disabilities, employers and, 5/36

MicroPatent, 6/6, 8/12

Minimum wage, 4/3

    tips credited against, 4/5

Miranda warning, 18/15-16

Misdemeanor, 18/4

Mold exposure, landlord liability, 3/15-16

Money issues. *See* Financial issues

Mortgages and loans, 1/2-5

Mortuary services, 12/23

Myvesta/org, 9/12, 9/17

N

Names. *See* Business names; Changing your name; Surnames

National Anatomical Service, 12/25

National Center for Lesbian Rights, 16/25

National Congress for Fathers and Children, 16/25

National Domestic Violence Hotline, 15/27, 15/28

National Foundation for Consumer Credit, 9/12, 9/18

National Fraud Information Center, 9/4-5

National Lead Information Center, 1/13, 3/15

National Student Loan Data System, 9/16

Natural Hazard Disclosure Statement, 1/12

NDAs, 5/40

Neighbor law, 2/1-11

    boundaries, 2/2-3

    fences, 2/3-4

    noise, 2/8-11

    trees, 2/4-6

    views, 2/6-8

New homes, buying, 1/7

Newspaper Association of America, 1/6

New York City Gay & Lesbian Anti-Violence Project, 15/28

New York City indoor air quality guidelines, 3/16

9to5, National Association of Working Women, 4/25

No-fault auto insurance, 10/15, 10/24

No-fault divorce, 15/18

Noise disputes, 2/8-11

Nondischargeable debts in bankruptcy, 9/26

Nondisclosure agreements, 5/40

"Nonobvious" requirement and patents, 6/5-6

Nonprofit corporations, 5/11, 5/15-18

Notarization

    deeds, 1/16

    healthcare directives, 13/7

    wills, 12/4

Notice

    copyright, 7/6-7

    trademark, 8/10

Notice requirements

    of entry by landlord, 3/8

    in leases and rental agreements, 3/2-3

"Novel" requirement and patents, 6/5

Nuisance

    mold as, 3/16

    tree as, 2/6

O

Occupational Safety and Health Act (OSHA), 4/9-10

Occupational Safety and Health Administration

    asbestos regulations, 3/15-16

    tobacco smoke, 4/11

Offers for home

    contingencies and, 1/8

    counteroffer of seller, 1/12

Office of the Americans with Disabilities Act, 4/28

Office supplies, deducting on taxes, 5/21

Official Gazette, 8/15

Older Americans, 14/1-22
  driver's licenses and, 10/18
  Medicare, 14/8-12
  pensions, 14/12-18
  prescription drugs and, 14/11
  retirement plans, 14/19-22
  Social Security benefits, 14/2-7

Older Women's League, 4/20

Older Workers Benefit Protection Act, 4/19, 4/20

On-call time, 4/6

Open adoptions, 16/9-10

Organ donations, 12/25

O.R. release of defendant, 18/19

OSHA. *See* Occupational Safety and Health Act (OSHA)

Overbooked flights, compensation for, 11/6-7, 11/8

Overtime pay
  exempt executives, 4/3-4
  forcing to work, 4/4-5

P

Pain medication, healthcare directives and, 13/5-6

Palimony, 15/2-3

Parenting agreements, 16/21

Parents and children, 16/1-35
  adopting a child, 16/2-17
  child custody and visitation, 16/18-25
  child support, 16/25-31
  guardianship of children, 16/31-35
  unmarried couples, 15/5
  wills and, 12/4-5

Partnerships, 5/9, 5/11, 5/22

Partners living together, 15/2-6

Patent and Trademark Depository Libraries, 6/7, 8/13-14

Patent and Trademark Office (PTO)
  electronic registration for trademarks, 8/17-18
  Official Gazette, 8/15
  patent applications, 6/7-9
  patents and, 6/2-3

trademark databases, 8/12
  trademark registration, 8/14-18

Patents, 6/1-16
  commercial opportunities, 6/12-15
  copyrights compared to, 6/14
  enforcement, 6/9-12
  obtaining, 6/7-9
  Provisional Patent Application, 6/8
  qualifying for, 6/2-7
  trademarks compared to, 6/15, 8/18-19

Pay-on-death designations, 12/14

Pendente lite action, 15/25

Pension Benefit Guaranty Corp., 14/17

Pension plans, 14/12-18

Pension Rights Center, 14/18

Personal injuries
  hotel's liability and, 11/20
  landlord's liability and, 3/10-11

Personal Injury Protection, 10/15

Personnel files, 5/33-34

Plant patents, 6/2, 6/3

PMI (private mortgage insurance), 1/6-7

"Point" system and driver's licenses, 10/18

Police actions
  arrests and interrogations, 18/14-17
  emergency protective orders issued by, 15/27-28
  frisks by, 18/9
  questioning by, 18/8-10
  searches and seizures, 18/10-14
  searches of cars, 10/20
  traffic stops, 10/19-20

Police reports, traffic accidents and, 10/25

Posting bail, 18/17-18

Pot trust, for children, 12/5

Powers of attorney. *See* Durable powers of attorney

PPA (Provisional Patent Application), 6/8

Premarital agreements, 15/6-8

Prepayment plans for final arrangements, 12/24

Prescription drugs and older Americans, 14/11

Prices for cars, 10/2-3

Principal Register for trademarks, 8/15

Privacy rights
  hotel rooms and, 11/18
  IRS tax files, 9/19

police searches and, 18/10-11
prospective employees, 5/31-32
of tenants, 3/8
Private mortgage insurance (PMI), 1/6-7
Probate, 12/8-9
avoidance techniques, 12/13-15
Pro bono representation, 17/3-4
Professional corporation, 5/11
Professional limited liability company, 5/12
Property boundaries. *See* Boundaries
Property managers, landlord liability for, 3/14
Protect Your Family from Lead in Your Home, 1/13,
3/14, 3/15
Provisional Patent Application, 6/8
Proxy for healthcare, 13/4-5
PTO. *See* Patent and Trademark Office (PTO)
Public defenders, 17/3, 18/21-22
Public domain material, 7/7-8
Purchasing a house, 1/2-9
Purchasing cars, 10/2-7, 10/10-12
Purchasing goods and services, 9/2-7

Q

QPAT, 6/7
QTIP trust, 12/20
Qualified privilege doctrine, 5/41
Questel/Orbit, 6/7
"Quiet Enjoyment," noise and rentals, 2/9
"Quiet hours," 2/9
Quitclaim deed, 1/15

R

Real estate agents and brokers, 1/5
negotiating for reduced commission, 1/10-11
Rear-ended accidents and fault, 10/24-25
Reasonable accommodation, 4/27
Rebuilding credit, 9/28-32
Reciprocal Beneficiaries Law, 15/14
Recording, deeds, 1/16
Recordkeeping, for small businesses, 5/18-19
References for fired worker, 5/40-41
Refunds for purchases, 9/6
Relatives, disinheriting, 12/6-7
Religious discrimination claims, 5/38
Remedies, patent infringement, 6/10
Renewal records, copyright, 7/8

Rental agreements and leases, 3/2-4
Rental cars, 11/11-16
Rent and security deposits, 3/6-7
Rent control, 3/7
Renter's insurance, 3/17
Reorganization bankruptcy, 9/25
Repair and maintenance of rental property, 3/9-11
Repossession of car, 9/12-13
Reservations at hotels, 11/17-18
travel agents and, 11/22
Residency requirements, for divorce, 15/22,
15/23-24
Retirement
early retirement and pensions, 14/14
forcing early retirement, 4/19
Retirement benefits, 14/3
See also Social Security benefits
Retirement plans, 14/19-22
Revised Uniform Reciprocal Enforcement of
Support Act, 16/29
Revoked licenses, 10/18, 10/19
Roth IRAs, 14/20-21

S

Saegis, 8/12
Safe houses, finding, 15/26-27
Safety in the workplace, 4/9-11
Sallie Mae, 9/15
Same-sex marriage, 15/13-14
See also Gays and lesbians
San Francisco Community United Against
Violence, 15/28
Scams
goods and services, 9/4-5
travel, 11/25-31
S corporation, 5/11
Screening drivers by rental car company, 11/12-13
Searches
for birthparents, 16/16
copyright renewal records, 7/8
patent databases, 6/6-7
trademark databases, 8/11-12
trademark search firms, 8/13-14
Searches and seizures, 18/10-14
Search warrants, 18/11-12
Secondhand smoke, 4/11

Secret warranty adjustments for car repairs, 10/6-7

Section 179 deduction, 5/21-22

Security deposits, for rental property, 3/7

Seizure of house by IRS, 9/20-21

Self-defense, 18/6-7

Self-employment. *See* Small businesses; Sole proprietorships

Self-representation in court, 17/2-13
    criminal cases, 18/24, 18/25

Selling goods and services
    on consignment, 5/6-7
    consumer protection laws and, 5/6

"Separated" married persons, 15/17-18

SEPs, 14/21

Servicemarks, 8/2-3
    See also Trademarks

Severance pay, 4/31

Sexual harassment, 4/21-25
    complaint handling by employer, 5/36-38

Shipping delays and cancelling orders, 9/6

Sick leave, 4/7-8

Signature requirements
    healthcare directives, 13/7
    wills, 12/4

SIMPLE IRAs, 14/21

Single people and adopting a child, 16/3

Small businesses, 5/1-43
    employers' rights & responsibilities, 5/29-42
    home-based businesses, 5/24-29
    legal structures for, 5/8-15
    nonprofit corporations, 5/15-18
    startup issues, 5/2-8
    taxes, 5/18-24

Small claims court, 17/13-20
    avoiding court, 17/17-18
    judgment collection, 17/18
    limits on claims by state, 17/15-16
    reference book, 3/21, 17/20
    time limits on filing, 17/14, 17/17

Smoke (tobacco) in the workplace, 4/11, 5/38-39

Social justice issues and pro bono representation, 17/3-4

Social Security Administration, 14/7

Social Security benefits, 14/2-7
    claiming, 14/6, 14/7

disability benefits, 4/14, 4/32

earnings and benefit statement, 14/4

eligibility for, 14/2

error correction, 14/4-5

types of, 14/3

Sole proprietorships, 5/8-9, 5/11

Spending plan, 9/28-29

Spite fence, 2/4

Spouses. *See* Marriage

Springing power of attorney, 13/8

State laws
    age discrimination, 4/18-19
    antidilution statutes, trademarks and, 8/9
    blood tests for marriage license, 15/11-12
    child custody and sexual orientation, 16/20
    child custody decree handling, 16/21-22
    common law marriage states, 15/6
    community property states, 15/22
    credit card transaction and personal
        information, 9/9
    divorce, grounds for, 15/20-21
    divorce residency requirements, 15/23-24
    inheritance taxes, 12/19
    landlord-tenant codes, 3/19-20
    lemon laws, 10/5, 10/12
    Medicare billing limits, 14/12
    premarital agreements, 15/7
    refund policies, 9/6
    researching, A/4-6
    small claim court limits, 17/15-16
    vehicle codes, 10/24
    See also California; Hawaii; Vermont

Statute of limitations, small claims court, 17/14,
    17/17

Statutory codes. *See* State laws

Statutory subject matter and inventions, 6/2

Stepparents
    adoptions by, 16/12-14
    child support, 16/26

Stolen items
    ATM/debit cards, 9/11
    credit/charge cards, 9/8
    hotel's limited liability for, 11/20-21
    See also Lost items

Student loans, 9/14-16

Student travel, 11/26

Sunnyvale Center on Innovation, Invention and Ideas, 8/13-14
Supplemental Register for trademarks, 8/15-16
Surnames, as trademarks, 8/10
Surveyors and property boundaries, 2/2
Survivors benefits, 14/3
Suspended licenses, 10/18, 10/19

T

Taxes
   avoidance schemes, 9/20
   cheating on, 9/19
   corporations and, 5/13-14
   estate and gift taxes, 12/18-21
   exemption table for estate taxes, 12/18
   federal estate taxes, 12/19
   gift tax exemption, 12/20-21
   house sale and, 1/14
   nonprofits and 501(c)(3) exemption, 5/17-18
   retention time for records, 9/18
   small businesses and, 5/18-24
   See also IRS
Temporary restraining order (TRO), domestic violence and, 15/27-29
Tenants
   discrimination issues, 3/4-6
   drug dealing and, 3/13-14
   landlord's failure to maintain property and, 3/9-10
   noise problems, 2/9
   privacy rights, 3/8
   renter's insurance, 3/17
   selecting, 3/4
Termination notice, leases and, 3/3-4
Thomson & Thomson, 8/14
Three-day right to cancel, 9/5-6
Tickets received in other states, 10/17
Time off
   employers and, 5/34-35
   and fair pay, 4/2-9
Timeshares, 11/26-28
Tips and minimum wages, 4/5
Title X
   exempt rental properties, 3/15
   lead-based paint hazard, 1/13, 3/14
Tobacco smoke in the workplace, 4/11, 5/38-39

Trade dress, 8/3
Trade-in car prices, 10/3
Trademark/com, 8/12
Trademark Express, 8/14
Trademark Register, 8/12
Trademarks, 8/1-20
   copyright compared to, 8/18
   exceptions to protection, 8/6-7, 8/15
   patents compared to, 6/15, 8/18-19
   protections for, 8/5-8
   registering, 8/14-18
   searches, 8/11-14
   types of, 8/2-4
   using and enforcing, 8/8-10
Trade names, 8/4
Trade secret protection, 5/39-40
Traffic accidents, 10/23-25
Transfer of copyright, 7/6
Trans Union, 9/29, 9/30
Travel, 11/1-32
   airlines, 11/2-11
   hotels and other accommodations, 11/16-21
   rental cars, 11/11-16
   scams, 11/25-31
   travel agents, 11/21-24
Trees
   and neighbors, 2/4-6
   and views, 2/7
TROs and domestic violence, 15/27-29
Trust deed, 1/16
Trusts
   for children, 12/5
   living trusts, 12/15-18
Truth in Lending Act, cancelling loans, 9/5

U

Unemployment insurance, 4/32
Uniform Child Custody Jurisdiction Act (UCCJA), 16/21-22
Uniform Premarital Agreement Act, 15/7
Uniform Transfers to Minors Act (UTMA), 12/5
Uninsured motorist coverage, 10/14-15
Unmarried couples
   adopting a child, 16/3-4
   child custody and visitation, 16/20-21
   living together, 15/2-6

Unordered products, 9/5
USA Group, 9/15
Used cars, buying, 10/10-12
Utility bill payment problems, 9/14
Utility patents, 6/2-3

V

Vacation benefits, 4/7
Vacation certificates, legitimacy of, 11/28-29
Vacations and business expenses, 5/23-24
VA loans, 1/4
Vermont
    Civil Union Law, 15/15
    See also State laws
Vested benefits
    pension plan, 14/14
    retirement plan, 14/21
View disputes, 2/6-8

W

Wage garnishment, 9/16-17
Wages and time off, 4/2-9
Waivers, not to sue employer, 4/20
Warranties
    adjustments for car repairs, 10/6-7
    for goods and services, 9/2-4
    for homes, 1/13
    for used cars, 10/11-12
Warrantless searches, 18/13

Warranty deed, 1/15
Westlaw, A/8
Wills and estate planning, 12/1-26
    avoiding probate, 12/13-15
    body and organ donations, 12/25
    estate and gift taxes, 12/18-21
    executors, 12/9-13
    funerals and other final arrangements,
        12/22-24
    living trusts, 12/15-18
    probate, 12/8-9
    wills, 12/2-8
Workers' compensation, 4/12-17, 4/32
Workplace rights, 4/1-33
    age discrimination, 4/17-20
    disability discrimination, 4/25-28
    fair pay and time off, 4/2-9
    health and safety, 4/9-11
    losing or leaving your job, 4/29-33
    sexual harassment, 4/21-25
    workers' compensation, 4/12-17
    See also Employers' rights & responsibilities
Works made for hire, 7/4-5

Z

Zoning
    business location, 5/5-6
    and fences, 2/3-4
    home-based businesses and, 5/24-26 ■

Remember:

Little publishers have big ears.
We really listen to you.

Take 2 Minutes & Give Us Your 2 cents

Your comments make a big difference in the development and revision of Nolo books and software. Please take a few minutes and register your Nolo product—and your comments—with us. Not only will your input make a difference, you'll receive special offers available only to registered owners of Nolo products on our newest books and software. Register now by:

PHONE
1-800-728-3555

FAX
1-800-645-0895

EMAIL
cs@nolo.com

or **MAIL** us
this registration card

fold here

Registration Card

NAME _____ DATE _____

ADDRESS _____

_____

CITY _____ STATE _____ ZIP _____

PHONE _____ EMAIL _____

WHERE DID YOU HEAR ABOUT THIS PRODUCT? _____

WHERE DID YOU PURCHASE THIS PRODUCT? _____

DID YOU CONSULT A LAWYER? (PLEASE CIRCLE ONE)   YES   NO   NOT APPLICABLE

DID YOU FIND THIS BOOK HELPFUL?   (VERY)   5   4   3   2   1   (NOT AT ALL)

COMMENTS _____

_____

_____

WAS IT EASY TO USE?   (VERY EASY)   5   4   3   2   1   (VERY DIFFICULT)

We occasionally make our mailing list available to carefully selected companies whose products may be of interest to you.
❏ If you do not wish to receive mailings from these companies, please check this box.
❏ You can quote me in future Nolo promotional materials.
   Daytime phone number _____.

EVL 4.0